GUIDE TO
FIRST EDITION PRICES

EIGHTH EDITION

Guide to
First Edition Prices

Eighth Edition

R.B. Russell

Tartarus Press

Guide to First Edition Prices
Eighth Edition
by R.B. Russell

Published by Tartarus Press, October 2010, at:
Coverley House, Carlton, Leyburn, North Yorkshire, DL8 4AY. UK.
www.tartaruspress.com
Book printed and bound by MPG Biddles.

ISBN 978-1-905784-24-0

Wherever possible each value in this *Guide* has been checked against copies of the book offered for sale in the previous twelve months. The greatest care has been taken to ensure that the information included in the guide is accurate, but the editor cannot be held accountable for any losses that may occur as a result of the information contained herein. The prices represent the perceived average prices asked by reputable book-dealers.

This edition is dedicated to Tim Russell,
who knows a good book when he sees one.

Contents:

INDEX OF AUTHORS

INTRODUCTION

This eighth edition of the Tartarus Press *Guide to First Edition Prices* has been once again completely revised and updated. Designed to appeal to book collectors, dealers and readers, it now contains suggested values for 50,000 sought-after books by over 700 collectable authors. Useful appendices provide a checklist of author pseudonyms, publishers' conventions for identifying a First Edition and useful reference works. The entries for each author have been brought up to date and expanded wherever possible, and it is our aim to provide a complete bibliography for each author.

The format of the *Guide* has changed for this edition: the colour illustrations have been removed so that it can remain affordable as it continues to grow in size and scope.

What is a First Edition?

The term 'First Edition' is generally applied to the first ever appearance in print of a particular work in book format. A First Edition is valuable to collectors because it is the form in which the work was first published, despite the fact that later editions of the work may have been corrected, expanded, illustrated, or by other means improved upon.

The value of a First Edition will be determined primarily by the law of supply and demand: in other words, by how many collectors are interested in obtaining a copy, compared with the numbers of copies available.

This *Guide* gives a suggested retail value for collectable books in their first British and American editions. Books are not always published simultaneously on both sides of the Atlantic and the edition which enjoys chronological precedence is usually listed first. However, the 'follow the flag' principle means that even if a book was published after an edition in another country, its desirability is not necessarily reduced: collectors will often favour the First Edition published in their own country, or be guided by the nationality of the author. Really serious collectors will, of course, seek both editions!

Identifying a First Edition

Not all First Editions identify themselves as such. The most obvious sign that a book is not a First Edition is a note, usually on the copyright page, alluding to previous editions or printings. Simple detective work can usually identify reprints: if the book or its dust wrapper contains a list of works by the same author that post-date the first publication of the book, then it must be a later edition. Quotes from reviews of the book may suggest that it is a later edition, although this is not always the case. You will need to verify, though, that the book has its original wrapper.

It is also vital to check that the publisher of the book is the same as the one stated in this *Guide*: reprints undertaken by book clubs often omit previous publication histories and may look like First Editions to the over-eager collector.

For books published before 1900, the most common means of identification is the date printed on the title page. In the years between 1850-1900 this will be found typically on the back of the title page along with copyright information. After 1900, publishers began not to date books, although many identified First Editions as such on the copyright page.

The various other terms discussed elsewhere in this Introduction may also be used: First 'Edition', 'Printing', 'Impression' etc.

In more recent years, many publishers have adopted the practice of printing a row of numbers on the copyright page. Even if the book claims to be a First Edition, the important thing to look for is the lowest value number present in this row. It is usually the case that the lowest number given is the number of the printing, so the presence of such rows as '1 2 3 4 5 6 7 8 9 10', '10 9 8 7 6 5 4 3 2 1' or '1 3 5 7 9 10 8 6 4 2' denote a First Edition because the number '1' is present. If, for example, the row is printed '2 3 4 5 6 7 8 9 10', then the book is likely to be a second edition. You can find more detailed information on how individual publishers identify First Editions in Appendix III of this book.

The methods discussed above should help you to ascertain whether most books are First Editions or not, but for some the collector will need to refer to points identified by specialist bibliographers, such as the exact binding style, the colouring of the edges of the pages, or some typographical point. In this *Guide* we give, wherever possible, an indication of such points, but please remember that this is only a brief guide. Limitations of space make it impossible to comment adequately on the complexities of different 'states', variant bindings, etc. If you are in any doubt, and especially if you are about to make an expensive purchase, then it would be advisable to consult an author-specific bibliography. We include in Appendix II a list of published bibliographies which often give more detailed information. If in doubt, ask a reputable book-dealer for help in tracking them down.

Values

A rare book will have little value if it is not sought by collectors, and conversely, a book printed in a run of many thousands can still be worth a great deal if there are more collectors eager to acquire a copy than there are copies available. There will always be exceptions, of course, but the fact that a famous author's piece of embarrassing juvenilia may be worth a great deal more than the classic works of their more mature years is usually because their first efforts were printed in small runs, i.e. in editions of only a few hundreds or thousands. It is a fact of life that publishers have always been less willing to invest heavily in a young, unknown first-time author than a proven literary heavy-weight. And true collectors will often want to own a copy of every book by an author, regardless of literary merit.

Just as important for the value of any book is the condition in which it has survived. Even the smallest of faults can affect the value of an otherwise collectable book. If you are not able to inspect the book yourself before you purchase it; if, for example, you are buying the book by mail order from a printed catalogue or Internet listing; then you will need to pay careful attention to the dealer's description of its condition. For more information please see the 'Condition' section of this Introduction.

This *Guide* suggests the prices that a book-dealer might charge a collector, and not the price at which the dealer would necessarily buy books for his or her own stock. My own experience is that a dealer will offer the vendor a quarter of the re-sale value of an ordinary book. For a large number of less desirable titles, the offer will be considerably lower. However, a very collectable and expensive book might command a price much closer to its eventual re-sale value. When offering a book for sale, you should remember that there is nothing wrong with a dealer attempting to make an honest profit. Most dealers choose their profession out of a love of books, but they would not be there to sell you books if they could not make a living out of it. A private sale to another collector would, of course, expect to realise an amount more akin to the full retail value of the book.

The rate of appreciation in the value of collectable First Editions is impossible to predict, but it would be wise to remember that copies in poor condition, acquired for little, will almost always have a similarly low re-sale value. If you can afford it, it is always a better investment to buy a fine copy. In the following excerpt John Ruskin (1819-1900) was writing about wine, but the advice it contains applies equally to book collecting: '*It is unwise to pay too much, but it's worse to pay too little. When you pay too much, you lose a little money—that's all. When you pay too little you sometimes lose everything, because the thing you bought is incapable of doing the thing it was bought to do. The common law of business balance prohibits paying a little and getting a lot—it can't be done. If you deal with the lowest bidder, it is well to add something for the risk you run. And if you do that, you will have enough to pay for something better.*'

Advertisements for investment opportunities always carry the caveat (usually in smaller print than this) that prices may go down as well as up. Books, along with much else in life, go in and out of fashion. A well-received film of a book, or media hype of a title can cause the price to soar, but it will always be more risky to buy at the top end of the market. It has been noted, however, that the values of books that go out of fashion rarely drop too much, as the collector or dealer who has paid a high price for a book will probably keep it on their shelf indefinitely rather than sell it at a loss.

Condition

The condition of a book can cause widely-varying prices to be asked for a title. Simply put, collectors prefer to have their books in a state as close as possible to that when they were first published. Any signs of wear or damage, such as bumps to the corners or creasing to the spine from opening the book roughly or too often will decrease its value. Inscriptions by previous owners, notes in margins, bookplates, etc, can also seriously affect the value of a book, unless the author or some famous person made them. And even then, a mint copy of a fragile book may have more value than a scruffy copy inscribed by the author.

The level of wear or damage that can be tolerated will depend upon the age and/or scarcity of the book, but, in general, minor defects such as ripped pages will devalue the book. Major defects, such as missing pages, will render most books worthless.

Remainder marks, even the most discreet ones, indicating discounting by the publisher when the book was first for sale, will also have an effect on the value. Some publishers, such as Random House, stamp their logo on books that are being disposed of through remainder outlets, but others may simply put a small line or dot in pen on the underside of the book block. The book may well be a First Edition, and the mark very small, but some collectors will still reject it out of hand.

The importance of the dust wrapper cannot be over-emphasised: the most extreme variations in the price of modern First Editions occur between books offered with dust wrappers in varying states of preservation. For some books, dust wrappers almost never survive in a mint state, so when they do a premium can be asked by a dealer. It may be hard to believe, but small nicks or creases in dust wrappers can halve the value of some books. Even an otherwise perfectly-preserved wrapper is devalued if an owner or purchaser has clipped the price from the front flap. So take care of your books and treat them kindly.

The vast majority of established book-dealers will take condition into account when pricing books, and will usually describe any faults in meticulous detail. Do not be put off if a dealer points out a number of small nicks and scuffs in their description of a book and assume that a copy simply described by another dealer as 'good' will be in better condition. There is an art to reading and interpreting descriptions of the condition of books, and the majority of complaints from collectors relate to poor descriptions offered by inexperienced dealers. One dealer's definition of 'good' will equate to 'fine' by another dealer with lesser standards, and 'poor' to one with exacting values.

Recent Trends in Book Values

In earlier editions of this *Guide* I noted that prices asked for collectable First Editions seemed to have risen inexorably. However, in the last few years there has been something of a slow-down. The exchange rate and international economic conditions have had an effect, but perhaps the biggest change has come from the availability of books on the Internet. It has been fascinating to watch the world of book collecting change from the days when most collectors relied on browsing the shelves of local bookshops and waited for catalogues to arrive through the post. Serious collectors will still keep up contact with favourite dealers, but every year more and more books become available to anyone who can access the Internet. There are a number of websites where you can search the stock of thousands of dealers and you will be offered a previously unimagined range of titles. And those dealers who advertise their stock on the Internet now find they have many hundreds of thousands of potential new customers.

The result is that both the supply and the demand sides of the value equation have grown, and the laws of basic economics have gradually come into play. It has been slow: the immediate result appeared to be that the value of the most common books was levelled downwards, but middle-ranking books appeared to increase. The reason for prices rising was simply that there was no reason why a small provincial dealer should not ask as much as a well-known specialist. Finally, though, 'supply and demand' is bringing the value of most books back down to more realistic levels as more dealers add stock to Internet search engines at a price just below that of their competitors.

The sheer volume of books made available to collectors means that those previously described by dealers as 'rare' have to be called, at best, 'uncommon'. At the top end of the market 'blue chip' books by highly sought-after authors such as Graham Greene, Ernest Hemingway and F. Scott Fitzgerald have retained their value. The only books that continue to rise in value are those that are genuinely super-rare and in hitherto unknown fine condition. Some mind-boggling prices are being asked for such books, and who can say that they are not worth the large sums asked for them?

It should also be pointed out that trends in book prices affect the various 'fields' and 'genres' in different ways. Many dealers and collectors of 'Modern Firsts' have noticed that the field continues to be rather depressed. One simple factor is that the majority of collectable, fashionable modern firsts were published in very large numbers and the Internet has once again revealed that many of them are far more commonly available than anyone had perceived. First books by such authors, printed in more conservative runs, can still command a premium, but they have to be in especially fine condition.

Areas in which prices have held steady, and even continued to rise, are the more specialist genres. In golden-age detective fiction, classic ghost stories, early science fiction etc, there are collectable books known to dedicated fans who will pay large sums to add to their collections, irrespective of exchange rates etc. One problem with assessing the value of such books is that they are often sold privately, among fans, without ever appearing publicly for sale.

There are still a few bargains to be found on the Internet, but not many, as there is no longer any reason why a book-seller should be ignorant of a book's value. And if a gem has been offered at a ludicrously low price, there are plenty of people who will pounce on it. Those bargains that it is still possible to find are usually among the little-known, special-ity and genre books, but you need specific knowledge to find them.

Terminology

The term 'First Printing' is often synonymous with 'First Edition', though it is a description employed more by publ-ishers than book collectors or dealers. It refers specifically to the printing of the pages, some of which may have been bound at a later date (a later 'issue'), and therefore does not constitute the first form in which the book was published. Other terms must also be considered with care, for if a book was reprinted from the original printers' plates without altera-tions being made to the text then this will not technically constitute a new edition. This is a new 'impression' which will generally be less desirable than the first. Different 'states' refer to various alterations made to the book by the publisher, and over the years collectors and dealers have gauged which 'variants' are considered more or less desirable.

Other publishing and collecting terms can mislead the unwary. 'First published edition', for example, implies that the work may have been printed previously for a restricted circulation, although it can be assumed that it was probably never offered for sale to the public at large. 'First separate edition' usually implies that the material in the book had been previously published, albeit with other matter. 'First thus' is a term that should be treated with great caution as it usually denotes a reprint, although it will be the first time that the material has been presented in that particular format.

Books that may have appeared in print *before* the publi-cation of the First Edition include 'copyright editions', produced in the 19th and early 20th centuries. These were typically bound up in small numbers, of which only one copy might have been sold so as to establish copyright. If the author is collectable, these copyright editions can be very valuable indeed. Even today, books can appear in various forms before publication, usually as 'proof' copies, and more recently as 'advance reading copies' for publicity purposes.

While these may have some value they are not considered true First Editions. The practice of some modern publishers of issuing signed, numbered proof or advance copies can mean that the true collector ends up with three or four variant printings of exactly the same book!

Reprints

Not all of the collectable books listed in this *Guide* are First Editions. It may be the case that the First Edition is so rare and expensive that realistic collectors are happy to pay for a later edition, especially if it is similar to the first. Some re-prints may contain important new matter not included in the First Edition, and the value of such reprints is once again de-termined primarily by supply and demand.

The *Guide* also lists 'special editions' of books. These take a variety of forms and are often published in limited numbers, with something extra to appeal to the collector, such as fine quality paper or bindings, the author's signature or even the addition of further material that does not appear in the ordinary 'trade' edition. Although the limited nature of such editions may add to their value, it must be remembered that they are usually recognised as something special by even the most disinterested of owners and may often survive in greater numbers than the dowdier, ordinary edition.

Print on Demand

Modern 'print on demand' technology allows publishers to produce books only when a customer orders a copy. They use it where the perceived demand for a book is low or they are unwilling to take the financial risk of printing a longer run by more traditional methods. As the opportunity exists for the publisher to keep producing identical copies, print on demand books are unlikely to have any real value to collectors.

Where to Obtain First Editions

A lot of enjoyment can be had in finding First Editions at garage sales and general charity shops, but great discoveries will not be common, and the likelihood of unearthing specific books that you collect is very small. Traditionally, specialist bookshops and book-dealers have been the main source of books for serious collectors. And then came the Internet. . . .

The Internet is a mixed blessing for both dealers and collectors. The great advantage has been in enabling so many books to be made available to so many customers, but problems are inevitable when inexperienced collectors and dealers come into the field. It is recommended to both parties in any expensive transaction that personal contact be made at least through email, by telephone, and by making available photographs of the book in question. For those who have embraced the Internet and use it wisely the world of book collecting has been enriched.

Bookshops, however, do still exist! There are not as many as there were and if they are to remain in business they need to be supported. There is, as yet, no Internet application that can replicate the experience of browsing the shelves of a real bookshop and making unexpected and happy discoveries therein.

Specialist charity bookshops have become a more import-ant factor in high street sales of secondhand books in the last few years. Specialists in the field such as Oxfam have been blamed for the demise of private bookshops because of advantages they have: free stock, lower rents and rates, etc. This is only one of the reasons that private bookshops struggle, however, and it should be remembered that charity shops have these advantages because of their charitable aims. As with any bookshop, the level of expertise and experience in charity bookshops will vary and collectors get to know which establishments they can trust. It is always more satisfying to buy a book from a book-seller with a good reputation and several years experience in the trade.

How to Use This *Guide*

Entries are listed alphabetically by author, then chronologically by publication, within subject classifications such as 'Fiction' and 'Non-Fiction.' The default assumption is that books listed are traditional hardbacks.

If a book is not a hardback then it will be described as either 'pbk' (denoting what is popularly thought of as a paperback), or 'wraps'. This latter description applies to a number of binding styles but is generally a publication bound with paper covers.

Where two values are given for a book the first is usually for an example with a dust wrapper (d/w) and the second for a copy without. If only one price is quoted, it is for a book without a dust wrapper.

For books with slipcases (with or without d/ws), or other associated components (eg additional booklets, prints etc), the first price is for the book complete with all these, the second for the book without any of them.

Books published before 1920 are given a single value because the survival of dust wrappers earlier than this date is rare. If an early wrapper does survive, then it is often impossible to gauge the added value this will add to the book.

All books valued in the *Guide* are assumed to be in very good condition 'for their age'. For example, a fragile item, poorly bound a hundred years ago, will be unlikely to survive in mint condition and some wear and tear is expected. The majority of books from the last thirty or forty years, however, are expected to be in fine condition.

Books are assumed to be in their original bindings, although those published before 1800 are usually valued on the assumption that they will have been rebound in the 19th century (a common practice): original bindings will greatly increase their value, whereas a more recent re-binding will decrease the value.

The known limitation of a First Edition is noted simply as *x copies*. If a book is 'signed', it is assumed that it was the author who did the signing, unless specified otherwise. If a book was re-issued later under a new title, then it is listed under the original title but noted thus:

ditto, as ***The Murder of Geraldine Foster***, Collins Crime
    Club (London), 1931 .   .   .   .   .   . £750/£50

If a book was issued pseudonymously then a note follows the date, i.e. '(pseud. 'Fred Smith')'. A list of many authors' pseudonyms is printed in Appendix IV to this volume.

Any information provided in the *Guide* listing that does not appear in the book is given in square brackets: [Such as the date of publication].

Acknowledgements

I am grateful to the many people who have helped me to compile this *Guide*, but as editor I must assume all responsibility for any errors which, inevitably, may have crept in. I welcome any suggestions, corrections, etc. at the publisher's address. A continuing criticism of previous editions of the *Guide* has been the omission of certain authors. We will never be able to do justice to every collectable author, but new entries suggested by dealers and collectors are always included in each new edition.

Many of the bibliographies in this *Guide* are based on those previously published by other indefatigable researchers and these are acknowledged in Appendix II. I also owe a great debt to the countless book-dealers who have advertised books for sale over the years, often with accompanying valuable bibliographical information.

I would like to specifically thank Anne Osinga for continuing assistance in the preparation of the *Guide*, and to Rosalie Parker not only for her proof-reading (what a vast undertaking!) but also her support when the revision and expansion of each new Guide has sometimes appeared overwhelming.

A number of people have been very generous with their time and expertise in the preparation of previous editions, and this Eighth Edition continues to benefit from their help. These include John Abrahamson, Donn Albright, Douglas Anderson, Mike Ashley, Phil Baker, Mark Benham, Mike Berro, Richard Caton, Dr Glen Cavaliero, Shelley Cox, Nigel Cozens, Clarissa Cridland, Richard Dalby, Andrew Detheridge, Michael DiRuggie, David Downes, Nicolas Granger-Taylor, Norman Gates, Michael Gauntlett, James Goddard, Dan Gregory, Clive Harper, Hunter Hayes, Malcolm Henderson, Susan Hill, Richard Humphries, Kevin Johnson, Jonathan Kearns, Lawrence Knapp, Rick Loomis, Edward Mendelson, Gary Morris & the Compton-Burnett Cabal, CeCe Motz, John Potter and the Alan Bennett Society, Barry Pike, Ryan Roberts, Colin Smythe, Colin Scott-Sutherland, Ed Seiler, David Tibbetts, and Mark Valentine.

And Finally . . .

No one can learn the tricks of the book trade overnight. This *Guide* does not explain how to become a book-dealer, or how to get one step ahead of the trade. It is unlikely that it will help anyone make their fortune, and no one person can be an expert on all of the titles listed here. It is simply a 'guide', and I hope that it is of use and interest to collectors and dealers alike.

EDWARD ABBEY

(b.1927 d.1989)

Abbey was an American author and essayist noted for his advocacy of environmental issues and his criticism of public land policies. His best-known works include the novel *The Monkey Wrench Gang*, his first book to deal explicitly with the ecological and environmental themes that dominate his later writings. Abbey described his first book, *Jonathan Troy*, as 'bad Thomas Wolfe' and would not allow it to be reprinted. *The Brave Cowboy* was the basis of the film, *Lonely Are the Brave*, starring Kirk Douglas.

Fiction

Jonathan Troy, Dodd, Mead (New York), 1954 . . . . £1,500/£250

The Brave Cowboy: An Old Tale in a New Time, Dodd, Mead & Co. (New York), 1956 . . . £3,500/£400

ditto, Eyre & Spottiswoode (London), 1957 . . £650/£50

Fire on the Mountain, Dial Press (New York), 1962 . . . . £650/£100

ditto, Eyre & Spottiswoode (London), 1963 . . £250/£40

Black Sun, Simon & Schuster (New York), 1971 . £150/£25

ditto, as **Sunset Canyon**, Talmy, Franklin (London), 1972 . . . . £50/£10

The Monkey Wrench Gang, J.B. Lippincott (Philadelphia, PA), 1975 . . . . . . £250/£35

ditto, Canongate (Edinburgh, Scotland), 1978 . . £65/£10

ditto, Dream Garden Press (Salt Lake City, UT), 1985 (illustrated by Robert Crumb) . . . . . £45/£15

ditto, Dream Garden Press (Salt Lake City, UT), 1985 (15 signed, lettered copies; print signed by Crumb; slipcase; no d/w) . . . . £1,250/£900

ditto, Dream Garden Press (Salt Lake City, UT), 1985 (250 signed, numbered copies; print signed by Crumb; slipcase; no d/w) . . . . . . £650/£450

Good News, E.P. Dutton (New York), 1980 . . £75/£15

The Fool's Progress: An Honest Novel, Henry Holt (New York), 1988 (first issue dust jacket with 'mist' for 'myth' on front flap) . . . . . . £15/£5

ditto, Bodley Head (London), 1989 . . . . £10/£5

Hayduke Lives!, Little, Brown (Boston), 1989 . £10/£5

Poetry

Earth Apples, St Martin's Press (New York), 1994 £10/£5

Non-Fiction

Desert Solitaire, McGraw-Hill (New York), 1968 . £350/£45

Appalachian Wilderness: The Great Smoky Mountains, E.P. Dutton (New York), 1970 (colour photos by Eliot Porter) . . . . £100/£25

Slickrock: The Canyon Country of Southeast Utah, The Sierra Club (San Francisco), 1971 (colour photographs by Philip Hyde) . . . . £125/£25

Cactus Country, Time-Life Books (New York), 1973 (with single 'hourglass' symbol at bottom of final page of text) . . . . £75/£15

The Hidden Canyon: A River Journey, Viking (New York), 1977 (photographs by John Blaustein) . . . £135/£25

The Journey Home: Some Words in Defense of the American West, E.P. Dutton (New York), 1977 (illustrations by Jim Stiles) . . . . £100/£20

Desert Images: An American Landscape, Harcourt Brace Jovanovich (New York), 1979 (photographs by David Muench; slipcase but no d/w) . . . . . £125/£30

Abbey's Road, E.P. Dutton (New York), 1980 . £200/£45

Down the River, E.P. Dutton (New York), 1982 . £300/£35

Beyond the Wall: Essays from the Outside, Holt, Rinehart & Winston (New York), 1984 . . . . . £100/£15

In Praise of Mountain Lions: Original Praises by Edward Abbey and John Nichols, The Sierra Club (Albuquerque, NM), 1984 (pamphlet; approx 600 copies; with 'Some Words in Behalf of a Predator' by John Nichols, and 'The Mountain Lion in New Mexico' by Carol Cochran) . £50

Confessions of a Barbarian, Capra Press (Santa Monica, CA), 1986 (pbk bound back-to-back with *Red Knife Valley* by Jack Curtis) £10

One Life at a Time, Please, Henry Holt (New York), 1988 . . . . £15/£5

Vox Clamantis in Deserto: Some Notes from a Secret Journal, The Rydal Press (Santa Fe, NM), 1989 (225 numbered copies of 250, slipcase) . . . . £100/£45

ditto, as *A Voice Crying in the Wilderness*, St Martin's Press (New York), 1990 . . . . . . £10/£5

Postcards From Ed: Dispatches and Salvos from an American Iconoclast, Milkweed Editions (Minneapolis, MN), 2006 (letters) . . . . £10/£5

Anthologies

Slumgullion Stew: An Edward Abbey Reader, E.P. Dutton (New York), 1984 . . . . . . £75/£20

ditto, E.P. Dutton (New York), 1984 (simultaneous pbk issue) £5

ditto, as *The Best of Edward Abbey*, Sierra Club (San Francisco), 1984 (pbk) £5

The Serpents of Paradise: A Reader, Henry Holt (New York), 1995 . . . . £10/£5

ANTHONY ABBOT

(b.1893 d.1952)

Abbot was the pseudonym of Fulton Oursler, whose 'Thatcher Colt' novels are examples of 'Golden Age' detective fiction. He wrote many other books under his own name. The first four 'Covici Friede' titles were initially published in yellow cloth with purple lettering. All of the Collins Crime Club first editions were published in orange cloth with black lettering and have wrappers priced 7/6.

'Thatcher Colt' Novels

About the Murder of Geraldine Foster, Covici Friede (New York), 1930 . . . . £750/£65

ditto, as *The Murder of Geraldine Foster*, Collins Crime Club (London), 1931 . . . . . . £750/£50

About the Murder of the Clergyman's Mistress, Covici Friede (New York), 1931 . . . . . . £650/£50

ditto, as *The Crime of the Century*, Collins Crime Club (London), 1931 . . . . . . £500/£45

About the Murder of the Night Club Lady, Covici Friede (New York), 1931 . . . . . . £500/£20

ditto, as *The Murder of the Night Club Lady*, Collins Crime Club (London), 1932 . . . . . £500/£20

About the Murder of the Circus Queen, Covici Friede (New
  York), 1932 . . . . £350/£25
ditto, as *The Murder of the Circus Queen*, Collins Crime
  Club (London), 1933 . . . . . . £200/£20
About the Murder of a Startled Lady, Farrar & Rinehart
  (New York), 1935 . . . . £200/£25
ditto, as *Murder of a Startled Lady*, Collins Crime Club
  (London), 1936 . . . . £100/£20
About the Murder of a Man Afraid of Women, Farrar &
  Rinehart (New York), 1937 . . . . £200/£25
ditto, as *Murder of a Man Afraid of Women*, Collins Crime
  Club (London), 1937 . . . . . . £100/£20
The Creeps, Farrar & Rinehart (New York), 1939 (red cloth,
  black lettering, date on copyright page) . . . £125/£20
ditto, as *Murder at Buzzards Bay*, Collins Crime Club
  (London), 1940 . . . . £125/£20
The Shudders, Farrar & Rinehart (New York), 1943
  (blue/green cloth, black lettering, date on copyright page).
  . . . . £100/£15
ditto, as *Deadly Secret*, Collins Crime Club (London), 1943
  . . . . £100/£15

Anonymous Crime Title
Dark Masquerade, Green Circle (New York), 1936 . .
  . . . . £500/£45

Other Titles as Anthony Abbot
The Flower of the Gods, Green Circle (New York), 1936
  (with Achmed Abdullah) . . . . . £125/£35
The President's Mystery Story, Farrar & Rinehart (New
  York), 1935 (with Franklin D Roosevelt, Rupert Hughes,
  Samuel Hopkins Adams, Rita Weiman, S.S. Van Dine,
  John Erskine and Erle Stanley Gardner). . . £45/£10
ditto, Bodley Head (London), 1936 . . . £45/£10
These Are Strange Tales: Short Stories, John C. Winston,
  (Philadelphia, PA), 1948 . . . . . £75/£15

PETER ABRAHAMS
(b.1919)

Abrahams left South Africa in 1939 aged 20, but the impact of the South African system upon him has meant that
most of his work is set in Africa and deals with racial
conflict, oppression and economic injustice. He is acknowledged not only for his own literary achievements, but also
for the   example he provided as one of the first black
African writers of the 1950s and 60s.

Novels
Song of the City, Crisp (London), [1945] . . . £75/£20
Mine Boy, Crisp (London), [1946] . . . £60/£15
ditto, Knopf (New York), 1955 (pbk). . . . £10
The Path of Thunder, Harper & Brothers (New York), 1948
  . . . . £30/£10
ditto, Faber (London), 1952 . . . . . . £30/£10
Wild Conquest, Harper & Brothers (New York), 1950. .
  . . . . £30/£10
ditto, Faber (London), 1951 . . . . . . £35/£10
A Wreath for Udomo, Knopf (New York), 1956 . £30/£10
ditto, Faber (London), 1956 . . . . . . £25/£10
A Night of Their Own, Knopf (New York), 1965 . £25/£10
ditto, Faber (London), 1965 . . . . . . £25/£10

This Island Now, Faber (London), 1966 . . . £20/£10
ditto, Knopf (New York), 1967 . . . . . £20/£10

Others
Dark Testament, George Allen & Unwin (London), 1942
  (short stories) . . . . £200/£50
A Blackman Speaks of Freedom, Durban, 1942 (poetry;
  wraps) £250
Return to Goli, Faber (London), 1953 . . £35/£10
Tell Freedom: Memories of Africa, Knopf (New York), 1954
  . . . . £35/£10
ditto, Faber (London), 1954 . . . . . . £35/£10
Jamaica: An Island Mosaic, H.M.S.O. (London), 1957 .
  . . . . £40/£15

J.R. ACKERLEY
(b.1896 d.1967)

For many years the literary editor of *The Listener*, Ackerley
encouraged several young writers, including Auden,
Isherwood and Spender. His own literary output was small,
but candid and frank. *My Father and Myself*, which deals
with his experiences of 'coming-out' as a gay man, is
considered by many to be his masterpiece. He also edited
Escapers All (Bodley Head, London, 1932).

Poetry
Cambridge Poets 1914-1920, Heffers (Cambridge, UK),
  1920 (edited by E. Davison, two poems by Ackerley, plus
  poems by Brooke, Sassoon and others) . . £300/£75
Poems by Four Authors, Bowes & Bowes (Cambridge, UK),
  1923 (poems by J.R. Ackerley, A.Y. Campbell, Edward
  Davison, and Frank Kendon, grey cloth spine, green stiff
  paper boards, printed paper title label with spare tipped in
  at rear) . . . . £200/£35
Micheldever and Other Poems, McKelvie (London), 1972
  (350 numbered copies, plain stiff paper wraps with illustrated yellow d/w, frontispiece of Ackerley by Don
  Bachardy tipped-in) . . . . . . £45/£25

Novel
We Think the World of You, Bodley Head (London), 1960.
  . . . . £75/£20
ditto, Ivan Obolensky (New York), 1961 (states 'First printing') . . . . £65/£15

Other Titles
The Prisoners of War: A Play in Three Acts, Chatto &
  Windus (London), 1925 (printed paper title label) £250/£65
Hindoo Holiday: An Indian Journey, Chatto & Windus
  (London), 1932 . . . . £200/£75
ditto, Viking (New York), 1932 . . . . £75/£25
ditto, Chatto & Windus (London), 1952 (revised edition) .
  . . . . £25/£10
My Dog Tulip: Life with an Alsatian, Secker & Warburg
  (London), 1956 . . . . £35/£10
ditto, Fleet Publishing (New York), 1965 (expanded edition)
  . . . . £10/£5
My Father and Myself, Bodley Head (London), 1968 . .
  . . . . £20/£5
ditto, Coward-McCann (New York), 1969 (first state binding
  with 'Ackerly' on spine) . . . . . £15/£10

ditto, Coward-McCann (New York), 1969 (second state with name correct) . . . . . . £10/£5
E.M. Forster: A Portrait, McKelvie (London), 1972 (green card wraps) £10
The Letters of J.R. Ackerley, Duckworth (London), 1975 .
. . . . £15/£5
ditto, as **The Ackerley Letters**, Harcourt Brace Jovanovich (New York), 1975 . . . . . £15/£5
My Sister and Myself: The Diaries of J.R. Ackerley, Hutchinson (London), 1982 . . . . £15/£5

PETER ACKROYD
(b.1949)

A wide-ranging and versatile British writer, Ackroyd is best known as a novelist and biographer, although he started out as a poet. His life of T.S. Eliot won the Whitbread and Heinemann (London) Awards for 1984, and his monumental biography of Dickens is much acclaimed. His work often exhibits a fascination with the city of London and his most recent works are biographies of London itself, and it's river, The Thames.

Novels
The Great Fire of London, Hamish Hamilton (London), 1982 . . . . £250/£35
ditto, Univ of Chicago Press (Chicago), 1982 (pbk) . £10
The Last Testament of Oscar Wilde, Hamish Hamilton (London), 1983 . . . . £35/£10
ditto, Harper & Row (New York), 1983 . . . £15/£5
Hawksmoor, Hamish Hamilton (London), 1985 . £25/£5
ditto, Harper & Row (New York), 1985 . . £25/£5
Chatterton, Hamish Hamilton (London), 1987 £15/£5
ditto, Hamish Hamilton (London), 1987 (150 signed, numbered copies, 1/4 blue cloth lettered in gilt, marbled boards unprinted glassine d/w). . . . £25/£20
ditto, Grove Press (New York), 1988. . . £10/£5
First Light, Hamish Hamilton (London), 1989 . £15/£5
ditto, Grove Weidenfeld (New York), 1989 . . £10/£5
English Music, Hamish Hamilton (London), 1992. £15/£5
ditto, London Limited Editions (London), 1992 (150 signed, numbered copies, 1/4 blue cloth lettered in gilt, marbled boards unprinted glassine d/w). . . . £40/£30
ditto, Knopf (New York), 1992 (advance reading copy signed by author, in illustrated slipcase). . . £10/£5
ditto, Knopf (New York), 1992 . . . . £10/£5
ditto, The Franklin Library (Franklin Centre, PA), 1992 (full leather, signed, limited edition) £20
The House of Doctor Dee, Hamish Hamilton (London), 1993 . . . . £15/£5
Dan Leno and the Limehouse Golem, Sinclair-Stevenson (London), 1994 . . . . . . £15/£5
ditto, as 'The Trial of Elizabeth Cree', Nan A. Talese/ Doubleday (New York), 1995 . . . £10/£5
Milton in America, Sinclair-Stevenson (London), 1996 .
. . . . £10/£5
ditto, Nan A. Talese/Doubleday (New York), 1997 £10/£5
The Plato Papers, Chatto & Windus (London), 1999 £10/£5
ditto, Nan A. Talese/Doubleday (New York), 1999 £10/£5
The Clerkenwell Tales, Chatto & Windus (London), 2003 .
. . . . £10/£5
ditto, Nan A. Talese/Doubleday (New York), 2004. £10/£5

The Lambs of London, Chatto & Windus (London), 2004 .
. . . . £10/£5
ditto, Nan A. Talese/Doubleday (New York), 2006 £10/£5
The Fall of Troy, Chatto & Windus (London), 2006 £10/£5
ditto, Nan A. Talese/Doubleday (New York), 2007 £10/£5
The Casebook of Victor Frankenstein, Chatto & Windus (London), 2008 . . . . £10/£5
The Canterbury Tales: A Retelling, Penguin (London), 2009
. . . . £10/£5

Poetry
Ouch, The Curiously Strong Press (London), vol. IV no.2 1971 (xeroxed copies, sheets, usually in stapled wraps) .
. . . . £200
London Lickpenny, Ferry Press (London), 1973 (26 signed copies of edition of 500, illustrated stapled card wraps) .
. . . . £200
ditto, Ferry Press (London), 1973 (474 unsigned copies of edition of 500, illustrated stapled card wraps) . . £65
Country Life, Ferry Press (London), 1978 (324 signed copies of edition of 350, stapled card wraps) . . . £25
ditto, Ferry Press (London), 1978 (26 signed copies of edition of 350, with additional holograph poem, stapled card wraps) £200
The Diversions of Purley, Hamish Hamilton (London), 1987
. . . . £25/£10

Biography
Ezra Pound and His World, Thames & Hudson (London), 1980 . . . . £25/£5
ditto, Scribner's (New York), 1980 . . . £20/£5
T.S. Eliot, Hamish Hamilton (London), 1984 . . £20/£5
ditto, Simon & Schuster (New York), 1984 . . £15/£5
Dickens, Sinclair-Stevenson (London), 1990 . . £20/£5
ditto, London Limited Editions (London), 1990 (150 signed, numbered copies, 1/4 cloth lettered in gilt, marbled boards unprinted glassine d/w) . . . . . £75/£50
ditto, HarperCollins (New York), 1990 . . £15/£5
Blake, Sinclair-Stevenson (London), 1995 . £15/£5
ditto, Knopf (New York), 1996 . . . . £10/£5
The Life of Thomas More, Chatto & Windus (London), 1998 . . . . £10/£5
ditto, Doubleday (New York), 1998 . . . £10/£5
Chaucer (Ackroyd's Brief Lives), Chatto & Windus (London), 2004 . . . . £10/£5
ditto, Nan A. Talese/Doubleday (New York), 2005 £10/£5
Shakespeare: The Biography, Chatto & Windus, 2005 .
. . . . £10/£5
ditto, Nan A. Talese/Doubleday (New York), 2005 £10/£5
Turner (Ackroyd's Brief Lives), Chatto & Windus, 2005 .
. . . . £10/£5
ditto, Nan A. Talese/Doubleday (New York), 2006. £10/£5
Newton (Ackroyd's Brief Lives), Chatto & Windus, 2006 .
. . . . £10/£5
ditto, Nan A. Talese/Doubleday (New York), 2008 £10/£5
Poe: A Life Cut Short, Chatto & Windus (London), 2008 .
. . . . £10/£5
ditto, Nan A. Talese/Doubleday (New York), 2008 £10/£5

Miscellaneous
Notes for a New Culture: An Essay on Modernism, Vision Press (London), 1976 . . . . . . £35/£10
ditto, Barnes & Noble (New York), 1976 . . £35/£10

Dressing Up, Transvestism and Drag: The History of an Obsession, Thames & Hudson (London), 1979 . £45/£10
ditto, Simon & Schuster (New York), 1979 . . £20/£10
Dickens' London: An Imaginative Vision, Headline (London), 1987 (introduced by Peter Ackroyd) . £15/£5
Introduction to Dickens, Sinclair-Stevenson (London), 1991 . . . . £15/£5
ditto, Ballantine (New York), 1992 (pbk) £5
London: The Biography, Chatto & Windus (London), 2000 . . . . £15/£5
ditto, Nan A. Talese/Doubleday (New York), 2001 £10/£5
The Collection: Journalism, Reviews, Essays, Short Stories, Lectures, Chatto & Windus (London), 2001 . . £10/£5
Dickens: Public Life and Private Passion, BBC Books (London), 2002 . . . . . . £10/£5
ditto, Hydra (New York), 2002 . . . . . £10/£5
Albion: The Origins of the English Imagination, Chatto & Windus (London), 2002 . . . . . £10/£5
ditto, Nan A. Talese/Doubleday (New York), 2003 £10/£5
Illustrated London, Chatto & Windus (London), 2003 . . . . £10/£5
The Thames: Sacred River, Chatto & Windus (London), 2007 . . . . £10/£5
Venice: Pure City, Chatto & Windus (London), 2009 £10/£5

Voyages Through Time
Escape from Earth, Dorling Kindersley (London/New York), 2003 . . . . £10/£5
The Beginning, Dorling Kindersley (London/New York), 2003 . . . . £10/£5
Ancient Americas, Dorling Kindersley (London/New York), 2004 . . . . £10/£5
Ancient Egypt, Dorling Kindersley (London/New York), 2004 . . . . £10/£5
Cities of Blood, Dorling Kindersley (London/New York), 2004 . . . . £10/£5
Ancient Rome, Dorling Kindersley (London/New York), 2006 . . . . £10/£5
Kingdom of the Dead, Dorling Kindersley (London/New York), 2006 . . . . . . £10/£5

DOUGLAS ADAMS
(b.1952 d.2001)

The Hitch Hiker's Guide To The Galaxy (which is inconsistently hyphenated in the books) was first on the radio before becoming a successful novel and television series. It has also been adapted as a computer game, a comic book, a stage play and a film. Asteroids have been named after both Adams and Arthur Dent (the bewildered hero of *The Hitch Hiker's Guide to the Galaxy*). The hardest hardback edition of the five books in the *Hitch Hiker's* trilogy (!) to obtain is *Life, The Universe and Everything*.

'The Hitch Hiker's Guide To The Galaxy' Series
The Hitch Hiker's Guide To The Galaxy, Pan (London), 1979 (pbk) £10
ditto, Barker (London), 1979 [1980] (first hardback edition) . . . . £300/£35
ditto, Harmony (New York), 1980 . . . . £75/£20
The Restaurant At The End Of The Universe, Pan (London), 1980 (pbk) £5

ditto, Barker (London), 1980 (first hardback edition) . . . . £100/£15
ditto, Harmony (New York), 1980 . . . . £35/£5
Life, The Universe and Everything, Pan (London), 1982 (pbk) £5
ditto, Barker (London), 1982 (first hardback edition) . . . . £450/£15
ditto, Harmony (New York), 1982 . . . . £20/£5
So Long, And Thanks For All The Fish, Pan (London), 1984 . . . . £25/£5
ditto, Harmony (New York), 1985 . . . . £10/£5
Mostly Harmless, Heinemann (London), 1992 . £15/£5
ditto, Harmony (New York), 1992 . . . £10/£5

'Dirk Gently' Series
Dirk Gently's Holistic Detective Agency, Heinemann (London), 1987 . . . . £25/£5
ditto, Simon & Schuster (New York), 1987 . £15/£5
The Long Dark Tea-Time Of The Soul, Heinemann (London), 1988 . . . . £25/£5
ditto, Simon & Schuster (New York), 1988 . . £15/£5

Collected Editions
The Hitch Hiker's Trilogy, Harmony (New York), 1983 . . . . £25/£10
The Hitch Hiker's Guide To The Galaxy: The Original Radio Scripts, Pan (London), 1985 (pbk) . . . £10
ditto, Harmony (New York), [c.1985] (pbk) . . . £10
The Compleat Hitch Hiker, Pan (London), 1986 (proof only, with d/w) £300
The Hitch Hiker's Guide To The Galaxy: A Trilogy in Four Parts, Heinemann (London), 1986 . . . . £40/£10
ditto, as *The Hitch Hiker's Quartet*, Harmony (New York), 1986 . . . . £25/£10
The More Than Complete Hitch Hiker's Guide, Bonanza (New York), 1989 . . . . . . £15/£5
The Hitch Hiker's Guide To The Galaxy: A Trilogy in Five Parts, Heinemann (London), 1995 . . . . £15/£5
The Dirk Gently Omnibus, Heinemann (London), 2001 . . . . £10/£5

Non-Fiction
The Meaning of Liff, Pan (London), 1983 (with John Lloyd; pbk) £10
ditto, Harmony (New York), 1984 . . . . £10/£5
The Deeper Meaning of Liff, Pan (London), 1990 (with John Lloyd) . . . . £10/£5
ditto, Harmony (New York), 1990 . . . . £10/£5
Last Chance To See ..., Heinemann (London), 1990 (with Mark Carwardine) . . . . . . £15/£5
ditto, Harmony (New York), 1992 . . . . £10/£5

Others
Doctor Who, Serial 5M, 'Shada', BBC (London), 1979 (pbk) £25
Doctor Who - Pirate Planet, Titan Books (London), 1994 (pbk) £5
Douglas Adams's Starship Titanic, Pan (London), 1997 (with Terry Jones) £5
ditto, Harmony (New York), 1997 . . . . £10/£5
The Salmon of Doubt, Heinemann (London), 2002 £10/£5
ditto, Random House/Harmony (New York), 2002 . £10/£5

RICHARD ADAMS
(b.1920)

Richard Adams is a British novelist whose sophisticated
fantasy novels are often concerned with man's cruelty to
animals. *Watership Down* won the Guardian Award and
Carnegie Medal. The first issue of his *The Girl in a Swing*
was withdrawn through fear of libel, and among the
changes made was the name of the heroine.

Novels
Watership Down, Rex Collings (London), 1972 (colour
folding map fixed to rear endpapers) . . £1,250/£100
ditto, Macmillan (New York), 1972 . . . .£200/£15
ditto, Penguin (London), 1976 (first illustrated edition, in
slipcase with d/w) . . . . £80/£15
ditto, Paradine (London), 1976 (deluxe illustrated edition
limited to 250 signed, numbered copies, bound in full green
morocco by Sangorski and Sutcliffe, slipcase) . . .
. . . . £1,250/£1,000
ditto, Paradine (London), 1976 (approx 30 copies of the
above edition with an original illustration) . . £2,000
ditto, Paradine (London), 1976 (10 copies of the 30-copy
limited edition with an original fore-edge painting) £3,500
Shardik, Allen Lane (London), 1974. . . . £15/£5
ditto, Simon & Schuster (New York), [1974] . . £10/£5
Plague Dogs, Allen Lane (London), 1977 . . £15/£5
ditto, Knopf (New York), 1978 . . . . £10/£5
The Girl in a Swing, Allen Lane (London), 1980 (withdrawn
first issue with 'Kathe Geutner' character, 'Allen Lane' on
title-page) . . . . £50/£15
ditto, Knopf (New York), 1980 (withdrawn issue) . £40/£15
ditto, Allen Lane (London), 1980 (second issue, revised
edition, with 'Karin Förster' character, without 'Allen Lane'
on title-page) . . . . £10/£5
ditto, Knopf (New York), 1980 (revised edition) . £10/£5
The Legend of Te Tuna, Sylvester & Orphanos (Los
Angeles, CA), 1982 (300 of 330 signed copies; no slipcase
or d/w) £45
ditto, Sylvester & Orphanos (Los Angeles, CA), 1982 (26
lettered and signed copies and 4 copies with recipient's
name printed, of 330, slipcase). . . . £150/£100
ditto, Sidgwick & Jackson (London), 1986 . £10/£5
Maia, Viking (London), 1984 . . . . . £10/£5
ditto, Knopf (New York), 1985 . . . . £10/£5
Traveller, Knopf (New York), 1988 . . . £10/£5
ditto, Hutchinson (London), 1988 . . . £10/£5
Daniel, Wrecking Ball Press, Hull, 2006 . . £10/£5
ditto, Wrecking Ball Press, Hull, 2006 (1,000 signed, boxed
copies) . . . . £25/£10

Short Stories
The Iron Wolf and Other Stories, Allen Lane (London),
1980 . . . . £10/£5
ditto, as *The Unbroken Web: Stories & Fables*, Crown
(New York), 1980 . . . . . . £10/£5
The Bureaucats, Viking Kestrel (London), 1985 . £15/£5
Tales from Watership Down, Hutchinson (London), 1996 .
. . . . £10/£5
ditto, Knopf (New York), 1996 . . . . £10/£5

Poetry
The Tyger Voyage, Cape (London), 1976. . . £20/£10

ditto, Knopf (New York), 1976 . . . . . £20/£10
The Ship's Cat, Cape (London), 1977 . . . £20/£10
ditto, Knopf (New York), 1977 . . . . . £20/£10

Non-Fiction
Nature Through the Seasons, Kestrel (London), 1975 (with
Max Hooper) . . . . £15/£5
ditto, Simon & Schuster (New York), 1975 . . £15/£5
Nature Day and Night, Kestrel (London), 1978 (with Max
Hooper) . . . . £15/£5
ditto, Viking (New York), 1978 . . . . £15/£5
Voyage Through the Antarctic, Allen Lane (London), 1982
(with Ronald Lockley) . . . . . . £15/£5
ditto, Knopf (New York), 1983 . . . . £10/£5
A Nature Diary, Viking (London), 1985 . . . £10/£5
ditto, Viking (New York), 1985 . . . . £10/£5
Day Gone By, Hutchinson (London), 1990 . . £10/£5
ditto, Knopf (New York), 1991 . . . . £10/£5

CHAS ADDAMS
(b.1912 d.1988)

An American cartoonist with a dark sense of humour who
is best known for creating the Addams Family. This
macabre family first made an appearance in 1938, but
Morticia, Gomez *et al* only received their names when
christened by the makers of the 1960s TV series. Most of
Addams' cartoons appeared first in magazines, notably the
New Yorker.

Cartoons
Drawn and Quartered, Random House (New York), 1942 .
. . . . £125/£45
ditto, Hamish Hamilton (London), 1943 . . £100/£30
Addams and Evil, Random House (New York), 1947 £75/£25
ditto, Hamish Hamilton (London), 1947 . . £65/£25
Monster Rally, Simon & Schuster (New York), 1950 £65/£25
ditto, Hamish Hamilton (London), 1951 . . . £50/£20
Homebodies, Simon & Schuster (New York), 1954 £60/£25
ditto, Hamish Hamilton (London), 1954 . . . £50/£20
Nightcrawlers, Simon & Schuster (New York), 1957 £60/£25
ditto, Hamish Hamilton (London), 1957 . . . £50/£20
Black Maria, Simon & Schuster (New York), 1960 £60/£25
ditto, Hamish Hamilton (London), 1960 . . . £50/£20
The Penguin Charles Addams, Penguin (Harmondsworth,
Middlesex), 1962 (pbk) £10
The Groaning Board, Simon & Schuster (New York), 1964
. . . . £40/£15
ditto, Hamish Hamilton (London), 1964 . . . £40/£15
The Chas Addams Mother Goose, Windmill Books/Harper
(New York), 1967 . . . . £40/£15
ditto, Collins (London), 1967 . . . . £40/£15
My Crowd, Simon & Schuster (New York), 1970 . £40/£15
ditto, Tom Stacey (London), 1971 . . . . £40/£15
Favourite Haunts, Simon & Schuster (New York), 1976 .
. . . . £30/£10
ditto, W.H. Allen (London), 1977 . . . £30/£10
Creature Comforts, Simon & Schuster (New York), 1981 .
. . . . £25/£10
ditto, Heinemann (London), 1981 . . . £25/£10
The Addams Family Album, Hamish Hamilton (London),
1991 (pbk) £5

The World of Chas Addams, Knopf (New York), 1991   .
.   .   .   .   £25/£10
ditto, Hamish Hamilton (London), 1992 .   .   . £25/£10

Others
Afternoon in the Attic by John Kobler, Dodd, Mead (New
York), 1950 .   .   .   . £45/£15
Dear Dead Days, Putnam (New York), 1959 .   . £30/£10
ditto, Hamlyn (London), [1960] .   .   .   . £30/£10

JAMES AGEE
(b.1909 d.1955)

U.S. poet, novelist, journalist, film critic, and social activist, Agee led an unorthodox, driven life and died young.
His best known work is the posthumously published novel
A Death in the Family, which won the Pulitzer Prize in
1957. It tells of the tragic impact of a man's death on his
wife and family.

Reportage
Let Us Now Praise Famous Men, Houghton Mifflin
(Boston), 1941 (with Walker Evans, black cloth stamped in
silver) .   .   .   . £2,500/£250
ditto, Peter Owen (London), 1965 .   .   . £45/£15
A Way of Seeing, Viking (New York), 1965 (with Helen
Levitt) .   .   .   . £500/£50

Poetry
Permit Me Voyage, Yale Univ Press (New Haven, CT), 1934
.   .   .   . £450/£65
The Collected Poems of James Agee, Houghton Mifflin
(Boston), 1968 .   .   .   .   .   . £30/£10
ditto, Calder & Boyars (London), 1972 .   . £30/£10

Novels
The Morning Watch, Botteghe Oscure (Rome, Italy) 1950
(offprint from *Botteghe Oscure VI*, printed wraps, glassine
d/w) £500
ditto, Houghton Mifflin (Boston), 1951 .   . £125/£15
ditto, Secker & Warburg (London), 1952 .   . £50/£10
A Death in the Family, McDowell Obolensky (New York),
1957 (first issue 'walking' for 'waking' on p.80). £150/£20
ditto, McDowell Obolensky (New York), 1957 (second
issue) .   .   .   . £45/£10
ditto, Gollancz (London), 1958 .   .   .   . £45/£10

Others
Knoxville: Summer of 1915 for Voice and Orchestra, by
Samuel Barber (music) and Agee (words), Schirmer (New
York), 1949 .   .   .   . £35
ditto, as *Knoxville: Summer 1915*, Aliquando (Toronto),
1970 (100 numbered copies, no music) .   .   . £100
Agee on Film: Reviews and Comments, McDowell Obolensky (New York), 1958 .   .   .   .   . £75/£15
ditto, Peter Owen (London), 1963 .   .   . £30/£10
Agee on Film, Volume Two: Five Film Scripts, McDowell
Obolensky (New York), 1960 .   .   .   . £50/£10
ditto, Peter Owen (London), 1965 .   .   . £30/£10
Letters of James Agee to Father Flye, Braziller (New York),
1962 .   .   .   .   £20/£5
ditto, Peter Owen (London), 1964 .   .   . £15/£5

Four Early Stories, Cummington Press (West Branch, IA),
1964 (285 copies; last of four etchings signed in pencil by
the artist, Keith Achepohl; plain d/w) .   . £125/£100
The Collected Short Prose of James Agee, Houghton
Mifflin (Boston), 1968 .   .   .   .   . £25/£5
ditto, Calder & Boyars (London), 1972 .   .   . £20/£5
The Last Letter of James Agee to Father Flye, Godine
(Boston), 1969 (500 copies; stapled pamphlet) .   . £20

ROBERT AICKMAN
(b.1914 d.1981)

A British short story writer, critic, lecturer and novelist,
Aickman also edited *The Fontana Book of Great Ghost
Stories* between 1964 and 1972. He was the founder of the
Inland Waterways Association, which was instrumental in
saving Britain's rivers and canals.

Short Stories
We Are For the Dark: Six Ghost Stories, Cape (London),
1951 (with Elizabeth Jane Howard). .   . £300/£100
Dark Entries, Collins (London), 1964 .   . £300/£100
Powers of Darkness, Collins (London), 1966 . £250/£100
Sub Rosa, Gollancz (London), 1968 .   .   . £250/£100
ditto, Gollancz (London), 1968 (40 signed copies) .   .
.   .   .   . £450/£300
Cold Hand in Mine, Gollancz (London), 1975 [1976] .   .
.   .   .   . £50/£15
ditto, Scribner's (New York), 1975 [1977] .   . £25/£10
Tales of Love and Death, Gollancz (London), 1977 £75/£20
Painted Devils: Strange Stories, Scribner's (New York),
1979 .   .   .   . £25/£10
Intrusions: Strange Tales, Gollancz (London), 1980 .   .
.   .   .   . £75/£20
Night Voices: Strange Stories, Gollancz (London), 1985 .
.   .   .   . £25/£10
The Wine-dark Sea, Arbor House (New York), 1988 .   .
.   .   .   . £20/£10
ditto, Mandarin (London), 1990 (pbk) £5
The Unsettled Dust, Mandarin (London), 1990 (pbk) . £10
The Collected Strange Stories, Tartarus/Durtro (Horam/
London), 1999 (2 vols) .   .   .   .   . £175/£100

Novels
The Late Breakfasters, Gollancz (London), 1964 £250/£100
ditto, Portway/Chivers (Bath, UK), 1978 .   . £45/£15
The Model, Arbor House (New York), 1987 .   . £10/£5
ditto, Robinson (London), 1988 .   .   .   . £10/£5

Canals
Know Your Waterways, Coram (London), [1955] (wraps) .
.   .   .   . £10
ditto, Coram (London), [1956] .   .   .   . £35/£10
The Story of Our Inland Waterways, Pitman (London),
1955 .   .   .   . £25/£10

Autobiography
The Attempted Rescue, Gollancz (London), 1966 . £150/£60
ditto, Tartarus Press (Carlton-in-Coverdale), 2001 . £20/£5
The River Runs Uphill, Pearson (Burton on Trent, UK),
1986 .   .   .   . £75/£25

CONRAD AIKEN

(b.1889 d.1973)

A poet and novelist, born in Savannah, Georgia, Aiken made his name with his first collection of verse, *Earth Triumphant*. *Selected Poems* was awarded the 1930 Pulitzer Prize. He wrote short stories and novels and an autobiography (*Ushant*). He held the Library of Congress poetry chair from 1950–57 and received the National Medal for Literature in 1969.

Poetry

Earth Triumphant and Other Tales in Verse, Macmillan (New York), 1914 . . . . . £85
Turns and Movies and Other Tales in Verse, Houghton Mifflin (Boston), 1916 (stiff wraps in a d/w attached at the spine) . . . . £100/£15
ditto, Constable (London), 1916 (US sheets used, stiff wraps in a d/w attached at the spine, as above). . . £100/£15
The Jig of Forslin: A Symphony, Four Seas (Boston), 1916 (assumed first issue with 'r' missing in 'warm' on p.117, line 1) . . . . £125/£50
Nocturne of Remembered Spring and Other Poems, Four Seas (Boston), 1917 . . . . £175/£75
The Charnel Rose; Senlin: A Biography; and Other Poems, Four Seas (Boston), 1918 . . . £150/£50
ditto, as *Senlin: A Biography*, Hogarth Press (London), 1925 . . . . £65
The House of Dust: A Symphony, Four Seas (Boston), 1920 . . . . £125/£25
Punch: The Immortal Liar, Documents in His History, Knopf (New York), 1921 . . . . . £125/£25
ditto, Secker (London), 1921 . . . . £125/£25
Priapus and the Pool, Dunster House (Cambridge, MA), 1922 (50 numbered copies) . . . £300/£175
ditto, Dunster House (Cambridge, MA), 1922 (425 copies) . . . . £125/£65
ditto, as *Priapus and the Pool and Other Poems*, Boni & Liveright (New York), 1925 . . . . £125/£25
The Pilgrimage of Festus, Knopf (New York), 1923 £50/£10
Prelude, Random House (New York), 1929 (475 copies; sewn salmon wraps) £25
Selected Poems, Scribner's (New York), 1929 . £125/£35
ditto, Scribner's (New York), 1929 (210 numbered, signed copies in slipcase) . . . . £200/£125
John Deth, a Metaphysical Legend and Other Poems, Scribner's (New York), 1930 . . . . £125/£25
Gehenna, Random House (New York), 1930 (875 copies; stiff paper wraps with paper spine label) . . . £20
The Coming Forth by Day of Osiris Jones, Scribner's (New York), 1931 (with 'THE MUSIC' in caps on p.37) . .
. . . . £125/£25
ditto, Scribner's (New York), 1931 (with 'The Music'). .
. . . . £100/£20
Preludes for Memnon, Scribner's (New York), 1931 £65/£15
Landscape West of Eden, Dent (London), 1934 . £45/£10
ditto, Scribner's (New York), 1935 . . . . £40/£10
Time in the Rock: Preludes to Definition, Scribner's (New York), 1936 . . . . £40/£15
And in the Human Heart, Duell, Sloan & Pearce (New York), 1942 . . . . £35/£10

Brownstone Eclogues and Other Poems, Duell, Sloan & Pearce (New York), 1942 . . . . . £40/£10
The Soldier: A Poem, New Directions (Norfolk, CT), 1944.
. . . . £40/£10
ditto, New Directions (Norfolk, CT), 1944 (paper wraps with attached d/w) . . . . £15/£5
ditto, Editions Poetry London/Nicholson & Watson (London), [1946]. . . . . £30/£10
The Kid, Duell, Sloan & Pearce (New York), 1947 £25/£10
ditto, John Lehmann (London), 1947. . . . £25/£10
The Divine Pilgrim, Univ of Georgia Press (Athens, GA), 1949 . . . . £30/£10
Skylight One: Fifteen Poems, O.U.P. (New York), 1949 .
. . . . £30/£10
ditto, John Lehmann (London), 1951. . . . £30/£10
Collected Poems, O.U.P. (New York), 1953 . £50/£20
A Letter From Li Po and Other Poems, O.U.P. (New York), 1955 . . . . £25/£10
Sheepfold Hill: Fifteen Poems, Sagamore Press (New York), 1958 . . . . £25/£10
The Morning Song of Lord Zero, O.U.P. (New York), 1963 . . . . £25/£10
A Seizure of Limericks, Holt, Rinehart & Winston (New York), 1964 . . . . £20/£5
ditto, W.H. Allen (London), 1965 . . . £20/£5
Thee, Braziller (New York), 1967 . . . £25/£10
ditto, Braziller (New York), 1967 (100 numbered copies signed by Aiken and Baskin of 500, slipcase) . £125/£50
ditto, Braziller (New York), 1967 (400 numbered copies signed by Aiken and Baskin of 500) . . . £75/£45
ditto, Inca Books (London), 1973 (100 numbered copies signed by Aiken of 500, slipcase) . . . £125/£50
ditto, Inca Books (London), 1973 (400 numbered copies signed by Aiken of 500) . . . . . £75/£50
The Clerk's Journal, Eakins Press (New York), 1971 . .
. . . . £10/£5
ditto, Eakins Press (New York), 1971 (300 signed copies, slipcase). . . . . £65/£45

Novels

Blue Voyage, Gerald Howe (London), 1927 . £75/£20
ditto, Scribner's (New York), 1927 . . . £100/£25
ditto, Scribner's (New York), 1927 (125 signed copies, slipcase). . . . . £200/£150
Great Circle, Scribner's (New York), 1933 . £100/£25
ditto, Wishart (London), 1933 . . . . £100/£25
King Coffin, Scribner's (New York), 1935 (bright green cloth, lettered in blue/purple) . . . . £300/£200
ditto, Scribner's (New York), 1935 (yellow cloth, lettered in black) . . . . £75/£25
ditto, Scribner's (New York), 1935 (grey/blue cloth, lettered in gilt) . . . . £75/£25
ditto, Dent (London), 1935 . . . . . £100/£25
A Heart for the Gods of Mexico, Secker (London), 1939 .
. . . . £225/£50
Conversation: or a Pilgrim's Progress, Duell, Sloan & Pearce (New York), 1940 . . . . . £25/£10
ditto, Rodney, Phillips & Green (London), 1940 £25/£10
Ushant: An Essay, Duell, Sloan & Pearce (New York), 1952 . . . . £20/£5
ditto, W.H. Allen (London), 1963 . . . £15/£5
The Collected Novels of Conrad Aiken, Holt, Rinehart & Winston (New York), 1964 . . . . £20/£5
Three Novels, W.H. Allen (London), 1965 . . £25/£10

Short Stories
Bring! Bring! And Other Stories, Secker (London), 1925 .
. . . . £125/£25
ditto, Boni & Liveright (New York), 1925 . . £125/£25
Costumes By Eros, Scribner's (New York), 1928 . £100/£15
Among the Lost People, Scribner's (New York), 1934 . .
. . . . £75/£20
The Short Stories of Conrad Aiken, Duell, Sloan & Pearce
(New York), 1950 . . . . £25/£10
The Collected Short Stories of Conrad Aiken, World
Publishing Co. (Cleveland, OH), 1960 . . . £15/£5

Children's Books
Cats and Bats and Things with Wings, Atheneum (New
York), 1965 . . . . £35/£10
A Little Who's Zoo of Mild Animals, Atheneum (New
York), 1977 . . . . £35/£10
ditto, Cape (London), 1977 (laminated boards; no d/w). £20

Literary Criticism
Scepticisms: Notes on Contemporary Poetry, Knopf (New
York), 1919 (first issue binding burgundy cloth lettered in
gilt). £45
ditto, Knopf (New York), 1919 (second issue black printed
spine & cover) £30
A Reviewer's ABC, Meridian Books (New York), 1958 .
. . . . £25/£10
*Collected Criticism of Conrad Aiken from 1916 to the
Present*, W.H. Allen (London), 1961 . . . £25/£10

Others
Mr Arcularis, Harvard Univ Press (Cambridge, MA), 1957
(play) . . . . £30/£10
Selected Letters of Conrad Aiken, Yale Univ Press (New
Haven, CT), 1978 . . . . £25/£10

JOAN AIKEN

(b.1924 d.2004)

Joan Aiken was the daughter of the American poet, Conrad
Aiken. She worked for the BBC for several years before
her first major novel was published in 1961, after which
she became a full-time writer. She was the author mainly of
children's books and thrillers, and she received the Guardian Award (1969) and the Edgar Allan Poe Award (1972).

'The Wolves of Willoughby Chase' Series
The Wolves of Willoughby Chase, Cape (London), 1962 .
. . . . £125/£25
ditto, Doubleday (Garden City, NY), 1963 . . £75/£10
Black Hearts in Battersea, Cape (London), 1965 . £75/£15
ditto, Doubleday (Garden City, NY), 1964 . . £30/£10
Nightbirds on Nantucket, Cape (London), 1966 . £45/£10
ditto, Doubleday (Garden City, NY), 1966 . . £25/£10
The Whispering Mountain, Cape (London), 1968 . £30/£10
ditto, Doubleday (Garden City, NY), 1969 . . £20/£5
The Cuckoo Tree, Cape (London), 1971 . . . £25/£10
ditto, Doubleday (Garden City, NY), 1971 . . £15/£5
Midnight is a Place, Cape (London), 1974 . . £30/£10
ditto, Viking (New York), 1974 . . . . . £20/£5
The Stolen Lake, Cape (London), 1981 . . . £25/£10

ditto, Delacorte (New York), 1981 . . . . £20/£5
Dido and Pa, Cape (London), 1986 . . . . £20/£5
ditto, Delacorte (New York), 1987 . . . . £15/£5
Is, Cape (London), 1992 . . . . £10/£5
ditto, Delacorte (New York), 1992 . . . . £10/£5
Cold Shoulder Road, Cape (London), 1995 . . £10/£5
ditto, Delacorte (New York), 1995 . . . . £10/£5
Limbo Lodge, Cape (London), 1999 . . . . £10/£5
ditto, as *Dangerous Games*, Delacorte (New York), 1999 .
. . . . £10/£5
Midwinter Nightingale Cape (London), 2003 . . £10/£5
ditto, Delacorte (New York), 2003 . . . . £10/£5
The Witch of Clatteringshaws Cape (London), 2005 £10/£5
ditto, Delacorte (New York), 2005 . . . . £10/£5

'Felix' Novels
Go Saddle the Sea, Doubleday (Garden City, NY), 1977 .
. . . . £15/£5
ditto, Cape (London), 1978 . . . . . . £10/£5
Bridle the Wind, Cape (London), 1983 . . . £15/£5
ditto, Delacorte (New York), 1983 . . . . £10/£5
The Teeth of the Gale, Cape (London), 1988 . . £15/£5
ditto, Harper & Row (New York), 1988 . . . £10/£5

Other Novels for Children
The Kingdom and the Cave, Abelard-Schuman (London),
1960 . . . . £350/£40
ditto, Doubleday (Garden City, NY), 1974 . . £35/£10
The Shadow Guests, Cape (London), 1980 . . £15/£5
ditto, Delacorte (New York), 1980 . . . . £10/£5
The Moon's Revenge, Cape (London), 1987 (no d/w) . £10
ditto, Knopf (New York), 1988 . . . . . £10/£5
The Shoemaker's Boy, Hodder & Stoughton (London), 1991
. . . . £10/£5
ditto, Simon & Schuster (New York), 1994 . . £10/£5
Song of Mat and Ben, Random House (London), 2001 .
. . . . £10/£5
Bone And Dream, Random House (London), 2001 £10/£5
The Scream, Macmillan (London), 2002 . . . £10/£5
Snow White and the Seven Dwarfs, Dorling Kindersley
(London/New York), 2002 . . . . . £10/£5

'Arabel and Mortimer' Short Stories
Arabel's Raven, BBC/Cape (London), 1972 . . £75/£25
ditto, Doubleday (Garden City, NY), 1974 . . £50/£15
The Escaped Black Mamba, BBC (London), 1973 (pbk) £15
The Bread Bin, BBC (London), 1974 (pbk) . . . £5
Mortimer's Tie, BBC (London), 1976 (pbk) . . . £5
Mortimer and the Sword Excalibur, BBC (London), 1979
(pbk) £5
The Spiral Stair, BBC (London), 1979 (pbk) . . . £5
Arabel and Mortimer, Cape (London), 1980 . . £20/£5
ditto, Doubleday (Garden City, NY), 1981 . . £15/£5
Mortimer's Portrait on Glass, BBC (London), 1980 (pbk) .
. . . . £5
Mr Jones's Disappearing Taxi, BBC (London), 1980 (pbk)
. . . . £5
Mortimer's Cross, BBC/Cape (London), 1983 . . £20/£5
ditto, Harper & Row (New York), 1983 . . . £15/£5
Mortimer Says Nothing, Cape (London), 1985 (Contains:
*Mortimer Says Nothing, Arabels Birthday, Mr Jones's Rest
Cure* and *A Call at the Joneses*) . . . . £20/£5
ditto, Harper & Row (New York), 1985 . . . £15/£5

Other Short Stories for Children

All You've Ever Wanted and Other Stories, Cape (London), 1953 . . . . £85/£15

More Than You Bargained For and Other Stories, Cape (London), 1955 . . . . . £75/£15

ditto, Abelard-Schuman (New York), 1957 . . £65/£15

A Necklace of Raindrops and Other Stories, Cape (London), 1968 . . . . . . £150/£25

ditto, Doubleday (Garden City, NY), 1968 . . £100/£15

A Small Pinch of Weather and Other Stories, Cape (London), 1969 . . . . . . £25/£10

All and More, Cape (London), 1971 (contains *All You've Ever Wanted* and *More Than You Bargained For*) £20/£5

The Kingdom Under the Sea and Other Stories, Cape (London), 1971 . . . . . . £30/£10

A Harp of Fishbones and Other Stories, Cape (London), 1972 . . . . £25/£10

All But A Few, Puffin (London), 1974 (pbk) . . . £5

Not What You Expected: A Collection of Short Stories, Doubleday (Garden City, NY), 1974 . . £30/£10

A Bundle of Nerves: Stories of Horror, Suspense and Fantasy, Gollancz (London), 1976 . . . £45/£10

The Faithless Lollybird and Other Stories, Cape (London), 1977 . . . . £30/£10

ditto, Doubleday (Garden City, NY), 1978 . . £25/£10

Tales of A One-Way Street and Other Stories, Cape (London), 1978 . . . . . . £25/£10

ditto, Doubleday (Garden City, NY), 1979 . . £20/£5

Mice and Mendelson, Cape (London), 1978 . . £20/£5

A Touch of Chill: Stories of Horror, Suspense and Fantasy, Gollancz (London), 1979 . . . £20/£5

ditto, Delacorte (New York), 1980 . . . £15/£5

A Whisper in the Night: Stories of Horror, Suspense and Fantasy, Gollancz (London), 1982 . . . £20/£5

ditto, Delacorte (New York), 1984 . . . £15/£5

The Kitchen Warriors, BBC (London), 1983 . . £15/£5

Up The Chimney Down and Other Stories, Cape (London), 1984 . . . . £25/£5

ditto, Harper & Row (New York), 1984 . . . £20/£5

Fog Hounds, Wind Cat, Sea Mice, Macmillan (London), 1984 . . . . £10/£5

The Last Slice of Rainbow and Other Stories, Cape (London), 1985 . . . . . . £25/£5

ditto, Harper & Row (New York), 1988 . . . £20/£5

Past Eight O'Clock, Cape (London), 1986 . . £15/£5

ditto, Viking Kestrel (New York), 1987 . . . £15/£5

A Foot in the Grave, Cape (London), 1989 . . £20/£5

ditto, Viking (New York), 1991 . . . . £20/£5

A Fit of Shivers, Gollancz (London), 1990 . . £25/£5

ditto, Delacorte (New York), 1992 . . . £20/£5

Creepy Company, Gollancz (London), 1993 . . £10/£5

A Handful of Gold, Cape (London), 1995 . . £10/£5

Moon Cake, Hodder & Stoughton (London), 1998. £10/£5

Adult Novels

The Silence of Herondale, Gollancz (London), 1965 . . . . £30/£10

ditto, Doubleday (Garden City, NY), 1964 . . £15/£5

The Fortune Hunters, Doubleday (Garden City, NY), 1965 . . . . £10/£5

Trouble With Product X, Gollancz (London), 1966 £30/£10

ditto, as *Beware of the Bouquet*, Doubleday (Garden City, NY), 1966 . . . . £10/£5

Hate Begins at Home, Gollancz (London), 1967 . £30/£10

ditto, as *Dark Interval*, Doubleday (Garden City, NY), 1967 . . . . £10/£5

The Ribs of Death, Gollancz (London), 1967 . . £30/£10

ditto, as *The Crystal Crow*, Doubleday (Garden City, NY), 1968 . . . . £10/£5

Night Fall, Holt Rinehart & Winston (New York), 1969 . . . . £25/£10

The Embroidered Sunset, Gollancz (London), 1970 £45/£10

ditto, Doubleday (Garden City, NY), 1970 . . £20/£5

Died on a Rainy Sunday, Gollancz (London), 1972 £20/£10

ditto, Holt Rinehart & Winston (New York), 1972 . £15/£5

The Butterfly Picnic, Gollancz (London), 1972 . £35/£10

ditto, as *A Cluster of Separate Sparks*, Doubleday (Garden City, NY), 1972 . . . . . . £10/£5

Voices in an Empty House, Gollancz (London), 1975 . . . . £20/£5

ditto, Doubleday (Garden City, NY), 1975 . . £10/£5

Castle Barebane, Gollancz (London), 1976 . . £15/£5

ditto, Viking (New York), 1976 . . . . £10/£5

Last Movement, Gollancz (London), 1977 . . £15/£10

ditto, Doubleday (Garden City, NY), 1977 . . £10/£5

The Five-Minute Marriage, Gollancz (London), 1977 . . . . £15/£5

ditto, Doubleday (Garden City, NY), 1978 . . £10/£5

The Smile of the Stranger, Gollancz (London), 1978 £15/£5

ditto, Doubleday (Garden City, NY), 1978 . . £10/£5

The Young Lady From Paris, Gollancz (London), 1978 . . . . £15/£5

ditto, as *The Girl From Paris*, Doubleday (Garden City, NY), 1980 . . . . £10/£5

The Lightning Tree, Gollancz (London), 1980 . £15/£5

ditto, as *The Weeping Ash*, Doubleday (Garden City, NY), 1980 . . . . £10/£5

Foul Matter, Gollancz (London), 1983 . . . £15/£5

ditto, Doubleday (Garden City, NY), 1983 . . £10/£5

Mansfield Revisited, Gollancz (London), 1984 . £15/£5

ditto, Doubleday (Garden City, NY), 1985 . . £10/£5

Deception, Gollancz (London), 1987. . . . £15/£5

ditto, as *If I Were You*, Doubleday (Garden City, NY), 1987 . . . . £10/£5

Blackground, Gollancz (London), 1989 . . . £15/£5

ditto, Doubleday (New York), 1989 . . . . £10/£5

Jane Fairfax, Gollancz (London), 1990 . . . £15/£5

ditto, St Martin's Press (New York), 1990 . . £10/£5

The Haunting of Lamb House, Cape (London), 1991 . . . . £15/£5

ditto, St Martin's Press (New York), 1993. . . £10/£5

Morningquest, Gollancz (London), 1992 . . . £10/£5

ditto, St Martin's Press (New York), 1993 . . £10/£5

Eliza's Daughter, Gollancz (London), 1994 . . £10/£5

ditto, St Martin's Press (New York), 1994 . . £10/£5

Emma Watson: The Watsons Completed, Gollancz (London), 1996 (with Jane Austen). . . . £10/£5

ditto, St Martin's Press (New York), 1996 . . £10/£5

The Cockatrice Boys, Gollancz (London), 1996 . £10/£5

ditto, Tor (New York), 1996 . . . . . £10/£5

The Youngest Miss Ward: A Jane Austen Entertainment, Gollancz (London), 1998 . . . . . . £10/£5

ditto, St Martin's Press (New York), 1998 . . £10/£5

Lady Catherine's Necklace Gollancz (London), 1999 £10/£5

ditto, St Martin's Press (New York), 2000 . . £10/£5

Adult Short Stories
Armitage, Armitage, Fly Away Home, Doubleday (Garden City, NY), 1968 . . . . £45/£10
The Windscreen Weepers, Gollancz (London), 1969 . .
. . . . £75/£10
Smoke From Cromwell's Time and Other Stories, Doubleday (Garden City, NY), 1970 . . . £40/£10
The Green Flash and Other Tales of Horror, Suspense and Fantasy, Holt Rinehart & Winston (New York), 1971 .
. . . . £30/£10
The Far Forests: Tales of Romance, Fantasy and Suspense, Viking (New York), 1977 . . . £15/£5
A Goose On Your Grave, Gollancz (London), 1987 £15/£5
The Erl King's Daughter, Heinemann (London), 1988 (pictorial boards). £10
Voices, Scholastic/Hippo (London), 1988 (pbk) . . £5
ditto, as *Return to Harken House*, Delacorte (New York), 1990 . . . . £10/£5
Give Yourself A Fright: Thirteen Tales of the Super-natural, Delacorte (New York), 1989 . . . £10/£5

Plays
Winterthing, Holt Rinehart & Winston (New York), 1972 .
. . . . £15/£5
Winterthing and The Mooncusser's Daughter, Cape (London), 1973 . . . . £15/£5
The Mooncusser's Daughter, Viking (New York), 1974 .
. . . . £15/£5
Street: A Play, Viking (New York), 1978 (illustrated by Arvis Stewart; music by John Sebastian Brown) . £15/£5

Others
Angel Inn, Cape (London), 1976 (translated by Aiken from a story by the Comtesse de Segur) . . . . £15/£5
ditto, Stemmer House (New York), 1978 . . . £15/£5
The Skin Spinners, Viking (New York), 1976 (poetry). .
. . . . £10/£5
The Way To Write For Children, Elm Tree (London), 1982
. . . . £10/£5
ditto, St Martin's Press (New York), 1983 . . £10/£5

KATHLEEN AINSLIE
(b.? d.?)

A British author and illustrator, Ainslie's small books with their Dutch doll characters and handwritten text were influenced by the earlier work of Florence Upton. Her books and calendars were bound in card covers stitched with cord, with red tassels, and each contained full-colour chromolithographs.

Books
Mother's Cherub, Castell (London), [c.1900] . . .£100
Me and Catherine Susan, Castell (London), [1903] .£100
Me and Catherine Susan Earns an Honest Penny, Castell (London), [1903]. £75
Oh! Poor Amelia Jane!, Castell (London), [1905]. . £75
Catherine Susan's Little Holiday, Castell (London), [1905]
. . . . £100
At Great Aunt Martha's, Castell (London), [1905] . £75
Lady Tabitha and Us, Castell (London), [1905] . £75

Catherine and Me's Coming Out, Castell (London), [1905]
. . . . £75
Catherine and Me Goes Abroad, Castell (London), [1905] .
. . . . £75
Sammy Goes A' Hunting, Castell (London), [1905] . £75
Dear Dirty Dolly, Castell (London), [1905] . . . £75
'What I Did', Castell (London), [1905] £75
Mops Versus Tails, Castell (London), [1907] . . . £75
Catherine Susan in Hot Water, Castell (London), [1910] .
. . . . £75
Votes for Catherine Susan and Me, Castell (London), [1910] £75

Calendars
Catherine Susan's Calendar, 1906, Castell (London), [1905] £75
Catherine Susan's Calendar, 1907, Castell (London), [1906] £75
Catherine Susan's Calendar, 1909, Castell (London), [1908] £75
Catherine Susan's Calendar, 1910, Castell (London), [1909] £75

W. HARRISON AINSWORTH
(b.1805 d.1882)

William Harrison Ainsworth was a British historical novelist, born in Manchester, England. He was trained for a career in the law, but after trying publishing took up journalism and literature. *Rookwood*, a 'romance' in which Dick Turpin is the lead character, was his first success. A successor to Sir Walter Scott, he became the leading historical novelist of the mid-nineteenth century. The values suggested here for rebound copies assume plain bindings (very nice bidings in leather etc will be worth more).

Fiction
December Tales, G. & B.W. Whitaker (London), 1823 (anonymous; original boards) £1,000
ditto, G. & B.W. Whitaker (London), 1823 (rebound) .£250
Sir John Chiverton: A Romance, John Ebers (London), 1826 (anonymous; with J.P. Aston; original boards) £1,000
ditto, John Ebers (London), 1826 (rebound) . . £250
Rookwood: A Romance, Richard Bentley (London), 1834 (anonymous; 3 vols; original boards) . . . £2,000
ditto, Richard Bentley (London), 1834 (3 vols; rebound) .
. . . .£350
ditto, Richard Bentley (London), 1834 (second edition; Ainsworth credited as author) £500
ditto, Carey, Lea & Blanchard (Philadelphia, PA), 1835 (2 vols). £750
Crichton, Richard Bentley (London), 1837 (3 vols; original boards) £1,000
ditto, Richard Bentley (London), 1837 (3 vols rebound) .
. . . .£250
ditto, Harper (New York), 1837 (2 vols) £650
Jack Shepard: A Romance, Richard Bentley (London), 1839 (3 vols; original boards; 29 illustrations by Cruikshank) .
. . . . £1,000

ditto, Richard Bentley (London), 1837 (3 vols rebound) £300

The Tower of London, Bentley (London), 1840 (13 monthly parts in 12; wraps; 40 etchings and 58 woodcuts by Cruikshank) £650

ditto, Richard Bentley (London), 1840 (original boards) £400

ditto, Richard Bentley (London), 1840 (rebound) . . £45

ditto, Lea & Blanchard (Philadelphia, PA), 1841 . . £200

Guy Fawkes; or The Gunpowder Treason, Richard Bentley (London), 1841 (3 vols; 22 illustrations by Cruikshank) £1,500

ditto, Lea & Blanchard (Philadelphia, PA), 1841 . . £200

Old Saint Paul's; A Tale of the Plague and the Fire, Hugh Cunningham (London), 1841 (3 vols; 20 illustrations by Franklin) £1,000

ditto, E.P. Williams (Boston), 1844 . . . . £150

The Miser's Daughter, Cunningham & Mortimer (London), 1842 (3 vols; 20 illustrations by Cruikshank) . £1,500

Windsor Castle, Henry Colburn (London) 1843 (3 vols; 3 frontispieces by Cruikshank) £1,000

Modern Chivalry; or, a New Orlando Furioso, John Mortimer (London), 1843 (with Mrs C.F. Gore; 2 vols; 6 illustrations by Cruikshank) £350

St James's; or The Court of Queen Anne, John Mortimer (London), 1844 (3 vols; 9 illustrations by Cruikshank) £750

James the Second; or The Revolution of 1688, Henry Colburn (London), 1848 (3 vols; 3 frontispieces by Buss). £1,500

ditto, Carey and Hart (Philadelphia, PA), 1848 . . £350

The Lancashire Witches: A Novel, printed for private circulation, 1849 . . . . £400

ditto, as **The Lancashire Witches: A Romance of Pendle Forest**, Henry Colburn (London), 1849 (3 vols) . . £750

Auriol; or, The Elixir of Life, Chapman & Hall (London), 1850 (Vol XII in the Uniform Collected Edition; 15 illustrations by 'Phiz') £150

The Flitch of Bacon; or The Customs of Dunmow: A Tale of English Home, George Routledge (London), 1854 (8 illustrations by Gilbert) £125

The Star Chamber, George Routledge (London), 1854 (2 vols; 8 illustrations by 'Phiz') £150

ditto, T.B. Peterson & Bros. (Philadelphia, PA), [187-?] (1 vol). £75

The Spendthrift, George Routledge (London), 1857 (8 illustrations by 'Phiz') £100

The Life and Adventures of Mervyn Clitheroe, Chapman & Hall (London), December 1851-March 1852 (parts 1-4), and George Routledge (London), December 1957-June 1958 (parts 5-12, with 11 and 12 a double number) (wraps; 24 illustrations by 'Phiz') £1,000

ditto, as **Mervyn Clitheroe**, George Routledge (London), 1858 (24 illustrations by 'Phiz') £150

ditto, H. Long & T.B. Peterson (New York/Philadelphia), 1854 (2 vols; with The Life and Adventures of Percival Mayberry) £65

Ovingdean Grange: A Tale of the South Downs, Routledge, Warne, and Routledge, 1860 (8 illustrations by 'Phiz') £125

The Constable of the Tower, Chapman & Hall (London), 1861 (3 vols; 6 illustrations by Gilbert) . . . £350

The Lord Mayor of London; or City Life in the Last Century, Chapman & Hall (London), 1862 (3 vols) . £350

Cardinal Pole; or The Days of Philip and Mary, Chapman & Hall (London), 1863 (3 vols) £350

John Law, Chapman & Hall (London), 1864 (3 vols) . £350

The Spanish Match; or, Charles Stuart at Madrid, Chapman & Hall (London), 1865 (3 vols) . . . £350

The Constable de Bourbon, Chapman & Hall (London), 1866 (3 vols) £250

Old Court, Chapman & Hall (London), 1867 (3 vols) . £250

Myddleton Pomfret, Chapman & Hall (London), 1868 (3 vols) £500

Hilary St Ives, Chapman & Hall (London), 1870 (3 vols) £750

Talbot Harland: A Tale of the Days of Charles the Second, John Dicks (London), 1871 (wraps; 10 illustrations by Gilbert) £225

The South-Sea Bubble: A Tale of the Year 1720, John Dicks (London), 1871 (wraps; 19 illustrations by Corbould) £225

Tower Hill, John Dicks (London), 1871 (wraps; 11 illustrations by Gilbert) £225

Boscobel; or, The Royal Oak: A Tale of the Year 1651, Tinsley Brothers (London), 1872 (3 vols; 12 illustrations by Rimbault) £500

The Good Old Times: The Story of the Manchester Rebels of '45, Tinsley Brothers (London), 1873 (3 vols). . £750

ditto, as **The Manchester Rebels of the Fatal '45**, Tinsley Brothers (London), 1874 . . . . . . £100

Merry England; or, Nobles and Serfs, Tinsley Brothers (London), 1874 (3 vols) £350

The Goldsmith's Wife, Tinsley Brothers (London), 1875 (3 vols) £350

Preston Fight; or, The Insurrection of 1715, Tinsley Brothers (London), 1875 (3 vols) £500

Chetwynd Calverley, Tinsley Brothers (London), 1876 (3 vols) £350

The League of Lathom: A Tale of the Civil War in Lancashire, Tinsley Brothers (London), 1876 (3 vols) £350

The Fall of Somerset, Tinsley Brothers (London), 1877 (3 vols) £350

Beatrice Tyldesley, Tinsley Brothers (London), 1878 (3 vols) £350

Beau Nash; or, Bath in the Eighteenth Century, George Routledge (London), 1879 (3 vols). . . . £350

Stanley Brereton, George Routledge (London), 1881 (3 vols) £350

Verse

Poems by Cheviot Ticheburn, John Arliss (London), 1822 . . . . £750

The Works of Cheviot Ticheburn, Manchester, 1825 . £750

Letters from Cockney Lands, John Ebers (London), 1826 . . . . £500

Ballads: Romantic, Fantastical, and Humorous, George Routledge (London), 1853 (8 illustrations by Gilbert) £75

The Combat of the Thirty, from a Breton Lay of the Fourteenth Century, Chapman & Hall (London), 1859 (wraps) £200

Political Tract

Considerations on the Best Means of Affording Immediate Relief to the Operative Classes in the Manufacturing Districts, John Ebers (London), 1826 . . . . £500

ALAIN-FOURNIER
(b.1886 d.1914)

'Alain-Fournier' was the pen-name of Henri Fournier, author of one novel, *Le Grand Meaulnes*, published in France in 1913. Often translated into English as *The Wanderer* or *The Lost Domain*, it is a classic novel of a lost childhood love. *Miracles* is a collection of prose poems.

Le Grand Meaulnes, Emile-Paul Frères (Paris), 1913 (1,000 copies; pbk) £5,000
Miracles, Gallimard (Paris), 1924 . . . . .£200
The Wanderer, Houghton Mifflin (Boston), 1928 (first translation into English of *Le Grand Meaulnes*, by Françoise Delisle) . . . .£250/£40
ditto, Constable (London), 1929 . . . . . £200/£40
Towards the Lost Domain: Letters from London, 1905, Carcanet (Manchester), 1986 (edited and translated by W.J. Strachan) . . . . £15/£5
Le Grand Meaulnes and *Miracles*, Tartarus Press (Horam, UK), 1999 (first translation of *Miracles* into English, by Adrian Eckersley) . . . . . . £50/£15

ALASTAIR
(b.1887 d.1969)

Alastair was the pseudonym of Hans Henning Voight, an illustrator who owed a great debt to Aubrey Beardsley, but succeeded in offering a decadent style all of his own. *Red Skeletons* is especially rare as the author, Harry Crosby, destroyed many copies by firing a shotgun at them and setting them on fire.

Books Illustrated by Alastair
Forty-Three Drawings by Alastair (with a note of Exclamation by Robert Ross), John Lane (London), 1914 (500 copies; 43 illustrations plus endpaper and cover designs) .
. . . .£650
Poèmes pour Pâques, by Loïs Cendré (Geneva), privately printed, 1915 (printed anonymously by 'Celui qui aime l'amour', 7 illustrations) £500
The Sphinx, by Oscar Wilde, John Lane (London), 1920 (1,000 copies, 10 illustrations, 8 initial letters, 2 endpaper designs, 1 cover design) £600
Carmen, by Prosper Mérimée, Verlag Rascher (Zurich), 1920 (50 copies on Japon paper, 12 illustrations). .£800
ditto, Verlag Rascher (Zurich), 1920 (ordinary edition of 450 copies, 12 illustrations) £300
Die Büchse der Pandora, by Frank Wedekind, George Muller Verlag (Munich), [1921] (12 illustrations) .£300
Erdgeist, by Frank Wedekind, George Muller Verlag (Munich), [1921] (12 illustrations) £200
Salome, by Oscar Wilde, G. Crès (Paris), 1922 (9 illustrations; white printed paper wraps) £100
ditto, G. Crès (Paris), 1922 (100 copies on Imperial Japon paper, 9 illustrations) £500
Die Rache einer Frau, by Barbey d'Aurevilly, (Vienna), 1924 (9 illustrations) £125
Sebastian van Storck, by Walter Pater, Im Avalun Verlag (Vienna), 1924 (480 copies, 8 illustrations) . . £200

ditto, John Lane & Dodd, Mead (London, New York), 1927 (1050 copies, 8 illustrations, of which one is signed in pencil by the artist, slipcase) . . . . £150/£125
ditto, Propyläen Verlag (Frankfurt), 1974 (facsimile reprint of 1924 edition, limited to 400 copies, 8 illustrations) £25
Fifty Drawings, by Alastair, Knopf (New York), 1925 (1025 copies in box) . . . . £300/£200
Red Skeletons, by Harry Crosby, Editions Narcisse (Paris), 1927 (ordinary edition of 337 copies, 9 illustrations) .£600
ditto, Editions Narcisse (Paris), 1927 (33 copies on Imperial Japon paper, 9 illustrations) £1,000
The Fall of the House of Usher, by Edgar Allan Poe, Editions Narcisse (Paris), 1928 (1 copy only on old Japon paper containing the original drawings, 5 illustrations) . £20,000
ditto, Editions Narcisse (Paris), 1928 (307 copies, 5 illustrations; glassine d/w) . . . . . £200/£150
L'Anniversaire de L'Infant, by Oscar Wilde, Black Sun Press (Paris), 1928 (9 illustrations) £250
The Birthday of the Infanta, by Oscar Wilde, Black Sun Press (Paris), 1928 (100 copies, as above but text in English; 9 illustrations; slipcase and glassine d/w) £1,000/£600
Manon Lescaut, by Abbé Prévost, John Lane & Dodd, Mead (London, New York), 1928 (1850 copies, 11 illustrations) . . . .£175/£75
ditto, privately printed for Rarity Press (New York), 1933 (a very poor reprint of the above, 11 illustrations) . . £10
Les Liaisons Dangereuses, by Choderlos de Laclos (translated by Ernest Dowson), Black Sun Press (Paris), 1929 (2 vols, edition of 15 sets on Japon paper, 7 illustrations) .
. . . . £2,500
ditto, Black Sun Press (Paris), 1929 (ordinary edition of 1005 sets, 7 illustrations; bound in card wraps with french-fold printed d/w; slipcase) . . . . . . £3000/£200
ditto, privately printed for William Godwin (New York), 1933 (as *Dangerous Acquaintances*, a very poor reprint of Vol. 1 of above edition) £10
Alastair: Illustrator of Decadence, Thames & Hudson (London), 1979 . . . . £45/£20
ditto, Thames & Hudson (London), 1979 (pbk) . .£5

Poetry
Das Flammende Tal, Hyperion Verlag (Munich), 1920 (680 copies) £350

EDWARD ALBEE
(b.1928)

An American playwright perhaps best-known for *Who's Afraid of Virginia Woolf?* Albee's early work is reminiscent of European Absurdists such as Samuel Beckett, but his theatricalism and an unsympathetic examination of modern America, often with biting dialogue, made him distinct from his contemporaries. Albee has received a number of prizes for his work including three Pulitzer Prizes for drama (for *A Delicate Balance*, *Seascape* and *Three Tall Women*).

Plays
The Zoo Story and *The Sandbox*, Dramatists Play Service (New York), 1960 (stapled pale green wraps) . .£100
The Zoo Story, The Death of Bessie Smith, The Sandbox: Three Plays, Coward-McCann (New York), 1960 (d/w price $2.75) . . . .£175/£45

ditto, Coward-McCann (New York), 1960 (second state d/w with price clipped and $3.50 added) . . . £125/£45
ditto, Coward-McCann (New York), 1960 (pbk) . . £15
ditto, as *The Zoo Story and Other Plays*, Cape (London), 1962 . . . . £50/£10
The American Dream, Coward-McCann (New York), 1961 . . . . £100/£25
ditto, Coward-McCann (New York), 1961 (pbk) . . £15
ditto, French (London), 1961 (pbk) £10
ditto, Cape (London), 1962 . . . . . £40/£10
Who's Afraid of Virginia Woolf?, Atheneum (New York), 1962 . . . . £300/£35
ditto, Cape (London), 1964 . . . . . . £100/£10
The American Dream, The Death of Bessie Smith, Fam and Yam: Three Plays, Dramatists Play Service (New York), 1962 (stapled orange paper wraps) . . . £10
The Ballad of the Sad Café, Houghton Mifflin/Atheneum (Boston/New York), 1963 (from the novel by Carson McCullers) . . . . £45/£10
ditto, Houghton Mifflin/Atheneum (Boston/New York), 1963 (pbk) £10
ditto, Cape (London), 1965 . . . . . £20/£10
Tiny Alice, Atheneum (New York), 1965 . . £10/£5
ditto, Cape (London), 1966 . . . . . £10/£5
Malcolm, Atheneum (New York), 1966 (from the novel by James Purdy) . . . . £20/£5
ditto, Cape/Secker & Warburg (London), 1967 £15/£5
A Delicate Balance, Atheneum (New York), 1966. £20/£5
ditto, Cape (London), 1968 . . . . . £15/£5
Everything in the Garden, Atheneum (New York), 1968 (from a play by British playwright Giles Cooper) £15/£5
Box and *Quotations from Chairman Mao Tse-Tung: Two Inter-Related Plays*, Atheneum (New York), 1969 £15/£5
ditto, Cape (London), 1970 . . . . . £15/£5
All Over, Atheneum (New York), 1971 . . £15/£5
ditto, Cape (London), 1972 . . . . . £15/£5
Seascape, Atheneum (New York), 1975 . . £15/£5
ditto, Cape (London), 1976 (pbk) £10
Counting the Ways & Listening, Two Plays, Atheneum (New York), 1977 . . . . . . £15/£5
The Lady From Dubuque, Atheneum (New York), 1980 . . . . £10/£5
Lolita, Dramatists Play Service (New York), 1984 (from the novel by Vladimir Nabokov; pbk) £10
Three Tall Women, Dutton (New York), 1995 £10/£5
ditto, Penguin (London), 1995 (pbk) £5
Edward Albee's Fragments, A Sit-around, Dramatists Play Service (New York), 1995 (pbk) £10
The Play about the Baby, The Overlook Press (Woodstock, NY), 2003 . . . . . . £10/£5
ditto, Methuen (London), 2004 . . . . £10/£5
The Goat, Or Who Is Sylvia?, The Overlook Press (Woodstock, NY), 2003 . . . . . £10/£5
ditto, Methuen (London), 2004 . . . . £10/£5

Collected Editions
Plays, Volume 1, Coward, McCann & Geoghegan (New York), 1981 (pbk) £5
Plays, Volume 2, Atheneum (New York), 1982 (pbk) . £5
Plays, Volume 3, Atheneum (New York), 1982 (pbk) . £5
Plays, Volume 4, Atheneum (New York), 1982 (pbk) . £5
The Collected Plays of Edward Albee: Volume 1, 1958-1965, Overlook Press (Woodstock, NY), 2004 . £10/£5
ditto, Duckworth (London), 2004 . . . . £10/£5

The Collected Plays of Edward Albee: Volume 2, 1966-1977, Overlook Press (Woodstock, NY), 2005 . £10/£5
ditto, Duckworth (London), 2005 . . . . £10/£5
The Collected Plays of Edward Albee: Volume 3, 1978-2003, Overlook Press (Woodstock, NY), 2006 . £10/£5
ditto, Duckworth (London), 2006 . . . . £10/£5

Non-Dramatic Writings
Stretching My Mind: Essays 1960-2005, Carroll & Graf (New York), 2005 . . . . . . £10/£5

LOUISA MAY ALCOTT
(b.1832 d.1888)

Best known as a writer for children, this American novelist's first success was with the widely-reprinted *Little Women*. However, Alcott also wrote a number of thrillers and potboilers, a few of which were published under the pseudonym 'A.M. Barnard', but most of which were printed anonymously in magazines. These latter works have been collected in various volumes since the 1970s.

Margaret Lyon, Crosby, Nichols & Co. (Boston), 1854 (from magazine plates) £2,500
Flower Fables, George W. Briggs & Co (Boston), 1855 (frontispiece and 5 plates; various colours of cloth blocked in gilt) £1,000
ditto, Roberts Bros (Boston), 1855 (brown cloth binding) £600
Hospital Sketches, Redpath (Boston), 1863 (advert on back announcing Wendell Phillips' *Speeches* at $2.50, not $2.25; bound in boards) £400
Hospital Sketches, Redpath (Boston), 1863 (second issue bound in cloth) £300
ditto, as Hospital Sketches and Camp & Fireside Stories, Roberts Bros (Boston), 1869 . . . . £125
ditto, as Hospital Sketches and Camp & Fireside Stories, Sampson Low (London), 1870. . . . . . £100
On Picket Duty, Redpath (Boston), [1864] (green, printed wraps) £1,000
The Rose Family: A Fairy Tale, Redpath (Boston), 1864 (wraps) £1,000
Moods, Loring (Boston), 1865 (without copyright notice) £100
ditto, Loring (Boston), 1865 (copyright notice printed on a slip of paper pasted to the verso of the title-page) . £75
ditto, Routledge (London), 1866. . . . . £75
Nelly's Hospital, [Boston, 1865] (self-wraps) . . £1,500
The Foundling, Thomas & Talbot (Boston), [1867] (pseud 'Perley Parker'; printed wraps). £2,500
The Mysterious Key, and What It Opened, Elliott, Thomas & Talbot (Boston), [1867] (blue wraps; various imprints on front wrapper) £1,000
Morning-Glories and Other Stories, H.B. Faller (Boston), 1868 . . . . £450
Kitty's Class Day, Loring (Boston) [1867] (printed buff wraps; Loring copyright notice pasted over imprint of Rockwell & Rollins) £1,000
Aunt Kipp, Loring (Boston) [1868] (printed buff wraps) £1,000
Psyche's Art, Loring (Boston) [1868] (printed buff wraps) £1,000

Louisa M. Alcott's Proverb Stories, Loring (Boston) [1868] (printed wraps) £1,000

Little Women, or Meg, Jo, Beth and Amy, Roberts Bros (Boston), 1868 (without 'Part One' on spine; frontispiece and 3 plates). £4,000

ditto, Sampson Low (London), 1868 . . . . . £300

Three Proverb Stories: Kitty's Class-Day; Aunt Kipp; Psyche's Art, Loring (Boston), 1868 . . . . £35

ditto, Sampson Low (London), 1882 . . . . . £30

Little Women Part 2, Roberts Bros (Boston), 1869 (no reference on p.iv to 'Little Women, Part First') . £3,000

ditto, as *Good Wives*, Sampson Low (London), 1869 . £200

An Old Fashioned Girl, Roberts Bros (Boston), 1870 (first printing without ads on copyright page). . . . £75

ditto, Sampson Low (London), 1870 . . . . . £35

V.V.: or, Plots and Counterplots, Thomas & Talbot (Boston), 1865 [1870] (pseud 'A.M. Brannard'; blue printed wraps) £1,500

Will's Wonder Book, Horace B. Fuller (Boston), [1870] £1,500

Little Men, Life at Plumfield with Jo's Boys, Sampson Low (London), 1871 (frontispiece; blue cloth) . . £150

ditto, Roberts Bros (Boston), 1871 (green cloth; first issue with adverts at front listing *Pink and White Tyranny* as nearly ready). £450

Aunt Jo's Scrap-Bag: My Boys, Sampson Low (London), 1871. . . . . £75

ditto, Roberts Bros (Boston), 1872 . . . . . £150

Aunt Jo's Scrap-Bag: Shawl Straps, Roberts Bros (Boston), 1872 . . . . £75

ditto, Sampson Low (London), 1873 [1872] . . £75

Work, A Story of Experience, Sampson Low (London), 1873 (2 vols) £125

ditto, Roberts Bros (Boston), 1873 (1 vol) . . £75

Aunt Jo's Scrap-Bag: Cupid & Chow Chow, Sampson Low (London), 1873 . . . . £35

ditto, Roberts Bros (Boston), 1874 . . . . . £75

Something To Do, Ward Lock (London), [1873] . . £60

Fireside & Camp Stories, Ward Lock (London), 1873 . £60

Eight Cousins, or The Aunt Hill, Roberts Bros (Boston), 1875 . . . . £200

ditto, Sampson Low (London), 1875 . . . . . £75

Beginning Again, Being A Continuation of 'Work', Sampson Low (London), 1875. . . . . . £75

Silver Pitchers and Other Stories, Roberts Bros (Boston), 1876 . . . . £75

ditto, Sampson Low (London), 1876 . . . . . £75

Rose in Bloom, A Sequel To 'Eight Cousins', Roberts Bros (Boston), 1876 . . . . £100

ditto, Sampson Low (London), 1877 . . . . . £75

A Modern Mephistopheles, Roberts Bros (Boston), 1877 (anonymous). £100

ditto, Sampson Low (London), 1877 . . . . . £45

Aunt Jo's Scrap-Bag: My Girls, Roberts Bros (Boston), 1878 . . . . £75

Under the Lilacs, Sampson Low (London), 1877-78 (issued in 11 monthly parts) £200

ditto, Sampson Low, 1878 (first book edition). . . £50

ditto, Roberts Bros (Boston), 1878 . . . . . £200

Aunt Jo's Scrap-Bag: Jimmy's Cruise in the 'Pinafore', Sampson Low (London), 1879. . . . . . £20

ditto, Roberts Bros (Boston), 1879 . . . . . £75

Jack and Jill: A Village Story, Roberts Bros (Boston), 1880 . . . . £75

ditto, Sampson Low (London), 1880 . . . . . £20

Aunt Jo's Scrap-Bag: An Old Fashioned Thanksgiving And Other Stories, Roberts Bros (Boston), 1882 . £75

ditto, Sampson Low (London), 1882 . . . . . £15

Spinning Wheel Stories, Roberts Bros (Boston), 1884 . £75

ditto, Sampson Low (London), 1884 . . . . . £30

Lulu's Library, Roberts Bros (Boston), 1886-9 (3 vols) £75

ditto, Sampson Low (London), 1884 . . . . . £30

Jo's Boys And How They Turned Out, Roberts Bros (Boston), 1886 . . . .£200

ditto, Sampson Low (London), 1886 . . . . .£100

Lulu's Library: The Frost King, Roberts Bros (Boston), 1887 (mainly reprint material from *Flower Fables*) . £40

A Garland For Girls, Roberts Bros (Boston), 1888 . £65

ditto, Blackie & Sons (London), 1888 . . . . £30

Lulu's Library: Recollections, Roberts Bros (Boston), 1889 . . . . £40

ditto, as *Recollections of My Childhood Days*, Sampson Low (London), 1890 . . . . £35

Comic Tragedies, Written by 'Jo' and 'Meg', Roberts Bros (Boston), 1893 . . . . £75

ditto, Sampson Low (London), 1893 . . . . . £40

A Hole in the Wall, Little, Brown (Boston), [1899] . £45

Marjorie's Three Gifts, Little, Brown (Boston), [1899] £45

May Flowers, Little, Brown (Boston), [1899] . . £45

The Candy Country, Little, Brown (Boston), [1900] . £45

Poppies and Wheat, Little, Brown (Boston), [1900] . £45

A Christmas Dream, Little, Brown (Boston), [1901] . £45

Little Button Rose, Little, Brown (Boston), [1901] . £45

The Doll's Journey, Little, Brown (Boston), [1902] . £45

Pansies and Water-Lilies, Little, Brown (Boston), [1902] £45

Mountain-Laurel and Maidenhair, Little, Brown (Boston), [1903] £45

Morning-Glories and Queen Aster, Little, Brown (Boston), [1904] £45

Behind a Mask, The Unknown Thrillers of Louisa M. Alcott, Morrow (New York), 1975 . . . . £15/5

ditto, W.H. Allen (London), 1976 . . . . £10/£5

Plots and Counterplots, Morrow (New York), 1976 £10/£5

ditto, W.H. Allen, 1977. . . . . . £10/£5

Diana and Persis, Arno (New York), 1978 (unfinished) . . . . £50/£15

A Long Fatal Love Chase, Random House (New York), 1995 (written 1866) . . . . . . £10/£5

ditto, as *The Chase, or A Long Fatal Love Chase*, Century (London), 1995 . . . . £10/£5

The Inheritance, Dutton (New York), 1997 (written 1849) . . . . £10/£5

ditto, Penguin (London), 1998 (wraps) . . . £5

The Hidden Louisa May Alcott, Avenal (New York), 1984. . . . . £10/£5

A Double Life: Newly Discovered Thrillers of Louisa May Alcott, Little, Brown (Boston), 1988 . . £10/£5

Freaks of Genius: Unknown Thrillers of Louisa May Alcott, Greenwood (Westport, CT), 1991 . . £10/£5

From Jo March's Attic: Stories of Intrigue and Suspense, Northeastern Univ Press (Boston), 1993 . £10/£5

A Whisper in the Dark: Twelve Thrilling Tales, Barnes & Noble (New York), 1996 . . . . . . £10/£5

CECIL ALDIN
(b.1870 d.1935)

Aldin studied at South Kensington School of Art and worked as a comic illustrator in the 1890s. He later became a successful sporting artist, being an extremely adroit observer and illustrator of dogs. Aldin also contributed illustrations to the *Boy's Own Paper* and the *Oxford Annual*.

Spot, An Autobiography, Houlston (London), 1894 (14 b/w illustrations) £135
Wonderland Wonders, by Rev. John Isabell, Home Words (London), 1895 (frontispiece and 19 plates) . . . £100
Every-Day Characters, by Winthrop Mackworth Praed, Kegan, Paul, Trench, Trubner & Co. (London), 1896 (b/w illustrations) £165
Prehistoric Man and Beast, by Henry Neville, Hutchinson, Smith, Elder & Co (London), 1896 . . . . . £75
Two Little Runaways, by James Buckland, Longman (London), 1898 . . . . £100
Two Well-Worn Shoe Stories, Sands & Co. (London), 1899 (illustrations by Aldin and John Hassall) £250
A Cockney in Arcadia, by Harry Spurr, George Allen (London), 1899 (28 illustrations by Aldin and John Hassall) £80
ditto, Harper, New York, 1899 . . . . . £75
Ten Little Puppy Dogs, Sands & Co. (London), [1902]. £225
A Sporting Garland, Sands & Co. (London), 1902 (23 colour plates) £650
Faithful Friends, Blackie (London), 1902 . . . £100
Bubble and Squeak, by P. Robinson, Isbister (London), 1902 . . . . £300
A Dog Day, or The Angel in the House, by Walter Emanuel, Heinemann (London), 1902 (28 full-page black, white & red on brown plates) £125
The House Annual, Gale & Palden (London), 1902 . £75
The Young Folks Birthday Book, Hills (London), 1902 £50
The Snob: Some Episodes In a Mis-spent Youth, by Walter Emanuel, Lawrence & Bullen (London), 1904 (19 colour plates) £125
A Gay Dog: The Story of a Foolish Year, by Walter Emanuel, Heinemann (London), 1905 (24 colour plates) .
. . . . £150
The Dogs of War, by Walter Emanuel, Bradbury Agnew (London), [1906] (frontispiece and 11 colour plates) . £200
The Happy Annual, Heinemann (London), 1907 (with John Hassall) £75
Old Christmas, by Washington Irving, Hodder & Stoughton (London), 1908 (27 colour plates, 6 b/w illustrations). £150
Farm Friends for Little Folk, Blackie (London), 1908. £100
The Playtime Picture Books, Lawrence & Jellicoe (London), 1909 (series). . . . . £175 each
Pussy and Her Ways, Henry Frowde/Hodder & Stoughton (London), [1909]. £200
Doggie and His Ways, Henry Frowde/Hodder & Stoughton (London), [1909]. £200
The Black Puppy Book, Henry Frowde/Hodder & Stoughton (London), [1909]. £225
The White Puppy Book, Henry Frowde/Hodder & Stoughton (London), [1909] (12 colour plates) . . . £225
ditto, O.U.P. (New York), [1929] . . . . £125/£45

The White Kitten Book, Henry Frowde/Hodder & Stoughton (London), [1909] (11 colour plates) . . . £225
Pickles, A Puppy Dog's Tale, Henry Frowde/Hodder & Stoughton (London), [1909] (24 colour plates) . . £350
The Perverse Widow, and *The Widow* by R. Steele, and Washington Irving, Heinemann (London), 1909 (3 colour plates) £25
Wives, and *The Henpecked Man* by Washington Irving, and R. Steele, Heinemann (London), 1909 (3 colour plates) £25
Bachelors, and *Bachelor's Confessions* by Washington Irving, Heinemann (London), 1909 (3 colour plates) . £25
Rough and Tumble, Henry Frowde/Hodder & Stoughton (London), [1910]. £350
Field Babies, Henry Frowde/Hodder & Stoughton (London), [1910] (24 colour plates) £200
The Twins, Henry Frowde/Hodder & Stoughton (London), [1910] (24 colour plates) £325
The Red Puppy Book, Henry Frowde/Hodder & Stoughton (London), [1910] (12 colour plates) . . . £200
My Pets, Henry Frowde/Hodder & Stoughton (London), [1910] £100
An Old-Fashioned Christmas Eve, by Washington Irving, Hodder & Stoughton (London), 1910 . . . £50
An Old-Fashioned Christmas Day, by Washington Irving, Hodder & Stoughton (London), 1910 (6 colour plates) £50
The Posthumous Papers of the Pickwick Club, by Charles Dickens, Chapman & Hall/Lawrence & Jellicoe (London), 1910 (2 vols, vol. I with 13 colour plates, vol. II with 11 colour plates) £150
ditto, Chapman & Hall/Lawrence & Jellicoe (London), 1910 (as above but 250 signed copies) £250
My Book of Doggies: Stories and Pictures for Little Folk, Blackie (London), [1910] £100
Farm Babies, by May Byron, Henry Frowde/Hodder & Stoughton (London), [1911] (24 colour plates) . . £300
Handley Cross, Or Mr. Jorrock's Hunt, by Robert Smith Surtees, Edward Arnold (London), [1911] (12 colour plates in each of 2 vols) £100
Farmyard Puppies, Henry Frowde/Hodder & Stoughton (London), [1911] (12 colour plates) . . . £250
Merry and Bright, Henry Frowde/Hodder & Stoughton (London), [1911] (24 colour plates) . . . £350
Mac: A Story of a Dog, Henry Frowde/Hodder & Stoughton (London), [1912] (24 colour plates) . . . £350
The Mongrel Puppy Book, Henry Frowde/Hodder & Stoughton (London), [1912] (12 colour plates) . . £200
Puppy Tails, by Richard Waylett, Lawrence & Jellicoe (London), [1912]. £125
Black Beauty, by Anna Sewell, Jarrold (London), [1912] (18 colour plates) £100
ditto, Jarrold (London), [1912] (250 copies) . . £300
White-Ear and Peter: The Story of a Fox and a Fox-Terrier, by Neils Heiberg, Macmillan (London), 1912 (16 colour plates) £150
Cecil Aldin's Happy Family, by May Byron, Henry Frowde/Hodder & Stoughton (London), [1912] (6 parts, illustrated in colour) . . . . . . £75 each
ditto, Henry Frowde/Hodder & Stoughton (London), [1912] (single volume edition) £100
Cecil Aldin's Merry Party, by May Byron, Henry Frowde/Hodder & Stoughton (London), [1913] (6 parts, illustrated in colour) . . . . . . £75 each
ditto, Henry Frowde/Hodder & Stoughton (London), [1913] (single volume edition) £100

My Dog, by Maurice Maeterlinck, Allen (London), 1913 (6 colour plates) £100

Zoo Babies, by G.E. Farrow, Henry Frowde/Hodder & Stoughton (London), 1913 . . . . .£125

The Merry Puppy Book, Milford (London), 1913 (36 colour plates) £275

The Underdog, by Sidney Trist, Animals' Guardian (London), 1913 (4 plates) £75

Cecil Aldin's Rag Book, The Animals' School Treat, by Clifton Bingham, Dean: 'Rag Book' series No. 70, [1913] (24 colour plates). £175

The Bobtail Puppy Book, Henry Frowde/Hodder & Stoughton (London), [1914] (12 colour plates) . .£225

Jack and Jill, by May Byron, Henry Frowde/Hodder & Stoughton (London), [1914] (24 colour plates) . .£400

The Dog Who Wasn't What He Thought He Was, by Walter Emanuel, Raphael Tuck (London), [1914] (24 colour plates) £250

Animal Revels, by May Byron, Henry Frowde/Hodder & Stoughton (London), [1915] £100

Moufflou, by Ouida, T.C. & E.C. Jack (London), 1915. £100

The Cecil Aldin Painting Books, Lawrence & Jellicoe (London), [1915]. £125

Jock and Some Others, by Richard Waylett, Gale & Polden (London), [1916] (16 colour plates) £250

Animal Frolics, by May Byron, Henry Frowde/Hodder & Stoughton (London), [1916] £100

The Merry Party, Humphrey Milford (London), [1918] £150

Bunnyborough, Humphrey Milford (London), [1919] . £275

ditto, Eyre & Spottiswoode (London), 1946 (15 colour plates) . . . .£75/£25

Gyp's Hour of Bliss, by Gladys Davidson, Collins (London), 1919 . . . .£200

The Great Adventure, Humphrey Milford (London), [1921] (17 colour plates). £250

Cecil Aldin Letter Books, Humphrey Milford (London), [1921] (6 parts) £125

Old Inns, Heinemann (London), 1921 (16 plates) .£150/£75

ditto, Heinemann (London), 1921 (380 signed copies) .£200

ditto, Doubleday, Page (Garden City, NY), 1921 .£125/£45

Us, Humphrey Milford (London), [1922] . .£150/£75

Right Royal by John Masefield, Heinemann (London), 1922 (4 plates) . . . .£100/£25

Old Manor Houses, Heinemann (London), 1923 (12 plates) . . . .£100/£65

Jack Frost Days, Collins (London), 1923 (with John Hassall) . . . .£150/£75

Cathedrals and Abbey Churches of England, Eyre & Spottiswoode (London), 1924 (16 plates) . .£35/£10

ditto, Eyre & Spottiswoode (London), 1929 (375 signed copies) £250

Ratcatcher to Scarlet, Eyre & Spottiswoode (London), 1926 . . . .£125/£45

Dogs of Character, Eyre & Spottiswoode (London), 1927 . . . .£125/£45

ditto, Eyre & Spottiswoode (London), 1927 (250 signed copies with an original signed sketch) £500

A Dozen Dogs Or So, by P.R. Chalmers, Eyre & Spottiswoode (London), 1927 (13 colour plates) .£150/£65

ditto, Eyre & Spottiswoode (London), 1927 (13 colour plates, 250 copies, signed by Aldin and Chalmers) .£300

Berkshire Vale, by Wilfred Howe-Nurse, Basil Blackwell (Oxford), 1927 (22 plates). . . . .£150/£100

The Romance of the Road, Eyre & Spottiswoode (London), 1928 (12 colour plates and colour map of London in front pocket) . . . .£225/£150

Forty Fine Ladies, Eyre & Spottiswoode (London), 1929 . . . .£200/£125

ditto, Eyre & Spottiswoode (London), 1929 (250 signed copies) £300

Sleeping Partners: A Series of Episodes, Eyre & Spottiswoode (London), [1929] (20 colour plates) . £300/£200

Jerry: The Story of an Exmoor Pony, by Eleanor E. Helme and Nance Paul, Eyre & Spottiswoode (London), [1930] (11 b/w illustrations) . . . . . .£50/£10

Roads and Vagabonds, by Kenneth Hare, Eyre & Spottiswoode (London), [1930] . . . .£175/£75

ditto, Eyre & Spottiswoode (London), [1930] (50 copies signed by Hare and Aldin). £225

ditto, Scribner's (New York), 1930 . . . .£125/£45

An Artist's Models, H.F. & G. Witherby (London), 1930 (20 colour plates) . . . . . .£250/£175

ditto, H.F. & G. Witherby (London), 1930 (250 signed copies) £350

ditto, Scribner's (Mew York), 1930 . . .£150/£50

Riding, by Lady Hunloke, Eyre & Spottiswoode (London), 1931 . . . .£45/£20

Mrs Tickler's Caravan, Eyre & Spottiswoode (London), 1931 . . . .£75/£30

ditto, Scribner's (New York), 1931 . . . .£65/£15

Lost, Stolen or Strayed, by Marion Ashmore, Eyre & Spottiswoode (London), 1931 (30 b/w illustrations and colour frontispiece) . . . .£65/£25

ditto, Scribner's (New York), 1931 . . . .£50/£20

Flax, Police Dog, by Svend Fleuron, Eyre & Spottiswoode (London), [1931] (10 b/w illustrations) . . .£65/£35

The Bunch Book, by James Douglas, Eyre & Spottiswoode (London), 1932 (51 b/w illustrations and coloured frontispiece) . . . .£50/£20

ditto, Appleton (New York), 1932 . . . .£45/£15

The Joker, and Jerry Again, by Eleanor E. Helme and Nance Paul, Eyre & Spottiswoode (London), 1932 . . . .£45/£15

The Cecil Aldin Book, Eyre & Spottiswoode (London), 1932 (8 colour plates and 95 b/w illustrations) . .£75/£45

Scarlet, Blue and Green, by Duncan Fife, Macmillan (London), 1932 (5 colour plates, 7 half-tone and 25 b/w illustrations). . . . .£100/£50

His Apologies, by Rudyard Kipling, Doubleday Doran (Garden City, NY), 1932 . . . . . .£65/£35

Dogs of Every Day, by Patrick Chalmers, Eyre & Spottiswoode (London), 1933 (12 full-page mono plates) . . . .£100/£65

Who's Who in the Zoo, Eyre & Spottiswoode (London), 1933 (4 colour plates and 35 full-page b/w illustrations) . . . .£65/£30

ditto, Houghton Mifflin (Boston), 1933 . .. .£50/£25

Scarlet to M.F.H., Eyre & Spottiswoode (London), 1933 (21 plates) . . . .£175/£50

Hotspur the Beagle, by John Vickerman, Constable (London), 1934 . . . .£65/£45

Time I Was Dead: Pages from my Autobiography, Eyre & Spottiswoode (London), 1934 . . . .£65/£45

Just Among Friends, Eyre & Spottiswoode (London), 1934 . . . .£300/£150

ditto, Scribner's (New York), 1934 . . . .£200/£75

How to Draw Dogs, John Lane/Bodley Head (London), 1935
.   .   .   .   £150/£100
ditto, Bridgman (Pelham, NY), [1936]   .   .   £100/£45
Exmoor, The Riding Playground of England, Witherby
(London), 1935 (4 plates) .   .   .   .   .   £50/£20
Smuggler's Gallows, by William E.S. Hope, Eyre &
Spottiswoode (London), 1936 .   .   .   .   £35/£20
Hunting Scenes, Eyre & Spottiswoode (London), 1936   .
.   .   .   .   £175/£100
ditto, Scribner's (New York), 1936 .   .   .   . £125/£45
Last Muster, Eyre & Spottiswoode (London), 1939 £75/£45

RICHARD ALDINGTON
(b.1892 d.1962)

Richard Aldington was an English poet, novelist and
literary scholar. He is probably best known for his war
poetry (he served on the Western Front from 1916-18), but
he was also one of the first three Imagist poets, along with
his first wife, H.D., and Ezra Pound. He moved to the
United States in 1942, where he began to write biographies,
the last being of T.E. Lawrence, of whom he was highly
critical.

Novels
Death of a Hero, Chatto & Windus (London), 1929   .   .
.   .   .   .   £100/£40
ditto, Covici Friede (New York), 1929   .   .   £45/£20
ditto, Babou & Kahane (Paris), 1930 (first unexpurgated
edition, 300 copies, 2 vols, tissue d/w; slipcase) £400/£300
The Colonel's Daughter. A Novel, Chatto & Windus
(London), 1931 .   .   .   .   .   .   £25/£5
ditto, Chatto & Windus (London), 1931 (210 signed,
numbered copies) £40
ditto, Doubleday (Garden City, NY), 1931   .   £20/£5
Stepping Heavenward - A Record, Orioli (Florence), 1931
(808 signed, numbered copies).   .   .   £45/£30
ditto, Chatto & Windus (London), 1931 .   .   £25/£5
All Men are Enemies: A Romance, Chatto & Windus
(London), 1932 .   .   .   .   .   .   £25/£5
ditto, Chatto & Windus (London), 1933 (110 signed copies)
.   .   .   .£100
ditto, Doubleday (Garden City, NY), 1933   .   £25/£5
Women Must Work, Chatto & Windus (London), 1934 £35/£5
ditto, Doubleday (Garden City, NY), 1934   .   £30/£5
Very Heaven, Heinemann (London), 1937   .   . £15/£5
ditto, Doubleday (Garden City, NY), 1937   .   £15/£5
Seven Against Reeves: A Comedy-Farce, Heinemann
(London), 1938 .   .   .   .   .   .   £10/£5
ditto, Doubleday (Garden City, NY), 1938   .   £10/£5
Rejected Guest, Viking (New York), 1939   .   £15/£5
ditto, Heinemann (London), 1939   .   .   .   £10/£5
The Romance of Casanova: a Novel, Duell, Sloan & Pearce
(New York), 1946 .   .   .   .   .   £15/£5
ditto, Heinemann (London), 1946   .   .   £10/£5

Short Stories
Roads to Glory, Chatto & Windus (London), 1930. £65/£15
ditto, Chatto & Windus (London), 1930 (360 numbered
copies) £75
ditto, Doubleday (Garden City, NY), 1931   .   £30/£10

Two Stories, Elkin Mathews & Marrot (London), 1930 (530
signed, numbered copies) .   .   .   .   £65/£35
At All Costs, Heinemann (London), 1930   .   . £15/£5
ditto, Heinemann (London), 1930 (275 signed, numbered
copies). £35
Last Straws, Hours Press (Paris), 1930 (500 numbered
copies out of 700) £50
ditto, Hours Press (Paris), 1930 (200 signed, numbered
copies out of 700) £150
Soft Answers, Chatto & Windus (London), 1932 . £20/£5
ditto, Chatto & Windus (London), 1932 (110 signed copies)
.   .   .   .   £65
ditto, Doubleday (Garden City, NY), 1932   .   £20/£5

Poetry
Images (1910-1915), The Poetry Bookshop (London), 1915
(sewn wraps) £100
ditto, as *Images Old and New*, Four Seas Company (Boston),
1916 .   .   .   .   £65/£25
*The Love of Myrrhine and Konallis And Other Prose
Poems*, The Clerk's Press (Cleveland, OH), 1917 (40
copies; sewn wraps) £250
ditto, Pascal Covici (Chicago), 1926 (150 signed copies)   .
.   .   .   .   £75/£45
ditto, Pascal Covici (Chicago), 1926 (unsigned copies).   .
.   .   .   .   £25/£5
Reverie, A Little Book of Poems for H.D., The Clerk's Press
(Cleveland, OH), 1917 (50 copies; sewn wraps) .   .£150
Images of War, Beaumont Press (London), 1919 (30
numbered, signed copies, in box) £400
ditto, Beaumont Press (London), 1919 (50 copies on
cartridge paper numbered 31 to 80).   .   .   £200
ditto, Beaumont Press (London), 1919 (120 unsigned copies
on handmade paper, numbered 81 to 200)   .   .   £75
ditto, Allen & Unwin (London), 1919   .   .   .   £45
ditto, Four Seas Company (Boston), 1921 (paper-covered
boards) £45
Images of Desire, Elkin Mathews/Riverside Press (London),
1919 (wraps). £25
Images, The Egoist Ltd (London), 1919 .   .   .   £30
War and Love (1915-1918), Four Seas Company (Boston),
1919 .   .   .   .   £35
The Berkshire Kennet, Curwen Press (London), 1923 (50
copies; wraps) £150
Collected Poems 1915-1923, Allen & Unwin (London),
1923 .   .   .   .   £35/£15
Exile and Other Poems, Allen & Unwin (London), 1923
(700 unsigned copies of 750)   .   .   .   £25/£10
ditto, Allen & Unwin (London), 1923 (50 signed copies of
750) .   .   .   .   £250/£150
A Fool i' the Forest: a Phantasmagoria, Allen & Unwin
(London), 1924 .   .   .   .   .   £35/£10
Hark the Herald, Hours Press (Paris), 1928 (100 numbered,
signed copies) £175
The Eaten Heart, Hours Press (Paris), 1929 (200 numbered,
signed copies) £100
ditto, Chatto & Windus (London), 1933 .   .   £10/£5
Love and the Luxembourg, Covici Friede (New York), 1930
(475 signed copies, slipcase) .   .   .   .   £45/£25
ditto, as *A Dream in the Luxembourg*, Chatto & Windus
(London), 1930 (308 signed copies)   .   .   £45/£25
*Movietones: Invented and Set Down by Richard Aldington,
1928-1929*, privately printed, 1932 (10 copies) .   £6,500

The Poems of Richard Aldington, Doubleday (Garden City, NY), 1934 . . . . . . £15/£5
Life Quest, Chatto & Windus (London), 1935 . . £15/£5
ditto, Doubleday (Garden City, NY), 1935 . . £10/£5
The Crystal World, Heinemann (London), 1937 . £10/£5
ditto, Doubleday (Garden City, NY), 1937 . . £10/£5

Others
Literary Studies and Reviews, Allen & Unwin (London), 1924 . . . . £25/£10
ditto, Lincoln MacVeagh/Dial Press (New York), 1924. . . . . £25/£10
Voltaire, Routledge (London), 1925 . . . £30/£10
French Studies and Reviews, Allen & Unwin (London), 1926 . . . . £45/£20
ditto, Dial Press (New York), 1926 . . . £45/£20
D.H. Lawrence: An Indiscretion, Univ of Washington Book Store, Seattle, WA), 1927 (purple wraps) . . £25
ditto, as *D.H. Lawrence*, Chatto & Windus (London), 1930 (250 signed copies) £45
ditto, as *D.H. Lawrence*, Chatto & Windus (London), 1930 (orange wraps) £15
Remy de Gourmont. A Modern Man of Letters, Univ of Washington Book Store (Seattle, WA), 1928 (wraps). £25
Balls and Another Book for Suppression, Lahr (London), 1930 (100 copies; stapled wraps) £45
ditto, Lahr (London), 1930 (unlimited edition; stapled wraps) £25
Balls, privately printed (Westport, CT), 1932 (99 + copies, single folded sheet) £150
The Squire Heinemann (London), 1934 . . £2,500
D.H. Lawrence: A Complete List of His Works, Together with a Critical Appreciation, Heinemann (London), 1935 (stapled wraps) £10
Artifex: Sketches and Ideas, Chatto & Windus (London), 1935 . . . . £20/£5
ditto, Doubleday (Garden City, NY), 1936 . . £15/£5
W. Somerset Maugham, An Appreciation, Doubleday (Garden City, NY), 1939 (stapled wraps) . . £15
Life for Life's Sake, A Book of Reminiscences, Viking (New York), 1941 . . . . . £25/£10
ditto, Cassell (London), 1968 . . . . £25/£10
The Duke, Being an Account of the Life and Achievements of the 1st Duke of Wellington, Viking (New York), 1943. . . . . £15/£5
ditto, as *Wellington*, Heinemann (London), 1946 . £15/£5
Jane Austen, Ampersand Press (Pasadena, CA), 1948 (white tissue d/w) . . . . . . £25/£15
Four English Portraits 1801-1851, Evans (London), 1948 . . . . £20/£5
The Strange Life of Charles Waterton, Evans (London), 1949 . . . . £20/£5
ditto, Duell, Sloan & Pearce (New York), 1949 . £20/£5
D.H. Lawrence: An Appreciation, Penguin (Harmondsworth, Middlesex), 1950 (stapled wraps) . . £5
ditto, as *D.H. Lawrence, Portrait of a Genius, But ...*, Heinemann (London), 1950 . . . . £20/£5
ditto, as *D.H. Lawrence, Portrait of a Genius, But ...*, Duell, Sloan & Pearce (New York), 1950 . . £20/£5
Pinorman: Personal Recollections of Norman Douglas, Pino Orioli, and Charles Prentice, Heinemann (London), 1954 . . . . . . £25/£10

Ezra Pound & T.S. Eliot - A Lecture, The Peacocks Press (Hurst, Reading, UK), 1954 (350 signed, numbered copies, glassine d/w, slipcase) . . . . . £75/£25
ditto, The Peacocks Press (Hurst, Reading, UK), 1954 (10 trial copies, azure paper, signed) £250
Lawrence L'Imposteur: T.E. Lawrence, the Legend and the Man, Amiot-Dumont (Paris), 1954 (wraps; glassine d/w) . . . . £45/£35
ditto, as *Lawrence of Arabia: A Biographical Enquiry*, Collins (London), 1955 (first issue with errata slip at p. 332) . . . . £35/£15
ditto, as *Lawrence of Arabia: A Biographical Enquiry*, Regnery (Chicago, IL), 1955 . . . . £35/£15
A.E. Housman & W.B. Yeats: Two Lectures, The Peacocks Press (Hurst, Reading, UK), 1955 (350 copies of 360, glassine d/w). . . . . £75/£25
Introduction to Mistral, Heinemann (London), 1956 £15/£5
ditto, Southern Illinois Univ Press (Carbondale, IL), 1960 . . . . £10/£5
Frauds, Heinemann (London), 1957. . . £10/£5
Portrait of a Rebel, The Life and Works of Robert Louis Stevenson, Evans (London), 1957 . . . £10/£5
A Tourist's Rome, The Mélissa Press (Draguignan, France), [1960 or 1961] (stapled wraps). £15
D.H. Lawrence in Selbstzeugnissen und Bilddokumenten, Rowohlt Taschenbuch (Hamburg), 1961 . £10/£5
A Letter from Richard Aldington and a Summary Bibliography of Count Potocki's Published Works, The Mélissa Press (Draguignan, France), 1962 . . £65
Selected Critical Writings 1928-60, Southern Illinois Univ Press (Carbondale, IL), 1970 . . £10/£5
A Passionate Prodigality: Letters to Alan Bird from Richard Aldington 1949-1962, New York Public Library & Readers Books (New York), 1975 . . £10/£5
Literary Lifelines: The Richard Aldington - Lawrence Durrell Correspondence, Faber (London), 1981 . £15/£5
ditto, Viking (New York), 1981 . . . . £15/£5

BRIAN ALDISS
(b.1925)

Aldiss is best known for his science fiction novels, which push the genre to the limits of convention. *Billion Year Spree* is considered a landmark history of science fiction, successfully arguing that the field's first important work was *Frankenstein* by Mary Shelley. His mainstream novel *Life in the West* was selected by Anthony Burgess as one of the 99 best novels published in England since 1945.

Novels
The Brightfount Diaries, Faber & Faber (London), 1955 (copyright page states 'First published in mcmlv') £85/£15
Non-Stop, Faber & Faber (London), 1958 (first printing red boards) . . . . £200/£40
ditto, Faber & Faber (London), 1958 (second printing in brown cloth). . . . . . . £175/£15
ditto, as *Starship*, Criterion (New York), 1959 (textual differences) . . . . £50/£10
Vanguard from Alpha, Ace (New York), 1959 (pbk double with Kenneth Bulmer's *The Changeling Worlds*). . £10
ditto, as *Equator*, Digit (London), 1961 (first printing includes 'Segregation' pp.107-[160]; pbk) . . £10

ditto, as **Equator**, Digit (London), 1961 (second printing includes 'Segregation' pp.105-157; pbk) . . . £5

Bow Down to Nul, Ace (New York), 1960 (pbk double with Manly Wade Wellman's *The Dark Destroyers*) . . £10

ditto, as **The Interpreter**, Digit (London), 1961 (pbk) . £10

The Male Response, Galaxy Publishing Corp/Beacon Press (New York), 1961 (pbk) £15

ditto, Dobson (London), 1963 . . . . . £45/£10

The Primal Urge, Ballantine (New York), 1961 (pbk) . £5

ditto, Sphere (London), 1967 (pbk) . . . £5

The Long Afternoon of Earth, Signet (New York), 1962 (abridged; pbk) £5

ditto, as **Hothouse**, Faber (London), 1962 (full text) .
. . . . £300/£35

The Dark Light Years, Faber (London), 1964 . £40/£10

ditto, Signet (New York), 1964 (pbk) £5

Greybeard, Harcourt Brace (New York), 1964 . £60/£10

ditto, Faber (London), 1964 . . . . . £75/£10

Earthworks, Faber (London), 1965 . . . £45/£10

ditto, Doubleday (Garden City, NY), 1966 . £20/£5

An Age, Faber (London), 1967 . . . £25/£10

ditto, as **Cryptozoic**, Doubleday (Garden City, NY), 1968 .
. . . . £15/£5

Report on Probability A, Faber (London), 1968 . £25/£5

ditto, Doubleday (Garden City, NY), 1969 . £25/£5

Barefoot in the Head, Faber (London), 1969 . £25/£5

ditto, Doubleday (Garden City, NY), 1970 . £25/£5

The Hand-Reared Boy, Weidenfeld & Nicolson (London), 1970 . . . . £25/£5

ditto, McCall (New York), 1970 . . . . £20/£5

A Soldier Erect, Weidenfeld & Nicolson (London), 1971 .
. . . . £20/£5

ditto, Coward McCann Geoghegan (New York), 1971 .
. . . . £15/£5

Frankenstein Unbound, Cape (London), 1973 . £15/£5

ditto, Random House (New York), [1974] . . £15/£5

The Eighty-Minute Hour, Doubleday (Garden City, NY), 1974 . . . . £20/£5

ditto, Cape (London), 1974 . . . . . £15/£5

The Malacia Tapestry, Cape (London), 1976 . £25/£5

ditto, Harper & Row (New York), [1977] . . £15/£5

Brothers of the Head, Pierrot (London), 1977 . £35/£5

ditto, Pierrot (London), 1977 (pbk) £10

ditto, Pierrot/Two Continents (New York), 1977 . £35/£5

ditto, Pierrot/Two Continents (New York), 1977 (pbk) . £10

ditto, as **Brothers of the Head**, and **Where the Lines Converge**, Panther (London), 1979 (pbk) . . . £5

Enemies of the System, Cape (London), 1978 . £15/£5

ditto, Harper & Row (New York), 1978 . . £10/£5

A Rude Awakening, Weidenfeld & Nicolson (London), 1978
. . . . £10/£5

ditto, Random House (New York), 1979 . . £10/£5

Life in the West, Weidenfeld & Nicolson (London), 1980 .
. . . . £20/£5

ditto, Carroll & Graf (New York), 1990 . . £15/£5

Moreau's Other Island, Cape (London), 1980 . £20/£5

ditto, as **An Island Called Moreau**, Simon & Schuster (New York), 1981 . . . . . . £15/£5

Helliconia Spring, Cape (London), 1982 . . £20/£5

ditto, Atheneum (New York), 1982 . . . £15/£5

Helliconia Summer, Cape (London), 1983 . £20/£5

ditto, Atheneum (New York), 1983 . . . £15/£5

Helliconia Winter, Atheneum (New York), 1985 . £20/£5

ditto, Cape (London), 1985 . . . . . £20/£5

Ruins, Century Hutchinson (London), 1987 . . £10/£5

The Year Before Yesterday, Watts (New York), 1987 . .
. . . . £15/£5

ditto, as **Cracken at Critical**, Kerosina (Worcester Park, UK), 1987 . . . . £15/£5

ditto, Kerosina (Worcester Park, UK), 1987 (250 signed, numbered copies, with d/w and in slipcase with *The Magic of the Past*) . . . . £25 the set

ditto, Kerosina (Worcester Park, UK), 1987 (26 lettered, ¼ leather copies) £125

Forgotten Life, Gollancz (London), 1988 . . £10/£5

ditto, Atheneum (New York), 1989 . . £10/£5

Dracula Unbound, HarperCollins (New York), 1991 £10/£5

ditto, Easton Press (Norwalk, CT), 1991 (signed edition; full leather boards; priority between this and HarperCollins edition not determined) £35

ditto, Grafton (London), 1991 . . . . . £10/£5

Remembrance Day, HarperCollins (New York), 1992 . .
. . . . £10/£5

ditto, St Martin's Press (New York), 1993 . £10/£5

Somewhere East of Life, Flamingo (London), 1994 £10/£5

ditto, Easton Press (Norwalk, CT), 1994 (signed edition; full leather boards) £35

ditto, Carroll & Graf (London), 1994 . . . £10/£5

White Mars, or, The Mind Set Free: A 21st Century Utopia, Little, Brown (Boston), 1999 . . . £10/£5

ditto, St Martin's Press (New York), 1999 . £10/£5

A Chinese Perspective, James Goddard (East Yorkshire, UK), 2000 (300 copies; wraps) £10

Super-State, Orbit (London), 2002 . . . £10/£5

The Cretan Teat, House of Stratus (London), 2002 £10/£5

Affairs at Hampden Ferrers, Little, Brown (London), 2004
. . . . £10/£5

Jocasta, The Rose Press (Pinner, Middlesex), 2004 (750 numbered copies) . . . . . . £25/£10

Sanity And The Lady, PS Publishing (Harrogate, UK), 2005 (500 signed numbered copies, d/w) . . . £15/£5

ditto, PS Publishing (Harrogate, UK), 2005 (200 signed numbered copies, d/w and slipcase) . . . £40/£20

Harm, Ballantine (New York), 2007 . . . . £10/£5

ditto, Duckworth (London), 2007 . . . . £10/£5

Short Stories

Space, Time and Nathaniel, Faber (London), 1957 £125/£20

ditto, as **No Time Like Tomorrow**, Signet (New York), 1959 (pbk) £10

The Canopy of Time, Faber (London), 1959 . £75/£15

ditto, as **Galaxies Like Grains of Sand**, Signet (New York), 1960 (pbk) £5

The Airs of Earth, Faber (London), 1963 . . £50/£20

ditto, as **Starswarm**, Signet (New York), 1964 (pbk) . £5

Best Science Fiction Stories of Brian W. Aldiss, Faber (London), 1965 . . . . . . £30/£5

ditto, as **Who Can Replace a Man?**, Harcourt Brace (New York), 1966 . . . . £15/£5

ditto, as **Best Science Fiction Stories of Brian W. Aldiss**, Faber (London), 1971 (revised edition) . . £15/£5

The Saliva Tree and Other Strange Growths, Faber (London), 1966 . . . . . . £50/£10

ditto, Gregg Press (Boston, MA), 1987 (no d/w) . £20

Intangibles Inc. and Other Stories, Faber (London), 1969 .
. . . . £20/£5

ditto, as **Neanderthal Planet**, Avon (New York), 1970 (pbk)
. . . . £5

ditto, as *Neanderthal Planet*, Avon, Science Fiction Book
Club (New York), 1970   .   .   .   .   .   £10/£5
The Inner Landscape, Allison & Busby (London), 1969
(contains three original novellas: 'Boy in Darkness' by
Mervyn Peake; 'The Voices of Time' by J.G. Ballard;
'Danger: Religion!' by Brian Aldiss)   .   .   .   £20/£5
The Moment of Eclipse, Faber (London), 1970   .   £30/£5
ditto, as *Moment of Eclipse*, Doubleday (Garden City, NY),
1972   .   .   .   .   £10/£5
The Book of Brian Aldiss, Daw Books (New York), 1972
(pbk) £5
ditto, as *The Comic Inferno*, N.E.L. (London), 1973 (pbk) .
        .   .   .   .   £5
Excommunication, Postcard Partnership (London), 1975
(very short story printed on a postcard)   .   .   .   £5
Last Orders, Cape (London), 1977   .   .   .   £20/£5
ditto, Carroll & Graf (New York), 1989   .   .   £10/£5
New Arrivals, Old Encounters, Cape (London), 1979 £20/£5
ditto, Harper & Row (New York), 1979   .   .   £10/£5
A Romance of the Equator, Birmingham Science Fiction
Group (Birmingham, UK), 1980 (stapled wraps) .   .   £15
Foreign Bodies, Chopmen (Singapore), 1981 .   .   £45/£10
ditto, Chopmen (Singapore), 1981 (wraps)   .   .   £20
Best of Aldiss, Viaduct Publications (London), 1983
(magazine format; wraps) £15
Seasons in Flight, Cape (London), 1984 .   .   .   £10/£5
ditto, Atheneum (New York), 1986   .   .   .   £10/£5
My Country 'Tis Not Only of Thee, Aldiss Appreciation
Society, 1986 (100 copies) £5
ditto, Aldiss Appreciation Society, 1986 (signed copies) .
        .   .   .   .   £35
The Magic of the Past, Kerosina (Worcester Park, UK),
1987 (350 copies; pbk) £5
ditto, Kerosina (Worcester Park, UK), 1987 (250 cloth copies
without jacket, in slipcase with *Cracken at Critical*)   .   .
        .   .   .   .   £25 the set
Science Fiction Blues, Avernus (London), 1987 (programme
booklet; stapled wraps) £5
Science Fiction Blues, Avernus (London), 1988 (short
stories with poetry and stage sketches; pbk)   .   .   £5
Best SF Stories of Brian W. Aldiss, Gollancz (London),
1988 (new collection).   .   .   .   .   .   £15/£5
ditto, as *Man in His Time*, Atheneum (New York), 1989   .
        .   .   .   .   £10/£5
A Romance of the Equator: Best Fantasy Stories, Gollancz
(London), 1989   .   .   .   .   £15/£5
ditto, Atheneum (New York), 1990   .   .   .   £10/£5
Bodily Functions, Avernus (London), 1991 (100 signed
copies)   .   .   .   .   £20/£10
Journey to the Goat Star, Pulphouse Publishing (Eugene,
OR), 1991 (pbk) £5
A Tupolev Too Far, HarperCollins (London), 1993   £10/£5
ditto, St Martin's Press (New York), 1994   .   £10/£5
The Secret of This Book, HarperCollins (London), 1995   .
        .   .   .   .   £10/£5
ditto, as *Common Clay: 20 Odd Stories*, St Martin's Press
(New York), 1996   .   .   .   .   .   £10/£5
The Rain Will Stop, The Pretentious Press (Rochester, MI),
2000 (85 signed, numbered copies; stapled wraps)   .   £25
*Supertoys Last All Summer Long and Other Stories of
Future Time*, Orbit (London), 2001 (pbk)   .   .   £5
Cultural Breaks, Tachyon Publications (San Francisco, CA),
2005   .   .   .   .   £10/£5

Poetry

Summer 1773, The Bellvue Press (Binghamton, NY), 1976
(single poem on a postcard) £5
Pile: Petals from St Klaed's Computer, Cape (London),
1979 (illustrated by Mike Wilks, laminated boards, no d/w)
        .   .   .   .   £5
ditto, Cape (London), 1979 (unspecified number signed by
author and artist on tipped-in bookplate)   .   .   £15
ditto, Holt Rinehart & Winston (New York), 1980 .   .   £5
Farewell to a Child, Priapus (Berkhampstead, UK), 1982
(315 of 350 unsigned copies; stapled wraps)   .   .   £5
ditto, Priapus (Berkhampstead, UK), 1982 (35 signed,
numbered copies of 350; stapled wraps).   .   .   £25
Home Life With Cats, Grafton (London), 1992 (laminated
boards, no d/w) £10
At the Caligula Hotel, Sinclair Stevenson (London), 1995
(pbk) £5
*Songs from the Steppes of Central Asia: The Collected
Poems of Makhtumkuli*, The Society of Friends of
Makhtumkuli, 1995 (translated by Dr Youssef Azemoun
and versified by Aldiss)   .   .   .   .   £30/£5
A Plutonian Monologue, The Frogmore Press (Folkestone,
UK), 2000 (200 signed, numbered copies; wraps)   .   £5
At a Bigger House, Avernus (London), 2002 (20 copies with
eight coloured plates; wraps) £60
A Prehistory of Mind, Mayapple Press (Bay City, MI), 2008
(pbk) £10

Non-Fiction

Cities and Stones: A Traveller's Yugoslavia, Faber
(London), 1966   .   .   .   .   .   .   £30/£5
The Shape of Further Things, Faber (London), 1970 £30/£5
ditto, Doubleday (Garden City, NY), 1971   .   £15/£5
Billion Year Spree: The History of Science Fiction,
Weidenfeld & Nicolson (London), 1973   .   £15/£5
ditto, Doubleday (Garden City, NY), 1973   .   £10/£5
Science Fiction Art, New English Library (London), 1975
(oversized soft cover). £35
ditto, Bounty Books (New York), 1975   .   .   £20
Science Fiction as Science Fiction, Bran's Head Books
(Hayes, UK), 1978 (stiff printed wraps)   .   .   £5
*This World and Nearer Ones: Essays Exploring the
Familiar*, Weidenfeld & Nicolson (London), 1979 £10/£5
ditto, Kent State (Kent, OH), 1981 (pbk) .   .   .   £5
The Pale Shadow of Science, Serconia Press (Seattle, WA),
1985   .   .   .   .   £15/£5
Trillion Year Spree: The History of Science Fiction,
Gollancz (London), 1986 (with David Wingrove) £25/£10
ditto, Gollancz (London), 1986 (100 signed copies of 126,
slipcase). £100
ditto, Gollancz (London), 1986 (26 signed, lettered copies of
126) £125
ditto, Atheneum (New York), 1986   .   .   .   £25/£5
...And the Lurid Glare of the Comet, Serconia Press (Seattle,
WA), 1986   .   .   .   .   £15/£5
Bury My Heart at W.H. Smith's, Hodder & Stoughton
(London), 1990   .   .   .   .   .   .   £10/£5
ditto, Avernus (London), 1990 (250 signed, numbered
copies, with six extra chapters).   .   .   .   £30/£10
The Detached Retina, Liverpool Science Fiction Texts and
Studies, No.4 (Liverpool), 1994   .   .   .   £30/£10
ditto, Liverpool Science Fiction Texts and Studies, No.4
(Liverpool), 1994 (pbk) £10
ditto, Syracuse Univ Press (Syracuse, NY), 1995 . £30/£10

ditto, Syracuse Univ Press (Syracuse, NY), 1995 (pbk)   £10
The Twinkling of an Eye, Little, Brown (London), 1998 .
  .   .   .   .   £10/£5
ditto, St Martin's (New York), 1999 .   .   .   £10/£5
When the Feast is Finished, Little, Brown (London), 1999 .
  .   .   .   .   £10/£5

Omnibus Editions
A Brian Aldiss Omnibus, Sidgwick & Jackson (London), 1969
  .   .   .   .   £50/£10
Brian Aldiss Omnibus 2, Sidgwick & Jackson (London), 1971
  .   .   .   .   £60/£10

Miscellaneous
The Life of Samuel Johnson, as edited [written] by Aldiss,
  Oxford Polytechnic Press (Oxford, UK), 1980 (60 signed,
  numbered copies) £45
Science Fiction Quiz, Weidenfeld & Nicolson (London),
  1983 (laminated boards) £10
Sex and the Black Machine, Avernus: Titan Books
  (London), 1988 (pbk). £20
Kindred Blood at Kensington Gore, Avernus (London),
  1992 (pbk) £15
Art After Apogee, Avernus (London), 2000 (50 copies
  signed by author and artist, hardback, no d/w)   .   £50
ditto, Avernus (London), 2000 (50 copies signed by author
  and artist; pbk) £25

NELSON ALGREN

(b.1908 d.1981)

An American writer who identified with society's out-
siders. It is said that this was in part due to his experience
in jail, the result of trying to steal a typewriter from an
abandoned classroom.

'Thundermug', The Windsor Quarterly (no place), [1935]
  (offprint, unbound sheets, 26 pages)   .   .   .   £500
Somebody in Boots, The Vanguard Press (New York), 1935
  (orange cloth; top page edge stained reddish brown) .   .
  .   .   .   .   £3,000/£500
ditto, The Vanguard Press (New York), 1935 (smooth tan
  cloth; top page edge unstained)   .   .   £2,750/$400
ditto, Constable (London), 1935 (blue-grey cloth stamped
  dark blue; top page edge stained red)   .   £1,250/£150
ditto, Constable (London), 1935 (red-orange cloth stamped
  black)   .   .   .   .   £1,000/£100
ditto, as *The Jungle*, Avon (New York), 1957 (pbk; abridged
  version of the above) £20
Never Come Morning, Harper's (New York), 1942 £250/£30
ditto, Harper's (New York), 1942 (promotional issue signed
  by author on leaf inserted between free front endpaper and
  half title)   .   .   .   .   .   .   £300/£150
ditto, Spearman (London), 1958 .   .   .   .   £65/£10
The Neon Wilderness, Doubleday & Co (Garden City, NY),
  1947 (ads for other books on back of d/w)   .   £175/£20
ditto, Doubleday & Co (Garden City, NY), 1947 (reviews for
  this book on back of d/w)   .   .   .   .   £125/£20
ditto, Andre Deutsch (London), 1965.   .   .   £50/£10
The Man With the Golden Arm, Doubleday & Co (Garden
  City, NY), 1949 (top page edge stained grey)   .   £300/£35

ditto, Doubleday & Co (Garden City, NY), 1949 (signed on
  tipped-in sheet)   .   .   .   .   .   .   £500/£150
ditto, Spearman (London), 1959 .   .   .   .   £75/£15
Chicago: City on the Make, Doubleday & Co (Garden City,
  NY), 1951   .   .   .   .   £45/£10
A Walk on the Wild Side, Farrar, Straus and Cudahy (New
  York), 1956   .   .   .   .   £65/£15
ditto, Spearman (London), 1957 .   .   .   .   £45/£10
Nelson Algren's Own Book of Lonesome Monsters, Lancer
  (New York), 1962 (pbk) £15
ditto, Panther (London), 1964 (pbk) £5
Who Lost An American?, Macmillan (New York), 1963   .
  .   .   .   .   £45/£10
ditto, Andre Deutsch (London), 1963.   .   .   £35/£5
Conversations with Nelson Algren, Hill & Wang (New
  York), 1964   .   .   .   .   £25/£5
Notes from a Sea Diary…, G.P. Putnam's Sons (New York),
  1965   .   .   .   .   £20/£5
ditto, Andre Deutsch (London), 1966.   .   .   £20/£5
The Last Carousel, G.P. Putnam's Sons (New York), 1973.
  .   .   .   .   £15/£5
The Devil's Stockings, Arbor House Library of Contemp-
  orary Americana (New York), 1983 (early d/w with *Puss in
  Boots* on rear flap)   .   .   .   .   .   £20/£5
ditto, Arbor House Library of Contemporary Americana
  (New York), 1983 (later d/w with *Someone in Boots* on
  rear flap)   .   .   .   .   £15/£5
ditto, Arbor House Library of Contemporary Americana
  (New York), 1983 (pbk) £10
America Eats, Univ of Iowa Press (Iowa City, IA), 1992   .
  .   .   .   .   £20/£5
He Swung and He Missed, Creative Education (Mankato,
  MN), 1993   .   .   .   .   £10/£5
The Texas Stories of Nelson Algren, Univ of Texas Press
  (Austin, TX), 1995   .   .   .   .   .   £15/£5
ditto, Univ of Texas Press (Austin, TX), 1995 (pbk)   .   £5
Nonconformity: Writing on Writing, Seven Stories Press
  (New York), 1996   .   .   .   .   .   £10/£5

GRANT ALLEN

(b.1848 d.1899)

Canadian Charles Grant Blairfindie Allen's early publications were scientific and evolutionary works, but he
became known as the author of novels and short stories,
and is principally remembered for *The Woman Who Did*, an
1890s *succès de scandale*. He is collected today for his
detective stories (*An African Millionaire* is a 'Queen's
Quorum' title) and tales of supernatural horror (*Strange
Tales* etc).

Novels
Philistia, Chatto & Windus (London), 1884 (pseud 'Cecil
  Power'; three vols) £750
ditto, Harper & Brothers (New York), [c1884]   .   £125
Babylon, Chatto & Windus (London), 1885 (pseud 'Cecil
  Power') £450
ditto, Appleton (New York), 1885   .   .   .   .   £250
Kalee's Shrine, Arrowsmith (London), 1886 (with May
  Coates) £200
ditto, New Amsterdam Book Company (New York), 1897   .
  .   .   .   .   £150

For Maimie's Sake: A Tale of Love and Dynamite, Chatto & Windus (London), 1886 . . . . . £200

ditto, Appleton (New York), 1886 . . . . £125

In All Shades, Chatto & Windus (London), 1886 (3 vols) .
. . . . £400

ditto, Rand, McNally (Chicago), 1886 (?). . . £45

A Terrible Inheritance, SPCK (London), [1887] . . £85

ditto, Crowell (New York), [c.1887] £75

The White Man's Foot, Hatchards (London), 1888 . £125

The Devil's Die, Chatto & Windus (London), 1888 . £300

ditto, Lovell (New York), 1888 . . . . . £225

This Mortal Coil, Chatto & Windus (London), 1888 (3 vols)
. . . . £250

ditto, Appleton (New York), 1889 . . . . £45

Dr Palliser's Patient, Samuel Mullen (London), 1889 . £165

The Tents of Shem, Chatto & Windus (London), 1889 (3 vols) £300

ditto, Rand, McNally (Chicago), 1889 . . . . £75

The Jaws of Death, Simpkin Marshall (London), [1889] .
. . . . £125

ditto, New Amsterdam Book Company (New York), 1896 .
. . . . £65

A Living Apparition, SPCK (London), [1889] . . £125

ditto, E & J.B. Young, 1889. . . . . . £100

The Great Taboo, Chatto & Windus (London), 1890 . £85

ditto, Harper & Brothers (New York), 1891 . . £65

The Sole Trustee, SPCK (London), [1890] . . . £100

Wednesday the Tenth, Lothrop (Boston), 1890 . £65

ditto, as *The Cruise of the Albatross; or, When was Wednesday the Tenth? A Story of the South Pacific*, Lothrop (Boston), 1898 . . . . . . £45

Dumaresq's Daughter, Chatto & Windus (London), 1891 (3 vols) £300

ditto, Harper & Brothers (New York), 1891 . . £65

Recalled to Life, Arrowsmith (London), [1891] . £150

ditto, H. Holt and Company (New York), 1891 . £125

What's Bred in the Bone, Tit-Bits Offices (London), 1891 .
. . . . £125

ditto, Tucker (New York), 1891 . . . . . £75

The Duchess of Powysland, US Book Co (New York), 1891
. . . . £65

ditto, Chatto & Windus (London), 1892 (3 vols) . £300

Blood Royal, Cassell (New York), 1892 . . . £125

ditto, Chatto & Windus (London), 1893 . . . £125

The Scallywag, Chatto & Windus (London), 1893 (3 vols) .
. . . . £225

ditto, Cassell (New York), [c1893] £65

Michael's Crag, Leadenhall Press (London), 1893. £65

ditto, Rand, McNally (Chicago), 1893 . . . . £50

An Army Doctor's Romance, Tuck (New York), 1893 . £125

ditto, Raphael Tuck (London), [1894] . . . £125

At Market Value, Chatto & Windus (London), 1894 (2 vols)
. . . . £175

ditto, F.T. Neely (Chicago), 1894 . . . . £65

Under Sealed Orders, Chatto & Windus (London), 1895 (3 vols) £250

ditto, P.F. Collier (New York), 1894 . . . . £65

The Woman Who Did, John Lane (London), 1895. £100

ditto, Roberts Bros (Boston), 1895 . . . . £45

The British Barbarians, John Lane (London), 1895 . £100

ditto, New York, London, G.P. Putnam's sons, 1895 . £40

A Splendid Sin, F.V. White (London), 1896 . . £125

ditto, F.M. Buckles & Co (New York), 1899 . . £50

The Typewriter Girl, C. Arthur Pearson (London), 1897 (pseud 'Olive Pratt Rayner') £150

ditto, Street & Smith (New York) [1900] . . . £75

Tom, Unlimited, Grant Richards (London), 1897 (pseud 'Martin Leach Warborough') £125

The Incidental Bishop, C. Arthur Pearson (London), 1898 .
. . . . £150

ditto, Appleton (New York), 1898 . . . . £75

Linnet, Grant Richards (London), 1898 . . . . £65

ditto, New Amsterdam Book Company (New York), 1900 .
. . . . £25

Rosalba, C. Arthur Pearson (London), 1899 (pseud 'Olive Pratt Rayner') £100

ditto, G.P. Putnam's (New York), 1899 . . . £75

Short Stories

Strange Stories, Chatto & Windus (London), 1884 . £250

The Beckoning Hand and Other Stories, Chatto & Windus (London), 1887 . . . . £125

The General's Will, Butterworth (London), 1892 . £125

Ivan Greet's Masterpiece, Chatto & Windus (London), 1893
. . . . £125

The Desire of the Eyes, Digby Long (London), 1895 . £125

ditto, R.F. Fenno & Co (New York), 1895 . . . £75

A Bride from the Desert, R.F. Fenno & Co (New York), 1896 . . . . £50

An African Millionaire, Grant Richards (London), 1897 .
. . . . £400

ditto, Arnold (New York), 1897 . . . . . £250

Twelve Tales with a Headpiece, a Tailpiece, and an Intermezzo . . ., Grant Richards (London), 1899 . £200

Miss Cayley's Adventures, Grant Richards (London), 1899.
. . . . £200

ditto, G.P. Putnam's Sons (New York), 1899 . . £125

Hilda Wade, Grant Richards (London), 1900 . . £200

ditto, G.P. Putnam's Sons (New York), 1900 . . £125

The Backslider, Lewis Scribner (London/New York), 1901
. . . . £125

Sir Theodore's Guest and Other Stories, Arrowsmith (London), 1902 . . . . £100

Travel

Paris, Grant Richards (London), 1897 . . . £30

ditto, A. Wessels Co (New York), 1900 . . . £25

Florence, Grant Richards (London), 1897 . . £30

ditto, A. Wessels Co (New York), 1900 . . . £25

Cities of Belgium, Grant Richards (London), 1897 . £25

ditto, L.C. Page & Co (Boston), 1904 [1903] . . £25

Venice, Grant Richards (London), 1898 . . . £25

ditto, A. Wessels Co (New York), 1902 . . . £25

The European Tour, Grant Richards (London), 1899 . £25

ditto, Dodd, Mead and Co (New York) . . . £25

Others

Physiological Aesthetics, H.S. King (London), 1877 . £150

ditto, Appleton (New York), 1877 . . . . £85

Colour Sense: Its Origin and Development, Trubner (London), 1879 . . . . £65

Anglo-Saxon Britain, SPCK (London), 1881 . . £35

ditto, E. & J.B. Young & Co (New York), 1901 . . £35

The Evolutionist at Large, Chatto & Windus (London), 1881 . . . . £75

ditto, J. Fitzgerald (New York), 1881. . . . £65

Vignettes from Nature, Chatto & Windus (London), 1881 .
. . . . £60
ditto, J. Fitzgerald (New York), [1882] £45
The Colours of Flowers, Macmillan (London), 1882 . £40
Colin Clout's Calendar, Chatto & Windus, 1882 . . £35
ditto, Funk & Wagnalls (New York), [1883] . . . £35
Flowers and their Pedigrees, Green & Co (London), 1883 .
. . . . £35
ditto, Appleton (New York), 1884 . . . . . £30
Biographies of Working Men, SPCK (London), 1884 . £30
Darwin, Longmans (London), 1885 . . . . . £65
ditto, Appleton (New York), 1885 . . . . . £45
Force and Energy: A Theory of Dynamics, Longmans, 1888
. . . . £50
Falling In Love, Smith Elder (London), 1889 . . . £30
ditto, Appleton (New York), 1890 . . . . . £30
Science in Arcady, Lawrence & Bullen (London), 1892 £30
Lower Slopes, John Lane (London), 1894 (600 copies). £45
Post Prandial Philosophy, Chatto & Windus (London), 1894
. . . . £30
The Story of Plants, Newnes (London),1895 . . . £15
ditto, Appleton (New York), 1895 . . . . . £15
In Memoriam G.P. Macdonell, Percy Lund (London), 1895
. . . . £25
Moorland Idylls, Chatto & Windus (London), 1896 . £35
The Evolution of the Idea of God, Grant Richards (London),
1897 . . . . £65
Natural Inequality: Forecasts of the Coming Century, The
Labour Press (Manchester, UK), 1897 (wraps) . . £30
Flashlights on Nature, Newnes (London), 1899 . . £30
ditto, Doubleday & McClure (New York), [c1898]. . £25
The New Hedonism, The Tucker Publishing Co (New York),
[1900] (wraps) £30
Country and Town in England, Grant Richards (London),
1901 . . . . £35
In Nature's Workshop, Newnes (London), 1901 . . £20
Evolution in Italian Art, Grant Richards (London), 1908 £20
ditto, A. Wessels Co (New York), 1908 . . . . £20
The Hand of God and Other Posthumous Essays, Watts
(London), 1909 . . . . £25

MARGERY ALLINGHAM

(b.1904 d.1966)

An author of detective fiction from its 'Golden Age',
whose principal hero is an urbane, aristocratic adventurer
known as Albert Campion. Her first novel, *Blackerchief
Dick*, was written while she was still in her teens.
Allingham's artist husband Philip Youngman Carter
designed the d/ws of some twenty of her books.

'Albert Campion' Titles
The Crime at Black Dudley, Jarrolds (London), [1929]
(pink/tan cloth; lettered in black on spine and front board)
. . . . £1,750/£200
ditto, as *The Black Dudley Murder*, Doubleday (Garden
City, NY), 1930 . . . . . . £250/£65
Mystery Mile, Jarrolds (London), [1930] (red cloth with
black lettering on spine only; one map) . . £1,500/£150
ditto, Doubleday (Garden City, NY), 1930 . . £150/£20
Look to the Lady, Jarrolds (London), [1931] (black cloth,
green lettering on spine only; two maps) . £1,500/£150

ditto, as *The Gyrth Chalice Mystery*, Doubleday (Garden
City, NY), 1931 . . . .£125/£20
Police at the Funeral, Heinemann (London), 1931 (with
illustrated endpapers) . . . . . £1,250/£125
ditto, Doubleday (Garden City, NY), 1932 . .£125/£20
Sweet Danger, Heinemann (London), 1933 (black lettering
on a red triangle; illustrated endpapers) . . £1,000/£125
ditto, as *Kingdom of Death*, Doubleday (Garden City, NY),
1933 . . . .£125/£20
Death of a Ghost, Heinemann (London), 1934 (with
illustrated endpapers) . . . . . £1,000/£100
ditto, Doubleday (Garden City, NY), 1934 . .£125/£20
Flowers for the Judge, Heinemann (London), 1936 (with
illustrated endpapers) . . . . . .£600/£50
ditto, Doubleday (Garden City, NY), 1936 . .£100/£15
Dancers in Mourning, Heinemann (London), 1937 (with
illustrated endpapers) . . . . . .£500/£50
ditto, Doubleday (Garden City, NY), 1937 . .£75/£15
The Case of the Late Pig, Hodder & Stoughton (London),
1937 (pbk; yellow cover with title and illustration blue;
black spine with yellow lettering) £175
Mr Campion Criminologist, Doubleday (Garden City, NY),
1937 . . . .£125/£25
The Fashion in Shrouds, Heinemann (London), 1938 (green
endpapers) . . . .£500/£50
ditto, Doubleday (Garden City, NY), 1938 . .£75/£15
Mr Campion and Others, Heinemann (London), [1939]
(green endpapers) . . . . . £1,000/£125
Traitor's Purse, Heinemann (London), 1941 . .£600/£65
ditto, Doubleday (Garden City, NY), 1941 . .£75/£15
Coroner's Pidgin, Heinemann (London), 1945 .£200/£50
ditto, as *Pearls Before Swine*, Doubleday (Garden City,
NY), 1945 . . . .£75/£10
The Case Book of Mr Campion, Spivak (New York), 1947
(pbk) £75
More Work for the Undertaker, Heinemann (London), 1948
(with illustrated endpapers) . . . .£100/£20
ditto, Doubleday (Garden City, NY), 1949 . .£40/£10
The Tiger in the Smoke, Chatto & Windus (London), 1952
(gilt lettering on spine only) . . . .£45/£10
ditto, Doubleday (Garden City, NY), 1952 . .£25/£5
The Beckoning Lady, Chatto & Windus (London), 1955 (gilt
lettering on spine only) . . . .£40/£10
ditto, as *The Estate of the Beckoning Lady*, Doubleday
(Garden City, NY), 1955 . . . . .£25/£5
Hide My Eyes, Chatto & Windus (London), 1958 (gilt
lettering on spine only) . . . . .£40/£10
ditto, as *Tether's End*, Doubleday (Garden City, NY), 1958
. . . .£25/£5
The China Governess, Doubleday (Garden City, NY), 1962
(red cloth, gilt lettering on spine) . . . .£35/£10
ditto, Chatto & Windus (London), 1963 (gilt lettering on
mauve background in gilt frame) . . . .£25/£5
The Mysterious Mr Campion, An Allingham Omnibus,
Chatto & Windus (London), 1963 (red cloth) .£30/£5
The Mind Readers, Morrow (New York), 1965 .£30/£5
ditto, Chatto & Windus (London), 1965 (gilt lettering on
spine only) . . . .£25/£5
Mr Campion's Lady, An Allingham Omnibus, Chatto &
Windus (London), 1965 (red cloth). . . .£25/£5
Mr Campion's Clowns, An Allingham Omnibus, Chatto &
Windus (London), 1967 (red cloth) . . . .£15/£5
Cargo of Eagles, Chatto & Windus (London), 1968 £25/£5
ditto, Morrow (New York), 1968 . . . .£20/£5

The Allingham Casebook, Chatto & Windus (London), 1969
. . . . £15/£5
ditto, Morrow (New York), 1969 . . . . £15/£5
The Allingham Minibus, Chatto & Windus (London), 1973
. . . . £20/£5
ditto, Morrow (New York), 1973 . . . . £15/£5
ditto, as **Mr Campion's Lucky Day and other Stories**,
Penguin (London), 1992 (pbk). £5
ditto, Carroll & Graf (New York), 1992 (pbk). . . £5
The Return of Mr Campion, Hodder & Stoughton (London),
1989 (blue cloth; gilt lettering on spine). . . £10/£5
ditto, St Martin's Press (New York), 1990 . £10/£5

Books Written as 'Maxwell March'
Other Man's Danger, Collins (London), 1933 (mauve cloth,
silver lettering, d/w priced 7/6). . . . .£750/£65
ditto, as **The Man of Dangerous Secrets**, Doubleday
(Garden City, NY), 1933 . . . . . .£200/£35
The Rogues' Holiday, Collins (London), 1935 (mauve cloth,
silver lettering, d/w priced 7/6). . . . .£750/£65
ditto, Doubleday (Garden City, NY), 1935 . .£200/£35
The Shadow in the House, Collins Crime Club, 1936
(orange cloth, black lettering, d/w priced 7/6) .£750/£65
ditto, Doubleday (Garden City, NY), 1936 . .£200/£35

Other Crime Titles
The White Cottage Mystery, Jarrolds (London), [1928]
(purple cloth, orange lettering on spine and front boards) .
. . . . £1,750/£200
ditto, Carroll & Graf (New York), 1990 (pbk). . . £5
Six against the Yard, Selwyn & Blount (London), 1936
(stories by Margery Allingham, Anthony Berkeley, Freeman
Wills Crofts, Ronald Knox; Dorothy L. Sayers and Russell
Thorndyke) . . . . £1,500/£100
ditto, as **Six against Scotland Yard**, Doubleday (Garden
City, NY), 1936 . . . .£500/£35
Black Plumes, Doubleday (Garden City, NY), 1940 (yellow
cloth; black lettering on spine; skeletal horse's head on
front and back; gunman in upper right corner) .£200/£35
ditto, Heinemann (London), 1940 . . . .£650/£45
Wanted: Someone Innocent, Stamford House (New York),
1946 (pbk) £25
Deadly Duo, Doubleday (Garden City, NY), 1949 . £30/£10
ditto, as **Take Two at Bedtime**, World's Work (Kingswood,
Surrey, UK), 1950 (black spine lettering; blue cloth) . .
. . . . £30/£10
No Love Lost, World's Work (Kingswood, Surrey, UK),
1954 (black spine lettering; green cloth) . . £40/£10
ditto, Doubleday (Garden City, NY), 1954 . £25/£10
The Darings of the Red Rose, Crippen & Landru (Norfolk,
VA), 1995 (pbk) £35

Other Titles
Blackkerchief Dick, Hodder & Stoughton (London), 1923 .
. . . . £750/£125
ditto, as **Black'erchief Dick**, Doubleday (Garden City, NY),
1923 . . . . £500/£100
Dance of the Years, Joseph (London), 1943 . £50/£10

Plays
Water in a Sieve, Samuel French (London), 1925 (wraps) .
. . . . £35
Room to Let, Crippen & Landru (Norfolk, VA), 1999 (247
copies; wraps) £20

Non-Fiction
The Oaken Heart, Joseph (London), 1941 . . £75/£35
ditto, Doubleday (Garden City, NY), 1941 . . £65/£25

ERIC AMBLER
(b.1909 d.1998)

A popular and influential thriller writer who deftly directs
his heroes through fast-moving plots. He was once
described by Graham Greene as 'the greatest living writer
of the novel of suspense'. Ian Fleming acknowledged
Ambler's influence by giving James Bond a copy of *The
Mask of Dimitrios* to read in *From Russia With Love*.

Thrillers
The Dark Frontier, Hodder & Stoughton (London), 1936 .
. . . . £3,500/£250
ditto, Mysterious Press (New York), 1990 . . £20/£5
Uncommon Danger, Hodder & Stoughton (London), 1937 .
. . . . £3,000/£250
ditto, as **Background to Danger**, Knopf (New York), 1937 .
. . . . £400/£35
Epitaph for a Spy, Hodder & Stoughton (London), 1938 .
. . . . £2,750/£200
ditto, Knopf (New York), 1952 . . . .£100/£25
Cause for Alarm, Hodder & Stoughton (London), 1938 .
. . . . £1,750/£125
ditto, Knopf (New York), 1939 . . . . .£400/£35
The Mask of Dimitrios, Hodder & Stoughton (London),
1939 . . . . £4,500/£350
ditto, as **A Coffin for Dimitrios**, Knopf (New York), 1939 .
. . . . £1,000/£75
Journey into Fear, Hodder & Stoughton (London), 1940 .
. . . . £1,500/£150
ditto, Knopf (New York), 1940 . . . . .£450/£40
Skytip, Doubleday (Garden City, NY), 1950 (pseud 'Eliot
Reed', written with Charles Rhoda) . . .£125/£15
ditto, Hodder & Stoughton (London), 1951 . £75/£15
Judgement on Deltchev, Hodder & Stoughton (London),
1951 . . . . £50/£25
ditto, Knopf (New York), 1951 . . . . . £25/£10
Tender to Danger, Doubleday (Garden City, NY), 1951
(pseud 'Eliot Reed', written with Charles Rhoda) £75/£15
ditto, as **Tender to Moonlight**, Hodder & Stoughton
(London), 1951 . . . . £75/£15
The Malas Affair, Collins (London), 1953 (pseud 'Eliot
Reed', written with Charles Rhoda) . . . £75/£15
The Schirmer Inheritance, Heinemann (London), 1953 .
. . . . £75/£20
ditto, Knopf (New York), 1953 . . . . . £45/£15
Charter to Danger, Collins (London), 1954 (pseud 'Eliot
Reed', written with Charles Rhoda) . . . £75/£15
The Night-Comers, Heinemann (London), 1956 . £25/£10
ditto, as **State of Siege**, Knopf (New York), 1956 . £25/£10
Passage of Arms, Heinemann (London), 1959 . £25/£10
ditto, Knopf (New York), 1959 . . . . . £15/£5
The Light of Day, Heinemann (London), 1962 . £25/£10
ditto, Knopf (New York), 1963 . . . . . £15/£5
A Kind of Anger, Bodley Head (London), 1964 . £25/£10
ditto, Atheneum (New York), 1964 . . . . £15/£5
The Jealous God, Stellar Press (New York), 1964 (200
copies; sewn wraps) £50

Dirty Story, Bodley Head (London), 1967   .   .   £25/£10
ditto, Atheneum (New York), 1967   .   .   .   .   £15/£5
The Intercom Conspiracy, Atheneum (New York), 1969   .
.   .   .   .   £25/£10
ditto, Weidenfeld & Nicolson (London), 1970.   £25/£10
The Levanter, Weidenfeld & Nicolson (London), 1972 .   .
.   .   .   .   £25/£10
ditto, Atheneum (New York), 1972   .   .   .   .   £15/£5
Doctor Frigo, Weidenfeld & Nicolson (London), 1974.   .
.   .   .   .   £25/£10
ditto, Atheneum (New York), 1974   .   .   .   .   £15/£5
Send No More Roses, Weidenfeld & Nicolson (London),
1977   .   .   .   .   £15/£5
ditto, as *The Siege of the Villa Lipp*, Random House (New
York), 1977 .   .   .   .   £20/£5
The Care of Time, Farrar Straus Giroux (New York), 1981 .
.   .   .   .   £15/£5
ditto, Farrar Straus Giroux (New York), 1981 (300 signed
copies, slipcase)   .   .   .   .   .   .   £50/£35
ditto, Weidenfeld & Nicolson (London), 1981.   .   £15/£5

Short Stories
The Army of the Shadows and Other Stories, Eurographica
(Helsinki), 1986 (350 signed copies)   .   .   £50/£40
Waiting for Orders, Mysterious Press (New York), 1991   .
.   .   .   .   £10/£5
ditto, Mysterious Press (New York), 1991 (26 signed copies,
slipcase).   .   .   .   .   .   .   £125/£100
The Story So Far, Weidenfeld & Nicolson (London), 1993 .
.   .   .   .   £15/£5

Essays
The Ability to Kill and Other Pieces, Bodley Head
(London), 1962 (first issue with essay)   .   .   £125/£75
ditto, Bodley Head (London), 1963 (second issue) .   £35/£10
ditto, as *The Ability to Kill: True Tales of Bloody Murder*,
The Mysterious Press (New York), [1987] (250 signed,
numbered copies; slipcase)   .   .   .   .   £25/£15
ditto, The Mysterious Press (New York), [1987] (26 signed,
lettered copies; slipcase)   .   .   .   .   £40/£20
ditto, The Mysterious Press (New York), [1987] (unlimited
edition in d/w)   .   .   .   .   .   .   £10/£5

Autobiography
Here Lies Eric Ambler, Weidenfeld & Nicolson (London),
1985   .   .   .   .   £20/£5
ditto, Farrar Straus Giroux (New York), 1986 .   .   £10/£5
ditto, Farrar Straus Giroux (New York), 1986 (100 signed
copies, slipcase)   .   .   .   .   .   .   £50/£35

KINGSLEY AMIS
(b.1922 d.1995)

A poet and novelist who had the ability to be satirical and
inventive whilst remaining thoroughly readable. His
bibliography ranges from comic fiction to political pamphlets, and from poetry to studies of science fiction. His
first novel, *Lucky Jim*, is a seminal work of the 1950s. He
was knighted in 1991.

Novels
Lucky Jim, Gollancz (London), 1953 [1954] .   £2,500/£450
ditto, Doubleday (Garden City, NY), 1954   .   £250/£35

That Uncertain Feeling, Gollancz (London), 1955 £150/£20
ditto, Harcourt Brace (New York), 1956   .   .   .   £50/£15
I Like it Here, Gollancz (London), 1958   .   .   .   £75/£20
ditto, Harcourt Brace (New York), 1958   .   .   .   £45/£15
Take a Girl Like You, Gollancz (London), 1960   .   £75/£20
ditto, Harcourt Brace (New York), 1961   .   .   .   £25/£10
One Fat Englishman, Gollancz (London), 1963   .   £35/£10
ditto, Harcourt Brace (New York), 1964   .   .   .   £20/£5
The Egyptologists (with Robert Conquest), Cape (London),
1965   .   .   .   .   £45/£15
ditto, Random House (New York), 1966   .   .   .   £25/£10
The Anti-Death League, Gollancz (London), 1966 £25/£10
ditto, Harcourt Brace (New York), 1966   .   .   .   £20/£5
Colonel Sun, Cape (London), 1968 (pseud 'Robert
Markham')   .   .   .   .   £60/£15
ditto, Harper (New York), 1968   .   .   .   .   £40/£10
I Want it Now, Cape (London), 1968.   .   .   .   £25/£5
ditto, Harcourt Brace (New York), 1969   .   .   .   £20/£5
The Green Man, Cape (London), 1969   .   .   .   £50/£15
ditto, Harcourt Brace (New York), 1970 .   .   .   £35/£10
Girl, 20, Cape (London), 1971   .   .   .   .   £25/£5
ditto, Harcourt Brace (New York), 1972   .   .   .   £25/£5
The Riverside Villas Murder, Cape (London), 1973   £25/£5
ditto, Harcourt Brace (New York), 1973   .   .   .   £20/£5
Ending Up, Cape (London), 1974   .   .   .   .   £20/£5
ditto, Harcourt Brace (New York), 1974   .   .   .   £20/£5
The Alteration, Cape (London), 1976   .   .   .   £20/£5
ditto, Viking (New York), 1977   .   .   .   .   £15/£5
Jake's Thing, Hutchinson (London), 1978   .   .   £20/£5
ditto, Viking (New York), 1979   .   .   .   .   £15/£5
Russian Hide-and-Seek, Hutchinson (London), 1980 £20/£5
Stanley and the Women, Hutchinson (London), 1984 £15/£5
ditto, Summit (New York), 1985.   .   .   .   .   £15/£5
The Old Devils, Hutchinson (London), 1986   .   £20/£5
ditto, Hutchinson/London Limited Editions (London), 1986
(250 signed copies, tissue jacket)   .   .   .   £50/£45
ditto, Summit (New York), 1986.   .   .   .   .   £10/£5
Difficulties With Girls, Hutchinson (London), 1988   £10/£5
ditto, Hutchinson (London), 1988 (500 numbered proof
copies; pbk) £15
ditto, Summit (New York), 1989.   .   .   .   .   £10/£5
The Folks That Live on the Hill, Hutchinson (London),
1990   .   .   .   .   £10/£5
ditto, Hutchinson (London), 1990 (500 numbered proof
copies) £15
ditto, Summit (New York), 1990.   .   .   .   .   £10/£5
We Are All Guilty, Reinhardt Books/Viking (New York),
1991   .   .   .   .   £10/£5
The Russian Girl, Hutchinson (London), 1992   .   £10/£5
ditto, Viking (New York), 1992   .   .   .   .   £10/£5
The Kingsley Amis Omnibus, Hutchinson (London), 1992 .
.   .   .   .   £10/£5
You Can't Do Both, London Limited Editions (London),
1994 (150 copies in glassine d/w)   .   .   .   £50/£40
ditto, Hutchinson (London), 1994   .   .   .   .   £10/£5
The Biographer's Moustache, Flamingo/Harper Collins
(London), 1995   .   .   .   .   .   .   £10/£5

Short Stories
My Enemy's Enemy, Gollancz (London), 1962   .   £75/£10
ditto, Harcourt Brace (New York), 1963   .   .   .   £50/£10
Dear Illusion, Covent Garden Press [London], 1972 (500
copies; stapled pictorial wraps) £20

ditto, Covent Garden Press [London], 1972 (100 signed copies; stapled pictorial wraps) £50
The Darkwater Hall Mystery, Tragara Press (Edinburgh), 1978 (150 of 165 copies; marbled paper wraps) . . £100
ditto, Tragara Press (Edinburgh), 1978 (15 signed copies of 165) £400
Collected Short Stories, Hutchinson (London), 1980 £15/£5
The Crime of the Century, Dent (London), 1987 (pbk) £10
ditto, Hutchinson (London), 1989 . . . . £10/£5
ditto, Mysterious Press (New York), 1989 . . £10/£5
ditto, Mysterious Press (New York), 1989 (100 signed, numbered copies in slipcase) . . . . . £30/£20
ditto, Mysterious Press (New York), 1989 (26 signed, lettered copies in slipcase) . . . . . £50/£40
Mrs Barrett's Secret and Other Stories, Hutchinson (London), 1993 . . . . £10/£5

Poetry
Bright November, Fortune Press (London), [1947] . .
. . . . £1,000/£250
A Frame of Mind, Reading School of Art (Reading, UK), 1953 (150 numbered copies; stapled wraps) . . . £500
Fantasy Poets No.22, Fantasy Press (Swinford, UK), 1954 (stapled wraps) £300
A Case of Samples: Poems, 1946-1956, Gollancz (London), 1956 . . . . £75/£25
ditto, Harcourt Brace (New York), 1957 . . . £60/£15
Penguin Modern Poets No.2, Penguin (Harmondsworth, Middlesex), 1962 (with Moraes and Porter; pbk) . . £5
The Evans Country, Fantasy Press (Oxford), 1962 (stapled wraps) £70
A Look Round the Estate: Poems, 1957-1967, Cape (London), 1967 . . . . £45/£15
ditto, Harcourt Brace (New York), 1968 . . £20/£5
Wasted and **Kipling at Batemans**, Poem-of-the-Month-Club (London), 1973 (broadsheet) £15
Collected Poems 1944-1979, Hutchinson (London), 1979 .
. . . . £15/£5
ditto, Viking (New York), 1980 . . . . . £15/£5

Non-Fiction
Socialism and the Intellectuals, Fabian Society (London), 1957 (stapled wraps) £50
New Maps of Hell: A Survey of Science Fiction, Harcourt Brace (New York), 1960 . . . . . £40/£10
ditto, Gollancz (London), 1961 . . . . . £40/£10
The James Bond Dossier, Cape (London), 1965 . £50/£15
ditto, NAL (New York), 1965 . . . . . £35/£10
The Book of Bond, or Every Man His Own 007 Dossier, Cape (London), 1965 (pseud 'Lt.-Colonel William ('Bill') Tanner'; reversible d/w) . . . . . £75/£15
ditto, Viking (New York), 1965 (single-sided d/w). £45/£15
Lucky Jim's Politics, Conservative Policy Centre (London), 1968 (wraps). £30
What Became of Jane Austen? and Other Questions, Cape (London), 1970 . . . . £35/£10
ditto, Harcourt Brace (New York), 1971 . . £25/£10
On Drink, Cape (London), 1972. . . . . £35/£10
ditto, Harcourt Brace (New York), 1973 . . £25/£10
Rudyard Kipling and his World, Thames & Hudson (London), 1975 . . . . £15/£5
ditto, Scribner's (New York), 1975 . . . . £15/£5
An Arts Policy?, Centre for Policy Studies (London), 1979 (stapled wraps) £10

Every Day Drinking, Hutchinson (London), 1983 . £15/£5
How's Your Glass? A Quizzical Look at Drinks and Drinking, Weidenfeld & Nicolson (London), 1984 £15/£5
The Amis Collection: Selected Non-Fiction, 1954-1990, Hutchinson (London), 1990 . . . . £15/£5
Memoirs, Hutchinson (London), 1991 . . . £10/£5
ditto, Summit (New York), 1991. . . . . £10/£5
The King's English: A Guide to Modern Usage, HarperCollins (London), 1997 . . . . . £10/£5
ditto, St Martin's Press (New York), 1998 . . £10/£5
The Letters of Kingsley Amis, HarperCollins, 2000 £10/£5
ditto, Miramax (New York), 2001 . . . . £10/£5

MARTIN AMIS
(b.1949)

The son of Kingsley Amis, Martin had his first novel published at the age of 24. He is highly regarded for a style that owes a debt to Vladimir Nabokov and Saul Bellow. Amis is considered one of the 'big names' of contemporary British fiction, and is also a regular contributor to many newspapers, magazines and journals.

Novels
The Rachel Papers, Cape (London), 1973. . . £450/£65
ditto, Knopf (New York), 1974 . . . . . £125/£15
Dead Babies, Cape (London), 1975 . . . £300/£30
ditto, Knopf (New York), 1976 . . . . . £75/£15
ditto, as **Dark Secrets**, Triad, 1977 (pbk) . . . £10
Success, Cape (London), 1978 . . . . . £200/£25
ditto, Harmony (New York), 1987 . . . . £15/£5
Other People: A Mystery Story, Cape (London), 1981 . .
. . . . £75/£10
ditto, Viking (New York), 1981 . . . . . £30/£5
Money: A Suicide Note, Cape (London), 1984 . £90/£15
ditto, Viking (New York), 1985 . . . . . £40/£5
London Fields, Cape (London), 1989 . . . £15/£5
ditto, London Limited Editions (London), 1989 (150 signed copies, glassine d/w) . . . . . £75/£50
ditto, Harmony (New York), 1990 . . . . £15/£5
Time's Arrow, or the Nature of the Offence, Cape (London), 1991 . . . . £10/£5
ditto, London Limited Editions (London), 1991 (200 signed copies, glassine d/w) . . . . . £75/£50
ditto, Harmony (New York), 1991 . . . . £10/£5
The Information, Flamingo, 1995 . . . . £10/£5
ditto, Flamingo, 1995 (350 signed, numbered copies of 376, slipcase). . . . . £75/£55
ditto, Flamingo, 1995 (26 signed, lettered copies of 376, slipcase). . . . . £250/£225
ditto, Harmony (New York), 1995 . . . . £10/£5
ditto, Harmony (New York), 1995 (100 signed, numbered copies of 126, slipcase) . . . . £175/£150
ditto, Harmony (New York), 1995 (26 signed, lettered copies of 126, slipcase) . . . . . £225/£200
Night Train, Cape (London), 1997 . . . . £10/£5
ditto, Harmony (New York), 1998 . . . . £10/£5
Yellow Dog, Cape (London), 2003 . . . . £10/£5
ditto, Hyperion/Miramax (New York), 2003 . . £10/£5
House of Meetings, Cape (London), 2006. . . £10/£5
ditto, Knopf (New York), 2007 . . . . . £10/£5

Short Stories

Einstein's Monsters, Cape (London), 1987 . . £10/£5

ditto, Harmony (New York), 1987 . . . . £10/£5

Two Stories, Moorhouse & Sorensen, 1994 (26 signed copies, bound in aluminium, of 326) £400

ditto, Moorhouse & Sorensen, 1994 (100 signed copies bound in cloth of 326) £100

ditto, Moorhouse & Sorensen, 1994 (200 signed copies in card covers of 326) £45

God's Dice, Penguin (London), 1995 (small pbk) . £5

Heavy Water and Other Stories, Cape (London), 1998. .
. . . . £10/£5

ditto, Harmony (New York), 1999 . . . . £10/£5

The Coincidence of the Arts, Coromandel Express (Paris), 1999 (individual pages in a metal container, illustrated by 7 prints by photographer Mario Testino; 55 copies signed by Amis and Testino) £2,000

Vintage Amis, Vintage Books (New York), 2004 (pbk) £5

House of Meetings, Cape (London), 2006 . . £10/£5

ditto, Knopf (New York), 2007 . . . . £10/£5

Non-Fiction

Invasion of the Space Invaders, Hutchinson (London), 1982 (pbk) £100

ditto, Celestial Arts (Millbrae, CA), 1982 (pbk) . £100

The Moronic Inferno and Other Visits to America, Cape (London), 1986 . . . . . . £15/£5

ditto, Viking (New York), 1987 . . . . £15/£5

Visiting Mrs Nabokov and Other Excursions, Cape (London), 1993 . . . . £10/£5

ditto, Harmony (New York), 1994 . . . . £10/£5

Experience, Cape (London), 2000 . . . . £10/£5

ditto, Cape (London), 2000 (150 signed leatherbound copies, slipcase). . . . . £125/£100

ditto, Hyperion (New York), 2000 . . . . £10/£5

The War Against Cliché: Essays and Reviews 1971-2000, Cape (London), 2001 . . . . . . £10/£5

ditto, Hyperion/Talk Miramax (New York), 2001 . £10/£5

Koba the Dread, Hyperion/Talk Miramax (New York), 2002
. . . . £10/£5

ditto, Cape (London), 2002 . . . . . £10/£5

Pornoland, Thames & Hudson (London), 2004. . £10/£5

ANNE ANDERSON

(b.1874 d.1930)

An Art Nouveau illustrator primarily of books for children, Anderson was born in Scotland, spent her childhood in Argentina, but settled in Berkshire, England when, in 1912, she married the painter Alan Wright with whom she often collaborated.

Children's Books Written and Illustrated by Anderson

The Dandy Andy Book, Nelson (London), [1911] (twelve colour plates by Anderson) £125

The Funny Bunny ABC: A Book of Bunnies and Bairnies with Pictures for Painting, Nelson (London), [1912] . £100

The Maisie-Daisie Book, Nelson (London), [1912] . £75

The Daring-Duckie Book, Nelson (London), 1914 (with Alan Wright; twelve colour plates by Anderson) . £75

The Little Busy Bee Book, Nelson (London), [1915] . £75

The Busy Bunny Book, Nelson (London), [1916] (with Alan Wright) £75

The Naughty Neddy Book, Nelson, [1916] (with Alan Wright) £75

The Gilly Flower Garden Book, Nelson (London), [c.1916]
. . . . £100

The Rosie Posy Book, Nelson (London), [c.1917] . . £100

Two Bold Sportsmen, Nelson (London), 1918 (with Alan Wright) £65

The Patsy Book: Being the Adventures of Patsy, Patty and Pat, Nelson (London), [1919] £65

Hop O'My Thumb, Nelson (London), [c.1920] . . £65

The Jackie Jackdaw Book, Nelson (London), 1920 . £75

The Jacky Horner ABC, Dean (London), [c.1920] . £65

The Anne Anderson Fairy Tale Book, Nelson (London), [1923] £75

The Old Mother Goose Nursery Rhyme Book, Nelson (London), [1926]. £75

The Cuddly Kitty and the Busy Bunny, Nelson (London), 1926 (with Alan Wright) £75

The Old Mother Goose Nursery Rhyme Book, Nelson (London), 1926 . . . . £65

The Podgy-Puppy, Nelson (London), [1927] (with Alan Wright) £100

A Series of Fairy Tales, Nelson (London), [1928] (6 parts) .
. . . . £30 each

A Series of Fairy Tales, Nelson (London), [1929] (3 parts) .
. . . . £30 each

Playtime ABC, Collins (London), 1930 . . . £45

Merry Folk, Collins (London), 1930 . . . . £65

The Cosy Corner Book, Collins, [1943] . . . £75

**Children's Books Written by Others,
Illustrated by Anderson**

Aucassin and Nicolette, translated and edited with introduction by Harold Child, A. & C. Black, 1911 . £75

The Gateway to Chaucer, Nelson (London), 1912 (16 colour plates by Anderson) £65

Old French Nursery Songs, Horace Mansion, Harrap (London), [1915] (8 colour plates by Anderson) . £100

Old English Nursery Songs, Horace Mansion, Harrap (London), [1915] (8 colour plates by Anderson) . £100

Rip, by E.W. Garrett, Humphrey Milford (London), 1919 .
. . . . £65

Tub Time Tales, by Madeline Barnes, Blackie (London), 1920 . . . . £75

The Cosy-Comfy Book, by Ethel Talbot, Collins (London), 1920 . . . . £65

My Big Picture Book, by Mrs H. Strang, Humphrey Milford/ O.U.P. (London), [1920] £75

The House Above the Trees, by Ethel C. Eliot, Thornton Butterworth (London), 1921 . . . . . £125

Fireside Stories, by Madeleine Barnes, Blackie (London), 1922 . . . . £75

Grimm's Fairy Tales, Collins (London), [1922] . £75

Sing-Song Stories, by Agnes Grozier Herbertson, Milford (London), [1922] (illustrated with Alan Wright) . £75

Cosy-Time Tales, by Natalie Joan, Nelson (London), [1922]
. . . . £75

Fairy Tales, by Hans Christen Andersen, Collins (London), [1924] £100

Cosy Chair Stories, by Peggy Morrison, Collins (London), [1924] £75

The Isle of Wirrawoo, An Australian Fairy Tale, by A.L.
   Purse, Humphrey Milford/O.U.P. (London), 1923 (with
   Alan Wright) £65
Heidi, by Johanna Spyri, Harrap (London), 1924 (translated
   by Helene S. White) £75
Wanda and the Garden of the Red House, by E.W. Garrett,
   Humphrey Milford/O.U.P. (London), 1924 . . . £65
The Water Babies, by Charles Kingsley, T.C. & E.C. Jack,
   (London), [1924]. £125
Little Rhymes for Little Folk, by Mrs. H. Strang, Humphrey
   Milford/O.U.P. (London), 1925 . . . . £45
Mr. Pickles and the Party, by Constance Howard, Warne
   (London), [1926]. £65
Once Upon a Time Stories, by S. Southwold, Collins
   (London), 1927 . . . . £65
The Anne Anderson Picture Book, Collins, [1943] (fairy
   tales by Hans Andersen and the Grimm brothers) . £100
Pretender Peggy, by Violet Methley, T.C. & E.C. Jack
   (London), no date £45
The Sleepy Song Book, by Horace Mansion, Harrap
   (London), no date £100

HANS CHRISTIAN ANDERSEN

(b.1805 d.1875)

Danish writer Hans Christian Andersen can be said to have
created the Fairy Story genre single-handedly. Following
the example of Perrault and the Brothers Grimm, who
collected traditional tales, Anderson invented new stories
for children and gave the world 'The Ugly Duckling', 'The
Emporer's New Clothes', 'The Princess and The Pea', etc.
Although he was also a novelist, poet, dramatist and travel-
writer, his fairy stories are his legacy to the history of
literature.

Collections of Fairy Stories
Wonderful Stories for Children, Chapman & Hall (London),
   1846 (translated by Howitt) £750
A Danish Story Book, Cundall (London), 1846 (translated
   by Boner; illustrated by Count Pocci) . . . £500
ditto, C.S. Francis (New York), 1857. . . . . £300
Danish Fairy Legends and Tales, Pickering (London), 1846
   (translated by Peachey) £500
The Shoes of Fortune and Other Tales, Chapman & Hall
   (London), 1847 (translated by Boner; illustrated by Otto
   Speckter) £125
ditto, J. Wiley (New York), 1848 . . . . £125
A Picture Book Without Pictures, Bogue (London), 1847
   (translated by Taylor). £125
ditto, C.S. Francis & Co (New York) 1848 . . £125
Tales for the Young, Burns (London), 1847 (illustrated by
   the Dalziel Brothers) £125
A Christmas Greeting to My English Friends, Bentley
   (London), 1847 (translayed by Charles Lohmeyer) . £150
ditto, James Miller (New York), 1847 . . . £150
The Dream of Little Tuk and Other Tales, Grant & Griffiths
   (London), 1848 (translated by Charles Boner; illustrated by
   Count Pocci). £350
ditto, James Munroe & Co. (Boston & Cambridge), 1848 .
   . . . . £350

Tales and Fairy Stories, George Routledge (London), 1853
   (translated by Madame de Chatelain; illustrated by Henry
   Warren). £125
Diamond Sparks, George Routledge (London), 1853
   (illustrated by Henry Warren) £100
The Sand-Hills of Jutland, Richard Bentley (London), 1860
   (translated by Anne Bushby) £100
ditto, Ticknor and Fields (Boston), 1860 . . . . £100
The Ice Maiden, Richard Bentley (London), 1863 (translated
   by Anne Bushby illustrated by Johann Zwecker). . £100
ditto, F. Leypoldt etc (Philadelphia, PA), 1863 . . £100
The Wild Swans, J. Haddock (London), 1863 . . £75
Stories and Tales, George Routledge, 1864 (translated by
   H.W. Dulken; illustrated by Alfred W. Bayes) . £125
ditto, Houghton Mifflin (Boston, [1871] £75
What the Moon Saw and Other Tales, George Routledge
   (London), 1866 [1865] (translated by H.W. Dulken
   illustrated by Alfred W. Bayes) £100
Out of the Heart: Spoken to the Little Ones, George
   Routledge, 1867 (translated by H.W. Dulken illustrated by
   Alfred W. Bayes) £75
The Will-O' The-Wisps Are In Town and Other Tales,
   Alexander Strahan (London), 1867 (translated by A.
   Plesner & S. Rugeley-Powers illustrated by Swain) . £150
Later Tales, Bell & Daldy (London), 1869 (translated by
   Caroline Peachey, A. Plesner, H. Ward, and others
   illustrated by Otto Speckler and others). . . . £100
The Wood Nymph, Sampson Low (London), 1870
   (translated by A.M. & A. Plesner) £75
The White Swan and Other Tales, Hildesheimer & Faulkner
   (London), 1873 (translated by Mrs H.B. Paull; illustrated
   by Alice Havers). £75
Fairy Tales, Sampson Low (London), 1872 [1871]
   (illustrated by E.V.B. [Eleanor Vere Boyle]). . £500
ditto, Sampson Low (London), 1872 [1871] (smaller format
   edition with two extra plates) £750
Stories and Fairy Tales, George Allen (London), 1893
   (illustrated by Arthur Gaskin; 2 vols; 300 sets) . £250
Danish Fairy Tales and Legends, Bliss Sands & Co.
   (London), 1897 (illustrated by W. Heath Robinson) . £100
ditto, Page & Co (Boston), 1898 . . . . . £100
Fairy Tales from Hans Christian Andersen, Dent (London),
   1899 (illustrated by W. Heath Robinson) . . . £150
Fairy Tales and Stories, The Century Co (New York), 1900
   (translated by H.L. Brækstad; illustrated by Hans Tegner)
   . . . . £125
Fairy Tales, J.M. Dent (London), 1910 (illustrated by
   Maxwell Armfield) £50
Stories from Hans Andersen, Hodder & Stoughton
   (London), 1911 (illustrated by Edmund Dulac; 28 colour
   plates) £500
ditto, Hodder & Stoughton (London), 1911 (deluxe edition,
   750 signed copies, 28 colour plates) . . . £1,750
ditto, Hodder & Stoughton (London), 1911 (deluxe edition,
   100 signed copies, morocco binding, 28 colour plates) .
   . . . . £3,000
Fairy Tales, A. & C. Black (London), 1912 (illustrated by A.
   Duncan Carse) £35
ditto, A. & C. Black (London), 1912 (500 signed, deluxe
   copies) £150
Hans Andersen's Fairy Tales, Constable (London), 1913
   (illustrated by W. Heath Robinson). . . . £500
ditto, Constable (London), 1913 (100 signed copies, bound
   in vellum) £2,500

ditto, Holt (New York), 1913 . . . . . £100

Hans Andersen's Fairy Tales, Raphael Tuck (London), [1914] (12 colour plates by Mabel Lucie Attwell) . £150

Hans Andersen's Fairy Tales, Harrap (London), [1916] (illustrated by Harry Clarke; 125 signed copies) . £2,500

ditto, Harrap (London), [1916] (full leather edition) . £600

ditto, Harrap (London), [1916] (cloth edition) . . £250

ditto, Brentano's (New York), 1916 . . . . £250

Fairy Tales, Nelson (London), [1920] (illustrated by Honor C. Appleton). £200

Hans Andersen's Fairy Tales, Hodder & Stoughton (London), [1924] (12 colour plates by Kay Nielsen) . .

. . . . £1,500/£750

ditto, Hodder & Stoughton (London), [1924] (deluxe edition, approx 250 of 500 signed copies, issued with d/w) . .

. . . . £3,500/£1,500

ditto, Hodder & Stoughton (London), [1924] (deluxe edition, approx 250 of 500 signed copies, white vellum binding) .

. . . . £2,500

ditto, Doran (New York), 1924 . . . £1,000/£250

Hans Andersen, Forty Stories, Faber (London), 1930 (translated by M.R. James; illustrated by Christine Jackson)

. . . . £65/£25

ditto, Lippincott (Philadelphia, PA), 1930. . £65/£25

Fairy Tales, Harrap (London), 1932 (illustrated by Arthur Rackham; 8 colour and 19 b&w drawings, rose-red cloth).

. . . . £300/£150

ditto, Harrap (London), 1932 (deluxe 525 signed copies, full vellum) £1,750

ditto, Harrap (London), 1932 (publisher's special binding, full morocco) £300

ditto, McKay (Philadelphia), 1932 . . £300/£150

Fairy Tales and Legends, Cobden-Sanderson (London), 1935 (illustrated by Rex Whistler) . . . £40/£10

ditto, Cobden-Sanderson (London), 1935 (200 signed copies)

. . . . £300

ditto, O.U.P. (New York), 1936 . . . . £35/£10

Fairy Tales, O.U.P. (London), 1961 (translated by L.W. Kingland; illustrated by E.H. Shepard) . . £30/£10

ditto, Walck (New York), 1962 . . . . £30/£10

Ardizzone's Hans Andersen, Deutsch (London), 1978 (illustrated by Edward Ardizzone) . . £35/£15

ditto, Atheneum (New York), 1979 . . £35/£15

Novels

The Improvisatore, Richard Bentley (London), 1845 (2 vols; translated by Mary Howitt) £650

ditto, Hurd and Houghton (New York), 1869 (1 vol) . £45

Only A Fiddler! and **O.T, or Life in Denmark**, Richard Bentley (London), 1845 (2 vols; translated by Mary Howitt) £650

ditto, Hurd and Houghton (New York), 1876 (1 vol) . £45

The Two Baronesses, Richard Bentley (London), 1848 (2 vols; translated by Charles Beckwith) . . . £650

To Be, Or Not To Be?, Richard Bentley (London), 1857 (translated by Mrs Bushby) £250

Travel

A Poet's Bazaar, Richard Bentley (London), 1846 (3 vols; translated by Charles Beckwith) £750

Rambles in the Romantic Regions of the Hartz Mountains, Richard Bentley (London), 1848 (translated by Charles Beckwith) £500

Pictures of Sweden, Richard Bentley (London), 1851 (translated by Charles Beckwith) £250

ditto, as **In Sweden**, Richard Bentley (London), 1852 (translated by K.R.K. MacKenzie) £200

In Spain, Richard Bentley (London), 1864 (translated by Mrs Bushby). £200

In Spain and A Visit to Portugal, Hurd & Houghton (New York), 1870 . . . . £150

A Poet's Bazaar: Pictures of Travel in Germany, Italy, Greece, and the Orient, Hurd & Houghton (New York), 1871 . . . . £125

Pictures of Travel In Sweden, Among the Hartz Mountains, and In Switzerland, with A Visit at Charles Dickens' House, Hurd & Houghton (New York), 1871 . £125

A Visit to Portugal, 1866, Peter Owen (London), 1972 (translated, with introduction and notes by Grace Thornton) . . . . £10/£5

A Visit to Spain, 1862, Peter Owen (London), 1975 (translated, with introduction and notes, by Grace Thornton) . . . . £10/£5

A Visit to Germany, Italy and Malta, 1840-1841, Peter Owen (London), 1985 (translated, with introduction and notes, by Grace Thornton). . . . . £10/£5

Autobiography

The True Story of My Life, Richard Bentley (London), 1847 (translated by Mary Howitt) £250

ditto, J. Munroe & Co. (Boston), 1847 . . . £200

Letters

Hans Christian Andersen's Correspondence with the Late Grand Duke of Saxe-Weimar, Charles Dickens etc, Dean (London), 1891 . . . . £50

The Andersen-Scudder Letters, Univ of California Press (Berkeley, CA), 1949 . . . . . . £35/£15

Complete Works

The Complete Works of Hans Christian Andersen, Hurd and Houghton (New York), 1870-1874 (10 vols: **The Improvisatore, Wonder Stories Told for Children, The Two Baronesses, In Spain and a Visit to Portugal, O.T., A Danish Romance, Only a Fiddler, Pictures of Travel, A Poet's Bazaar, Stories and Tales, The Story of My Life**) .

. . . . £75 each

SHERWOOD ANDERSON

(b.1876 d.1941)

An American novelist and short story writer, Anderson's prose style is said to have had a significant impact on the direction of 20th-century American literature. Although critics suggest that none of his novels are wholly successful, his fascination with a simple, innocent narrator and a believable, rhythmic style made him popular and influential with other writers.

Novels

Windy McPherson's Son, John Lane (New York), 1916 .

. . . . £200

Marching Men, John Lane (New York), 1917 . £300/£65

Poor White, Huebsch (New York), 1920 . . . £350/£65

ditto, Cape (London), 1921 . . . . . £250/£30

Many Marriages, Huebsch (New York), 1923 . £125/£20

Dark Laughter, Boni & Liveright (New York), 1925 .   .
.   .   .   . £125/£20
ditto, Boni & Liveright (New York), 1925 (370 signed,
numbered copies, slipcase)   .   .   .   .   £150/£100
ditto, Jarrolds (London), 1926   .   .   .   . £200/£30
Beyond Desire, Liveright (New York), 1932 .   £75/£15
ditto, Liveright (New York), 1932 (165 signed, numbered
copies, slipcase) .   .   .   .   .   .   £175/£125
Kit Brandon: A Portrait, Scribner's (New York), 1936   .
.   .   .   . £75/£10
ditto, Hutchinson (London), 1937   .   .   . £65/£10

Short Stories
*Winesburg, Ohio: A Group of Tales of Ohio Small Town
Life*, Huebsch (New York), 1919 (yellow cloth, paper label
on spine, first issue, with line 5 of p.86 reading 'lay' and
with broken type in 'the' in line 3 of p.251, map endpapers,
top edge stained yellow)   .   .   .   . £6,000/£400
ditto, Huebsch (New York), 1919 (yellow cloth, paper label
on spine, presumed second issue with unstained top edge)
.   .   .   . £6,500/£150
ditto, Cape (London), 1922 .   .   .   .   . £250/£75
The Triumph of the Egg and Other Stories, Huebsch (New
York), 1921 (first issue with top edge stained yellow)   .
.   .   .   . £250/£35
ditto, Cape (London), 1922   .   .   .   .   . £200/£45
*Horses and Men: Tales, Long & Short from Our American
Life*, Huebsch (New York), 1923 (first issue with top edge
stained orange)   .   .   .   . £250/£30
ditto, Cape (London), 1924   .   .   .   .   . £150/£35
Alice and the Lost Novel, Elkin Mathews & Marrot
(London), 1929 (350 signed copies)   .   .   £75/£40
Death in the Woods and Other Stories, Liveright (New
York), 1933 .   .   .   . £150/£30

Play
Winesburg and Others, Scribner's (New York), 1937 .   .
.   .   .   . £75/£15

Poetry
Mid-American Chants, John Lane (New York), 1918 .   .
.   .   .   . £350/£45
A New Testament, Boni & Liveright (New York), 1927   .
.   .   .   . £100/£20
ditto, Boni & Liveright (New York), 1927 (265 signed,
numbered copies)   .   .   .   .   .   . £150/£75

Others
A Story Teller's Story, Huebsch (New York), 1924 £90/£15
ditto, Cape (London), 1925 .   .   .   .   . £75/£15
The Modern Writer, The Lantern Press (San Francisco, CA),
1925 (950 copies in slipcase)   .   .   .   . £100/£60
ditto, The Lantern Press (San Francisco, CA), 1925 (50
signed copies on vellum, in slipcase)   .   . £300/£200
Sherwood Anderson's Notebook, Boni & Liveright (New
York), 1926 .   .   .   . £75/£25
ditto, Boni & Liveright (New York), 1926 (225 signed
copies, slipcase)   .   .   .   .   .   . £175/£125
Tar: A Midwest Childhood, Boni & Liveright (New York),
1926 .   .   .   . £100/£20
ditto, Boni & Liveright (New York), 1926 (350 signed
copies, glassine d/w, slipcase) .   .   .   . £150/£75
Hello Towns!, Horace Liveright (New York), 1929   .   .
.   .   .   . £100/£25

Nearer the Grass Roots, Westgate Press (San Francisco,
CA), 1929 (500 signed copies, printed by Grabhorn Press)
.   .   .   .   £75
The American County Fair, Random House (New York),
1930 (6 prose quartos in wraps; slipcase, 875 copies).   .
.   .   .   . £100/£65
Perhaps Women, Horace Liveright (New York), 1931 .   .
.   .   .   . £65/£15
No Swank, Centaur Press (Philadelphia, PA), 1934 (1,000
copies, glassine d/w)   .   .   .   .   . £75/£40
ditto, Centaur Press (Philadelphia, PA), 1934 (50 signed,
numbered copies, glassine d/w)   .   .   . £250/£200
Puzzled America, Scribner's (New York), 1935 . £100/£20
A Writer's Conception of Realism, Olivet College
(Kankakee, IL), 1939 (wraps) £250
Home Town, Alliance Book Corporation (New York), 1940
.   .   .   . £100/£35
Sherwood Anderson's Memoirs, Harcourt Brace (New
York), 1942 .   .   .   . £75/£15
The Sherwood Anderson Reader, Houghton Mifflin Co.
(Boston), 1947 .   .   .   . £35/£5
The Portable Sherwood Anderson, Viking Press (New
York), 1949 .   .   .   . £20/£5
Letters of Sherwood Anderson, Little, Brown (Boston),
1953 .   .   .   . £10/£5
Return to Winesburg, Univ of North Carolina (Chapel Hill,
NC), 1967 .   .   .   . £15/£5
*Sherwood Anderson/Gertrude Stein: Correspondence and
Personal Essays*, Univ of North Carolina (Chapel Hill,
NC), 1972 .   .   .   . £10/£5
France and Anderson: Paris Notebook, 1921, Louisiana
State Univ Press (Baton Rouge, LA), 1977 .   £10/£5
Letters to Bab, Univ of Illinois Press (Urbana, IL), 1985   .
.   .   .   . £10/£5
The Sherwood Anderson Diaries 1936-1941, Univ of
Georgia Press (Athens, GA), 1987 .   .   . £10/£5
Sherwood Anderson: Early Writings, Kent State Univ Press
(Kent, OH), 1989.   .   .   .   .   .   . £10/£5
*Sherwood Anderson's Love Letters to Eleanor Copenhaver
Anderson*, Univ of Georgia Press (Athens, GA), 1989
.   .   .   . £10/£5
*Sherwood Anderson's Secret Love Letters: For Eleanor, a
Letter a Day*, Louisiana State Univ Press (Baton Rouge,
LA), 1991 .   .   .   . £10/£5
Certain Last Things: Selected Short Stories, Four Walls
Eight Windows Press (New York), 1992   .   . £10/£5

MAYA ANGELOU
(b. 1928)

Maya Angelou is a poet, historian, author, playwright,
actress, civil-rights activist, producer and director. She has
a reputation as an incisive commentator on black American
culture, especially the challenges and potential of black
American women. Her books of autobiography have
become international bestsellers.

Autobiography
I Know Why the Caged Bird Sings, Random House (New
York), 1969 .   .   .   . £200/£30
ditto, Virago (London), 1984 (pbk) £5

Gather Together in My Name, Random House (New York),
  1974 . . . . £45/£10
ditto, Virago (London), 1985 (pbk) £5
Singin' and Swingin' and Gettin' Merry Like Christmas,
  Random House (New York), 1976 . . . £10/£5
ditto, Virago (London), 1985 (pbk) £5
The Heart of a Woman, Random House (New York), 1981
  . . . . £10/£5
ditto, Virago (London), 1986 (pbk) £5
All God's Children Need Travelling Shoes, Random House
  (New York), 1986 . . . . . £10/£5
ditto, Franklin Library (Franklin Centre, PA), 1986 (signed,
  limited edition) £15
ditto, Virago (London), 1987 (pbk) £5
A Song Flung Up to Heaven, Random House (New York),
  2002 . . . . £10/£5
ditto, Virago (London), 2002 . . . . £10/£5
Collected Autobiographies, The Modern Library (New
  York), 2004 . . . . £15/£5

Essays
Wouldn't Take Nothing for my Journey Now, Random
  House (New York), 1993 . . . . . £10/£5
ditto, Virago (London), 1994 . . . . £10/£5
Even the Stars Look Lonesome, Random House (New
  York), 1997 . . . . £10/£5
ditto, Virago (London), 1998 (300 numbered copies) . £30
ditto, Virago (London), 1998 . . . . £10/£5
*Hallelujah! The Welcome Table: A Lifetime of Memories
  with Recipes*, Random House (New York), 2004 . £10/£5
ditto, Virago (London), 2005 . . . . £10/£5
Mother: A Cradle to Hold Me, Random House (New York),
  2006 . . . . £10/£5
ditto, Virago (London), 2006 . . . . £10/£5
Letter to My Daughter, Random House (New York), 2008 .
  . . . . £10/£5
ditto, Virago (London), 2008 . . . . £10/£5

Poetry
Just Give Me a Cool Drink of Water 'fore I Diiie, Random
  House (New York), 1971 . . . . . £50/£20
ditto, Virago (London), 1988 (pbk) £5
Oh Pray My Wings are Gonna Fit Me Well, Random House
  (New York), 1975 . . . . . . £25/£5
And Still I Rise, Random House (New York), 1978 £40/£10
ditto, Virago (London), 1986 (pbk) £5
Shaker, Why Don't You Sing?, Random House (New York),
  1983 . . . . £15/£5
Now Sheba Sings the Song, Dutton/Dial (New York), 1987
  . . . . £10/£5
ditto, Virago (London), 1987 . . . . £15/£5
I Shall Not Be Moved, Random House (New York), 1990 .
  . . . . £10/£5
ditto, Virago (London), 1990 (pbk) £5
On the Pulse of the Morning, Random House (New York),
  1993 (pbk) £5
The Complete Collected Poems of Maya Angelou, Random
  House (New York), 1994 . . . . £10/£5
ditto, Virago (London), 1994 . . . . £10/£5
Phenomenal Woman: Four Poems Celebrating Women,
  Random House (New York), 1994 . . . £10/£5
A Brave and Startling Truth, Random House (New York),
  1995 . . . . £10/£5

Poems, Bantam Doubleday Dell (New York), 1997 (pbk) .
  . . . . £5
Amazing Peace: A Christmas Poem, Random House (New
  York), 2005 . . . . £10/£5
Celebrations, Rituals of Peace and Prayer, Random House
  (New York), 2006 . . . . . £10/£5
ditto, Virago (London), 2006 . . . . £10/£5
Poetry for Young People, Sterling (Canada), 2007. £10/£5

Children's Titles
Mrs Flowers, Redpath Press (Minneapolis, MN), 1986 .
  . . . . £10/£5
Life Doesn't Frighten Me, Stewart, Tabori and Chang (New
  York), 1993 . . . . £35/£10
My Painted House, My Friendly Chicken, And Me,
  Clarkson Potter Inc (New York), 1994 . . . £15/£5
Kofi and His Magic, Clarkson Potter Inc (New York), 1996
  . . . . £20/£5
Angelina of Italy, Random House, 2004 (pbk) . . £5
Izak of Lapland, Random House, 2004 (pbk) . . £5
Mikale of Hawaii, Random House, 2004 (pbk) . . £5
Renee Marie of France, Random House, 2004 (pbk) . £5

EDWARD ARDIZZONE
(b.1900 d.1979)

Ardizzone studied at the Westminster School of Art and in
1927 and became a full-time artist. He illustrated books
written by others and himself, and during the Second
World War worked as an official war artist. He is best
known for the 'Tim' series, featuring the maritime adventures of the eponymous young hero.

Children's Books Written and Illustrated by Ardizzone
Little Tim and the Brave Sea Captain, O.U.P. (Oxford, UK),
  [1936] . . . . £600/£300
ditto, O.U.P. (New York), [1936] . . . £500/£250
ditto, O.U.P. (Oxford, UK), 1955 (revised edition). £45/£15
ditto, Walck (New York), 1955 . . . . . £45/£15
Lucy Brown and Mr Grimes, O.U.P. (Oxford, UK), [1937].
  . . . . £500/£250
ditto, O.U.P. (Oxford, UK), 1970 (revised edition). £50/£15
ditto, Walck (New York), [1971] . . . £45/£15
Tim and Lucy go to Sea, O.U.P. (Oxford, UK), [1938].
  . . . . £500/£250
ditto, O.U.P. (Oxford, UK), 1958 (revised edition). £45/£20
ditto, Walck (New York), [1958] . . . . £45/£10
Nicholas the Fast-Moving Diesel, Eyre & Spottiswoode
  (London), [1947]. . . . . . £350/£175
ditto, Walck (New York), 1959 . . . . £45/£10
Paul, The Hero of the Fire, Penguin (Harmondsworth,
  Middlesex), 1948 (pictorial stiff card wraps in d/w)
  . . . . £100/£35
ditto, Constable (London), 1962 (revised edition) . £40/£15
ditto, Walck (New York), [1963] . . . . £65/£25
Tim to the Rescue, O.U.P. (Oxford, UK), 1949 . £150/£45
ditto, Walck (New York), [196-?] . . . . £65/£25
Tim and Charlotte, O.U.P. (Oxford, UK), 1951 . £150/£45
ditto, Lothrop, Lee & Shepard Books (New York), 2000 .
  . . . . £10/£5
Tim in Danger, O.U.P. (Oxford, UK), 1953 . . £150/£45
ditto, Walck (New York), [196-?] . . . . £65/£25

Tim all Alone, O.U.P. (Oxford, UK), 1956 . . £100/£25
ditto, Walck (New York), [196-?] . . . . £65/£25
Johnny the Clockmaker, O.U.P. (Oxford, UK), 1960 . .
. . . .£100/£25
ditto, Walck (New York), 1960 . . . . . £65/£25
Tim's Friend Towser, O.U.P. (Oxford, UK), 1962. £100/£25
ditto, Walck (New York), 1962 . . . . . £65/£25
Peter the Wanderer, O.U.P. (Oxford, UK), 1963 . £75/£25
ditto, Walck (New York), 1963 . . . . . £65/£25
Diana and her Rhinoceros, Bodley Head (London), 1964 .
. . . . £75/£25
ditto, Walck (New York), 1964 . . . . . £65/£25
Sarah and Simon and No Red Paint, Constable (London),
[1965] . . . . £75/£25
ditto, Delacorte Press (New York), [1966] . . £65/£25
Tim and Ginger, O.U.P. (Oxford, UK), 1965 . . £75/£25
ditto, Walck (New York), 1965 . . . . . £65/£25
The Little Girl and the Tiny Doll, Constable (London), 1966
(with Aingelda Ardizzone) . . . . . £75/£25
ditto, Delacorte (New York), 1966 . . . . £60/£25
Tim to the Lighthouse, O.U.P. (Oxford, UK), 1968 £75/£25
ditto, Walck (New York), [1968] . . . . £50/£20
Johnny's Bad Day, Bodley Head (London), 1970 . £65/£25
ditto, as *The Wrong Side of the Bed*, Doubleday (Garden
City, NY), 1970 . . . . £25/£10
Tim's Last Voyage, Bodley Head (London), 1972 . £50/£20
ditto, Walck (New York), 1972 . . . . . £50/£20
Ship's Cook Ginger: Another Time Story, Bodley Head
(London), 1977 . . . . £35/£15
ditto, Macmillan (New York), 1978 . . . . £35/£15
The Adventures of Tim, Bodley Head (London), 1977 . .
. . . . £35/£15

Children's Books Illustrated by Ardizzone
Tom, Dick and Harriet, by Albert N. Lyons, Cresset Press
(London), 1937 . . . .£250/£75
Great Expectations, by Charles Dickens, Heritage Press
(New York), 1939 (slipcase) . . . . . £40/£20
MIMFF: the Story of a Boy Who Was Not Afraid, by H.J.
Kaeser, O.U.P. (Oxford, UK), 1939 . . . £75/£35
Peacock Pie, by Walter de la Mare, Faber (London), 1946 .
. . . . £70/£25
The Pilgrim's Progress, by John Bunyan, Faber (London),
1947 . . . . £85/£35
Three Brothers and a Lady, by Margaret Black, Acorn Press
(London), 1947 . . . . £75/£25
*A True and Pathetic History of Desbarollda, The Waltzing
Mouse*, by Noel Langley, Lindsay Drummond (London),
1947 . . . . £75/£25
Hey Nonny Yes: Passions and Conceits from Shakespeare,
edited by Hallam Fordham, Saturn Press (London), 1947 .
. . . . £25/£10
The Life and Adventures of Nicholas Nickleby, by Charles
Dickens, Ealing Studios (London), 1947 (colour wraps) .
. . . . £75
Charles Dickens' Birthday Book, edited by Enid Dickens
Hawksley, Faber (London), 1948 . . . £65/£20
The Otterbury Incident, by Cecil Day Lewis, Putnam
(London), 1948 . . . . £45/£15
ditto, Viking (New York), 1949 . . . . . £20/£5
The Rose and the Ring, by William Makepeace Thackeray,
Guildford Press/Wilfrid David (London), 1948 . £45/£10
MIMFF in Charge, by H.J. Kaeser, O.U.P. (Oxford, UK),
1949 (translated by David Ascoli) . . . £60/£25

Ali Baba and the Forty Thieves, Limited Editions Club
(New York), 1949 (2,500 signed copies with two other
books for children; glassine d/w and slipcase) . £100/£65
Somebody's Rocking My Dreamboat, by Noel Langley and
Hazel Pynegar, Barker (London), 1949 . . . £50/£15
The Humour of Dickens, News Chronicle (London), 1952
(wraps in d/w; with Ronald Searle, Vicky, Low, Osbert
Sitwell, Giles, Illingworth and Michael Cummings, Horner
and Joss . . . . £20/£5
The Blackbird in the Lilac, by James Reeves, O.U.P.
(Oxford, UK), 1952 . . . . . . £50/£20
ditto, Dutton (New York), 1959 . . . . . £20/£5
MIMFF Takes Over, by H.J. Kaeser, O.U.P. (Oxford, UK),
1954 . . . . £30/£10
*The Fantastic Tale of the Plucky Sailor and the Postage
Stamp*, by Stephen Corrin, Faber (London), 1954 £75/£35
The Little Bookroom, by Eleanor Farjeon, O.U.P. (Oxford,
UK), 1955 . . . . £50/£20
ditto, Walck (New York), 1955 . . . . . £35/£10
The Suburban Child, by James Kenward, C.U.P.
(Cambridge, UK), 1955 . . . . . . £30/£10
Minnow on the Say, by Phillippa Pearce, O.U.P. (Oxford,
UK), 1955 . . . . £25/£10
ditto, World (Cleveland, OH), 1955 . . . . £20/£5
ditto, as *The Minnow Leads to Treasure*, Gregg Press
(Boston, MA), 1980 . . . . . . £25/£10
David Copperfield, by Charles Dickens, O.U.P. (Oxford,
UK), 1955 (abridged by S. Wood) . . . £45/£20
Bleak House, by Charles Dickens, O.U.P. (Oxford, UK),
1955 (abridged by S. Wood) . . . . £45/£20
Sun Slower, Sun Faster, by Meriol Trevor, Collins
(London), 1955 . . . . £45/£20
ditto, Sheed and Ward (New York), 1955 . . . £10/£5
Pigeons and Princesses, by James Reeves, Heinemann
(London), 1956 . . . . £40/£15
Marshmallow, by Claire Newberry, Studio (London), 1956.
. . . . £30
St Luke's Life of Christ (translated by J.B. Phillips), Collins
(London), 1956 . . . . £15/£5
ditto, Collins (London), 1956 (150 signed copies; slipcase;
no d/w) . . . .£100/£75
A Stickful of Nonpareil, by George Scurfield, C.U.P.
(Cambridge, UK), 1956 (500 copies) . . . £100
Hunting with Mr Jorrocks, by Robert Surtees (edited by
Lionel Gough) O.U.P. (Oxford, UK), 1956 . . £45/£10
Wandering Moon, by James Reeves, Heinemann (London),
1957 . . . . £35/£10
ditto, Dutton (New York), 1960 . . . . . £25/£5
Prefabulous Animiles, by James Reeves, Heinemann
(London), 1957 . . . . £50/£20
The School in Our Village, by Joan M. Goldman, Batsford
(London), 1957 . . . . £40/£10
The Boy Down Kitchener Street, by Leslie Paul, Faber
(London), 1957 . . . . £25/£10
Lottie, by John Symonds, Bodley Head (London), 1957 .
. . . . £50/£20
Ding Dong Bell, by Walter de la Mare, Dobson (London),
1957 . . . . £65/£25
ditto, Dover (New York), 1969 . . . . . £30/£10
MIMFF-Robinson, by H.J. Kaeser, O.U.P. (Oxford, UK),
1958 (translated by Ruth Michaelis and Jena & Arthur
Ratcliff) . . . . £40/£10
The Story of Joseph, by Walter de la Mare, Faber (London),
1958 . . . . £25/£10

Jim at the Corner, by Eleanor Farjeon, O.U.P. (Oxford, UK), 1958 . . . . £75/£25
ditto, Walck (New York), 1958 . . . . . £75/£25
Pinky Pye, by Eleanor Estes, Constable (London), 1959 . . . . £45/£15
ditto, Harcourt, Brace & World (New York), 1959. £40/£10
The Nine Lives of Island Mackenzie, by Ursula Moray Williams, Chatto & Windus (London), 1959. . £45/£15
Titus in Trouble, by James Reeves, Bodley Head (London), 1959 . . . . £25/£10
ditto, Walck (New York), 1960 . . . . £25/£10
Exploits of Don Quixote, by Cervantes, Blackie (London), [1959] (abridged by James Reeves). . . . £50/£20
ditto, Bedrick Books (New York), 1985 . . . £15/£5
Story of Moses, by Walter de la Mare, Faber (London), 1959 . . . . £25/£10
Elfrida and the Pig, by John Symonds, Harrap (London), 1959 . . . . £50/£20
ditto, Franklin Watts (New York), 1959 . . . £45/£15
Holiday Trench, by Joan Ballantyne, Nelson (London), 1959 . . . . £35/£10
The Godstone and the Blackymor, by T.H. White, Cape (London), 1959 . . . . £40/£15
ditto, Putnam (New York), 1959 . . . . . £35/£10
The Story of Samuel and Saul, by Walter de la Mare, Faber (London), 1960 . . . . . . £35/£10
Kidnappers at Coombe, by Joan Ballantyne, Nelson (London), 1960 . . . . £45/£15
The Rib of the Green Umbrella, by Naomi Mitchison, Collins (London), 1960 . . . . . £30/£10
Eleanor Farjeon's Book, edited by Eleanor Graham, Puffin (Harmondsworth, Middlesex), 1960 (pbk) . . . £10
ditto, as *A Book for Eleanor Farjeon*, Walck (New York), 1966 . . . . £25/£5
Merry England, by Cyril Ray, Vista Books (London), 1960 . . . . £30/£10
Italian Peepshow, by Eleanor Farjeon, O.U.P. (Oxford, UK), 1960 . . . . £30/£10
ditto, Walck (New York), 1960 . . . . . £30/£10
The Penny Fiddle: Poems for Children, by Robert Graves, Cassell (London), 1960 . . . . . £75/£30
ditto, Doubleday (Garden City, NY), 1960 . £40/£10
Boyhoods of the Great Composers, O.U.P. (Oxford, UK), 1960 & 1963 (2 vols) . . . . . . £65/£25
Hurdy Gurdy, by James Reeves, Heinemann (London), 1961 (pbk) £20
No Mystery for the Maitlands, by Joan Ballantyne, Nelson (London), 1961 . . . . £35/£5
Down in the Cellar, by Nicholas Gray, Dobson (London), 1961 . . . . £50/£25
The Adventures of Huckleberry Finn, by Mark Twain, Heinemann (London), 1961 . . . . £45/£10
The Adventures of Tom Sawyer, by Mark Twain, Heinemann (London), 1961 . . . . £45/£10
Stories from the Bible, by Walter de la Mare, Faber (London), 1961 . . . . £40/£10
ditto, Knopf (New York), 1961 . . . . . £40/£10
The Witch Family, by Eleanor Estes, Constable (London), 1962 . . . . £50/£20
ditto, Harcourt Brace Jovanovich (New York), [1990] . . . . £20/£5
Naughty Children, edited by Christianna Brand, Gollancz (London), 1962 . . . . £50/£15
ditto, Dutton (New York), 1963 . . . . £40/£10

Sailor Rumbelow and Britannia, by James Reeves, Heinemann (London), 1962 . . . . . £45/£15
Peter Pan, by J.M. Barrie, Brockhampton Press (Leicester, UK), 1962 . . . . £35/£10
ditto, Scribner's (New York), [1962] . . . . £35/£10
A Ring of Bells, by John Betjeman, Murray (London), 1962 . . . . £20/£5
ditto, Houghton Mifflin (Boston), 1963 . . . £20/£5
The Story of Let's Make an Opera, by Eric Crosier, O.U.P. (Oxford, UK), 1962 . . . . . . £50/£20
The Singing Cupboard, by Dana Farralla, Blackie (London), 1962 . . . . £45/£20
Mrs Malone, by Eleanor Farjeon, O.U.P. (Oxford, UK), 1962 . . . . £75/£25
ditto, Walck (New York), 1962 . . . . . £50/£15
Island of Fish in the Trees, by Eva-Lis Wuorio, World (Cleveland, OH), 1962 . . . . . £45/£10
ditto, Dobson (London), 1964 . . . . . £45/£10
Stig of the Dump, by Clive King, Puffin Original (Harmondsworth, Middlesex), 1963 (pbk) . . . £20
Kaleidoscope, by Eleanor Farjeon, O.U.P. (Oxford, UK), 1963 . . . . £30/£10
ditto, Walck (New York), 1963 . . . . . £25/£10
Swanhilda-of-the-Swans, by Dana Farralla, Blackie (London), [1964] . . . . £35/£10
Ann at Highwood Hall, by Robert Graves, Cassell (London), 1964 . . . . £60/£20
ditto, Doubleday (Garden City, NY), 1964 . . £45/£15
Three Tall Tales, by James Reeves, Abelard-Schuman (London), 1964 . . . . £45/£15
ditto, Abelard-Schuman (New York), 1964 . £45/£15
The Alley, by Eleanor Estes, Harcourt Brace (New York), 1964 . . . . £35/£10
Hello, Elephant, by Jan Wahl, Holt, Rinehart & Winston (New York), [1964] . . . . . . £50/£15
The Land of Right Up and Down, by Eva-Lis Wuorio, World (Cleveland, OH), [1964] (illustrated boards; no d/w) £30
ditto, Dobson (London), 1968 (illustrated boards; no d/w) £30
Nurse Matilda, by Christianna Brand, Brockhampton Press (Leicester, UK), 1964 . . . . . . £75/£20
ditto, Dutton (New York), 1964 . . . . . £65/£15
The Story of Jackie Thimble, by James Reeves, Dutton (New York), 1964 . . . . £35/£15
ditto, Chatto & Windus (London), 1965 . . . £35/£15
Open the Door, edited by Margery Fisher, Brockhampton Press (Leicester, UK), 1965 . . . . . £30/£10
Old Perisher, by Diana Ross, Faber (London), 1965 £45/£15
The Old Nurse's Stocking Basket, by Eleanor Farjeon, O.U.P. (Oxford, UK), 1965 . . . . . £45/£15
ditto, Walck (New York), 1965 . . . . . £45/£15
The Truants and Other Poems for Children, by John Walsh, Heinemann (London), 1965 . . . . £25/£10
ditto, Rand McNally (New York), [1968] . . . £25/£10
The Growing Summer, by Noel Streatfield, Collins (London), 1966 . . . . £45/£15
ditto, as *The Magic Summer*, Random House (New York), 1967 . . . . £40/£10
Long Ago When I Was Young, by E. Nesbit, Whiting & Wheaton (London), 1966 . . . . . £30/£10
ditto, Watts (New York), [1966] . . . . . £30/£10
Daddy Long-legs, by Jean Webster, Brockhampton Press (Leicester, UK), 1966 . . . . . . £30/£10

The Land of Green Ginger, by Noel Langley, Puffin (Harmondsworth, Middlesex), 1966 (pbk) . . £10
ditto, Penguin Books (New York), [1966] (pbk) . . £5
The Dragon, by Archibald Marshall, Warne (London), 1966 . . . . £40/£15
ditto, Dutton (New York), [1967] . . . £40/£10
The Secret Shoemakers and Other Stories, by James Reeves, Abelard-Schuman (London), 1966 . . £25/£10
ditto, Abelard-Schuman (New York), 1966 . . £25/£10
Timothy's Song, by W.J. Lederer, Lutterworth Press (London), 1966 . . . . £35/£10
ditto, Norton (New York), [1965] . . . £35/£10
The Year Round, by Leonard Clark, Hart Davis (London), 1966 (illustrated card covers) £20
The Muffletumps; the story of four dolls, by Jan Wahl, Holt Rinehart & Winston (New York), [1966] . . £40/£10
Rhyming Will, by James Reeves, Hamish Hamilton (London), 1967 . . . . £45/£15
ditto, McGraw-Hill (New York), [1968] . . £45/£15
Travels with a Donkey, by Robert Louis Stevenson, Folio Society (London), 1967 (slipcase; no d/w) . £15/£5
Miranda The Great, by Eleanor Estes, Harcourt Brace (New York), 1967 . . . . £35/£10
ditto, Harcourt, Brace & World (New York), [1967] £30/£10
A Likely Place, by Paula Fox, Macmillan (London) [1967] . . . . £25/£10
ditto, Macmillan (New York), [1967]. . . . £20/£5
Kali and the Golden Mirror, by Eva-Lis Wuorio, World Publishing (Cleveland, OH), 1967 . . . £25/£10
The Stuffed Dog, by John Symonds, Barker (London), 1967 . . . . £30/£10
Nurse Matilda Goes to Town, by Christianna Brand, Brockhampton Press (Leicester, UK), 1967 . £75/£20
ditto, Dutton (New York), [1968] . . . £60/£10
Robinson Crusoe, by Daniel Defoe, Nonesuch Press (London), 1968 . . . . £30/£10
Upsidedown Willie, by Dorothy Clewes, Hamish Hamilton (London), 1968 . . . . £30/£10
Special Branch Willie, by Dorothy Clewes, Hamish Hamilton (London), 1969 . . . . . £30/£10
The Angel and the Donkey, by James Reeves, Hamish Hamilton (London), 1969 . . . . £70/£20
ditto, McGraw-Hill (New York), [1970] . . £45/£10
A Riot of Quiet, by Virginia Sicotte, Holt, Rinehart and Winston (New York), [1969] . . . . £30/£10
Dick Whittington, retold by Kathleen Lines, Bodley Head (London), 1970 . . . . . . £25/£10
ditto, Walck (New York), [1970] . . . £25/£10
Fire Brigade Willie, by Dorothy Clewes, Hamish Hamilton (London), 1970 . . . . . £30/£10
Home From the Sea, by Robert Louis Stevenson, Bodley Head (London), 1970 . . . . . . £20/£10
How the Moon Began, by James Reeves, Abelard-Schuman (London), 1971 . . . . . . £35/£10
The Old Ballad of the Babes in the Wood, Bodley Head (London), 1972 . . . . . . £20/£10
ditto, Walck (New York), [1972] . . . . £15/£5
The Second Best Children in the World, by Mary Lavin, Longmans (London), 1972 . . . . £30/£10
ditto, Houghton Mifflin (Boston), 1972 . . £30/£10
The Tunnel of Hugsy Goode, by Eleanor Estes, Harcourt Brace (New York), 1972 . . . . £25/£5
Rain, Rain, Don't Go Away, by Shirley Morgan, Dutton (New York), [1972] . . . . . . £20/£5

The Little Fire Engine, by Graham Greene, Bodley Head (London), 1973 . . . . £50/£20
ditto, Doubleday (Garden City, NY), 1973 . . £50/£20
The Little Train, by Graham Greene, Bodley Head (London), 1973 . . . . £50/£20
ditto, Doubleday (Garden City, NY), 1973 . . £50/£20
Complete Poems for Children, by James Reeves, Heinemann (London), 1973 . . . . £30/£10
The Night Ride, by Aingelda Ardizzone, Bodley Head (London), 1973 . . . . £30/£10
ditto, Windmill Books (New York), 1975 . . £25/£10
The Little Horse Bus, by Graham Greene, Bodley Head (London), 1974 . . . . £50/£20
ditto, Doubleday (Garden City, NY), 1974 . . £45/£20
The Little Steam Roller, by Graham Greene, Bodley Head (London), 1974 . . . . £50/£20
ditto, Doubleday (Garden City, NY), 1974 . . £45/£20
The Lion That Flew, by James Reeves, Chatto & Windus (London), 1974 (issued without d/w) . . . £20
Nurse Matilda Goes to Hospital, by Christianna Brand, Brockhampton Press (Leicester, UK), 1974 . . £70/£20
ditto, Dutton (New York), 1974 . . . . £60/£10
More Prefabulous Animiles, by James Reeves, Heinemann (London), 1975 . . . . £25/£10
Ardizzone's Kilvert, Cape (London), 1976 . . £25/£10
Arcadian Ballads, by James Reeves, Heinemann (London), 1978 . . . . £25/£10
ditto, Heinemann (London), 1978 (200 signed, numbered copies; slipcase) . . . . . . £150/£100
Ardizzone's Hans Andersen, Deutsch (London), 1978 . . . . £35/£15
ditto, Atheneum (New York), 1979 . . . £30/£10
A Child's Christmas in Wales, by Dylan Thomas, Dent (London), 1978 . . . . £50/£15
ditto, Godine (Boston), 1980 . . . . . £35/£10
The James Reeves Story Book, Heinemann (London), 1978 . . . . £25/£10
Ardizzone's English Fairy Tales, Deutsch (London), 1980 . . . . £20/£5

Adult Books Written and Illustrated by Ardizzone
Baggage to the Enemy, Murray (London), 1941 . £75/£25
The Young Ardizzone: An Autobiographical Fragment, Studio Vista (London), 1970 . . . . . £20/£5
ditto, Macmillan (New York), 1970 . . . . £20/£5
Diary of a War Artist, Bodley Head (London), 1974 £30/£10
From Edward Ardizzone's Indian Diary, Stellar Press/ Bodley Head (London), 1983 (225 copies; wraps) . £25
Indian Diary, Bodley Head (London), 1984 . . £25/£10

Adult Books Illustrated by Ardizzone
In a Glass Darkly, by Sheridan Le Fanu, Peter Davis (London), 1929 (first impression, black cloth, with pictorial d/w) . . . . £250/£125
ditto, Peter Davis (London), 1929 (second impression, orange cloth, plain d/w) . . . . . . £125/£65
The Library, by George Crabbe, De la More Press (London), 1930 (pictorial paper-covered boards) £40
The Mediterranean, edited by Paul Bloomfield, Cassell (London), 1935 . . . . £125/£35
The Local, by Maurice Gorham, Cassell (London), 1939 . . . . £400/£250
My Uncle Silas, by H.E. Bates, Cape (London), 1939 . . . . £150/£45

The Road to Bordeaux, by C.D. Freeman and D. Cooper, Cresset Press (London), 1940 . . . . . £45/£20

The Battle of France, by A. Maurois, Bodley Head (London), 1940 . . . . £30/£10

Women, O.U.P. (Oxford, UK), 1943 (pictorial wraps; one vol in series of four) £25

The Poems of Francois Villon, Cresset Press (London), 1946 . . . . £40/£10

Back to the Local, by Maurice Gorham, Percival Marshall (London), 1949 . . . . £30/£10

The Londoners, by Maurice Gorham, Percival Marshall (London), 1951 . . . . £40/£10

Showmen and Suckers, by Maurice Gorham, Percival Marshall (London), 1951 . . . . . £35/£10

The Modern Prometheus, by Zara Nuber, Forge Press (London), 1952 . . . . £35/£15

The Warden, by Anthony Trollope, O.U.P. (Oxford, UK), 1952 . . . . £25/£10

Barchester Towers, by Anthony Trollope, O.U.P. (Oxford, UK), 1953 (2 vols) . . . . £35/£10

ditto, Franklin Library (Franklin Centre, PA), 1982 (full leather edition) £5

Christmas Eve, by C. Day Lewis, Faber (London), 1954 (sewn orange wraps) £5

The Newcomes, by William Makepeace Thackeray, Limited Edition Club (Cambridge, UK, and New York), 1954 (1,500 signed copies, slipcase, 2 vols) . . . £45/£30

Let's Have a Party, Blumenthals (London), 1956 (stapled wraps printed in black and red) £75

The Tale of an Old Tweed Jacket, by Eric Keown, Moss Bros (London), [1955] (stapled pictorial wraps) . £75

The History of Henry Esmond, by William Makepeace Thackeray, The Limited Editions Club (New York), 1956 (1,500 signed, numbered copies, glassine d/w and slipcase) . . . . £15/£10

Sugar for the Horse, by H.E. Bates, Joseph (London), 1957 . . . . £35/£10

Brief to Counsel, by Henry Cecil, Joseph (London), 1957 . . . . £20/£5

Not Such An Ass, by Henry Cecil, Hutchinson (London), 1961 . . . . £20/£5

Folk Songs of England, Ireland, Scotland and Wales, by W. Cole, Doubleday (Garden City, NY), 1961 . £35/£10

London Since 1912, by John T. Hayes, Museum of London (London), 1962 . . . . £35/£10

The Thirty-Nine Steps, by John Buchan, Dent (London), 1964 . . . . £20/£5

The Milldale Riot, by Freda P. Nichols, Ginn (London), 1965 . . . . £35/£10

Know About English Law, by Henry Cecil, Blackie (London), 1965 . . . . £35/£10

Mr Visconti, by Graham Greene, Bodley Head (London), 1969 (300 copies; d/w over unprinted white wraps) . . . . £150/£75

The Short Stories, by Charles Dickens, Limited Edition Club (New York), 1971 (1,500 signed copies, slipcase) £65/£25

Learn About English Law, by Henry Cecil, William Luscombe (London), 1974 . . . . . £20/£10

MICHAEL ARLEN
(b.1895 d.1956)

Born Dikran Kouyoumdjian in Bulgaria of Armenian ancestry, Arlen became a naturalised British subject in 1922. A novelist and short story writer, Arlen chronicled the lives of the young, rich and fashionable of the period, resulting in comparisons with F. Scott Fitzgerald. He was the model for Michaelis, the successful playwright with whom Connie has an affair in *Lady Chatterley's Lover*.

Short Stories
The Romantic Lady and Other Stories, Collins (London), [1921] . . . . £75/£20
ditto, Doran (New York), 1921 . . . . . £50/£10
These Charming People, Collins (London), [1923] £45/£10
ditto, Doran (New York), 1924 . . . . . £35/£10
May Fair, In Which Are Told the Last Adventures of These Charming People, Collins (London), [1925] . £50/£10
ditto, Doran (New York), [1925] . . . £35/£5
ditto, Doran (New York), [1925] (550 signed copies; slipcase) . . . . £60/£40
Ghost Stories, Collins (London), [1927] . . £250/£125
Babes in the Wood, Hutchinson (London), [1929]. £40/£10
ditto, Doran (New York), 1929 . . . . . £30/£10
The Ancient Sin and Other Stories, Collins (London), 1930 . . . . £30/£10
The Short Stories of Michael Arlen, Collins (London), 1933 . . . . £20/£5
The Crooked Coronet and Other Misrepresentations of the Real Facts of Life, Heinemann (London), 1937 . £25/£5
ditto, Doran (New York), 1937 . . . . . £20/£5

Novels
The London Venture, Heinemann (London), 1920 [1919] (first issue in paper boards wrongly dated 1920) . £125/£45
ditto, Heinemann (London), 1919 (second issue bound in cloth and dated 1919) . . . . £100/£25
ditto, Doran (New York), 1920 . . . . . £100/£20
'Piracy': A Romantic Chronicle of These Days, Collins (London), [1922] . . . . £50/£10
ditto, Doran (New York), 1923 . . . . . £40/£10
The Green Hat: A Romance for a Few People, Collins (London), 1924 . . . . £200/£30
ditto, Doran (New York), 1924 . . . . . £125/£20
Young Men in Love, Hutchinson (London), [1927] £45/£10
ditto, Doran (New York), 1927 . . . . . £40/£10
Lily Christine, Hutchinson (London), [1928] . £30/£15
ditto, Doran (New York), 1928 . . . . . £25/£10
Men Dislike Women, Heinemann (London), 1931 . £45/£15
ditto, Doran (New York), 1931 . . . . . £35/£15
A Young Man Comes to London, Keliher & Co. (London), 1931 (brochure to promote Dorchester Hotel) . £40
Man's Mortality, Heinemann (London), 1933 . . £45/£5
ditto, Doran (New York), 1933 . . . . . £25/£5
Hell! Said the Duchess: A Bed-Time Story, Heinemann (London), [1934] . . . . £50/£10
ditto, Doran (New York), 1934 . . . . . £35/£5
The Flying Dutchman, Heinemann (London), 1939 £40/£10
ditto, Doran (New York), 1939 . . . . . £35/£10

Plays
The Green Hat: A Romance, Doran (New York), 1925 (175 signed copies, glassine d/w and slipcase) . £100/£65

The Zoo, French (London), 1927 (wraps; with Winchell Smith) £15
Good Losers, French (London), 1933 (wraps; with Walter Hackett). £15

'Michael Arlen Booklets'
The Lady in the Stage-Box, Collins, [1927] (wraps)   .   £50
Ghost Stories, Collins, [1927] (wraps)   .   .   .   £60
Cavalier of the Streets, Collins, [1927] (wraps)   .   .   £40
The Ghoul of Golders Green, Collins, [1927] (wraps) .   £65

DAISY ASHFORD
(b.1881 d.1972)

Written when the author was a child, Ashford's books, full of social observation, are classics of unconscious humour. *The Young Visiters*, written when she was just nine years old, parodies the upper-class society of late 19th century England. The novella was published in 1919 with a foreword by J.M. Barrie and remains in print in the U.K. to this day.

The Young Visiters or, Mr Salteenas Plan, Chatto & Windus (London), 1919 (preface by J.M. Barrie). £250/£45
ditto, Doran (New York), 1919   .   .   .   .   £75/£20
Daisy Ashford: Her Book, Chatto & Windus (London), 1920   .   .   .   .   £50/£15
ditto, Doran (New York), 1920   .   .   .   .   £50/£15
Love and Marriage, Hart Davis (London), 1965 (illustrated by Ralph Steadman)   .   .   .   .   .   £25/£5
Where Love Lies Deepest, Hart Davis (London), 1966 (illustrated by Ralph Steadman)   .   .   .   £20/£5
The Hangman's Daughter, O.U.P. (Oxford, UK), 1983 (pbk) £5

ISAAC ASIMOV
(b.1920 d.1992)

Born in Russia, Asimov was taken to the U.S. in infancy. Although he wrote on many subjects, he is best known as a hugely successful science fiction writer. Asimov's most famous work is the 'Foundation Series', which he later combined with two other series, the 'Galactic Empire' and 'Robot' books. His many non-fiction writings have helped to make scientific ideas more popular and easily understandable.

Novels
Pebble in the Sky, Doubleday (Garden City, NY), 1950   .
.   .   .   .   £750/£85
ditto, Sidgwick & Jackson (London), 1968   .   £250/£35
The Stars, Like Dust, Doubleday (Garden City, NY), 1951 .
.   .   .   .   £225/£30
ditto, Panther (London), 1958 (pbk) £5
ditto, Grafton (London), 1986   .   .   .   .   £15/£5
Foundation, Gnome Press (New York), 1951 (first binding in cloth; width of sheets 1.9cm; first printing of jacket with rear panel advertising 3 titles)   .   .   .   £1,250/£225

ditto, Gnome Press (New York), 1951[1954] (second binding in boards; width of sheets 1.4cm; retains statement 'First Edition' and is dated 1951 on copyright page, but was apparently issued in 1954; second printing of jacket with rear panel advertising 32 titles).   .   .   £750/£100
ditto, Weidenfeld & Nicolson (London), 1953.   .£300/£50
Foundation and Empire, Gnome Press (New York), 1952 (first binding red boards lettered in black with publisher's imprint on spine 2.2cm wide; first printing width of sheets 1.8cm; first issue pictorial jacket with 26 titles listed on rear panel)   .   .   .   .   .   £500/£100
ditto, Gnome Press (New York), 1952 (second binding red boards lettered in black with publisher's imprint on spine 2.8cm wide; second printing width of sheets 2.3cm; second issue jacket printed in blue and black with 32 titles listed on rear panel)   .   .   .   .   .   .   £200/£50
ditto, Gnome Press (New York), 1952 (third binding green boards lettered in black with publisher's imprint on spine 2.8cm wide; second printing width of sheets 2.3cm; second issue jacket printed in blue and black with 32 titles listed on rear panel)   .   .   .   .   .   £200/£40
ditto, Panther (London), 1962 (pbk) £5
ditto, Granada (London), 1983   .   .   .   .   £15/£5
The Currents of Space, Doubleday (Garden City, NY), 1952 .
.   .   .   .   £250/£45
ditto, Boardman (London), 1955.   .   .   .   .£125/£20
Second Foundation, Gnome Press (New York), 1953 (first binding blue boards lettered in brown)   .   .   £500/£100
ditto, Gnome Press (New York), 1953 (later bindings)   .
.   .   .   .   £450/£45
ditto, Digit (London), 1958 (pbk) £5
ditto, Granada (London), 1983   .   .   .   .   £15/£5
The Caves of Steel, Doubleday (Garden City, NY), 1954   .
.   .   .   .   £450/£50
ditto, Boardman (London), 1954.   .   .   .   .£200/£20
The End of Eternity, Doubleday (Garden City, NY), 1955 .
.   .   .   .   £175/£15
ditto, Panther (London), 1959 (pbk) £5
The Naked Sun, Doubleday (Garden City, NY), 1957 .
.   .   .   .   £750/£50
ditto, Joseph (London), 1958   .   .   .   .   £350/£45
The Death Dealers, Avon (New York), 1958 (pbk)   .   £25
ditto, as *A Whiff of Death*, Walker (New York), 1968 .   .
.   .   .   .   £100/£20
ditto, Gollancz (London), 1968   .   .   .   .   £75/£15
Fantastic Voyage, Houghton Mifflin (Boston), 1966   .   .
.   .   .   .   £125/£20
ditto, Dobson (London), 1966   .   .   .   .   £35/£10
The Gods Themselves, Doubleday (Garden City, NY), 1972 .
.   .   .   .   £100/£20
ditto, Gollancz (London), 1972   .   .   .   .   £45/£10
Murder at the ABA, Doubleday (Garden City, NY), 1976 .
.   .   .   .   £40/£10
ditto, as *Authorised Murder*, Gollancz (London), 1976.   .
.   .   .   .   £40/£10
Foundation's Edge, Doubleday (Garden City, NY), 1982   .
.   .   .   .   £35/£10
ditto, Whispers Press (Binghampton, NY), 1982 (1,000 signed, numbered copies, no d/w) £100
ditto, Whispers Press (Binghampton, NY), 1982 (26 signed, lettered copies, all edges gilt, slipcase, no d/w)   .   £350
ditto, Granada (London), 1983   .   .   .   .   £15/£5
Robots of Dawn, Doubleday (Garden City, NY), 1983 .   .
.   .   .   .   £75/£25

ditto, Phantasia Press (Huntington Woods, MT), 1983 (750 signed, numbered copies, slipcase and d/w) . . £100/£75
ditto, Phantasia Press (Huntington Woods, MT), 1983 (35 signed, lettered copies, bound in black leather metal and plastic inserts in the front cover; no slipcase or d/w) . .
. . . . £1,250
ditto, Granada (London), 1984 . . . . . £15/£5
Robots and Empire, Doubleday (Garden City, NY), 1985 .
. . . . £45/£10
ditto, Phantasia Press (West Bloomfield, MT), 1985 (650 signed, numbered copies, slipcase) . . . £100/£75
ditto, Phantasia Press (West Bloomfield, MT), 1985 (35 signed, lettered copies bound in black leather, no slipcase or d/w) £650
ditto, Granada (London), 1985 . . . . . £20/£5
Foundation and Earth, Doubleday (Garden City, NY), 1986
. . . . £20/£5
ditto, Doubleday (Garden City, NY), 1986 (300 signed, numbered copies, slipcase) . . . £250/£200
ditto, Grafton (London), 1986 . . . . . £15/£5
Fantastic Voyage II: Destination Brain, Doubleday (New York), 1987 . . . . £20/£5
ditto, Doubleday (New York), 1987 (450 signed, numbered copies; slipcase) . . . . . . £65/£50
ditto, Grafton (London), 1987 . . . . . £20/£5
Prelude to Foundation, Doubleday (New York), 1988 . .
. . . . £10/£5
ditto, Doubleday (New York), 1988 (500 signed copies, slipcase). . . . . £125/£75
ditto, Easton Press (Norwalk, CT), 1988 (signed copies, full leather) £150
ditto, Grafton (London), 1988 . . . . . £10/£5
Nemesis, Doubleday (New York), 1989 . . . £10/£5
ditto, Doubleday (New York), 1989 (500 signed, numbered copies, slipcase) . . . . . . £85/£60
ditto, Doubleday (U.K.), 1989 . . . . . £10/£5
Child of Time, Gollancz (London), 1991 . . . £10/£5
ditto, as **The Ugly Little Boy**, Doubleday (New York), 1992
. . . . £10/£5
The Positronic Man, Doubleday (New York), 1992 (with Robert Silverberg) . . . . £10/£5
ditto, Gollancz (London), 1992 . . . . . £10/£5
Forward the Foundation, Doubleday (New York), 1993 .
. . . . £10/£5
ditto, Doubleday (U.K.), 1993 . . . . . £10/£5

Short Stories
I, Robot, Gnome Press (New York), 1950 . £1,500/£250
ditto, Grayson & Grayson (London), 1952 . . £300/£45
The Martian Way and Other Stories, Doubleday (Garden City, NY), 1955 . . . . £375/£50
ditto, Dobson (London), 1964 . . . . . £200/£35
Earth Is Room Enough, Doubleday (Garden City, NY), 1957
. . . . £175/£35
ditto, Panther (London), 1960 (pbk) £5
Nine Tomorrows: Tales of the Near Future, Doubleday (Garden City, NY), 1959 . . . . £125/£25
ditto, Dobson (London), 1963 . . . . . £45/£10
The Rest of the Robots, Doubleday (Garden City, NY), 1964 .
. . . . £100/£20
ditto, Dobson (London), 1967 . . . . . £75/£15
Through a Glass, Clearly, Four Square Books (London), 1967 (pbk) £5
ditto, Ian Henry Publications (Hornchurch, Essex) . £20/£5

Asimov's Mysteries, Doubleday (Garden City, NY), 1968 .
. . . . £45/£10
ditto, Rapp & Whiting (London), 1968 . . . £45/£10
Nightfall and Other Stories, Doubleday (Garden City, NY), 1969 . . . . £100/£25
ditto, Rapp & Whiting (London), 1970 . . . £75/£15
ditto, as **Nightfall and Other Stories**, Doubleday (Garden City, NY), 1990 (with Robert Silverberg) . . £15/£5
ditto, Doubleday (Garden City, NY), 1990 (750 signed copies, slipcase) . . . . . . £75/£50
ditto, as **Nightfall: Twenty SF Stories**, Gollancz (London), 1990 . . . . £10/£5
The Early Asimov, Doubleday (Garden City, NY), 1972 .
. . . . £50/£10
ditto, Gollancz (London), 1973 . . . . . £35/£10
The Best of Isaac Asimov, Sidgwick & Jackson (London), 1973 . . . . £45/£10
ditto, Doubleday (Garden City, NY), 1974 . £45/£10
Tales of the Black Widowers, Doubleday (Garden City, NY), 1974
. . . . £75/£10
ditto, Gollancz (London), 1975 . . . . . £50/£10
Have You Seen These?, NESFA Press (Boston, MA), 1974 (500 signed, numbered copies). . . . £100/£45
The Heavenly Host, Walker (New York), 1975 . £25/£10
ditto, Penguin (Harmondsworth, Middlesex), 1978 (pbk) £5
Buy Jupiter and Other Stories, Doubleday (Garden City, NY), 1975 . . . . £65/£10
ditto, Gollancz (London), 1976 . . . . . £20/£5
The Bicentennial Man and Other Stories, Doubleday (Garden City, NY), 1976 . . . . . £65/£10
ditto, Gollancz (London), 1977 . . . . . £30/£10
More Tales of the Black Widowers, Doubleday (Garden City, NY), 1976 . . . . £65/£10
ditto, Gollancz (London), 1977 . . . . . £30/£10
The Dream; Benjamin's Dream; & Benjamin's Bicentennial Blast, Benjamin Franklin Keepsakes (New York), 1976 (approx 200 copies) £35
Good Taste, Apocalypse Press (Topeka, KA), 1976 (500 signed, numbered copies) £100
ditto, Apocalypse Press (Topeka, KA), 1976 (500 facsimile signed, numbered copies) £45
The Key Word and Other Mysteries, Walker (New York), 1977 . . . . £35/£10
ditto, Piccolo/Pan (London), 1982 (pbk) £5
The Casebook of the Black Widowers, Doubleday (Garden City, NY), 1980 . . . . £50/£10
ditto, Gollancz (London), 1980 . . . . . £40/£5
Three Science Fiction Tales, Targ Editions (New York), 1981 (250 signed copies in plain d/w) . . £125/£100
The Complete Robot, Doubleday (Garden City, NY), 1982 .
. . . . £100/£25
ditto, Granada (London), 1982 . . . . . £65/£15
The Winds of Change and Other Stories, Doubleday (Garden City, NY), 1983 . . . . . £35/£10
ditto, as **The Winds of Change**, Granada (London), 1983 .
. . . . £25/£10
The Union Club Mysteries, Doubleday (Garden City, NY), 1983 . . . . £25/£10
ditto, Granada (London), 1984 . . . . . £15/£5
Banquets of the Black Widowers, Doubleday (Garden City, NY), 1984 . . . . £15/£5
ditto, Granada (London), 1985 . . . . . £15/£5
The Edge of Tomorrow, Tor (New York), 1985 . £15/£5
ditto, Harrap (London), 1986 . . . . . £10/£5

It's Such a Beautiful Day, Creative Education (Mankato, MN), 1985 (no d/w) £10
Alternate Asimovs, Doubleday (Garden City, NY), 1986 . . . . £15/£5
ditto, Panther/Grafton (London), 1987 (pbk) . . £5
Science Fiction by Asimov, Davis (New York), 1986 (pbk). £5
The Best Science Fiction of Isaac Asimov, Doubleday (Garden City, NY), 1986 . . . . £15/£5
ditto, Grafton (London), 1987 . . . . . £10/£5
Robot Dreams, Berkley (New York), 1986 (pbk) . £5
ditto, Berkley (New York), 1986 (300 signed, numbered copies; hardback in slipcase; no d/w) . . £125/£100
ditto, Gollancz (London), 1987 . . . . . £50/£15
The Best Mysteries of Isaac Asimov, Doubleday (Garden City, NY), 1986 . . . . . . £10/£5
ditto, Grafton (London), 1987 . . . . . £10/£5
Other Worlds of Isaac Asimov, Avenel (New York), 1987 . . . . £10/£5
Sally, Creative Education (Mankato, MN), 1988 (no d/w) £10
Azazel, Doubleday (New York), 1988 . . . £10/£5
ditto, Doubleday (U.K.), 1989 . . . . . £10/£5
The Asimov Chronicles: Fifty Years of Isaac Asimov, Dark Harvest (Arlington Heights, IL), 1989 . . £25/£10
ditto, Dark Harvest (Arlington Heights, IL), 1989 (52 signed, lettered copies, slipcase) . . . . £300/£250
ditto, Dark Harvest (Arlington Heights, IL), 1989 (500 signed copies) . . . . . £150/£100
ditto, Century (London), 1991 . . . . . £15/£5
All The Troubles of the World, Creative Education (Mankato, MN), 1989 (no d/w) £10
Franchise, Creative Education (Mankato, MN), 1989 (no d/w) £10
Robbie, Creative Education (Mankato, MN), 1989 (no d/w) £10
Robot Visions, Roc (New York), 1990 . . . £15/£5
ditto, Gollancz (London), 1990 . . . . . £15/£5
Puzzles of the Black Widowers, Doubleday (New York), 1990 . . . . £25/£5
ditto, Doubleday (U.K.), 1990 . . . . . £15/£5
The Complete Stories Volume I, Doubleday (New York), 1990 . . . . £25/£5
The Complete Stories Volume II, Doubleday (New York), 1992 . . . . £15/£5
The Complete Stories, Harper/Collins (London), 1992 £15/£5
Gold: The Final Science Fiction Collection, Harper Collins (London), 1995 . . . . £10/£5
Magic: The Final Fantasy Collection, Harper (New York), 1996 . . . . £10/£5
ditto, Voyager (London), 1996 . . . . . £10/£5

Children's Titles Written as 'Paul French'
David Starr: Space Ranger, Doubleday (Garden City, NY), 1953 . . . . £150/£45
ditto, World's Work (Kingswood, Surrey, UK), 1953 . . . . £100/£30
Lucky Starr and the Pirates of the Asteroids, Doubleday (Garden City, NY), 1954 . . . . £125/£45
ditto, World's Work (Kingswood, Surrey, UK), 1954 . . . . £100/£30
Lucky Starr and the Oceans of Venus, Doubleday (Garden City, NY), 1954 . . . . . . £75/£15
ditto, as *Oceans of Venus*, New English Library (London), 1974 (pbk) £5

Lucky Starr and the Big Sun of Mercury, Doubleday (Garden City, NY), 1956 . . . . . £75/£15
ditto, as *The Big Sun of Mercury*, New English Library (London), 1974 (pbk). £5
Lucky Starr and the Moons of Jupiter, Doubleday (Garden City, NY), 1957 . . . . £75/£15
ditto, as *The Moons of Jupiter*, New English Library (London), 1974 (pbk). £5
Lucky Starr and the Rings of Saturn, Doubleday (Garden City, NY), 1958 . . . . £75/£15
ditto, as *The Rings of Saturn*, New English Library (London), 1974 (pbk). £5
Norby the Mixed-Up Robot, Walker (New York), 1983 (with Janet Asimov) . . . . £50/£10
ditto, Methuen (London), 1984 . . . . . £30/£5
Norby's Other Secret, Walker (New York), 1984 (with Janet Asimov). . . . . £50/£10
ditto, Methuen (London), 1985 . . . . . £30/£5
Norby and the Lost Princess, Walker (New York), 1985 (with Janet Asimov) . . . . . . £50/£10
ditto, Methuen (London), 1986 . . . . . £30/£5

Others
Futuredays: A Nineteenth-Century Vision of the Year 2000, Virgin/Lucy-Carroll (London), 1986 . . £20/£5
ditto, Henry Holt (New York), 1986 (pbk) . . . £5

MABEL LUCIE ATTWELL
(b.1879 d.1964)

Attwell illustrated not only classic children's books such as *Alice in Wonderland*, but also drew comic strips and produced her own books, postcards and annuals. She contributed to a number of magazines including *The Strand* and *Pearsons*.

'Bunty and the Boo Boos' Titles
Bunty and the Boo Boos, Valentine (Dundee), [1921] . £200
The Boo Boos and Bunty's Baby, Valentine (Dundee), [1921] £200
The Boo Boos at School, Valentine (Dundee), [1921] . £200
The Boo Boos at the Seaside, Valentine (Dundee), [1921] £200
The Boo Boos at Honeysweet Farm, Valentine (Dundee), [1921] £200
The Boo Boos and Santa Claus, Valentine (Dundee), [1921] £200

Annuals
The Lucie Attwell Annual No. 1, Partridge (London), 1922 . . . . £225
The Lucie Attwell Annual No. 2, Partridge (London), 1923 . . . . £200
The Lucie Attwell Annual No. 3, Partridge (London), 1924 . . . . £200
Lucie Attwell's Children's Book, Partridge (London), 1925-32 . . . . £175 each
Lucie Attwell's Annual, Dean (London), 1934-35, 1937-41 . . . . £100 each
Lucie Attwell's Annual, Dean (London), 1942 . . £75
Lucie Attwell's Annual, Dean (London), 1945-68 . £75/£45
Lucie Attwell's Annual, Dean (London), 1969-74 . £50/£35

Others Written and Illustrated by Attwell

Peggy: The Lucie Attwell Cut-Out Dressing Doll, Valentine (Dundee), [1921]. £175

Stitch Stitch, Valentine (Dundee), [1922]. . . . £135

Comforting Thoughts, Valentine (Dundee), [1922] . £75

Baby's Book, Raphael Tuck (London), [1922] . . £125

Fairy Tales, Valentine (Dundee), [1922] (full colour frontispiece, 4 full-page drawings, 6 quarter-page drawings) £150

All About Bad Babies, John Swain (London), [c1925] . £75

All About the Seaside, John Swain (London), [c1925] . £60

All About Fairies, John Swain (London), [c1925] . . £65

All About the Country, John Swain (London), [c1925]. £65

All About School, John Swain (London), [c1925] . . £65

All About Fido, John Swain (London), [c1925] . . £65

Lucie Attwell's Rainy-Day Tales, Partridge (London) [1931] (with other authors) £125

Lucie Attwell's Rock-Away Tales, London, 1931 (with other authors) £100

Lucie Attwell's Fairy Book, Partridge (London), 1932 (12 colour plates plus b&w illustrations) . . . £200

Lucie Attwell's Happy-Day Tales, Partridge (London), [1932] £100

Lucie Attwell's Quiet Time Tales, Partridge (London), [1932] £100

Lucie Attwell's Painting Book, Dean (London), [1934] £75

Lucie Attwell's Great Big Midget Book, Dean (London), [1934] £100

Lucie Attwell's Great Big Midget Book, Dean (London), [1935] (different from above) £100

Lucie Attwell's Playtime Pictures, Carlton Publishing Co. (U.S.), 1935. . . . . £75

Lucie Attwell Picture Book, Whitman Publishing Co. (Racine, WI), 1936 . . . . . . £300/£125

Lucie Attwell's Story Book, Dean (London), [1943] . £65

Lucie Attwell's Story Book, Dean (London), [1945] (different from above) £65

Lucie Attwell's Jolly Book, Dean (London), [1953] £65/£25

Lucie Attwell's Nursery Rhymes Pop-Up Book, Dean (London), 1958 . . . . £45

Lucie Attwell's Storytime Tales, Dean (London), [1959] . . . . £35/£15

Lucie Attwell's Book of Verse, Dean (London), 1960 . . . . £35/£15

Lucie Attwell's Book of Rhymes, Dean (London), 1962 . . . . £35/£15

Stories for Everyday, Dean (London), 1964 . . £25/£10

A Little Bird Told Me, Dean (London), 1964 . . £25/£10

A Little Bird Told Me Another Story, Dean (London), 1966 . . . . £25/£10

Tinie's Book of Prayers, Dean (London), 1967 . £25/£10

Lucie Attwell's Tiny Rhymes Pop-Up Book, Dean (London), 1967 . . . . £45

Lucie Attwell's Tell Me A Story Pop-Up Book, Dean (London), 1968 . . . . £45

Lucie Attwell's Book of Rhymes, Dean (London), 1969 . . . . £25/£10

Books Illustrated by Attwell

That Little Limb, by May Baldwin, Chambers (London), 1905 . . . . £75

The Amateur Cook, by K. Burrill, Chambers (London), 1905 . . . . £50

Troublesome Ursula, by Mabel Quiller-Couch, Chambers (London), 1905 . . . . £65

Dora: A High School Girl, by May Baldwin, Chambers (London), 1906 . . . . £75

A Boy and a Secret, by Raymond Jacberns, Chambers (London), 1908 . . . . £40

Busy Bees, by Grace C. Floyd, Raphael Tuck & Sons, Ltd. (London), [1908]. £200

The Little Tin Soldier, by Graham Mar, Chambers (London), 1909 (frontispiece plus 5 b&w plates) . . . £50

The February Boys, by Mrs Molesworth, Chambers (London), 1909 . . . . £60

Old Rhymes, Raphael Tuck (London), 1909 . . . £45

The Old Pincushion, by Mrs Molesworth, Chambers (London), 1910 . . . . £60

Mother Goose, Raphael Tuck (London), 1910. . . £150

Alice in Wonderland, by Lewis Carroll, Raphael Tuck (London), [1910] (12 colour plates, plus b&w illustrations) £250

My Dolly's House ABC, Raphael Tuck (London), [c.1910] £150

Grimm's Fairy Tales, Cassell (London), [1910] (4 full-page illustrations). £125

Tabitha Smallways, by Raymond Jacberns, Chambers (London), 1911 (6 colour plates) £65

Grimm's Fairy Stories, Raphael Tuck (London), 1912 (12 colour plates) £150

Troublesome Topsy and Her Friends, by May Baldwin, Chambers (London), 1913. . . . . . £50

Hans Andersen's Fairy Tales, Raphael Tuck (London), [1914] (12 colour plates) £150

A Band of Mirth, by L.T. Meade, Chambers (London), 1914 . . . . £50

The Water Babies, by Charles Kingsley, Raphael Tuck (London), [1915] (12 colour plates, plus b&w illustrations) £200

Children's Stories from French Fairy Tales, by Doris Ashley, Raphael Tuck (London), 1917 (12 colour plates, plus b&w illustrations) £165

Peeping Pansy, by Marie, Queen of Roumania, Hodder & Stoughton (London), [1919] (issued with d/w) . £250

Wooden, by Archibald Marshall, Collins (London), [1920] (4 colour plates) . . . . £125/£65

Peter Pan and Wendy, by J.M. Barrie, Hodder & Stoughton (London), [1921]. . . . . £300/£100

ditto, Charles Scribner's Sons (New York), 1921 £300/£100

The Lost Princess: A Fairy Tale, by Marie, Queen of Roumania, Partridge (London), 1924 (6 colour plates, plus b&w illustrations) . . . . . £300/£125

Little Red Riding Hood and Other Stories, by The Brothers Grimm, Raphael Tuck (London), 1925 (4 colour plates, plus b&w illustrations) £75

The Frog Prince and Other Stories, by The Brothers Grimm, Raphael Tuck (London), [1925?] (2 colour plates, plus b&w illustrations) £75

Children's Stories, Whitman Publishing Co. (Racine, WI), [c.1930]. . . . . £300/£125

Feeding Your Baby, Robinsons (London), [c.1960] (wraps) £50

MARGARET ATWOOD
(b.1939)

Atwood is a Canadian writer most popularly known for her prose, following the success of *Cat's Eye*. A versatile writer, she works successfully in various genres and her writing often focuses on feminist issues and concerns. She is also known for her interest in Canada and Canadian fiction.

Poetry

Double Persephone, Hawkshead Press (Toronto), 1961 (printed white stiff wraps) £1,500
The Circle Game, Cranbrook Academy (Bloomfield Hills, MI), 1964 (15 numbered copies; hardback without d/w) .
. . . . £3,000
ditto, Contact Press (Toronto), 1966 (50 copies) . £1,000
ditto, Contact Press (Toronto), 1966 (200 copies; white, printed wraps with French flaps) £450
ditto, House of Anansi (Toronto), 1967 (100 signed copies).
. . . . £200
ditto, House of Anansi (Toronto), 1967 (pbk) . . . £15
Talismans for Children, Cranbrook Academy (Bloomfield Hills, MI), 1965 (10 copies) £3,000
Kaleidoscopes: Baroque, Cranbrook Academy (Bloomfield Hills, MI), 1965 (20 copies) £2,500
Speeches for Doctor Frankenstein, Cranbrook Academy (Bloomfield Hills, MI), 1966 (10 copies) . . £3,000
Expeditions, Cranbrook Academy (Bloomfield Hills, MI), 1966 (15 copies) £2,500
The Animals in that Country, O.U.P. (Toronto), 1968 .
. . . . £200/£45
ditto, O.U.P. (Toronto), 1968 (pbk) £30
ditto, Little, Brown (Boston), [1969] . . . £45/£10
What Was in the Garden?, Unicorn (Santa Barbara, CA), 1969 (broadside) £40
The Journals of Susanna Moodie, O.U.P. (Toronto), 1970 (pbk) £35
ditto, Manuel & Abel Bello-Sanchez (Canada), 1980 (20 deluxe signed copies, numbered I-XX) . . . £750
ditto, Manuel & Abel Bello-Sanchez (Canada), 1980 (100 signed copies) £200
ditto, Bloomsbury (London), 1997 (slipcase) . £75/£50
Oratorio for Sasquatch, Man and Two Androids: Poems for Voices, C.B.C. (Canada), 1970 . . . . £25
Procedures for Underground, O.U.P. (Toronto), 1970 (pbk)
. . . . £15
ditto, Little, Brown (Boston), 1970 . . . £25/£10
Power Politics, Anansi (Toronto), 1971 . . £100/£25
ditto, Anansi (Toronto), 1971 (pbk) £15
ditto, Harper (New York), 1973 . . . . £20/£5
You Are Happy, O.U.P. (Toronto), 1974 (pbk) . . £20
ditto, Harper (New York), 1974 . . . . £15/£5
Selected Poems, O.U.P. (Toronto), 1976 (pbk) . . £20
ditto, Simon & Schuster (New York), 1978 . . £15/£5
Marsh, Hawk, Dreadnought (Toronto), 1977 (broadside) £35
Two-headed Poems, O.U.P. (Toronto), 1978 (pbk) . £20
ditto, Simon & Schuster (New York), 1980 . . £15/£5
A Poem for Grandmothers, Square Zero Editions (no place, U.S.), 1978 (26 copies of 126, single sheet) . . £100
ditto, Square Zero Editions (no place, U.S.), 1978 (100 copies of 126, single sheet) £35
True Stories, O.U.P. (Toronto), 1981 (pbk) . . £10

ditto, Simon & Schuster (New York), 1982 . . £20/£10
ditto, Cape (London), 1982 (pbk) £10
Notes Towards a Poem that can Never be Written, Salamander Press (Toronto), 1981 (200 numbered, signed copies; handbound pbk) £125
Snake Poems, Salamander Press (Toronto), 1983 (100 numbered, signed copies, accordion fold) . . £175
Interlunar, O.U.P. (Toronto), 1984 (pbk). . . . £5
ditto, Cape (London), 1988 (pbk) £10
Selected Poems II: Poems Selected & New 1976-1986, O.U.P. (Toronto), 1986 (pbk) £10
ditto, Houghton Mifflin (Boston), 1987 . . . £10/£5
ditto, as *Poems, 1976-1986*, Virago (London), 1992 (pbk) £5
Selected Poems, 1966-1984, O.U.P. (Toronto), 1990 (pbk) .
. . . . £10
Poems, 1965-1975, Virago (London), 1991 (pbk) . . £5
ditto, Houghton Mifflin (Boston), 1987 . . . £10/£5
Good Bones, Harbourfront Reading Series (Toronto), 1992 (150 signed, numbered copies; wraps) . . . £30
ditto, Harbourfront Reading Series (Toronto), 1992 (350 unsigned copies; wraps) £10
ditto, Coach House Press (Toronto, Canada), 1992. £10/£5
ditto, Bloomsbury (London), 1992 . . . £10/£5
Good Bones and Simple Murders, Doubleday (New York), 1994 . . . . £10/£5
Morning in the Burned House, McClelland & Stewart (Toronto), [1995]. . . . . £10/£5
ditto, Virago (London), 1995 (pbk) £5
ditto, Houghton Mifflin (Boston), 1995 . . . £10/£5
Eating Fire; Selected Poems, 1965-1995, Virago (London), 1998 . . . . £5
ditto, Little, Brown (New York), 1998 . . . £10/£5
The Door McClelland & Stewart (Toronto), 2007 . £10/£5
ditto, Virago (London), 2007 . . . . . £10/£5
ditto, Houghton Mifflin (Boston), 2007 . . . £10/£5

Novels

The Edible Woman, McClelland & Stewart (Toronto), 1969
. . . . £300/£35
ditto, Deutsch (London), 1969 . . . . . £150/£25
ditto, Little, Brown (Boston), 1970 . . . . £150/£25
Surfacing, McClelland & Stewart (Toronto), 1972 £50/£15
ditto, Deutsch (London), 1973 . . . . . £50/£15
ditto, Simon & Schuster (New York), 1973 . . £35/£5
Lady Oracle, McClelland & Stewart (Toronto), 1976 £30/£5
ditto, Simon & Schuster (New York), 1976 . . £30/£5
ditto, Deutsch (London), 1977 . . . . . £30/£5
Life Before Man, McClelland & Stewart (Toronto), 1979 .
. . . . £30/£5
ditto, Simon & Schuster (New York), 1979 . . £15/£5
ditto, Cape (London), 1980 . . . . . . £15/£5
Bodily Harm, McClelland & Stewart (Toronto), 1981 £15/£5
ditto, Simon & Schuster (New York), 1982 . . £10/£5
ditto, Cape (London), 1982 . . . . . . £10/£5
The Handmaid's Tale, McClelland & Stewart (Toronto), 1985 . . . . £35/£10
ditto, Houghton Mifflin (Boston), 1986 . . . £25/£5
ditto, Cape (London), 1986 . . . . . . £25/£5
The Margaret Atwood Omnibus, Deutsch (London), 1987 .
. . . . £10/£5
Cat's Eye, McClelland & Stewart (Toronto), 1988. £15/£5
ditto, Doubleday (New York), 1989 . . . . £15/£5
ditto, Bloomsbury (London), 1989 . . . . £15/£5
Robber Bride, McClelland & Stewart (Toronto), 1993 .
. . . . £15/£10

ditto, Doubleday (New York), 1993 . . . . £15/£5
ditto, Bloomsbury (London), 1993 . . . . £10/£5
Alias Grace, McClelland & Stewart (Toronto), 1996 £15/£10
ditto, Doubleday (New York), 1996 . . . . £15/£5
ditto, Bloomsbury (London), 1996 . . . . £10/£5
The Blind Assassin, McClelland & Stewart (Toronto), 2000
. . . . £15/£10
ditto, Doubleday (New York), 2000 . . . . £10/£5
ditto, Bloomsbury (London), 2000 . . . . £10/£5
Oryx and Crake, McClelland & Stewart (Toronto), 2003 .
. . . . £10/£5
ditto, Talese/Doubleday (New York), 2003 (800 copies) .
. . . . £25/£10
ditto, Doubleday (New York), 2003 . . . . £10/£5
ditto, Bloomsbury (London), 2003 . . . . £10/£5
The Year of the Flood, McClelland & Stewart (Toronto),
2009. . . . . £10/£5
ditto, Talese/Doubleday (New York), 2009 . . £10/£5
ditto, Bloomsbury (London), 2003 . . . . £10/£5

Short Stories
Dancing Girls and Other Stories, McClelland & Stewart
(Toronto), 1977 . . . . £40/£10
ditto, Simon & Schuster (New York), 1982 . . £25/£5
ditto, Cape (London), 1982 . . . . . £25/£5
Encounters with the Element Man, Ewert (Concord, NH),
1982 (60 signed, numbered copies, boards, no d/w) . £125
ditto, Ewert (Concord, NH), 1982 (100 signed, numbered
copies; wraps) £75
Murder in the Dark: Short Fictions and Prose Poems,
Coach House Press (Toronto, Canada), 1983 (first issue
with 'pocket' typo p.61; pbk) £20
ditto, Coach House Press (Toronto, Canada), 1983 (second
issue with 'pockets' p.61; pbk). £5
ditto, Cape (London), 1984 . . . . . £15/£5
Bluebeard's Egg and Other Stories, McClelland & Stewart
(Toronto), 1983 . . . . £10/£5
ditto, Houghton Mifflin (Boston), 1986 . . . £10/£5
ditto, Cape (London), 1987 . . . . . £10/£5
Unearthing Suite, Grand Union Press (Toronto), 1983 (175
signed, numbered copies, boards with no d/w) . . £200
Hurricane Hazel and Other Stories, Eurographica
(Helsinki), 1987 (350 signed copies, stiff card covers and
printed textured d/w) £60
Wilderness Tips, McClelland & Stewart (Toronto), 1991 .
. . . . £10/£5
ditto, Doubleday (New York), 1991 . . . . £10/£5
ditto, Bloomsbury (London), 1991 . . . . £10/£5
Good Bones, Coach House (Toronto), 1992 . . £10/£5
ditto, Bloomsbury (London), 1992 . . . . £10/£5
Good Bones and Simple Murders, Doubleday (New York),
1994 . . . . £10/£5
ditto, Doubleday (New York), 1994 (50 copies) . £100/£75
ditto, as *Bones and Murder*, Virago (London), 1995 (pbk) £5
Nightingale, Harbourfront Reading Series (Toronto), 2000
(26 signed, lettered copies in quarter calf binding, no d/w)
. . . . £150
ditto, Harbourfront Reading Series (Toronto), 2000 (5 signed
copies in half calf binding) £200
ditto, Harbourfront Reading Series (Toronto), 2000 (39
signed, roman-numeralled copies) £90
ditto, Harbourfront Reading Series (Toronto), 2000 (31
signed, roman-numeralled copies) £100
ditto, Harbourfront Reading Series (Toronto), 2000 (5
signed, roman-numeralled copies) £150

ditto, Harbourfront Reading Series (Toronto), 2000 (150
signed, numbered copies in stapled wraps) . . . £25
ditto, Harbourfront Reading Series (Toronto), 2000 (300
unsigned copies; stapled wraps) £10
Bottle, Hay Festival Press, 2004 (2004) (100 numbered,
signed copies, no d/w) £100
ditto, Hay Festival Press, 2004 (2004) (900 copies, no d/w) .
. . . . £15
The Tent, Doubleday (New York), 2006 . . . £10/£5
ditto, Doubleday (New York), 2006 . . . . £10/£5
ditto, Bloomsbury (London), 2006 . . . . £10/£5
Moral Disorder, McClelland & Stewart (Toronto), 2006 .
. . . . £10/£5
ditto, Doubleday (New York), 2006 . . . . £10/£5
ditto, Bloomsbury (London), 2006 . . . . £10/£5

Children's Titles
Up in the Tree, McClelland & Stewart (Toronto), 1978
(decorative boards; no d/w) £65
Anna's Pet, Lorimer (Toronto), 1980 (with Joyce Barkhouse,
no d/w) £20
For the Birds, Douglas & McIntyre (Toronto), 1990 (wraps)
. . . . £10
Princess Prunella and the Purple Peanut, Key Porter Kids
(Toronto), 1995 . . . . £15/£5
Rude Ramsay and the Roaring Radishes, Key Porter Kids
(Toronto), 2003 . . . . £10/£5
ditto, Bloomsbury (New York), 2004. . . . £10/£5
Bashful Bob and Doleful Dorinda, Key Porter Kids
(Toronto), 2004 . . . . £10/£5

Criticism
Survival: A Thematic Guide to Canadian Literature,
Anansi (Toronto), 1972 ('first' issue binding printed by
Web. Offset Ltd., with 'first' issue d/w without blurbs on
the rear panel) . . . . £125/£45
ditto, Anansi (Toronto), 1972 (second issue binding printed
by T.H. Best, with 'second' issue d/w with blurbs) £35/£10
Second Words: Selected Critical Prose, Anansi (Toronto),
1982 . . . . £30/£10
ditto, Beacon Press (Boston), 1984 . . . . £20/£5
*Strange Things: The Malevolent North in Canadian
Literature*, O.U.P. (Oxford, UK), 1995 . . . £10/£5
Negotiating with the Dead: A Writer on Writing, C.U.P.
(Cambridge, UK), 2002 . . . . . . £10/£5

Others
Margaret Atwood: Conversations, Ontario Review Press
(Princeton, NJ), 1990 . . . . . . £15/£5
ditto, Virago (London), 1991 (pbk) £10
*Winner of the Welsh Arts Council International Writer's
Prize*, Welsh Arts Council, 1992 (wraps) . . . £5
Murder in the Dark, Cape (London), 1994 . . £10/£5
Moving Targets: Writing with Intent 1982-2004, House of
Anansi (Toronto), 2004 . . . . . £10/£5
ditto, Carroll & Graf (New York), 2005 . . . £10/£5
Curious Pursuits, Virago (London), 2005 . . £10/£5
The Penelopiad: The Myth of Penelope and Odysseus,
Cannongate (Edinburgh), 2005. . . . . £10/£5
ditto, Cannongate (New York), 2005 . . . . £10/£5
ditto, Knopf (Toronto), 2005 . . . . . £10/£5
ditto, Cannongate (Edinburgh), 2005 (box set, *Myths*, also
containing *Weight* by Jeanette Winterson, *A Short History*

of Myth by Karen Armstrong, and an introductory pamphlet, *A Word or Two About Myth* by Philip Pullman) £45
ditto, Cannongate (Edinburgh), 2005 (1,500 numbered box sets, as above but each book signed by the authors)   .   £80
Waltzing Again, Ontario Review Press (Princeton, NJ), 2006 (wraps) £5

W.H. AUDEN
(b.1907 d.1973)

Auden's early poetry was markedly left-wing, but Christianity was the dominant influence in his later life and art. He is considered one of the most influential poets of the 20th century. Although born in Britain, Auden emigrated to the United States in 1939 with Christopher Isherwood and became an American citizen in 1946.

Poetry
Poems, privately printed by Stephen Spender, 1928 (30 copies, orange wraps). £25,000
Poems, Faber (London), 1930 (wraps)   .   .   .   £450
ditto, Random House (New York), 1934   .   .   £100/£25
The Orators: an English Study, Faber (London), [1932]   .
   .   .   .   .   £225/£65
ditto, Random House (New York), 1967   .   .   £25/£5
The Dance of Death, Faber (London), 1933   .   £150/£30
The Witnesses, privately printed, 1933 (broadside, 20 copies, illustrated by Gwen Raverat) £2,750
Poem, privately printed, 1933 (22 copies; wraps)   .   £4,000
Two Poems, privately printed, 1934 (22 copies; wraps).   .
   .   .   .   .   £4,000
Our Hunting Fathers, privately printed, 1935 (22 copies; wraps) £4,000
Sonnet, privately printed, 1935 (22 copies; wraps).   £4,000
Look Stranger!, Faber (London), 1936   .   .   £125/£30
ditto, as *On This Island*, Random House (New York), [1937]
   .   .   .   .   £125/£30
Spain, Faber (London), [1937] (wraps)   .   .   .   £75
Deux Poemes, Hours Press (Paris), 1937 (100 copies) £1,000
Night Mail, G.P.O., 1938 (broadside)   .   .   .   £75
Selected Poems, Faber (London), 1938   .   .   £125/£25
Journey to a War, Faber (London), 1939 (with Christopher Isherwood)   .   .   .   .   £150/£35
ditto, Random House (New York), 1939   .   .   £85/£20
Another Time, Faber (London), 1940   .   .   £225/£45
ditto, Random House (New York), 1940   .   .   £225/£35
Some Poems, Faber (London), 1940   .   .   .   £40/£10
The Double Man, Random House (New York), 1941   .   .
   .   .   .   .   £150/£35
ditto, as *New Year Letter*, Faber (London), 1941   .£125/£30
Three Songs for St Cecilia's Day, privately printed, 1941 (250 copies; wraps) £125
For the Time Being, Random House (New York), 1944   .
   .   .   .   .   £100/£25
ditto, Faber (London), 1945.   .   .   .   .   £100/£25
The Collected Poetry, Random House (New York), 1945   .
   .   .   .   .   £75/£20
Litany and Anthem for St Matthew's Day, privately printed, 1946 (single sheet) £65
The Age of Anxiety, Random House (New York), [1947]   .
   .   .   .   .   £100/£25
ditto, Faber (London), 1948.   .   .   .   .   £75/£20

Collected Shorter Poems 1930-1944, Faber (London), 1950
   .   .   .   .   £75/£15
Nones, Random House (New York), 1951   .   .   £60/£15
ditto, Faber (London), 1952.   .   .   .   .   £60/£15
Mountains, Faber (London), 1954 (wraps)   .   .   £25
The Shield of Achilles, Random House (New York), 1955   .
   .   .   .   .   £35/£10
ditto, Faber (London), 1955.   .   .   .   .   £35/£10
The Old Man's Road, Voyages Press (New York), 1956 (50 signed copies of 750; wraps in printed paper d/w)   .
   .   .   .   .   £300/£250
ditto, Voyages Press (New York), 1956 (700 unsigned copies of 750; wraps) £40
W.H. Auden: A Selection by the Author, Penguin (Harmondsworth, Middlesex), 1958 (pbk)   .   .   .   £5
ditto, as *Selected Poetry of W.H. Auden*, Modern Library (New York), 1959   .   .   .   .   .   .   £15/£5
Goodbye to the Mezzogiorno, All'Insegna del Pesce d'Oro (Spain), 1958 (1,000 numbered copies; wraps with integral d/w and wraparound band)   .   .   .   £25/£15
Homage to Clio, Random House (New York), 1960 £40/£10
ditto, Faber (London), 1960.   .   .   .   .   £40/£10
The Platonic Blow, Fuck You Press (New York), 1965 (300 copies; wraps) £35
ditto, Fuck You Press (New York), 1965 (10 copies)   .£300
About the House, Random House (New York), 1965   .   .
   .   .   .   .   £30/£10
ditto, Faber (London), 1966.   .   .   .   .   £30/£10
Collected Shorter Poems, 1927-1957, Faber (London), 1966
   .   .   .   .   £45/£15
ditto, Random House (New York), 1967   .   .   £45/£15
Marginalia, Ibex Press (Cambridge, MA), 1966 (150 signed, numbered copies, sewn white wraps, with marbled paper cover; white printed cover label) £150
ditto, Ibex Press (Cambridge, MA), 1966 (26 signed, lettered copies, sewn white wraps, with marbled paper cover; white printed cover label) £200
Selected Poems, Faber (London), 1968 (pbk)   .   .   £5
Collected Longer Poems, Faber (London), 1968   .   £35/£10
ditto, Random House (New York), 1969   .   .   £30/£10
City Without Walls, Faber (London), 1969   .   .   £15/£5
ditto, Random House (New York), 1970   .   .   £15/£5
Natural Linguistics, Poem-of-the-Month-Club (London), 1970 (1,000 signed copies, broadsheet)   .   .   .£100
Academic Graffiti, Faber (London), 1971   .   .   £15/£5
ditto, Random House (New York), 1972   .   .   £15/£5
Epistle to a Godson, Faber (London), 1972   .   .   £10/£5
ditto, Random House (New York), 1972   .   .   £10/£5
The Ballad of Barnaby, no publisher, no place, 1973 (broadside) £65
Thank You Fog: Last Poems, Faber (London), 1974 £10/£5
ditto, Random House (New York), 1974   .   .   £10/£5
Collected Poems, Faber (London), 1976   .   .   £20/£5
ditto, Random House (New York), 1976   .   .   £20/£5
ditto, Franklin Library (Franklin Centre, PA), 1976 (full leather) £20
The English Auden, Faber (London), 1977   .   .   £15/£5
ditto, Random House (New York), 1978   .   .   £15/£5
Norse Poems, Athlone Press, 1981   .   .   .   £20/£5

Plays
The Dog Beneath the Skin, Faber (London), 1935 (with Christopher Isherwood)   .   .   .   .   £135/£20
ditto, Random House (New York), 1935   .   .   £135/£20

The Ascent of F6, Faber (London), 1936 (with Christopher Isherwood) . . . . £135/£20
ditto, Random House (New York), 1937 (revised) . £100/£15
On the Frontier, Faber (London), [1938] (with Christopher Isherwood) . . . . £100/£20
ditto, Random House (New York), 1939 . . . £65/£10

Prose
Letters from Iceland, Faber (London), 1937 (with Louis MacNeice) . . . . £125/£25
ditto, Harcourt Brace (New York), 1937 . . £100/£15
Education Today and Tomorrow, Hogarth Press (London), 1939 (with T.S. Worsley; wraps) £75
The Enchafèd Flood or The Romantic Iconography of the Sea, Random House (New York), 1950 . . . £50/£10
ditto, Faber (London), 1951 . . . . . £50/£10
Making, Knowing and Judging, O.U.P. (Oxford, UK), 1956 (wraps) £35
The Dyer's Hand, Random House (New York), 1962 .
. . . . £75/£15
ditto, Faber (London), 1963 . . . . . £65/£15
Louis MacNeice - A Memorial Address, privately printed Faber (London), 1963 (1,500 copies; wraps). . . £50
Selected Essays, Faber (London), 1964 (pbk) . . £10
Secondary Worlds, Random House (New York), 1968 . .
. . . . £15/£5
ditto, Faber (London), 1969 . . . . . £15/£5
Forewords and Afterwords, Faber (London), 1973 £20/£5
ditto, Viking (New York), 1973 . . . . £20/£5

Others
The Rake's Progress, Boosey & Hawkes Ltd (London), 1951 (libretto, with Chester Kallman; wraps) . . £65
The Magic Flute, Random House (New York), 1956 (libretto, with Chester Kallman) . . . £35/£15
ditto, Faber (London), 1957 . . . . . £35/£15
Elegy for Young Lovers, Schott (Mainz, Germany), 1961 (libretto, with Chester Kallman; wraps) . . . £30
The Bassarids, Schott (Mainz, Germany), 1966 (libretto with Chester Kallman; wraps) £25
A Certain World, Viking (New York), [1970]. . £25/£5
ditto, Faber (London), 1971 . . . . . £25/£5
Lectures on Shakespeare, Princeton Univ Press (Princeton, NJ), 2000 . . . . £10/£5
ditto, Faber (London), 2001 . . . . . £10/£5

JANE AUSTEN

(b.1775 d.1817)

Jane Austen is generally regarded as the greatest of English women novelists. Although her first novel, *Northanger Abbey* (published posthumously), parodies the Gothic novels of Ann Radcliffe, Austen's reputation rests on her later works, which are notable for their sparkling social comedy and accurate portrayal of human relationships. Rebound copies vary greatly in value based on the condition of the original pages (not only the title pages but the half-titles should ideally be present) rather than the binding itself.

Sense and Sensibility, T. Egerton (London), 1811 (pseud 'A Lady'; 3 vols in original blue paper boards with brown paper spine, or pink paper boards with cream paper spine; pink or white paper labels; dated on title-page) . £45,000
ditto, T. Egerton (London), 1811 (rebound) . £17,500
ditto, Carey & Lea (Philadelphia, PA), 1833 (2 vols; drab paper boards; purple cloth spine; white paper labels) . £7,500
ditto, Carey & Lea (Philadelphia, PA), 1833 (rebound) £2,500
Pride and Prejudice, T. Egerton (London), 1813 (pseud 'By the Author of *Sense and Sensibility*'; 3 vols in original blue paper boards and brown paper spine; white paper label; dated on title-page) £45,000
ditto, T. Egerton (London), 1813 (rebound) . £15,000
ditto, as *Elizabeth Bennet, or Pride and Prejudice*, Carey & Lea (Philadelphia, PA), 1832 (2 vols; drab paper boards; purple cloth spine; white paper labels) . . . £7,500
ditto, as *Elizabeth Bennet, or Pride and Prejudice*, Carey & Lea (Philadelphia, PA), 1832 (rebound). . . £2,500
Mansfield Park, T. Egerton (London), 1814 (pseud 'By the Author of *Sense and Sensibility* and *Pride and Prejudice*'; 3 vols in original blue paper boards and brown paper spine; white paper label; dated on title-page) . . . £30,000
ditto, T. Egerton (London), 1814 (rebound) . £12,000
ditto, Carey & Lea (Philadelphia, PA), 1832 (2 vols; drab paper boards; purple cloth spine; white paper labels) .
. . . . £7,000
ditto, Carey & Lea (Philadelphia, PA), 1832 (rebound). .
. . . . £2,000
Emma, J. Murray (London), 1816 (pseud 'By the Author of *Pride and Prejudice* . . .'; 3 vols in original brown paper boards and spine, or blue paper boards and darker blue spine; white paper labels; dated on title-page) . £25,000
ditto, J. Murray (London), 1816 (rebound) . £7,500
ditto, Carey & Lea (Philadelphia, PA), 1833 (2 vols; drab paper boards; purple cloth spine; white paper labels) . .
. . . . £6,000
ditto, Carey & Lea (Philadelphia, PA), 1833 (rebound). .
. . . . £2,000
Northanger Abbey and *Persuasion*, J. Murray (London), 1818 (pseud 'By the Author of *Pride and Prejudice*. . .'; 4 vols in original blue-grey paper boards and brown paper spine, or pink paper boards and spine; white paper labels).
. . . . £20,000
ditto, J. Murray (London), 1818 (rebound) . £6,500
ditto, *Northanger Abbey* only, Carey & Lea (Philadelphia, PA), 1833 (2 vols; drab paper boards; purple cloth spine; white paper labels) £5,000
ditto, *Northanger Abbey* only, Carey & Lea (Philadelphia, PA), 1833 (rebound) £1,500
Persuasion, Carey & Lea (Philadelphia, PA), 1832 (2 vols; drab paper boards; purple cloth spine; white paper labels).
. . . . £5,000
ditto, Carey & Lea (Philadelphia, PA), 1832 (rebound). .
. . . . £1,500

Miscellaneous
Letters, R. Bentley (London), 1884 (2 vols) . . . £400
Charades, Spottiswoode & Co. (London), 1895 (wraps) .
. . . . £400
Love and Freindship (sic) *and Other Early Works (Volume the second)*, Chatto & Windus (London), 1922 . £150/£50
ditto, Chatto & Windus (London), 1922 (260 copies, special edition) £400
ditto, Stokes (New York), 1922 . . . . £140/£40
ditto, (*Volume the First*), Clarendon Press (Oxford), 1933 .
. . . . £75/£25

ditto, (***Volume the Second***), Clarendon Press (Oxford), 1951
 . . . . £50/£20
The Watsons, Parsons (London), 1923 . . .£150/£25
ditto, Appleton (New York), 1923 . . .£150/£25
Five Letters from Jane Austen to her Niece, Fanny Knight,
 Clarendon Press (Oxford), 1924 (250 copies, no d/w). £125
Fragment of a Novel, O.U.P. (Oxford), 1925 ('Sanditon', no
 d/w). £40
ditto, O.U.P. (Oxford), 1925 (250 copies on handmade
 paper) £125
Lady Susan, O.U.P. (Oxford), 1925 (no d/w). . .£40
ditto, O.U.P. (Oxford), 1925 (250 copies on handmade
 paper). £125
The Letters of Jane Austen, The Bodley Head (London),
 1925 . . . .£45/£15
Two Chapters from Persuasion, O.U.P. (Oxford), 1926 £65
Plan of a Novel, Clarendon Press (Oxford), 1926 (350
 copies, no d/w). £25
Letters, O.U.P. (Oxford), 1932 (2 vols) . . .£100
Three Evening Prayers, Colt Press (San Francisco), 1940
 (300 copies). £200
Sanditon: A Facsimile of the Manuscript, Scolar/Clarendon
 (London/Oxford), 1975 . . . .£40/£25
ditto, Houghton Mifflin (Boston), 1975 . . £40/£25
Jane Austen's Sir Charles Grandison, O.U.P. (Oxford),
 1980
 £30/£10

PAUL AUSTER
(b. 1947)

Paul Auster is an American author whose work is often considered 'postmodern' because it combines absurdism with crime fiction, as in The New York Trilogy (1987), *Moon Palace* (1989) and *The Brooklyn Follies* (2005).

The New York Trilogy
City of Glass, Sun & Moon Press (Los Angeles, CA), 1985
 (first state d/w without publisher's device on spine). .
 . . . . £600/£100
ditto, Sun & Moon Press (Los Angeles, CA), 1985 (second
 state d/w with publisher's device tipped in on lower spine)
 . . . . £500/£100
ditto, Sun & Moon Press (Los Angeles, CA), 1985 (third
 state d/w with publisher's device printed on spine) . .
 . . . . £300/£100
ditto, Sun & Moon Press (Los Angeles, CA), 1985 (26
 signed, lettered copies) . . . £1,250/£1,000
Ghosts, Sun & Moon Press (Los Angeles, CA), 1986. .
 . . . . £100/£15
ditto, Sun & Moon Press (Los Angeles, CA), 1986 (26
 signed, lettered copies) . . . £400/£350
The Locked Room, Sun & Moon Press (Los Angeles, CA),
 1986 . . . . £100/£15
ditto, Sun & Moon Press (Los Angeles, CA), 1986 (26
 signed, lettered copies) . . . £400/£350
The New York Trilogy, Faber (London), 1987 .£60/£15
ditto, Penguin (New York), 1990 (pbk) . . . £10
ditto, Sun & Moon Press (Los Angeles, CA), 1994. £45/£10
ditto, Sun & Moon Press (Los Angeles, CA), 1994 (200
 signed, numbered copies) . . . £300/£200

Other Novels
Squueze Play: A Novel, Alpha-Omega Publishers (New
 York), 1982 (pbk; pseud Paul Benjamin) . . .£250
ditto, Avon (New York), 1984 (pbk). . . . £20
ditto, Faber (London), 1991 (pbk) £10
In the Country of Last Things, Viking (New York), 1987.
 . . . . £10/£5
ditto, Faber (London), 1988. . . . . £10/£5
Moon Palace, Viking (New York), 1989. . . £10/£5
ditto, Faber (London), 1990. . . . . £10/£5
The Music of Chance, Viking (New York), 1990. £10/£5
ditto, Faber (London), 1991. . . . . £10/£5
Leviathan, Viking (New York), 1992 . . £10/£5
ditto, Faber (London), 1992. . . . . £10/£5
Mr Vertigo, Faber (London/Boston), 1994 (export edition
 with ISBN 0-571- 17111-7; priced £12.99). .£15/£5
ditto, Faber (London/Boston), 1994 (ISBN 0-571-17092-7,
 priced at £14.99). . . . . . £10/£5
ditto, Viking (New York), 1994. . . . £10/£5
ditto, Viking (New York), 1994 (special ABA pbk issue)
 . . . . £10
Timbuktu, Faber (London), 1999. . . £10/£5
ditto, Henry Holt (New York), 1999. . . . £10/£5
The Book of Illusions, Henry Holt (New York), 2002. .
 . . . . £10/£5
ditto, Faber (London), 2002. . . . . £10/£5
Threebies, Faber (London), 2003 (pbk; contains *In the
 Country of the Last Things*, *Mr Vertigo* and *The Music Of
 Chance*). £5
Oracle Night, Henry Holt (New York), 2003. . £10/£5
ditto, Faber (London), 2004. . . . . £10/£5
The Brooklyn Follies, Faber (London), 2005. . £10/£5
ditto, Henry Holt (New York), 2006. . . £10/£5
Travels in the Scriptorium, Faber (London), 2006. £10/£5
ditto, Henry Holt (New York), 2007. . . £10/£5

Short Story
Auggie Wren's Christmas Story, The Delos Press/William
 Drenttel (Birmingham, UK/New York), 1992 (300
 numbered copies; marbled paper wraps) . . . £35
ditto, The Delos Press/William Drenttel (Birmingham,
 UK/New York), 1992 (100 signed, numbered copies;
 bound in quarter buckram boards) £85
ditto, The Delos Press/William Drenttel (Birmingham,
 UK/New York), 1992 (50 signed, numbered copies; bound
 in black goatskin; marbled slipcase) . . £200/£135

Poetry
Unearth, Living Hand 3 (Weston, CT), 1974 (wraps).£100
ditto, Maeght éditeur (Collection Argile, Paris) 1980 (500
 numbered copies; wraps) £100
ditto, Maeght éditeur (Collection Argile, Paris) 1980 (40
 numbered copies signed by Auster and artist Jean-Paul
 Riopelle; with an extra suite of wide-margined lithographs;
 bound in cloth; slipcase) £600
ditto, Maeght éditeur (Collection Argile, Paris) 1980 (80
 numbered copies signed by Auster and artist Jean-Paul
 Riopelle; with an extra suite of lithographs; bound in cloth;
 slipcase). £450
ditto, Maeght éditeur (Collection Argile, Paris) 1980 (20
 Roman numeral numbered copies signed by Auster and
 artist Jean-Paul Riopelle; issued hors commerce; bound in
 cloth; slipcase) . . . . . £250/£200

Wall Writing, The Figures (Berkeley, CT), 1976 (474 copies; pbk) £125

ditto, The Figures (Berkeley, CT), 1976 (26 signed, lettered copies; pbk) £250

Effigies, Orange Export Ltd (Paris), 1976 (9 signed and lettered copies; wraps) £300

ditto, Orange Export Ltd (Paris), 1976 (4 signed and numbered copies; wraps) £400

Fragments from Cold, Parenthèse (Brewster, NY), 1977 (730 copies; stapled wraps in in d/w) . . . £125/£75

ditto, Parenthèse (Brewster, NY), 1977 (20 numbered copies signed by Auster and artist Norman Bluhm, stapled wraps in in d/w) . . . . . . £400/£300

Facing the Music, Station Hill (Barrytown, New York), 1980 (pbk) £35

ditto, Station Hill (Barrytown, New York), 1980 (43 signed, numbered copies) £200

Disappearances: Selected Poems, Overlook Press, Woodstock (New York), 1988 . . . . £25/£10

Early History of a Writer, [The Figures] ([Great Barrington]), no date [1995] (signed, lettered broadside in a collection of 26 issued in a box as *Writings for Bernadette*) . . . . . . £350 the set

Selected Poems, Faber (London), 1998 (pbk) . . £5

Accident Report, (Pressed Wafer), no place (1999) (broadside, approx 30 copies) £75

Collected Poems, The Overlook Press (New York), 2004 . . . . £10/£5

Screenplays

The Music of Chance, Viking (New York), 1993 . £10/£5

ditto, Faber (London), 1991 . . . . . £10/£5

Smoke and Blue in the Face, Miramax/Hyperion (New York), 1995 (pbk) £5

ditto, Faber (London), 1995 (pbk) £5

Lulu on the Bridge, Owl/Henry Holt (New York), 1999 (pbk) £5

ditto, Faber (London), 1998 (pbk) £5

The Inner Life of Martin Frost, Picador (New York), 2007 (pbk) £5

Essays, Memoirs, and Autobiographies

White Spaces, Station Hill (Barrytown, New York), 1980 (pbk) £35

ditto, Station Hill (Barrytown, New York), 1980 (43 signed, numbered copies) £200

The Art of Hunger And Other Essays, The Menard Press (London), 1982 (pbk) £100

ditto, as *The Art of Hunger, Essays, Prefaces & Interviews*, Sun & Moon Press (Los Angeles, CA), 1992 (expanded edition) . . . . £10/£5

ditto, Sun & Moon Press (Los Angeles, CA), 1992 (300 signed, numbered copies) . . . . . £45/£35

The Invention of Solitude, Sun (New York), 1982 (pbk) £30

ditto, Faber (London), 1988 (pbk) £25

The Red Notebook, Faber (London), 1995 . £15/£5

ditto, New Directions (New York), 2002 (pbk) . . £5

Why Write?, Burning Deck (Providence, RI), 1996 (pbk) £5

ditto, Burning Deck (Providence, RI), 1996 (500 hardback copies) . . . . £10/£5

ditto, Burning Deck (Providence, RI), 1996 (50 signed, numbered copies £65

Hand to Mouth, Henry Holt (New York), 1997 . £10/£5

ditto, Faber (London), 1988 . . . . . . £10/£5

Collected Prose, Faber (London), 2003 . . . £10/£5

Translations

A Little Anthology of Surrealist Poems, Siamese Banana Press (New York), [no date, 1972] (stapled mimeographed sheets) £125

ditto, Rain Taxi (Minneapolis, MN), 2002 (pbk; 300 copies) £10

Fits and Starts, Selected Poems of Jacques Dupin, Living Hand (Salisbury, UK), 1973 (wraps) . . . £30

ditto, Living Hand (Salisbury, UK), 1973 (100 copies signed by author and translator; slipcase, with a signed, numbered lithograph by Alexander Calder as the frontispiece) . . . . £600/£500

Saul Friedländer & Mahmoud Hussein, Arabs and Israelis, A Dialogue, Holmes & Meier (New York), 1975 (translated with Lydia Davis) . . . . . £65/£10

Miró: Paining & Sculpture 1969-74, Pierre Matisse Gallery (New York), 1975 (wraps; translation by Auster of an essay by Jacques Dupin) £50

Marc Chagall, The Four Seasons, Pierre Matisse Gallery (New York), 1975 (wraps). £50

Hantaï, Paintings Watercolours 1871-75, Pierre Matisse Gallery (New York), 1975 (wraps) £50

The Uninhabited: Selected Poems of Andre du Bouchet, Living Hand 7 (Weston, CT), 1976 (wraps; 500 numbered copies) £40

Marc Cgahall: A Celebration, Pierre Matisse Gallery (New York), 1977 (wraps) £50

Life/Situations: Essays Written and Spoken, by Jean-Paul Sartre, Pantheon Books (New York), 1977 (translated with Lydia Davis). . . . . £25/£10

ditto, as *Satre in the Seventies, Interviews and Essays*, Andre Deutsch (London), 1978 . . . £25/£10

China from the 1911 Revolution to Liberation, by Jean Chesneaux, Pantheon Books (New York), 1977 (translated with Lydia Davis) . . . . £35/£10

ditto, Harvester Press (London), 1978 . . . £35/£10

Mao Tse-Tung, A Guide to His Thought, by Alain Bouc, St Martin's Press (New York), 1977 (translated with Lydia Davis) . . . . £35/£10

China, The People's Republic, 1948-76, by Jean Chesneaux, Pantheon Books (New York), 1979 (translated with Lydia Davis) . . . . £35/£10

ditto, Harvester Press (London), 1979 . . . £35/£10

African Trio: Talatalia, Tropic Moon, Aboard the Aquitaine, by Georges Simenon, Harcourt Brace Jovanovich (New York), 1979 (Auster translates the last novella) . . . . £20/£5

ditto, Hamish Hamilton (London), 1979 . . £20/£5

Selected Poetry and Prose, by Stéphane Mallarmé, New Directions (New York), 1982 . . . £25/£10

The Notebooks of Joseph Joubert, A Selection, North Point Press (San Francisco, CA), 1983 (pbk in d/w) . £25/£10

A Tomb for Anatole, by Stéphane Mallarmé, North Point Press (San Francisco, CA), 1983 (pbk in d/w) . £25/£10

On The High Wire, by Philippe Petit, Random House (New York), 1985 (pbk) £35

Vicious Circles: Two fictions & 'After the Fact', by Maurice Blanchot, Station Hill (Barrytown, New York), 1985 (hardcover without d/w) £35

ditto, Station Hill (Barrytown, New York), 1985 (pbk) . £10

Miró/Artigas, by Joan Gardy Artigas, Pierre Matisse Gallery (New York), 1985 . . . . . . £30/£10
Joan Miró, Selected Writings and Interviews, G.K. Hall & Co, (Boston), 1986 . . . . . . £30/£10
ditto, Thames & Hudson, (London), 1987. . . £20/£5
ditto, as *Joan Miró, A Retrospective*, Solomon R. Guggenheim Museum/Yale Univ Press (New York/New Haven, CT), 1987 . . . . . . £40/£10
Selected Poems of René Char, New Directions (New York), 1992 . . . . £10/£5
Jacques Dupin: Selected Poems, Wake Forest Univ Press (Winston-Salem, NC), 1992 (pbk; translation by Auster and others) £10
ditto, Bloodaxe, (Newcastle Upon Tyne), 1992 (pbk) . £10
Translations, Marsilio (New York), 1997 (pbk) . . £5
Chronicle of the Guayaki Indians, by Pierre Clastres, Zone Books (New York), 1998 . . . . . £10/£5
ditto, Faber, (London), 1998 (pbk) £5
The Station Hill Blanchot Reader, Station Hill/Barrytown Ltd (Barrytown, NY), 1999 (pbk) £5

Misc
Ground Work, Selected Poems and Essays 1970-79, Faber (London), 1990 . . . . . . £15/£5
Paul Auster's New Tork, Henry Holt (New York), 1997 (no d/w) £30
Double Game and The Gotham Handbook, Violette Editions (London), 1999 (with Sophie Calle) . £20/£5
The Story of My Typewriter, Distributed Art Publishers (New York), 2002 . . . . . . £10/£5

Edited by Auster
The Random House Book of Twentieth Century French Poetry, Random House (New York), 1982 (dual-language edition edited and introduction by Auster, who translated 42 poems) . . . . £25/£10
I Thought My Father Was God, Henry Holt (New York), 2001 . . . . £10/£5
ditto, as *True Tales of American Life*, Faber (London), 2001 . . . . £10/£5

REV. W. AWDRY & CHRISTOPHER AWDRY
(b. 1911 d.1997, b.1940)

Thomas the Tank Engine is the most famous of all of the Rev. Awdry's railway characters, in a series which has been continued by his son, Christopher.

'Railway Series' Titles by Rev. W. Awdry
1. The Three Railway Engines, Edmund Ward (London), 1945 (illustrated by Middleton) . . . . £135/£15
2. Thomas the Tank Engine, Edmund Ward (London), 1946 (illustrated by Payne) . . . . . . £180/£25
3. James the Red Engine, Edmund Ward (London), 1948 (illustrated by Dalby) . . . . . £125/£15
4. Tank Engine Thomas Again, Edmund Ward (London), 1949 (illustrated by Dalby) . . . . £165/£25
5. Troublesome Engines, Edmund Ward (London), 1950 (illustrated by Dalby) . . . . . £135/£15

6. Henry the Green Engine, Edmund Ward (London), 1951 (illustrated by Dalby) . . . . . . £125/£15
7. Toby the Tram Engine, Edmund Ward (London), 1952 (illustrated by Dalby) . . . . . £125/£15
8. Gordon the Big Engine, Edmund Ward (London), 1953 (illustrated by Dalby) . . . . . £125/£15
9. Edward the Blue Engine, Edmund Ward (London), 1954 (illustrated by Dalby) . . . . . £125/£15
10. Four Little Engines, Edmund Ward (London), 1955 (illustrated by Dalby) . . . . . £125/£15
11. Percy the Small Engine, Edmund Ward (London), 1956 (illustrated by Dalby) . . . . . £100/£15
12. The Eight Famous Engines, Edmund Ward (London), 1957 (illustrated by Kenney) . . . . £100/£15
13. Duck and the Diesel Engine, Edmund Ward (London), 1958 (illustrated by Kenney) . . . . £75/£10
14. The Little Old Engine, Edmund Ward (London), 1959 (illustrated by Kenney) . . . . . £75/£10
15. The Twin Engines, Edmund Ward (London), 1960 (illustrated by Kenney) . . . . . £75/£10
16. Branch Line Engines, Edmund Ward (London), 1961 (illustrated by Kenney) . . . . . £75/£10
17. Gallant Old Engine, Edmund Ward (London), 1962 (illustrated by Kenney) . . . . . £75/£10
18. Stepney the 'Bluebell' Engine, Edmund Ward (London), 1963 (illustrated by G. & P. Edwards) . . £75/£10
19. Mountain Engines, Edmund Ward (London), 1964 (illustrated by G. & P. Edwards) . . . £75/£10
20. Very Old Engines, Edmund Ward (London), 1965 (illustrated by G. & P. Edwards) . . . £75/£10
21. Main Line Engines, Edmund Ward (London), 1966 (illustrated by G. & P. Edwards) . . . £75/£10
22. Small Railway Engines, Kaye & Ward (London), 1967 (illustrated by G. & P. Edwards) . . . £75/£10
23. Enterprising Engines, Kaye & Ward (London), 1968 (illustrated by G. & P. Edwards) . . . £75/£10
24. Oliver the Western Engine, Kaye & Ward (London), 1969 (illustrated by G. & P. Edwards) . . £75/£10
25. Duke the Lost Engine, Kaye & Ward (London), 1970 (illustrated by G. & P. Edwards) . . . £75/£10
26. Tramway Engines, Kaye & Ward (London), 1972 (illustrated by G. & P. Edwards) . . . . £50/£5

'Railway Series' Titles by Christopher Awdry
(laminated boards; no d/w)
27. Really Useful Engines, Kaye & Ward (London), 1983 (illustrated by Spong) £10
28. James and the Diesel Engines, Kaye & Ward (London), 1984 (illustrated by Spong) £10
29. Great Little Engines, Kaye & Ward (London), 1985 (illustrated by Spong) £10
30. More about Thomas the Tank Engine, Kaye & Ward (London), 1986 (illustrated by Spong) . . £10
31. Gordon the High-Speed Engine, Kaye & Ward (London), 1987 (illustrated by Spong) . . . £10
32. Toby, Trucks and Trouble, Kaye & Ward (London), 1988 (illustrated by Spong) £5
33. Thomas and the Twins, Heinemann (London), 1989 (illustrated by Spong, boards) £5
34. Jock the New Engine, Heinemann (London), 1990 (illustrated by Spong, boards) £5
35. Thomas and the Great Railway Show, Heinemann (London), 1991 (illustrated by Spong, boards) . . £5

36. Thomas Comes Home, Heinemann (London), 1992
(illustrated by Spong, boards) £5
37. Henry and the Express, Heinemann (London), 1993
(illustrated by Spong, boards) £5
38. Wilbert the Forest Engine, Heinemann (London), 1994
(illustrated by Spong, boards) £5
39. Thomas and the Fat Controller's Engines, Heinemann
(London), 1995 (illustrated by Spong, boards) . . £5
40. New Little Engine, Heinemann (London), 1996
(illustrated by Spong, boards) £5

ALAN AYCKBOURN
(b.1939)

Ayckbourn excels at highlighting the neuroses and
anxieties of the British suburban middle-class. He has also
been recognised as something of a stylistic innovator who
experiments with theatrical styles within the boundaries set
by popular tastes. His plays have won many awards and
have been translated into over 30 languages. They are
performed internationally on stage and television.

Individual plays
How the Other Half Loves, Evans, 1972 (pbk) . . £40
Relatively Speaking, Evans, 1972 (pbk) . . . £40
Time and Time Again, Samuel French (London), 1973 (pbk)
. . . . £20
Absurd Person Singular, Samuel French (London), 1974
(pbk) £15
Living Together, Samuel French (London), 1975 (pbk) £15
Round & Round The Garden, Samuel French (London),
1975 (pbk) £15
Absent Friends, Samuel French (London), 1975 (pbk) . £15
Confusions, Samuel French (London), 1977 (first issue,
'frought' for 'fraught' on lower wrapper; pbk) . . £15
Bedroom Farce, Samuel French (London), 1978 (pbk) . £15
Just Between Ourselves, Samuel French (London), 1978
(pbk) £10
Ten Times Table, Samuel French (London), 1978 (pbk) £10
Joking Apart, Samuel French (London), 1979 (pbk) . £10
Season's Greetings, Samuel French (London), 1981 (pbk) .
. . . . £10
Taking Steps, Samuel French (London), 1981 (pbk) . £10
Sisterly Feelings, Samuel French (London), 1981 (pbk) £10
Suburban Strains, Samuel French (London), 1982 (pbk) £5
Way Upstream, Samuel French (London), 1983 (pbk) . £5
A Chorus of Disapproval, Samuel French (London), 1985
(pbk) £5
Intimate Exchanges, Samuel French (London), 1985 (2 vols;
pbks) £15
Woman in Mind, Faber (London), 1986 (pbk) . . £10
A Small Family Business, Faber (London), 1987 (pbk) £10
Henceforward, Faber & Faber (London), 1987 (pbk) . £10
Table Manners, Samuel French (London), 1988 (pbk) . £5
Mr A's Amazing Maze Plays, Faber (London), 1989 (pbk) .
. . . . £5
Invisible Friends, Faber (London), 1991 . . . £5
The Revengers' Comedies, Faber (London), 1991 (pbk) £5
Man of the Moment, Faber, 1991 (pbk) . . . £5
Mr Whatnot, Samuel French (London), 1992 (pbk) . £5
Wildest Dreams, Samuel French (London), 1993 (pbk). £5

Time of My Life, Samuel French (London), 1994 (pbk). £5
My Very Own Story, Faber, 1995 (pbk) . . . £5
Communicating Doors, Faber (London), 1995 . £15/£5
Callisto 5, Samuel French (London), 1995 (pbk) . £5
This Is Where We Came In, Samuel French (London), 1995
(pbk) £5
A Word from Our Sponsor, Samuel French (London), 1996
(pbk) £5
Dreams from a Summer House, Samuel French (London),
1997 (pbk) £5
Family Circles, Samuel French (London), 1997 (pbk) . £5
Things We Do For Love, Faber (London), 1998 (pbk) . £5
It Could Be Any One Of Us, Samuel French (London), 1998
(pbk) £5
Comic Potential, Faber (London), 1999 (pbk). . . £5
The Boy Who Fell into a Book, Faber (London), 2000 (pbk)
. . . . £5
House and Garden, Faber (London), 2000 (pbk) . . £5
The Champion of Paribanou, Samuel French (London),
2000 . . . . £5
Body Language, Samuel French (London), 2002 . . £5
Whenever, Faber (London), 2002 (pbk) . . . £5
My Sister Sadie, Faber (London), 2003 (pbk) . . £5
Orvin--Champion of Champions, Faber (London), 2003
(pbk) £5
GamePlan, Samuel French (London), 2004 (pbk) . . £5
FlatSpin, Samuel French (London), 2004 (pbk) . . £5
RolePlay, Samuel French (London), 2004 (pbk) . . £5
Snake in the Grass, Samuel French (London), 2004 (pbk) £5

Collected Editions
The Norman Conquests, Chatto & Windus (London), 1975
(contains: *Table Manners, Living Together, Round and
Round the Garden*) . . . . . . £25/£10
Three Plays, Chatto & Windus (London), 1977 (contains:
Absurd Person Singular, Absent Friends and *Bedroom
Farce*) . . . . £25/£10
ditto, Grove Press (New York), 1979 . . . £25/£10
Joking Apart and Two Other Plays, Chatto & Windus
(London), 1979 (contains: *Joking Apart, Ten Times Table,
Just Between Ourselves*) . . . . . £25/£10
Sisterly Feelings & Taking Steps, Chatto & Windus
(London), 1981 (contains: *Sisterly Feelings, Taking Steps*)
. . . . £15/£5
Plays 1, Faber & Faber (London), 1995 (contains:
*Henceforward..., A Chorus of Disapproval, Man of the
Moment, A Small Family Business*). . . . £15/£5
Plays 2, Faber (London), 1998 (contains: *The Champion Of
Paribanou, Invisible Friends, My Very Own Story, This Is
Where We Came In, Ernie's Incredible Illucinations*). .
. . . . £10/£5
Damsels in Distress, Faber (London), 2002 (contains:
GamePlan, RolePlay and *FlatSpin*). . . . £10/£5
Plays 3, Faber, 2005 (contains: *Haunting Julia, Private
Fears in Public Places, Sugar Daddies* and *Drowning on
Dry Land*) . . . . £10/£5

Others
Playbill One, edited by Alan Durband, Hutchinson
Educational (London), 1969 (contains *Ernie's Incredible
Illucinations*; pbk) £10
The Crafty Art of Playmaking, Faber (London), 2002 £10/£5

H.C. BAILEY
(b.1878 d.1961)

H.C. Bailey's reputation is based on his dandy detective, Reggie Fortune, who appears in short stories and novels. These elegant tales are rather complex and belie a savage undertow. There is some debate about the publication date of his first collection, *Call Mr Fortune*, as the date 17/6/19 is printed at the end of the book. Bailey also wrote eleven novels involving the lawyer Joshua Clunk.

'Reggie Fortune' Short Story Collections

Call Mr Fortune, Methuen (London), 1920   .   . £500/£65
ditto, Dutton (New York), 1921 .   .   .   .   . £250/£40
Mr Fortune's Practice, Methuen (London), 1923 . £350/£45
ditto, Dutton (New York), 1924 .   .   .   .   . £250/£40
Mr Fortune's Trials, Methuen (London), 1925   . £300/£35
ditto, Dutton (New York), 1926 .   .   .   .   . £200/£30
Mr Fortune, Please, Methuen (London), 1927   . £300/£35
ditto, Dutton (New York), 1928 .   .   .   .   . £200/£30
Mr Fortune Speaking, Ward Lock (London), 1929 £300/£35
ditto, Dutton (New York), 1931 .   .   .   .   . £200/£25
Mr Fortune Explains, Ward Lock (London), 1930 £275/£30
ditto, Dutton (New York), 1931 .   .   .   .   . £175/£25
Case for Mr Fortune, Ward Lock (London), 1932. £275/£30
ditto, Dutton (New York), 1932 .   .   .   .   . £175/£25
Mr Fortune Wonders, Ward Lock (London), 1933 £250/£30
ditto, Dutton (New York), 1933 .   .   .   .   . £175/£25
Mr Fortune Objects, Gollancz (London), 1935   . £250/£30
ditto, Doubleday (Garden City, NY), 1935   . £150/£20
Clue for Mr Fortune, Gollancz (London), 1936   . £250/£30
ditto, as *A Clue for Mr Fortune*, Doubleday (Garden City, NY), 1936 .   .   .   . £65/£10
This is Mr Fortune, Gollancz (London), 1938   . £200/£30
ditto, Doubleday (Garden City, NY), 1938   . £65/£10
Mr Fortune Here, Gollancz (London), 1940 .   . £200/£30
ditto, Doubleday (Garden City, NY), 1940   . £65/£10
Meet Mr Fortune: A Reggie Fortune Omnibus, Doubleday (Garden City, NY), 1942 .   .   .   .   . £65/£10

'Reggie Fortune' Novels

Shadow on the Wall, Gollancz (London), 1934   . £300/£40
ditto, Doubleday (Garden City, NY), 1934   . £125/£30
Black Land, White Land, Gollancz (London), 1937 .   .
.   .   .   . £250/£35
ditto, Doubleday (Garden City, NY), 1937   . £100/£20
The Great Game, Gollancz (London), 1939 .   . £300/£35
ditto, Doubleday (Garden City, NY), 1939   . £100/£20
The Bishop's Crime, Gollancz (London), 1940   . £225/£30
ditto, Doubleday (Garden City, NY), 1941   . £100/£15
No Murder, Gollancz (London), 1942 .   .   . £150/£35
ditto, as *The Apprehensive Dog*, Doubleday (Garden City, NY), 1942 .   .   .   . £75/£15
Mr Fortune Finds a Pig, Gollancz (London), 1943 £125/£30
ditto, Doubleday (Garden City, NY), 1943   . £75/£15
The Cat's Whisker, Doubleday (Garden City, NY), 1944   .
.   .   .   . £35/£10
ditto, as *Dead Man's Effects*, Macdonald (London), n.d. [1945] .   .   .   . £65/£10
The Life Sentence, Macdonald (London), 1946   . £45/£10
ditto, Doubleday (Garden City, NY), 1946   . £35/£10
Saving a Rope, Macdonald (London), 1948 .   . £40/£10

ditto, as *Save a Rope*, Doubleday (Garden City, NY), 1948 .
.   .   .   . £35/£10

'Joshua Clunk' Novels

Garstons, Methuen (London), 1930 .   .   .   . £250/£35
ditto, as *The Garston Murder Case*, Doubleday (Garden City, NY), 1930 .   .   .   . £100/£20
The Red Castle, Ward Lock (London), 1932 .   . £250/£35
ditto, as *The Red Castle Mystery*, Doubleday (Garden City, NY), 1932 .   .   .   . £100/£20
The Sullen Sky Mystery, Gollancz (London), 1935 £250/£35
ditto, Doubleday (Garden City, NY), 1935   . £75/£15
Clunk's Claimant, Gollancz (London), 1937 .   . £250/£35
ditto, as *The Twittering Bird Mystery*, Doubleday (Garden City, NY), 1937 .   .   .   .   .   . £75/£10
The Veron Mystery, Gollancz (London), 1939   . £250/£35
ditto, as *Mr Clunk's Text*, Doubleday (Garden City, NY), 1939 .   .   .   . £45/£10
The Little Captain, Gollancz (London), 1941 .   . £150/£30
ditto, as *Orphan Ann*, Doubleday (Garden City, NY), 1941.
.   .   .   . £45/£10
Dead Man's Shoes, Gollancz (London), 1942 .   . £150/£30
ditto, as *Nobody's Vineyard*, Doubleday (Garden City, NY), 1942 .   .   .   . £45/£10
Slippery Ann, Gollancz (London), 1944 .   .   . £65/£10
ditto, as *The Queen of Spades*, Doubleday (Garden City, NY), 1944 .   .   .   . £45/£10
The Wrong Man, Doubleday (Garden City, NY), 1945.   .
.   .   .   . £45/£10
ditto, Macdonald, n.d. [1946] .   .   .   .   . £45/£10
Honour Among Thieves, Macdonald (London), 1947 .   .
.   .   .   . £35/£10
ditto, Doubleday (Garden City, NY), 1947   . £35/£10
Shrouded Death, Macdonald (London), 1950.   . £35/£10

Other Novels

My Lady of Orange, Longman's (London), 1901 .   . £45
ditto, Longmans (New York), 1901 .   .   .   .   . £35
Raoul, Gentleman of Fortune, Hutchinson & Co (London), 1907 .   .   .   . £40
ditto, Appleton (New York), 1907 .   .   .   .   . £40
The God of Clay, Hutchinson & Co (London), 1908   . £20
ditto, Brentanos (New York), 1908 .   .   .   .   . £20
Colonel Stow, Hutchinson & Co (London), 1908 .   . £15
Storm and Treasure, Methuen (London), 1910 .   . £15
ditto, Brentanos (New York), 1910 .   .   .   .   . £15
The Lonely Queen, Methuen (London), 1911 .   .   . £20
ditto, Doran (New York), 1911 .   .   .   .   .   . £20
The Gentleman Adventurer, Methuen (London), 1914. £20
The Highwayman, Methuen (London), 1915 .   .   . £20
ditto, Dutton (New York), 1915 .   .   .   .   .   . £20
Barry Leroy, Methuen (London), 1919 .   .   .   . £10
ditto, Dutton (New York), 1919 .   .   .   .   .   . £10
The Fool, Methuen (London), 1921 .   .   .   . £40/£10
ditto, Dutton (New York), 1927 .   .   .   .   . £40/£10
Knight at Arms, Methuen, 1924 .   .   .   .   . £40/£10
ditto, Dutton (New York), 1925 .   .   .   .   . £40/£10
The Man in the Cape, Benn (London), 1933 .   . £200/£45

BERYL BAINBRIDGE
(b.1934 d.2010)

Bainbridge spent her early years working as an actress, leaving the theatre to have her first child. It was at this time that she wrote her first novel, *Harriet Said...*, which was rejected by several publishers who found it 'repulsive', and 'indecent'. It eventually became her third published novel. Bainbridge's books, usually controversial, often involve several deaths.

Novels
A Weekend with Claud, New Authors Limited, Hutchinson (London), 1967 . . . . £150/£30
ditto, as *A Weekend with Claude*, Duckworth (London), 1981 (rewritten) . . . . . . £20/£5
ditto, Braziller (New York), 1982 . . . . £10/£5
Another Part of the Wood, Hutchinson (London), 1968 .
. . . . £50/£15
ditto, Duckworth (London), 1979 . . . £20/£5
ditto, Braziller (New York), 1980 . . . . £10/£5
Harriet Said ..., Duckworth (London), 1972 . . £75/£15
ditto, Braziller (New York), 1973 . . . £10/£5
The Dressmaker, Duckworth (London), 1973 . . £75/£15
ditto, as *The Secret Glass*, Braziller (New York), 1974 . .
. . . . £10/£5
The Bottle Factory Outing, Duckworth (London), 1974 .
. . . . £20/£5
ditto, Braziller (New York), 1975 . . . £10/£5
Sweet William, Duckworth (London), 1975 . . £10/£5
ditto, Braziller (New York), 1976 . . . £10/£5
A Quiet Life, Duckworth (London), 1976 . . £10/£5
ditto, Braziller (New York), 1977 . . . £10/£5
Injury Time, Duckworth (London), 1977 . . £10/£5
ditto, Braziller (New York), 1977 . . . £10/£5
Young Adolf, Duckworth (London), 1978 . £10/£5
ditto, Braziller (New York), 1979 . . . £10/£5
Winter Garden, Duckworth (London), 1980 . £10/£5
ditto, Braziller (New York), 1981 . . . £10/£5
Watson's Apology, Duckworth (London), 1984 . £10/£5
ditto, McGraw-Hill (New York), 1985 . . £10/£5
Filthy Lucre, Duckworth (London), 1986 . . £10/£5
An Awfully Big Adventure, Duckworth (London), 1989 .
. . . . £10/£5
ditto, HarperCollins (New York), 1991 . . £10/£5
The Birthday Boys, Duckworth (London), 1991 . £10/£5
ditto, Carroll & Graf (New York), 1994 . . £10/£5
Every Man for Himself, Duckworth (London), 1996 £10/£5
ditto, Carroll & Graf (New York), 1996 . . £10/£5
Master Georgie, Duckworth (London), 1998 . £10/£5
ditto, Carroll & Graf (New York), 1998 . £10/£5
According to Queeney, Carroll & Graf (New York), 2001 .
. . . . £10/£5
ditto, Little, Brown (London), 2001 . . . £10/£5

Short Stories
Mum and Mr Armitage: Selected Stories, Duckworth (London), 1985 . . . . £10/£5
ditto, McGraw-Hill (New York), 1987 . . . £10/£5
Collected Stories, Penguin (London), 1994 (pbk) . . £5

Others
English Journey: or, The Road to Milton Keynes, Duckworth (London), 1984 . . . . . £10/£5

ditto, Braziller (New York), 1984 . . . . £10/£5
Forever England: North and South, Duckworth (London), 1987 . . . . £10/£5
ditto, Carroll & Graf (New York), 1999 . . . £10/£5
A Bainbridge Omnibus, Duckworth (London), 1989 £10/£5
Something Happened Yesterday, Duckworth (London), 1993 (pbk) £5
ditto, Carroll & Graf (New York), 1998 . . . £10/£5
Front Row: Evenings at the Theatre, Continuum, 2005 .
. . . . £10/£5

FRANK BAKER
(b.1908 d.1983)

Frank Baker was an author, actor, musician and scriptwriter. His novel, *The Birds*, was published in 1936 by Peter Davies, for whom Daphne Du Maurier was working as a reader at the time. Her later short story, 'The Birds' is very similar, and was used as the basis for Hitchcock's film.

Novels
The Twisted Tree, Peter Davies (London), 1935 . £45/£15
The Birds, Peter Davies (London), 1936 . . . £75/£25
ditto, Panther (London), 1964 (pbk; revised edition) . £25
Miss Hargreaves: A fantasy, Eyre & Spottiswoode (London), 1940 . . . . £100/£20
ditto, Coward-McCann (New York), 1941 . £75/£15
Allanayr, Eyre & Spottiswoode (London), 1941 . £35/£10
Sweet Chariot, Eyre & Spottiswoode (London), 1942 . .
. . . . £45/£10
ditto, Coward-McCann (New York), 1943 . £45/£10
Full Score, Coward-McCann (New York), 1942 . £25/£10
Mr Allenby Loses the Way, Coward-McCann (New York), 1945 . . . . £35/£10
ditto, Boardman (London), 1946 . . . £35/£10
Before I Go Hence: Fantasia on a Novel, Andrew Dakers (London), 1946 . . . . £35/£10
ditto, Coward-McCann (New York), 1947 . . £35/£10
Embers: A Winter Tale, Coward-McCann (New York), 1946
. . . . £25/£10
ditto, Andrew Dakers (London), 1947 . . . £25/£10
The Downs So Free, Andrew Dakers (London), 1948 . .
. . . . £35/£10
My Friend the Enemy, Boardman (London), 1948 . £25/£10
ditto, Coward-McCann (New York), 1948 . . £25/£10
Lease of Life, Angus & Robertson (London), 1954 £15/£5
ditto, as *Nearer to Heaven*, Westminster Press (Philadelphia, PA), 1955 . . . . £15/£5
Talk of the Devil, Angus & Robertson (London), 1956 . .
. . . . £15/£5
Teresa: A Journey Out of Time, Peter Davies (London), 1960 . . . . £15/£5
ditto, Coward-McCann (New York), 1961 . . £15/£5

Short Stories
Blessed Are They: Eight Stories, Society of St Paul (London), 1953 . . . . £15/£5
ditto, Newman Press (Westminster, MD), 1951 . £15/£5
Stories of the Strange and Sinister, William Kimber (London), 1983 . . . . £15/£5

Play
Playing With Punch, Boardman (London), 1944 .   £15/£5

Non-Fiction
The Road Was Free, Boardman (London), 1948 . £25/£10
I Follow But Myself, Peter Davies (London), 1968 £25/£10
The Call of Cornwall, Robert Hale (London), 1976 (photos
   by David Pitt and others) .   .   .   .   .   . £10/£5

JAMES BALDWIN
(b.1924 d.1987)

Baldwin was an American novelist, writer, playwright,
poet, essayist, and civil rights activist. Most of Baldwin's
work deals with racial and sexual issues in mid-20th
century United States. His novels are notable for the
personal way in which they explore questions of identity as
well as for the way in which they mine complex social and
psychological pressures related to being black and
homosexual.

Novels
Go Tell It On The Mountain, Knopf (New York), 1953   .
   .   .   .   .   £1,750/£200
ditto, Joseph (London), 1954 .   .   .   . £150/£20
Giovanni's Room, Dial Press (New York), 1956 . £300/£35
ditto, Joseph (London), 1957 .   .   .   . £75/£20
Another Country, Dial Press (New York), 1962 . £100/£15
ditto, Joseph (London), 1963 .   .   .   . £40/£10
Tell Me How Long the Train's Been Gone, Dial Press (New
   York), 1968 .   .   .   . £15/£5
ditto, Joseph (London), 1968   .   .   .   . £15/£5
If Beale Street Could Talk, Dial Press (New York), 1974 .
   .   .   .   . £10/£5
ditto, Dial Press (New York), 1974 (250 signed, numbered
   copies) .   .   .   . £150/£125
ditto, Joseph (London), 1974 .   .   .   . £10/£5
Just Above My Head, Dial Press (New York), 1979 £10/£5
ditto, Dial Press (New York), 1979 (500 signed, numbered
   copies) .   .   .   . £100/£75
ditto, Joseph (London), 1979   .   .   .   . £10/£5

Plays
Blues for Mister Charlie, Dial Press (New York), 1964   .
   .   .   .   . £75/£10
ditto, Joseph (London), 1965 .   .   .   . £45/£10
The Amen Corner, Dial Press (New York), 1968 . £35/£10
ditto, Joseph (London), 1969   .   .   .   . £20/£5

Essays
Notes of a Native Son, Beacon Press (Boston), 1955   .
   .   .   .   . £150/£20
ditto, Joseph (London), 1964 .   .   .   . £20/£5
Nobody Knows My Name, Dial Press (New York), 1961   .
   .   .   .   . £35/£10
ditto, Joseph (London), 1964   .   .   .   . £20/£5
The Fire Next Time, Dial Press (New York), 1963   £10/£5
ditto, Joseph (London), 1963 .   .   .   . £10/£5
No Name in the Street, Dial Press (New York), 1972 £10/£5
ditto, Joseph (London), 1972   .   .   .   . £10/£5
The Devil Finds Work, Dial Press (New York), 1976 £10/£5
ditto, Joseph (London), 1976   .   .   .   . £10/£5

The Evidence of Things Not Seen, Holt Rinehart and
   Winston, New York, 1985.   .   .   .   . £10/£5
ditto, Joseph (London), 1986   .   .   .   . £10/£5
The Price of the Ticket; Collected Nonfiction 1948-1945, St
   Martin's Press/Marek (New York), 1985 .   . £10/£5
ditto, Joseph (London), 1986   .   .   .   . £10/£5

Short Stories
Going to Meet the Man, Dial Press (New York), 1965 .   .
   .   .   .   . £20/£5
ditto, Joseph (London), 1965 .   .   .   . £15/£5

Poetry
Jimmy's Blues, Joseph (London), 1983 .   .   . £10/£5
ditto, St Martins Press (New York), 1985.   .   . £10/£5

With Others
Nothing Personal, Atheneum (New York), 1964 (slipcase;
   with d/w) .   .   .   . £100/£65
ditto, Penguin (London), 1964   .   .   .   . £100/£65
A Rap on Race, Lippincott (Philadelphia, PA), 1971 (with
   Margaret Mead) .   .   .   .   .   . £10/£5
ditto, Joseph (London), 1971   .   .   .   . £10/£5
*One Day When I Was Lost: A Scenario based on Alex
   Haley's The Autobiography of Malcolm X*, Joseph
   (London), 1972 .   .   .   .   .   . £50/£10
ditto, Dial Press (New York), 1973 .   .   . £50/£10
A Dialogue, Lippincott (Philadelphia, PA), 1973 (with Nikki
   Giovanni) .   .   .   . £40/£10
ditto, Joseph (London), 1975   .   .   .   . £40/£10
Little Man Little Man: A Story of Childhood, Dial Press
   (New York), 1976 (illustrated by Yoran Cazac) . £15/£5
ditto, Joseph (London), 1976   .   .   .   . £15/£5

R.M. BALLANTYNE
(b.1825 d.1894)

A Scottish author, Ballantyne was born into a family of
printers and publishers. For some time he was employed by
the publishers Constable, but in 1856 he gave up business
for literature, and began the series of adventure stories for
the young for which he became famous. His first published
work was about his life as a fur trader in Canada. By the
time of his death he had written over 80 books in 40 years.

Children's Titles
The Life and Adventures of Simon Gupple, by Ralph Rover,
   No.1, privately printed, 1855 (single sheet of paper printed
   in black on one side) £1,750
Naughty Boys, by Champfleury (pseud 'Jules Francois Felix
   Husson'; Ballantyne drew the illustrations and edited his
   sister's translation of the text), Hamilton, Adams & Co.
   (London), 1855 (bound in brown morocco-grain cloth;
   blocked on front in gilt and blind; blocked on back in blind;
   and lettered in gilt on spine; dated on title-page) .   £200
Snowflakes and Sunbeams, or The Young Fur-Traders,
   Nelson (London), 1856 (bound in diagonal ripple-grain
   cloth; blocked on front and back in blind; lettered in gilt on
   spine; pale yellow endpapers; dated on title-page; 6 full-
   page illustrations plus frontispiece and pictorial title-page)
   .   .   .   . £1,250

Three Little Kittens, Nelson (London), [1856] (pseud 'Comus'; bound in ripple-grain cloth, blocked on front in gold and in blind; back blocked in blind; spine blank; yellow endpapers; all edges gilt; no title-page; 6 full-page colour illustrations plus frontispiece; first issue with a red diamond design on the carpet on the plate on page 10; without red flowers or red cloth on the plate at page 24)   .
.   .   .   .   £350

ditto, Nelson (London), [1856] (as above but second issue without a red diamond design on the carpet on the plate on page 10 and with red flowers and red cloth on the plate at page 24). £100

Mister Fox, Nelson (London), 1857 (pseud 'Comus'; bound in coarse morocco diagonal-grained cloth; blocked on front in gilt and blind, back blocked in blind, spine plain, yellow endpapers; all edges gilt; dated on title-page; 7 full-page illustrations plus frontispiece) £100

My Mother, Nelson (London), 1857 (pseud 'Comus'; bound in ripple-grain cloth; blocked on front in gilt and blind; back blocked in blind; spine plain; yellow endpapers; all edges gilt; dated on title-page; 7 full-page illustrations plus frontispiece) £100

The Butterfly's Ball, Nelson (London), 1857 (pseud 'Comus'; bound in coarse morocco hessian-grain cloth; blocked on front in gilt and blind; back in blind; spine plain; cream endpapers; all edges gilt; dated on title-page; 7 full-page illustrations plus frontispiece)   .   .   .   £125

ditto, Nelson (London), 1857 (pseud 'Comus'; as above but special binding in glazed, ivory-coloured cloth embossed in gilt; back and spine plain) £250

The Life of a Ship, Nelson (London), 1857 ('by the author of "Three Little Kittens", &tc'; bound in bead-grain cloth; blocked on front in gilt and blind; back blocked in blind; spine plain; yellow endpapers; all edges gilt; dated on title-page; 7 full-page illustrations plus frontispiece)   .   .   £125

Ungava, A Tale of Esquimaux Land, Nelson (London), 1858 [1857] (first issue binding ripple-grain cloth; blocked in gilt and blind on front; blind on back; spine in gilt; pale yellow endpapers; dated on title-page; 6 full-page illustrations plus frontispiece, and engraved title-page)   .   .   £125

ditto, Nelson (London), 1858 [1857] (as above but variant issue blocked in blind on front and back; spine blocked in gilt). £125

ditto, Nelson (London), 1858 [1857] (later issue in wavy-grain cloth blocked in blind on front and back; spine blocked in gilt) £100

The Coral Island, A Tale of the Pacific Ocean, Nelson (London), 1858 [1857] (first issue, binding in diagonal ripple-grain cloth; blocked on front in gilt and blind, back in blind, spine in gilt; pale yellow endpapers; dated on title-page; 6 full-page illustrations plus frontispiece and pictorial title-page) £6,000

ditto, Nelson (London), 1858 [1857] (second issue as above, but binding blocked on front in blind only)   .   .   £4,000

ditto, Nelson (London), 1858 [1857] (third issue bound as second issue, but plates printed in 2 colours only)   £3,000

ditto, Nelson (London), 1913 (deluxe edition with 8 coloured illustrations by S.E. Scott and preface written by J.M. Barrie; red cloth blocked in gold; grey d/w printed in red).
.   .   .   .   £2,500

The Robber Kitten, Nelson (London), 1858 (pseud 'Comus'; bound in bead-grain cloth, blocked on front in gilt and blind; back blocked in blind; spine plain; yellow endpapers; all edges gilt; dated on title-page; 7 full-page

illustrations plus frontispiece; lettering under each illustration in red on first edition). £100

Martin Rattler, or A Boy's Adventures in the Forests of Brazil, Nelson (London), 1858 (bound in diagonal ripple-grain cloth, blocked on front in gilt and blind, back in blind; spine in gilt; pale yellow endpapers; dated on title-page; 3 full-page illustrations plus frontispiece)   .   .   £100

Mee-a-ow! or Good Advice to Cats and Kittens, Nelson (London), 1859 (bound in bead-grain cloth; blocked on front in gilt and blind; back blocked in blind; spine plain; cream endpapers; all edges gilt; dated on title-page; 5 full-page illustrations plus frontispiece).   .   .   .   £100

The World of Ice, or Adventures in the Polar Regions, Nelson (London), 1860 [1859] (bound in bead-grain cloth; blocked on front in gilt and blind; back blocked in blind; spine blocked in gold; pale yellow endpapers; dated on title-page; 3 full-page illustrations plus frontispiece)   .   £100

The Dog Crusoe, A Tale of the Western Prairies, Nelson (London), 1861 [1860] (bound in bead-grain cloth; blocked on front in gilt and blind; back blocked in blind; spine blocked in gold; pale yellow endpapers; dated on title-page; 3 full-page colour illustrations plus colour frontispiece) £175

The Gorilla Hunters, A Tale of the Wilds Of Africa, Nelson (London), 1861 (bound in wavy-line cloth; blocked on front in gilt and blind; back blocked in blind; spine blocked in gold; yellow endpapers; dated on title-page; 5 full-page illustrations plus frontispiece and pictorial title)   .   £1,500

The Golden Dream, or Adventures in the Far West, Shaw (London), 1861 [1860] (bound in hessian-grain cloth; front and back blocked in blind; spine blocked in gold; pale yellow endpapers; dated on title-page; 3 full-page illustrations plus frontispiece; first issue with 24 pages of advertisement headed 'Religious, General and Educational Works'). £225

ditto, Shaw (London), 1861 [1860] (later issue as above but adverts start with 'Eight Hundred and Eight Psalms and Hymns'). £175

The Red Eric, or The Whaler's Last Cruise: A Tale, Routledge (London), 1861 (bound in bubble-grain cloth; blocked on front in gilt and blind; back blocked in blind; spine blocked in gold; yellow endpapers; dated on title-page; 7 full-page illustrations plus frontispiece)   .   .   £125

The Wild Man of the West, A Tale of the Rocky Mountains, Routledge (London), 1863 [1862] (bound in ripple-grain cloth; blocked on front in gilt and blind, back blocked in blind; spine blocked in gold; buff endpapers; dated on title-page; 7 full-page illustrations plus frontispiece)   .   .   £200

Man on the Ocean, A Book for Boys, Nelson (London), 1863 [1862] (bound in hessian-grain cloth; blocked on front in gilt and blind; back blocked in blind; spine blocked in gold; yellow endpapers; dated on title-page; 7 full-page colour illustrations, colour frontispiece, with further illustrations in text) £150

Ballantyne's Miscellany, Nisbet (London), 1863-1886 (15 volumes, all identified on title-page with date)   .   £650

Gascoyne, The Sandal-Wood Trader, A Tale of the Pacific, Nisbet (London), 1864 [1863] (bound in morocco-grain cloth; blocked on front in gilt and blind; back blocked in blind; spine blocked in gold; orange-brown endpapers; dated on title-page; 7 full-page coloured illustrations plus coloured frontispiece). £125

The Lifeboat, A Tale of Our Coast Heroes, Nisbet (London), 1864 (bound in sand-grain cloth; blocked on front and back in blind; spine blocked in gold; brown end-papers; dated on title-page) £100

Freaks on the Fells, or Three Months' Rustication: And Why I did not Become a Sailor, Routledge (London), 1865 [1864] (bound in sand-grain cloth; blocked on front in gold and blind; back blocked in blind; spine blocked in gold; dated on title-page; 7 full-page illustrations plus frontis-piece) £100

The Lighthouse, Being the Story of a Great Fight Between Man and the Sea, Nisbet (London), 1865 (bound in sand-grain cloth; blocked on front and back in blind; spine blocked in gold; grey endpapers; dated on title-page). £75

Shifting Winds, A Tough Yarn, Nisbet (London), 1866 (bound in sand-grain cloth; blocked on front and back in blind; spine blocked in gold; light-grey endpapers; dated on title-page) £100

Silver Lake, or Lost in the Snow, Jackson (London), 1867 (bound in sand-grain cloth; blocked on front in gilt and on back in blind; spine blocked in gold; yellow endpapers; dated on title-page) £75

Fighting the Flames, A Tale of the London Fire Brigade, Nisbet (London), 1868 (bound in sand-grain cloth; blocked on front and back in blind; spine blocked in gold; grey endpapers; dated on title-page). £100

Away in the Wilderness, or Life Among the Red-Indians and Fur-Traders of North America, Porter & Coates (Philadelphia, PA), 1869 . . . . £125

Deep Down, A Tale of the Cornish Mines, Nisbet (London), 1869 (bound in fine-grain cloth; blocked on front and back in blind; spine blocked in gold; grey endpapers; dated on title-page) £100

Erling the Bold, A Tale of the Norse Sea-Kings, Nisbet (London), 1869 (bound in fine-grain cloth; blocked on front and back in blind; spine blocked in gold; grey end-papers; dated on title-page) £75

The Floating Lights of the Godwin Sands, A Tale, Nisbet (London), 1870 (bound in sand-grain cloth; blocked on front and back in blind; spine blocked in gold; light-grey endpapers; dated on title-page). £75

The Iron Horse, or Life on the Line: A Tale of the Grand National Trunk Railway, Nisbet (London), 1871 (bound in fine-grain cloth; blocked on front in black and back in blind; spine blocked in gold and black; grey endpapers; dated on title-page; 4 full-page illustrations plus frontis-piece and pictorial title) £125

The Norsemen in the West, or America Before Columbus, Nisbet (London), 1872 (bound in fine-grain cloth; blocked on front in black, and back in blind; spine blocked in gold and black; grey endpapers; dated on title-page) . . £100

The Pioneers, A Tale of the Western Wilderness, Nisbet (London), 1872 (first issue bound in sand-grain cloth; blocked on front in gold and black, and back in blind; spine blocked in gold and black; grey endpapers; dated on title-page; frontispeice and pictorial title only; adverts dated 'June 1872'). £125

ditto, Nisbet (London), 1872 (second issue as above but adverts dated 'October 1872.') £100

Life in the Red Brigade, A Story for Boys, Routledge (London), [1873] (first issue bound in fine morocco-grain cloth; blocked on front in gold and black, and back in blind; spine blocked in gold and black; cream endpapers; not dated on title-page; 4 full-page illustrations plus frontispiece; 32 pages of adverts dated '28th November, 1872') £75

ditto, Routledge (London), [1873] (later issues as above but 16 pages of adverts) £65

Black Ivory, A Tale of Adventure among the Slavers of East Africa, Nisbet (London), 1873 (bound in fine-grain cloth; blocked on front in black, and back in blind; spine blocked in gold and black; grey endpapers; dated on title-page; 4 full-page illustrations plus frontispiece and pictorial title) £100

Tales of Adventure on the Sea, Nisbet (London), 1873 (bound in fine-grain cloth; blocked on front in black, and back in blind; spine blocked in gold and black; grey end-papers; dated on title-page; each story has 2 full-page illustrations and a pictorial title-page, plus frontispiece) .

. . . . £75

Tales of Adventure by Flood, Field Mountain and Sea, Nisbet (London), 1874 (bound in fine-grain cloth; blocked on front in black, and back in blind; spine blocked in gold and black; grey endpapers; dated on title-page; each story has 2 full-page illustrations and a pictorial title-page, plus frontispiece) £75

Tales of Adventure or Wild Work in Strange Places, Nisbet (London), 1874 (bound in fine-grain cloth; blocked on front in black, and back in blind; spine blocked in gold and black; grey endpapers; dated on title-page; each story has 2 full-page illustrations and a pictorial title-page, plus frontispiece) £75

The Ocean and Its Wonders, Nelson (London), 1874 (bound in fine-ribbed diagonal cloth; blocked on front in gold and black, and back in blind; spine blocked in gold and black, cream endpapers; dated on title-page) . . . £45

Tales of Adventure on the Coast, Nisbet (London), 1875 (bound in fine-grain cloth; blocked on front in black, and back in blind; spine blocked in gold and black; grey end-papers; dated on title-page; each story has 2 full-page illustrations and a pictorial title-page, plus frontispiece) .

. . . . £75

The Pirate City, An Algerine Tale, Nisbet (London), 1875 (bound in fine-grain cloth; blocked on front in black, and back in blind; spine blocked in gold; grey endpapers; dated on title-page; 4 full-page illustrations plus frontispiece and pictorial title) £100

Rivers of Ice, A Tale Illustrative of Alpine Adventure and Glacier Action, Nisbet (London), 1875 (bound in fine-grain cloth; blocked on front in black, and back in blind; spine blocked in gold and black; grey endpapers; dated on title-page; 4 full-page illustrations plus frontispiece and pictorial title) £75

Under the Waves, or Diving In Deep Waters, A Tale, Nisbet (London), 1876 (bound in fine-grain cloth; blocked on front in black, and back in blind; spine blocked in gold and black; grey endpapers; dated on title-page; 4 full-page illustrations plus frontispiece and pictorial title) . . £75

The Settler and the Savage, A Tale of Peace and War in South Africa, Nisbet (London), 1877 (bound in fine-grain cloth; blocked on front in black, and back in blind; spine blocked in gold; dated on title-page; 4 full-page illustra-tions plus frontispiece and pictorial title) . . . £100

Jarwin and Cuffy, A Tale, Warne (London), [1878] (first issue bound in fine-grain cloth; blocked on front in gold and black 'Jarwin / and Cuffy / Incident / & / Adventure / Library', and back in blind; spine blocked in gold and black; yellow endpapers; not dated on title-page). . £100

ditto, Warne (London), [1878] (later issue bound in morocco-grain cloth; blocked on front in gold and black

'Warne's / Incident & Adventure / Library / Jarwin / and Cuffy / Illustrated') £75

In the Track of the Troops, A Tale of Modern War, Nisbet (London), 1878 (bound in fine-grain cloth; blocked on front in black, and back in blind; spine blocked in gold; grey endpapers; dated on title-page; 5 full-page illustrations plus frontispiece). £75

Six Months at the Cape, or Letters to Periwinkle from South Africa, Nisbet (London), 1879 [1878] (bound in diagonal, fine-ribbed cloth; blocked on front in gold and black, and back in blind; spine blocked in gold and black, cream endpapers; dated on title-page; 11 full-page illustrations plus frontispiece) £100

The Red Man's Revenge, A Tale of the Red River Flood, Nisbet (London), 1880 (bound in diagonal, fine-ribbed cloth; blocked on front in gold and black, and back in blind; spine blocked in gold and black, brown endpapers; dated on title-page; frontispiece and illustrations on text paper) £100

Philosopher Jack, A Tale of the Southern Seas, Nisbet (London), 1880 (bound in diagonal, fine-ribbed cloth; blocked on front in gold and black, and back in blind; spine blocked in gold and black, brown endpapers; dated on title-page; frontispiece and 10 illustrations on text paper) . £75

Post Haste, A Tale of Her Majesty's Mails, Nisbet (London), 1880 [1879] (bound in diagonal, fine-ribbed cloth; blocked on front in gold and black, and back in blind; spine blocked in gold and black; dated on title-page; 4 full-page illustrations plus frontispiece and pictorial title; first issue with 16 pages of adverts starting with 'Post Haste', priced at 3/6d) £125

ditto, Nisbet (London), 1880 [1879] (second issue as above but in adverts the price for 'Post Haste' corrected to 5/- in ink). £100

ditto, Nisbet (London), 1880 [1879] (later issues as above but in adverts the price for 'Post Haste' printed as 5/-) £75

The Lonely Island, or the Refuge of the Mutineers, Nisbet (London), 1880 (bound in diagonal, fine-ribbed cloth; blocked on front in gold and black, and back in blind; spine blocked in gold and black; dated on title-page; 4 full-page illustrations plus frontispiece and pictorial title) . . £75

My Doggy and I, Nisbet (London), [1881] (bound in fine-grain cloth; blocked on front in gold and black, and back in blind; spine blocked in gold and black, brown endpapers; dated on title-page; 5 full-page illustrations plus frontispiece all on text paper) £75

The Kitten Pilgrims, or Great Battles and Grand Victories, Nisbet (London), [1882] (glazed, coloured pictorial boards; spine plain brown diagonal-ribbed cloth; white endpapers; edges stained red; not dated on title-page; 10 full-page colour illustrations plus frontispiece and pictorial title) .
. . . . £100

The Giant of the North, or Pokings Round the Pole, Nisbet (London), 1882 [1881] (bound in diagonal, fine-ribbed cloth; blocked on front in gold and black, and back in blind; spine blocked in gold and black; brown endpapers; dated on title-page; 5 full-page illustrations plus frontispiece and pictorial title) £100

The Battery and the Boiler, or Adventures in the Laying of Submarine Cable, Nisbet (London), 1883 [1882] (bound in diagonal, fine-ribbed cloth; blocked on front in gold and black, and back in blind; spine blocked in gold and black; dark brown endpapers; dated on title-page; 4 full-page illustrations plus frontispiece and engraved title) . . £100

Battles with the Sea, or Heroes of the Lifeboat and Rocket, Nisbet (London), 1883 (bound in diagonal, fine-ribbed cloth; blocked on front in gold and black, and back in blind; spine blocked in gold and black, yellow endpapers; dated on title-page; frontispiece and illustrations on text paper) £75

The Madman and the Pirate, Nisbet (London), 1883 (bound in diagonal, fine-ribbed cloth; blocked on front in gold and black, and back in blind; spine blocked in gold and black; yellow endpapers; dated on title-page; 6 illustrations and frontispiece on text paper) £75

Dusty Diamonds Cut and Polished, A Tale of City-Arab Life and Adventure, Nisbet (London), 1884 [1883] (bound in smooth cloth; blocked on front in gold and black, and back in blind; spine blocked in gold and black; brown endpapers; dated on title-page; 4 full-page illustrations plus frontispiece and pictorial title-page) £75

The Young Trawler, A Story of Life and Death and Rescue on the North Sea, Nisbet (London), 1884 (bound in fine-grain cloth; blocked on front in gold and black, and back in blind; spine blocked in gold and black; brown endpapers; dated on title-page; 4 full-page illustrations plus frontispiece and pictorial title-page) £75

Twice Bought, A Tale of the Oregon Gold Fields, Nisbet (London), 1885 [1884] (bound in diagonal, fine-ribbed cloth; blocked on front in gold and black, and back in blind; spine blocked in gold and black; dated on title-page; 6 illustrations plus frontispiece and pictorial title-page) .
. . . . £75

The Rover of the Andes, A Tale of Adventure in South America, Nisbet (London), 1885 (bound in diagonal, fine-ribbed cloth; blocked on front in gold and black, and back in blind; spine blocked in gold and black; dark brown endpapers; dated on title-page; 4 full-page illustrations plus frontispiece and pictorial title-page) £75

The Island Queen, A Tale of the Southern Hemisphere, Nisbet (London), 1885 (bound in diagonal, fine-ribbed cloth; blocked on front in gold and black, and back in blind; spine blocked in gold and black; yellow endpapers; dated on title-page; 6 illustrations plus frontispiece) . £75

Red Rooney, or Last of the Crew, Nisbet (London), 1886 (bound in smooth cloth; blocked on front in gold and colours, and back has publisher's device; spine blocked in gold and colours; dark brown endpapers; dated on title-page; 4 full-page illustrations plus frontispiece and pictorial title-page) £75

The Prairie Chief, Nisbet (London), 1886 (bound in diagonal, fine-ribbed cloth; blocked on front in gold and black, and back in blind; spine blocked in gold and black; yellow endpapers; dated on title-page; 10 full-page illustrations plus frontispiece and pictorial title-page) . . . £75

The Fugitives, Nisbet (London), 1887 (bound in smooth cloth; blocked on front in gold and colours, and back has publisher's device; spine blocked in gold and colours; dark brown endpapers; dated on title-page; 4 full-page illustrations plus frontispiece and pictorial title-page) . . £75

The Big Otter, A Tale of the Great Nor'West, Routledge (London), 1887 [1886] (bound in diagonal, fine-ribbed cloth; blocked on front in gold, black, white, brown and green, and back in blind; spine blocked in gold, white, brown and black; grey, patterned endpapers; dated on title-page; 7 full-page illustrations plus frontispiece) . . £75

Blue Lights, or Hot Work in the Soudan: A Tale of Soldier Life, Nisbet (London), 1888 (bound in smooth cloth;

blocked on front in gold and colours, and back has publisher's device; spine blocked in gold; yellow end-papers; dated on title-page; 4 full-page illustrations plus frontispiece and pictorial title-page) £75

The Middy and the Moors, An Algerine Story, Nisbet (London), 1888 (bound in smooth cloth; blocked on front in gold and black, and back has publisher's device; spine blocked in gold colours; dark brown endpapers; dated on title-page; frontispiece and other illustrations on text paper) £75

The Crew of the Water Wagtail, A Story of Newfoundland, Nisbet (London), [1889] (bound in diagonal, fine-ribbed cloth; blocked on front in gold and black, and back in blind; spine blocked in gold and black; yellow endpapers; dated on title-page; 3 full-page illustrations plus frontis-piece) £75

The Eagle Cliff, Partridge (London), [1889] (bound in smooth cloth; blocked on front in gold and colours, and back has publisher's device; spine blocked in gold and black; green, flowered endpapers; all edges gilt; 16 pages of advertisements starting with 'Eagle's Cliff' and ending with 'The Mother's Companion'; not dated on title-page; all illustrations are on text paper) £65

ditto, Partridge (London), [1889] (later editions have no adverts and the edges are not gilt) £65

Blown to Bits, Nisbet (London), 1889 (bound in smooth cloth; blocked on front in gold and colours, and back has publisher's device; spine blocked in gold and colours; dark brown endpapers; dated on title-page; 4 full-page illustra-tions plus frontispiece and pictorial title-page) . . £65

The Garrett and the Garden, or Low Life High Up, and *Jeff Benson, or The Young Coastguardsman*, Nisbet (London), [1890] (bound in diagonal, fine-ribbed cloth; blocked on front in gold and black, and back in blind; spine blocked in gold and black; yellow endpapers; not dated on title-page; 3 full-page illustrations plus frontispiece) £65

Charlie to the Rescue, A Tale of the Sea and the Rockies, Nisbet (London), 1890 (bound in smooth cloth; blocked on front in gold and colours, and back has publisher's device; spine blocked in gold and colours; dark brown endpapers; dated on title-page; 4 full-page illustrations plus frontis-piece and pictorial title) £65

The Buffalo Runners, Nisbet (London), 1891 (bound in smooth cloth; blocked on front in gold and colours, and back has publisher's device; spine blocked in gold and colours; dark brown endpapers; dated on title-page; 4 full-page illustrations plus frontispiece and pictorial title). £65

The Coxswain's Bride, or The Rising Tide and Other Tales, Nisbet (London), 1891 (bound in smooth cloth; blocked on front in gold and colours, back plain; spine blocked in gold and colours; yellow endpapers; dated on title-page; 3 full-page illustrations plus frontispiece). £65

Hunted and Harried, A Tale of the Scottish Covenanters, Nisbet (London), [1892] (bound in smooth cloth; blocked on front in gold and colours, back plain; spine blocked in gold and colours; yellow endpapers; not dated on title-page; 3 full-page illustrations plus frontispiece, all on text paper. No adverts) £65

ditto, Nisbet (London), [1892] (later issue as above but with 32 pages of adverts) £65

The Hot Swamp, A Romance of Old Albion, Nisbet (London), 1892 (bound in smooth cloth; blocked on front in gold and colours, and back has publisher's device; spine blocked in gold and colours; black/brown endpapers; dated

on title-page; 4 full-page illustrations plus frontispiece and pictorial title) £65

The Walrus Hunters, A Romance of the Realms of Ice, Nisbet (London), 1893 (bound in smooth cloth; blocked on front in gold and colours, back plain; spine blocked in gold and colours; plain yellow endpapers; all edges gilt; dated on title-page; 4 full-page illustrations plus frontispiece and pictorial title) £65

Reuben's Luck, S.P.C.K (London), [1896] (coloured pictorial wraps; not dated) £100

The Jolly Kitten Book, Blackie (London), [1925] . £50/£20

Ballantyne Omnibus for Boys, Collins (London), [1932] . . . . £35/£10

Other Titles

Hudson's Bay, or Every-day Life in the Wilds of North America, Blackwood (Edinburgh), 1848 (privately issued first edition; bound in red morocco; blocked in gilt on front board and lettered in gilt on spine; cream endpapers; all edges gilt; dated on title-page where it is noted as a private edition; 3 full-page illustrations plus frontispiece, and other illustrations in text; perhaps no more than 6 copies) £2,000

ditto, Blackwood (Edinburgh/London), 1848 (first trade edition; bound in dark green/grey cloth; blocked on front and back in blind, lettered in gilt on spine, cream/yellow endpapers; dated on title-page; 3 full-page illustrations plus frontispiece, and other illustrations in text) . . . £500

The Northern Coasts of America, Nelson (London), 1853 (written with Patrick Fraser Tyler; bound in ripple-grain cloth; blocked on front and back in blind, lettered in gilt on spine; yellow endpapers; dated on title-page; 5 full-page illustrations plus frontispiece) £200

Handbook to the New Gold Fields, Strahan/Adams (Edin-burgh/London), 1858 (yellow paper covered boards, printed in red, white endpapers; dated on title-page; contains folding map). £650

Environs and Vicinity of Edinburgh, Nelson (London), 1859 (bound in heavy-grain cloth; blocked on front in gilt and blind, back in blind, lettered in gilt on spine; yellow endpapers; dated on title-page; 12 coloured illustrations; folding map). £125

Ships - The Great Eastern and Lesser Craft, Nelson (London), 1859 (glazed paper, red printed wraps; dated on title-page; 12 coloured illustrations) £150

Lakes of Killarney, Nelson (London), 1859 (bound in bead-grain cloth; blocked on front in gilt and blind, back in blind, lettered in gilt on spine; yellow endpapers; dated on title-page; eleven full-page coloured illustrations plus frontispiece; folding map; 16 pages of advertisements dated May 1858) £125

How Not to do it, Constable/Adams (Edinburgh/London), 1859 ('By one of Themselves'; orange paper wraps printed on front in black, back and spine blank; dated on title-page) £125

Discovery and Adventure in the Polar Seas and Regions, by Leslie, Murray and Ballantyne, Nelson (London), 1860 (bound in morocco grain cloth; blocked on front in gilt and blind, back in blind; lettered in gilt on spine; pale yellow endpapers; dated on title-page; 12 inserted illustrations plus frontispiece, pictorial title-page, and other illustrations in text, some full-page; folding chart of the polar seas) . £125

The Volunteer Levee, Constable/Adams (Edinburgh/London), 1860 (pseud 'Ensign Sopht'; pictorial yellow paper wraps; dated on title-page) £125

Ensign Sopht's Volunteer Almanack, Nimmo/Simpkin Marshall (Edinburgh/London), 1861 (pseud 'Ensign Sopht'; pictorial yellow paper wraps; dated on title-page)   . £125

Photographs of Edinburgh, Duthie/Simpkin Marshall (Edinburgh/London), 1868 (pseud 'Ensign Sopht'; bound in fine-grain cloth; blocked on front in gold, on back in blind; spine plain; brown endpapers; all edges gilt; not dated on title-page)   . £150

The Collected Works of Ensign Sopht, Late of the Volunteers, Nisbet (London), 1881 ('edited' by Ballantyne; pictorial yellow paper boards; back and spine plain; white endpapers; dated on title-page). £175

ditto, Nisbet (London), 1881 (as above but later binding of fine-grain cloth, front blocked in gold and black, back in blind; spine in gold; yellow endpapers, all edges gilt). £150

Personal Reminiscences in Book-making, Nisbet (London), [1893] (bound in smooth cloth; blocked on front in gold and colours with picture of man in boat, back plain; spine blocked in gold and colours; cream endpapers; not dated on title-page; 8 pages of adverts; frontispiece and pictorial title only) £75

ditto, Nisbet (London), [1893] (simultaneous issue as above but binding with no picture on front but author's signature in gilt) £75

ditto, Nisbet (London), [1893] (later issues as above but with picture on front and only 2pps of adverts)   .   .   . £50

J.G. BALLARD

(b.1930 d.2009)

Despite shifting from avant-garde science fiction to surreal contemporary writing, Ballard is best known as the author of the controversial novels *Crash*, and *Empire of the Sun*, the latter based on his own experiences of internment by the Japanese in World War Two.

Novels

The Wind from Nowhere, Berkley (New York), 1962 (pbk)
.   .   .   . £15

ditto, Doubleday (Garden City, NY), 1965 (with *The Drowned World*)   .   .   .   . £75/£20

ditto, Penguin (Harmondsworth, Middlesex), 1967 (pbk) £10

The Drowned World, Berkley (New York), 1962 (pbk)   £20

ditto, Gollancz (London), 1962   .   .   .   . £650/£75

The Burning World, Berkley (New York), 1964 (pbk) . £15

ditto, as *The Drought*, Cape (London), 1965   . £500/£50

The Crystal World, Cape (London), 1966.   . £300/£40

ditto, Farrar Straus Giroux (New York), 1966 .   . £75/£10

Crash, Cape (London), 1973   .   .   .   . £750/£45

ditto, Farrar Straus Giroux (New York), 1973 . . £100/£25

Concrete Island, Cape (London), 1974   .   . £100/£20

ditto, Farrar Straus Giroux (New York), 1974 .   . £15/£5

High-Rise, Cape (London), 1975   .   .   . £75/£15

ditto, Holt Rinehart & Winston (New York), 1977 . £35/£5

The Unlimited Dream Company, Cape (London), 1979
.   .   .   . £35/£5

ditto, Holt Rinehart & Winston (New York), 1979 . £15/£5

Hello America, Cape (London), 1981   .   . £10/£5

ditto, Carroll & Graf (New York), 1988   .   . £10/£5

Empire of the Sun, Gollancz (London), 1984 (first issue d/w with 2 reviews on back)   .   .   .   . £30/£5

ditto, Gollancz (London), 1984 (second issue d/w with 6 reviews).   .   .   .   . £15/£5

ditto, Gollancz (London), 1984 (100 signed copies, slipcase)
.   .   .   . £300/£200

ditto, Simon & Schuster (New York), 1984   . . £20/£5

The Day of Creation, Gollancz (London), 1987   . £10/£5

ditto, Gollancz (London), 1987 (100 signed copies, slipcase)
.   .   .   . £150/£75

ditto, Farrar Straus Giroux (New York), 1988 .   . £10/£5

Running Wild, Hutchinson (London), 1988 (novella) £10/£5

ditto, Farrar Straus Giroux (New York), 1989 .   . £10/£5

The Kindness of Women, Harper Collins (London), 1991 .
.   .   .   . £10/£5

ditto, Farrar Straus Giroux (New York), 1991 .   . £10/£5

Rushing to Paradise, Harper Collins/Flamingo (London), 1994   .   .   .   . £10/£5

ditto, Picador (New York), 1995.   .   .   . £10/£5

Cocaine Nights, Harper Collins/Flamingo (London), 1996 .
.   .   .   . £10/£5

ditto, Counterpoint (Washington, DC), 1998 .   . £10/£5

Super-Cannes, Harper Collins/Flamingo (London), 2000 .
.   .   .   . £10/£5

ditto, Picador (New York), 2001.   .   .   . £10/£5

Millennium People, Flamingo (London), 2003   . £10/£5

Kingdom Come, Fourth Estate (London), 2006   . £10/£5

Short Stories

Billenium and Other Stories, Berkley (New York), 1962 (pbk; reprints sometimes spelt 'Billennium').   .   . £10

The Voices of Time and Other Stories, Berkley (New York), 1962 (pbk) £10

The Four-Dimensional Nightmare, Gollancz (London), 1963   .   .   .   .   .   . £650/£125

ditto, Gollancz (London), 1974 (drops 2 stories and adds 2 others)   .   .   .   . £70/£15

ditto, as *The Voices of Time*, Gollancz (London), 1985 .
.   .   .   . £15/£5

Passport to Eternity and Other Stories, Berkley (New York), 1963 (pbk) £10

Terminal Beach, Berkley (New York), 1964 (pbk)   . £10

The Terminal Beach, Gollancz (London), 1964 (not the same as above)   .   .   .   .   .   . £400/£40

The Impossible Man and Other Stories, Berkley (New York), 1966 (pbk) £5

The Day of Forever, Panther (London), 1967 (pbk)   . £5

ditto, Gollancz (London), 1986 (hardback)   . £25/£5

The Disaster Area, Cape (London), 1967.   . £175/£25

The Overloaded Man, Panther (London), 1967 (pbk) . £5

The Inner Landscape, Allison & Busby (London), 1969 (contains three original novellas: 'Boy in Darkness' by Mervyn Peake; 'The Voices of Time' by J.G. Ballard; 'Danger: Religion!' by Brian Aldiss)   .   . £20/£5

The Atrocity Exhibition, Cape (London), 1970   . £175/£45

ditto, Doubleday (Garden City, NY), 1970 (withdrawn)
.   .   .   .   .   . £3,500/£3,000

ditto, as *Love and Napalm: Export USA*, Grove Press (New York), 1972   .   .   .   .   .   . £15/£5

ditto, as *The Atrocity Exhibition*, Re/Search (San Francisco), 1990 (pbk) £10

ditto, as *The Atrocity Exhibition*, Re/Search (San Francisco), 1990 (400 signed copies)   .   .   .   . £145/£100

Chronopolis and Other Stories, Putnam (New York), 1971.
.   .   .   . £65/£15

Vermilion Sands, Berkley (New York), 1971 (pbk)   . £15

ditto, Cape (London), 1973   .   .   .   . £175/£25

Low-Flying Aircraft and Other Stories, Cape (London), 1976   .   .   .   . £125/£20

The Best Science Fiction of J.G. Ballard, Orbit/Futura (London), 1977 (pbk) £5
The Best Short Stories of J.G. Ballard, Holt Rinehart & Winston (New York), 1978 . . . . £15/£5
The Venus Hunters, Granada (London), 1980 (pbk) . £5
ditto, Gollancz (London), 1986 . . . . . £20/£5
Myths of the Near Future, Cape (London), 1982 . £15/£5
ditto, Farrar Straus Giroux (New York), 1991 . . £15/£5
Memories of the Space Age, Arkham House (Sauk City, WI), 1988 . . . . £10/£5
War Fever, Collins (London), 1990 . . . £10/£5
ditto, Farrar Straus Giroux (New York), 1990 . . £10/£5
The Complete Short Stories, Flamingo (London), 2001 .
. . . . £45/£10

Others
Why I Want to Fuck Ronald Reagan, Unicorn Bookshop (Brighton), 1968 (50 signed copies of 250) . . . £800
ditto, Unicorn Bookshop (Brighton), 1968 (200 unsigned copies of 250) £500
News from the Sun, Interzone (London), 1982 (unsigned copies of 750; stapled wraps) £10
ditto, Interzone (London), 1982 (100 signed copies of 750; stapled wraps) £30
ditto, Interzone (London), 1982 (20 signed, lettered copies of 750; stapled wraps) £75
A Users Guide to the Millennium: Essays and Review, Harper-Collins (London), 1996 . . . . £10/£5
ditto, Picador (New York), 1996 . . . . £10/£5
Quotes, RE/Search Publications (San Francisco, CA), 2004 (pbk) £5
Miracles of Life: Shanghai to Shepperton: An Autobiography, Fourth Estate (London), 2008 . . £10/£5
ditto, Fourth Estate (London), 2008 (1,000 signed copies; slipcase) . . . . £50/£25

IAIN BANKS
(b.1954)

Iain Menzies Banks writes mainstream novels as Iain Banks and science fiction as Iain M. Banks. *The Wasp Factory* was a controversial success, and Banks has become more than a cult writer. His subsequent fiction and science fiction often stray into the realm of the bizarre and the sinister. Apparently, Banks produces his novels in three months of uninterrupted work, then takes nine months off.

Novels Written as 'Iain Banks'
The Wasp Factory, Macmillan (London), 1984 . £150/£35
ditto, Houghton Mifflin (Boston), 1984 . . . £25/£5
Walking on Glass, Macmillan (London), 1985 . £25/£5
ditto, Houghton Mifflin (Boston), 1986 . . . £20/£5
The Bridge, Macmillan (London), 1986 . . . £65/£10
ditto, St Martin's Press (New York), 1989 . . £15/£5
Espedair Street, Macmillan (London), 1987 . . £25/£5
Canal Dreams, Macmillan (London), 1989 . . £15/£5
ditto, Doubleday (Garden City, NY), 1991 . . £10/£5
The Crow Road, Scribner's (London), 1992 . . £25/£5
Complicity, Little, Brown (London), 1993 . . £10/£5
ditto, Doubleday (New York), 1995 . . . £10/£5
Whit, Or Isis among the Unsaved, Little, Brown (London), 1995 . . . . £10/£5
A Song of Stone, Abacus (London), 1997 . £10/£5

ditto, Simon & Schuster (New York), 1998 . . £10/£5
The Business, Little, Brown (London), 1999 . . £10/£5
ditto, Simon & Schuster (New York), 2000 . . £15/£5
Dead Air, Little, Brown (London), 2002 . . . £10/£5
The Steep Approach to Garbadale, Little, Brown (London), 2007 . . . . £10/£5
ditto, Little, Brown (London), 2007 (1,000 signed, numbered copies; slipcase) . . . . . . £40/£25

Novels Written as 'Iain M. Banks'
Consider Phlebas, Macmillan (London), 1987 . £40/£10
ditto, Macmillan (London), 1987 (176 signed copies, slipcase) . . . . £175/£100
ditto, St Martin's Press (New York), 1988 . . £15/£5
The Player of Games, Macmillan (London), 1988 . £40/£10
ditto, Macmillan (London), 1988 (201 signed copies, slipcase) . . . . £150/£65
ditto, St Martin's Press (New York), 1989 . . £15/£5
Use of Weapons, Orbit (London), 1990 . . . £50/£10
ditto, Bantam (New York), 1992 . . . . £10/£5
Against a Dark Background, Orbit (London), 1993 £25/£5
ditto, Bantam (New York), 1993 (pbk) . . . £5
Feersum Endjinn, Orbit (London), 1994 . . . £15/£5
ditto, Bantam (New York), 1995 (pbk) . . . £5
Excession, Orbit (London), 1996 . . . £10/£5
ditto, Bantam (New York), 1997 (pbk) . . . £5
Inversions, Orbit (London), 1998 . . . £10/£5
ditto, Pocket Books (New York), 2000 . . . £10/£5
Look To Windward, Orbit (London), 2000 . . £10/£5
ditto, Pocket Books (New York), 2001 . . . £10/£5
The Algebraist, Orbit (London), 2004 . . . £10/£5
ditto, Nightshade Books (Portland, OR), 2005 . . £10/£5
ditto, Nightshade Books (Portland, OR), 2005 (200 signed, numbered copies) . . . . £40/£20
Matter, Orbit (London), 2008 . . . . £10/£5

Others
Cleaning Up, Birmingham Science Fiction Group (Birmingham, UK), 1987 (500 signed, numbered copies; stapled wraps) £75
The State of the Art, Ziesing (Willimantic, CT), 1989 £10/£5
ditto, Ziesing (Willimantic, CT), 1989 (400 signed copies) .
. . . . £20/£10
ditto, Orbit (London), 1991 (adds further stories) . £10/£5
Raw Spirit: In Search of the Perfect Dram, Century (London), 2003 . . . . £10/£5

HELEN BANNERMAN
(b.1863 d.1946)

Born in Scotland, Bannerman married an army doctor and settled in India where she wrote *Little Black Sambo* for her own children. The heroes of many of her books are recognisably south Indian or Tamil children in the illustrations. Although her books are not in themselves racist, they have often been censored or banned because the name Sambo has caused offence.

The Story of Little Black Sambo, Grant Richards' 'Dumpy Books for Children' (London), No. 4, 1899 (anonymous) .
. . . . £5,000
ditto, Stokes (New York), 1901 . . . . £1,000

The Story of Little Black Mingo, Nisbet (London), 1901
(anonymous). £400
ditto, Stokes (New York), 1901 . . . . . £150
The Story of Little Black Quibba, Nisbet (London), 1902
(anonymous). £400
ditto, Stokes (New York), 1903 . . . . . £150
Little Degchie-Head: An Awful Warning to Bad Babas,
Nisbet (London), 1903 (anonymous) £200
Pat and the Spider: The Biter Bit, Nisbet (London), 1904
(anonymous). £200
ditto, Stokes (New York), 1905 . . . . . £150
The Story of the Teasing Monkey, Nisbet (London), 1906
(anonymous). £200
ditto, Stokes (New York), 1907 . . . . . £150
The Story of Little Black Quasha, Nisbet (London), 1908
(anonymous). £150
ditto, Stokes (New York), 1908 . . . . . £150
The Story of Little Black Bobtail, Nisbet (London), 1909
(anonymous). £75
ditto, Stokes (New York), 1909 . . . . . £50
The Story of Sambo and the Twins, Stokes (New York),
1936 . . . . £50
ditto, Nisbet (London), 1937 . . . . . £150/£50
The Story of Little White Squibba, Chatto & Windus
(London), 1966 . . . . £75/£20

JOHN BANVILLE

(b.1945)

John Banville is a well respected Irish author, whose novel
The Book of Evidence was shortlisted for the Booker prize.
It won the Guinness Peat Aviation Award in the same year.
Banville is known for his inventive, precise prose style, and
for the dark humour of his narrators. He is the literary
editor of the *Irish Times*.

Novels

Nightspawn, Secker & Warburg (London), 1971 . £350/£45
ditto, Norton (New York), 1971 . . . . . £100/£25
Birchwood, Secker & Warburg (London), 1971 . £150/£25
ditto, Norton (New York), 1973 . . . . . £50/£10
Doctor Copernicus, Secker & Warburg (London), 1976 .
. . . . £150/£25
ditto, Norton (New York), 1976 . . . . £35/£10
Kepler, Secker & Warburg (London), 1981 . £150/£25
ditto, Godine (Boston), 1983 . . . . . £25/£5
The Newton Letter: An Interlude, Secker & Warburg
(London), 1982 . . . . £150/£15
ditto, Godine (Boston), 1987 . . . . . £20/£5
Mefisto, Secker & Warburg (London), 1986 . £15/£5
ditto, Godine (Boston), 1989 . . . . . £10/£5
The Book of Evidence, Secker & Warburg (London), 1989.
. . . . £10/£5
ditto, Scribner's (New York), 1990 . . . £10/£5
Ghosts, Secker & Warburg (London), 1993 . £10/£5
ditto, Knopf (New York), 1993 . . . . £10/£5
Athena, Secker & Warburg (London), 1995 . £10/£5
ditto, Knopf (New York), 1995 . . . . £10/£5
The Untouchable, Picador (London), 1997 . £10/£5
ditto, Knopf (New York), 1997 . . . . £10/£5
Eclipse, Bridgewater Press (London), 2000 (100 signed,
numbered copies, bound in cloth) £50

ditto, Bridgewater Press (London), 2000 (26 signed copies
lettered A-Z, bound in quarter cloth and marbled paper
boards) £125
ditto, Bridgewater Press (London), 2000 (12 signed copies
numbered I-XII, bound in quarter library calf) . £250
ditto, Picador (London), 2000 . . . . . £10/£5
ditto, Knopf (New York), 2001 . . . . £10/£5
Shroud, Picador (London), 2002 . . . . £10/£5
ditto, McCann/Picador (Oxford/London), 2002 (65 signed
copies, no d/w) £100
ditto, McCann/Picador (Oxford/London), 2002 (15 signed
copies, quarter leather, no d/w). £150
ditto, Knopf (New York), 2003 . . . . £10/£5
The Sea, Picador (London), 2005 . . . . £30/£5
ditto, Knopf (New York), 2005 . . . . £10/£5
ditto, McCann/Picador (Oxford/London), 2006 (46 signed
copies, glassine d/w) £225
ditto, McCann/Picador (Oxford/London), 2006 (10 signed
copies, glassine d/w) £350
Infinities, Picador (London), 2009 . . . . £30/£5
ditto, Picador/London Review Bookshop (London), 2006 (35
signed, numbered copies in quarter-bound Beech Nut cloth)
. . . . £100
ditto, Picador/London Review Bookshop (London), 2006 (25
signed, numbered copies quarter-bound in Harmatan
Toffee Beige leather) £200
ditto, Picador/London Review Bookshop (London), 2006 (10
signed, lettered copies quarter-bound in Harmatan Toffee
Beige leather; slipcase) £300

Collected Editions

The Revolutions Trilogy, Picador (London), 2000 (contains
Doctor Copernicus, *Kepler* and *The Newton Letter: An
Interlude*) . . . . £20/£5
Frames Trilogy, Picador (London), 2001 (contains *Athena*,
The Book of Evidence and *Ghosts*) . . . . £20/£5

Novel as Benjamin Black

Christine Falls, Picador (London), 2006 . . . £10/£5
ditto, Holt (New York), 2006 . . . . . £10/£5

Short Stories

Long Lankin, Secker & Warburg (London), 1970 . £500/£75
ditto, Gallery Press (Dublin), 1984 (revised edition) £45/£10

Plays

The Broken Jug, Gallery Press (Dublin), 1987 (240 copies)
. . . . £45/£15
God's Gift, Gallery Press (Dublin), 2000 . . £35/£10
ditto, Gallery Press (Dublin), 2000 (pbk) . . . £10

Non-Fiction

Prague Pictures: Portrait of a City, Bloomsbury (London),
2003 . . . . £10/£5
ditto, Bloomsbury (New York), 2004. . . . £10/£5

CICELY MARY BARKER
(b.1895 d.1973)

Cicely Mary Barker was a British author and illustrator, largely self-taught, who is best-known for her *Flower Fairies* books. In these popular stories child fairies are shown dressed as different types of flowers. Her publisher, Blackie, did not print a date in her books so it can be hard to tell the difference between first and later editions. However, the presence of a d/w with the price '1s' or 1s6d' is a sure indication of a first edition.

Written and Illustrated by Barker
Flower Fairies of the Spring, Blackie (London), [1923] (24 colour plates) . . . . . . £125/£30
ditto, Macmillan (New York), 1927 (24 colour plates) .
. . . . £75/£20
Flower Fairies of the Summer, Blackie (London), [1925] (24 colour plates). . . . . . £100/£25
ditto, Macmillan (New York), 1927 (24 colour plates) . .
. . . . £100/£20
Flower Fairies of the Autumn: With the Nuts and Berries they Bring, Blackie (London), [1926] (24 colour plates) .
. . . . £75/£25
ditto, Macmillan (New York), 1927 (24 colour plates) .
. . . . £75/£20
Beautiful Bible Pictures, Blackie (London), [1932] (6 cards painted by Barker) . . . . £40 the set
A Flower Fairy Alphabet, Blackie (London), [1934] (24 colour plates) . . . . . . £100/£30
The Lord of the Rushie River, Blackie (London), [1938] .
. . . . £65/£15
ditto, as *The Fairy Necklaces*, Warner (London), 1991. .
. . . . £10/£5
Fairies of the Trees, Blackie (London), 1940 (24 colour plates) . . . . £75/£25
Flower Fairies of the Garden, Blackie (London), [1944] (24 colour plates) . . . . . £75/£15
Groundsel and Necklaces, Blackie (London), [1946] (12 colour pictures) . . . . . £60/£15
Flower Fairies of the Wayside, Blackie (London), [1948] (24 colour plates). . . . . £60/£15
Lively Stories, Macmillan (London), 1954-55 (5 books: *The Little House, Do You Know?, The Click-Clock Man, The Why Girl* and *Hutch the Peg Doll*) . . . £45 each
Cicely Barker's Flower Fairy Picture Book, Blackie (London), [1955]. . . . . . £125/£35
Lively Numbers, Macmillan (London), 1960-1962 (3 books: *The Little Man, The Little Boats* and *The Lazy Giant*) .
. . . . £45 each
The Rhyming Rainbow, Blackie (London), 1977 . £15/£5
The Fairies' Gift, Blackie (London), 1977 . . £15/£5
Flower Fairies of the Winter, Blackie (London), 1985. .
. . . . £10/£5
Simon the Swan: A Sequel to the Lord of the Rushie River, Blackie (London), 1988 . . . . . £15/£5
ditto, Peter Bedrick Books (Columbus, OH), 1989 . £15/£5

Illustrated by Barker
The Children's Book of Hymns, Blackie & Son (London), [1929] (12 colour plates plus numerous black & white drawings) . . . . £45/£10
ditto, as *The Little Picture Hymn Book*, Blackie (London), [1933] (as UK edition but without music) . . £20/£5

Old Rhymes for All Times, Blackie (London), [1928] (12 colour plates and numerous black & white illustrations) .
. . . . £150/£45
ditto, Artists and Writers Guild (Poughkeepsie, NY), c.1935
. . . . £125/£35
A Little Book of Rhymes New and Old, Blackie (London), [1933] (12 colour plates) . . . . . £45/£15
A Little Book of Old Rhymes, Blackie (London), [1936] .
. . . . £40/£10
He Leadeth Me: A Book of Bible Stories, by Dorothy O. Barker, Blackie (London), [1936] (16 colour plates plus black & white drawings) . . . . . £40/£15
ditto, M.S. Mill Co (New York), [1938] . . . £40/£15

With music by Olive Linnell
Autumn Songs With Music, Blackie (London), [1926] (from *Flower Fairies of the Autumn* with music by Olive Linnell; 12 coloured plates) . . . . . £150/£45
ditto, Dodge (New York), 1927 . . . . £125/£35
Spring Songs With Music, Blackie (London), [1926] (from *Flower Fairies of the Spring* with music by Olive Linnell; 12 coloured plates) . . . . . £125/£40
Summer Songs With Music, Blackie (London), [c.1926] (from *Flower Fairies of the Summer* with music by Olive Linnell; 12 coloured plates) . . . . £125/£40
Flower Songs of the Seasons, Blackie (London), [c.1930] (music by Olive Linnell; 12 coloured plates). . £125/£40
When Spring Came In at the Window: A One-Act Play, Blackie (London), 1942 (songs from *Flower Fairies of the Spring*) . . . . £65/£15

Collected Editions
The Book of the Flower Fairies, Blackie (London), [1927] (collects *Flower Fairies of the Spring, Flower Fairies of the Summer* and *Flower Fairies of the Autumn*; 72 colour plates) . . . . £250/£75
Fairies of the Flowers and Trees, Blackie (London), [1950] (contains *Flower Fairies of the Wayside, Flower Fairies of the Garden* and *Fairies of the Trees*; 72 colour plates) .
. . . . £200/£45
Flower Fairies Miniature Library, Blackie & Son Intervisual (London), 1981 (4 miniature books: *Spring Flower Fairies, Summer Flower Fairies, Blossom Flower Fairies* and *Berry Flower Fairies*; slipcase) . £40 the set

---

CLIVE BARKER
(b.1952)

Clive Barker's early short stories and novels are pure horror, but he has since moved towards epic modern fantasy. His work explores the idea of hidden fantastical worlds existing alongside our own, sexuality in the supernatural and the construction of coherent, complex and detailed mythologies. He also illustrates his own work, and writes, directs and produces for the stage and screen.

Novels
The Damnation Game, Weidenfeld & Nicolson (London), 1985 . . . . £20/£5
ditto, Weidenfeld & Nicolson (London), 1985 (250 signed, numbered copies, slipcase, no d/w) . . . . £125/£75
ditto, Ace/Putnam (New York), 1987. . . . £10/£5

Weaveworld, Poseidon Press (New York), 1987 . £10/£5
ditto, Poseidon Press (New York), 1987 (500 signed, numbered copies, slipcase, unprinted acetate d/w) £75/£40
ditto, Poseidon Press (New York), 1987 (52 signed copies lettered a-zz, slipcase, no d/w) . . . . £175/£125
ditto, Collins (London), 1987 . . . . . £10/£5
ditto, Collins (London), 1987 (500 signed, numbered copies, quarter leather-bound, slipcase, no d/w) . . . £125/£65
ditto, Collins (London), 1987 (26 signed, numbered copies, quarter leather-bound, all edges gilt, slipcase, no d/w) .
. . . . £175/£135
Cabal: The Nightbreed, Poseidon Press (New York), 1988 .
. . . . £10/£5
ditto, Poseidon Press (New York), 1988 (750 signed, numbered copies, no d/w) . . . . . . £45/£25
ditto, Fontana (London), 1988 (pbk) £5
ditto, Collins (London), 1989 . . . . £10/£5
The Great and Secret Show: The First Book of the Art, Collins (London), 1989 . . . . . £10/£5
ditto, Collins (London), 1989 (500 signed, numbered copies, full leather binding, all edges gilt, velvet-lined box) . .
. . . .£100/£65
ditto, Collins (London), 1989 (26 signed, lettered copies, full leather binding, all edges gilt, velvet-lined box) £200/£125
ditto, Harper & Row (New York), 1990 . . . £10/£5
Imajica, HarperCollins (London), 1991 . . . £10/£5
ditto, HarperCollins (New York), 1991 . . . £10/£5
ditto, HarperCollins (New York), 1991 (500 signed copies, slipcase, no d/w) . . . .£125/£75
ditto, HarperCollins (New York), 1991 (26 signed copies, slipcase, no d/w) . . . . . £175/£125
The Hellbound Heart, Fontana (London), 1991 (pbk) . £5
ditto, Harper (New York), 1991 (pbk) £5
The Thief of Always: A Fable, HarperCollins (London), 1992 . . . . £10/£5
ditto, HarperCollins (New York), 1992 . . . £10/£5
ditto, HarperCollins (New York), 1992 (500 signed copies, slipcase, no d/w) . . . .£125/£75
ditto, HarperCollins (New York), 1992 (26 signed copies, slipcase, no d/w) . . . . . £150/£100
Everville: The Second Book of the Art, HarperCollins (London), 1994 . . . . £10/£5
ditto, HarperCollins (London), 1994 (limited edition of 2,000 numbered copies with facsimilie signature) . . £25/£15
ditto, HarperCollins (New York), 1994 . . . £10/£5
ditto, HarperCollins (New York), 1994 (500 signed copies, slipcase, no d/w) . . . . . . £50/£35
ditto, HarperCollins (New York), 1994 (26 signed copies, slipcase, no d/w) . . . . . .£125/£75
Sacrament, HarperCollins (London), 1994 . . £10/£5
ditto, HarperCollins (New York), 1996 . . £10/£5
Galilee: A Romance, HarperCollins (New York), 1998 .
. . . . £10/£5
ditto, HarperCollins/Trice (New York), 1998 (26 signed copies, slipcase, no d/w) . . . . £175/£125
ditto, HarperCollins/Trice (New York), 1998 (125 signed copies, slipcase, no d/w) . . . £150/£100
ditto, HarperCollins (London), 1998 . . . £10/£5
Coldheart Canyon: A Hollywood Ghost Story, HarperCollins (London), 2001 . . . . £10/£5
ditto, HarperCollins (New York), 2001 . . . £10/£5
ditto, HarperCollins (New York), 2001 (2,500 signed copies)
. . . . £20/£5

ditto, HarperCollins/Trice (New York), 2001 (26 signed copies, slipcase, no d/w) . . . . . £125/£100
ditto, HarperCollins/Trice (New York), 2001 (150 signed copies, slipcase, no d/w) . . . . .£100/£65
Abarat, HarperCollins (London), 2002 . . . £10/£5
ditto, HarperCollins (New York), 2002. . . . £10/£5
ditto, HarperCollins/Trice (New York), 2002 (175 signed copies, slipcase, no d/w) . . . . .£125/£75
ditto, HarperCollins/Trice (New York), 2002 (50 signed copies with additional artwork, d/w) . £350/£300
Abarat Book Two: Days of Magic, Nights of War, Joanna Cotler/HarperCollins (New York), 2004 . £10/£5
ditto, Trice (New Orleans), 2004 (175 signed, numbered copies, slipcase, no d/w) . . . . £175/£100
ditto, HarperCollins/Trice (New York), 2004 (50 signed copies with additional artwork, d/w) . . £350/£300
ditto, Voyager/HarperCollins (London), 2004 . . £10/£5
Mister B Gone, Harper Voyager (London), 2007 . £10/£5
ditto, Harper Voyager (London), 2007 (1,000 signed copies; slipcase). . . . . £35/£20
ditto, HarperCollins (New York), 2007 . . . £10/£5

Short Stories and Novellas
Books of Blood, Vol. 1, Sphere (London), 1984 (first issue with original covers; pbk) £10
ditto, Sphere (London), 1984 (second issue with Barker designed covers; pbk). £5
ditto, Weidenfeld & Nicolson (London), 1985. . £30/£5
ditto, Weidenfeld & Nicolson (London), 1985 (200 signed, numbered sets with vols 2 and 3, slipcase) . £200/£75
ditto, Berkley Books (New York), 1986 (pbk). . £5
Books of Blood, Vol. 2, Sphere (London), 1984 (first issue with original covers; pbk) £10
ditto, Sphere (London), 1984 (second issue with Barker designed covers; pbk). £5
ditto, Weidenfeld & Nicolson (London), 1985. . £30/£5
ditto, Berkley Books (New York), 1986 (pbk). . . £5
Books of Blood, Vol. 1 and 2, Sphere (London), 1984 . .
. . . . £25/£10
Books of Blood, Vol. 3, Sphere (London), 1984 (first issue with original covers; pbk) £10
ditto, Sphere (London), 1984 (second issue with Barker designed covers; pbk). £5
ditto, Weidenfeld & Nicolson (London), 1985 . £30/£5
ditto, Berkley Books (New York), 1986 (pbk). . . £5
Books of Blood, Vol. 4, Sphere (London), 1985 (first issue with original covers; pbk) £10
ditto, Sphere (London), 1985 (second issue with Barker designed covers; pbk). £5
ditto, Weidenfeld & Nicolson (London), 1985. . £25/£5
ditto, Weidenfeld & Nicolson (London), 1985 (200 signed, numbered sets with vols 5 and 6, slipcase) . .£175/£75
ditto, Poseidon Press (New York), 1986 . . £25/£5
ditto, Scream Press (Santa Cruz, CA), 1987 (333 signed copies, slipcase) . . . . £45/£20
Books of Blood, Vol. 5, Sphere (London), 1985 (first issue with original covers; pbk) £10
ditto, Sphere (London), 1985 (second issue with Barker designed covers; pbk). £5
ditto, Weidenfeld & Nicolson (London), 1985. . £25/£5
ditto, Poseidon Press (New York), 1986 . . £25/£5
ditto, Scream Press (Santa Cruz, CA), 1988 (333 signed copies, slipcase) . . . . £45/£20

Books of Blood, Vol. 4 and 5, Weidenfeld & Nicolson/
Leisure Circle (London), 1985 .   .   .   .   £25/£10
Books of Blood, Vol. 6, Sphere (London), 1985 (first issue
with original covers; pbk) £10
ditto, Sphere (London), 1985 (second issue with Barker
designed covers; pbk). £5
ditto, Weidenfeld & Nicolson (London), 1985.   .   £25/£5
ditto, Scream Press (Santa Cruz, CA), 1991 (333 signed
copies, slipcase) .   .   .   .   .   .   £45/£20
Books of Blood, Vol. 1, 2 and 3, Scream Press (Santa Cruz,
CA), 1985 (250 signed numbered copies, slipcase)   .   .
.   , ...   £125/£100
ditto, Scream Press (Santa Cruz, CA), 1985 (17 signed
lettered copies, slipcase) £200
ditto, Scream Press (Santa Cruz, CA), 1985 (10 signed
copies, slipcase) £200
ditto, Weidenfeld & Nicolson (London), 1987.   .   £15/£5
ditto, Ace/Putnam (New York), 1988.   .   .   £15/£5
In the Flesh, Poseidon Press (New York), 1986   .   £10/£5
The Inhuman Condition, Poseidon Press (New York), 1986
.   .   .   .   £10/£5
Books of Blood, Vol. 4, 5 and 6, Weidenfeld & Nicolson
(London), 1988 .   .   .   .   .   .   £15/£5
The Essential Clive Barker, HarperCollins (London), 1999
.   .   .   .   £10/£5
ditto, HarperCollins (New York), 2000   .   .   £10/£5
Books of Blood, Vol. 1-6, Stealth Press (Lancaster, PA),
2001   .   .   .   .   £25/£5
ditto, Stealth Press (Lancaster, PA), 2001 (500 signed
numbered copies, slipcase)   .   .   .   £100/£65
ditto, Stealth Press (Lancaster, PA), 2001 (52 signed lettered
copies, in wooden box with brass plate).   .   £300/£200
Tapping the Vein, Checker Book Publishing Group
(Centerville, OH), 2002 (comic art adaptations of Barker
stories; hardback; no d/w) £15
ditto, Checker Book Publishing Group (Centerville, OH),
2002 (pbk) £5

Collected Plays
Incarnations, HarperPrism (New York), 1995   .   £10/£5
ditto, HarperCollins (London), 1996.   .   .   £10/£5
Forms Of Heaven, HarperPrism (New York), 1997   £10/£5
ditto, HarperCollins (London), 1998.   .   .   £10/£5

Non-Fiction
Clive Barker's A-Z of Horror, BBC Books (London), 1997
(with Stephen Jones; pbk) £5
ditto, HarperPrism (New York), 1997   .   .   £10/£5
Rare Flesh, Universe (New York), 2003 (with David E.
Armstrong, no d/w) £30
The Hellraiser Chronicles, Titan (London), 2004 (with Peter
Atkins and Stephen Jones; pbk)   .   .   .   £5
Visions Of Heaven & Hell: The Art Of Clive Barker,
Rizzoli (New York), 2005 (hardback; no d/w)   .   . £20

PAT BARKER
(b.1943)

Pat Barker is a novelist, short story writer and historian
who has gained critical acclaim for her First World War
series, the 'Regeneration Trilogy', which documents the
wartime experiences of the poets Siegfried Sassoon and
Wilfred Owen, the psychiatrist W.H.R. Rivers, and the fictional Lt. Billy Prior. *The Ghost Road*, the last book of the
trilogy, won the Booker Prize in 1995.

Novels
Union Street, Virago (London), 1982 (pbk)   .   .   £20
ditto, Virago (London), 1982   .   .   .   . £300/£35
ditto, Putnam (New York), 1983 .   .   .   . £40/£10
Blow Your House Down, Virago (London), 1984 (pbk)   £15
ditto, Virago (London), 1984   .   .   .   . £150/£20
ditto, Putnam (New York), 1984 .   .   .   . £20/£5
The Century's Daughter, Virago (London), 1986 (pbk)   £5
ditto, Virago (London), 1986   .   .   .   . £50/£10
ditto, Putnam (New York), 1986 .   .   .   . £15/£5
ditto, as *Liza's England*, Virago (London) 1990 (pbk)   .   £5
The Man Who Wasn't There, Virago (London), 1989 .   .
.   .   .   .   £15/£5
ditto, Ballantine (New York), 1990 (pbk) .   .   .   £5
Regeneration, Viking (London), 1991   .   . £125/£15
ditto, Dutton (New York), 1992 .   .   .   . £40/£10
The Eye in the Door, Viking (London), 1993 .   . £45/£10
ditto, Dutton (New York), 1994 .   .   .   . £10/£5
The Ghost Road, Viking (London), 1995 .   .   . £45/£10
ditto, Dutton (New York), 1995 .   .   .   . £10/£5
The Regeneration Trilogy, Viking (London), 1996   £10/£5
Another World, Viking (London), 1998 .   .   . £10/£5
ditto, Farrar, Straus & Giroux (New York), 1999   . £10/£5
Border Crossing, Viking (London), 2001.   .   . £10/£5
ditto, Farrar, Straus & Giroux (New York), 2001   . £10/£5
Double Vision, Hamish Hamilton (London), 2003 . £10/£5
ditto, Farrar, Straus & Giroux (New York), 2003   . £10/£5
Life Class, Hamish Hamilton (London), 2007 .   . £10/£5
ditto, Farrar, Straus & Giroux (New York), 2007   . £10/£5

ROBERT BARNARD
(b.1936)

Barnard is the author of many light and entertaining
detective novels. His policemen range from the nonchalant,
aristocratic Perry Trethowan through to the rather more
robust Mike Oddie. Barnard has been a recipient of the
Crime Writer's Association Golden Handcuffs Award, and
has been nominated several times for the Edgar Allan Poe
Award.

'Trethowan' Novels
Sheer Torture, Collins Crime Club (London), 1981   £45/£10
ditto, as *Death by Sheer Torture*, Scribner's (New York),
1982   .   .   .   .   £25/£5
Death and the Princess, Collins Crime Club (London), 1982
.   .   .   .   £30/£10
ditto, Scribner's (New York), 1982 .   .   .   £20/£5
The Missing Brontë, Collins Crime Club (London), 1983.
.   .   .   .   £45/£10

ditto, as *The Case of the Missing Brontë*, Scribner's (New York), 1983 . . . . £20/£5
Bodies, Collins Crime Club (London), 1986 . . £20/£5
ditto, Scribner's (New York), 1986 . . . . £10/£5
Death in Purple Prose, Collins Crime Club (London), 1987 . . . . £20/£5
ditto, as *The Cherry Blossom Corpse*, Scribner's (New York), 1987 . . . . £10/£5

'Charlie Peace' Novels
Death and the Chaste Apprentice, Collins Crime Club (London), 1989 . . . . . . £15/£5
ditto, Scribner's (New York), 1989 . . . . £10/£5
A Fatal Attachment, Bantam (London), 1992 . . £15/£5
ditto, Scribner's (New York), 1992 . . . . £10/£5
A Hovering of Vultures, Bantam (London), 1993 . £15/£5
ditto, Scribner's (New York), 1993 . . . . £10/£5
Bad Samaritan, Collins (London), 1995 . . . £15/£5
ditto, Scribner's (New York), 1995 . . . . £10/£5
The Corpse at the Haworth Tandoori, Collins (London), 1998 . . . . £25/£5
ditto, Scribner's (New York), 1999 . . . . £10/£5
Unholy Dying, Collins (London), 2000 . . . £10/£5
ditto, Scribner's (New York), 2001 . . . . £10/£5
Bones in the Attic, Collins (London), 2001 . . £10/£5
ditto, Scribner's (New York), 2002 . . . . £10/£5

'Oddie' Novel
A City of Strangers, Bantam (London), 1990 . . £15/£5
ditto, Scribner's (New York), 1990 . . . . £10/£5

'Meredith' Novels
Unruly Son, Collins Crime Club (London), 1978 . £75/£10
ditto, as *Death of a Mystery Writer*, Scribner's (New York), 1979 . . . . £10/£5
At Death's Door, Collins Crime Club (London), 1988 . . . . £25/£10
ditto, Scribner's (New York), 1988 . . . . £10/£5

Other Novels
Death of an Old Goat, Collins Crime Club (London), 1974 . . . . £250/£25
ditto, Walker (New York), 1977 . . . . . £75/£15
A Little Local Murder, Collins Crime Club (London), 1976 . . . . £145/£15
ditto, Scribner's (New York), 1983 . . . . £25/£5
Death on the High C's, Collins Crime Club (London), 1977 . . . . £125/£15
ditto, Walker (New York), 1978 . . . . . £75/£10
Blood Brotherhood, Collins Crime Club (London), 1977 . . . . £200/£45
ditto, Walker (New York), 1978 . . . . . £75/£10
Posthumous Papers, Collins Crime Club (London), 1979 . . . . £20/£5
ditto, as *Death of a Literary Widow*, Scribner's (New York), 1980 . . . . £20/£5
Death in a Cold Climate, Collins Crime Club (London), 1980 . . . . £30/£10
ditto, Scribner's (New York), 1981 . . . . £15/£5
Mother's Boys, Collins Crime Club (London), 1981 £30/£10
ditto, as *Death of a Perfect Mother*, Scribner's (New York), 1981 . . . . £15/£5
Little Victims, Collins Crime Club (London), 1983 £30/£10

ditto, as *School for Murder*, Scribner's (New York), 1984 . . . . £15/£5
A Corpse in a Gilded Cage, Collins Crime Club (London), 1984 . . . . £30/£10
ditto, Scribner's (New York), 1984 . . . . £15/£5
Out of the Blackout, Collins Crime Club (London), 1985 . . . . £25/£5
ditto, Scribner's (New York), 1985 . . . . £15/£5
The Disposal of the Living, Collins Crime Club (London), 1985 . . . . £20/£5
ditto, as *Fete Fatale*, Scribner's (New York), 1985 £15/£5
Political Suicide, Collins Crime Club (London), 1986 £20/£5
ditto, Scribner's (New York), 1986 . . . . £10/£5
The Skeleton in the Grass, Collins Crime Club (London), 1987 . . . . £15/£5
ditto, Scribner's (New York), 1988 . . . . £10/£5
A Scandal in Belgravia, Bantam (London), 1991 . £15/£5
ditto, Scribner's (New York), 1991 . . . . £10/£5
Masters of the House, Collins (London), 1994 . £15/£5
ditto, Scribner's (New York), 1994 . . . . £10/£5
No Place of Safety, Collins (London), 1997 . . £15/£5
ditto, Scribner's (New York), 1997 . . . . £10/£5
Touched by the Dead, Collins (London), 1999 . £15/£5
ditto, as *Murder in Mayfair*, Scribner's (New York), 2000 . . . . £10/£5
The Mistress of Alderley, Allison & Busby (London), 2002 . . . . £10/£5
ditto, Scribner's (New York), 2003 . . . . £10/£5
A Cry from the Dark, Allison & Busby (London), 2003 . . . . £10/£5
ditto, Scribner's (New York), 2004 . . . . £10/£5
The Graveyard Position, Allison & Busby (London), 2004 . . . . £10/£5
ditto, Scribner's (New York), 2005 . . . . £10/£5
Dying Flames, Allison & Busby (London), 2005 . £10/£5
ditto, Scribner's (New York), 2006 . . . . £10/£5
A Fall from Grace, Allison & Busby (London), 2005 £10/£5
ditto, Scribner's (New York), 2006 . . . . £10/£5
Last Post, Allison & Busby (London), 2008 . . £10/£5
ditto, Scribner's (New York), 2008 . . . . £10/£5

Short Stories
Death of a Salesperson: And Other Untimely Exits, Collins Crime Club (London), 1989 . . . . . £15/£5
ditto, Scribner's (New York), 1990 . . . . £10/£5
The Habit of Widowhood: And other Murderous Proclivities, Collins (London), 1996 . . . . . £10/£5
ditto, Scribner's (New York), 1996 . . . . £10/£5

Novels Written as 'Bernard Bastable'
To Die like a Gentleman, Macmillan (London), 1993 £15/£5
ditto, St Martin's Press (New York), 1993 . . £15/£5
Too Many Notes, Mr. Mozart, Little, Brown (London), 1995 . . . . £10/£5
ditto, Carroll & Graf (New York), 1995 . . . £10/£5
Dead, Mr. Mozart, Little, Brown (London), 1995 . £10/£5
ditto, St Martin's Press (New York), 1995 . . £10/£5
A Mansion and It's Murder, Carroll & Graf (New York), 1998 . . . . £10/£5

Non-Fiction
Imagery and Theme in the Novels of Dickens, Universitetsforlaget/Humanities Press (Bergen, Norway/New York), 1974 (wraps). £10

Talent to Deceive: An Appreciation of Agatha Christie,
Collins (London)1980 . . . . . £25/£5
ditto, Dodd, Mead & Co (New York), 1980 . . £20/£5
A Short History of English Literature, Blackwell/
Universitets-forlaget (Oxford, UK/Norway), 1984 £40/£10
Emily Brontë, The British Library (London), 2000 (pbk) .
. . . . £10
ditto, O.U.P. (New York), 2000 (pbk) £10
A Brontë Encyclopedia, Blackwell (London), 2007 (with
Louise Barnard) . . . . . . £50/£25

DJUNA BARNES

(b.1892 d.1982)

Djuna Barnes played an important role in the development
of 20th-century Modernist writing, although her books
became collector's items rather than popular successes. Her
novel *Nightwood* became a cult work of modern fiction,
helped by an introduction written by T.S. Eliot. Barnes was
one of the key figures in 1920s and 30s bohemian Paris.

Fiction
*The Book of Repulsive Women; 8 Rhythms and 5 Draw-
ings*, Guido Bruno (New York), 1915 (stapled yellow
printed wraps) £500
ditto, Alicat Bookshop (New York), 1948 (1,000 copies;
stapled brown/black wraps printed in pink and green) £25
A Book, Boni & Liveright (New York), [1923] . £750/£75
ditto, as *A Night among the Horses*, Liveright (New York),
1929 (three stories added) . . . . £300/£50
ditto, as *Spillway*, Faber (London), 1962 . . £25/£10
ditto, as *Spillway*, Harper & Row (New York), 1972 (pbk) .
. . . . £5
Ryder, Liveright (New York), 1928 (3,000 copies). £300/£45
Nightwood, Faber (London), 1936 . . . . £250/£75
ditto, Harcourt, Brace (New York), 1937 . . . £125/£30
Vagaries Malicieux: Two Stories, Hallman (New York),
1974 (500 copies; a few copies issued with d/w) . £100/£25
Smoke and Other Early Stories, Sun & Moon Press (Los
Angeles, CA), 1982 . . . . . £20/£5
Collected Stories, Sun & Moon Press (Los Angeles, CA),
1996 . . . . £10/£5

Plays
The Antiphon, Faber (London), 1958 . . . £40/£10
ditto, Farrar, Straus (New York), 1958 . . . £35/£5
To The Dogs, The Press of the Good Mountain (Rochester,
NY), 1982 (110 copies; accordion-fold, marbled boards,
slipcase). . . . . £100/£65

Others
Ladies Almanack, Titus (Paris), 1928 (pseud 'A Lady of
Fashion', 1,000 copies; pictorial wraps). . . . £250
ditto, Titus (Paris), 1928 (pseud 'A Lady of Fashion', 40
copies on Rives paper; wraps) £600
ditto, Titus (Paris), 1928 (pseud 'A Lady of Fashion', 10
signed copies on Vergé de Vidalon; wraps) . . £2,000
ditto, Harper & Row (New York), 1972 . . . £15/£5
Selected Works, Farrar, Straus (New York), 1962 (contains:
Spillway, *The Antiphon* and *Nightwood*) . . £20/£5
ditto, Faber (London), 1980 . . . . . £15/£5

Creatures in an Alphabet, Dial Press (New York), 1982 .
. . . . £15/£5
Interviews, Sun & Moon Press (Los Angeles, CA), 1986 .
. . . . £15/£5
New York, Sun & Moon Press (Los Angeles, CA), 1989 .
. . . . £15/£5
Poe's Mother, Sun & Moon Press (Los Angeles, CA), 1995
. . . . £15/£5

JULIAN BARNES

(b.1946)

An inventive postmodernist writer, Barnes moves between
genres, probing the boundaries of convention. He has been
twice short-listed for the Booker Prize (for *Flaubert's
Parrot* in 1984 and *England, England* in 1998). He also
writes crime fiction under the pseudonym 'Dan Kavanagh'.

Novels
Metroland, Cape (London), 1980 . . . . £300/£35
ditto, St Martin's Press (New York), 1980 . . £75/£10
Before She Met Me, Cape (London), 1982 . . £50/£10
ditto, McGraw-Hill (New York), 1986 (pbk) . . . £5
Flaubert's Parrot, Cape (London), 1984 . . . £175/£25
ditto, Knopf (New York), 1985 . . . . £15/£5
Staring at the Sun, Cape (London), 1986 . . £10/£5
ditto, London Limited Editions (London), 1986 (150 signed
copies, glassine d/w) . . . . . . £55/£30
ditto, Knopf (New York), 1987 . . . . . £10/£5
A History of the World in 10½ Chapters, Cape (London),
1989 . . . . £15/£5
ditto, Knopf (New York), 1989 . . . . £10/£5
Talking it Over, Cape (London), 1991 . . . £10/£5
ditto, London Limited Editions (London), 1991 (200 signed
copies, glassine d/w) . . . . . . £65/£30
ditto, Knopf (New York), 1991 . . . . £10/£5
Bodlivo Svinche, Obsidian (Bulgaria), 1992 (pbk). . £10
ditto, as *The Porcupine*, Cape (London), 1992 (novella) .
. . . . £10/£5
ditto, Knopf (New York), 1992 . . . . . £10/£5
England, England, Cape (London), 1998 . . £10/£5
ditto, Knopf (New York), 1999 . . . . . £10/£5
Love, etc, Cape (London), 2000 . . . . £10/£5
ditto, Knopf (New York), 2001 . . . . £10/£5
Arthur & George, Cape (London), 2005 (wraparound band
but no d/w) . . . . £15/£5
ditto, Cape (London), 2005 (125 signed, numbered copies,
quarter bound in cloth with patterned boards; slipcase) .
. . . . £250/£200
ditto, Knopf (New York), 2006 . . . . . £10/£5

Novels Written as 'Dan Kavanagh'
Duffy, Cape (London), 1980 . . . . . £45/£10
ditto, Pantheon (New York), 1986 (pbk) . . . £5
Fiddle City, Cape (London), 1981 . . . . £65/£10
ditto, Pantheon (New York), 1986 (pbk) . . . £5
Putting the Boot In, Cape (London), 1985 . . £40/£10
Going to the Dogs, Viking (London), 1987 . . £15/£5
ditto, Pantheon (New York), 1987 . . . . £10/£5
The Duffy Omnibus, Penguin (London), 1991 (pbk) . £5

Short Stories
Cross Channel, Cape (London), 1996 . . . £10/£5
ditto, Cape (London), 1996 (50 special copies, signed and numbered; full leather) £250
ditto, Knopf (New York), 1996 . . . . . £15/£5
Evermore, Palawan (London), 1996 (with 6 etchings by Sir Howard Hodgkin, 50 copies signed by Barnes and Hodgkin with two individual, signed prints in a portfolio) . £2,000
ditto, Palawan (London), 1996 (with 6 etchings by Sir Howard Hodgkin, 150 copies signed by Barnes and Hodgkin, hand-painted wraps and slipcase) . . £1,000
ditto, Penguin (London), 1996 (pbk) £5
The Lemon Table, Cape (London), 2004 . . . £10/£5
ditto, Knopf (New York), 2004 . . . . . £10/£5

Translations
The Truth about Dogs, by Volker Kriegel; Bloomsbury (London), 1988 . . . . £15/£5
ditto, Harper (New York), 1988 . . . . . £15/£5
In the Land of Pain, by Alphonse Daudet; Cape (London), 2002 . . . . £10/£5
ditto, Knopf (New York), 2003 . . . . . £10/£5

Others
Letters from London, 1990-1995, Picador (London), 1995 (pbk) £5
ditto, Vintage (New York), 1995 (pbk) £5
Something to Declare, Picador (London), 2002 (pbk) . £5
ditto, Knopf, 2002 . . . . £10/£5
The Pedant in the Kitchen, Atlantic Books (London), 2003 . . . . £10/£5
Nothing To Be Frightened Of, Cape (London), 2008 £10/£5
ditto, Knopf (New York), 2008 . . . . . £10/£5
ditto, Cape/London Review Bookshop (London), 2008 (100 signed, numbered copies quarter bound in leather; slipcase) £150

J.M. BARRIE
(b.1860 d.1937)

Sir James Matthew Barrie, Bt., O.M., who wrote as J.M. Barrie, was a Scottish novelist and dramatist. He is best known for his creation of Peter Pan, the boy who would never grow up. In 1924, he specified that the copyright of *Peter Pan* should be owned by Great Ormond Street Hospital in London.

Children's Novels
The Little White Bird, Hodder & Stoughton (London), 1902 (first appearance of the Peter Pan character) . . £125
ditto, Scribner's (New York), 1902. . . . . £75
Peter Pan in Kensington Gardens, Hodder & Stoughton (London), 1906 (deluxe edition of 500 copies signed by artist; frontispiece and 49 colour plates by Arthur Rackham; captioned tissue guards; bound in vellum; gilt titles and decoration to upper board and spine; yellow silk ties, top edge gilt but others untrimmed) £4,000
ditto, Hodder & Stoughton (London), 1906 (trade edition) £650
ditto, Scribner's (New York), 1906. . . . . £500

ditto, Hodder & Stoughton (London), 1910 (24 colour plates) £100
ditto, Hodder & Stoughton (London), 1912 (bound in green buckram; 50 colour plates, 12 drawings) . . . £500
ditto, Hodder & Stoughton (London), 1912 (deluxe edition bound in decorative vellum covers; unsigned; 50 colour plates, 12 drawings) £1,250
Peter and Wendy, Hodder & Stoughton (London), 1911 (illustrated by Bedford) £200
ditto, Scribner's (New York), 1911 . . . . . £150
The Peter Pan Portfolio, Hodder & Stoughton (London), [1912] (500 boxed portfolios numbered 101-600, signed by the publishers) £8,000
ditto, Hodder & Stoughton (London), 1912 (approx 20 boxed portfolios signed by the artist) £15,000
ditto, Brentano's (New York), 1912 (300 unsigned boxed portfolios) £2,000

Adult Novels
Better Dead, Swan Sonnenschein & Co (London), 1888 [1887] (yellow wraps lettered in black) . . . £400
ditto, Rand McNally (New York), 1891 (salmon-coloured paper covers lettered in black and red) . . . £150
When a Man's Single, A Tale of Literary Life, Hodder & Stoughton (London), 1888 . . . . . . £40
ditto, Harper (New York), 1889 . . . . . £35
The Little Minister, Cassell (London), 1891 (3 vols) . £300
ditto, Lovell, Coryell & Co. (New York), [1891] . . £40
Sentimental Tommy, Cassell (London), 1896 . . . £35
ditto, Scribner's (New York), 1896 . . . . £30
Tommy and Grizel, Cassell (London), 1900 . . . £25
ditto, Scribner's (New York), 1900 . . . . . £25
Farewell Miss Julie Logan: A Wintry Tale, The Times, December 24, 1931 (large folio, printed wraps, 8 pps) £35
ditto, Hodder & Stoughton (London), 1932 . . £40/£10
ditto, Scribner's (New York), 1932 . . . . £40/£10

Sketches and Short Stories
Auld Licht Idylls, Hodder & Stoughton (London), 1888 . . . . £45
ditto, Macmillan (New York), 1891 . . . . . £45
ditto, Hodder & Stoughton (London), 1895 (50 signed copies of 550 numbered) £200
ditto, Hodder & Stoughton (London), 1895 (500 unsigned copies of 550 numbered) £50
A Window in Thrums, Hodder & Stoughton (London), 1889 . . . . £45
ditto, Cassell (New York), 1892 . . . . . . £40
ditto, as *The Sabbath Day*, Hodder & Stoughton (London), 1895 (issued without wraps, a reprint of the first chapter of *A Window in Thrums*). £35
ditto, as *Jess*, Dana Estes (Boston), 1898 (reprint of the first 16 stories from *A Window in Thrums*) £35
A Holiday in Bed and Other Sketches, New York Publishing Co. (New York), [1892] (wraps) . . . £300
ditto, New York Publishing Co. (New York), [1892] (boards) £40
An Auld Licht Manse, John Knox (New York), [1893] (wraps) £100
ditto, John Knox (New York), [1893] (boards) . £35
Two of Them, Lovell, Coryell & Co. (New York), 1893 (wraps) £75
ditto, Lovell, Coryell & Co. (New York), 1893 (boards) £35

A Tillyloss Scandal, Lovell, Coryell & Co. (New York), 1893 (first issue with address at 43, 45 and 47 East Tenth Street; wraps) £125

ditto, Lovell, Coryell & Co. (New York), 1893 (first issue with address at 43, 45 and 47 East Tenth Street; boards)   .

.   .   .   .£100

ditto, Lovell, Coryell & Co. (New York), 1893 (second issue with address at East 10th Street, boards)   .   .   .£75

A Powerful Drug and Other Stories, Ogilvie (New York), [1893] (wraps) £100

A Lady's Shoe, Brentano's (New York), 1898 (blue/green cloth lettered in gilt and black). £35

Life in a Country Manse, Ogilvie (New York), 1899 (bound with *The Mystery of No.13* by Helen Mathers; wraps).   £50

ditto, Neely (New York), 1899 (wraps)   .   .   .£45

Plays

Richard Savage, privately printed, 1891 (wraps; title-page serves as front cover). £1,500

The Wedding Guest, Scribner's (New York), 1900 (copyright copies) £750

ditto, Fortnightly Review (London), 1900 (supplement to *Fortnightly Review*) £45

Walker, London, French (London), 1907 (wraps)   .   .£75

Quality Street, Hodder & Stoughton (London), 1913   .£40

ditto, Hodder & Stoughton (London), 1913 (1,000 signed copies) £200

Half Hours, Scribner's (New York), 1914   .   .   .£30

ditto, Hodder & Stoughton (London), [1914]   .   .   .£30

The Admirable Crichton, Hodder & Stoughton (London), 1914 (illustrated by Hugh Thompson)   .   .   .£50

ditto, Hodder & Stoughton (London), 1914 (500 copies signed by Thompson). £400

Der Tag, Hodder & Stoughton (London), [1914]   .   .£30

Echoes of the War, Hodder & Stoughton (London), [1918].

.   .   .   .£50

ditto, Scribner's (New York), 1918   .   .   .   .£45

What Every Woman Knows, Hodder & Stoughton (London), [1918] (from the *Uniform Edition*) £20

Alice-Sit-by-the-Fire, Hodder & Stoughton (London), [1919] (from the *Uniform Edition*) £20

A Kiss for Cinderella, Hodder & Stoughton (London), [1920] (from the *Uniform Edition*)   .   .   .£45/£20

ditto, Scribner's (New York), 1920   .   .   .£45/£15

The Twelve Pound Look and Other Plays, Hodder & Stoughton (London), [1921] (from the *Uniform Edition*)   .

.   .   .   .£45/£20

The Old Lady Shows Her Medals, Hodder & Stoughton (London), [1921-2] (from the *Uniform Edition*)   .£35/£10

Dear Brutus, Hodder & Stoughton (London), [1922] (from the *Uniform Edition*)   .   .   .   .   .£45/£15

ditto, Scribner's (New York), 1922   .   .   .£45/£15

Mary Rose, Hodder & Stoughton (London), [1924] (from the *Uniform Edition*).   .   .   .   .   .£45/£15

ditto, Scribner's (New York), 1924   .   .   .£35/£10

Representative Plays, Scribner's (New York), 1926 £25/£10

Plays of J.M. Barrie, Hodder & Stoughton (London), 1928.

.   .   .   .£35/£10

Peter Pan or The Boy Who Would Not Grow Up, Hodder & Stoughton (London), 1928   .   .   .£150/£45

ditto, Scribner's (New York), 1928   .   .   .£125/£40

Shall We Join the Ladies?, Hodder & Stoughton (London), 1929   .   .   .   .£45/£15

The Boy David, Peter Davies (London), 1938 .   .   £15/£5

ditto, Scribner's (New York), 1938   .   .   .   .£15/£5

When Wendy Grew Up: An Afterthought, Nelson (London), 1957   .   .   .   .£25/£10

Others

The New Amphion, David Douglas (Edinburgh), 1886 (contains 'The Scotch Student's Dream' by Barrie, pps.105-117). £200

An Edinburgh Eleven: Pen Portraits from College Life, The 'British Weekly' (London), 1889 (wraps)   .   .£40

My Lady Nicotine, Hodder & Stoughton (London), 1890 £75

ditto, Rand McNally (New York), 1891   .   .   .£65

Jane Annie, Or the Good Conduct Prize, Chappell (London), 1893 (with Sir Arthur Conan Doyle; wraps) £750

Allahakbarrie C. C., privately printed, 1893 (wraps; title-page serves as front cover) £50

Scotland's Lament: A Poem on the Death of Robert Louis Stevenson, December 3rd, 1894, privately printed for T.J. Wise (without wraps, 12 copies) £100

ditto, privately printed for Clement Shorter, 1918 (25 copies; wraps) £45

Margaret Ogilvy, Scribner's (New York), 1896   .   .£25

ditto, Hodder & Stoughton (London), 1896   .   .   .£25

Allahakbarrie Book of Broadway Cricket for 1899, privately printed, (520 copies, Japanese vellum wraps)   .

.   .   .   .£250

The Boy Castaways of Black Lake Island, privately printed, 1901   .   .   .   .£300

George Meredith, Constable (London), 1909   .   .   .£40

ditto, Mosher (Portland, ME), 1909   .   .   .   .£40

ditto, as *Neither Dorking Nor the Abbey* Browne's Bookstore (Chicago, IL), 1910 (wraps)   .   .   .£30

Charles Frohman: A Tribute, privately printed for Clement Shorter (London), 1915 (20 copies).   .   .   .£125

Shakespeare's Legacy, privately printed for Clement Shorter (London), [1916] (25 copies) £125

Who Was Sarah Findlay?, privately printed for Clement Shorter (London), 1917 (25 copies).   .   .   .£125

Courage, Hodder & Stoughton (London), [1922]   .£35/£10

ditto, Scribner's (New York), 1922   .   .   .£30/£10

The Ladies' Shakespeare, privately printed for Clement Shorter (London), [1925] (25 copies)   .   .   .£125

Neil and Tintinnabulum, privately printed, 1925 (52 copies; wraps) £125

The Author, privately printed for Lawson McClung Melish (Cincinnati, OH), 1925 (20 copies).   .   .   .£100

Cricket, privately printed for Clement Shorter (London), 1926 (25 copies) £300

The Entrancing Life, Hodder & Stoughton (London), 1930

.   .   .   .£20

ditto, Scribner's (New York), 1930   .   .   .   .£20

The Greenwood Hat: Being a Memoir of James Anon 1885-1887, Peter Davies (London), 1937   .   .£50/£20

ditto, Scribner's (New York), 1938   .   .   .£50/£20

M'Connachie and JMB: Speeches, Peter Davies (London), 1938   .   .   .   .£35/£10

Letters of J.M. Barrie, Peter Davies, 1942   .   .£35/£10

ditto, as *Letters of James M. Barrie*, Scribner's (New York), 1947   .   .   .   .£35/£10

Collected Editions

Thistle Edition, Scribner's (New York), 1896-1911 (12 vols)

.   .   .   .£75

ditto, Scribner's (New York), 1896-1911 (12 vols, 150 copies on Imperial handmade Japan paper, vol 1 signed) .
. . . . £250
Kirriemur Edition, Hodder & Stoughton (London), 1913 (10 vols, limited to 1,000 sets, the first vol signed) . . £200
Uniform Edition of Plays, Hodder & Stoughton (London), 1918-1924 (11 vols) £200
The Works of J.M. Barrie, Scribner's (New York), 1918 (10 vols) £100
Peter Pan Edition, Scribner's (New York), 1929 (14 vols, 130 signed sets of 1,000) . . . . £1,000/£500
ditto, Scribner's (New York), 1929 (14 vols, 870 unsigned sets of 1,000) . . . . . . £750/£350

JOHN BARTH
(b.1930)

An American novelist and short story writer, Barth's writing balances self-conscious postmodernism with more traditional plots and characterisation. In 1974 Barth was elected to the American Academy of Arts and Letters and the American Academy of Arts and Sciences. He received the F. Scott Fitzgerald Award for Distinguished Achievement in American Fiction in 1997.

Fiction
The Floating Opera, Appleton Century-Crofts (New York), 1956 ('1' in parentheses on last page of book under the last word of text; no reviews on back panel of d/w which is priced $3.95 on front flap). . . . . £200/£30
ditto, Secker & Warburg (London), 1968 . . £25/£10
The End of the Road, Doubleday (Garden City, NY), 1958.
. . . . £200/£50
ditto, Secker & Warburg (London), 1962 . . £45/£10
The Sot-Weed Factor, Doubleday (Garden City, NY), 1960
. . . . £200/£50
ditto, Secker & Warburg (London), 1961 . . £45/£10
ditto, Franklin Library (Franklin Centre, PA), 1960 (signed; full leather) £30
Giles Goat-Boy, or, The Revised New Syllabus, Doubleday (Garden City, NY), 1966 . . . . . £200/£50
ditto, Doubleday (Garden City, NY), 1966 (250 signed, numbered copies; slipcase, no d/w). . . £100/£50
ditto, Secker & Warburg (London), 1967 . . £25/£10
Letters, G.P. Putnam's Sons (New York), 1979 £15/£5
ditto, G.P. Putnam's Sons (New York), 1979 (500 signed, numbered copies; slipcase, no d/w). . . £40/£20
ditto, Secker & Warburg (London), 1980 . . £10/£5
Sabbatical: A Romance, G.P. Putnam's Sons (New York), 1982 . . . . £15/£5
ditto, G.P. Putnam's Sons (New York), 1982 (750 signed, numbered copies; slipcase, no d.w) . . . £35/£15
ditto, Secker & Warburg (London), 1980 . . £10/£5
The Tidewater Tales, G.P. Putnam's Sons (New York), 1987
. . . . £15/£5
ditto, Methuen (London), 1988 . . . . £10/£5
The Last Voyage of Somebody the Sailor, Little, Brown (Boston), 1991 . . . . £10/£5
ditto, Hodder & Stoughton (London), 1991 . . £10/£5
Once upon a Time: A Floating Opera, Little, Brown (Boston), 1994 . . . . £10/£5
ditto, Sceptre (London), 1994 . . . . £10/£5

Coming Soon!!!: A Narrative, Houghton Mifflin (Boston/New York), 2001. . . . . £10/£5
ditto, Atlantic (London), 2002 (pbk) £5

Short Stories
Lost in the Funhouse: Fiction for Print, Tape, Live Voice, Doubleday (Garden City, NY), 1968 . . . £10/£5
ditto, Secker & Warburg (London), 1968 . . . £10/£5
Chimera, Random House (New York), 1972 £10/£5
ditto, Random House (New York), 1972 (300 signed, numbered copies; acetate d/w; slipcase). . . £45/£35
ditto, Andre Deutsch (London), 1974. . . £10/£5
On with the Story, Little, Brown (Boston), 1996 . £10/£5
The Book of Ten Nights and a Night: Eleven Stories, Houghton Mifflin (Boston/New York), 2004 . £10/£5
ditto, Atlantic (London), 2005 . . . . . £10/£5
Where Three Roads Meet, Houghton Mifflin (Boston/New York), 2005 . . . . £10/£5

Others
A Conversation with John Barth, Union College (Schenectady, NY), 1972 (pbk) £10
Todd Andrews to the Author, Lord John (Northridge, CA), 1979 (300 signed, numbered copies; no d/w) . . £30
ditto, Lord John (Northridge, CA), 1979 (50 signed, numbered, leather-bound copies) £50
The Literature of Exhaustion and the Literature of Replenishment, Lord John (Northridge, CA), 1982 (300 signed, numbered copies; no d/w) £30
ditto, Lord John (Northridge, CA), 1982 (100 signed, numbered, copies) £45
Don't Count on It: A Note on the Number of the 1001 Nights, Lord John (Northridge, CA), 1984 (150 signed, numbered copies; no d/w). £30
ditto, Lord John (Northridge, CA), 1984 (50 signed, numbered, copies) £50

Non-Fiction
The Friday Book; Essays & Other Non-Fiction, G.P. Putnam's Sons (New York), 1984 . . . £15/£5
Further Fridays, Little, Brown (Boston), 1995 . £10/£5

DONALD BARTHELME
(b.1931 d.1989)

Barthelme was an American author of rather compact short stories which typically avoid traditional plot structures and rely on an accumulation of seemingly-unrelated detail. The bulk of his work was originally published in *The New Yorker*. He also wrote novels, and worked as a journalist, was director of the Contemporary Arts Museum in Houston, was co-founder of *Fiction*, and a professor at several universities.

Short Stories
Come Back, Dr Caligari, Little, Brown (Boston), 1964 .
. . . . £75/£10
ditto, Little, Brown (Boston), 1964 (signed by author on tipped-in leaf) . . . . £100/£40
ditto, Eyre & Spottiswoode (London), 1965 . £40/£10
Unspeakable Practices, Unnatural Acts, Farrar, Straus & Giroux (New York), 1968 . . . . . £30/£10

ditto, Cape (London), 1969 . . . . . £25/£10
City Life, Farrar, Straus & Giroux (New York), 1970 £20/£5
ditto, Cape (London), 1971 . . . . . £20/£5
Sadness, Farrar, Straus & Giroux (New York), 1972 £15/£5
ditto, Cape (London), 1973 . . . . . £10/£5
Guilty Pleasures, Farrar, Straus and Giroux (New York), 1974 . . . . £10/£5
Amateurs, Farrar, Straus and Giroux (New York), 1976 . . . . £10/£5
Great Days, Farrar, Straus and Giroux (New York), 1979 . . . . £10/£5
ditto, Routledge & Kegan Paul (London), 1979 . £10/£5
Presents, Pressworks (Dallas, TX), 1980 (350 signed, numbered copies; no d/w) £30
ditto, Pressworks (Dallas, TX), 1980 (26 signed, lettered copies; no d/w) £100
Sixty Stories, Putnam (New York), 1981 . . . £10/£5
ditto, Putnam (New York), 1981 (500 signed, numbered copies; no d/w; slipcase) . . . . . £45/£35
ditto, Secker & Warburg (London), 1989 . . . £10/£5
Overnight to Many Distant Cities, Putnam (New York), 1983 . . . . £10/£5
Sam's Bar, Doubleday (New York), 1987 . . £10/£5
Forty Stories, Putnam (New York), 1987 . . . £10/£5
ditto, Secker & Warburg (London), 1988 . . . £10/£5
Flying to America: 45 More Stories, Shoemaker & Hoard (Washington, DC), 2007 . . . . . £10/£5

Novels
Snow White, Atheneum (New York), 1967 . . £50/£10
ditto, Cape (London), 1968 . . . . . £25/£10
The Dead Father, Straus & Giroux (New York), 1975 . .
. . . . £10/£5
ditto, Routledge & Kegan Paul (London), 1977 . £10/£5
Paradise, Putnam (New York), 1986 . . . . £10/£5
The King, Harper (New York), 1990 . . . £10/£5

Others
The Slightly Irregular Fire Engine or the Hithering Thithering Djinn, Farrar, Straus, Giroux (New York), 1971 . . . . £45/£10
She, Codier & Erstrom (New York), 1971 (wraps; exhibition catalgue with text by Barthelme) £20
Robert Morris, Washburn Gallery (New York), 1976 (wraps; exhibition catalgue with text by Barthelme) . . . £20
Here in the Village, Lord John (Northridge, CA), 1978 (275 signed, numbered copies) £45
ditto, Lord John (Northridge, CA), 1978 (50 signed, numbered, copies) £100
Sunny Marge, Toothpaste Press [St Paul, MN], 1980 (125 signed, numbered copies; broadside) . . . £20
ditto, Toothpaste Press [St Paul, MN], 1980 (26 signed, lettered copies; broadside) £45
Bride, Lord John (Northridge, CA), 1980 (150 signed, numbered, copies; two-line poem by William Watson, illustrated by Barthelme) £45
The Emerald, Sylvester & Orphanos (Los Angeles, CA), 1980 (300 signed, numbered copies; no d/w) . . £40
ditto, Sylvester & Orphanos (Los Angeles, CA), 1980 (26 signed, lettered copies; no d/w) £75
The Teachings of Don B.: Satires, Parodies, Fables, Illustrated Stories and Plays of Donald Barthelme, edited by Kim Herzinger, Turtle Bay Books (New York), 1992 .
. . . . £10/£5

Not-Knowing: The Essays and Interviews of Donald Barthelme, Random House (New York), 1997 . £10/£5

H.E. BATES
(b.1906 d.1974)

A British author of popular novels, novellas and short stories, many of which depict life in the rural Midlands of England, and especially his native Northamptonshire. Bates is perhaps best known for the Larkin family novels, including *The Darling Buds of May*, set in Kent. The success of this series was, however, posthumous, following the television adaptation.

Novels
The Two Sisters, Cape (London), 1926 (maroon cloth, blocked in gold on spine, with device on back cover; white endpapers; white d/w lettered in black with illustration in blue, black, white and orange) . . . . £275/£75
ditto, Viking (New York), 1926 (quarter dark green linen cloth, pale green cloth covers flecked with dark green, cream paper label printed in red on spine, top edges dyed green, white endpapers, dated on title-page) . £250/£50
Catherine Foster, Cape (London), 1929 (grey-green rough cloth with muslin-weave pattern printed in brown, spine stamped in gold, white endpapers; white d/w printed in orange and black) . . . . . . £250/£50
ditto, Viking (New York), 1929 (quarter black cloth, green cloth sides, title lettered within ornamental border in silver on front, lettering on spine in silver; top edge dyed red, white endpapers, dated on title-page, illustrated d/w in green, orange, black and white) . . . £225/£45
Charlotte's Row, Cape (London), 1931 (blue cloth lettered on spine in gold, white endpapers, white d/w lettered in black with vignette) . . . . . . £85/£35
ditto, Cape (London), 1931 (107 signed, numbered copies, marbled boards, white endpapers) £125
ditto, Viking (New York), 1931 (black cloth, spine lettered in gold, top edge dyed black, white endpapers; yellow d/w printed in black) . . . . £85/£35
The Fallow Land, Cape (London), 1932 (olive green cloth, spine lettered in red, white endpapers, illustrated d/w printed in green and black) . . . . £75/£20
ditto, Ballou (New York), 1933 . . . . . £75/£15
The Poacher, Cape (London), 1935 (brown cloth lettered in green on front cover and spine, white endpapers, green d/w with white lettering and black & white illustration) . .
. . . . £75/£20
ditto, Macmillan (New York), 1935 (fine green cloth stamped in gold and black on front and spine; d/w printed in black, orange, blue and white) . . . . £65/£15
A House of Women, Cape (London), 1936 (pale green cloth lettered on front and spine in blue; white endpapers. d/w printed purple, white and black) . . . . £125/£20
ditto, Henry Holt (New York), 1936 (green cloth lettered on front and spine in black, top edge dyed green, white endpapers, d/w in white, black and green) . £100/£15
'Spella Ho', Cape (London), 1938 (tourquoise cloth lettered in gilt, top edge dyed green, white endpapers, d/w in white black, orange and yellow) . . . . . £100/£15
ditto, Little, Brown (Boston), 1938 . . . . £85/£10

Fair Stood the Wind for France, Joseph (London), 1944 . . . . £45/£10
ditto, Little, Brown (Boston), 1944 . . . £40/£10
The Cruise of the 'Breadwinner', Joseph (London), 1946 . . . . £45/£150
The Purple Plain, Joseph (London), 1947 . £45/£10
ditto, Little, Brown (Boston), 1947 . . . £45/£10
The Jacaranda Tree, Joseph (London) [1949] . £40/£10
ditto, Little, Brown (Boston), 1949 . . . £40/£10
The Scarlet Sword, Joseph (London), 1950 . £30/£5
ditto, Little, Brown (Boston), 1951 . . . £30/£5
Love for Lydia, Joseph (London), 1952 . . £25/£5
ditto, Little, Brown (Boston), 1952 . . . £25/£5
The Feast of July, Joseph (London), 1954 . £25/£5
ditto, Little, Brown (Boston), 1954 . . . £20/£5
The Sleepless Moon, Joseph (London), 1956 . . £25/£5
ditto, Little, Brown (Boston), 1956 . . . £20/£5
The Darling Buds of May, Joseph (London), 1958 £45/£15
ditto, Little, Brown (Boston), 1958 . . . £40/£10
A Breath of French Air, Joseph (London), 1959 . £40/£10
ditto, Little, Brown (Boston), 1959 . . . £35/£10
When the Green Woods Laugh, Joseph (London), 1960 . . . . £25/£5
The Day of the Tortoise, Joseph (London), 1961 . £30/£5
The Crown of Wild Myrtle, Joseph (London), 1962 £15/£5
ditto, Farrar, Straus Giroux (New York), 1963 . £15/£5
Oh! to be in England, Joseph (London), 1963 . £25/£10
ditto, Farrar, Straus Giroux (New York), 1964. . £20/£5
A Moment in Time, Joseph (London), 1964 . . £15/£5
ditto, Farrar, Straus Giroux (New York), 1964. . £15/£5
The Distant Horns of Summer, Joseph (London), 1967 . . . . £15/£5
A Little of What You Fancy, Joseph (London), 1970 . . . . £25/£10
The Triple Echo, Joseph (London), 1970 . . £15/£5

Novellas and Short Stories

The Spring Song, and In View of the Fact That ... Two Stories, Archer (London), 1927 (100 numbered, signed copies, violet and yellow marbled wraps) . . . £200
ditto, Lantern Press (San Francisco, CA), 1927 (50 signed copies) £250
Day's End and Other Stories, Cape (London), 1928 (green cloth, shot with yellow, spine lettered in gold) . £125/£30
ditto, Viking (New York), 1928 . . . . . £65/£15
Seven Tales and Alexander, Scholartis Press (London), 1929 (full blue cloth binding, 50 signed copies of an edition of 1,000) £200
ditto, Scholartis Press (London), 1929 (quarter blue cloth and cream paper boards, spine lettered in gold, cream d/w lettered in blue, 950 unsigned copies of an edition of 1,000) . . . . £75/£30
ditto, Viking (New York), 1930 . . . . . £65/£30
The Hessian Prisoner, Furnival Books (London), 1930 (550 signed copies) £100
The Tree, A Story, Blue Moon Booklets (London), 1930 (blue wraps lettered in black) £50
ditto, Blue Moon Booklets (London), 1930 (100 large paper copies, printed on vellum, white wraps lettered black) £125
Mrs. Esmond's Life, privately printed by E.H. Lahr (London), 1931 (300 signed copies) £75
ditto, privately printed by E.H. Lahr (London), 1931 (50 signed copies, leaf of manuscript bound in) . . . £250

A German Idyll, Golden Cockerel Press (Waltham St Lawrence, Berks), 1932 (307 signed copies). . . £150
The Black Boxer, Pharos Editions (London), 1932 (100 signed copies) £145
ditto, Pharos Editions (London), 1932 . . £100/£25
Sally Go Round the Moon, White Owl Press (London), 1932 . . . . £50/£15
ditto, White Owl Press (London), 1932 (129 signed copies). £125
ditto, White Owl Press (London), 1932 (21 signed copies, with leaf of manuscript bound in) £250
The Story Without an End and The Country Doctor, White Owl Press (London), 1932. . . . . . £50/£15
ditto, White Owl Press (London), 1932 (105 signed copies) £150
ditto, White Owl Press (London), 1932 (25 signed copies, leaf of manuscript bound in) £325
The House with the Apricot and Two Other Tales, Golden Cockerel Press (Waltham St Lawrence, Berks), 1933 (300 signed copies) £200
The Woman Who Had Imagination, Cape (London), 1934. . . . . £100/£25
ditto, Macmillan (New York), 1934 . . . £75/£20
Thirty Tales, Cape, Traveller's Library (London), 1934 . . . . £15/£5
The Duet, A Story, Grayson & Grayson (London), 1935 (285 signed copies) . . . . £150/£65
Cut and Come Again: Fourteen Stories, Cape (London), 1935 . . . . £125/£30
Something Short and Sweet, Cape (London), 1937 £100/£25
Country Tales, Readers Union (London), 1938 (tissue jacket) . . . . £40/£30
ditto, Cape (London), 1940 (the story 'The Palace' is replaced by 'The Captain') . . . . . £45/£15
My Uncle Silas, Cape (London), 1939 (illustrated by Edward Ardizzone) . . . . £150/£45
ditto, Graywolf Press (Port Townsend, WA), 1984. £25/£10
The Flying Goat, Cape (London), 1939 . . £125/£25
The Beauty of the Dead and Other Stories, Cape (London), 1940 . . . . £100/£25
The Greatest People in the World, Cape (London), 1942 (pseud 'Flying Officer "X"') . . . . . £45/£15
ditto, as *There's Something in the Air*, Knopf (New York), 1943 . . . . £45/£15
How Sleep the Brave and other Stories, Cape (London), 1943 (pseud 'Flying Officer "X"') . . . . £40/£15
The Bride Comes to Evensford, Cape (London), 1943 . . . . £100/£25
The Daffodil Sky, Joseph (London), 1943 . £40/£10
Thirty-One Selected Tales, Cape (London), 1947 . £20/£5
Dear Life, Little, Brown (Boston), 1949 . . £30/£10
ditto, Joseph (London), 1950 . . . . £30/£10
Colonel Julian and Other Stories, Joseph (London), 1951 . . . . £30/£10
ditto, Little, Brown (Boston), 1952 . . . £30/£10
Twenty Tales, Cape (London), 1951 . . . £15/£5
The Nature of Love, Joseph (London), 1953 . £30/£10
ditto, Little, Brown (Boston), 1954 . . . £30/£10
Sugar for the Horse, Joseph (London), 1957 . £35/£10
Death of a Huntsman, Joseph (London), 1957 . £35/£10
ditto, as *Summer in Salandar*, Little, Brown (Boston), 1957 . . . . £25/£5
The Watercress Girl and other Stories, Joseph (London), 1959 . . . . £35/£10

ditto, Little, Brown (Boston), 1959 . . . . £30/£5
An Aspidistra in Babylon: Four Novellas, Joseph (London), 1960 . . . . £25/£10
Now Sleeps the Crimson Petal and Other Stories, Joseph (London), 1961 . . . . . . £25/£5
The Golden Oriole: Five Novellas, Joseph (London), 1962 .
. . . . £25/£5
ditto, Little, Brown (Boston), 1962 . . . £20/£5
Seven by Five: Stories 1926-1961, Joseph (London), 1963 .
. . . . £20/£10
ditto, as *The Best of H.E. Bates*, Little, Brown (Boston), 1963 . . . . £15/£5
The Fabulous Mrs V., Joseph (London), 1964 . £20/£5
The Wedding Party, Joseph (London), 1965 . . £20/£5
The Wild Cherry Tree, Joseph (London), 1968 . £20/£5
The Four Beauties, Joseph (London), 1968 . . £20/£5
The Song of the Wren, Joseph (London), 1972 . £15/£5
The Yellow Meads of Asphodel, Joseph (London), 1976 .
. . . . £15/£5
A Month by the Lake & Other Stories, New Directions (Norfolk, CT), 1987 . . . . . £20/£5
Elephants Nest in a Rhubarb Tree & Other Stories, New Directions (Norfolk, CT), 1989 . . . £20/£5

Plays
The Last Bread, Labour Publishing Co. (London), 1926 (buff stapled wraps printed in blue; dated copyright page).
. . . . £65
The Day of Glory, Joseph (London), 1945 . £50/£10

Children's Titles
The Seekers, Bumpus (London), 1926 (tissue jacket) £35/£15
The Seasons and the Gardener, C.U.P. (Cambridge, UK), 1940 . . . . £75/£25
Achilles the Donkey, Dobson Books (London), 1962 £75/£20
ditto, Franklin-Watts (New York), 1963 . . £65/£15
Achilles and Diana, Dobson Books (London), 1963 £75/£20
ditto, Franklin-Watts (New York), 1963 . . £65/£15
Achilles and the Twins, Dobson Books (London), 1964 .
. . . . £75/£20
ditto, Franklin-Watts (New York), 1964 . . £65/£15
The White Admiral, Dobson Books (London), 1968 £35/£10

Poetry
Song for December, privately printed by Charles Lahr (London), 1928 (single sheet folded; white card printed with green text) £125
Christmas 1930, privately printed by E. & Charles Lahr (London), 1930 (single sheet folded; white card printed with blue and black text) £125
Holly and Sallow, Blue Moon (London), 1931 (100 numbered, signed copies, single sheet folded) . £125

Autobiography
The Vanished World, Joseph (London), 1969 . . £30/£5
ditto, Univ of Missouri Press (Columbia, MO), 1969 £30/£5
The Blossoming World, Joseph (London), 1971 . £20/£5
ditto, Univ of Missouri Press (Columbia, MO), 1971 £20/£5
The World in Ripeness, Joseph (London),1972 . £20/£5
ditto, Univ of Missouri Press (Columbia, MO), [1972] . .
. . . . £15/£5

Others
A Threshing Day, Foyle (London), 1931 (300 signed copies)
. . . . £75
Flowers and Faces, Golden Cockerel Press (Waltham St Lawrence, Berks), 1935 (325 signed copies; engravings by John Nash) £300
ditto, Golden Cockerel Press (Waltham St Lawrence, Berks), 1935 (60 copies signed by the author, with an extra set of the 4 full-page wood-engravings, each signed by John Nash) £2,000
Through the Woods: The English Woodland - April to April, Gollancz (London), 1936 . . . £100/£45
ditto, Macmillan (New York), 1936 . . . £65/£25
Down the River, Gollancz (London), 1937 . £65/£25
ditto, Henry Holt & Co. (New York), 1937 . £35/£10
The Modern Short Story, Nelson (London), 1940 . £40/£10
You Have Seen Their Faces, H.M.S.O. (London), 1941 (anonymous; stapled wraps) £35
In the Heart of the Country, Country Life (London), 1942 (illustrated by Tunnicliffe) . . . £75/£25
O More Than Happy Countryman, Country Life (London), 1943 (illustrated by Tunnicliffe) . . . £45/£15
Country Life, Penguin Books (Harmondsworth, Middlesex), 1943 (pbk) £5
There's Freedom in the Air: The Official Story of the Allied Air Forces from the Occupied Countries, H.M.S.O. (London), 1944 (anonymous; stapled wraps) . £30
Night Battle of Britain, H.M.S.O. (London), 1944 (anonymous; stapled wraps) . . . £30
The Tinkers of Elstow: The Story of the Royal Ordnance Factory, privately printed, 1946 (300 signed, numbered copies) £150
ditto, Bemrose & Sons (London), 1946 (no d/w) . £40
The Country Heart, Joseph (London), 1949 . £45/£10
Edward Garnett, Parrish (London), 1950 . . £35/£10
Flower Gardening, C.U.P. (Cambridge, UK), 1950 (stapled wraps) £10
The Country of White Clover, Joseph (London), 1952 £35/£5
ditto, Joseph (London), 1952 (100 signed copies) . £175
The Face of England, Batsford Ltd (London), 1952 £25/£5
Pastoral on Paper, Medway Corrugated Paper Co. (Maidstone, Kent), [1956] (slipcase and d/w) . £125/£35
A Love of Flowers, Joseph (London), 1971 . . £15/£5
Fountain of Flowers, Joseph (London), 1974 . . £15/£5

L. FRANK BAUM
(b.1856 d.1919)

An American author who had a varied career until he started to write for children with *Mother Goose in Prose*. Three years later he brought out the classic *The Wonderful Wizard of Oz*. In this and its 13 sequels, Baum was attempting to write fantasies with distinctly American origins.

'Oz' Books
The Wonderful Wizard of Oz, George M. Hill Co. (Chicago & New York), 1900 (illustrated by W.W. Denslow; green cloth; first issue with publisher's ads enclosed in a box on p.2 and at end of book, and with an 11-line colophon; publisher's imprint at base of spine stamped in green) .
. . . . £15,000

ditto, George M. Hill Co. (Chicago & New York), 1900 (second issue with no box around ads, colophon of 13 lines, and imprint stamped in red) £10,000

ditto, as *The New Wizard of Oz*, Bobbs-Merrill (Indianapolis, IN), [1903] £750

ditto, Hodder & Stoughton (London), 1906 . . £1,250

The Marvellous Land of Oz, Reilly & Britton Co. (Chicago), 1904 (first issue without 'Published July, 1904', although has 1904 on title page; first state in green boards) £3,500

ditto, Reilly & Britton Co. (Chicago), 1904 (second issue with date on copyright page; first state in green boards) .
. . . . £2,000

ditto, Reilly & Britton Co. (Chicago), 1904 (first edition, second state in red boards) £1,750

ditto, Reilly & Britton Co. (Chicago), 1904 (with title on cover shortened to *The Land of Oz*). £200

ditto, Revell (New York), 1906 (copyright edition) £1,000

ditto, Hodder & Stoughton (London), 1906 . . .£400

Ozma of Oz, Reilly & Britton Co. (Chicago), 1907 (first issue with illustration on p.221 in colour; spine imprint 'The Reilly & Britton Co.') £650

ditto, Reilly & Britton Co. (Chicago), 1907 (second issue with spine imprint 'Reilly & Britton') £350

ditto, Hutchinson (London), 1942 . . . .£100/£25

Dorothy and the Wizard in Oz, Reilly & Britton Co. (Chicago), 1908 (first issue, with 'The Reilly & Britton Co.' at bottom of spine) £1,000

ditto, Reilly & Britton Co. (Chicago), 1908 (second issue, with 'Reilly & Britton' at bottom of spine) . . £1,000

The Road to Oz, Reilly & Britton Co. (Chicago), 1909 (first 2 pages of ads at end with colour-tinted text sheets; later printings have an ad for *Rinkitink in Oz* (1916), on verso of ownership page) £800

The Emerald City of Oz, Reilly & Britton Co. (Chicago), 1910 . . . . £1,000

The Patchwork Girl of Oz, Reilly & Britton Co. (Chicago), 1913 (first state with light green pictorial cloth; the 'C' in chapter 3 touching text) £1,000

ditto, Reilly & Britton Co. (Chicago), 1913 (second state with tan cloth and correction made) . . .£600

Tik-Tok of Oz, Reilly & Britton Co. (Chicago), 1914 .£750

The Scarecrow of Oz, Reilly & Britton Co. (Chicago), 1915
. . . .£500

Rinkitink in Oz, Reilly & Britton Co. (Chicago), 1916 .£500

The Lost Princess of Oz, Reilly & Britton Co. (Chicago), 1917 . . . .£450

The Tin Woodman of Oz, Reilly & Britton Co. (Chicago), 1918 . . . .£450

The Magic of Oz, Reilly & Britton Co. (Chicago), 1919 £400

Glinda of Oz, Reilly & Britton Co. (Chicago), 1920 .£400

'Little Wizard' Books

(First issues in wraps stapled at centre, printed on semi-glossy paper with shadowed areas below the lion and tiger on endpapers printed in solid blue. Second issues have half the value and are printed on slightly rough wove paper stock with shadowed area in blue halftone stipple)

The Cowardly Lion and the Hungry Tiger, Reilly & Britton Co. (Chicago), 1913 . . . .£125

Little Dorothy and Toto, Reilly & Britton Co. (Chicago), 1913 . . . .£125

Tik-Tok and the Nome King, Reilly & Britton Co. (Chicago), 1913 . . . .£125

Ozma and the Little Wizard, Reilly & Britton Co. (Chicago), 1913 . . . .£125

ditto, as *Princess Ozma of Oz*, Hutchinson (London), 1942 .
. . . .£50

Jack Pumpkinhead and the Sawhorse, Reilly & Britton Co. (Chicago), 1913 . . . .£125

The Scarecrow and the Tin Woodman, Reilly & Britton Co. (Chicago), 1913 . . . .£125

ditto, as *Scarecrow and the Tin Woodman of Oz*, Hutchinson (London), 1942 . . . . . .£50

Little Wizard Stories of Oz, Reilly & Britton Co. (Chicago), 1914 (all the *Little Wizard* titles collected; first state in yellow cloth with colour pictorial label on front cover; one inch thick) £400

Other 'Oz' Titles

Pictures from the 'Wonderful Wizard of Oz', Ogilvie (New York), [1903] (illustrated stiff pictorial card covers) .£250

Denslow's Scarecrow and the Tin Man, Dillingham (New York), 1904 (wraps) £250

The Woggle-Bug Book, Reilly & Britton Co. (Chicago), 1905 (first state with front cover printed in colours, background field of grey-green, no printing on back cover)
. . . . £1,000

ditto, Reilly & Britton Co. (Chicago), 1905 (second state front cover background field of pale-yellow and yellow lettering on back cover) £750

The Oz Toy Book: Cut Outs for the Kiddies, Reilly & Britton Co. (Chicago), 1915 . . . . .£500

The Land of Oz Story Book, Hutchinson (London), 1941 £75

Other Titles

Mother Goose in Prose, Way & Williams (Chicago, IL), [1897] (first issue with gatherings of 8 and 4 leaves at end concluding on p.268) £3,000

ditto, Duckworth (London), 1899 . . . .£750

Father Goose, His Book, George M. Hill (Chicago, IL), 1899 . . . . £3,000

ditto, Werner (London), 1899 . . . . . £1,500

A New Wonderland, Russell (New York), 1900 . £2,000

ditto, Russell (New York), 1900 (second binding with blank endpapers) £1,000

ditto, as *The Surprising Adventures of the Magical Monarch of Mo and His People*, Bobbs-Merrill (Indianapolis, IN), [1903] £750

The Army Alphabet, George M. Hill (Chicago, IL), 1900 (pictorial boards). £1,000

The Navy Alphabet, George M. Hill (Chicago, IL), 1900 .
. . . . £1,000

American Fairy Tales, George M. Hill (Chicago, IL), 1901 .
. . . .£500

Dot and Tot of Merryland, George M. Hill (Chicago, IL), 1901 . . . .£750

The Master Key: An Electrical Fairy Tale, Bobbs-Merrill (Indianapolis, IN), 1901 (first issue with signatures of 8 pages and second line on copyright page $1^{21}/_{32}$ inches wide)
. . . .£350

ditto, Bobbs-Merrill (Indianapolis, IN), 1901 (second issue with signatures of 16 pages) £250

ditto, Bobbs-Merrill (Indianapolis, IN), 1901 (third issue with second line on copyright page $1^{25}/_{32}$ inches wide) £100

ditto, Stevens & Brown (London), [1902]. . . .£500

The Life and Adventures of Santa Claus, Bobbs-Merrill (Indianapolis, IN), 1902 (first state with headings 'Book First', 'Book Second' and 'Book Third'.) . . £1,000 *ditto*, Bobbs-Merrill (Indianapolis, IN), 1902 (second state with headings 'Youth', 'Manhood' and 'Old Age') . £650

ditto, Stevens & Brown (London), 1902 . . . . £850

The Enchanted Island of Yew, Bobbs-Merrill (Indianapolis, IN), [1903] (first state with Braunworth's imprint on copyright page, and illustration on page 238 incorrectly positioned over text) £600

Queen Zixi of Ix, Century (New York), 1905 (first state with terra-cotta and black text illustrations on pps.169-236) £750

ditto, Century (New York), 1905 (second state with illustrations in turquoise and black on pps.169-84 and 221-36) £450

ditto, Hodder & Stoughton (London), 1905 . . . £500

John Dough and The Cherub, Reilly & Britton Co. (Chicago), 1906 . . . . £600

ditto, Reilly & Britton Co. (Chicago), 1906 (with John Dough Mystery form). £700

ditto, Constable (London), 1906 . . . . . £500

The Last Egyptian: A Romance of the Nile, Reilly & Britton Co. (Chicago), 1908 . . . . . . £300

ditto, Sisley's (London), 1908 . . . . . £300

The Daring Twins: A Story for Young Folk, Reilly & Britton Co. (Chicago), 1911 . . . . . £150

The Sea Fairies, Reilly & Britton Co. (Chicago), 1911 (first issue with three heads on cover label) . . . £500

ditto, Reilly & Britton Co. (Chicago), 1911 (second issue has cover label showing girl on a sea horse). . . £500

Sky Island, Reilly & Britton Co. (Chicago), 1912 . £400

Phoebe Daring: A Story for Young Folk, Reilly & Britton Co. (Chicago), 1912 . . . . . . £125

Written as As Edith Van Dyne

Aunt Jane's Nieces, Reilly & Britton Co. (Chicago), 1906 £65

Aunt Jane's Nieces Abroad, Reilly & Britton Co. (Chicago), 1906 . . . . £60

Aunt Jane's Nieces at Millville, Reilly & Britton Co. (Chicago), 1908 . . . . £25

Aunt Jane's Nieces at Work, Reilly & Britton Co. (Chicago), 1906 . . . . £25

Aunt Jane's Nieces in Society, Reilly & Britton Co. (Chicago), 1910 . . . . £20

Aunt Jane's Nieces and Uncle John, Reilly & Britton Co. (Chicago), 1911 . . . . £20

The Flying Girl, Reilly & Britton Co. (Chicago), 1911 . £75

Aunt Jane's Nieces on Vacation, Reilly & Britton Co. (Chicago), 1912 . . . . £20

The Flying Girl and Her Chum, Reilly & Britton Co. (Chicago), 1912 . . . . £75

Aunt Jane's Nieces on the Ranch, Reilly & Britton Co. (Chicago), 1913 . . . . £20

Aunt Jane's Nieces Out West, Reilly & Britton Co. (Chicago), 1914 . . . . £20

Aunt Jane's Nieces in the Red Cross, Reilly & Britton Co. (Chicago), 1915 . . . . £20

Mary Louise, Reilly & Britton Co. (Chicago), 1916 . £75

Mary Louise in the Country, Reilly & Britton Co. (Chicago), 1916 . . . . £45

Mary Louise Solves a Mystery, Reilly & Britton Co. (Chicago), 1917 . . . . £50

Mary Louise and the Liberty Girls, Reilly & Britton Co. (Chicago), 1918 . . . . £45

Mary Louise Adopts a Soldier, Reilly & Britton Co. (Chicago), 1919 (ghostwritten, based on a fragment by Baum) £45

Written as Floyd Akers

Sam Steele's Adventures on Land and Sea, by Capt. Hugh Fitzgerald, Reilly & Britton Co. (Chicago), 1906. . £250

ditto, as **The Boy Fortune Hunters in Alaska**, Reilly & Britton Co. (Chicago), 1906 . . . . . £150

The Boy Fortune Hunters in Panama, Reilly & Britton Co. (Chicago), 1907 . . . . £125

The Boy Fortune Hunters in Egypt, Reilly & Britton Co. (Chicago), 1908 . . . . £100

The Boy Fortune Hunters in China, Reilly & Britton Co. (Chicago), 1909 . . . . £100

The Boy Fortune Hunters in Yucatan, Reilly & Britton Co. (Chicago), 1910 . . . . £100

The Boy Fortune Hunters in the South Seas, Reilly & Britton Co. (Chicago), 1911 . . . . . £100

Written as Schuyler Staunton

The Fate of a Crown, Reilly & Britton Co. (Chicago), 1905 . . . . £65

Daughters of Destiny, Reilly & Britton Co. (Chicago), 1906 . . . . £50

Written as John Estes Cooke

Tamawaca Folks: A Summer Comedy, Tamawaca Press (Cicago), 1907 . . . . £500

Written as Suzanne Metcalf

Annabel, A Story for Young Folks, Reilly & Britton Co. (Chicago), 1906 . . . . £650

Written as Laura Bancroft

Mr Woodchuck, Reilly & Britton Co. (Chicago), 1906 . £200

Twinkle's, Reilly & Britton Co. (Chicago), 1906 . . £200

Sugar Loaf Mountain, Reilly & Britton Co. (Chicago), 1906 . . . . £200

Prince Mudturtle, Reilly & Britton Co. (Chicago), 1906 . . . . £200

Bandit Jim Crow, Reilly & Britton Co. (Chicago), 1906 . . . . £200

Prairie Dog Town, Reilly & Britton Co. (Chicago), 1906 . . . . £200

Policeman Bluejay, Reilly & Britton Co. (Chicago), 1907 . . . . £200

'BB'

(b.1905 d.1990)

'BB' was the pseudonym used by Denys James Watkins-Pitchford, an author and illustrator of countryside books for both adults and children. His career began when he obtained the position of Art Master at Rugby School, during which time he wrote his first book, *Wild Lone*. It was an immediate success and invited comparisons with the writing of Henry Williamson. While his books were written under the name 'BB', he always signed his illustrations with his real name.

Adult Books Written and Illustrated by 'BB'

The Sportsman's Bedside Book, Eyre & Spottiswoode (London), 1937 . . . . . . £200/£45

The Countryman's Bedside Book, Eyre & Spottiswoode (London), 1941 . . . . . . £125/£30

The Idle Countryman, Eyre & Spottiswoode (London), 1943
. . . . £50/£15
The Fisherman's Bedside Book, Eyre & Spottiswoode
(London), 1945 . . . . £125/£25
ditto, Scribner's (New York), 1946 . . . . £75/£25
The Wayfaring Tree, Hollis & Carter (London), 1945 . .
. . . . £50/£15
The Shooting Man's Bedside Book, Eyre & Spottiswoode
(London), 1948 . . . . . . £100/£25
ditto, Scribner's (New York), 1948 . . £65/£20
A Stream in Your Garden, Eyre & Spottiswoode (London),
1948 . . . . £35/£15
Be Quiet and Go A-Angling, Lutterworth Press (London),
1949 (pseud 'Michael Traherne') . . . £400/£150
Confessions of a Carp Fisher, Eyre & Spottiswoode
(London), 1950 . . . . £250/£75
Letters from Compton Deverell, Eyre & Spottiswoode
(London), 1950 . . . . . . £45/£15
Tide's Ending, Hollis & Carter (London), 1950 . £175/£50
ditto, Scribner's (New York), 1950 . . . £150/£45
Dark Estuary, Hollis & Carter (London), 1953 . £175/£50
A Carp Water (Wood Pool), Putnam (London), 1958 . .
. . . . £500/£100
ditto, as *Wood Pool*, Meddlar Press, 1996 (77 copies bound
in leather) £400
Autumn Road to the Isles, Kaye (London), 1959 . £60/£15
The White Road Westward, Kaye (London), 1961 . £60/£15
The September Road to Caithness, Kaye (London), 1962 .
. . . . £60/£15
Pegasus Book of the Countryside, Hamish Hamilton
(London), 1964 . . . . . . £750/£150
The Summer Road to Wales, Kaye (London), 1964 . .
. . . . £60/£15
A Summer on the Nene, Kaye (London), 1967 . £125/£35
dtto, Little Egret Press (Port Eliot, Cornwall), 2005 (570 of
600 copies) . . . . £25/£10
dtto, Little Egret Press (Port Eliot, Cornwall), 2005 (30
copies bound in leather) £250
Recollections of a Longshore Gunner, Boydell Press
(London), 1976 . . . . . . £100/£25
A Child Alone: The Memoirs of 'BB', Joseph (London),
1978 . . . . £100/£35
Ramblings of a Sportsman-Naturalist, Joseph (London),
1979 . . . . £65/£20
The Naturalist's Bedside Book, Joseph (London), 1980 .
. . . . £45/£15
The Quiet Fields, Joseph (London), 1981. . . £65/£15
Indian Summer, Joseph (London), 1984 . . . £75/£15
The Best of 'BB', Joseph (London), 1985 . . £65/£15
Fisherman's Folly, Boydell Press (London), 1987 (pbk) £25
dtto, Little Egret Press (Port Eliot, Cornwall), 2003 (570 of
600 copies) . . . . £25/£10
dtto, Little Egret Press (Port Eliot, Cornwall), 2003 (30
copies bound in leather) £250

Children's Books Written and Illustrated by 'BB'
Wild Lone: The Story of a Pytchley Fox, Eyre &
Spottiswoode (London), 1938 . . . . £150/£40
ditto, Scribner's (New York), 1938 . . . £145/£40
Manka, The Sky Gipsy, Eyre & Spottiswoode (London),
1939 . . . . £150/£40
The Little Grey Men: A Story for the Young in Heart, Eyre
& Spottiswoode (London), 1942 (without colour plates) .
. . . . £200/£40

ditto, Eyre & Spottiswoode (London), 1946 (8 colour plates)
. . . . £200/£50
ditto, Scribner's (New York), 1949 . . . £175/£50
Brendon Chase, Hollis & Carter (London), 1944 . £225/£25
ditto, Scribner's (New York), 1945 . . . £125/£25
Down the Bright Stream, Eyre & Spottiswoode (London),
[1948] . . . . £250/£50
ditto, as *The Little Grey Men Go Down the Bright Stream*,
Methuen (London), 1977 . . . . . £35/£10
BB's Fairy Book: Meeting Hill, Hollis & Carter (London),
1948 . . . . £250/£50
The Wind in the Wood, Hollis & Carter (London), 1952 .
. . . . £200/£50
The Forest of Boland Light Railway, Eyre & Spottiswoode
(London), 1955 . . . . . . £125/£25
Monty Woodpig's Caravan, Ward, 1957 . . . £400/£75
Ben the Bullfinch, Hamish Hamilton (London), 1957 . .
. . . . £400/£75
Wandering Wind, Hamish Hamilton (London), 1957 . .
. . . . £400/£75
Alexander, Blackwell (Oxford), 1957 [1958] (no d/w issued)
. . . . £300
Monty Woodpig and his Bubblebuzz Car, Ward (London),
1958 . . . . £400/£75
Mr Bumstead, Eyre & Spottiswoode (London), 1958 . .
. . . . £250/£45
The Wizard of Boland, Ward (London), 1959 . . £300/£45
Bill Badger's Winter Cruise, Hamish Hamilton (London),
1959 . . . . £350/£45
Bill Badger and the Pirates, Hamish Hamilton (London),
1960 . . . . £350/£45
Bill Badger's Finest Hour, Hamish Hamilton (London),
1961 . . . . £200/£35
ditto, as *Bill Badger and the Secret Weapon*, Methuen
(London), 1983 . . . . £100/£25
The Badgers of Bearshanks, Benn (London), 1961 . .
. . . . £150/£40
Bill Badger's Whispering Reeds Adventure, Hamish
Hamilton (London), 1962 . . . . . £350/£45
Lepus the Brown Hare, Benn (London), 1962 . £125/£35
Bill Badger's Big Mistake, Hamish Hamilton (London),
1963 . . . . £250/£40
Bill Badger and the Big Store Robbery, Hamish Hamilton
(London), 1967 . . . . £350/£50
The Whopper, Benn (London), 1967. . . £500/£150
dtto, as *The Monster Fish*, Scholastic Book Services (New
York), 1970 (illustrated by Bernard D'Andrea; pbk) . £65
dtto, as *The Monster Fish*, Scholastic Book Services
(London), 1975 (illustrated by Bernard D'Andrea; pbk) £65
dtto, as *The Whopper*, Meddlar Press, 1997 (98 copies
bound in leather) £300
At the Back O'Ben Dee, Benn (London), 1968 . £250/£45
Bill Badger's Voyage to the World's End, Kaye & Ward
(London), 1969 . . . . £250/£65
The Tyger Tray, Methuen (London), 1971 . . £200/£45
The Pool of the Black Witch, Methuen (London), 1974 .
. . . . £125/£30
dtto, Little Egret Press (Port Eliot, Cornwall), 2002 (475 of
500 copies) . . . . £25/£10
dtto, Little Egret Press (Port Eliot, Cornwall), 2002 (25
copies bound in leather) £250
Lord of the Forest, Methuen (London), 1975 . . £100/£25

Other Books Illustrated by 'BB'

Sport in Wildest Britain, by H.V. Prichard, Philip Allan (London), 1936 . . . . . . £125/£35

Winged Company, by R.G. Walmsley, Eyre & Spottiswoode (London), 1940 . . . . . £125/£35

England is a Village, by C.H. Warren, Eyre & Spottiswoode (London), 1940 . . . . . £45/£15

ditto, Dutton & Co (New York), 1941 . . . £45/£15

Southern English, by E. Benfield, Eyre & Spottiswoode (London), 1942 . . . . . £100/£25

Narrow Boat, by L.T.C. Rolt, Eyre & Spottiswoode (London), 1944 . . . . . £100/£25

It's My Delight, by B. Vesey-Fitzgerald, Eyre & Spottiswoode (London), 1947 . . . . £50/£20

Philandering Angler, by A. Applin, Hurst & Blackett (London), [1948]. . . . . . £75/£25

A Sportsman Looks at Eire, by J.B. Drought, Hutchinson (London), 1949 . . . . . . £75/£20

Landmarks, by A.G. Street, Eyre & Spottiswoode (London), 1949 . . . . . . £45/£15

Red Vagabond, by G.D. Adams, Batchworth Press (London), 1951 . . . . £65/£25

Fairy Tales of Long Ago, by M.C. Carey, Dent (London), 1952 . . . . £75/£25

The White Foxes of Gorfenletch, by H. Tegner, Hollis & Carter (London), 1954 . . . . . £35/£15

The Secret of Orra, by E. Vipont, Blackwell (Oxford), 1957 (no d/w). £200

The Long Night, by William Mayne, Blackwell (Oxford), 1957 [1958] (no d/w) £125

The Long-Bow, by Ronald Welch, Blackwell (Oxford), 1958 (no d/w). £150

Sailors All by Peter Dawlish, Blackwell (Oxford), 1958 (no d/w) £150

A Snowdon Stream, by W.H. Canaway, Putnam: Fisherman's Choice Series (London), 1958 . £75/£20

Trout Fisherman's Saga, by I.D. Owen, Putnam: Fisherman's Choice Series (London), 1959 . £45/£10

Thirteen O'Clock by William Mayne, Blackwell (Oxford), 1959. . . . . . . £75/£25

Vix: The Story of a Fox Cub, by A. Windsor-Richards, Benn (London), 1960 . . . . . £50/£15

Beasts of the North Country, by H. Tegner, Galley Press (London), 1961 . . . . . £50/£15

Birds of the Lonely Lake, by A. Windsor-Richards, Benn (London), 1961 . . . . . . £50/£15

Prince Prigio and Prince Ricardo, by Andrew Lang, Dent (London), 1961 . . . . . . £45/£15

The Rogue Elephant, by Arthur Catherall, Dobson (London), 1962 . . . . . . £200/£45

ditto, Macrae Smith (Philadelphia, PA), 1962 . £100/£25

Guns This Way, by H.W. Pearson-Rogers, Witherby (London), 1962 . . . . . . £75/£20

Granny's Wonderful Chair, by Frances Browne, Dent (London), 1963 . . . . . . £50/£15

King Todd, by N. Burke, Putnam (London), 1963 . £75/£25

A Cabin in the Woods, by A. Windsor-Richards, Friday Press (London), 1963 . . . . . £250/£60

Red Ivory, by A.R. Channel, Dobson (London), 1964 (pseud 'Arthur Catherall') . . . . . £125/£40

ditto, Macrae Smith (Philadelphia, PA), 1964 . £100/£25

The Lost Princess, by George Macdonald, Dent (London), 1965 . . . . £35/£10

To Do With Birds, by H. Tegner, H. Jenkins (London), 1965 . . . . £25/£15

The Wild White Swan, by A. Windsor-Richards, Friday Press (Penshurst, Kent), 1965 . . . £250/£75

Jungle Rescue, by A.R. Channel, Dobson (London), 1967 . . . . £225/£45

ditto, Phillips (New York), [1968] . . . . £150/£25

The Shadow on the Moor, by I. Alan, 8th Duke of Northumberland, privately printed, 1967 (200 copies) . £1,000

Where Vultures Fly, by G. Summers, Collins (London), 1974 . . . . £35/£10

Stories of the Wild, by A.L.E. Fenton and A. Windsor-Richards, Benn (London), 1975 . . . £60/£15

More Stories of the Wild, by A. Windsor-Richards, Benn (London), 1977 . . . . £65/£15

THE BEANO

The Beano is arguably the most famous of all British children's comics, first appearing on 30th July 1938. The first *Beano* annual was issued in 1940. Dennis the Menace did not appear in *The Beano* until 1951, since when he has become a much-loved character, warranting his own annual from 1956.

Comics

No.1, D.C. Thomson, 30th July 1938 (with Whoopee Mask) £12,500

ditto, D.C. Thomson, 30th July 1938 (without Whoopee Mask) £3,500

No.2, D.C. Thomson, 1938 . . . . . . £650

No.3, D.C. Thomson, 1938 . . . . . . £600

No.4, D.C. Thomson, 1938 . . . . . . £600

No.5, D.C. Thomson, 1938 . . . . . . £600

1938-39 . . . . £500 each

1940s. . . . . £75 each

1941-45 . . . . £45 each

1946-50 . . . . £25 each

1950-60 . . . . £10 each

1961-71 . . . . £5 each

1971 to today . . . . 45p each

Annuals

The Beano Book 1940, D.C. Thomson . . . £3,000

The Beano Book 1941, D.C. Thomson . . . £1,000

The Beano Book 1942, D.C. Thomson . . . £1,000

The Magic Beano Book 1943, D.C. Thomson. . £8,000

The Magic Beano Book 1944, D.C. Thomson. . £600

The Magic Beano Book 1945, D.C. Thomson. . £500

The Magic Beano Book 1946, D.C. Thomson. . £400

The Magic Beano Book 1947, D.C. Thomson. . £300

The Magic Beano Book 1948, D.C. Thomson. . £300

The Magic Beano Book 1949, D.C. Thomson. . £250

The Magic Beano Book 1950, D.C. Thomson. . £250

The Beano Book 1951, D.C. Thomson . . . £175

The Beano Book 1952, D.C. Thomson . . . £100

The Beano Book 1953, D.C. Thomson . . . £100

The Beano Book 1954, D.C. Thomson . . . £90

The Beano Book 1955, D.C. Thomson . . . £90

The Beano Book 1956, D.C. Thomson . . . £90

The Beano Book 1957, D.C. Thomson . . . £90

The Beano Book 1958, D.C. Thomson . . . £90

The Beano Book 1959, D.C. Thomson . . . £80

The Beano Book 1960, D.C. Thomson . . . £80
The Beano Book 1961, D.C. Thomson . . . £75
The Beano Book 1962, D.C. Thomson . . . £75
The Beano Book 1963, D.C. Thomson . . . £75
The Beano Book 1964, D.C. Thomson . . . £65
The Beano Book 1965, D.C. Thomson . . . £65
The Beano Book 1966, D.C. Thomson . . . £50
The Beano Book 1967, D.C. Thomson . . . £50
The Beano Book 1968, D.C. Thomson . . . £50
The Beano Book 1969, D.C. Thomson . . . £20
The Beano Book 1970-75, D.C. Thomson . £15 each
The Beano Book 1976-80, D.C. Thomson . £10 each
The Beano Book 1981-90, D.C. Thomson . £7.50 each
The Beano Book 1991 to today, D.C. Thomson . £5 each

'Dennis the Menace' Annuals
Dennis the Menace, D.C. Thomson, 1956 (Dennis walking
with a tin of paint) £150
Dennis the Menace, D.C. Thomson, 1958 (Dennis on a
buggy) £75
Dennis the Menace, D.C. Thomson, 1960 (Dennis attempts
dive) £35
Dennis the Menace, D.C. Thomson, 1962 (papermache
model of Dennis' head) £35
Dennis the Menace, D.C. Thomson, 1964 (Dennis bursts on
to front cover) £30
Dennis the Menace, D.C. Thomson, 1966. . . £40
Dennis the Menace, D.C. Thomson, 1967-69 . . £25
Dennis the Menace, D.C. Thomson, 1970-79 . £15 each
Dennis the Menace, D.C. Thomson, 1980s to today £5 each

AUBREY BEARDSLEY
(b.1872 d.1898)

A British illustrator and writer who came to prominence in
the 1890s. His sinuous black-and-white illustrations became as synonymous with the 'decadence' of the period as
the name of Oscar Wilde. See also under 'Keynotes', 'The
Yellow Book' and 'The Savoy' for further publications
containing his illustrations.

Major Works
Le Morte d'Arthur, by Thomas Malory, Dent (London),
1893-4 (12 parts, green wraps). . . . the set £4,500
ditto, Dent (London), 1893-4 (12 parts, handmade paper,
grey wraps) . . . . the set £7,500
ditto, Dent (London), 1893 and 1894 (2 vols, 1,500 ordinary
copies) £2,500
ditto, Dent (London), 1893 (3 vols, 300 copies on handmade
paper) £4,000
ditto, Dent (London), 1909 (second edition, 1 vol., 1,300
copies of 1,500) £250
ditto, Dutton (New York), 1909 (1 vol., 300 copies of 1,500)
. . . . £250
ditto, Dent (London), 1927 (third edition, 1,600 copies) .
. . . . £650/£200
Bon-Mots of Sydney Smith and R. Brinsley Sheridan, Dent
(London), 1893 . . . . £65
ditto, Dent (London), 1893 (100 numbered copies, large
paper issue) £450
Bon-Mots of Charles Lamb and Douglas Jerrold, Dent
(London), 1893 . . . . £65

ditto, Dent (London), 1893 (100 numbered copies, large
paper issue) £450
Bon-Mots of Samuel Foot and Theodore Hook, Dent
(London), 1894 . . . . £65
ditto, Dent (London), 1894 (100 numbered copies, large
paper issue) £450
Salomé, by Oscar Wilde, Lane & Mathews (London), 1894
(755 copies, blue cloth; 12 illustrations). . . £1,750
ditto, Lane & Mathews (London), 1894 (125 copies, on
Japan vellum, large paper issue, bound in green silk; 12
illustrations) £9,000
ditto, Melmoth & Co. [Smithers] (London), 1904 (250
numbered copies; 12 illustrations) £350
ditto, Melmoth & Co. [Smithers] (London), 1904 (50
numbered copies; 12 illustrations) £500
ditto, Lane & Mathews (London), 1907 (16 illustrations; all
of Beardsley's intended illustrations which were previously
cancelled or 'bowdlerised') £500
ditto, Limited Editions Club (London & Paris), 1938 (16
illustrations by Beardsley, with a companion volume which
has French text and 10 illustrations by André Dérain; both
vols in cleap d/ws; slipcase) . . . . £225/£175
The Rape of the Lock, by Alexander Pope, privately printed
[Smithers] (London), 1896 (1,000 copies; 8 illustrations) .
. . . . £300
ditto, privately printed [Smithers] (London), 1896 (25 copies
on Japanese vellum; 8 illustrations). . . . £4,000
ditto, Leonard Smithers (London), 1897 (special 'bijou'
edition, 50 copies on Japanese vellum; vellum binding; 8
illustrations) £2,500
ditto, Leonard Smithers (London), 1897 (ordinary 'bijou'
edition, 1,000 copies; 8 illustrations) . . . £125
Lysistrata of Aristophanes, privately printed [Smithers]
(London), 1896, (100 copies; 8 tipped-in plates; vellum
backed blue paper covered boards and printed label pasted
onto the upper cover) £7,000
ditto, Beardsley Press (London), 1927 (750 numbered
copies) £125
ditto, Odyssey Publications (New York), 1967 (515
numbered copies; slipcase, no d/w) . . . £125/£95
A Book of Fifty Drawings, Smithers (London), 1897 (500
copies) £450
ditto, Smithers (London), 1897 (50 copies on Japanese
vellum) £3,000
ditto, Grolier Club (New York), 1923 (300 copies printed on
Dutch antique paper) £200
The Pierrot of the Minute, by Ernest Dowson, Smithers
(London), 1897 (300 copies; frontispiece, 2 vignettes and
an initial letter by Beardsley) £350
ditto, Smithers (London), 1897 (30 copies on Japanese
vellum) £2,000
A Second Book of Fifty Drawings, Smithers (London), 1898
(1,000 copies) £200
ditto, John Lane (New York), 1899 (1,000 copies). . £200
Volpone, by Ben Jonson, Smithers (London), 1898 (1,000
numbered copies; frontispiece, 5 initial letters and front
cover design by Beardsley) £200
ditto, Smithers (London), 1898 (100 numbered copies on
Japanese vellum) £1,250
ditto, John Lane (New York), 1898 (1,000 numbered copies)
. . . . £150
The Early Work of Aubrey Beardsley, Bodley Head
(London), 1899 (157 plates, including photogravure
frontispiece portrait, photogravure portrait, and title) . £300

ditto, Bodley Head (London), 1899 (100 copies) . . £650
ditto, Bodley Head (London), 1912 . . . . . £75
The Later Work of Aubrey Beardsley, Bodley Head (London), 1901 (photogravure frontispiece and 173 plates)
. . . . £300
ditto, Bodley Head (London), 1901 (100 copies) . . £650
ditto, Bodley Head (London), 1912 . . . . . £75
Under the Hill, Lane (London), 1904 (17 illustrations). £250
ditto, Lane (London), 1904 (50 copies on Japanese vellum).
. . . . £1,000
ditto, Olympia Press (Paris), 1959 (3,000 numbered copies).
. . . . £35
ditto, Grove Press (New York), 1959. . . . £20/£5
The Uncollected Works of Aubrey Beardsley, Bodley Head (London), 1925 (162 plates, including photogravure frontispiece portrait and four double-page plates) . £250/£150
ditto, Bodley Head (London), 1925 (100 copies) . . £300
ditto, Dodd, Mead (New York), 1925 . . £250/£150

Other Titles With Designs by Beardsley
Evelina, by Frances Burney, Dent (London), 1893 (title-page, cover and spine design by Beardsley; 2 vols) . £45
ditto, Dent (London), 1893 (200 numbered large paper copies; 2 vols) £100
Pastor Sang, by Bjornstjerne Bjornson, Longmans (London), 1893 (frontispiece by Beardsley) £50
The Wonderful History of Virgilus the Sorceror of Rome, Nutt (London), 1893 (frontispiece by Beardsley). . £100
The Pagan Papers, by Kenneth Grahame, Mathews & Lane (London), 1894 (450 [615] copies, title-page design by Beardsley) £100
Plays, by John Davidson, Mathews & Lane (London), 1894 (frontis-piece and title-page vignette by Beardsley) . £60
The Land of Heart's Desire, by W.B. Yeats, Unwin (London), 1894 (500 copies; mauve wraps; presumed first state without 2 fleurons after 'Desire' on front cover, design by Beardsley on cover and title-page) . . £750
ditto, Unwin (London), 1894 (presumed second state with 2 fleurons) £450
ditto, Stone and Kimball (Chicago), [1894] (450 copies in glazed boards, date incorrect on title-page as 1814, frontispiece by Beardsley). £400
Baron Verdigris, by Jocelyn Quilp, Henry (London), 1894 (frontis-piece by Beardsley) £100
Good Reading About Many Books, Unwin (London), 1894 (2 designs by Beardsley) £45
ditto, Unwin (London), 1894 (100 large paper copies signed by publisher, 2 designs by Beardsley) . . . £75
Lucian's True History, by Lucian, [Lawrence & Bullen] (London), 1894 (251 numbered copies, illustrated by Beardsley, Strang and Clark) £150
ditto, by Lucian, [Lawrence & Bullen] (London), 1894 (54 numbered copies with extra plate) £350
A London Garland, Macmillan (London), 1895 (various artists) £75
Tales of Mystery and Wonder, by Edgar Allan Poe, Stone & Kimball (Chicago), 1895 . . . . . . £200
Earl Lavender, by John Davidson, Ward & Downey (London), 1895 (frontispiece by Beardsley) . . £100
Young Ofeg's Ditties, by Ola Hansson, Lane (London), 1895 (title-page design by Beardsley) £75
Sappho, by H.T. Wharton, Lane (London), 1895 (front cover by Beardsley) £100

An Evil Motherhood, by Walt Ruding, Mathews (London), 1896 ('Black Coffee' frontispiece) £750
ditto, Mathews (London), 1896 ('Portrait of the Author' frontispiece) £100
ditto, Mathews (London), 1896 (remainder issue with 'Portrait of the Author' frontispiece glued in and 'Black Coffee' inserted or tipped-in) £100
The Barbarous Britishers, by H.D.Traill, Lane (London), 1896 (front cover, title-page and key design by Beardsley)
. . . . £100
Verses, by Ernest Dowson, Smithers (London), 1896 (300 copies; front cover design by Beardsley) . . .£650
ditto, Smithers (London), 1896 (30 copies on Japanese vellum) £2,500
A Book of Bargains, by V. O'Sullivan, Smithers (London), 1896 (frontispiece by Beardsley) £300
Pierrot!, by Henry de Vere Stacpoole, Lane (London), 1896 (front cover, back cover, spine, title-page and endpapers designed by Beardsley) £100
My Little Lady Anne, by Mrs Egerton Castle, Lane (London), 1896 (front cover, back cover, spine, title-page and endpapers designed by Beardsley) £75
Simplicity, by A.T.G. Price, Lane (London), 1896 (front cover, back cover, spine, title-page and endpapers designed by Beardsley) £75
My Brother, by Vincent Brown, Lane (London), 1896 (front cover, back cover, spine, title-page and endpapers designed by Beardsley) £75
The Life and Times of Madame du Barry, by Douglas, Smithers (London), 1897 (front cover design by Beardsley)
. . . . £75
Le Comédie Humaine, Scenes of Parisian Life, by Honoré de Balzac, Smithers (London), 1897 (11 vols, 250 sets, each with front cover, back cover and spine designed by Beardsley) £450
ditto, Smithers (London), 1897 (50 sets on Japanese vellum)
. . . . £750
Le Comédie Humaine, Scenes of Private Life, by Honoré de Balzac, Smithers (London), 1897-98 (11 vols, cover designs by Beardsley as above) £250
The Souvenirs of Leonard, by Jean Leonard, Smithers (London), 1897 (2 vols, 250 numbered sets; front cover design by Beardsley) £100
The House of Sin, by V. O'Sullivan, Smithers (London), 1897 (front and back cover design by Beardsley; 400 numbered copies) £350
A History of Dancing, Gaston Vuillier, Heinemann (London), 1898 (2 vols, Beardsley plate in 35 numbered copies on Japanese vellum only) £500
Decorations, in Verse & Prose, by Ernest Dowson, Smithers (London), 1899 . . . .£350
The Poems of Ernest Dowson, Lane (London), 1905 (edited and with a memoir by Arthur Symons) £100

Portfolios of Illustrations
Mademoiselle de Maupin, by Theophile Gautier, Smithers (London), 1898 (portfolio, 50 numbered copies; six illustrations) £3,000
An Issue of Five Drawings Illustrative of Juvenal and Lucian, Smithers (London), 1906 (5 drawings by Beardsley; 120 numbered copies) . . . £1,250
Nineteen Early Drawings by Aubrey Beardsley, From the Collection of Mr. Harold Hartley..., privately printed

(London?) 1919 (150 copies signed by Hartley; with an 8
page pamphlet and 19 collotype plates) £250
Le Morte d'Arthur, by Thomas Malory, Dent (London),
1927 (11 unpublished designs, 300 copies) . . . £650

Other Titles Containing Illustrations by Beardsley

Aubrey Beardsley, by Arthur Symons, Unicorn Press
(London), 1898 . . . . £75
ditto, Dent (London), 1905 . . . . £25
The Last Letters of Aubrey Beardsley, ed. by John Gray,
Longmans (London), 1904 . . . . . . £45
Aubrey Beardsley, by Robert Ross, Lane (London), 1909 £65
The Beardsley Period, by O. Burdett, Bodley Head
(London), 1925 . . . . £75/£25
ditto, Boni & Liveright (New York), 1925 . . £75/£25
The Best of Beardsley, by R.A. Walker, Bodley Head
(London), 1948 . . . . £50/£20
A Beardsley Miscellany, ed. by R.A. Walker, Bodley Head
(London), 1949 . . . . £50/£20
Beardsley: A Catalogue of an Exhibition, V&A Museum
(London), 1966 . . . . £15

Others

*Fifty Drawings by Aubrey Beardsley. Selected from the
Collection Owned by Mr. H.S. Nichols,* H.S. Nichols, For
Subscribers Only (New York), 1920 (500 signed copies;
the illustrations are blatant forgeries) £175
The Story of Venus and Tanhauser, A Romantic Novel,
Smithers (London), 1907 ('Under the Hill', 250 numbered
copies on hand-made paper, no illustrations) . . £250
ditto, Smithers (London), 1907 ('Under the Hill', 50 numbered copies on Japanese vellum, no illustrations) . £650
Letters to Leonard Smithers, First Editions Club (London),
1937 . . . . £75

SAMUEL BECKETT
(b.1906 d.1989)

An individual and experimental Irish playwright, novelist
and poet, Beckett's minimalist writing is deeply pessimistic
about human nature and the human condition. His work
became increasingly enigmatic in later years and his style
more attenuated. He received the Nobel Prize for Literature
in 1969. Note: reprints under different titles do not necessarily mean that the same text is reproduced: one work is
often a progression of another.

Plays

En Attendant Godot, Éditions de Minuit (Paris), 1952 (white
wraps printed in blue and black) £2,000
ditto, Éditions de Minuit (Paris), 1952 (35 numbered large
paper copies; wraps) £6,000
ditto, Éditions de Minuit (Paris), 1952 [1956] (30 numbered
copies, six photographs; wraps) . . . £6,000
ditto, as *Waiting for Godot*, Grove Press (New York), 1954
. . . . £1,250/£250
ditto, Faber (London), 1956 . . . . . £600/£125
Tous Ceux Qui Tombent, Éditions de Minuit (Paris), 1957
(white wraps printed in blue and black) £65
ditto, Éditions de Minuit (Paris), 1957 (80 numbered copies;
wraps) £200
ditto, as *All That Fall*, Grove Press (New York), 1957 . .
. . . . £65/£30

ditto, Grove Press (New York), 1957 (100 numbered copies,
acetate jacket) . . . . £175/£125
ditto, Grove Press (New York), 1957 (25 signed, numbered
copies) £1,000
ditto, Faber (London), 1958 (pbk) £25
Fin de Partie, Éditions de Minuit (Paris), 1957 (white wraps
printed in blue and black) £200
ditto, Éditions de Minuit (Paris), 1957 (50 numbered large
paper copies) £4,000
ditto, as *Endgame*, Faber (London), 1958. . . £150/£45
ditto, Grove Press (New York), 1958. . . . £125/£45
ditto, Grove Press (New York), 1958 (100 signed copies,
glassine d/w). . . . . £300/£250
Krapp's Last Tape and Embers, Faber (London), 1959
(bound in stiff cardboard covers with attached pale blue-
green d/w with black and red titles). £35
ditto, Evergreen (New York), 1960 . . . . £35/£10
ditto, as *La dernière bande*, Éditions de Minuit (Paris), 1959
[1960] (white wraps printed in blue and black) . . £40
ditto, Éditions de Minuit (Paris), 1959 [1960] (40 numbered
copies; wraps) £450
Happy Days, Grove Press (New York), 1961 (pbk) . £25
ditto, Faber (London), 1962 . . . . . . £40/£10
ditto, as *Oh Les Beaux Jours*, Éditions de Minuit (Paris),
1963 (87 numbered large paper copies of 412; wraps) £250
ditto, as *Oh Les Beaux Jours*, Éditions de Minuit (Paris),
1963 (325 copies of 412; wraps) £150
ditto, as *Oh Les Beaux Jours*, Éditions de Minuit (Paris),
1963 (wraps). £45
Play and Two Short Pieces for Radio, Faber (London), 1964
. . . . £50/£15
ditto, as *Comédie et actes divers*, Éditions de Minuit (Paris),
1966 (112 numbered copies; wraps) £200
ditto, Éditions de Minuit (Paris), 1966 (wraps) . . £25
ditto, as *Cascando and Other Short Dramatic Pieces*, Grove
Press (New York), 1968 (pbk) £25
Eh Joe and Other Writings, Faber (London), 1967 £35/£10
Come and Go, Calder (London), 1967 . . . £65/£20
ditto, Calder (London), 1967 (100 signed copies, slipcase) .
. . . . £600/£550
Film, Grove Press (New York), 1969 (pbk) . . . £20
ditto, Grove Press (New York), 1969 (200 numbered copies)
. . . . £125
ditto, Faber (London), 1972 (glossy, pictorial wraps) . £35
ditto, Éditions de Minuit (Paris), 1972 (342 copies) . £150
Breath and Other Shorts, Faber (London), 1972 . £60/£25
ditto, Faber (London), 1972 (pbk) £15
Not I, Faber (London), 1973 (stapled wraps) . . . £15
ditto, as *Pas Moi*, Éditions de Minuit (Paris), 1975 (150
numbered copies of 242; wraps) £45
ditto, Éditions de Minuit (Paris), 1975 (92 numbered copies
of 242; wraps) £75
That Time, Faber (London), 1976 (stapled wraps) . . £10
ditto, as *Cette Fois*, Éditions de Minuit (Paris), 1978 (100
numbered copies; wraps) £250
Footfalls, Faber (London), 1976 (wraps) £10
ditto, Grove Press (New York), 1976. . . . £25/£10
ditto, as *Pas*, Éditions de Minuit (Paris), 1977 (135
numbered copies of 227; wraps) £200
Pas Suivi de Quatre Esquisses, Éditions de Minuit (Paris),
1976 (86 copies; wraps) £75
Ends and Odds: Eight New Dramatic Pieces, Grove Press
(New York), 1976 . . . . £20/£5

ditto, as ***Ends and Odds: Plays and Sketches***, Faber (London), 1977 . . . . £25/£10
Rockaby and Other Short Pieces, Grove Press (New York), 1981 . . . . £25/£10
ditto, as ***Three Occasional Pieces***, Faber (London), 1982 (stapled black and white wraps) £10
ditto, as ***Berceuse suivi de Impromptu d'Ohio***, Éditions de Minuit (Paris), 1982 (99 numbered large paper copies; wraps) £150
Solo suivi de Catastrophe, Éditions de Minuit (Paris), 1982 (99 numbered copies; wraps) £200
ditto, as ***Catastrophe***, Lord John Press (Northridge, CA), 1983 (100 numbered signed copies, broadside) . . £300
ditto, Lord John Press (Northridge, CA), 1983 (26 lettered signed copies, broadside) £1,000
ditto, Faber (London), 1984 (pbk) £10
Quoi Où, Éditions de Minuit (Paris), 1983 (99 copies; wraps)
. . . . £75
ditto, as ***What Where***, Faber (London), 1984 . . . £10
Three Plays: Ohio Impromptu, Catastrophe, What Where, Grove Press (New York), 1984 . . . . £20/£5
Collected Shorter Plays, Faber (London), 1984 . £20/£5
ditto, Grove Press (New York), 1984 . . . £20/£5
Eleutheria, Éditions de Minuit (Paris), 1995 (wraps) . £10
ditto, Foxrock (New York), 1995 (250 signed, numbered copies) £125
ditto, Faber (London), 1996 (pbk) £10

Novels and Short Stories

More Pricks than Kicks, Chatto & Windus (London), 1934
. . . . £3,500/£2,000
ditto, Calder & Boyars (London), 1966 (textured brown/mauve paper covered boards stamped in gold at spine, in green and white d/w) . . . . . . £100/£45
ditto, Calder & Boyars (London), 1970 (100 signed copies, vellum-backed boards in slipcase) . . . £300/£200
ditto, Grove Press (New York), 1970 . . . . £30/£10
Murphy, Routledge (London), 1938 . . £4,500/£2,500
ditto, Bordas (Paris), 1947 (wraps [95 copies]) . £1,250
ditto, Éditions de Minuit/Bordas (Paris), 1947 [1951] . £250
ditto, Grove Press (New York), [1957] . . . £150/£35
ditto, Grove Press (New York), [1957] (100 signed copies, acetate d/w) . . . . . . £1,500/£1,000
Molloy, Éditions de Minuit (Paris), 1951 (trade edition of 3000 copies; wraps) £50
ditto, Éditions de Minuit (Paris), 1951 (500 numbered copies; wraps) £150
ditto, Éditions de Minuit (Paris), 1951 (50 large paper numbered copies; wraps) £2,500
ditto, Olympia Press (Paris), 1955 (wraps) . . £100
ditto, Grove Press (New York), 1955 . . . . £100/£35
ditto, Calder (London), 1959 . . . . £100/£45
Malone Meurt, Éditions de Minuit (Paris), [1951] (wraps) .
. . . . £200
ditto, Éditions de Minuit (Paris), [1951] (47 numbered copies; wraps) £2,000
ditto, as ***Malone Dies***, Grove Press (New York), 1956 . .
. . . . £65/£35
ditto, Grove Press (New York), 1956 (500 numbered copies, acetate d/w) . . . . . . £150/£100
ditto, Calder (London), 1958 . . . . . £100/£45
L'Innommable, Éditions de Minuit (Paris), 1953 (wraps) £75
ditto, Éditions de Minuit (Paris), 1953 (50 signed copies; wraps) £2,000

ditto, as ***The Unnamable***, Grove Press (New York), 1958 (100 numbered copies, acetate d/w) . . £150/£100
ditto, Grove Press (New York), 1958 (26 signed, lettered copies, acetate d/w) . . . . . £2,500/£2,000
ditto, Grove Press (New York), 1958 (acetate d/w) . .
. . . . £125/£100
ditto, Grove Press (New York), 1958 (pbk) . . . £25
ditto, Calder (London), 1975 . . . . . £25/£10
Watt, Olympia Press (Paris), 1953 (1,100 numbered copies; wraps) £400
ditto, Olympia Press (Paris), 1953 (25 signed, lettered copies) £2,500
ditto, Grove Press (New York), 1953 . . . £200/£40
ditto, Grove Press (New York), 1953 (100 numbered copies)
. . . . £250
ditto, Grove Press (New York), 1953 (26 signed, lettered copies) £2,500
ditto, Olympia Press (Paris), 1958 . . . . £75/£25
ditto, Calder (London), 1963 (wraps) £75
Nouvelles et Textes pour Rien, Éditions de Minuit (Paris), 1955 (1,100 numbered copies of 1,185; wraps) . £150
ditto, Éditions de Minuit (Paris), 1955 (50 numbered *hors commerce* copies of 1,185; wraps) . . . £1,500
ditto, Éditions de Minuit (Paris), 1955 (35 signed copies of 1,185; wraps) £2,500
ditto, Éditions de Minuit (Paris), 1958 (2,000 numbered copies, illustrated; wraps) £65
ditto, as ***Stories & Texts for Nothing***, Grove Press (New York), 1967 . . . . £35/£10
From an Abandoned Work, Faber (London), 1958 (stapled wraps) £45
Molloy, Malone Dies, The Unnamable: A Trilogy, Olympia Press (Paris), 1959 (wraps) £50
ditto, Calder (London), 1959 . . . . £60/£20
ditto, as ***Three Novels***, Grove Press (New York), 1959 . .
. . . . £45/£15
Comment c'est, Éditions de Minuit (Paris), 1961 (wraps) .
. . . . £100
ditto, Éditions de Minuit (Paris), 1961 (80 numbered copies of 88; wraps) £350
ditto, Éditions de Minuit (Paris), 1961 (8 *hors commerce* of 88 copies; wraps) £350
ditto, Éditions de Minuit (Paris), 1961 (100 of 110 copies for the 'Club l'édition originale'; wraps) £350
ditto, Éditions de Minuit (Paris), 1961 (10 'H.C.' of 110 copies for the 'Club l'édition originale'; wraps) . £350
ditto, as ***How It Is***, Calder (London), 1964 . . £60/£20
ditto, as ***How It Is***, Calder (London), 1964 (100 signed copies, slipcase) . . . . . . £500/£400
ditto, Grove Press (New York), 1964 . . . . £60/£30
Imagination Morte Imaginez, Éditions de Minuit (Paris), 1965 (612 signed copies) £150
ditto, as ***Imagination Dead Imagine***, Calder (London), 1965 (wraps) £35
ditto, Calder (London), 1965 (100 signed, numbered copies) .
. . . . £500/£450
ditto, as ***All Strange Away***, Gotham Book Mart (New York), 1976 . . . . £50/£15
ditto, Gotham Book Mart (New York), 1976 (200 signed, numbered copies, slipcase) . . . . £1,000/£900
ditto, Calder (London), 1979 . . . . . £20/£5
Assez, Éditions de Minuit (Paris), 1966 (112 numbered copies of 662) £125

ditto, Éditions de Minuit (Paris), 1966 (100 *hors commerce* copies of 662) £150

ditto, Éditions de Minuit (Paris), 1966 (450 numbered copies of 662; wraps) £125

Bing, Éditions de Minuit (Paris), 1966 (100 numbered copies of 762; wraps) £150

ditto, Éditions de Minuit (Paris), 1966 (112 numbered copies reserved for La Librairie des Éditions de Minuit; wraps) £150

ditto, Éditions de Minuit (Paris), 1966 (550 numbered copies of 762; wraps) £100

ditto, as ***Le Dépeupleur***, Éditions de Minuit (Paris), 1970 (99 copies on pure thread 'lafuma' of 399 copies) . . £150

ditto, Éditions de Minuit (Paris), 1970 (201 of 399 copies, numbered 100-300) £75

ditto, Éditions de Minuit (Paris), 1970 (92 numbered copies reserved for publisher) £75

ditto, Éditions de Minuit (Paris), 1970 (7 *hors commerce* copies) £200

ditto, as ***Séjour***, Georges Richar (Paris), 1970 (5 full-page etchings by Louis Maccard after drawings by Jean Deyrolle; loose sheets housed in a wrapper folder and folding box) £300

ditto, as ***The Lost Ones***, Calder (London), 1972 . £40/£15

ditto, Calder (London), 1972 (100 signed copies, slipcase) . . . . £450/£350

ditto, Grove Press (New York), 1972 . . . £40/£15

ditto, as ***The North***, Enitharmon Press (London), 1973 (137 signed, numbered copies; wraps) £650

ditto, Enitharmon Press (London), 1973 (15 signed copies with three extra etchings, heavyweight paper; wraps) £2,000

No's Knife, Calder (London), 1967 . . . . £40/£10

ditto, Calder (London), 1967 (100 signed copies, 'printed A (*hors commerce*)', slipcase) . . . . £600/£500

ditto, Calder (London), 1967 ('a second series of 100 numbered copies printed B and signed by the author (*hors commerce*)', slipcase) . . . . . £600/£500

Sans, Éditions de Minuit (Paris), 1969 (742 copies; wraps) £125

ditto, as ***Lessness***, Calder (London), 1970 . . £65/£20

ditto, Calder (London), 1970 (100 signed copies, slipcase) . . . . £450/£400

Premier Amour, Éditions de Minuit (Paris), 1970 (92 of 399 copies) £150

ditto, Éditions de Minuit (Paris), 1970 (106 numbered large paper copies of 399) £75

ditto, Éditions de Minuit (Paris), 1970 (201 of 399 copies) £75

ditto, as ***First Love***, Calder (London), 1973 . £40/£15

ditto, Grove Press (New York), 1974 . . . £40/£15

Mercier et Camier, Éditions de Minuit (Paris), 1970 (99 numbered large paper copies of 399) . . . £150

ditto, Éditions de Minuit (Paris), 1970 (92 of 399 copies; wraps) £65

ditto, Éditions de Minuit (Paris), 1970 (7 *hors commerce* copies; wraps) £300

ditto, Éditions de Minuit (Paris), 1970 (201 of 399 copies; wraps) £45

ditto, as ***Mercier and Camier***, Calder (London), 1974 . . . . £35/£10

ditto, Grove Press (New York), 1974 . . . £35/£10

Six Residua, Calder (London), 1978 . . . £50/£15

ditto, Calder (London), 1978 (pbk) £10

Still, M'Arte Edizioni (Milan), 1974 (30 signed copies with extra portfolio of plates, slipcase) . . . £2,000

ditto, M'Arte Edizioni (Milan), 1974 (signed copies, slipcase) £1,000

ditto, as ***Immobile***, Éditions de Minuit (Paris), 1976 (100 numbered copies of 125; wraps) £45

ditto, Éditions de Minuit (Paris), 1976 (25 *hors commerce* copies; wraps) £45

Pour finir encore et autres foirades, Éditions de Minuit (Paris), 1976 (125 numbered copies; wraps) . . £75

ditto, as ***Foirades/Fizzles***, Petersburg Press (London/New York), 1976 (33 lithographs by Jasper Johns, 300 signed, numbered copies; wraps) £10,000

ditto, as ***For to End Yet Again and Other Fizzles***, Calder (London), 1976 . . . . £30/£10

ditto, as ***Fizzles***, Grove Press (New York), 1977 . £30/£10

Four Novellas, Calder (London), 1978 . . . £25/£10

Compagnie, Éditions de Minuit (Paris), 1980 (106 numbered copies; wraps) £75

ditto, as ***Company***, Calder (London), 1980 . £25/£10

ditto, Calder (London), 1980 (100 signed copies, slipcase) . . . . £450/£400

ditto, Grove Press (New York), 1980 . . . £25/£10

Mal vu mal dit, Éditions de Minuit (Paris), 1981 (114 numbered copies; wraps) £75

ditto, Éditions de Minuit (Paris), 1981 (99 numbered copies; wraps) £150

ditto, as ***Ill Seen Ill Said***, Grove Press (New York), 1981 . . . . £25/£10

ditto, Calder (London), 1982 . . . . £25/£10

ditto, Lord John Press (Northridge, CA), 1982 (299 signed copies of 325) £300

ditto, Lord John Press (Northridge, CA), 1982 (26 signed, lettered copies of 325) £750

Worstward Ho, Calder (London), 1983 . . . £25/£10

ditto, Grove Press (New York), 1983 . . . £25/£10

ditto, as ***Cap au pire***, Éditions de Minuit (Paris), 1991 (wraps) £15

Collected Shorter Prose, 1945-1980, Calder (London), 1984 . . . . £20/£5

As the Story Was Told: Uncollected and Late Prose, Rampant Lions Press (Cambridge, UK), 1987 (325 numbered copies) £100

ditto, Calder (London), 1990 . . . . . £25/£10

L'Image, Éditions de Minuit (Paris), 1988 (wraps) . £40

ditto, as ***The Image***, Calder (London), 1990 . £25/£10

ditto, Riverrun Press (New York), 1990 . . £20/£5

Stirrings Still, Calder/Blue Moon Books (London), [1988] (200 of 226 signed, numbered copies, slipcase) . £1,500

ditto, Calder/Blue Moon Books (London), [1988] (26 lettered, signed copies of 226, slipcase) . . £2,000

ditto, Calder/Blue Moon Books, [1988] (15 Roman-numeralled 'hors de commerce' copies, slipcase) . £2,000

Nohow On, Calder (London), 1989 . . . . £25/£10

ditto, Limited Editions Club (New York), [1989] (550 signed copies in box) £2,000

Dream of Fair to Middling Women, Black Cat Press (Dublin), 1992 . . . . £25/£10

ditto, Calder (London), 1993 . . . . . £25/£10

Poetry

Whoroscope, Hours Press (Paris), 1930 (200 numbered copies of 300; wraps) £2,000

ditto, Hours Press (Paris), 1930 (100 signed, numbered copies of 300; wraps) £4,000
ditto, Grove Press (New York), 1957 . . . . £45/£15
Echo's Bones, Europa Press (Paris), 1935 (25 signed copies) £2,500
ditto, Europa Press (Paris), 1935 (250 numbered copies; wraps) £650
ditto, Europa Press (Paris), 1935 (50 *hors commerce* copies) £650
Poems in English, Calder (London), 1961 . £75/£35
ditto, Calder (London), 1961 (100 signed copies, slipcase) .
. . . . £600/£500
ditto, Grove Press (New York), 1963 . . . . £60/£30
ditto, as **Poèmes**, Éditions de Minuit (Paris), 1968 (550 copies of 762; wraps) £125
ditto, Éditions de Minuit (Paris), 1968 (100 numbered copies of 762; wraps) £200
Poèmes, Éditions de Minuit (Paris), 1968 (550 copies; wraps) £125
Collected Poems in French and English, Calder (London), 1977 . . . . £25/£10
Poèmes [suivi de mirlitonnades, 1976-1978], Éditions de Minuit (Paris), 1978 (wraps) £10
Collected Poems, 1930-1978, Calder (London), 1984 £20/£5
Comment dire, Éditions de Minuit (Paris), 1989 (single sheet folded) £15

Essays
Our Exagmination Round His Factification for Incamination of 'Work in Progress', Shakespeare & Co (Paris), 1929 (contains essay by Beckett 'Dante... Bruno... Vico... Joyce', 300 copies; wraps) £300
ditto, Shakespeare & Co (Paris), 1929 (96 large paper copies)
. . . . £750
ditto, Faber (London), 1936 . . . . . £150/£65
ditto, New Directions (Norfolk, CT), 1939 . £125/£50
Proust, Chatto & Windus (London), 1931 . £200/£100
ditto, Grove Press (New York), 1957 (250 signed copies) .
. . . . £450
ditto, Grove Press (New York), 1957 (pbk) . £40
Proust and Three Dialogues with Georges Duthuit, Calder (London), 1965 . . . . £65/£15
Disjecta, Calder (London), 1983 . . . . £30/£10
ditto, Grove Press (New York), 1983 . . . £15/£5
Le Monde et le Pantalon, Éditions de Minuit (Paris), 1989 (99 copies; wraps) £45

Collected Edition
The Collected Works, Grove Press (New York), (16 vols 200 signed, numbered sets) £1,000

Translations
La Manivelle/The Old Tune, by Robert Pinget, Éditions de Minuit (Paris), 1960 (wraps) £500
Zone, by Apollinaire Guillaume, Dolmen Press/Calder (Dublin/London), 1972 . . . . . £45/£10
ditto, by Apollinaire Guillaume, Dolmen Press/Calder (Dublin/London), 1972 (250 copies signed by Beckett; slipcase, no d/w) . . . . . £400/£300
The Drunken Boat, by Arthur Rimbaud, Whiteknights Press (Reading, UK), 1976 (200 copies, signed by Beckett). £400
ditto, by Arthur Rimbaud, Whiteknights Press (Reading, UK), 1976 (100 copies, signed by Beckett) . . £600

WILLIAM BECKFORD
(b.1759 d.1844)

Beckford is remembered equally for his oriental horror story, *Vathek*, and for the creation of the Gothic abbey at Fonthill, Wiltshire. *Vathek* was originally written in French, but the Reverend Samuel Henley had his English translation published first in June 1876, against Beckford's wishes. The author had it published in its original French in December 1786, under the title *Vathek*, and then in another edition a few months later.

'Vathek'
An Arabian Tale, Johnson (London), 1786 (anonymous; English translation by Rev. Henley from the French text) .
. . . . £1,000
ditto, Johnson (London), 1786 (anonymous; large paper edition) £1,250
ditto, as **Vathek**, Isaac Hignou (Lausanne, France), 1787 [1786] (anonymous; French text; dark purple wraps) . £750
ditto, as **Vathek**, Poincot (Paris), 1787 (anonymous; French text white wraps) £650
ditto, as **Vathek**, Clarke (London), 1815 (anonymous; French text; first edition containing all of the episodes) . £650
The Episodes of Vathek, Stephen Swift (London), 1912 (translated by Sir Frank T. Marzials) £65

Travel
Dreams, Waking Thoughts and Incidents in a Series of Letters from Various Parts of Europe, J. Johnson/P. Elmsley, 1783 (anonymous) £350
Italy, With Sketches of Spain and Portugal, Richard Bentley, 1834 ('by the author of "Vathek"'; 2 vols) . £200
Recollections of an Excursion to the Monasteries of Alcobaca and Batalha, Richard Bentley, 1835 ('by the author of "Vathek"') £200
Italy, Spain and Portugal, with **Recollections of an Excursion to the Monasteries of Alcobaca and Batalha**, Richard Bentley, 1840 ('by the author of "Vathek"') . £200
The Travel-Diaries of William Beckford, Constable/ Houghton Mifflin, 1928 (edited by Chapman; 2 vols; 750 sets; slipcase) . . . . . £150/£100
The Journal of William Beckford in Portugal and Spain, Hart-Davis, 1954 (edited by Boyd Alexander) . £25/£5
Life at Fonthill 1807-1822, With Interludes in Paris and London, From the Correspondence of William Beckford, Hart-Davis, 1957 (translated and edited by Boyd Alexander) . . . . £25/£5

Poetry
The Transient Gleam: A Bouquet of Beckford's Poesy, Aylesford Press, 1991 (300 copies) . . . £20/£10

Miscellaneous
Biographical Memoirs of Extraordinary Painters, J Robson, 1780 (anonymous) £600
Popular Tales of the Germans, John Murray, 1791 (anonymous; translated from the German of J.C.A. Musaeus; 2 vols) £450
Modern Writing, or The Elegant Enthusiast; and the Interesting Emotions of Arabella Bloomville: A Rhapsodical Romance, G.G. & J. Robinson, 1796 (pseud 'the Right Hon Lady Harriet Marlow') £300

Azemia: A Descriptive and Sentimental Novel, Sampson Low, 1797 (pseud 'Agneta Mariana Jenks'; 2 vols) . £300
The Story of Al Raoui: A Tale from the Arabic, C. Geisweiler, 1799 (anonymous). £200
Epitaphs: Some of Which have Appeared in the 'Literary Gazette' of March and April 1823, privately printed, [1825] (anonymous; wraps) £200
The Vision and *Liber Veritastis*, Constable/Richard R. Smith, 1930 (edited and with introduction and notes by Guy Chapman; limited to 750 copies; slipcase) . £50/£15

FRANCIS BEEDING
(b.1898 d.1951)

'Francis Beeding' is the best known pseudonym of Hilary St George Saunders under which name he co-wrote crime novels with John Palmer (1885-1944). Alfred Hitchcock successfully adapted The *House of Doctor Edwardes* for his classic film *Spellbound*, staring Ingrid Bergman and Gregory Peck.

'Francis Beeding' Novels
The Seven Sleepers, Little, Brown (Boston), 1925 . £300/£25
ditto, Hutchinson (London), [1925] . . . . £800/£25
The Little White Hag, Hutchinson (London), [1926] . .
. . . . £750/£25
ditto, Little, Brown (Boston), 1926 . . . £250/£20
The Hidden Kingdom, Hodder & Stoughton (London), [1927] . . . . £750/£25
ditto, Little, Brown (Boston), 1927 . . . £250/£20
The House of Doctor Edwardes, Hodder & Stoughton (London), [1927]. . . . . . £1,000/£45
ditto, Little, Brown (Boston), 1928 . . . £1,000/£45
ditto, as *Spellbound*, World Publishing Co. (Cleveland, OH), 1945 . . . . £50/£10
The Six Proud Walkers, Little, Brown (Boston), 1928 . .
. . . . £200/£20
ditto, Hodder & Stoughton (London), [1928] . . £750/£25
The Five Flamboys, Hodder & Stoughton (London), [1929]
. . . . £750/£25
ditto, Little, Brown (Boston), 1929 . . . £200/£20
Pretty Sinister, Hodder & Stoughton (London), [1929]. .
. . . . £750/£25
ditto, Little, Brown (Boston), 1929 . . . £200/£20
The Four Armourers, Little, Brown (Boston), 1930 . .
. . . . £750/£20
ditto, Hodder & Stoughton (London), 1930 . . £200/£25
The League of Discontent, Little, Brown (Boston), 1930 .
. . . . £700/£15
ditto, Hodder & Stoughton (London), 1930 . . £175/£20
Death Walks in Eastrepps, Hodder & Stoughton (London), 1931 . . . . £700/£15
ditto, Mystery League (New York), 1931 . . £150/£10
The Three Fishers, Little, Brown (Boston), 1931 . £600/£10
ditto, Hodder & Stoughton (London), [1931] . £100/£10
Take It Crooked, Little, Brown (Boston), 1932 . £600/£10
ditto, Hodder & Stoughton (London), 1932 . £100/£10
Murder Intended, Little, Brown (Boston), 1932 . £600/£10
ditto, Hodder & Stoughton (London), 1932 . £100/£10
The Two Undertakers, Hodder & Stoughton (London), 1933
. . . . £500/£10
ditto, Little, Brown (Boston), 1933 . . . £75/£10

The Emerald Clasp, Little, Brown (Boston), 1933 . £75/£10
ditto, Hodder & Stoughton (London), 1933 . . £500/£10
The One Sane Man, Hodder & Stoughton (London), 1934 .
. . . . £500/£10
ditto, Little, Brown (Boston), 1934 . . . £75/£10
Mr Bobadil, Hodder & Stoughton (London), 1934. £500/£10
ditto, as *The Street of the Serpents*, Harper (New York), 1934
. . . . £75/£10
Death in Four Letters, Hodder & Stoughton (London), 1935
. . . . £500/£10
ditto, Harper (New York), 1935 . . . . £75/£10
The Norwich Victims, Hodder & Stoughton (London), 1935
. . . . £500/£10
ditto, Harper (New York), 1935 . . . . £65/£10
The Eight Crooked Trenches, Hodder & Stoughton (London), 1936 . . . . . . £450/£10
ditto, Harper (New York), 1936 . . . . £60/£10
ditto, as *Coffin for One*, Avon (New York), 1943 (pbk) £10
The Nine Waxed Faces, Hodder & Stoughton (London), 1936 . . . . £400/£10
ditto, Harper (New York), 1936 . . . £60£10
Hell Let Loose, Hodder & Stoughton (London), 1937 . .
. . . . £400/£10
ditto, Harper (New York), 1937 . . . . £60/£10
The Erring Secretary, Hodder & Stoughton (London), 1937 (pbk) £15
No Fury, Hodder & Stoughton (London), 1937 . £400/£10
ditto, as *Murdered: One by One*, Harper (New York), 1937
. . . . £60/£10
The Black Arrows, Hodder & Stoughton (London), 1938 .
. . . . £400/£10
ditto, Harper (New York), 1938 . . . £60/£10
The Big Fish, Hodder & Stoughton (London), 1938 . .
. . . . £400/£10
ditto, as *Heads off at Midnight*, Harper (New York), 1938 .
. . . . £50/£10
The Ten Holy Horrors, Hodder & Stoughton (London), 1939 . . . . £350/£10
ditto, Harper (New York), 1939 . . . . £45/£10
He Could Not Have Slipped, Hodder & Stoughton (London), 1939 . . . . £350/£10
ditto, Harper (New York), 1939 . . . . £35/£10
Eleven Were Brave, Hodder & Stoughton (London), 1940 .
. . . . £200/£10
ditto, Harper (New York), 1941 . . . . £25/£10
Not a Bad Show, Hodder & Stoughton (London), 1940. .
. . . . £175/£10
ditto, as *The Secret Weapon*, Harper (New York), 1940 .
. . . . £25/£10
The Twelve Disguises, Hodder & Stoughton (London), 1942
. . . . £125/£10
ditto, Harper (New York), 1942 . . . . £35/£10
There are Thirteen, Hodder & Stoughton (London), 1946 .
. . . . £25/£10
ditto, Harper (New York), 1946 . . . . £25/£10

'David Pilgrim' Novels, Written with John Palmer
So Great A Man, Macmillan (London), 1937 . . £35/£10
ditto, Harper (New York), 1937 . . . . £35/£10
No Common Glory, Macmillan (London), 1941 . £25/£5
ditto, Harper (New York), 1941 . . . . £25/£5
The Grand Design, Macmillan (London), 1944 . £20/£5
ditto, Harper (New York), 1944 . . . . £20/£5
The Emperor's Servant, Macmillan (London), 1946 £15/£5

'Barum Browne' Novel, Written with Geoffrey Dennis
The Devil and X.Y.Z., Gollancz (London), 1931 . £65/£15
ditto, Doubleday (Garden City, NY), 1931 . . £65/£15

'Cornelius Coffyn' Novel, Written with John de Vere Loder
The Death Riders, Gollancz (London), 1935 . . £45/£10
ditto, Knopf (New York), 1935 . . . . £45/£10

As Hilary St George Saunders
Return at Dawn, New Zealand Tourist and Publicity Department, 1943 (pbk) £15
Per Ardua, O.U.P. (Oxford, UK), 1944 . . . £20/£5
Pioneers! Pioneers!, Macmillan (London), 1944 . £15/£5
Ford at War, Harrison & Sons (London), 1946 (pbk) . £10
The Left Handshake, Collins (London), 1948 . . £25/£10
Valiant Voyaging, Faber (London), 1948 . . £25/£10
The Middlesex Hospital, 1745-1948, Max Parrish (London), 1949 . . . . £20/£5
The Green Beret, Joseph (London), 1949 . . £20/£5
The Red Beret, Joseph (London), 1950 . . £20/£5
The Red Cross and the White, Hollis & Carter (London), 1949 . . . . £20/£5
The Sleeping Bacchus, Joseph (London), 1951 £20/£5
Westminster Hall, Joseph (London), 1951 . £20/£5
Royal Air Force 1939-1945, H.M.S.O. (London), 1953-4 (3 vols, with Denis G. Richards; stapled wraps) £40 the set

Anonymous Publications
The Battle of Britain, H.M.S.O./Ministry of Information (London), 1941 (stapled wraps) £10
ditto, Doubleday (Garden City, NY), 1941 (wraps) . £10
Bomber Command, H.M.S.O./Ministry of Information (London), 1941 (stapled wraps) £10
ditto, Doubleday (Garden City, NY), 1941 (stapled wraps) £10
Air-Sea Rescue, H.M.S.O./Ministry of Information (London), 1942 (stapled wraps) £10
Bomber Command Continues, H.M.S.O./Ministry of Information (London), 1942 (stapled wraps). . £10
Coastal Command, H.M.S.O./Ministry of Information (London), 1943 (stapled wraps) £10
ditto, Macmillan (New York), 1943 (stapled wraps) . £10
Combined Operations, H.M.S.O./Ministry of Information (London), 1943 (stapled wraps) £10
ditto, Macmillan (New York), 1943 (stapled wraps) . £10
By Air to Battle, H.M.S.O./Ministry of Information (London), 1945 (stapled wraps) £10

MAX BEERBOHM

(b.1872 d.1956)

Sir Max Beerbohm was a humorist, caricaturist, essayist and novelist. A contributor to the *The Yellow Book* in 1894, his first book, *The Works of Max Beerbohm*, was published in 1896. One of his best known works is the story of 'Enoch Soames', a poet who makes a deal with the Devil in order to discover how posterity will remember him.

Fiction
The Happy Hypocrite, Wayside Press/John Lane (Springfield, Mass./London), 1896/1897 (green wraps; title-page dated 1897, but colophon dated Dec. 1896; first state with full stop after 'One' on front cover) £125

ditto, Wayside Press/John Lane (Springfield, Mass./London), 1896/1897 (as above, second state without full stop after 'One' on front cover) £100
Zuleika Dobson, Heinemann (London), 1911 (first issue, smooth cloth) £100
ditto, Heinemann (London), 1911 (second issue, rough cloth) £75
ditto, John Lane (New York), 1912 . . . . £75
A Christmas Garland, Heinemann (London), 1912 . £65
ditto, Dutton & Co. (New York), 1912 . . . £50
Seven Men, Heinemann (London), 1919 . . . £100/£35
ditto, Knopf (New York), 1920 (2,000 numbered copies) .
. . . . £75/£25
ditto, as *Seven Men and Two Others*, Heinemann (London), 1946 . . . . £15/£5
The Dreadful Dragon of Hay Hill, Heinemann (London), 1928 . . . . £45/£15

Non-Fiction
The Works of Max Beerbohm, Scribner's (New York), 1896 (1,000 copies, of which 401 were pulped) . . . £165
ditto, John Lane (London), 1896 . . . . . £100
More, John Lane (London), 1899 . . . . . £60
Yet Again, Chapman & Hall (London), 1909 . . . £40
ditto, Knopf (New York), 1923 . . . . . £50/£15
And Even Now, Heinemann (London), 1920 . £45/£10
ditto, Dutton (New York), 1921 . . . . . £45/£10
A Peep into the Past, privately printed [Max Harzof, New York], 1923 (300 copies on Japanese vellum, slipcase) .
. . . . £100/£75
Around Theatres, Heinemann (London), 1924 (2 vols).
. . . . £200/£50
ditto, Knopf (New York), 1930 (2 vols) . . . £150/£45
A Variety of Things, Heinemann (London), 1928 . £40/£10
ditto, Knopf (New York), 1928 (2,000 numbered copies) .
. . . . £40/£10
Lytton Strachey, C.U.P. (Cambridge, UK), 1943 (wraps) £10
ditto, Knopf (New York), 1943 . . . . . £25/£10
Mainly on the Air, Heinemann (London), 1946 . £20/£5
ditto, Knopf (New York), 1947 . . . . . £15/£5
Sherlockiana: A Reminiscence of Sherlock Holmes, Edwin B. Hill (Tempe, AZ), 1948 (36 copies) . . . £350
More Theatres, Hart Davis (London), 1969 . . £10/£5
ditto, Taplinger (New York), 1969 . . . . £10/£5
Last Theatres, Hart Davis (London), 1970. . £10/£5
ditto, Knopf (New York), 1970 . . . . . £10/£5
Letters Of Max Beerbohm, 1892-1956, Murray (London), 1988 . . . . £15/£5
ditto, Norton (New York), 1989 . . . . . £15/£5

Drawings and Caricatures
Caricatures of Twenty-Five Gentleman, Leonard Smithers (London), 1896 (25 plates; first issue with 'Leonard/Smithers' on spine) £450
ditto, Leonard Smithers (London), 1896 (second issue with 'Leonard/Smithers/& Co' on spine) £350
Poet's Corner, Heinemann (London), 1904 (20 colour plates, pictorial boards) £200
ditto, Heinemann (London), 1904 (pictorial wraps). . £200
A Book of Caricatures, Methuen (London), 1907 (colour frontispiece, 48 drawings) £200
Cartoons: The Second Childhood of John Bull, Stephen Swift (London), [1911] (first issue, 15 full-page colour plates bound in book) £125

ditto, Stephen Swift (London), [1911] (second issue, 15 colour plates in cloth folder) £100
Fifty Caricatures, Heinemann (London), 1913 (50 black & white plates). £100
ditto, Dutton (New York), 1913 . . . . . £75
A Survey, Heinemann (London), 1921 (coloured frontispiece and 52 plates) . . . . . . £100/£45
ditto, Heinemann (London), 1921 (275 signed, numbered copies) . . . . . . £225/£150
ditto, Doubleday, Page & Co. (New York), 1921 . £100/£45
Rossetti and His Circle, Heinemann (London), 1922 (colour frontispiece and 22 colour plates) . . . £175/£45
ditto, Heinemann (London), 1922 (380 signed, numbered copies) . . . . £400/£350
Things New and Old, Heinemann (London), 1923 (coloured frontispiece and 49 black & white plates) . £150/£50
ditto, Heinemann (London), 1923 (350 signed, numbered copies, with additional signed coloured plate) £300/£200
Observations, Heinemann (London), 1925 (coloured frontispiece and 51 plates). . . . . £150/£50
ditto, Heinemann (London), 1925 (250 copies with extra signed colour plate) £300
The Heroes and Heroines of Bitter Sweet, [Leadley (London), 1931] (900 numbered copies; portfolio; mounted facsimile of a Beerbohm letter and 5 colour plates) . £200

Edited by Beerbohm
Herbert Beerbohm Tree, Hutchinson (London), 1920 .
. . . . £200/£45
ditto, Dutton (New York), [1920] . . . £200/£45

Collected Edition
Works, Heinemann (London), 1922-28 (10 vols, 780 signed, numbered sets) . . . . . . £1,500/£450

BRENDAN BEHAN

(b.1923 d.1964)

Irish playwright Behan spent many years in prison as a result of his I.R.A. activities. Released in 1947, he had begun to write whilst still behind bars, and his first success came with the publication of *The Quare Fellow* in 1956. Behan found fame difficult to deal with, and his drink problem and diabetes resulted in infamous drunken public appearances on stage and television.

Plays
The Quare Fellow, Methuen (London), 1956 . . £125/£25
ditto, Grove Press (New York), 1956. . . . £40/£10
ditto, Grove Press (New York), 1956 (pbk) . . £10
ditto, Grove Press (New York), 1956 (100 numbered copies, acetate d/w) . . . . . . £200/£150
The Hostage, Methuen (London), 1958 . . . £65/£15
ditto, Grove Press (New York), 1958. . . . £40/£20
ditto, Grove Press (New York), 1958 (pbk) . . £10
ditto, Grove Press (New York), 1958 (26 signed, lettered copies) £1,000
Borstal Boy, Random House (New York), 1971 (adapted for the stage by Frank McMahon) . . . . £35/£10
Richard's Cork Leg, Methuen (London), 1973 . £20/£5
ditto, Grove Press (New York), 1974. . . . £20/£5

An Giall and *The Hostage*, Catholic Univ of America Press/ Colin Smythe (Washington, DC/Gerrards Cross), 1987 .
. . . . £10/£5
Moving Out and *A Garden Party: Two Plays*, Proscenium Press (Dixon, CA), 1967 (stapled wraps) £5
The Complete Plays, Grove Press (New York), 1978 (pbk) .
. . . . £10
ditto, Methuen (London), 1978 (pbk). . . . £10

Novel
The Scarperer, Doubleday (Garden City, NY), 1964 . .
. . . . £30/£5
ditto, Hutchinson (London), 1964 . . . . £30/£5

Others
Borstal Boy, Hutchinson (London), 1958. . . £75/£15
ditto, Knopf (New York), 1959 . . . . £65/£15
Brendan Behan's Island: An Irish Sketchbook, Hutchinson (London), 1962 (with drawings by Paul Hogarth) £30/£5
ditto, Bernard Geis (New York), 1962 . . . £25/£5
Hold Your Hour and Have Another, Hutchinson (London), 1963 (with decorations by Beatrice Behan) . . £40/£10
ditto, Little, Brown (Boston), 1963 . . . . £25/£10
Brendan Behan's New York, Hutchinson (London), 1964 (with drawings by Paul Hogarth) . . . . £20/£5
ditto, Bernard Geis (New York), 1964 . . . £20/£5
Confessions of an Irish Rebel, Hutchinson (London), 1965
. . . . £20/£5
ditto, Bernard Geis Associates (New York), 1966 . £15/£5
Poems and Stories, Liffey Press (Dublin), 1978 (500 copies; pbk) £20
Poems and *A Play in Irish*, Gallery Press (Dublin), 1981 .
. . . . £25/£10
After the Wake: Twenty-One Prose Works Including Previously Unpublished Material, O'Brien Press (Dublin), 1981 . . . . £20/£5
The Letters of Brendan Behan, Macmillan (London), 1992
. . . . £20/£5
ditto, McGill-Queen's Univ Press (Montreal, QC), 1992 .
. . . . £20/£5
The King of Ireland's Son, Andersen Press (London), 1996 (illustrated by P.J. Lynch) . . . . . . £10/£5
ditto, Orchard Books (New York), 1997 . . . £10/£5
The Dubbalin Man, Farmar (Dublin), 1997 . . £25/£10

JOSEPHINE BELL

(b.1897 d.1987)

Bell is collected principally for her many detective novels, although these are not widely known outside of the genre because her themes varied greatly and she did not stick to a recognisable formula. Many of her early novels feature a doctor, David Wintringham, drawing on the author's own career in the medical profession.

'Dr David Wintringham' novels
Murder in Hospital, Longmans Green (London), 1937 (yellow-brown cloth, red lettering) . . . £400/£100
Death on the Borough Council, Longmans Green (London), 1937 (deep red cloth, black lettering) . . . £350/£75
Fall over Cliff, Longmans Green (London), 1938 (blue cloth, black lettering) . . . . £300/£75
ditto, Macmillan (New York), 1956 . . . . £20/£5

Death at Half-Term, Longmans Green (London), 1939 (blue cloth, black lettering) . . . . . . £250/£45

ditto, as *Curtain Call for a Corpse*, Macmillan (New York), 1965 . . . . £20/£5

ditto, as *Curtain Call for a Corpse*, White Lion (London), 1976 (pbk) £5

From Natural Causes, Longmans Green (London), 1939 (red cloth, black lettering) . . . . . £250/£45

All is Vanity, Longmans Green (London), 1940 (blue cloth, black lettering) . . . . £200/£40

Death at the Medical Board, Longmans Green (London), 1944 (green cloth, red lettering) . . . £50/£10

ditto, Ballantine (New York), 1964 (pbk) . . . £5

Death in Clairvoyance, Longmans Green (London), 1949 (green cloth/gilt lettering to spine) . . . £45/£10

The Summer School Mystery, Methuen (London), 1950 (blue cloth/gilt lettering) . . . . . £45/£10

Bones in the Barrow, Methuen (London), 1953 (red cloth/gilt lettering) . . . . . £45/£10

ditto, Macmillan (New York), 1955 . . . £20/£5

The China Roundabout, Hodder & Stoughton (London), 1956 (blue cloth/gilt lettering to spine) . . £45/£10

ditto, as *Murder on the Merry-go-round*, Ballantine (New York), 1965 . . . . £5

The Seeing Eye, Hodder & Stoughton (London), 1958 (blue cloth/gilt lettering to spine) . . . £30/£5

Other Detective Novels

The Port of London Murders, Longmans Green (London), 1938 (red cloth, black lettering) . . . £200/£35

ditto, Macmillan (New York), 1958 . . . £20/£5

Trouble at Wrekin Farm, Longmans Green (London), 1942 (yellow/brown cloth, red lettering) . . . £150/£25

To Let – Furnished, Methuen (London), 1952 (blue cloth/gilt lettering to spine) . . . . £45/£10

ditto, as *Stranger on a Cliff*, Ace (New York), 1964 (pbk) £5

Fires at Fairlawn, Methuen (London), 1954 (blue cloth/gilt lettering to spine) . . . . . . £35/£10

Death in Retirement, Methuen (London), 1956 (blue cloth/gilt lettering to spine) . . . . £35/£10

ditto, Macmillan (New York), 1956 . . . £20/£5

Double Doom, Hodder & Stoughton (London), 1957 (blue cloth/gilt lettering to spine) . . . . £35/£10

ditto, Macmillan (New York), 1958 . . . £20/£5

The House above the River, Hodder & Stoughton (London), 1959 (maroon cloth/gilt lettering to spine) . £30/£5

Easy Prey, Hodder & Stoughton (London), 1959 (red cloth/ilt lettering to spine) . . . . . . £30/£5

ditto, Macmillan (New York), 1959 . . . £20/£5

A Well-Known Face, Hodder & Stoughton (London), 1960 (green cloth/gilt lettering to spine) . . . £30/£5

ditto, Ives Washburn (New York), 1960 . . . £20/£5

New People at the Hollies, Hodder & Stoughton (London), 1961 (green cloth/gilt lettering to spine) . . £30/£5

ditto, Macmillan (New York), 1961 . . . £20/£5

Adventure With Crime, Hodder & Stoughton (London), 1961 (green cloth/gilt lettering to spine) . . £25/£5

A Flat Tyre in Fulham, Hodder & Stoughton (London), 1963 (red cloth/gilt lettering to spine) . . £25/£5

ditto, as *Fiasco in Fulham*, Macmillan (New York), 1963 . . . . £15/£5

ditto, as *Room for a Body* Ballantine (New York), 1964 (pbk) £5

The Hunter and the Trapped, Hodder & Stoughton (London), 1963 (orange cloth/gilt lettering to spine) £25/£5

The Upfold Witch, Hodder & Stoughton (London), 1964 (blue cloth/gilt lettering to spine) . . . £25/£5

ditto, Macmillan (New York), 1964 . . . £15/£5

No Escape, Hodder & Stoughton (London), 1965 (blue cloth/gilt lettering to spine) . . . . £25/£5

ditto, Macmillan (New York), 1966 . . . £15/£5

Death on the Reserve, Hodder & Stoughton (London), 1966 (blue cloth/gilt lettering to spine) . . . £25/£5

ditto, Macmillan (New York), 1966 . . . £15/£5

The Catalyst, Hodder & Stoughton (London), 1966 (blue cloth/gilt lettering to spine) . . . . £25/£5

ditto, Macmillan (New York), 1967 . . . £10/£5

Death of a Con Man, Hodder & Stoughton (London), 1968 (maroon cloth/gilt lettering to spine) . . £20/£5

ditto, Lippincott (Philadelphia, PA), 1968. . . £10/£5

The Wilberforce Legacy, Hodder & Stoughton (London), 1969 (green cloth/gilt lettering to spine). . £20/£5

ditto, Walker (New York), 1969 . . . . £10/£5

The Fennister Affair, Hodder & Stoughton (London), 1969 (black cloth/gilt lettering to spine) . . . £20/£5

ditto, Stein & Day (New York), 1977. . . £10/£5

A Hydra with Six Heads, Hodder & Stoughton (London), 1970 (blue cloth/gilt lettering to spine) . . £15/£5

ditto, Stein & Day (New York), 1977. . . £10/£5

A Hole in the Ground, Hodder & Stoughton (London), 1971 (blue cloth/gilt lettering to spine) . . . £15/£5

ditto, Ace (New York), 1973 (pbk) £5

Death of a Poison-Tongue, Hodder & Stoughton (London), 1972 (maroon cloth/gilt lettering to spine) . £15/£5

ditto, Stein & Day (New York), 1977. . . £10/£5

A Pigeon among the Cats, Hodder & Stoughton (London), 1974 (blue cloth/gilt lettering to spine) . . £15/£5

ditto, Stein & Day (New York), 1977. . . £10/£5

Victim, Hodder & Stoughton (London), 1975 (black cloth/gilt lettering to spine) . . . . £15/£5

ditto, Walker (New York), 1976 . . . . £10/£5

The Trouble in Hunter Ward, Hodder & Stoughton (London), 1976 (red cloth/gilt lettering to spine) . £15/£5

ditto, Walker (New York), 1977 . . . . £10/£5

Such a Nice Client, Hodder & Stoughton (London), 1977 (blue cloth/gilt lettering to spine) . . . £10/£5

ditto, as *The Stroke of Death*, Walker (New York), 1977 . . . . £10/£5

A Swan-Song Betrayed, Hodder & Stoughton (London), 1978 (maroon cloth/gilt lettering to spine) . . £10/£5

ditto, as *Treachery in Type*, Walker (New York), 1980. . . . . £10/£5

Wolf! Wolf!, Hodder & Stoughton (London), 1979 (blue cloth/gilt lettering to spine) . . . . £10/£5

ditto, Walker (New York), 1980 . . . . £10/£5

A Question of Inheritance, Hodder & Stoughton (London), 1980 (black cloth/gilt lettering to spine). . £10/£5

ditto, Walker (New York), 1981 . . . . £10/£5

The Innocent, Hodder & Stoughton (London), 1982 (green cloth/gilt lettering to spine) . . . . £10/£5

ditto, as *A Deadly Place to Stay*, Walker (New York), 1983 . . . . £10/£5

Other Novels

The Bottom of the Well, Longmans Green (London), 1940 . . . . £45/£10

Martin Croft, Longmans Green (London), 1941 . £35/£10

Alvina Foster, Longmans Green (London), 1943 . £30/£10
Compassionate Adventure, Longmans Green (London), 1946 . . . . £25/£5
Total War at Haverington, Longmans Green (London), 1947 . . . . £25/£5
Wonderful Mrs Marriot, Longmans Green (London), 1948. . . . . £20/£5
The Whirlpool, Methuen (London), 1949. . . £20/£5
The Backing Winds, Methuen (London), 1951 . £20/£5
Cage-Birds, Methuen (London), 1953 . . £20/£5
Two Ways to Love, Methuen (London), 1954 . . £15/£5
Hell's Pavement, Methuen (London), 1955 . £15/£5
The Convalescent, Bles (London), 1960 . . . £10/£5
Safety First, Bles (London), 1962 . . . . £10/£5
The Alien, Bles (London), 1964 . . . . £10/£5
Tudor Pilgrimage, Bles (London), 1967 . . . £10/£5
Jacobean Adventure, Bles (London), 1969 . . £10/£5
Over the Seas, Bles (London), 1970 . . . . £10/£5
The Dark and the Light, Bles (London), 1971 . £10/£5
To Serve a Queen, Bles (London), 1972 . . £10/£5
In the King's Absence, Bles (London), 1973 . £10/£5
A Question of Loyalties, Bles (London), 1974 . £10/£5

Non-Fiction

Crime in Our Time, Nicholas Vane (London), 1961 £25/£10
ditto, Abelard Schuman (New York), 1962 . . £15/£10

GEORGE BELLAIRS

(b.1902 d.1985)

Bellairs was the *nom de plume* of UK crime writer Harold Blundell who wrote more than 50 books, most featuring detective Inspector Littlejohn. He also contributed articles to the *Manchester Guardian* and, once he had retired to the Isle of Man, to such publications as *Manx Life*.

Novels

Littlejohn on Leave, John Gifford (London), 1941. £350/£75
Death of a Busybody, John Gifford (London), 1942 . . . . £150/£50
ditto, Macmillan (New York), 1943 . . £75/£25
The Dead Shall Be Raised, John Gifford (London), 1942 . . . . £150/£50
ditto as *Murder Will Speak*, Macmillan (New York), 1943 . . . . £75/£25
The Four Unfaithful Servants, John Gifford (London), 1942 . . . . £125/£50
Calamity at Harwood, John Gifford (London), 1943 . . . . £125/£50
ditto, Macmillan (New York), 1945 . . £75/£25
Murder of a Quack, John Gifford (London), 1943. £125/£40
ditto, Macmillan (New York), 1944 . . £75/£25
Turmoil in Zion, John Gifford (London), 1943 . £125/£40
ditto as *Death Stops the Frolic*, Macmillan (New York), 1944 . . . . £75/£25
Death in the Night Watches, John Gifford (London), 1945 . . . . £65/£25
ditto, Macmillan (New York), 1946 . . . £40/£15
He'd Rather Be Dead, John Gifford (London), 1945 . . . . £75/£25
The Case of the Scared Rabbits, John Gifford (London), 1946 . . . . £50/£15

The Crime at Halfpenny Bridge, John Gifford (London), 1946 . . . . £50/£15
Death on the Last Train, John Gifford (London), 1948 . . . . £50/£15
ditto, Macmillan (New York), 1949 . . . £25/£10
The Case of the Seven Whistlers, John Gifford (London), [1948] . . . . £50/£15
ditto, Macmillan (New York), 1948 . . . £25/£10
Outrage on Gallows Hill, Thriller Book Club (London), 1948 . . . . £25/£10
ditto, John Gifford (London), 1949 . . . £35/£10
The Case of the Famished Parson, John Gifford (London), 1949 . . . . £35/£10
ditto, Macmillan (New York), 1949 . . . £25/£10
The Case of the Demented Spiv, John Gifford (London), 1949 . . . . £35/£10
ditto, Macmillan (New York), 1950 . . . £25/£10
The Case of the Headless Jesuit, John Gifford (London), 1950 . . . . £35/£10
ditto as *Death Brings In The New Year*, Macmillan (New York), 1951 . . . . . £75/£25
Dead March for Penelope Blow, John Gifford (London), 1951 . . . . £35/£10
ditto, Macmillan (New York), 1951 . . . £25/£10
Death in Dark Glasses, John Gifford (London), 1952 . . . . £35/£10
ditto, Macmillan (New York), 1952 . . . £25/£10
Lepers' Hollow, John Gifford (London), 1952 . £35/£10
A Knife for Harry Dodd, John Gifford (London), 1953 . . . . £35/£10
Half-Mast for the Deemster, John Gifford (London), 1953 . . . . £35/£10
Corpses in Enderby, John Gifford (London), 1954 £35/£10
The Cursing Stones Murder, John Gifford (London), 1954. . . . . £35/£10
Death in Room Five, John Gifford (London), 1955 £25/£10
Death Treads Softly, John Gifford (London), 1956 £35/£10
Death Drops the Pilot, John Gifford (London), 1956 . . . . £35/£10
Death in High Provence, John Gifford (London), 1957 . . . . £35/£10
Death Sends for the Doctor, John Gifford (London), 1957 . . . . £35/£10
Corpse at the Carnival, John Gifford (London), 1958 . . . . £25/£10
Murder Makes Mistakes, John Gifford (London), 1958 . . . . £25/£10
Bones in the Wilderness, John Gifford (London), 1959 . . . . £25/£10
Toll The Bell For Murder, John Gifford (London), 1959 . . . . £25/£10
Death in the Fearful Night, John Gifford (London), 1960 . . . . £25/£10
Death in Despair, John Gifford (London), 1960 . £25/£10
Death of a Tin God, John Gifford (London), 1961. £25/£10
The Body in the Dumb River, John Gifford (London), 1961 . . . . £25/£10
ditto, as *Murder Masquerade*, Tower (New York), 1981 (pbk) £5
The Tormentors, John Gifford (London), 1962 . £25/£10
Death Before Breakfast, John Gifford (London), 1962. . . . . £25/£10
Death in the Wasteland, John Gifford (London), 1963 . . . . £25/£10

Surfeit of Suspects, John Gifford (London), 1964 .   £15/£5
Death of a Shadow, John Gifford (London), 1964 .   £15/£5
Death Spins the Wheel, John Gifford (London), 1965 .   .
.   .   .   .   £15/£5
Intruder in the Dark, John Gifford (London), 1966   £15/£5
Strangers Among the Dead, John Gifford (London), 1966 .
.   .   .   .   £15/£5
Death in Desolation, John Gifford (London), 1967   £15/£5
Single Ticket to Death, John Gifford (London), 1967 .   .
.   .   .   .   £15/£5
Fatal Alibi, John Gifford (London), 1968.   .   £15/£5
Murder Gone Mad, John Gifford (London), 1968 .   £15/£5
Tycoon's Death Bed, John Gifford (London), 1970   £15/£5
The Night They Killed Joss Varran, John Gifford (London),
1970   .   .   .   .   £15/£5
Pomeroy Deceased, John Gifford (London), 1971 .   £15/£5
Murder Adrift, John Gifford (London), 1972 .   .   £15/£5
Devious Murder, John Gifford (London),1973   .   £15/£5
ditto, Walker (New York), 1980 .   .   .   .   £10/£5
Fear Round About, John Gifford (London), 1975 .   £10/£5
ditto, Walker (New York), 1975 .   .   .   .   £10/£5
Close All Roads to Sospel, John Gifford (London), 1976   .
.   .   .   .   £10/£5
ditto, as *All Roads to Sospel*, Walker (New York), 1981   .
.   .   .   .   £10/£5
The Downhill Ride of Leeman Popple, John Gifford
(London), 1978   .   .   .   .   .   .   £10/£5
An Old Man Dies, John Gifford (London), 1980 .   £10/£5

Novels by 'Hilary Landon'
Murder at Morning Prayers, John Gifford (London), 1947.
.   .   .   .   £45/£15
Circle Round A Corpse, John Gifford (London), 1948 .   .
.   .   .   .   £45/£15
Choose Your Own Verdict, John Gifford (London), 1949   .
.   .   .   .   £45/£15
Exit Sir Toby Belch, John Gifford (London), 1950   £45/£15

HILAIRE BELLOC

(b.1870 d.1953)

Belloc was a poet, novelist, essayist and travel writer, but is
best known and most often collected for his humorous
verse for children. 'Matilda', one of his 'cautionary tales'
tells how a girl who was a liar was burnt to death. *The Path
to Rome*, an account of a walking trip he took from central
France to Rome, has remained continuously in print.

Poetry
Verses and Sonnets, Ward & Downey (London), 1896. £300
The Bad Child's Book of Beasts, Alden Press (Oxford),
1896 (pseud 'H.B.') £250
More Beasts (For Worse Children), Edward Arnold
(London), 1897   .   .   .   .   £75
The Modern Traveller, Edward Arnold (London), 1898   £75
A Moral Alphabet, Edward Arnold (London), 1899   .   £65
Cautionary Tales for Children, Eveleigh Nash (London),
1907   .   .   .   .   £75
Verses, Duckworth (London), 1910   .   .   .   .   £50
More Peers, Stephen Swift & Co (London), 1911 .   .   £45
Sonnets and Verse, Duckworth (London), 1923   .   £50/£10
ditto, Duckworth (London), 1923 (525 signed copies) .   £75

ditto, McBride (New York), 1924   .   .   .   .   £20/£5
ditto, McBride (New York), 1924 (500 numbered copies)   .
.   .   .   .   £20/£10
The Chanty of the Nona, Faber, Ariel Poem (London), 1928
(sewn wraps) £15
ditto, Faber, Ariel Poem (London), 1928 (500 signed, large
paper copies; boards) £50
New Cautionary Tales, Duckworth (London), 1930 £75/£25
ditto, Duckworth (London), 1930 (110 signed copies) .£175
ditto, Harper (New York), 1931 .   .   .   .   £75/£20
In Praise of Wine: A Heroic Poem, privately printed/Peter
Davies (London), 1932 (100 copies)   .   .   .£175
Ladies and Gentlemen, Duckworth (London), 1932 £40/£15
The Verse of Hilaire Belloc, The Nonesuch Press (London),
1954 (1,250 numbered copies) £35

Novels
Emmanuel Burden, Methuen (London), 1904 (34 full-page
plates by G.K. Chesterton) £40
ditto, Scribner (New York), 1904   .   .   .   .   £35
Mr Clutterbuck's Election, Eveleigh Nash (London), 1908 .
.   .   .   .   £35
A Change in the Cabinet, Methuen (London), 1909   .   £30
Pongo and the Bull, Constable (London), 1910   .   .   £25
The Girondin, Nelson (London), 1911   .   .   .   £30
The Green Overcoat, Arrowsmith (London), 1912.   .   £45
ditto, McBride (New York), 1912   .   .   .   .   £40
The Mercy of Allah, Chatto & Windus (London), 1922   .
.   .   .   .   £75/£20
ditto, Appleton (New York), 1922   .   .   .   .   £75/£20
Mr Petre, Arrowsmith (London), 1925   .   .   .   £75/£20
ditto, Robert M. McBride (New York), 1925   .   £75/£20
The Emerald of Catherine the Great, Arrowsmith (London),
1926 (illustrated by G.K. Chesterton)   .   .   £50/£15
ditto, as *The Emerald*, Harper & Brothers (New York), 1926
.   .   .   .   £50/£15
The Haunted House, Arrowsmith (London), 1927. £200/£65
ditto, Harper & Brothers (New York), 1928   .   .£150/£50
But Soft, We Are Observed, Arrowsmith (London), 1928   .
.   .   .   .   £50/£15
ditto, as *Shadowed!*, Harper & Brothers (New York), 1929 .
.   .   .   .   £50/£15
Belinda, Constable (London), 1928   .   .   .   £65/£15
ditto, Harper & Brothers (New York), 1929   .   £50/£10
The Missing Masterpiece, Arrowsmith (London), 1929
(illustrated by G.K. Chesterton)   .   .   .£100/£40
ditto, Harper & Brothers (New York), 1929   .   £75/£25
The Man Who Made Gold, Arrowsmith (London), 1930   .
.   .   .   .   £75/£15
ditto, Harper & Brothers (New York), 1931   .   £65/£15
The Postmaster General, Arrowsmith (London), 1932 .   .
.   .   .   .£100/£25
ditto, Lippincott (Philadelphia, PA), 1932.   .   £75/£10
The Hedge and the Horse, Cassell (London), 1936   £35/£10

History
Danton, John Nisbet & Co. (London), 1899   .   .   £50
ditto, Scribner (New York), 1899   .   .   .   .   £40
Robespierre, John Nisbet & Co. (London), 1901   .   £40
ditto, Scribner (New York), 1902   .   .   .   .   £35
The Eye Witness, Eveleigh Nash (London), 1908 .   .   £40
Marie Antoinette, Methuen (London), 1909   .   .   £40
ditto, Doubleday, Page & Co (New York), 1909   .   .   £20

The French Revolution, Williams & Norgate (London), 1911 . . . . £30
ditto, as *High Lights of the French Revolution*, Century (New York), 1915 . . . . . . £20
The Battle of Blenheim, Stephen Swift & Co (London), 1911 . . . . £20
Malplaquet, Stephen Swift & Co (London), 1911 . . £20
Crecy, Stephen Swift & Co (London), 1911 . . . £20
Poitiers, Stephen Swift & Co (London), 1911 . . . £20
Waterloo, Stephen Swift & Co (London), 1912 . . £20
Turcoing, Stephen Swift & Co (London), 1912 . . £20
Warfare in England, Williams & Norgate (London), 1912 .
. . . . £20
The Book of the Bayeaux Tapestry, Chatto & Windus (London), 1914 . . . . £30
ditto, Putman's (New York), 1914 . . . . . £25
History of England, Catholic Publications Society of America (New York), 1912-15 (11 vols; with John Lingard) .
. . . . £75 the set
Land and Water Map of the War, Land & Water (London), 1915 . . . . £25
A General Sketch of the European War: The First Phase, Nelson (London), 1915 . . . . . £25
The Two Maps of Europe, Arthur Pearson (London), 1915 .
. . . . £30
The Last Days of the French Monarchy, Chapman & Hall (London), 1916 . . . . £10
A General Sketch of the European War: The Second Phase, Nelson (London), 1916. . . . . £25
The Second Year of the War, Land & Water (London), 1916 . . . . £30
The Principles of War, by Foch, Chapman & Hall (London), 1919 (translation) £20
Precepts and Judgements, by Foch, Chapman & Hall (London), 1919 (translation) £25
The Jews, Constable (London), 1922. . . . £75/£35
ditto, Houghton Mifflin (Boston), 1922 . . . £75/£35
The Campaign of 1812, Nelson (London), 1924 £75/£15
ditto, as *Napoleon's Campaign of 1812 and the Retreat from Moscow*, Harper & Brothers (New York), 1926. .
. . . . £75/£15
History of England Vol. 1, Methuen (London), 1925 .
. . . . £25/£10
ditto, Putnam (New York), 1925. . . . . £25/£10
Miniatures of French History, Nelson (London), 1925 .
. . . . £35/£15
Mrs Markham's New History of England, Cayme Press (London), 1926 . . . . . . £35/£15
History of England Vol. 2, Methuen (London), 1927 . .
. . . . £25/£10
ditto, Putnam (New York), 1927. . . . . £25/£10
Oliver Cromwell, Benn (London), 1927 . . . £30/£10
History of England Vol. 3, Methuen (London), 1928 . .
. . . . £25/£10
ditto, Putnam (New York), 1928. . . . . £25/£10
James II, Faber & Gwyer (London), 1928 . . £35/£15
ditto, as *James the Second*, Lippincott (Philadelphia, PA), 1928 . . . . £35/£15
How the Reformation Happened, Cape (London), 1928 .
. . . . £25/£10
ditto, McBride & Co (New York), 1928 . . . £25/£10
Joan of Arc, Cassell (London), 1929. . . . £30/£10
ditto, Little, Brown (Boston), 1929 . . . £30/£10
Richelieu, Lippincott (Philadelphia, PA), 1929 . £30/£10

ditto, Benn (London), 1930 . . . . . £30/£10
Wolsey, Cassell (London), 1930 . . . . . £30/£10
ditto, Lippincott (Philadelphia, PA), 1930. . £30/£10
History of England Vol. 4, Methuen (London), 1931 £25/£5
ditto, Putnam (New York), 1925. . . . . £25/£10
Cranmer, Cassell (London), 1931 . . . . £35/£10
ditto, Lippincott (Philadelphia, PA), 1931. . . £35/£10
The Tactics and Strategy of the Great Duke of Marlborough, Arrowsmith (London), 1931 . . . £100/£50
Six British Battles, Arrowsmith (London), 1931 £40/£15
Napoleon, Cassell (London), 1932 . . . . £25/£10
ditto, Lippincott (Philadelphia, PA), 1932. . . £25/£10
William the Conqueror, Peter Davies (London), 1933 . .
. . . . £25/£10
ditto, Appleton (New York), 1934 . . . . £25/£10
Beckett, Catholic Truth Society, 1933 (stapled wraps) . £10
Charles I, Cassell (London), 1933 . . . . £25/£5
ditto, Lippincott (Philadelphia, PA), 1933. . . £15/£5
Cromwell, Cassell (London), 1934 . . . . £15/£5
ditto, Lippincott (Philadelphia, PA), 1934 . . £15/£5
A Shorter History of England, Harrap, 1934 . . £25/£10
Milton, Cassell (London), 1935 . . . . . £25/£10
ditto, Lippincott (Philadelphia, PA), 1935. . . £25/£10
The Battleground, Cassell (London), 1936 . . £20/£5
ditto, Lippincott (Philadelphia, PA), 1936. . . £20/£5
Characters of the Reformation, Sheed & Ward (London), 1936 . . . . £15/£5
ditto, Sheed & Ward (New York), 1936 . . . £15/£5
The Crusade, Cassell (London), 1937 . . . £25/£10
ditto, as *The Crusades*, Bruce Publishing Company (Milwaukee, OR), 1937 . . . . . . £25/£10
The Crisis of Our Civilization, Cassell (London), 1937 .
. . . . £25/£10
ditto, Fordham Univ Press (New York), 1937 . . . £10
The Great Heresies, Sheed & Ward (London), 1938 £20/£5
ditto, Sheed & Ward (New York), 1938 . . . £20/£5
Monarchy: A Study of Louis XIV, Cassell (London), 1938 .
. . . . £25/£10
ditto, as *Louis XIV*, Harper (New York), 1938 . £25/£10
Charles II: The Last Rally, *ditto*, Harper & Brothers (New York), 1939 . . . . £20/£5
ditto, as *The Last Rally: A Study of Charles II*, Cassell (London), 1940 . . . . £20/£5
Elizabethan Commentary, Cassell (London), 1942 £15/£5

Travel
Paris, Henry T. Coates (Philadelphia), 1898 . . . £25
ditto, Edward Arnold (London), 1900 . . . . £25
The Path to Rome, George Allen (London), 1902 . . £25
The Old Road, Constable (London), 1904 . . . £75
Esto Perpetua, Duckworth (London), 1906 . . . £45
Sussex, A. & C. Black (London), 1906 . . . . £30
The Historic Thames, Dent (London), 1907 . . . £65
The Pyrenees, Methuen (London), 1909 . . . . £25
The River of London, T.N. Foulis (London), 1912. . £25
The Four Men, Nelson (London), 1912 . . . . £20
ditto, Bobbs-Merrill (Indianapolis, IN), 1912 . . £10
The Stane Street, Constable (London), 1913 . . £10
ditto, Dutton (New York), 1913 . . . . . £10
The Road, Charles W. Hobson for The British Reinforced Concrete Engineering Co (Manchester), 1923 . £25
ditto, Harper & Brothers (New York), [c.1926] . £25/£10
The Contrast, Arrowsmith (London), 1923 . . £20/£5
ditto, McBride (New York), 1924 . . . . £20/£5

The Cruise of the Nona, Constable (London), 1925 £45/£15
ditto, Houghton Mifflin (Boston), 1925 . . . . £40/£15
The Highway and its Vehicles, The Studio (London), 1926
   (1,250 numbered copies) . . . . . £75/£25
Many Cities, Constable (London), 1928 . . . £25/£10
Return to the Baltic, Constable (London), 1938 . £25/£10
On Sailing the Sea, Methuen (London), 1939 . . £15/£5
Places, Sheed and Ward (New York), 1941 . . £15/£5
ditto, Cassell (London), 1942 . . . . . £15/£5

Politics

Socialism and the Servile State, Independent Labour Party
   (London), 1910 . . . . £10
The Party System and Cecil Chesterton, Stephen Swift &
   Co (London), 1911 . . . . £15
The Servile State, T.N. Foulis (London), 1912 . . £20
ditto, Henry Holt (New York), 1946 . . . . £10/£5
The Free Press, Allen & Unwin (London), 1918 . . £15
The House of Commons and the Monarchy, Allen & Unwin
   (London), 1920 . . . . £45/£10
Economics for Helen, Arrowsmith (London), 1924 £20/£10
ditto, Arrowsmith (London), 1924 (250 signed copies) . £175
ditto, Putnam (New York), 1924 . . . . £20/£10
The Political Effort, True Temperance Association, 1924 £15

Literature

Caliban's Guide to Letters, Duckworth (London), 1903 £30
The Romance of Tristan and Iseult, George Allen
   (London), 1903 (translation) £20
ditto, Albert & Charles Boni (New York), 1927 . . £20
*Avril, Being Essays on the Poetry of the French Renais-
sance*, Duckworth (London), 1904 . . . . . £20
On the Place of Gilbert Chesterton in English Letters,
   Sheed & Ward (London), 1940 . . . £20/£5
ditto, Sheed & Ward (New York), 1940 . . . £20/£5

Religion

An Open Letter on the Decay of Faith, Burns & Oates
   (London), 1906 . . . . £20
The Catholic Church and Historical Truth, W. Watson
   (London), 1908 . . . . £10
An Examination of Socialism, Catholic Truth Society
   (London), 1908 (stapled wraps) £10
The Church and Socialism, Catholic Truth Society
   (London), 1908 (stapled wraps) £10
The Ferrer Case, Catholic Truth Society (London), 1909
   (stapled wraps) £10
Anti-Catholic History, Catholic Truth Society (London),
   1914 (stapled wraps) £10
Religion and Liberty, Catholic Truth Society (London), 1918
   (stapled wraps) £10
The Catholic Church and the Purchase of Private Property,
   Catholic Truth Society (London), 1920 (stapled wraps) £10
A Companion to Mr Wells' Outline of History, Sheed &
   Ward (London), 1926 . . . . . . £25/£10
ditto, Ecclesiastical Supply Association (San Francisco, CA)
   1927 . . . . £25/£10
Mr Belloc Still Objects, Sheed & Ward (London), 1927 .
   . . . . £15/£5
ditto, Ecclesiastical Supply Association (San Francisco, CA)
   1927 . . . . £15/£5
The Catholic Church and History, Burns, Oates &
   Washbourne (London), 1927 . . . . . £10/£5

Survivals and New Arrivals, Sheed & Ward (London), 1929
   . . . . £10/£5
ditto, Macmillan (New York), 1929 . . . . £10/£5
The Case of Dr Coulton, Sheed & Ward (London), 1931 .
   . . . . £10/£5
The Catholic and the War, Burns & Oates (London), 1940 .
   . . . . £10/£5

Essays

At the Sign of the Lion, Mosher (Portland, ME), 1896 (950
   copies) £25
ditto, Mosher (Portland, ME), 1916 . . . . £15
Hills and Seas, Methuen (London), 1906 . . . £25
On Nothing, Methuen (London), 1908 . . . . £15
On Everything, Methuen (London), 1909 . . . £15
On Anything, Constable (London), 1910 . . . £15
On Something, Methuen (London), 1910 . . . £15
First and Last, Methuen (London), 1911 . . . £10
ditto, Dutton (New York), 1912 . . . . . £10
This and That, Methuen (London), 1912 . . . £10
On, Methuen (London), 1923 . . . . £15/£5
Hilaire Belloc: Essays, Harrap (London), 1926 . £15/£5
Short Talks with the Dead, Cayme Press (London), 1926 .
   . . . . £25/£10
ditto, Harper & Brothers (New York), 1926 . . £25/£10
A Conversation with an Angel, Cape (London), 1928 . .
   . . . . £25/£10
ditto, Harper & Brothers (New York), 1929 . . £25/£10
Conversations with a Cat, Cassell (London), 1930 £25/£10
ditto, Harper & Brothers (New York), 1931 . . £20/£5
Essays of a Catholic, Sheed & Ward (London), 1931 £15/£5
Nine Nines, Blackwell (Oxford), 1931 . . . . £15
An Essay on the Restoration of Property, Distributist
   League (London), 1936 . . . . . . £10
ditto, Sheed & Ward (New York), 1936 . . . £15/£5
An Essay on the Nature of Contemporary England,
   Constable (London), 1937 . . . . . £15/£5
ditto, Sheed & Ward (New York), 1937 . . . £15/£5
The Silence of the Sea, Sheed & Ward (New York), 1940 .
   . . . . £15/£5
ditto, Cassell (London), 1941 . . . . . £15/£5

Others

Lambkin's Remains, by 'H.B.', The Proprietors of the J.C.R.
   at J. Vincent's (Oxford, U.K.), 1900 . . . . £75
The Great Inquiry, Duckworth (London), 1903 . £65
A Pamphlet, 1930, privately printed (for Belloc's 60th
   birthday; wraps) £65
On Translation, Clarendon Press (Oxford, UK), 1931 . .
   . . . . £30/£15
The Issue, Sheed & Ward (London), 1937 . £15/£5
The Question and the Answer, Bruce Publishing (New
   York), 1932 . . . . £15/£5
ditto, Longman's Green (London), 1938 . . . £15/£5
The Test in Poland, Weekly Review (London), 1939 . £10

SAUL BELLOW

(b.1915 d.2005)

A Canadian-born American Jewish writer whose work often addresses the problems of those living in urban areas and their place in the modern world. Considered one of the foremost novelists of the 20th century, Bellow is the first writer to win the American National Book Award three times. He was awarded the Nobel Prize for Literature in 1976.

Novels

Dangling Man, Vanguard Press (New York), 1944 . .
. . . . £1,750/£125
ditto, Lehmann (London), 1946 . . . . £250/£30
The Victim, Vanguard Press (New York), 1947 . £500/£45
ditto, Lehmann (London), 1948 . . . . £125/£25
The Adventures of Augie March, Viking (New York), 1953
. . . . £175/£30
ditto, Weidenfeld & Nicolson (London), 1954. £100/£15
Seize the Day, with Three Short Stories and a One Act Play,
Viking (New York), 1956 . . . . . £125/£15
ditto, Weidenfeld & Nicolson (London), 1957. £100/£10
Henderson the Rain King, Viking (New York), 1959 . .
. . . . £100/£15
ditto, Weidenfeld & Nicolson (London), 1959. £75/£15
Herzog, Viking (New York), 1964 . . . £65/£10
ditto, Weidenfeld & Nicolson (London), 1965. £25/£5
Mr Sammler's Planet, Viking (New York), 1970 . £15/£5
ditto, Weidenfeld & Nicolson (London), 1970. £15/£5
Humboldt's Gift, Viking (New York), 1975 . £25/£5
ditto, Alison Press/Secker & Warburg (London), 1975 .
. . . . £15/£5
ditto, Franklin Library (Franklin Centre, PA), 1980 (full
leather) £20
The Dean's December, Harper (New York), 1982. £10/£5
ditto, Harper (New York), 1982 (500 signed copies, glassine
wrapper, slipcase) . . . . . £75/£45
ditto, Secker & Warburg (London), 1982 . . £10/£5
ditto, Franklin Library (Franklin Centre, PA), 1982 (full
leather) £20
More Die of Heartbreak, Morrow (New York), 1987 £10/£5
ditto, Alison Press (London), 1987 . . . £10/£5
A Theft, Alison Press (London), 1989 . . £45/£10
ditto, Penguin (New York), 1989 (pbk) . . . £5
The Bellarosa Connection, Alison Press (London), 1989 .
. . . . £45/£10
ditto, Penguin (New York), 1989 (pbk) . . . £5
The Actual, Viking (London), 1997 . . . £10/£5
ditto, Penguin (New York), 1997 (pbk) . . . £5
Ravelstein, Viking (New York), 2000 . . £10/£5
ditto, Viking (London), 2000 . . . . £10/£5

Short Stories

Mosby's Memoirs and Other Stories, Viking (New York),
1968 . . . . £40/£10
ditto, Weidenfeld & Nicolson (London), 1969. £30/£5
The Portable Saul Bellow, Viking (New York), 1974 £20/£5
Him with His Foot in His Mouth and Other Stories, Harper
(New York), 1984 . . . . . £25/£5
ditto, Secker & Warburg (London), 1984 . . £20/£5
Something to Remember Me By, Viking (New York), 1991
. . . . £20/£5
ditto, Secker & Warburg (London), 1992 . . £15/£5

Collected Stories, Viking (New York), 2001 . . £10/£5
ditto, Viking (London), 2001 . . . . . £10/£5

Plays

The Last Analysis, Viking (New York), 1965 . . £65/£10
ditto, Weidenfeld & Nicolson (London), 1966. . £50/£10

Others

Recent American Fiction, Library of Congress (Washington,
DC), 1963 (stapled wraps). £10
To Jerusalem and Back, Viking (New York), 1976 £35/£5
ditto, Secker & Warburg (London), 1976 . . £25/£5
The Nobel Lecture, U.S. Information Service (Stockholm),
1977 (350 signed copies, tissue d/w) . . . £65/£40
It All Adds Up: from the Dim Past to the Uncertain Future,
Penguin (New York), 1994 . . . . . £10/£5
ditto, Secker & Warburg (London), 1994 . . . £10/£5
Conversations with Saul Bellow, Univ of Mississippi Press
(Jackson, MS), 1994 . . . . . . £25/£10

LUDWIG BEMELMANS

(b.1898 d.1962)

An artist and writer in various genres, Bemelmans is best known for his little French schoolgirl character, Madeline. All of these stories are told in rhymes, and each begins: 'In an old house in Paris, that was covered with vines, lived twelve little girls in two straight lines ... the smallest one was Madeline.'

'Madeline' Books

Madeline, Simon & Schuster (New York), 1939 £650/£125
ditto, Derek Verschoyle (London), [1953] . £200/£35
Madeline's Rescue, Viking (New York), 1953 . £350/£75
ditto, Derek Verschoyle (London), 1953 . . £200/£35
Madeline and the Bad Hat, Viking (New York), 1956 (985
signed copies, slipcase) . . . . £500/£350
ditto, Viking (New York), 1956 . . . . £300/£75
ditto, Deutsch (London), 1958 . . . . £175/£45
Madeline and the Gypsies, Viking (New York), 1959 . .
. . . . £300/£75
ditto, Deutsch (London), 1961 . . . . £145/£45
Madeline in London, Viking (New York), 1961 . £225/£65
ditto, Deutsch (London), 1962 . . . . £135/£35
Madeline's Christmas, McCall (New York), 1956 (stapled
wraps; issued in December 1956 as a supplement to the
Christmas edition of *McCall's* magazine) . . . £65
Viking/Kestrel (New York), 1985 (completed by Madeline
and Barbara Bemelmans) . . . . . £15/£5
ditto, Deutsch (London), 1985 . . . . £15/£5

Other Children's Books

Hansi, Viking (New York), 1934 . . . . £275/£65
ditto, Lovat Dickson (London), 1935. . . £150/£30
The Golden Basket, Viking (New York), 1936 . £200/£45
The Castle Number 9, Viking (New York), 1937 . £200/£45
Quito Express, Viking (New York), 1938 . . £150/£35
Rosebud, Viking (New York), 1942 . . . £125/£30
A Tale of Two Glimps, Columbia Broadcasting Systems
(New York), 1947 (glassine d/w) . . . £125/£100
The Happy Place, Little, Brown (Boston), 1952 . £50/£20
The High World, Harper (New York), 1954 . . £50/£20

ditto, Hamish Hamilton (London), 1958 . . . £50/£15
Parsley, Harper (New York), 1955 . . . . £50/£15

Poetry
Fifi, Simon & Schuster (New York), 1940 . .£150/£35
Sunshine, Simon & Schuster (New York), 1950 .£125/£30
Welcome Home, Harper (New York), 1960 . . £65/£20
ditto, Hamish Hamilton (London), 1961 . . £35/£15
Marina, Harper (New York), 1962 . . . . £65/£20

Novels for Adults
Now I Lay Me Down to Sleep, Viking (New York), 1943 .
. . . . £50/£15
ditto, Viking (New York), 1943 (500 signed copies; slipcase;
no d/w) . . . .£100/£65
ditto, Hamish Hamilton (London), 1944 . . £35/£10
The Blue Danube, Viking (New York), 1945 . £25/£10
ditto, Hamish Hamilton (London), 1946 . . £25/£10
Dirty Eddie, Viking (New York), 1947 . . . £25/£10
ditto, Hamish Hamilton (London), 1948 . . £25/£10
The Eye of God, Viking (New York), 1949 . . £25/£10
ditto, as *The Snow Mountain*, Hamish Hamilton (London),
1950 . . . . £25/£10
The Woman of My Life, Viking (New York), 1957 £25/£10
ditto, Hamish Hamilton (London), 1957 . . . £25/£10
Are You Hungry, Are You Cold, World (Cleveland, OH),
1960 . . . . £20/£5
ditto, Deutsch (London), 1961 . . . . £20/£5
The Street Where the Heart Lies, World (Cleveland, OH),
1963 . . . . £20/£5

Short Stories
Small Beer, Viking (New York), 1939 . . . £65/£20
ditto, Viking (New York), 1939 (175 signed copies with a
signed, original colour illustration by Bemelmans, slipcase)
. . . . £250/£200
ditto, John Lane (London), 1940 . . . . £45/£10
I Love You, I Love You, I Love You, Viking (New York),
1942 . . . . £50/£10
ditto, Hamish Hamilton (London), 1943 . . . £45/£10

Travel
The Donkey Inside, Viking (New York), 1941 . £25/£10
ditto, Viking (New York), 1941 (175 deluxe copies with a
signed, original colour illustration by Bemelmans, slipcase)
. . . . £200/£165
ditto, Hamish Hamilton (London), 1947 . . . £20/£5
The Best of Times, Simon & Schuster (New York), 1948 .
. . . . £35/£10
ditto, Cresset Press (London), 1949 . . . £30/£10
How To Travel Incognito, Little, Brown (Boston), 1952 .
. . . . £25/£10
ditto, Hamish Hamilton (London), 1952 . . . £20/£5
Father, Dear Father, Viking (New York), 1953 . £25/£10
ditto, Viking (New York), 1953 (151 signed, deluxe copies
with a signed, original colour illustration by Bemelmans,
slipcase) . . . . £200/£150
ditto, Hamish Hamilton (London), 1953 . . . £20/£5
Holiday in France, Houghton Mifflin (Boston), 1957 £30/£10
ditto, Deutsch (London), 1958 . . . . £20/£5
How To Have Europe All To Yourself, European Travel
Commission (New York), 1960 (pbk) £10
Italian Holiday, Houghton Mifflin (Boston), 1961. £35/£15
On Board Noah's Ark, Viking (New York), 1962 £15/£5
ditto, Collins (London), 1962 . . . . . £15/£5

Others
My War with the United States, Viking (New York), 1937 .
. . . . £65/£20
ditto, Gollancz (London), 1938 . . . . £40/£15
Life Class, Viking (New York), 1938 . . . £40/£10
ditto, John Lane (London), 1939. . . . . £15/£5
At Your Service, Peterson (Evanston, IL), 1941 (colour
decorated beige cloth) £15
Hotel Splendide, Viking (New York), 1941 . .£100/£25
ditto, Viking (New York), 1941 (305 signed, deluxe copies,
slipcase) . . . . £125/£100
ditto, Hamish Hamilton (London), 1942 . . £50/£15
Hotel Bemelmans, Viking (New York), 1946 . . £30/£10
ditto, Hamish Hamilton (London), 1956 . . £20/£5
To The One I Love the Best, Viking (New York), 1955 .
. . . . £50/£15
ditto, Hamish Hamilton (London), 1955 . . £30/£10
The World of Bemelmans, Viking (New York), 1955 . .
. . . . £25/£10
My Life in Art, Harper (New York), 1958 . . £30/£10
ditto, Deutsch (London), 1958 . . . . £25/£5
La Bonne Table, Simon & Schuster (New York), 1964 .
. . . . £20/£5
ditto, Hamish Hamilton (London), 1964 . . £20/£5

ALAN BENNETT
(b.1934)

An actor and playwright, Alan Bennett's quiet, self-
effacing, comic style has been as popular with television
audiences as it has with the readers of his books. The
majority of Bennett's more popular characters are rather
sad and unfortunate, and he often lets them realise the
hopelessness of their situation in a typically bleak con-
clusion.

Plays
Beyond the Fringe, Souvenir Press (London), 1963 £75/£20
ditto, Random House (New York), 1963 . . . £50/£15
Forty Years On, Faber (London), 1969 . . . £75/£20
ditto, Faber (London), 1969 (pbk) £5
Getting On, Faber (London), 1972 . . . £20/£5
ditto, Faber (London), 1972 (pbk) £5
Habeas Corpus, Faber (London), 1973 . . £20/£5
ditto, Faber (London), 1973 (pbk) £5
The Old Country, Faber (London), 1978 (pbk) . £10
Enjoy, Faber (London), 1980 (pbk) £10
Office Suite: Two One-Act Plays, Faber (London), 1981
(pbk) £15
Objects of Affection and Other Plays for Television, BBC
(London), 1982 (pbk). £10
Say Something Happened, French (London), 1982 (pbk) £30
The Writer in Disguise, Faber (London), 1985 (pbk) . £10
Two Kafka Plays, Faber (London), 1987 (pbk) . . £5
Talking Heads, BBC (London), 1988 (pbk) . . £5
Single Spies, Faber (London), 1989 (pbk) . . £5
Single Spies and *Talking Heads*, Summit (New York), 1990
. . . . £15/£5
The Wind in the Willows, Faber (London), 1991 (pbk) . £5
The Madness of George III, Faber (London), 1992 (pbk) £5
The Complete Talking Heads, BBC (London), 1998 £10/£5

Screenplays
A Private Function, Faber (London), 1984 (pbk) . . £10
Prick Up Your Ears, Faber (London), 1987 (pbk) . . £10
The Madness of King George, Faber (London), 1995 (pbk)
. . . . £5
ditto, Random House (New York), 1995 (pbk) . . £5
The History Boys, Faber (London), 2004 (pbk) . . £5

Novellas and Short Stories
The Clothes They Stood Up In, Profile Books/London
Review of Books (London), 1998 . . . £10/£5
ditto, Random House (New York), 1998 . . £10/£5
Father! Father! Burning Bright, Profile Books/London
Review of Books (London), 2000 . . . £10/£5
Laying On Of Hands, Profile Books/London Review of
Books, 2001 (London) . . . . . £10/£5
ditto, Picador (New York), 2002 . . . . £10/£5

Prose
The Lady in the Van, London Review of Books (London),
1990 (pbk) £20
Writing Home, Faber (London), 1994 . . £10/£5
ditto, Random House (New York), 1995 . . £10/£5
ditto, Faber (London), 1997 (with additional material; pbk) £5
Telling Tales, BBC (London), 2000 . . . £10/£5
Untold Stories, Faber/Profile Books (London), 2005 £10/£5
The Uncommon Reader, Faber/Profile (London), 2007 .
. . . . £10/£5
ditto, Faber/Profile (London), 2007 (2,000 signed copies;
slipcase). . . . . £65/£50
ditto, Farrar Straus & Giroux (New York), 2007 . £10/£5

ARNOLD BENNETT

(b.1867 d.1931)

Arnold Bennett was born in Hanley, Stoke-on-Trent, Staffordshire, one of five towns in the area known as the
Potteries. A novelist, short story writer, playwright and
journalist, Bennett's reputation today rests principally on
his novels about the lives of ordinary people. During World
War One he was Director of Propaganda at the War Ministry. He refused a knighthood in 1918.

Novels
A Man from the North, John Lane (London), 1898 . £100
Anna of the Five Towns, Chatto & Windus (London), 1902
. . . . £60
ditto, McClure Phillips (New York), 1903 . . £50
The Grand Babylon Hotel, Chatto & Windus (London),
1902 . . . . £100
ditto, as *T. Racksole and Daughter*, New Amsterdam (New
York), 1902 . . . . £60
ditto, as *The Grand Babylon Hotel*, Doran (New York),
1913 . . . . £45
The Gates of Wrath, Chatto & Windus (London), 1903 £45
ditto, Doran (New York), 1915 . . . . . £35
Leonora, Chatto & Windus (London), 1903 . . £60
ditto, Mershon (New York), [1903] . . . £35
A Great Man, Chatto & Windus (London), 1904 . . £60
ditto, Doran (New York), 1910 . . . . . £35
Teresa of Watling Street, Chatto & Windus (London), 1904
. . . . £75

Sacred and Profane Love, Chatto & Windus (London), 1905
. . . . £50
ditto, as *The Book of Carlotta*, Doran (New York), 1911 .
. . . . £40
Hugo, Chatto & Windus (London), 1906 . . . £75
ditto, Buckles (New York), 1906 . . . . £35
The Sinews of War (with Eden Philpotts), T. Werner Laurie
(London), 1906 . . . . . . £40
ditto, as *Doubloons*, McClure, Phillips & Co. (New York),
1906 . . . . £20
Whom God Hath Joined, David Nutt (London), 1906 . £45
ditto, Doran (New York), 1911 . . . . £30
The City of Pleasure, Chatto & Windus (London), 1907 £50
ditto, Doran (New York), 1913 . . . . £30
The Ghost: A Fantasia on Modern Times, Chatto & Windus
(London), 1907 . . . . . . £50
ditto, Turner (U.S.), 1907 . . . . . £30
Buried Alive, Chapman & Hall (London), 1908 . . £30
ditto, Brentanos (New York), 1910 . . . £25
The Old Wives' Tale, Chapman & Hall (London), 1908 £400
ditto, Hodder & Stoughton (New York), 1909 . . £50
ditto, Ernest Benn (London/New York), 1927 (500 signed
copies; facsimile; 2 vols; slipcase) . . £145/£125
The Statue (with Eden Philpotts), Cassell (London), 1908 .
. . . . £45
ditto, Moffat, Yard (New York), 1908 . . . £45
The Glimpse: An Adventure of the Soul, Chapman & Hall
(London), 1909 . . . . . . £50
ditto, Appleton (New York), 1909 . . . . £40
Clayhanger, Methuen (London), 1910 . . . £25
ditto, Dutton (New York), 1910 . . . . . £20
Helen with the High Hand, Chapman & Hall (London),
1910 . . . . £20
ditto, Doran (New York), 1910 . . . . £20
The Card, Methuen (London), 1911 . . . . £45
ditto, as *Denry the Audacious*, Dutton (New York), 1911 .
. . . . £45
Hilda Lessways, Methuen (London), 1911 . . . £35
ditto, Dutton (New York), 1911 . . . . . £25
The Regent, Methuen (London), 1913 . . . £30
ditto, as *The Old Adam*, Doran (New York), 1913 . . £25
The Price of Love, Methuen (London), 1914 . . £25
ditto, Harper (New York), 1914 . . . . . £25
These Twain, Methuen (London), 1916 . . . £30
ditto, Doran (New York), 1915 . . . . . £25
The Lion's Share, Cassell (London), 1916 . . . £20
ditto, Doran (New York), 1916 . . . . . £20
The Pretty Lady, Cassell (London), 1918 . . . £20
ditto, Doran (New York), [1918] £20
The Roll Call, Hutchinson (London), 1918 . . . £20
ditto, Doran (New York), 1918 . . . . . £20
Lilian, Cassell (London), 1922 . . . . £75/£15
ditto, Doran (New York), 1922 . . . . £75/£15
Mr Prohack, Methuen (London), 1922 . . . £65/£15
ditto, Doran (New York), 1922 . . . . £65/£10
Riceyman Steps, Cassell (London), 1923 . . £75/£20
ditto, Doran (New York), 1923 . . . . £65/£10
The Clayhanger Family, Methuen (London), 1925 £45/£15
ditto, Methuen (London), 1925 (200 signed copies) . £75
Lord Raingo, Cassell (London), 1926 . . . £25/£5
ditto, Doran (New York), 1926 . . . . £25/£5
The Vanguard, Doran, 1927 . . . . . £25/£5
ditto, as *The Strange Vanguard*, Cassell (London), 1929 .
. . . . £50/£15

Accident, Doubleday (Garden City, NY), 1928 . £25/£5
ditto, Cassell (London), 1929 . . . . . £25/£5
Piccadilly, Readers Library Publishing Co. (London), 1929.
. . . . £65/£15
Imperial Palace, Cassell (London), 1930 . . . £30/£5
ditto, Cassell (London), 1930 (100 signed copies; 2 vols; slipcase). . . . . . . £175/£125
ditto, Doran (New York), 1931 . . . . £25/£5
Venus Rising from the Sea, Cassell (London), 1931 (350 numbered copies, in slipcase, signed by the artist McKnight Kauffer). £200
Dream of Destiny and *Venus Rising from the Sea*, Cassell (London), 1932 . . . . £45/£15
ditto, as *Stroke of Luck* and *Venus Rising from the Sea*, Doubleday (Garden City, NY), 1932 . . . £35/£10

Short Stories
The Loot of Cities, Rivers (London), 1904 (boards) . £400
ditto, Rivers (London), 1904 (wraps). £300
ditto, Train (Philadelphia, PA), 1972 . . £10/£5
Tales of the Five Towns, Chatto & Windus (London), 1905
. . . .£50
The Grim Smile of the Five Towns, Chatto & Windus (London), 1907 . . . . £50
The Matador of the Five Towns, Methuen (London), 1912 .
. . . . £30
The Matador of the Five Towns, Doran (New York), [1912] (different selection of stories from above) . . . £30
Elsie and the Child: A Tale of Riceyman Steps And Other Stories, Cassell (London), 1924 . . . £50/£20
ditto, Doran (New York), 1924 . . . . £50/£20
ditto, Cassell (London), 1929 (750 numbered copies, title story only, illustrated by McKnight Kauffer) . £75
The Woman Who Stole Everything and Other Stories, Cassell (London), 1927 . . . . . £50/£20
ditto, Doran (New York), [1927]. . . . £50/£20
The Night Visitor and Other Stories, Cassell (London), 1931 . . . . £30/£15
ditto, Doubleday (Garden City, NY), 1931 . £25/£10

Plays
Polite Farces for the Drawing Room, Doran (New York), 1899 (copyright edition) £100
ditto, Lamley & Co. (London), 1900 . . . .£100
ditto, Doran (New York), 1912 . . . . . £30
Cupid and Commonsense, New Age Press (London), 1909.
. . . . £20
ditto, Doran (New York), 1910 . . . . . £20
What the Public Wants, Duckworth (London), 1909 . £20
ditto, McClure, Phillips & Co. (New York), 1910 . . £20
The Honeymoon, Methuen (London), 1911 . . £20
ditto, Doran (New York), 1912 . . . . . £20
Milestones, Methuen (London), 1912 (with Edward Knoblauch) £20
ditto, Doran (New York), 1912 . . . . . £20
The Great Adventure, Methuen (London), 1913 . . £15
ditto, Doran (New York), 1913 . . . . . £15
The Title, Chatto & Windus (London), 1918 . . £15
ditto, Doran (New York), 1918 . . . . . £15
Judith, Chatto & Windus (London), 1919 . . £15
ditto, Doran (New York), 1919 . . . . . £15
Sacred and Profane Love, Chatto & Windus (London), 1919
. . . . £15
ditto, Doran (New York), [1920]. £15

The Love Match, Chatto & Windus (London), 1922 £45/£15
ditto, Doran (New York), 1922 . . . . £45/£15
Body and Soul, Chatto & Windus (London), 1922. £45/£15
ditto, Doran (New York), 1922 . . . . £45/£15
Don Juan de Marana, T. Werner Laurie (London), 1923 (1,000 signed copies). . . . . . £75/£35
ditto, Doran (New York), 1923 (possibly unpublished) . .
. . . . £200/£150
The Bright Island, Golden Cockerel Press (Waltham St Lawrence, Berks), 1924 (200 signed, numbered copies) .
. . . .£125
ditto, Doran (New York), 1925 . . . £45/£15
London Life (with Edward Knoblauch), Chatto & Windus (London), 1924 . . . . . . £65/£20
ditto, Doran (New York), 1924 . . . . . £65/£20
Mr Prohack, Chatto & Windus (London), 1927 . £60/£20
ditto, Doran (New York), 1927 . . . . . £60/£20

Journals
Things That Interested Me, privately printed (Burslem), 1906 (100 copies) £150
ditto as *Things That Have Interested Me*, Chatto & Windus (London), 1921 . . . .£40/£10
ditto Doran (New York), 1921 . . . . £40/£10
Things That Interested Me, Second Series, privately printed (Burslem), 1907 (100 copies) £150
ditto as *Things That Have Interested Me, Second Series*, Chatto & Windus (London), 1923 . . . £40/£10
ditto Doran (New York), 1923 . . . . £40/£10
Things That Interested Me, Third Series, privately printed (Burslem), 1908 (100 copies) £200
ditto as *Things That Have Interested Me, Third Series*, Chatto & Windus (London), 1926 . . . £35/£10
ditto Doran (New York), 1926 . . . . £35/£10
Journal, 1929, Cassell (London), 1930 . . £25/£10
ditto, Cassell (London), 1930 (75 copies) £125
ditto as *Journal of Things Old and New*, Doran (New York), 1930 . . . . £25/£10
The Journals of Arnold Bennett, Cassell (London), 1932-1933 (3 vols; 1896-1910, 1911-1920, 1921-1928) £75/£40
ditto, Viking (New York), 1932-1933 (3 vols). . £75/£40
Florentine Journal, Chatto & Windus (London), 1967. .
. . . . £25/£10

Others
Journalism for Women: A Practical Guide, John Lane (London), 1898 . . . .£100
Fame and Fiction, Grant Richards (London), 1901 . £50
ditto, Dutton (New York), 1901 . . . . . £45
How to Become an Author: A Practical Guide, C. Arthur Pearson (London), 1903 . . . . . . £30
The Truth About An Author, Constable (London), 1903 (anonymous; first issue) £50
ditto, Constable (London), 1903 (anonymous; second issue, remainder bindings) £20
ditto, Doran (New York), [1911]. £20
The Reasonable Life, A. C. Fifield (London), 1907 . £25
ditto, Doran (New York), 1911 . . . . . £20
ditto, as *Mental Efficiency*, Doran (New York), 1911 . £10
ditto, Hodder & Stoughton (London), 1912 . . . £5
How to Live on 24 Hours a Day, New Age Press (London), 1908 . . . . £10
ditto, Doran (New York), 1910 . . . . . £10
The Human Machine, New Age Press (London), 1908. £10

ditto, Doran (New York), 1910 . . . . . £10

Literary Taste: How To Form It, New Age Press (London), 1909 . . . . £35

ditto, Doran (New York), 1910 . . . . £20

The Feast of St. Friend, Hodder & Stoughton (London), 1911 . . . . £15

ditto, Doran (New York), 1911 . . . . . £25

ditto, as *Friendship and Happiness*, Hodder & Stoughton (London), 1914 . . . . £5

Your United States: Impressions of a First Visit, Harper (New York), 1912 . . . . . £30

ditto, as *Those United States*, Secker (London), 1912 . £25

Paris Nights, Hodder & Stoughton (London), 1913 . £25

ditto, Doran (New York), 1913 . . . . . £20

The Plain Man and His Wife, Hodder & Stoughton (London), [1913] £10

ditto, Doran (New York), 1913 . . . . . £25

ditto, as *Marriage: The Plain Man and His Wife*, Hodder & Stoughton (London), 1916 . . . . . . £5

From the Log of the Velsa, Century (New York), 1914 £20

ditto, Chatto & Windus (London), 1920 . . £50/£20

Liberty: A Statement of the British Case, Hodder & Stoughton (London), 1914 . . . . . £20

ditto, Doran (New York), 1914 . . . . . £20

The Author's Craft, Hodder & Stoughton (London), 1914 .
. . . . £20

ditto, Doran (New York), 1914 . . . . . £20

Over There, Methuen (London), 1915 . . . £60

ditto, Doran (New York), 1915 . . . . . £45

Books and Persons, Chatto & Windus (London), 1917. £15

ditto, Doran (New York), 1917 . . . . . £15

Self and Self Management, Hodder & Stoughton (London), 1918 . . . . £5

ditto, Doran (New York), [1918]. £5

Our Women: Chapters on the Sex Discord, Cassell (London), 1920 . . . . £45/£15

ditto, Doran (New York), 1920 . . . . £45/£15

How to Make the Best of Life, Hodder & Stoughton (London), 1923 . . . . . . £40/£10

ditto, Doran (New York), 1923 . . . . £40/£10

Mediterranean Scenes, Cassell (London), 1928 (1,000 numbered copies) . . . . . . £200/£60

The Savour of Life: Essays in Gusto, Cassell (London), 1928 . . . . £35/£10

ditto, Doran (New York), 1928 . . . . £35/£10

The Letters of Arnold Bennett, O.U.P. (London), 1966-1986 (4 vols) . . . . £90/£60 the set

E.F. BENSON

(b.1867 d.1940)

E.F Benson was the son of an Archbishop of Canterbury and a member of a distinguished and eccentric family. Benson's first book, *Dodo*, was a huge success and he is known for his light society novels, especially the 'Mapp and Lucia' series. Of his supernatural fiction *The Room in the Tower* is the most highly regarded.

Novels
Dodo: A Detail of Today, Methuen (London), 1893 (2 vols)
. . . . £600

ditto, Appleton (New York), 1893 . . . . . £400

The Rubicon, Methuen (London), 1894 (2 vols) . . £250

ditto, Appleton (New York), 1894 . . . . . £200

The Judgement Books, Osgood McIlvaine (London), 1895.
. . . . £175

Limitations, Innes (London), 1896 . . . . . £65

ditto, Harper (New York), 1896 . . . . . £30

The Babe, B.A., Putnam (London), 1896 . . . . £60

ditto, Putnams (New York), 1897 . . . . . £50

The Vintage, Methuen (London), 1898 . . . . £75

ditto, Harper (New York), 1898 . . . . . £35

The Money Market, Arrowsmith (London), 1898 . . £75

ditto, Drexel Biddle (Philadelphia, PA), 1898 . . . £65

The Capsina, Methuen (London), 1899 . . . . £100

ditto, Harper (New York), 1899 . . . . . £75

Mammon and Co., Heinemann (London), 1899 . . £60

ditto, Appleton (New York), 1899 . . . . . £45

The Princess Sophia, Heinemann (London), 1900 . . £75

ditto, Harper (New York), 1900 . . . . . £45

The Luck of the Vails, Heinemann (London), 1901 . £75

ditto, Appleton (New York), 1901 . . . . . £35

Scarlet and Hyssop, Heinemann (London), 1902 . . £60

ditto, Appleton (New York), 1902 . . . . . £30

The Book of Months, Heinemann (London), 1903. . £60

ditto, Harper & Bros (New York), 1903 . . . . £30

An Act in a Backwater, Heinemann (London), 1903 . £100

ditto, Appleton (New York), 1903 . . . . . £75

The Valkyries, Dean & Son (London), 1903 . . . £100

The Relentless City, Heinemann (London), 1903 . . £60

ditto, Harper & Bros (New York), 1903 . . . . £30

The Challoners, Heinemann (London), 1904 . . . £45

ditto, Lippincott (Philadelphia, PA), 1904. . . . £25

The Image in the Sand, Heinemann (London), 1905 . £100

ditto, Lippincott (Philadelphia, PA), 1905. . . . £75

The Angel of Pain, Lippincott (Philadelphia, PA), 1905 £75

ditto, Heinemann (London), 1906 . . . . . £45

Paul, Heinemann (London), 1906 . . . . . £60

ditto, Lippincott (Philadelphia, PA), 1906. . . . £30

The House of Defence, Heinemann (London), 1907 . £50

ditto, Authors and Newspapers Association (New York), 1906 . . . . £40

Sheaves, Stanley Paul (London), 1907 . . . . £50

ditto, Doubleday (New York), 1907 . . . . . £30

The Blotting Book, Heinemann (London), 1908 . . £50

ditto, Doubleday (New York), 1908 . . . . . £30

The Climber, Heinemann (London), 1908 . . . £45

ditto, Doubleday (New York), 1909 . . . . . £30

A Reaping, Heinemann (London), 1909 . . . . £50

ditto, Doubleday (New York), 1910 . . . . . £30

Daisy's Aunt, Nelson (London), 1910 . . . . £50

ditto, as *The Fascinating Mrs Halton*, Doubleday (New York), 1910 . . . . £30

The Osbornes, Smith Elder (London), 1910 . . . £45

ditto, Doubleday (New York), 1910 . . . . . £30

Margery, Doubleday (New York), 1910 . . . . £45

ditto, as *Juggernaut*, Heinemann (London), 1911 . . £30

Account Rendered, Heinemann (London), 1911 . . £40

ditto, Doubleday (New York), 1911 . . . . . £30

Mrs Ames, Hodder & Stoughton (London), 1912 . . £40

ditto, Doubleday (New York), 1912 . . . . . £30

The Weaker Vessel, Heinemann (London), 1913 . . £40

ditto, Dodd, Mead (New York), 1913 . . . . £30

Thorley Weir, Smith, Elder (London), 1913 . . . £40

ditto, Lippincott (Philadelphia), 1913 . . . . £30

Dodo's Daughter: A Sequel to Dodo, Century Co. (New York), 1913 . . . . £65
ditto, as *Dodo the Second*, Hodder & Stoughton (London), 1914 . . . . £60
Arundel, Unwin (London), 1914 . . . . £40
ditto, Doran (New York), [1915]. £30
The Oakleyites, Hodder & Stoughton (London), 1915 . £40
ditto, Doran (New York), 1915 . . . . . £20
David Blaize, Hodder & Stoughton (London), 1916 . £40
ditto, Doran (New York), 1916 . . . . £30
Mike, Cassell (London), 1916 . . . . £45
ditto, as *Michael*, Doran (New York), 1916 . . £30
The Freaks of Mayfair, Foulis (London), 1916 . . £65
ditto, Doran (New York), [1918]. . . . £40
Mr Teddy, Unwin (London), 1917 . . . £40
ditto, as *The Tortoise*, Doran (New York), 1917 . . £25
An Autumn Sowing, Collins (London), 1917 . . . £40
ditto, Doran (New York), 1918 . . . . . £25
David Blaize and the Blue Door, Hodder & Stoughton (London), 1918 . . . . £45
ditto, Putnam (New York), 1918 . . . . £25
Up and Down, Hutchinson (London), 1918 . . . £40
ditto, Doran (New York), 1918 . . . . £25
Across the Stream, Murray (London), 1919 . . £40
ditto, Doran (New York), 1919 . . . . . £30
Robin Linnet, Hutchinson (London), 1919 . . . £40
ditto, Doran (New York), 1919 . . . . . £30
Queen Lucia, Hutchinson (London), 1920 . £300/£145
ditto, Doran (New York), 1920 . . . . . £250/£50
Dodo Wonders, Hutchinson (London), 1921 . £200/£45
ditto, Doran (New York), [1921]. . . . £200/£45
Lovers and Friends, Unwin (London), 1921 . £100/£35
ditto, Doran (New York), [1921]. . . . £200/£45
Miss Mapp, Hutchinson (London), 1922 . . £300/£145
ditto, Doran (New York), 1923 . . . . £225/£45
Peter, Cassell (London), 1922 . . . . £50/£15
ditto, Doran (New York), 1922 . . . . . £45/£15
Colin: A Novel, Hutchinson (London), [1923] . £50/£15
ditto, Doran (New York), 1923 . . . . . £45/£15
David of King's, Hodder & Stoughton (London), 1924 . . . . £50/£15
ditto, as *David Blaize of Kings*, Doran (New York), 1924 . . . . £45/£15
Alan, Unwin (London), 1924 . . . . £50/£15
ditto, Doran (New York), 1925 . . . . . £45/£15
Colin II, Hutchinson (London), [1925] . . £50/£15
ditto, Doran (New York), 1925 . . . . . £45/£15
Rex, Hodder & Stoughton (London), 1925 . £50/£15
ditto, Doran (New York), 1925 . . . . . £45/£15
Mezzanine, Cassell (London), 1926 . . . £50/£15
ditto, Doran (New York), 1926 . . . . . £45/£15
Pharisees and Publicans, Hutchinson (London), 1926 . . . . £30/£10
ditto, Doran (New York), 1927 . . . . £45/£15
Lucia in London, Hutchinson (London), 1927 £300/£125
ditto, Doubleday (New York), 1928 . . . £250/£65
Paying Guests, Hutchinson (London), 1929 . . £50/£15
ditto, Doubleday (New York), 1929 . . . £50/£15
The Inheritor, Hutchinson (London), [1930] . £65/£25
ditto, Doubleday (New York), 1930 . . . £65/£25
Mapp & Lucia, Hodder & Stoughton (London), 1931 . . . . £275/£75
ditto, Doran (New York), 1931 . . . . . £275/£65
Secret Lives, Hodder & Stoughton (London), 1932 £45/£15

ditto, Doubleday (New York), 1932 . . . . £45/£15
Travail of Gold, Hodder & Stoughton (London), 1933 . . . . £35/£15
ditto, Doubleday (New York), 1933 . . . £35/£15
Raven's Brood, Barker (London), 1934 . . £45/£15
ditto, Doran (New York), 1934 . . . . £35/£15
Lucia's Progress, Hodder & Stoughton (London), 1935 . . . . £250/£75
ditto as *Worshipful Lucia*, Doubleday (New York), 1935 . . . . £100/£15
All About Lucia, Doubleday (New York), 1936 (the first four Lucia novels in one vol.) . . . £65/£25
Old London, Appleton-Century (New York), 1937 (4 vols in d/ws, slipcase) . . . . . . £100/£65
Trouble for Lucia, Hodder & Stoughton (London), 1939 . . . . £200/£45
ditto, Doran (New York), 1939 . . . . £100/£35

Short Stories
Six Common Things, Osgood McIlvaine (London), 1893 . . . . £100
ditto, as *A Double Overture*, C.H. Sergel (Chicago), 1894 . . . . £100
The Countess of Lowndes Square and Other Stories, Cassell (London), 1920 . . . . £350/£125
The Male Impersonator, Elkin Mathews & Marrot (London), 1929 (530 signed copies) . . . £65/£50
Desirable Residences, O.U.P. (Oxford, UK), 1991. £15/£5
Fine Feathers, O.U.P. (Oxford, UK), 1994 . . £15/£5

Ghost Stories
The Room in the Tower, Mills & Boon (London), [1912] £250
ditto, Knopf (New York), 1929 . . . . £250/£75
Visible and Invisible, Hutchinson (London), 1923 £450/£100
ditto, Doran (New York), 1924 . . . . . £300/£75
'And the Dead Spake' & The Horror Horn, Doran (New York), 1923 . . . . £300/£100
Expiation & Naboth's Vineyard, Doran (New York), 1924. . . . . £300/£100
The Face, Doran (New York), 1924 . . . £350/£100
The Temple, Doran (New York), 1925 . . £350/£100
A Tale of an Empty House & Bagnell Terrace, Doran (New York), 1925 . . . . . £350/£100
ditto, as *The Tale of an Empty House*, Black Swan/Corgi (London), 1985 (pbk). £5
ditto, Black Swan/Corgi (London), 1986 (hardback; no d/w) £25
Spook Stories, Hutchinson (London), [1928] . £600/£200
The Step, H.V. Marrot (London), 1930 . . £200/£75
More Spook Stories, Hutchinson (London), [1934] . . . . £500/£125
The Horror Horn, Panther (London), 1974 (pbk) . . £5
The Flint Knife, Equation (London), 1988 (pbk) . £10
ditto, Chivers Press (Bath), 1990 (pictorial boards; no d/w) £35
The Terror by Night, Ash-Tree Press (Ashcroft, Canada), 1998 (600 copies) . . . . . . £25/£10
The Passenger, Ash-Tree Press (Ashcroft, Canada), 1999 (600 copies) . . . . £25/£10
Mrs Amworth, Ash-Tree Press (Ashcroft, Canada), 2001 (600 copies) . . . . £25/£10
The Face, Ash-Tree Press (Ashcroft, Canada), 2003 (600 copies) . . . . £25/£10

Sea Mist, Ash-Tree Press (Ashcroft, Canada), 2005 (600 copies) . . . . £25/£10

Collaborations with Eustace Miles
Daily Training, Hurst & Blackett (London), 1902 . . £45
Cricket of Abel, Hirst and Shrewsbury, Hurst & Blackett (London), 1903 . . . . £75
ditto, Dutton (New York), 1903 . . . . . £65
The Mad Annual, Grant Richards (London), 1903. . £45
A Book of Golf, Hurst Blackett (London), 1903 . . £75
Diversions Day by Day, Hurst & Blackett (London), 1905 . . . . £45

Non-Fiction
Sketches from Marlborough, 1888 (anonymous) . . £125
English Figure-Skating, Bell (London), 1908 . . £200
Skating Calls, Bell (London), 1909 . . . . £65
Winter Sports in Switzerland, George Allen (London), 1913 . . . . £200
Deutschland Uber Allah, Hodder & Stoughton (London), 1917 (stapled wraps) £75
Crescent and Iron Cross, Hodder & Stoughton (London), 1918 . . . . £65
ditto, Doran (New York), [1918]. £65
The White Eagle of Poland, Hodder & Stoughton (London), 1918 . . . . £30
ditto, Doran (New York), 1919 . . . . . £25
Poland and Mittel-Europa, Hodder & Stoughton (London), 1918 . . . . £15
The Social Value of Temperance, True Temperance Association (London), 1919 . . . . £15
Our Family Affairs, 1867-1896, Cassell (London), 1920 .
. . . . £50/£25
ditto, Doran (New York), 1921 . . . . £40/£15
Mother, Hodder & Stoughton (London), 1925 . £100/£25
ditto, Doran (New York), 1925 . . . . £75/£15
Sir Frances Drake, John Lane/Bodley Head (London), 1927
. . . . £35/£15
ditto, Harper (New York), 1927 . . . . £30/£10
The Life of Alcibiades, Ernest Benn (London), 1928 . .
. . . . £45/£15
ditto, Appleton (New York), 1929 . . . £35/£15
Ferdinand Magellan, John Lane/Bodley Head (London), 1929 . . . . £35/£15
ditto, Harper (New York), 1930 . . . . £30/£15
Henry James: Letters to A.C. Benson/Auguste Monod, Elkin Mathews & Marrot (London), 1930 (1,050 numbered copies) £30
As We Were: A Victorian Peepshow, Longmans (London), 1930 . . . . £35/£15
As We Are: A Modern Revue, Longmans (London), 1932 .
. . . . £30/£15
Charlotte Brontë, Longmans (London), 1932 . £30/£15
ditto, Longmans (New York), 1932 . . . £35/£15
King Edward VII, Longmans (London), 1933. . £35/£15
ditto, Longmans (New York), 1933 . . . £35/£15
The Outbreak of War, Peter Davies (London), 1933 £65/£20
ditto, Putnams (New York), 1934 . . . £50/£15
The Kaiser and English Relations, Longmans (London), 1934 . . . . £25/£10
Queen Victoria, Longmans (New York), 1935 . £30/£10
ditto, Longmans (London), 1935. . . . £30/£10
Queen Victoria's Daughters, Appleton-Century (New York), 1938 . . . . £25/£10

ditto, as *Daughters of Queen Victoria*, Cassell (London), 1939 . . . . £25/£10
Final Edition: An Informal Autobiography, Longmans (London), 1940 . . . . £30/£15
ditto, Appleton-Century (New York), 1940 . . £30/£15

Others
Bensoniana: Maxims by E.F. Benson, Siegle Hill Watteau (London), 1912 . . . . £75
ditto, A.L. Humphreys, 1912 . . . . . £65
Thoughts from E.F. Benson, Harrap (London), 1913 (compiled by E.E. Morton) £40
Thoughts from E.F. Benson, Holden & Hardingham (London), 1916 (compiled by H.B. Elliott, leather-bound).
. . . . £75
ditto, Holden & Hardingham (London), 1916 (cloth bound).
. . . . £30

E.C. BENTLEY
(b.1875 d.1956)

Although E.C. Bentley's oeuvre is very small, his first book, *Trent's Last Case*, is an acknowledged classic of detective fiction. There is some debate as to which is the true first edition of this classic novel: Nelson's *Trent's Last Case*, or Century's *The Woman in Black*.

Edmund Clerihew Bentley is also collected for his odd comic verse-form known as the clerihew.

Novels
Trent's Last Case, Nelson (London), [1913] (blue cloth, elaborate blind-stamping to front board, gilt and blind stamped spine; colour frontispiece; illustrated endpapers) .
. . . . £300/£85
ditto, as *The Woman in Black*, Century (New York), 1913 (black cloth, lettered in gilt) . . . . £250/£65
Trent's Own Case, Constable (London), 1936 (with H. Warner Allen; orange cloth lettered on front and spine in blue) . . . . £450/£25
ditto, Constable (London), 1936 (later issue with note tipped-in on title-page apologising for any offence caused to 'The Association for Moral and Social Hygiene') . £450/£25
ditto, Knopf (New York), 1936 (orange cloth lettered in black) . . . . £150/£25
Elephant's Work, Hodder & Stoughton (London), 1950 (maroon cloth, white lettering on spine). . . £45/£10
ditto, Knopf (New York), 1950 (pink patterned cloth, decorated and printed in black) . . . £25/£5
ditto, as *The Chill*, Dell (New York), 1953 (pbk) . £10

Collaboration
The Scoop and *Behind the Screen*, Gollancz (London), 1983 (chain novels; chapters by Bentley, Hugh Walpole, Agatha Christie, Dorothy L. Sayers, Anthony Berkeley, E.C. Bentley, Ronald Knox, Freeman Wills Crofts and Clemence Dane) . . . . . . £20/£5
ditto, Harper (New York), 1984 . . . . £20/£5

Short Stories
Trent Intervenes, Nelson (London), 1938 (blue cloth, lettered in white on spine). . . . . £250/£35
ditto, Knopf (New York), 1938 . . . . £150/£25

Clerihews
Biography for Beginners, Werner Laurie (London), 1905
(pseud 'E. Clerihew'). £150
More Biography, Methuen (London), 1929 . £50/£15
Baseless Biography, Constable (London), 1939 . £35/£10
Clerihews Complete, Werner Laurie (London), 1951 £25/£10
The Complete Clerihews of E. Clerihew Bentley, O.U.P.
(London), 1981 . . . . £10/£5
The First Clerihews, O.U.P. (London), 1982 . . £10/£5

Other Titles
*Peace Year in the City, 1918-1919: An Account of the
Outstanding Events in the City of London During Peace
Year*, privately printed, 1920 (no d/w) . . . £20
Those Days, Constable, 1940 . . . £15/£5

THOMAS BERGER
(b.1924)

American novelist Thomas Berger is best known for his
novel *Little Big Man*, which was made into a film staring
Dustin Hoffman. It tells the story of a 19th century boy
who survives an attack by Native Americans on a wagon
train of white settlers, and is subsequently raised by the
leader of the Cheyenne people.

Novels
Crazy in Berlin, Charles Scribner's (New York), 1958 (first
state d/w with no mention of Dial Prize) . £150/£15
ditto, Charles Scribner's (New York), 1958 (second state d/w
with Dial Prize mentioned) . . . . £75/£15
Reinhart in Love, Charles Scribner's (New York), 1962 .
. . . . £85/£15
ditto, Eyre and Spottiswoode (London), 1963 . . £65/£10
Little Big Man, Dial Press (New York), 1964 (first state d/w
with no mention of Dial Prize) . . . . £350/£40
ditto, Dial Press (New York), 1964 (second state d/w with
Dial Prize mentioned). . . . . . £125/£40
ditto, Eyre and Spottiswoode (London), 1965 . £100/£15
Killing Time, Dial Press (New York), 1967 . £30/£10
Vital Parts, Richard W. Baron (New York), 1970 . £20/£5
ditto, Eyre and Spottiswoode (London), 1971 . £10/£5
Regiment of Women, Simon & Schuster (New York), 1973
. . . . £20/£5
ditto, Eyre, Methuen (London), 1974. . . . £10/£5
Sneaky People, Simon & Schuster (New York), 1975 . .
. . . . £15/£5
ditto, Magnum (London), 1980 (pbk). . . . £5
Who Is Teddy Villanova?, Delacorte Press (New York),
1977 . . . . £15/£5
ditto, Eyre, Methuen (London), 1977. . . . £10/£5
Arthur Rex: A Legendary Novel, Delacorte Press (New
York), 1978 . . . . £15/£5
ditto, Magnum (London), 1979 (pbk). . . . £5
Neighbours, Delacorte Press (New York), 1980 . £15/£5
ditto, Magnum (London), 1981 (pbk). . . . £5
Reinhart's Women, Delacorte Press (New York), 1981 .
. . . . £15/£5
ditto, Methuen (London), 1982 . . . . £10/£5
The Feud, Delacorte Press (New York), 1983. . £15/£5
ditto, Methuen (London), 1984 . . . . £10/£5

Granted Wishes, Lord John Press (Northridge, CA), 1984
(250 signed copies; no d/w or slipcase) £25
ditto, Lord John Press (Northridge, CA), 1984 (26 signed,
lettered copies) £45
Nowhere, Delacorte Press (New York), 1985 . . £10/£5
ditto, Methuen (London), 1986 . . . . . £10/£5
Being Invisible, Little, Brown (Boston), 1987. . £15/£5
ditto, Methuen (London), 1988 . . . . . £10/£5
The Houseguest, Little, Brown (Boston), 1988 . £10/£5
ditto, Weidenfeld & Nicolson (London), 1989. . £10/£5
Changing the Past, Little, Brown (Boston), 1989 . £10/£5
ditto, Weidenfeld & Nicolson (London), 1990. . £10/£5
Orrie's Story, Little, Brown (Boston), 1990 . . £10/£5
Meeting Evil, Little, Brown (Boston), 1992 . . £10/£5
Robert Crews, William Morrow (Boston), 1994 . £10/£5
Suspects, William Morrow (Boston), 1996 . . £10/£5
The Return of Little Big Man, Little, Brown (Boston), 1999
. . . . £10/£5
ditto, Little, Brown (Boston), 1999 (signed by author on
tipped-in leaf) . . . . £20/£10
ditto, Harvill (London), 1999 . . . . . £10/£5
Best friends, Simon & Schuster (Boston), 2003 . £10/£5
Adventures of the Artificial Woman, Simon & Schuster
(Boston), 2004 . . . . £10/£5

ANTHONY BERKELEY
(b.1893 d.1971)

Anthony Berkeley Cox was a British crime fiction writer
who wrote under the pen-names Francis Iles, Anthony
Berkeley, A.B. Cox and A. Monmouth Platts. He worked
as a journalist for many years before taking up the post of
reviewer for *John O'London's Weekly* and the *Daily
Telegraph* in 1938, writing as Francis Iles. He was a
prominent member of The Crime Club.

Roger Sherringham Books
The Layton Court Mystery, Jenkins (London), 1925
(anonymous). . . . . £3,500/£500
ditto, Doubleday (New York), 1929 (all US editions credited
to Anthony Berkeley). . . . . . £1,000/£65
The Wychford Poisoning Case, Collins (London), 1926 (by
the author of *The Layton Court Mystery*) . £3,00/£450
ditto, Doubleday (New York), 1930 . . . £1,000/£65
Roger Sheringham and the Vane Mystery, Collins
(London), 1927 . . . . . . £3,000/£450
ditto, as *The Mystery at Lovers' Cave*, Simon & Schuster
(New York), 1927 . . . . £750/£45
The Silk Stocking Murders, Collins (London), 1928 . .
. . . . £2,500/£400
ditto, Doubleday (New York), 1928 . . . . £750/£45
The Poisoned Chocolates Case, Collins (London), 1929 .
. . . . £2,500/£400
ditto, Doubleday (New York), 1929 . . . . £600/£30
The Second Shot, Hodder & Stoughton (London), 1930 .
. . . . £2,500/£400
ditto, Doubleday (New York), 1931 . . . . £400/£15
Top Storey Murder, Hodder & Stoughton (London), 1931 .
. . . . £2,000/£400
ditto, as *Top Story Murder*, Doubleday (New York), 1931 .
. . . . £200/£15
Murder in the Basement, Hodder & Stoughton (London),
1932 . . . . £2,000/£400

ditto, Doubleday (New York), 1932 . . . .£100/£15
Jumping Jenny, Hodder & Stoughton (London), 1933 . .
. . . .£500/£45
ditto, as ***Dead Mrs Stratton***, Doubleday (New York), 1933 .
. . . . £65/£10
Panic Party, Hodder & Stoughton (London), 1934 £500/£40
ditto, as ***Mr Pidgeon's Island***, Doubleday (New York), 1934
. . . . £65/£10
***The Avenging Chance and Other Mysteries from Roger
Sheringham's Casebook***, Crippen & Landru (Norfolk,
VA), 2004 . . . . £15/£5

Books Written as Francis Iles
Malice Aforethought, Gollancz (London) 1931 £1,500/£300
ditto, Harper (New York), 1931 . . . . .£200/£15
Before the Fact, Gollancz (London) 1932 . £1,500/£300
ditto, Doubleday (New York), 1932 . . . .£200/£15
As for the Woman, Jarrolds (London), [1939] £1,000/£125
ditto, Doubleday (New York), 1939 . . . . £50/£10

Novel by A. Monmouth Platts
Cicely Disappears, John Long (London), 1927 £3,000/£450
ditto, Harper (New York), 1931 . . . . £1,000/£65

Novel by A.B. Cox
Mr Priestley's Problem, Collins (London), 1927 £3,000/£450
ditto, as ***The Amateur Crime***, Doubleday (New York), 1928
. . . . £1,000/£65
ditto, Penguin (London), 1947 (pbk: written as Anthony
Berkeley) £5

Other Books
Professor On Paws, Collins (London), 1926 . .£500/£75
ditto, L. MacVeagh, Dial Press (New York), 1927 (written as
'A.B. Cox') . . . .£200/£25
The Piccadilly Murder, Collins (London), 1929 £1,000/£85
ditto, Doubleday (New York), 1930 . . . .£100/£15
Trial and Error, Hodder & Stoughton (London), 1937 . .
. . . .£500/£35
ditto, Doubleday (New York), 1937 . . £75/£15
Not To Be Taken, Hodder & Stoughton (London), 1938 .
. . . .£500/£35
ditto, as ***A Puzzle in Poison***, Doubleday (New York), 1938 .
. . . .£100/£15
Death in the House, Hodder & Stoughton (London), 1939 .
. . . .£500/£35
ditto, Doubleday (New York), 1939 . . . .£100/£15

Novels With Other Members of the Detection Club
The Floating Admiral, Hodder & Stoughton (London),
[1931] (chain novel; chapters also contributed by
Chesterton, Dorothy L. Sayers, Agatha Christie, John
Rhode, Ronald A. Knox, Freeman Wills Crofts, and others)
. . . . £1,500/£100
ditto, Doubleday (New York), 1932 . . . .£500/£30
Ask a Policeman, Barker (London), [1933] (chain novel;
chapters contributed by Gladys Mitchell, John Rhode,
Dorothy L. Sayers and others) . . . . £1,000/£100
ditto, Morrow (New York), 1933 . . . .£500/£65
The Scoop and ***Behind the Screen***, Gollancz (London), 1983
(chain novels; chapters by Dorothy L. Sayers, Agatha
Christie, Hugh Walpole, E.C. Bentley, Freeman Wills
Crofts and others) . . . . . . £25/£10

LORD BERNERS
(b.1883 d.1950)

Millionaire, aesthete and eccentric, Gerald Hugh Tyrwhitt-
Wilson, 14th Baron Berners was also an author, composer
of classical music and painter. His most controversial book
is perhaps his roman-à-clef *The Girls of Radcliff Hall*, in
which he depicts himself and friends such as Cecil Beaton
and Olivier Messel as girl pupils at a girls' school.

Fiction
The Camel, Constable (London), 1936 . . . £65/£15
ditto, in ***Collected Tales and Fantasies***, Turtle Point Press
(New York), 1999 (pbk) £5
The Girls of Radcliff Hall, privately published, 1937
(wraps) £125
Far from the Madding War, Constable (London), 1941 .
. . . . £65/£15
Count Omega, Constable (London), 1941 . . £50/£15
Percy Wallingford and Mr Pidger, Blackwell (Oxford),
1941 (wraps). £85
The Romance of a Nose, Constable (London), 1941 £65/£15

Autobiography
First Childhood, Constable (London), 1934 . .£75/£45
ditto, Farrar & Rinehart (New York), 1934 . .£45/£15
A Distant Prospect, Constable (London), 1945 . £35/£10
ditto, Turtle Point Press (New York), 1998 (pbk) . . £5

Music
Trois Chansons, J. & W. Chester Ltd (London), 1920
(quarto; wraps) £85
Intermezzo from 'The Triumph of Neptune', J. & W.
Chester Ltd (London), 1927 (quarto; wraps). . . £75
Three Songs in the German Manner, J. & W. Chester Ltd
(London), [n.d.] (quarto; wraps) £95
Luna Park-Fantastic Ballet in One Act, J. & W. Chester Ltd
(London), [n.d., c.1930] (quarto; wraps) . . .£150
Suite from The Triumph of Neptune, J. & W. Chester Ltd
(London), [n.d.] (quarto; wraps) £50

Other
Lord Berners, privately printed [London, by Lord Berners?],
[1922] (essays; wraps) £100

JOHN BETJEMAN
(b.1906 d.1984)

As a broadcasting personality commenting on the superficial and the middle class, Betjeman with his bumbling
image somehow failed to gain serious recognition for his
verse during his lifetime, despite becoming Poet Laureate
in 1972. He also worked as a journalist for a number of
years and wrote on architectural matters.

Poetry
Mount Zion or In Touch with the Infinite, James Press
(London), [1931] (blue and gold patterned boards, no d/w)
. . . . £1,000
ditto, James Press (London), [1931] (striped boards, no d/w)
. . . .£500

Continual Dew, Murray (London), 1937 . . . £175/£65
Sir John Piers by 'Epsilon', Mullingar (Ireland), 1938 (50 copies; wraps) £1,250
Old Lights for New Chancels, Murray (London), 1940 . .
. . . . £150/£60
ditto, Murray (London), 1940 (limited, signed edition; printed on blue laid paper). £500
New Bats in Old Belfries, Murray (London), 1945. £75/£25
ditto, Murray (London), 1945 (50 signed copies) . .£450
Slick But Not Streamlined, Doubleday (New York), 1947 (edited by W.H. Auden) . . . . £75/£30
Selected Poems, Murray (London), 1948 . . . £45/£15
ditto, Murray (London), 1948 (18 signed copies) . .£600
Verses Turned in Aid of Public Subscription Toward the Restoration of the Church of St Katherine, Chislehampton, Oxon, St Katherine's Church (Oxford, UK), 1952 (wraps) £150
A Few Late Chrysanthemums, Murray (London), 1954 .
. . . . £65/£20
ditto, Murray (London), 1954 (50 signed copies) . .£350
Poems in the Porch, S.P.C.K. (London), 1954 (stapled wraps) £20
John Betjeman: A Selection, Edward Hulton Pocket Poets (London), 1958 (pbk). £5
Collected Poems, Murray (London), 1958 . . £20/£5
ditto, Murray (London), 1958 (100 signed copies, marbled paper slipcase) . . . . . £300/£250
ditto, Houghton Mifflin (Boston), 1959 . . £20/£5
Lament for Moira McCavendish, Browne (Lismore, Ireland), [1958] (pseud 'Coras Jompair Eireann'; 20 copies, single sheet of blue-green paper) £800
Ireland's Own, or The Burial of Thomas Moore, Browne (Lismore, Ireland), [1958] (pseud 'Ian MacBetjeman'; 20 copies, single sheet of mauve paper) £800
Summoned by Bells, Murray (London), 1960 . £20/£10
ditto, Murray (London), 1960 (125 signed, numbered copies; frontispiece portrait etching of Betjeman does not appear in the regular issue) £350
ditto, Houghton Mifflin (Boston), 1960 . . £20/£10
ditto, John Murray/Paradine (London), 1976 (100 numbered copies signed by the author and bound for the Silver Jubilee of Queen Elizabeth II; this enlarged edition adds the text of 'Cricket Master/(An Incident)', a portrait of Betjeman and a page in facsimile of the draft typescript; slipcase). . . . . £300/£250
A Ring of Bells, Murray (London), 1962 . . . £20/£5
ditto, Houghton Mifflin (Boston), 1963 . . £20/£5
High and Low, Murray (London), 1966 . . £35/£10
ditto, Murray (London), 1966 (100 signed copies) . .£325
ditto, Houghton Mifflin (Boston), 1967 . . £25/£10
Six Betjeman Songs, Duckworth (London), 1967 (wraps) £35
A Wembley Lad and The Crem, Poem-of-the-Month-Club (London), 1971 (signed broadsheet) £75
A Nip in the Air, Murray (London), 1974. . . £10/£5
ditto, Murray (London), 1974 (175 signed copies) . .£175
ditto, Norton (New York), [1974] . . . . £10/£5
Betjeman in Miniature, Selected Poems, Gleniffer Press (no place), 1976 (250 copies) £65
The Best of Betjeman, Murray (London), 1978 . £10/£5
Five Betjeman Songs, Weinberger, 1980 (wraps) . .£25
Ode on the Marriage of H.R.H. Prince Charles to Lady Diana Spencer, Warren Editions (London), 1981 (125 signed copies, broadsheet). £250

Church Poems, Murray (London), 1980 (first issue, withdrawn, with text of 'Bristol and Clifton' poem incomplete)
. . . . £75/£25
ditto, Murray (London), 1981 (second issue, poem complete)
. . . . £20/£10
ditto, Murray (London), 1981 (100 copies, signed by the author and John Piper) £300
St Mary-le-Strand, St Mary-le-Strand (London), 1981 (signed broadsheet) £75
Uncollected Poems, Murray (London), 1982 . £10/£5
ditto, Murray (London), 1982 (100 signed copies) . .£300
Betjeman's Cornwall, Murray (London), 1984 . £25/£10
Ah Middlesex, Warren Editions (London), 1984 (250 copies)
. . . .£50

Prose

Ghastly Good Taste, Chapman & Hall (London), 1933 (first issue with pages 119/120 bound in and errata at page 1; fold-out plate tipped-in at rear flyleaf) . . £300/£175
ditto, Chapman & Hall (London), 1933 (second issue with pages 119/120 cancelled, ie replaced; fold-out plate tipped-in at rear flyleaf) . . . . . . £200/£100
ditto, Chapman & Hall (London), 1933 (200 signed copies in a slipcase) . . . . £400/£350
ditto, Anthony Blond (London) 1970. . . . £15/£5
ditto, Anthony Blond (London), 1970 (200 signed copies, slipcase). . . . . £175/£125
ditto, St Martin's Press (New York), 1971 . . £15/£5
Cornwall Illustrated in a series of views, Architectural Press (London), 1934 (spiral-bound). £85
Devon, Architectural Press (London), 1936 (spiral-bound) .
. . . .£80
An Oxford University Chest, John Miles (London), 1938 .
. . . . £250/£65
A Handbook on Paint, with Hugh Casson, Silicate Paint Co., 1939 . . . .£500
Antiquarian Prejudice, Hogarth Sixpenny Pamphlets No. 3 (London), 1939 (stapled wraps) £25
Vintage London, Collins (London), 1942 . . £50/£20
English Cities and Small Towns, Britain in Pictures/Collins (London), 1943 . . . . £15/£5
John Piper, Penguin Modern Painters (Harmondsworth, Middlesex), 1944 (stapled wraps) £10
Murray's Buckinghamshire Architectural Guide, Murray (London), 1948 (edited with John Piper) . . £30/£10
Murray's Berkshire Architectural Guide, Murray (London), 1949 (edited with John Piper) . . . . £30/£10
Shropshire, Faber Shell Guide (London), 1951 . £25/£10
The English Scene, C.U.P./N.B.L. (London), 1951 (stapled wraps) £15
First and Last Loves, Murray (London), 1952 . £75/£25
The English Town in the Last Hundred Years, C.U.P. (Cambridge, UK), 1956 (Rede Lecture; sewn wraps) . £20
Collins Guide to English Parish Churches, Collins (London), 1958 . . . . £25/£10
Ground Plan to Skyline (pseud 'Richard M. Farran'), Newman Neame (London), 1960 (stapled wraps) . £20
English Churches, with Basil Clarke, Studio Vista (London), 1964 . . . . £20/£10
The City of London Churches, Pitkin Pictorial (London), 1965 (pbk) £5
Victorian and Edwardian London from Old Photographs, Batsford (London), 1969 . . . . . £15/£5
ditto, Viking (New York), 1969 . . . . . £10/£5

Ten Wren Churches, Editions Elector (London), 1970 (100 copies, folder) £200
Victorian and Edwardian Oxford from Old Photographs, with David Vaisey, Batsford (London), 1971 . £15/£5
Victorian and Edwardian Brighton from Old Photographs, with J. S. Gray, Batsford (London), 1972 . £15/£5
London's Historic Railway Stations, Murray (London), 1972 . . . . £25/£5
A Pictorial History of English Architecture, Murray (London), 1972 . . . . £15/£5
ditto, Murray (London), 1972 (100 signed copies, slipcase) . . . . £300/£250
ditto, Macmillan (New York), 1972 . . . . £10/£5
West Country Churches, Society of Saints Peter & Paul (London), 1973 (stapled wraps) £15
Victorian and Edwardian Cornwall from Old Photographs, with A. L. Rowse, Batsford (London), 1974 . . £15/£5
Plea for Holy Trinity Church, Sloane Street, Church Literature Association (London), 1974 (wraps) . £150
Souvenir of Metroland, Warren Editions (London), 1977 (220 copies) £200
Archie and the Strict Baptists, Murray (London), 1977 . . . . £35/£15
ditto, Lippincott (Philadelphia, PA), 1978. . . £20/£10
Letters, Volume One, 1926-1951, Methuen (London), 1994 . . . . £10/£5
Letters, Volume Two, 1951-1984, Methuen (London), 1995 . . . . £10/£5

A.I. BEZZERIDES
(b.1908 d.2007)

Bezzirides is probably best-known as a screenwriter who produced *noir* and action films, including Mick Spillaine's *Kiss Me Deadly*. His work also included some of Warners' 'social conscience' movies of the Forties. He only wrote three novels, and all are highly collectable.

Novels
Long Haul, Carrick and Evans (New York), 1938 . £500/£65
ditto, Cape (London), 1938 . . . . . . £250/£30
There Is A Happy Land, Henry Holt (New York), 1942 . . . . £250/£35
Thieves' Market, Scribners (New York), 1942 . £250/£35

Other
William Faulkner: A Life on Paper, Univ of Mississippi Press (Jackson, MI), 1980 . . . . . . £15/£10

AMBROSE BIERCE
(b.1842[1] d.1914?)

Ambrose Bierce was an American journalist, short story writer and satirist. He is best known for his cynical *The Devil's Dictionary* and short stories such as 'An Occurrence at Owl Creek Bridge'.

Humour
The Fiend's Delight, John Camden Hotten (London), [1872] (pseud 'Dod Grile'; cloth) £350

ditto, John Camden Hotten (London), [1872] (pseud 'Dod Grile'; wraps) £350
ditto, A.L. Lyster (New York), 1873 (cloth; without publisher's ads) £300
Nuggets and Dust Panned Out in California, Chatto & Windus (London), [1873] (pseud 'Dod Grile'; wraps) £350
Cobwebs from an Empty Skull, George Routledge & Sons (London), 1874 (pseud 'Dod Grile') £300
ditto, as *Cobwebs: Being the Fables of Zimbri, the Parsee*, 'Fun' Office (London), [c.1884] (pseud 'Dod Grile'; wraps or cloth) £150
The Dance of Death, H. Keller (San Francisco, CA), 1877 (pseud 'William Herman'; written with Thomas A. Harcourt) £350
Fantastic Fables, Putnam's (New York), 1899 (with ads at rear starting with 'By Anna Fuller') . . . £200
The Cynic's Word Book, Doubleday Page (New York), 1906 (presumed first issue without frontispiece) . . . £225
ditto, Doubleday Page (New York), 1906 (frontispiece inserted) £200
ditto, as *The Devil's Dictionary*, A. & C. Boni (New York), 1926 . . . . £25/£10
The Enlarged Devil's Dictionary, Doubleday (Garden City, NY), 1967 (edited by Ernest Jerome Hopkins) . £20/£5

Poetry
Black Beetles in Amber, Western Authors Publishing Co. (New York), 1892 . . . . £200
ditto, Western Authors Publishing Co. (New York), 1892 (second issue; printed grey wraps; printed by Johnson & Emigh) £150
Shapes of Clay, W.E. Wood (San Francisco, CA), 1903 (first issue with lines 5 and 6 transposed on p.71) . . £200
ditto, W.E. Wood (San Francisco, CA), 1903 (second issue corrected) £150
An Invocation, Book Club of California (San Francisco, CA), 1928 (300 copies; marbled paper boards) . . £25
A Vision of Doom, Donald M. Grant (West Kingston, RI), 1980 (edited by Donald Sidney-Fryer) . . . £10/£5

Short Stories
Tales of Soldiers and Civilians, E.L.G. Steele (New York), 1891 . . . . £200
ditto, E.L.G. Steele (New York), 1891 (copies with 'Compliments of' on preliminary leaf, signed by Bierce) £1,000
ditto, as *In the Midst of Life: Tales of Soldiers and Civilians*, Chatto & Windus (London), 1892 (blue cloth) £150
Can Such Things Be?, Cassell (New York), 1893 (cloth) £325
ditto, Cassell (New York), 1893 (wraps) . . . £300
ditto, Jonathan Cape Travellers' Library (London), 1926 . . . . £15/£5
A Son of the Gods and A Horseman in the Sky, Paul Elder & Co. (San Francisco, CA), 1907 . . . . £45/£15
Ten Tales, First Edition Club (London), 1925 (500 copies) £40
Ghost and Horror Stories, Dover (New York), 1964 (edited by E.F. Bleiler; pbk) £5
Stories and Fables, Stemmer House (Owings Mills, MD), 1977 (edited by Edward Wagenknecht; wraps) . . £5
An Occurrence At Owl Creek Bridge, Tartarus Press (Carlton-in-Coverdale), 2008 (300 copies) . . £30/£10

Essays and Miscellany

The Shadow on the Dial and Other Essays, A.M. Robertson (San Francisco, CA), 1909 . . . . . £100

Write It Right: A Little Blacklist of Literary Faults, Neale Publishing Co. (New York), 1909 (first issue 5¾x3 inches) £250

ditto, Neale Publishing Co. (New York), 1909 (second issue 6x4 inches) £125

Letters, Book Club of California (San Francisco, CA), 1922 (edited by Bertha Clark Pope; black cloth spine, marbled boards, paper label) £40

Twenty-one Letters, George Kirk (Cleveland, OH), 1922 (edited by Samuel Loveman) £50

Battle Sketches, First Edition Club (London), 1930 (350 copies; slipcase) . . . . . £200/£150

Selections from 'Prattle', Book Club of California (San Francisco, CA), 1936 (edited by Carroll D. Hall; 500 copies) £25

The Ambrose Bierce Satanic Reader, Doubleday (Garden City, NY), 1968 (edited by Jerome Hopkins) . £20/£5

Translation

The Monk and the Hangman's Daughter, by Richard Voss, F.J. Schulte (Chicago), 1892 (with G.A. Danziger; yellow wraps) £250

ditto, by Richard Voss, F.J. Schulte (Chicago), 1892 (grey cloth) £200

ditto, Jonathan Cape Travellers' Library (London), 1927 . . . . £45/£20

Collected Works

Collected Works, Neale Publishing Co (Washington, DC), 1909-1912 (12 vols) £1,000

Collected Writings, Citadel Press (New York), 1946 £20/£5

EARL DERR BIGGERS

(b.1884 d.1933)

Earl Derr Biggers was an American author whose novel *Seven Keys to Baldpate* inspired seven films of the same title and perhaps two with different titles but identical plots (*House of Long Shadows*, *Haunted Honeymoon*). He is best remembered for his character Charlie Chan, a Chinese-American detective created as an alternative to Yellow Peril stereotypes like Fu Manchu.

Charlie Chan Series

The House Without a Key, Bobbs-Merrill (Indianapolis, IN), 1925 . . . . £1,250/£75

ditto, Harrap (London), 1926 . . . . £450/£45

The Chinese Parrot, Bobbs-Merrill (Indianapolis, IN), 1926 . . . . £1,000/£70

ditto, Harrap (London), 1927 . . . . £400/£40

Behind That Curtain, Bobbs-Merrill (Indianapolis, IN), 1928 (Bobbs-Merrill symbol on copyright page) . £750/£65

ditto, Harrap (London), 1928 . . . . . £350/£35

The Black Camel, Bobbs-Merrill (Indianapolis, IN), 1929 . . . . £450/£50

ditto, Cassell (London), 1930 . . . . . £350/£35

Charlie Chan Carries On, Bobbs-Merrill (Indianapolis, IN), 1930 . . . . £250/£30

ditto, Cassell (London), 1931 . . . . . £250/£30

The Keeper of the Keys, Bobbs-Merrill (Indianapolis, IN), 1932 . . . . £200/£25

ditto, Cassell (London), 1932 . . . . . £200/£25

Celebrated Cases of Charlie Chan, Bobbs-Merrill (Indianapolis, IN), 1933 . . . . . £150/£20

ditto, Cassell (London), 1933 . . . . . £150/£20

Novels

Seven Keys to Baldpate, Bobbs-Merrill (Indianapolis, IN), 1913 . . . . £100

ditto, Mills and Boon (London), 1914 . . . . £100

Love Insurance, Bobbs-Merrill (Indianapolis, IN), 1914 £25

Inside the Lines, Bobbs-Merrill (Indianapolis, IN), 1915 (with Robert Welles Ritchie) £25

The Agony Column, Bobbs-Merrill (Indianapolis, IN), 1916 . . . . £25

ditto, as *Second Floor Mystery*, Gosset & Dunlap (New York), 1930 . . . . £75/£15

Fifty Candles, Bobbs-Merrill (Indianapolis, IN), 1926 . . . . £60/£15

Others

If You're Only Human, 1912 . . . . . . £200

Earl Derr Biggers Tells Ten Stories, Bobbs-Merrill (Indianapolis, IN), 1933 . . . . . £225/£25

R.D. BLACKMORE

(b.1825 d.1900)

Richard Doddridge Blackmore was called to the Bar in 1852 but he preferred to spend his time writing and market gardening. His first real success was *Lorna Doone*. This historical novel, set on Exmoor, was not an initial hit, but a reviewer mistakenly claimed that the novel told the history of one of the ancestors of the fiancé of Princess Louise, daughter of Queen Victoria. It was suddenly a great success, and even after the mistake had been revealed it continued to be popular, over-shadoweding his later work.

Novels

Clara Vaughan, Macmillan (London), 1864 (anonymous; 3 vols) £450

ditto, Harper (New York), 1880 . . . . . £75

Cradock Nowell: A Tale of the New Forest, Chapman & Hall (London), 1866 (3 vols) £400

ditto, Harper (New York), 1866 . . . . . £150

Lorna Doone: A Romance of Exmoor, Sampson Low & Marston (London), 1869 (3 vols) £2,000

ditto, Harper (New York), 1874 . . . . . £200

The Maid of Sker, Blackwood (London), 1872 (3 vols) £350

ditto, Harper (New York), [1872] £125

Alice Lorraine: A Tale of the South Downs, Sampson Low (London), 1875 (3 vols) £350

ditto, Harper (New York), 1875 . . . . . £100

Cripps the Carrier: A Woodland Tale, Sampson Low (London), 1876 (3 vols) £300

ditto, Harper (New York), 1876 . . . . . £100

Erema, or My Father's Sin, Smith Elder (London), 1877 (3 vols) £300

ditto, Harper (New York), 1877 (1 vol) £100

Mary Anerley: A Yorkshire Tale, Sampson Low (London), 1880 (3 vols) £275
ditto, Harper (New York), 1880 (1 vol) . . . £75
Christowell: A Dartmoor Tale, Sampson Low (London), 1882 (3 vols) £275
ditto, Harper (New York), 1882 (1 vol) . . . £75
The Remarkable History of Sir Thomas Upmore, Bart, M.P., Sampson Low (London), 1884 (2 vols) . £250
ditto, Harper (New York), 1884 (1 vol) . . . £65
Springhaven: A Tale of the Great War, Sampson Low (London)), 1887 (3 vols) £250
ditto, Harper (New York), 1887 (1 vol) . . . £65
Kit and Kitty: A Story of West Middlesex, Sampson Low (London), 1890 [1889] (3 vols) £200
ditto, Harper (New York), 1889 (1 vol) . . . £65
Perlycross: A Tale of the Western Hills, Sampson Low (London), 1894 (3 vols) £200
ditto, Harper (New York), 1889 (1 vol) . . . £65
Tales from the Telling House, Sampson Low (London), 1896 . . . . £75
ditto, as *Slain by the Doons*, Dodd, Mead (New York), 1895 . . . . £45
Dariel: A Romance of Surrey, Blackwood (London), 1897 . . . . £25
ditto, Dodd, Mead (New York), 1897 . . . £25

Poetry
Poems, Robert Hardwicke, 1854 (pseud 'Melanter') . £100
Epullia, Hope, 1854 . . . . £100
The Bugle of the Black Sea, Robert Hardwicke, 1855 . £75
The Fate of Franklin, Robert Hardwicke, 1860 . . £75
The Farm and Fruit of Old: A Translation of the First and Second Georgics of Virgil, Sampson Low (London), 1862 (pseud 'A Market-gardener'; light blue cloth) . . £75
ditto, as *The Georgics of Virgil*, Sampson Low (London), 1871 . . . . £65
Fringilla: Some Tales in Verse, Elkin Mathews (London), 1895 . . . . £50
ditto, Elkin Mathews (London),1895 (deluxe edition limited to 25 copies on hand-made paper; vellum binding) . £350
ditto, Burrows Brothers (Cleveland, OH), 1895 (600 numbered copies) £200

ALGERNON BLACKWOOD

(b.1869 d.1951)

An influential British writer of supernatural fiction, Blackwood mined all aspects of the genre from tales of reincarnation, through hauntings, to stories of nature deities. His best stories are masterpieces of atmosphere and suggestion, and many reflect his love of the natural world. Towards the end of his life he became something of a radio and television personality, often reading his own stories live on air.

Novels
Jimbo: A Fantasy, Macmillan (London), 1909 . £100
ditto, Macmillan (New York), 1909 . . . . £65
The Education of Uncle Paul, Macmillan (London), 1909 . . . . £65

ditto, Paget (New York), 1909 (abridged; wraps) . . £75
ditto, Holt (New York), 1914 . . . . . £30
The Human Chord, Macmillan (London), 1910 . £75
The Centaur, Macmillan (London), 1911. . . . £85
A Prisoner in Fairyland, Macmillan (London), 1913 . £40
ditto, Macmillan (New York), 1913 . . . . . £35
The Extra Day, Macmillan (London), 1915 . . £35
ditto, Macmillan (New York), 1915 . . . . £35
Julius Levallon, Cassell (London), 1916 . . . . £45
ditto, Dutton (New York), 1916 . . . . . £40
The Wave: An Egyptian Aftermath, Macmillan (London), 1916 . . . . £45
ditto, Dutton (New York), 1916 . . . . . £40
The Promise of Air, Macmillan (London), 1918 . £30
ditto, Dutton (New York), 1918 . . . . . £25
The Garden of Survival, Macmillan (London), 1918 . £30
ditto, Dutton (New York), 1918 . . . . . £25
The Bright Messenger, Cassell (London), 1921 . £150/£45
ditto, Dutton (New York), 1922 . . . . . £150/£45

Short Story Collections
The Empty House and Other Ghost Stories, Eveleigh Nash (London), 1906 . . . . £600
ditto, Vaughan (New York), 1915 (limited to 500 copies) £175
The Listener and Other Stories, Eveleigh Nash (London), 1907 . . . . £300
ditto, Vaughan & Gomme (New York), 1914 (limited to 500 copies) £125
John Silence, Physician Extraordinary, Eveleigh Nash (London), 1908 . . . . £250
ditto, John W. Luce (Boston), 1909 . . . . £100
ditto, Brentano's (New York), 1909 (unauthorised). . £65
The Lost Valley and Other Stories, Eveleigh Nash (London), 1910 . . . . £300
ditto, Vaughan & Gomme (New York), 1914 (limited to 500 copies) £100
Pan's Garden, A Volume of Nature Stories, Macmillan (London), 1912 . . . . £75
ditto, Tartarus Press (Carlton-in Coverdale), 2000 . £30/£5
Ten Minute Stories, Murray (London), 1914 . . £75
ditto, Dutton (New York), 1914 . . . . . £75
Incredible Adventures, Macmillan (London), 1914 . £75
ditto, Macmillan (New York), 1914 . . . . £65
Day and Night Stories, Cassell (London), 1917 . £125
ditto, Dutton (New York), 1917 . . . . . £65
The Wolves of God, Cassell (London), 1921 (with Wilfrid Wilson) . . . . £400/£175
ditto, Dutton (New York), 1921 . . . £250/£75
Tongues of Fire and Other Sketches, Jenkins (London), 1924 . . . . £400/£100
ditto, Dutton (New York), 1925 . . . . . £300/£65
Ancient Sorceries and Other Tales, Collins (London), [1927] . . . . £200/£50
The Dance of Death and Other Tales, Jenkins (London), 1927 . . . . £150/£65
ditto, Dial Press (New York), 1928 . . . £75/£25
Strange Stories, Heinemann (London), 1929 . £45/£20
ditto, as *The Best Supernatural Tales of Algernon Blackwood*, Causeway Books (New York), 1973 (abridged facsimile of above edition) . . . . £25/£10
Full Circle, Mathews & Marrot (London), 1929 (530 signed, numbered copies) . . . . . . £100/£65

Short Stories of Today and Yesterday, Harrap & Co
(London), 1930 . . . . . . £35/£20
The Willows and Other Queer Tales, Collins (London),
[1932] . . . . £150/£45
Shocks, Grayson & Grayson (London), 1935 . . £125/£25
ditto, Dutton (New York), 1936 . . . . £125/£25
The Tales of Algernon Blackwood, Secker (London), 1938
. . . . £45/£15
ditto, Dutton (New York), 1939 . . . . £45/£15
Selected Tales of Algernon Blackwood, Penguin (Har-
mondsworth, Middlesex), 1942 (pbk) . . . £15
Selected Short Stories of Algernon Blackwood, Armed
Services Editions (New York), [1942] (stapled pbk) . £20
The Doll and One Other, Arkham House (Sauk City, WI),
1946 . . . . £45/£20
Tales of the Uncanny and Supernatural, Nevill (London),
1949 . . . . £15/£5
ditto, Castle (New York), 1974 . . . . £15/£5
In the Realm of Terror, Pantheon Books (New York), 1957
. . . . £15/£5
Selected Tales of Algernon Blackwood, John Baker
(London), 1964 . . . . . £15/£5
ditto, Dutton (New York), 1965 . . . . £15/£5
Tales of the Mysterious and Macabre, Spring Books
(London), 1967 . . . . . £10/£5
ditto, Castle (New York), 1974 . . . . £10/£5
Ancient Sorceries and Other Stories, Penguin (Harmonds-
worth, Middlesex), 1968 (pbk). £10
Best Ghost Stories of Algernon Blackwood, Dover (New
York), 1973 (pbk) £10
The Magic Mirror, Equation (Wellingborough, Northants),
1989 (pbk) £5

Children's Books
Sambo and Snitch, Blackwell (Oxford), 1927. . £100/£75
ditto, Appleton (New York), 1927 . . . £85/£65
Mr Cupboard, Blackwell (Oxford), 1928 . . . £100/£75
Dudley and Gilderoy: A Nonsense, Benn (London), 1929 .
. . . . £75/£25
ditto, Dutton (New York), 1929 . . . . £45/£20
By Underground, Blackwell (Oxford), 1930 . . £100/£65
The Parrot and the Cat, Blackwell (Oxford), 1931 £100/£65
The Italian Conjuror, Blackwell (Oxford), 1932 . £100/£65
Maria (Of England) In the Rain, Blackwell (Oxford), 1933
. . . . £100/£65
Sergeant Poppett and Policeman James, Blackwell
(Oxford), 1934 . . . . . £100/£65
The Fruit Stoners, Grayson & Grayson (London), [1934] .
. . . . £75/£25
ditto, Dutton (New York), 1935 . . . £65/£20
ditto, Blackwell (Oxford), 1935 (extract) . . £65/£40
How the Circus Came to Tea, Blackwell (Oxford), 1936 .
. . . . £100/£65
The Adventures of Dudley and Gilderoy, Dutton (New
York), 1941 (adapted by Marion B. Cottren). . £45/£15
ditto, Faber (London), 1941 . . . . £45/£15

Plays
Karma: A Reincarnation Play, Macmillan (London), 1918
(with Violet Pearn) £50
ditto, Dutton (New York), 1918 . . . . £45
Through the Crack, French (London), 1925 (with Violet
Pearn; wraps) £25

Other Works
Episodes Before Thirty, Cassell (London), 1923 . £200/£35
ditto, Dutton (New York), 1924 . . . . £200/£35
ditto, as *Adventures Before Thirty*, Cape (London), 1934 .
. . . . £40/£15

ROBERT BLOCH
(b.1917 d.1994)

Psycho became the best known of Bloch's novels
following Alfred Hitchcock's classic film. He was a
prolific author of crime fiction, science fiction, and perhaps
most influentially, horror fiction. He received a Hugo
Award, the Bram Stoker Award, and the World Fantasy
Award, and also served a term as President of the Mystery
Writers of America.

Novels
The Scarf, Dial Press (New York), 1947 . . . £150/£25
ditto, New English Library (London), 1972 (pbk) . . £10
The Kidnapper, Lion (New York), 1954 (pbk) . . £50
Spiderweb, Ace (New York), 1954 (pbk double with David
Alexander's *The Corpse in My Bed*) . . . £25
The Will to Kill, Ace (New York), 1954 (pbk). . £25
Shooting Star, Ace (New York), 1958 (pbk double with
Bloch's *Terror In The Night And Other Stories*) . £25
Psycho, Simon & Schuster (New York), 1959 . £1,000/£150
ditto, Robert Hale (London), 1960 . . . £500/£75
The Dead Beat, Simon & Schuster (New York), 1960 .
. . . . £60/£15
ditto, Robert Hale (London), 1971 . . £50/£10
Firebug, Regency (Evanston, IL), 1961 (pbk). . £15
ditto, Corgi (London), 1977 (pbk) . . . £5
The Couch, Fawcett (Greenwich, Conn), 1962 (pbk) . £10
Terror, Belmont (New York), 1962 (pbk). . . £10
ditto, Corgi (London), 1964 (pbk) . . . £5
The Star Stalker, Pyramid (New York), 1968 (pbk) . £20
The Todd Dossier, Delacorte (New York), 1969 (pseud
'Collier Young') . . . . . £35/£10
ditto, Macmillan (London), 1969 (pseud 'Collier Young') .
. . . . £25/£10
It's All In Your Mind, Curtis (New York), 1971 (pbk) . £10
Sneak Preview, Paperback Library (New York), 1971 (pbk)
. . . . £10
Night World, Simon & Schuster (New York), 1972 £15/£5
ditto, Robert Hale (London), 1974 . . . £15/£5
American Gothic, Simon & Schuster (New York), 1974 .
. . . . £25/£10
ditto, W.H. Allen (London), 1975 . . . £20/£5
Strange Eons, Whispers Press (Chapel Hill, NC), 1978
[1979] . . . . . . £10/£5
ditto, Whispers Press (Chapel Hill, NC), 1978 [1979] (300
signed copies, slipcase) . . . . £30/£15
ditto, Whispers Press (Chapel Hill, NC), 1978 [1979] (26
lettered, signed copies, slipcase) . . . £100/£65
There is a Serpent in Eden, Zebra Books (London), 1979
(pbk) £10
Psycho II, Warner Books (New York), 1982 (pbk) . £5
ditto, Whispers Press (Binghamton, NY), 1982 . £10/£5
ditto, Whispers Press (Binghamton, NY), 1982 (750 signed,
numbered copies, slipcase) . . . . £15/£10

ditto, Whispers Press (Binghamton, NY), 1982 (26 signed, lettered copies, d/w and slipcase) . . . £125/£75
ditto, as **Psycho 2**, Transworld (London), 1982 . £10/£5
ditto, as **Psycho 2**, Transworld (London), 1982 (26 lettered copies in slipcase) . . . . £100/£65
Twilight Zone - The Movie, Warner Books (New York), 1983 (pbk) £5
ditto, Transworld (London), 1983 (pbk) £5
Night of the Ripper, Robert Hale (London), 1984 . £10/£5
ditto, Doubleday (New York), 1984 . . . . £10/£5
Unholy Trinity, Scream Press (Santa Cruz, CA), 1986 . .
. . . . £15/£5
ditto, Scream Press (Santa Cruz, CA), 1986 (250 signed, numbered copies, d/w and slipcase) . . . £25/£15
ditto, Scream Press (Santa Cruz, CA), 1986 (26 signed, lettered copies, d/w and slipcase) . . . . £75/£45
Lori, Tor (New York), 1989. . . . . . £10/£5
Screams, Underwood/Miller (San Rafael, CA/Lancaster, PA), 1989 . . . . £10/£5
ditto, Underwood/Miller (San Rafael, CA/Lancaster, PA), 1989 (300 signed copies, slipcase) . . . £30/£15
Psycho III: The Psycho House, Tor (New York), 1990 .
. . . . £10/£5
ditto, Robert Hale (London), 1995 . . . £10/£5
The Jekyll Legacy, Tor (New York), 1990 . . £10/£5

Short Stories
Sea Kissed, Utopian Publications (London), [1945] (first issue printed in Great Britain; stapled wraps) . . £750
ditto, Utopian Publications (London), [1945] (second issue printed in Eire; stapled wraps) £350
The Opener of the Way, Arkham House (Sauk City, WI), 1945 . . . . £175/£45
ditto, Neville Spearman (London), 1974 . . . £35/£10
Terror in the Night, Ace (New York), 1958 (pbk) . . £30
Pleasant Dreams, Arkham House (Sauk City, WI), 1960 .
. . . . £75/£20
ditto, Whiting & Wheaton (London), 1967 . . £40/£10
Blood Runs Cold, Simon & Schuster (New York), 1961 .
. . . . £65/£10
ditto, Robert Hale (London), 1963 . . . . £45/£10
Nightmares, Belmont (New York), 1961 (pbk) . . £10
Yours Truly, Jack the Ripper, Belmont (New York), [1962] (pbk) £10
ditto, as **The House of the Hatchet**, Tandem (London), 1965 (pbk) £5
Atoms and Evil, Fawcett (Greenwich, Conn), 1962 (pbk) .
. . . . £10
ditto, Frederick Muller (London), 1963 (pbk) . . . £5
ditto, Robert Hale (London), 1976 . . . £45/£10
More Nightmares, Belmont (New York), [1962] (pbk). £5
Horror-7, Belmont (New York), 1963 (pbk) . . £10
ditto, Four Square (London), 1965 (pbk) . . . £5
Bogey Men: Ten Tales, Pyramid Books (New York), 1963 (pbk) £5
Tales in a Jugular Vein, Pyramid Books (New York), 1965 (pbk) £5
ditto, Sphere (London), 1970 (pbk) £5
The Skull of the Marquis de Sade, Pyramid Books (New York), 1965 (pbk) £15
ditto, Robert Hale (London), 1975 . . . . £65/£15
Chamber of Horrors, Award (New York), 1966 (pbk) . £5
ditto, Corgi (London), 1977 (pbk) £5
The Living Demons, Belmont (New York), 1967 (pbk) £5

ditto, Sphere (London), 1970 (pbk) £5
Dragons and Nightmares, Mirage Press (Baltimore, MD), 1968 (1,000 numbered copies) . . . . . £20/£10
Ladies' Day/This Crowded Earth, Belmont (New York), 1968 (pbk) £5
Bloch and Bradbury, Tower [New York], [1969] (pbk) £5
ditto, as **Fever Dream and Other Fantasies**, Sphere (London), 1970 (pbk) £5
ditto, as **Bloch & Bradbury: Whispers From Beyond**, Peacock Press (Chicago), 1972 (pbk; with additional material by others) £5
Fear Today, Gone Tomorrow, Award (New York), 1971 (pbk) £5
The King of Terrors, Mysterious Press (New York), 1977 (250 signed copies, slipcase and d/w) . . . £30/£15
ditto, Mysterious Press (New York), 1977 . . £10/£5
ditto, Robert Hale (London), 1978 . . . . £10/£5
Cold Chills, Doubleday (New York), 1977 . . £15/£10
ditto, Robert Hale (London), 1978 . . . . £15/£5
The Best of Robert Bloch, Ballantine (New York), 1977 (pbk) £5
Out of the Mouths of Graves, Mysterious Press (New York), 1978 . . . . £10/£5
ditto, Mysterious Press (New York), 1978 (26 signed, lettered copies, slipcase) . . . . . . £45/£35
ditto, Mysterious Press (New York), 1978 (250 signed, numbered copies, slipcase) . . . . . £25/£10
Such Stuff As Screams Are Made Of, Ballantine (New York), 1978 (pbk) £5
Mysteries Of The Worm, Zebra Books (New York), 1981 (pbk) £5
Lost in Time and Space With Lefty Feep, Creatures at Large Press (Pacifica, CA), 1987 (pbk) £5
ditto, Creatures at Large Press (Pacifica, CA), 1987 (250 signed copies in d/w and slipcase) . . . . £45/£25
The Selected Stories of Robert Bloch, Underwood/Miller (Los Angeles, CA/Columbia, PA), 1987 (3 vols, 500 copies, slipcase, no d/ws) . . . £25 each, £75 the set
ditto, Underwood/Miller (Los Angeles, CA/Columbia, PA), 1987 (11 signed, numbered, leather-bound sets, 3 vols, slipcase, no d/ws) £450
Midnight Pleasures, Doubleday (New York), 1987 £10/£5
Fear and Trembling, Tor (New York), 1989 (pbk) . £5
The Early Fears, Fedogan and Bremer (Minneapolis, MN), 1994 . . . . £15/£5
ditto, Fedogan and Bremer (Minneapolis, MN), 1994 (100 signed, numbered copies, slipcase and d/w) . £200/£150

Non-Fiction
The Eighth Stage of Fandom, Advent (Chicago), 1962 (125 numbered, signed copies, no d/w) £125
ditto, Advent (Chicago), 1962 (200 copies) . £100/£25
ditto, Advent (Chicago), 1962 (400 copies; pbk) . . £15
The First World Fantasy Convention: Three Authors Remember, Necronomicon Press (West Warwick, RI), 1980 (stapled wraps) £25
Out Of My Head, NESFA Press (Framingham, MA), 1986 .
. . . . £25/£10
ditto, NESFA Press (Framingham, MA), 1986 (200 signed, numbered copies, slipcase and d/w) . . £35/£25
Once Around The Bloch: An Unauthorized Autobiography, Tor (New York), 1993 . . . . . . £10/£5

EDMUND BLUNDEN

(b.1896 d.1974)

Blunden is remembered primarily as a war poet, having enlisted in 1915 in the Royal Sussex Regiment and serving with them until the end of the War. He took part in the actions at Ypres and the Somme where he won the Military Cross. In 1922, he was awarded the prestigious Hawthornden Prize for Poetry. His later poetry was inspired by his adopted county of Kent.

Poetry

Poems 1913 and 1914, privately printed by Price & Co (Horsham, Sussex), 1914 (100 copies; wraps) . £1,500

Poems Translated from the French, printed by Price & Co (Horsham, Sussex), 1914 (100 copies; wraps) . £1,250

The Barn, privately printed (Framfield, Sussex), 1916 (50 copies; wraps) £1,250

Three Poems, privately printed (Framfield, Sussex), 1916 (50 copies; wraps) £1,250

The Harbingers, privately printed (Framfield, Sussex), 1916 (200 copies, 'The Barn' and 'Three Poems' bound together; wraps) £850

Pastorals, Erskine Macdonald (London), 1916 (wraps). £50

ditto, Erskine Macdonald (London), 1916 (50 cloth copies) £350

The Waggoner and Other Poems, Sidgwick & Jackson (London), 1920 . . . . . . £125/£35

The Shepherd and Other Poems of Peace and War, Cobden-Sanderson (London), 1922. . . . £75/£20

ditto, Knopf (New York), 1922 . . . . . £75/£15

Dead Letters, Pelican Press (London), 1923 (50 numbered copies; wraps) £200

To Nature, The Beaumont Press (London), 1923 (310 numbered copies) £45

ditto, The Beaumont Press (London), 1923 (80 signed, numbered copies) £125

Masks of Time: A New Collection of Poems, The Beaumont Press (London), 1925 (310 numbered copies) . . £40

ditto, The Beaumont Press (London), 1925 (80 signed, numbered copies) £125

The Augustan Books of Modern Poetry, Benn (London), 1925 (stapled wraps) £5

English Poems, Cobden-Sanderson (London), 1926 £35/£15

ditto, Knopf (New York), 1926 . . . . . £30/£10

Retreat, Cobden-Sanderson (London), 1928 . £40/£10

ditto, Cobden-Sanderson (London), 1928 (112 signed, numbered copies) . . . . . . £86/£45

ditto, Doubleday (New York), 1928 . . . . £40/£10

Japanese Garland, The Beaumont Press (London), 1928 (310 numbered copies) £60

ditto, The Beaumont Press (London), 1928 (80 signed, numbered copies) £150

Winter Nights: A Reminiscence, Faber (London), 1928 (sewn wraps) £10

ditto, Faber (London), 1928 (500 signed, numbered, large paper copies) £25

Near and Far, Cobden-Sanderson (London), 1929 £25/£10

ditto, Cobden-Sanderson (London), 1929 (160 signed, numbered copies) £35

ditto, Harper (New York), 1930 . . . . £25/£10

Poems 1914-1930, Cobden-Sanderson (London), 1930. . . . . £35/£10

ditto, Cobden-Sanderson (London), 1930 (200 signed, numbered copies) £175

ditto, Harper (New York), 1930 . . . . . £35/£10

Halfway House: A Miscellany of New Poems, Cobden-Sanderson (London), 1932 . . . . £30/£10

ditto, Cobden-Sanderson (London), 1932 (70 signed, numbered copies) £140

Choice or Chance: New Poems, Cobden-Sanderson (London), 1934 . . . . £30/£10

ditto, Cobden-Sanderson (London), 1934 (45 signed, numbered copies) £150

An Elegy and Other Poems, Cobden-Sanderson (London), 1937 . . . . £35/£10

Poems 1930-1940, Macmillan (London), 1940 . £25/£10

ditto, Macmillan (New York), 1940 . . . . £25/£10

Shells by a Stream: New Poems, Macmillan (London), 1944 . . . . £20/£10

After the Bombing and Other Short Poems, Macmillan (London), 1949 . . . . £15/£5

Eastward: A Selection of Verses, privately printed, 1950 (250 copies) £85

Poems of Many Years, Collins (London), 1957 . £15/£5

A Hong Kong House: Poems 1951-1981, Collins (London), 1962 . . . . £10/£5

Eleven Poems, The Golden Head Press, 1965 [1966] (wraps) £25

ditto, The Golden Head Press, 1965 [1966] (21 signed copies) £200

A Selection of the Shorter Poems, privately printed, 1966 (wraps) £10

The Midnight Skaters: Poems for Young Readers, Bodley Head (London), 1968 . . . . . . £10/£5

A Selection from the Poems, privately printed, 1969 (wraps) £10

Selected Poems, Carcanet (Manchester), 1982. . . £5

Overtones of War: Poems of the First World War, Duckworth (London), 1996 . . . . . £10/£5

Prose

The Bonadventure: A Random Journal of an Atlantic Holiday, Cobden-Sanderson (London), 1922 . £45/£15

ditto, Putnam (New York), 1923 . . . . . £30/£10

Christ's Hospital: A Retrospect, Christophers (London), 1923 . . . . £100/£35

On the Poems of Henry Vaughan, Cobden-Sanderson (London), 1927 . . . . £25/£10

Undertones of War, Cobden-Sanderson (London), 1928 . . . . £250/£45

ditto, Doubleday (New York), 1929 . . . £75/£20

ditto, The Folio Society (London), 1989 (slipcase) . £10/£5

Nature in English Literature, The Hogarth Press (London), 1929 . . . . £45/£15

ditto, Harcourt (New York), 1929 . . . . £35/£10

Leigh Hunt, Cobden-Sanderson (London), 1930 . £40/£15

ditto, Harper (New York), 1930 . . . . . £30/£10

De Bello Germanico: A Fragment of Trench History, G.A. Blunden (Hawstead), 1930 (250 copies). . . £150

ditto, G.A. Blunden (Hawstead), 1930 (25 signed copies) £300

Votive Tablets: Studies Chiefly Appreciative of English Authors and Books, Cobden-Sanderson (London), 1931 . . . . £45/£15

ditto, Cobden-Sanderson (London), 1931 (50 signed, numbered copies) £200

ditto, Harper (New York), 1932 . . . . £45/£15
The Face of England, Longmans Green (London), 1932 .
. . . . £35/£10
We'll Shift our Ground, or Two On a Tour, Cobden-
Sanderson (London), 1933 (with Sylvia Norman) £45/£15
Charles Lamb and His Contemporaries, C.U.P. (Cam-
bridge, UK), 1933 . . . . . . £10/£5
ditto, Macmillan (New York), 1933 . . . £10/£5
The Mind's Eye, Cape (London), 1934 . . . £15/£5
Keats's Publisher: A Memoir of John Taylor (1781-1864),
Cape (London), 1938 . . . . . £35/£10
English Villages, Collins (London), 1941 . . £15/£5
ditto, Hastings House (New York), [n.d.] . . £10/£5
Thomas Hardy, Macmillan (London), 1941 [1942] £30/£10
Cricket Country, Collins (London), 1944 . . £20/£5
Shelley: A Life Story, Collins (London), 1946 . £35/£10
ditto, Viking Press (New York), 1947 . . . £25/£10
John Keats, British Council, Longmans (London), 1950
(stapled wraps) £5
Charles Lamb, British Council, Longmans (London), 1954
(stapled wraps) £5
War Poets 1914-1918, British Council, Longmans (London),
1958 (stapled wraps) £5
Guest of Thomas Hardy, Toucan Press (Beaminster, Dorset),
1964 (sewn wraps) £10

ENID BLYTON

(b.1897 d.1968)

A prolific children's author, Blyton is best known for the
'Famous Five', 'Secret Seven' and 'Noddy' books. Her
output was huge and her books were very popular in
Britain and Australia and have remained so despite
becoming rather dated. They have been translated into at
least 40 languages and are also successful in many European countries. Books by Blyton are listed under the
following categories: Adventure and Mystery Series,
School Series, Noddy Titles, Family Series, Series for
Younger Children, Books Written as 'Mary Pollock',
Poetry, Plays, Other Titles, Books Edited by Enid Blyton.

Adventure and Mystery Series:

'Adventure' Series

The Island of Adventure, Macmillan (London), 1944 . .
. . . . £700/£75
The Castle of Adventure, Macmillan (London), 1946 . .
. . . . £400/£25
The Valley of Adventure, Macmillan (London), 1947 . .
. . . . £200/£25
The Sea of Adventure, Macmillan (London), 1948 £200/£25
The Mountain of Adventure, Macmillan (London), 1949 .
. . . . £150/£20
The Ship of Adventure, Macmillan (London), 1950 . .
. . . . £125/£20
The Circus of Adventure, Macmillan (London), 1952 . .
. . . . £100/£20
The River of Adventure, Macmillan (London), 1955 . .
. . . . £100/£20

'The Adventurous Four' Series

The Adventurous Four, Newnes (London), 1941 . £100/£25
The Adventurous Four Again, Newnes (London), 1947 .
. . . . £75/£20

'Barney Junior Mystery' Series

The Rockingdown Mystery, Collins (London), [1949] . .
. . . . £65/£15
The Rilloby Fair Mystery, Collins (London), [1950] £45/£15
The Ring O'Bells Mystery, Collins (London), 1951 £35/£10
The Rubadub Mystery, Collins (London), 1952 . £35/£10
The Rat-A-Tat Mystery, Collins (London), 1956 . £35/£10
The Ragamuffin Mystery, Collins (London), 1959 £35/£10

'Famous Five' Series

Five on a Treasure Island: An Adventure Story, Hodder &
Stoughton (London), 1942 . . . . £1,250/£125
Five Go Adventuring Again, Hodder & Stoughton
(London), 1943 . . . . £850/£75
Five Run Away Together, Hodder & Stoughton (London),
1944 . . . . £750/£65
Five Go To Smuggler's Top, Hodder & Stoughton
(London), 1945 . . . . £600/£65
Five Go off in a Caravan, Hodder & Stoughton (London),
1946 . . . . `.` . . £450/£40
Five on Kirrin Island Again, Hodder & Stoughton
(London), 1947 . . . . £450/£40
Five Go Off to Camp, Hodder & Stoughton (London), 1948
. . . . £250/£35
Five Get Into Trouble, Hodder & Stoughton (London), 1949
. . . . £125/£25
Five Fall into Adventure, Hodder & Stoughton (London),
1950 . . . . £65/£15
Five on a Hike Together, Hodder & Stoughton (London),
1951 . . . . £65/£15
Five Have a Wonderful Time, Hodder & Stoughton
(London), [1952] . . . . £65/£15
Five Go Down to the Sea, Hodder & Stoughton (London),
1953 . . . . £65/£15
Five Go to Mystery Moor, Hodder & Stoughton (London),
1954 . . . . £50/£10
Five Have Plenty of Fun, Hodder & Stoughton (London),
1955 . . . . £50/£10
Five on a Secret Trail, Hodder & Stoughton (London), 1956
. . . . £50/£10
Five Go To Billycock Hill, Hodder & Stoughton (London),
1957 . . . . £45/£10
Five get into a Fix, Hodder & Stoughton (London), [1958].
. . . . £35/£10
The Famous Five Special, Hodder & Stoughton (London),
1959 (contains *Five Go Off to Camp*, *Five Go Off in a
Caravan* and *Five Have a Wonderful Time*) . £35/£10
Five on Finniston Farm, Hodder & Stoughton (London),
[1960] . . . . £35/£10
Five Go To Demon's Rocks, Hodder & Stoughton (London),
1961 . . . . £35/£10
Five Have a Mystery to Solve, Hodder & Stoughton
(London), 1962 . . . . £35/£10
Five are Together Again, Hodder & Stoughton (London),
1963 . . . . £35/£10
The Famous Five Big Book, Hodder & Stoughton (London),
1964 (contains *Five on a Treasure Island*, *Five Go Adven-
turing Again* and *Five Run Away Together*) . £35/£10

'Mystery' Series

The Mystery of the Burnt Cottage, Methuen (London), 1943
.   .   .   . £500/£35

The Mystery of the Disappearing Cat, Methuen (London), 1944   .   .   .   .   .   . £250/£30

The Mystery of the Secret Room, Methuen (London), 1945.
.   .   .   . £175/£25

The Mystery of the Spiteful Letters, Methuen (London), 1946   .   .   .   .   .   . £125/£20

The Mystery of the Missing Necklace, Methuen (London), 1947   .   .   .   .   .   . £100/£20

The Mystery of the Hidden House, Methuen (London), 1948
.   .   .   . £100/£15

The Mystery of the Pantomime Cat, Methuen (London), 1949   .   .   .   .   .   . £100/£15

The Mystery of the Invisible Thief, Methuen (London), 1950
.   .   .   . £85/£10

The Mystery of the Vanished Prince: Being the Ninth Adventure of the Five Find-Outers and Dog, Methuen (London), 1951   .   .   .   .   . £85/£15

The Mystery of the Strange Bundle, Methuen (London), 1952   .   .   .   .   .   . £65/£15

The Mystery of Holly Lane, Methuen (London), 1953 .   .
.   .   .   . £65/£15

The Mystery of Tally-Ho Cottage, Methuen (London), 1954
.   .   .   . £65/£15

The Mystery of the Missing Man, Methuen (London), 1956
.   .   .   . £65/£15

The Mystery of the Strange Messages, Methuen (London), 1957   .   .   .   .   .   . £65/£15

The Mystery of Banshee Towers, Methuen (London), 1961
.   .   .   . £65/£15

'Secret' Series

The Secret Island, Blackwell (Oxford), 1938 . £1,000/£100
The Secret of Spiggy Holes, Blackwood (London), [1940] .
.   .   .   . £175/£25

The Secret Mountain: Being the Third Story of the Strange Adventures of the Secret Island Children, Blackwell (Oxford), 1941   .   .   .   .   . £150/£35

The Secret of Killimoon, Blackwell (Oxford), 1943   .   .
.   .   .   . £125/£35

The Secret of Moon Castle, Blackwell (Oxford), 1953 .   .
.   .   .   . £100/£25

'Secret Seven' Series

At Seaside Cottage, Brockhampton Press (Leicester, UK), [1947] (no d/w) £75

Secret of the Old Mill, Brockhampton Press (Leicester, UK), [1948]   (no d/w) £65

The Secret Seven, Brockhampton Press (Leicester, UK), 1949   .   .   .   . £75/£15

Secret Seven Adventure, Brockhampton Press (Leicester, UK), 1950   .   .   .   .   .   . £45/£10

Well Done, Secret Seven, Brockhampton Press (Leicester, UK), 1951   .   .   .   .   .   . £45/£10

Secret Seven on the Trail, Brockhampton Press (Leicester, UK), 1952   .   .   .   .   .   . £45/£10

Go Ahead Secret Seven, Brockhampton Press (Leicester, UK), 1953   .   .   .   .   .   . £40/£10

Good Work, Secret Seven, Brockhampton Press (Leicester, UK), 1954   .   .   .   .   .   . £40/£10

Secret Seven Win Through, Brockhampton Press (Leicester, UK), 1955   .   .   .   .   .   . £40/£10

Three Cheers Secret Seven, Brockhampton Press (Leicester, UK), 1956   .   .   .   .   .   . £30/£10

Secret Seven Mystery, Brockhampton Press (Leicester, UK), 1957   .   .   .   .   .   . £25/£10

Puzzle for the Secret Seven, Brockhampton Press (Leicester, UK), 1958   .   .   .   .   .   . £25/£10

Secret Seven Fireworks, Brockhampton Press (Leicester, UK), 1959   .   .   .   .   .   . £25/£10

Good Old Secret Seven, Brockhampton Press (Leicester, UK), 1960   .   .   .   .   .   . £25/£5

Shock for the Secret Seven, Brockhampton Press (Leicester, UK), 1961   .   .   .   .   .   . £25/£5

Look out Secret Seven, Brockhampton Press (Leicester, UK), 1962   .   .   .   .   .   . £25/£5

Fun for the Secret Seven, Brockhampton Press (Leicester, UK), 1963   .   .   .   .   .   . £20/£5

School Series:

'Malory Towers' Series

First Term at Malory Towers, Methuen (London), 1946   .
.   .   .   . £200/£30

The Second Form at Malory Towers, Methuen (London), 1947   .   .   .   . £125/£25

Third Year at Malory Towers, Methuen (London), 1948   .
.   .   .   . £100/£25

The Upper Fourth at Malory Towers, Methuen (London), 1949   .   .   .   . £75/£20

In the Fifth at Malory Towers, Methuen (London), 1950   .
.   .   .   . £65/£15

Last Term at Malory Towers, Methuen (London), 1951   .
.   .   .   . £45/£10

'Naughtiest Girl' Series

The Naughtiest Girl in the School, Newnes (London), 1940
.   .   .   . £100/£25

The Naughtiest Girl Again, Newnes (London), 1942   .   .
.   .   .   . £75/£20

The Naughtiest Girl is a Monitor, Newnes (London), 1945
.   .   .   . £65/£20

'St Clare's School' Series

The Twins at St Clare's, Methuen (London), 1941 £250/£25
The O'Sullivan Twins, Methuen (London), 1942 . £75/£20
Summer Term at St Clare's, Methuen (London), 1943 .   .
.   .   .   . £65/£15

Claudine at St Clare's, Methuen (London), 1944 . £65/£15
The Second Form at St Clare's, Methuen (London), 1944 .
.   .   .   . £65/£15

Fifth Formers at St Clare's, Methuen (London), 1945 .   .
.   .   .   . £65/£15

Noddy Titles:

Numbered 'Noddy' Titles

Nos 1-15 were originally priced 3/6 on the d/w, and 16-24 at 4/6. Nos 1-6 have full name and address of Sampson Low on title page, the others do not. Nos. 1-6 have thicker paper and rounded spines.

No.1, *Noddy Goes to Toyland*, Sampson Low (London), 1949   .   .   .   . £85/£20

No.2, *Hurrah for Little Noddy*, Sampson Low (London), 1950   .   .   .   . £80/£20

No.3, *Noddy and His Car*, Sampson Low (London), 1951 .
.   .   .   . £80/£20

No.4, *Here Comes Noddy Again!*, Sampson Low (London), 1951 . . . . £80/£15

No.5, *Well Done, Noddy!*, Sampson Low (London), 1952 . . . . £65/£15

No.6, *Noddy Goes to School*, Sampson Low (London), 1952 . . . . £65/£15

No.7, *Noddy at the Seaside*, Sampson Low (London), 1953 . . . . £60/£15

No.8, *Noddy Gets Into Trouble*, Sampson Low (London), 1954 . . . . £60/£15

No.9, *Noddy and the Magic Rubber*, Sampson Low (London), 1954 . . . . . . £50/£15

No.10, *You Funny Little Noddy*, Sampson Low (London), 1955 . . . . £50/£15

No.11, *Noddy Meets Father Christmas*, Sampson Low (London), 1955 . . . . . . £50/£15

No.12, *Noddy and Tessie Bear*, Sampson Low (London), 1956 . . . . £50/£15

No.13, *Be Brave, Little Noddy*, Sampson Low (London), 1956 . . . . £50/£15

No.14, *Noddy and the Bumpy-Dog*, Sampson Low (London), 1957 . . . . . . £50/£15

No.15, *Do Look Out Noddy*, Sampson Low (London), 1957 . . . . £50/£15

No.16, *You're a Good Friend Noddy!*, Sampson Low (London), 1958 . . . . . . £25/£15

No.17, *Noddy Has An Adventure*, Sampson Low (London), 1958 . . . . £25/£15

No.18, *Noddy Goes to Sea*, Sampson Low (London), 1959 . . . . £50/£15

No.19, *Noddy and the Bunkey*, Sampson Low (London), 1959 . . . . £50/£15

No.20, *Cheer Up Little Noddy!*, Sampson Low (London), 1960 . . . . £50/£15

No.21, *Noddy Goes to the Fair*, Sampson Low (London), 1960 . . . . £50/£15

No.22, *Mr Plod and Little Noddy*, Sampson Low (London), 1961 . . . . . . £50/£15

No.23, *Noddy and the Tootles*, Sampson Low (London), 1962 . . . . £50/£15

No.24, *Noddy and the Little Aeroplane*, Sampson Low (London), 1964 . . . . . . £50/£15

'Noddy' Hardback Strip Books

Noddy Has Some Adventures, Sampson Low (London), 1951 . . . . £50

Noddy Colour Strip Book, Sampson Low (London), 1952 . . . . £50

The New Noddy Colour Strip Book, Sampson Low (London), 1953 . . . . £50

How Funny You Are, Noddy!, Sampson Low (London), 1954 . . . . £50

'Noddy' Little Colour Strip Books

(stapled wraps)

Noddy and the Witch's Wand, Sampson Low (London), 1952 . . . . £30

Noddy's Penny Wheel Car, Sampson Low (London), 1952 . . . . £30

Noddy's Car Gets a Squeak, Sampson Low (London), 1952 . . . . £30

Noddy and the Cuckoo's Nest, Sampson Low (London), 1953 . . . . £30

Noddy Gets Captured, Sampson Low (London), 1953 . £25

Noddy Is Very Silly, Sampson Low (London), 1953 . £25

Noddy Goes Dancing, Sampson Low (London), 1954 . £25

Noddy and the Snow House, Sampson Low (London), 1954 . . . . £25

Noddy the Cry Baby, Sampson Low (London), 1954 . £25

Noddy and the Tricky Teddy, Sampson Low (London), 1957 . . . . £25

Noddy Tricks Mr Sly, Sampson Low (London), 1957 . £25

Noddy and the Bear Who Lost His Growl, Sampson Low (London), 1957 . . . . £25

Noddy's Car Gets Into Trouble, Sampson Low (London), 1960 . . . . £25

Noddy and the Runaway Wheel, Sampson Low (London), 1960 . . . . £25

Noddy's Bag of Money, Sampson Low (London), 1960 £25

'Noddy' Cartons of Books

Noddy's House of Books, Sampson Low (London), [1951] (The Tiny Noddy Book Nos. 1-6, in card case, no d/ws. Contains: 1. *A Tale of Little Noddy*, 2. *Noddy Has More Adventures*, 3. *Noddy Goes to the Seaside*, 4. *Noddy Has a Shock*, 5. *Noddy Off to Rocking Horse Land*, 6. *Noddy and Big Ears Have a Picnic*) . . . . . £175 the set

Enid Blyton's Noddy's Ark of Books, Sampson Low (London), [1952] (5 books, cardboard case, no d/ws. Contains: 1. *Noddy and the Flying Elephant*, 2. *Big-Ears Loses Some Jewels*, 3. *Noddy and the Three Bears*, 4. *Noddy's Car Rides in the Air*, 5. *Noddy and the Big Balloon*) . . . . £165 the set

Noddy's Garage of Books, Sampson Low (London), [1953] (5 books, in cardboard case, no d/ws. Contains: 1. *Noddy Loses His Clothes*, 2. *Noddy and the Naughty Toys*, 3. *Noddy Makes a Mistake*, 4. *Noddy Wins a Prize*, 5. *Noddy and Jimmy Giraffe*) . . . . . £165 the set

Noddy's Castle of Books, Sampson Low (London), [1954] (5 books, in cardboard case, no d/ws. Contains: 1. *Noddy Visits the Land of Tops*, 2. *Noddy and the Magic Goldfish*, 3. *Noddy in the Land of King Ho-Ho*, 4. *Noddy and Mr. Roundy in Clowntown*, 5. *Noddy and Mr. Cheery*) . . £165 the set

The Noddy Toy Station Book Nos. 1-5, Sampson Low (London), [1956] (Contains: 1. *Noddy and His Passengers*, 2. *Noddy and the Magic Boots*, 3. *Noddy Flies a Kite*, 4. *Noddy and Naughty Gobby*, 5. *Noddy Has Hankie Troubles*) . . . . £150 the set

Noddy's Shop of Books Nos. 1-5, Sampson Low (London), [1958] (Contains: 1. *Noddy Buys a Spell*, 2. *Noddy Helps Tinny Build a House*, 3. *Noddy Drives Much Too Fast*, 4. *Noddy Complains to Mr Plod*, 5. *Noddy Buys Tinny a Present*) . . . . £150 the set

'Noddy' Big Books

The Big Noddy Book, Sampson Low (London), 1951 . . . . £125/£25

The Big Noddy Book Number 2, Sampson Low (London), 1952 . . . . £125/£25

The New Big Noddy Book Number 3, Sampson Low (London), 1953 . . . . £100/£25

The New Big Noddy Book Number 4, Sampson Low (London), 1954 . . . . £75/£20

The New Big Noddy Book Number 5, Sampson Low (London), 1955 . . . . £75/£20

The New Big Noddy Book Number 6, Sampson Low (London), 1956 . . . . £75/£20

The New Big Noddy Book Number 7, Sampson Low (London), 1957 . . . . £75/£20
The New Big Noddy Book Number 8, Sampson Low (London), 1958 . . . . £75/£20

'Noddy's' Tall Books
Noddy's Tall Blue Book, Sampson Low (London), [1960] £45
Noddy's Tall Green Book, Sampson Low (London), [1960] £45
Noddy's Tall Orange Book, Sampson Low (London), [1960] £45
Noddy's Tall Pink Book, Sampson Low (London), [1960] £45
Noddy's Tall Red Book, Sampson Low (London), [1960] £45
Noddy's Tall Yellow Book, Sampson Low (London), [1960] £45
The set of 6 *'Noddy's' Tall Books* £150

Other 'Noddy' Titles
Noddy Cut-Out Model Book: Adventure for the Noah's Ark, Sampson Low (London), 1953 . . . . £150
Enid Blyton's Book of Her Famous Play: Noddy in Toyland, Sampson Low (London), 1956 . . £75/£25

Family Series

Caravan Family Series
The Caravan Family, Lutterworth Press (London), 1945 . . . . £35/£10
The Saucy Jane Family, Lutterworth Press (London), 1947 . . . . £30/£10
The Pole Star Family, Lutterworth Press (London), 1950 . . . . £35/£10
The Seaside Family, Lutterworth Press (London), 1950 . . . . £30/£10
The Buttercup Farm Family, Lutterworth Press (London), 1951 . . . . £30/£10
The Queen Elizabeth Family, Lutterworth Press (London), 1951 . . . . £25/£10

Cherry Tree Farm/Willow Farm Series
The Children of Cherry-Tree Farm, Country Life (London), 1940 . . . . £60/£15
The Children of Willow Farm: A Tale of Life on a Farm, Country Life (London), 1942 . . . . £60/£15
More Adventures on Willow Farm, Country Life (London), 1942 . . . . £45/£10
Adventures on Willow Farm, Collins (London), 1968 . . . . £15/£5

Happy House Children Series
The Children at Happy House, Blackwell (Oxford), 1946 . . . . £50/£15
The Happy House Children Again, Blackwell (Oxford), 1947 . . . . £45/£15
Benjy and the Others, Latimer House (London), 1955 . . . . £35/£10
The Happy House Children, Collins (London), 1966 £15/£5

Six Cousins Series
Six Cousins at Mistletoe Farm, Evans (London), 1948. . . . . £50/£10
Six Cousins Again, Evans (London), 1950 . . £50/£10

Series for Younger Children

Bom Series
Bom The Little Toy Drummer, Brockhampton Press (Leicester, UK), 1956. . . . . . . £30/£10
Bom and His Magic Drumstick, Brockhampton Press (Leicester, UK), 1957. . . . . . . £30/£10
Enid Blyton's Bom Painting Book, Dean (London), [1957] . . . . £25/£15
Bom Goes Adventuring, Brockhampton Press (Leicester, UK), 1958 . . . . £25/£10
Bom and the Rainbow, Brockhampton Press (Leicester, UK), 1959 . . . . £25/£10
Hello Bom and Wuffy Dog, Brockhampton Press (Leicester, UK), [1959] . . . . £25/£10
Bom and the Clown, Brockhampton Press (Leicester, UK), 1959 . . . . £25/£10
Bom Goes to Magic Town, Brockhampton Press (Leicester, UK), 1960 . . . . £20/£5
Here Comes Bom, Brockhampton Press (Leicester, UK), [1960] . . . . £20/£5
Bom at the Seaside, Brockhampton Press (Leicester, UK), 1961. . . . . £20/£5
Bom Goes to the Circus, Brockhampton Press (Leicester, UK), [1961] . . . . £20/£5

Brer Rabbit Stories
Tales of Brer Rabbit Retold, Nelson (London), 1928 . . . . £50/£15
Heyo, Brer Rabbit! Tales of Brer Rabbit and His Friends, Newnes (London), 1938 . . . . £75/£15
The Further Adventures of Brer Rabbit, Newnes (London), 1942 . . . . £45/£15
Enid Blyton's Brer Rabbit Book, Latimer House (London), 1948 (1-8) . . . . . . £25/£10 each
Brer Rabbit and His Friends, Coker (London), 1948 . . . . £35/£10
Brer Rabbit Again, Dean (London), 1963 . . £15/£5
Enid Blyton's Brer Rabbit's A Rascal, Dean (London), 1965 . . . . £15/£5
Brer Rabbit and the Tar Baby, Hodder & Stoughton (London), 1975 . . . . £15/£5

Clicky Series
Strip books with stapled pictorial card wraps and cloth spine
Clicky the Clockwork Clown, Brockhampton Press (Leicester, UK), 1953. . . . . £15
Clicky Gets Into Trouble, Brockhampton Press (Leicester, UK), [1958] £15
Clicky and Tiptoe, Brockhampton Press (Leicester, UK), 1960 . . . . £15
Happy Birthday Clicky, Brockhampton Press (Leicester, UK), [1961] £15
Happy Holiday, Clicky, Brockhampton Press (Leicester, UK), 1961 . . . . £15

Faraway Tree Series
The Magic Faraway Tree, Newnes (London), 1943 . . . . £750/£65
The Folk of the Faraway Tree, Newnes (London), 1946 . . . . £150/£35
Up The Faraway Tree, Newnes (London), 1951 . £75/£25

John Jolly Series
John Jolly At Christmas Time, Evans (London), 1942
(wraps) £75
John Jolly By the Sea, Evans (London), 1943 (wraps) . £75
John Jolly on the Farm, Evans (London), 1943 (wraps) £75
John Jolly at the Circus, Evans (London), 1945 (wraps) £75

Josie, Click and Bun Series
*The Little Tree-House: Being the Adventures of Josie, Bun
and Click*, Newnes (London), [1940] . . . £100/£25
ditto, as *Josie, Click and Bun, and The Little Tree House*,
Newnes (London), [1951] . . . . . £35/£15
The Further Adventures of Josie, Bun and Click, Newnes
(London), [1941]. . . . . . £65/£15
Josie, Click and Bun Again, Newnes (London), [1946] .
. . . . £65/£20
The Little Green Duck and Other Stories, Brockhampton
Press (Leicester, UK), 1947 . . . . £35/£10
More About Josie, Click and Bun, Newnes (London), 1947
. . . . £45/£15
Welcome, Josie, Click and Bun!, Newnes (London), 1952 .
. . . . £35/£15

Mary Mouse Series
Mary Mouse and the Dolls House, Brockhampton Press
(Leicester, UK), [1942] (wraps) £25
More Adventures of Mary Mouse, Brockhampton Press
(Leicester, UK), [1943] (wraps) £25
Little Mary Mouse Again, Brockhampton Press (Leicester,
UK), [1944] (wraps) £20
Hallo, Little Mary Mouse, Brockhampton Press (Leicester,
UK), [1945] (wraps) £20
Mary Mouse and Her Family, Brockhampton Press
(Leicester, UK), [1946] (wraps) £20
Here Comes Mary Mouse Again, Brockhampton Press
(Leicester, UK), 1947 (wraps). £20
How Do You Do, Mary Mouse, Brockhampton Press
(Leicester, UK), 1948 (wraps) £20
We Do Love Mary Mouse, Brockhampton Press (Leicester,
UK), 1950 (wraps) £15
Welcome Mary Mouse, Brockhampton Press (Leicester,
UK), [1950] (wraps) £20
A Prize for Mary Mouse, Brockhampton Press (Leicester,
UK), [1951] (wraps) £15
Hurrah for Mary Mouse, Brockhampton Press (Leicester,
UK), 1951 (wraps) £15
Mary Mouse and Her Bicycle, Brockhampton Press
(Leicester, UK), [1952] (wraps) £15
Mary Mouse and the Noah's Ark, Brockhampton Press
(Leicester, UK), [1953] (wraps) £15
Mary Mouse to the Rescue, Brockhampton Press (London),
[1954] (wraps) £15
Mary Mouse in Nursery Rhyme Land, Brockhampton Press
(Leicester, UK), [1955] (wraps) £15
A Day With Mary Mouse, Brockhampton Press (Leicester,
UK), [1956] (wraps) £15
Mary Mouse and the Garden Party, Brockhampton Press
(Leicester, UK), [1957] (wraps) £15
Mary Mouse Goes to the Fair, Brockhampton Press
(Leicester, UK), [1958] (wraps) £15
Mary Mouse Has a Wonderful Idea, Brockhampton Press
(Leicester, UK), [1959] (wraps) £15
Mary Mouse Goes to Sea, Brockhampton Press (Leicester,
UK), [1960] (wraps) £15

Mary Mouse Goes Out for the Day, Brockhampton Press
(Leicester, UK), [1961] (wraps) £15
Fun With Mary Mouse, Brockhampton Press (Leicester,
UK), 1962 (wraps) £15
Mary Mouse and the Little Donkey, Brockhampton Press
(Leicester, UK), [1964] (wraps) £15

Mr Meddle Series
Mister Meddle's Mischief, Newnes (London), 1940 £75/£20
Mister Meddle's Muddles, Newnes (London), 1950 £35/£15
Merry Mistle Meddle!, Newnes (London), 1954 . £35/£15

Mr Pink-Whistle Series
The Adventures of Mr Pink-Whistle, Newnes (London),
1941 . . . .£150/£35
Mr Pink-Whistle Interferes, Newnes (London), 1950 . .
. . . . £35/£15
Mr Pink-Whistle's Party, Newnes (London), 1955 £35/£15
Mr Pink-Whistle's Big Book, Evans (London), 1958 . .
. . . . £45/£15

Mr Tumpy Series
Mr Tumpy and His Caravan, Sidgwick & Jackson
(London), 1949 . . . . £45/£10
Mr Tumpy Plays A Trick on Saucepan, Sampson Low
(London), 1952 (wraps) £15
Mr Tumpy in the Land of Wishes, Sampson Low (London),
1953 (wraps). £15
Mr Tumpy in the Land of Boys and Girls, Sampson Low
(London), [1955] (wraps) £15

Mr Twiddle Series
Hello, Mr Twiddle!, Newnes (London), 1942 . . £45/£15
Don't Be Silly, Mr Twiddle, Newnes (London), 1949 . .
. . . . £35/£15
Well Really, Mr Twiddle!, Newnes (London), 1953 £35/£15

Pip Series
The Adventures of Pip, Sampson Low (London), [1948] .
. . . . £35/£10
More Adventures of Pip, Marston (London), [1948] £35/£10

Twins Series
The Twins Go To Nursery-Rhyme Land, Brockhampton
Press (Leicester, UK), [1945] £25
Tales of the Twins, Brockhampton Press (Leicester, UK),
[1948] £20
Hello Twins, Brockhampton Press (Leicester, UK), 1951
(stapled card wraps; cloth spine) £15
Come Along Twins, Brockhampton Press (Leicester, UK),
1952 (stapled card wraps; cloth spine) . . . £15
Here Come the Twins, Brockhampton Press (Leicester, UK),
1953 (stapled wraps) £15
Trouble for the Twins, Brockhampton Press (Leicester, UK),
1964 (stapled wraps) £15

Wishing Chair Series
Adventures of the Wishing Chair, Newnes (London), [1937]
. . . .£750/£45
The Wishing Chair Again, Newnes (London), 1950 £65/£20

Amelia Jane Series
Naughty Amelia Jane!, Newnes (London), 1939 .£125/£30
Amelia Jane Again, Newnes (London), 1946 . . £65/£20
More About Amelia Jane!, Newnes (London), 1954 £45/£15

Books Written as 'Mary Pollock'

Children of Kidillin, Newnes (London), 1940. . £45/£10
Three Boys and a Circus, Newnes (London), 1940 £45/£10
The Adventures of Scamp, Newnes (London), 1943 £45/£10
Smuggler Ben, Laurie (London), 1943 . . . £45/£10
Mischief at St Rollo's, Newnes Tower House series (London), 1947 . . . . £45/£10
The Secret of Cliff Castle, Newnes Tower House series (London), 1947 . . . . . . £45/£10

Poetry

Child Whispers, J. Saville (London), [1922] (pictorial card wraps) £225
ditto, J. Saville (London), 1923 . . . £225/£100
Real Fairies, J. Saville (London), 1923 . £225/£100
ditto, J. Saville (London), 1923 (yellow pictorial card covers) £200
Ten Songs From Child Whispers, J. Saville (London), 1924 (card wraps) £100
Silver and Gold, Nelson (London), [1925] . £225/£75

Plays

A Book of Little Plays, Nelson (London), 1927 . £65/£20
The Play's the thing: Musical Plays for Children, Home Library Book Co., Newnes (London), [1927] . £250/£75
Six Enid Blyton Plays, Methuen (London), 1936 . £60/£15
The Wishing Bean and Other Plays, Blackwell (Oxford), 1939 . . . . £50/£20
The Blyton-Sharman Musical Plays for Juniors, Wheaton (London), 1939 . . . . . . £15 each
Cameo Plays Book, No 4, Edited by Holroyd, Arnold (London), 1939 . . . . . . £25/£10
How the Flowers Grow and Other Musical Plays, Wheaton (London), 1939 . . . . £15
School Plays: Six Plays for School, Blackwell (Oxford), 1939 . . . . £45/£10
Plays for Older Children, Newnes (London), [1940] £45/£10
Plays for Younger Children, Newnes (London), [1940] .
. . . . £45/£10
Finding the Tickets, Evans (London), 1955 (wraps) . £35
The Mother's Meeting, Evans (London), 1955 (wraps). £35
Mr Sly-One and the Cats, Evans (London), 1955 (wraps) £35
Who Will Hold the Giant, Evans (London), 1955 (wraps) .
. . . . £35

Other Titles

Responsive Singing Games, J. Saville (London), 1923 (stapled card covers; d/w) . . . . £300/£125
The Zoo Book, Newnes (London), [1924] . £65/£30
The Enid Blyton Book of Fairies, Newnes (London), [1924]
. . . . £125/£45
Sports and Games, Birn (London), 1924 (picture boards) .
. . . . £150
ditto, as *Playtime*, Birn (London), 1932 (picture boards) £150
Songs of Gladness, J. Saville (London), 1924 (wraps) . £125
The Enid Blyton Book of Bunnies, Newnes (London), [1925] . . . . £125/£45
Reading Practice, Nos 1-5,8,9 & 11, Nelson (London), [1925-1926] (no d/ws) . . . . . £15 each
The Enid Blyton Book of Brownies, Newnes (London), [1926] . . . . £125/£45
Tales Half Told, Nelson (London), 1926 . . £125/£45
The Bird Book, Newnes (London), [1926] . £35/£15
The Animal Book, Newnes (London), [1927] . £35/£15

The Wonderful Adventure, Birn (London), 1927 (picture boards) £325
Let's Pretend, Nelson (London), [1928] . . . £75/£15
Aesop's Fables Retold, Nelson (London), 1928 . £50/£15
Old English Tales Retold, Nelson (London), 1928. £50/£15
Pinkity's Pranks and Other Nature Fairy Stories: Retold, Nelson (London), 1928 . . . . . £50/£15
Enid Blyton's Nature Lessons, Evans (London), 1929 . .
. . . . £50/£15
Tarrydiddle Town, Nelson (London), 1929 . £35/£15
The Book Around Europe, Birn (London), 1929 (picture boards) £150
The Knights of the Round Table, Newnes (London), [1930]
. . . . £45/£15
Tales from the Arabian Nights, Retold, Newnes (London), [1930] . . . . £45/£15
Tales of Ancient Greece, Newnes (London), [1930] £45/£15
Tales of Robin Hood, Newnes (London), [1930] . £45/£15
My First Reading Book, Birn (London), [1933] . . £20
Cheerio! A Book for Boys and Girls, Birn (London), [1933]
. . . . £60
Five Minute Tales: Sixty Short Stories for Children, Methuen (London), 1933 . . . . . £50/£15
Let's Read, Birn (London), [1933] £25
Read to Us, Birn (London), 1933 . . . . £25
Letters from Bobs, privately printed for Blyton (London), 1933 (wraps). £75
The Adventures of Odysseus: Stories from World History Retold, Evans (London), 1934 . . . . £45/£10
The Story of the Siege of Troy: Stories from World History Retold, Evans (London), 1934 . . . . £45/£10
Tales of the Ancient Greeks and Persians: Stories from World History Retold, Evans (London), 1934 . £45/£10
Tales of the Romans: Stories from World History Retold, Evans (London), 1934 . . . . . £45/£10
The Enid Blyton Poetry Book, Methuen (London), 1934 .
. . . . £50/£15
The Red Pixie Book, Newnes (London), [1934] . £125/£45
Round the Year With Enid Blyton: A Year's Nature Study for Children, Evans (London), [1934] (94 vols, no d/ws) .
. . . . £20 the set
Ten-Minute Tales: Twenty-Nine Varied Stories for Children, Methuen (London), 1934 . . . £45/£10
The Old Thatch Series, Johnston (London), 1934-1935 (8 vols, pictorial limp linen covers; no d/ws) . £10 each
The Strange Tale of Mr Wumble, Coker (London), [1935] (wraps) £20
Hop, Skip and Jump, Coker (London), [1935] (wraps). £20
The Talking Teapot and Other Tales, Coker (London), [1935] . . . . £35/£10
The Children's Garden, Newnes (London), [1935] £45/£15
The Green Goblin Book, Newnes (London), [1935] £75/£15
Hedgerow Tales, Methuen (London), 1935 . £40/£10
Nature Observation Pictures, Warne (London), 1935 (32 pictures in four folders) £45
Fifteen-Minute Tales: Nineteen Stories for Children, Methuen (London), 1936 . . . . . £35/£10
The Famous Jimmy, Muller (London), 1936 . £35/£10
The Yellow Fairy Book, Newnes (London), [1936] £75/£20
The Adventures of Binkle and Flip, Newnes (London), [1936] . . . . £45/£15
Billy-Bob Tales, Methuen (London), 1936 . £45/£10
Enid Blyton's Sunny Stories, Newnes (London), 1937-1953 (stapled wraps; new series) . . . . £5 each

More Letters from Bobs, privately printed for Blyton (London), 1937 (wraps) £75
Mr Galliano's Circus, Newnes (London), [1938] . £300/£65
The Old Thatch, Johnston (London), 1938-1939 (8 vols, pictorial limp linen covers; no d/ws; second series) . £10 each
Hurrah for the Circus! Being the Further Adventures of Mr Galliano and his Famous Circus, Newnes (London), 1939 . . . . £125/£35
The Enchanted Wood, Newnes (London), 1939   £750/£125
News Chronicle Boys' and Girls' Circus Book, News Chronicle (London), [1940] . . . . £75/£25
Boys' and Girls' Circus Book, Newnes (London), [1940] .
. . . . £75/£20
Boys' and Girls' Story Book, Newnes (London), 1940 . .
. . . . £75/£20
News Chronicle Boys' and Girls' Book, News Chronicle (London), 1940 . . . . £75/£20
Birds of Our Gardens, Newnes (London), 1940 . £45/£15
Twenty-Minute Tales, Methuen (London), 1940 . £40/£10
Tales of Betsy-May, Methuen (London), 1940 . £45/£15
The Treasure Hunters, Newnes (London), 1940 . £150/£35
Bobs Again, privately printed for Blyton (London), 1940 (wraps) £75
Five O'Clock Tales: Sixty Five-Minute Stories for Children, Methuen (London), 1941 . . . £30/£10
The Babar Story Book, Methuen (London), 1941 . £75/£15
A Calendar for Children, Newnes (London), 1941 . . £100
Enid Blyton's Book of the Year, Evans (London), 1941 .
. . . . £35/£10
Six O'Clock Tales: Thirty-Three Short Stories for Children, Methuen (London), 1942 . . . £30/£10
Shadow, the Sheep-Dog, Newnes (London), 1942 . £75/£25
The Land of Far-Beyond, Methuen (London), 1942 £45/£15
I'll Tell You a Story, Macmillan (London), 1942 . £25/£10
I'll Tell You Another Story, Macmillan (London), 1942 .
. . . . £25/£10
Enid Blyton's Happy Story, Hodder & Stoughton (London), 1942 . . . . £35/£10
Enid Blyton's Little Books, Evans (London), [1942] (stapled pictorial wraps) . . . . £15 each, £80 the set
Circus Days Again, Newnes (London), 1942 . £45/£15
Enid Blyton's Readers, Macmillan (London), 1942-50 (Books 1-12). . . . . £10 each
The Children's Life of Christ, Methuen (London), 1943 .
. . . . £30/£10
Seven O'Clock Tales: Thirty Short Stories for Children, Methuen (London), 1943 . . . . . £30/£10
Dame Slap and Her School, Newnes (London), [1943] .
. . . . £45/£15
Enid Blyton's Merry Story Book, Hodder & Stoughton (London), 1943 . . . . £35/£10
Bimbo and Topsy, Newnes (London), 1943 . £45/£15
The Jolly Family Picture Story Book, Evans (London), [1943] (wraps) £25
The Toys Come to Life, Brockhampton Press (Leicester, UK), [1944] . . . . £45/£10
Billy and Betty at the Seaside, Valentine (London), [1944] (wraps) £60
The Boy Next Door, Newnes (London), 1944 . £125/£25
Enid Blyton's Nature Lover's Book, Evans (London), 1944
. . . . £45/£10
The Christmas Book, Macmillan (London), 1944 . £25/£10
Come to the Circus, Brockhampton Press (Leicester, UK), [1944] . . . . £45/£10

Eight O'Clock Tales, Methuen (London), 1944 . £30/£10
Enid Blyton's Jolly Story Book, Hodder & Stoughton (London), 1944 . . . . £35/£10
Polly Piglet, Brockhampton Press (Leicester, UK), [1944] .
. . . . £45/£10
Rainy Day Stories, Evans (London), [1944] . . £45/£10
Tales From the Bible, Methuen (London), 1944 . £30/£10
At Appletree Farm, Brockhampton Press (Leicester, UK), 1944 . . . . £45/£10
Tales of Toyland, Newnes (London), 1944 . . £45/£15
A Book of Naughty Children, Methuen (London), 1944 .
. . . . £45/£15
The Dog That Went To Fairyland, Brockhampton Press (Leicester, UK), 1944 . . . . . . £35/£10
Jolly Little Jumbo, Brockhampton Press (Leicester, UK), 1944 . . . . £45/£10
The Three Golliwogs, Newnes (London), 1944 . £75/£25
The Blue Story Book, Methuen (London), 1945 . £35/£10
Round the Clock Stories, National Magazine Co. (London), 1945 . . . . £65/£20
The Brown Family, News Chronicle (London), [1945].
. . . . £100/£45
The Conjuring Wizard and Other Stories, Macmillan (London), 1945 . . . . £45/£15
The Family at Red Roofs, Lutterworth Press (London), 1945
. . . . £45/£15
The First Christmas, Methuen (London), 1945 . £25/£10
Hollow Tree House, Lutterworth Press (London), 1945 .
. . . . £35/£15
The Runaway Kitten, Brockhampton Press (Leicester, UK), [1945] . . . . £45/£10
Enid Blyton's Sunny Story Book, Hodder & Stoughton (London), 1945 . . . . £35/£10
The Teddy Bear's Party, Brockhampton Press (Leicester, UK), [1945] . . . . £45/£10
The Bad Little Monkey, Brockhampton Press (Leicester, UK), [1946] . . . . £45/£10
Chimney Corner Stories, National Magazine Co. (London), 1946 . . . . £65/£20
The Enid Blyton Holiday Book, Sampson Low (London), [1946]. . . . . £25 each
Enid Blyton's Gay Story Book, Hodder & Stoughton (London), 1946 . . . . £35/£10
The Little White Duck and Other Stories, Macmillan (London), 1946 . . . . £35/£10
The Put-Em-Rights, Lutterworth Press (London), 1946 .
. . . . £25/£10
The Red Story Book, Methuen (London), 1946 . £35/£10
Tales of Green Hedges, National Magazine Co. (London), 1946 . . . . £65/£20
The Surprising Caravan, Brockhampton Press (Leicester, UK), 1946 . . . . £45/£10
The Train That Lost Its Way, Brockhampton Press (Leicester, UK), [1946] . . . . . . £45/£10
The Green Story Book, Methuen (London), 1947 . £35/£10
House-At-The-Corner, Lutterworth Press (London), 1947 .
. . . . £45/£15
Jinky Nature Books, Arnold (London), [1947] (4 vols) .
. . . . £15/£5 each
Enid Blyton's Lucky Story Book, Hodder & Stoughton (London), 1947 . . . . £35/£10
Rambles With Uncle Nat, National Magazine Co. (London), [1947] . . . . £65/£20

A Second Book of Naughty Children: Twenty-Four Short Stories, Methuen (London), 1947 . . . . £40/£15

The Smith Family, Arnold (London), [1947] (Books 1-3 by Blyton) . . . . £15/£5 each

Enid Blyton's Treasury, Evans (London), 1947 (published for Boots) . . . . £35/£10

Before I Go To Sleep: A Book of Bible Stories and Prayers for Children at Night, Latimer House (London), 1947 .
. . . . £35/£10

The Very Clever Rabbit, Brockhampton Press (Leicester, UK), 1947 . . . . £45/£10

Mister Icey-Cold, Blackwell (Oxford), 1948 . £35/£10

The Boy With the Loaves and Fishes, Lutterworth Press (London), 1948 . . . . £15/£5

Just Time For A Story, Macmillan (London), 1948 £25/£10

Let's Garden, Latimer House (London), 1948. £35/£10

Let's Have A Story, Pitkin (London), [1948] . . £60/£20

The Little Button-Elves, Coker (London), [1948] . £35/£10

The Little Girl at Capernaum, Lutterworth Press (London), 1948 . . . . £15/£5

Enid Blyton's Bedtime Series, Brockhampton Press (Leicester, UK), 1948 (2 vols) . . . £15/£5 each

Children of Other Lands, Coker (London), [1948] £35/£10

Come to the Circus, Newnes (London), 1948 . £35/£10

Now For A Story, Harold Hill (London), 1948 . £25/£10

The Red-Spotted Handkerchief and Other Stories, Brockhampton Press, [1948] . . . . . . £35/£10

Tales of Old Thatch, Coker (London), 1948 . £35/£10

They Ran Away Together, Brockhampton Press (Leicester, UK), [1948] . . . . £25/£5

We Want a Story, Pitkin (London), [1948] . . £60/£20

Nature Tales, Johnston (London), 1948 . . £20/£5

Tales After Tea, Werner Laurie (London), 1948 . £35/£10

Enid Blyton's Merry Christmas Cards, Pitkin (London), 1948 (card covers) £50

Enid Blyton's Birthday Cards, Pitkin (London), 1948 (card covers) £50

Enid Blyton's Bluebell Story Book, Gifford (London), [1949] . . . . £45/£15

Humpty Dumpty and Belinda, Collins (London), [1949] .
. . . . £40/£10

A Book of Magic, Macmillan (London), 1949 . £25/£10

Bumpy and His Bus, Newnes (London), 1949 £35/£15

Enid Blyton's Daffodil Story Book, Gifford (London), [1949] . . . . £45/£15

The Dear Old Snowman, Brockhampton Press (Leicester, UK), [1949] . . . . £35/£10

The Enid Blyton Bible Stories: Old Testament, Macmillan (London), 1949 . . . . £25/£10

The Enid Blyton Pictures: Old Testament, by John Turner, Macmillan (London), 1949 . . . . £25/£10

Jinky's Joke and Other Stories, Brockhampton Press (Leicester, UK), [1949]) . . . . . £35/£10

My Enid Blyton Bedside Book, 1-12, Barker (London), 1949
. . . . £45/£20 each

A Story Party at Green Hedges, Hodder & Stoughton (London), 1949 . . . . £35/£10

Tales After Supper, Werner Laurie (London), 1949 £25/£10

A Cat In Fairyland, Pitkin (London), 1949 . £50/£15

Chuff the Chimney Sweep, Pitkin (London), 1949. £50/£15

The Circus Book, Latimer House (London), 1949 . £35/£10

Those Dreadful Children, Lutterworth Press (London), 1949
. . . . £45/£15

Enid Blyton's Good Morning Book, National Magazine Co. (London), 1949 . . . . £40/£10

Oh, What A Lovely Time, Brockhampton Press (Leicester, UK), 1949 . . . . £35/£10

Robin Hood Book, Latimer House (London), 1949 £35/£10

Tiny Tales, Littlebury (London), 1949 . . . £30/£10

The Strange Umbrella and Other Stories, Pitkin (London), [1949] . . . . £50/£15

The Enchanted Sea and Other Stories, Pitkin (London), [1949] . . . . £50/£15

A Rubbalong Tale Showbook, Werner Laurie (London), 1950 (complete with cut-outs) £300

Mary Mouse Showbook, Werner Laurie (London), 1950 (complete with cut-outs) £300

The Astonishing Ladder and Other Stories, Macmillan (London), 1950 . . . . £35/£10

The Magic Knitting Needles and Other Stories, Macmillan (London), 1950 . . . . £35/£10

The Magic Snow-Bird and Other Stories, Pitkin (London), [1950] . . . . £50/£15

The Three Naughty Children and Other Stories, Macmillan (London), 1950 . . . . £35/£10

Smuggler Ben, Werner Laurie (London), 1950 . £25/£10

Tricky the Goblin and Other Stories, Macmillan (London), 1950 . . . . £35/£10

Rubbalong Tales, Macmillan (London), 1950. £45/£15

Enid Blyton's Poppy Story Books, Gifford (London), [1950]
. . . . £40/£15

Enid Blyton's Book of the Year, Evans (London), 1950 .
. . . . £45/£15

Enid Blyton Little Book Nos 1-6, Brockhampton Press (Leicester, UK), [1950] . . . . . £10 each

The Enid Blyton Pennant Series, Macmillan (London), 1950 (30 vols) . . . . £10 each

Round the Year With Enid Blyton, Evans (London), 1950 .
. . . . £45/£10

Round the Year Stories, Coker (London), 1950 . £25/£10

Tales About Toys, Brockhampton Press (Leicester, UK), 1950 . . . . £35/£10

What An Adventure, Brockhampton Press (Leicester, UK), 1950 . . . . £35/£10

The Yellow Story Book, Newnes (London), 1950 . £35/£15

Pippy and the Gnome and Other Stories, Pitkin (London), 1951 . . . . £50/£15

The Proud Golliwog, Brockhampton Press (Leicester, UK), 1951 . . . . £25/£5

Benjy and the Princess and Other Stories, Pitkin (London), [1951] . . . . £50/£15

The Book of Brownies, Newnes (London), [1951]. £35/£15

Enid Blyton's Buttercup Story Book, Gifford (London), [1951] . . . . £35/£10

The Flying Goat and Other Stories, Pitkin (London), [1951]
. . . . £50/£15

Enid Blyton's Gay Street Book, Latimer House (London), [1951] . . . . £35/£10

A Picnic Party With Enid Blyton, Hodder & Stoughton (London), 1951 . . . . £35/£10

The Runaway Teddy Bear and Other Stories, Pitkin (London), [1951]. . . . . £50/£15

The Six Bad Boys, Lutterworth Press (London), 1951 . .
. . . . £35/£15

'Too-Wise' the Wonderful Wizard and Other Stories, Pitkin (London), [1951]. . . . . . . £50/£15

Down at the Farm, Sampson Low (London), 1951 £35/£10

Father Christmas and Belinda, Collins (London), 1951   .
.   .   .   . £30/£10
Feefo, Tuppeny and Jinks, Staples Press (London), 1951   .
.   .   .   . £45/£15
The Little Spinning Mouse and Other Stories, Pitkin
(London), 1951   .   .   .   .   .   .   £50/£15
Enid Blyton's Animal Lover's Book, Evans (London), 1952
.   .   .   . £45/£10
Enid Blyton's Bright Story Book, Brockhampton Press
(Leicester, UK), 1952.   .   .   .   .   . £50/£20
The Enid Blyton Bible Pictures: New Testament, Macmil-
lan, [1952]   .   .   .   . £25/£10
The Queer Adventure, Staples Press (London), 1952 £45/£15
The Story of My Life, Pitkin (London), [1952]   . £75/£25
The Very Big Secret, Lutterworth Press (London), 1952   .
.   .   .   . £35/£15
Enid Blyton's Snowdrop Story Book, Gifford (London),
[1952]   .   .   .   . £35/£10
Enid Blyton's Omnibus!, Newnes (London), 1952   £35/£15
Enid Blyton Tiny Strip Books, Sampson Low (London),
[1952]   .   .   .   . £15 each
My First Enid Blyton Book, Latimer House (London), 1952
.   .   .   . £30/£10
My First Nature Book, Macmillan (London), 1952   £15/£5
The Children's Jolly Book, Odhams (London), 1952 £30/£10
The Mad Teapot, Brockhampton Press (Leicester, UK), 1952
.   .   .   . £25/£5
The Two Sillies and Other Stories, Coker (London), 1952   .
.   .   .   . £35/£10
Mandy, Mops and Cubby Again, Sampson Low (London),
1952   .   .   .   . £15
Mandy, Mops and Cubby Find a House, Sampson Low
(London), 1952   .   .   .   . £15
Mandy Makes Cubby a Hat, Sampson Low (London), 1953
.   .   .   . £15
Snowball the Pony, Lutterworth Press (London), 1953 .   .
.   .   .   . £35/£15
The Story of Our Queen, Muller (London), 1953   . £35/£10
The Children's Book of Prayers, Muller (London), [1953] .
.   .   .   . £25/£10
Enid Blyton's Christmas Story, Hamilton (London), [1953]
(advent calendar). £30
The Enid Blyton Bible Stories: New Testament, Macmillan
(London), 1953 [1954] (14 vols)   .   .   . £5 each
Enid Blyton's Magazine, Evans (London), 1953+ . £15 each
Gobo and Mr Fierce, Sampson Low (London), 1953 £20/£5
Little Gift Books, Hackett (London), 1953 (translated by
Blyton)   .   .   .   .   .   . £25/£10 each
Playways Annual, Lutterworth Press (London), 1953 (by
Blyton and others)   .   .   .   .   .   . £25/£10
Visitors in the Night, Brockhampton Press (Leicester, UK),
1953 (wraps). £15
The Adventure of the Secret Necklace, Lutterworth Press
(London), 1954   .   .   .   .   .   .   £35/£15
The Castle Without a Door and Other Stories, Pitkin
(London), [1954].   .   .   .   .   .   £50/£15
The Children at Green Meadows, Lutterworth Press
(London), 1954   .   .   .   .   .   .   £35/£15
Enid Blyton's Friendly Story Book, Brockhampton Press
(Leicester, UK), 1954.   .   .   .   .   . £25/£5
Enid Blyton's Good Morning Book, Juvenile Productions
(London), [1954].   .   .   .   .   .   £25/£10
The Greatest Book in the World, British & Foreign Bible
Society (London), [1954] .   .   .   .   . £25/£10

The Little Toy Farm and Other Stories, Pitkin (London),
1954   .   .   .   .   £50/£15
Enid Blyton's Marigold Story Book, Gifford (London),
[1954]   .   .   .   .   £35/£10
Enid Blyton's Magazine Annual, Evans (London), [1954] .
.   .   .   . £15
Little Strip Picture Books, Sampson Low (London), 1954
(wraps).   .   .   .   . £10 each
A Surprise for Mary, Brent Press (London), 1954 (wraps)   .
.   .   .   . £25
A Happy Birthday, Brent Press (London), 1954 (wraps) £25
The Two Birthdays, Brent Press (London), 1954 (wraps) £25
The Wonderful Birthday, Brent Press (London), 1954
(wraps) £25
All About Babies, Brent Press (London), 1954 (wraps).   £25
Tales About Toys, Brent Press (London), 1954 (wraps)   £25
Enid Blyton's Away Goes Sooty, Collins (London), [1955].
.   .   .   . £30/£10
Bible Stories from the Old Testament, Muller (London),
[1955]   .   .   .   . £15/£5
Enid Blyton's Bobs, Collins (London), [1955]   . £30/£10
Enid Blyton's Foxglove Story Book, Gifford (London),
[1955]   .   .   .   . £35/£10
Holiday House, Evans (London), [1955] .   .   £45/£10
Enid Blyton's Little Bedtime Books, Sampson Low
(London), [1955] (8 vols)   .   .   .   .   . £10 each
Mandy, Mops and Cubby and the Whitewash, Sampson
Low (London), [1955] £15
Gobo in the Land of Dreams, Sampson Low (London),
[1955] £15
Mischief Again!, Collins (London), 1955.   .   £50/£15
More Chimney Corner Stories, Macdonald (London), 1955
.   .   .   . £30/£10
Enid Blyton's Neddy the Little Donkey, Collins (London),
[1955]   .   .   .   .   £30/£10
Playing At Home: A Novelty Book, Methuen (London),
1955 (spiral bound) £150
Run-About's Holiday, Lutterworth Press (London), 1955   .
.   .   .   . £35/£10
Enid Blyton's Christmas With Scamp and Bimbo, Collins
(London), [1955].   .   .   .   .   .   £30/£10
Enid Blyton's Sooty, Collins (London), [1955]   £30/£10
The Troublesome Three, Sampson Low (London), [1955] .
.   .   .   . £25/£10
Enid Blyton's 'What Shall I Be?', Collins (London), [1955]
.   .   .   . £20/£5
Bimbo and Blackie Go Camping, Collins (London), 1955   .
.   .   .   . £20/£5
*Enid Blyton's Favourite Book of Fables, from the Tales of
La Fontaine*, Collins (London), 1955   .   .   £35/£10
Golliwog Grumbled, Brockhampton Press (Leicester, UK),
1955   .   .   .   .   £30/£10
Laughing Kitten, Harvill (London), 1955.   .   £25/£10
The Child Who Was Chosen, Waterlow (London), 1955
(wraps) £30
Let's Have a Club of Our Own, Waterlow (London), 1955
(wraps) £30
Enid Blyton's Animal Tales, Collins (London), [1956].   .
.   .   .   . £30/£10
The Clever Little Donkey, Collins (London), [1956] £30/£10
Colin the Cow-Boy, Collins (London), [1956].   £30/£10
Four in a Family, Lutterworth Press (London), 1956 £25/£10
Let's Have a Party, Harvill Press (London), 1956   . £25/£10
Scamp at School, Collins (London), [1956]   .   £30/£10

A Story of Jesus, Macmillan (London), 1956 .   £15/£5
Children's Own Painting Book, Odhams (London), 1957 £15
New Testament Picture Books, Nos 1-2, Macmillan
(London), 1957 .   .   .   .   .   . £10/£5 each
The Birthday Kitten, Lutterworth Press (London), 1958   .
.   .   .   . £45/£10
Enid Blyton's Little Bedtime Books, Sampson Low
(London), [1958] (4 vols) .   .   .   . £10 each
Rumble and Chuff, Juvenile Productions (London), [1958].
.   .   .   . £45/£15
Tales After Tea, Collins (London), 1958 .   .   . £15/£5
Enid Blyton's Mystery Stories, Collins (London), 1959   .
.   .   .   . £15/£5
Enid Blyton's Dog Stories, Collins (London), 1959 £15/£5
Adventure Stories, Collins (London), 1960 .   . £15/£5
Adventure of the Strange Ruby, Brockhampton Press
(Leicester, UK), 1960.   .   .   .   . £25/£10
Happy Day Stories, Evans (London), 1960 .   . £35/£10
Will the Fiddler, Instructive Arts (London), [1960] £30/£10
Old Testament Picture Books, Macmillan (London), 1960 .
.   .   .   . £10/£5 each
Tales At Bedtime, Collins (London), 1960 .   . £15/£5
The Big Enid Blyton Book, Hamlyn (London), 1961 £25/£10
The Mystery That Never Was, Collins (London), 1961.   .
.   .   .   . £25/£10
Circus Days Again, May Fair Books (London), 1962 £15/£5
The Four Cousins, Lutterworth Press (London), 1962 .   .
.   .   .   . £25/£10
Stories for Monday, Oliphants (London), 1962 (no d/w) £35
Stories for Tuesday, Oliphants (London), 1962 (no d/w) £35
The Boy Who Wanted A Dog, Lutterworth Press (London),
1963   .   .   .   . £25/£10
Tales of Brave Adventure, Dean (London), [1963] £15/£5
The Enid Blyton Storybook for Fives to Sevens, Parrish
(London), [1964].   .   .   .   .   . £35/£10
Happy Hours Story Book, Dean (London), [1964]. £25/£5
Enid Blyton's Sunshine Picture Story Book, World Distrib-
utors (London), [1964]   .   .   .   .   . £20/£5
Storytime Book, Dean (London), 1964   .   . £15/£5
Tell-A-Story Books, World Distributors (London), 1964   .
.   .   .   . £15/£5 each
Enid Blyton's Sunshine Book, Dean (London), [1965]   .
.   .   .   . £15/£5
The Boy Who Came Back, Lutterworth Press (London),
1965   .   .   .   . £25/£10
The Man Who Stopped to Help, Lutterworth Press
(London), 1965 .   .   .   .   .   . £25/£10
Easy Reader, Collins (London), 1965 (no d/w)   .   . £5
Tales of Long Ago, Dean (London), 1965   .   . £15/£5
Enid Blyton's Pixie Tales, Collins (London), 1966   £15/£5
Enid Blyton's Pixieland Story Book, Collins (London),
1966   .   .   .   . £15/£5
Enid Blyton's Playbook, Collins (London), [1966]   £15/£5
Enid Blyton's Fireside Tales, Collins (London), 1966 £15/£5
Enid Blyton's Bedtime Annual, Manchester (London), 1966
.   .   .   . £15/£5
The Fairy Folk Story Book, Collins (London), 1966 £20/£5
Enid Blyton's Gift Book, Purnell (London), 1966 . £20/£5
Stories for Bedtime, Dean (London), 1966   .   . £15/£5
Stories for You, Dean (London), 1966   .   .   . £15/£5
John and Mary, Brockhampton Press (Leicester, UK), 1966-
68 (9 vols) .   .   .   .   .   . £10/£5 each
Holiday Annual Stories, Low Marston (London), 1967   .
.   .   .   . £20/£5

Holiday Magic Stories, Low Marston (London), 1967 £20/£5
Holiday Pixie Stories, Low Marston (London), 1967 £20/£5
Holiday Toy Stories, Low Marston (London), 1967   £20/£5
The Playtime Story Book, Nos 1-14, World Distributors
(London), 1967 .   .   .   .   . £10/£5 each
Brownie Tales, Collins (London), 1968 .   .   . £15/£5
Once Upon A Time, Collins (London), 1968 .   . £15/£5
The Bear With Boot-Button Eyes and Other Stories, Purnell
(London), 1975 .   .   .   .   .   . £10/£5
Dame Roundy's Stockings and Other Stories, Purnell
(London), 1975 .   .   .   .   .   . £10/£5
The Dog With the Long Tail and Other Stories, Purnell
(London), 1975 .   .   .   .   .   . £10/£5
The Goblin and the Dragon and Other Stories, Purnell
(London), 1975 .   .   .   .   .   . £10/£5
The Good Old Rocking Horse and Other Stories, Purnell
(London), 1975 .   .   .   .   .   . £10/£5
The Little Sugar Mouse and Other Stories, Purnell
(London), 1975 .   .   .   .   .   . £10/£5

Books Edited by Enid Blyton
The Teacher's Treasury, Newnes (London), [1926] (3 vols)
.   .   .   . £30/£15 each
Sunny Stories for Little Folks, Newnes (London), [1926-
1936] (240 issues)   .   .   .   .   . £10 each
Pictorial Knowledge, Newnes (London), 1930 (10 vols)   .
.   .   .   . £100/£40 the set
Treasure Trove Readers, Wheaton (London), 1934-35 (the
'Junior' series compiled by Blyton, no d/ws)   . £10 each
Birds of the Wayside and Woodland, by Thomas A. Coward,
Warne (London), 1936 .   .   .   .   . £30/£10

NELSON S. BOND
(b.1908 d. 2006)

Nelson S. Bond is better known in the United States than in
the United Kingdom, where he is appreciated as one of the
most important fantasy writers of the mid-20th century. An
early science fiction author, often combining the humorous
with the weird, he published many short stories in the pulp
magazines of the 1930s and 40s.

Novels
Exiles of Time, Prime Press (Philadelphia, PA), 1949 .   .
.   .   .   . £30/£10
ditto, Prime Press (Philadelphia, PA), 1949 (112 signed,
numbered copies, slipcase)   .   .   .   . £80/£50
That Worlds May Live, Wildside Press (Holicong, PA), 2002
(pbk) £5

Short Stories
Mr Mergenthwirker's Lobblies and Other Fantastic Tales,
Coward-McCann (New York), [1946] .   .   . £40/£10
The Thirty-First of February, Gnome Press (New York),
[1949]   .   .   .   . £25/£10
ditto, Gnome Press (New York), [1949] (112 signed,
numbered copies, slipcase)   .   .   . £150/£100
The Remarkable Exploits of Lancelot Biggs: Spaceman,
Doubleday (New York), 1950 .   .   .   . £45/£10
No Time Like the Future, Avon (New York), 1956 (pbk) £5
Nightmares and Daydreams, Arkham House (Sauk City,
WI), 1968 .   .   .   . £20/£5

The Far Side of Nowhere, Arkham House (Sauk City, WI),
2002 . . . . £15/£5

Plays
Mr Mergenthwirker's Lobblies, Samuel French (New York),
1957 (stapled wraps) £20
State of Mind, Samuel French (New York), 1958 (stapled
wraps) £10
Animal Farm: A Fable in Two Acts, Samuel French (New
York), 1964 (stapled wraps) (adapted from Orwell's novel)
. . . . £10

LUCY M. BOSTON
(b.1892 d.1990)

A British author, Boston was inspired to write *The Children of Green Knowe* after buying the 800 year-old Grey
Manor in Cambridgeshire in 1935. (The Manor is one of
the oldest permanently inhabited houses in Britain.) Boston
did not have her first book published until she was over 60
years old.

'Green Knowe' Novels
The Children of Green Knowe, Faber (London), 1954 . .
. . . . £300/£45
ditto, Harcourt Brace (New York), 1955 . . . £200/£30
The Chimneys of Green Knowe, Faber (London), 1958 .
. . . . £175/£25
ditto, as *Treasure of Green Knowe*, Harcourt Brace (New
York), 1958 . . . . £100/£20
The River at Green Knowe, Faber (London), 1959 £85/£15
ditto, Harcourt Brace (New York), 1959 . . £65/£10
A Stranger at Green Knowe, Faber (London), 1961 £85/£15
ditto, Harcourt Brace (New York), 1961 . . £65/£10
An Enemy at Green Knowe, Faber (London), 1964 £50/£10
ditto, Harcourt Brace (New York), 1964 . . £45/£10
The Stones of Green Knowe, Faber (London), 1976 £50/£10
ditto, Harcourt Brace (New York), 1976 . . £45/£10

Other Novels
Yew Hall, Faber (London), 1954. . . . . £75/£15
The Castle of Yew, Bodley Head (London), 1965 . £35/£5
ditto, Harcourt Brace (New York), 1964 . . £25/£5
The Sea Egg, Faber (London), 1967 . . . £25/£5
ditto, Harcourt Brace (New York), 1967 . . £25/£5
The House that Grew, Faber (London), 1969 . . £45/£5
Persephone, Collins (London), 1969. . . . £45/£5
Nothing Said, Faber (London), 1971. . . . £25/£5
ditto, Harcourt Brace (New York), 1971 . . . £25/£5
The Guardians of the House, Bodley Head (London), 1974
. . . . £25/£5
ditto, Atheneum (New York), 1975 . . . £25/£5
The Fossil Snake, Bodley Head (London), 1975 . £25/£5
ditto, Atheneum (New York), 1976 . . . £25/£5

Poetry
Time is Undone, privately printed, 1954 (750 copies; wraps)
. . . . £25

Play
The Horned Man, Faber (London), 1970 . . £25/£5

Autobiography
Memory in a House, Bodley Head (London), 1973 £30/£10
ditto, Macmillan (New York), 1974 . . . . £20/£5
Perverse and Foolish, Bodley Head (London), 1979 £20/£5
ditto, Atheneum (New York), 1979 . . . . £15/£5
Memories, Colt Books (Cambridge, UK), 1992 . £15/£5

ELIZABETH BOWEN
(b.1899 d.1973)

An Anglo-Irish novelist and short story writer noted for her
attention to detail and subtlety of style. She was a part of
the Bloomsbury Group and became good friends with Rose
Macaulay, who helped her find a publisher for her first
book, *Encounters*. Bowen inherited her family home in
County Cork, Bowen's Court, in 1930 but did not move
there permanently until 1952. The house was knocked
down seven years later.

Short Stories
Encounters: Stories, Sidgwick & Jackson (London), 1923
(blue cloth, design and titles stamped in gilt) £1,000/£150
ditto, Boni & Liveright (New York), 1926 . . £200/£40
Ann Lee's and Other Stories, Sidgwick & Jackson
(London), 1926 (brown cloth lettering on spine in gilt) .
. . . . £500/£45
ditto, Boni & Liveright (New York), 1926 . . £100/£25
Joining Charles and Other Stories, Constable (London),
1929 (red cloth) . . . . £175/£30
ditto, Dial Press (New York), 1929 . . . £100/£25
The Cat Jumps and Other Stories, Gollancz (London), 1934
(black cloth) . . . . £200/£45
Look at All Those Roses, Gollancz (London), 1941 £75/£15
ditto, Knopf (New York), 1941 . . . . . £25/£10
The Demon Lover and Other Stories, Cape, [1945] £75/£20
ditto, as *Ivy Gripped the Steps and Other Stories*, Knopf
(New York), 1946 . . . . £30/£10
Selected Stories, Fridberg (Dublin), 1946 (wraps with d/w) .
. . . . £15/£5
Early Stories, Knopf (New York), 1951 . . . £20/£5
Stories, Knopf (New York), 1959 . . . . £15/£5
A Day in the Dark and Other Stories, Cape (London), 1965
. . . . £15/£5
ditto, Random House (New York), 1982 . . . £20/£5
The Collected Stories, Cape (London), 1981 . . £20/£5
ditto, Random House (New York), 1982 . . . £20/£5

Novels
The Hotel, Constable (London), 1927 . . . £350/£30
ditto, Dial Press (New York), 1928 . . . £50/£15
The Last September, Constable (London), 1929 . £300/£25
ditto, Dial Press (New York), 1929 . . . £175/£20
Friends and Relations, Constable (London), 1931. £300/£25
ditto, Dial Press (New York), 1931 . . . £175/£20
To the North, Gollancz (London), 1931 . . £250/£20
ditto, Knopf (New York), 1933 . . . . £75/£15
The House in Paris, Gollancz (London), 1935 . £150/£20
ditto, Knopf (New York), 1936 . . . . £75/£15
The Death of the Heart, Gollancz (London), 1938. £145/£20
ditto, Knopf (New York), 1939 . . . . £75/£15
The Heat of the Day, Cape (London), 1949 . . £15/£5
ditto, Knopf (New York), 1949 . . . . £15/£5

A World of Love, Cape (London), 1955 . . . £15/£5
ditto, Knopf (New York), 1955 . . . . £15/£5
The Little Girls, Cape (London), 1964 . . . £15/£5
ditto, Knopf (New York), 1964 . . . £15/£5
Eva Trout, Knopf (New York), 1968. . . . £15/£5
ditto, Cape (London), 1969 . . . . . £15/£5

Non-Fiction
Bowen's Court, Longmans, Green and Co (London), 1942 .
. . . . £125/£25
ditto, Knopf (New York), 1942 . . . £40/£10
English Novelists, Collins (London), 1942 . £15/£5
ditto, Hastings House (New York), 1942 . . £15/£5
Seven Winters, Cuala Press (Dublin), 1942 (450 numbered copies, plain glassine d/w). . . . £125/£100
ditto, Longmans, Green and Co (London), 1943 . £15/£5
ditto, Knopf (New York), 1943 . . . . £10/£5
Anthony Trollope: A New Judgement, O.U.P. (Oxford, UK), 1946 (stapled wraps). £5
ditto, O.U.P. (New York), 1946 (stapled wraps) . £5
ditto, O.U.P. (New York), 1946 (unprinted tissue d/w) .
. . . . £30/£20
Why Do I Write?: An Exchange of Views Between Elizabeth Bowen, Graham Greene, and V.S. Pritchett, Marshall (London), 1948 . . . . £125/£35
Collected Impressions, Longmans, Green and Co (London), 1950 . . . . £10/£5
ditto, Knopf (New York), 1950 . . . . £10/£5
The Shelbourne, Harrap (London), 1951 . . . £25/£10
ditto, as *The Shelbourne Hotel*, Knopf (New York), 1951 .
. . . . £20/£5
A Time in Rome, Longmans, Green and Co (London), 1960
. . . . £20/£5
ditto, Knopf (New York), 1960 . . . . £15/£5
Afterthought: Pieces About Writing, Longmans, Green and Co (London), 1962 . . . . . £20/£5
ditto, Knopf (New York), 1962 . . . . £15/£5
Pictures and Conversations, Cape (London), 1975 £10/£5
ditto, Knopf (New York), 1975 . . . . £10/£5
The Mulberry Tree, Virago (London), 1986 . £10/£5
ditto, Harcourt Brace Jovanovich (New York), [1987] .
. . . . £10/£5

Children's Titles
The Good Tiger, Knopf (New York), 1965 . . £35/£5
ditto, Cape (London), 1970 . . . . . £30/£5

JANE BOWLES

(b.1917 d.1973)

Jane Bowles was an American author and playwright, married to the writer Paul Bowles. For many years she enjoyed a glamorous literary reputation, based in part on the extreme rarity for several years of her novel *Two Serious Ladies*. Tennessee Williams and Truman Capote both considered her to be one of the finest and most underrated writers of American fiction.

Novel
Two Serious Ladies, Knopf (New York), 1943 £1,000/£250
ditto, Peter Owen (London), 1965 . . . . £45/£10

Short Stories
Plain Pleasures, Peter Owen (London), 1966 . . £65/£10
Feminine Wiles, Black Sparrow Press (Santa Barbara, CA), 1976 (hardback in acetete d/w). . . . £45/£40
ditto, Black Sparrow Press (Santa Barbara, CA), 1976 (50 numbered copies; slipcase) . . . . £85/£65
ditto, Black Sparrow Press (Santa Barbara, CA), 1976 (pbk)
. . . . £10
Everything is Nice, Virago Press (London), 1989 (pbk) £5

Plays
In the Summer House, A Play in Two Acts, Random House (New York), 1954 . . . . . . £100/£20

Others
Song of an Old Woman, Schirmer (New York), 1946 (sheet music; with words by Jane Bowles and music by Paul Bowles) £45
Two Skies, Schirmer (New York), 1946 (sheet music) . £45
The Collected Works of Jane Bowles, Farrar, Straus & Giroux (New York), 1966 . . . . £30/£10
ditto, as *My Sister's Hand in Mine, The Collected Works of Jane Bowles*, The Ecco Press (New York), 1978 (pbk; expanded) £10
ditto, Peter Owen (London), 1984 . . . £20/£5
Out in the World, Letters of Jane Bowles, Black Sparrow Press (Santa Barbara, CA), 1985 (500 hardback copies; acetate d/w) . . . . . . £25/£20
ditto, Black Sparrow Press (Santa Barbara, CA), 1985 (200 numbered hardback copies signed by editor; acetate d/w) .
. . . . £45/£35
ditto, Black Sparrow Press (Santa Barbara, CA), 1985 (26 lettered hardback copies signed by editor; acetate d/w) .
. . . . £45/£35
ditto, Black Sparrow Press (Santa Barbara, CA), 1985 (pbk)
. . . . £10
Conversations, Univ Press of Mississippi (Jackson, MI), 1993 . . . . £10/£5
The Portable Paul and Jane Bowles, Penguin Books (New York), 1994 (pbk) £5

PAUL BOWLES

(b.1910 d.1999)

An American novelist and musician, Bowles was born in New York City. On a trip to France in 1931 he became a part of Gertrude Stein's literary and artistic circle and on her advice made his first visit to Tangier, where he subsequently lived in self-imposed exile. Although he lived in Morocco for 52 years, he was buried in New York next to the graves of his parents and grandparents.

Novels
The Sheltering Sky, John Lehmann (London), 1949 . .
. . . . £2,250/£175
ditto, New Directions (Norfolk, CT), 1949 . £750/£50
Let It Come Down, Random House (New York), 1952 . .
. . . . £100/£15
ditto, John Lehmann (London), 1952 . . . £100/£15
ditto, Black Sparrow Press (Santa Barbara, CA), 1980 (350 signed copies; acetate d/w) . . . . . £75/£60

ditto, Black Sparrow Press (Santa Barbara, CA), 1980 (1,000 copies bound in quarter cloth, decorated boards; acetate d/w) . . . . £20/£15
The Spider's House, Random House (New York), 1955 .
. . . . £65/£15
ditto, Macdonald & Co. (London), 1957 . . . £50/£10
ditto, Black Sparrow Press (Santa Barbara, CA), 1982 (350 signed copies) . . . . £50/£40
Up Above the World, Simon & Schuster (New York), 1966.
. . . . £45/£10
ditto, Peter Owen (London), 1967 . . . . £45/£10
Too Far From Home, Peter Owen (London), 1994 £15/£5
ditto, Peter Owen (London), 1994 (100 signed, numbered copies) £100

Short Stories
A Little Stone, John Lehmann (London), 1950 (light green cloth stamped in dark green and gilt on the spine) £250/£25
ditto, as *Call at Corazón and Other Stories*, Peter Owen (London), 1988 . . . . £10/£5
The Delicate Prey, Random House (New York), 1950 . .
. . . . £250/£25
The Hours After Noon, Heinemann (London), 1959 . .
. . . . £175/£30
A Hundred Camels in the Courtyard, City Lights (San Francisco), 1962 (wraps) £20
ditto, Cadmus (Santa Barbara, CA), 1981 (100 signed, numbered copies, 2 vinyl L.P.s laid into a cloth sleeve with pictorial colour label on front cover) . . . £125
The Time of Friendship, Holt, Rinehart & Winston (New York), 1967 . . . . £50/£15
Pages From Coldpoint and Other Stories, Peter Owen (London), 1968 . . . . . . £100/£15
Things Gone and Things Still Here, Black Sparrow Press (Santa Barbara, CA), 1977 (500 copies, acetate d/w) . .
. . . . £35/£20
ditto, Black Sparrow Press (Santa Barbara, CA), 1977 (26 lettered, signed copies, acetate d/w) £200
ditto, Black Sparrow Press (Santa Barbara, CA), 1977 (250 numbered, signed copies, acetate d/w) . . £85/£75
Collected Stories 1939-1976, Black Sparrow Press (Santa Barbara, CA), 1979 (750 unsigned copies; wraps) . £40
ditto, Black Sparrow Press (Santa Barbara, CA), 1979 (300 copies signed by Bowles, acetate d/w) . . £125/£100
ditto, Black Sparrow Press (Santa Barbara, CA), 1979 (60 copies signed by Bowles and Vidal, acetate d/w) £400/£350
Midnight Mass and Other Stories, Black Sparrow Press (Santa Barbara, CA), 1981 (350 signed copies, acetate d/w)
. . . . £65/£50
ditto, Black Sparrow Press (Santa Barbara, CA), 1981 (750 unsigned copies, acetate d/w) . . . . £35/£25
ditto, Peter Owen (London), 1985 . . . . £25/£10
Unwelcome Words, Tombouctou Books (Bolinas, CA), 1988 (wraps) £10
ditto, Tombouctou Books (Bolinas, CA), 1988 (hardback, no d/w) £45
ditto, Tombouctou Books (Bolinas, CA), 1988 (100 signed copies, no d/w) £125
A Thousand Days for Mokhtar, Peter Owen (London), 1989
. . . . £15/£5

Poetry
Two Poems, Modern Editions Press (New York), 1934 (string-tied wraps) £10,000

Next To Nothing, Starstreams (Kathmandu), 1976 (500 numbered copies; wraps) £100
Next To Nothing: Collected Poems 1926-1977, Black Sparrow Press (Santa Barbara, CA), 1981 (wraps) . £10
ditto, Black Sparrow Press (Santa Barbara, CA), 1981 (500 unsigned hardbackcopies, acetate d/w) . . . £35/£30
ditto, Black Sparrow Press (Santa Barbara, CA), 1981 (300 signed, numbered hardback copies, acetate d/w) . £80/£60
ditto, Black Sparrow Press (Santa Barbara, CA), 1981 (26 signed, lettered hardback copies, acetate d/w) £225/£175

Others
Yallah, Macdowell, Obolensky (New York), 1956 (photographs by Haeberlin, commentary by Bowles) . £75/£25
Their Heads Are Green and Their Hands Are Blue, Random House (New York), 1963 . . . . £30/£10
ditto, as *Their Heads Are Green*, Peter Owen (London), 1963 . . . . £35/£10
Without Stopping, Putnam's (New York), 1972 . £15/£5
ditto, Peter Owen (London), 1972 . . . . £20/£5
Points in Time, Peter Owen (London), 1982 . . £10/£5
ditto, The Ecco Press (New York), 1984 . . . £10/£5
Two Years Beside the Strait: Tangier Journal 1987-1989, Peter Owen (London), 1990 . . . . £10/£5
ditto, Peter Owen (London), 1990 (75 signed copies) . .
. . . . £100/£75
Too Far From Home: The Selected Writings of Paul Bowles, The Ecco Press (Hopewell New Jersey), 1993 .
. . . . £10/£5
Morocco, Abrams (New York), 1993 (photographs by Barry Brukoff). . . . . £15/£5
ditto, Abrams (New York), 1993 (50 signed, numbered copies in quarter leather; original photograph was laid in; slipcase). . . . . £150/£100

WILLIAM BOYD
(b.1952)

Born in Ghana of Scottish descent, Boyd was educated in Great Britain. *A Good Man in Africa* won the Whitbread Book award and the Somerset Maugham Award in 1981. *An Ice Cream War* was nominated for the Booker Prize for Fiction in 1982 and won the John Llewellyn Rhys Prize in the same year. He became a C.B.E. in 2005.

Novels
A Good Man in Africa, Hamish Hamilton (London), 1981 .
. . . . £350/£40
ditto, Morrow (New York), 1982 . . . . £45/£10
An Ice Cream War, Hamish Hamilton (London), 1982 .
. . . . £60/£10
ditto, Morrow (New York), 1983 . . . . £25/£5
Stars and Bars, Hamish Hamilton (London), 1984. £25/£5
ditto, Morrow (New York), 1985 . . . . £25/£5
The New Confessions, Hamish Hamilton (London), 1987 .
. . . . £25/£5
ditto, Morrow (New York), 1988 . . . . £15/£5
Brazzaville Beach, Sinclair Stevenson (London), 1990. .
. . . . £20/£5
ditto, London Limited Editions (London), 1990 (150 signed, numbered copies, cellophane d/w) . . . £60/£50
ditto, Morrow (New York), 1991 . . . . £10/£5

The Blue Afternoon, Sinclair Stevenson (London), 1993   .
.   .   .   .   .   .   £10/£5
ditto, London Limited Editions (London), 1993 (150 signed,
numbered copies, cellophane d/w) .   .   .   £50/£45
ditto, Knopf (New York), 1995   .   .   .   .   £10/£5
Transfigured Night, One Horse Press (London), 1995
(wraps) (2,000 signed, numbered copies, with intact
wraparound band) £25
Armadillo, Hamish Hamilton (London), 1998 .   .   £10/£5
ditto, Knopf (New York), 1998   .   .   .   .   £10/£5
Nat Tate: An American Artist: 1928-1960, 21 Publishing
(Cambridge, UK), 1998   .   .   .   .   .   £25/£10
Any Human Heart, Hamish Hamilton (London), 2002 .   .
.   .   .   .   .   .   £10/£5
ditto, Knopf (New York), 2003   .   .   .   £10/£5
Restless, Bloomsbury (London), 2006   .   .   £10/£5
ditto, Bllomsbury (New York), 2006 .   .   .   £10/£5
Ordinary Thunderstorms, Bloomsbury (London), 2009   .
.   .   .   .   .   .   £10/£5

Short Stories
On the Yankee Station and Other Stories, Hamish Hamilton
(London), 1981   .   .   .   .   .   £300/£35
ditto, Morrow (New York), 1984   .   .   .   £25/£5
School Ties, Hamish Hamilton (London), 1985   .   £25/£5
ditto, Penguin (Harmondsworth, Middlesex), 1985 (wraps) .
.   .   .   .   .   .   £5
ditto, as *School Ties: Two Screenplays*, Morrow (New
York), 1986   .   .   .   .   .   .   £20/£5
Cork, Ulysses (London), 1994 (frontispiece and cover design
by Ian Beck; 150 numbered copies)   .   .   .   £35
ditto, Ulysses (London), 1994 (60 numbered copies signed
by artist and author) £85
ditto, Ulysses (London), 1994 (26 lettered copies signed by
artist and author) £150
Killing Lizards, Penguin (London), 1995 (wraps)   .   £5
The Destiny of Nathalie 'X' and Other Stories, Sinclair
Stevenson (London), 1995.   .   .   .   .   £10/£5
ditto, Knopf (New York), 1997   .   .   .   £10/£5
A Haunting, Bridgewater Press (London), 2000 (100 signed,
numbered copies of 138 copies)   .   .   .   £45
ditto, Bridgewater Press (London), 2000 (26 signed, lettered
copies of 138 copies) £150
ditto, Bridgewater Press (London), 2000 (12 signed copies,
numbered I-XII, with an original signed drawing by Boyd)
.   .   .   .   .   .   £300
Fascination, Hamish Hamilton (London), 2004   .   £10/£5
ditto, Knopf (New York), 2005   .   .   .   £10/£5
'Visions Fugitives', Cuckoo Press (London), 1997 (wraps) .
.   .   .   .   .   .   £10
The Dream Lover, Bloomsbury (London), 2008 (wraps)   £5

Non-Fiction
Protobiography, Bridgewater Press (London), 1998 (26
signed, lettered copies of 138 copies)   .   .   .   £125
ditto, Bridgewater Press (London), 1998 (100 signed,
numbered copies of 138 copies)   .   .   .   £50
ditto, Bridgewater Press (London), 1998 (12 signed copies,
numbered I-XII) £400
Bamboo, Penguin (London), 2005   .   .   .   £10/£5

KAY BOYLE
(b.1903 d.1992)

An American novelist, short story writer and poet, Boyle
lived for many years in Europe and between 1946-1954
was a foreign correspondent for the *New Yorker*. She was a
member of the American Academy of Arts and Letters,
won two O. Henry Awards for her short stories, received
two Guggenheim Fellowships and was given a lifetime
achievement award from the National Endowment for the
Arts.

Novels
Plagued by the Nightingale, Jonathan Cape & Harrison
Smith (New York), 1931 (turquoise cloth lettered in gilt) .
.   .   .   .   .   .   £200/£30
ditto, Lehmann (London), 1951 .   .   .   .   £75/£15
Year Before Last, Harrison Smith (New York), 1932 (red
cloth lettered in gilt) .   .   .   .   .   £125/£25
ditto, Faber (London), 1932 .   .   .   .   £100/£25
Gentlemen, I Address You Privately, Harrison Smith &
Robert Haas (New York), 1933 (black cloth lettered in gilt)
.   .   .   .   .   .   £150/£25
ditto, Faber (London), 1934 .   .   .   .   £75/£25
My Next Bride, Harcourt, Brace (New York), 1934 (green
cloth lettered in silver)   .   .   .   .   £125/£25
ditto, Faber (London), 1935 .   .   .   .   £50/£20
Death of a Man, Harcourt, Brace (New York), [1936] (grey
cloth lettered in silver)   .   .   .   .   £45/£15
ditto, Faber (London), 1936 .   .   .   .   £50/£20
Monday Night, Harcourt, Brace (New York), 1938 (dark
blue cloth lettered in silver)   .   .   .   £125/£25
ditto, Faber (London), 1938 .   .   .   .   £65/£20
The Crazy Hunter: Three Short Novels, Harcourt, Brace
(New York), 1940   .   .   .   .   .   £125/£15
ditto, Faber (London), 1940 .   .   .   .   £100/£10
Primer for Combat, Simon & Schuster (New York), 1942 .
.   .   .   .   .   .   £45/£10
ditto, Faber (London), 1943 .   .   .   .   £35/£10
Avalanche, Simon & Schuster (New York), 1944 .   £30/£10
ditto, Faber (London), 1945 .   .   .   .   £25/£10
A Frenchman Must Die, Simon & Schuster (New York),
1946   .   .   .   .   £30/£10
ditto, Faber (London), 1946 .   .   .   .   £25/£10
1939, Simon & Schuster (New York), 1948   .   £25/£10
ditto, Faber (London), 1948 .   .   .   .   £25/£10
His Human Majesty, Whittlesey House (New York), 1949 .
.   .   .   .   .   .   £25/£10
ditto, Faber (London), 1950 .   .   .   .   £25/£10
The Seagull on the Step, Knopf (New York), 1955   £25/£10
ditto, Faber (London), 1955 .   .   .   .   £25/£10
Generation Without Farewell, Knopf (New York), 1960   .
.   .   .   .   .   .   £25/£10
ditto, Faber (London), 1960 .   .   .   .   £25/£10
The Underground Woman, Doubleday (New York), 1975 .
.   .   .   .   .   .   £25/£10

Short Stories
Short Stories, Black Sun Press (Paris), 1929 (15 signed copies
on Japan paper; wraps in tied protected boards)   .   £1,000
ditto, Black Sun Press (Paris), 1929 (20 copies on Arches
paper; wraps in tied protected boards)   .   .   .   £750

ditto, Black Sun Press (Paris), 1929 (150 copies on Van Gelder paper; wraps in tied protected boards) . . £450

Wedding Day and Other Stories, Jonathan Cape & Harrison Smith (New York), 1930 (blue cloth lettered in gilt) . .

. . . . £250/£25

ditto, Pharos Edition (London), 1932. . . . £200/£20

The First Lover and Other Stories, Harrison Smith & Robert Haas (New York), 1933 (blue cloth lettered in gilt) . .

. . . . £150/£25

ditto, Faber (London), 1937 . . . . . . £100/£25

The White Horses of Vienna and Other Stories, Harcourt, Brace (New York), [1936] (blue cloth lettered in silver) .

. . . . £150/£25

ditto, Faber (London), 1937 . . . . . £100/£20

Thirty Stories, Simon & Schuster (New York), 1946 . .

. . . . £100/£20

ditto, Faber (London), 1948 . . . . . . £40/£10

The Smoking Mountain: Stories of Post-War Germany, McGraw-Hill (New York), 1951 . . . . £35/£10

ditto, Faber (London), 1952 . . . . . . £35/£10

Three Short Novels, Beacon Press (Boston), 1958 (wraps) .

. . . . £20

Nothing Ever Breaks Except the Heart, Doubleday (New York), 1966 . . . . £25/£10

Poetry

A Statement, Modern Edition Press (New York), 1932 (175 signed, numbered copies; sewn wraps) £65

A Glad Day, New Directions (Norfolk, CT), 1938 . £35/£15

American Citizen: Naturalized in Leadville, Colorado, Simon & Schuster (New York), 1944 (wraps) . . £30

Collected Poems, Knopf (New York), 1962 . . £25/£10

Testament for My Students, Doubleday (New York), 1970 .

. . . . £25/£10

Others

The Youngest Camel, Little, Brown (Boston), 1939 £60/£15

ditto, Faber (London), 1939 . . . . . . £40/£15

Breaking the Silence: Why a Mother Tells Her Son about the Nazi Era, Institute of Human Relations Press (New York), 1962 (wraps) £20

Pinky: The Cat Who Liked to Sleep, Crowell-Collier (New York), 1966 . . . . £45/£15

Pinky in Persia, Crowell-Collier (New York), 1968 £40/£15

Being Geniuses Together, Doubleday (New York), 1968

ditto, Joseph (London), 1970 . . . . . £20/£5

The Long Walk at San Francisco State and Other Essays, Grove (New York), 1970 . . . . . £20/£5

Four Visions of America, Capra Press (Santa Barbara, CA), 1977 (with Erica Jong, Thomas Sanchez and Henry Miller) .

. . . . £20/£5

ditto, Capra Press (Santa Barbara, CA), 1977 (225 copies signed by all four authors). . . . . £75/£50

ditto, Capra Press (Santa Barbara, CA), 1977 (wraps) . £5

MALCOLM BRADBURY
(b.1932 d.2000)

A novelist and critic, *The History Man* is Bradbury's best regarded novel, satirising the university culture of the 1960s and 70s. Bradbury has been compared to David Lodge, another exponent of the campus novel, but Bradbury's books are altogether darker and less playful. He became a Commander of the British Empire in 2000 for services to literature.

Novels

Eating People is Wrong, Secker & Warburg (London), 1959

. . . . £125/£45

ditto, Knopf (New York), 1960 . . . . . £45/£15

Stepping Westward, Secker & Warburg (London), 1965 .

. . . . £75/£25

ditto, Houghton Mifflin (Boston), 1966 . . . £15/£5

The History Man, Secker & Warburg (London), 1975 £40/£10

ditto, Houghton Mifflin (Boston), 1976 . . . £15/£5

Rates of Exchange, Secker & Warburg (London), 1983 .

. . . . £15/£5

ditto, Knopf (New York), 1983 . . . . . £10/£5

Doctor Criminale, Secker & Warburg (London), 1992 £10/£5

ditto, Viking (New York), 1992 . . . . . £10/£5

To the Hermitage, Picador (London), 2000 . . £10/£5

ditto, Overlook Press (Woodstock, NY), 2000. . £10/£5

Novella

Cuts, Hutchinson (London), 1987 . . . . £15/£5

ditto, Harper (New York), 1987 . . . . . £15/£5

Short Stories

Who Do You Think You Are?, Secker & Warburg (London), 1976 . . . . £15/£5

Criticism etc.

Phogey! How to Have Class in a Classless Society, Parrish (London), 1960 . . . . . . £25/£10

All Dressed Up and Nowhere to Go, Parrish (London), 1962

. . . . £25/£10

Evelyn Waugh, Oliver & Boyd (Edinburgh), 1964 (wraps) .

. . . . £25

What is a Novel?, Arnold (London), 1969 . . £15

The Social Context of Modern English Literature, Blackwell (Oxford), 1971 . . . . . £20/£5

ditto, Schocken (New York), 1971 . . . . £20/£5

Possibilities: Essays on the State of the Novel, O.U.P. (Oxford, UK), 1973 . . . . £10

Saul Bellow, Methuen (London), 1982 (wraps) . £10

The Expatriate Tradition in American Literature, British Association for American Studies (Durham, UK), 1982 (wraps) £5

The Modern American Novel, O.U.P. (Oxford, UK), 1983 .

. . . . £10/£5

ditto, Viking (New York), 1993 . . . . . £10/£5

Why Come to Slaka?, Secker & Warburg (London), 1986 .

. . . . £10

ditto, Penguin (New York), 1988 (wraps). . . £10

My Strange Quest for Mensonge: Structuralism's Hidden Hero, Deutsch (London), 1987. . . . £10/£5

ditto, Penguin (New York), 1988 (wraps). . . £10

No, Not Bloomsbury, Deutsch (London), 1987 . £10/£5

ditto, Columbia Univ Press (New York), 1988. . £10/£5
The Modern World: Ten Great Writers, Secker & Warburg
(London), 1988 . . . . . £10/£5
ditto, Viking (New York), 1989 . . . . £10/£5
Unsent Letters: Irreverent Notes from a Literary Life,
Deutsch (London), 1988 . . . . . £10/£5
ditto, Viking (New York), 1988 . . . . £10/£5
ditto, Penguin (London), 1995 (revised and expanded
edition; pbk) £5
***From Puritanism to Postmodernism: A History of
American Literature***, Routledge (London), 1991 (with
Richard Ruland) . . . . . . £10/£5
ditto, Viking (New York), 1991 . . . . £10/£5
The Modern British Novel, Secker & Warburg (London),
1993 . . . . £10/£5
Dangerous Pilgrimages, Secker & Warburg (London), 1995
. . . . £10/£5
ditto, Viking (New York), 1996 . . . . £10/£5

Plays
The After Dinner Game: Three Plays for Television, Arrow
(London), 1982 (pbk) £5
Inside Trading: A Comedy in Three Acts, Methuen
(London), 1997 (pbk) £5

RAY BRADBURY
(b.1920)

An American author who has worked in many genres, Ray
Bradbury originally emerged in the science fiction pulp
magazines and is considered a leading writer in the field.
His work, however, crosses genres and tends to blur the
distinctions between them. Confusingly, he has often
written short stories which he later collects together,
amends, and publishes as a 'novel'.

Novels
Fahrenheit 451, Ballantine (New York), 1953 (pbk) . £45
ditto, Ballantine (New York), 1953 (author's copies in red
cloth, lettered in gilt) £3,500
ditto, Ballantine (New York), 1953 (red boards lettered in
yellow) . . . . £2,500/£500
ditto, Ballantine (New York), 1953 (200 signed, numbered
copies, asbestos boards, no statement of printing on
copyright page, no d/w) £7,500
ditto, Hart Davis (London), 1954 (title novel only). £500/£50
ditto, Limited Editions Club (New York), 1982 (2,000
signed, numbered copies, slipcase) . . . £150/£100
ditto, Simon & Schuster (New York), 1994 (500 signed,
numbered copies, slipcase) . . . . £175/£100
Dandelion Wine, Doubleday (New York), 1957 (yellow
cloth stamped in grey and gold on spine) . £750/£75
ditto, Hart Davis (London), 1957 . . . £350/£35
Something Wicked This Way Comes, Simon & Schuster
(New York), 1962 (yellow cloth, stamped in black on front
board and spine) . . . . . . £450/£50
ditto, Hart Davis (London), 1963 (black cloth stamped in
silver) . . . . £175/£20
ditto, Gauntlet Press (Springfield, PA), 1999 (500 signed,
numbered copies, d/w and slipcase) . . £200/£125
ditto, Gauntlet Press (Springfield, PA), 1999 (52 signed,
numbered deluxe copies, traycase) . . £400/£250

The Novels of Ray Bradbury, Granada (London), 1984 .
. . . . £35/£10
Death is a Lonely Business, Knopf (New York), 1985 . .
. . . . £25/£5
ditto, Knopf (New York), 1985 (70-75 signed presentation
copies) £200
ditto, Franklin Library (Franklin Centre, PA), 1985 (signed,
limited edition, full leather) £45
ditto, Grafton (London), 1986 . . . . £15/£5
A Graveyard for Lunatics: Another Tale of Two Cities,
Knopf (New York), 1990 . . . . . £15/£5
ditto, Grafton (London), 1990 . . . . £10/£5
Green Shadows, White Whale, Knopf (New York), 1992 .
. . . . £10/£5
ditto, Ultramarine Press (New York), 1992 (38 signed copies,
no d/w) £250
ditto, Harper-Collins (London), 1992 . . . £10/£5
From the Dust Returned, Easton Press (Norwalk, CT), 2001
(1,400 signed copies) £125
ditto, Morrow (New York), 2001 . . . £10/£5
ditto, Earthlight (London), 2001 . . . . £10/£5
Let's All Kill Constance, Morrow (New York), 2003 £10/£5
Farewell Summer, Morrow (New York), 2006 . £10/£5
ditto, Subterranean Press (Burton, MI), 2006 (250 signed,
numbered copies; slipcase) . . . . £100/£75
ditto, Harper Voyager (London), 2008 . . . £10/£5

Short Stories
Dark Carnival, Arkham House (Sauk City, WI), 1947 . .
. . . . £1,000/£250
ditto, Hamish Hamilton (London), 1948 (abridged edition,
only collected 20 of 27 stories). . . . £350/£30
ditto, as ***The Small Assassin***, Ace/New English Library
(London), 1962 (pbk) £10
ditto, as ***Dark Carnival***, Gauntlet Press (Springfield, PA),
2001 (700 numbered copies signed by Bradbury and Clive
Barker, d/w and slipcase) . . . . £250/£150
ditto, Gauntlet Press (Springfield, PA), 2001 (52 lettered
deluxe copies signed by Bradbury and Clive Barker,
traycase, with a numbered chapbook and CD) £500/£250
The Martian Chronicles, Doubleday (New York), 1950
(green binding, first state d/w with price of $2.50 printed at
top right corner of front flap) . . . . £1,750/£400
ditto, Doubleday (New York), 1950 (green binding, second
state d/w with price of $2.50 blocked out and price raised
to $2.75) . . . . £1,500/£400
ditto, as ***The Silver Locusts***, Hart Davis (London), 1951
(deletes one story and adds another) . . £200/£45
ditto, as ***The Martian Chronicles***, Science Fiction Book
Club (London), 1953 (adds story 'Wilderness') . £75/£15
The Illustrated Man, Doubleday (New York), 1951 .
. . . . £600/£65
ditto, Hart Davis (London), 1952 (deletes four stories and
adds two new ones) . . . . . . £200/£35
ditto, Gauntlet Press (Springfield, PA), 1996 (600 numbered
copies signed by Bradbury, William F. Nolan and Ed
Gorman, d/w and slipcase) . . . . £145/£100
ditto, Gauntlet Press (Springfield, PA), 1996 (52 lettered
deluxe copies signed by Bradbury, William F. Nolan and
Ed Gorman, traycase) . . . . £500/£350
The Golden Apples of the Sun, Doubleday (New York),
1953 . . . . £300/£35
ditto, Hart Davis (London), 1953 (deletes two stories) . .
. . . . £145/£25

The October Country, Ballantine (New York), 1955 (50 copies for author's use, red cloth lettered in gold) . . . . £500/£125

ditto, Ballantine (New York), 1955 (dull red cloth lettered in black, BB monogram printed upside down on spine) . . . . £450/£75

ditto, Ballantine (New York), 1955 (dull red cloth lettered in black, BB monogram printed correctly on spine). £425/£65

ditto, Ballantine (New York), 1955 (red boards lettered in black) . . . . £400/£60

ditto, Hart Davis (London), 1956 . . £200/£25

Sun and Shadow, Quenian Press (Berkley, CA), 1957 (90 copies; wraps) £700

A Medicine for Melancholy, Doubleday (New York), 1959 . . . . £165/£20

ditto, as *The Day it Rained Forever*, Hart Davis (London), 1959 (deletes four stories from *A Medicine for Melancholy* and adds five new ones) . . . . . £135/£25

The Machineries of Joy, Simon & Schuster (New York), 1964 . . . . £90/£20

ditto, Hart Davis (London), 1964 (deletes one story) £90/£20

The Pedestrian, Roy Squires (Glendale, CA), [1964] (280 copies, card wraps) £80

The Vintage Bradbury, Vintage Books (New York), 1965 (pbk) £10

ditto, Vintage Books (New York), 1965 (orange cloth stamped in gold and black, no d/w). . . . £600

The Autumn People, Ballantine (New York), 1965 (cartoons; pbk) £15

Tomorrow Midnight, Ballantine (New York), 1966 (cartoons; pbk) £15

Twice Twenty-Two, Doubleday (New York), 1966 (first edition dated on title-page; later editions delete date) . . . . £125/£20

I Sing the Body Electric!, Knopf (New York), 1969 . . . . £75/£10

ditto, Hart Davis (London), 1970 . . . £45/£10

Bloch and Bradbury, Tower [New York], [1969] (pbk) £5

ditto, as *Fever Dream and Other Fantasies*, Sphere (London), 1970 (pbk) £5

ditto, as *Bloch & Bradbury: Whispers From Beyond*, Peacock Press (Chicago), 1972 (pbk; with additional material by others) £5

Long After Midnight, Knopf (New York), 1976 . £20/£5

ditto, Hart-Davis MacGibbon (London), 1977 . £20/£5

The Best of Bradbury, Bantam (New York), 1976 (pbk) £5

To Sing Strange Songs, Wheaton (Exeter, Devon), 1979 (pbk) £5

The Stories of Ray Bradbury, Knopf (New York), 1980 . . . . £15/£5

ditto, Granada (London), 1980 (two vols; pbks) . £5

The Last Circus, and The Electrocution, Lord John Press (Northridge, CA), 1980 (illustrated by William F. Nolan, 100 deluxe, signed copies of 400, slipcase) . £100/£65

ditto, Lord John Press (Northridge, CA), 1980 (300 of 400 signed copies, slipcase) . . . . . £65/£40

The Other Foot, Perfection Form Co. (Logan, IA) 1982 (stapled wraps) £5

ditto, Creative Education, Inc. (Mankato, MN), 1987 £10/£5

The Veldt, Perfection Form Co. (Logan, IA) 1982 (stapled wraps) £5

ditto, Creative Education, Inc. (Mankato, MN), 1987 £10/£5

Dinosaur Tales, Bantam (New York), 1983 (pbk) . £5

A Memory of Murder, Dell (New York), 1984 (pbk) . £5

The April Witch, Creative Education, Inc. (Mankato, MN), 1987 . . . . £10/£5

Fever Dream, St Martin's (New York), 1987 . . £10/£5

The Fog Horn, Creative Education, Inc. (Mankato, MN), 1987 . . . . £10/£5

The Toynbee Convector, Knopf (New York), 1988 £15/£5

ditto, Knopf (New York), 1988 (350 signed copies) £125/£65

ditto, Grafton (London), 1989 . . . . . £10/£5

The Dragon, Footsteps Press (Round Top, NY), 1988 (26 signed, lettered copies of 300; stapled wraps with d/w) . . . . £65/£50

ditto, Footsteps Press (Round Top, NY), 1988 (numbered copies; stapled wraps with d/w) . . . . £30/£15

Classic Stories Volume One, Bantam (New York), 1990 (pbk) £5

Classic Stories Volume Two, Bantam (New York), 1990 (pbk) £5

The Smile, Creative Education, Inc. (Mankato, MN), 1991 . . . . £10/£5

Quicker Than The Eye, Avon (New York), 1996 . £10/£5

ditto, Franklin Library (Franklin Centre, PA), 1996 (signed, limited edition) £90

Driving Blind, Avon (New York), 1997 . . . £10/£5

One More For the Road, Morrow (New York), 2002 £10/£5

Bradbury Stories: 100 of His Most Celebrated Tales, Easton Press (Norwalk, CT), 2003 (1,000 signed copies) . £75

ditto, Morrow (New York), 2003 . . . . £10/£5

Time Intervening/Is That You, Herb?, Gauntlet Press (Springfield, PA), 2001 (two signed, numbered chapbooks) £15

The Cat's Pajamas: Stories, Morrow (New York), 2004 . . . . £10/£5

ditto, Hill House (Ossining, NY), 2004 (1,000 signed, numbered copies; slipcase) . . . . £100/£75

ditto, Hill House (Ossining, NY), 2004 (52 signed, lettered copies; slipcase) . . . . . £150/£125

Now and Forever: Somewhere a Band is Playing & Leviathan '99, Morrow (New York), 2007 . . £10/£5

Summer Morning, Summer Night, Subterranean Press (Burton, MI), 2008 . . . . £25/£10

We'll Always Have Paris, Morrow (New York), 2009 . . . . £10/£5

Poetry

Old Ahab's Friend, and friend to Noah, Speaks His Piece, Squires (Glendale, CA), 1971 (445 unsigned copies of 485; wraps) £45

ditto, Squires (Glendale, CA), 1971 (40 signed copies of 485) £150

That Son of Richard III, Squires (Glendale, CA), 1974 (400 unsigned copies of 485; wraps) £45

ditto, Squires (Glendale, CA), 1974 (85 signed copies of 485) £100

Twin Hieroglyphs that Swim the River Dust, Lord John Press (Northridge, CA), 1978 (300 signed copies of edition of 326) £75

ditto, Lord John Press (Northridge, CA), 1978 (26 signed, lettered deluxe copies) £200

The Bike Repairman, Lord John Press (Northridge, CA), 1978 (broadside) £65

The Poet Considers His Resources, Lord John Press (Northridge, CA), 1979 (200 signed copies, broadside) £45

ditto, Lord John Press (Northridge, CA), 1979 (26 lettered, signed copies, broadside) £75

The Aqueduct, Squires (Glendale, CA), 1979 (230 copies; wraps) £75

Beyond 1984: Remembrance of Things Future, Targ Editions (New York), 1979 (350 signed copies) . £50/£40

The Attic Where The Meadow Greens, Lord John Press (Northridge, CA), 1980 (300 copies, signed) . . £50

ditto, Lord John Press (Northridge, CA), 1980 (75 deluxe copies, signed) £100

Then Is All Love? It Is, It Is!, Orange County Book Society (Orange, CA), 1981 (230 signed copies, broadside) . £40

The Complete Poems of Ray Bradbury, Ballantine (New York), 1982 (pbk) £5

The Love Affair, Lord John Press (Northridge, CA), 1983 (300 signed copies) . . . . . . £45/£30

ditto, Lord John Press (Northridge, CA), 1983 (100 signed deluxe copies) £65

Forever and the Earth, Croissant (Athens, OH), 1984 (300 signed copies, tissue d/w) . . . . . £150/£125

Death Has Lost Its Charm For Me, Lord John Press (Northridge, CA), 1987 (trade edition, no d/w) . . £20

ditto, Lord John Press (Northridge, CA), 1987 (150 signed copies, no d/w) £80

ditto, Lord John Press (Northridge, CA), 1987 (26 lettered, signed copies, no d/w) £200

ditto, Lord John Press (Northridge, CA), 1987 (25 presentation copies, no d/w) £150

The Climate of Palettes, Lord John Press (Northridge, CA), 1989 (150 signed, numbered copies; slipcase, no d/j) . £45

ditto, Lord John Press (Northridge, CA), 1989 (26 signed, lettered copies; slipcase, no d/j) £75

With Cat for Comforter, Gibbs-Smith (Layton, UT), 1997 . . . . £10/£5

I Live By The Invisible: New and Selected Poems, Salmon (Cliffs of Moher, Co. Clare, Ireland), 2002 (pbk). . £10

They Have Not Seen The Stars: The Collected Poetry of Ray Bradbury, Stealth Press (Lancaster, PA), 2002 (200 signed, numbered copies in slipcase) . . . £100/£65

ditto, Stealth Press (Lancaster, PA), 2002. . . £20/£5

Plays

The Anthem Sprinters and Other Antics, Dial Press (New York), 1963 (wraps) £35

ditto, Dial Press (New York), 1963 . . . . £100/£35

The Day it Rained Forever: A Comedy in One Act, French (New York), 1966 (stapled wraps) £25

The Pedestrian: A Fantasy in One Act, French (New York), 1966 (stapled wraps) £20

The Wonderful Ice Cream Suit and Other Plays, Bantam (New York), 1972 (pbk) £10

ditto, Hart-Davis MacGibbon (London), 1973 . . £35/£10

Pillar of Fire and Other Plays of Today, Tomorrow and Beyond Tomorrow, Bantam (New York), 1975 (pbk). £15

A Device Out of Time, The Dramatic Publishing Company (Woodstock, IL), 1976 (stapled wraps) . . . £20

That Ghost, that Bride of Time: Excerpts from a Play-in-Progress, Squires (Glendale, CA), 1976 (150 signed copies of 400; wraps) £100

ditto, Squires (Glendale, CA), 1976 (250 unsigned copies of 400; wraps) £30

Falling Upward, The Dramatic Publishing Company (Woodstock, IL), 1988 (stapled wraps) . . . £20

Ray Bradbury On Stage: A Chrestomathy of Plays, Donald Fine, Inc (New York), 1991 (wraps) £5

Children's Books

Switch on the Night, Pantheon (New York), 1955 (first state with 'Pantheon Books' mentioned on title-page) . £600/£75

ditto, Pantheon (New York), 1955 (later state with 'Pantheon Books, A Division of Random House' mentioned verso title-page) . . . . £500/£45

ditto, Hart Davis (London), 1955 . . . . £200/£35

R is for Rocket, Doubleday (New York), [1962] . £175/£25

ditto, Hart Davis (London), 1968 . . . . £150/£20

S is for Space, Doubleday (New York), 1966 . . £135/£20

ditto, Hart Davis (London), 1968 . . . . £100/£20

The Halloween Tree, Knopf (New York), 1972 (black cloth stamped in orange and white) . . . . £100/£20

ditto, Knopf (New York), 1972 (white cloth stamped in black orange and brown reproducing d/w design, but issued without d/w). £20

ditto, Hart-Davis MacGibbon (London), [1975] . £45/£15

When Elephants Last in the Dooryard Bloomed: Celebrations for Almost Any Day in the Year, Knopf (New York), 1973 . . . . £25/£5

ditto, Hart-Davis MacGibbon (London), 1975 . . £20/£5

Where Robot Mice and Robot Men Run Round in Robot Towns: New Poems both Light and Dark, Knopf (New York), 1977 . . . . £25/£5

ditto, Granada (London), 1979 . . . . . £15/£5

The Haunted Computer and the Android Pope, Knopf (New York), 1981 . . . . £15/£5

ditto, Granada (London), 1981 . . . . . £15/£5

Dogs Think That Every Day Is Christmas, Gibbs-Smith (Layton, UT), 1997 . . . . £15/£5

Ahmed and the Oblivion Machines, Avon (New York), 1998 . . . . £10/£5

Miscellaneous

No Man is an Island, Brandeis Univ (Los Angeles, CA), 1952 (stapled wraps) £200

The Circus of Dr Lao and Other Improbable Stories, Bantam (New York), 1956 (edited by Ray Bradbury; pbk) £5

The Essence of Creative Writing, San Antonio Public Library (Texas), 1962 (wraps) £5

Creative Man Among His Servant Machines, Stromberg Datagraphix (San Diego, CA), 1967 (xeroxed typescript essay of twelve stapled leaves). £65

Teacher's Guide: Science Fiction with Lewy Olfson, Bantam (New York), 1969 (pbk) £10

Madrigals for the Space Age for Mixed Chorus and Narrator with Piano, Associated Music Publishers (New York), 1972 (music by Lalo Schifrin; wraps) . . £40

Mars and the Mind of Man, Harper (New York), 1973 . . . . £15/£5

Zen and the Art of Writing, and The Joy of Writing, Capra Press (Santa Barbara, CA), 1973 (250 signed copies, no d/w) £100

ditto, Capra Press (Santa Barbara, CA), 1973 (wraps) . £10

The Mummies of Guanajuato, Abrams (New York), 1978 (photographs by Archie Lieberman) . . . £50/£20

The God in Science Fiction, Santa Susana Press, Northridge, CA, 1978 (stapled wraps) £20

Flatland: A Romance of Many Dimensions, by Edwin Abbott, Arion Press (San Francisco, CA), 1980 (56 accordion-style folded panels, comprising 112 pp, with an introduction by Bradbury, 275 copies) . . . £1,000

Fantasmas Para Siempre, Ediciones Libreria (Buenos Aires, Argentina), 1980 . . . . . £75/£45
ditto, as *The Ghosts of Forever*, Rizzoli (New York), 1981 . . . . £40/£25
Los Angeles, Skyline Press (Toronto, Canada), 1984 (photographs by West Light) . . . . £10/£5
The Last Good Kiss, California State at Northridge (Northridge, CA), 1984 (60 signed, numbered copies with portfolio of prints by Hans Burkhardt) . . . £250
Orange County, Skyline Press (Toronto, Canada), 1985 (photographs by Bill Ross and others) . . £10/£5
The Art of 'Playboy', Alfred Van Der Marck (New York), 1985 . . . . £15/£5
Zen in the Art of Writing, Joshua Odell/Capra Press (Santa Barbara, CA), 1990 . . . . . £30/£10
ditto, Joshua Odell/Capra Press (Santa Barbara, CA), 1990 (wraps) £5
Yestermorrow: Obvious Answers to Impossible Futures, Capra Press (Santa Barbara, CA), 1991 . . £10/£5
A Chapbook for Burnt-Out Priests, Rabbis and Ministers, Cemetery Dance (Forest Hills, MD), 2001 (350 signed, numbered copies; d/w and slipcase) . . £40/£30
ditto, Cemetery Dance (Forest Hills, MD), 2001 (26 signed, lettered copies; with framed print) £250
Bradbury, An Illustrated Life: Journey to Far Metaphor, Morrow (New York), 2002 . . . . £10/£5
It Came From Outer Space, Gauntlet Press (Springfield, PA), 2004 (750 signed, numbered copies) . £50/£35
Futuria Fantasia, Graham Press (Los Angeles, CA), 2007 . . . . £20/£10
ditto, Graham Press (Los Angeles, CA), 2007 (300 signed, numbered copies in d/w and slipcase) . . £75/£50
ditto, Graham Press (Los Angeles, CA), 2007 (52 signed, lettered copies handbound in cloth and leather with handmade clamshell box) £250

JOHN BRAINE

(b.1922 d.1986)

John Braine was born in Bradford, Yorkshire, leaving grammar school at 16 to work in a shop, a laboratory and a factory before becoming a librarian. As a novelist he is best known for *Room at the Top*, a classic novel of the 'Angry Young Men' school, which was successfully filmed in 1959.

Room at the Top, Eyre & Spottiswoode (London), 1957 . . . . £250/£25
ditto, Eyre & Spottiswoode (London), 1957 (with yellow wrap-around band) £300
ditto, Houghton Mifflin (Boston), 1957 . . £35/£10
The Vodi, Eyre & Spottiswoode (London), 1959 . £25/£5
ditto, as *From the Hand of the Hunter*, Houghton Mifflin (New York), 1960 . . . . . £25/£10
Life at the Top, Eyre & Spottiswoode (London), 1962 . . . . £30/£10
ditto, Houghton Mifflin (Boston), 1962 . . £25/£5
The Jealous God, Eyre & Spottiswoode (London), 1964 . . . . £15/£5
ditto, Houghton Mifflin (Boston), 1965 . . £10/£5
The Crying Game, Eyre & Spottiswoode (London), 1968 . . . . £15/£5

ditto, Houghton Mifflin (Boston), 1968 . . . £10/£5
Stay with Me till Morning, Eyre & Spottiswoode (London), 1970 . . . . £10/£5
ditto, as *The View from Tower Hill*, Coward-McCann (New York), 1971 . . . . £10/£5
The Queen of a Distant Country, Methuen (London), 1972 . . . . £10/£5
ditto, Coward, McCann & Geoghegan (New York), 1973 . . . . £10/£5
Writing a Novel, Eyre Methuen (London), 1974 . £10/£5
ditto, Coward, McCann & Geoghegan (New York), 1974 . . . . £10/£5
The Pious Agent, Eyre Methuen (London), 1975 . £10/£5
ditto, Atheneum (New York), 1976 . . . . £10/£5
Waiting for Sheila, Eyre Methuen (London), 1976 £10/£5
ditto, Methuen (New York), 1980 . . . £10/£5
Finger of Fire, Eyre Methuen (London), 1977 . £10/£5
J.B. Priestley, Weidenfeld & Nicolson (London), 1978 . . . . £10/£5
ditto, Barnes and Noble (New York), 1979 . . £10/£5
One and Last Love, Eyre Methuen (London), 1981 £10/£5
The Two of Us, Methuen (London), 1984. . . £10/£5
These Golden Days, Methuen (London), 1985 . £10/£5

ERNEST BRAMAH

(b.1868 d.1942)

Ernest Bramah Smith is read today for his 'Max Carrados' and 'Kai Lung' stories, each a rather individual series of tales. The former feature the exploits of a blind but remarkably percipient detective. The latter are the stories of a Chinese philosopher, marked by a dry irony and an absurd parody of what was considered the over-formal Chinese mode of expression.

'Kai Lung' Titles
The Wallet of Kai Lung, Grant Richards (London), 1900 (first issue with 'Recent Fiction' list facing title page and 1.5 inches thick) £225
ditto, Grant Richards (London), 1900 (second issue without half-title list) £150
ditto, L.C. Page and Company (Boston), 1900 . . £125
ditto, Grant Richards's Colonial Library (London), 1900 . . . . £125
ditto, Grant Richards (London), 1923 (200 signed copies) . . . . £250/£175
ditto, Doran (New York), [1923] . . . . £150/£60
The Transmutation of Ling, Grant Richards (London)/ Brentano's (New York), 1911 (500 copies; brown cloth) £85
ditto, Brentano's (New York), 1912 (blue cloth) . £65
Kai Lung's Golden Hours, Grant Richards (London), 1922 . . . . £125/£35
ditto, Doran (New York), 1923 . . . . £125/£35
ditto, Grant Richards (London), 1924 (250 signed copies) . . . . £250/£150
The Story of Wan and the Remarkable Shrub ..., Doubleday Doran (New York), 1927 (wraps) . . . £150
ditto, as *Kai Lung Unrolls His Mat*, Richards Press (London), 1928 (the above title comprises two chapters from this book) . . . . £75/£20
ditto, Doran (New York), 1928 . . . . £75/£20

The Moon of Much Gladness, Cassell (London), 1932. .
.   . £100/£30
ditto, as *The Return of Kai Lung*, Sheridan House (New
York), 1937 .   .   .   .   .   . £75/£25
The Kai Lung Omnibus, Philip Allan (London), 1936 .   .
.   .   .   . £75/£25
Kai Lung Beneath the Mulberry-Tree, Richards Press
(London), 1940   .   .   .   .   . £150/£45
ditto, Arno Press (New York), 1978 .   .   .   . £15
Kin Weng and the Miraculous Tusk, City of Birmingham
School of Printing (Birmingham, UK), 1941 .   .   . £50
The Celestial Omnibus, Richards Press (London), 1963   .
.   .   .   . £35/£10
Kai Lung: Six, Non-Profit Press (Tacoma, Washington),
1974 (250 copies)   .   .   .   .   . £75/£45

'Max Carrados' Titles
Max Carrados, Methuen (London), 1914 (adverts dated
1913)   .   .   .   . £1,000/£250
ditto, Methuen (London), 1914 (later issue with adverts dated
1915)   .   .   .   . £1,000/£150
ditto, Hyperion Press (New York), 1975 .   .   . £25
The Eyes of Max Carrados, Grant Richards (London), 1923
.   .   .   . £750/£100
ditto, Doran (New York), 1924 .   .   .   . £500/£45
Max Carrados Mysteries, Hodder & Stoughton (London),
1927   .   .   .   . £500/£100
ditto, Penguin (New York), 1964 (wraps) .   .   . £10
The Bravo of London, Cassell (London), 1934   £600/£175

'Kai Lung' & 'Max Carrados' Titles
The Specimen Case, Hodder & Stoughton (London), 1924 .
.   .   .   . £600/£45
ditto, Doran (New York), 1925 .   .   .   . £450/£40
Short Stories of Today and Yesterday, Harrap (London),
1929   .   .   .   . £25/£5

Other Fiction
The Mirror of Kong Ho, Chapman & Hall (London), 1905 .
.   .   .   . £65
ditto, Doubleday (New York), 1930   .   .   . £100/£35
What Might Have Been: The Story of a Social War, John
Murray (London), 1907 (anonymous)   .   .   . £65
ditto, as *The Secret of The League: The Story of a Social
War*, Nelson (London), [1909] (by Bramah) .   .   . £30
A Little Flutter, Cassell (London), 1930 .   .   . £125/£20

Non-Fiction
English Farming and Why I Turned It Up, Leadenhall
Press (London), 1894 .   .   .   .   . £125
A Hand Book for Writers and Artists, Charles William
Deacon (London), 1898 (anonymous)   .   .   . £65
*A Guide to the Varieties and Rarity of English Regal
Copper Coins, Charles II – Victoria, 1671-1860*, Methuen
(London), 1929   .   .   .   .   .   . £60/£20

CHRISTIANNA BRAND
(b.1907 d.1988)

Christianna Brand was a British mystery writer and
children's author. Inspector Cockrill is perhaps her best-
known detective, with *Green for Danger* considered by
many to be her masterpiece. She is the author of the
children's series *Nurse Matilda*, which was adapted to film
as *Nanny McPhee* (2005).

Inspector Cockrill Novels
Heads You Lose, Bodley Head (London), 1941 [1942]. .
.   .   .   . £275/£25
ditto, Dodd Mead (New York), 1942 .   .   . £75/£15
Green For Danger, Dodd Mead (New York), 1944 £200/£25
ditto, Bodley Head (London), 1945 .   .   . £250/£25
The Crooked Wreath, Dodd Mead (New York), 1946 .   .
.   .   .   . £150/£20
ditto, as *Suddenly At His Residence*, Bodley Head (London),
1947   .   .   .   . £125/£20
Death of Jezebel, Dodd Mead (New York), 1948 . £75/£15
ditto, Bodley Head (London), 1949 .   .   . £75/£15
London Particular, Michael Joseph (London), 1952 £40/£10
ditto, as *Fog of Doubt*, Scribner (New York), 1953 £25/£10
Tour de Force, Michael Joseph (London), 1955 . £35/£10
ditto, Scribner (New York), 1955 .   .   . £25/£10

Other Crime Novels
Death in High Heels, Bodley Head (London), 1941 .   .
.   .   .   . £400/£25
ditto, Scribner (New York), 1942 .   .   . £75/£15
Cat and Mouse, Michael Joseph (London), 1950 . £50/£10
ditto, Alfred A. Knopf (New York), 1950 .   .   . £35/£10
Starrbelow, Hutchinson (London), 1958 (pseud China
Thompson)   .   .   .   .   .   . £10/£5
ditto, Scribner (New York), 1958 .   .   . £10/£5
Alas For Her That Met Me, Star Books (New York), 1976
(pseud Mary Ann Ashe; pbk) £5
A Ring of Roses, Star Books (New York), 1977 (pseud Mary
Ann Ashe; pbk) £5
ditto, W.H. Allen (London), 1977 (written as Christianna
Brand) .   .   .   . £10/£5
The Honey Harlot, W.H. Allen (London),1978 . £15/£5
The Rose in the Darkness, Michael Joseph (London), 1979
.   .   .   . £10/£5
The Brides of Aberdar, Michael Joseph (London), 1982 .
.   .   .   . £15/£5
ditto, St Martin's Press (New York), 1983 .   . £10/£5

Short Stories
What Dread Hand?, Michael Joseph (London), 1968 .   .
.   .   .   . £25/£10
Brand X, Michael Joseph (London), 1974 .   . £15/£5
Buffet for Unwelcome Guests, Southern Illinois Univ Press
(Carbondale, IL), 1983 .   .   .   .   . £15/£5
*The Spotted Cat, and Other Mysteries from Inspector
Cockrill's Casebook*, Crippen & Landru (Norfolk, VA),
2002   .   .   .   . £10/£5

Other Novels
The Single Pilgrim, Crowell (New York), 1946 (pseud
'Mary Roland') .   .   .   . £25/£10
ditto, Sampson Low (London), 1946 .   .   . £25/£10

The Three-Cornered Halo, Michael Joseph (London), 1957
. . . . £25/£10
ditto, Scribner (New York), 1957   .   .   .   £15/£5
Court of Foxes, Michael Joseph (London), 1969 .   £15/£5
ditto, Brooke House (New York), 1977   .   .   £10/£5
The Radiant Dove, Michael Joseph (London), 1974 (pseud
'Annabel Jones') .   .   .   .   .   .   £10/£5
ditto, St Martin's Press (New York), 1975   .   £10/£5

Children's Books
Danger Unlimited, Dodd Mead (New York), 1948 £35/£10
ditto, as *Welcome to Danger*, Foley House Press, 1949
(illustrated by William Stobbs) .   .   .   £35/£10
Naughty Children, edited by Christianna Brand, Gollancz
(London), 1962 (edited by Christianna Brand; illustrated by
Edward Ardizzone) .   .   .   .   .   £50/£15
ditto, Dutton (New York), 1963 .   .   .   £40/£10
Nurse Matilda, Brockhampton Press (Leicester, UK), 1964
(illustrated by Edward Ardizzone) .   .   .   £75/£20
ditto, Dutton (New York), 1964 .   .   .   £65/£15
Nurse Matilda Goes to Town, by Christianna Brand,
Brockhampton Press (Leicester, UK), 1967 (illustrated by
Edward Ardizzone) .   .   .   .   .   £75/£20
ditto, Dutton (New York), [1968]   .   .   £60/£10
Nurse Matilda Goes to Hospital, by Christianna Brand,
Brockhampton Press (Leicester, UK), 1974 .   £70/£20
ditto, Dutton (New York), 1974 .   .   .   £60/£10

Miscellaneous
Making a Film: The Making of 'Secret People', George
Allen & Unwin (London), 1952 (edited by Lindsay
Anderson; screenplay by Christianna Brand)   £15/£5
ditto, Macmillan (New York), 1952 .   .   £15/£5
Heaven Knows Who, Michael Joseph (London), 1960 £15/£5
ditto, Scribner (New York), 1960   .   .   .   £15/£5

RICHARD BRAUTIGAN
(b.1935 d.1984)

Brautigan was an American writer whose first published
novel, *A Confederate General from Big Sur* was his first
published novel and met with little success. However, his
second novel, *Trout Fishing in America* catapulted him to
international fame and he was hailed by literary critics as
the writer most representative of the emerging counter-
culture youth-movement of the late 1960s. He died of an
apparently self-inflicted gunshot-wound to the head in
1984.

Novels
A Confederate General From Big Sur, Grove Press (New
York), 1964 .   .   .   .   .   .   £125/£30
ditto, Cape (London), 1970 .   .   .   .   £75/£50
Trout Fishing in America, Four Seasons Foundation (San
Francisco, CA), 1967 (pbk) £200
ditto, Cape (London), 1970 .   .   .   .   £75/£50
In Watermelon Sugar, Four Seasons Foundation (San
Francisco, CA), 1968 (pbk) £45
ditto, Four Seasons Foundation (San Francisco, CA), 1968
(50 signed, numbered hardback copies) .   .   £300
ditto, Cape (London), 1970 .   .   .   .   £45/£10

The Abortion: An Historical Romance 1966, Simon &
Schuster (New York), 1971   .   .   .   .   £100/£15
ditto, Cape (London), 1973 .   .   .   .   £35/£10
The Hawkline Monster: A Gothic Western, Simon &
Schuster (New York), 1974   .   .   .   .   £65/£10
ditto, Cape (London), 1975 .   .   .   .   £35/£10
Willard and His Bowling Trophies: A Perverse Mystery,
Simon & Schuster (New York), 1975   .   .   £40/£10
ditto, Cape (London), 1976 .   .   .   .   £20/£5
Sombrero Fallout: A Japanese Novel, Simon & Schuster
(New York), 1976 .   .   .   .   .   £25/£10
ditto, Cape (London), 1977 .   .   .   .   £20/£5
Dreaming of Babylon: A Private Eye Novel 1942, Delacorte
(New York), 1977 .   .   .   .   .   £25/£10
ditto, Cape (London), 1978 .   .   .   .   £20/£5

Short Stories
Revenge of the Lawn, Simon & Schuster (New York), 1971
.   .   .   .   £75/£15
ditto, Cape (London), 1972 .   .   .   .   £45/£10

Poetry
Four New Poets, Inferno Press (San Francisco, CA), 1957
(with Martin Hoberman, Carl Larsen and James Singer;
white wraps illustrated with handprints on front cover, but
not the names of the poets whose work is included.) . £400
The Return of the Rivers, Inferno Press (San Francisco,
CA), 1958 (a single sheet, glued into wraps).   £1,750
The Galilee Hitch-Hiker, White Rabbit Press (San
Francisco, CA), 1958 (200 copies; sewn wraps) .   £500
Lay the Marble Tea, Carp Press (San Francisco, CA), 1959
(wraps) £500
The Octopus Frontier, Carp Press (San Francisco, CA),
1960 (stapled wraps) £300
September California, San Francisco Arts Festival
Commission (San Francisco, CA), 1964 (300 copies;
broadside) £100
Karma Repair Kit, Communication Company (San
Francisco, CA), 1967 (broadside) .   .   .   £75
All Watched Over by Machines of Loving Grace,
Communication Company (San Francisco, CA), 1963
(yellow wraps bound with yellow cord tie) .   .   £175
Please Plant This Book, Graham Mackintosh (San Francisco
and Santa Barbara), 1968 (card folder with eight seed
packets each with printed poem) .   .   .   £300
The Pill versus the Springhill Mine Disaster, Four Seasons
Foundation (San Francisco, CA), 1968 (wraps) .   £45
ditto, Four Seasons Foundation (San Francisco, CA), 1968
(50 signed, numbered hardback copies) .   .   £250
ditto, Cape (London), 1970 .   .   .   .   £45/£50
Rommel Drives on Deep into Egypt, Delacorte (New York),
1970 .   .   .   .   £65/£15
Loading Mercury with a Pitchfork, Simon & Schuster (New
York), 1976 .   .   .   .   .   .   £45/£10
June 30th, June 30th, Delacorte (New York), 1977 £45/£10
The Edna Webster Collection of Undiscovered Writings,
Weiss & James (Berkeley, CA, 1999 (65 numbered copies
signed by editor; marbled board) .   .   .   £100
ditto, Mariner/Houghton Mifflin (New York), 1999 (pbk) £5

Others
The San Francisco Public Library: A Publishing House,
self published (San Francisco, CA), 1968 (Stapled
mimeograph) £1,000

The Tokyo-Montana Express, Targ (New York), 1979 (350 signed copies in boards with glassine d/w) . £75/£50
ditto, Cape (London), 1981 . . . . . £20/£5
So The Wind Won't Blow It All Away, Delacorte (New York), 1982 . . . . £25/£10
An Unfortunate Woman: A Journey, Creative Arts Book Company (San Francisco, CA), 1984 . . . £20/£5
ditto, Rebel Inc (Edinburgh), 2000 . . . . £10/£5

ANGELA BRAZIL
(b.1868 d.1947)

A British-born author of school stories for girls. Brazil was popular with readers because her heroines were instantly believable, although there were contemporary complaints about the schoolgirl slang used in the books. Latterly, authors like Elinor Brent-Dyer threatened to become more popular and relevant to young girls, but Brazil remained queen of the genre right into the 1930s.

School Stories
A Terrible Tomboy, Gay & Bird (London), 1904 . . £145
The Fortunes of Philippa, Blackie (London), 1907 [1906] £85
The Third Class at Miss Kaye's, Blackie (London), 1909 [1908] £85
The Nicest Girl in the School, Blackie (London), 1910 £75
Bosom Friends: A Seaside Story, Nelson (London), [1910] £60
The Manor House School, Blackie (London), 1911 . £50
A Fourth Form Friendship, Blackie (London), 1912 . £45
The New Girl at St. Chad's, Blackie (London), 1912 . £45
A Pair of Schoolgirls, Blackie (London), [1912] . . £40
The Leader of the Lower School, Blackie (London), [1914] £40
The Youngest Girl in the Fifth, Blackie (London), [1914] £40
The Girls of St. Cyprian's, Blackie (London), [1914] . £35
The School by the Sea, Blackie (London), [1914] . . £35
The Jolliest Term on Record, Blackie (London), [1915] £35
For the Sake of the School, Blackie (London), [1915] . £35
The Luckiest Girl in the School, Blackie (London), [1916]. £30
The Slap-Bang Boys, T.C. & E.C. Jack (Edinburgh and London), [1917] £30
The Madcap of the School, Blackie (London), [1918] . £30
A Patriotic Schoolgirl, Blackie (London), [1918] . . £25
For the School Colours, Blackie (London), [1918] . £25
A Harum-Scarum Schoolgirl, Blackie (London), [1919] £25
The Head Girl at The Gables, Blackie (London), [1919] £25
Two Little Scamps and a Puppy, Nelson (London), [1919] £25
A Gift from the Sea, Nelson (London), [1920] . £150/£25
A Popular Schoolgirl, Blackie (London), [1920] . £150/£25
The Princess of the School, Blackie (London), [1920] . . . . £145/£25
A Fortunate Term, Blackie (London), [1921] . . £145/£25
Loyal to the School, Blackie (London), [1921] . £145/£25
Moniteress Merle, Blackie (London), [1922] . £145/£25
The School in the South, Blackie (London), [1922] . . . . £145/£25

The Khaki Boys and Other Stories, Nelson (London), [1923] . . . . £145/£25
Schoolgirl Kitty, Blackie (London), [1923] . £145/£25
Captain Peggie, Blackie (London), [1924] . £135/£25
Joan's Best Chum, Blackie (London), [1926]. . £135/£25
Queen of the Dormitory and Other Stories, Cassell (London), [1926]. . . . . . . £100/£25
Ruth of St. Ronans, Blackie (London), [1927] . £100/£25
At School with Rachel, Blackie (London), [1928] . £100/£20
St. Catherine's College, Blackie (London), [1929] £100/£20
The Little Green School, Blackie (London), [1931] . . . . £100/£20
Nesta's New School, Blackie (London), [1932] . £85/£20
Jean's Golden Term, Blackie (London), [1934] . £85/£20
The School at the Turrets, Blackie (London), [1935] . . . . £85/£20
An Exciting Term, Blackie (London), [1936] . . £75/£15
Jill's Jolliest School, Blackie (London), 1937. . £75/£15
The School on the Cliff, Blackie (London), [1938] £75/£15
The School on the Moor, Blackie (London), [1939] £70/£10
The New School at Scawdale, Blackie (London), [1940] . . . . £70/£10
Five Jolly Schoolgirls, Blackie (London), [1941] . £70/£10
The Mystery of the Moated Grange, Blackie (London), [1942] . . . . £50/£10
The Secret of the Border Castle, Blackie (London), [1943]. . . . . £50/£10
The School in the Forest, Blackie (London), [1944] £45/£10
Three Terms at Uplands, Blackie (London), [1945] £45/£10
The School on the Loch, Blackie (London), [1946] £45/£10

Plays
The Mischievous Brownie, Paterson, 'Children's Plays' series No. 1 (London), [1913] (stapled wraps) . £40
The Fairy Gifts, Paterson, 'Children's Plays' series No. 2 (London), [1913] (stapled wraps) £40
The Enchanted Fiddle, Paterson, 'Children's Plays' series No. 3 (London), [1913] (stapled wraps). . . . £40
The Wishing Princess, Paterson, 'Children's Plays' series No. 4 (London), [1913] (stapled wraps). . . . £40

Autobiography
My Own Schooldays, Blackie (London), [1925] . £125/£35

ELINOR BRENT-DYER
(b.1894 d.1969)

Born Gladys Elinor May Dyer, this British author of stories for girls worked for many years as a teacher. Her 'Chalet School' stories are still very popular and even spawned a 'Chalet Club' with its own newsletter. The Club and its literature seems to have been used by Brent-Dyer as a sophisticated form of market research, helping her discover what readers wanted from the books.

'Chalet School' Titles
The School at the Chalet, Chambers (London), 1925 . . . . £500/£175
Jo of the Chalet School, Chambers (London), 1926 . . . . £450/£150
The Princess of the Chalet School, Chambers (London), 1927 . . . . £350/£100

The Head Girl of the Chalet School, Chambers (London), 1928 . . . . £350/£100

The Rivals of the Chalet School, Chambers (London), 1929 . . . . £350/£100

Eustacia Goes to the Chalet School, Chambers (London), 1930 . . . . £350/£100

The Chalet School and Jo, Chambers (London), 1931 . . . . £350/£100

The Chalet School in Camp, Chambers (London), 1932 . . . . £350/£100

The Exploits of the Chalet Girls, Chambers (London), 1933 . . . . . £350/£100

The Chalet School and the Lintons, Chambers (London), 1934 . . . . £350/£100

The New House at the Chalet School, Chambers (London), 1935 . . . . £350/£100

Jo Returns to the Chalet School, Chambers (London), 1936 . . . . . £350/£100

The New Chalet School, Chambers (London), 1938 . . . . £275/£75

The Chalet School in Exile, Chambers (London), 1940 (Nazi d/w) . . . . £500/£60

The Chalet School Goes To It, Chambers (London), 1941 . . . . £175/£60

The Highland Twins at the Chalet School, Chambers (London), 1942 . . . . . £175/£60

Lavender Laughs in the Chalet School, Chambers (London), 1943 . . . . £175/£60

Gay from China at the Chalet School, Chambers (London), 1944 . . . . £175/£60

Jo to the Rescue, Chambers (London), 1945 . . £175/£60

The Chalet Book for Girls, Chambers (London), [1947] (no d/w) £100

The Second Chalet Book for Girls, Chambers (London), 1948 (no d/w) £100

The Third Chalet Book for Girls, Chambers (London), 1949 . . . . £200/£75

Three Go to the Chalet School, Chambers (London), 1949 . . . . £175/£50

The Chalet School and the Island, Chambers (London), 1950 . . . . £175/£50

Peggy of the Chalet School, Chambers (London), 1950 . . . . £175/£50

Carola Storms the Chalet School, Chambers (London), 1951 . . . . £175/£50

The Chalet School and Rosalie, Chambers (London), 1951 (wraps) £250

The Wrong Chalet School, Chambers (London), 1952 . . . . £175/£50

Shocks for the Chalet School, Chambers (London), 1952 . . . . £175/£50

The Chalet School in the Oberland, Chambers (London), 1952 . . . . £150/£60

Bride Leads the Chalet School, Chambers (London), 1953 . . . . £175/£65

Changes for the Chalet School, Chambers (London), 1953 . . . . £150/£60

The Chalet Girls' Cook Book, Chambers (London), 1953 . . . . £200/£100

Joey Goes to the Oberland, Chambers (London), 1954 . . . . £150/£65

The Chalet School and Barbara, Chambers (London), 1954 . . . . £175/£50

Tom Tackles the Chalet School, Chambers (London), 1955 . . . . £150/£60

The Chalet School Does it Again, Chambers (London), 1955 . . . . £200/£75

A Chalet Girl from Kenya, Chambers (London), 1955 . . . . £150/£45

Mary-Lou of the Chalet School, Chambers (London), 1956 . . . . £175/£50

A Genius at the Chalet School, Chambers (London), 1956 . . . . £150/£50

A Problem for the Chalet School, Chambers (London), 1956 . . . . £150/£50

The New Mistress at the Chalet School, Chambers (London), 1957 . . . . . £150/£50

Excitements at the Chalet School, Chambers (London), 1957 . . . . £150/£50

The Coming of Age at the Chalet School, Chambers (London), 1958 . . . . £150/£50

The Chalet School and Richenda, Chambers (London), 1958 . . . . £150/£50

Trials for the Chalet School, Chambers (London), 1959 . . . . £125/£50

Theodora and the Chalet School, Chambers (London), 1959 . . . . £125/£50

Joey and Co. in Tirol, Chambers (London), 1960 . £125/£50

Ruey Richardson, Chaletian, Chambers (London), 1960 . . . . £125/£50

A Leader in the Chalet School, Chambers (London), 1961 . . . . £125/£50

The Chalet School Wins the Trick, Chambers (London), 1961 . . . . £125/£50

A Future Chalet School Girl, Chambers (London), 1962 . . . . £125/£50

The Feud in the Chalet School, Chambers (London), 1962 . . . . £125/£50

The Chalet School Triplets, Chambers (London), 1963 . . . . £125/£50

The Chalet School Reunion, Chambers (London), 1963 (with d/w, chart and yellow band) . . . . £250/£65

Jane and the Chalet School, Chambers (London), 1964 . . . . £125/£50

Redheads at the Chalet School, Chambers (London), 1964 . . . . £125/£50

Adrienne and the Chalet School, Chambers (London), 1965 . . . . £125/£50

Summer Term at the Chalet School, Chambers (London), 1965 . . . . . . £125/£50

Challenge for the Chalet School, Chambers (London), 1966 . . . . £150/£50

Two Sams at the Chalet School, Chambers (London), 1967 . . . . £175/£50

Althea Joins the Chalet School, Chambers (London), 1969 . . . . £200/£50

Prefects of the Chalet School, Chambers (London), 1970 . . . . £225/£50

'La Rochelle' Titles

Gerry Goes to School, Chambers (London), 1922 £350/£100

ditto, Lippincott (Philadelphia, PA), 1923. . £350/£100

A Head Girl's Difficulties, Chambers (London), 1923 . . . . £350/£100

The Maids of La Rochelle, Chambers (London), 1924 . . . . £350/£100

Seven Scamps, Chambers (London), 1927 . £350/£100

Heather Leaves School, Chambers (London), 1929   .   .
.   .   .   .   £350/£100
Janie of La Rochelle, Chambers (London), 1932   £350/£100
Janie Steps in, Chambers (London), 1953   .   .£125/£25

'Chudleigh Hold' Titles
Fardingales, Latimer House (London), 1950   .   .£250/£50
The 'Susannah' Adventure, Chambers (London), 1953   .
.   .   .   .£125/£40
Chudleigh Hold, Chambers (London), 1954   .   .£125/£40
The Condor Crags Adventure, Chambers (London), 1954   .
.   .   .   .£125/£40
Top Secret, Chambers (London), 1955   .   .   .£125/£40

Other Titles
A Thrilling Term at Janeways, Nelson (London), 1927   .
.   .   .   .£250/£100
The New Housemistress, Nelson (London), 1928   .£75/£25
Judy the Guide, Nelson (London), 1928   .   .£200/£75
The School by the River, Burns, Oates & Washbourne
(London), 1930   .   .   .   .   .   .£600/£150
The Feud in the Fifth Remove, Girl's Own Paper (London),
1931   .   .   .   .£150/£50
The Little Marie-Jose, Burns, Oates & Washbourne
(London), 1932   .   .   .   .   .   £600/£150
Carnation of the Upper Fourth, Girl's Own Paper
(London), 1934   .   .   .   .   .   .£150/£45
Elizabeth the Gallant, Butterworth (London), 1935   .
.   .   .   .£450/£175
Monica Turns Up Trumps, Girl's Own Paper (London),
1936   .   .   .   .£125/£50
Caroline the Second, Girl's Own Paper (London), 1937   .
.   .   .   .£400/£150
They Both Liked Dogs, Girl's Own Paper (London), 1938   .
.   .   .   .£400/£150
The Little Missus, Chambers (London), 1942   .   .£150/£50
The Lost Staircase, Chambers (London), 1946   .£150/£45
Lorna at Wynyards, Lutterworth Press (London), 1947   .
.   .   .   .£150/£45
Stepsisters for Lorna, Temple (London), 1948   .£150/£45
Verena Visits New Zealand, Chambers (London), 1951
(wraps) £250
Bess on Her Own in Canada, Chambers (London), 1951
(wraps) £250
Quintette in Queensland, Chambers (London), 1951 (wraps)
.   .   .   .£250
Sharlie's Kenya Diary, Chambers (London), 1951 (wraps)   .
.   .   .   .£250
Nesta Steps Out, Oliphants (London), 1954   .£125/£25
Kennelmaid Nan, Lutterworth (London), 1954   .£125/£25
Beechy of the Harbour School, Oliphants (London), 1955   .
.   .   .   .£125/£25
Leader in Spite of Herself, Oliphants (London), 1956   .
.   .   .   .£125/£25
The School at Skelton Hall, Max Parrish (London), 1962   .
.   .   .   .£125/£40
Trouble at Skelton Hall, Max Parrish (London), 1963   .   .
.   .   .   .£125/£40

Short Stories
Sunday and Everyday Reading for the Young (contains
'Jack's Revenge'), Wells, Gardner, Darton (London), 1914
.   .   .   .£50

The Big Book for Girls (contains 'The Lady in the Yellow
Gown'), Humphrey Milford (London)/O.U.P. (Oxford,
UK), 1925   .   .   .   .£35
The Golden Story Book for Girls (contains 'The Lady in the
Yellow Gown'), Humphrey Milford (London)/O.U.P.
(Oxford, UK), 1931   .   .   .   .   .   .£25
Stories of the Circus, Book 4 (contains 'Carlotta to the
Rescue', magazine), c.1931   .   .   .   .   .£50
The Children's Circus Book (contains 'Carlotta to the
Rescue'), Associated Newspapers (London), c.1934   .£35
Come to the Circus (contains 'Carlotta to the Rescue'), P.R.
Gawthorn (London), c.1938   .   .   .   .   .£35
The Second Coronet Book for Girls (contains 'Cavalier
Maid'), Sampson Low (London), [n.d.]   .   .   .£25
My Favourite Story (contains 'Rescue in the Snows'),
Thames (London) [n.d.] £25
Sceptre Girls' Story Annual (contains 'House of Secrets'),
Purnell (London) [n.d.] £25
Girl's Own Annual, Vol 57 (contains 'The Robins Make
Good'), Girl's Own (London) [n.d.]   .   .   .£50
My Treasure Hour Bumper Annual (contains 'The Chalet
School Mystery'), Murrays Sales and Service Co.
(London), 1970   .   .   .   .£25

ANNE BRONTË
(b.1820 d.1849)

The youngest of six, Anne was the sister of Charlotte and
Emily, whose work tends to overshadow that of their
younger sister. *Agnes Grey* was first published alongside
Emily's *Wuthering Heights*. Anne's works were originally
published under the pseudonym 'Acton Bell'.

Poems, (with Charlotte and Emily Brontë under the
pseudonyms of 'Currer, Ellis and Acton Bell'), Aylott &
Jones (London), 1846 (first issue, first binding, dark green
cloth) £25,000
ditto, Aylott & Jones (London), 1846 (first issue, second binding, lighter green cloth with blind-stamped harp).   £25,000
ditto, Smith, Elder & Co (London), 1846 [1848], (second
issue with cancel title-page stating 'Smith, Elder & Co')   .
.   .   .   .£2,500
ditto, Lea and Blanchard (Philadelphia, PA), 1848.   £2,000
Wuthering Heights with *Agnes Grey*, Newby (London),
1847 (pseud 'Ellis and Acton Bell', 3 vols, of which the
third is *Agnes Grey*, purple cloth)   .   .   .£60,000
ditto, Newby (London), 1847 (as above but half cloth boards
with labels) £60,000
ditto, Harper & Brothers (New York), 1848   .   .£6,000
The Tenant of Wildfell Hall, Newby (London), 1848 (pseud
'Acton Bell', 3 vols, purple cloth)   .   .   .£30,000
ditto, Harper (New York), 1848   .   .   .   .£15,000

CHARLOTTE BRONTË
(b.1816 d.1855)

Sister to Emily and Anne, Charlotte was the only Brontë to achieve literary fame in her own lifetime. Her novels were considered coarse by critics and there was great speculation as to who 'Currer Bell' really was. The enormous popular success of *Jane Eyre* led Charlotte to reveal her identity and she became friends with other writers such as Elizabeth Gaskell and William Makepeace Thackeray. Charlotte was a champion of the female spirit; *Jane Eyre* an enduring classic.

Poems, (with Charlotte and Emily Brontë under the pseudonyms of 'Currer, Ellis and Acton Bell'), Aylott & Jones (London), 1846 (first issue, first binding, dark green cloth) £25,000
ditto, Aylott & Jones (London), 1846 (first issue, second binding, lighter green cloth with blind-stamped harp). £25,000
ditto, Smith, Elder & Co (London), 1846 [1848], (second issue with cancel title-page stating 'Smith, Elder & Co') .
. . . . £2,500
ditto, Lea and Blanchard (Philadelphia, PA), 1848 . £2,000
Jane Eyre: An Autobiography, Smith, Elder & Co. (London), 1847 (first issue, 'edited' by Currer Bell; 3 vols; advertisements dated June, 1847) . . . £32,500
ditto, Smith, Elder & Co. (London), 1847 (second issue, with Currer Bell as author; 3 vols; ads dated October, 1847) .
. . . . £6,500
ditto, Harper (New York), 1848 (wraps) . . . £1,500
Shirley: A Tale, Smith, Elder & Co. (London), 1849 (3 vols, credited as by Charlotte Brontë, plum coloured cloth) .
. . . . £3,500
ditto, Harper (New York), 1850 (1 vol.) £450
Villette, Smith, Elder & Co. (London), 1853 (3 vols, olive/brown cloth, credited as by Charlotte Brontë) .
. . . . £2,750
ditto, Harper (New York), 1853 (1 vol.) £500
The Professor, Smith, Elder & Co. (London), 1857 (2 vols, plum coloured cloth, credited as by Charlotte Brontë) .
. . . . £2,500
ditto, Smith, Elder & Co. (London), 1857 (second state, 2 vols rebound together) £350
ditto, Harper (New York), 1857 (1 vol.) . . . £225

Minor Works
The Last Sketch - Emma: A Fragment, The Cornhill Magazine Vol I (London), 1860 . . . . . £65
The Twelve Adventurers and Other Stories, Hodder & Stoughton (London), 1925 (limited to 1,000 copies) . .
. . . . £125/£45
ditto, Hodder & Stoughton (New York), 1925 . . £85/£30
The Spell, O.U.P. (Oxford, UK), 1931 . . £50/£35
Legends of Angria, edited by Fannie E. Ratchford, Yale Univ Press (New Haven, CT), 1933 . . £75/£30
The Poems of Charlotte Brontë and Patrick Branwell Brontë, edited by T.J. Wise and J.A. Symington, O.U.P. (Oxford, UK), 1934 . . . . . £75/£25
The Miscellaneous and Unpublished Writings of Charlotte and Patrick Branwell Brontë, edited by T.J. Wise and J.A. Symington, O.U.P. (Oxford, UK), 1934 (2 vols, 1,000 copies) . . . . £125/£75

Tales from Angria, edited by Phyllis Bentley, Collins (London), 1954 . . . . £45/£15
The Search After Happiness, Harvill Press (London), 1969
. . . . £20/£5
ditto, Simon & Schuster (New York), 1969 . . £20/£5
Five Novelettes, edited by Winifred Gerin, The Folio Society (London), 1971 (slipcase) . . . . . £20/£10
A Leaf from an Unopened Volume, The Brontë Society, 1986 (wraps). £15

EMILY BRONTË
(b.1818 d.1848)

Wuthering Heights received mixed reviews when first published but is now regarded as a literary classic. It was published shortly after Charlotte's Brontë's *Jane Eyre*, and there was speculation that the pseudonyms used by the sisters concealed the identity of a single male author. Emily's poems are considered some of the finest lyric verse in the English language.

Poems, (with Charlotte and Anne Brontë under the pseudonyms of 'Currer, Ellis and Acton Bell'), Aylott & Jones (London), 1846 (first issue, first binding, dark green cloth) £25,000
ditto, Aylott & Jones (London), 1846 (first issue, second binding, lighter green cloth with blind-stamped harp). £25,000
ditto, Smith, Elder & Co (London), 1846 [1848], (second issue with cancel title-page stating 'Smith, Elder & Co') .
. . . . £2,500
ditto, Lea and Blanchard (Philadelphia, PA), 1848 . £2,000
Wuthering Heights with *Agnes Grey*, Newby (London), 1847 (pseud 'Ellis and Acton Bell', 3 vols, of which the third is *Agnes Grey*, purple cloth) . . . £60,000
ditto, Newby (London), 1847 (as above but half cloth boards with labels) £60,000
ditto, Harper & Brothers (New York), 1848 . . £6,000

JOCELYN BROOKE
(b.1908 d.1966)

A novelist and poet, Brooke is considered a fine stylist. His Proustian 'Orchid' trilogy takes as a theme the author's abiding interest in botany and especially the native orchids of Britain. He also published brief studies of other writers and edited a selection of the work of Denton Welch.

The 'Orchid' Series
The Military Orchid, Bodley Head (London), 1948 £75/£15
A Mine of Serpents, Bodley Head (London), 1949. £65/£15
The Goose Cathedral, Bodley Head (London), 1950 .
. . . . £60/£15
The Orchid Trilogy, Secker & Warburg (London), 1981 .
. . . . £30/£10

Other Fiction
The Scapegoat, Bodley Head (London), 1948 . . £75/£15
ditto, Harper (New York), 1949 . . . . . £25/£10

The Image of a Drawn Sword, Bodley Head (London), 1950
. . . . £60/£20
ditto, Knopf (New York), 1951 . . . . £15/£5
The Passing of a Hero, Bodley Head (London), 1953 . .
. . . . £65/£15
Private View: Four Portraits, Barrie, 1954 . £35/£15
The Dog at Clambercrown, Bodley Head (London), 1955 .
. . . . £75/£15
ditto, Vanguard Press (New York), 1955 . . £20/£10
The Crisis in Bulgaria, or Ibsen to the Rescue!, Chatto &
Windus (London), 1956 . . . . . £45/£10
Conventional Weapons, Faber (London), 1961 . £25/£10
ditto, as *The Name of Greene*, Vanguard Press (New York),
1961 . . . . £20/£10

Poetry
Six Poems, privately printed, 1928 (50 signed, numbered
copies; wraps) £300
December Spring, Bodley Head (London), 1946 . £85/£25
The Elements of Death and other poems, Hand & Flower
Press (Aldington, Kent), 1952 (stapledwraps) . £25

Children's Titles
The Wonderful Summer, Lehmann (London), 1949 £65/£25

Non-Fiction
The Wild Orchids of Britain, Bodley Head (London), 1950
(40 specially bound, signed copies of 1,140). £1,000/£750
ditto, Bodley Head (London), 1950 (1,100 copies of 1,140)
. . . . £175/£145
Ronald Firbank: A Critical Study, Barker (London), 1951 .
. . . . £25/£10
ditto, Roy (New York), 1951 . . . . £20/£5
The Flower in Season, Bodley Head (London), 1952 . .
. . . . £35/£15
Elizabeth Bowen, British Council/Longmans Green
(London), 1952 (stapled wraps) £5
Aldous Huxley, British Council/Longmans Green (London),
1953 (stapled wraps) £5
ditto, revised edition, British Council/Longmans Green
(London), 1958 (stapled wraps) £5
Ronald Firbank and John Betjeman, British Council/
Longmans Green (London), 1962 (stapled wraps) . £5
The Birth of a Legend, Bertram Rota (London), 1964 (65
signed, numbered copies; wraps) £100

RUPERT BROOKE
(b.1887 d.1915)

Born and educated at Rugby, Brooke went to Cambridge
University. Although already a published poet, he achieved
his greatest fame posthumously. (He died of blood-
poisoning aboard ship on his way to the great engagement
of the Dardanelles at the age of 28.) His verse is charac-
teristically Georgian, and his good looks and early death
make him one of the most celebrated of the war poets.

Poetry
The Pyramids, privately printed (Rugby), 1904 (wraps) .
. . . . £10,000
The Bastille, privately printed by A.J. Lawrence (Rugby),
1905 (blue wraps) £6,000

ditto, privately printed by George E. Over (Rugby), 1905
[1920] (wraps) £500
Prize Compositions, privately printed by the Rugby Press
(Rugby), 1905 (wraps) £2,500
Poems, Sidgwick & Jackson (London), 1911 (dark blue
cloth, paper label, no d/w) £750
1914 and Other Poems, Sidgwick & Jackson (London),
1915 (dark blue cloth, paper label; frontispiece) . £400
ditto, Doubleday, Page (New York), 1915 (87 copyright
copies, bound or unbound) £1,000
1914, Five Sonnets, Sidgwick & Jackson (London), 1915
(wraps; in printed envelope) . . . . £100/£45
War Poems, privately printed, 1915 . . . . £100
The Collected Poems of Rupert Brooke, Lane (New York),
1915 (with a Memoir by Edward Marsh) . . . £50
ditto, Lane (New York), 1915 (100 copies bound for
members of the Woodberry Society) . . . £600
ditto, Sidgwick & Jackson (London), 1918 . . . £50
ditto, Riccardi Press (London), 1919 (1,000 numbered
copies) £150
ditto, Riccardi Press (London), 1919 (13 copies in full
vellum) £1,250
The Old Vicarage, Grantchester, Sidgwick & Jackson
(London), 1916 (grey wraps) £100
Selected Poems, Sidgwick & Jackson (London), 1917 . £20
Fragments Now First Collected, privately printed (Hartford,
CT), 1925 (94 copies). £250
ditto, privately printed (Hartford, CT), 1925 (5 numbered
copies on vellum) £450
Twenty Poems, Sidgwick & Jackson (London), 1935 . .
. . . . £50/£20
The Poetical Works of Rupert Brooke, Faber & Faber
(London), 1946 . . . . £35/£10
Poems, Folio Society (London), 1948 (slipcase) . £25/£15
Four Poems, Scolar Press (London), 1974 (100 copies
signed by editor of 500, slipcase) . . . £200/£150
ditto, Scolar Press (London), 1974 (400 unsigned copies of
500) £75

Prose
The Authorship of the Later 'Appius and Virginia',
privately printed, [1913] (20 copies) . . . £1,250
Lithuania, A Drama in One Act, Chicago Little Theatre
(Chicago), 1915 (200 copies; pictorial brown stapled
wraps) £350
ditto, Sidgwick & Jackson (London), 1935 . £75/£25
ditto, Sidgwick & Jackson (London), 1935 (wraps) . £25
Letters from America, Scribner's (New York), 1916 . £25
ditto, Sidgwick & Jackson (London), 1916 . . . £25
John Webster and the Elizabethan Drama, John Lane (New
York), 1916 . . . . £50
ditto, Sidgwick & Jackson (London), 1916 . . . £40
A Letter to the Editor of the Poetry Review, Watch Hill
Press (Peekskill, NY), 1929 (50 copies). . . £175
Democracy and the Arts, Hart Davis (London), 1946
(preface by Geoffrey Keynes) . . . . £25/£10
ditto, Hart Davis (London), 1946 (240 numbered copies) .
. . . . £100
The Prose of Rupert Brooke, Sidgwick & Jackson (London),
1956 (edited and with an introduction by Christopher
Hassall). . . . . £25/£10
The Letters of Rupert Brooke, Faber & Faber (London), 1968
. . . . £30/£10
ditto, Harcourt Brace (New York), 1968 . . . £30/£10

Song of Love: The Letters of Rupert Brooke and Noel
  Olivier, Bloomsbury, 1991 . . . . . £25/£10
ditto, Crown (New York), 1992 . . . . . £25/£10

ANITA BROOKNER
(b.1928)

An English novelist and art historian. In 1967 Brookner became the first woman to hold the Slade professorship at Cambridge University and since 1977 she has been associated with the Courtauld Institute of Art. She is best known as a novelist, after winning the Booker Prize in 1984 for *Hotel du Lac*. Her novels are haunted by solitary, sad women and the failures of their relationships.

Novels
A Start in Life, Cape (London), 1981 . . . £125/£15
ditto, Cape (London), 1981 (price clipped, with new price
  sticker, but otherwise fine) . . . . . £65/£15
ditto, as *The Debut*, Linden Press (New York), 1981 £35/£5
Providence, Cape (London), 1982 . . . . £65/£15
ditto, Pantheon (New York), 1984 . . . . £25/£5
Look at Me, Cape (London), 1983 . . . £60/£5
ditto, Pantheon (New York), 1983 . . . . £20/£5
Hotel Du Lac, Cape (London), 1984 . . . £65/£10
ditto, Pantheon (New York), 1985 . . . . £20/£5
Family and Friends, Cape (London), 1985 . . £20/£5
ditto, London Limited Editions (London), 1985 (250 signed
  copies) . . . . £45/£35
ditto, Pantheon (New York), 1985 . . . . £20/£5
A Misalliance, Cape (London), 1986. . . . £20/£5
ditto, as *The Misalliance*, Pantheon (New York), 1987 . .
  . . . . £20/£5
A Friend From England, Cape (London), 1987 . £20/£5
ditto, Pantheon (New York), 1988 . . . . £20/£5
Latecomers, Cape (London), 1988 . . . . £15/£5
ditto, Pantheon (New York), 1989 . . . . £15/£5
Lewis Percy, Cape (London), 1989 . . . . £15/£5
ditto, Pantheon (New York), 1990 . . . . £15/£5
Brief Lives, Cape (London), 1990 . . . . £15/£5
ditto, Random House (New York), 1991 . . . £15/£5
A Closed Eye, Cape (London), 1991 . . . . £15/£5
ditto, Random House (New York), 1992 . . . £15/£5
Fraud, Cape (London), 1992 . . . . . £15/£5
ditto, Random House (New York), 1992 . . . £15/£5
A Family Romance, Cape (London), 1993 . . £15/£5
ditto, as *Dolly*, Random House (New York), 1993 . £15/£5
A Private View, Cape (London), 1994 . . . £10/£5
ditto, Random House (New York), 1994 . . . £10/£5
Incidents in the Rue Laugier, Cape (London), 1995 £10/£5
ditto, Random House (New York), 1994 . . . £10/£5
Altered States, Cape (London), 1996. . . . £10/£5
ditto, Random House (New York), 1996 . . . £10/£5
Visitors, Cape (London), 1997 . . . . . £10/£5
ditto, Random House (New York), 1998 . . . £10/£5
Falling Slowly, Viking (London), 1998 . . . £10/£5
ditto, Random House (New York), 1999 . . . £10/£5
Undue Influence, Viking (London), 1999 . . £10/£5
ditto, Random House (New York), 1999 . . . £10/£5
The Bay of Angels, Viking (London), 2001 . . £10/£5
ditto, Random House (New York), 2001 . . . £10/£5
The Next Big Thing, Viking (London), 2002 . . £10/£5

ditto, Random House (New York), 2002 . . . £10/£5
The Rules of Engagement, Viking (London), 2003 £10/£5
ditto, Random House (New York), 2003 . . . £10/£5
Leaving Home, Viking (London), 2005 . . . £10/£5
ditto, Random House (New York), 2006 . . . £10/£5

Essays
J.A. Dominique Ingres, Purnell (Paulton, Somerset), 1965
  (The Masters #16; wraps) £5
Jacques-Louis David, Purnell (Paulton, Somerset), 1967
  (The Masters #91; wraps) £25
Watteau, Hamlyn (London), 1967 . . . . £30/£10
The Genius of the Future: Studies in French Art Criticism,
  Phaidon (London), 1971 . . . . . . £30/£10
ditto, as *The Genius of the Future: Essays in French Art*
  Criticism, Cornell Univ Press (Ithaca, NY), 1988 £25/£10
Greuze: The Rise and Fall of an Eighteenth-Century
  Phenomenon, New York Graphic Society (Greenwich,
  CT), 1972 . . . . £30/£10
ditto, Elek (London),1972 . . . . . . £30/£10
Jacques-Louis David: A Personal Interpretation, O.U.P.
  (London), 1974 (stapled wraps) £20
Jacques-Louis David, Chatto & Windus (London), 1980 .
  . . . . £25/£10
ditto, Harper (New York), 1980 . . . . . £25/£10
Soundings, Harvill (London), 1997 . . . £10/£5
Romanticism and Its Discontent, Viking, 2000 . £10/£5
ditto, Farrar Straus (New York), 2000 . . . £10/£5

DAN BROWN
(b.1964)

Dan Brown is an American author of thrillers, best-known for the controversial *The Da Vinci Code*. His first three novels had some success, but *The Da Vinci Code* became a runaway bestseller and is now credited with being one of the most popular books of all time. It has however, been widely attacked by literary critics.

Novels
Digital Fortress, St Martin's Press (New York), 1998 . .
  . . . . £400/£60
ditto, Bantam (London), 2005 . . . . . £25/£10
Angels and Demons, Simon & Schuster (New York), 2000 .
  . . . . £300/£30
ditto, Bantam (London), 2005 . . . . . £25/£10
Deception Point, Simon & Schuster (New York), 2001 .
  . . . . £50/£10
ditto, Bantam (London), 2005 . . . . . £25/£10
The Da Vinci Code, Doubleday (New York), 2003 ('Lyon'
  for 'Lille' on p.152; 'skitoma' for 'scotoma' on p.243) .
  . . . . £50/£5
ditto, Bantam (London), 2003 . . . . . £45/£5

Other Books
187 Men to Avoid: A Survival Guide for the Romantically
  Frustrated Woman, Berkley Publishing Group (New
  York), 1995 (co-written with Blythe Brown under the
  pseudonym 'Danielle Brown'; pbk) £10
The Bald Book, Pinnacle Books (New York), 1998 (co-
  written with and credited to Blythe Brown; pbk) . . £5

FREDRIC BROWN

(b.1906 d.1972)

One of the most collectable authors of the pulp era, Brown's work is usually very original, well-plotted and fast-moving. Many of his short stories are essentially extended jokes and he wrote in an engaging style. His novels are also humorous: *What Mad Universe* explores the clichés of the genre by placing the editor of a pulp magazine in a parallel world based on a naïve fan's understanding of the magazine's stories.

Novels

The Fabulous Clipjoint, Dutton (New York), 1947 . . . . £400/£50
ditto, Boardman (London), 1949 (pbk) . . . £35
The Dead Ringer, Dutton (New York), 1948 . . £250/£35
ditto, Boardman (London), 1949 (pbk) . . . £30
Murder Can be Fun, Dutton (New York), 1948 . £200/£35
ditto, Boardman (London), 1951 . . . . . £75/£25
The Bloody Moonlight, Dutton (New York), 1949 . £200/£35
ditto, as *Murder in Moonlight*, Boardman (London), 1949 . . . . £50/£15
The Screaming Mimi, Dutton (New York), 1949 . £275/£50
ditto, Boardman (London), 1950 . . . . . £75/£20
What Mad Universe, Dutton (New York), 1949 . £200/£35
ditto, Boardman (London), 1951 . . . . . £75/£20
Compliments of a Fiend, Dutton (New York), 1950 . . . . £200/£35
ditto, Boardman (London), 1951 . . . . . £75/£20
Here Comes a Candle, Dutton (New York), 1950 . £200/£35
ditto, Boardman (London), 1951 . . . . . £75/£20
Night of the Jabberwock, Dutton (New York), 1950 . . . . £200/£35
ditto, Boardman (London), 1951 . . . . . £75/£20
The Case of the Dancing Sandwiches, Dell (New York), 1951 (pbk) £200
Death Has Many Doors, Dutton (New York), 1951 . . . . £175/£25
ditto, Boardman (London), 1952 . . . . . £75/£20
The Far Cry, Dutton (New York), 1951 . . £175/£25
ditto, Boardman (London), 1952 . . . . . £75/£20
We All Killed Grandma, Dutton (New York), 1951 . . . . £150/£25
ditto, Boardman (London), 1952 . . . . . £50/£15
The Deep End, Dutton (New York), 1952 . £150/£25
ditto, Boardman (London), 1953 . . . . . £50/£15
Madball, Dell (New York), 1953 (pbk) . . . £50
The Lights in the Sky are Stars, Dutton (New York), 1953 . . . . £125/£25
ditto, as *Project Jupiter*, Boardman (London), 1954 £50/£15
His Name Was Death, Dutton (New York), 1954 . £125/£25
ditto, Boardman (London), 1955 . . . . . £50/£15
The Wench is Dead, Dutton (New York), 1955 . £125/£25
Martians Go Home, Dutton (New York), 1955 . £150/£35
ditto, Grafton (London), 1987 (pbk) . . . £10
The Lenient Beast, Dutton (New York), 1956 . £125/£25
ditto, Boardman (London), 1957 . . . . . £50/£15
Rogue in Space, Dutton (New York), 1957 . £125/£25
One For the Road, Dutton (New York), 1958 . £125/£25
ditto, Boardman (London), 1959 . . . . . £50/£15

The Office, Dutton (New York), 1958 . . . £200/£35
ditto, Dennis McMillan (Miami Beach, FL), 1987 (425 numbered copies, signed by Philip Jose Farmer) . £40/£10
The Late Lamented, Dutton (New York), 1959 . £100/£20
ditto, Boardman (London), 1959 . . . . . £50/£15
Knock Three-One-Two, Dutton (New York), 1959 £150/£35
ditto, Boardman (London), 1960 . . . . . £50/£15
The Murderers, Dutton (New York), 1961 . . £100/£20
ditto, Boardman (London), 1962 . . . . . £45/£15
The Mind Thing, Bantam (New York), 1961 (pbk) . £15
ditto, Hamlyn (London), 1979 (pbk) £10
The Five-Day Nightmare, Dutton (New York), 1963 . . . . £100/£20
ditto, as *Five Day Nightmare*, Boardman (London), 1963 . . . . £45/£15
Mrs Murphy's Underpants, Dutton (New York), 1963 . . . . £100/£20
ditto, Boardman (London), 1965 . . . . . £45/£15
Four Novels, Zomba (London), 1983 (*Night of the Jabberwock*, *The Screaming Mimi*, *Knock Three-One-Two* and *The Fabulous Clipjoint*) . . . . . . £30/£10

Short Stories

Space on My Hands, Shasta (Chicago), 1951 . . £250/£35
ditto, Corgi (London), 1953 (pbk) £10
Mostly Murder: Eighteen Short Stories, Dutton (New York), 1953 . . . . £150/£35
ditto, Boardman (London), 1954 . . . . . £100/£25
Angels and Spaceships, Dutton (New York), 1954 £125/£25
ditto, Gollancz (London), 1955 . . . . . £50/£15
Honeymoon in Hell, Bantam (New York), 1958 (pbk) . £15
Nightmares and Geezenstacks, Bantam (New York), 1961 (pbk) £20
ditto, Corgi (London), 1962 (pbk) £10
The Shaggy Dog and Other Murders, Dutton (New York), 1963 . . . . £125/£25
ditto, Boardman (London), 1954 . . . . . £45/£15
Daymares, Lancer (New York), 1968 (pbk) . . £10
Paradox Lost, Random House (New York), 1973 . £25/£5
ditto, Hale (London), 1975 . . . . . . £20/£5
The Best of Fredric Brown, Doubleday (New York), 1976 . . . . £35/£10
The Best Short Stories of Fredric Brown, New English Library (London), 1982 (pbk) £5
Carnival of Crime, Southern Illinois Univ Press (Carbondale, IL), 1985 . . . . £35/£10
And the Gods Laughed, Phantasia Press (West Bloomfield, MI), 1987 (1,525 copies) . . . . . £25/£10
ditto, Phantasia Press (West Bloomfield, MI), 1987 (475 numbered copies) . . . . . . £50/£15

Fredric Brown in the 'Pulp Detectives'

Homicide Sanatarium, Dennis McMillan (San Antonio, TX), 1984 (300 numbered copies) . . . £100/£25
Before She Kills, Dennis McMillan (San Diego, CA), 1984 (350 numbered copies) . . . . . £75/£20
Madman's Holiday, Dennis McMillan (Volcano, HI), 1985 (350 numbered copies) . . . . . £75/£20
The Case of the Dancing Sandwiches, Dennis McMillan (Volcano, HI), 1985 (400 numbered copies) . . £75/£20
The Freak Show Murders, Dennis McMillan (Belan, NM), 1985 (350 numbered copies) . . . £50/£15
30 Corpses Every Thursday, Dennis McMillan (Belan, NM), 1985 (375 numbered copies) . . . . £50/£15

Pardon My Ghoulish Laughter, Dennis McMillan (Miami Beach, FL), 1986 (400 numbered copies) . . £50/£15
Red is the Hue of Hell, Dennis McMillan (Miami Beach, FL), 1986 (400 numbered copies) . . . . £50/£15
Sex Life on the Planet Mars, Dennis McMillan (Miami Beach, FL), 1986 (400 numbered copies) . . £100/£25
Brother Monster, Dennis McMillan (Miami Beach, FL), 1987 (400 numbered copies) . . . . £50/£15
Nightmare in the Darkness, Dennis McMillan (Miami Beach, FL), 1987 (425 numbered copies) . . £50/£15
Who Was That Blonde I Saw You Kill Last Night?, Dennis McMillan (Miami Beach, FL), 1988 (450 numbered copies) . . . . £40/£10
Three Corpse Parlay, Dennis McMillan (Missoula, MT), 1988 (450 numbered copies) . . . . £40/£10
Selling Death Short, Dennis McMillan (Missoula, MT), 1988 (450 numbered copies) . . . . £30/£10
Whispering Death, Dennis McMillan (Missoula, MT), 1989 (450 numbered copies) . . . . . £30/£10
Happy Ending, Dennis McMillan (Missoula, MT), 1990 (450 numbered copies) . . . . . £30/£10
The Water Walker, Dennis McMillan (Missoula, MT), 1990 (425 numbered copies) . . . . £30/£10
The Gibbering Night, Dennis McMillan (Hilo, HI), 1991 (425 numbered copies) . . . . £25/£10
The Pickled Punks, Dennis McMillan (Hilo, HI), 1991 (450 numbered copies) . . . . £25/£10

Poetry
Fermented Ink, privately published (U.S.), 1932 (string bound wraps) £750
Shadow Suite, privately published (U.S.), 1932 (wraps) £750

Children's Title
Mitkey Astromouse, Quist (New York/London), 1971 . . . . £45/£10

ELIZABETH BARRETT BROWNING

(b.1806 d.1861)

A poet who started writing and publishing verse at an early age, she had already established a literary reputation before corresponding with, meeting and finally marrying in secret the poet Robert Browning in 1846. She was proposed as Poet Laureate after the death of Wordsworth, but it was the publication of *Aurora Leigh* which secured her reputation.

Poetry
The Battle of Marathon: A Poem, Lindsell (London), 1820 (50 copies; wraps) £40,000
An Essay on Mind, With Other Poems, James Duncan (London), 1826 (published anonymously; blue-grey boards; first issue with 'found' in line 15, p.75) . £1,250
Prometheus Bound and Miscellaneous Poems, A.J. Valpey (London), 1833 (anonymous; cloth covered boards) £4,000
ditto, C.S. Francis (New York), 1851. . . . . £450
The Seraphim and Other Poems, Saunders & Otley (London), 1838 (boards) £200

Poems, Edward Moxon (London), 1844 (2 vols; adverts in vol 1 dated 'June 1') £750
ditto, Edward Moxon (London), 1844 (2 vols; no adverts) £600
Poems: New Edition, Chapman & Hall (London), 1850 (2 vols; containing first appearance of 'Sonnets from the Portugese') £1,500
Casa Guidi Windows, Chapman & Hall (London), 1851 . . . . £150
Two Poems, Chapman & Hall (London), 1854 (with Robert Browning; wraps) £225
Aurora Leigh, Chapman & Hall (London), 1857 . . £300
ditto, C.S. Francis (New York), 1857. . . . . £150
Poems Before Congress, Chapman & Hall (London), 1860 (red cloth; first impression p.25, line 1 with single quote mark '...different scarce') £250
ditto, Chapman & Hall (London), 1860 (red cloth; second impression reads '...different scarce') £175
Last Poems, Chapman & Hall (London), 1862 . . £150
The Greek Christian Poets and the English Poets, Chapman & Hall (London), 1863 . . . . £65
Psyche Apocalypse: A Lyrical Drama, privately printed (Aylesbury, UK), 1876 (with Richard Hengist Horne) £175
New Poems by Robert and Elizabeth Barrett Browning, Smith Elder (London), 1914 (edited by Frederic G. Kenyon) £75
Elizabeth Barrett Browning: Hitherto Unpublished Poems and Stories, with an Unedited Autobiography, Bibliophile Society (New York), 1914 (2 vols; edited by H. Buxton Forman) £175
Diary by E.B.B.: The Unpublished Diary of Elizabeth Barrett Browning, 1831-1832, Ohio Univ Press (Cleveland, OH), 1969 . . . . £45/£15

Collected Editions
The Poetical Works of Elizabeth Barrett Browning, Smith Elder (London), 1889-1890 (6 vols) . . £200 the set
The Complete Works of Elizabeth Barrett Browning, Crowell (New York), 1900 (6 vols). . . £200 the set

Letters
Letters of Elizabeth Barrett Browning Addressed to Richard Hengist Horne, Richard Bentley (London), 1877 (2 vols) £75
The Letters of Elizabeth Barrett Browning, Smith Elder (London), 1897 (2 vols) £100
Elizabeth Barrett Browning: Letters to Her Sister, 1846-1859, John Murray (London), 1929. . . . £35/£15
Elizabeth Barrett to Miss Mitford: The Unpublished Letters of Elizabeth Barrett Browning to Mary Russell Mitford, John Murray (London), 1954 . . . . . £25/£10
The Brownings' Correspondence: 1809-1849, Wedgestone Press (US)/Athlone (London), 1984-1998 (14 volumes) £1,000

ROBERT BROWNING
(b.1812 d.1889)

Robert Browning was a successful English poet and
playwright, much influenced by Percy Bysshe Shelley.
Many of his best known works were published as
pamphlets by Edward Moxon under the general heading of
Bells and Pomegranates. He married Elizabeth Barrett in
1846 after a two year courtship which also resulted in one
of the most celebrated epistolary correspondences in
literary history.

Individual Works
Pauline, a Fragment of a Confession, Saunders and Otley
(London), 1833 (only 5 known copies, two of which are in
the British Museum; grey or brown boards, paper label)   .
    .   .   .   . £25,000
ditto, T. J. Wise (London), 1886 (400 copies)   .   .   . £150
ditto, T. J. Wise (London), 1886 (25 large paper copies) £300
Paracelsus, Effingham Wilson (London), 1835 (first issue
with 8 pages of adverts at front dated Dec 1, 1842; drab
boards, paper label on spine) £750
ditto, Effingham Wilson (London), 1835 (as above but
rebound) £350
Strafford: An Historical Tragedy, Longman etc (London),
1837 (drab wraps with paper label on front)   .   .   . £300
Sordello, Edward Moxon (London), 1840 (drab boards, label
on spine) £500
ditto, Edward Moxon (London), 1840 (green cloth)   . £250
Bells and Pomegranates, Edward Moxon (London) 1841-
1846 (8 parts, printed wraps: No.1: Pippa Passes. 1841,
No.2: King Victor and King Charles. 1842, No.3: Dramatic
Lyrics. 1842, No.4: The Return of the Druses. 1843, No.5:
A Blot in the 'Scutcheon. 1843, No.6: Colombe's Birthday.
1844, No.7: Dramatic Romances and Lyrics. 1845, No.8:
Luria; A Soul's Tragedy. 1846)   .   .   . £750 the set
ditto, Edward Moxon (London) 1846 (8 parts bound in one
volume) £200
Christmas Eve and Easter Day: A Poem, Chapman & Hall,
1850 (first issue with adverts dated August, 1849; green
cloth) £200
Two Poems, Chapman & Hall (London), 1854 (with
Elizabeth Barrett Browning; wraps)   .   .   . £250
Cleon, Edward Moxon (London), 1855 (mauve wraps; a
forgery by Wise) £100
The Statue and the Bust, Edward Moxon (London), 1855
(red wraps; a Wise forgery) £100
Men and Women, Chapman & Hall (London), 1855 (2 vols;
green cloth; no half-titles) £200
ditto, Ticknor and Fields (Boston), 1856   .   .   . £100
Gold Hair: a Legend of Pornic, [London], 1864 (pink
wraps; a forgery by Wise) £100
Dramatis Personae, Chapman & Hall (London), 1864 (red
cloth) £250
The Ring and the Book, Smith, Elder (London), 1868-69 (4
vols; dark green cloth with the spines of the first two vols
in Arabic numbers, and the last 2 in Roman numerals) £400
Balaustion's Adventure, Smith Elder (London), 1871 (no
half-title; brown cloth) £65
Prince Hohenstiel-Schwangau: Saviour of Society, Smith,
Elder (London), 1871 (no half-title; blue cloth)   .   . £45
Fifine at the Fair, Smith, Elder (London), 1872 (brown
cloth) £45

Red Cotton Nightcap Country; or Turf and Towers, Smith,
Elder (London), 1873 (green cloth). £45
ditto, Osgood (Boston), 1873   .   .   .   .   . £45
The Inn Album, Smith, Elder (London), 1875.   . £45
La Saisiaz: The Two Poets of Croisic, Smith, Elder
(London), 1878   .   .   .   . £40
***Pacchiarotto and how he worked in distemper: with other
poems***, Smith, Elder (London), 1876   .   .   . £35
Dramatic Idyls, Smith, Elder (London), 1879 .   .   . £45
ditto, Smith, Elder (London), 1879 (later binding has 'First
Series' on spine) £25
Dramatic Idyls (Second Series), Smith, Elder (London),
1880   .   .   .   . £35
Jocoseria, Smith, Elder (London), 1883 (red cloth)   . £30
Ferishtah's Fancies, Smith, Elder (London), 1884 (green
cloth) £30
***Parleyings with Certain People of Importance in their Day.
Introduced by a Dialogue between Apollo and the Fates,
etc***, Smith, Elder (London), 1887 (brown cloth)   . £25
Pied Piper of Hamelin, Routledge (London), [1888]
(illustrated by Kate Greenaway) £150
ditto, Harrap (London), 1934 (illustrated by Arthur
Rackham; 4 colour and 14 b&w illustrations; wraps with
d/w)   .   .   .   . £125/£60
ditto, Harrap (London), 1934 (illustrated by Arthur
Rackham; deluxe 410 signed copies, limp vellum)   . £750
ditto, Lippincott (Philadelphia), 1934 (illustrated by Arthur
Rackham; red or green cloth with pictorial panel) £125/£50
Asolando: Fancies and Facts, Smith, Elder (London), 1890
[1889] (red bevelled cloth) £45

JEAN de BRUNHOFF
(b.1899 d.1937)

Jean de Brunhoff was a French writer and illustrator who
co-created Babar the Elephant, the stories having been told
originally to their son by his wife Cecile. After Jean's
death, the son, Laurent de Brunhoff, continued the series.
The first seven titles were reprinted in abridged form, with
only 30 pages per book rather than the original 48.

'Babar' Books by Jean de Brunhoff
Histoire de Babar le Petit Éléphant, Editions Du Jardin Des
Modes (Paris, France), 1931   .   .   .   . £800/£400
ditto, as ***The Story of Babar, the Little Elephant***, Smith &
Haas (New York), 1933   .   .   .   . £600/£300
ditto, Methuen (London), 1934 (Preface by A.A. Milne)   .
    .   .   .   . £500/£200
Le Voyage De Babar, Editions Du Jardin Des Modes (Paris,
France), 1932   .   .   .   .   .   . £800/£375
ditto, as ***Travels of Babar***, Smith & Haas (New York), 1934
    .   .   .   . £500/£250
ditto, as ***Babar's Travels***, Methuen (London), 1935   .
    .   .   .   . £500/£200
Le Roi Babar, Editions Du Jardin Des Modes (Paris,
France), 1933   .   .   .   .   .   . £400/£175
ditto, as ***Babar the King***, Smith & Haas (New York), 1935 .
    .   .   .   . £400/£175
ditto, Methuen (London), 1936   .   .   . £400/£175
Vacances de Zéphir, Hachette (Paris, France), 1936   .   .
    .   .   .   . £225/£125

ditto, as **Zephir's Holidays**, Random House (New York), 1937 . . . . £225/£125
ditto, as **Babar's Friend Zephir**, Methuen (London), 1937 .
. . . . £225/£125
ABC de Babar, Editions Du Jardin Des Modes (Paris, France), 1937 . . . . . . £400/£175
ditto, **A B C of Babar**, Smith & Haas (New York), 1937 . . . . £400/£175
ditto, as **Babar's ABC**, Methuen (London), 1937 £400/£175
Babar en Famille, Hachette (Paris, France), 1938 £300/£150
ditto, as **Babar and His Children**, Random House (New York), 1938 . . . . . £300/£150
ditto, as **Babar at Home**, Methuen (London), 1938 £300/£150
Babar et Le Père Noël, Hachette (Paris, France), 1940 . .
. . . . £275/£145
ditto, as **Babar and Father Christmas**, Random House (New York), 1940 . . . . . . £275/£145
ditto, Methuen (London), 1940 . . . £350/£145

'Babar' Books by Laurent de Brunhoff
Babar and that Rascal Arthur, Methuen (London), 1948 .
. . . . £250/£100
Picnic at Babar's, Methuen (London), 1950 . £250/£100
Babar's Visit to Bird Island, Methuen (London), 1952. .
. . . .£200/£75
Babar's Castle, Methuen (London), 1962. . .£175/£65
Babar's French Lessons, Cape (London), 1965 .£150/£45
Babar Goes Visiting, Methuen (London), 1969 .£125/£35
Babar Goes to America, Collins (London), 1969 .£125/£35
Babar's Fair, Methuen (London), 1969 . .£125/£35
Babar Learns to Drive, Methuen (London), 1969 .£100/£35
Babar Keeps Fit!, Methuen (London), 1970 . £65/£25
Babar at the Seaside, Methuen (London), 1971 . £65/£25
Babar in the Snow, Methuen (London), 1971 . . £45/£20
Babar the Gardener, Methuen (London), 1971 . £45/£20
Babar's Birthday Surprise, Methuen (London), 1971 £45/£20
Babar's Day Out, Methuen (London), 1971 . . £45/£20
Babar and the Christmas Tree, Methuen (London), 1972 .
. . . . £35/£15
Babar and the Doctor, Methuen (London), 1972 . £35/£10
Babar and the Professor, Methuen (London), 1972 £35/£10
Babar Goes Camping, Methuen (London), 1972 . £35/£10
Babar and the Artist, Methuen (London), 1972 . £35/£10
Babar on the Secret Planet, Methuen (London), 1973 . .
. . . . £35/£10
Babar the Cook, Methuen (London), 1973 . . £25/£5
Babar the Musician, Methuen (London), 1973 . £25/£5
Babar the Pilot, Methuen (London), 1973 . . £25/£5
Babar the Sportsman, Methuen (London), 1973 . £25/£5
Babar and the Wully-Wully, Methuen (London), 1977. .
. . . . £25/£5
Babar's Mystery, Methuen (London), 1979 . . £25/£5
Babar and the Ghost, Methuen (London), 1981 . £15/£5
Babar's ABC, Methuen (London), 1984 . . . £15/£5
Babar's Book of Colour, Methuen (London), 1985 £15/£5
Babar's Counting Book, Methuen (London), 1986 £10/£5
Babar's Little Girl, Methuen (London), 1988 . £10/£5
Babar's Busy Week, Methuen (London), 1990 . £10/£5
Babar's Battle, Methuen (London), 1992 . . £10/£5
The Rescue of Babar, Methuen (London), 1993 . £10/£5

'Serafina' books by Laurent de Brunhoff
Serafina the Giraffe, Methuen (London), 1964 [1965] . .
. . . .£100/£25

Serafina's Lucky Find, Methuen (London), 1967 . £75/£20
Captain Serafina, Methuen (London), 1969 . . £65/£20

BILL BRYSON
(b.1951)

Bill Bryson, O.B.E., is a best-selling American author of humorous works on travel, as well as books on the English language. He was a resident of North Yorkshire, England, for many years before moving to Norfolk in 2003.

Travel Books
The Palace Under the Alps and Over 200 Other Unusual, Unspoiled, and Infrequently Visited Spots in 16 European Countries, Congdon & Weed (New York), 1985. £100/£15
The Lost Continent: Travels in Small-Town America, Secker & Warburg (London), 1989. . . . £50/£10
ditto, Harper & Row (New York), 1989 . . £50/£10
Neither Here Nor There: Travels in Europe, Secker & Warburg (London), 1991 . . . . . £50/£10
ditto, Morrow (New York), 1992 . . . . £50/£10
Notes from a Small Island, Doubleday (London), 1995 .
. . . . £15/£5
ditto, Morrow (New York), 1995 . . . . £15/£5
A Walk in the Woods: Rediscovering America on the Appalachian Trail, Doubleday (London), 1997 . £10/£5
ditto, Broadway Books (New York), 1998 . . £10/£5
Notes from a Big Country, Doubleday (London), 1998 .
. . . . £10/£5
ditto, as **I'm A Stranger Here Myself: Notes on Returning to America after Twenty Years Away**, Broadway Books (New York), 1999 . . . . . . £10/£5
Down Under, Doubleday (London), 2000 . £10/£5
ditto, as **In a Sunburned Country**, Broadway Books (New York), 2000 . . . . £10/£5
Bill Bryson's African Diary, Doubleday (London), 2002 .
. . . . £10/£5
ditto, Broadway Books (New York), 2002 . . £10/£5

Language Books
The Penguin Dictionary of Troublesome Words, Allen Lane (London), 1984 (edited by Bryson) . . . . £15/£5
ditto, as **The Facts on File Dictionary of Troublesome Words**, Facts on File (New York), 1984. . . £15/£5
ditto, as **Troublesome Words**, Viking (London), 1997 (revised) . . . . £10/£5
ditto, as **Bryson's Dictionary of Troublesome Words**, Broadway Books (New York), 2002 . . £10/£5
The Mother Tongue: English and How it Got That Way, Hamish Hamilton (London), 1990 . . . . £35/£10
ditto, Morrow (New York), 1990 . . . . £35/£10
Made in America: An Informal History of the English Language in the United States, Secker & Warburg (London), 1994 . . . . £45/£10
ditto, Morrow (New York), 1994 . . . . £45/£10

Science
A Short History of Nearly Everything, Doubleday (London), 2003 . . . . £10/£5
ditto, Broadway (New York), 2003 . . . . £10/£5

Memoir
The Life and Times of the Thunderbolt Kid, Doubleday
(London), 2006 . . . . £10/£5
ditto, Broadway Books (New York), 2006 . . £10/£5

Biography
Shakespeare: The World as Stage, HarperCollins (London),
2007 . . . . £10/£5
ditto, Atlas Books/HarperCollins (New York), 2007 £10/£5

JOHN BUCHAN

(b.1875 d.1940)

Buchan was a prolific Scottish writer whose talents ranged
across novels, biographies, essays and poetry. Buchan's
'Richard Hannay' mystery novels are still popular, and his
historical romances have attracted much praise. *The Thirty-
Nine Steps* became famous when it was filmed by Alfred
Hitchcock.

Historical Romances
*Sir Quixote of the Moors: Being Some Account of an
Episode in the Life of the Sieur de Rohaine*, Fisher Unwin
(London), 1895 . . . . £450
ditto, Henry Holt and Co (New York), 1895 . . . £100
John Burnet of Barns, John Lane (London), 1898 . £200
Grey Weather, Moorland Tales, John Lane (London), 1899
. . . . £250
A Lost Lady of Old Years: A Romance, John Lane
(London), 1899 . . . . £250
Salute to Adventurers, Nelson (London), [1915] . £100
ditto, Doran (New York), 1915 . . . . . £65
The Path of the King, Hodder & Stoughton (London),
[1921] . . . . £400/£50
ditto, Doran (New York), 1921 . . . . £125/£30
Midwinter, Hodder & Stoughton (London), [1923] £250/£45
ditto, Doran (New York), 1923 . . . . £200/£35
Witch Wood, Hodder & Stoughton (London), 1927 £300/£50
ditto, Houghton Mifflin (Boston), 1927 . . £100/£20
The Blanket of the Dark, Hodder & Stoughton (London),
1931 . . . . £125/£25
ditto, Houghton Mifflin (Boston), 1931 . . £50/£15
The Free Fishers, Hodder & Stoughton (London), 1934 .
. . . . £125/£25
ditto, Houghton Mifflin (Boston), 1934 . . . £50/£15

The 'Richard Hannay' Books
The Thirty-Nine Steps, Blackwood (Edinburgh and
London), 1915 . . . . . £10,000/£300
ditto, Doran (New York), 1915 . . . . . £200
Greenmantle, Hodder & Stoughton (London), 1916 .
. . . . £5,000/£125
ditto, Doran (New York), 1916 . . . . . £65
Mr Standfast, Hodder & Stoughton (London), 1918 .
. . . . £2,000/£150
ditto, Doran (New York), 1919 . . . . . £75
The Three Hostages, Hodder & Stoughton (London), [1924]
. . . . £1,000/£25
ditto, Houghton Mifflin (Boston), 1924 . £125/£20
The Courts of the Morning, Hodder & Stoughton (London),
1929 . . . . £350/£50
ditto, Houghton Mifflin (Boston), 1929 . . £75/£15

The Island of Sheep, Hodder & Stoughton (London), 1936.
. . . . £100/£10

The 'Edward Leithen' Books
The Power House, Blackwood (Edinburgh and London),
1916 . . . . £100
ditto, Doran (New York), 1916 . . . . . £75
John MacNab, Hodder & Stoughton (London), [1925]. .
. . . . £300/£65
ditto, Houghton Mifflin (Boston), 1925 . . £200/£45
The Dancing Floor, Hodder & Stoughton (London), [1926]
. . . . £250/£45
ditto, Houghton Mifflin (Boston), 1926 . . £150/£35
The Runagates Club and Other Stories, Hodder &
Stoughton (London), 1928 . . . . £250/£50
ditto, Houghton Mifflin (Boston), 1928 . . £125/£30
The Gap in the Curtain, Hodder & Stoughton (London),
1932 . . . . £250/£45
ditto, Houghton Mifflin (Boston), 1932 . . £75/£20
Sick Heart River, Hodder & Stoughton (London), 1941 .
. . . . £75/£15
ditto, as *Mountain Meadow*, Houghton Mifflin (Boston),
1941 . . . . £50/£10

The 'Dickson McCunn' Books
Huntingtower, Hodder & Stoughton (London), 1922 . .
. . . . £300/£50
ditto, Doran (New York), 1916 . . . . £250/£35
Castle Gay, Hodder & Stoughton (London), 1930 . £200/£40
ditto, Houghton Mifflin (Boston), 1930 . . £100/£30
The House of the Four Winds, Hodder & Stoughton
(London), 1935 . . . . . . £200/£30
ditto, Houghton Mifflin (Boston), 1935 . . £100/£30

Contemporary Adventures
The Half-Hearted, Isbister (London), 1900 . . . £250
ditto, Houghton Mifflin (Boston), 1928 . . £50/£15
The Watcher by the Threshold and Other Tales, Blackwood
(Edinburgh and London), 1902 . . . . £250
ditto, Doran (New York), 1918 . . . . . £250
Prester John, Nelson (London), 1910 . . . . £150
ditto, Doran (New York), 1910 . . . . . £125
A Prince of the Captivity, Hodder & Stoughton (London),
1933 . . . . £125/£15
ditto, Houghton Mifflin (Boston), 1933 . . £50/£15

Miscellaneous
A Lodge in the Wilderness, Blackwood (Edinburgh and
London), 1906 . . . . £450
The Moon Endureth, Tales and Fancies, Blackwood
(Edinburgh and London), 1912 . . . . £250
ditto, Sturgis & Walton (New York), 1912 . . £125
The Island of Sheep (by 'Cadmus & Harmonia'), Hodder &
Stoughton (London), 1919 . . . . . £50
ditto, Houghton Mifflin (Boston), 1920 . . £150/£45

Omnibus Editions
The Four Adventures of Richard Hannay, Hodder &
Stoughton (London), 1930 . . . . £100/£15
The Adventures of Sir Edward Leithen, Hodder &
Stoughton (London), 1933 . . . . £65/£10
Four Tales, Hodder & Stoughton (London), 1936 . £65/£10
The Adventures of Dickson McCunn, Hodder & Stoughton
(London), 1937 . . . . £50/£10

A Five-Fold Salute to Adventure, Hodder & Stoughton (London), 1939 . . . . . . £65/£10

Adventures of Richard Hannay, Houghton Mifflin (Boston), 1939 . . . . £35/£5

Adventurers All, Houghton Mifflin (Boston), 1942 £100/£20

Poetry

Sir Walter Raleigh, Blackwell (Oxford, UK), 1897 (mustard cloth with black lettering) £200

The Pilgrim Fathers, Blackwell (Oxford, UK), 1898 (wraps) £200

Poems, Scots and English, T.C. & E.C. Jack (Edinburgh and London), 1917 . . . . . . £75

ditto, T.C. & E.C. Jack (Edinburgh and London), 1917 (50 signed, numbered large paper copies) . . . £750

Children's Titles

Sir Walter Raleigh, T. Nelson & Sons (London), [1911] £125

ditto, Henry Holt (New York), 1911 . . . . £45

The Magic Walking Stick, Hodder & Stoughton (London), 1932 . . . . £100/£20

ditto, Houghton Mifflin (Boston), 1932 . . £75/£20

The Long Traverse, Hodder & Stoughton (London), 1941 . . . . £65/£15

Non-Fiction

Scholar Gipsies, John Lane (London), 1896 . . £250

ditto, Macmillan (New York), 1896 . . . £175

Brasenose College, F.E. Robinson (London), 1898 . £175

The African Colony, Blackwood (Edinburgh and London), 1903 . . . . £150

The Law Relating to Taxation of Foreign Income ..., Stevens and Sons (London), 1905 . . . . £300

Some Eighteenth Century Byways and other essays, Blackwood (Edinburgh and London), 1908 . . £125

Nine Brasenose Worthies, Clarendon Press (Oxford, UK), 1909 . . . . £175

What the Home Rule Bill Means, Smythe, 1912 . £250

The Marquis of Montrose, T. Nelson & Sons (London), 1913 . . . . £45

ditto, Scribner's (New York), 1913 . . . . £35

Andrew Jameson, Lord Ardwall, Blackwood (Edinburgh and London), 1913 . . . . £65

Britain's War By Land, O.U.P. (Oxford, UK), 1915 . £350

Nelson's History of the War, T. Nelson & Sons (London), [1915-1919] (24 vols) £125

ditto, as *A History of the Great War*, Nelson (London), 1921-22 (4 vols, condensed version of the above) . £60

ditto, Nelson (London), 1921-22 (500 numbered, signed copies, 4 vols) £150

ditto, Houghton Mifflin (Boston), 1923 (4 vols) . £60

The Achievement of France, Methuen (London), 1915. £250

Ordeal by Marriage, Clay (London), 1915 . . £500

The Future of the War, Boyles, Sons & Watchurst, 1916 . . . . £175

The Purpose of War, Dent (London), 1916 . . £175

The Battle of Jutland, Nelson (London), 1916 (stapled wraps) £65

The Battle of The Somme, First Phase, Nelson (London), 1916 . . . . £75

The Battle of The Somme, Second Phase, Nelson (London), 1917 . . . . £75

The Battle of The Somme, Doran (New York), 1917 . £75

The Battle-Honours of Scotland, Outram (Glasgow), 1919. . . . . £125

These for Remembrance, Reminiscences of Men Killed in the War, Medici (London), 1919 . . . . £500

The History of the South African Forces in France, T. Nelson & Sons (London), [1920] . . . £165/£75

Francis and Riversdale Grenfell: A Memoir, T. Nelson & Sons (London), [1920] . . . . . £100/£45

A Book of Escapes and Hurried Journeys, T. Nelson & Sons (London), [1922] . . . . . £150/£45

The Last Secrets: the final mysteries of exploration, T. Nelson & Sons (London), [1923]. . . . £150/£35

ditto, Houghton Mifflin (Boston), 1924 . . . £45/£10

Days to Remember: the British Empire in the Great War, T. Nelson & Sons (London), 1923 (with Henry Newbolt) . . . . £150/£35

Some Notes on Walter Scott, English Association/O.U.P. (London/Oxford), 1924 (stitched wraps) . . . £15

Lord Minto: A Memoir, T. Nelson & Sons (London), [1924] . . . . £75/£20

Two Ordeals of Democracy, Houghton Mifflin (Boston), 1925 . . . . £125/£45

The Man and the Book: Sir Walter Scott, Nelson (London), 1925 . . . . £100/£30

The History of the Royal Scots Fusiliers, 1678-1918, T. Nelson & Sons (London), [1925] . . . £145/£45

The Fifteenth (Scottish) Division, Blackwood (Edinburgh and London), 1926 (with J. Stewart) . . . £125/£45

Homilies and Recreations, T. Nelson & Sons (London), [1926] . . . . £125/£35

ditto, T. Nelson & Sons (London), [1926] (large paper edition, 200 signed and numbered copies) . . £200

Montrose, T. Nelson & Sons (London), [1928] . £75/£20

ditto, Houghton Mifflin (Boston), 1928 . . £45/£15

The Causal and the Casual in History, C.U.P. (Cambridge, UK), 1929 . . . . £125/£35

Montrose and Leadership, O.U.P. (Oxford, UK), 1930 . . . . £145/£40

The Kirk in Scotland, 1560-1929, Hodder & Stoughton (London), [1930] (with George Adam Smith) . £75/£20

Lord Rosebery, British Academy/Milford (London), 1930 . . . . £125/£30

The Novel and the Fairy Tale, English Association (London), 1931 (stapled wraps) £15

Sir Walter Scott, Cassell (London), [1932] . £45/£10

ditto, Coward-McCann (New York), [1932] . £35/£10

Julius Caesar, Peter Davies (London), 1932 . £45/£10

Andrew Lang and the Border, O.U.P. (Oxford, UK), 1933 . . . . £100/£20

The Massacre of Glencoe, Peter Davies (London), 1933 . . . . £75/£15

ditto, Putnam (New York), 1933. . . . . £65/£15

The Margins of Life, Birkbeck College (London), 1933 . . . . £145/£45

Gordon at Khartoum, Peter Davies (London), 1934 £125/£25

Oliver Cromwell, Hodder & Stoughton (London), [1934] . . . . £100/£25

ditto, Houghton Mifflin (Boston), 1934 . . £85/£20

The King's Grace: 1910-35, Hodder & Stoughton (London), [1935] . . . . £40/£10

ditto, Hodder & Stoughton (London), 1935 (large paper edition, 500 numbered, signed copies) . . . £75

Men and Deeds, Peter Davies (London), 1935 . £45/£15

Augustus, Hodder & Stoughton (London), 1937 . £45/£15

ditto, Houghton Mifflin (Boston), 1937   .   .   . £40/£10
Naval Episodes of the Great War, Nelson (London), 1938 .
.   .   .   .   £50/£15
The Interpreter's House, Hodder & Stoughton (London),
1938   .   .   .   . £45/£10
Unchanging Germany, Nelson (London), 1939   . £100/£30
Memory Hold-the-Door, Hodder & Stoughton, 1940 £15/£5
Comments and Characters, T. Nelson & Sons (London),
[1940]   .   .   .   . £40/£10
Canadian Occasions, Hodder & Stoughton (London), [1940]
.   .   .   . £35/£10
The Clearing House: a John Buchan Anthology, Hodder &
Stoughton (London), 1946   .   .   .   . £20/£5
Life's Adventure: a John Buchan Anthology, St Hugh's
Press/Hodder & Stoughton (London), 1947 .   . £15/£5

ANTHONY BUCKERIDGE

(b.1912 d.2004)

Anthony Buckeridge was a teacher whose first successes
were radio plays for adults. The immortal Jennings
appeared later on, at first in tales told to his own pupils
based on an old schoolfellow, Diarmid Jennings. These
stories then surfaced as a series of radio plays for the
BBC's *Children's Hour*, and then as a series of children's
novels. He was awarded the O.B.E. in 2003.

'Jennings' Books
Jennings Goes to School, Collins (London), 1950. £125/£15
Jennings Follows a Clue, Collins (London), 1951. £100/£15
Jennings' Little Hut, Collins (London), 1951 .   £75/£15
Jennings and Darbishire, Collins (London), 1952.   £65/£15
Jennings' Diary, Collins (London), 1953.   .   . £65/£15
According to Jennings, Collins (London), 1954   . £50/£15
Our Friend Jennings, Collins (London), 1955   . £50/£15
Thanks to Jennings, Collins (London), 1957 .   . £45/£15
Take Jennings, for Instance, Collins (London), 1958 .   .
.   .   .   . £45/£10
Jennings, as Usual, Collins (London), 1959 .   . £45/£10
The Trouble with Jennings, Collins (London), 1960 £40/£10
Just Like Jennings, Collins (London), 1961   .   . £40/£10
Leave It to Jennings, Collins (London), 1963.   . £40/£10
Jennings, of Course!, Collins (London), 1964   . £40/£10
Especially Jennings!, Collins (London), 1965   . £40/£10
A Bookful of Jennings!, Collins (London), 1966 (anthology)
.   .   .   . £100/£20
ditto, as *The Best of Jennings*, Collins (London), 1972   .
.   .   .   . £35/£10
Jennings Abounding, Collins (London), 1967   . £40/£10
Jennings in Particular, Collins (London), 1968   . £40/£10
Trust Jennings!, Collins (London), 1969.   .   . £40/£10
The Jennings Report, Collins (London), 1970   . £75/£15
Typically Jennings!, Collins (London), 1971 .   . £45/£10
Speaking of Jennings, Collins (London), 1973   . £40/£10
Jennings at Large, Armada (London), 1977 (pbk).   . £15
ditto, Severn House (London), 1980   .   .   . £35/£10
Jennings Abounding, A Comedy with Music, French
(London), 1980 (wraps) £5
Jennings Again!, Macmillan (London), 1991 .   . £20/£5
That's Jennings, Macmillan (London), 1994 .   . £20/£5
Jennings Sounds The Alarm: Seven Plays for Radio, David
Schutte (Petersfield, Hampshire), 1999 (pbk)   .   . £10

ditto, David Schutte (Petersfield, Hampshire), 1999 (100
signed, numberd copies; pbk) £35
Jennings Breaks the Record: Seven More Plays for Radio,
David Schutte (Petersfield, Hampshire), 2000 (pbk)   . £10
ditto, David Schutte (Petersfield, Hampshire), 2000 (100
signed, numbered copies; pbk) £35
*Jennings Joins the Search Party: Plays for Radio Volume
3*, David Schutte (Petersfield, Hampshire), 2001 (pbk)   £10
ditto, David Schutte (Petersfield, Hampshire), 2001 (100
signed, numbered copies; pbk) £35
Jennings To the Rescue: Plays for Radio Volume 4, David
Schutte (Petersfield, Hampshire), 2002 (pbk)   .   . £10
ditto, David Schutte (Petersfield, Hampshire), 2002 (100
signed, numbered copies; pbk) £35
*Jennings And the Roman Remains: Plays for Radio
Volume 5*, David Schutte (Petersfield, Hampshire), 2002
(pbk) £10
ditto, David Schutte (Petersfield, Hampshire), 2002 (100
signed, numbered copies; pbk) £35

'Rex Milligan' Books
Rex Milligan's Busy Term, Lutterworth Press (London),
1953   .   .   .   . £40/£10
Rex Milligan Raises the Roof, Lutterworth Press (London),
1955   .   .   .   . £40/£10
Rex Milligan Holds Forth, Lutterworth Press (London), 1955
.   .   .   . £40/£10
Rex Milligan Reporting, Lutterworth Press (London), 1961
.   .   .   . £40/£10
Introducing Rex Milligan, David Schutte (Petersfield,
Hampshire), 2002 (pbk) £5
ditto, David Schutte (Petersfield, Hampshire), 2002 (100
signed copies; pbk) £25

Others
*A Funny Thing Happened! The First Adventure of the
Blighs*, Lutterworth Press (London), [1953] .   . £40/£10
While I Remember, Romansmead, 1999 (100 copies; pbk) .
.   .   .   . £15
ditto, David Schutte (Petersfield, Hampshire), 2002   . £5

CHARLES BUKOWSKI

(b.1920 d.1994)

Henry Charles Bukowski was an American poet and
novelist, influenced by the geography and atmosphere of
his home city of Los Angeles. A very prolific and
influential author and poet, his style is frequently imitated.
The majority of Black Sparrow Press hardbacks were
issued with unprinted d/ws.

Poetry
20 Tanks from Kasseldown, Black Sun Press (Washington,
DC), 1946 (broadside; 1,000 copies; issued in *Portfolio III*)
.   .   .   . £400
His Wife, The Painter, Hearse Press (Eureka, CA), 1960
(broadside; 50 copies issued from a total of 201) .   £2,000
Flower, Fist and Bestial Wail, Hearse Press (Eureka, CA),
1960 (200 copies; stapled wraps)   .   .   . £2,500
Longshot Poems for Broke Players, 7 Poets Press (New
York), 1962 (c.200 copies; wraps)   .   .   . £1,250

Poems and Drawings, *Epos* (Crescent City, FL), 1962 (*Epos*
extra issue, 1962; stapled wraps)   .   .   .   £1,000
Run with the Hunted, Midwest Press (Chicago IL), 1962
(c.300 copies; stapled wraps) £1,250
Penny Poetry: The Priest and the Matador, [not known]
1962 (broadside) £350
**It Catches My Heart in its Hands: New and Selected
Poems, 1955-1963**, Loujon Press (New Orleans LA), 1963
(777 copies; wraps) £600
The Paper on the Floor, Hearse Press (Eureka, CA), 1964
[printed in 1960] (broadside; 150 copies; issued in portfolio
Coffin I). £650
The Old Man on the Corner, Hearse Press (Eureka, CA),
1964 (broadside; 150 copies; issued in portfolio *Coffin I*) .
.   .   .   . £650
Waste Basket, Hearse Press (Eureka, CA), 1964 (broadside;
150 copies; issued in portfolio *Coffin I*).   .   . £650
Crucifix in a Deathhand: New Poems, 1963-1965, Lyle
Stuart/Loujon Press (New Orleans LA), 1965 (wraps) £200
ditto, Lyle Stuart/Loujon Press (New Orleans LA), 1965 (12
specially inscribed copies with saffron covers)   . £800
Cold Dogs in the Courtyard, Leterary Times-Cyfoeth
(Chicago IL), 1965 (c.500 copies; stapled wraps)   . £300
**Confessions of a Man Insane Enough to Live with Beasts:
Fragments from a Disorder**, Mimeo Press (Bensenville
IL), 1965 (500 copies; stapled wraps)   .   .   . £250
ditto, Mimeo Press (Bensenville IL), 1965 (25 copies with
autographed drawing by author)   .   .   .   £1,250
True Story, Philip Klein for the Black Sparrow Press (Los
Angeles), 1966 (broadside; 30 copies)   .   .   £3,000
On Going Out to Get the Mail, Philip Klein for the Black
Sparrow Press (Los Angeles), 1966 (broadside; 30 copies)
.   .   .   . £3,000
To Kiss the Worms Goodnight, Philip Klein for the Black
Sparrow Press (Los Angeles), 1966 (broadside; 30 copies)
.   .   .   . £3,000
The Genius of the Crowd, 7 Flowers Press (Cleveland OH),
1966 (103 copies; wraps) £1,000
The Girls. For the Mercy-Mongers, Philip Klein for the
Black Sparrow Press (Los Angeles), 1966 (broadside; 30
copies) £3,000
All the Assholes in the World and Mine, Open Skull Press
(Bensenville, IL), 1966 (400 copies; stapled wraps)   . £350
The Flower Lover. I Met a Genius, Philip Klein for the
Black Sparrow Press (Los Angeles), 1966 (broadside; 30
copies) £3,000
2 Poems, Black Sparrow Press (Los Angeles, CA), 1967
(111 copies; wraps) £500
**The Curtains Are Waving and People Walk Through the
Afternoon Here in Berlin and in New York City and in
Mexico**, Black Sparrow Press (Los Angeles, CA), 1967
(125 copies; wraps) £650
At Terror Street and Agony Way, Black Sparrow Press (Los
Angeles, CA), 1968 (765 unsigned copies; pbk)   . £175
ditto, Black Sparrow Press (Los Angeles, CA), 1968 (90
hardback copies). £400
ditto, Black Sparrow Press (Los Angeles, CA), 1968 (75
signed, numbered hardback copies with artwork).   £1,500
Poems Written Before Jumping Out of an 8 Story Window,
Poetry X/Change/Litmus (Glendale CA), 1968 (c.400
unsigned copies; stapled wraps)   .   .   .   £125
ditto, Poetry X/Change/Litmus (Glendale CA), 1968 (25
signed copies with drawings)   .   .   .   £1,000

A Bukowski Sampler, Quixote Press (Madison, WI), 1969
(c.400 copies; stapled wraps) £75
Charles Bukowski, Philip Lamantia, Harold Norse,
Penguin (Harmondsworth, Middlesex), 1969 (Penguin
Modern Poets, no. 13)   .   .   .   .   . £45/£20
ditto, Penguin (Harmondsworth, Middlesex), 1969 (pbk) £10
The Nature of the Threat and What to Do, Nevada/Tattoo
Press (San Francisco, CA), 1969 (broadside; issued in
portfolio *Peace Amongst the Arts*) £75
If We Take, Black Sparrow Press (Los Angeles, CA), 1970
[Dec. 1969] (350 unsigned copies; sewn wraps)   . £40
ditto, Black Sparrow Press (Los Angeles, CA), 1970 [Dec
1969] (101 signed copies; wraps)   .   .   . £125
The Days Run Away Like Wild Horses Over the Hills,
Black Sparrow Press (Los Angeles CA), 1969 [Dec 1969]
(pbk) £45
ditto, Black Sparrow Press (Los Angeles CA), 1969 [Dec
1969] (250 signed, numbered hardback copies)   . £450
ditto, Black Sparrow Press (Los Angeles CA), 1969 [Dec
1969] (50 signed hardback copies with artwork) . £3,000
Fire Station, Capricorn Press (Santa Barbara CA), 1970 (100
hardback copies). £450
ditto, Capricorn Press (Santa Barbara CA), 1970 (100 pbk
copies) £100
Another Academy, Black Sparrow Press (Los Angeles CA),
1970 (broadside; 250 signed, numbered copies)   . £75
Chilled Green, Alternative Press (Detroit), 1970 (postcard;
c.400 copies) £30
An Answer to a Critic of Sorts, [s.l., s.n., ca. 1970]
(broadside) £75
Mockingbird Wish Me Luck, Black Sparrow Press (Los
Angeles CA), 1972 (wraps) £20
ditto, Black Sparrow Press (Los Angeles CA), 1972 (250
signed hardback copies) £250
ditto, Black Sparrow Press (Los Angeles CA), 1972 (50
signed hardback copies with artwork)   .   .   £2,000
Me and You Sometimes Love Poems, Kisskill Press (Los
Angeles, CA), 1972 (c.100 copies; by Bukowski and Linda
King) £250
While the Music Played, Black Sparrow Press (Los Angeles,
CA), 1973 (958 copies; stapled wraps)   .   .   . £20
Love Poems to Marina, Black Sparrow Press (Los Angeles,
CA), 1973 (broadside) £20
ditto, Black Sparrow Press (Los Angeles, CA), 1973
(broadside; 100 signed copies). £150
**Burning in Water, Drowning In Flame: Selected Poems
1955-1973**, Black Sparrow Press (Los Angeles, CA), 1974
(wraps) £15
ditto, Black Sparrow Press (Los Angeles, CA), 1974 (221
hardback copies) £75
ditto, Black Sparrow Press (Los Angeles, CA), 1974 (300
signed, numbered hardback copies).   .   .   . £350
ditto, Black Sparrow Press (Los Angeles, CA), 1974 (50
signed, numbered hardback copies with artwork).   £2,000
Africa, Paris, Greece, Black Sparrow Press (Los Angeles,
CA), 1975 (unsigned copies; stapled wraps).   .   . £20
ditto, Black Sparrow Press (Los Angeles, CA), 1975 (20
signed copies) £200
86'd, Nitty-gritty, Goldermood Rainbow Press (Pasco, WA),
1975 (broadside; unsigned copies) £40
ditto, Goldermood Rainbow Press (Pasco, WA), 1975
(broadside; 50 signed copies) £125
Weather Report, Pomegranate Press (North Cambridge,
MA), 1975 (broadside; 125 signed, numbered copies) £225

ditto, Pomegranate Press (North Cambridge, MA), 1975 (broadside; 20 numbered unsigned copies) . . . £175

Winter, Ravine Press (Chicago), 1975 (broadside; 199 signed copies; silkscreen design by Darsie Sanders) . £225

Face of a Political Candidate on a Street Billboard, Old Marble Press [Black Sparrow Press (Santa Barbara, CA)], 1975 (broadside) £40

ditto, Old Marble Press, Press [Black Sparrow Press (Santa Barbara, CA)], 1975 (broadside; 50 signed copies) . £150

Tough Company, by Bukowski and *The Last Poem,* by Diana Wakowski, Black Sparrow Press (Santa Barbara, CA), 1976 (sewn wraps) £15

ditto, Black Sparrow Press (Santa Barbara, CA), 1976 (150 signed, numbered copies) £125

ditto, Black Sparrow Press (Santa Barbara, CA), 1976 (26 signed, lettered copies) . . . . £300/£200

Scarlet, Black Sparrow Press (Santa Barbara CA), 1976 (140 signed, numbered hardback copies) £250

ditto, Black Sparrow Press (Santa Barbara CA), 1976 (40 signed, numbered hardback copies with artwork). £1,250

462-0614, Second Coming Press (San Francisco, CA), 1976 (broadside) £30

If I Suffer at This Typewriter Think How I Feel Among the Lettuce-pickers of Solinas?, Realities Library (?), 1976 (business card sized broadside) £25

Art, Black Sparrow Press (Santa Barbara CA), 1977 (wraps) £20

ditto, Black Sparrow Press (Santa Barbara CA), 1977 (100 signed, numbered copies) £225

ditto, Black Sparrow Press (Santa Barbara CA), 1977 (26 signed, lettered copies, slipcase) . . . £300/£250

Maybe Tomorrow, Black Sparrow Press (Santa Barbara CA), 1977 (stapled wraps) £10

ditto, Black Sparrow Press (Santa Barbara CA), 1977 (20 copies bound in cloth with a paper label on the front cover and with a signed original oil painting by Bukowski bound in) £2,000

What They Want, Maurice Neville (Santa Barbara CA), 1977 (wraps). £10

ditto, Maurice Neville (Santa Barbara CA), 1977 (75 signed copies) £65

Love is a Dog from Hell: Poems 1974-77, Black Sparrow Press (Santa Barbara CA), 1977 (pbk) . . . £15

ditto, Black Sparrow Press (Santa Barbara CA), 1977 (hardback copies) £100

ditto, Black Sparrow Press (Santa Barbara CA), 1977 (300 signed, numbered hardback copies). . . . £250

ditto, Black Sparrow Press (Santa Barbara CA), 1977 (75 signed, numbered hardback copies with artwork). £2,000

You Kissed Lilly, Black Sparrow Press (Santa Barbara CA), 1978 (200 signed, numbered copies) . . £250/£200

ditto, Black Sparrow Press (Santa Barbara CA), 1978 (75 signed, numbered copies with artwork) . . £350/£300

We'll Take Them, Black Sparrow Press (Santa Barbara CA), 1978 (wraps). £10

ditto, Black Sparrow Press (Santa Barbara CA), 1978 (20 signed copies) £100

Legs, Hips, and Behind, Wormwood Review Press (Stockton, CA), 1978 (700 unsigned copies; wraps) . £75

ditto, Wormwood Review Press (Stockton, CA), 1978 (60 signed copies) £250

A Note Upon a Workshop Instructor with Tiny Hairs Under His Chin, Pomegranate Press (Cambridge, MA), 1978 (broadside; 125 signed copies) £175

A Love Poem, Black Sparrow Press (Santa Rosa CA), 1979 (900 unsigned copies; wraps) £10

ditto, Black Sparrow Press (Santa Rosa CA), 1979 (176 signed, numbered copies) . . . . £150/£100

ditto, Black Sparrow Press (Santa Rosa CA), 1979 (26 signed, lettered copies) . . . . £200/£150

Play the Piano Drunk Like a Percussion Instrument Until the Fingers Begin to Bleed a Bit, Black Sparrow Press (Santa Barbara CA), 1979 (pbk) £10

ditto, Black Sparrow Press (Santa Barbara CA), 1979 (500 hardback copies) £100

ditto, Black Sparrow Press (Santa Barbara CA), 1979 (300 signed, numbered copies) £150

ditto, Black Sparrow Press (Santa Barbara CA), 1979 (100 signed, numbered copies with a silkscreen print tipped) £300

Night Work, Toothpaste Press (West Branch, IA), 1981 (postcard) £20

Dangling in the Tournefortia, Black Sparrow Press (Santa Barbara CA), 1981 (pbk) £15

ditto, Black Sparrow Press (Santa Barbara CA), 1981 (750 hardback copies) £75

ditto, Black Sparrow Press (Santa Barbara CA), 1981 (350 signed, numbered hardback copies). . . . £150

ditto, Black Sparrow Press (Santa Barbara CA), 1981 (100 signed, numbered hardback copies with artwork). £1,000

The Last Generation, Black Sparrow Press (Santa Barbara CA), 1982 (sewn wraps) £10

ditto, Black Sparrow Press (Santa Barbara CA), 1982 (150 signed, numbered copies) £125

ditto, Black Sparrow Press (Santa Barbara CA), 1982 (26 signed, lettered copies) £175

Horsemeat, Black Sparrow Press (Santa Barbara CA), 1982 (130 signed copies; photographs by Michael Monfort) £1,000

Sparks, Black Sparrow Press (Santa Barbara CA), 1983 (stapled wraps) £10

ditto, Black Sparrow Press (Santa Barbara CA), 1983 (200 signed, numbered copies; hardback) £75

ditto, Black Sparrow Press (Santa Barbara CA), 1983 (26 signed, lettered copies; hardback) £125

Playing It Out, Toothpaste Press (West Branch, IA), 1983 (small broadside). £15

Aftermath of a Lengthy Rejection Slip, Printed by the Grenfell Press for Thomas Goff at Blackrose Editions (New York), 1983 (176 copies) £200

One for the Old Boy, Black Sparrow Press (Santa Barbara CA), 1984 (stapled wraps). £15

ditto, Black Sparrow Press (Santa Barbara CA), 1984 (200 signed, numbered copies; hardback) £75

ditto, Black Sparrow Press (Santa Barbara CA), 1984 (26 signed, lettered copies; hardback) £125

Talking to My Mailbox, Black Sparrow Press (Santa Barbara CA), 1984 (broadside) £15

ditto, Black Sparrow Press (Santa Barbara CA), 1984 (broadside; 100 signed copies). £125

War All the Time: Poems 1981-84, Black Sparrow Press (Santa Barbara CA), 1984 (pbk) £20

ditto, Black Sparrow Press (Santa Barbara CA), 1984 (500 signed hardback copies) £100

ditto, Black Sparrow Press (Santa Barbara CA), 1984 (400 signed hardback copies) £200

ditto, Black Sparrow Press (Santa Barbara CA), 1984 (26 signed, lettered hardback copies with artwork) . £1,000

Going Modern, Ruddy Duck (Fremont, CA), 1984 (suppressed and largely destroyed; unsigned and un-numbered despite colophon statement; stapled wraps) £15

Blow 6, Grey Whale Press (Portland, OR), 1984 (edited by Karol Kleinheksel; stapled wraps) £30

Alone in a Time of Armies, Black Sparrow Press (Santa Rosa CA), 1985 (stapled wraps) £15

ditto, Black Sparrow Press (Santa Rosa CA), 1985 (200 signed, numbered copies; hardback) . . . £75

ditto, Black Sparrow Press (Santa Rosa CA), 1985 (26 signed, lettered copies; hardback) . . . £150

Cornered, Burn Again Press [Black Sparrow Press] (Santa Barbara, CA), 1985 (30 signed copies; wraps) . . £750

Pig in a Pamphlet, [Harry Calhoun] Pittsburgh, 1985 (stapled wraps) £40

The Wedding, Brown Buddah Books (San Pedro, CA), 1986 (40 signed copies; photographs by Michael Montfort) .
. . . . £2,000

Gold in Your Eye, Black Sparrow Press (Santa Barbara CA) 1986 (stapled wraps) £10

ditto, Black Sparrow Press (Santa Barbara CA), 1986 (200 signed, numbered copies; hardback) . . . £75

ditto, Black Sparrow Press (Santa Barbara CA), 1986 (26 signed, lettered copies; hardback) £125

The Day It Snowed in L.A.: The Adventures of Clarence Hiram Sweetmeat, Paget Press (Sutton West, Ont. & Santa Barbara, CA), 1986 (wraps) £15

ditto, Paget Press (Sutton West, Ont. & Santa Barbara, CA), 1986 (200 signed hardback copies). . . . £150

You Get So Alone at Times that It Just Makes Sense, Black Sparrow Press (Santa Rosa CA), 1986 (pbk). . £15

ditto, Black Sparrow Press (Santa Rosa CA), 1986 (400 signed, numbered hardback copies). . . . £125

ditto, Black Sparrow Press (Santa Rosa CA), 1986 (100 signed, numbered hardback copies with signed print). £200

ditto, Black Sparrow Press (Santa Rosa CA), 1986 (26 signed, lettered hardback copies with artwork) . . £400

Relentless as the Tarantula, Planet Detroit Chapbooks (Detroit), 1986 (500 copies; stapled wraps) . . £75

Luck, Black Sparrow Press (Santa Rosa, CA), 1987 (stapled wraps) £10

ditto, Black Sparrow Press (Santa Rosa CA), 1987 (200 signed, numbered copies; hardback) . . . £65

ditto, Black Sparrow Press (Santa Rosa CA), 1987 (26 signed, lettered copies; hardback) £100

A Visitor Complains of My Disenfranchise, Illuminati (Los Angeles, CA), 1987 (225 copies; sewn wraps with a tiny doorknob affixed to the front cover) . . . £200

The Movie Critics, Black Sparrow Press (Santa Rosa, CA), 1988 (stapled wraps) £10

ditto, Black Sparrow Press (Santa Rosa CA), 1988 (200 signed, numbered copies; hardback) . . . £65

ditto, Black Sparrow Press (Santa Rosa CA), 1988 (26 signed, lettered copies; hardback) £85

The Cage, Limberlost Press (Boise, ID), 1987 (postcard issued in *A Collection of Poetry Postcards from Limberlost Press*) £25

The Roominghouse Madrigals: Early Selected Poems, 1946-1966, Black Sparrow Press (Santa Rosa CA), 1988 (stapled wraps) £10

ditto, Black Sparrow Press (Santa Rosa CA), 1988 (500 hardback copies). £75

ditto, Black Sparrow Press (Santa Rosa CA), 1988 (400 signed, numbered hardback copies). . . . £100

ditto, Black Sparrow Press (Santa Rosa CA), 1988 (150 signed, numbered hardback copies with signed print). £250

ditto, Black Sparrow Press (Santa Rosa CA), 1988 (26 signed, lettered hardback copies with signed print) . £300

Red, Burn Again Press (Hollywood, CA) [Black Sparrow Press (Santa Rosa, CA)], 1989 (50 signed copies) . £300

If You Let Them Kill You, They Will, Black Sparrow Press (Santa Rosa, CA), 1989 (stapled wraps). . . £10

ditto, Black Sparrow Press (Santa Rosa CA), 1989 (200 signed, numbered copies; hardback) . . . £65

ditto, Black Sparrow Press (Santa Rosa CA), 1989 (26 signed, lettered copies; hardback) £100

We Ain't Got No Money, Honey, But We Got Rain, Black Sparrow Press (Santa Rosa CA), 1990 (stapled wraps) £10

ditto, Black Sparrow Press (Santa Rosa CA), 1990 (200 signed, numbered copies; hardback) . . . £65

ditto, Black Sparrow Press (Santa Rosa CA), 1990 (26 signed, lettered copies; hardback) £100

Septuagenarian Stew: Stories and Poems, Black Sparrow Press (Santa Rosa CA), 1990 (pbk). . . . £10

ditto, Black Sparrow Press (Santa Rosa CA), 1990 (hardback) £40

ditto, Black Sparrow Press (Santa Rosa CA), 1990 (500 signed, numbered hardback copies). . . . £100

ditto, Black Sparrow Press (Santa Rosa CA), 1990 (225 signed, numbered hardback copies with signed print). £150

Not Quite Bernadette, Graybeard Press (Compton, CA), 1990 (75 signed, numbered copies; etchings by James W. Johnson) £500

ditto, Graybeard Press (Compton, CA), 1990 (15 numbered copies signed by Bukowski and Johnson with drawing by Johnson, and two extra etchings enclosed in a secret pocket in the back) £1,500

This, Burn Again Press (Andernach, CA) [Black Sparrow Press (Santa Rosa, CA)], 1990 (50 signed copies, boards).
. . . . £300

Darkness & Ice, Burn Again Press (Arctic Circle) [Black Sparrow Press (Santa Rosa, CA)], 1990 (50 signed copies)
. . . . £300

Upon This Most Delicate Profession, Second Coming (San Francisco, CA), 1990 (broadside issued with *Second Coming*, vol. 18, no. 7.) £50

In the Morning and at Night, Black Sparrow Press (Santa Rosa, CA), 1991 (stapled wraps) £10

ditto, Black Sparrow Press (Santa Rosa CA), 1991 (200 signed, numbered copies; hardback) . . . £65

ditto, Black Sparrow Press (Santa Rosa CA), 1991 (26 signed, lettered copies; hardback) £100

In the Shadow of the Rose, Black Sparrow Press (Santa Rosa CA), 1991 (750 signed, numbered copies) . £125

ditto, Black Sparrow Press (Santa Rosa CA), 1991 (26 signed lettered). £250

A Couple of Winos, Fantagraphics Books (Seattle, WA), 1991 (with Matthias Schultheiss; wraps) . . . £25

The Bluebird, Published for the friends of the Black Sparrow Press (Santa Rosa, CA), 1991 (broadside) . £15

Husk, Beat Scene (Binley Woods, North Coventry, CA), 1991 (broadside issued with *Beat Scene*, no. 15) . £20

Pastoral, Limberlost Press (Boise, ID), 1991 (broadside) £25

Now, Black Sparrow Press (Santa Rosa, CA), 1992 (stapled wraps) £10

ditto, Black Sparrow Press (Santa Rosa CA), 1992 (200 signed, numbered copies; hardback) . . . £65 *ditto*, Black Sparrow Press (Santa Rosa CA), 1992 (26 signed, lettered copies; hardback) £100

The Last Night of the Earth Poems, Black Sparrow Press (Santa Rosa CA), 1992 (pbk) £15

ditto, Black Sparrow Press (Santa Rosa CA), 1992 (hardback) £75

ditto, Black Sparrow Press (Santa Rosa CA), 1992 (750 signed, numbered hardback copies). £100

ditto, Black Sparrow Press (Santa Rosa CA), 1992 (251 signed, numbered hardback copies with silkscreen print) £150

Three Poems, Black Sparrow Press (Santa Rosa, CA), 1992 (stapled wraps) £10

ditto, Black Sparrow Press (Santa Rosa, CA), 1992 (103 signed hardback copies) £100

Those Marvelous Lunches, Black Sparrow Press (Santa Rosa, CA), 1993 (stapled wraps) £10

ditto, Black Sparrow Press (Santa Rosa CA), 1993 (200 signed, numbered copies; hardback) £65

ditto, Black Sparrow Press (Santa Rosa CA), 1993 (26 signed, lettered copies; hardback) £100

Run With the Hunted: A Charles Bukowski Reader, HarperCollins (New York), 1993 (edited by John Martin). . . . . £25/£10

ditto, Black Sparrow Press (Santa Rosa CA)/HarperCollins (New York), 1993 (300 signed, numbered copies, slipcase) £125

ditto, Black Sparrow Press (Santa Rosa CA)/HarperCollins (New York), 1993 (26 signed, lettered copies, slipcase) £200

ditto, Eden Grove Editions (London), 1994 (pbk) . . £5

Between the Earthquake, the Volcano and the Leopard, Black Sparrow Press (Santa Rosa, CA), 1994 (stapled wraps) £10

ditto, Black Sparrow Press (Santa Rosa CA), 1994 (200 signed, numbered copies; hardback) £50

ditto, Black Sparrow Press (Santa Rosa CA), 1994 (26 signed, lettered copies; hardback) £75

French Quarter, Perdido Press (New Orleans), 1994 (broadside) £10

Confessions of a Coward, Black Sparrow Press (Santa Rosa, CA), 1995 (stapled wraps). £10

ditto, Black Sparrow Press (Santa Rosa CA), 1995 (200 signed, numbered copies; hardback) £45

ditto, Black Sparrow Press (Santa Rosa CA), 1995 (26 signed, lettered copies; hardback) £65

Heat Wave, Black Sparrow Press (Santa Rosa, CA), 1995 (74 page folio with compact disc of Bukowski reading poetry mounted on the inside front cover; a tray, built into the book, holds 15 serigraphs by Ken Price; the entire portfolio is housed in a polished plexi slipcase; 170 copies signed by Price) £250

ditto, Black Sparrow Press (Santa Rosa, CA), 1995 (26 copies signed by Price) £1,000

Fencing with the Shadows, Pneumatic Press (San Francisco, CA), 1995 (broadside; 250 copies; X-Ray Broadside, no. 4 issued in *X-Ray* magazine, no. 4) £65

Body Slam, Pneumatic Press (San Francisco, CA), 1995 (broadside; 250 copies; X-Ray Broadside, no. 5 issued in *X-Ray* magazine, no. 4) £65

The Laughing Heart, Black Sparrow Press (Santa Rosa, CA), 1996 (stapled wraps). £5

ditto, Black Sparrow Press (Santa Rosa CA), 1996 (200 numbered copies; hardback) £35

ditto, Black Sparrow Press (Santa Rosa CA), 1996 (26 lettered copies; hardback) £50

Betting on the Muse: Poems and Stories, Black Sparrow Press (Santa Rosa, CA), 1996 (pbk) . . . £10

ditto, Black Sparrow Press (Santa Rosa CA), 1996 (200 signed, numbered copies; hardback) £45

ditto, Black Sparrow Press (Santa Rosa CA), 1996 (26 signed, lettered copies; hardback) £100

A New War, Black Sparrow Press (Santa Rosa, CA), 1997 (stapled wraps) £5

ditto, Black Sparrow Press (Santa Rosa, CA), 1997 (200 numbered copies; hardback) £35

ditto, Black Sparrow Press (Santa Rosa, CA), 1997 (26 lettered copies; hardback) £50

Bone Palace Ballet: New Poems, Black Sparrow Press (Santa Rosa CA), 1997 (pbk) £5

ditto, Black Sparrow Press (Santa Rosa CA), 1997 (750 hardback copies) £40

ditto, Black Sparrow Press (Santa Rosa CA), 1997 (400 numbered hardback copies) £75

ditto, Black Sparrow Press (Santa Rosa CA), 1997 (26 lettered hardback copies) £150

To Lean Back Into It, Black Sparrow Press (Santa Rosa, CA), 1998 (stapled wraps). £5

ditto, Black Sparrow Press (Santa Rosa CA), 1998 (200 numbered copies; hardback) £30

ditto, Black Sparrow Press (Santa Rosa CA), 1998 (26 lettered copies; hardback) £40

The Word, X-Ray (San Francisco, CA), 1998 (broadside issued in *X-Ray*, no. 7) £10

The Singer, Black Sparrow Press (Santa Rosa, CA), 1999 (stapled wraps) £5

ditto, Black Sparrow Press (Santa Rosa CA), 1999 (150 numbered copies; hardback) £20

ditto, Black Sparrow Press (Santa Rosa CA), 1999 (26 lettered copies; hardback) £40

Crime & Punishment, Black Sparrow Press (Santa Rosa, CA), 1999 (broadside) £10

What Matters Most Is How Well You Walk Through the Fire, Black Sparrow Press (CA), 1999 (pbk) . £5

ditto, Black Sparrow Press (CA), 1999 (750 unnumbered hardback copies) £25

ditto, Black Sparrow Press (CA), 1999 (400 numbered hardback copies with artwork) £100

ditto, Black Sparrow Press (CA), 1999 (26 lettered hardback copies with signed artwork) £150

Open All Night: New Poems, Black Sparrow Press (CA), 2000 (pbk) £5

ditto, Black Sparrow Press (CA), 2000 (hardback) . £20

ditto, Black Sparrow Press (CA), 2000 (400 numbered copies) £30

ditto, Black Sparrow Press (CA), 2000 (26 lettered copies) £40

Novels

Post Office, Black Sparrow Press (Santa Barbara CA), 1971 (pbk) £75

ditto, Black Sparrow Press (Santa Barbara CA), 1971 (250 signed, numbered hardback copies). . . . £650

ditto, Black Sparrow Press (Santa Barbara CA), 1971 (50 signed, numbered hardback copies with artwork). £3,000

ditto, London Magazine Editions (London), 1974 . £75/£25

Factotum, Black Sparrow Press (Santa Barbara CA), 1975 (pbk) . . . . £75 *ditto*, Black Sparrow Press (Santa Barbara CA), 1975 (750 hardback copies) £150

ditto, Black Sparrow Press (Santa Barbara CA), 1975 (250 signed, numbered hardback copies). £650

ditto, Black Sparrow Press (Santa Barbara CA), 1975 (75 signed, numbered hardback copies with artwork). £2,000

ditto, W.H. Allen (London), 1981 . . . . £35/£10

Women, Black Sparrow Press (Santa Barbara CA), 1978 (pbk) £25

ditto, Black Sparrow Press (Santa Barbara CA), 1978 (hardback copies) £150

ditto, Black Sparrow Press (Santa Barbara CA), 1978 (300 signed, numbered copies) £1,000

ditto, Black Sparrow Press (Santa Barbara CA), 1978 (75 signed, numbered copies with artwork) . . . £1,500

ditto, W.H. Allen (London), 1981 . . . . £65/£15

Ham On Rye, Black Sparrow Press (Santa Barbara CA), 1982 (pbk) £65

ditto, Black Sparrow Press (Santa Barbara CA), 1982 (hardback copies) £125

ditto, Black Sparrow Press (Santa Barbara CA), 1982 (350 signed, numbered copies) £650

ditto, Black Sparrow Press (Santa Barbara CA), 1982 (100 signed, numbered copies with artwork) . . £1,500

Hollywood: A Novel, Black Sparrow Press (Santa Rosa CA), 1989 (pbk) £15

ditto, Black Sparrow Press (Santa Rosa CA), 1989 (hardback) £45

ditto, Black Sparrow Press (Santa Rosa CA), 1989 (500 signed, numbered hardback copies). . . . £150

ditto, Black Sparrow Press (Santa Rosa CA), 1989 (150 signed, numbered hardback copies with signed print). £200

ditto, Black Sparrow Press (Santa Rosa CA), 1989 (26 signed, numbered hardback copies with signed print). £250

Pulp, Black Sparrow Press (Santa Rosa CA), 1994 (pbk) £5

ditto, Black Sparrow Press (Santa Rosa CA), 1994 (hardback copies) £15

ditto, Black Sparrow Press (Santa Rosa CA), 1994 (750 signed, numbered hardback copies). . . . £125

ditto, Black Sparrow Press (Santa Rosa CA), 1994 (300 signed, numbered hardback copies with artwork). £200

ditto, Black Sparrow Press (Santa Rosa CA), 1994 (26 signed, numbered hardback copies with artwork). £250

Short Stories

Erections, Ejaculations, Exhibitions, and General Tales of Ordinary Madness, City Lights Books (San Francisco, CA), 1972 (pbk) £145

ditto, as **Life and Death in the Charity Ward**, London Magazine Editions (London), 1974 (abridged) . £125/£25

ditto, as **The Most Beautiful Woman in Town and Other Stories**, City Lights Books (San Francisco, CA), 1983, and **Tales of Ordinary Madness**, City Lights Books (San Francisco, CA), 1983 (pbks) . . . . £10 each

South of No North: Stories of the Buried Life, Black Sparrow Press (Los Angeles CA), 1973 (wraps) . £25

ditto, Black Sparrow Press (Los Angeles CA), 1973 (300 signed, numbered hardback copies). . . . £250

ditto, Black Sparrow Press (Los Angeles CA), 1973 (50 signed, numbered hardback copies with artwork). £650

Hot Water Music, Back Sparrow (Santa Barbara CA), 1983 (hardback) £40

ditto, Back Sparrow (Santa Barbara CA), 1983 (400 signed, numbered copies) £200

ditto, Back Sparrow (Santa Barbara CA), 1983 (100 signed, numbered copies with artwork) . . . £1,500

Bring Me Your Love, Black Sparrow Press (Santa Barbara CA), 1983 (illustrated by Robert Crumb; pbk) . £10

ditto, Black Sparrow Press (Santa Barbara CA), 1983 (350 numbered copies signed by author and illustrator) . £250

ditto, Black Sparrow Press (Santa Barbara CA), 1983 (26 lettered copies signed by author and illustrator) . . £450

There's No Business, Black Sparrow Press (Santa Rosa CA), 1984 (wraps). £10

ditto, Black Sparrow Press (Santa Rosa CA), 1984 (400 numbered hardback copies) £50

ditto, Black Sparrow Press (Santa Rosa CA), 1984 (400 numbered copies signed by author and illustrator) . £75

ditto, Black Sparrow Press (Santa Rosa CA), 1984 (26 lettered copies signed by author and illustrator) . . £300

Jaggernaut, a Short Story, Beat Scene Press (Coventry), 1995 (200 copies; wraps) £20

Non-Fiction

Notes of a Dirty Old Man, Essex House (N. Hollywood CA), 1969 (pbk) £65

Shakespeare Never Did This, City Lights Books (San Francisco, CA), 1979 (photographs by Michael Montfort). . . . . £135/£65

ditto, City Lights Books (San Francisco, CA), 1979 (pbk) £15

ditto, Black Sparrow Press (Santa Rosa), 1995 (enlarged edition; hardback) £40

ditto, Black Sparrow Press (Santa Rosa), 1995 (200 numbered copies signed by Montfort) . . . £75

ditto, Black Sparrow Press (Santa Rosa), 1995 (26 lettered copies signed by Montfort) £150

The Captain is Out to Lunch and the Sailors Have Taken Over the Ship, Black Sparrow Press (Santa Rosa CA), 1997 (wraps). £10

ditto, Black Sparrow Press (Santa Rosa CA), 1997 (hardback copies) £40

ditto, Black Sparrow Press (Santa Rosa CA), 1997 (400 numbered copies with a serigraph portrait of Bukowski signed by Robert Crumb tipped-in) £100

ditto, Black Sparrow Press (Santa Rosa CA), 1997 (175 numbered copies in slipcase without d/w; with 5 full colour serigraph prints each individually signed by Robert Crumb) £400

ditto, Black Sparrow Press (Santa Rosa CA), 1997 (26 specially bound lettered copies with an colour serigraph portrait of Bukowski signed by Robert Crumb) . . £175

Letters

The Bukowski/Purdy Letters, 1964-1974: A Decade of Dialogue, Paget Press (Sutton West, Ontario), 1983 (edited by Seamus Cooney; hardback) £35

ditto, Paget Press (Sutton West, Ontario), 1983 (200 copies signed by Bukowski and Purdy) £150

ditto, Paget Press (Sutton West, Ontario), 1983 (26 copies signed by Bukowski and Purdy) £200

Screams from the Balcony: Selected Letters 1960-1970, Black Sparrow Press (Santa Rosa CA), 1993 (pbk) . £10

ditto, Black Sparrow Press (Santa Rosa, CA), 1993 (hardback) £20

ditto, Black Sparrow Press (Santa Rosa CA), 1993 (600 signed, numbered hardback copies). . . . £75

ditto, Black Sparrow Press (Santa Rosa CA), 1993 (300 signed, numbered hardback copies with signed artwork) £125

ditto, Black Sparrow Press (Santa Rosa CA), 1993 (26 signed, numbered hardback copies with signed artwork) .
. . . . £175
Living on Luck: Selected Letters 1960s-1970s, Black Sparrow Press (Santa Rosa CA), 1995 (pbk). . . £5
ditto, Black Sparrow Press (Santa Rosa CA), 1995 (hardback) £15
ditto, Black Sparrow Press (Santa Rosa CA), 1995 (216 hardback copies containing a tipped in signature) . £100
Reach for the Sun: Selected Letters, 1978-1994, Black Sparrow Press (Santa Rosa CA), 1999 (pbk). . . £5
ditto, Black Sparrow Press (Santa Rosa CA), 1999 (hardback) £15
ditto, Black Sparrow Press (Santa Rosa CA), 1999 (350 numbered hardback copies with artwork) . . . £45
ditto, Black Sparrow Press (Santa Rosa CA), 1999 (26 lettered hardback copies with artwork) . . . £75
Beerspit Night and Cursing: The Correspondence of Charles Bukowski and Sheri Martinelli 1960-1967, Black Sparrow Press (Santa Rosa, CA), 2001 (pbk) . . £5
ditto, Black Sparrow Press (Santa Rosa, CA), 2001 (hardback) £15
ditto, Black Sparrow Press (Santa Rosa CA), 2001 (500 numbered hardback copies with artwork) . . . £40
ditto, Black Sparrow Press (Santa Rosa CA), 2001 (26 lettered hardback copies with artwork) . . . £75

Others

Mockingbird Wish Me Luck: A New Book of Poems, Black Sparrow Press (Los Angeles CA), 1972 (broadside prospectus) £15
ditto, Black Sparrow Press (Los Angeles CA), 1972 (100 signed copies) £150
Play the Piano Drunk Like a Percussion Instrument Until the Fingers Begin to Bleed a Bit: Previously Uncollected Poems, Black Sparrow Press (Santa Barbara CA), 1979 (broadside prospectus) £20
ditto, Black Sparrow Press (Santa Barbara CA), 1979 (broadside prospectus; 100 signed copies) . . £75
ditto, Black Sparrow Press (Santa Barbara CA), 1979 (broadside prospectus; 26 signed lettered copies). . £150
Ham On Rye: A New Novel, Black Sparrow Press (Santa Barbara CA), 1982 (broadside prospectus; unsigned copies)
. . . . £20
ditto, Black Sparrow Press (Santa Barbara CA), 1982 (broadside prospectus; 100 signed copies) . . £125
Hot Water Music: A New Book of Short Stories, Black Sparrow Press (Santa Barbara CA), 1983 (promotional broadside) £25
Hot Water Music: A New Book of Short Stories, Black Sparrow Press (Santa Barbara CA), 1983 (promotional broadside; 50 signed, numbered copies). . . £125
Barfly: The Continuing Saga of Henry Chinaski, Paget Press (Sutton West, Ontario), 1984 (pbk) . . £15
ditto, Paget Press (Sutton West, Ontario), 1984 (220 signed copies) £200
The Movie 'Barfly': An Original Screenplay, Black Sparrow Press (Santa Rosa CA), 1987 (500 hardback copies) £65
ditto, Black Sparrow Press (Santa Rosa CA), 1987 (400 numbered hardback copies signed by Bukowski only) £125
ditto, Black Sparrow Press (Santa Rosa CA), 1987 (140 numbered signed by Bukowski, Barbet Schroeder, Faye Dunaway, and Mickey Rourke) £300

ditto, Black Sparrow Press (Santa Rosa CA), 1987 (26 lettered signed by Bukowski, Barbet Schroeder, Faye Dunaway, and Mickey Rourke) . . . £400
Charles Bukowski: Laughing with the Gods, Sun Dog Press (Northville, MI), 2000 (interview by Fernanda Pivano, translated from the Italian by Pivano and Simona Viciani; pbk) £5

MIKHAIL BULGAKOV
(b.1891 d.1940)

Bulgakov was a Russian novelist and playwright born and educated in Kiev. He graduated as a doctor in 1916 but abandoned medicine to write. After a lifetime at odds with the Soviet regime he died in poverty, shortly after completing his best-known novel *The Master and Margarita*. The *New York Times Book Review* called one it of the greatest novels of the 20th century. None of his major fiction was published during his lifetime.

Novels

The Master and Margarita, Collins/Harvill (London), 1967 (translated by Michael Glenny) . . . £100/£15
ditto, Harper & Row (New York), 1967 . . £75/£10
ditto, Grove Press (New York), 1967 (translated by Mirra Ginsburg) . . . . £75/£10
Black Snow: A Theatrical Novel, Hodder & Stoughton (London), 1967 (translated by Michael Glenny) . £25/£5
ditto, Simon & Schuster (New York), 1967 . . £25/£5
A Country Doctor's Notebook, Collins-Harvill (London), 1975 (translated by Michael Glenny) . . . £15/£5

Short Stories

Heart of a Dog and Other Stories, Collins/Harvill (London), 1968 (translated by Michael Glenny) . . . £20/£5
ditto, Harcourt, Brace & Wolff (New York), 1968 . £20/£5
ditto, Grove Press (New York), 1968 (translated by Mirra Ginsburg) . . . . £20/£5
Diaboliad and Other Stories, Indiana Univ Press (Bloomington, IA), 1972 (translated by Carl R. Proffer) . £25/£10
ditto, Harvill (London), 1991 . . . . . £10/£5
Notes on the Cuff & Other Stories, Ardis (Ann Arbor, MI), 1991 (translated by Alison Rice) . . . £15/£5
The Fatal Eggs and Other Soviet Satire, 1918-1963, Quartet (London), 1993 (edited and translated by Mirra Ginsburg; pbk) £5

Plays

Flight; A Play In Eight Dreams & Four Acts, Grove Press (New York), 1969 (translated and with an introduction by Mirra Ginsburg; pbk) £5
The White Guard, Collins-Harvill (London), 1971 (translated by Michael Glenny) . . . . . £20/£5
ditto, McGraw Hill (New York), 1971 . . £15/£5
The Early Plays of Mikhail Bulgakov, Indiana Univ Press (Bloomington, IA), 1972 (translated by Carl R. Proffer and Ellendea Proffer). . . . . . . £15/£5
Flight and Bliss, New Directions (New York), 1985 (pbk) £5
Zoya's Apartment: A Tragic Farce In Three Acts, Samuel French (New York), 1991 (translated by Nicholas Saunders and Frank Dwyer) £10

Six Plays, Methuen (London), 1991 (contains *The White Guard, Madame Zoyka, Flight, Molière, Adam and Eve, The Last Days*; translated by William Powell, Michael Glenny and Michael Earley) . . . . £10/£5

Non-Fiction
The Life of Monsieur de Molière, Funk & Wagnalls (New York), 1970 (translated by Mirra Ginsburg) . . £20/£5
Manuscripts Don't Burn, A Life in Diaries and Letters, Bloomsbury (London), 1991 . . . . £20/£5
ditto, The Overlook Press (Woodstock, NY), 1992. £20/£5

ANTHONY BURGESS
(b.1917 d.1993)

Born John Burgess Wilson, this inventive, satirical author often presents a bleak outlook on life. He has written distinctive, well received novels, the best known being the classic *The Clockwork Orange*. He also wrote critical studies of Joyce, Hemingway, Shakespeare and D.H. Lawrence, and was a poet, playwright, composer, librettist, screenwriter, journalist, broadcaster and translator.

Novels
Time for a Tiger, Heinemann (London), 1956. . £450/£45
The Enemy in the Blanket, Heinemann (London), 1958 . . . . . £150/£30
Beds in the East, Heinemann (London), 1959. . £100/£15
The Right to an Answer, Heinemann (London), 1960 . . . . . £100/£10
ditto, Norton (New York), 1961 . . . £35/£10
The Doctor is Sick, Heinemann (London), 1960 . £225/£30
ditto, Norton (New York), 1966 . . . £30/£10
The Worm and the Ring, Heinemann (London), 1961 . . . . £500/£125
Devil of a State, Heinemann (London), 1961 . . £75/£10
ditto, Norton (New York), 1962 . . . £25/£5
One Hand Clapping, Peter Davies (London), 1961 (pseud 'Joseph Kell') . . . . . £325/£45
ditto, Knopf (New York), 1972 . . . £25/£5
A Clockwork Orange, Heinemann (London), 1962 (first issue, black boards, d/w priced 16s and with flaps with a margin of approx 1 inch) . . . £2,500/£125
ditto, Heinemann (London), 1962 (second issue, black boards, d/w priced 18s and narrower flaps) . £2,000/£125
ditto, Heinemann (London), 1962 (third issue, purple boards with a decimal price sticker) . . . £1,000/£75
ditto, Norton (New York), 1963 . . . £300/£50
The Wanting Seed, Heinemann (London), 1962 . £75/£35
ditto, Norton (New York), 1963 . . . £25/£5
Honey for the Bears, Heinemann (London), 1963 . £75/£10
ditto, Norton (New York), 1964 . . . £25/£5
Inside Mr Enderby, Heinemann (London), 1963 (pseud 'Joseph Kell') . . . . . £275/£60
Nothing Like the Sun, Heinemann (London), 1964 £75/£10
ditto, Norton (New York), 1964 . . . £30/£5
The Eve of Saint Venus, Sidgwick & Jackson (London), 1964 . . . . . £45/£10
ditto, Norton (New York), 1970 . . . £15/£5
A Vision of Battlements, Sidgwick & Jackson (London), 1965 . . . . . £45/£10
ditto, Norton (New York), 1966 . . . £15/£5

Tremor of Intent, Heinemann (London), 1966 . £40/£10
ditto, Norton (New York), 1966 . . . £15/£5
Enderby Outside, Heinemann (London), 1968 . £50/£10
ditto, as *Enderby*, Norton (New York), 1968 . £20/£5
MF, Cape (London), 1971 . . . . £30/£5
ditto, Knopf (New York), 1971 . . . £15/£5
Napoleon Symphony, Cape (London), 1974 . £30/£5
ditto, Knopf (New York), 1974 . . . £15/£5
The Clockwork Testament; or Enderby's End, Hart-Davis MacGibbon (London), 1974 . . . £30/£5
ditto, Knopf (New York), 1974 . . . £15/£5
Beard's Roman Women, McGraw-Hill (New York), 1976 . . £15/£5
ditto, Hutchinson (London), 1977 . . . £15/£5
Abba Abba, Faber (London), 1977 . . . £35/£5
ditto, Little, Brown (Boston), 1977 . . . £35/£5
1985, Hutchinson (London), 1978 . . . £20/£5
ditto, Little, Brown (Boston), 1978 . . . £15/£5
Man of Nazareth, McGraw-Hill (New York), 1979 £20/£5
ditto, Magnum (London), 1980 . . . £15/£5
Earthly Powers, Hutchinson (London), 1980 . £30/£5
ditto, Simon & Schuster (New York), 1980 . £15/£5
The End of the World News, Hutchinson (London), 1982 . . . . . £20/£5
ditto, McGraw-Hill (New York), 1983 . . £15/£5
Enderby's Dark Lady, Hutchinson (London), 1984 £20/£5
ditto, McGraw-Hill (New York), 1984 . . £15/£5
The Kingdom of the Wicked, Hutchinson (London), 1985 . . . . £20/£5
ditto, Franklin Library (Franklin Centre, PA), 1985 (signed, limited edition) £25
ditto, Arbor House (New York), 1985 . . £10/£5
The Pianoplayers, Hutchinson (London), 1986 . £15/£5
ditto, Arbor House (New York), 1986 . . £10/£5
Any Old Iron, Hutchinson (London), 1989 . £15/£5
ditto, Random House (New York), 1989 . . £10/£5
Mozart and the Wolf Gang, Hutchinson (London), 1991 . . . . . £10/£5
ditto, as *On Mozart: a Paean for Wolfgang*, Ticknor and Fields (Boston), 1991 . . . £10/£5
A Dead Man in Deptford, Hutchinson (London), 1993 . . . . . £10/£5
ditto, Carroll & Graf (New York), 1995 . . £10/£5
Byrne, Hutchinson (London), 1995 . . . £10/£5
ditto, Carroll & Graf (New York), 1997 . . £10/£5

Short Stories
The Devil's Mode, Hutchinson (London), 1989 . £15/£5
ditto, Random House (New York), 1989 . . £15/£5

Autobiography
Little Wilson and Big God, Weidenfeld & Nicolson (New York), 1986 . . . . . £20/£5
ditto, Heinemann (London), 1987 . . . £15/£5
ditto, Franklin Library (Franklin Centre, PA), 1987 (signed, limited edition) £25
You've Had Your Time, Heinemann (London), 1990 £20/£5
ditto, Grove Weidenfeld (New York), 1991 . £15/£5

Literary Criticism & Biography
English Literature: A Survey for Students, Longmans, Green (London), 1958 (pseud 'John Burgess Wilson', no d/w) £250

The Novel Today, Longmans, Green (London), 1963 (stapled wraps) £15
Language Made Plain, English Univ Press (London), 1964 . . . . £45/£10
ditto, Crowell (New York), 1965 . . . £25/£5
Here Comes Everybody: An Introduction to James Joyce for the Ordinary Reader, Faber (London), 1965 . £50/£10
ditto, as *Re James Joyce*, Norton (New York), 1965 (wraps) £10
The Novel Now: A Student's Guide to Contemporary Fiction, Faber (London), 1967 . . £25/£10
ditto, as *The Novel Now: A Guide to Contemporary Fiction*, Norton (New York), 1967 . . . £20/£5
Urgent Copy: Literary Studies, Cape (London), 1968 . . . . £30/£10
ditto, Norton (New York), 1969 . . . . £20/£5
Shakespeare, Cape (London), 1970 . . £25/£10
ditto, Knopf (New York), 1970 . . . £20/£5
Joysprick: An Introduction to the Language of James Joyce, Deutsch (London), 1973 . . £30/£10
ditto, Harcourt Brace Jovanovich (New York), 1975 (pbk) £10
Obscenity and the Arts, Malta Library Association (Valletta, Malta), 1973 (wraps) £25
Will and Testament, Plain Wrapper Press (Verona, Italy), 1977 (full leather in box; with eight screenprints by Joe Tilson, 86 numbered copies signed by Tilson and Burgess) £2,000
A Christmas Recipe, Plain Wrapper Press (Verona, Italy), 1977 (illustrated by Fulvio Testa, 180 copies) . . £750
Ernest Hemingway and His World, Thames & Hudson (London), 1978 . . . . . £20/£5
ditto, Scribner's (New York), 1978 . . £15/£5
Ninety-Nine Novels, Allison & Busby (London), 1984 . . . . £20/£5
ditto, Summit (New York), 1984. . . . £15/£5
Flame into Being: The Life and Works of D.H. Lawrence, Heinemann (London), 1985 . . £15/£5
ditto, Arbor House (New York), 1985 . . £15/£5
Mouthful of Air, Hutchinson (London), 1992 . £10/£5
ditto, Morrow (New York), 1992 . . . £10/£5

Miscellaneous Works
Coaching Days of England, Elek (London), 1966 . £45/£15
The Age of the Grand Tour, Elek (London), 1967 (with Francis Haskell) . . . . . £45/£15
ditto, Crown (New York), 1967 . . . £45/£15
A Long Trip to Teatime, Dempsey & Squires (London), 1976 . . . . £15/£5
ditto, Stonehill (New York), 1976 . . £10/£5
Moses: A Narrative, Dempsey & Squires (London), 1976 . . . . £20/£5
ditto, Stonehill (New York), 1976 . . £15/£5
New York, Time-Life Books (Amsterdam), 1977 . £15/£5
The Land Where Ice-Cream Grows, Benn (London), 1979 . . . . £15/£5
ditto, Doubleday (New York), 1979 . . £15/£5
On Going to Bed, Deutsch (London), 1982 . £15/£5
ditto, Abbeville Press (New York), 1982 . £15/£5
This Man and Music, Hutchinson (London), 1982 £10/£5
ditto, McGraw-Hill (New York), 1983 . £10/£5
Homage to QWERT YUIOP: Essays, Hutchinson (London), 1986 . . . . . . £10/£5

ditto, as *But Do Blondes Prefer Gentlemen? Homage to QWERT YUIOP and Other Writings*, McGraw-Hill (New York), 1986 . . . . £10/£5
Oberon Old and New, Hutchinson (London), 1985 (new libretto for the opera by Carl Maria Von Weber; pbk) . £10
Blooms of Dublin: A Musical Play Based on James Joyce's Ulysses, Hutchinson (London), 1986 (pbk) . . . £10
One Man's Chorus: The Uncollected Writings, Carroll & Graf (New York), 1998 . . . . . £10/£5

JAMES LEE BURKE
(b.1936)

One of the biggest selling crime writers in America, Burke is best known for his novels about Vietnam veteran Dave Robicheaux. Burke has apparently worked at a wide variety of jobs over the years, including in the oil industry, as a reporter, an English teacher and social worker. His daughter, Alafair Burke, is also a mystery novelist.

'Dave Robicheaux' Books
The Neon Rain, Henry Holt & Co. (New York), 1987 . . . . £125/£25
ditto, Mysterious/Century (London), 1989 . £125/£25
ditto, Mysterious/Century (London), 1989 (pbk) . £10
Heaven's Prisoners, Henry Holt (New York), 1988 . . . . £75/£15
ditto, Century (London), 1990 . . . . £75/£15
Black Cherry Blues, Little, Brown (Boston), 1989. £50/£15
ditto, Century (London), 1990 . . . . £45/£10
A Morning for Flamingos, Little, Brown (Boston), 1990 . . . . £45/£10
ditto, Century (London), 1992 . . . £35/£5
A Stained White Radiance, Hyperion (New York), 1992 . . . . £35/£10
ditto, Century (London), 1993 . . . £25/£10
In the Electric Mist with the Confederate Dead, Hyperion (New York), 1993 . . . . £30/£5
ditto, Hyperion (New York), 1993 (150 signed, numbered copies, slipcase) . . . . . . £100/£65
ditto, Hyperion (New York), 1993 (26 signed, lettered copies, slipcase) . . . . £250/£200
ditto, Orion (London), 1993. . . . . £20/£5
Dixie City Jam, Hyperion (New York), 1994 . £25/£5
ditto, Hyperion, (New York), 1994 (1,525 signed, numbered copies, slipcase) . . . . £40/£30
ditto, Orion (London), 1994. . . . . £20/£5
Burning Angel, Hyperion (New York), 1995 . £20/£5
ditto, Trice (New Orleans), 1995 (150 signed, numbered copies, slipcase) . . . . £65/£50
ditto, Trice (New Orleans), 1995 (26 signed, lettered copies, slipcase) . . . . £125/£100
ditto, Orion (London), 1995. . . . . £15/£5
Cadillac Jukebox, Hyperion (New York), 1996 . £20/£5
ditto, Hyperion (New York), 1996 (ABA collectors edition) . . . . £25/£10
ditto, Trice (New Orleans), 1996 (175 signed, numbered copies, slipcase) . . . . £60/£45
ditto, Trice (New Orleans), 1996 (26 signed, lettered copies, slipcase). . . . . £175/£150
ditto, Orion (London), 1996. . . . . £15/£5
Sunset Limited, Doubleday (New York), 1998 . £20/£5

ditto, Orion (London), 1998 . . . . £15/£5
ditto, Scorpion Press (Blakeney, Glos), 1998 (110 signed, numbered copies) £65
ditto, Scorpion Press (Blakeney, Glos), 1998 (16 signed, lettered copies) £175
Purple Cane Road, Doubleday (New York), 2000 . £15/£5
ditto, Trice (New Orleans), 2000 (150 signed, numbered copies, slipcase) . . . . . . £65/£45
ditto, Trice (New Orleans), 2000 (26 signed, lettered copies, slipcase). . . . . . £125/£100
ditto, Orion (London), 2000 . . . . . £10/£5
Jolie Blon's Bounce, Simon & Schuster (New York), 2002. . . . . £10/£5
ditto, Trice (New Orleans), 2002 (150 signed, numbered copies, slipcase) . . . . . £65/£45
ditto, Trice (New Orleans), 2002 (26 signed, lettered copies, slipcase). . . . . . .£100/£75
ditto, Orion (London), 2002 . . . . . £10/£5
Last Car to Elysian Field, Simon & Schuster (Riverside, NJ), 2003 . . . . . £10/£5
ditto, Orion (London), 2003 . . . . . £10/£5
Crusader's Cross, Simon & Schuster (Riverside, NJ), 2005. . . . . £10/£5
ditto, Scorpion Press (Blakeney, Glos), 2005 (15 signed, lettered copies) £175
ditto, Scorpion Press (Blakeney, Glos), 2005 (90 signed, numbered copies) £65
ditto, Orion (London), 2006 . . . . . £10/£5
Pegasus Descending, Simon & Schuster (Riverside, NJ), 2006 . . . . £10/£5
ditto, Orion (London), 2006 . . . . . £10/£5
ditto, Scorpion Press (Blakeney, Glos), 2006 (80 signed, numbered copies) £65
The Tin Roof Blowdown, Simon & Schuster (Riverside, NJ), 2007 . . . . £10/£5
ditto, Orion (London), 2007 . . . . . £10/£5
ditto, Scorpion Press (Blakeney, Glos), 2007 (80 signed, numbered copies) £65
ditto, Scorpion Press (Blakeney, Glos), 2007 (16 signed, lettered copies) £200
Swan Peak, Simon & Schuster (Riverside, NJ), 2008 £10/£5
ditto, Orion (London), 2008 . . . . . £10/£5
ditto, Scorpion Press (Blakeney, Glos), 2008 (80 signed, numbered copies) £65
ditto, Scorpion Press (Blakeney, Glos), 2008 (16 signed, lettered copies) £200

'Billy Bob Holland' Books
Cimarron Rose, Orion (London), 1997 . . . £20/£10
ditto, Hyperion (New York), 1997 . . . . £15/£5
ditto, Trice (New Orleans), 1997 (150 signed, numbered copies, slipcase) . . . . £60/£45
ditto, Trice (New Orleans), 1997 (26 signed, lettered copies, slipcase). . . . . . £150/£125
Heartwood, Doubleday (New York), 1999 . . £15/£5
ditto, Trice (New Orleans), 1999 (26 signed, lettered copies, slipcase). . . . . . £150/£125
ditto, Trice (New Orleans), 1999 (150 signed, numbered copies, slipcase) . . . . £65/£50
ditto, Orion (London), 1999 . . . . . £15/£5
Bitterroot, Simon & Schuster (New York), 2001 . £10/£5
ditto, Trice (New Orleans), 2001 (150 signed, numbered copies, slipcase) . . . . £65/£50

ditto, Trice (New Orleans), 2001 (26 signed, lettered copies, slipcase). . . . . . .£100/£75
ditto, Orion (London), 2001 . . . . . £10/£5
In the Moon of Red Ponies, Simon & Schuster (Riverside, NJ), 2004 . . . . £10/£5
ditto, Orion (London), 2004 . . . . . £10/£5

Other Books
Half of Paradise, Houghton Mifflin (Boston), 1965 . . . . £1,250/£200
To the Bright and Shining Sun, Scribner's (New York), 1970 . . . . £600/£125
ditto, James Cahill (Huntington Beach, CA), 1992 (400 signed copies, slipcase) . . . . . £50/£35
Lay Down My Sword and Shield, Crowell (New York), 1971 . . . . £500/£75
Two for Texas, Pocket Books (New York), 1982 (pbk). £15
ditto, James Cahill (Huntington Beach, CA), 1992 (400 numbered, signed copies, slipcase) . . . £65/£45
The Lost Get-Back Boogie, Louisiana State Univ Press (Baton Rouge, LA), 1986 . . . . . .£150/£30
White Doves at Morning, Simon & Schuster (New York), 2003 . . . . £10/£5
ditto, Orion (London), 2003 . . . . . £10/£5
Rain Gods, Simon & Schuster (Riverside, NJ), 2009 £10/£5
ditto, Orion (London), 2008 . . . . . £10/£5
ditto, Scorpion Press (Blakeney, Glos), 2009 (80 signed, numbered copies) £65

Short Stories
The Convict, Louisiana State Univ Press (Baton Rouge, LA), 1985 . . . . . . £1,750/£750
ditto, Louisiana State Univ Press (Baton Rouge, LA), 1985 (pbk) £75
ditto, Orion (London), 1995 . . . . . .£40/£10
Winter Light, James Cahill (Huntington Beach, CA), 1992 (26 signed, lettered copies) £200
ditto, James Cahill (Huntington Beach, CA), 1992 (300 signed, numbered copies) £75
Texas City 1947, Lord John Press (Northridge, CA), 1992 (26 signed, lettered copies) £175
ditto, Lord John Press (Northridge, CA), 1992 (275 signed, numbered copies, slipcase) . . . . £60/£50
Jesus Out to Sea, Simon & Schuster (Riverside, NJ), 2007 (pbk) £5
ditto, Orion (London), 2008 . . . . . £10/£5

W.J. BURLEY

(b.1914 d.2002)

Burley was an engineer until he won a mature state scholarship to Oxford, where he read Zoology. He then worked as a teacher. His first novel, *A Taste of Power*, features the criminologist and professor of Zoology, Dr Henry Pym, but Burley soon found a more successful formula with detective novels featuring Chief Superintendent Charles Wycliffe, set in Cornwall.

'Wycliffe' Novels
Three Toed Pussy, Gollancz (London), 1968 . .£350/£25
To Kill A Cat, Gollancz (London), 1970 . . .£125/£20
ditto, Walker (New York), 1972 . . . . .£40/£10

Guilt Edged, Gollancz (London), 1971 . . . £125/£20
ditto, Walker (New York), c.1972 . . . . £40/£10
ditto, as ***Wycliffe and the Guilt Edged Alibi***, Corgi (London), 1994 (pbk). £5
Death in a Salubrious Place, Gollancz (London), 1973 .
. . . . £100/£10
ditto, Walker (New York), 1973 . . . . £30/£5
ditto, as ***Wycliffe and Death in a Salubrious Place***, Corgi (London), 1995 (pbk). £5
Death in Stanley Street, Gollancz (London), 1974. £100/£10
ditto, Walker (New York), 1974 . . . . £30/£5
ditto, as ***Wycliffe and Death in Stanley Street***, Corgi (London), 1990 (pbk). £5
Wycliffe and the Pea-Green Boat, Gollancz (London), 1975
. . . . £75/£15
ditto, Walker (New York), 1975 . . . . £20/£5
Wycliffe and the Schoolgirls, Gollancz (London), 1976 .
. . . . £75/£15
ditto, Walker (New York), 1976 . . . . £20/£5
Wycliffe and the Scapegoat, Gollancz (London), 1978 . .
. . . . £65/£10
ditto, Doubleday (New York), 1979 . . . £20/£5
Wycliffe in Paul's Court, Gollancz (London), 1980 £65/£10
ditto, Doubleday (New York), 1980 . . . £20/£5
Wycliffe's Wild Goose Chase, Gollancz (London), 1982 .
. . . . £45/£10
ditto, Doubleday (New York), 1982 . . . £20/£5
Wycliffe and the Beales, Gollancz (London), 1983 £25/£5
ditto, Doubleday (New York), 1984 . . . £20/£5
Wycliffe and the Four Jacks, Gollancz (London), 1985 .
. . . . £25/£5
ditto, Doubleday (New York), 1986 . . . £15/£5
Wycliffe and the Quiet Virgin, Gollancz (London), 1986 .
. . . . £25/£5
ditto, Doubleday (New York), 1986 . . . £15/£5
Wycliffe and the Winsor Blue, Gollancz (London), 1987 .
. . . . £20/£5
ditto, Doubleday (New York), 1987 . . . £10/£5
Wycliffe and the Tangled Web, Gollancz (London), 1988 .
. . . . £15/£5
ditto, Doubleday (New York), 1989 . . . £10/£5
Wycliffe and the Cycle of Death, Gollancz (London), 1990.
. . . . £15/£5
ditto, Doubleday (New York), 1991 . . . £10/£5
Wycliffe and the Dead Flautist, Gollancz (London), 1991 .
. . . . £15/£5
ditto, St Martin's Press (New York), 1992 . . £10/£5
Wycliffe and the Last Rites, Gollancz (London), 1992 . .
. . . . £10/£5
ditto, St Martin's Press (New York), 1993 . £10/£5
Wycliffe and the Dunes Mystery, Gollancz (London), 1994
. . . . £10/£5
ditto, St Martin's Press (New York), 1994 . £10/£5
Wycliffe and the House of Fear, Gollancz (London), 1995 .
. . . . £10/£5
ditto, St Martin's Press (New York), 1996 . £10/£5
Wycliffe Omnibus, Gollancz (London), 1996 . £10/£5
Wycliffe and the The Redhead, Gollancz (London), 1997 .
. . . . £10/£5
ditto, St Martin's Press (New York), 1998 . £10/£5
Wycliffe and the Guild of Nine, Gollancz (London), 2000 .
. . . . £10/£5

'Pym' Novels
A Taste of Power, Gollancz (London), 1966 . .£200/£30
Death in Willow Pattern, Gollancz (London), 1969 . .
. . . . £175/£30
ditto, Walker (New York), 1970 . . . . £45/£10

Other Novels
The Schoolmaster, Gollancz (London), 1977 . . £35/£10
ditto, Walker (New York), 1977 . . . . £20/£5
The Sixth Day, Gollancz (London), 1978. . . £45/£10
Charles and Elizabeth: A Gothic Novel, Gollancz (London), 1979 . . . . £25/£10
ditto, Walker (New York), 1981 . . . . £10/£5
The House of Care, Gollancz (London), 1981 . £35/£10
ditto, Walker (New York), 1981 . . . . £10/£5

Non-Fiction
City of Truro, 1877-1977, O. Blackford (Truro, Cornwall), 1977 (wraps). £10

FRANCES HODGSON BURNETT
(b.1849 d.1924)

A novelist and playwright, Burnett was born in Manchester but spent many years in America, where she died. Her sentimental novels for children have often been filmed, with varying degrees of success. After her first son, Lionel, died in 1890, Burnett became interested in spiritualism and wrote of her beliefs about life after death in the novella *The White People*.

Children's Books
Little Lord Fauntleroy, Scribner's (New York), 1886 (first issue with 'De Vinne' imprint on page 210) . . .£475
ditto, Scribner's (New York), 1886 (second issue with 'J.J. Little' imprint) £300
ditto, Warne (London), 1886 . . . . . .£300
Sara Crewe; or What Happened at Miss Minchin's, Unwin (London), 1887 . . . . £45
ditto, Scribner's (New York), 1888 . . . . £35
ditto, as ***Sara Crewe, and Editha's Burglar***, Warne (London), 1888 . . . . £30
Editha's Burglar, Jordan, Marsh (Boston), 1888 . . £50
Little Saint Elizabeth and Other Child Stories, Scribner's (New York), 1890 . . . . £30
ditto, Warne (London), 1890 . . . . . £30
Children I Have Known, Osgood McIlvaine (Boston), 1892 [1891] £30
ditto, as ***Giovanni and the Other***, Scribner's (New York), 1892 . . . . £30
The One I Knew the Best of All, Scribner's (New York), 1893 . . . . £25
ditto, Warne (London), 1893 . . . . . £25
The Captain's Youngest and Other Stories, Warne (London), 1894 . . . . £20
ditto, as ***Piccino and Other Child Stories***, Scribner's (New York), 1894 . . . . £20
Two Little Pilgrims' Progress, Scribner's (New York), 1895
. . . . £25
ditto, Warne (London), 1895 . . . . . £25

A Little Princess, Scribner's (New York), 1905 . . £100
ditto, Warne (London), 1905 . . . . . £125
Racketty Packetty House, Century (New York), 1906 . £30
ditto, Warne (London), 1907 . . . . . £30
The Troubles of Queen Silver-Bell, Century (New York), 1907 . . . . £30
ditto, Warne (London), 1907 . . . . . £30
The Cozy Lion, Century (New York), 1907 . . £25
ditto, Tom Stacey (London), 1972 . . . £10/£5
The Spring Cleaning, Century (New York), 1909 . . £30
ditto, Tom Stacey (London), 1973 . . . £10/£5
The Land of the Blue Flower, Moffat, Yard (New York), 1909 . . . . £30
ditto, Putnam (London), 1912 . . . . . £30
The Secret Garden, Stokes (New York), 1911 . . £500
ditto, Heinemann (London), 1911 . . . . £500
My Robin, Stokes (New York), 1912. . . . . £30
ditto, Putnam (London), 1913 . . . . . £25
The Lost Prince, Century (New York), 1915 . . . £35
ditto, Hodder & Stoughton (London), 1915 . . . £30
The Little Hunchback Zia, Stokes (New York), 1916 . £50
ditto, Heinemann (London), 1916 . . . . . £50

Novels and Novellas for Adults
That Lass O'Lowrie's: A Lancashire Story, Warne (London), [1877]. £30
ditto, Scribner's (New York), 1887 . . . . £75
Dolly: A Love Story, Porter & Coates (Philadelphia, PA), 1877 . . . . £20
ditto, Routledge (London), [1877] £20
ditto, Warne (London), 1893 (new edition) . . . £10
Theo: A Love Story, Peterson (Philadelphia, PA), 1877 £20
ditto, Ward Lock (London), [1877] £20
ditto, Warne (London), 1877 (new edition) . . . £20
ditto, as *Vagabondia*, Scribner's (New York), 1883 (*Theo* and *Dolly*) £20
Pretty Polly Pemberton: A Love Story, Peterson (Philadelphia, PA), 1877 . . . . . . £20
ditto, Routledge (London), 1878 . . . . . £20
Kathleen: A Love Story, Peterson (Philadelphia, PA), 1878.
. . . . £20
ditto, Routledge (London), 1878 . . . . . £20
ditto, as *Kathleen Mavourneen*, Chatto & Windus (London), 1879 . . . . £20
Miss Crespigny: A Love Story, Peterson (Philadelphia, PA), 1878 . . . . £20
ditto, Routledge (London), [1878] £20
Haworth's, Scribner's (New York), 1879 (1 vol) . . £35
ditto, Macmillan (London), 1879 (2 vols) . . . £50
Louisiana, Scribner's (New York), 1880 . . . £30
Louisiana, and That Lass O'Lowrie's, Macmillan (London), 1880 . . . . £30
A Fair Barbarian, Osgood (Boston), 1881 . . £25
ditto, Warne (London), [1881] £25
Through One Administration, Osgood & Co. (Boston), 1883 . . . . £75
ditto, Warne (London), 1883 (3 vols) £75
A Woman's Will; or, Miss Defarge, Warne (London), 1887
. . . . £20
The Fortunes of Philippa Fairfax, Warne (London), 1888 .
. . . . £30
The Pretty Sister of Jose, Scribner's (New York), 1889 £25
ditto, Spencer Blackett, 1889 (wraps) . . . £25
A Lady of Quality, Scribner's (New York), 1896 . £25

ditto, Warne (London), 1896 . . . . . £25
His Grace of Ormonde, Scribner's (New York), 1897 . £20
ditto, Warne (London), 1897 . . . . . £20
In Connection with the De Willoughby Claim, Scribner's (New York), 1899 . . . . £15
ditto, Warne (London), 1899 . . . . . £15
The Making of a Marchioness, Stokes (New York), 1901 .
. . . . £20
ditto, Smith Elder (London), 1901 . . . . £15
The Methods of Lady Walderhurst, Stokes (New York), 1901 . . . . £20
ditto, Smith Elder (London), 1902 . . . . £20
In the Closed Room, McClure, Phillips & Co. (New York), 1904 . . . . £50
ditto, Hodder & Stoughton (London), 1904 . . . £50
The Dawn of Tomorrow, Scribner's (New York), 1906 £15
ditto, Warne (London), 1907 . . . . . £15
The Shuttle, Stokes (New York), 1907 . . . . £15
ditto, Heinemann (London), 1907 . . . . £15
T. Tembarom, Century (New York), 1913 . . . £15
ditto, Hodder & Stoughton (London), [1913] . . . £15
The White People, Harper & Bros (New York), 1917 . £15
ditto, Heinemann (London), 1920 . . . . £25/£5
The Head of the House of Coombe, Stokes (New York), 1922 . . . . £25/£5
ditto, Heinemann (London), 1922 . . . . £25/£5
Robin, Stokes (New York), 1922 . . . . £25/£5
ditto, Heinemann (London), 1922 . . . . £25/£5

Short Stories for Adults
Surly Tim and Other Stories, Scribner, Armstrong & Co (New York), 1877 . . . . £30
ditto, Ward Lock (London), [1877] £20
Earlier Stories, Scribner's (New York), 1878 (2 vols) . £35
Our Neighbour Opposite, Routledge (London), [1878]. £20
Natalie and Other Stories, Warne (London), [1879] . £20
Lindsay's Luck, Scribner's (New York), 1879 . . £20
ditto, Routledge (London), 1879 . . . . . £20
A Quiet Life and *The Tide on the Moaning Bar*, Peterson (Philadelphia, PA), 1878 . . . . . . £20
ditto, Routledge (London), [1879] £20

W.R. BURNETT
(b.1899 d.1982)

Burnett was an American novelist and screenwriter, forced to take a job as night-clerk in a seedy Chicago hotel. The unsavoury characters he associated with inspired *Little Caesar* which was an overnight success and landed him a job as a Hollywood screenwriter.

Novels
Little Caesar, Lincoln MacVeagh/Dial Press (New York), 1929 . . . . £2,000/£200
ditto, Cape (London), 1929 . . . . . £250/£45
Iron Man, Lincoln MacVeagh/Dial Press (New York), 1930 . . . . £200/£30
ditto, Heinemann (London), 1930 . . . . £100/£25
Saint Johnson, Lincoln MacVeagh/Dial Press (New York), 1930 . . . . £300/£35
ditto, Heinemann (London), 1931 . . . . £100/£25

The Silver Eagle, Lincoln MacVeagh/Dial Press (New York), 1931 . . . . £500/£45
ditto, Heinemann (London), 1932 . . . . £100/£25
The Goodhues of Sinking Creek, The Raven's Head Press (Los Angeles, CA), 1931 (50 numbered copies; pbk) . £350
ditto, Harper & Brothers (New York), 1934 . . £50/£10
The Giant Swing, Harper & Brothers (New York), 1932 .
. . . . £150/£20
ditto, Heinemann (London), 1932 . . . £100/£25
Dark Hazard, Harper & Brothers (New York), 1933 (green cloth stamped in black and orange) . . . £200/£45
ditto, Harper & Brothers (New York), 1933 (blue cloth stamped with green racing greyhounds) . . . £50/£10
ditto, Heinemann (London), 1934 . . . £100/£25
Goodbye to the Past, Harper & Brothers (New York), 1934.
. . . . £100/£15
ditto, Robert Hale (London), 1981 . . . . £50/£10
King Cole, Harper & Brothers (New York), 1936 . £300/£35
ditto, as *Six Days Grace*, Heinemann (London), 1937 . .
. . . . £100/£15
The Dark Command, Harper & Brothers (New York), 1938
. . . . £250/£30
ditto, Heinemann (London), 1938 . . . £100/£25
High Sierra, Harper & Brothers (New York), 1940 £300/£35
ditto, Heinemann (London), 1940 . . . £125/£20
The Quick Brown Fox, Knopf (New York), 1942 . £200/£25
ditto, Heinemann (London), 1943 . . . £50/£15
Nobody Lives Forever, Knopf (New York), 1943 . £125/£15
ditto, Heinemann (London), 1944 . . . £45/£10
Tomorrow's Another Day, Knopf (New York), 1945 .
. . . . £125/£15
ditto, Heinemann (London), 1946 . . . £35/£10
Romelle, Knopf (New York), 1946 . . . £40/£10
ditto, Heinemann (London), 1947 . . . £45/£10
The Asphalt Jungle, Knopf (New York), 1949 . £175/£25
ditto, Macdonald (London), 1950 . . . £75/£15
Stretch Dawson, Fawcett (Gold Medal) (New York), 1950 (pbk) £35
Little Men, Big World, Knopf (New York), 1951 . £50/£10
ditto, Macdonald (London), 1952 . . . £35/£5
Vanity Row, Knopf (New York), 1952 . . £50/£10
ditto, Macdonald (London), 1953 . . . £20/£5
Adobe Walls, Knopf (New York), 1953 . . £50/£10
ditto, Macdonald (London), 1954 . . . £20/£5
Big Stan, Fawcett (Gold Medal) (New York), 1953 (pbk) .
. . . . £20
Captain Lightfoot, Knopf (New York), 1954 . . £35/£10
It's Always Four O'Clock, Random House (New York), 1956 . . . . £100/£15
Pale Moon, Knopf (New York), 1956 . . £50/£10
ditto, Macdonald (London), 1957 . . . £20/£5
Underdog, Knopf (New York), 1957 . . . £45/£10
ditto, Macdonald (London), 1957 . . . £45/£10
Bitter Ground, Knopf (New York), 1958 . . £50/£10
ditto, Macdonald (London), 1958 . . . £45/£10
Mi Amigo, Knopf (New York), 1959 . . . £50/£10
Conant, Popular Library (New York), 1961 (pbk) . £20
Round the Clock at Volari's, Fawcett (Gold Medal) (New York), 1961 (pbk) £20
Sergeants 3, Pocket Books (New York), 1962 (pbk) . £15
The Goldseekers, Doubleday (New York), 1962 . £40/£10
ditto, as *The Gold Seekers*, Macdonald (London), 1963 .
. . . . £25/£10
The Widow Barony, Macdonald (London), 1962 . £75/£15

The Abilene Samson, Pocket Books (New York), 1963 (pbk)
. . . . £10
The Roar of the Crowd, Clarkson N. Potter (New York), 1964 . . . . £25/£5
The Winning of Mickey Free, Bantam Books (New York), 1965 (pbk) £10
The Cool Man, Fawcett (Gold Medal) (New York), 1968 (pbk) £15
Good-bye Chicago, St Martin's Press (New York), 1981 .
. . . . £15/£5
ditto, Robert Hale (London), 1982 . . . . £50/£10

FANNY BURNEY
(b.1752 d.1840)

A respected woman of letters, Fanny Burney moved in circles which included Samuel Johnson and David Garrick. A novelist, and playwright, her work is considered to provide a link between the early 18th-century novels of Samuel Richardson and Henry Fielding (her influences) and the early 19th-century books of Jane Austen, who read and admired Burney.

Novels
Evelina, or A Young Lady's Entrance into the World, T. Lowndes (London), 1778 (3 vols, anonymous) . £5,000
ditto, Dent (London), 1893 (title-page, cover and spine design by Beardsley) £100
ditto, George Newnes (London), 1898 (16 b&w illustrations by Arthur Rackham, first issue with one page advert at rear, grey/blue cloth) £150
Cecilia, or Memoirs of an Heiress, T. Payne & T. Cadell (London), 1782 (5 vols; 'By the Author of "Evelina" ') .
. . . . £1,000
Camilla, or A Picture of Youth, T. Payne, T. Cadell Jun & W. Davies (London), 1796 (5 vols; 'By the Author of "Evelina" and "Cecilia" ') £500
The Wanderer, or Female Difficulties, Longman, Hurst & Co. (London), 1814 (5 vols; 'By the Author of "Evelina" ')
. . . . £500

Plays
A Busy Day, Rutgers Univ Press (New Brunswick, NJ), 1984
. . . . £10
The Witlings, Colleagues Press (London), 1995 . . £10
The Complete Plays of Frances Burney, William Pickering (London), 1995 (2 vols) £25

Miscellaneous
Brief Reflections Relative to the Emigrant French Clergy, 1793 (pamphlet, 'By the Author of "Evelina" and "Cecilia"') £200
Memoirs of Doctor Burney, Edward Moxon, 1832 (3 vols; 'arranged . . . by His Daughter') £250
The Diary and Letters of Madame D'Ardblay, 1778-1840, Henry Colburn, 1842-6 (7 vols) £250
The Early Diary of Frances Burney, 1768-1778, G. Bell (London), 1889 (2 vols) £60
The Journals and Letters of Fanny Burney, 1791-1840, Clarendon Press (Oxford), 1972-1984 (12 vols) . £150/£65

The Early Journals and Letters of Fanny Burney, 1768-1779, Clarendon Press (Oxford), 1988-1994 (3 vols) . . . . £75/£30

ROBERT BURNS

(b.1759 d.1796)

A self-taught poet, Robert Burns was as adept at composing in English as in the Scottish vernacular, and is the best known of the Lowland Scots poets. Burns also collected folk songs from across Scotland, usually revising or adapting them along the way. His poem (and song) 'Auld Lang Syne' is often sung at Hogmanay, or New Year's Eve. Values are given for copies in the original binding.

Poems Chiefly in the Scottish Dialect, John Wilson (Kilmarnock, Scotland), 1786 . . . . . £5,000
ditto, John Wilson (Kilmarnock, Scotland), 1786 (wraps) £17,500
ditto, Creech (Edinburgh, Scotland), 1787 (second edition, first issue with 'Boxburgh' in the list of subscribers, and 'skinking' on p263) £3,000
ditto, Creech (Edinburgh, Scotland), 1787 (second edition, second issue with 'Roxburgh' and 'stinking') . £2,000
The Poetical Miscellany, Stewart & Melkie (Glasgow), [1800] £600
The Works of Robert Burns, McCreery (Liverpool), 1800 (4 vols) . . . . £500 the set
Poems by Robert Burns, Oliver & Co (Edinburgh), 1801 (2 vols) . . . . £250 the set
Poems Ascribed to Robert Burns, Thomas Stewart (Glasgow), 1801 . . . .£200
Letters Addressed to Clarinda, Stewart/Macgoun (Glasgow), 1802 . . . .£200
The Prose Works of Robert Burns, Mackenzie & Dent (Newcastle), 1819 . . . .£500
Tam O'Shanter, Essex House Press (London), 1902 (150 numbered copies illustrated by W. Strang and C.R. Ashbee) £350

EDGAR RICE BURROUGHS

(b.1875 d.1950)

American author Burroughs is best known for his creation of the jungle hero Tarzan, although his many 'Martian' and other science fiction stories are of seminal importance in the development of the genre. The town of Tarzana north of Los Angeles is named after the ranch that he bought and renamed in 1919. Burroughs' also has a Martian crater named after him.

'Tarzan' Books
Tarzan of the Apes, McClurg (Chicago), 1914 (dark red cloth with front cover ruled in blind and lettered in gilt and spine ruled and lettered in gilt, first edition, first printing with 'W.F. Hall Printing Co./Chicago' set in Old English

type on two lines on verso of title leaf, first binding without acorn device on spine panel) . . . £25,000/£2,000
ditto, Methuen (London), 1917 (orange cloth, adverts dated Autumn) . . . . £1,250/£350
The Return of Tarzan, McClurg (Chicago), 1915 (states 'Published March, 1915' on copyright page; 'W.F. HALL PRINTING COMPANY, CHICAGO' at bottom of copyright page; green cloth, front panel stamped in gold and ruled in blind, spine panel stamped in gold) . £6,000/£500
ditto, Methuen (London), 1918 . . . . £1,000/£200
The Beasts of Tarzan, McClurg (Chicago), 1916 (states 'Published March, 1916' on copyright page; 'W.F. HALL PRINTING COMPANY, CHICAGO' at bottom of copyright page) . . . . £6,000/£500
ditto, Methuen (London), 1918 . . . . . £1,000/£50
The Son of Tarzan, McClurg (Chicago), 1917 (first printing with 'W.F. HALL PRINTING COMPANY, CHICAGO' at bottom of copyright page, and without dedication page) . . . . £4,000/£250
ditto, Methuen (London), 1919 . . . . . £1,000/£50
Tarzan and the Jewels of Opar, McClurg (Chicago), 1918 (states 'Published, April, 1918' on copyright page; 'W.F. HALL PRINTING COMPANY, CHICAGO' at bottom of copyright page) . . . . £2,000/£250
ditto, Methuen (London), 1919 . . . . . .£750/£60
Jungle Tales of Tarzan, McClurg (Chicago), 1919 (orange cloth; first binding with publisher's imprint on spine panel set on three lines) . . . . £1,250/£175
ditto, McClurg (Chicago), 1919 (orange cloth; second binding with publisher's imprint on spine panel set on two lines) . . . . £1,250/£125
ditto, Methuen (London), 1919 . . . . . .£750/£60
Tarzan the Untamed, McClurg (Chicago), 1920 (states 'Published April, 1920' on copyright page; 'M.A. DONOHUE & CO., PRINTERS AND BINDERS, CHICAGO' at bottom of copyright page) . £2,000/£100
ditto, Methuen (London), 1920 . . . . .£750/£60
Tarzan the Terrible, McClurg (Chicago), 1921 (states 'Published June, 1921' on copyright page; 'M.A. DONOHUE & CO., PRINTERS AND BINDERS, CHICAGO' at bottom of copyright page) . . . £2,000/£100
ditto, Methuen (London), 1921 . . . . . .£750/£60
Tarzan and the Golden Lion, McClurg (Chicago), 1923 (states 'Published March, 1923' on copyright page; 'M.A. DONOHUE & CO., PRINTERS AND BINDERS, CHICAGO' at bottom of copyright page) . . £2,000/£100
ditto, Methuen (London), 1924 . . . . . .£750/£60
Tarzan and the Ant Men, McClurg (Chicago), 1924 (states 'Published September, 1924' on copyright page; first binding with A.C. McClurg/& Co. on spine). £2,000/£125
ditto, McClurg (Chicago), 1924 (second binding with GROSSET/& DUNLAP on spine) . . . £2,000/£75
ditto, Methuen (London), 1925 . . . . . .£225/£60
The Tarzan Twins, Volland (Joilet, IL), 1924 (pictorial boards with cloth spine; issued in cardboard box without d/w) . . . .£750/£75
ditto, Volland (Joilet, IL), 1924 (first issue with d/w from later printing) . . . .£450/£75
ditto, Collins (London), 1930 . . . . . £500/£100
The Eternal Lover, McClurg (Chicago), 1925 (states 'Published October, 1925' on copyright page; 'M.A. DONOHUE & CO., PRINTERS AND BINDERS, CHICAGO' on copyright page) . . . . £2,000/£100
ditto, Methuen (London), 1927 . . . . . .£500/£60

ditto, as **The Eternal Savage**, Ace Books, Inc. (New York), [1963] (pbk) £5

Tarzan, Lord of the Jungle, McClurg (Chicago), 1928 (no statement of printing on copyright page; McClurg acorn device on copyright page) . . . . £2,000/£100

ditto, Cassell (London), 1928 . . . . . £750/£60

Tarzan and the Lost Empire, Metropolitan (New York), 1929 (no printing statement on copyright page; first binding orange cloth lettered in black; 'METROPOLITAN' at bottom of spine) . . . . . . £1,000/£65

ditto, Metropolitan (New York), 1929 (second binding red cloth lettered in black; GROSSET/&DUNLAP at bottom of spine) . . . . £1,000/£45

ditto, Cassell (London), 1931 . . . . . £750/£60

Tarzan at the Earth's Core, Metropolitan (New York), 1930 (no statement of printing on copyright page; first binding green cloth lettered in black; METROPOLITAN at bottom of spine) . . . . £1,000/£65

ditto, Metropolitan (New York), 1930 (second binding ed cloth lettered in black. GROSSET/&DUNLAP at bottom of spine) . . . . £1,000/£45

ditto, Methuen (London), 1938 . . . . . £750/£60

Tarzan the Invincible, ERB Inc. (Tarzana, CA), 1931 (no statement of printing on copyright page) . . £500/£45

ditto, John Lane (London), 1933 . . . . . £750/£60

Tarzan Triumphant, ERB Inc. (Tarzana, CA), 1932 (no statement of printing on copyright page) . . £400/£45

ditto, John Lane (London), 1933 . . . . . £400/£60

Tarzan and the City of Gold, ERB Inc. (Tarzana, CA), 1933 (states 'first edition' on copyright page) . . £400/£45

ditto, John Lane (London), 1936 . . . . . £400/£60

Tarzan and the Leopard Men, ERB Inc. (Tarzana, CA), 1933 (states 'first edition' on copyright page) . £400/£45

ditto, John Lane (London), 1936 . . . . . £300/£60

Tarzan and the Lion Man, ERB Inc. (Tarzana, CA), 1934 (states 'first edition' on copyright page) . . £400/£45

ditto, Mark Goulden Ltd (London), 1950 (pbk) . . £10

Tarzan's Quest, ERB Inc. (Tarzana, CA), 1936 (states 'first edition' on copyright page) . . . . £350/£40

ditto, Methuen (London), 1938 . . . . . £300/£60

Tarzan and the Tarzan Twins with Jad-Bal-Ja the Golden Lion, Whitman (Racine, WI), 1936 (no statement of printing on copyright page; first binding spine reads down, TARZAN [small circular picture of Tarzan] /EDGAR/ RICE/BURROUGHS/4056; no d/w) . . . £200

ditto, Whitman (Racine, WI), 1936 (second binding blank spine save for series number; no d/w) £165

ditto, Whitman (Racine, WI), 1936 (third binding solid black spine; no d/w) £150

Tarzan and the Forbidden City, ERB Inc. (Tarzana, CA), 1938 (states 'first edition' on copyright page) . £300/£30

ditto, Mark Goulden Ltd (London), 1950 (pbk) . . £10

Tarzan the Magnificent, ERB Inc. (Tarzana, CA), 1939 (states 'first edition' on copyright page) . . £200/£30

ditto, Methuen (London), 1940 . . . . . £150/£50

Tarzan and the Foreign Legion, ERB Inc. (Tarzana, CA), 1947 (states 'first edition' on copyright page) . £100/£25

ditto, W.H. Allen (London), 1949 . . . . £45/£10

Tarzan the Madman, Canaveral (New York), 1964 (states 'first edition' on copyright page) . . . £75/£25

ditto, Four Square (London), 1966 (pbk) . . . £5

Tarzan and the Castaways, Canaveral (New York), 1965 [1964] (states 'first edition' on copyright page; 400 copies without sticker on copyright page) . . £75/£25

ditto, Canaveral (New York), 1965 (later copies, distributed in 1965, have cancel sticker affixed to copyright page bearing corrected date '© 1964.') . . . £75/£25

ditto, Four Square (London), 1966 (pbk) . . . £5

Tarzan: The Lost Adventure, Dark Horse (Milwaukie, OR), 1995 . . . . £10/£5

ditto, Dark Horse (Milwaukie, OR), 1995 (1,000 signed copies) . . . . £25/£10

'Tarzan' in the Pulp Magazines

Tarzan of the Apes, *All-Story*, October 1912 . . £12,000

The Return of Tarzan, *New Story*, June to December 1913 (seven issues) . . . . £1,000 the set

The Eternal Lover, *All-Story weekly*, 7 March 1914 . £350

The Beasts of Tarzan, *All-Story Cavalier Weekly*, 16 May to 13 June 1914 (five issues) . . . . £450 the set

The Son of Tarzan, *All-Story Weekly*, 4 December 1915 to 8 January 1916 (six issues) . . . . £250 the set

Tarzan and the Jewels of Opar, *All-Story Weekly*, 18 November to 16 December 1916 (five issues) £250 the set

New Stories of Tarzan (aka *Jungle Tales of Tarzan*), *Blue Book Magazine*, September 1916 to August 1917 (twelve issues) . . . . £175 the set

Tarzan the Untamed, *Red Book*, March to August 1919 (six issues) . . . . £75 the set

Tarzan the Terrible, *Argosy All-Story Weekly*, 12 February to 26 March 1921 (seven issues) . . £75 the set

Tarzan and the Golden Lion, *Argosy All-Story Weekly*, 9 December, 1922 to 20 January 1923 (seven issues) . . . . £75 the set

Tarzan and the Ant Men, *Argosy All-Story Weekly*, 2 February to 15 March 1924 (seven issues) . £75 the set

Tarzan, Lord of the Jungle, *Blue Book Magazine*, December 1927 to May 1928 (six issues) . . £85 the set

Tarzan and the Lost Empire, *Blue Book Magazine*, October 1928 to February 1929 (five issues) . £85 the set

Tarzan at the Earth's Core, *Blue Book Magazine*, September 1929 to March 1930 (seven issues) £85 the set

Tarzan Guard of the Jungle (aka *Tarzan the Invincible*), *Blue Book Magazine*, October 1930 to April 1931 (seven issues) . . . . £85 the set

The Triumph of Tarzan (aka *Tarzan Triumphant*), *Blue Book Magazine*, October 1931 1929 to March 1932 (six issues) . . . . £85 the set

Tarzan and the City of Gold, *Argosy Weekly*, 12 March to 16 April 1932 (six issues) . . . . £40 the set

Tarzan and the Leopard Men, *Blue Book Magazine*, August 1932 to January 1933 (six issues) . . £85 the set

Tarzan and the Lion Man, *Liberty*, 11 November 1933 to 6 January 1934 (nine issues) . . . . £30 the set

Tarzan and the Immortal Men (aka *Tarzan's Quest*), *Blue Book Magazine*, October 1935 to March 1936 (six issues). . . . . £50 the set

Tarzan and the Magic Men, *Argosy All-Story Weekly*, 19 September to 3 October 1936 (three issues) . £20 the set

The Red Star of Tarzan (aka *Tarzan and the Forbidden City*), *Argosy All-Story Weekly*, 19 March to 23 April, 1938 (six issues) . . . . £20 the set

Tarzan and the Champion, *Blue Book Magazine*, April 1940 . . . . £25

The Quest of Tarzan, *Argosy All-Story Weekly*, 23 August to 6 September 1941 (three issues) . . . £15 the set

'Mars' Titles

A Princess of Mars, McClurg (Chicago), 1917 (states 'Published October, 1917' on copyright page; 'W.F. HALL PRINTING COMPANY, CHICAGO' at bottom of copyright page) . . . . . £6,000/£500
ditto, Methuen (London), 1920 . . . . £1,000/£65
The Gods of Mars, McClurg (Chicago), 1918 (states 'Published September, 1918' on copyright page; 'W.F. HALL PRINTING COMPANY, CHICAGO' at bottom of copyright page) . . . . . . £3,000/£200
ditto, Methuen (London), 1920 . . . . .£750/£65
The Warlord of Mars, McClurg (Chicago), 1919 (states 'Published September, 1919' on copyright page; first printing with 'W.F. HALL PRINTING COMPANY, CHICAGO' at bottom of copyright page; publisher's imprint at bottom of spine in three lines: A.C./McCLURG/& CO.; first printing dust jacket with price $1.40 printed at center of spine panel) . £3,000/£225
ditto, McClurg (Chicago), 1919 (second printing with no printer's details on copyright page; publisher's imprint at bottom of spine in two lines A.C. McClurg/& Co.; second printing jacket with no printed price on spine panel.) . .
. . . . £2,500/£165
ditto, Methuen (London), 1920 . . . . .£750/£60
Thuvia, Maid of Mars, McClurg (Chicago), 1920 (states 'Published October, 1920' on copyright page; 'M.A. DONOHUE & CO., PRINTERS AND BINDERS, CHICAGO' at bottom of copyright page) . £2,000/£100
ditto, Methuen (London), 1921 . . . . .£650/£50
Chessmen of Mars, McClurg (Chicago), 1922 (states 'Published November, 1922' on copyright page; 'M.A. DONOHUE & CO., PRINTERS AND BINDERS, CHICAGO' at bottom of copyright page) . £2,000/£100
ditto, Methuen (London), 1923 . . . . .£600/£45
Master Mind of Mars, McClurg (Chicago), 1928 (no printing statement on copyright page; McClurg acorn device on copyright page) . . . . . £2,000/£100
ditto, Methuen (London), 1939 . . . . .£200/£45
Fighting Man of Mars, Metropolitan (New York), 1931 (no printing statement on copyright page; first binding with *METROPOLITAN* at bottom of spine panel) . £750/£60
ditto, Metropolitan (New York), 1931 (second binding with GROSSET & DUNLAP at bottom of spine panel) £750/£40
ditto, Bodley Head (London), 1932 . . . .£250/£45
Swords of Mars, ERB Inc. (Tarzana, CA), 1936 (states 'first edition' on copyright page) . . . £1,250/£65
ditto, Four Square (London), 1966 (pbk) £5
Synthetic Men of Mars, ERB Inc. (Tarzana, CA), 1940 (states 'first edition' on copyright page). . .£400/£40
ditto, Methuen (London), 1941 . . . . .£150/£35
John Carter of Mars, Whitman Publishing Company (Racine, Wisconsin), [1940] (graphic boards; no printing statement on copyright page; although attributed to Edgar Rice Burroughs the story was the work of his son, John Coleman Burroughs) £45
Llana of Gathol, ERB Inc. (Tarzana, CA), 1948 (states 'first edition' on copyright page) . . . .£200/£45
ditto, Four Square (London), 1967 (pbk) £5
John Carter of Mars, Canaveral (New York), 1964 (first binding title incorrectly reads *John Carter and the Giant of Mars*) . . . .£100/£30
ditto, Canaveral (New York), 1964 (second binding with correct title) . . . .£100/£20
ditto, Four Square (London), 1967 (pbk) £5

'Venus' Titles

Pirates of Venus, ERB Inc. (Tarzana, CA), 1934 (states 'first edition' on copyright page) . . . .£400/£35
ditto, John Lane (London), 1935. . . . .£200/£35
Lost on Venus, ERB Inc. (Tarzana, CA), 1935 (states 'first edition' on copyright page) . . . .£400/£25
ditto, Methuen (London), 1937 . . . . .£200/£35
Carson of Venus, ERB Inc. (Tarzana, CA), 1939 (states 'first edition' on copyright page) . . . .£400/£25
ditto, Mark Goulden Ltd (London), 1950 (pbk) . . £10
Escape on Venus, ERB Inc. (Tarzana, CA), 1946 (states 'first edition' on copyright page) . . . .£250/£25
ditto, Four Square (London), 1966 (pbk) £5
Wizard of Venus, Ace Books, Inc. (New York), [1970] (no printing statement on copyright page; pbk) . . £5
ditto, New English Library (London), 1973 (pbk) . . £5

'Pellucidar' Titles

At the Earth's Core, McClurg (Chicago), 1922 (states 'Published July, 1922' on copyright page; 'M.A. DONOHUE & CO., PRINTERS AND BINDERS, CHICAGO' at bottom of copyright page) . . . . . £2,000/£100
ditto, Methuen (London), 1923 . . . . .£600/£50
Pellucidar, McClurg (Chicago), 1923 (states 'Published September, 1923' on copyright page) . . £2,000/£100
ditto, Methuen (London), 1924 . . . . .£600/£50
Tanar of Pellucidar, Metropolitan (New York), 1930 (no printing statement on copyright page) . £1,000/£50
ditto, Methuen (London), 1939 . . . . .£400/£50
Back to the Stone Age, ERB Inc. (Tarzana, CA), 1937 (states 'first edition' on copyright page) . . . .£500/£35
ditto, Tandem (London), 1974 (pbk) £5
Land of Terror, ERB Inc. (Tarzana, CA), 1944 (states 'first edition' on copyright page) . . . .£500/£35
ditto, Tandem (London), 1974 (pbk) £5
Savage Pellucidar, Canaveral (New York), 1963 (no printing statement on copyright page) . . .£250/£25
ditto, Tandem (London), 1974 (pbk) £5

'Old West' Titles

The Bandit of Hell's Bend, McClurg (Chicago), 1925 (states 'Published June, 1925' on copyright page; 'M.A. DONOHUE & CO., PRINTERS AND BINDERS, CHICAGO' at bottom of copyright page) . £2,000/£100
ditto, Methuen (London), 1926 . . . . .£750/£50
The War Chief, McClurg (Chicago), 1927 (no statement of printing on copyright page; McClurg acorn device on copyright page) . . . . . . £1,500/£75
ditto, Methuen (London), 1926 . . . . .£500/£45
Apache Devil, ERB Inc. (Tarzana, CA), 1933 (no printing statement on copyright page) . . . .£600/£50
The Oakdale Affair/The Rider, ERB Inc. (Tarzana, CA), 1937 (states 'first edition' on copyright page) .£750/£50
ditto, as *The Oakdale Affair*, Ace Books, Inc. (New York), [1974] (pbk; restores full text) £10
The Deputy Sheriff of Comanche Country, ERB Inc. (Tarzana, CA), 1940 (states 'first edition' on copyright page) . . . .£400/£35

Others

The Mucker, McClurg (Chicago), 1921 (states 'Published October, 1921' on copyright page) . . .£3,000/£150
ditto, as *The Mucker* and *The Man Without a Soul*, Methuen (London), 1921 and 1922 . . . .£500/£50

The Girl from Hollywood, McCauley (New York), 1923 (first printing with the frontispiece including: 'he said' in the caption; the first binding is coarse mesh weave red cloth lettered in yellow-green; the earliest d/w advertises 6 titles on the rear panel beginning with *Smoke of the .45* by Harry Sinclair Drago and ends with *Ride Him, Cowboy!* by Kenneth Perkins, and the publisher's address is 15-17 W. 38th St. New York) . . . . £2,000/£50
ditto, Methuen (London), 1924 . . . . £350/£60
The Land That Time Forgot, McClurg (Chicago), 1924 (states 'Published June, 1924' on copyright page; M.A. DONOHUE & CO., PRINTERS AND BINDERS, CHICAGO' at bottom of copyright page) . £4,500/£50
ditto, Methuen (London), 1927 . . . . £350/£60
ditto, as *The Land That Time Forgot, The People That Time Forgot*, and *Out of Time's Abyss*, Ace Books, Inc. (New York), [1963] (3 vols; pbk reprint of the 1918 magazine version) . . . . £5 each
The Cave Girl, McClurg (Chicago), 1925 (states 'Published March, 1925' on copyright page; 'M.A. DONOHUE & CO., PRINTERS AND BINDERS, CHICAGO' at bottom of copyright page; first binding 'A.C. McClurg/& CO' on spine) . . . . . . £1,000/£75
ditto, McClurg (Chicago), 1925 (second binding 'GROSSET/& DUNLAP' on spine) . £1,000/£40
ditto, Methuen (London), 1927 . . . . £600/£50
The Moon Maid, McClurg (Chicago), 1926 (states 'Published February, 1926' on copyright page) . £1,000/£50
ditto, as *The Moon Men*, Canaveral (New York), 1962. .
. . . . £150/£25
ditto, as *The Moon Maid*, Tom Stacey (London), 1972. .
. . . . £50/£10
The Mad King, McClurg (Chicago), 1926 (states 'published August, 1926' on copyright page; first state with textual errors on pages 12 and 92). . . . £1,000/£65
ditto, McClurg (Chicago), 1926 (errors corrected with cancel leaves) . . . . £1,000/£45
The Outlaw of Torn, McClurg (Chicago), 1929 (no statement of printing on copyright page; McClurg acorn device on copyright page) . . . . . £600/£35
ditto, Methuen (London), 1929 . . . . £200/£20
The Monster Men, McClurg (Chicago), 1929 (no printing statement on copyright page; McClurg acorn device on copyright page) . . . . £2,000/£50
ditto, Tandem (London), 1976 (pbk) £5
Jungle Girl, ERB Inc. (Tarzana, CA), 1932 (no printing statement on copyright page; 'W.F. HALL PRINTING COMPANY, CHICAGO' at bottom of copyright page; first binding in orange cloth with publisher's spine imprint in three lines) . . . . . . £175/£50
ditto, Odhams (London), [1934] . . . £175/£45
ditto, as *The Land of Hidden Men*, Ace Books, Inc. (New York), [1963] (pbk) £5
The Resurrection of Jimber Jaw, Argosy (New York), 1937 (wraps) £120
The Lad and the Lion, ERB Inc. (Tarzana, CA), 1938 (states 'first edition' on copyright page) . . . £175/£50
The Scientists Revolt, Fantastic Adventures (New York), July 1939 (wraps) £100
Beyond Thirty: A Tale of the 22nd Century, N.p., 1953 (unprinted self wraps, stapled, without any printing statement) £350
ditto, as *Beyond Thirty and The Man-Eater*, Science Fiction and Fantasy Publications (New York), 1957. . £250/£75

ditto, as *The Lost Continent*, Ace Books, Inc. (New York), [1963] (pbk). £5
ditto, as *The Lost Continent*, Tandem (London), 1977 (pbk) £5
The Man-Eater, Lloyd A. Eshbach, c.1955 (300 copies; wrappers; no printing statement) £45
ditto, as *The Man-Eater (Ben, King of Beasts)*, Fantasy House (North Hollywood, California), 1974 (stapled wraps) £5
The Girl from Farris's, Wilma Co. (Tacoma, WA), 1959 (150 copies in rust marbled boards, blue cloth tape spine).
. . . . £250
ditto, Wilma Co. (Tacoma, WA), 1959 (20 copies in black leatherette) £350
ditto, Wilma Co. (Tacoma, WA), 1959 (80 copies in sewn self wraps) £150
Tales of Three Planets, Canaveral (New York), 1964 (states 'first edition' on copyright page; contains *Beyond the Farthest Star*) . . . . . . £125/£20
Beyond the Farthest Star, Ace Books, Inc. (New York), [1964] (pbk). £5
The Efficiency Expert, House of Greystoke (Kansas City, MO), 1966 (stapled wraps; states 'Authorized first edition' on copyright page) £60
I Am A Barbarian, ERB Inc. (Tarzana, CA), 1967 (states 'first edition' on copyright page) . . . £100/£20
Pirate Blood, Ace (New York), 1970 (pbk) . . . £5

WILLIAM S. BURROUGHS
(b.1914 d.1997)

Burroughs was a controversial American novelist, essayist, social critic and spoken word performer. His early writing is associated with the Beat Generation, and he was close friends with other Beat authors including Allen Ginsberg and Jack Kerouac. He wrote of his experiences as a heroin addict in *Junkie* and *The Naked Lunch*. The latter became a cult classic, banned on the grounds of obscenity.

Novels

Junkie: Confessions of an Unredeemed Drug Addict, Ace (New York), 1953 (pseud 'William Lee', pbk double with *Narcotic Agent*; pbk) £400
ditto, Digit (London), 1957 (pseud 'William Lee'). . £75
ditto, Ace (New York), 1964 (as William Burroughs, containing only *Junkie*) £10
ditto, David Bruce & Watson (London), 1973. . £200/£30
ditto, as *Junky*, Penguin (Harmondsworth, Middlesex), 1977
. . . . £5
The Naked Lunch, Olympia Press (Paris), 1959 (first issue with green border on title-page and 'Francs 1500' on back cover; pbk; with d/w). . . . . £1,250/£250
ditto, Olympia Press (Paris), 1959 (later issue with price change stamped on the back cover; pbk; with d/w)
. . . . £600/£250
ditto, as *Naked Lunch*, Grove Press (New York), 1959 [1962] . . . . £225/£35
ditto, Calder (London), 1964 . . . . £100/£20
ditto, Grove Press (New York), 1984 (500 signed copies in box) . . . . £200/£125

The Soft Machine, Olympia Press (Paris), 1961 (pbk; with d/w) . . . . £300/£75
ditto, Grove Press (New York), 1966 . . . £100/£25
ditto, Calder & Boyars (London), 1968 . . . £75/£15
The Ticket That Exploded, Olympia Press (Paris), 1962 (pbk; with d/w) . . . . . . £150/£100
ditto, Grove Press (New York), 1967 . . . £100/£25
ditto, Calder & Boyars (London), 1968 . . . £45/£15
Dead Fingers Talk, Calder/Olympia Press (London), 1963 .
. . . . £75/£20
Nova Express, Grove Press (New York), 1964 . £50/£15
ditto, Cape (London), 1966 . . . . . £45/£15
The Wild Boys: A Book of the Dead, Grove Press (New York), 1971 . . . . £65/£20
ditto, Calder & Boyars (London), 1972 . . £65/£20
Exterminator!, Viking (New York), 1973 . £30/£10
ditto, Calder & Boyars (London), 1974 . . £30/£10
Port of Saints, Covent Garden/Am Here (London/Ollon, Switzerland), 1973 [1975] (100 signed copies of 200, d/w and slipcase) . . . . . . £250/£175
ditto, Covent Garden/Am Here (London/Ollon, Switzerland), 1973 [1975] (100 unsigned copies of 200) . £150/£125
ditto, Blue Wind Press (Berkeley, CA), 1980 . £25/£5
ditto, Blue Wind Press (Berkeley, CA), 1980 (200 signed copies, slipcase) . . . . . £100/£75
ditto, Calder (London), 1983 . . . . £25/£5
Short Novels, Calder (London), 1978 . . . £35/£10
Cities of the Red Night, Calder (London), 1981 . £25/£10
ditto, Holt Rinehart (New York), 1981 . . £40/£10
ditto, Holt Rinehart (New York), 1981 (500 signed, numbered copies, slipcase, no d/w) . . £100/£75
ditto, Holt Rinehart (New York), 1981 (26 signed, lettered copies, slipcase, no d/w) . . . £150/£125
The Place of Dead Roads, Holt Rinehart (New York), 1983
. . . . £25/£5
ditto, Holt Rinehart (New York), 1983 (300 signed, numbered copies, slipcase, no d/w) . . £100/£75
ditto, Calder (London), 1984 . . . . £25/£5
Queer, Viking (New York), 1985 . . . £20/£5
ditto, Picador (London), 1986 . . . . £20/£5
The Western Lands, Viking (New York), 1987 . £15/£5
ditto, Picador (London), 1988 . . . . £15/£5

Short Stories

Early Routines, Cadmus (Santa Barbara, CA), 1981 (26 copies of 500 signed by Burroughs and Hockney) £600/£500
ditto, Cadmus (Santa Barbara, CA), 1981 (125 signed copies of 151, glassine d/w) . . . . £150/£125
ditto, Cadmus (Santa Barbara, CA), 1981 (349 copies; pbks)
. . . . £25
Tornado Alley, Cherry Valley Editions (New York), 1989 (500 unsigned copies) £35
ditto, Cherry Valley Editions (New York), 1989 (100 signed hardback copies, no d/w) £150
ditto, Cherry Valley Editions (New York), 1989 (pbk) . £10

Poetry

The Exterminator, Auerhahn Press (San Francisco, CA), 1960 (with Brion Gysin; pbk) £60
Minutes to Go, Two Cities Editions (Paris), 1960 (with Brion Gysin, Gregory Corso and Sinclair Beiles; stapled wraps) £50
ditto, Beach Books/City Lights (San Francisco, CA), 1968 (pbk) £15

Others

Letter from a Master Addict to Dangerous Drugs, privately published, 1957 (stapled sheets) £250
Takis, Galleria Schwarz (Milan), 1962 (exhibition catalogue; stapled wraps) £30
The Yage Letters, City Lights (San Francisco, CA), 1963 (with Allen Ginsberg; pbk) £50
Roosevelt After Inauguration, Fuck You Press (New York), 1964 (pseud 'Willy Lee'; stapled pamphlet) . . £200
ditto, as *Roosevelt After Inauguration and Other Atrocities*, City Lights (San Francisco, CA), 1979 (pbk) . £25
Time, 'C' Press (New York), 1965 (with Brion Gysin, 886 copies of 986; stapled wraps) £75
ditto, 'C' Press (New York), 1965 (100 signed copies of 986; stapled wraps) £375
ditto, 'C' Press (New York), 1965 (14 copies with page of manuscript and an original drawing by Gysin) . £1,500
ditto, Urgency Press Rip-Off (London), 1972 (495 copies) .
. . . . £100
Valentine's Day Reading, American Theatre for Poets (New York), 1965 (stapled wraps) £75
Health Bulletin: Apo-33, Fuck You Press (New York), 1965
. . . . £500
ditto, as *Apo-33 Bulletin: A Metabolic Regulator*, Beach Books (San Francisco, CA), 1966 (stapled wraps) . £75
So Who Owns Death TV?, Beach Books (San Francisco, CA), 1967 (first issue, 50 cent price, with Claude Pélieu and Carl Weissner; stapled wraps) . . . £100
ditto, Beach Books (San Francisco, CA), 1967 (second issue, 75 cent price; stapled wraps) £50
The Dead Star, Nova Broadcast Press (San Francisco, CA), 1969 (stapled wraps) £50
Fernseh-Tuberkulose, Nova Press (Frankfurt), 1969 (with Claude Pélieu and Carl Weissner; stapled wraps) . £100
Entretiens avec William Burroughs, Pierre Belfond (Paris), 1969 (by Daniel Odier; pbk) £40
ditto, as *The Job, Interviews with William S. Burroughs*, Grove Press (New York), 1970 . . . £75/£25
ditto, Cape (London), 1970 . . . . £50/£15
ditto, Calder (London), 1984 (pbk) £5
The Last Words of Dutch Schultz, Cape Goliard (London), 1970 (pbk) £25
ditto, Cape Goliard (London), 1970 (hardback issue) £40/£25
ditto, Cape Goliard (London), 1970 (100 signed, numbered copies, glassine d/w) . . . . . £200/£165
ditto, as *The Last Words of Dutch Schultz: A Fiction in the Form of a Film Script*, Viking (New York), 1975 £30/£10
Ali's Smile, Unicorn Books (Brighton, UK), 1971 (99 signed hardback copies without d/w, with 12" record) . £1,500
ditto, as *Ali's Smile/Naked Scientology*, Expanded Media Editions (Göttingen), 1978 (pbk) £35
Electronic Revolution, 1970-71, Blackmoor Head Press (Cambridge, England), 1971 (50 signed copies of 500; pbk)
. . . . £1,750
ditto, Blackmoor Head Press (Cambridge, England), 1971 (450 copies of 500; pbk) £200
ditto, Expanded Media Editions (Göttingen), 1976 (pbk) £40
White Subway, Aloes Books (London), [1973] (975 copies of 1,000; stapled wraps) £40
ditto, Aloes Books (London), [1973] (25 signed copies of 1,000) £750
Mayfair Academy Series More or Less, Urgency Press Rip Off (Brighton, England), [1973] (650 copies; wraps) . £75

The Book of Breething, Chopin (Ingastone, Essex), 1974
(350 un-numbered copies; wraps) £225
ditto, Chopin (Ingastone, Essex, 1974 (50 signed copies) .
. . . . £1,000
ditto, Blue Wind Press (Berkeley, CA), 1975 (pbk) . £10
ditto, Blue Wind Press (Berkeley, CA), 1975 (175 signed,
numbered copies) £125
Sidetripping, Strawberry Hill (New York), 1975 (photographs by Charles Gatewood; pbk) £65
Snack, Aloes Books (London), 1975 (interviews by Eric
Mottram; stapled wraps) £25
Cobble Stone Gardens, Cherry Valley Editions (New York),
1976 (50 handbound, numbered and signed copies) . £250
ditto, Cherry Valley Editions (New York), 1976 (pbk) . £15
The Retreat Diaries, City Moon (New York), 1976 (stapled
wraps) £30
The Third Mind, Viking (New York), 1978 . . £30/£10
ditto, Calder (London), 1979 . . . . £25/£10
Letters to Allen Ginsberg, Givaudan/Am Here Press
(Geneva), 1978 (400 numbered copies) . . . £65
ditto, Givaudan/Am Here Press (Geneva), 1978 (100 signed,
numbered copies) £300
Blade Runner: A Movie, Blue Wind Press (Berkeley, CA),
1979 . . . . £125/£30
ditto, Blue Wind Press (Berkeley, CA), 1979 (100 signed,
numbered copies) . . . . . £225/£150
ditto, Blue Wind Press (Berkeley, CA), 1979 (pbk) . £10
Dr Benway: A Passage from 'The Naked Lunch', Brad
Morrow (Santa Barbara, CA), 1979 (324 numbered copies;
wraps) £60
ditto, Brad Morrow (Santa Barbara, CA), 1979 (150 signed,
numbered copies) . . . . . . £150/£100
Ah, Pook is Here and Other Texts, Calder (London), 1979 .
. . . . £50/£20
ditto, Calder (London)/Riverrun Press (New York), 1979
(pbk) £10
Streets of Chance, Red Ozier Press (New York), 1981 (160
signed, numbered copies) £265
With William Burroughs: A Report from the Bunker,
Seaver Books (New York), 1981 . . . . £25/£10
Sinki's Sauna, Pequod Press (New York), 1982 (500
numbered copies; wraps) £50
A William Burroughs Reader, Picador (London), 1982
(pbk) £10
Ruski, Hand Job Press (Brooklyn, NY), 1984 (500 numbered
copies; stapled wraps) £150
ditto, Odd Job Press (US), 1984 (50 bootleg copies; stapled
wraps) £100
The Four Horsemen of the Apocalypse, Expanded Media
Editions (Göttingen), 1984 (pbk) £10
The Burroughs File, City Lights (San Francisco, CA), 1984
. . . . £75/£20
ditto, City Lights (San Francisco, CA), 1984 (pbk). . £10
The Adding Machine, Selected Essays, Calder (London),
1985 . . . . £25/£5
ditto, Seaver Books (New York), 1986 . . . £25/£5
The Cat Inside, Grenfell Press (New York), 1986 (115 folio
copies, quarter vellum, signed by Burroughs and Gysin) .
. . . . £500
ditto, Grenfell Press (New York), 1986 (18 folio copies, full
vellum, signed by Burroughs and Gysin) . . £1,500
ditto, Viking (New York), 1992 (pictorial boards) . . £10
ditto, Penguin (London), 1992 (pictorial boards) . . £10

Apocalypse, George Mulder Fine Arts (New York), [1988]
(250 copies; pbk with d/w) . . . . . £65/£20
Interzone, Picador (London), 1989 . . . £25/£10
ditto, Viking (New York), 1989 . . . . £25/£10
Ghost of a Chance, Whitney Museum (New York), 1991
(160 copies, 10 signed lithographs, slipcase). £750/£500
ditto, Serpent's Tail/High Risk Press (New York), 1995 (125
signed, numbered copies, slipcase) . . . £700/£500
ditto, Serpent's Tail/High Risk Press (New York), 1995
(pictorial boards). £15
Paper Cloud, Thick Pages, Kyoto Shoin International
(Tokyo, Japan), 1992 (hardcover, no d/w) . . . £25
The Letters of William S. Burroughs, 1945-59, Picador
(London), 1993 . . . . £25/£5
ditto, Viking (New York), 1993 . . . . £15/£5
My Education, A Book of Dreams, Picador (London), 1995
. . . . £20/£5
ditto, Viking (New York), 1995 . . . . £20/£5
Word Virus: The William Burroughs Reader, Grove (New
York), 1998 . . . . £15/£5
ditto, HarperCollins (London), 1999 . . . £15/£5
Last Words: The Final Journals of William S. Burroughs,
Grove (New York), 2000 . . . . . £15/£5
ditto, Flamingo (London), 2000 . . . . £15/£5

ROBERT BURTON

(b.1577 d.1640)

Burton was a fellow of Brasenose College, Oxford. His
claim to fame is the composition of *The Anatomy of Melancholy*, written under the pseudonym of 'Democritus Junior'. It was published in 1621 and became popular immediately, being a favourite of Dr Johnson's. The book was
constantly revised and expanded by Burton and subsequent
editions increase in size. It has been suggested that he
committed suicide, but this is unlikely as he received a
Christian burial at Christ Cathedral Church, Oxford.

The Anatomy of Melancholy, Lichfield & Short for Henry
Cripps (Oxford), 1621 . . . . . . £16,500
ditto, Lichfield & Short for Henry Cripps (Oxford), 1624
(second edition) £2,250
ditto, T. Wardle (Philadelphia, PA), 1836 (2 vols) . . £300

CHRISTOPHER BUSH

(b.1885 d.1973)

All sixty-three of the novels by the British-born Christopher
Bush feature his urbane investigator Ludovic Travers.
These are restrained exercises in detection rather than
thrillers and thus can be placed at the heart of the 'Golden
Age' of detective fiction. He also wrote *The Economics of
a Spendthrift*, *World Markets* and *The Stockbrokers
Breviary*.

'Travers' Novels
The Plumley Inheritance, Jarrolds (London), n.d. [1926] .
. . . . £1,000/£125
The Perfect Murder Case, Heinemann (London), 1929 .
. . . . £800/£100

ditto, Doubleday (New York), 1929 . . . . £250/£50
Dead Man Twice, Heinemann (London), 1930   £800/£100
ditto, Doubleday (New York), 1930 . . . . £250/£50
The Death of Cosmo Revere, Doubleday (New York), 1930
. . . . £450/£75
ditto, as **Murder at Fenwold**, Heinemann (London), 1930 .
. . . . £425/£65
Dancing Death, Heinemann (London), 1931 . . £800/£75
ditto, Doubleday (New York), 1931 . . . . £250/£35
Dead Man's Music, Heinemann (London), 1931 . £700/£70
ditto, Doubleday (New York), 1932 . . . . £300/£35
Cut Throat, Heinemann (London), 1932 . . . £500/£50
ditto, Morrow (New York), 1932 . . . . £200/£25
The Case of the Unfortunate Village, Cassell (London),
1932 . . . . £500/£50
The Case of the April Fools, Cassell (London), 1933 .
. . . . £500/£50
ditto, Morrow (New York), 1933 . . . . £200/£25
The Case of the Three Strange Faces, Cassell (London),
1933 . . . . £500/£50
ditto, as **The Crank in the Corner**, Morrow (New York),
1933 . . . . £200/£25
The Case of the 100% Alibis, Cassell (London), 1934 . .
. . . . £500/£50
ditto, as **The Kitchen Cake Murder**, Morrow (New York),
1934 . . . . £175/£45
The Case of the Dead Shepherd, Cassell (London), 1934 .
. . . . £500/£50
ditto, as **The Tea-tray Murders**, Morrow (New York), 1934
. . . . £175/£45
The Case of the Chinese Gong, Cassell (London), 1935 .
. . . . £500/£50
ditto, Holt (New York), 1935 . . . . £175/£45
The Case of the Monday Murders, Cassell (London), 1936
. . . . £500/£50
ditto, as **Murder on Mondays**, Holt (New York), 1936 . .
. . . . £175/£45
The Case of the Bonfire Body, Cassell (London), 1936 .
. . . . £500/£50
ditto, as **The Body in the Bonfire**, Holt (New York), 1936 .
. . . . £175/£45
The Case of the Missing Minutes, Cassell (London), 1937 .
. . . . £450/£45
ditto, as **Eight O'clock Alibi**, Holt (New York), 1937 . .
. . . . £175/£45
The Case of the Hanging Rope, Cassell (London), 1937 .
. . . . £450/£45
ditto, as **The Wedding Night Murder**, Holt (New York),
1937 . . . . £175/£45
The Case of the Tudor Queen, Cassell (London), 1938, Holt
(New York), 1938 . . . . . . £450/£45
The Case of the Leaning Man, Cassell (London), 1938 .
. . . . £450/£45
ditto, as **The Leaning Man**, Holt (New York), 1938 . .
. . . . £175/£45
The Case of the Green Felt Hat, Cassell (London), 1939 .
. . . . £450/£45
ditto, Holt (New York), 1939 . . . . £175/£45
The Case of the Flying Ass, Cassell (London), 1939 . .
. . . . £450/£45
The Case of the Climbing Rat, Cassell (London), 1940 .
. . . . £400/£45
The Case of the Murdered Major, Cassell (London), 1941 .
. . . . £400/£45

The Case of the Kidnapped Colonel Cassell (London), 1942
. . . . £400/£45
The Case of the Fighting Soldier, Cassell (London), 1942 .
. . . . £300/£35
The Case of the Magic Mirror, Cassell (London), 1943 .
. . . . £300/£35
The Case of the Running Mouse, Cassell (London), 1944 .
. . . . £300/£35
The Case of the Platinum Blonde, Cassell (London), 1944 .
. . . . £250/£25
ditto, Macmillan (New York), 1949 . . . . £60/£15
The Case of the Corporal's Leave, Cassell (London), 1945.
. . . . £150/£25
The Case of the Missing Men, Macdonald (London), n.d.
(1946) . . . . £75/£20
ditto, Macmillan 1947 . . . . . £25/£10
The Case of the Second Chance, Macdonald (London),
1946 . . . . £50/£15
ditto, Macmillan (New York) 1947 . . . . £25/£10
The Case of the Curious Client, Macdonald (London), 1947
. . . . £50/£15
ditto, Macmillan (New York) 1948 . . . . £25/£10
The Case of the Haven Hotel, Macdonald (London), 1948 .
. . . . £50/£15
The Case of the Housekeeper's Hair, Macdonald (London),
1948 . . . . £50/£15
ditto, Macmillan (New York) 1949 . . . . £25/£10
The Case of the Seven Bells, Macdonald (London), 1949 .
. . . . £50/£15
ditto, Macmillan (New York) 1950 . . . . £25/£10
The Case of the Purloined Picture, Macdonald (London),
1949 . . . . £50/£15
ditto, Macmillan (New York) 1951 . . . . £25/£10
The Case of the Happy Warrior, Macdonald (London), 1950
. . . . £50/£15
ditto, as **The Case of the Frightened Mannequin**, Macmillan
(New York) 1951 . . . . . . £25/£10
The Case of the Corner Cottage, Macdonald (London), 1951
. . . . £50/£15
ditto, Macmillan (New York) 1952 . . . . £25/£10
The Case of the Fourth Detective, Macdonald (London),
1951 . . . . £40/£10
The Case of the Happy Medium, Macdonald (London),
1952 . . . . £40/£10
ditto, Macmillan (New York) 1952 . . . . £25/£10
The Case of the Counterfeit Colonel, Macdonald (London),
1952 . . . . £40/£10
ditto, Macmillan (New York) 1953 . . . . £25/£10
The Case of the Burnt Bohemian, Macdonald (London),
1953 . . . . £40/£10
ditto, Macmillan (New York) 1954 . . . . £25/£10
The Case of the Silken Petticoat, Macdonald (London),
1953 . . . . £40/£10
ditto, Macmillan (New York) 1954 . . . . £25/£10
The Case of the Red Brunette, Macdonald (London), 1954 .
. . . . £40/£10
ditto, Macmillan (New York) 1955 . . . . £25/£10
The Case of the Three Lost Letters, Macdonald (London),
1954 . . . . £40/£10
ditto, Macmillan (New York) 1955 . . . . £25/£10
The Case of the Benevolent Bookie, Macdonald (London),
1955 . . . . £40/£10
ditto, Macmillan (New York) 1956 . . . . £25/£10

The Case of the Amateur Actor, Macdonald (London), 1955
. . . . £35/£10
ditto, Macmillan (New York) 1956 . . . £25/£10
The Case of the Extra Man, Macdonald (London), 1956 .
. . . . £35/£10
ditto, Macmillan (New York) 1957 . . . £25/£10
The Case of the Flowery Corpse, Macdonald (London),
1956 . . . . £30/£10
ditto, Macmillan (New York) 1957 . . . £25/£10
The Case of the Russian Cross, Macdonald (London), 1957
. . . . £35/£10
ditto, Macmillan (New York) 1958 . . . £20/£5
The Case of the Treble Twist, Macdonald (London), 1958 .
. . . . £35/£10
ditto, as *The Case of the Triple Twist*, Macmillan (New
York) 1958 . . . . £20/£5
The Case of the Running Man, Macdonald (London), 1958
. . . . £35/£10
ditto, Macmillan (New York) 1959 . . . £20/£5
The Case of the Careless Thief, Macdonald (London), 1959
. . . . £35/£10
ditto, Macmillan (New York) 1960 . . . £20/£5
The Case of the Sapphire Brooch, Macdonald (London),
1960 . . . . £30/£10
ditto, Macmillan (New York) 1961 . . . £20/£5
The Case of the Extra Grave, Macdonald (London), 1961 .
. . . . £30/£10
ditto, Macmillan (New York) 1962 . . . £15/£5
The Case of the Dead Man Gone, Macdonald (London),
1961 . . . . £25/£10
ditto, Macmillan (New York) 1962 . . . £15/£5
The Case of the Three-Ring Puzzle, Macdonald (London),
1962 . . . . £20/£10
ditto, Macmillan (New York) 1963 . . . £10/£5
The Case of the Heavenly Twin, Macdonald (London), 1963
. . . . £15/£5
ditto, Macmillan (New York) 1964 . . . £10/£5
The Case of the Grand Alliance, Macdonald (London), 1964
. . . . £15/£5
ditto, Macmillan (New York) 1965 . . . £10/£5
The Case of the Jumbo Sandwich, Macdonald (London),
1965 . . . . £10/£5
ditto, Macmillan (New York) 1966 . . . £10/£5
The Case of the Good Employer, Macdonald (London),
1966 . . . . £10/£5
ditto, Macmillan (New York) 1967 . . . £10/£5
The Case of the Deadly Diamonds, Macdonald (London),
1967 . . . . £10/£5
ditto, Macmillan (New York) 1969 . . . £10/£5
The Case of the Prodigal Daughter, Macdonald (London),
1968 . . . . £10/£5
ditto, Macmillan (New York) 1969 . . . £10/£5

Novels Written as 'Michael Home'
The Place of Little Birds, Methuen (London), 1941 £50/£15
The House of Shade, Methuen (London), 1942 . £45/£15
City of the Soul, Methuen (London), 1943 . £45/£10
The Cypress Road, Methuen (London), 1945 . £35/£10
The Strange Prisoner, Methuen (London), 1947 (with John
Benham) . . . . £35/£10
The Auber File, Methuen (London), 1953 (uncollected
stories, with John Benham) . . . . £30/£10

A.S. BYATT
(b.1936)

A novelist and critic, Byatt is the sister of Margaret
Drabble and a great rivalry is said to exist between the two
of them. Byatt won the Booker Prize for *Possession*, her
best known work, and is not only a critically acclaimed
novelist but a popular one. She caused controversy by
pouring scorn on readers of J.K. Rowling's 'Harry Potter'
books and was defended by Fay Weldon, who at the same
time admitted that she sounded 'like a bit of a spoilsport'.
Byatt was awarded a C.B.E. in 1990 and was made a
D.B.E. in 1999.

Novels
Shadow of a Sun, Chatto & Windus (London), 1964 . .
. . . . £250/£20
ditto, Harcourt Brace (New York), 1964 . . . £75/£10
ditto, as *The Shadow of the Sun*, Random House (London),
1991 (pbk) £5
ditto, as *The Shadow of the Sun*, Harcourt Brace (New
York), 1991 (pbk) £5
The Game, Chatto & Windus (London), 1967 . . £100/£20
ditto, Scribner's (New York), 1968 . . . £75/£15
The Virgin in the Garden, Chatto & Windus (London), 1978
. . . . £100/£20
ditto, Knopf (New York), 1979 . . . . £75/£15
Still Life, Chatto & Windus and The Hogarth Press
(London), 1985 . . . . . . £30/£5
ditto, Scribner's (New York), 1985 . . . £15/£5
Possession: A Romance, Chatto & Windus (London), 1990
. . . . £75/£10
ditto, Random House (New York), 1990 . . £65/£10
Babel Tower, Chatto & Windus (London), 1996 . £15/£5
ditto, Random House (New York), 1996 . . £15/£5
ditto, Franklin Library (Franklin Centre, PA), 1996 (signed,
limited edition) £35
The Biographer's Tale, Chatto & Windus (London), 2000 .
. . . . £15/£5
ditto, Knopf (New York), 2001 . . . . £15/£5
A Whistling Woman, Chatto & Windus (London), 2002 .
. . . . £15/£5
ditto, Knopf (New York), 2002 . . . £15/£5
The Children's Book, Chatto & Windus (London), 2009 .
. . . . £10/£5
ditto, Chatto & Windus (London), 2009 (1,000 signed,
numbered copies; slipcase) . . . . £50/£35
ditto, Knopf (New York), 2009 . . . . £10/£5

Short Stories and Novellas
Sugar and Other Stories, Chatto & Windus (London), 1987
. . . . £45/£10
ditto, Scribner's (New York), 1987 . . . £40/£10
Angels and Insects, Chatto & Windus (London), 1992 . .
. . . . £15/£5
ditto, London Limited Editions (London), 1992 (150 signed
copies, acetate d/w) . . . . . £60/£45
ditto, as *Angels and Insects: Two Novellas*, Random House
(New York), 1992 . . . . . . £10/£5
ditto, Franklin Library (Franklin Centre, PA), 1993 (signed,
limited edition) £35
The Matisse Stories, Chatto & Windus (London), 1993 .
. . . . £15/£5

ditto, Random House (New York), 1993 . . . £10/£5

The Djinn in the Nightingale's Eye, Five Fairy Stories, Chatto & Windus (London), 1994 . . . . £10/£5

ditto, Random House (New York), 1994 . . . £10/£5

Elementals: Stories of Fire and Ice, Chatto & Windus (London), 1998 . . . . £10/£5

ditto, Random House (New York), 1999 . . . £10/£5

Little Black Book of Stories, Chatto & Windus (London), 2003 . . . . £10/£5

ditto, Random House (New York), 2004 . . . £10/£5

Non-Fiction

Degrees of Freedom: The Novels of Iris Murdoch, Chatto & Windus (London), 1965 . . . . . £75/£25

ditto, Barnes & Noble (New York), 1965 . . . £65/£20

Wordsworth and Coleridge in Their Time, Nelson (London), 1970 . . . . £75/£20

ditto, Crane, Russak (New York), 1973 . . . £35/£10

ditto, as **Unruly Times: Wordsworth and Coleridge in Their Times**, Hogarth Press (London), 1989 . . £10/£5

Iris Murdoch, Longman (London), 1970 (stapled wraps) £10

Ford Madox Ford and the Prose Tradition, Chatto & Windus (London), 1982 . . . . . £25/£10

ditto, Knopf (New York), 1982 . . . . . £20/£10

Passions of the Mind: Selected Writings, Chatto & Windus (London), 1991 . . . . . . £15/£5

ditto, Turtle Bay (New York), 1992 . . . . £10/£5

Imagining Characters, Six Conversations about Women Writers, Chatto & Windus (London), 1995 (with Ignes Sodre) . . . . £25/£10

ditto, as **Imagining Characters: Conversations about Women Writers**, Vintage Books (New York), 1997 £10/£5

On Histories and Stories: Selected Essays, Chatto & Windus (London), 2000 . . . . . £15/£5

ditto, Harvard Univ Press (Cambridge, MA), 2000 £15/£5

Portraits in Fiction, Chatto & Windus (London), 2001 .
. . . . £15/£5

LORD BYRON

(b.1788 d.1824)

George Gordon, 6th Baron Byron was an Anglo-Scottish poet and a leading figure in the Romantic movement. He was regarded as one of the greatest European poets during his lifetime, and is still widely read. His fame rests, perhaps, on his extravagant living, many love affairs, debts, and allegations of incest, as much as on his writings; he was famously described by Lady Caroline Lamb as 'mad, bad, and dangerous to know'.

Fugitive Pieces, privately printed by J. Ridge (Newark), [1806] (66pps booklet in green/grey wrappers) . £35,000

Poems on Various Occasions, privately printed by J. Ridge (Newark), 1807 (boards with paper label printed 'Poems')
. . . . £4,000

Hours of Idleness: a Series of Poems, S. & J. Ridge (Newark), 1807 (boards; first issue p22, line 2 reads 'Those tissues of fancy...') £1,750

ditto, S. & J. Ridge (Newark), 1807 (boards; second issue p22, line 2 reads 'Those tissues of falsehood . . .' and is a cancel leaf) £1,250

English Bards and Scottish Reviewers, James Cawthorn (London), [1809] (wraps; first issue no Preface) . . £375

ditto, James Cawthorn (London), [1809] (wraps; second issue contains a Preface) £175

Imitations and Translations, Longman (London), 1809 (boards) £300

Childe Harold's Pilgrimage: Cantos I & II, John Murray (London), 1812 (boards; first issue poem on p.189 is headed 'Written beneath a picture of J-V-D') . £400

ditto, John Murray (London), 1812 (boards; second issue poem headed 'Written beneath a picture') . . . £225

Childe Harold's Pilgrimage: Canto III, John Murray (London), 1816 (plain wraps; first issue with 'L' in 'Lettre' under the word 'La' in line above on title page; at end of first line of second stanza on p.4 there is no exclamation mark) £200

ditto, John Murray (London), 1816 (second issue with 'L' under 'U' in 'CGLU'; exclamation mark added at end of first line of second stanza on p.4) £150

Childe Harold's Pilgrimage: Canto IV, John Murray (London), 1818 (paper-covered boards; first issue p.155 ends with 'the impressions of'). £400

The Curse of Minerva, T. Davison (London), 1812 (25pps in wrappers) £125

The Genuine Rejected Addresses Presented to Drury Lane Theatre, B. McMillan, 1812 (wraps) £500

The Waltz: An Apostrophic Hymn, Sherwood, Neely and Jones (London), 1813 (pseudonym 'Horace Hornem'; wraps) £5,000

The Giaour: a Fragment of a Turkish Tale, John Murray (London), 1813 (41pps; wrappers) £150

The Bride of Abydos: a Turkish Tale, John Murray (London), 1813 (72 pps; wrappers; first issue p.47 has 20 lines; errata slip) £250

ditto, John Murray (London), 1813 (72 pps; wrappers; second issue p.47 has 22 lines; no errata slip) . £175

The Corsair: a Tale, John Murray (London), 1814 (wraps; first issue ends at p 100) £275

ditto, John Murray (London), 1814 (wraps; second issue ends at p 108) £175

Ode to Napoleon Buonoparte, John Murray (London), 1814 (wraps; 14pps) £1,000

Lara: a Tale, John Murray (London), 1814 (boards; issued with **Jacqueline: a Tale** by Samuel Rogers) . . . £150

Hebrew Melodies, John Murray (London), 1815 (wraps; first issue has notice of Roger's 'Jacqueline') . . . £650

ditto, John Murray (London), 1815 (wraps; second issue without notice of 'Jacqueline'). £300

Poems, John Murray (London), 1816 (boards; first issue with Notes on p.39) £175

ditto, John Murray (London), 1816 (boards; second issue with poem 'To Samuel Rogers' on p.39; Notes on p.40) .
. . . . £100

The Siege of Corinth: a Poem, John Murray (London), 1816 (wraps) £175

The Prisoner of Chillon, John Murray (London), 1816 (wraps; first issue last leaf in blank and verso has adverts)
. . . . £250

ditto, John Murray (London), 1816 (wraps; second issue last leaf has adverts and verso blank) £175

Monody on the Death of R.B. Sheridan, John Murray (London), 1816 (wraps) £150

Lament of Tasso, John Murray (London), 1817 (wraps) .
. . . . £2,000

Manfred: a Dramatic Poem, John Murray (London), 1817
(wraps; first issue verso title page has two-line printer's
imprint) £400
ditto, John Murray (London), 1817 (wraps; second issue
verso title page has one-line printer's imprint)   .   .£150
Beppo: a Venetian Story, John Murray (London), 1818
(wraps) £500
Mazeppa, John Murray (London), 1819 (wraps; first issue
imprint on p.70) £400
ditto, John Murray (London), 1819 (wraps; second issue
imprint on verso p.71) £200
Don Juan: Cantos 1 & 2, John Murray (London), 1819
(boards) £200
ditto: Cantos 3, 4, & 5, Murray (London),1821 (boards) £200
ditto: Cantos 6, 7 & 8, Hunt (London), 1823 (boards)   .£200
ditto: Cantos 9 to 14, Hunt (London), 1823 (boards)   .£200
ditto: Cantos 15 & 16, Hunt (London), 1824 (boards)   .£200
ditto: the set £1,500
Marino Faliero: The Doge of Venice and *The Prophecy of
Dante*, John Murray (London), 1821 (blue boards; first
issue: on p151 the Doge's speech begins 'What Crimes?')
    .   .   .   .£200
ditto, John Murray (London), 1821 (blue boards; second
issue: on p151 the Doge's speech begins 'His Crimes!')   .
    .   .   .   .£175
Sardanapalus: a Tragedy; *The Two Foscari*; *Cain: a
Mystery*, John Murray (London), 1821 (paper boards) £200
*Letter to **** ****** [John Murray] on the Rev. W.L.
Bowles*, John Murray (London), 1821 (wraps; first issue
with adverts dated March 1821)   .   .   .£100
ditto, John Murray (London), 1821 (wraps; second issue with
4 leaves before adverts, on paper watermarked '1819')   £75
*Cain: A Mystery, With a Letter From the Author to Mr.
Murray*, R. Carlile (London), 1822.   .   .   .£100
The Liberal: Verse and Prose from the South, John Hunt
(London), 1822-23 (by Byron and others; 4 parts bound
into 2 volumes) £500
Werner: a Tragedy, John Murray (London), 1823 (unlettered
wraps; first issue with advertisment for 'Werner' p188)   .
    .   .   .   .£350
ditto, John Murray (London), 1823 (second issue with no
advert on p.188 but with 'The End' followed by the
imprint) £175
The Age of Bronze, John Hunt (London), 1823 (unlettered
wraps; anonymous) £250
The Island or Christian and his Comrades, John Hunt
(London), 1823 (unlettered wraps; paper watermarked
'1822') £150
The Deformed Transformed: a Drama, J. & H.L. Hunt
(London), 1824 (wraps) £200
Parliamentary Speeches of Lord Byron, Rodwell & Martin
(London), 1824 (wraps) £350
The Correspondence of Lord Byron, [1824] (boards)   .£100

Collected Editions

The Works of Lord Byron, John Murray (London), 1815 (4
vols) £250
*The Works of Lord Byron, with his Letters and Journals,
and his Life by Thomas Moore*, John Murray (london),
1832/33 (17 vols) £200

JAMES M. CAIN
(b. 1892 d.1977)

James Mallahan Cain was an American journalist and
novelist. He is commonly associated with the hardboiled
school of American crime fiction and is considered one of
the creators of *noir* fiction. In all of his novels (apart from
Mildred Pierce) a man falls for a *femme fatale* and
becomes involved in criminal activity with her, and is
eventually betrayed by her. Cain continued writing until his
death but his later novels were not as critically or
commercially successful.

Novels and Novellas

The Postman Always Rings Twice, Knopf (New York),
1934   .   .   .   .   .   . £2,000/£250
ditto, Cape (London), 1934 (d/w price 5/-)   . £1,000/£150
Serenade, Knopf (New York), 1937 (three d/w variants
noted but no priority established)   .   .   .£200/£25
ditto, Cape (London), 1938 (d/w price 7/6)   .   .£100/£15
Mildred Pierce, Knopf (New York), 1941   . £500/£45
ditto, Robert Hale (London), 1943 (d/w price 8/6)   . £200/£25
Love's Lovely Counterfeit, Knopf (New York), 1942   .   .
    .   .   .   .£150/£20
Double Indemnity, Avon (New York), 1943 (pbks)   . £45
The Embezzler, Avon (New York), 1944 (pbk)   .   . £45
Career in C Major and Other Stories, Avon (New York),
1945 (pbk) £35
Past All Dishonor, Knopf, 1946.   .   . £75/£15
The Butterfly, Knopf (New York), 1947   .   . £65/£10
Sinful Woman, Avon (New York), 1947 (pbk)   .   . £60
ditto, World (Cleveland, OH), 1948   .   .   . £75/£25
The Moth, Knopf (New York), 1948.   .   . £75/£15
ditto, Robert Hale (London), 1950   .   .   . £65/£15
Jealous Woman, Avon (New York), 1950 (pbk)   . £65
ditto, Robert Hale (London), 1955 (with *Sinful Woman*)   .
    .   .   .   .£150/£25
The Root of His Evil, Avon (New York), 1951   .   . £40
ditto, Robert Hale (London), 1954   .   .   . £75/£15
Galatea, Knopf (New York), 1953   .   .   . £30/£5
ditto, Robert Hale (London), 1954   .   .   . £50/£10
Mignon, Dial (New York), 1962.   .   .   . £35/£10
ditto, Robert Hale (London), 1963   .   .   . £50/£10
The Magician's Wife, Dial (New York), 1965   . £25/£10
ditto, Robert Hale (London), 1966   .   .   . £25/£10
Rainbow's End, Mason-Charter (New York), 1975   £25/£10
ditto, W.H. Allen (London), 1975   .   .   . £25/£10
The Institute, Mason-Charter (New York), 1976   . £25/£10
ditto, Robert Hale (London), 1977   .   .   . £25/£10
Cloud Nine, Mysterious Press (New York), 1984   . £20/£5
The Enchanted Isle, Mysterious Press (New York), 1984   .
    .   .   .   .£20/£5

Collections of Novels and Novellas

Three of a Kind, Knopf (New York), 1943 (contains: *Career
in C Major*, *The Embezzler* and *Double Indemnity*; d/w
with price of $2.75 and $2.50)   .   .   . £300/£40
ditto, Knopf (New York), 1943 (d/w clipped so retaining
only one price)   .   .   .   .   .£200/£40
ditto, Robert Hale (London), 1945   .   .   . £225/£35
Three of Hearts, Robert Hale (London), 1949 (contains:
Love's Lovely Counterfeit, *Past All Dishonour* and *The
Butterfly*)   .   .   .   .   .   .£60/£15

Cain x 3, Knopf (New York), 1969 (contains: *The Postman Always Rings Twice*, *Mildred Pierce* and *Double Indemnity*) . . . . . . £20/£5

The Baby in the Icebox and Other Short Fiction, Holt, Rinehart and Winston (New York), 1981 . . £20/£5

ditto, Franklin Library (Franklin Centre, PA), 1981. . £25

ditto, Robert Hale (London), 1982 . . . . £20/£5

Hard Cain, Gregg Press (Boston), 1980 (Contains: *Sinful Woman*, *Jealous Woman* and *The Root of His Evil*) £30/£10

Others

Our Government, Knopf (New York), 1930 (first issue printed d/w) . . . . £300/£40

ditto, Knopf (New York), 1930 (second issue pictorial d/w). . . . . £200/£40

Sixty Years of Journalism, Bowling Green State Univ Popular Press (Bowling Green, OH), 1985 . . £25/£5

ditto, Bowling Green State Univ Popular Press (Bowling Green, OH), 1985 (pbk) £5

PAUL CAIN

(b. 1902 d.1966)

Paul Cain was the pseudoym used by George Carrol Sims for his pulp career. He wrote seventeen hard-boiled detective tales for *Black Mask*, five of which were brought together to form his one published novel, *Fast One*. As a screenwriter he used the name Peter Ruric.

Novels

Fast One, Doubleday (Garden City, NY), 1933 £4,000/£300

ditto, Constable (London), 1936 . . . . £3,500/£300

Short Stories

7 Slayers, Saint Enterprises (Hollywood), 1946 (pbk) . £100

ditto, as **Seven Slayers**, No Exit (Harpenden, Herts), 1988 . . . . £45/£10

RANDOLPH CALDECOTT

(b.1846 d.1886)

A British illustrator, Caldecott produced innovative and popular picture books in the Victorian era. He was among the first to see that words are not needed if the picture illustrates a point, and *vice versa*. He is said to have influenced, amongst other artists, Beatrix Potter.

'Picture Books'

The Diverting History of John Gilpin, Routledge (London), [1878] £50

The House that Jack Built, Routledge (London), [1878] £45

The Mad Dog, Routledge (London), [1879] . . . £75

The Babes in the Wood, Routledge (London), [1879] . £45

The Three Jovial Huntsmen, Routledge (London), [1880] .
. . . . £45

Sing a Song for Sixpence, Routledge (London), [1880] £45

The Queen of Hearts, Routledge (London), [1881] . £45

The Farmer's Boy, Routledge (London), [1881] . . £40

The Milkmaid, Routledge (London), [1882] . . . £40

Hey Diddle Diddle and Baby Bunting, Routledge (London), [1882] £40

The Fox Jumps Over the Parson's Gate, Routledge (London), [1883] £35

A Frog He Would A-Wooing Go, Routledge (London), [1883] £35

Come Lasses and Lads, Routledge (London), [1884] . £35

Ride a Cock Horse to Banbury Cross and A Farmer Went Trotting upon his Grey Mare, Routledge (London), [1884] £35

An Elegy on the Glory of Her Sex, Mrs Mary Blaize, by Dr Oliver Goldsmith, Routledge (London), [1885] . . £35

The Great Panjandrum Himself, Routledge (London), [1885] £30

R. Caldecott's Picture Book, Vol. 1, Routledge (London), [1879] (containing the first 4 'Picture Books') . . £50

R. Caldecott's Picture Book, Vol. 2, Routledge (London), [1881] (containing the second 4 'Picture Books') . £50

R. Caldecott's Collection of Pictures and Songs, Routledge (London), [1881] (reissue of Caldecott's 'Picture Book' Vols 1 and 2) £50

The Hey Diddle Diddle Picture Book, Routledge (London), [1883] (contains 4 'Picture Books') £50

The Panjandrum Picture Book, Routledge (London), [1885] (contains 4 'Picture Books') £50

The Complete Collection of Randolph Caldecott's Pictures and Songs, Routledge (London), [1887] (contains all 16 'Picture Books', 800 copies) £300

R. Caldecott's Picture Books, Routledge (London), [1889-1892] (contains the first 4 'Picture Books') . . . £50

Randolph Caldecott's Second Collection of Pictures and Songs, Warne (London), [1895] (reissue of *The Hey Diddle Diddle Picture Book* and *The Panjandrum Picture Book*) .
. . . . £50

Other Titles Illustrated by Randolph Caldecott

Frank Mildmay, or The Naval Officer, by Captain Marryat, Routledge (London), [1873] £50

Baron Bruno, or The Unbelieving Philosopher and Other Fairy Stories, by Louisa Morgan, Macmillan (London), 1875 . . . . £50

Old Christmas, From the Sketchbook of Washington Irving, Macmillan (London), 1876 . . . . . £45

Bracebridge Hall, or The Humorists, by Washington Irving, Macmillan (London), 1877 [1876] . . . £45

What the Blackbird Said, A Story in Four Chirps, by Mrs Frederick Locker, Routledge (London), 1881 . £50

Jackanapes, by Juliana Horatia Ewing, S.P.C.K. (London), 1884 [1883] £30

Some of Aesop's Fables with Modern Instances, Macmillan (London), 1883 . . . . £35

Daddy Darwin's Dovecote, A Country Tale, by Juliana Horatia Ewing, S.P.C.K. (London), [1884] . . £30

Lob Lie-By-The-Fire, by Juliana Horatia Ewing, S.P.C.K. (London), [1885] £30

Fables de la Fontaine, Macmillan (London), 1885 £35

Jack and the Beanstalk, by Hallam Tennyson, Macmillan (London), 1886 . . . . £35

The Owls of Olynn Belfry, by A.Y.D., Field & Tuer (London), [1886]. £40

The Complete Collection of Randolph Caldecott's Contributions to The Graphic, Routledge (London), 1888 (1,250 copies signed by publisher and printer) . £250

Jackanapes, by Juliana Horatia Ewing, S.P.C.K. (London),
[1892] (contains *Daddy Darwin's Dovecote* and *Lob Lie-
By-The-Fire*). £30
Randolph Caldecott's Painting Book, S.P.C.K. (London),
[1895] £65

ALBERT CAMUS
(b.1913 d.1960)

Camus was a French author and philosopher and one of the
principal exponents of Existentialism. He is also considered
the originator of the related philosophy of Absurdism, and
was one of the very few international goalkeepers to have
gone on to establish a literary reputation, for which he was
awarded the Nobel Prize for Literature in 1957.

Novels
The Outsider, Hamish Hamilton (London), 1946 (translated
by Stuart Gilbert).   .   .   .   .   .   . £350/£40
ditto, as *The Stranger*, Knopf (New York), 1946 . £350/£40
The Plague, Hamish Hamilton (London), 1948 (translated by
Stuart Gilbert)   .   .   .   .   .   . £200/£25
ditto, Knopf (New York), 1948   .   .   .   . £200/£20
The Rebel, Hamish Hamilton (London), 1953 (translated by
Anthony Bower)   .   .   .   .   .   . £100/£15
ditto, Knopf (New York), 1954   .   .   .   . £75/£15
The Fall, Hamish Hamilton (London), 1957 (translated by
Justin O'Brien)   .   .   .   .   .   . £100/£15
ditto, Knopf (New York), 1957   .   .   .   . £100/£15
A Happy Death, Hamish Hamilton (London), 1972 (translated by Richard Howard) .   .   .   .   . £25/£5
ditto, Knopf (New York), 1972   .   .   .   . £25/£5

Short Stories
Exile and the Kingdom, Hamish Hamilton (London), 1958
(translated by Justin O'Brien)   .   .   .   . £65/£15
ditto, Knopf (New York), 1958   .   .   .   . £65/£10

Plays
Caligula and *Cross Purpose*, Hamish Hamilton (London),
1947 (translated by Justin Kaplan)   .   .   . £100/£15
ditto, New Directions (Norfolk, CT), 1947   .   . £75/£15
ditto, Knopf (New York), 1948   .   .   .   . £30/£10
The Possessed, Hamish Hamilton (London), 1960 (translated
by Justin O'Brien)   .   .   .   .   .   . £65/£15
ditto, Knopf (New York), 1960   .   .   .   . £50/£10
Others
The Myth of Sisyphus, Hamish Hamilton (London), 1955
(translated by Justin O'Brien)   .   .   .   . £65/£15
ditto, Knopf (New York), 1955   .   .   .   . £50/£10
Nobel Prize Acceptance Speech, Knopf (New York), 1958
(translated by Justin O'Brien; stapled wraps)   .   . £30
Reflections on the Guillotine, Fridtjof-Karla (U.S.), 1959 .
.   .   .   . £75/£20
Resistance, Rebellion and Death, Hamish Hamilton
(London), 1961 (translated by Justin O'Brien)   . £25/£5
ditto, Knopf (New York), 1961   .   .   .   . £25/£5
Carnets 1935-1942, Hamish Hamilton (London), 1963
(translated by Justin O'Brien)   .   .   .   . £40/£15
ditto, as *Notebooks 1935-1942*, Knopf (New York), 1963 .
.   .   .   . £40/£15

Carnets 1942-1951, Hamish Hamilton (London), 1965
(translated by Justin O'Brien)   .   .   .   . £40/£15
ditto, as *Notebooks 1942-1951*, Knopf (New York), 1965 .
.   .   .   . £40/£15
Lyrical and Critical, Hamish Hamilton (London), 1967
(translated by Ellen Conroy Kennedy)   .   .   . £25/£5
ditto, Knopf (New York), 1968   .   .   .   . £25/£5
Youthful Writings, Knopf (New York), 1976 (translated by
Ellen Conroy Kennedy)   .   .   .   .   . £25/£5
ditto, Hamilton (London), 1977   .   .   .   . £25/£5

TRUMAN CAPOTE
(b.1924 d.1984)

An American short story writer and novelist whose career
developed after he won the O. Henry Prize in 1946. He
became a best seller with his 'non-fiction novel' *In Cold
Blood*, which fictionalised the real-life motiveless murder
of a family of four in rural Kansas. Capote is perhaps best
known, though, for the novella *Breakfast at Tiffany's*.

Novels
Other Voices, Other Rooms, Random House (New York),
1948   .   .   .   . £250/£45
ditto, Heinemann (London), 1948   .   .   . £125/£20
ditto, Franklin Library (Franklin Centre, PA), 1979 (signed,
limited edition) £100
The Grass Harp, Random House (New York), [1951] .   .
.   .   .   . £150/£25
ditto, Heinemann (London), 1952   .   .   . £75/£20
Answered Prayers: The Unfinished Novel, Hamish
Hamilton (London), 1986 .   .   .   .   . £25/£5
ditto, Random House (New York), 1987   .   . £20/£5
Summer Crossing, Random House (New York), 2005 £10/£5
ditto, Penguin, 2005   .   .   .   .   .   . £10/£5

Short Stories
A Tree of Night and Other Stories, Random House (New
York), 1949 .   .   .   . £125/£25
ditto, Heinemann (London), 1950   .   .   . £100/£20
Breakfast at Tiffany's, Random House (New York), 1958 .
.   .   .   . £750/£40
ditto, Hamish Hamilton (London), 1958   .   . £125/£20
A Christmas Memory, Random House (New York), 1966
(slipcase, no d/w).   .   .   .   .   .   . £65/£45
ditto, Random House (New York), 1966 (600 signed copies,
slipcase, no d/w) .   .   .   .   .   . £500/£450
One Christmas, Random House (New York), 1983 (no d/w,
slipcase).   .   .   .   . £50/£30
ditto, Random House (New York), 1983 (500 numbered
copies signed by the author)   .   .   .   . £250/£200
ditto, Hamish Hamilton (London), 1983   .   . £20/£5
Three by Truman Capote, Random House (New York),
1985   .   .   .   . £20/£5

Plays
The Grass Harp, Random House (New York), [1952] .   .
.   .   .   . £250/£75
The Thanksgiving Visitor, Random House (New York),
1967 (300 signed, numbered copies, slipcase)   £300/£250
ditto, Random House (New York), 1968 (slipcase). £65/£45
ditto, Hamish Hamilton (London), 1969   .   . £45/£10

House of Flowers, Random House (New York), 1968 (with Harold Arlen) . . . . . £225/£75
Trilogy: An Experiment in Multimedia, Macmillan (New York), 1969 (with Elinor and Frank Perry) . . £30/£10

Non-Fiction
Local Color, Random House (New York), 1950 . £125/£30
ditto, Heinemann (London), 1950 . . . £45/£10
ditto, Heinemann (London), 1950 (200 numbered copies) £250
The Muses are Heard: An Account, Random House (New York), 1956 . . . . £50/£25
ditto, as *The Muses are Heard: An Account of the Porgy and Bess Visit to Leningrad*, Heinemann (London), 1957. . . . . £25/£10
Observations, Simon & Schuster (New York), 1959 (photographs by Richard Avedon, glassine d/w, slipcase) . . . . £175/£150
ditto, Weidenfeld and Nicolson (London), 1959 (glassine d/w, slipcase) . . . . . £175/£150
In Cold Blood: A True Account of a Multiple Murder and its Consequences, Random House (New York), 1965 . . . . £30/£10
ditto, Random House (New York), 1965 (trade edition with extra signed leaf inserted) . . . . £300/£175
ditto, Random House (New York), 1965 (500 signed, numbered copies, slipcase) . . . £600/£500
ditto, Hamish Hamilton (London), 1966 . . £50/£10
The Dogs Bark: Public People and Private Places, Random House (New York), 1973 . . . . £20/£5
ditto, Weidenfeld and Nicolson (London), 1974 £15/£5
Then it All Came Down: Criminal Justice Today Discussed by Police, Criminals and Correcting Officers with Comments by Truman Capote, Random House (New York), 1976 . . . . £35/£10
Music for Chameleons, Random House (New York), 1980 . . . . £25/£10
ditto, Random House (New York), 1980 (350 signed copies, slipcase). . . . . . . £200/£150
ditto, Hamish Hamilton (London), 1980 . . £25/£10

Collections
Selected Writings of Truman Capote, Random House (New York), 1963 . . . . . . £25/£5
ditto, Hamish Hamilton (London), 1963 . . £20/£5
A Capote Reader, Random House (New York), 1987 £10/£5
ditto, Hamish Hamilton (London), 1987 . . £10/£5

PETER CAREY
(b.1943)

In the early days of his literary career, Australian writer Peter Carey wrote advertising copy. He has lived in London, but is now based in New York. Carey's novels and stories have been described as postmodern fables. *Illywacker* was nominated for the Booker Prize Best Novel in 1985, and *Oscar and Lucinda* and *Jack Maggs* both won that prize in 1988 and 2001 respectively.

Novels
Bliss, Univ of Queensland Press (St Lucia, Australia), 1981 . . . . £65/£15

ditto, Faber (London), 1981 . . . . . £35/£10
ditto, Harper (New York), 1981 . . . . £35/£10
Illywhacker, Univ of Queensland Press (St Lucia, Australia), 1985 . . . . £45/£10
ditto, Faber (London), 1985 . . . . . £25/£5
ditto, Harper (New York), 1985 . . . . £20/£5
Oscar and Lucinda, Univ of Queensland Press (St Lucia, Australia), 1988 . . . . . £35/£10
ditto, Faber (London), 1988 . . . . . £25/£5
ditto, Harper (New York), 1988 . . . . £20/£5
The Tax Inspector, Univ of Queensland Press (St Lucia, Australia), 1991 . . . . . £20/£5
ditto, Faber (London), 1991 . . . . . £15/£5
ditto, Knopf (New York), 1991 . . . . £15/£5
ditto, Franklin Library (Franklin Centre, PA), 1991 (signed, limited edition) £40
The Unusual Life of Tristan Smith, Univ of Queensland Press (St Lucia, Australia), 1994 . . . £15/£5
ditto, Faber (London), 1994 . . . . . £15/£5
ditto, Knopf (New York), 1995 . . . . £15/£5
Jack Maggs, Univ of Queensland Press (St Lucia, Australia), 1997 . . . . £10/£5
ditto, Faber (London), 1997 . . . . . £10/£5
ditto, Knopf (New York), 1998 . . . . £10/£5
True History of the Kelly Gang, Univ of Queensland Press (St Lucia, Australia), 2000 . . . £15/£5
ditto, Faber (London), 2001 . . . . . £10/£5
ditto, Knopf (New York), 2001 . . . . £10/£5
My Life as a Fake, Knopf (Sydney, Australia), 2003 £10/£5
ditto, Faber (London), 2003 . . . . . £10/£5
ditto, Knopf (New York), 2003 . . . . £10/£5
Theft: A Love Story, Knopf (Sydney, Australia), 2006 . . . . £10/£5
ditto, Faber (London), 2006 . . . . . £10/£5
ditto, Knopf (New York), 2006 . . . . £10/£5
His Legal Self, Knopf/Random House (Sydney, Australia), 2008 . . . . £10/£5
ditto, Knopf (New York), 2008 . . . . £10/£5
ditto, Faber (London), 2008 . . . . . £10/£5
ditto, Faber/London Review Bookshop (London), 2008 (75 signed, numbered copies; bound in green cloth and Eric Ravilious-designed boards; slipcase) . . . £85/£50
ditto, Faber/London Review Bookshop (London), 2008 (40 signed, roman numeraled copies; bound in quarter leather; slipcase). . . . . £250/£200

Short Stories
The Fat Man in History, Univ of Queensland Press (St Lucia, Australia), 1974 . . . . . £400/£85
ditto, Faber (London), 1980 . . . . . £45/£10
ditto, Random House (New York), 1980 . . £25/£10
War Crimes, Univ of Queensland Press (St Lucia, Australia), 1979 . . . . £125/£30
Collected Stories, Univ of Queensland Press (St Lucia, Australia), 1994 . . . . . . £25/£5
ditto, Faber (London), 1995 . . . . . £20/£5

Others
Bliss: The Screenplay, Univ of Queensland Press (St Lucia, Australia), 1986 . . . . . £10/£5
ditto, as *Bliss: The Film*, Faber (London), 1986 . £10/£5
A Letter to Our Son, Univ of Queensland Press (St Lucia, Australia), 1994 . . . . . £25/£10
Big Bazoohley, Faber (London), 1995 . . £25/£5

ditto, Holt (New York), 1995 . . . . £25/£5
30 Days in Sydney: A Wildly Distorted Account,
Bloomsbury (London), 2001 . . . £10/£5
ditto, Bloomsbury (New York), 2001 . . . £10/£5
Four Easy Pieces, Belmont Press (London), 2002 (26
lettered copies of 226, signed by author and artist, with two
additional prints signed by artist) £250
ditto, Belmont Press (London), 2002 (100 copies numbered
1-100 signed by author and artist, with one additional print
signed by artist) £125
ditto, Belmont Press (London), 2002 (100 copies numbered
101-200, signed by author and artist) . . . £75
Wrong About Japan, Knopf (Sydney, Australia), 2004.
. . . . £10/£5
ditto, Faber (London), 2005 . . . . . £10/£5

J.L. CARR
(b.1912 d.1994)

Carr's reputation rests mainly on *A Month in the Country*
(successfully filmed in 1987) which, along with *The Battle
of Pollock's Crossing*, was short-listed for the Booker
Prize. Other than these highlights, though, Carr's writing
was not commercially successful and he finally resorted to
self-publishing under his Quince Tree Press imprint. As a
'small press' his sales were quite impressive. He also
published a series of maps of the British counties.

Novels
A Day In Summer, Barrie & Rockliff (London), 1963 . .
. . . . £450/£45
A Season in Sinji, Alan Ross (London), 1967 . . £300/£35
The Harpole Report, Secker & Warburg (London), 1972 .
. . . . £100/£15
How Steeple Sinderby Wanderers Won the F.A. Cup,
London Magazine Editions (London), 1975 . . £100/£20
A Month in the Country, Harvester Press (Brighton), 1980 .
. . . . £125/£20
ditto, St Martin's Press (New York), 1983 . . £35/£5
The Battle of Pollock's Crossing, Viking (London), 1985 .
. . . . £10/£5
What Hetty Did, Quince Tree Press (Kettering, Northants),
1988 (pbk; limited to 2,850 copies) £15
Harpole & Fowbarrow, General Publishers, Quince Tree
Press (Kettering, Northants), 1992 (pbk; limited to 4,000
copies) £10

Other Titles
Old Timers, privately printed (Huron, SD), 1957
(mimeograph limited to 50 copies) . . . £1,250
The Red Windcheater, Macmillan (London), 1970 (pbk) £5
The Dustman, Macmillan (London), 1972 (pbk). . £5
The Garage Mechanic, Macmillan (London), 1972 (pbk) £5
The Old Farm Coat, Macmillan (London), 1974 (pbk). £5
Red Foal's Coat, Macmillan (London), 1974 (pbk) . £5
The Green Children of the Woods, Longman (London),
1976 (pbk) £5
An Ear-Ring for Anna Beer, Macmillan (London), 1976
(pbk; as Jim Carr) £5
Carr's Dictionary of Extra-Ordinary English Cricketers,
Quince Tree Press (Kettering, Northants), 1977 (pbk). £20

*Carr's Dictionary of English Queens, Kings' Wives,
Celebrated Paramours, Handfast Spouses, and Royal
Changlelings*, Quince Tree Press (Kettering, Northants),
1977 (pbk) £10
Gone With the Whirlwind, Macmillan (London), 1980 (pbk;
as Jim Carr) £5
*Carr's Illustrated Dictionary of Extra-Ordinary English
Cricketers*, Quartet Books/Solo Books, 1983 (pbk) . £10
*An Inventory and a History of the Quince Tree Press
(Kettering, Northants) to Mark its 21st Year and the Sale
of its 500,000th Small Book, August 1987*, Quince Tree
Press (Kettering, Northants), 1987 (pbk) . . . £10
*Carr's Dictionary of English Kings, Consorts, Pretenders,
Usurpers,Unnatural Claimants & Royal Aethlings*,
Quince Tree Press (Kettering, Northants), [no date] (pbk) .
. . . . £10
*A Dictionary of Extra-Ordinary English Cricketers,
Volume 2*, Quince Tree Press (Kettering, Northants), [no
date] (pbk) £10
The Territory Versus Flaherty, Quince Tree Press
(Kettering, Northants), [no date] (pbk) . . . £10
A Christmas Book, Quince Tree Press (Kettering,
Northants), [no date] (pbk) £10
The Death of Parcy Reed, Quince Tree Press (Kettering,
Northants), [no date] (pbk) £10
Gidner's Brief Lives of the Frontiers, Quince Tree Press
(Kettering, Northants), [no date] (pbk) . . . £10
Welbourne's Dictionary, Quince Tree Press (Kettering,
Northants), [no date] (pbk) £10
Churches in Retirement: A Gazetteer, H.M.S.O. (London),
1990 (pbk) £20
*The First Saturday in May: An Echo of 'A Shropshire
Lad'*, Tern Press (Market Drayton, Shropshire), 1993 (8
wood engravings by Nicholas Parry, 140 numbered copies
signed by Nicholas and Mary Parry) £30
Sydney Smith: The Smith of Smiths, J.L. Carr Publishing,
[undated] (pbk) £10
The Poor Man's Guide to the Revolt of 1381, J.L. Carr
Publishing/Quince Tree Press (Kettering, Northants),
[undated] (pbk) £10

JOHN DICKSON CARR
(b.1906 d.1977)

American-born John Dickson Carr was a prolific author of
detective fiction and is considered one of the classic
authors of 'locked room' mysteries. His work often features
an eccentric detective who solves apparently impossible
crimes. His literary influences include Gaston Leroux and
G.K. Chesterton. Indeed, Carr apparently modelled Dr
Gideon Fell, one of his detectives, on Chesterton. In a
number of his books the pages revealing the identity of the
murderer were contained with a paper seal.

'Dr Gideon Fell' Titles
Hag's Nook, Harper (New York), 1933 (seal unbroken on
last section) . . . . £1,250/£350
ditto, Harper (New York), 1933 (seal opened) . £1,250/£100
ditto, Hamish Hamilton (London), 1933 . . £1,250/£100
The Mad Hatter Mystery, Harper (New York), 1933 (seal
unbroken) . . . . £1,250/£300
ditto, Harper (New York), 1933 (seal opened). £1,250/£100

ditto, Hamish Hamilton (London), 1933 .   . £1,250/£100
The Eight of Swords, Harper (New York), 1934 (seal
unbroken)   .   .   .   . £1,250/£300
ditto, Harper (New York), 1934 (seal opened) . £1,250/£100
ditto, Hamish Hamilton (London), 1934   .   £1,250/£100
The Blind Barber, Harper (New York), 1934 (seal
unbroken)   .   .   .   . £1,000/£250
ditto, Harper (New York), 1934 (seal opened) . £1,000/£100
ditto, Hamish Hamilton (London), 1934 .   . £1,000/£100
Death Watch, Hamish Hamilton (London), 1935 £1,000/£100
ditto, Harper (New York), 1935 (seal unbroken) £1,000/£250
ditto, Harper (New York), 1935 (seal opened) . £1,000/£100
The Three Coffins, Harper (New York), 1935 (seal
unbroken)   .   .   .   . £750/£200
ditto, Harper (New York), 1935 (seal unbroken)   . £750/£75
ditto, as **The Hollow Man**, Hamish Hamilton (London), 1935
.   .   .   . £750/£75
The Arabian Nights Murder, Hamish Hamilton (London),
1936 .   .   .   . £750/£75
ditto, Harper (New York), 1936 .   .   .   . £750/£75
To Wake the Dead, Hamish Hamilton (London), 1937 .   .
.   .   .   . £500/£75
ditto, Harper (New York), 1938 .   .   .   . £500/£75
The Crooked Hinge, Harper (New York), 1938   . £500/£75
ditto, Hamish Hamilton (London), 1938 .   . £500/£75
The Problem of the Green Capsule, Harper (New York),
1939 .   .   .   . £450/£65
ditto, as **The Black Spectacles**, Hamish Hamilton (London),
1939 .   .   .   . £450/£65
The Problem of the Wire Cage, Harper (New York), 1939 .
.   .   .   . £300/£50
ditto, Hamish Hamilton (London), 1940 .   . £300/£50
The Man Who Could Not Shudder, Harper (New York),
1940 .   .   .   . £250/£40
ditto, Hamish Hamilton (London), 1940 .   . £250/£40
The Case of the Constant Suicides, Harper (New York),
1941 .   .   .   . £250/£40
ditto, Hamish Hamilton (London), 1941 .   . £250/£40
Death Turns the Tables, Harper (New York), 1941 (seal
unbroken)   .   .   .   . £250/£75
ditto, Harper (New York), 1941 (seal unbroken)   . £250/£40
ditto, as **The Seat of the Scornful**, Hamish Hamilton
(London), 1942   .   .   .   .   .   . £250/£40
Till Death Do Us Part, Harper (New York), 1944 . £175/£30
ditto, Hamish Hamilton (London), 1944   .   . £175/£30
He Who Whispers, Harper (New York), 1946 .   . £150/£25
ditto, Hamish Hamilton (London), 1946   .   . £150/£25
The Sleeping Sphinx, Harper (New York), 1947 . £150/£25
ditto, Hamish Hamilton (London), 1947 .   . £150/£25
Dr Fell, Detective and Other Stories, The American
Mercury/Lawrence Spivak (New York), 1947 (pbk)   . £50
Below Suspicion, Harper (New York), 1949 .   . £65/£10
ditto, Hamish Hamilton (London), 1950 .   . £65/£10
The Dead Man's Knock, Harper (New York), 1958 £35/£10
ditto, Hamish Hamilton (London), 1958 .   . £35/£10
In Spite of Thunder, Harper (New York), 1960 (seal
unbroken)   .   .   .   . £75/£35
ditto, Harper (New York), 1960 (seal opened) .   . £35/£10
ditto, Hamish Hamilton (London), 1960 .   . £35/£10
The House at Satan's Elbow, Harper (New York), 1965   .
.   .   .   . £35/£10
ditto, Hamish Hamilton (London), 1965 .   . £35/£10
Panic in Box C, Harper (New York), 1966   . £35/£10
ditto, Hamish Hamilton (London), 1966 .   . £35/£10

Dark of the Moon, Harper (New York), 1967 .   . £35/£10
ditto, Hamish Hamilton (London), 1968 .   .   . £35/£10

'Henri Bencolin' Titles
It Walks by Night, Harper (New York), 1930 (seal unbroken)
.   .   .   . £2,000/£350
ditto, Harper (New York), 1930 (seal opened) . £1,750/£125
ditto, Harper (London), 1930 (no logo on the d/w, though it
originally came with the blue promotional band; the front
and back panels of the jacket contain a slit that the band
ends slip through; seal unbroken)   .   . £2,000/£350
ditto, Harper (London), 1930 (seal opened)   . £1,750/£125
The Lost Gallows, Harper (New York), 1931 (seal unbroken)
.   .   .   . £1,500/£300
ditto, Harper (New York), 1931 (seal opened) . £1,300/£100
ditto, Hamish Hamilton (London), 1931 (seal unbroken)   .
.   .   .   . £1,500/£300
ditto, Hamish Hamilton (London), 1931 (seal opened) .   .
.   .   .   . £1,300/£100
Castle Skull, Harper (New York), 1931 (seal unbroken)   .
.   .   .   . £1,500/£300
ditto, Harper (New York), 1931 (seal opened) . £1,300/£100
ditto, Severn House (London), 1976 .   .   .   . £15/£5
The Waxworks Murder, Hamish Hamilton (London), 1932.
.   .   .   . £1,250/£100
ditto, as **The Corpse in the Waxworks**, Harper (New York),
1932 (seal unbroken)   .   .   .   .   . £1,500/£300
ditto, as **The Corpse in the Waxworks**, Harper (New York),
1932 (seal opened)   .   .   .   .   . £1,300/£100
The Four False Weapons, Harper (New York), 1937 .   .
.   .   .   . £1,000/£100
ditto, Hamish Hamilton (London), 1938 .   . £1,000/£100
The Door to Doom and Other Detections, Harper, 1980   .
.   .   .   . £10/£5
ditto, Hamish Hamilton (London), 1981 .   .   . £10/£5

'Sir Henry Merrivale' Titles by 'Carter Dickson'
The Plague Court Murders, Morrow (New York), 1934   .
.   .   .   . £750/£100
ditto, Heinemann (London), 1935 .   .   . £750/£100
The White Priory Murders, Morrow (New York), 1934   .
.   .   .   . £750/£100
ditto, Heinemann (London), 1935 .   .   . £750/£100
The Red Widow Murders, Morrow (New York), 1935 .   .
.   .   .   . £750/£100
ditto, Heinemann (London), 1935 .   .   . £750/£100
The Unicorn Murders, Morrow (New York), 1935   .   .
.   .   .   . £750/£100
ditto, Heinemann (London), 1936 .   .   . £750/£100
The Magic Lantern Murders, Heinemann (London), 1936 .
.   .   .   . £750/£100
ditto, as **The Punch and Judy Murders**, Morrow (New
York), 1937 .   .   .   . £750/£100
The Peacock Feather Murders, Morrow (New York), 1937
.   .   .   . £650/£75
ditto, as **The Ten Teacups**, Heinemann (London), 1937   .
.   .   .   . £650/£75
The Judas Window, Morrow (New York), 1938 . £450/£75
ditto, Heinemann (London), 1938 .   .   . £450/£75
Death in Five Boxes, Heinemann (London), 1938 . £350/£65
ditto, Morrow (New York), 1938 .   .   .   . £350/£65
The Reader is Warned, Heinemann (London), 1939   .   .
.   .   .   . £650/£85
ditto, Morrow (New York), 1939 .   .   .   . £650/£85

And So To Murder, Morrow (New York), 1940 . £650/£85
ditto, Heinemann (London), 1941 . . . . £650/£85
Murder in the Submarine Zone, Heinemann (London), 1940
. . . . £650/£85
ditto, as *Nine–And Death Makes Ten*, Morrow (New York),
1940 . . . . £650/£85
Seeing is Believing, Morrow (New York), 1941 . £650/£85
ditto, Heinemann (London), 1942 . . . . £650/£85
The Gilded Man, Morrow (New York), 1942 . . £250/£40
ditto, Heinemann (London), 1942 . . . . £250/£40
She Died a Lady, Morrow (New York), 1943 . . £250/£40
ditto, Heinemann (London), 1943 . . . . £250/£40
He Wouldn't Kill Patience, Morrow (New York), 1944 .
. . . . £150/£25
ditto, Heinemann (London), 1944. . . . £150/£25
The Curse of the Bronze Lamp, Morrow (New York), 1945
. . . . £100/£20
ditto, as *Lord of the Sorcerers*, Heinemann (London), 1946
. . . . £100/£20
My Late Wives, Morrow (New York), 1946 . . £75/£15
ditto, Heinemann (London), 1947 . . . . £75/£15
The Skeleton in the Clock, Morrow (New York), 1948. .
. . . . £75/£15
ditto, Heinemann (London), 1949 . . . . £75/£15
A Graveyard to Let, Morrow (New York), 1949 . £75/£15
ditto, Heinemann (London), 1950 . . . . £65/£10
Night at the Mocking Widow, Morrow (New York), 1950 .
. . . . £65/£10
ditto, Heinemann (London), 1951 . . . . £65/£10
Behind the Crimson Blind, Morrow (New York), 1952 .
. . . . £65/£10
ditto, Heinemann (London), 1952 . . . £65/£10
The Cavalier's Cup, Morrow (New York), 1953 . £65/£10
ditto, Heinemann (London), 1954 . . . . £65/£10

Other Titles
Poison in Jest, Harper (New York), 1932 (seal unbroken) .
. . . . £1,250/£350
ditto, Harper (New York), 1932 (seal opened). £1,000/£100
ditto, Hamish Hamilton (London), 1932 . £1,000/£100
The Bowstring Murders, Morrow (New York), 1933 (pseud
'Carr Dickson') . . . . £750/£75
ditto, Heinemann (London), 1934 (pseud 'Carter Dickson') .
. . . . £750/£75
Devil Kinsmere, Hamish Hamilton (London), 1934 (pseud
'Roger Fairbairn') . . . . . £1,000/£100
ditto, Harper (New York), 1934 . . . . . £750/£50
The Murder of Sir Edmund Godfrey, Hamish Hamilton
(London), 1936 . . . . . . £1,000/£65
ditto, Harper (New York), 1936 . . . . . £450/£45
The Third Bullet, Hodder & Stoughton, 1937 (by 'Carter
Dickson'; pbk) £200
The Burning Court, Harper (New York), 1937 . £650/£45
ditto, Hamish Hamilton (London), 1937 . . £800/£45
Drop to His Death, Heinemann (London), 1939 (pseud
'Carter Dickson', with 'John Rhode') . . £750/£65
ditto, as *Fatal Descent*, Dodd Mead (New York), 1939
(pseud 'Carter Dickson', with 'John Rhode') . £650/£45
The Department of Queer Complaints, Heinemann
(London), 1940 . . . . £600/£55
ditto, Morrow (New York), 1940 . . . . £450/£45
The Emperor's Snuffbox, Harper (New York), 1942 . .
. . . . £250/£45
ditto, Hamish Hamilton (London), 1943 . . £250/£45

The Life of Sir Arthur Conan Doyle, Harper (New York),
1948 . . . . £40/£10
ditto, Hamish Hamilton (London), 1949 . . £35/£10
The Bride of Newgate, Harper (New York), 1950 . £50/£15
ditto, Hamish Hamilton (London), 1950 . . £50/£15
The Devil in Velvet, Harper (New York), 1951 £50/£15
ditto, Hamish Hamilton (London), 1951 . . . £50/£15
The Nine Wrong Answers, Harper (New York), 1952 . .
. . . . £60/£15
ditto, Hamish Hamilton (London), 1952 . . . £60/£15
The Third Bullet and Other Stories, Harper (New York),
1954 . . . . £60/£20
ditto, Hamish Hamilton (London), 1954 . . £60/£20
The Exploits of Sherlock Holmes, Random House (New
York), 1954 (with Adrian Conan Doyle) . . £45/£10
ditto, Murray (London), 1954 . . . . . £45/£10
Captain Cut Throat, Harper (New York), 1955 . £50/£15
ditto, Hamish Hamilton (London), 1955 . . . £50/£15
Patrick Butler for the Defence, Harper (New York), 1956 .
. . . . £50/£10
ditto, Hamish Hamilton (London), 1956 . . . £50/£10
Fear is the Same, Morrow (New York), 1956. . £50/£10
ditto, Heinemann (London), 1956 . . . . £50/£10
Fire, Burn!, Harper (New York), 1957 . . . £50/£10
ditto, Hamish Hamilton (London), 1957 . . . £50/£10
Scandal at High Chimneys, Harper (New York), 1959. .
. . . . £50/£10
ditto, Hamish Hamilton (London), 1959 . . . £50/£10
The Witch of the Low-Tide, Harper (New York), 1961. .
. . . . £50/£10
ditto, Hamish Hamilton (London), 1961 . . . £50/£10
The Demoniacs, Harper (New York), 1962 . . £50/£10
ditto, Hamish Hamilton (London), 1962 . . . £50/£10
The Men Who Explained Miracles, Harper (New York),
1963 . . . . £35/£10
ditto, Hamish Hamilton (London), 1964 . . £35/£10
Most Secret, Harper (New York), 1964 . . . £50/£10
ditto, Hamish Hamilton (London), 1964 . . . £50/£10
Papa La-Bas, Harper (New York), 1968 . . . £50/£10
ditto, Hamish Hamilton (London), 1969 . . . £50/£10
The Ghosts' High Noon, Harper (New York), 1969 £50/£10
ditto, Hamish Hamilton (London), 1970 . . . £50/£10
Deadly Hall, Harper (New York), 1971 . . . £45/£10
ditto, Hamish Hamilton (London), 1971 . . . £45/£10
The Hungry Goblin, Harper (New York), 1972 . £45/£10
ditto, Hamish Hamilton (London), 1972 . . . £45/£10
The Dead Sleep Lightly, Doubleday (New York), 1983 .
. . . . £25/£10

Omnibus Editions
A John Dickson Carr Trio, Harper (New York), 1957
(includes *The Three Coffins*, *The Crooked Hinge* and *The
Case of the Constant Suicides*). . . . . £25/£5
A Dr Fell Omnibus, Hamish Hamilton (London), 1959
(includes *The Mad Hatter Mystery*, *Death-Watch, The
Black Spectacles* and *The Seat of the Scornful*) . £25/£5
Three Detective Novels, Harper (New York), 1959 (includes
Arabian Nights Murder, *The Burning Court* and *The
Problem of the Wire Cage*) . . . . . £25/£5

Collaborations
No Flowers by Request & *Crime on the Coast*, Gollancz
(London), 1984 (chain novel; chapters by Carr and others)
. . . . £10/£5

LEWIS CARROLL
(b.1832 d.1898)

Born Charles Lutwidge Dodgson, Carroll was a British author, mathematician, logician, Anglican clergyman and photographer whose best-known work is *Alice's Adventures in Wonderland*. His books have remained popular since they were first published and have influenced not only much children's literature, but also major 20th-century writers such as James Joyce and Jorge Luis Borges.

Alice's Adventures in Wonderland, Macmillan (London), 1865 (withdrawn, 42 illustrations by Sir John Tenniel) £200,000
ditto, Appleton (New York), 1866 (illustrated by Sir John Tenniel). £7,500
ditto, Macmillan (London), 1866 [1865] (first UK edition on general sale). £5,000
ditto, as *Alice's Adventures Under Ground*, Macmillan (London), 1886 (red cloth) £250
ditto, as *Alice's Adventures Under Ground*, Macmillan (London), 1886 (variant binding) . . £1,500
ditto, as *Alice's Adventures in Wonderland* Macmillan (London), 1889 (illustrated by Gertrude Thomson, withdrawn) £250
ditto, Macmillan (London), 1889 (illustrated by Gertrude Thomson) £125
ditto, Wessels (New York), 1899 (illustrated by Blanche McManus) £150
ditto, Harper (New York), 1901 (illustrated by Peter Newell) £165
ditto, Ward Lock (London), 1907 (illustrated by Blanche McManus) £75
ditto, Cassell (London), 1907 (illustrated by Charles Robinson) £150
ditto, Heinemann (London), [1907] (illustrated by Arthur Rackham; green cloth) £300
ditto, Heinemann (London), [1907] (illustrated by Arthur Rackham, deluxe edition of 1,130 copies) . . £1,750
ditto, Doubleday (New York), [1907] (illustrated by Arthur Rackham, 550 signed copies) £1,750
ditto, Doubleday (New York), [1907] (illustrated by Arthur Rackham, trade edition) £300
ditto, Routledge (London), 1907 (illustrated by Thomas Maybank) £100
ditto, Chatto & Windus (London), 1907 (illustrated by Millicent Sowerby) £125
ditto, Nelson (London), 1908 (illustrated by Harry Rountree) £100
ditto, Raphael Tuck (London), [1910] (12 colour plates by Mabel Lucie Attwell; illustrated boards) . . £200
ditto, Raphael Tuck (London), [1910] (12 colour plates by Mabel Lucie Attwell; deluxe edition) . . £350
ditto, Dutton (New York), 1929 (illustrated by Willy Pogány) . . . . £250/£75
ditto, Dutton (New York), 1929 (200 signed, numbered copies, illustrated by Willy Pogány) . £500/£400
ditto, Black Sun Press (Paris), 1930 (illustrated by Marie Lurencin) £2,000
ditto, Black Sun Press (Paris), 1930 (illustrated by Marie Lurencin, with extra plates) £5,000

ditto, Random House (New York), 1969 (illustrated by Salvador Dali) £3,000
ditto, Random House (New York), 1969 (illustrated by Salvador Dali; folio; loose sheets in full leather portfolio; 200 copies on Rives paper, signed by Dali on the title page, with an extra suite of the 13 plates on Japan vellum) £6,000
Phantasmagoria and Other Poems, Macmillan (London), 1869. . . . . £300
ditto, Macmillan (London), 1911 (miniature edition) . £30
Through the Looking Glass, Macmillan (London), 1872 (illustrated by Sir John Tenniel) £350
ditto, Wessels (New York), 1899 (illustrated by Blanche McManus) £100
ditto, Harper (New York), 1902 (illustrated by Peter Newell) £100
The Hunting of the Snark, An Agony in Eight Fits, Macmillan (London), 1876 (100 copies in red cloth stamped in gilt) £450
ditto, Macmillan (London), 1876 (buff boards printed in black) £250
ditto, Chatto & Windus (London), 1941 (illustrated by Mervyn Peake; yellow boards). . . . £75/£20
ditto, Chatto & Windus (London), 1941 (illustrated by Mervyn Peake, large format, pink boards) . £125/£35
Doublets: A Word Puzzle, Macmillan (London), 1879 . . . . £200
Rhyme? and Reason?, Macmillan (London), 1883 . £150
A Tangled Tale, Macmillan (London), 1885 . . £125
The Game of Logic, Macmillan (London), 1886 (with envelope, card and 9 counters. Approx 50 copies) £1,250
ditto, Macmillan (London), 1887 (with envelope, card and 9 counters) £250
Sylvie and Bruno, Macmillan (London), 1889 . . £75
Sylvie and Bruno Concluded, Macmillan (London), 1893 . . . . £65
Symbolic Logic, Macmillan (London), 1896 . . £350
Three Sunsets and Other Poems, Macmillan (London), 1898 . . . . £65
The Lewis Carroll Picture Book, T. Fisher Unwin (London), 1899 . . . . £125
Feeding the Mind, Chatto & Windus (London), 1907 (boards). £40
ditto, Chatto & Windus (London), 1907 (wraps) . . £35
ditto, Chatto & Windus (London), 1907 (leather binding) £50
Bruno's Revenge, Collins (London), [1924] . . £50/£10
Further Nonsense, Verse and Prose, T. Fisher Unwin (London), 1926 . . . . £50/£15
The Collected Verse of Lewis Carroll, Macmillan (London), 1932 . . . . £100/£20
For the Train, Denis Archer (London), 1932 . . £65/£20
ditto, Denis Archer (London), 1932 (100 signed, numbered copies) . . . . £200/£100
The Rectory Umbrella and Mischmasch, Cassell & Co. (London), 1932 . . . . £65/£20
Alice in Wonderland and *Through the Looking Glass*, The Continental Book Company (Stockholm, Sweden), 1946 (illustrated by Mervyn Peake; wraps with d/w) . £200/£75
ditto, Allan Wingate (London), 1954. . . . £100/£35
ditto, Schocken (New York), 1979 . . . . £25/£10
Useful and Instructive Poetry, Butler and Tanner (London), 1954 . . . . £40/£10
ditto, Macmillan (New York), 1954 . . . . £40/£10

The Diaries of Lewis Carroll, Cassell (London), 1953
[1954] (2 vols) . . . . £125/£45
The Rectory Magazine, Univ of Texas Press (Austin, TX),
1975 . . . . £25/£10
The Letters of Lewis Carroll, Macmillan (London), 1979 (2
vols) . . . . £45/£20
ditto, as *The Selected Letters of Lewis Carroll*, Macmillan
(London), 1982 (1 vol.) . . . . . £15/£5

**Other Books Published as 'Charles L. Dodgson'/
'Anonymous'/'An Oxford Chiel'**
Syllabus of Plane Algebraical Geometry, James Wright
(Oxford), 1860 . . . . £600
The Formulae of Plane Trigonometry, James Wright
(Oxford), 1861 . . . . £600
An Index to 'In Memoriam', Edward Moxon (London), 1862
. . . . £125
*A Guide to the Mathematical Student in Reading,
Reviewing and Working Examples*, James Wright
(Oxford), 1864 . . . . £1,000
The Dynamics of a Particle, J. Vincent (Oxford), 1865 (wraps)
. . . . £150
ditto, James Parker (Oxford), 1874 (wraps). . . £125
*An Elementary Treatise on Determinants: Their Application
to Equations*, Macmillan (London), 1867 . . £650
The New Belfry of Christ Church, Oxford, James Parker
(Oxford), 1872 (wraps) £150
The Vision of the Streets, James Parker (Oxford), 1873 (wraps)
. . . . £150
Notes By An Oxford Chiel, James Parker (Oxford), 1874
(wraps) £250
The Blank Cheque, James Parker (Oxford), 1874 (wraps) .
. . . . £150
The New Method of Evaluation, James Parker (Oxford), 1874
(wraps) £150
Euclid: Book V Proved Algebraically, James Parker (Oxford),
1874 . . . . £600
Euclid and His Modern Rivals, Macmillan (London), 1879 .
. . . . £500
ditto, Macmillan (London), 1885 . . . . . £450
Euclid: Books I & II, Macmillan (London), 1882 . £150
ditto, Macmillan (London), 1885 (revised) . . . £125
*Lawn Tennis Tournaments: The True Method of Assigning
Prizes, with a Proof of the Fallacy of the Present Method*,
Macmillan (London), 1883 (wraps) £500
The Principles of Parliamentary Representation, Harrison &
Sons (London), 1884 . . . . . . £600
Twelve Months in a Curatorship, E. Baxter (Oxford), 1884 .
. . . . £600
Three Years in a Curatorship, E. Baxter (Oxford), 1886 . £600
Curiosa Mathematica, Part I: A New Theory of Parallels,
Macmillan (London), 1888 . . . . . £450
Curiosa Mathematica, Part II: Pillow-Problems, Macmillan
(London), 1893 . . . . £350

RACHEL CARSON
(b.1907 d.1964)

Carson was an American marine biologist and best-selling
nature writer. In *Silent Spring* she turned her attention to
conservation and environmental problems caused by
synthetic pesticides, making the American public aware of
environmental concerns for the first time. The creation of
the U.S. Environmental Protection Agency was a direct
result of the concerns she raised, and Carson was posthumously awarded the Presidential Medal of Freedom.

Books
Under the Sea-Wind: A Naturalist's Picture of Ocean Life,
Simon & Schuster (New York), 1941 . . . £200/£50
ditto, Staples (London), 1952 . . . . . £40/£10
The Sea Around Us, O.U.P. (New York), 1951 (first state
d/w without excerpts from reviews) . . . £150/£25
ditto, O.U.P. (New York), 1951 (later d/w with excerpts from
reviews and 1952 National Book Award noted) . £75/£25
ditto, Staples (London), 1951 . . . . . £30/£10
ditto, Limited Editions Club (New York), 1980 (2,000
numbered copies signed by Alfred Eisenstaedt; slipcase) .
. . . . £75/£50
ditto, Golden Press (New York), 1958 (juvenile edition) .
. . . . £20/£5
ditto, as *Mountains in the Sea*, Science Research Institute,
1962 (wraps; 32 pages; excerpt from above). . . £20
ditto, as *Life Under the Sea*, Golden Press (Racine, WI),
1968 (pictorial boards, no d/w; excerpts from above) . £5
The Edge of the Sea, Houghton Mifflin (Boston), 1955 .
. . . . £65/£15
ditto, Staples (London), 1955 . . . . . £25/£10
ditto, as *The Rocky Coast*, McCall Publishing (New York),
1971 (photographs by Charles Pratt and drawings by Bob
Hines; selections from above) . . . . £15/£5
Silent Spring, Houghton Mifflin (Boston), 1962 . £150/£30
ditto, Hamish Hamilton (London), 1963 . . . £30/£10
ditto, as *Rivers of Death*, National Wildlife Federation
(Washington, DC), 1962 (wraps; excerpt from above) £25
*The Sea/The Sea Around Us/Under the Sea-Wind/The
Edge of the Sea*, MacGibbon & Kee (London), 1964 . .
. . . . £25/£10
The Sense of Wonder, Harper & Row (New York/Evanston),
1965 (text by Carson, photos by Charles Pratt etc) £20/£10
The House of Life; Rachel Carson At Work..., by Paul
Brooks, Houghton Mifflin (Boston), 1972 (contains
selections from Carson's published and unpublished
writings) . . . . £10/£5
ditto, Allen & Unwin (London), 1973 . . . £10/£5
*Always Rachel: The Letters Of Rachel Carson And
Dorothy Freeman 1952-1964*, Beacon Press (Boston),
1995 . . . . £10/£5
Lost Woods, The Discovered Writing of Rachel Carson,
Beacon Press (Boston), 1998 (pbk) £5

Others
Food From the Sea: Fish and Shellfish of New England,
United States Government Printing Office (Washington,
DC), 1943 (wraps; Conservation Bulletin 33) . . £75
Food From Home Waters: Fishes of the Middle West,
United States Government Printing Office (Washington,
DC), 1943 (wraps; Conservation Bulletin 34) . . £75

Fish and Shellfish of the South Atlantic and Gulf Coasts, United States Government Printing Office (Washington, DC), 1944 (wraps; Conservation Bulletin 37) . . £65

Fish and Shellfish of the Middle Atlantic Coast, United States Government Printing Office (Washington, DC), 1945 (wraps; Conservation Bulletin 38). . . . £65

Chincoteague: A National Wildlife Refuge, United States Government Printing Office (Washington, DC), 1947 (wraps; 'Conservation in Action Number One') . £45

Mattamuskeet: A National Wildlife Refuge, United States Government Printing Office (Washington, DC), 1947 (wraps) £45

Parker River: A National Wildlife Refuge, United States Government Printing Office (Washington, DC), 1947 (wraps; 'Conservation in Action Number Two') . . £45

Guarding Our Wildlife Resources, United States Government Printing Office (Washington, DC), 1948 (wraps; 'Conservation in Action Number Three') . £45

Bear River National Wildlife Refuge, United States Government Printing Office (Washington, DC), 1950 (wraps; 'Conservation in Action Number Eight'). . £45

Of Man and the Stream of Time, Scripps College (Claremont, CA), 1962 (wraps) £40

ANGELA CARTER

(b.1940 d.1992)

Carter was an English novelist and short story writer whose work explores the territory of magic realism. She travelled widely, and spent much of the late 1970s and 1980s as writer in residence at universities in Britain, the U.S. and Australia. Her works *The Magic Toyshop* and *The Company of Wolves* have been adapted into films.

Novels

Shadow Dance, Heinemann (London), 1966 . . £175/£25

ditto, as *Honeybuzzard*, Simon & Schuster (New York), 1966 . . . . £75/£25

The Magic Toyshop, Heinemann (London), 1967 . £300/£45

ditto, Simon & Schuster (New York), 1968 . . £100/£15

Several Perceptions, Heinemann (London), 1968 . £135/£25

ditto, Simon & Schuster (New York), 1968 . . £50/£10

Heroes and Villains, Heinemann (London), 1969 . £200/£30

ditto, Simon & Schuster (New York), 1969 . . £40/£15

Love, Hart Davis (London), 1971 . . . . £45/£10

ditto, Chatto & Windus (London), 1987 (revised edition) . . . . £20/£5

The Infernal Desire Machines of Doctor Hoffman, Hart Davis (London), 1972. . . . . . . £75/£15

ditto, as *The War of Dreams*, Harcourt Brace (New York), 1974 . . . . £25/£10

The Passion of New Eve, Gollancz (London), 1977 £35/£10

ditto, Harcourt Brace (New York), 1977 . . £25/£5

Nights at the Circus, Chatto & Windus (London), 1984 . . . . £20/£5

ditto, Viking (New York), 1985 . . . . £20/£5

Wise Children, Chatto & Windus (London), 1991 . £20/£5

ditto, Farrar Straus (New York), 1992 . . . £10/£5

Short Stories

Fireworks: Nine Profane Pieces, Quartet (London), 1974 . . . . £40/£10

ditto, as *Fireworks: Nine Stories in Various Disguises*, Harper & Row (New York), 1981 . . . . £15/£5

ditto, as *Artificial Fire,* McClelland & Stewart (Toronto, Canada), 1988 (revised edition) . . . . £10/£5

The Bloody Chamber and Other Stories, Gollancz (London), 1979 . . . . £65/£10

ditto, Harper & Row (New York), 1979 . . . £20/£5

Black Venus's Tale, Next Editions (London), 1980 (woodcuts by Philip Sutton; spiral bound) . . . £10

Black Venus, Chatto & Windus/Hogarth Press (London), 1985 . . . . £20/£5

ditto, as *Saints and Strangers*, Viking (New York), 1986 . . . . £20/£5

American Ghosts and Old World Wonders, Chatto & Windus (London), 1993 . . . . . £20/£5

Burning Your Boats, The Complete Short Stories, Chatto & Windus (London), 1995 . . . . . £20/£10

ditto, as *Burning Your Boats: The Collected Short Stories*, Holt (New York), 1996 . . . . . £15/£5

Children's Fiction

Miss Z, The Dark Young Lady, Heinemann (London), 1970 . . . . £45/£10

ditto, Simon & Schuster (New York), 1970 . . £30/£10

The Donkey Prince, Simon & Schuster (New York), 1970 . . . . £25/£10

The Fairy Tales of Charles Perrault, Gollancz (London), 1977 (translated by Carter) . . . . £40/£20

Martin Leman's Comic and Curious Cats, Gollancz (London), 1979 (illustrations by Martin Leman) . £20/£5

ditto, as *Comic and Curious Cats*, Harmony/Crown (New York), 1979 . . . . £20/£5

The Music People, Hamish Hamilton (London), 1980 (with Leslie Carter) . . . . £15/£5

Moonshadow, Gollancz (London), 1982 (with Justin Todd, no d/w) £100

Sleeping Beauty and Other Favourite Fairy Tales, Gollancz (London), 1982 . . . . £15/£5

ditto, Schocken (New York), 1984 . . . . £15/£5

Poetry

Unicorn, Tlaloc (Leeds, UK), 1966 (150 copies, mimeographed sheets, stapled) £1,000

Others

The Sadeian Woman and the Ideology of Pornography, Pantheon (New York), 1978 . . . . . £35/£10

The Sadeian Woman: An Exercise in Cultural History, Virago (London), 1979 . . . . . £35/£10

Nothing Sacred, Selected Writings, Virago (London), 1982 (pbk) £10

Come unto These Yellow Sands: Four Radio Plays, Bloodaxe Books (Newcastle Upon Tyne, UK), 1984 . . . . £50/£15

Expletives Deleted: Selected Writings, Chatto & Windus (London), 1992 . . . . £15/£5

The Curious Room, Collected Dramatic Works, Chatto & Windus (London), 1996 . . . . . £15/£5

Shaking a Leg: Collected Journalism and Writings, Chatto & Windus (London), 1997 . . . . £10/£5

ditto, as *Shaking a Leg: Collected Writings*, Penguin (New York), 1998 (pbk) £5

RAYMOND CARVER

(b.1938 d.1988)

An American short story writer and poet, Carver's work has been translated into more than 20 languages. Many of his short stories were first published in magazines such as the *New Yorker* and *Esquire* and it was perhaps in writing for these markets that he acquired and perfected his minimalist prose style. Carver's short stories were the subject of Robert Altman's film *Short Cuts.*

Fiction

Put Yourself in My Shoes, Capra Press (Santa Barbara, CA), 1974 (500 copies; wraps) £75

ditto, Capra Press (Santa Barbara, CA), 1974 (75 numbered copies in hard covers). £400

Will You Please Be Quiet, Please?, McGraw-Hill (New York), 1976 . . . . £300/£50

Furious Seasons and Other Stories, Capra Press (Santa Barbara, CA), 1977 (100 signed copies; black cloth; no d/w) £700

ditto, Capra Press (Santa Barbara, CA), 1977 (pbk) . £75

What We Talk About When We Talk About Love, Knopf (New York), 1981 . . . . . . £100/£20

ditto, Collins (London), 1982 . . . . £75/£15

The Pheasant, Metacom (Worcester, MA), 1982 (150 signed copies; hand-sewn into a soft French marble wraps) . £125

ditto, Metacom (Worcester, MA), 1982 (26 lettered signed hardback copies, no d/w) £650

Cathedral, Knopf (New York), 1983 . . . . £35/£10

ditto, Collins (London), 1984 . . . . £35/£10

If It Please You, Lord John Press (Northridge, CA), 1984 (200 signed, numbered copies). £100

ditto, Lord John Press (Northridge, CA), 1984 (26 signed, lettered copies) £250

The Stories of Raymond Carver, Picador (London), 1985 (pbk) £10

Glimpses, Basement Press (Northampton, MA), 1985 (15 numbered copies) £600

My Father's Life, Babcock & Koontz (Derry, NH/Ridgewood, NJ), 1986 (200 signed, numbered copies of 240; sewn into Fabriano Roma wraps) £100

ditto, Babcock & Koontz (Derry, NH/Ridgewood, NJ), 1986 (40 copies of 240, sewn into Mouchete de Pombie wraps, each numbered in Roman and signed by both author and illustrator) £150

Intimacy, Ewert (Concord, NH), 1987 (75 signed copies, no d/w) £200

Those Days: Early Writings by Raymond Carver, Raven (Elmwood, CT), 1987 (100 signed, numbered copies; sewn wraps) £125

ditto, Raven (Elmwood, CT), 1987 (26 signed, lettered copies) £400

ditto, Raven (Elmwood, CT), 1987 (14 signed, presentation copies, quarter leather) £500

Where I'm Calling From: New and Selected Stories, Atlantic Monthly (New York), 1988 . . . £15/£5

ditto, Atlantic Monthly (New York), 1988 (250 signed copies, slipcase) . . . . . . £150/£100

ditto, Franklin Library (Franklin Centre, PA), 1988 (signed, limited edition) £35

ditto, Harvill (London), 1993 . . . . £15/£5

Elephant, Jungle Garden Press (Fairfax, CA), 1988 (200 signed copies; wraps) £150

Elephant and Other Stories, Collins Harvill (London), 1988 . . . . £30/£5

Three Stories, Engdahl Typography (Vineburg, CA), 1990 (400 numbered copies) . . . . . £75/£50

Short Cuts, Vintage Books (New York), 1993 (pbk) . £5

Poetry

Near Klamath, English Club of Sacramento State College (Sacramento, CA), 1968 (wraps) . . . £3,000

Winter Insomnia, Kayak (Santa Cruz, CA), 1970 (mustard-coloured wraps) £65

ditto, Kayak (Santa Cruz, CA), 1970 (white wraps) £1,250

At Night the Salmon Move, Capra Press (Santa Barbara, CA), 1976 (100 signed hardback copies; no d/w). . £300

ditto, Capra Press (Santa Barbara, CA), 1976 (1000 copies; pbk) £75

ditto, Capra Press (Santa Barbara, CA), 1983 (revised text) £45

ditto, Capra Press (Santa Barbara, CA), 1983 (revised text, 25 signed, numbered copies) £250

Distress Sale, Lord John Press (Northridge, CA), 1981 (150 signed copies, single printed sheet). . . . £75

Two Poems, Scarab (Salisbury, MD), 1982 (100 signed copies; wraps) £175

My Crow, Ewert (Concord, NH), 1984 (150 unsigned copies; sewn wraps). £25

ditto, Ewert (Concord, NH), 1984 (36 signed, numbered copies; sewb wraps) £100

For Tess, Ewert (Concord, NH), 1984 (broadside, 125 signed copies) £250

This Water, Ewert (Concord, NH), 1985 (100 signed copies; sewn wraps) £75

ditto, Ewert (Concord, NH), 1985 (36 signed, hardback copies, no d/w) £200

Where Water Comes Together with Other Water, Random House (New York), 1985 . . . . . £25/£10

The Window, Ewert (Concord, NH), 1985 (broadside, 100 unsigned copies) £25

ditto, Ewert (Concord, NH), 1985 (36 numbered, signed copies) £125

Early for the Dance, Ewert (Concord, NH), 1986 (100 signed, numbered copies; sewn wraps) . . . £75

ditto, Ewert (Concord, NH), 1986 (36 Roman numeralled copies, hardcover, no d/w). £145

The River, Ewert (Concord, NH), 1986 (broadside; 100 signed, numbered copies) £100

ditto, Ewert (Concord, NH), 1986 (broadside; 26 signed, lettered copies) £250

Batavia, Shadow Editions (Burlington, VT), [1986] (broadside with portfolio of photographs, 50 numbered copies) £500

ditto, Shadow Editions (Burlington, VT), [1986] (10 lettered copies) £750

ditto, Shadow Editions (Burlington, VT), [1986] (signed, over-run copies) £200

Ultramarine, Random House (New York), 1986 . £25/£10

Two Poems, Ewert (Concord, NH), 1986 (100 copies; sewn wraps) £30

ditto, Ewert (Concord, NH), 1986 (26 signed copies; sewn wraps) £100

In a Marine Light: Selected Poems, Collins Harvill (London), 1987 . . . . £40/£15

Afghanistan, Ewert/Firefly Press (Concord, NH) 1988 (broadside, 50 signed, unnumbered copies) . . . £200

His Bathrobe Pockets Stuffed with Notes, Raven (Elmwood, CT), 1988 (50 numbered, signed copies; wraps) . . £175

ditto, Raven (Elmwood, CT), 1988 (15 numbered, signed presentation copies, marbled wraps) £400

The Toes, Ewert (Concord, NH), 1988 (100 unnumbered copies; sewn wraps) £45

ditto, Ewert (Concord, NH), 1988 (36 lettered copies, sewn wraps in printed red Fabriano d/w) £75

In Memory: Raymond Carver 1938-1988, Saint Peter's Church (New York), 1988 (broadside) . . . £75

The Painter and the Fish, Ewert (Concord, NH), 1988 (26 signed copies, hardcover) £150

ditto, Ewert (Concord, NH), 1988 (74 signed, numbered copies; sewn wraps) £75

ditto, Ewert (Concord, NH), 1988 (15 signed publisher's copies, hardcover) £150

A New Path to the Waterfall, Atlantic Monthly (New York), 1989 . . . . £25/£10

ditto, Atlantic Monthly (New York), 1989 (200 copies signed by editor, blue cloth stamped in gold, in red cloth slipcase) . . . . £75/£50

ditto, Collins Harvill (London), 1989. . . £25/£10

All of Us, Collins Harvill (London), 1996. . . £30/£10

ditto, Knopf (New York), 1998 . . . . £20/£10

Essays, etc
Fires, Capra Press (Santa Barbara, CA), 1983 (250 signed, hardback copies, acetate d/w) . . . . £150/£135

ditto, Capra Press (Santa Barbara, CA), 1983 (unsigned hardback copies) . . . . . . £150/£135

ditto, Capra Press (Santa Barbara, CA), 1983 (pbk) . £15

ditto, Collins Harvill (London), 1985. . . £35/£15

Music, Ewert (Concord, NH), 1985 (26 signed, lettered copies; sewn wraps) £125

ditto, Ewert (Concord, NH), 1985 (100 signed, numbered copies; sewn wraps) £75

No Heroics, Please: Uncollected Writings, Collins Harvill (London), 1991 . . . . . . £35/£10

ditto, Vintage Contemporaries (New York), 1992 (pbk). £10

Screenplays/Plays
Dostoevsky: A Screenplay, Capra Press (Santa Barbara, CA), 1985 (with Tess Gallagher, bound in with *King Dog* by Le Guin; pbk) £10

ditto, Capra Press (Santa Barbara, CA), 1985 (200 copies signed by all authors; pbk) £85

Carnations: A Play in One Act, Engdahl Typography (Vineburg, CA), 1992 (124 numbered copies; no d/w) £100

ditto, Engdahl Typography (Vineburg, CA), 1992 (26 lettered copies with slipcase; no d/w) . . . £200

Call If You Need Me: The Uncollected Fiction and Prose, Harvill (London), 2000 . . . . . £35/£10

ditto, Harvill (London), 2000 (pbk) £5

ditto, Vintage Books (New York), 2001 (pbk). . . £5

JOYCE CARY
(b.1888 d.1957)

Irish novelist Cary studied art in Paris and Edinburgh before turning to literature. He is perhaps best known for *The Horse's Mouth*, a novel about a disreputable artist named Gulley Jimson, which was made into a film with Alec Guinness. *Mister Johnson*, however, is widely regarded as his greatest novel, and like his other novels set in Africa it drew from his own experiences in Nigeria.

Novels
Aissa Saved, Benn (London), 1932 . . . . £400/£50

ditto, Harper & Row (New York), 1962 . . . £30/£10

An American Visitor, Benn (London), 1933 . . £145/£20

ditto, Harper & Row (New York), 1961 . . . £25/£10

The African Witch, Gollancz (London), 1936. . £125/£25

ditto, Morrow (New York), 1936 . . . £25/£5

Castle Corner, Gollancz (London), 1938 . . . £75/£20

ditto, Harper & Row (New York), 1963 . . £25/£10

Mister Johnson, Gollancz (London), 1939 . . £200/£40

ditto, Harper & Row (New York), 1948 . . £25/£10

Charley Is My Darling, Joseph (London), 1940 . £100/£15

ditto, Harper & Row (New York), 1959 . . £20/£5

A House of Children, Joseph (London), 1941. . £35/£10

ditto, Harper & Row (New York), 1955 . . £20/£5

Herself Surprised, Joseph (London), 1941 . . £35/£10

ditto, Harper & Row (New York), 1941 . . £20/£5

To Be a Pilgrim, Joseph (London), 1942 . . £35/£10

ditto, Harper & Row (New York), 1942 . . £20/£5

The Horse's Mouth, Joseph (London), 1944 . . £150/£20

ditto, Harper & Row (New York), 1944 . . £45/£5

The Moonlight, Joseph (London), 1946 . . £35/£10

ditto, Harper & Row (New York), 1946 . . £20/£5

A Fearful Joy, Joseph (London), 1949 . . . £25/£10

ditto, Harper & Row (New York), 1949 . . £20/£5

Prisoner of Grace, Joseph (London), 1952 . . £25/£10

ditto, Harper & Row (New York), 1952 . . £20/£5

Except the Lord, Joseph (London), 1953 . . £20/£5

ditto, Harper & Row (New York), 1953 . . £20/£5

Not Honour More, Joseph (London), 1955 . . £20/£5

ditto, Harper & Row (New York), 1955 . . £20/£5

The Old Strife at Plant's, New Bodlean (Oxford, UK), 1956 (100 signed, numbered copies; wraps) . . . £150

The Horse's Mouth and The Old Strife at Plant's, George Rainbird/Joseph (London), 1957 (1,500 numbered copies; slipcase, acetate d/w) . . . . . . £20/£15

The Captive and the Free, Joseph (London), 1959. £20/£10

ditto, Harper & Row (New York), 1959 . . £15/£5

Spring Song and Other Stories, Joseph (London), 1960 . . . . £15/£10

ditto, Harper & Row (New York), 1960 . . £15/£5

Cock Jarvis, Joseph (London), 1974 . . . £10/£5

ditto, St Martin's Press (New York), 1975 . . £10/£5

Others
Power in Men, Liberal Book Club/Nicholson & Watson (London), 1939 . . . . . . £20/£10

ditto, Univ of Washington Press (Seattle, WA), 1963 £15/£5

The Case for African Freedom, Secker & Warburg (London), 1941 . . . . . . £25/£10

ditto, Secker & Warburg (London), 1941 (revised edition) . . . . £20/£10

ditto, as *The Case for African Freedom and Other Writings on Africa*, Univ of Texas (Austin, TX), 1962 . £10/£5
Process of Real Freedom, Joseph (London), 1943 (wraps) .
. . . . £25
Marching Soldier, Joseph (London), 1945 . . £30/£10
Britain and West Africa, Longman's Green and Co. (London), 1946 (pbk) £25
The Drunken Sailor: A Ballad-Epic, Joseph (London), 1947 . . . . £30/£10
Art and Reality, Ways of the Creative Process, C.U.P. (Cambridge, UK), 1958 . . . . . £20/£5
ditto, Harper & Row (New York), 1958 . . £20/£5
Memoir of the Bobotes, Univ of Texas (Austin, TX), 1960 .
. . . . £20/£5
ditto, Joseph (London), 1964 . . . . £20/£5
Selected Essays, Joseph (London), 1976 . . . £20/£5
ditto, St Martin's Press (New York), 1976 . . £20/£5

WILLA CATHER
(b.1873 d.1947)

Willa Cather is one of America's most prominent female authors, known for her depictions of U.S. prairie life. *O Pioneers* was her first popular success, and serious critical recognition was to come with the award of the Pulitzer Prize for *One of Ours*, and the Prix Femina Americaine in 1933.

Novels
Alexander's Bridge, Houghton Mifflin/Riverside Press (Boston), 1912 (first state binding blue or purple cloth, 'Willa S. Cather' on spine) £200
ditto, Houghton Mifflin/Riverside Press (Boston), 1912 (later issues, other cloth colours) £100
ditto, Heinemann (London), 1912 . . . . £75
O Pioneers!, Houghton Mifflin/Riverside Press (Boston), 1913 (first issue, light yellow/brown vertical ribbed cloth, with stop after 'Co' on spine touching 'o', 'Willa S. Cather' on spine) £350
ditto, Houghton Mifflin/Riverside Press (Boston), 1913 (second issue, pale cream/yellow vertical ribbed cloth, with 'Co' as above, 'Willa S. Cather' on spine) . . . £300
ditto, Houghton Mifflin/Riverside Press (Boston), 1913 (third issue, light yellow/brown linen cloth, with stop after 'Co' on spine separated from 'o', 'Willa S. Cather' on spine) £200
ditto, Houghton Mifflin/Riverside Press (Boston), 1913 (later issue with 'Willa Cather' on spine, brown cloth) . . £40
ditto, Heinemann (London), 1913 . . . . . £300
The Song of the Lark, Houghton Mifflin/Riverside Press (Boston), 1915 (first issue with boxed adverts for 3 books on copyright page, 'moment' for 'moments' on page 8, three lines from the bottom) £50
ditto, Houghton Mifflin/Riverside Press (Boston), 1915 (second issue with adverts facing half title, page 8 corrected) £30
ditto, Murray (London), 1916 . . . . . . £40
My Ántonia, Houghton Mifflin/Riverside Press (Boston), 1918 (first issue with illustrations on inserted coated paper)
. . . . £300
ditto, Houghton Mifflin/Riverside Press (Boston), 1918 (second issue with illustrations on text paper) . . £100

ditto, Heinemann (London), 1919 . . . . . £30
One of Ours, Knopf (New York), 1922 (35 signed copies on Japanese vellum, glassine d/w) . . .£2,000/£1,650
ditto, Knopf (New York), 1922 (310 signed of 345 copies, slipcase) . . . . £450/£350
ditto, Knopf (New York), 1922 (150 of 250 special copies in the US 'Made for Bookseller friends…') . . . £500
ditto, Macmillan (Toronto), 1922 (95 of 250 special copies, without limitation leaf) £400
ditto, Knopf (New York), 1922 (first trade edition states 'Second printing, September 1922') . . £450/£40
ditto, Heinemann (London), 1923 . . . . £100/£25
A Lost Lady, Knopf (New York), 1923 (first issue, green cloth, title at top of spine) . . . . . £300/£100
ditto, Knopf (New York), 1923 (second issue, Cather's name at top of spine) . . . . . . £200/£25
ditto, Knopf (New York), 1923 (200 signed copies, slipcase)
. . . . £650/£550
ditto, Knopf (New York), 1923 (20 signed, lettered copies, slipcase) . . . .£1,650/£1,500
ditto, Heinemann (London), 1924 . . . . £75/£25
The Professor's House, Knopf (New York), 1925 (40 signed, on Japanese vellum of 225 copies, glassine d/w) .
. . . .£1,500/£1,250
ditto, Knopf (New York), 1925 (185 signed of 225 copies, slipcase) . . . . £500/£400
ditto, Knopf (New York), 1925 (this first trade edition states 'first and second printings before publication') . £650/£35
ditto, Heinemann (London), 1925 . . . . £250/£40
My Mortal Enemy, Knopf (New York), 1926 (220 signed copies, slipcase) . . . . . . £300/£250
ditto, Knopf (New York), 1926 (this first trade edition states 'first and second printings before publication') . £65/£20
ditto, Heinemann (London), 1928 . . . . £35/£10
Death Comes for the Archbishop, Knopf (New York), 1927 (50 signed copies on Japanese vellum, slipcase) . . .
. . . .£4,500/£4,000
ditto, Knopf (New York), 1927 (175 signed copies, d/w and slipcase) . . . . . . £3,500/£2,000
ditto, Knopf (New York), 1927 (this first trade edition states 'first and second printings before publication') . £650/£45
ditto, Heinemann (London), 1927 . . . . £350/£45
ditto, Knopf (New York), 1929 (170 signed copies, slipcase)
. . . . £1,500/£1,000
Shadows on the Rock, Knopf (New York), 1931 . £100/£15
ditto, Knopf (New York), 1931 (199 signed, numbered copies on Japanese vellum; d/w and slipcase) £600/£300
ditto, Knopf (New York), 1931 (619 signed, numbered copies; d/w and slipcase) . . . . £300/£200
ditto, Cassell (London), 1932 . . . . . £50/£10
Lucy Gayheart, Knopf (New York), 1935 . £50/£10
ditto, Knopf (New York), 1935 (749 signed, numbered copies, d/w and slipcase) . . . . £300/£125
ditto, Cassell (London), 1935 . . . . . £25/£10
Sapphira and the Slave Girl, Knopf (New York), 1940
. . . . £45/£10
ditto, Knopf (New York), 1940 (525 signed, numbered copies) . . . . £200/£150
ditto, Cassell (London), 1941 . . . . . £15/£5

Short Stories
The Troll Garden, McClure, Phillips & Co. (New York), 1905 . . . .£700
ditto, McClure, Phillips & Co. (New York), 1905 (second issue with 'Doubleday, Page & Co.' at foot of spine) . £250

Youth and the Bright Medusa, Knopf (New York), 1920 .
. . . . £300/£75
ditto, Knopf (New York), 1920 (35 signed copies) . . .
. . . . £1,250/£1,000
ditto, Heinemann (London), 1921 . . . £300/£100
The Fear that Walks by Noonday, Phoenix Bookshop (New
York), 1931 (30 numbered copies) £1,000
Obscure Destinies, Knopf (New York), 1932 (260 signed,
numbered copies, d/w and slipcase) . . £400/£300
ditto, Knopf (New York), 1932 . . . . £75/£15
ditto, Cassell (London), 1932 . . . . £75/£15
The Old Beauty and Others, Knopf (New York), 1948. .
. . . . £45/£10
ditto, Cassell (London), 1956 . . . . £25/£5
Five Stories, Vintage Books (New York), 1956 (pbk) . £30
Father Junipero's Holy Family, Robbins (San Francisco,
CA), 1955 (200 copies; wraps). £150
ditto, Carolyn Hammer at The Anvil Press, (Lexington, KT),
1956 (hardback, no d/w) £125
Early Stories of Willa Cather, Dodd, Mead (New York),
1957 . . . . £25/£10
Willa Cather's Collected Short Fiction, Univ of Nebraska
Press (Lincoln, NE), 1965. . . . . £20/£5
Uncle Valentine and Other Stories, Univ of Nebraska Press
(Lincoln, NE), 1973 . . . . . . £15/£5

Poetry
April Twilights, Gorham Press (Boston), 1903 . £1,000
April Twilights and Other Poems, Knopf (New York), 1923
(450 signed, numbered copies, slipcase). . £350/£250
ditto, Knopf (New York), 1923 . . . . £100/£25
ditto, Heinemann (London), 1924 . . . £200/£35

Essays
Not Under Forty, Knopf (New York), 1936 . . £50/£15
ditto, Knopf (New York), 1936 (313 signed, numbered
copies on Japanese vellum, d/w and slipcase) £300/£200
ditto, Cassell (London), 1936 . . . . £35/£10

Others
My Autobiography, Stokes (New York), 1914 (pseud 'S.S.
McClure', first issue with 'Sept, 1914' on copyright page)
. . . . £250
ditto, Stokes (New York), 1914 (second issue with 'May,
1914' on copyright page) £150
ditto, Murray (London), 1914 . . . . £25
December Night, Knopf (New York), 1933 . £75/£35
Willa Cather on Writing, Knopf (New York), 1949 £30/£10
Writing from Willa Cather's Campus Years, Univ of
Nebraska Press (Lincoln, NE), 1950 . . £25/£10
Willa Cather in Europe, Knopf (New York), 1956 £20/£5
*The Kingdom of Art: Willa Cather's First Principles and
Critical Statements 1893-1902*, Univ of Nebraska Press
(Lincoln, NE), 1966 . . . . . £25/£10
*The World and the Parish: Willa Cather's Articles and
Reviews 1893-1902*, Univ of Nebraska Press (Lincoln,
NE), 1970 (2 vols) . . . . . . £30/£10
Willa Cather In Person, Univ of Nebraska Press (Lincoln,
NE), 1987 . . . . £20/£10

NICK CAVE
(b.1957)

Cave is an Australian musician, songwriter, author and
screenwriter. His first novel, the Southern Gothic *And the
Ass Saw the Angel* was a critical success.

Novels
And the Ass Saw the Angel, Black Spring Press (London),
1989 . . . . £50/£15
ditto, Black Spring Press (London), 1989 (75 numbered,
signed copies in full leather) £750
ditto, HarperCollins (New York), 1990 . . . £25/£10
The Death of Bunny Munro, Canongate (Edinburgh), 2009
. . . . £10/£5
ditto, Canongate (Edinburgh), 2009 (500 signed, numbered
copies; with dvd; slipcase). . . . . £125/£100
ditto, Faber (New York), 2009 . . . . £10/£5

Lyrics
King Ink, Black Spring Press (London), 1988. . £50/£15
King Ink II, Black Spring Press (London), 1997 . £25/£10

RAYMOND CHANDLER
(b.1888 d.1959)

Born in America, Chandler became a British citizen in
1907, but returned to the U.S. in 1912. A novelist and short
story writer, Chandler was 45 before he began writing, and
in *The Big Sleep* introduced one of the most famous
fictional detectives, Philip Marlowe. Chandler's influence
on modern crime fiction, particularly his writing style and
attitude, has been immense.

Novels
The Big Sleep, Knopf (New York), 1939 . . £7,000/£600
ditto, Hamish Hamilton (London), 1939 . . £2,000/£250
ditto, World (Cleveland, OH), 1946 (motion picture edition
with photographs from the film) . . . . £75/£25
Farewell My Lovely, Knopf (New York), 1940 £3,000/£250
ditto, Hamish Hamilton (London), 1940 . . £1,500/£100
The High Window, Knopf (New York), 1942 . £2,500/£250
ditto, Hamish Hamilton (London), 1943 . . £750/£100
The Lady in the Lake, Knopf (New York), 1943 £3,000/£250
ditto, Hamish Hamilton (London), 1944 . . £750/£100
The Little Sister, Hamish Hamilton (London), 1949 £750/£65
ditto, Houghton Mifflin (Boston), 1949 . . £650/£65
The Long Goodbye, Hamish Hamilton (London), 1953. .
. . . . £650/£75
ditto, Houghton Mifflin (Boston), 1954 . . £500/£75
Playback, Hamish Hamilton (London), 1958 . £150/£25
ditto, Houghton Mifflin (Boston), 1958 . . £100/£20
Poodle Springs, Putnam (New York), 1989 (completed by
Robert Parker) . . . . £15/£5
ditto, Macdonald (London), 1990 . . . £15/£5
ditto, Macdonald (London), 1990 (250 copies signed by
Parker, slipcase, no d/w) . . . . . £50/£30

Short Stories
Five Murderers, Avon (New York), 1944 (pbk) . . £125
Five Sinister Characters, Avon (New York), 1945 (pbk) £125

Finger Man and Other Stories, Avon (New York), [1946]
(pbk) £75
Red Wind, World (New York), 1946 .   .   . £65/£15
Spanish Blood, World (New York), 1946.   . £65/£15
Trouble is My Business, Penguin (Harmondsworth,
Middlesex), 1950 (pbk £10
ditto, Pocket Books (New York), 1951 (pbk   .   . £15
The Simple Art of Murder, Houghton Mifflin (Boston),
1950   .   .   .   . £250/£30
ditto, Hamish Hamilton (London), 1950   .   . £200/£30
Pick-Up on Noon Street, Pocket Books (New York), 1952
(pbk) £15
Smart-Aleck Kill, Hamish Hamilton (London), 1953 £400/£35
Pearls are a Nuisance, Hamish Hamilton (London), 1953
(pbk) £40
ditto, as *Finger Man*, Ace Books (New York), 1960 (pbk) £40
Killer in the Rain, Hamish Hamilton (London), 1964   .
.   .   .   . £175/£30
ditto, Houghton Mifflin (Boston), 1964   . £100/£15
The Smell of Fear, Hamish Hamilton (London), 1965   .   .
.   .   .   . £100/£15
Goldfish, Penguin (London), 1995 (pbk)   .   .   . £5
Collected Stories, Random House (New York), 2002 £10/£5

Omnibus Editions
Raymond Chandler's Mystery Omnibus, World (New
York), 1944 .   .   .   . £50/£10
The Raymond Chandler Omnibus, Hamish Hamilton
(London), 1953   .   .   .   .   . £200/£30
ditto, Knopf (New York), 1964   .   .   . £45/£10
The Second Chandler Omnibus, Hamish Hamilton
(London), 1962   .   .   .   .   . £100/£20
The Midnight Raymond Chandler, Houghton Mifflin
(Boston), 1971   .   .   .   .   .   . £35/£10

Others
Raymond Chandler On Writing, Houghton Mifflin
(Boston), 1962 (pbk) £150
Raymond Chandler Speaking, Hamish Hamilton (London),
1962   .   .   .   . £75/£15
ditto, Houghton Mifflin (Boston), 1962   .   . £50/£15
Chandler On Proof Reading, Merrion Press, 1963 (wraps) .
.   .   .   . £200
*Down These Mean Streets a Man Must Go: Raymond
Chandler's Knight*, Univ of North Carolina (Chapel Hill,
NC), 1963   .   .   .   .   .   . £35/£10
*Chandler Before Marlowe: Raymond Chandler's Early
Prose and Poetry, 1908-1912*, Univ of South Carolina
Press (Columbia, SC), 1973 (pbk)   .   .   . £10
ditto, Univ of South Carolina Press (Columbia, SC), 1973
(499 numbered copies, slipcase, no d/w)   .   . £75
The Blue Dahlia, Southern Illinois Univ Press (Carbondale,
IL), 1976   .   .   .   .   .   . £45/£10
ditto, Elm Tree Books (London), 1976   .   . £20/£5
*The Notebooks of Raymond Chandler and English Summer
- A Gothic Romance*, The Ecco Press (New York), 1976 .
.   .   .   . £45/£20
ditto, Weidenfeld & Nicolson (London), 1977.   . £25/£10
Letters, Raymond Chandler and James M. Fox, Nevile &
Yellin (Santa Barbara, CA), 1978 (350 numbered copies,
no d/w) £60
ditto, Nevile & Yellin (Santa Barbara, CA), 1978 (26 lettered
copies, no d/w) £125
The Selected Letters of Raymond Chandler, Columbia Univ
Press (New York), 1981   .   .   .   . £40/£15

ditto, Cape (London), 1981   .   .   .   .   . £25/£10
Backfire: Story for the Screen, Santa Teresa Press (Santa
Barbara, CA), 1984 (200 copies; sewn wraps)   .   . £30
ditto, Santa Teresa Press (Santa Barbara, CA), 1984 (26
lettered copies, signed by Robert Parker, slipcase, no d/w)
.   .   .   . £200
ditto, Santa Teresa Press (Santa Barbara, CA), 1984 (100
signed, numbered copies, slipcase, no d/w)   .   . £75
*Raymond Chandler's Unknown Thriller: The Screenplay
of 'Playback'*, Mysterious Press (New York), 1985 £30/£15
ditto, Mysterious Press (New York), 1985 (250 copies,
signed by Robert Parker, slipcase)   .   .   . £100/£75
ditto, Mysterious Press (New York), 1985 (26 signed,
lettered copies, slipcase)   .   .   .   . £200/£175
ditto, Harrap (London), 1985   .   .   .   . £20/£10
*The Raymond Chandler Papers: Selected Letters and
Nonfiction, 1909-1959*, Atlantic Monthly Press (New
York), 2000 .   .   .   . £25/£10
ditto, Hamish Hamilton (London), 2000   .   . £25/£10

LESLIE CHARTERIS
(b.1907 d.1993)

Charteris was born in Singapore to a Chinese father and
English mother. Educated and living in England for several
years he wrote a number of crime novels before creating
Simon Templar, a gentleman burglar nicknamed 'The
Saint'. He moved to America in 1932 but was excluded
from permanent residency by the Oriental Exclusion Act.
An Act of Congress subsequently granted him the right of
permanent residence and he became a U.S. citizen in 1941.

'Saint' Novels
Meet the Tiger!, Ward Lock (London), 1928   . £2,500/£650
ditto, Doubleday (New York), 1929   .   . £1,500/£600
ditto, as *The Saint Meets The Tiger*, Hodder & Stoughton
(London), 1963   .   .   .   . £75/£10
The Last Hero, Hodder & Stoughton (London), [1930]   .
.   .   .   . £1,250/£75
ditto, Doubleday (New York), 1931   .   . £750/£65
ditto, as *The Saint Closes The Case*, Hodder & Stoughton
(London), 1951   .   .   .   .   .   . £75/£10
Knight Templar, Hodder & Stoughton (London), [1930]   .
.   .   .   . £1,250/£75
ditto, as *The Avenging Saint*, Doubleday (New York), 1931
.   .   .   . £750/£65
ditto, as *The Avenging Saint*, Hodder & Stoughton
(London), 1949   .   .   .   .   .   . £75/£10
She Was A Lady, Hodder & Stoughton (London), 1931   .
.   .   .   . £1,250/£75
ditto, as *Angels of Doom*, Doubleday (New York), 1932   .
.   .   .   . £750/£65
ditto, as *The Saint Meets His Match*, Hodder & Stoughton
(London), 1950   .   .   .   .   .   . £75/£10
Getaway, Hodder & Stoughton (London), 1932 £1,250/£75
ditto, as *Getaway: The New Saint Mystery*, Doubleday (New
York), 1933   .   .   .   .   .   . £750/£65
ditto, as *The Saint's Getaway*, Hodder & Stoughton
(London), 1950   .   .   .   .   .   . £75/£10
The Saint in New York, Hodder & Stoughton (London),
1935   .   .   .   . £1,250/£75
ditto, Doubleday (New York), 1935   .   .   . £650/£65

The Saint Overboard, Hodder & Stoughton (London), 1936
. . . . £1,250/£75
ditto, Doubleday (New York), 1936 . . . . £350/£35
Thieves' Picnic, Hodder & Stoughton (London), 1937 . .
. . . . £1,000/£65
ditto, Doubleday (New York), 1937 . . . . £300/£25
ditto, as *The Saint Bids Diamonds*, Hodder & Stoughton
(London), 1950 . . . . £75/£10
Prelude for War, Hodder & Stoughton (London), 1938 .
. . . . £650/£50
ditto, Doubleday (New York), 1938 . . . . £300/£30
ditto, as *The Saint Plays With Fire*, Hodder & Stoughton
(London), 1951 . . . . £75/£10
The Saint in Miami, Doubleday (New York), 1940 £250/£20
ditto, Hodder & Stoughton (London), 1941 . £200/£20
The Saint Steps In, Doubleday (New York), 1943 . £250/£20
ditto, Hodder & Stoughton (London), 1944 . £200/£20
The Saint Sees it Through, Doubleday (New York), 1946 .
. . . . £150/£15
ditto, Hodder & Stoughton (London), 1947 . £100/£10
The Saint and the Fiction Makers, Doubleday (New York),
1968 . . . . £75/£10
ditto, Hodder & Stoughton (London), 1969 . £75/£10
The Saint in Pursuit, Doubleday (New York), 1970 . .
. . . . £125/£25
ditto, Hodder & Stoughton (London), 1971 . £125/£25
The Saint and the People Importers, Hodder & Stoughton
(London), 1971 (pbk) £10
ditto, Doubleday (New York), 1972 . . . £135/£25
ditto, Hodder & Stoughton (London), 1973 . £100/£15
The Saint and the Hapsburg Necklace, Doubleday (New
York), 1976 . . . . £25/£10
ditto, Hodder & Stoughton (London), 1976 . £60/£10
Send for The Saint, Hodder & Stoughton (London), 1977 .
. . . . £35/£10
ditto, Doubleday (New York), 1978 . . . £35/£10
The Saint and the Templar Treasure, Doubleday (New
York), 1979 . . . . £35/£10
ditto, Hodder & Stoughton (London), 1979 . £35/£10
Count on The Saint, Doubleday (New York), 1980 £25/£5
ditto, Hodder & Stoughton (London), 1980 . £25/£5
Salvage for The Saint, Doubleday (New York), 1983 £20/£5
ditto, Hodder & Stoughton (London), 1983 . £20/£5

'Saint' Novellas and Short Stories
Enter The Saint, Hodder & Stoughton (London), [1930] .
. . . . £1,250/£75
ditto, Doubleday (New York), 1931 . . . . £750/£65
Featuring The Saint, Hodder & Stoughton (London), 1931
. . . . £1,250/£75
Alias The Saint, Hodder & Stoughton (London), 1931 . .
. . . . £1,250/£75
Wanted for Murder, Doubleday (New York), 1931 (contains
Featuring the Saint and *Alias the Saint*) . . £750/£65
ditto, as *Paging the Saint*, Jacobs (New York), 1945 (pbk) .
. . . . £30
The Holy Terror, Hodder & Stoughton (London), 1932 .
. . . . £1,250/£75
ditto, as *The Saint Versus Scotland Yard*, Doubleday (New
York), 1932 . . . . £750/£65
ditto, as *The Saint Versus Scotland Yard*, Hodder &
Stoughton (London), 1949 . . . . £75/£10
Once More The Saint, Hodder & Stoughton (London), 1933
. . . . £1,000/£75

ditto, as *The Saint and Mr Teal*, Doubleday (New York),
1933 . . . . £750/£65
The Brighter Buccaneer, Hodder & Stoughton (London),
1933 . . . . £1,000/£75
ditto, Doubleday (New York), 1933 . . . . £650/£65
The Misfortunes of Mr Teal, Hodder & Stoughton
(London), 1934 . . . . . . £1,000/£75
ditto, Doubleday (New York), 1934 . . . . £500/£45
ditto, as *The Saint In London*, Hodder & Stoughton
(London), 1952 . . . . £75/£10
Boodle, Hodder & Stoughton (London), 1934 . £1,000/£75
ditto, *The Saint Intervenes*, Doubleday (New York), 1934 .
. . . . £500/£45
The Saint Goes On, Hodder & Stoughton (London), 1934 .
. . . . £1,000/£75
ditto, Doubleday (New York), 1935 . . . . £650/£65
The Ace of Knaves, Hodder & Stoughton (London), 1937 .
. . . . £600/£45
ditto, Doubleday (New York), 1937 . . . . £250/£30
Follow The Saint, Doubleday (New York), 1938 . £450/£35
ditto, Hodder & Stoughton (London), 1939 . £200/£30
The Happy Highwayman, Doubleday (New York), 1939 .
. . . . £450/£25
ditto, Hodder & Stoughton (London), 1939 . £175/£25
The Saint Goes West, Doubleday (New York), 1942 £75/£15
ditto, Hodder & Stoughton (London), 1942 . £75/£15
The Saint on Guard, Doubleday (New York), 1944 £75/£15
ditto, Hodder & Stoughton (London), 1945 . £75/£15
Call For The Saint, Doubleday (New York), 1948 £30/£15
ditto, Hodder & Stoughton (London), 1948 . £30/£10
Saint Errant, Doubleday (New York), 1948 . £30/£10
ditto, Hodder & Stoughton (London), 1949 . £30/£10
The Saint in Europe, Doubleday (New York), 1953 £30/£10
ditto, Hodder & Stoughton (London), 1954 . £30/£10
The Saint on the Spanish Main, Doubleday (New York),
1955 . . . . £30/£10
ditto, Hodder & Stoughton (London), 1956 . £30/£10
The Saint Around the World, Doubleday (New York), 1956
. . . . £30/£10
ditto, Hodder & Stoughton (London), 1957 . £25/£10
Thanks to The Saint, Doubleday (New York), 1957 £25/£10
ditto, Hodder & Stoughton (London), 1958 . £25/£10
Señor Saint, Doubleday (New York), 1958 . £25/£10
ditto, Hodder & Stoughton (London), 1959 . £25/£10
The Saint to the Rescue, Doubleday (New York), 1959 .
. . . . £25/£10
ditto, Hodder & Stoughton (London), 1961 . £25/£10
Trust The Saint, Doubleday (New York), 1962 . £25/£10
ditto, Hodder & Stoughton (London), 1962 . £25/£10
The Saint in the Sun, Doubleday (New York), 1963 £25/£10
ditto, Hodder & Stoughton (London), 1964 . £25/£10
Vendetta for The Saint, Doubleday (New York), 1964 . .
. . . . £25/£10
ditto, Hodder & Stoughton (London), 1965 . £25/£10
The Saint on TV, Doubleday (New York), 1968 . £25/£10
ditto, Hodder & Stoughton (London), 1968 . £25/£10
The Saint Returns, Doubleday (New York), 1968 . £25/£10
ditto, Hodder & Stoughton (London), 1969 . £25/£10
The Saint Abroad, Doubleday (New York), 1969 . £20/£5
ditto, Hodder & Stoughton (London), 1970 . £20/£5
Catch The Saint, Hodder & Stoughton (London), 1975. .
. . . . £15/£5
ditto, Doubleday (New York), 1975 . . . £15/£5
The Saint in Trouble, Doubleday (New York), 1978 £15/£5
ditto, Hodder & Stoughton (London), 1979 . £15/£5

Collected Editions
The First Saint Omnibus, Hodder & Stoughton (London), 1939 . . . . £75/£15
ditto, Doubleday (New York), 1939 . . . . £75/£15
ditto, as *Arrest the Saint*, PermaBooks (New York), 1951 .
. . . . £25/£10
The Saint Two in One, Sun Dial Press (New York), 1942 .
. . . . £35/£5
The Saint at Large, Sun Dial Press (New York), 1943 £35/£5
The Second Saint Omnibus, Doubleday (New York), 1951.
. . . . £35/£10
ditto, Hodder & Stoughton (London), 1952 . £35/£10
Concerning The Saint, Avon (New York), 1958 (pbk). £15
The Saint Cleans Up, Avon (New York), 1959 (pbk) . £15
The Saint Magazine Reader, Doubleday (New York), 1966
. . . . £15/£5
ditto, as *The Saint's Choice*, Hodder & Stoughton (London), 1976 . . . . £15/£5
Saints Alive, Hodder & Stoughton (London), 1974 £15/£5
The Saint: Good as Gold, The Ellery Queen Mystery Club (Roslyn, NY), 1979 . . . . . . £15/£5
The Fantastic Saint, Doubleday (New York), 1982 £10/£5
ditto, Hodder & Stoughton (London), 1982 . £10/£5
The Saint: Five Complete Novels, Avenel Books (New York), 1983 . . . . £10/£5

Other Titles
X Esquire, Ward Lock (London), 1927 . . £1,450/£125
The White Rider, Ward Lock (London), 1928 . . £500/£50
ditto, Doubleday (New York), 1930 . . . £350/£35
Daredevil, Ward Lock (London), 1929 . . . £300/£50
ditto, Doubleday (New York), 1929 . . . £200/£25
The Bandit, Ward Lock (London), 1929 . . . £300/£75
ditto, Doubleday (New York), 1930 . . . £200/£25
Killer of Bulls, Heinemann (London), 1937 (with Juan Belmonte) . . . . £75/£25
ditto, Doubleday (New York), 1937 . . . £50/£15
Lady on a Train, Shaw Press (Pasadena,CA), 1945 (pbk) £40
Spanish for Fun, Hodder & Stoughton (London), 1964 (pbk) £10
Paleneo: A Universal Sign Language, Hodder & Stoughton (London), 1972 (pbk). £10

BRUCE CHATWIN
(b.1940 d.1989)

Travel writer and novelist Chatwin's first book, *In Patagonia*, won both the Hawthornden Prize and the E.M. Forster Award of the American Academy of Arts and Letters. His story-telling and spare style are much admired, but since his death it has been alleged that his travel books distort the details of real people, places and events.

Novels
The Viceroy of Ouidah, Cape (London), 1980 . £40/£10
ditto, Summit (New York), 1980. . . . . £30/£10
On the Black Hill, Cape (London), 1982 . . . £35/£10
ditto, Viking (New York), 1983 . . . . £25/£10
The Songlines, Cape (London), 1987 . . . £45/£10
ditto, London Limited Editions (London), 1987 (150 signed copies, glassine wrapper) . . . . £300/£250
ditto, Viking (New York), 1987 . . . . £40/£5

ditto, Franklin Library (Franklin Centre, PA), 1987 (signed limited edition) £35
Utz, Cape (London), 1988 . . . . . . £15/£5
ditto, Viking (New York), 1989 . . . . . £10/£5

Travel
In Patagonia, Cape (London), 1977 (map endpapers) . .
. . . . £700/£350
ditto, Cape (London), 1977 (white endpapers). £450/£100
ditto, Summit (New York), 1978 . . . . £125/£25
Patagonia Revisited, Russell (Wilton, Salisbury, UK), 1985 (with Paul Theroux) . . . . . . £25/£10
ditto, Russell (Wilton, Salisbury, UK), 1985 (250 numbered copies signed by both authors, cellophane d/w) £200/£175
ditto, Houghton Mifflin (Boston), 1986 . . . £20/£10
ditto, as *Nowhere is a Place: Travels in Patagonia*, Sierra Club (San Francisco, CA), 1991 . . . £20/£10

Short Stories
The Attractions of France, Colophon Press (London), 1993 (26 lettered copies, cloth) £175
ditto, Colophon Press (London), 1993 (175 numbered copies; sewn wraps) £50

Biography
What Am I Doing Here?, Cape (London), 1989 . £25/£5
ditto, Viking (New York), 1989 . . . . £20/£5
Photographs and Notebooks, Cape (London), 1993 £35/£10
ditto, as *Far Journeys: Photographs and Notebooks*, Viking (New York), 1993 . . . . . . £25/£10

Others
Animal Style: Art From East to West, Asia Society (New York), 1970 (with Emma Bunker and Ann Farkas) £35/£15
ditto, Asia Society (New York), 1970 (pbk) . . £15
Lady Lisa Lyon, Viking (New York), 1983 (photographs by Robert Mapplethorpe; wraps) £10
ditto, St Martin's Press (New York), 1983 . £100/£15
ditto, Blond & Briggs (London), 1983 . . £100/£15
ditto, Blond & Briggs (London), 1983 (wraps) . £10
The Morality of Things, Typographeum (Francestown, NH), 1993 (175 copies, cloth, no d/w) . . . £125
Anatomy of Restlessness, Selected Writings, 1969-89, Cape (London), 1996 . . . . . . £30/£10
ditto, Viking (New York), 1996 . . . . £25/£5
Winding Paths: Photographs by Bruce Chatwin, Cape (London), 1999 (pbk). £10

GEOFFREY CHAUCER
(b.1340? d.1400)

Chaucer gave English literature its form and inspiration, and well over 500 years later his work can still be outrageous and entertaining. First editions of the *Canterbury Tales* are only available to wealthy institutions, but 16th-century editions of Chaucer's work are within the reach of committed collectors.

Canterbury Tales, William Caxton (London), [c.1478]. .
. . . . £6,000,000
ditto, William Caxton (London), 1483 (with woodcut illustrations). £3,000,000

JOHN CHEEVER
(b.1912 d.1982)

An American short story writer and novelist, Cheever's most important works include the 'Wapshot' books (*The Wapshot Chronicle* won the National Book Award in 1958) and a collection *The Stories of John Cheever*, which won the Pulitzer Prize in 1978. He was a frequent contributor to the *New Yorker*.

Fiction
The Way Some People Live: A Book of Stories, Random House (New York), 1943 . . . . . £650/£100
The Enormous Radio and Other Stories, Funk & Wagnalls (New York), 1953 . . . . . . £165/£25
ditto, Gollancz (London), 1953 . . . . £75/£15
The Wapshot Chronicle, Harper & Row (New York), 1957 . . . . £125/£25
ditto, Gollancz (London), 1957 . . . . £50/£10
ditto, Franklin Library (Franklin Centre, PA), 1978 (signed, limited edition) £50
The Housebreaker of Shady Hill and Other Stories, Harper (New York), [1958] . . . . . £45/£10
ditto, Gollancz (London), 1958 . . . . £45/£10
Some People, Places, and Things That Will Not Appear in My Next Novel, Harper (New York), 1961 . £75/£15
ditto, Gollancz (London), 1961 . . . . £65/£15
The Wapshot Scandal, Harper (New York), 1964 . £65/£10
ditto, Gollancz (London), 1964 . . . . £40/£10
The Brigadier and the Golf Widow, Harper (New York), 1964 . . . . £40/£5
ditto, Gollancz (London), 1965 . . . . £35/£5
Bullet Park, Knopf (New York), 1969 . . £40/£10
ditto, Cape (London), 1969 . . . . . £40/£10
The World of Apples, Knopf (New York), 1973 . £30/£10
ditto, Cape (London), 1974 . . . . . £25/£10
Falconer, Knopf (New York), 1977 . . . £25/£10
ditto, Cape (London), 1977 . . . . . £25/£10
The Stories of John Cheever, Knopf (New York), 1978 . . . . £25/£10
ditto, Cape (London), 1979 . . . . . £20/£5
The Wapshot Chronicle/The Wapshot Scandal, Harper (New York), 1979 . . . . . . £30/£10
Oh, What a Paradise it Seems, Knopf (New York), 1982 . . . . £20/£5
ditto, Cape (London), 1982 . . . . . £20/£5
The Letters of John Cheever, Simon & Schuster (New York), 1988 (ed. by Benjamin Cheever). . £25/£10
ditto, Cape (London), 1989 . . . . . £20/£5
The Journals of John Cheever, Knopf (New York), 1991 . . . . £20/£5
ditto, Cape (London), 1991 . . . . . £15/£5

Others
Homage to Shakespeare, Country Squires Books (Stevenson, CT), 1968 (150 signed, numbered copies) £125/£100
The Day the Pig Fell into the Well, Lord John Press (Northridge, CA), 1978 (275 signed, numbered copies, cloth; no d/w) £50
ditto, Lord John Press (Northridge, CA), 1978 (26 signed, lettered copies, slipcase) . . . . £200/£150
The Leaves, The Lion-Fish and the Bear, Sylvester & Orphanos (Los Angeles, CA), 1980 (300 signed, numbered copies) £45

ditto, Sylvester & Orphanos (Los Angeles, CA), 1980 (26 signed, lettered copies, slipcase) . . . £200/£150
ditto, Sylvester & Orphanos (Los Angeles, CA), 1980 (4 signed copies bearing printed name of recipient, slipcase) . . . . £350/£300
The National Pastime, Sylvester & Orphanos (Los Angeles, CA), 1982 (300 signed, numbered copies) . . . £50
ditto, Sylvester & Orphanos (Los Angeles, CA), 1982 (26 signed, lettered copies, slipcase) . . . £200/£150
ditto, Sylvester & Orphanos (Los Angeles, CA), 1982 (4 signed copies bearing printed name of recipient, slipcase) . . . . £350/£300
Atlantic Crossing: Excerpts from the Journals of John Cheever, Ex Ophidia (Cottondale, AL), 1986 (90 copies, slipcase). . . . . £375/£325
Expelled, Sylvester & Orphanos (Los Angeles, CA), 1988 (a miniature book with a Preface by Malcom Cowley, an Afterword by John Updike, designed and illustrated by Warren Chappell, 150 copies signed by Cheever, Cowley, Updike and Chappell, slipcase) . . . £175/£125
ditto, Sylvester & Orphanos (Los Angeles, CA), 1988 (26 lettered copies, signed by contributors, slipcase) . . . . £250/£200
ditto, Sylvester & Orphanos (Los Angeles, CA), 1988 (4 copies bearing printed name of recipient, signed by contributors, slipcase) . . . . . £350/£300

G.K. CHESTERTON
(b.1874 d.1936)

A Poet, novelist, journalist and essayist, Chesterton wrote around 80 books, several hundred poems, 200 short stories, 4,000 essays and a handful of plays. He is best remembered for his detective stories featuring Father Brown, an unassuming Catholic priest. He was also a columnist for the *Daily News*, *Illustrated London News*, and his own paper, *G.K's Weekly*.

'Father Brown' Stories
The Innocence of Father Brown, Cassell (London), 1911 . . . . £350
ditto, John Lane (New York), 1911 . . . . £100
The Wisdom of Father Brown, Cassell (London), 1914 £150
ditto, John Lane (New York), 1915 . . . . £50
The Incredulity of Father Brown, Cassell (London), 1926 . . . . £1,500/£50
ditto, Dodd, Mead (New York), 1927 . . £500/£35
The Secret of Father Brown, Cassell (London), 1927 . . . . £1,500/£35
ditto, Harper & Bros (New York), 1928 . . £500/£30
The Father Brown Stories, Cassell (London), 1929 . . . . £250/£25
ditto, as *The Father Brown Omnibus*, Dodd, Mead (New York), 1933 . . . . . . £175/£20
The Scandal of Father Brown, Cassell (London), 1935 . . . . £600/£25
ditto, Dodd, Mead (New York), 1935 . . £200/£25

Novels
The Napoleon of Notting Hill, John Lane (London), 1904 . . . . £100
ditto, John Lane (New York), 1906 . . . . £100

The Man Who Was Thursday, Arrowsmith (London), [1908] £150
ditto, Dodd, Mead (New York), 1908 . . £150
The Ball and the Cross, John Lane (New York),1909 . £45
ditto, Wells Gardner (London), 1910 . . . . £40
Manalive, Nelson (London), 1912 . . . . £35
ditto, John Lane (New York), 1912 . . . . £30
The Flying Inn, Methuen (London), 1914 . . . £45
ditto, John Lane (New York), 1914 . . . . £35
The Return of Don Quixote, Chatto & Windus (London), 1927 . . . . £225/£30
ditto, Dodd, Mead (New York), 1927 . . . £100/£25

Short Stories
The Club of Queer Trades, Harper & Bros (London), 1905. . . . . £250
ditto, Harper & Bros (New York), 1905 . . . £200
The Man Who Knew Too Much, Cassell (London), 1922 . . . . £750/£100
ditto, Harper & Bros (New York), 1922 . . £250/£45
Tales of the Long Bow, Cassell (London), 1925 . £500/£75
ditto, Dodd, Mead (New York), 1925 . . £300/£40
The Sword of Wood, Elkin Mathews & Marrot (London), 1928 (530 signed copies) . . . . £125/£75
The Poet and the Lunatics, Cassell (London), 1929 £600/£65
ditto, Dodd, Mead (New York), 1929 . . £325/£45
Four Faultless Felons, Cassell (London), 1930 . £500/£50
ditto, Dodd, Mead (New York), 1930 . . £300/£40
The Paradoxes of Mr Pond, Cassell (London), 1937 . . . . £225/£40
ditto, Dodd, Mead (New York), 1937 . . £125/£25

Plays
Magic, A Fantastic Comedy, Martin Secker (London), 1913 (pbk) £45
ditto, Martin Secker (London), 1913 (150 signed copies, tissue d/w) . . . . . . £300/£250
ditto, Putnam's (New York), 1913 (pbk) . . . £30
The Judgement of Dr Johnson, Sheed & Ward (London), 1927 . . . . £75/£20
ditto, Putnam's (New York), 1928 . . . £50/£10
The Surprise, Sheed & Ward (London), 1952 . £50/£20
ditto, Sheed & Ward (New York), 1953 . . £50/£20

Poetry
Greybeards at Play, Brimley Johnson (London), 1900 . £500
The Wild Knight and Other Poems, Grant Richards (London), 1900 . . . . £100
The Ballad of the White Horse, Methuen (London), 1911 . . . . £45
ditto, Methuen (London), 1911 (100 signed copies, handmade paper) £200
The Nativity, Albany (New York), 1911 (wraps) . £65
Poems, Burns & Oates Ltd (London), 1915 . . £40
Wine, Water and Song, Methuen (London), 1915 . £45
The Ballad of St. Barbara and Other Verses, Cecil Palmer (London), 1922 . . . . . £150/£35
ditto, Putnam's (New York), 1923 . . . £75/£20
The Queen of Seven Swords, Sheed & Ward (London), 1926 . . . . £50/£20
Collected Poems, Cecil Palmer (London), 1927 . £65/£25
ditto, Cecil Palmer (London), 1927 (350 signed copies, slipcase) . . . . £150/£125
Gloria in Profundis, Faber & Gwyer (London), 1927 (wraps; in envelope; illustrated by Eric Gill) . . . £50/£35

ditto, by G.K. Chesterton, Faber & Gwyer (London), 1927 (350 copies signed by Gill; glassine wraps) . £150/£125
ditto, Rudge (New York), 1927 (27 copies for copyright purposes; stapled wraps) £125

Collaborations
The Floating Admiral, Hodder & Stoughton (London), [1931] (chain novel; chapters also contributed by Chesterton, Dorothy L. Sayers, Agatha Christie, John Rhode, Ronald A. Knox, Freeman Wills Crofts, and others) . . . . £1,500/£100
ditto, Doubleday (New York), 1932 . . . . £500/£30

Others
The Defendant, Brimley Johnson (London), 1901 . . £65
Twelve Types, Humphreys (London), 1902 . . . £65
ditto, as *Varied Types*, Dodd, Mead (New York), 1908 . £30
Robert Browning, Macmillan (London), 1903 . . £25
ditto, Macmillan (New York), 1903 . . . . £25
G.F. Watts (New York), Duckworth (London), 1904 . £25
ditto, Dutton (New York), 1904 . . . . . £25
Charles Dickens, Methuen (London), 1906 . . £45
ditto, as *Charles Dickens, a critical study*, Dodd, Mead (New York), 1906 . . . . £35
All Things Considered, Methuen (London), 1908 . . £45
Orthodoxy, John Lane (London), 1909 . . . . £30
George Bernard Shaw, John Lane/Bodley Head (London), 1909 . . . . £40
ditto, John Lane (New York), 1909 . . . . . £40
Tremendous Trifles, Methuen (London), 1909 . . £45
What's Wrong with the World, Cassell (London), 1910 . £35
Five Types, Humphries (London), 1910 (in slipcase) £45/£20
ditto, Holt (New York), 1911 . . . . . £45/£20
Alarms and Discursions, Methuen (London), 1910 . £45
ditto, Dodd, Mead (New York), 1911 . . . . £40
William Blake, Duckworth (London), 1910 . . . £40
Appreciations and Criticisms of the Works of Dickens, Dent & Sons (London), 1911 . . . . . . £40
ditto, Dutton (New York), 1911 . . . . . £40
The Future of Religion. Mr. G.K. Chesterton's Reply to Mr. Bernard Shaw, The Heretics Club (New York), 1911 (wire-stiched wraps) £50
A Miscellany of Men, Methuen (London), 1912 . . £40
ditto, Dodd, Mead (New York), 1912 . . . . £35
Victorian Age in Literature, Williams & Norgate (London), 1913 . . . . £35
The Barbarism of Berlin, Cassell (London), 1914 (pbk) £40
ditto, as *The Appetite of Tyranny*, Dodd, Mead (New York), 1915 . . . . £25
London, privately printed for Edmund D. Brooks and Alvin Langdon Coburn etc (London), 1914 . . . £500
The Crimes of England, Cecil, Palmer & Hayward (London), 1915 . . . . £65
ditto, Cecil, Palmer & Hayward (London), 1915 (pbk) . £25
Lord Kitchener, privately published, 1917 (wraps) . £75
A Short History of England, John Lane (London), 1917 £35
ditto, John Lane (New York), 1917 . . . . . £35
Utopia of Usurers and Other Essays, Boni & Liveright (New York), 1917 . . . . £35
Irish Impressions, John Lane (New York), 1920 . £75/£35
The Superstition of Divorce, Chatto & Windus (London), 1920 . . . . £75/£15
The New Jerusalem, Hodder & Stoughton (London), 1920 . . . . £125/£15

ditto, Doran (New York), 1921 . . . . £125/£15
Eugenics and Other Evils, Cassell (London), 1922 .
. . . . £125/£15
ditto, Dodd, Mead (New York), 1922 . . £125/£15
What I Saw In America, Hodder & Stoughton (London),
1922 . . . . £100/£25
Fancies Versus Fads, Methuen (London), 1923 . £100/£25
ditto, Dodd, Mead (New York), 1923 . . £100/£25
St Francis of Assisi, Hodder & Stoughton (London), 1923 .
. . . . £100/£25
The Superstitions of the Sceptic, Heffers (Oxford), 1925
(pbk) £45
The Everlasting Man, Dodd, Mead (New York), 1925 . .
. . . . £100/£25
William Cobbett, Hodder & Stoughton (London), 1925 .
. . . . £75/£15
The Outline of Sanity, Methuen (London), 1926 . £75/£25
ditto, Dodd, Mead (New York), 1927 . . £75/£25
The Catholic Church and Conversion, Burns, Oates &
Washbourne (London), 1926 . . . £75/£15
The Gleaming Cohort, Methuen (London), 1926 . £75/£25
Robert Louis Stevenson, Hodder & Stoughton (London),
[1927] . . . . £75/£30
ditto, Dodd, Mead (New York), 1928 . . £75/£30
Generally Speaking, Methuen (London), 1928 . £65/£25
**Do We Agree? A Debate Between G. K. Chesterton and
George Bernard Shaw. With Hilaire Belloc in the Chair**,
Cecil Palmer (London), 1928 . . . £75/£25
ditto, Mitchell (New York), 1928 . . . £75/£25
The Thing, Sheed & Ward (London), 1929 . £85/£30
ditto, Dodd, Mead (New York), 1930 . . £50/£20
The Resurrection of Rome, Hodder & Stoughton (London),
[1930] . . . . £75/£30
ditto, Dodd, Mead (New York), 1927 . . £75/£30
Come to Think of It, Methuen (London), 1930 . £75/£25
All Is Grist, Methuen (London), 1931 . . £75/£25
ditto, Dodd, Mead (New York), 1932 . . £65/£20
Chaucer, Faber & Faber (London), 1932 . . £75/£25
ditto, Farrar & Rinehart (New York), 1932 . £45/£15
**Sidelights on New London and Newer York and Other
Essays**, Sheed & Ward (London), 1933 . . £75/£30
ditto, Dodd, Mead (New York), 1932 . . £75/£30
Christendom in Dublin, Sheed & Ward (London), 1933 .
. . . . £75/£20
ditto, Sheed & Ward (New York), 1933 . . £75/£20
All I Survey, Methuen (London), 1933 . . £50/£15
ditto, Dodd, Mead (New York), 1933 . . £50/£15
St. Thomas Aquinas, Hodder & Stoughton (London), 1933.
. . . . £45/£15
ditto, Sheed & Ward (New York), 1933 . . £45/£15
Avowals and Denials, Methuen (London), 1934 . £45/£15
The Well and the Shallows, Sheed & Ward (London), 1935
. . . . £45/£15
ditto, Sheed & Ward (New York), 1935 . . £45/£15
Autobiography, Hutchinson (London), 1936 . £45/£15
ditto, Hutchinson (London), 1936 (250 deluxe copies;
slipcase). . . . . £95/£75
ditto, Sheed & Ward (New York), 1936 . . £40/£15
The Coloured Lands, Sheed & Ward (London), 1938 . .
. . . . £40/£15
ditto, Sheed & Ward (New York), 1938 . . £40/£15
The Common Man, Sheed & Ward (London), 1950 £30/£10
ditto, Sheed & Ward (New York), 1950 . . £30/£10

A Handful of Authors, Sheed & Ward (London), 1953 .
. . . . £35/£10
ditto, Sheed & Ward (New York), 1953 . . £35/£10
**The Glass Walking-Stick and Other Essays from the
Illustrated London News**, Metheun, 1955 . . £35/£10
Lunacy and Letters, Sheed & Ward (London), 1958 . .
. . . . £35/£10
ditto, Sheed & Ward (New York), 1958 . . £35/£10

PETER CHEYNEY
(b.1896 d.1951)

British author Cheyney's books may seem a little dated
now, but his brutal heroes still attract collectors of thrillers.
Towards the end of World War Two Cheyney's reputation
was at its height and his sales peaked at two-and-half-
million copies per year in the U.K. alone.

Novels
This Man is Dangerous, Collins (London), 1936 . £125/£15
ditto, Coward-McCann (New York), 1938 . . £65/£10
Poison Ivy, Collins (London), 1937 . . . £125/£15
Dames Don't Care, Collins (London), 1937 . . £100/£15
ditto, Coward-McCann (New York), 1938 . . £75/£10
Can Ladies Kill?, Collins (London), 1938 . . £100/£15
The Urgent Hangman, Collins (London), 1938 . £100/£15
ditto, Coward-McCann (New York), 1939 . . £75/£10
Don't Get Me Wrong, Collins (London), 1939 . £100/£10
Dangerous Curves, Collins (London), 1939 . . £75/£10
ditto, as **Callaghan**, Belmont (New York), 1973 . £20/£5
You'd Be Surprised, Collins (London), 1940 . . £75/£10
You Can't Keep the Change, Collins (London), 1940 . .
. . . . £75/£10
ditto, Dodd Mead (New York), 1944 . . . £50/£10
Another Little Drink, Collins (London), 1940. . £60/£10
ditto, as **A Trap For Bellamy**, Dodd Mead (New York), 1941
. . . . £45/£10
ditto, as **Premeditated Murder**, Avon (New York), 1943
(pbk) £10
Your Deal, My Lovely, Collins (London), 1941 . £60/£10
It Couldn't Matter Less, Collins (London), 1941 . £60/£10
ditto, Arcadia (New York), 1943. . . . £40/£10
Never a Dull Moment, Collins (London), 1942 . £60/£10
Sorry You've Been Troubled, Collins (London), 1942 . .
. . . . £50/£10
ditto, as **Farewell to the Admiral**, Dodd Mead (New York),
1943 . . . . £45/£10
Dark Duet, Collins (London), 1942 . . . £45/£10
ditto, Dodd Mead (New York), 1943 . . . £45/£10
ditto, as **The Counterspy Murder**, Avon (New York), 1944
(pbk) £10
You Can Always Duck, Collins (London), 1943 . £40/£10
The Stars Are Dark, Collins (London), 1943 . . £40/£10
ditto, Dodd Mead (New York), 1943 . . . £40/£10
ditto, as **The London Spy Murders**, Avon (New York), 1944
(pbk) £10
They Never Say When, Collins (London), 1944 . £30/£5
ditto, Dodd Mead (New York), 1945 . . . £30/£5
The Dark Street, Collins (London), 1944. . . £25/£5
ditto, Dodd Mead (New York), 1944 . . . £25/£5
ditto, as **The Dark Street Murders**, Avon (New York), 1946
(pbk) £10

I'll Say She Does, Collins (London), 1945 . . £20/£5
ditto, Dodd Mead (New York), 1946 . . £20/£5
Sinister Errand, Collins (London), 1945 . . . £20/£5
ditto, Dodd Mead (New York), 1945 . . . £20/£5
ditto, as *Sinister Murders*, Avon (New York), 1957 (pbk) £5
Uneasy Terms, Collins (London), 1946 . . £20/£5
ditto, Dodd Mead (New York), 1947 . . . £20/£5
Dark Hero, Collins (London), 1946 . . . £20/£5
ditto, Collins (London), 1946 (250 signed copies) . £100/£65
ditto, Dodd Mead (New York), 1946 . . . £20/£5
ditto, as *The Case of the Dark Hero*, Avon (New York), 1947 (pbk) £10
Dark Interlude, Collins (London), 1947 . . £20/£5
ditto, Dodd Mead (New York), 1947 . . . £20/£5
ditto, as *The Terrible Night*, Avon (New York), 1959 (pbk)
. . . . £5
The Curiosity of Etienne Macgregor, Hennel Locke (London), 1947 . . . . £20/£5
ditto, as *The Sweetheart of the Razors*, Four Square (London), 1942 (pbk) £5
Dance Without Music, Collins (London), 1947 . £20/£5
ditto, Dodd Mead (New York), 1948 . . . £20/£5
Dark Wanton, Collins (London), 1948 . . £20/£5
ditto, Dodd Mead (New York), 1949 . . . £20/£5
ditto, as *The Case of the Dark Wanton*, Avon (New York), 1948 (pbk) £5
Try Anything Twice, Collins (London), 1948 . . £20/£5
ditto, Dodd Mead (New York), 1948 . . . £20/£5
ditto, as *Undressed To Kill*, Avon (New York), 1959 (pbk) .
. . . . £5
You Can Call It A Day, Collins (London), 1949 . £20/£5
ditto, as *The Man Nobody Saw*, Dodd Mead (New York), 1949 . . . . £20/£5
One Of Those Things, Collins (London), 1949 . £20/£5
ditto, Dodd Mead (New York), 1950 . . . £20/£5
ditto, as *Mistress Murder*, Avon (New York), 1951 (pbk) £5
Lady, Behave!, Collins (London), 1950 . . £20/£5
ditto, as *Lady Beware*, Dodd Mead (New York), 1950 . .
. . . . £20/£5
Dark Bahama, Collins (London), 1950 . . £20/£5
ditto, Dodd Mead (New York), 1951 . . . £20/£5
ditto, as *I'll Bring Her Back*, Eton (New York), 1952 £20/£5
Set Up For Murder, Pyramid (New York), 1950 (pbk) . £5
Ladies Won't Wait, Collins (London), 1951 . £20/£5
ditto, Dodd Mead (New York), 1951 . . . £20/£5
ditto, as *Cocktails and the Killer*, Avon (New York), 1957 (pbk) £5

Short Story Collections
You Can't Hit A Woman and Other Stories, Collins (London), 1937 . . . . £100/£15
Knave Takes Queen, Collins (London), 1939 . £75/£10
Mr Caution – Mr Callaghan, Collins (London), 1941 .
. . . . £45/£10
Dressed to Kill, Todd (London), 1952 . . £20/£5
Velvet Johnnie and Other Stories, Collins (London), 1952 .
. . . . £20/£5
G Man At the Yard, Todd (London), 1953 . £20/£5
Calling Mr Callaghan, Todd (London), 1953 . . £20/£5
The Adventures of Julia and Two Other Spy Stories, Todd (London), 1954 . . . . . £15/£5
ditto, as *The Killing Game*, Belmont (New York), 1975 (pbk) £5

The Mystery Blues and Other Stories, Todd (London), 1954
. . . . £20/£5
ditto, as *Fast Work*, Four Square (London), 1965 (pbk) £5
He Walked In Her Sleep and Other Stories, Todd (London), 1954 . . . . £20
ditto, as *MacTavish*, Belmont (New York), 1973 (pbk). £5
The Best Stories of Peter Cheyney, Faber (London), 1954 .
. . . . £20/£5

Short Stories Published as Pamphlets
Adventures of Alonzo Mactavish, Todd (London), 1943 £20
Alonzo Mactavish Again, Todd (London), 1943 . . £20
Love With A Gun and Other Stories, Todd (London), 1943.
. . . . £20
The Murder of Alonzo, Todd (London), 1943 . . . £20
The Man With The Red Beard, Todd (London), 1943 . £20
Account Rendered, Vallencey Books (London), 1944 . £30
The Adventures of Julia, Poynings Press (Sussex, UK), 1945 . . . . £30
Dance Without Music, Vallencey Books (London), 1945 £30
Escape For Sandra, Poynings Press (Sussex, UK), 1945 £30
Night Club, Poynings Press (Sussex, UK), 1945 . . £30
A Tough Spot For Cupid and Other Stories, Vallencey Books (London), 1945 . . . . . . £30
Date After Dark and Other Stories, Todd (London), 1946 .
. . . . £20
G Man At the Yard, Poynings Press (Sussex, UK), 1946 £30
Time For Caution, Foster (Hounslow, Essex), 1946 . £25
He Walked In Her Sleep and Other Stories, Todd (London), 1946 . . . . £20
The Man With Two Wives and Other Stories, Todd (London), 1946 . . . . £20
A Spot of Murder and Other Stories, Todd (London), 1946
. . . . £20
Vengeance With A Twist and Other Stories, Vallencey Books (London), 1946 . . . . £5
You Can't Trust A Duchess and Other Stories, Vallencey Books (London), 1946 . . . . £5
Lady In Green and Other Stories, Bantam (London), 1947.
. . . . £5
A Matter of Luck and Other Stories, Bantam (London), 1947 . . . . £5
Cocktail For Cupid and Other Stories, Bantam (London), 1948 . . . . £5
Cocktail Party and Other Stories, Bantam (London), 1948 .
. . . . £5
Fast Work and Other Stories, Bantam (London), 1948. £5
Information Received and Other Stories, Bantam (London), 1948 . . . . £5
The Unhappy Lady and Other Stories, Bantam (London), 1948 . . . . £5
The Lady in Tears and Other Stories, Bantam (London), 1949 . . . . £5

Miscellaneous
Three Character Sketches, Reynolds (London), 1927 £30/£5
'I Guarded Kings': The Memoirs of a Political Police Officer, Stanley Paul (London), 1935 (pseud 'Harold Brust') . . . . £30/£10
In Plain Clothes: Further Memoirs of a Political Police Officer, Stanley Paul (London), 1937 (pseud 'Harold Brust') . . . . £30/£10
Making Crime Pay, Faber (London), 1944 . . £25/£10
No Ordinary Cheyney, Faber (London), 1948 . . £25/£10

AGATHA CHRISTIE
(b.1890 d.1976)

The Queen of detective fiction and creator of Hercule Poirot and Miss Marple, Dame Agatha Christie also wrote romances under the name 'Mary Westmacott'. She must be the world's best known author of detective fiction and the all time best selling author in any genre other than Shakespeare. Her stage play *The Mousetrap* holds the record for the longest run ever in London, opening in 1952 and still on stage today. All of the first editions are dated with exceptions noted below.

Novels

The Mysterious Affair at Styles, John Lane (New York), 1920 (brown cloth stamped in black) . £22,500/£5,000
ditto, John Lane, The Bodley Head (London), 1921 (brown cloth stamped in black) . . . £22,000/£5,000
The Secret Adversary, John Lane, The Bodley Head (London), 1922 (green cloth with green pattern; d/w priced at 7/6) . . . . . . £12,500/£1,450
ditto, Dodd, Mead (New York), 1922 (orange cloth stamped in black). . . . . . . £3,500/£450
Murder on the Links, John Lane, The Bodley Head (London), 1923 (orange cloth stamped in black; d/w priced at 7/6) . . . . . £15,000/£2,450
ditto, Dodd, Mead (New York), 1923 (green cloth stamped in orange). . . . . . £5,000/£600
The Man in the Brown Suit, John Lane, The Bodley Head (London), 1924 (light brown cloth stamped in dark brown; d/w priced at 7/6). . . . . £7,500/£750
ditto, Dodd, Mead (New York), 1924 (light brown cloth stamped in dark brown) . . . £2,000/£250
The Secret of Chimneys, John Lane, The Bodley Head (London), 1925 (blue cloth stamped in black; d/w priced at 7/6). . . . . . £7,500/£1,000
ditto, Dodd, Mead (New York), 1925 (purple cloth stamped in orange/red) . . . . . £2,000/£145
The Murder of Roger Ackroyd, Collins (London), 1926 (blue cloth stamped in red; d/w priced at 7/6) £12,000/£750
ditto, Dodd, Mead (New York), 1926 (grey cloth with lettering in black with a red question mark on the front boards) . . . . . . £2,000/£200
The Big Four, Collins (London), 1927 (blue cloth stamped in red; d/w priced at 7/6) . . . . £6,500/£450
ditto, Dodd, Mead (New York), 1927 (blue cloth stamped in orange). . . . . . £1,250/£125
The Mystery of the Blue Train, Collins (London), 1928 (blue cloth stamped in red; d/w priced at 7/6; not dated, simply stated 'Copyright' on verso title page) £6,000/£450
ditto, Dodd, Mead (New York), 1928 (blue cloth with design of train stamped on front board, stamped in orange) . . . . £750/£100
The Seven Dials Mystery, Collins (London), 1929 (black cloth stamped in red; d/w priced at 7/6) . . £6,000/£250
ditto, Dodd, Mead (New York), 1929 (orange cloth stamped in black). . . . . . £750/£100
The Murder at the Vicarage, Collins Crime Club (London), 1930 (orange/red cloth stamped in black; d/w priced at 7/6) . . . . £5,000/£350

ditto, Dodd, Mead (New York), 1930 (green cloth stamped in dark green) . . . . . . £750/£100
Giant's Bread, Collins (London), 1930 (pseud 'Mary Westmacott') . . . . . £1,500/£100
ditto, Doubleday (New York), 1930 . . . . £600/£75
The Sittaford Mystery, Collins Crime Club (London), 1931 (orange/red cloth stamped in black; d/w priced at 7/6) . . . . £6,000/£350
ditto, as *The Murder at Hazelmoor*, Dodd, Mead (New York), 1931 (orange cloth stamped in black) . £400/£45
Peril at End House, Collins Crime Club (London), 1932 (orange/red cloth stamped in black; d/w priced at 7/6) . . . . £5,000/£600
ditto, Dodd, Mead (New York), 1932 (brown cloth stamped in red) . . . . £400/£65
Lord Edgware Dies, Collins Crime Club (London), 1933 (orange/red cloth stamped in black; d/w priced at 7/6) . . . . £4,500/£250
ditto, as *Thirteen at Dinner*, Dodd, Mead (New York), 1933 (red cloth stamped in black) . . . . £500/£50
Murder on the Orient Express, Collins Crime Club (London), 1934 (orange/red cloth stamped in black; d/w priced at 7/6) . . . . £7,000/£1,500
ditto, as *Murder in the Calais Coach*, Dodd, Mead (New York), 1934 (yellow cloth stamped in black) £1,250/£100
Why Didn't They Ask Evans?, Collins Crime Club (London), 1934 (orange/red cloth stamped in black; d/w priced at 7/6) . . . . . £4,500/£250
ditto, as *Boomerang Clue*, in Six Redbook Novels, Redbook Magazine (New York), 1934 (red boards with black cloth spine; also contains abridged novels by Dashiell Hammet and others) £100
ditto, as *Boomerang Clue*, Dodd, Mead (New York), 1935 (grey cloth stamped in red) . . . . £400/£45
Murder in Three Acts, Dodd, Mead (New York), 1934 (orange cloth stamped in black) . . . £650/£75
ditto, as *Three-Act Tragedy*, Collins Crime Club (London), 1935 (orange/red cloth stamped in black; d/w priced at 7/6) . . . . £3,000/£250
Unfinished Portrait, Collins (London), 1934 (pseud 'Mary Westmacott') . . . . . £1,250/£75
ditto, Doubleday (New York), 1934 . . . . £450/£45
Death in the Clouds, Collins Crime Club (London), 1935 (orange/red cloth stamped in black; d/w priced at 7/6) . . . . £2,500/£150
ditto, as *Death in the Air*, Dodd, Mead (New York), 1935 (grey cloth stamped in orange/red) . . £750/£75
The A.B.C. Murders: A New Poirot Mystery, Collins Crime Club (London), 1936 (orange/red cloth stamped in black; d/w priced at 7/6). . . . . £3,500/£150
ditto, Dodd, Mead (New York), 1936 (yellow cloth stamped in green) . . . . . . £750/£75
ditto, as *The Alphabet Murders*, Pocket Books (New York), 1966 (pbk) £5
Murder in Mesopotamia, Collins Crime Club (London), 1936 (orange/red cloth stamped in black; d/w priced at 7/6) . . . . £2,750/£200
ditto, Dodd, Mead (New York), 1936 (green cloth stamped in black) . . . . £750/£75
Cards on the Table, Collins Crime Club (London), 19361936 (orange/red cloth stamped in black; d/w priced at 7/6) . . . . £2,750/£150
ditto, Dodd, Mead (New York), 1936 (orange cloth stamped in black). . . . . . . £650/£65

Dumb Witness, Collins Crime Club (London), 1937 (orange/red cloth stamped in black; d/w priced at 7/6) .
. . . . £5,000/£200
ditto, as *Poirot Loses a Client*, Dodd, Mead (New York), 1937 (orange cloth stamped in black) . . . £400/£50
Death on the Nile, Collins Crime Club (London), 1937 (orange/red cloth stamped in black; d/w priced at 7/6) .
. . . . £4,000/£125
ditto, Dodd, Mead (New York), 1938 (orange cloth stamped in black). . . . . £500/£75
Appointment With Death: A Poirot Mystery, Collins Crime Club (London), 1938 (orange/red cloth stamped in black; d/w priced at 7/6). . . . . . £1,750/£150
ditto, Dodd, Mead (New York), 1938 (orange cloth stamped in black). . . . . £650/£60
Hercule Poirot's Christmas, Collins Crime Club (London), 1939 (orange/red cloth stamped in black; d/w priced at 7/6; first impression has the top of 'Hercule' 7mm from the top of the spine) . . . . . . £2,000/£200
ditto, Collins Crime Club (London), 1939 (second impression has the top of 'Hercule' 14mm from the top of the spine) . . . . . . £2,000/£100
ditto, as *Murder for Christmas, A Poirot Story*, Dodd, Mead (New York), 1939 (black cloth stamped in green) . .
. . . . £750/£50
Murder Is Easy, Collins Crime Club (London), 1939 (orange/red cloth stamped in black; d/w priced at 7/6) .
. . . . £1,500/£100
ditto, as *Easy to Kill*, Dodd, Mead (New York), 1939 . .
. . . . £300/£40
Ten Little Niggers, Collins Crime Club (London), 1939 (orange/red cloth stamped in black; d/w priced at 7/6) .
. . . . £4,000/£500
ditto, as *And Then There Were None*, Dodd, Mead (New York), 1940 (beige boards stamped in orange) . £850/£75
ditto, as *Ten Little Indians*, Pocket Books (New York), 1965 (pbk) £5
Sad Cypress, Collins Crime Club (London), [1940] (orange/red cloth stamped in black; d/w priced at 8/3) .
. . . . £1,500/£150
ditto, Dodd, Mead (New York), 1940 (light blue cloth). .
. . . . £400/£40
One, Two, Buckle My Shoe, Collins Crime Club (London), 1940 (orange/red cloth stamped in black; d/w priced at 7/6)
. . . . £1,500/£150
ditto, as *The Patriotic Murders*, Dodd, Mead (New York), 1941 (red cloth stamped in black) . . . £400/£40
ditto, as *An Overdose of Death*, Dell (New York), 1953 (pbk) £5
Evil Under the Sun, Collins Crime Club (London), 1941 (orange/red cloth stamped in black; d/w priced at 7/6) .
. . . . £1,500/£150
ditto, Dodd, Mead (New York), 1941 (blue cloth stamped in black) . . . . £500/£35
N or M?, Collins Crime Club (London), 1941 (orange/red cloth stamped in black; d/w priced at 7/6) . £650/£90
ditto, Dodd, Mead (New York), 1941 (light blue cloth stamped in dark blue) . . . . £200/£25
The Body in the Library, Collins Crime Club (London), 1942 (orange/red cloth stamped in black; d/w priced at 7/6)
. . . . £1,000/£100
ditto, Dodd, Mead (New York), 1942 (orange cloth stamped in black). . . . . £250/£25

Five Little Pigs, Collins Crime Club (London), 1942 (orange/red cloth stamped in black; d/w priced at 8/-).
. . . . £650/£65
ditto, as *Murder in Retrospect*, Dodd, Mead (New York), 1942 (blue/green cloth) . . . . . £200/£25
The Moving Finger, Dodd, Mead (New York), 1942 (red cloth stamped in black) . . . . . £250/£30
ditto, Collins Crime Club (London), 1943 (orange/red cloth stamped in black; d/w priced at 7/6) . . £400/£35
Death Comes as the End, Dodd, Mead (New York), 1944 .
. . . . £200/£20
ditto, Collins Crime Club (London), 1945 (orange/red cloth stamped in black; d/w priced at 7/6) . . £200/£20
Towards Zero, Collins Crime Club (London), 1944 (orange/red cloth stamped in black; d/w priced at 7/6) .
. . . . £250/£25
ditto, Dodd, Mead (New York), 1944 (beige cloth stamped in brown) . . . . £100/£15
Absent in the Spring, Collins (London), 1944 (pseud 'Mary Westmacott'; light blue cloth stamped in gilt; d/w priced at 7/6). . . . . £100/£25
ditto, Farrar & Rinehart (New York), 1944 . £50/£10
Sparkling Cyanide, Collins Crime Club (London), 1945 (orange/red cloth stamped in black; d/w priced at 8/6) .
. . . . £100/£25
ditto, as *Remembered Death*, Dodd, Mead (New York), 1945 (beige cloth stamped in red) . . . . £75/£20
The Hollow, Collins Crime Club (London), 1946 (orange/red cloth stamped in black; d/w priced at 8/6) . £100/£15
ditto, Dodd, Mead (New York), 1946 (yellow cloth stamped in black). . . . . £75/£15
ditto, as *Murder after Hours*, Dell (New York), 1954 (pbk)
. . . . £5
Taken at the Flood, Collins Crime Club (London), 1948 (orange/red cloth stamped in black; d/w priced at 8/6) .
. . . . £65/£15
ditto, as *There is a Tide*, Dodd, Mead (New York), 1948 (grey cloth stamped in red) . . . . £50/£15
The Rose and the Yew Tree, Heinemann (London), 1948 (pseud 'Mary Westmacott') . . . . £50/£15
ditto, Rinehart (New York), 1948 . . . . £45/£10
Crooked House, Collins Crime Club (London), 1949 (orange/red cloth stamped in black; d/w priced at 8/6) .
. . . . £100/£15
ditto, Dodd, Mead (New York), 1949 (grey cloth) . £50/£10
A Murder is Announced, Collins Crime Club (London), 1950 (orange/red cloth stamped in black; d/w priced at 8/6)
. . . . £75/£15
ditto, Dodd, Mead (New York), 1950 . £65/£10
They Came to Baghdad, Collins Crime Club (London), 1951 (orange/red cloth stamped in black; d/w priced at 8/6) .
. . . . £65/£10
ditto, Dodd, Mead (New York), 1951 (green cloth stamped in red). . . . . £40/£10
Mrs McGinty's Dead, Collins Crime Club (London), 1952 (orange/red cloth stamped in black; d/w priced at 10/6) .
. . . . £50/£10
ditto, Dodd, Mead (New York), 1952 (blue cloth stamped in gilt). . . . . £35/£10
A Daughter's a Daughter, Heinemann (London), 1952 (pseud 'Mary Westmacott') . . . . £35/£10
They Do It with Mirrors, Collins Crime Club (London), 1952 (orange/red cloth stamped in black; d/w priced at 10/6) . . . . £40/£10

ditto, as **Murder with Mirrors**, Dodd, Mead (New York), 1952 . . . . £40/£10

After the Funeral, Collins Crime Club (London), 1953 (orange/red cloth stamped in black; d/w priced at 10/6; dated p.192) . . . . £35/£10

ditto, as **Funerals are Fatal**, Dodd, Mead (New York), 1953 . . . . £25/£5

A Pocket Full of Rye, Collins Crime Club (London), 1953 (orange/red cloth stamped in black; d/w priced at 10/6) . . . . £40/£10

ditto, Dodd, Mead (New York), 1954 . . . £40/£10

Destination Unknown, Collins Crime Club (London), 1954 (orange/red cloth stamped in black; d/w priced at 10/6) . . . . £40/£10

ditto, as **So Many Steps to Death**, Dodd, Mead (New York), 1955 . . . . £30/£5

Hickory, Dickory, Dock, Collins Crime Club (London), 1955 (orange/red cloth stamped in black; d/w priced at 10/6) . . . . £35/£5

ditto, as **Hickory, Dickory, Death**, Dodd, Mead (New York), 1955 . . . . £25/£5

Dead Man's Folly, Collins Crime Club (London), 1956 (orange/red cloth stamped in black; d/w priced at 12/6) . . . . £35/£5

ditto, Dodd, Mead (New York), 1956 . . . £25/£5

The Burden, Heinemann (London), 1956 (pseud 'Mary Westmacott') . . . . £35/£15

ditto, Arbor House (New York), 1956 . . . £25/£10

4.50 from Paddington, Collins Crime Club (London), 1957 (orange/red cloth stamped in black; d/w priced at 12/6) . . . . £35/£10

ditto, as **What Mrs McGillicuddy Saw!**, Dodd, Mead (New York), 1957 . . . . £25/£10

ditto, as **Murder, She Said**, Pocket Books (New York), 1961 (pbk) £5

Ordeal by Innocence, Collins Crime Club (London), 1958 (orange/red cloth stamped in black; d/w priced at 12/6) . . . . £25/£10

ditto, Dodd, Mead (New York), 1958 . . . £20/£5

Cat Among the Pigeons, Collins Crime Club (London), 1959 (orange/red cloth stamped in black; d/w priced at 12/6) . . . . £35/£5

ditto, Dodd, Mead (New York), 1959 . . . £25/£5

The Pale Horse, Collins Crime Club (London), 1961 (orange/red cloth stamped in black; d/w priced at 15/-) . . . . £20/£5

ditto, Dodd, Mead (New York), 1962 . . . £20/£5

The Mirror Crack'd from Side to Side, Collins Crime Club (London), 1962 (orange/red cloth stamped in black; d/w priced at 15/-) . . . . £15/£5

ditto, as **The Mirror Crack'd**, Dodd, Mead (New York), 1963 . . . . £15/£5

The Clocks, Collins Crime Club (London), 1963 (orange/red cloth stamped in black; d/w priced at 16/-) . . £15/£5

ditto, Dodd, Mead (New York), 1964 . . . £15/£5

A Caribbean Mystery, Collins Crime Club (London), 1964 (orange/red cloth stamped in gilt; d/w priced at 16/-) . . . . £15/£5

ditto, Dodd, Mead (New York), 1965 . . . £15/£5

At Bertram's Hotel, Collins Crime Club (London), 1965 (orange/red cloth stamped in gilt; d/w priced at 16/-) . . . . £15/£5

ditto, Dodd, Mead (New York), 1965 . . . £15/£5

Third Girl, Collins Crime Club (London), 1966 (orange/red cloth stamped in gilt; d/w priced at 18/-) . . £15/£5

ditto, Dodd, Mead (New York), 1967 . . . £15/£5

Endless Night, Collins Crime Club (London), 1967 (orange/red cloth stamped in gilt; d/w priced at 18/-) . . . . £15/£5

ditto, Dodd, Mead (New York), 1968 . . . £15/£5

By the Pricking of My Thumbs, Collins Crime Club (London), 1968 (orange/red cloth stamped in gilt; d/w priced at 21/-) . . . . £15/£5

ditto, Dodd, Mead (New York), 1968 . . . £15/£5

Hallowe'en Party, Collins Crime Club (London), 1969 (orange/red cloth stamped in gilt; d/w priced at 25/-) . . . . £15/£5

ditto, Dodd, Mead (New York), 1969 . . . £15/£5

Passenger to Frankfurt, Collins Crime Club (London), 1970 (orange/red cloth stamped in gilt; d/w priced at 25/-) . . . . £10/£5

ditto, Dodd, Mead (New York), 1970 . . . £10/£5

Nemesis, Collins Crime Club (London), 1971 (orange/red cloth stamped in gilt; d/w priced at £1.50) . . £10/£5

ditto, Dodd, Mead (New York), 1971 . . . £10/£5

Elephants Can Remember, Collins Crime Club (London), 1972 (orange/red cloth stamped in gilt; d/w priced at £1.60) . . . . £10/£5

ditto, Dodd, Mead (New York), 1972 . . . £10/£5

Postern of Fate, Collins Crime Club (London), 1973 (orange/red cloth stamped in gilt; d/w priced at £2.00) . . . . £10/£5

ditto, Dodd, Mead (New York), 1973 . . . £10/£5

Murder on Board: Three Complete Mystery Novels, Dodd, Mead (New York), 1974 . . . £10/£5

Curtain: Hercule Poirot's Last Case, Collins Crime Club (London), 1975 (orange/red cloth stamped in gilt; d/w priced at £2.95) . . . . . . £10/£5

ditto, Dodd, Mead (New York), 1975 . . . £10/£5

Sleeping Murder: Miss Marple's Last Case, Collins Crime Club (London), 1976 (orange/red cloth stamped in gilt; d/w priced at £3.50) . . . . . . £10/£5

ditto, Dodd, Mead (New York), 1976 . . . £10/£5

Omnibus Editions

An Agatha Christie Omnibus, John Lane (London), 1931 . . . . £350/£35

A Poirot Quintet, Collins (London), 1979 . . £10/£5

Short Stories

Poirot Investigates, John Lane (London), 1924 (yellow cloth stamped in blue; d/w wrapper priced at 7/6) . . . . £12,000/£1,750

ditto, Dodd, Mead (New York), 1924 (orange cloth stamped in black) . . . . £2,500/£150

Partners in Crime, Collins (London), 1929 (black cloth stamped in red; d/w priced at 7/6) . . £4,000/£200

ditto, Dodd, Mead (New York), 1929 (blue cloth stamped in red) . . . . £1,000/£100

Two New Crime Stories, Reader's Library (London), 1929 (includes 'The Under Dog' by Christie; maroon cloth stamped in gilt; book undated, small cheap format; first edition has description of stories on front flap) . £450/£75

The Mysterious Mr Quinn, Collins (London), 1930 (black cloth stamped in red; d/w priced at 7/6) . £4,000/£250

ditto, Dodd, Mead (New York), 1930 (pink cloth stamped in black) . . . . £1,000/£100

The Thirteen Problems, Collins Crime Club (London), 1932 (orange/red cloth stamped in black; d/d priced at 7/6).   .
.   .   .   . £5,000/£400
ditto, as *The Tuesday Club Murders*, Dodd, Mead (New York), 1933 .   .   .   .   . £1,750/£100
The Hound of Death and Other Stories, Odhams (London), 1933 (orange/red cloth stamped in black; d/w priced at 7/6)
.   .   .   . £350/£45
The Listerdale Mystery and Other Stories, Collins (London), 1934 (orange/red cloth stamped in black; d/w priced at 7/6)   .   .   .   . £5,000/£250
Parker Pyne Investigates, Collins (London), 1934 (orange/red cloth stamped in black; d/w priced at 7/6)   .
.   .   .   . £4,000/£200
ditto, as *Mr Parker Pyne, Detective*, Dodd, Mead (New York), 1934 (orange cloth stamped in black). £1,000/£150
Murder in the Mews and Other Stories, Collins Crime Club (London), 1937 (orange/red cloth stamped in black; d/w priced at 7/6)   .   .   .   . £3,000/£150
ditto, as *Dead Man's Mirror and Other Stories*, Dodd, Mead (New York), 1937 (blue cloth) .   .   . £1,500/£150
The Regatta Mystery and Other Stories, Dodd, Mead (New York), 1939 (orabge cloth stamped in black) £1,500/£250
The Labours of Hercules: Short Stories, Collins Crime Club (London), 1947 (orange/red cloth stamped in black; d/w priced at 8/6)   .   .   .   . £100/£15
ditto, as *Labors of Hercules*, Dodd, Mead (New York), 1947 (grey cloth stamped in black)   .   .   . £50/£10
Witness for the Prosecution, Dodd, Mead (New York), 1948
.   .   .   . £150/£25
Three Blind Mice and Other Stories, Dodd, Mead (New York), 1950 (stamped in red)   .   .   . £75/£15
ditto, as *The Mousetrap*, Dell (New York), 1960 (pbk).   £5
Under Dog and Other Stories, Dodd, Mead (New York), 1951 (orange cloth)   .   .   .   . £150/£25
The Adventure of the Christmas Pudding, Collins Crime Club (London), 1960 (orange/red cloth stamped in black; d/w priced at 12/6)   .   .   .   . £40/£10
Double Sin and Other Stories, Dodd, Mead (New York), 1961   .   .   .   .   .   . £25/£10
Thirteen for Luck, Dodd, Mead (New York), 1961   £15/£5
ditto, Collins (London), 1966   .   .   . £15/£5
Star Over Bethlehem, and Other Stories for Children, Collins (London), 1965 (by 'Agatha Christie Mallowan') .
.   .   .   . £15/£5
ditto, Dodd, Mead (New York), 1965   .   . £15/£5
Surprise! Surprise!, Dodd, Mead (New York), 1965 £15/£5
13 Clues for Miss Marple, Dodd, Mead (New York), 1966 .
.   .   .   . £15/£5
The Golden Ball and Other Stories, Dodd, Mead (New York), 1971   .   .   .   .   . £15/£5
Poirot's Early Cases, Collins Crime Club (London), 1974 (orange/red cloth stamped in gilt; d/w priced at £2.25)   .
.   .   .   . £15/£5
ditto, as *Hercule Poirot's Early Cases*, Dodd, Mead (New York), 1974 .   .   .   .   . £15/£5
Miss Marple's Final Cases and Two Other Stories, Collins Crime Club (London), 1979 (orange/red cloth stamped in gilt; d/w priced at £4.50)   .   .   . £10/£5
ditto, Dodd, Mead (New York), 1979   .   . £10/£5
The Agatha Christie Hour, Collins (London), 1982   £10/£5
Miss Marple: The Complete Short Stories, Dodd, Mead (New York), 1985   .   .   .   .   . £15/£5

Problem at Pollensa Bay, HarperCollins (London), 1991   .
.   .   .   . £10/£5
While the Light Lasts, HarperCollins (London), 1997 .   .
.   .   .   . £10/£5

Booklets
The Mystery of the Baghdad Chest, Todd/Bantam Books (London), 1943 .   .   .   .   .   . £40
The Problem at Pollensa Bay and *The Christmas Adventure*, Todd/Polybooks (London), 1943   . £40
Poirot on Holiday, Todd/Polybooks (London), 1943   . £40
The Veiled Lady and *The Baghdad Chest*, Francis Hodgson/ Polybooks (London), 1944   .   .   . £40
Poirot Knows the Murderer, Polybooks (London), 1946 £40
Poirot Lends a Hand, Polybooks (London), 1946 .   . £40
The Mystery of the Baghdad Chest, Vallencey Books (London), 1946 .   .   .   .   .   . £40
Crime in Cabin 66, Vallencey Books (London), 1946 . £40
Poirot and the Regatta Mystery, Vallencey Books (London), 1946   .   .   .   .   .   . £40

Collaborations
The Floating Admiral, Hodder & Stoughton (London), [1931] (chain novel; chapters by Christie and others) .   .
.   .   .   . £1,500/£100
ditto, Doubleday (New York), 1932 .   .   . £500/£30
The Scoop and *Behind the Screen*, Gollancz (London), 1983 (chain novels; chapters by Christie and others) . £25/£10

Poetry
The Road of Dreams, Bles (London), 1925 (green cloth with printed spine label)   .   .   . £1,250/£200
ditto, as *Poems*, Collins (London), 1973 (glassine d/w).
.   .   .   . £50/£45
ditto, Dodd, Mead (New York), 1973 (glassine d/w) £45/£40
Remembrance, Souvenir Press, 1988.   .   .   . £10/£5

Plays
Black Coffee, Alfred Ashley (London), 1934 (pbk)   . £125
ditto, French (London), 1952 (pbk)   .   .   . £35
Ten Little Niggers, French (London), 1944 (pbk)   . £50
ditto, as *Ten Little Indians*, French (New York), 1946 (pbk)
.   .   .   . £15
Appointment with Death, French (London), 1945 (pbk) £50
Murder on the Nile, French (London), 1946 (pbk).   . £75
ditto, French (New York), 1946 (pbk)   .   .   . £65
The Hollow, French (London), 1952 (pbk)   .   . £35
ditto, French (New York), 1952 (pbk)   .   .   . £20
The Mousetrap, French (London), 1954 (pbk)   . £100
ditto, French (New York), 1954 (pbk)   .   .   . £75
Witness for the Prosecution, French (New York), 1954 (pbk) £40
ditto, French (London), 1956 (pbk)   .   .   . £40
The Spider's Web, French (London), 1957 (pbk) . £30
ditto, French (New York), 1957 (pbk)   .   .   . £15
Towards Zero, Dramatist's Play Service (New York), 1957 (pbk) £50
ditto, French (London), 1958 (pbk)   .   .   . £35
Verdict, French (London), 1958 (pbk)   .   .   . £35
The Unexpected Guest, French (London), 1958 (pbk) . £35
Go Back for Murder, French (London), 1960 (pbk)   . £35
Rule of Three, French (London), 1963 (3 vols; pbk)   . £50
Akhmaton, Collins (London), 1973 .   .   . £15/£5
ditto, Dodd, Mead (New York), 1973 .   .   . £15/£5

Others
Come Tell Me How You Live, Collins (London), 1946 .
. . . . £50/£10
ditto, Dodd, Mead (New York), 1946 . . . £45/£10
Autobiography, Collins (London), 1977 . . . £20/£5
ditto, Dodd, Mead (New York), 1977 . . . £20/£5

WINSTON CHURCHILL
(b.1874 d.1965)

In earlier years Churchill was a soldier and journalist, and became an author and historian after his long career as parliamentarian and Prime Minister was over. His books were published under the name 'Winston Spencer Churchill' or 'Winston S. Churchill' in order to distinguish him from another author called Winston Churchill. He was awarded the Nobel Prize for Literature in 1953.

Novel
Savrola, Longmans, Green, and Co. (New York), 1900 (dark blue cloth lettered in gilt on front board and spine; dated on title-page, with no additional printings noted on copyright page; 24 pages of adverts at back of book) . . £1,000
ditto, Longmans, Green, and Co. (London), 1900 (blue-green cloth lettered in gilt on front board and spine; dated on title-page, no copyright statement on verso; 2 pages of advertisements at back of book; black endpapers) £1,000
ditto, Longmans, Green, and Co. (London), 1900 (as above, but second state with copyright notice verso title-page) .
. . . . £400
ditto, Newnes (London), 1908 (illustrated edition, paper wraps printed in red and blue; 'Newnes' Sixpenny Novels Illustrated') £350

Autobiography
My African Journey, Hodder & Stoughton (London), 1908 (red cloth with picture on front board of author and dead rhinocerous, lettered below in black, and the spine lettered in gilt; dated MCMVIII on title-page, with no additional printings noted on copyright page; 16 page catalogue at back) £500
ditto, Doubleday Doran (New York), 1909 . . . £350
ditto, Hodder & Stoughton (London), 1910 (brown card wraps with illustration, printed from first edition plates) .
. . . . £400
My Early Life, Thornton Butterworth Ltd (London), 1930 (wine-coloured cloth, lettered in gilt on front board and spine; states 'First Published … 1930' on copyright page with no additional printings) . . . £2,500/£150
ditto, as *A Roving Commission*, Charles Scribner's Sons (New York), 1930 (grey-blue cloth, lettered in gilt on spine; dated on title-page with no additional printings noted on copyright page) . . . . . . £700/£65

Biographies
Lord Randolph Churchill, Macmillan and Co. (London), 1906 (2 vols, plum cloth lettered in gilt on front board and spine; dated on title-page and copyright page) . £500
ditto, Macmillan and Co. (New York), 1906 (2 vols, maroon ribbed cloth lettered in gilt, top edges gilt; dated on title-page and copyright page) £400

ditto, Odhams Press Ltd (London), 1952 (extended one volume edition, red cloth, spine lettered and decorated in gilt). . . . . £40/£15
Marlborough: His Life and Times, Volume I, Harrap (London), 1933 (plum buckram with gilt coat of arms in front board and gilt lettering to spine, top edge gilt; Errata slip tipped-in before p.17; 1 folding map; no additional printings noted on copyright page) . . . . £75/£40
ditto, Harrap (London), 1933 (limited edition of 150 signed, numbered copies; full orange morocco with gilt coat of arms in front board and gilt lettering to spine, top edge gilt, marbled endpapers, in card slipcase with paper labels; errata slip tipped-in before p.17; 1 folding map) . . .
. . . . *see price for set*
ditto, *Volume II*, Harrap (London), 1934 (plum buckram with gilt coat of arms in front board and gilt lettering to spine, top edge gilt; no additional printings noted on copyright page; errata slip tipped-in facing p.434; 3 folding maps) . . . . £75/£40
ditto, Harrap (London), 1934 (limited edition of 150 signed, numbered copies; full orange morocco with gilt coat of arms in front board and gilt lettering to spine, top edge gilt, marbled endpapers, in card slipcase with paper labels; errata slip tipped-in facing p.434; 3 folding maps) . .
. . . . *see price for set*
ditto, *Volume III*, Harrap (London), 1936 (plum buckram with gilt coat of arms in front board and gilt lettering to spine, top edge gilt; no additional printings noted on copyright page; errata slip tipped-in facing p.18; 3 folding maps) . . . . £75/£40
ditto, Harrap (London), 1936 (limited edition of 150 signed, numbered copies; full orange morocco with gilt coat of arms in front board and gilt lettering to spine, top edge gilt, marbled endpapers, in card slipcase with paper labels; errata slip tipped-in facing p.18; 3 folding maps). . . .
. . . . *see price for set*
ditto, *Volume IV*, Harrap (London), 1938 (dark plum buckram with gilt coat of arms in front board and gilt lettering to spine, top edge gilt; no additional printings noted on copyright page; 2 folding maps) . . £75/£40
ditto, Harrap (London), 1938 (limited edition of 150 signed, numbered copies; full orange morocco with gilt coat of arms in front board and gilt lettering to spine, top edge gilt, marbled endpapers, in card slipcase with paper labels; 2 folding maps) . . . *see price for set*
ditto, Harrap (London), 1934; the complete set of 4 volumes in the trade edition . . . . . £800/£400
ditto, Harrap (London), 1934; the complete set of 4 volumes in the signed, limited edition, each volume in its original card slipcase. £8,500
Marlborough: His Life and Times, Volume I, Scribner's (New York), 1933 (deep green cloth with gilt lettering to spine; dated MCMXXXIII on title-page and 1933 on copyright page with no additional printings noted) £75/£40
ditto, *Volume II*, Scribner's (New York), 1933 (deep green cloth with gilt lettering to spine; dated MCMXXXIII on title-page and 1933 on copyright page with no additional printings noted; two folding maps) . . . . £75/£40
ditto, *Volume III*, Scribner's (New York), 1935 (deep green cloth with gilt lettering to spine; dated MCMXXV on title-page and 1935 on copyright page with no additional printings noted; three folding maps) . . . £75/£40
ditto, *Volume IV*, Scribner's (New York), 1935 (deep green cloth with gilt lettering to spine; dated MCMXXV on title-

page and 1935 on copyright page with no additional
printings noted; seven folding maps) .. . £75/£40

ditto, **Volume V**, Scribner's (New York), 1937 (deep green
cloth with gilt lettering to spine; dated MCMXXVII on
title-page and 1937 on copyright page with no additional
printings noted; errata slip tipped-in before p.17). £75/£40

ditto, **Volume VI**, Scribner's (New York), 1938 (deep green
cloth with gilt lettering to spine; dated MCMXXVIII on
title-page and 1938 on copyright page with no additional
printings noted; three folding maps) . . . £75/£40

ditto, Scribner's (New York), 1938; the complete set of 6
volumes . . . . £800/£400

Great Contemporaries, Thornton Butterworth Ltd (London),
1937 (dark blue buckram, lettered in gilt on front board and
spine, top edge stained blue; states 'First Published ...
1937' on copyright page with no additional printings) .
. . . . £300/£25

Historical Studies

The Story of the Malakand Field Force, Longmans, Green,
and Co. (London), 1898 (green cloth lettered in gilt on
front board and spine; dated on title-page, no additional
printings noted on copyright page; folding map tipped on to
stub of frontispiece; black endpapers) . . . £2,000

ditto, Longmans, Green, and Co. (London), 1898 (as above,
but second state with errata slip tipped-in before first
folding map). £1,000

The River War, Longmans, Green, and Co. (London), 1899
(2 vols; dark blue cloth with lettering and illustrations in
gilt on front board and spine; dated on title-pages, no
additional printings noted on copyright page; 10 folding
maps in volume 1, 9 folding maps in volume 2) . £3,000

ditto, Longmans, Green, and Co. (London), 1902 (revised 1
volume edition bound as above; dated on title-page,
bibliographical note on copyright page; 6 folding maps;
40pp catalogue bound in at back of book) . . £1,000

London to Ladysmith, Longmans, Green, and Co. (London),
1900 (fawn cloth with lettering and picture in black and red
to front board, and gilt and red to spine; dated on title-page,
with no additional printings noted on copyright page; black
endpapers; two folding maps) £400

Ian Hamilton's March, Longmans, Green, and Co.
(London), 1900 (dark red cloth with lettering in gilt to front
board and spine; dated on title-page, with no additional
printings noted copyright page; 32 pp catalogue at back of
book; black endpapers) £350

The World Crisis: Vol 1: 1911-1914, Thornton Butterworth
(London), 1923 (navy blue cloth, lettered in blind on top
board and in gilt on spine; states 'First Published ... April,
1923' on copyright page with no additional printings noted;
contains 5 folding maps; errata slip tipped-in before p.1) .
. . . . £750/£200

ditto, Scribner (New York), 1923. . . . £650/£150

ditto: Vol 2: 1915, Thornton Butterworth (London), 1923
(navy blue cloth, lettered in blind on top board and in gilt
on spine; states 'First Published ... October 1923' on
copyright page with no additional printings noted; contains
5 folding maps) . . . . . . £750/£200

ditto, Scribner (New York), 1923. . . . £650/£150

ditto, Vol 3: 1916-18, Part 1, Thornton Butterworth
(London), 1927 (navy blue cloth, lettered in blind on top
board and in gilt on spine; states 'First Published 1927' on
copyright page with no additional printings noted; contains
3 folding maps and two folding statistical tables; errata slip
tipped-in facing p.52). . . . . . £750/£200

ditto, Scribner (New York), 1923. . . . £650/£150

ditto, Vol 4: 1916-18, Part 2, Thornton Butterworth
(London), 1927 (navy blue cloth, lettered in blind on top
board and in gilt on spine; states 'First Published 1927' on
copyright page with no additional printings noted; contains
6 folding maps) . . . . . . £750/£200

ditto, Scribner (New York), 1923. . . . £650/£150

ditto, Vol 5: The Aftermath, Thornton Butterworth
(London), 1929 (navy blue cloth, lettered in blind on top
board and in gilt on spine; states 'First Published ... March
1929' on copyright page with no additional printings noted;
contains 4 folding maps) . . . . £500/£100

ditto, Scribner (New York), 1929. . . . £450/£100

ditto, Vol 6: The Eastern Front, Thornton Butterworth
(London), 1931 (navy blue cloth, lettered in blind on top
board and in gilt on spine; states 'First Published in 1931'
on copyright page with no additional printings noted;
contains 11 folding maps) . . . . £450/£100

ditto, as **The Unknown War**, Scribner (New York), 1923 .
. . . . £400/£100

ditto, Thornton Butterworth (London), 1923-1931; all six
vols. . . . . £4,000/£1,500

ditto, Scribner (New York), 1923-1931; all six vols . .
. . . . £3,000/£1,000

The Second World War: Vol 1: The Gathering Storm,
Houghton Mifflin (Boston), 1948 (red cloth with gilt
facsimile signature on front board and lettering to spine in
gilt; top edge yellow-brown; dated on title-page and
copyright page with no additional printings noted) £20/£5

ditto, Cassell (London), 1948 (black cloth with lettering to
spine in gilt; top edge red; states 'First Published 1948' on
copyright page with no additional printings noted; 1
folding map; errata slip facing p.610) . . . £20/£5

ditto, Vol 2: Their Finest Hour, Houghton Mifflin (Boston),
1949 (red cloth with gilt facsimile signature on front board
and lettering to spine in gilt; top edge yellow-brown; dated
on title-page and copyright page with no additional
printings noted) . . . . £20/£5

ditto, Cassell (London), 1949 (black cloth with lettering to
spine in gilt; top edge red; states 'First Published 1949' on
copyright page with no additional printings noted; 3
folding maps) . . . . £20/£5

ditto, Vol 3: The Grand Alliance, Houghton Mifflin
(Boston), 1950 (red cloth with gilt facsimile signature on
front board and lettering to spine in gilt; top edge yellow-
brown; dated on title-page and copyright page with no
additional printings noted). . . . . £20/£5

ditto, Cassell (London), 1950 (black cloth with lettering to
spine in gilt; top edge red; states 'First Published 1950' on
copyright page with no additional printings noted; 3
folding maps) . . . . £20/£5

ditto, Vol 4: The Hinge of Fate, Houghton Mifflin (Boston),
1950 (red cloth with gilt facsimile signature on front board
and lettering to spine in gilt; top edge yellow-brown; dated
on title-page and copyright page with no additional
printings noted) . . . . £20/£5

ditto, Cassell (London), 1951 (black cloth with lettering to
spine in gilt; top edge red; states 'First Published 1951' on
copyright page with no additional printings noted; 3
folding maps and 1 folding facsimile of a letter) . £20/£5

ditto, Vol 5: Closing the Ring, Houghton Mifflin (Boston),
1951 (red cloth with gilt facsimile signature on front board
and lettering to spine in gilt; top edge yellow-brown; dated
on title-page and copyright page with no additional
printings noted) . . . . £20/£5

ditto, Cassell (London), 1952 (black cloth with lettering to spine in gilt; top edge red; states 'First Published 1952' on copyright page with no additional printings noted; 3 folding maps and 1 folding facsimile of a minute)   £20/£5

ditto, Vol 6: Triumph and Tragedy, Houghton Mifflin (Boston), 1953 (red cloth with gilt facsimilie signature on front board and lettering to spine in gilt; top edge yellow-brown; dated on title-page and copyright page with no additional printings noted).   .   .   .   .   £20/£5

ditto, Cassell (London), 1954 (black cloth with lettering to spine in gilt; top edge red; states 'First Published 1954' on copyright page with no additional printings noted; 11 folding maps)   .   .   .   .   .   .   £20/£5

ditto, Houghton Mifflin (Boston), 1948-53; all six vols.   .
  .   .   .   .   £175/£45

ditto, Cassell (London), 1948-1954; all six vols   £175/£45

A History of the English-Speaking People: Vol 1: The Birth of Britain, Cassell (London), 1956 .   .   .   £15/£5

ditto, Vol 2: The New World, Cassell (London), 1956 .   .
  .   .   .   .   £15/£5

ditto, Vol 3: The Age of Revolution, Cassell (London), 1957
  .   .   .   .   £15/£5

ditto, Vol 4: The Great Democracies, Cassell (London), 1958   .   .   .   .   £15/£5

ditto, Cassell (London), 1956-1958 all four vols   . £100/£25

The American Civil War, Cassell (London), 1961 (red cloth with lettering to spine in gilt; no additional printings noted)
  .   .   .   .   £20/£5

ditto, Dodd Mead (New York), 1961 .   .   .   £20/£5

The Island Race, Cassell (London), 1964.   .   .   £20/£5

ditto, Dodd Mead (New York), 1964 .   .   .   £20/£5

Speeches, Lectures, Essays etc

Mr Broderick's Army, Arthur L. Humphreys (London), 1903 (dark red card, front cover printed in black the same as title-page but with price of 2d added; dated on title-page; 44pps; withdrawn) £15,000

ditto, Arthur L Humphreys (London), 1903 (dark red card, front cover printed in black the same as title-page but with price of 1s added; dated on title-page; 104pps)   .   £7,500

Mr Winston Churchill on the Aliens Bill, Liberal Publications Department (London), 1904 (dated, 2 page leaflet)   .
  .   .   .   .   £250

For Free Trade, Arthur L Humphreys (London), 1906 (dark red card, front cover printed in black the same as title-page but with price added; dated on title-page)   .   £15,000

National Demonstrations in Favour of Land and Housing Reform, Liberal Publications Department (London), 1907 (dated, 20 page pamphlet) £300

For Liberalism and Free Trade, John Leng (Dundee [Scotland]), 1908 (dated, 32 page pamphlet).   .   £300

Liberalism and Socialism, Liberal Publications Department (London), 1909 (dated, 16 page pamphlet)   .   £300

The Menace of Land Monopoly, Free Trade and Land Values League (Melbourne), 1909 (dated, 4 page pamphlet) £150

Liberalism and the Social Problem, Hodder & Stoughton (London), 1909 (dated MCMIX on title-page with no additional printings on copyright page, plum buckram with facsimilie signature in gilt on front board and spine lettering in gilt) £400

ditto, Doubleday Doran (New York), 1910   .   £250

The People's Rights, Hodder & Stoughton (London), 1910 (cherry-red cloth flecked with pink, with lettering to front board and spine in gilt; index at back)   .   .   .   £750

ditto, Hodder & Stoughton (London), 1910 (pbk edition of above with photograph of the author on cover)   .   . £750

ditto, Hodder & Stoughton (London), 1910 (second hardback issue as first but without index and a second appendix entitled 'Labour Exchanges and Unemployment Insurance' in its place) £100

Prisons and Prisoners, Cassell (London), 1910 (grey paper wraps printed in blue as on title-page but with price added)
  .   .   .   .   £1,000

Mr Churchill on the Peers, Liberal Publications Department (London), 1910 (dated, 2 page leaflet)   .   .   £150

An Address to Young Liberals, National League of Young Liberals (London), 1912 (dated, 12 page pamphlet)   . £150

Irish Home Rule, Liberal Publications Department (London), 1912 (dated, 16 page pamphlet)   .   .   £150

Mr Churchill's Message to Ulster, Home Rule Council (London), 1912 (dated, 12 page pamphlet)   .   .   £150

The Liberal Government and Naval Policy, Liberal Publications Department (London), 1912 (dated, 24 page pamphlet) £150

On Naval Armaments, American Association for International Conciliation (New York), 1913 (dated, 13 page pamphlet) £200

The Tories and the Army, Liberal Publications Department (London), 1914 (dated, 8 page pamphlet)   .   .   £200

Navy Estimates in the Great War, Liberal Publications Department (London), 1915 (dated, 20 page pamphlet)   . £200

The Fighting Line, Macmillan (London), 1916 (dated, 32 page pamphlet) £200

The Munitions Miracle, National War Aims Committee (London), 1918 (16 page pamphlet)   .   .   .   £200

The Rhine Army, Ministry of Information, H.M.S.O. (London), 1919 (8 page pamphlet) £200

Reason and Reality, W. Myers (London), 1920 (36 page pamphlet) £200

The Position at Home and Abroad, [Liberal Publications Department?] (London), 1920 (12 page pamphlet)   .£200

Dundee Parliamentary Election, John Leng (Dundee [Scotland]), 1922 (4 page pamphlet)   .   .   .   £100

The Alternative to Socialism, Harrison and Sons (London), 1924 (16 page pamphlet) £150

Shall We Commit Suicide?, Eilbert Printing Company (New York), 1924 (12 page pamphlet)   .   .   .   £150

Co-Ops and Income Tax, Conservative Party (London), 1927 (4 page pamphlet) £125

The Navy League, The Navy League (London), 1930 (8 page pamphlet) £150

Parliamentary Government and the Economic Problem, Clarendon Press (Oxford, U.K.), 1930 (grey tinted laid paper printed in green as title-page, stitched; dated on title-page) £200

India, Thornton Butterworth Ltd (London), 1931 (orange cloth, lettering in black to front board and spine; states 'First published in book form 1931' on copyright page with no further printings noted). £750

ditto, Thornton Butterworth Ltd (London), 1931 (pbk in orange wraps with lettering in black to front cover and spine; states 'First published in book form 1931' on copyright page with no further printings noted)   .   £750

Thoughts and Adventures, Thornton Butterworth Ltd (London), 1932 (sandy-brown cloth, lettering in gilt to front board and spine; states 'First Published ... 1932' on copyright page with no further printings noted)   . £500/£50

ditto, as *Amid These Storms*, Charles Scribner's Sons (New York), 1932 (carmine cloth, lettered in gilt on front board and spine; dated on title-page with no additional printings noted on copyright page) . . . . . £450/£45

The Truth About Hitler, Trustees for Freedom (London), 1936 (12 page booklet in yellow card wraps) . . £250

Speech, New Commonwealth (London), 1936 (12 page booklet in cream card wraps) £150

Arms and The Covenant, Harrap (London), 1938 (dark blue cloth, lettered in gilt on spine, top edge stained blue; no additional printings noted on copyright page) £600/£200

ditto, as **While England Slept**, Putnam's (New York), 1938 (blue cloth, lettered in silver on a red band on front board and spine. No additional printings noted on copyright page) . . . . £500/£150

Step by Step, Thornton Butterworth Ltd (London), 1939 (green cloth, lettering in gilt to spine; states 'First Published ... June 1939' on copyright page with no further printings noted) . . . . . £300/£150

U-Boat Warfare, Ministry of Information (London), 1939 (4 page pamphlet) £150

The War at Sea, Ministry of Information (London), 1939 (4 page pamphlet) £150

The Glorious Battle of the River Plate, Ministry of Information (London), 1939 (4 page pamphlet) . . £150

Allies Now In Their Stride, Ministry of Information (London), 1940 (8 page pamphlet) £150

The State of the War, Ministry of Information (London), 1940 (4 page pamphlet) £150

Navy Estimates, Ministry of Information (London), 1940 (8 page pamphlet) £150

A Sterner War, Ministry of Information (London), 1940 (4 page pamphlet) £150

The War at Sea, Ministry of Information (London), 1940 (8 page pamphlet) £150

Conquer We Shall, Ministry of Information (London), 1940 (4 page pamphlet) £150

Address by the Prime Minister . . . June 4, 1940, British Library of Information (New York), 1940 (8 page pamphlet; 'We shall fight on the beaches') . . £300

Speech by the Prime Minister . . . June 18, 1940, British Library of Information (New York), 1940 (8 page pamphlet; 'Their Finest Hour'). £300

Message from the Prime Minister . . . 4th July, 1940, [Ministry of Information?] (London), 1940 (1 page pamphlet) £100

Speech . . . July 14, 1940, British Library of Information (New York), 1940 (4 page pamphlet; 'War of the Unknown Warriors') £200

Speech by the Prime Minister . . . July 4, 1940, British Library of Information (New York), 1940 (6 page pamphlet) £200

A Speech . . . August 20th, 1940, Ministry of Information (London), 1940 (16 page booklet in light blue card wraps printed in maroon; 'The few') . . . £300

Britain's Strength, British Library of Information (New York), 1940 (8 page pamphlet). £150

Speech to the People of France, British Library of Information (New York), 1940 (4 page pamphlet) . £150

War Problems Facing Britain, British Library of Information (New York), 1940 (8 page pamphlet) . £150

Speech to the Italian People, British Library of Information (New York), 1940 (8 page pamphlet) . . £150

Do Not Despair, Ministry of Information (London), [1940] (postcard printed in blue-white-red) . . . £75

Speech ... to the Pilgrims . . . January 9, 1941, British Library of Information (New York), 1941 (4 page pamphlet) £100

Into Battle, Cassell (London), 1941 (light blue cloth lettered in gilt on spine; states 'First published 1941' on copyright page with no additional printings noted) . . £45/£15

ditto, Cassell (London), 1941 (second impression as above, but with an additional leaf tipped-in to the first section numbered 128a/b) . . . . . . £35/£10

ditto, as **Blood, Sweat and Tears**, Putnam's (New York), 1941 (blue cloth, top edge stained red. No additional printings noted on copyright page) . . . £35/£10

Speech . . . February 9th, 1941, British Library of Information (New York), 1941 (12 page pamphlet) . £100

Speech ... to the Pilgrim Society, March 18, 1941, British Library of Information (New York), 1941 (4 page pamphlet) £60

Beating the Invader, Ministry of Information etc (London), 1941 (2 page leaflet) £250

Speech . . . April 27, 1941, British Library of Information (New York), 1941 (8 page pamphlet) . . . £100

Broadcast . . . May 3, 1941, British Library of Information (New York), 1941 (2 page leaflet) £100

The War in the Middle East, Ministry of Information (London), 1941 (8 page pamphlet. Printed in English and Chinese) £250

Freedom's Cause, British Library of Information (New York), 1941 (4 page pamphlet). £100

Speech . . . June 22, 1941, British Library of Information (New York), 1941 (4 page pamphlet) . . . £100

Statement . . . July 29, 1941, British Library of Information (New York), 1941 (16 page pamphlet) . . . £100

The Atlantic Meeting, Ministry of Information (London), 1941 (8 page booklet in card wraps) . . . £200

The Assurance of Victory, Ministry of Information (London), 1941 (4 page pamphlet. Printed in English and Chinese) £200

Speech . . . August 24, 1941, British Library of Information (New York), 1941 (8 page pamphlet) . . . £100

The European War Reviewed, Ministry of Information (London), 1941 (6 page pamphlet; printed in English and Chinese) £200

Statement . . . September 30, 1941, British Library of Information (New York), 1941 (8 page pamphlet) . £100

Speech . . . November 10, 1941, British Library of Information (New York), 1941 (4 page pamphlet) . £100

Speech . . . November 12, 1941, British Library of Information (New York), 1941 (8 page pamphlet) . £100

Address . . . December 2, 1941, British Library of Information (New York), 1941 (12 page pamphlet) . £100

Speech . . . December 8, 1941, British Library of Information (New York), 1941 (4 page pamphlet) . £100

Speech . . . December 11, 1941, British Library of Information (New York), 1941 (8 page pamphlet) . £100

Address . . . December 26, 1941, British Library of Information (New York), 1941 (8 page pamphlet) . £100

Address ... December 26, 1941, United States Government Printing Office (Washington), 1941 (12 page pamphlet) £100

An Address . . . December 26, 1941, The Overbrook Press (Stamford, CT), 1942 (red buckram with paper label on front board; dated 'January 1942' on colophon page. 1,000 copies) £200

Speech . . . December 30, 1941, British Library of Information (New York), 1941 (8 page pamphlet) . £100

Canada and the War, Director of Public Information (Ottawa), 1942 (10 page pamphlet) £100

What Kind of People Do They Think We Are?, The Daily Telegraph and Morning Post (London), 1942 (8 page pamphlet) £75

Address . . . January 15, 1942, Bermuda Press (Hamilton), 1942 (4 page pamphlet) £75

Address . . . February 15, 1942, British Library of Information (New York), 1942 (8 page pamphlet) . £100

The Unrelenting Struggle, Cassell (London), 1942 (light blue cloth lettered in gilt on spine; states 'First Edition . . . 1942' on copyright page with no additional printings noted) . . . . £40/£10

ditto, Little, Brown (Boston), 1942 (dated on copyright page with no additional printings noted) . . . . £40/£10

Speech . . . November 29, 1942, British Library of Information (New York), 1942 (8 page pamphlet) . £75

On Human Rights, The Henry George Foundation (Melbourne), 1942 (16 page booklet in cream card wraps) £100

A Four Years Plan for Britain, The Times Publishing Company (London), 1943 (8 page pamphlet) . . £75

Address . . . May 19, 1943, United States Government Printing Office (Washington), 1943 (12 page pamphlet) £100

An Address . . . 19 May, 1943, The Overbrook Press (Stamford, CT), 1943 (black paper-covered boards with red paper label on front board; dated 'September 1943' on colophon page; 600 copies) £150

The End of the Beginning, Cassell (London), 1943 (light blue cloth lettered in gilt on spine; states 'First Published ... 1943' on copyright page with no additional printings noted) . . . . £40/£10

ditto, Little, Brown (Boston), 1943 (dated on copyright page with no additional printings noted) . . . £40/£10

The Last Days of Marlborough, The Times Publishing Company (London), 1943 (2 page leaflet) . . £75

Liberals' Part in Rebuilding Britain, Liberal Publications Department (London), 1943 (4 page pamphlet) . £100

Mr Churchill Pays Tribute to the Liberal Party, Liberal Publications Department (London), 1943 (2 page leaflet) £75

The Prime Minister's Speech . . . 28 October, 1943, The Univ Press (Cambridge, U.K.), 1943 (12 page booklet with card wraps) £125

The Eve of Action, W & G Baird (Belfast), 1944 (20 page booklet with card wraps) £125

Foreign Policy: The Prime Minister's Review, The Times Publishing Company (London), 1944 (12 page pamphlet) £100

The Tide of Triumph, The British Legation Press Department (Berne, Switzerland), 1944 (24 page pamphlet) . £100

Onwards to Victory, Cassell (London), 1944 (light blue cloth lettered in gilt on spine; states 'First Published ... 1944' on copyright page with no additional printings noted) £40/£10

ditto, Little, Brown (Boston), 1944 (dated on copyright page with no additional printings noted) . . . £40/£10

Country Before Party, S.H. Benson (London), 1945 (2 page leaflet) £100

Our Land, Our Food, S.H. Benson (London), 1945 (4 page pamphlet) £75

Premier's Pledge to Farmers and Farm-Workers, Conservative Party (London), 1945 (2 page leaflet) . £75

A Timely Deliverance, W & G Baird (Belfast), 1945 (10 page pamphlet) £75

Mr Churchill's Declaration of Policy to the Electors, S.H. Benson (London), 1945 (16 page pamphlet) . . £75

'Here is the course we steer', Conservative Party (London), 1945 (12 page booklet with pictorial paper wraps) . £75

The Dawn of Liberation, Cassell (London), 1945 (light blue cloth lettered in gilt on spine; states 'First Published 1945' on copyright page with no additional printings noted) . . . . £35/£10

ditto, Little, Brown (Boston), 1945 (dated on copyright page with no additional printings noted) . . . £35/£10

A True People's Party, Conservative Party (London), 1945 (12 page pamphlet) £75

Subaltern's Reading, The Times Publishing Company (London), 1945 (2 page leaflet) £65

We Fight for the People, Conservative Party (London), 1945 16 page pamphlet) £75

The Day Will Come, Conservative Party (London), 1946 (16 page pamphlet) £100

Victory, Cassell (London), 1946 (light blue cloth lettered in gilt on spine; states 'First Published . . . 1946' on copyright page with no additional printings noted) . £35/£10

ditto, Little, Brown (Boston), 1946 (dated on copyright page with no additional printings noted) . . . £35/£10

War Speeches, 1940-1945, Cassell (London), 1946 (white card wraps printed black on a blue background; states 'First Published . . . 1946' on copyright page with no additional printings noted) £20

Secret Session Speeches, Cassell (London), 1946 (light blue cloth, gilt rules on front board, lettered in gilt on spine; states 'First Published . . . 1946' on copyright page with no additional printings noted). . . . . £35/£10

ditto, Simon & Schuster (New York), 1946 (dated on copyright page with no additional printings noted) £35/£10

Speech . . . 5th October, 1946, Conservative Party (London), 1946 (16 page pamphlet) £75

United Europe: Newsletter of the United Europe Movement No.I, United Europe Movement (London), 1946 (4 page pamphlet) £75

A United Europe: One Way To Stop A New War, United Europe Movement (London), 1947 (8 page pamphlet) £75

The People's Peril, Conservative Party (London), 1947 (16 page pamphlet) £100

'Trust the People', Conservative Party (London), 1947 (16 page pamphlet) £75

Set the People Free, Conservative Party (London), 1948 (8 page booklet with card wraps) £75

'This Country Needs a New Parliament, Conservative Party (London), 1948 (12 page booklet with paper wraps) . £100

Opening Address by Mr Winston Churchill, United Europe Movement (London), 1948 (12 page pamphlet) . £75

The Sinews of Peace, Cassell (London), 1948 (orange-brown cloth, lettered in gilt on spine; states 'First Published . . . 1948' on copyright page with no additional printings noted) . . . . £35/£10

ditto, Houghton Mifflin (Boston), 1949 (dated on copyright page with no additional printings noted) . . £35/£10

The Right Road for Britain, Conservative Party (London), 1949 (20 page booklet with card wraps). . . . £150

The Days Ahead, Conservative Party (London), 1949 (20 page booklet with card wraps) £150

Europe Unite, Cassell (London), 1950 (dark green cloth, lettered in gilt on spine; states 'First Published . . . 1950' on copyright page with no additional printings noted) £35/£10

ditto, Houghton Mifflin (Boston), 1950 (dated on copyright page with no additional printings noted) . . £35/£10

Mr Churchill's Message To You, Conservative Party (London), 1950 (2 page leaflet) £75

In the Balance, Cassell (London), 1951 (dark blue cloth, lettered in gilt on spine; states 'FIRST PUBLISHED 1951' on copyright page with no additional printings noted) .

. . . . £30/£10

ditto, Houghton Mifflin (Boston), 1952 (dated on copyright page with no additional printings noted) . . £30/£10

Thanks to the Bunglers, Charles Knight (Orpington, Kent), 1951 (2 page leaflet) £75

The Manifesto of the Conservative and Unionist Party, Conservative Party (London), 1951 (8 page booklet with paper wraps) £50

The State of the Nation, Conservative Party (London), 1952 (8 page booklet with paper wraps) £50

Speech to the Congress of the United States of America, H.M.S.O. (London), 1952 (4 page pamphlet) . . £50

King George VI, The Times Publishing Company (London), 1952 (4 page pamphlet) £50

ditto, Achille J. St Onge (Worcester, MA), 1952 (purple goatskin, all edges gilt, red decorated endpapers, special imprint p.vi states printing of 750 copies) . . . £100

The War Speeches, Cassell (London), 1952 (3 vols; navy blue buckram, lettered in gilt on spine; fist volume states 'THIS EDITION FIRST PUBLISHED 1951' on copyright page with no additional printings noted, the second and third volume give the date as 1952). . £75/£25 the set

ditto, Houghton Mifflin (Boston), 1953 (dated on copyright page with no additional printings noted) £75/£25 the set

Stemming the Tide, Cassell (London), 1953 (maroon cloth, lettered in gilt on spine; states 'FIRST PUBLISHED 1953' on copyright page with no additional printings noted) .

. . . . £30/£10

ditto, Houghton Mifflin (Boston), 1954 (dated on copyright page with no additional printings noted) . . £30/£10

The Unwritten Alliance: Speeches 1953 to 1959, Cassell (London), 1961 (red cloth, lettered in gilt on spine; no additional printings noted). . . . . £30/£10

Other Title

Painting as a Pastime, Odhams Press/Ernest Benn (London), 1948 (fawn cloth lettered in gilt on front board and spine; copyright page states 'First Published in book form. 1948', with no additional printings noted) . . . £25/£10

TOM CLANCY
(b.1947)

Clancy is considered a master of the 'techno thriller', based on intelligence-gathering and the concepts of military science. He is a master of plotting and attention to technical detail, and the successful filming of his books has been an important factor in widening his readership. 'Tom Clancy' is also a brand name for similar books written by other authors.

Novels

The Hunt for Red October, Naval Institute Press (Annapolis, MD), 1984 (18 lines of text on the copyright page with no statement of edition, not printed at Berryville, VA.; six blurbs on back of d/w and no price) . . . £245/£15

ditto, Naval Institute Press (Annapolis, MD), 1984 (eight blurbs on back of d/w) . . . . . £75/£15

ditto, Collins (London), 1985 . . . . . £75/£15

Red Storm Rising, G.P. Putnam (New York), 1986 (with Larry Bond) . . . . £25/£5

ditto, Collins (London), 1987 . . . . . £25/£5

Patriot Games, G.P. Putnam (New York), 1987 (first state with errors on pp.227-228 and 230-231) . . £65/£15

ditto, G.P. Putnam (New York), 1987 (second state with errors corrected) . . . . £50/£5

ditto, Collins (London), 1987 . . . . . £50/£15

Clear and Present Danger, G.P. Putnam (New York), 1988

. . . . £25/£5

ditto, G.P. Putnam (New York), 1988 (250 signed, numbered copies in slipcase) . . . . . £175/£125

ditto, Collins (London), 1989 . . . . . £15/£5

The Cardinal of the Kremlin, G.P. Putnam (New York), 1988 . . . . £20/£5

ditto, Collins (London), 1988 . . . . . £20/£5

The Sum of All Fears, G.P. Putnam (New York), 1991 .

. . . . £10/£5

ditto, G.P. Putnam (New York), 1991 (600 signed, numbered copies in slipcase), ... £75/£50

ditto, HarperCollins (London), 1991 . . . . £15/£5

Without Remorse G.P. Putnam (New York), 1993 . £10/£5

ditto, G.P. Putnam (New York), 1993 (600 signed, numbered copies in slipcase) . . . . . . £75/£50

ditto, HarperCollins (London), 1993 . . . . £15/£5

Debt of Honor, G.P. Putnam (New York), 1994 . £10/£5

ditto, G.P. Putnam (New York), 1994 (450 signed, numbered copies in slipcase) . . . . . . £85/£60

ditto, Collins (London), 1994 . . . . . £10/£5

Executive Orders, G.P. Putnam (New York), 1996 £10/£5

ditto, G.P. Putnam (New York), 1996 (200 signed, numbered copies in slipcase), ... £75/£50

ditto, Collins (London), 1996 . . . . . £10/£5

Rainbow Six, G.P. Putnam (New York), 1998 . . £10/£5

ditto, G.P. Putnam (New York), 1998 (675 signed, numbered copies in slipcase) . . . . . . £100/£80

ditto, Joseph (London), 1998 . . . . . £10/£5

The Bear and the Dragon, G.P. Putnam (New York), 2000.

. . . . £10/£5

ditto, G.P. Putnam (New York), 2000 (425 signed, numbered copies in slipcase) . . . . . . £100/£80

ditto, Joseph (London), 2000 . . . . . £10/£5

Red Rabbit, G.P. Putnam (New York), 2002 . . £10/£5

ditto, G.P. Putnam (New York), 2002 (550 signed, numbered copies in slipcase) . . . . . . £75/£50

ditto, Joseph (London), 2002 . . . . . £10/£5

The Teeth of the Tiger, G.P. Putnam (New York), 2003 .

. . . . £10/£5

ditto, G.P. Putnam (New York), 2003 (300 signed, numbered copies in slipcase) . . . . . . £75/£50

ditto, Joseph (London), 2003 . . . . . £10/£5

Non-Fiction

Submarine, A Guided Tour inside a Nuclear Warship, G.P. Putnam (New York), 1993 (300 signed, numbered copies, slipcase). . . . . £150/£125

ditto, Berkley (New York), 1993 (pbk) £5

Armored Cav: A Guided Tour of an Armoured Cavalry Regiment, Putnam (New York), 1994 (150 signed, numbered copies, slipcase) . . . . £150/£125

ditto, Berkley (New York), 1994 (pbk) £5

ditto, as **Armoured Warfare**, HarperCollins (London), 1996
(pbk) £5
**Fighter Wing: A Guided Tour of an Airforce Combat
Wing**, Berkley (New York), 1995 (pbk). . . £5
ditto, HarperCollins (London), 1995 (pbk) . . £5
SSN: Strategies of Submarine Warfare, Berkley (New
York), 1996 (pbk) £5
Marine: A Guided Tour of a Marine Expeditionary Team,
Berkley (New York), 1996 (pbk) £5
Airborne: A Guided Tour of an Airborne Task Force,
Berkley (New York), 1997 (pbk) . . . £5
Into the Storm: A Study in Command, Putnam (New York),
1997 (with Fred Franks Jr) . . . . £20/£5
Carrier: A Guided Tour of an Aircraft Carrier, Berkley
(New York), 1999 (pbk) £5
Every Man a Tiger, Putnam (New York), 1999 (with Chuck
Horner) . . . . £20/£10
Special Ops, Berkley (New York), 2000 (pbk) . £5
Special Forces: A Guided Tour of U.S. Special Forces,
Berkley (New York), 2001 (with John Grisham; pbk). £5
ditto, Sidgwick & Jackson (London), 2001 (pbk) . £5
Shadow Warriors, Putnam (New York), 2002 (with Carl
Steiner) . . . . £10/£5
Battle Ready, Putnam (New York), 2004 (with General Tony
Zinni and Tony Koltz) . . . . . £10/£5

JOHN CLARE
(b.1793 d.1864)

Clare was a poet who excelled in his descriptions of
English rural life and the thoughts and feelings of ordinary
country people. The son of a farm labourer, he was inspired
to write poetry by reading Thomson's *Seasons*. Although
he gained recognition and became relatively wealthy for a
while, he died in the Northampton general lunatic asylum.
Largely forgotten during the 19th century, interest in his
work was revived by Edmund Blunden in 1920.

Poetry
Poems Descriptive of Rural Life and Scenery, Taylor &
Hessey (London), 1820 . . . . . £1,500
The Village Minstrel and Other Poems, Taylor & Hessey
(and) Stamford: E. Drury (London), 1821 (2 vols) . £750
The Shepherd's Calendar, Taylor (London), 1827 . £500
The Rural Muse, Whittaker & Co. (London), 1835 . £500
Poems by John Clare, G.E. Over (Rugby), 1901 (selected by
Norman Gale) £45
Poems by John Clare, Frowde (London), 1908 (selected by
Arthur Symons) £20
Poems Chiefly From Manuscript, Cobden-Sanderson
(London), 1920 . . . . . . £100/£40
Madrigals and Chronicles, Beaumont Press (London), 1924
(398 numbered copies, edited by Edmund Blunden) . £75

Others
The Life and Remains of John Clare, by J.L. Cherry, Warne
(London), 1873 . . . . £125
Sketches in the Life of John Clare, Cobden-Sanderson
(London), 1931 . . . . . . £75/£25
The Letters of John Clare, Routledge & Kegan Paul
(London), 1951 . . . . . . £35/£15

ARTHUR C. CLARKE
(b.1917 d.2008)

Clarke's much admired science fiction has successfully
popularised and experimented with speculative science.
Clarke wrote his novel *2001: A Space Odyssey* at the same
time that it was filmed by Stanley Kubrick: it was based on
an earlier short story 'The Sentinel'. He is considered one
of the greats of science fiction, along with Robert A.
Heinlein and Isaac Asimov, and has an asteroid, a species
of dinosaur and the 2001 Mars Odyssey orbiter named in
his honour.

Novels
Prelude to Space, World Editions (New York), 1951 (pbk) .
. . . . £25
ditto, Sidgwick & Jackson (London), 1953 . £150/£25
ditto, Gnome Press (New York), 1954 (blue boards, spine
lettered in yellow *or* black boards spine lettered in red) .
. . . . £65/£15
ditto, Gnome Press (New York), 1954 (grey boards, spine
lettered in red) . . . . . . £60/£10
The Sands of Mars, Sidgwick & Jackson (London), 1951 .
. . . . £150/£25
ditto, Gnome Press (New York), 1952 . . £125/£20
Islands in the Sky, Winston (Philadelphia), 1952 . £125/£35
ditto, Sidgwick & Jackson (London), 1952 . £100/£35
Against the Fall of Night, Gnome Press (New York), 1953.
. . . . £275/£45
Childhood's End, Ballantine (New York), 1953 £1,250/£200
ditto, Ballantine (New York), 1953 (pbk) . . . £75
ditto, Sidgwick & Jackson (London), 1954 . £450/£50
Earthlight, Ballantine (New York), 1955 . . £700/£75
ditto, Muller (London), 1955 . . . . £125/£45
The City and the Stars, Harcourt Brace (New York), 1956 .
. . . . £250/£35
ditto, Muller (London), 1956 . . . . £200/£35
The Deep Range, Harcourt Brace (New York), 1957 . . .
. . . . £100/£25
ditto, Muller (London), 1957 . . . . £75/£25
A Fall of Moondust, Harcourt Brace (New York), 1961 .
. . . . £75/£25
ditto, Gollancz (London), 1961 . . . . £75/£25
Dolphin Island, Holt Rinehart (New York), 1963 . £50/£20
ditto, Gollancz (London), 1963 . . . . £50/£20
Glide Path, Harcourt Brace (New York), 1963 £50/£20
ditto, Sidgwick & Jackson (London), 1969 . £50/£20
2001: A Space Odyssey, New American Library (New
York), 1968 (first issue d/w with price of $4.95) . £300/£45
ditto, New American Library (New York), 1968 (second
issue d/w with price of $6.95) . . . . £250/£45
ditto, Hutchinson (London), 1968 . . . £250/£40
The Lion of Comarre and **Against the Fall of Night**,
Harcourt Brace (New York), 1968 . . . £35/£10
ditto, Gollancz (London), 1970 . . . . £30/£10
Rendezvous with Rama, Harcourt Brace (New York), 1973.
. . . . £35/£10
ditto, Gollancz (London), 1973 . . . . £30/£10
Imperial Earth, Gollancz (London), 1975 . £25/£10
ditto, Harcourt Brace (New York), 1976 . . £25/£10

The Fountains of Paradise, Gollancz (London), 1979 .   .
  .   .   .   .   £25/£10
ditto, Harcourt Brace (New York), 1979   .   .   £25/£10
2010: Odyssey Two, Granada (London), 1982.   .   £20/£5
ditto, Granada (London), 1982 (author's name misspelt 'Clark' on title-page) .   .   .   .   .   £75/£45
ditto, Phantasia (Huntington Woods, MI), 1982 (650 signed copies, slipcase) .   .   .   .   .   £100/£75
ditto, Phantasia (Huntington Woods, MI), 1982 (26 signed, lettered copies, leather box)   .   .   .   £400/£350
ditto, Ballantine (New York), 1982   .   .   .   £15/£5
The Songs of Distant Earth, Grafton (London), 1986 .   .
  .   .   .   .   £15/£5
ditto, Ballantine (New York), 1986   .   .   .   £15/£5
2061: Odyssey Three, Ballantine (New York), 1988   £15/£5
ditto, Grafton (London), 1988   .   .   .   .   £15/£5
Cradle, Gollancz (London), 1988 (with Gentry Lee)   £15/£5
ditto, Warner (New York), 1988.   .   .   .   £15/£5
Rama II, Gollancz (London), 1989 (with Gentry Lee) .   .
  .   .   .   .   £20/£10
ditto, Ballantine (New York), 1989   .   .   .   £10/£5
Beyond the Fall of Night, Putnam (New York), 1990 (with Gregory Benford)   .   .   .   .   .   £10/£5
ditto, as *Against the Fall of Night*, Gollancz (London), 1991
  .   .   .   .   £10/£5
The Ghost from the Grand Banks, Bantam (New York), 1990   .   .   .   .   £10/£5
ditto, Gollancz (London), 1990   .   .   .   .   £10/£5
The Garden of Rama, Gollancz (London), 1991 (with Gentry Lee) .   .   .   .   £10/£5
ditto, Bantam (New York), 1991.   .   .   .   £10/£5
Rama Revealed, Gollancz (London), 1993 (with Gentry Lee)
  .   .   .   .   £10/£5
ditto, Bantam (New York), 1994.   .   .   .   £10/£5
The Hammer of God, Gollancz (London), 1993   .   £10/£5
ditto, Bantam (New York), 1993.   .   .   .   £10/£5
Richter 10, Gollancz (London), 1996 (with Mike McQuay).
  .   .   .   .   £10/£5
ditto, Bantam (New York), 1996.   .   .   .   £10/£5
3001: The Final Odyssey, Voyager (London), 1997   £10/£5
ditto, Ballantine (New York), 1997   .   .   .   £10/£5
The Trigger, Voyager (London), 1999 (with Michael P. Kube-McDowell).   .   .   .   .   .   £10/£5
ditto, Bantam (New York), 1999.   .   .   .   £10/£5
The Light of Other Days, Voyager (London), 2000 (with Stephen Baxter)   .   .   .   .   .   £10/£5
ditto, Tor (New York), 2000   .   .   .   .   £10/£5

Stories
Expedition to Earth, Ballantine (New York), 1953 £350/£40
ditto, Sidgwick & Jackson (London), 1954   .   £125/£25
Reach for Tomorrow, Ballantine (New York), 1956   .   .
  .   .   .   .   £600/£100
ditto, Gollancz (London), 1962   .   .   .   £125/£25
Tales from the White Hart, Ballantine (New York), 1957 (pbk) £100
ditto, Harcourt Brace (New York), 1970   .   .   £50/£15
ditto, Sidgwick & Jackson (London), 1972   .   £30/£10
The Other Side of the Sky, Harcourt Brace (New York), 1958   .   .   .   .   £150/£35
ditto, Gollancz (London), 1961   .   .   .   £35/£10
Tales of Ten Worlds, Harcourt Brace (New York), 1962   .
  .   .   .   .   £35/£10
ditto, Gollancz (London), 1963 .   .   .   .   £25/£10

The Nine Billion Names of God, Harcourt Brace (New York), 1967 .   .   .   .   .   .   £100/£15
The Wind from the Sun, Harcourt Brace (New York), 1971
  .   .   .   .   £35/£5
ditto, Gollancz (London), 1972   .   .   .   .   £35/£5
Of Time and Stars, Gollancz (London), 1972 .   . £100/£10
The Sentinel, Berkley (New York), 1983 .   .   .   £15/£5
ditto, Panther (London), 1985 (pbk) £5
Tales from Planet Earth, Century (London), 1989   £10/£5
ditto, Bantam (New York), 1990.   .   .   .   £10/£5

Miscellaneous Collections
Across the Sea of Stars, Harcourt Brace (New York), 1959 .
  .   .   .   .   £75/£15
From the Oceans, From the Stars, Harcourt Brace (New York), 1962 .   .   .   .   .   .   £50/£25
Prelude to Mars, Harcourt Brace (New York), 1965 £35/£10
An Arthur C. Clarke Omnibus, Sidgwick & Jackson (London), 1965   .   .   .   .   .   .   £25/£10
An Arthur C. Clarke Second Omnibus, Sidgwick & Jackson (London), 1968   .   .   .   .   .   £25/£10
Best of Arthur C. Clarke: 1937-1971, Sidgwick & Jackson (London), 1973   .   .   .   .   .   £25/£10

Non-Fiction
Interplanetary Flight, Temple Press (London), 1950   .   .
  .   .   .   .   £200/£45
ditto, Harper (New York), [1951]   .   .   . £125/£25
The Exploration of Space, Temple Press (London), 1951   .
  .   .   .   .   £125/£25
ditto, Harper (New York), 1951 .   .   .   . £125/£25
The Exploration of the Moon, Muller (London), 1954 .   .
  .   .   .   .   £125/£30
The Young Traveller in Space, Phoenix House (London), 1954   .   .   .   .   £100/£25
ditto, as *Into Space*, Harper (New York), 1971 (with Robert Silverberg)   .   .   .   .   .   .   £25/£5
The Coast of Coral, Muller (London), 1956   .   £75/£20
ditto, Harper (New York), 1956 .   .   .   .   £75/£20
The Making of a Moon, Muller (London), 1957   .   £40/£10
ditto, Harper (New York), 1957.   .   .   .   £40/£10
The Reefs of Taprobane, Muller (London), 1957   .   £35/£10
ditto, Harper (New York), 1957.   .   .   .   £35/£10
Boy Beneath the Sea, Harper (New York), [1958].   £50/£15
Voice Across the Sea, Muller (London), 1958.   .   £50/£10
ditto, Harper (New York), 1958 .   .   .   .   £50/£10
The Challenge of the Sea, Muller (London), 1960.   £40/£10
ditto, Holt, Reinhart (New York), 1960   .   .   £40/£10
The Challenge of the Spaceship, Muller (London), 1960   .
  .   .   .   .   £40/£10
ditto, Holt, Reinhart (New York), 1960   .   .   £40/£10
The First Five Fathoms, Harper (New York), 1960 £35/£10
Indian Ocean Adventure, Barker (London), 1962 .   £40/£10
Profiles of the Future, Gollancz (London), 1962   .   £35/£10
ditto, Harper (New York), 1962 .   .   .   .   £35/£10
Man and Space, Time (New York), 1964 (no d/w)   .   £20
The Treasure of the Great Reef, Barker (London), 1964   .
  .   .   .   .   £35/£10
ditto, Harper (New York), 1964 .   .   .   .   £35/£10
Indian Ocean Treasure, Harper (New York), 1964 (with Mike Wilson)   .   .   .   .   .   .   £15/£5
ditto, Sidgwick and Jackson (London), 1972   .   £15/£5
Voices from the Sky, Harper (New York), 1965   .   £35/£10
ditto, Gollancz (London), 1966 .   .   .   .   £35/£10

The Promise of Space, Hodder & Stoughton (London), 1968
. . . . £20/£5
ditto, Harper (New York), 1968 . . . . £20/£5
Report on Planet Three and Other Speculations, Gollancz
(London), 1972 . . . . £15/£5
ditto, Harper (New York), 1972 . . . . £15/£5
The Lost Worlds of 2001, New American Library (New
York), 1972 . . . . £25/£10
ditto, Sidgwick & Jackson (London), 1972 . £25/£10
Beyond Jupiter, Little, Brown (Boston), 1972 (with Chesley
Bonestell) . . . . £35/£10
The View from Serendip, Random House (New York), 1977
. . . . £20/£5
ditto, Gollancz (London), 1978 . . . . £20/£5
Arthur C. Clarke's Mysterious World, Collins (London),
1980 (with John Fairley and Simon Welfare) . £35/£10
1984: Spring, A Choice of Futures, Granada (London),
1984 . . . . £15/£5
ditto, Ballantine (New York), 1984 . . . £15/£5
Ascent to Orbit: A Scientific Autobiography, Wiley (New
York), 1984 . . . . £30/£10
The Odyssey File, Panther (London), 1985 (with Peter
Hyams; pbk). £5
Arthur C. Clarke's July 20, 2019, Macmillan (New York),
1986 . . . . £15/£5
Astounding Days: a Science Fictional Autobiography,
Gollancz (London), 1989 . . . . £15/£5
ditto, Bantam (New York), 1990. . . . £15/£5
How the World Was One, Gollancz (London), 1992 £15/£5
ditto, Bantam (New York), 1992. . . . £15/£5
The Fantastic Muse, Hilltop Press (Huddersfield,
Yorkshire), 1992 (wraps) £20
By Space Possessed, Gollancz (London), 1993 £20/£5
The Snows of Olympus, Gollancz (London), 1994. £15/£5
ditto, Norton (New York), 1995 . . . . £15/£5
Greetings, Carbon-Based Bipeds!, HarperCollins (London),
1999 . . . . £15/£5
ditto, St Martin's Press (New York), 1999 . £15/£5

HARRY CLARKE

(b.1889 d.1931)

An Irish artist in the tradition of Aubrey Beardsley, Clarke's
detail and decoration are distinctively his own. He had
begun work on illustrating Coleridge's *The Rime of the
Ancient Mariner* and Pope's *The Rape of the Lock* for
Harrap, but difficulties (work on the former was destroyed
in an uprising) led to *Hans Andersen's Fairy Tales*
becoming his first printed art work.

Illustrated by Clarke
Hans Andersen's Fairy Tales, Harrap (London), [1916]
(125 signed copies) £2,500
ditto, Harrap (London), [1916] (full leather edition) . £600
ditto, Harrap (London), [1916] (cloth edition). . . £250
ditto, Brentano's (New York), 1916 . . . . £250
Tales of Mystery and Imagination, by Edgar Allan Poe,
Harrap (London), 1919 (170 signed copies) . £2,500
ditto, Harrap (London), [1919] (morocco leather edition) .
. . . . £600
ditto, Harrap (London), [1919] (cloth edition). . . £250
ditto, Brentano's (New York), 1919 . . . . £250

ditto, Harrap (London), [1923] (new edition with colour
plates, antique leather) £275
ditto, Harrap (London), [1923] (new edition with colour
plates, cloth edition) . . . . . £350/£150
ditto, Brentano's (New York), 1923 (new edition with colour
plates, cloth edition) . . . . . £300/£150
The Year's at the Spring, Harrap (London), 1920 (250
signed copies) £1,000
ditto, Harrap (London), 1920 (cloth edition) . £300/£150
ditto, Brentano's (New York), 1920 . . £250/£125
The Fairy Tales of Perrault, Harrap (London), [1922]
(Persian levant leather edition). £700
ditto, Harrap (London), [1922] (Buckram edition) £600/£300
ditto, Harrap (London), [1922] (cloth edition) . £600/£250
ditto, Dodge (New York), [1922] . . . £600/£250
Faust, by Goethe, Harrap (London), 1925 (1,000 signed
copies) . . . . £750/£500
ditto, Harrap/Dingwall-Rock (New York), 1925 (1,000
signed copies) . . . . . . £750/£300
*Elixir of Life Being a slight account of the romantic rise to
fame of a great house*, by Geoffrey C. Warren, John
Jameson & Son Limited (Dublin), 1925. . £750/£450
Selected Poems of Algernon Charles Swinburne, John Lane
(London), 1928 . . . . . . £400/£125
ditto, Dodd, Mead (New York), 1928 . . £250/£125

MARY HIGGINS CLARK

(b.1927)

Mary Higgins Clark is an American author of best-selling
suspense novels. Her debut novel, *Aspire to the Heavens*,
was a fictionalised account of the life of George
Washington and did not sell well, but thereafter her work
became very popular and to date she has sold over 80
million books in the US alone. She was President of the
Mystery Writers of America (1987) and Chairman of the
International Crime Congress (1988). Among many
honours she received the Grand Prix de Littérature
Policière in 1980.

Novels
Aspire to the Heavens, A Portrait of George Washington,
Meredith Press (New York), 1968 . . . £150/£25
ditto, as *Mount Vernon Love Story*, Simon & Schuster (New
York), 2002 . . . . £10/£5
Where Are the Children?, Simon & Schuster (New York),
1975 . . . . £75/£15
ditto, Talmy Franklin (London), 1975 . . £45/£10
A Stranger is Watching, Simon & Schuster (New York),
1977 . . . . £45/£10
ditto, Collins (London), 1978 . . . . £30/£10
The Cradle Will Fall, Simon & Schuster (New York), 1980
. . . . £25/£10
ditto, Collins (London), 1980 . . . . £10/£5
A Cry in the Night, Simon & Schuster (New York), 1982 .
. . . . £25/£10
ditto, Collins (London), 1983 . . . . £10/£5
Stillwatch, Simon & Schuster (New York), 1984 . £15/£5
ditto, Collins (London), 1984 . . . . £10/£5
Weep No More, My Lady, Simon & Schuster (New York),
1987 . . . . £10/£5
ditto, Collins (London), 1987 . . . . £10/£5

While My Pretty One Sleeps, Simon & Schuster (New York), 1989 . . . . . . £10/£5
ditto, Century (London), 1989 . . . . £10/£5
Love Music, loves to Dance, Simon & Schuster (New York), 1991 . . . . . . £10/£5
ditto, Century (London), 1991 . . . . £10/£5
All Around the Town, Simon & Schuster (New York), 1992 . . . . £10/£5
ditto, Century (London), 1992 . . £10/£5
I'll Be Seeing You, Simon & Schuster (New York), 1993 . . . . £10/£5
ditto, Century (London), 1993 . . . . £10/£5
Remember Me, Simon & Schuster (New York), 1994 £10/£5
ditto, Simon & Schuster (London), 1994 . . . £10/£5
Let Me Call You Sweetheart, Simon & Schuster (New York), 1995 . . . . . . £10/£5
ditto, Simon & Schuster (London), 1995 . . £10/£5
Silent Night, Simon & Schuster (New York), 1995 £10/£5
ditto, Simon & Schuster (London), 1995 . . £10/£5
Moonlight Becomes You, Simon & Schuster (New York), 1996 . . . . £10/£5
Pretend You Don't See Her, Simon & Schuster (New York), 1997 . . . . . . £10/£5
ditto, Simon & Schuster (London), 1997 . . £10/£5
You Belong to Me, Simon & Schuster (New York), 1998 . . . . £10/£5
ditto, Simon & Schuster (London), 1998 . . £10/£5
All Through the Night, Simon & Schuster (New York), 1998 . . . . £10/£5
ditto, Simon & Schuster (London), 1998 . . £10/£5
We'll Meet Again, Simon & Schuster (New York), 1999 . . . . £10/£5
ditto, Simon & Schuster (London), 1999 . . £10/£5
Before I Say Good-bye, Simon & Schuster (New York), 2000 . . . . £10/£5
ditto, Simon & Schuster (London), 2000 . . £10/£5
Deck The Halls, Simon & Schuster (New York), 2000 . . . . £10/£5
ditto, Simon & Schuster (London), 2000 . £10/£5
On the Street Where You Live, Simon & Schuster (New York), 2001 . . . . . £10/£5
He Sees You When You're Sleeping, Simon & Schuster (New York), 2001 (written with Carol Higgins Clark) . . . . £10/£5
Daddy's Little Girl, Simon & Schuster (New York), 2002 . . . . £10/£5
The Second Time Around, Simon & Schuster (New York), 2003 . . . . . . £10/£5
ditto, Simon & Schuster (London), 2003 . . £10/£5
Nightime is My Time, Simon & Schuster (New York), 2004 . . . . £10/£5
ditto, Simon & Schuster (London), 2004 . . £10/£5
No Place Like Home, Simon & Schuster (New York), 2005 . . . . £10/£5
ditto, Simon & Schuster (London), 2005 . . £10/£5
Two Little Girls in Blue, Simon & Schuster (New York), 2006 . . . . . . £10/£5
ditto, Simon & Schuster (London), 2006 . £10/£5
I Heard That Song Before, Simon & Schuster (New York), 2007 . . . . . . £10/£5
ditto, Simon & Schuster (London), 2007 . . £10/£5
Where Are You Now?, Simon & Schuster (New York), 2008 . . . . £10/£5

Short Stories
The Anastasia Syndrome and Other Stories, Simon & Schuster (New York), 1989 . . . . . £10/£5
ditto, Century (London), 1990 . . . . £10/£5
Death on the Cape: and Other Stories, , Century (London), 1993 . . . . £10/£5
The Lottery Winner, Simon & Schuster (New York), 1994 . . . . £10/£5
My Gal Sunday, Simon & Schuster (New York), 1996. . . . . £10/£5
ditto, Simon & Schuster (London), 1996 . . £10/£5

Picture Book
Ghost Ship: A Cape Cod Story, Simon & Schuster (New York), 2007 . . . . . . £10/£5

Non-Fiction
Kitchen Priviliges, Simon & Schuster (New York), 2002 . . . . £10/£5
ditto, Simon & Schuster (London), 2003 . . . £10/£5

JAMES CLAVELL
(b.1924 d.1994)

James Clavell was an American novelist, screenwriter and director. He is best known for his epic Asian Saga series of novels, the first of which, *King Rat*, was a fictionalised account of his P.O.W. experiences. A best-seller, his books were filmed and also became phenomenally successful television series in the early 1980s.

The Asian Saga novels
King Rat, Little, Brown (Boston), 1962 . . . £250/£50
ditto, Michael Joseph (London), 1963 . . . £100/£15
Tai-Pan, Michael Joseph (London), 1966. . . £100/£15
ditto, Atheneum (New York), 1966 . . . £65/£10
Shogun, Atheneum (New York), 1975 . . . £65/£10
ditto, Hodder & Stoughton (London), 1975 . . £65/£10
Noble House: A Novel of Contemporary Hong Kong. Delacorte (New York), 1980 . . . . £25/£5
ditto. Delacorte (New York), 1980 (500 signed, numbered copies in slipcase; no d/w). . . . £125/£100
ditto, Hodder & Stoughton (London), 1981 . £25/£5
Whirlwind, Morrow (New York), 1986 . . . £20/£5
ditto, Morrow (New York), 1986 (75 signed copies; slipcase) . . . . £75/£65
ditto, Hodder & Stoughton (London), 1986 . . £15/£5
ditto, as *Escape*, Hodder & Stoughton (London), 1995 (shorter novel adapted from *Whirlwind*). . £10/£5
Gai-Jin, Delacorte (New York), 1993 . . . £10/£5
ditto, Delacorte (New York), 1993 (350 signed, numbered copies; slipcase) . . . . . £75/£65
ditto, Hodder & Stoughton (London), 1993 . . £10/£5

Others
The Making of James Clavell's Shogun, Delta/Dell (New York), 1980 (wraps) £5
ditto, Coronet (London), 1981 (wraps) £5
Art of War, by Sun Tzu, Hodder & Stoughton (London), 1981 (wraps; edited by Clavell) £10
ditto. Delacorte (New York), 1981 . . . . £10/£5
The Children's Story, Delacorte (New York), 1981 £10/£5

ditto, Hodder & Stoughton (London), 1982 . . £10/£5
Thrump-O-Moto, Hodder & Stoughton (London), 1986
(illustrated by George Sharp) . . . . £15/£5
ditto. Delacorte (New York), 1986 . . . . £10/£5
Ella's Trip to the Museum, Crown (New York), 1996 (no
d/w) £5

ROBERT M. COATES
(b.1897 d.1973)

The Eater of Darkness by Coates was an experimental work, called by some critics the first Dada novel. He is primarily collected today for his crime novels, but he spent many years working for *The New Yorker* for whom he wrote over 100 short stories, as well as serving as their art critic.

Novels
The Eater of Darkness, Contact Editions (Paris), 1926
(wraps) £400
ditto, Macaulay (New York), 1929 . . . . £200/£35
Yesterday's Burdens, Macaulay (New York), 1933 £50/£10
The Bitter Season, Harcourt, Brace & Co. (New York), 1946
. . . . £15/£5
ditto, Gollancz (London), 1949 . . . . £15/£5
Wisteria Cottage, Harcourt, Brace & Co. (New York), 1948
. . . . £50/£10
ditto, Gollancz (London), 1949 . . . . £25/£10
The Farther Shore, Harcourt, Brace & Co. (New York),
1955 . . . . £25/£10
ditto, as ***The Darkness of the Day***, Gollancz (London), 1955
. . . . £10/£5
ditto, as ***The Night is So Dark***, Popular Library (New York),
1955 (pbk) £5

Short Story Collections
All the Year Round: A Book of Stories, Harcourt, Brace &
Co. (New York), 1943 . . . . . £15/£5
The Hour After Westerly, Harcourt, Brace & Co. (New
York), 1957 . . . . £50/£10
ditto, as ***Accident at the Inn***, Gollancz (London), 1957. .
. . . . £25/£10
The Man Just Ahead of You, William Sloane (New York),
1964 . . . . £20/£5
ditto, Gollancz (London), 1965 . . . . £10/£5

History
***The Outlaw Years: The History of the Land Pirates of the
Natchez Trace***, Macaulay (New York), 1930 . £125/£45

Travel
Beyond the Alps: A Summer in the Italian Hill Towns,
William Sloane (New York), 1961 . . . £20/£5
ditto, Gollancz (London), 1962 . . . . £10/£5
***South of Rome: A Spring and Summer in Southern Italy
and Sicily***, William Morrow (New York), 1965 . £10/£5

Memoir
***The View from Here: Informal Recollections of Mostly
Happy Yesterdays***, Harcourt, Brace & Co. (New York),
1960 . . . . £30/£10

WILLIAM COBBETT
(b.1763 d.1835)

A journalist, farmer and M.P., Cobbett was also an English civil rights activist. He believed that the reform of Parliament and the abolition of rotten boroughs would relieve the poverty of farm labourers, and he also campaigned against the Corn Laws. Despite the apparent inconsistencies in his life, Cobbett was at heart opposed to all authority. Many of his publications were privately printed. *Rural Rides* is his best known work.

Books
Le Tuteur Anglais, Bradford (Philadelphia, PA), 1795 . £125
***A Collection of Facts and Observations Relative to the
Peace with Bonaparte***, Cobbett (London), 1801 . . £225
Letters to Aldington on the Fatal Effects of the Peace,
Cobbett (London), 1802 . . . . . . £165
Letters to Hawkesbury on the Peace with Bonaparte,
Cobbett (London), 1802 . . . . . . £100
***The Political Proteus: A View of the Public Character and
Conduct of R.B. Sheridan***, Budd (London), 1804 . £125
***Letters of the Late War between the United States and
Great Britain***, J. Belden & Co. (New York),1815 . £225
Paper Against Gold, printed by J. M'Creery (London), 1815
(2 vols) £165
An Address to the Journeymen and Labourers of England,
1816 . . . . £65
Mr Cobbett's Address to His Countrymen, Carlile (London),
1817 . . . . £65
A Journal of a Year's Residence in the United States,
Sherwood, Neely & Jones (London), 1818 & 1819 (3 parts)
. . . . £275 the set
A Grammar of the English Language, Clayton & Kingsland
(New York), 1818 . . . . £175
ditto, Thomas Dolby (London), 1819. . . . £175
The American Gardener, Charles Clement (London), 1821.
. . . . £175
Preliminary Paper Against Gold, John M. Cobbett
(London), 1821 . . . . £75
Cobbett's Sermons, Charles Clement (London), 1822 . £75
Cottage Economy, Charles Clement (London), 1822 . £125
ditto, Peter Davies (London), 1926 (preface by G.K.
Chesterton, illustrated by Eric Gill). . . . £20/£5
Cobbett's Collective Commentaries, J.M. Cobbett (London),
1822 . . . . £200
A History of the Protestant Reformation, William Cobbett
(London), 1824 & 1827 (2 parts) . . . £200 the set
A French Grammar, Charles Clement (London), 1824 £150
The Woodlands, William Cobbett (London), 1825 [1828] .
. . . . £150
A Treatise on Cobbett's Corn, William Cobbett (London),
1828 . . . . £175
The English Gardener, William Cobbett (London), 1829 .
. . . . £125
Advice to Young Men, William Cobbett (London), 1829
[1830] £125
The Emigrant's Guide, William Cobbett (London), 1829 .
. . . . £250
Rural Rides, William Cobbett (London), 1830 . . £600

History of the Regency and Reign of George IV, William Cobbett (London), 1830 . . . . . £125

A Spelling Book and Stepping-Stones to English Grammar, William Cobbett (London), 1831 . . . . £125

A Geographical Dictionary of England and Wales, W.H. Cobbett (London), 1832 . . . . . . £200

Three Lectures on the Political State of Ireland, R. Byrne (Dublin), 1834 . . . . . . £125

Legacy to Labourers, William Cobbett (London), 1834 [1835] £75

Legacy to Parsons, William Cobbett (London), 1835 . £75

Legacy to Peel, Cobbett's 'Register' Office (London), 1836 . . . . £75

Pamphlets

Observations on Dr Joseph Priestley's Emigration, Bradford (Philadelphia, PA), 1794 . . . . . £125

A Bone to Gnaw for the Democrats, Bradford (Philadelphia, PA), 1795 (2 parts) . . . . £100 the set

ditto, J. Wright (London), 1797 (with *A Rod for the Backs*) £600

A Kick for Bite, William Cobbett (Philadelphia, PA), 1795 . . . . £100

A New Year's Gift for the Democrats, Bradford (Philadelphia, PA), 1796 . . . . £100

The Political Censor, William Cobbett (Philadelphia, PA), 1796-7 (numbers 1-9). . . . . £250 the set

The Bloody Buoy, Benjamin Davies (Philadelphia, PA), 1796 . . . . £150

The Scare-Crow, William Cobbett (Philadelphia, PA), 1796 . . . . £125

The Life and Adventures of Peter Porcupine, William Cobbett (Philadelphia, PA), 1796 . . . . £150

ditto, Nonesuch Press (London), 1927 (1800 numbered copies) £40

Life of Thomas Paine, R. Gilbert (Philadelphia, PA), 1796 . . . . £150

A Letter to the Infamous Tom Paine, William Cobbett (Philadelphia, PA), 1796 . . . . . £100

ditto, Ogilvy & Son (London), 1797 . . . . £75

Observations on the Debates in the American Congress, William Cobbett (Philadelphia, PA), 1797 . £100

ditto, Ogilvy & Son (London), 1797 . . . . £75

Selections from Porcupine's Gazette, William Cobbett (Philadelphia, PA), 1797 . . . . . £125

The Democratic Judge, William Cobbett (Philadelphia, PA), 1798 . . . . £100

ditto, Wright (London), 1798 . . . . . £75

A Detection of a Conspiracy, Formed by the United Irishmen, Milliken (Philadelphia, PA), 1798 . £125

The Cannibal's Progress or The Dreadful Horrors of French Invasion, William Cobbett (London), 1798 . £125

French Arrogance, Published by Peter Porcupine (Philadelphia, PA), 1798 . . . . . . £100

Selections from Porcupine's Gazette, William Cobbett (London), 1798 . . . . £125

The Trial of Republicanism, William Cobbett (London), 1799 . . . . £100

ditto, Cobbett and Morgan (London), 1801 . £75

Cobbett's Advice, William Cobbett (London), 1800 . £75

Mr Cobbett's Taking Leave of His Countrymen, William Cobbett (London), 1817 . . . . . £100

The Farmer's Friend, William Cobbett (London), 1822 . . . . £100

The Farmer's Wife's Friend, William Cobbett (London), 1822 . . . . £100

Reduction No Robbery, C. Clement (London), 1822 . £100

Gold For Ever, C. Clement (London), 1825 . . £100

Good Friday, or The Murder of Jesus Christ by The Jews, printed for the Author (London), 1830 . . . £150

Surplus Population: A Comedy, William Cobbett (London), 1831 . . . . £125

Cobbett's Address to the Tax-Payers of England, William Cobbett (London), 1832 . . . . . . £100

The Rights of the Poor, William Cobbett (London), 1833 . . . . £75

The Flash in the Pan, William Cobbett (London), 1833 £75

LIZA CODY
(b.1944)

Crime writer Liza Cody is best known for her 'Anna Lee' novels about an everyday female detective. Cody studied painting at the Royal Academy School of Art and has worked as a furniture maker, photographer, and graphic designer. Her first novel, *Dupe*, won the John Creasey Award in 1980. *Bucket Nut* won the Crime Writers Association Silver Dagger Award in 1992.

'Anna Lee' Novels

Dupe, Collins (London), 1980 . . . . £250/£25

ditto, Scribner's (New York), 1981 . . . £65/£10

Bad Company, Collins (London), 1982 . . £95/£15

ditto, Scribner's (New York), 1981 . . . £45/£10

Stalker, Collins (London), 1984 . . . . £35/£10

ditto, Scribner's (New York), 1984 . . . £20/£10

Head Case, Collins (London), 1985 . . . £25/£10

ditto, Scribner's (New York), 1985 . . . £15/£15

Under Contract, Collins (London), 1986 . . . £20/£5

ditto, Scribner's (New York), 1986 . . . £20/£5

Backhand, Chatto & Windus (London), 1991 . . £15/£5

ditto, Little, Brown (Boston), 1991 . . . . £15/£5

Other Novels

Rift, Collins (London), 1988 . . . . . £20/£5

ditto, Scribner's (New York), 1988 . . . . £15/£5

Bucket Nut, Chatto & Windus (London), 1992 . £15/£5

ditto, Doubleday (New York), 1993 . . . . £15/£5

Monkey Wrench, Chatto & Windus (London), 1994 . . . . £15/£5

ditto, Mysterious Press (New York), 1995 . . £10/£5

Musclebound, Bloomsbury (London), 1997 . . £10/£5

ditto, Mysterious Press (New York), 1997 . . £10/£5

Gimme More, Bloomsbury (London), 2000 (pbk) . . £5

Short Stories

Lucky Dip and Other Stories, Crippen & Landru (Norfolk, VA), 2003 (250 signed, numbered copies, with pamphlet 'White Knights and Giggling Bimbos') . . . £20/£5

ditto, Crippen & Landru (Norfolk, VA), 2003 (pbk) . £5

J.M. COETZEE
(b.1940)

J.M. Coetzee is an author and academic from South Africa who has become an Australian citizen. He is known as a recluse and did not attend the award ceremonies for either of the Booker Prizes he has won, for *Life & Times of Michael K* in 1983, and *Disgrace* in 1999. He won the 2003 Nobel Prize for Literature.

Fiction
Dusklands, Ravan Press (Johannesburg, SA), 1974 . . . . £200/£65
ditto, Secker & Warburg (London), 1982 . . . £225/£60
ditto, Penguin (New York), 1985 (wraps) £40
In the Heart of the Country, Secker & Warburg (London), 1977 . . . . £175/£45
ditto as *From the Heart of the Country*, Harper (New York), 1977 . . . . £35/£10
ditto, Ravan Press (Johannesburg, SA), 1978 (pbk) . £45
Waiting for the Barbarians, Secker & Warburg (London), 1980 . . . . £175/£45
ditto, Ravan Press (Johannesburg, SA), 1981 . . £200/£45
ditto, Penguin (New York), 1982 (pbk) £10
Life & Times of Michael K, Secker & Warburg (London), 1983 . . . . £45/£10
ditto, Ravan Press (Johannesburg, SA), 1983 . . £25/£10
ditto, Viking (New York), 1984 . . . . . £10/£5
Foe, Secker & Warburg (London), 1986 . . . £25/£10
ditto, Ravan Press (Johannesburg, SA), 1986 . . £25/£10
ditto, Viking (New York), 1987 . . . . . £10/£5
Age of Iron, Secker & Warburg (London), 1990 . £10/£5
ditto, Random House (New York), 1990 . . . £10/£5
The Master of Petersburg, Secker & Warburg (London), 1994 . . . . £10/£5
ditto, Viking (New York), 1994 . . . . . £10/£5
Disgrace, Secker & Warburg (London), 1999 . . £10/£5
ditto, Viking (New York), 1999 . . . . . £10/£5
Elizabeth Costello, Secker & Warburg (London), 2003 . . . . £10/£5
ditto, Viking (New York), 2003 . . . . . £10/£5
Slow Man, Secker & Warburg (London), 2005 . £10/£5
ditto, Secker & Warburg (London), 2005 (100 signed, numbered copies) £450
ditto, Viking (New York), 2005 . . . . . £10/£5
Diary of a Bad Year, Harvill Secker (London), 2007 £10/£5
ditto, Harvill Secker (London), 2007 (100 signed, numbered copies) £300
ditto, Viking (New York), 2008 . . . . . £10/£5

Fictionalised Autobiography
Boyhood: Scenes from Provincial Life, Secker & Warburg (London), 1997 . . . . £15/£5
ditto, Viking (New York), 1997 . . . . . £10/£5
Youth: Scenes from Provincial Life II, Secker & Warburg (London), 2002 . . . . £10/£5
ditto, Viking (New York), 2002 . . . . . £10/£5

Non-Fiction
White Writing: On the Culture of Letters in South Africa, Radix (South Africa), 1988 (pbk) £45
ditto, Yale Univ Press (New haven, CT), 1988. . £100/£25

Doubling the Point: Essays and Interviews, Harvard Univ Press (Cambridge, MA), 1992 . . . . . £30/£5
Giving Offense: Essays on Censorship, The Univ of Chicago Press 1996 . . . . £10/£5
The Lives of Animals, Princeton Univ Press (Princeton, NJ), 1999 . . . . £10/£5
Stranger Shores: Literary Essays, 1986-1999, Secker & Warburg (London), 2001 . . . . . . £10/£5
ditto, Viking (New York), 2001 . . . . . £10/£5
Inner Workings: Literary Essays, 2000-2005, Harvill Secker (London), 2007 . . . . . . £10/£5
ditto, Viking (New York), 2008 . . . . . £10/£5

Translation/Introduction
Landscape with Rowers: Poetry from the Netherlands, Princeton Univ Press (Princeton, NJ), 2004 . . £10/£5

SAMUEL TAYLOR COLERIDGE
(b.1772 d.1834)

Coleridge was an English poet, critic, and philosopher who was one of the founders of the Romantic Movement in England along with his friend William Wordsworth. With Wordsworth he co-published *Lyrical Ballads*, and he is perhaps best-known today for 'Kubla-Khan' and 'The Rime of the Ancient Mariner'.

Poetry and Drama
The Fall of Robespierre: An Historical Drama, Printed by Benjamin Flower for W.H. Lunn and J. and J. Merrill (Cambridge), 1794 (written in collaboration with Robert Southey) £1,000
Poems on Various Subjects, C.G. and J. Robinson (London) and Joseph Cottle (Bristol), 1796 . . . . £2,000
ditto, as *Poems*, C.G. and J. Robinson (London) and Joseph Cottle (Bristol), 1797 (revised and enlarged edition with poems by Charles Lamb and Charles Lloyd) . . £1,250
Ode on the Departing Year, Printed by N. Biggs and Sold by J. Parsons (Bristol), 1796 . . . . . . £1,500
Fears in Solitude: Written in 1798, during the Alarm of an Invasion; to Which Are Added, 'France: An Ode' and 'Frost at Midnight', J. Johnson (London), 1798 . £1,500
Remorse: A Tragedy, in Five Acts, Printed for W. Pople (London), 1813 . . . . £250
Christabel; Kubla Khan, A Vision; The Pains of Sleep, Printed for John Murray by William Bulmer and Co. (London), 1816 . . . . £2,000
Sibylline Leaves: A Collection of Poems, Rest Fenner (London), 1817 . . . . £600
Zapolya: A Christmas Tale in Two Parts; the Prelude Entitled 'The Usurper's Fortune' and the Sequel Entitled 'The Usurper's Fate', Rest Fenner (London), 1817 . £500
The Devil's Walk: A Poem; by Professor Porson; Edited with a Biographical Memoir and Notes by H. W. Montagu; Illustrated with Beautiful Engravings on Wood by Bonner and Slader, after the Designs of R. Cruikshank, Marsh and Miller (London), [1828?]. (originally written by Coleridge, this poem was enlarged by Robert Southey in 1827; wrongly attributed to Richard Porson) £200

ditto, as *The Devil's Walk: A Poem; by S.T. Coleridge, Esq. and Robert Southey, Esq., LL.D., &c...*, Alfred Miller (London), H. Constable (Edinburgh), Griffin (Glasgow), Milliken (Dublin), 1830 . . . . . . £200

Osorio: A Tragedy; as Originally Written in 1797 by Samuel Taylor Coleridge; with the Variorum Readings of **Remorse** *and a Monograph on the History of the Play in Its Earlier and Later Form by the Author of* **Tennysonia**, John Pearson (London), 1873 . . . . £75

Lyrical Ballads; with a Few Other Poems, Printed by Biggs and Cottle (Bristol) for T.N. Longman (London), 1798 (anonymous; written with William Wordsworth; contains four poems by Coleridge: 'The Rime of the Ancyent Marinere,' 'The Foster-Mother's Tale', 'Lewti,' and 'The Dungeon') £15,000

ditto, J. & A. Arch (London), 1798 (second issue of first edition in which 'The Nightingale' replaces 'Lewti') . .
. . . . £3,000

ditto, Printed by Biggs and Cottle (Bristol) for T.N. Longman and O. Rees(London), 1800 (2 vols; revised version, Wordsworth moved the retitled 'The Ancient Mariner: A Poet's Reverie' from the front of the book to the back and added 'Love'. Wordsworth's wrote his 'Preface' for this edition) £2,000

Collected Poetry & Drama

The Poetical Works of Samuel Taylor Coleridge; Including the Dramas of Wallenstein, Remorse, and Zapolya, William Pickering (London), 1828 (3 vols) . . £500

Poetical Works, Pickering (London), 1877 (4 vols; edited by Richard Herne Shepherd) £50

ditto, Pickering (London), 1877 (100 large paper sets) . £250

The Complete Poetical Works of Samuel Taylor Coleridge; Including Poems and Versions of Poems Now Published for the First Time, O.U.P. (Oxford, UK), 1912 (2 vols, edited by Ernest Hartley Coleridge) . . . £100

Prose

A Moral and Political Lecture, Delivered at Bristol, George Routh (Bristol), 1795 (wraps) £1,500

Conciones ad Populum; or, Addresses to the People, Printed for the Author (Bristol), 1795 . . £1,250

The Plot Discovered; or, An Address to the People, against Ministerial Treason, Printed for the Author (Bristol), 1795
. . . . £1,250

The Statesman's Manual; or, The Bible the Best Guide to Political Skill and Foresight: A Lay Sermon, Addressed to the Higher Classes of Society; with an Appendix, Containing Comments and Essays connected with the Study of the Inspired Writings, Gale and Fenner (London), 1816 . . . . £400

A Lay Sermon, Addressed to the Higher and Middle Classes, on the Existing Distresses and Discontents, Gale and Fenner (London), 1817 . . . . . £400

The Friend: A Series of Essays, in Three Volumes, To Aid in the Formation of Fixed Principles in Politics, Morals, and Religion; with Literary Amusements Interspersed, Rest Fenner (London), 1818 (3 vols; the significantly revised and enlarged version of the periodical by the same title) £300

Aids to Reflection in the Formation of a Manly Character on the Several Grounds of Prudence, Morality, and Religion; Illustrated by Select Passages from Our Elder

Divines, Especially from Archbishop Leighton, Taylor and Hessey (London), 1825 . . . . . . £500

Biographia Literaria; or, Biographical Sketches of My Literary Life and Opinions, Rest Fenner (London), 1817 (2 vols) £450

On the Constitution of the Church and State according to the Idea of Each; with Aids toward a Right Judgment on the Late Catholic Bill, Hurst, Chance and Co. (London), 1830 . . . . £250

Translation

The Death of Wallenstein: A Tragedy in Five Acts; Translated from the German of Friedrich Schiller by S.T. Coleridge, T.N. Longman and O. Rees (London), 1800 .
. . . . £500

The Piccolomini; or, The First Part of Wallenstein: A Tragedy in Five Acts, T.N. Longman and O. Rees (London), 1800 . . . . £500

Periodicals

The Watchman, Published by the Author (Bristol), 1 March 1796 - 13 May 1796 (10 parts) . . . £3,000 the set

The Friend: A Literary, Moral, and Political Weekly Paper, Excluding Personal and Party Politics and the Events of the Day, J. Brown (Penrith), Longman and Co., and Clement (London), 1 June 1809 - 15 March 1810 (28 parts numbered 1 to 27, the issue of 11 January 1810 being supernumerary) . . . . . £3,000 the set

Correspondence & Table Talk

Specimens of the Table Talk of the Late Samuel Taylor Coleridge, John Murray (London), 1835 (2 cols; edited by H.N. Coleridge) £150

Unpublished Letters of Samuel Taylor Coleridge, Including Certain Letters Republished from Original Sources, Constable (London), 1932 (two vols; edited by Earl Leslie Griggs) . . . . £65/£35

ditto, Yale Univ Press (New Haven), 1933 (2 vols) £65/£35

Collected Letters, Clarendon Press (Oxford), 1956-1971 (6 vols; edited by Earl Leslie Griggs) . . . £400/£250

Unpublished Letters from Samuel Taylor Coleridge to the Rev. John Prior Estlin, Folcroft Press (Folcroft, PA), 1970 (edited by Henry A. Bright) . . . . . £40/£25

Samuel Taylor Coleridge: Selected Letters, Clarendon Press (Oxford), 1987 (edited by H.J. Jackson). . . £25/£10

Coleridge: The Early Family Letters, Clarendon Press (Oxford), 1994 (edited by Ed. James Engell) . £25/£10

Collected Works

Works, William Pickering and Edward Moxon (London), 1835-1853 (22 vols; general editor Henry Nelson Coleridge) £2,000

The Complete Works of Samuel Taylor Coleridge; with an Introductory Essay upon His Philosophical and Theological Opinions, Harper & Brothers (New York), 1853 (7 vols; edited by William G. T. Shedd) . . £200

The Collected Works of Samuel Taylor Coleridge, Princeton Univ Press (Princeton, NJ), 1969-2002 (16 vols; general editor Kathleen Coburn) £250

EOIN COLFER
(b.1965)

Eoin Colfer is an Irish author of children's books, most notably the Artemis Fowl series. His books often have recurring themes, although, like Terry Pratchett's 'Discworld' books, the books can be read without reference to others.

Artemis Fowl Books
Artemis Fowl, Viking (London), 2001 (holographic d/w)   .
.   .   .   .   £20/£5
ditto, Viking (London), 2001 (variant non-holographic d/w)
.   .   .   .   £50/£5
ditto, Hyperion (New York), 2001   .   .   .   £15/£5
The Arctic Incident, Puffin (London), 2002   .   £10/£5
ditto, Hyperion (New York), 2002   .   .   .   £10/£5
The Eternity Code, Puffin (London), 2003   .   £10/£5
ditto, Hyperion (New York), 2003   .   .   .   £10/£5
The Opal Deception, Puffin (London), 2005   .   £10/£5
ditto, Hyperion (New York), 2005   .   .   .   £10/£5
The Lost Colony, Puffin (London), 2006 .   .   £10/£5
ditto, Hyperion (New York), 2006   .   .   .   £10/£5
The Time Paradox, Puffin (London), 2008   .   £10/£5
ditto, Hyperion (New York), 2008   .   .   .   £10/£5

Artemis Fowl Companion Books
The Seventh Dwarf, Puffin (London), 2004 (pbk) .   .   £5
The Artemis Fowl Files, Puffin (London), 2004 (hardback;
no d/w) £10
ditto, Hyperion (New York), 2004 (hardback; no d/w)   £10
Artemis Fowl: The Graphic Novel, Puffin (London), 2007
(pbk) £5
ditto, Hyperion (New York), 2007   .   .   .   £10/£5

Ed Books
Ed's Funny Feet, O'Brien Press (Dublin), 2000   .   .   £5
Ed's Bed, O'Brien Press (Dublin), 2001   .   .   .   £5

Legend of... Books
Legend of Spud Murphy, Puffin, 2004   .   .   .   £10/£5
ditto, Hyperion (New York), 2004   .   .   .   £10/£5
Legend of Captain Crow's Teeth, Puffin, 2006   .   £10/£5
ditto, Hyperion (New York), 2006   .   .   .   £10/£5
Legend of the Worst Boy in the World, Puffin, 2007   £10/£5
ditto, Hyperion (New York), 2007   .   .   .   £10/£5

Other Books
Benny and Omar, O'Brien Press (Dublin), 1998 (pbk).   £65
ditto, Hyperion (New York), 2007   .   .   .   £10/£5
Benny and Babe, O'Brien Press (Dublin), 1999 (pbk) .   £45
ditto, Hyperion (New York), 2007   .   .   .   £10/£5
The Wish List, O'Brien Press (Dublin), 2000 .   .   £45
ditto, Hyperion (New York), 2003   .   .   .   £10/£5
The Supernaturalist, Puffin, 2004   .   .   .   £10/£5
ditto, Hyperion (New York), 2004   .   .   .   £10/£5
Half Moon Investigations, Puffin, 2006   .   .   £10/£5
ditto, Hyperion (New York), 2006   .   .   .   £10/£5
Airman, Puffin, 2008   .   .   .   .   .   £10/£5
ditto, Hyperion (New York), 2008   .   .   .   £10/£5

JOHN COLLIER
(b.1901 d.1980)

A British author who spent much of his life in Hollywood, Collier is perhaps best known for his clever short fantasies and stories with a twist-in-the-tail. An elegant writer, he mixes humour and horror in a way reminiscent of Saki and Roald Dahl, although he was perhaps more interested in the supernatural than they were. The novel *His Monkey Wife* is very highly regarded.

Short Stories
An Epistle to a Friend, Ulysses Press (London), 1932 (99
signed copies; green vellum wraps).   .   .   .   £150
ditto, Ulysses Press (London), 1932 (7 signed copies, each
containing an original page of manuscript)   .   .   £600
Green Thoughts, William Jackson (London), 1932 (550
signed copies)   .   .   .   .   £60/£25
The Devil and All, Nonesuch Press (London), 1934 (1,000
signed, numbered copies; glassine and foil d/w) . £100/£45
Variation on a Theme, Grayson & Grayson (London), 1935
(285 signed copies)   .   .   .   .   .   £100/£50
Witch's Money, Viking (New York), 1940 (350 signed
copies, tissue d/w)   .   .   .   .   .   £100/£75
Presenting Moonshine, Viking (New York), 1941.   £75/£25
ditto, Macmillan (London), 1941   .   .   .   £75/£25
The Touch of Nutmeg, and More Unlikely Stories, The
Readers Club (New York), 1943   .   .   .   £30/£10
Fancies and Goodnights, Doubleday (New York), 1951   .
.   .   .   .   £50/£15
ditto, as *Of Demons and Darkness*, Corgi (London), 1965
(abridged; wraps). £5
Pictures in the Fire, Hart Davis (London), 1958   . £35/£10

Novels
His Monkey Wife; or, Married to a Chimp, Peter Davies
(London), 1930   .   .   .   .   .   .   £250/£75
ditto, Appleton (New York), 1931   .   .   .   £175/£45
No Traveller Returns, White Owl Press (London), 1931
(185 copies on handmade paper of 210 signed, numbered
copies) £125
ditto, White Owl Press (London), 1931 (25 copies on
Japanese vellum of 210 signed, numbered copies)   . £250
Tom's A-Cold: A Tale, Macmillan (London), 1933 £200/£45
ditto, as *Full Circle*, Appleton (New York), 1933   . £150/£35
Defy the Foul Fiend; or, The Misadventures of a Heart,
Macmillan (London), 1934   .   .   .   .   £75/£25
ditto, Knopf (New York), 1934   .   .   .   .   £40/£15

Collected Edition
The John Collier Reader, Knopf (New York), 1972 £25/£10
ditto, Souvenir Press (London), 1975.   .   .   £20/£5

Poetry
Gemini, Ulysses Press (London), 1931 (185 signed copies) .
.   .   .   .   £125
ditto, Ulysses Press (London), 1931 (15 signed copies, each
containing an original page of manuscript)   .   .   £600
ditto, Harmsworth (London), 1931 (glassine d/w)   . £45/£30

Others
*Just The Other Day: An Informal History of Great Britain
Since the War*, Hamish Hamilton (London), 1932 (with
Iain Lang)   .   .   .   .   £35/£10

ditto, Harper (New York), 1932 . . . . £30/£10
Milton's Paradise Lost: Screenplay for Cinema of the Mind, Knopf (New York), 1973 . . . . £30/£10

WILKIE COLLINS
(b.1824 d.1889)

Collins was a popular and skilful author of sensation fiction, viewed today as a precursor of modern detective and suspense thrillers. He wrote effectively on issues relating to the role of women and class in Victorian society. As with many of his contemporaries, Collins first published most of his novels as serials in magazines.

Novels
Antonina, or the Fall of Rome, Bentley (London), 1850 (3 vols) £1,250
Basil: A Story of Modern Life, Bentley (London), 1852 (3 vols) £750
ditto, Appleton (New York), 1853 (1 vol). . . £500
ditto, as *The Crossed Path; or, Basil*, Peterson (Philadelphia, PA), 1861 (1 vol). . . . £200
Hide and Seek, Bentley (London), 1854 (3 vols) . £800
ditto, Dick (New York), 1858 (1 vol). . . . £400
The Dead Secret, Bradbury and Evans (London), 1857 (2 vols) £900
ditto, Miller & Curtis (New York), 1857 . . . £400
The Woman in White, Harper (New York), 1860 (1 vol, brown cloth; first state binding with woman stamped in white on spine). £3,250
ditto, Harper (New York), 1860 (1 vol, brown cloth; second state binding with woman stamped in blind on spine). . £2,000
ditto, Sampson Low (London), 1860 (3 vols, first issue with ads at end of vol 3 dated May 1, 1860) . . . £8,500
ditto, Sampson Low (London), 1860 (3 vols, later issues with ads at end of vol 3 dated August 1, 1860) . £6,000
ditto, Sampson Low (London), 1861 (1 vol) . . £600
No Name, Sampson Low (London), 1862 (3 vols). £1,500
ditto, Harper (New York), 1863 (1 vol) . . . £250
ditto, Gardner A. Fuller (Boston), 1863 (2 vols) . £300
Armadale, Smith, Elder & Co. (London), 1866 (2 vols) £850
ditto, Harper (New York), 1866 (1 vol) . . . £125
The Moonstone, Tinsley Brothers (London), 1868 (3 vols, first issue with 'treachesrouly' misspelled on line 24, p. 129 in Vol. II, and p. 10 and 11 transposed in Vol. I.). £8,500
ditto, Harper (New York), 1868 (1 vol) . . . £400
Man and Wife, F.S. Ellis (London), 1870 (3 vols) . £1,500
ditto, Harper (New York), 1870 (1 vol) . . . £200
Poor Miss Finch, Bentley (London), 1872 (3 vols) . £800
ditto, Harper (New York), 1872 (1 vol) . . . £100
The New Magdalen, Bentley (London), 1873 (2 vols) £800
ditto, Harper (New York), 1873 (1 vol) . . . £150
The Law and the Lady, Chatto & Windus (London), 1875 (3 vols) £750
ditto, Harper (New York), 1875 (1 vol, illustrated wraps) £300
ditto, Harper (New York), 1875 (1 vol) . . . £75
The Two Destinies, Chatto & Windus (London), 1876 (2 vols) £750

ditto, Harper (New York), 1876 (1 vol) . . . £100
My Lady's Money and *Percy and the Prophet*, Tauchnitz (Leipzig), 1877 (1 vol; pbk) £75
My Lady's Money. An Episode in the Life of a Young Girl, Harper (New York), 1878 (1 vol; pbk) . . . £175
The Haunted Hotel and *My Lady's Money*, Tauchnitz (Leipzig), 1878 (1 vol; pbk) £75
ditto, Chatto & Windus (London), 1879 [November, 1878] (2 vols) £800
ditto, Munro (New York), 1878 (1 vol) . . . £200
A Rogue's Life, Bentley (London), 1879 . . . £400
ditto, Appleton (New York), 1879 (1 vol). . . £75
The Fallen Leaves, Chatto & Windus (London), 1879 (3 vols) £850
ditto, Rose Belford (Chicago), 1879 (1 vol) . . £200
Jezebel's Daughter, Munro (New York), 1880 (1 vol; pbk). . £200
ditto, Chatto & Windus (London), 1880 (3 vols) . £750
The Black Robe, Chatto & Windus (London), 1881 (3 vols) . £750
ditto, Belford (Chicago), 1881 (1 vol) . . . £175
Heart and Science, Chatto & Windus (London), 1883 (3 vols) £750
ditto, Belford Clarke (Chicago), 1883 (1 vol) . . £100
'I Say No', Harper (New York), 1884 (1 vol) . . £200
ditto, Chatto & Windus (London), 1884 (3 vols) . £650
The Evil Genius, Harper (New York), 1886 (1 vol) . £200
ditto, Chatto & Windus (London), 1886 (3 vols) . £400
The Guilty River, Arrowsmith (Bristol and London), 1886 . £500
ditto, Harper (New York), 1886 (1 vol) . . . £75
The Legacy of Cain, Lovell (New York), 1888 (1 vol) . £100
ditto, Chatto & Windus (London), 1889 [November, 1888] (3 vols) £450
Blind Love, Chatto & Windus (London), 1890 (3 vols, completed by Walter Besant) £350
ditto, Appleton (New York), 1890 (1 vol). . . £65
Iolani; or, Tahiti As It Was: A Romance, Princeton Univ Press (Princeton, NJ), 1999 . . . . . £10/£5

Short Stories
Mr Wray's Cash-Box; or, the Mask and the Mystery, Bentley (London), 1852 [December, 1851] (1 vol) . £650
ditto, as *The Stolen Mask; or The Mysterious Cash Box*, Peterson (Philadelphia, PA), 1862 (1 vol) . . £250
After Dark, Smith & Elder (London), 1856 (2 vols) . £850
ditto, Dick (New York), 1856 (1 vol). . . . £400
The Queen of Hearts, Hurst & Blackett (London), 1859 (3 vols) £2,000
ditto, Harper (New York), 1859 (1 vol) . . . £250
A Plot in Private Life and Other Tales, Tauchnitz (Leipzig), 1859 (1 vol; wraps) £125
Miss or Mrs? and Other Stories, Tauchnitz (Leipzig), 1872 (1 vol; wraps) £75
ditto, Peterson (Philadelphia, PA), 1872 (1 vol) . £200
ditto, Bentley (London), 1873 . . . . . £500
The Dead Alive, Shepherd & Gill (Boston), 1874 [1873] . £125
The Frozen Deep and Other Tales, Bentley (London), 1874 (2 vols) £1,250
ditto, Gill (Boston), 1875 (1 vol). £200
The Ghost's Touch, Harper (New York), 1885 (1 vol) . £100
Little Novels, Chatto & Windus (London), 1887 (3 vols) . £750

Other Titles
Memoirs of the Life of William Collins, R.A., Longmans
(London), 1848 (2 vols) £1,000
***Rambles Beyond Railways: Notes in Cornwall Taken A-
Foot***, Bentley (London), 1851 .   .   .   .   .£450
My Miscellanies, Sampson Low (London), 1863 (2 vols) .
.   .   .   .   £1,000
ditto, Harper (New York), 1874 (1 vol) .   .   .£125
The Lazy Tour of Two Idle Apprentices, Chapman & Hall
(London), 1890 (in collaboration with Charles Dickens) .
.   .   .   .£200

IVY COMPTON-BURNETT
(b.1892 d.1969)

Compton-Burnett was the author of incisive, if somewhat
claustrophobic, English domestic novels. Her rather proper
Edwardian stories are told principally through the dialogue
between characters. They demand the continuous attention
of the reader as important information can often be
imparted casually in the middle of a sentence.

Novels
Dolores, William Blackwood (Edinburgh/London), 1911 .
.   .   .   .£650
Pastors and Masters, A Study, Heath Cranton (London),
1925 .   .   .   .£125/£35
Brothers and Sisters, Heath Cranton (London), 1929 .   .
.   .   .   .   £125/£75
ditto, Zero Press (New York), 1956 (with introductory
pamphlet) .   .   .   .£30/£10
Men and Wives, Heinemann (London), 1931 . £125/£40
ditto, Harcourt Brace (New York), [1939] .   £65/£20
More Women than Men, Heinemann (London), 1933 .   .
.   .   .   .£125/£40
ditto, Simon & Schuster (New York), 1965 (with *A Family
and Its Fortune*) .   .   .   .   .   .   £20/£5
A House and its Head, Heinemann (London), 1935 £125/£40
Daughters and Sons, Gollancz (London), 1937 . £100/£25
A Family and its Fortune, Gollancz (London), 1939 .
.   .   .   .   £75/£25
Parents and Children, Gollancz (London), 1941 . £65/£25
Elders and Betters, Gollancz (London), 1944 .   . £60/£20
Manservant and Maidservant, Gollancz (London), 1947 .
.   .   .   .   £45/£10
ditto, as ***Bullivant and the Lambs***, Knopf (New York), 1948
.   .   .   .   £40/£10
Two Worlds and their Ways, Gollancz (London), 1949 .
.   .   .   .   £40/£10
ditto, Knopf (New York), 1949 .   .   .   . £30/£10
Darkness and Day, Gollancz (London), 1951 .   . £30/£10
ditto, Knopf (New York), 1951 .   .   .   . £30/£10
The Present and the Past, Gollancz (London), 1953 £25/£5
ditto, Messner (New York), 1953 .   .   . £25/£5
Mother and Son, Gollancz (London), 1955 .   . £25/£5
ditto, Messner (New York), 1955 .   .   . £25/£5
A Father and his Fate, Gollancz (London), 1957 . £25/£5
ditto, Messner (New York), 1958 .   .   . £25/£5
A Heritage and its History, Gollancz (London), 1959 £25/£5
ditto, Simon & Schuster (New York), 1960 .   . £20/£5

The Mighty and their Fall, Gollancz (London), 1961 £20/£5
ditto, Simon & Schuster (New York), 1962 .   . £20/£5
A God and His Gifts, Gollancz (London), 1963 . £20/£5
ditto, Simon & Schuster (New York), 1964 .   . £20/£5
The Last and the First, Gollancz (London), 1971 . £15/£5
ditto, Knopf (New York), 1971 .   .   .   . £10/£5
Collected Works, Gollancz (London), 1972 (deluxe edition
of 500 sets in 19 vols).   .   .   .   . £450/£125

MICHAEL CONNELLY
(b.1956)

Michael Connelly is an American author of detective
novels, many featuring Hieronymus 'Harry' Bosch, a
LAPD detective. The first Bosch book, *The Black Echo*,
won the Mystery Writers of America's Edgar Award for
Best First Novel of 1992. Connelly has also written for
television.

Harry Bosch Novels
The Black Echo, Little, Brown (Boston, MA), 1992   .   .
.   .   .   .£100/£10
ditto, Headline (London), 1992 .   .   . £1,500/£200
The Black Ice, Little, Brown (Boston, MA), 1993 . £75/£10
ditto, Orion (London), 1993.   .   .   .   .£150/£20
The Concrete Blonde, Little, Brown (Boston, MA), 1994 .
.   .   .   .   £20/£5
ditto, Orion (London), 1994.   .   .   .   .£250/£20
The Last Coyote, Little, Brown (Boston, MA), 1995 £20/£5
ditto, Orion (London), 1995.   .   .   .   .£150/£10
Trunk Music, Orion (London), 1997.   .   . £20/£5
ditto, Little, Brown (New York), 1997 .   . £20/£5
Angels Flight, Orion (London), 1999 .   . £15/£5
ditto, Little, Brown (Boston, MA), 1999 .   . £15/£5
ditto, Scorpion Press (Blakeney, Glos), 1999 (115 signed,
numbered copies) £150
A Darkness More Than Night, B.E. Trice (New Orleans,
LA), 2001 (100 signed, numbered copies; slipcase) .   .
.   .   .   .£175/£125
ditto, B.E. Trice (New Orleans, LA), 2001 (400 signed,
numbered copies; slipcase) .   .   .   . £75/£50
ditto, Little, Brown (Boston, MA), 2001 .   . £15/£5
ditto, Orion (London), 2001.   .   .   .   . £15/£5
City of Bones, McMillan (New York), 2002 (104 signed,
lettered copies; slipcase) .   .   .   .   .£100/£75
ditto, McMillan (New York), 2002 (400 signed, numbered
copies; slipcase) .   .   .   .   . £50/£30
ditto, Little, Brown (Boston, MA), 2002 .   . £15/£5
ditto, Orion (London), 2002.   .   .   .   . £15/£5
Lost Light, B.E. Trice (New Orleans, LA), 2003 (300 signed
copies with CD; slipcase) .   .   .   . £75/£50
ditto, B.E. Trice (New Orleans, LA), 2003 (100 deluxe
signed copies with CD; slipcase) .   .   . £125/£85
ditto, Little, Brown (Boston, MA), 2003 .   . £15/£5
ditto, Orion (London), 2003.   .   .   .   . £15/£5
The Narrows, McMillan (New York), 2004 (156 signed,
lettered copies; slipcase) .   .   .   .   .£100/£75
ditto, McMillan (New York), 2004 (350 signed, numbered
copies; slipcase) .   .   .   .   . £50/£35
ditto, Little, Brown (New York), 2004 .   . £15/£5
ditto, Orion (London), 2004.   .   .   .   . £15/£5

The Closers, McMillan (New York), 2005 (40 signed, lettered copies; slipcase) . . . . £150/£125
ditto, McMillan (New York), 2005 (156 signed, numbered copies; slipcase) . . . . . . £100/£75
ditto, McMillan (New York), 2005 (300 signed, numbered copies; slipcase) . . . . . . £65/£45
ditto, Little, Brown (New York), 2005 . . £15/£5
ditto, Headline (London), 2005 . . . . £15/£5
Echo Park, McMillan (New York), 2006 (40 signed, lettered copies; slipcase) . . . . . £150/£125
ditto, McMillan (New York), 2006 (156 signed, numbered copies; slipcase) . . . . . . £100/£75
ditto, McMillan (New York), 2006 (300 signed, numbered copies; slipcase) . . . . . . £65/£45
ditto, Little, Brown (New York), 2006 . . £10/£5
ditto, Orion (London), 2006 . . . . . £10/£5
The Overlook, SCV Publishing (Los Angeles, CA), 2007 (100 signed, numbered copies; slipcase) . £125/£100
ditto, Little, Brown (New York), 2007 . . £10/£5
ditto, Orion (London), 2007 . . . . . £10/£5
The Brass Verdict, SCV Publishing (Los Angeles, CA), 2008 (200 signed, numbered copies; slipcase) £125/£100
ditto, Little, Brown (New York), 2008 . . £10/£5
ditto, Orion (London), 2008 . . . . . £10/£5
Nine Dragons, SCV Publishing (Los Angeles, CA), 2009 (150 signed, numbered copies; slipcase) . £125/£100
ditto, SCV Publishing (Los Angeles, CA), 2009 (50 deluxe signed, numbered copies; slipcase) . . £200/£150
ditto, Little, Brown (New York), 2009 . . £10/£5
ditto, Orion (London), 2009 . . . . . £10/£5

Other Novels
The Poet, Little, Brown (New York), 1996 . . £35/£5
ditto, Headline (Orion), 1996 . . . . £30/£5
ditto, Steven C. Vascik (Los Angeles, CA), 2004 (125 signed copies; slipcase) . . . . . £250/£200
Blood Work, McMillan (New York), 1997 (300 signed, numbered copies; slipcase) . . . . £750/£45
ditto, McMillan (New York), 1997 (100 signed, numbered copies; slipcase) . . . . . £125/£100
ditto, McMillan (New York), 1997 (26 signed, numbered copies; slipcase) . . . . . £350/£300
ditto, Little, Brown (New York), 1998 . . £15/£5
ditto, Headline (London), 1998 . . . . £15/£5
Void Moon, McMillan (New York), 1999 (400 signed, numbered copies; slipcase) . . . . £75/£45
ditto, McMillan (New York), 1999 (100 signed, numbered copies; slipcase) . . . . . £125/£100
ditto, Little, Brown (New York), 2000 . . £15/£5
ditto, Headline (London), 2000 . . . . £15/£5
Chasing The Dime, McMillan (New York), 2002 (104 signed, lettered copies; slipcase) . . . £100/£75
ditto, McMillan (New York), 2002 (400 signed, numbered copies; slipcase) . . . . . £65/£50
ditto, Little, Brown (New York), 2002 . . £15/£5
ditto, Headline (London), 2002 . . . . £15/£5
The Lincoln Lawyer, SCV Publishing (Los Angeles, CA), 2005 (75 signed copies numbered in red; slipcase) . . £300/£250
ditto, SCV Publishing (Los Angeles, CA), 2005 (275 signed copies numbered in black; slipcase) . . £125/£100
ditto, Little, Brown (New York), 2005 . . £15/£5
ditto, Orion (London), 2005 . . . . . £15/£5

The Scarecrow, McMillan (New York), 2009 (156 signed, lettered copies; slipcase) . . . . £125/£100
ditto, McMillan (New York), 2009 (300 signed, numbered copies; slipcase) . . . . . . £65/£50
ditto, Little, Brown (New York), 2009 . . . £10/£5
ditto, Headline (London), 2009 . . . . . £10/£5

Non-Fiction
Crime Beat: Selected Journalism 1984-1992, SCV Publishing (Los Angeles, CA), 2004 (150 signed, numbered copies; slipcase) . . . . . £100/£75
ditto, SCV Publishing (Los Angeles, CA), 2004 . £15/£5
ditto, as *Crime Beat: A Decade of Covering Cops and Killers*, Little, Brown (New York), 2006 . . £10/£5
ditto, Orion (London), 2006 . . . . . . £10/£5

CYRIL CONNOLLY
(b.1903 d.1974)

Principally a critic and literary editor, Connolly was educated at the same schools in the same year as George Orwell, who remained a life-long friend. Connolly founded the influential literary magazine *Horizon*, which he co-edited with Stephen Spender and Peter Watson. He was also literary editor of the *Observer*, and, after 1950, chief book reviewer for *The Sunday Times*.

The Rock Pool, Obelisk Press (Paris), 1936 (pbk) . . £275
ditto, Scribner's (New York), 1936 . . . . £150/£20
ditto, Hamish Hamilton (London), 1947 . . . £45/£10
Enemies of Promise, Routledge (London), 1938 . £200/£35
ditto, Little, Brown (Boston), 1939 . . £100/£25
The Unquiet Grave, Horizon (London), 1944 (500 numbered hardback copies of 1,000, pseud 'Palinurus') . £200/£65
ditto, Horizon (London), 1944 (500 numbered copies of 1,000; wraps) £125
ditto, Hamish Hamilton (London), [1945] (new edition) .
. . . . £20/£5
ditto, Harper (New York), 1945 (new edition) . . £30/£5
The Condemned Playground, Routledge (London), [1945].
. . . . £25/£10
ditto, Macmillan (New York), 1946 . . . . £15/£5
The Missing Diplomats, Queen Anne Press (London), 1952 (wraps, in d/w) . . . . £40/£20
Ideas and Places, Weidenfeld & Nicolson (London), 1953 .
. . . . £25/£10
ditto, Harper (New York), 1953 . . . . . £25/£10
The Golden Horizon, Weidenfeld & Nicolson (London), 1953 . . . . £15/£5
ditto, University Books (New York), 1955 . . £10/£5
Les Pavillons, Macmillan (New York), 1962 (with Jerome Zerbe) . . . . £25/£10
ditto, Hamish Hamilton (London), 1962 . . . £25/£10
Previous Convictions, Hamish Hamilton (London), 1963 .
. . . . £20/£10
ditto, Harper (New York), 1964 . . . . . £15/£5
The Modern Movement: 100 Key Books from England, France and America, 1880-1950, Deutsch/Hamilton (London), 1965 . . . . £30/£10
ditto, Atheneum (New York), 1966 . . . . £30/£10
The Evening Colonnade, Bruce & Watson (London), 1973.
. . . . £10/£5

ditto, Harcourt Brace (New York), 1975 . . . £10/£5
A Romantic Friendship: The Letters of Cyril Connolly to
Noel Blakiston, Constable (London), 1975 . . £15/£5
Journal and Memoir, Collins (London), 1983 . £10/£5
ditto, Ticknor & Fields (New York), 1984 . £10/£5
Shade Those Laurels, Bellew (London), 1990 . £10/£5
ditto, Pantheon (New York), 1991 . . . . £10/£5

JOSEPH CONRAD

(b.1857 d.1924)

Of Polish origin, Conrad served at sea for 20 years before
coming to England to write, becoming a naturalised British
subject in 1886. 'Heart of Darkness' was first published in
Youth: A Narrative, and Other Stories in 1902. His writing
is seen to connect the Realist literary tradition of writers
such as Dickens and Dostoevsky with the emergent
Modernism of the 20th century.

Novels

Almayer's Folly: A Story of an Eastern River, T. Fisher
Unwin (London), 1895 (dark green cloth; first issue, with
'e' omitted from 'generosity' at bottom of page 110) . £600
ditto, Macmillan (New York), 1895 (spine reads 'Macmillan
& Co') £500
ditto, Macmillan (New York), 1895 (spine reads 'The
Macmillan Company') £300
An Outcast of the Islands, T. Fisher Unwin (London), 1896
('this' for 'their' on line 31, p.26) £600
ditto, Appleton (New York), 1896 (pbk) . . .£250
ditto, Appleton (New York), 1896 (green cloth) . £150
ditto, Appleton (New York), 1896 (deluxe edition in 3/4 roan
and marbled boards) £400
The Children of the Sea: A Tale of the Forecastle, Dodd,
Mead (New York), 1897 . . . . . .£300
ditto, as ***The Nigger of the Narcissus: A Tale of the***
Forecastle, Heinemann (London), August 1898 (copyright
edition, 7 copies; pbk) £4,000
ditto, Heinemann (London), 1898 (first issue: 'H' in
'Heinemann (London)' on spine 5.5mm, 16 pages of
advertisements) £350
ditto, Heinemann (London), 1898 (second issue: 'Heinemann
(London)' on spine 3mm, 16 pages of advertisements)
. . . .£250
ditto, Heinemann (London), 1898 (second issue: 32 pages of
advertisements) £200
Lord Jim: A Tale, William Blackwood (Edinburgh/London),
1900 . . . . £2,000
ditto, as ***Lord Jim: A Romance***, Doubleday (New York),
1900 (copyright notice 1900) £600
ditto, Doubleday (New York), 1900 (copyright notice 1899
and 1900) £300
Nostromo: A Tale of the Seaboard, Harper (London), 1904
. . . .£600
ditto, Harper (New York), 1904 . . . . . £75
The Secret Agent: A Simple Tale, Methuen (London), 1907
(red cloth, 40 pages of adverts dated September) . £1,000
ditto, Harper (New York), 1907 . . . . .£150
Under Western Eyes, Methuen (London), 1911 . £250
ditto, Harper (New York), 1911 . . . . . £75
Chance: A Tale in Two Parts, Methuen (London), 1913
(first issue with 'First published in 1913' on verso of

integral title page, 'Methven' on spine, 32 page catalogue)
. . . . £1,500
ditto, Methuen (London), 1914 ('Methuen' on spine, no
catalogue) £1,000
ditto, Methuen (London), 1914 ('Methuen' on spine, with
'First published in 1914' on tipped-in page) . . .£500
ditto, Doubleday (New York), 1913 (150 copyright copies) .
. . . .£500
ditto, Doubleday (New York), 1914 . . . . .£100
Victory: An Island Tale, Doubleday (New York), 1915 £75
ditto, Methuen (London), 1915 . . . . . £65
The Shadow-Line: A Confession, Dent (London), 1917 £65
ditto, Doubleday (New York), 1917 . . . . . £50
The Arrow of Gold: A Story Between Two Notes,
Doubleday (New York), 1919 ('credentials and apparently'
in line 15, p.5) £35
ditto, Doubleday (New York), 1919 ('credentials and who' in
line 15, p.5) £25
ditto, T. Fisher Unwin (London), 1919 . . . £45
The Rescue: A Romance of the Shallows, Doubleday (New
York), 1920 ($1.90 d/w) . . . . . £200/£25
ditto, Doubleday (New York), 1920 ($2.00 d/w) . £150/£25
ditto, Dent (London), 1920 (40 copies for private
distribution) £1,000
ditto, Dent (London), 1920 (trade edition, green cloth) . .
. . . . £150/£25
The Rover, Doubleday (New York), 1923 (377 signed
copies, slipcase) . . . . . £500/£350
ditto, Doubleday (New York), 1923 . . .£100/£15
ditto, T. Fisher Unwin (London), 1923 . . .£100/£15
Suspense: A Napoleonic Novel, Dent (London), 1925 .
. . . . £150/£25
ditto, Doubleday (New York), 1925 (limited edition of 377
copies, glassine d/w, slipcase) . . . £175/£150
ditto, Doubleday (New York), 1925 . . .£125/£25
The Sisters, Crosby Gaige (New York), 1928 (926 copies) .
. . . . £75

Books Written with Ford Madox Hueffer/Ford

The Inheritors: An Extravagant Story, McClure, Phillips &
Co. (New York), 1901 (dedicated to Boys & Christina) .
. . . . £3,000
ditto, McClure, Phillips & Co. (New York), 1901 (dedicated
to Borys & Christina) £200
ditto, Heinemann (London), 1901 (top edge untrimmed, 32
pages adverts, publisher's device on spine with initials) .
. . . .£600
ditto, Heinemann (London), 1901 (top edge trimmed, no
catalogue, publisher's device on spine with initials) .£350
ditto, Heinemann (London), 1901 (without initials in
publisher's device) £300
ditto, Heinemann (London), 1901 (remainder issue, non-
pictorial cloth) £150
Romance, Smith Elder (London), 1903 . . .£150
ditto, McClure (New York), 1904 . . . .£125
The Nature of a Crime, Duckworth (London), 1924 . .
. . . . £125/£25
ditto, Doubleday (New York), 1924 . . .£125/£25

Short Stories

Tales of Unrest, Scribner's (New York), 1898 . £250
ditto, T. Fisher Unwin (London), 1898 (top edge gilt) .£300
ditto, T. Fisher Unwin (London), 1898 . . .£225

Youth: A Narrative, and Two Other Stories, William
 Blackwood (Edinburgh/London), 1902 (adverts dated
 '10/02') £200
ditto, William Blackwood (Edinburgh/London), 1902
 (adverts dated '11/02') £175
ditto, McClure, Phillips & Co. (New York), 1903 .   . £200
Typhoon, Putnam/Knickerbocker Press (New York), 1902
 (green cloth) £400
ditto, Putnam/Knickerbocker Press (New York), 1902
 (maroon cloth) £350
ditto, as *Typhoon and Other Stories*, Heinemann (London),
 1903 (grey cloth) £150
A Set of Six, Methuen (London), 1908 (first issue, adverts
 dated Feb. 1908, list of works including 'The Secret Agent
 (with Ford M. Hueffer)') £600
ditto, Methuen (London), 1908 (second issue, adverts dated
 Feb. 1908, list of works including 'The Secret Agent' with
 'FORD M. HUEFFER' below) £250
ditto, Methuen (London), 1908 (third issue, adverts dated
 June. 1908) £150
ditto, Doubleday (New York), 1915 .   .   . £100
The Point of Honor: A Military Tale, McClure (New York),
 1908 (first issue with McClure at base of spine) .   . £145
 ditto, McClure (New York), 1908 (second issue with
 Doubleday, Page & Co at base of spine)   .   . £50
'Twixt Land and Sea, Dent (London), 1912 (first issue with
 'Secret' instead of 'Seven' on front cover)   . £2,000
ditto, Dent (London), 1912 (second issue with 'Seven'
 stamped over erased 'Secret') £200
ditto, Dent (London), 1912 (third issue with front cover
 corrected) £100
ditto, Hodder & Stoughton/Doran (New York), 1912 . £100
Within the Tides: Tales, Dent (London), 1915 .   . £150
ditto, Doubleday (New York), 1916 .   .   . £100
Tales of Hearsay, T. Fisher Unwin (London), 1925   .   .
  .   .   .   . £150/£20
ditto, Doubleday (New York), 1925 .   .   . £125/£20

Plays

One Day More: A Play in One Act, privately printed,
 Clement Shorter (London), 1917 (25 copies; wraps) £1,500
ditto, Beaumont Press (London), 1919 (250 copies)   . £150
ditto, Beaumont Press (London), 1919 (24 signed copies on
 Japanese vellum) £1,500
ditto, Doubleday (New York), 1920 (377 signed, numbered
 copies) £250
The Secret Agent: Drama in Four Acts, Goulden
 (Canterbury, Kent), 1921 (50 copies, wraps) .   . £1,500
ditto, as *The Secret Agent: A Drama in Three Acts*, T.
 Werner Laurie (London), 1923 (printed for subscribers
 only, 1,000 signed and numbered copies)   . £450/£200
Laughing Anne, Morland Press, 1923 (200 signed,
 numbered copies bound in full vellum; no d/w; slipcase) .
  .   .   .   . £400
Laughing Anne and *One More Day*, John Castle (London),
 1924   .   .   .   . £75/£15
ditto, Doubleday (New York), 1925 .   .   . £35/£5
Three Plays, Methuen (London), 1934 (contains 'One Day
 More', 'The Secret Agent' and 'Laughing Anne') £35/£10

Miscellaneous

The Nigger of the Narcissus: A Preface, privately printed,
 1902 (100 copies; wraps) £2,000

The Mirror of the Sea: Memories and Impressions,
 Methuen (London), [1906] £200
ditto, Harper (New York), 1906 .   .   .   . £100
Some Reminiscences, Eveleigh Nash (London), 1912 . £100
ditto, as *A Personal Record*, Harper (New York), 1912 £100
Notes on Life and Letters, Dent (London), 1921 (33 copies,
 privately printed) £1,500
ditto, Dent (London), 1921 ('S' and 'a' missing from 'Sea',
 line 8 of table of contents) .   .   .   . £175/£45
ditto, Dent (London), 1921 (corrected page on cancel leaf) .
  .   .   .   . £150/£20
ditto, Doubleday (New York), 1921 .   .   . £150/£20
Notes on My Books, Doubleday (Garden City, NY), 1921
 (250 signed, numbered copies)   .   . £350/£250
ditto, Heinemann (London), 1921 (250 signed, numbered
 copies) .   .   .   . £350/£250
The Dover Patrol: A Tribute, privately printed (Canterbury,
 Kent), 1922 (75 copies, first state without title-page; stpled
 wraps) £250
ditto, privately printed (Canterbury, Kent), 1922 (75 copies,
 second state with added title-page; stapled wraps)   . £150
Five Letters by Joseph Conrad to Edward Noble in 1915,
 privately printed (London), 1925 (100 numbered copies
 signed by Noble; wraps with acetate d/w)   . £125/£75
*Notes by Joseph Conrad Written in a Set of First Editions
 in the Possession of Edward Curle*, privately printed
 (London), 1925 (100 numbered copies, signed by Curle) .
  .   .   .   . £200
Last Essays, Dent (London), 1926   .   .   . £125/£20
ditto, Doubleday (New York), 1926 .   .   . £100/£20
Joseph Conrad's Letters to His Wife, privately printed, 1927
 (220 copies, signed by his widow) .   .   . £175
Joseph Conrad: Life and Letters, Heinemann (London),
 1927 (2 volumes, edited by G. Jean-Aubry) .   . £125/£65
ditto, Doubleday (New York), 1927 (2 vols) .   . £100/£50
Letters from Joseph Conrad, 1895-1924, Nonesuch Press
 (London), 1928 (925 numbered copies, edited by Edward
 Garnett) £65
*Conrad to a Friend: 150 Selected Letters from Joseph
 Conrad to Richard Curle*, Sampson Low, Marston
 (London), 1928 .   .   .   .   .   . £45/£25
ditto, Doubleday (New York), 1928 .   .   . £45/£25
A Sketch of Joseph Conrad's Life Written by Himself,
 privately printed, 1939 (75 copies) .   .   . £100
*Letters of Joseph Conrad to Marguerite Poradowska, 1890-
 1920*, Yale Univ Press (New Haven CT), 1940 (edited by
 John A. Gee and Paul J. Strum)   .   .   . £20/£5
*Joseph Conrad: Letters to William Blackwood and David S.
 Meldrum*, Duke Univ Press (Durham, NC), 1958 (edited by
 William Blackburn) .   .   .   .   . £25/£10
*Joseph Conrad and Warrington Dawson: The Record of a
 Friendship*, Duke Univ Press (Durham, NC), 1958 (edited
 by Dale B.J. Randall) .   .   .   .   . £10/£5
*Conrad's Polish Background: Letters to and from Polish
 Friends*, O.U.P. (London), 1964 (edited by Zdzislaw
 Najder) .   .   .   .   .   . £20/£10 *Joseph
 Conrad's Letters to R.B. Cunninghame Graham*, C.U.P.
 (Cambridge, UK), 1969 (edited by C.T. Watts) . £20/£10
Congo Diary and Other Uncollected Pieces, Doubleday
 (New York), 1978 .   .   .   .   . £20/£10
*The Collected Letters of Joseph Conrad, Volume 1: 1861-
 1897*, C.U.P. (Cambridge, UK), 1983 .   . £25/£10
*The Collected Letters of Joseph Conrad, Volume 2: 1898-
 1902*, C.U.P. (Cambridge, UK), 1986 .   . £25/£10

The Collected Letters of Joseph Conrad, Volume 3: 1903-1907, C.U.P. (Cambridge, UK), 1988 . . . £25/£10
The Collected Letters of Joseph Conrad, Volume 4: 1908-1911, C.U.P. (Cambridge, UK), 1990 . . . £25/£10
The Collected Letters of Joseph Conrad, Volume 5: 1912-1916, C.U.P. (Cambridge, UK), 1996 . . . £25/£10
The Collected Letters of Joseph Conrad, Volume 6: 1917-1919, C.U.P. (Cambridge, UK), 2003 . . . £25/£10
The Collected Letters of Joseph Conrad, Volume 7: 1920-1922, C.U.P. (Cambridge, UK), 2005 . . . £25/£10

PAT CONROY
(b.1946)

Pat Conroy is a bestselling American author whose work has been heavily influenced by his upbringing and family tragedies. He self-published his first book, *The Boo*, which is a collection of stories based on his time at a military college. His second book, *The Water Is Wide* dealt with his experiences as a teacher, and his third book, the novel *The Great Santini*, describes a character based on his abusive father.

Novels

The Boo, McClure Press (Verona, VA), 1970 . £1,750/£200
ditto, Old New York Book Shop (Atlanta, GA), 1988 . .
. . . . £70/£10
ditto, Old New York Book Shop (Atlanta, GA), 1988 (250 signed, numbered copies; slipcase, no d/w) . £250/£200
ditto, Old New York Book Shop (Atlanta, GA), 1988 (20 signed, lettered copies; each copy includes a page of the original typed manuscript of the new introduction; slipcase, no d/w) . . . . £500/£450
ditto, Old New York Book Shop (Atlanta, GA), 1996 (500 signed copies) . . . . . . £65/£45
The Water is Wide, Houghton Mifflin (Boston), 1972 . .
. . . . £500/£75
The Great Santini. Houghton Mifflin, Boston, 1976 . .
. . . . £250/£30
ditto, Collins (London), 1977 . . . . £75/£15
ditto, Old New York Book Shop (Atlanta, GA), 2004 (facsimile reprint of first edition signed by Conroy on title page) . . . . £35/£10
The Lords of Discipline, Houghton Mifflin (Boston), 1980 (first issue d/w with review by James Dickey on back panel) . . . . £100/£20
ditto, Houghton Mifflin (Boston), 1980 (second issue d/w with four reviews on back panel) . . . £50/£20
ditto, Secker & Warburg (London), 1981 . . £50/£15
The Prince of Tides, Houghton Mifflin (Boston), 1986. .
. . . . £25/£5
ditto, Houghton Mifflin (Boston), 1986 (35 signed, unnumbered advance proof copies bound in blue vinyl simulated leather) £500
ditto, Houghton Mifflin (Boston), 1986 (20 signed, numbered advance uncorrected proof copies bound in dark brown or burgundy simulated leather) . . . £750
ditto, Bantam/Transworld (London), 1987 . £20/£5
Beach Music, Doubleday (New York), 1995 . . £10/£5
ditto, Doubleday (New York), 1995 (350 signed, numbered copies; in slipcase, no d/w) . . . . £100/£75
ditto, Doubleday (London), 1995 . . . . £10/£5

Memoir

My Loosing Season, Doubleday (New York), 2002 £10/£5
ditto, Doubleday (New York), 2002 (150 signed, numbered copies; slipcase, no d/w) . . . . . . £100/£75

Others

Conroy's World, Bantam (New York), 1987 (wraps; excerpts from four novels). £5
'To Describe Our Growing Up In The Low Country...', San Francisco Examiner (San Francisco, CA), 1992 (broadside) £25
Thomas Wolfe, Old New York Book Shop (Atlanta, GA), 2000 (250 signed, numbered copies; no d/w or slipcase) .
. . . . £75
ditto, Old New York Book Shop (Atlanta, GA), 2000 (24 signed, lettered copies with an original manuscript page inserted). £600
The Pat Conroy Cookbook, Doubleday (New York), 2004 .
. . . . £10/£5

JAMES FENIMORE COOPER
(b.1789 d.1851)

James Fenimore Cooper was a popular American author of the early nineteenth century, particularly remembered for *The Last of the Mohicans*, a novel which many people consider his masterpiece. He also wrote numerous sea-stories as well as the historical romances known as the *Leatherstocking Tales*, featuring the frontiersman Natty Bumppo.

Novels

Precaution, Goodrich (New York), 1820 (anonymous; first issue with errata leaf; in original boards; 2 vols) . £2,500
ditto, Goodrich (New York), 1820 (rebound) . . . £750
ditto, Henry Colburn (London), 1821 (3 vols) . . . £750
The Spy: A Tale of Neutral Ground, Wiley & Halstead (New York), 1821 (2 vols; 'by the author of "Precaution" ')
. . . . £4,500
ditto, as *The Spy: A Tale of the Neutral Ground*, Whittaker (London), 1822 (3 vols) £1,250
The Pioneers, or the Sources of the Susquehanna; a Descriptive Tale, Simpkin (London), 1823 (3 vols; 'by the author of "Precaution" ') £500
ditto, Charles Wiley (New York), 1823 (2 vols) . £750
The Pilot: A Tale of the Sea, Charles Wiley (New York), 1824 (2 vols) £350
ditto, John Miller (London), 1824 (3 vols; 'By the Author of "The Spy" ') £300
Lionel Lincoln; or, The Leaguer of Boston, Charles Wiley (New York), 1825 (2 vols; volume one dated '1824'). £350
ditto, John Miller (London), 1825 (3 vols) . . . £300
The Last of the Mohicans; a Narrative of 1757, Carey & Lea (Philadelphia, PA), 1826 (2 vols in original boards with paper labels) £10,000
ditto, Carey & Lea (Philadelphia, PA), 1826 (2 vols rebound)
. . . . £2,000
ditto, John Miller (London), 1826 (3 vols) . . £2,500
ditto, John Miller (London), 1826 (3 vols rebound) £1,000

The Prairie, Henry Colburn (London), 1827 (3 vols; 'By the Author of The Spy, The Pilot, &c &c.') £300

ditto, Carey, Lea & Carey (Philadelphia, PA), 1827 (2 vols) £300

The Red Rover, Henry Colburn (London), 1827 (3 vols) £350

ditto, Carey, Lea & Carey (Philadelphia, PA), 1828 (2 vols) £300

The Wept of Wish Ton-Wish, Carey, Lea & Carey (Philadelphia, PA), 1829 (2 vols) . £350

ditto, as *The Borderers; or, the Wept of Wish-ton-wish: A Tale*, Henry Colburn (London), 1829 (3 vols) . . £300

The Water-Witch; or, the Skimmer of the Seas, Henry Colburn (London), 1830 (3 vols) £400

ditto, Carey & Lea (Philadelphia, PA), 1830 [1831] (2 vols) £400

The Bravo; a Venetian Story, Colburn & Bentley (London), 1831 (3 vols) £400

ditto, Carey & Lea (Philadelphia, PA), 1831 (2 vols) . £250

The Heidenmauer; or, the Benedictines, Colburn & Bentley (London), 1832 (3 vols; 'By The Author of "The Pilot", "The Bravo" &c.') £300

ditto, Carey & Lea (Philadelphia, PA), 1832 (2 vols; 'By the Author of "The Prairie", "Red Rover", "Bravo" &c &c.') £300

The Headsman: or, the Abbaye des Vignerons, Bentley (London), 1833 (3 vols) £200

ditto, Carey, Lea & Blanchard (Philadelphia, PA), 1833 (2 vols) £300

The Monikins, Bentley (London), 1835 (3 vols) . £500

ditto, Carey, Lea & Blanchard (Philadelphia, PA), 1835 (2 vols) £350

Homeward Bound; or, The Chase; a Tale of the Sea, Carey, Lea & Blanchard (Philadelphia, PA), 1838 (2 vols) . £300

ditto, Bentley (London), 1838 (3 vols) . . . £300

Home As Found, Lea & Blanchard (Philadelphia, PA), 1838 (2 vols) £300

ditto, as *Eve Effingham; or, Home*, Bentley (London), 1838 (3 vols) £300

The Pathfinder; or, the Inland Sea, Bentley (London), 1840 (3 vols; boards as cloth with paper labels) . £1,500

ditto, Bentley (London), 1840 (3 vols; rebound) . £350

ditto, Lea & Blanchard (Philadelphia, PA), 1840 (2 vols) £750

Mercedes of Castile; or, The Voyage to Cathay, Lea & Blanchard (Philadelphia, PA), 1840 (2 vols) . . £250

ditto, Bentley (London), 1841 (3 vols) . . . £250

The Deerslayer, Lea & Blanchard (Philadelphia, PA), 1841 (2 vols) £1,000

ditto, Bentley (London), 1841 (3 vols) . . . £750

The Two Admirals; A Tale, Lea & Blanchard (Philadelphia, PA), 1842 (2 vols; 'By the Author of *The Pilot*') . £400

ditto, as *The Two Admirals. A Tale of the Sea*, Bentley (London), 1842 (3 vols; credited to Cooper) . . . £300

The Jack O'Lantern, Bentley (London), 1842 (3 vols; credited to Cooper) £300

ditto, as *The Wing-And-Wing*, Lea & Blanchard (Philadelphia, PA), 1842 (2 vols; wraps; 'By the Author of *The Pilot*') £750

Wyandote; or, the Hutted Knoll, Bentley (London), 1843 (3 vols) £1,000

ditto, Lea & Blanchard (Philadelphia, PA), 1843 (2 vols; wraps) £500

Afloat and Ashore; or, The Adventures of Miles Wallingford, Lea & Blanchard (Philadelphia, PA), 1844 (2 vols; wraps) £250

ditto, Bentley (London), 1844 (3 vols) . . . £250

Afloat and Ashore; Second Series, Burgess Stringer (New York), 1844 (2 vols; wraps) £250

ditto, Bentley (London), 1844 (3 vols) . . . £250

Satanstoe, Bentley (London), 1845 (3 vols) . . £500

ditto, Burgess Stringer (New York), 1845 (2 vols; wraps) £750

The Chainbearer, Bentley (London), 1845 (3 vols) . £250

ditto, Burgess Stringer (New York), 1845 (2 vols; wraps) £400

Ravensnest, Bentley (London), 1846 (3 vols) . . £450

ditto, as *The Redskins; or, Indian & Injin*, Burgess Stringer (New York), 1846 (2 vols; wraps) . . . £650

Mark's Reef; or, The Crater, Bentley (London), 1847 (3 vols) £250

ditto, as *The Crater: A Tale of the Pacific*, Burgess Stringer (New York), 1847 (2 vols; wraps) £225

Captain Spike, Bentley (London), 1848 (3 vols) . £250

ditto, as *Jack Tier*, Burgess Stringer (New York), 1848 (2 vols; wraps) £250

The Oak Openings; or, The Bee-Hunter, Burgess Stringer (New York), 1848 (2 vols; wraps) £400

ditto, as *The Bee Hunter*, Bentley (London), 1848 (3 vols) £800

The Sea Lions; or, The Lost Sealers, Stringer & Townsend (New York), 1849 2 vols) £200

ditto, Bentley (London), 1849 (3 vols; 'By the Author of "The Red Rover" ') £250

The Ways of the Hour, G.P. Putnam (New York), 1850 . . . . £200

ditto, Bentley (London), 1850 . . . . . £200

Miscellaneous

Notions of the Americans: Picked up by a Travelling Batchelor, Henry Colburn (London), 1828 (2 vols) . £250

ditto, Carey, Lea & Carey (Philadelphia, PA), 1828 (anonymous; 2 vols) £200

Letters of J. Fennimore Cooper to Gen. Lafeyette, Paris, 1831 (wraps). £500

A Letter to His Countrymen, John Wiley (New York), 1834 . . . . £250

Sketches of Switzerland, Carey, Lea & Carey (Philadelphia, PA), 1836 ('By An American') £200

ditto, as *Excursions in Switzerland*, Bentley (London), 1836 (2 vols) £200

Sketches of Switzerland: Part Second, Lea & Carey (Philadelphia, PA), 1836 ('By An American') . . £200

ditto, as *A Residence in France, with an Excursion Up the Rhine, and a Second Visit to Switzerland*, Bentley (London), 1836 . . . . £200

Gleanings in Europe, Carey, Lea & Carey (Philadelphia, PA), 1837 ('By An American') £200

ditto, as *Recollections of Europe*, Bentley (London), 1837 . . . . £150

Gleanings in Europe: England, Carey, Lea & Carey (Philadelphia, PA), 1837 ('By An American') . . £200

ditto, as *England; with Sketches of Society in the Metropolis*, Bentley (London), 1837 . . . £175

Gleanings in Italy, Carey, Lea & Carey (Philadelphia, PA), 1838 ('By An American') £200

ditto, as *Excursions in Italy*, Bentley (London), 1838 . £175

The American Democrat, H. & E. Phinney (Cooperstown, NY), 1838 . . . . £250
The Chronicles of Cooperstown, H. & E. Phinney (Cooperstown, NY), 1838 (anonymous). . . . £250
The History of the Navy of the United States of America, (Philadelphia, PA), 1839 (2 vols) £300
ditto, Bentley (London), 1839 (2 vols) . . . £250
Le Mouchoir: An Autobiographical Romance, (New York), 1843 (wraps). £200
ditto, as **The French Governess**, Bentley (London), 1843 . . . . £200
The Battle of Lake Erie, H. & E. Phinney (Cooperstown, NY), 1843 (wraps) £500
Proceedings of the Naval Court Martial in the Case of Alexander Slidell Mackenzie, (New York), 1844 . £250
Lives of Distinguished American Naval Officers, Carey & Hart (Philadelphia, PA), 1846 (2 vols) . . . £250
ditto, Carey & Hart (Philadelphia, PA), 1846 (2 vols; wraps) £400
Pages and Pictures, from the Writings, W.A. Townsend (New York), 1861 (With Notes by Susan Fenimore Cooper). £150
Stories of the World; or, Adventures in Leatherstocking, (New York) 1863 . . . . £125
The Correspondence of James Fennimore Cooper, Yale Univ Press (New Haven, CN), 1922 (2 vols; edited by J. Fenimore Cooper) £35
New York, W.F. Payson (New York), 1930 (750 copies) £50
The Letters and Journals of James Fenimore Cooper, Harvard Univ Press (Cambridge, MA), 1960-67 (6 vols; edited by James F. Beard) £100

A.E. COPPARD
(b.1878 d.1957)

An acknowledged master of the short story form, Coppard is at his best in his evocation of the English countryside and its characters. His first collection, *Adam and Eve and Pinch Me* was the first title published by the now highly collectable Golden Cockerel Press. Apparently, the proprietor of the press, Harold Midgley Taylor, made Coppard set some of the type and help with the printing and production of the book.

Short Stories

Adam and Eve and Pinch Me, Golden Cockerel Press (Waltham St Lawrence, Berks), 1921 (white buckram issue of 550 signed copies). £165
ditto, Golden Cockerel Press (Waltham St Lawrence, Berks), 1921 (orange boards issue of 550 signed copies) . £100
ditto, Cape (London), 1921 . . . . . £125/£75
ditto, Knopf (New York), 1922 . . . . £150/£25
Clorinda Walks in Heaven, Golden Cockerel Press (Waltham St Lawrence, Berks), 1922 . £60/£25
ditto, Golden Cockerel Press (Waltham St Lawrence, Berks), 1922 (20 signed copies on special paper) . £165/£125
The Black Dog and Other Stories, Cape (London), 1923 . . . . £65/£20
ditto, Knopf (New York), 1924 . . . . £60/£20
Fishmonger's Fiddle, Cape (London), 1925 . £50/£15
ditto, Cape (London), 1925 (60 signed copies) . £125/£75
ditto, Knopf (New York), 1925 . . . . £50/£15

The Field of Mustard, Cape (London), 1926 . . £45/£20
ditto, Cape (London), 1926 (85 signed, numbered copies) . . . . £100/£40
ditto, Knopf (New York), 1927 . . . . £65/£15
Silver Circus, Cape (London), 1928 . . . £45/£15
ditto, Cape (London), 1928 (125 signed copies) . £100/£75
ditto, Knopf (New York), 1929 . . . . £45/£15
Count Stefan, Golden Cockerel Press (Waltham St Lawrence, Berks), 1928 (600 signed copies, illustrated by Robert Gibbings). . . . . . . £75/£50
The Gollan, privately printed, 1929 (75 copies; wraps). £125
The Man from Kilsheelan, Furnival Books (London), 1930 (550 signed copies; illustrated by Gibbings) . . . £35
Pink Furniture: A Tale for Lovely Children with Noble Natures, Cape (London), 1930. . . . . £25/£5
ditto, Cape (London), 1930 (260 signed copies) . £75/£50
The Higgler, The Chochorua Press (New York), [c.1930] (39 copies) £250
The Hundredth Story, Golden Cockerel Press (Waltham St Lawrence, Berks), 1931 (1,000 copies, illustrated by Gibbings) . . . . £65/£45
Fares Please! An Omnibus, Cape (London), 1931 £30/£10
Nixey's Harlequin, Cape (London), 1931 . £25/£10
ditto, Cape (London), 1931 (304 signed copies) . £40/£25
ditto, Knopf (New York), 1932 . . . . £20/£10
Crotty Shinkwin, The Beauty Spot, Golden Cockerel Press (Waltham St Lawrence, Berks), 1932 (500 numbered copies; illustrated by Gibbings) . . . . £50/£25
Cheefoo, The Spiral Press (Croton Falls, NY), 1932 . £125
Dunky Fitlow, Cape (London), 1933. . . £25/£10
ditto, Cape (London), 1933 (300 signed copies) . £75/£30
Ring the Bells of Heaven, White Owl Press (London), 1933 . . . . £25/£10
ditto, White Owl Press (London), 1933 (150 signed copies, glassine d/w). . . . . £45/£35
Emergency Exit, Random House (New York), 1934 (350 signed copies) £40
Good Samaritans, privately printed by The Spiral Press (New York), 1934 (100 copies) £125
Polly Oliver, Cape (London), 1935 . . . £30/£10
The Ninepenny Flute: Twenty-One Tales, Macmillan (London), 1937 . . . . £35/£10
Tapster's Tapestry, Golden Cockerel Press (Waltham St Lawrence, Berks), 1938 . . . . . £50/£25
You Never Know, Do You? and Other Tales, Methuen (London), 1939 . . . . £25/£10
Ugly Anna and Other Tales, Methuen (London), 1944. . . . . £25/£10
Selected Tales, Cape (London), 1946 . . £35/£15
Fearful Pleasures, Arkham House (Sauk City, WI), 1946 . . . . £40/£10
ditto, Peter Nevill (London), 1951 . . £25/£10
Dark-Eyed Lady: Fourteen Tales, Methuen (London), 1947 . . . . £30/£10
Collected Tales, Knopf (New York), 1948 . £25/£10
Lucy in Her Pink Jacket, Peter Nevill (London), 1954. . . . . £20/£5
Selected Stories, Cape (London), 1972 . . £15/£5
Father Raven and Other Tales, Tartarus Press (Carlton-in-Coverdale), 2006. . . . . . . £30/£10

Poetry
Hips and Haws, Golden Cockerel Press (Waltham St Lawrence, Berks), 1922 (500 signed copies). . £75/£45

Pelagea and Other Poems, Golden Cockerel Press (Waltham St Lawrence, Berks), 1926 (425 numbered copies, illustrated by Gibbings) . . . . . £75/£30

Yokohama Garland and Other Poems, Centaur Press (Philadelphia, PA), 1926 (500 signed, numbered copies, glassine d/w). . . . . . . £50/£40

Collected Poems, Cape (London), 1928 . . £30/£10

ditto, Knopf (New York), 1928 . . . . £30/£10

Easter Day, [no publisher stated], [1931] (145 copies, last four lines written and signed, slipcase) . . £75/£50

Cherry Ripe, Hawthorn House (Windham, CT), 1935 (300 signed, numbered copies, slipcase) . . £50/£25

ditto, Tintern Press (Chepstow, Wales), 1935 (150 signed, numbered copies) £75

Others

Rummy, The Noble Game, Golden Cockerel Press (Waltham St Lawrence, Berks), 1932 (1,000 copies, with Gibbings) .
. . . . £75/£30

ditto, Golden Cockerel Press (Waltham St Lawrence, Berks), 1932 (250 signed copies on handmade paper, with Gibbings) . . . . . . £125/£75

ditto, Houghton Mifflin (Boston), 1933 . . £25/£10

It's Me, O Lord!, Methuen (London), 1957 . . £25/£10

BERNARD CORNWELL
(b.1944)

When British-born Bernard Cornwell married an American in 1980 and relocated to her home country, he was unable to obtain a Green Card to allow him to work and so started writing novels. He has become a successful and prolific historical novelist. Richard Sharpe, his most famous creation, is a common British infantryman made an officer by the Duke of Wellington during the Napoleonic Wars.

'Sharpe' Novels

Sharpe's Eagle, Collins (London), 1981 [1980] . £400/£25
ditto, Viking (New York), 1981 . . . . £45/£10
Sharpe's Gold, Collins (London), 1981 . . £200/£20
ditto, Viking (New York), 1982 . . . . £40/£10
Sharpe's Company, Collins (London), 1982 . £275/£35
ditto, Viking (New York), 1982 . . . . £40/£15
Sharpe's Sword, Collins (London), 1983 . . £750/£45
ditto, Viking (New York), 1983 . . . . £75/£15
Sharpe's Enemy, Collins (London), 1984 . £250/£35
ditto, Viking (New York), 1984 . . . £75/£15
Sharpe's Honour, Collins (London), 1985 . £250/£25
ditto, Viking (New York), 1985 . . . . £75/£15
Sharpe's Regiment, Collins (London), 1986 . £200/£20
ditto, Viking (New York), 1986 . . . . £60/£10
Sharpe's Siege, Collins (London), 1987 . . £150/£15
ditto, Viking (New York), 1987 . . . . £60/£10
Sharpe's Rifles, Collins (London), 1988 . . £75/£10
ditto, Viking (New York), 1988 . . . . £60/£10
Sharpe's Revenge, Collins (London), 1989 . £75/£10
ditto, Viking (New York), 1989 . . . . £50/£10
Sharpe's Waterloo, Collins (London), 1990 . £75/£10
ditto, as *Waterloo*, Viking (New York), 1990 . £40/£10
Sharpe's Devil, Collins (London), 1992 . . £65/£10
ditto, Viking (New York), 1992 . . . . £35/£10
Sharpe's Battle, HarperCollins (London), 1995 . £65/£10

ditto, HarperCollins (New York), 1995 . . . £35/£10
Sharpe's Tiger, HarperCollins (London), 1997 . £30/£10
ditto, HarperCollins (New York), 1997 (wraps) . . £5
ditto, Scorpion Press (Blakeney, Glos), 1997 (99 numbered, signed copies) £75
ditto, Scorpion Press (Blakeney, Glos), 1997 (15 lettered, signed copies) £175
Sharpe's Triumph, HarperCollins (London), 1998 . £20/£10
ditto, HarperCollins (New York), 1999 . . . £15/£5
Sharpe's Fortress, HarperCollins (London), 1999 . £15/£5
ditto, HarperCollins (New York), 2000 . . £15/£5
Sharpe's Trafalgar HarperCollins (London), 2000 £15/£5
ditto, HarperCollins (New York), 2001 . . £15/£5
ditto, Scorpion Press (Blakeney, Glos), 2000 (99 numbered, signed copies) £75
ditto, Scorpion Press (Blakeney, Glos), 2000 (15 lettered, signed copies) £175
Sharpe's Prey, HarperCollins (London), 2001 . £15/£5
ditto, HarperCollins (New York), 2002 . . . £15/£5
ditto, Scorpion Press (Blakeney, Glos), 2001 (90 numbered, signed copies) £75
ditto, Scorpion Press (Blakeney, Glos), 2001 (16 lettered, signed copies) £175
Sharpe's Havoc, HarperCollins (London), 2003 . £15/£5
ditto, HarperCollins (New York), 2003 . . . £15/£5
ditto, Scorpion Press (Blakeney, Glos), 2003 (85 numbered, signed copies) £75
ditto, Scorpion Press (Blakeney, Glos), 2003 (16 lettered, signed copies) £175
Sharpe's Escape, HarperCollins (London), 2004 . £15/£5
ditto, HarperCollins (New York), 2004 . . . £15/£5
ditto, Scorpion Press (Blakeney, Glos), 2004 (85 numbered, signed copies) £75
ditto, Scorpion Press (Blakeney, Glos), 2004 (16 lettered, signed copies) £175
Sharpe's Fury, HarperCollins (London), 2006 . £10/£5
ditto, HarperCollins (New York), 2006 . . . £10/£5
ditto, Scorpion Press (Blakeney, Glos), 2006 (80 numbered, signed copies) £75
ditto, Scorpion Press (Blakeney, Glos), 2006 (15 lettered, signed copies) £175

'Sharpe' Short Stories
Sharpe's Skirmish, HarperCollins (London), 1999 (pbk) .
. . . .£200
ditto, Sharpe Appreciation Society (West Chatham, MA), 1999 (pbk) £10
ditto, Sharpe Appreciation Society (Lowdham, Nottinghamshire), 2002 (pbk) £10
Sharpe's Christmas, Sharpe Appreciation Society (Lowdham, Nottinghamshire), 2003 (also includes 'Sharpe's Ransom'; pbk) £10
ditto, Sharpe Appreciation Society (West Chatham, MA), 2003 (pbk) £10

The 'Warlord' Chronicles
The Winter King, Joseph (London), 1995. . . £35/£10
ditto, St Martin's Press (New York), 1996 . . £30/£5
Enemy of God, Joseph (London), 1996 . . £30/£10
ditto, St Martin's Press (New York), 1997 . . £20/£5
Excalibur, Joseph (London), 1997 . . . . £30/£10
ditto, St Martin's Press (New York), 1998 . . £20/£5

Grail Quest Novels
Harlequin, HarperCollins (London), 2000 . . £10/£5
ditto, as *The Archer's Tale*, HarperCollins (New York),
2001 . . . . £10/£5
Vagabond, HarperCollins (London), 2002 . £10/£5
ditto, HarperCollins (New York), 2002 . . £10/£5
Heretic, HarperCollins (London), 2003 . . £10/£5
ditto, HarperCollins (New York), 2003 . . £10/£5

'Nathaniel Starbuck' Chronicles
Rebel, HarperCollins (London), 1993 . . . £30/£10
ditto, HarperCollins (New York), 1993 . . £15/£5
Copperhead, HarperCollins (London), 1994 . £25/£10
ditto, HarperCollins (New York), 1994 . . £10/£5
Battle Flag, HarperCollins (London), 1995 . £25/£10
ditto, HarperCollins (New York), 1995 . . £10/£5
The Bloody Ground, HarperCollins (London), 1996 £25/£10
ditto, HarperCollins (New York), 1996 . . £10/£5

Crowning Mercy Novels
(with Judy Cornwell, writing as Susannah Kells)
A Crowning Mercy, Collins (London), 1983 . £45/£10
ditto, Viking (New York), 1983 . . . . £45/£10
The Fallen Angels, Collins (London), 1984 . £45/£10
ditto, St Martins (New York), 1984 . . . £25/£10
Coat of Arms, Collins (London), 1986 . . £45/£10
ditto, as *The Aristocrats*, St Martins (New York), 1986 .
. . . . £45/£10

Alfred The Great Novels
The Last Kingdom, HarperCollins (London), 2004. £10/£5
ditto, HarperCollins (New York), 2005 . . £10/£5
The Pale Horseman, HarperCollins (London), 2005 £10/£5
ditto, HarperCollins (New York), 2006 . . £10/£5
The Lords of the North, HarperCollins (London), 2006 .
. . . . £10/£5
ditto, HarperCollins (New York), 2007 . . £10/£5
Sword Song, HarperCollins (London), 2007 . £10/£5
ditto, HarperCollins (New York), 2008 . . £10/£5
The Burning Land, HarperCollins (London), 2009 £10/£5

Other Novels
Redcoat, Joseph (London), 1987. . . . £45/£10
ditto, Viking (New York), 1988 . . . . £20/£5
Wildtrack, Joseph (London), 1988 . . . £35/£10
ditto, Putnam (New York), 1988. . . . £15/£5
Sea Lord, Joseph (London), 1989 . . . £35/£10
ditto, as *Killer's Wake*, Viking (New York), 1989 . £15/£5
Crackdown, Joseph (London), 1990 . . . £35/£10
ditto, HarperCollins (New York), 1990 . . £15/£5
Stormchild, Joseph (London), 1990 [1991] . £35/£10
ditto, HarperCollins (New York), 1991 . . £15/£5
Scoundrel, Joseph (London), 1992 . . . £35/£10
ditto, HarperCollins (New York), 2004 (pbk) . . . £5
Stonehenge, A Novel of 2000 BC, HarperCollins (London),
1999 . . . . £10/£5
ditto, HarperCollins (New York), 2000 . . £10/£5
Gallows Thief, HarperCollins (London), 2001 £10/£5
ditto, HarperCollins (New York), 2002 . £10/£5
Azincourt, HarperCollins (London), 2008 . £10/£5
ditto, as *Agincourt*, , HarperCollins (New York), 2009 . .
. . . . £10/£5

PATRICIA CORNWELL
(b.1956)

With her first 'Scarpetta' novel, *Post Mortem*, Cornwell
won four major awards. These influential titles rely heavily
on forensic science and it is here that the solution to her
mysteries is usually to be found. Cornwell has in the last
few years self-financed her search for evidence to support
her theory that British painter Walter Sickert was Jack the
Ripper.

'Scarpetta' Books
Postmortem, Scribner's (New York), 1990 . . £350/£35
ditto, Macdonald (London), 1990 . . . . £200/£30
Body of Evidence, Scribner's (New York), 1991 . £35/£10
ditto, Macdonald (London), 1991 . . . . £35/£150
All That Remains, Little, Brown (London), 1992 . £25/£10
ditto, Scribner's (New York), 1992 . . . £20/£10
Cruel and Unusual, Scribner's (New York), 1993. £25/£10
ditto, Little, Brown (London), 1993 . . . £20/£10
The Body Farm, Scribner's (New York), 1994 . £20/£10
ditto, Little, Brown (London), 1994 . . . £20/£10
From Potter's Field, Scribner's (New York), 1995 £20/£10
ditto, Little, Brown (London), 1995 . . . £20/£10
Cause of Death, Putnam (New York), 1996 . . £20/£10
ditto, Putnam (New York), 1996 (185 signed, numbered
copies, slipcase) . . . . . . £50/£40
ditto, Little, Brown (London), 1996 . . . £20/£10
Unnatural Exposure, Putnam (New York), 1997 . £20/£10
ditto, Putnam (New York), 1997 (175 signed, numbered
copies, slipcase) . . . . . . £45/£25
ditto, Little, Brown (London), 1997 . . . £20/£10
Point of Origin, Putnam (New York), 1998 . . £10/£5
ditto, Putnam (New York), 2000 (500 signed, numbered
copies, slipcase) . . . . . . £30/£15
ditto, Little, Brown (London), 1998 . . . £10/£5
Scarpetta's Winter Table, Wyrick & Company (Charleston,
SC), 1998 . . . . £10/£5
Black Notice, Putnam (New York), 1999 . . £10/£5
ditto, Putnam (New York), 1999 (200 signed, numbered
copies, slipcase) . . . . . . £45/£25
ditto, Little, Brown (London), 1999 . . . £10/£5
The Last Precinct, Putnam (New York), 2000. . £10/£5
ditto, Putnam (New York), 2000 (175 signed, numbered
copies, slipcase) . . . . . . £40/£25
ditto, Little, Brown (London), 2000 . . . £10/£5
Blow Fly, Putnam (New York), 2003. . . . £10/£5
ditto, Little, Brown (London), 2003 . . . £10/£5
Trace, Putnam (New York), 2004 . . . . £10/£5
ditto, Little, Brown (London), 2004 . . . £10/£5
Predator, Putnam (New York), 2005 . . . £10/£5
ditto, Little, Brown (London), 2005 . . . £10/£5
Book of the Dead, Putnam (New York), 2007 . . £10/£5
ditto, Little, Brown (London), 2007 . . . £10/£5
Scarpetta, Putnam (New York), 2008 . . . £10/£5
ditto, Little, Brown (London), 2008 . . . £10/£5
The Scarpetta Factor, Putnam (New York), 2009 . £10/£5
ditto, Little, Brown (London), 2009 . . . £10/£5

'Hammer'/'Brazil' Novels
Hornet's Nest, Putnam (New York), 1996 . . £20/£10
ditto, Little, Brown (London), 1997 . . . £20/£10
Southern Cross, Putnam (New York), 1999 . . £10/£5

ditto, Little, Brown (London), 1999 . . . . £10/£5
Isle of Dogs, Putnam (New York), 2001 . . . £10/£5
ditto, Little, Brown (London), 2001 . . . . £10/£5

'Winston Garano' Novels
At Risk, Putnam (New York), 2006 . . . . £10/£5
ditto, Little, Brown (London), 2006 . . . . £10/£5
The Front, Putnam (New York), 2008 . . . £10/£5
ditto, Little, Brown (London), 2008 . . . . £10/£5

Others
A Time for Remembering: The Ruth Bell Graham Story,
    Harper & Row (New York), 1983 . . . .£150/£20
ditto, Triangle (London), 1984 (pbk) £5
ditto, as *Ruth: A Portrait*, Hodder & Stoughton (London),
    1998 . . . . £15/£5
Life's Little Fable, Putnam (New York), 1999 . £10/£5
Food to Die For: Secrets from Kay Scarpetta's Kitchen,
    Putnam (New York), 2001 (with Marlene Brown) £10/£5
ditto, Little, Brown (London), 2001 . . . . £10/£5
Portrait of a Killer : Jack the Ripper - Case Closed, Putnam
    (New York), 2002 . . . . . . £10/£5
ditto, Little, Brown (London), 2002 . . . . £10/£5

HUBERT CRACKANTHORPE

(b.1870 d.1896)

Hubert Crackanthorpe edited the *Albermarle* between
1892-93, but it was the publication of *Wreckage* in 1893
that made him a sensation of the 'naughty nineties'.
Crackanthorpe's reputation was based on his willingness to
deal with taboo subjects such as adultery, prostitution and
social degradation. He also contributed to the notorious *The
Yellow Book*.

Wreckage: Seven Studies, Heinemann (London), 1893. £65
ditto, Cassell (New York), 1894 . . . . . . £50
Sentimental Studies & A Set of Village Tales, Heinemann
    (London), 1895 . . . . £85
ditto, Putnams (New York), 1895 . . . . . £65
Vignettes, A Miniature Journal of Whim and Sentiment,
    John Lane/Bodley Head (London), 1896 . . . £75
Last Studies, Heinemann (London), 1897. . . £65
The Light Sovereign: A Farcical Comedy in Three Acts,
    privately printed, Lady Henry Harland (London), 1917
    (with Henry Harland) £150
Collected Stories (1893-1897) of Hubert Crackanthorpe,
    Scholar's Facsimiles and Reprints (New York), 1969 £30

STEPHEN CRANE

(b.1871 d.1900)

Crane was an American novelist, poet and journalist who
only received acclaim for his work when he published the
Civil War novel *The Red Badge of Courage*. This success
secured highly paid positions as war correspondent in
Greece and Cuba for newspaper tycoons William Randolph
Hearst and Joseph Pulitzer. He is considered a pioneer of
literary realism.

Novels
Maggie: A Girl of the Streets, no publisher [New York],
    c.1893 (pseud Johnston Smith; yellow wraps printed in red
    and black; cover priced 50 cents; 1,100 copies, of which 38
    are known) £6,000
ditto, Appleton (New York), 1896 (second edition written as
    Stephen Crane; decorated tan buckram; 8-line title page in
    Gothic type; 12 pages of ads of which the last is headed
    The Story of the West Indies; title printed in upper and
    lower case letters) £600
ditto, Appleton (New York), 1896 (second edition, second
    printing; decorated tan buckram; 11-line title page in
    Roman type; title printed in upper case letters only) . £150
ditto, Appleton (New York), 1896 (second edition, third
    printing; as second printing but last page of ads headed *The
    Three Musketeers*) £75
ditto, as *Maggie: A Child of the Streets*, Heinemann
    (London), 1896 (cloth or wraps) £125
The Red Badge of Courage, Appleton (New York), 1895
    (first state, p.235 advertises three Gilbert Parker titles and
    last page of advertisements, p.238 ends with *The Land of
    the Sun*; printed on laid paper with horizontal chain lines;
    perfect type in the word 'congratulated' on p.225, line 6;
    title page printed in red and black and tipped in; top edges
    stained red) £2,000
ditto, Appleton (New York), 1895 (intermediate state; all
    printed on wove paper except signature 15 which is printed
    on laid paper; ads are headed 'Gilbert Parker's Best
    Books'; p.225 has unbroken type) £1,500
ditto, Appleton (New York), 1895 (second state; p.235
    advertises The *Red Badge of Courage*; Gilbert Parker not
    mentioned in ads; p.238 has A. Conan Doyle's ads; broken
    or distorted type on p.225, line 6; printed on wove paper, or
    on laid paper with vertical chain marks; top edge gilt) .
    . . . . £1,000
ditto, Appleton (New York), 1895 (third state; corrected type
    on p.226, but 'd' not straight £500
ditto, Heinemann (London), 1896 (olive green cloth, lettered
    in white; cover design of the wraps issue tipped in) . £600
ditto, Heinemann (London), 1896 (pictorial wraps) . . £500
George's Mother, Edward Arnold (New York), 1896 . £100
ditto, Edward Arnold (London), 1896 . . . . £100
The Third Violet, Appleton (New York), 1897 . . . £100
ditto, Heinemann (London), 1897 . . . . . £100
Active Service, Stokes (New York), 1899 (light green cloth
    lettered in dark green) £100
ditto, Stokes (New York), 1899 (pictorial green cloth,
    stamped in dark green and white) £125
ditto, Heinemann (London), 1899 . . . . . £75
Bowery Tales: George's Mother/Maggie, Heinemann
    (London), 1900 . . . . £200

ditto, Heinemann (London), 1900 (Times Book Club binding)
.   .£125

The O'Ruddy, Stokes (New York), 1903 (written with Robert
Barr)   .   .£100

ditto, Methuen (London), 1904 .   .   .   .   £75

Short Stories

***The Little Regiment and Other Episodes of the American
Civil War...***, Appleton (New York), 1896 (first state;
endpapers and flyleaves are laid unwatermarked paper;
p.197 with caption 'Gilbert Parker's Best Books'; last page
of ads, p.202, ends with *The Lilac Sunbonnet...*; bound in
tan buckram). £150

ditto, Appleton (New York), 1896 (second state; endpapers
and flyleaves are wove paper; p.197 advertises *The
Beginners of a Nation*; last page of ads, p.202, announces
The Story of the West Indies; bound in tan buckram) . £85

ditto, Appleton (New York), 1896 (third state; endpapers and
flyleaves are laid paper with Appleton watermark;
p.197 advertises *The Beginners of a Nation*).   .   £40

ditto, Heinemann (London), 1897 (olive green cloth) .£100

ditto, Heinemann (London), 1897 (wraps)   .   .   .£125

The Open Boat And Other Stories, Doubleday & McClure
(New York, 1898.   .   .   .   .   .£400

ditto, Heinemann (London), 1898 (contains nine stories not
present in the US edition; primary binding in lime green
cloth lettered in blue and stamped in gilt and blind) .£300

ditto, Heinemann (London), 1898 (later binding in tan linen,
lettered in red and black) £200

ditto, Heinemann (London), 1898 (Times Book Club issue in
blue cloth with circular seal on spine) .   .   .£150

ditto, Heinemann (London), 1898 (colonial issue in green
cloth; plain, unprinted covers; spine stamped in gilt) .£150

ditto, Heinemann (London), 1898 (colonial issue in wraps) .
.   .   .   .£150

The Lanthorn Book, Lanthorn (New York), 1898 (125
signed, numbered copies).   .   .   .£3,000

ditto, Lanthorn (New York), 1898 (unsigned copies) .£450

The Monster And Other Stories, Harper & Brothers (New
York), 1899 (red cloth) £150

ditto, Harper & Brothers (London), 1899 (rough brown/
orange cloth; different contents to US edition)   . £125

Whilomville Stories, Harper & Brothers (New York), 1900 .
.   .   .   .£150

ditto, Harper & Brothers (London), 1900 .   .   .£100

Wounds in the Rain, Methuen (London), 1900 (printed from
the American plates, but issued a few days before the US;
catalogue dated August 1900)   .   .   .£125

ditto, Methuen (London), 1900 (catalogue dated October
1900) £75

ditto, Stokes (New York), 1900 .   .   .   .£150

Last Words, Digby, Long & Co. (London), 1902 (primary
binding dark red cloth stamped in gilt)   .   .   .£500

ditto, Digby, Long & Co. (London), 1902 (later binding blue,
green, red or tan cloth lettered in black).   .   .£400

Men, Women and Boats, The Modern Library, Boni &
Liveright (New York), 1921 (first state with the word
'immediately' missing on p.69, line 19)   .   .£125/£45

ditto, The Modern Library, Boni & Liveright (New York),
1921 (second state with 'immediately' inserted after
'almost' on p.69, line 19) .   .   .£100/£20

The Pace of Youth And Other Stories, Haldeman-Julius
(Girard, KA), [1926] (wraps) .   .   .   £15

The Upturned Face And Other Stories, Haldeman-Julius
(Girard, KS), [1926] (wraps) .   .   .   £15

Twenty Stories..., Knopf (New York), 1940   . £40/£10

Selected Short Stories of Stephen Crane, Armed Services
Editions (New York) [1940?] (wraps)   .   .   £20

The Sullivan County Sketches, Syracuse Univ Press
(Syracuse, NY), 1949.   .   .   .   .£25/£10

The Bride Comes to Yellow Sky, Avon Books (New York),
1956 (wraps). £15

The Bride Comes to Yellow Sky, The Pemberton Press
(Austin, TX), 1978 (450 copies; wraps).   .   .   £15

ditto, Perfection Form Co. (Logan, IA), 1980 (wraps) .£10

The Complete Short Stories and Sketches of Stephen Crane,
Doubleday (Garden City, NY), 1963   .   .£20/£5

Poetry

The Black Riders And Other Lines, Copeland & Day
(Boston), 1895 (variant A: bound in cream laid paper over
boards with art nouveau orchid silhouetted in black and
title letters in black 'THE BLACK RIDERS | AND
OTHER | LINES | BY | STEPHEN | CRANE,' aligned to
the left margin) £500

ditto, Copeland & Day (Boston), 1895 (variant B: bound in
pale yellow paper over boards, otherwise as above) .£700

ditto, Copeland & Day (Boston), 1895 (variant C: bound in
pale yellow cloth over boards, otherwise as above) .£600

ditto, Copeland & Day (Boston), 1895 (variant D: bound in
grey laid paper over boards, otherwise as above). .£600

ditto, Copeland & Day (Boston), 1895 (variant E: bound in
light grey paper with small blue and red threads; black
orchid design repeated on back cover as in variant A, but
title and author lettering absent on back cover; front cover
lettering not aligned to left margin but first line indented
one space) £400

ditto, Copeland & Day (Boston), 1895 (limited edition reprint
of 50 copies in three variants; variant A: bound in white
paper over boards; spine lettering on paper label; text
printed in green) £2,000

ditto, Copeland & Day (Boston), 1895 (limited edition variant
B: bound in white vellum over boards; spine printed in
gold) £3,000

ditto, Copeland & Day (Boston), 1895 (limited edition variant
C: bound in full green morocco) .   .   .£3,000

ditto, Heinemann (London), 1896 (500 copies; bound in black
morocco) £250

ditto, privately printed by Small, Maynard & Co (Boston),
1905 (400 copies) £125

A Souvenir and a Medley..., Roycroft Printing Shop (East
Aurora, NY), 1896 (ictorial grey wraps).   .   .£400

Spanish-American War Songs..., Sidney A. Witherbee
(Detroit, MI), 1898 .   .   .   .   .£300

War Is Kind, Stokes (New York), 1899 (grey cartridge paper
boards; paper spine label) £600

The Collected Poems of Stephen Crane, Knopf (New York),
1930 (first state with running head The Black Riders at the
top of the left-hand page throughout book) . .£100/£20

A Lost Poem..., privately printed by Harvey Taylor/The
Harvard Press (New York), [1932] (100 numbered copies
signed by Taylor; single sheet folded to make four pps) £45

The Blood of the Martyr, Peter Pauper Press (Mt. Vernon,
NY), 1940 (200 copies) £150

Legends..., Edwin B. Hill (Ysleta, TX), 1942 (45 copies; buff
paper wraps; privately printed for the friends of Vincent
Starrett and Ames W. Williams) .   .   .£100

The Poetry of Stephen Crane, Columbia Univ Press (New York), 1957 . . . . £25/£10
The Poems of Stephen Crane: A Critical Edition, Cooper Square (New York), 1966 . . . . . £25/£10

Collected Editions
Pictures of War, Heinemann (London), 1898 (collects *The Red Badge of Courage*, *The Little Regiment*, *Three Miraculous Soldiers*, *A Mystery of Heroism*, *An Indiana Campaign*, *A Grey Sleeve* and *The Veteran*) . . . £250
ditto, Heinemann (London), 1898 (colonial issue) . . £200
The University of Virginia Edition of the Works of Stephen Crane, Univ Press of Virginia (Charlottesville, VA), 1969-1975 (10 vols; no d/ws) . . . . . £200 the set
Stephen Crane Omnibus, Knopf (New York) 1952. £25/£10
Stephen Crane, An Omnibus, Heinemann (London), 1954 . . . . £25/£10

Non-Fiction
Great Battles Of The World, Lippincott (Philadelphia, PA), 1901 . . . . £125
ditto, Chapman & Hall (London), 1901 (primary binding of brick-red cloth lettered in gilt) £125
ditto, Chapman & Hall (London), 1901 (later binding red pictorial cloth decorated in blue and black and lettered in gilt; all edges gilt) £100
The War Dispatches of Stephen Crane, New York Univ Press (New York), 1964 . . . . . £30/£10
ditto, Peter Owen (London), 1964 . . . . £30/£10
Stephen Crane in the West and Mexico, Kent State Univ Press (Kent, OH), 1970 . . . . . £25/£10

Letters
Two Letters from Stephen Crane to Joseph Conrad, The First Edition Club/Curwen Press (London), 1926 (220 sets of 12 different pamphlets in sewn wraps, in a double-compartment folding case) . . . . £150 the set
ditto, Crane pamphlet only £30
Stephen Crane's Love Letters to Nellie Crouse, Syracuse Univ Press (Syracuse, NY), 1954 . . . £25/£10
Stephen Crane, Letters, New York Univ Press (New York), 1960 . . . . £30/£10
ditto, Peter Owen (London), 1960 . . . . £30/£10
The Correspondence of Stephen Crane, Columbia Univ Press (New York), 1988 (2 vols) . . . £60/£20

Others
Pike County Puzzle, no publisher (Camp Interlaken, PA), 1894 (4-page spoof newspaper) £2,500
ditto, Stephen Crane Newsletter (no place), no date (70 numbered copies; facsimile on laid paper) . . £75
ditto, Stephen Crane Newsletter (no place), no date (300 copies) £50
Stephen Crane: Uncollected Writings, Uppsala Univ Press (Uppsala, Sweden), 1963 . . . . . £45
The Notebook of Stephen Crane, Bibliographical Society of the Univ of Virginia [Charlottesville, VA], 1969 (750 copies; no d/w) £20

WALTER CRANE
(b.1845 d.1915)

A successful British artist, Crane was a colleague of William Morris, sharing many of Morris's political and artistic beliefs. He produced paintings, illustrations, children's books, ceramic tiles and other decorative artefacts.

'Aunt Mavor' and Sixpenny Toy Books
The House that Jack Built, Ward, Lock & Tyler (London), 1865 . . . . £350
The Comical Cat, Ward, Lock & Tyler (London), 1865 £300
The Affecting Story of Jenny Wren, Ward, Lock & Tyler (London), 1865 . . . . £275
The Railroad Alphabet, Routledge (London), 1865 . £275
The Farmyard Alphabet, Routledge (London), 1865 . £265
Cock Robin, Frederick Warne (London), 1866 . . £265
A Gaping-Wide-Mouth Waddling Frog, Frederick Warne (London), [1866] £265
Sing A Song of Sixpence, Frederick Warne (London), 1866 . . . . £250
The Old Courtier, Frederick Warne (London), 1867 . £250
Multiplication Rule in Verse, Routledge (London), [1867] £250
Chattering Jack's Picture Book, Routledge (London), [1867] £250
How Jessie Was Lost, Routledge (London), [1868] . £250
Grammar in Rhyme, Routledge (London), [1868] . . £250
Annie and Jack in London, Routledge (London), [1869] £250
One, Two, Buckle My Shoe, Routledge (London), [1869] £250
The Fairy Ship, Routledge (London), 1870 . . . £250
The Adventures of Puffy, Routledge (London), 1870 . £250
This Little Pig Went To Market, Routledge (London), [1870] £250
King Luckieboy's Party, Routledge (London), 1870 . £325
King Luckieboy's Picture Book, Routledge (London), 1871 . . . . £350
Routledge's Book of Alphabets, Routledge (London), 1871 . . . . £250
Noah's Ark Alphabet, Routledge (London), 1872 . . £250
My Mother, Routledge (London), 1873 . . . . £250
Ali Baba and the Forty Thieves, Routledge (London), 1873 . . . . £100
The Three Bears, Routledge (London), 1873 . . . £225
Cinderella, Routledge (London), 1873 . . . . £225
Walter Crane's New Toy Book, Routledge (London), 1873 . . . . £325
Walter Crane's Picture Book, Routledge (London), 1874 . . . . £325
Valentine and Orson, Routledge (London), 1874 . . £225
Puss in Boots, Routledge (London), 1874 . . . £225
Old Mother Hubbard, Routledge (London), 1874 . . £225
The Marquis of Caraba's Picture Book, Routledge (London), [1874] £225
The Absurd ABC, Routledge (London), 1874 . . £200
The Frog Prince, Routledge: 'Walter Crane Shilling Series' (London), 1874 . . . . . . £225
Goody Two Shoes, Routledge: 'Walter Crane Shilling Series' (London), 1874 . . . . . . £225
Beauty and the Beast, Routledge: 'Walter Crane Shilling Series' (London), 1874 . . . . . . £225

The Alphabet of Old Friends, Routledge: 'Walter Crane Shilling Series' (London), 1874 . . . . . £225

Little Red Riding Hood, Routledge (London), 1875 . £225

Jack and the Beanstalk, Routledge (London), 1875 . £225

The Bluebeard Picture Book, Routledge (London), 1875 .
. . . . £225

Baby's Own Alphabet, Routledge (London), 1875 . . £225

The Yellow Dwarf, Routledge: 'Walter Crane Shilling Series' (London), 1875 . . . . . . £225

The Hind in the Wood, Routledge: 'Walter Crane Shilling Series' (London), 1875 . . . . . . £225

Princess Belle Etoile, Routledge: 'Walter Crane Shilling Series' (London), 1875 . . . . . . £225

Aladdin's Picture Book, Routledge: 'Walter Crane Shilling Series' (London), 1875 [1876] . . . £225

Song of Sixpence Toy Book, Warner, [1876] . . . £225

The Three Bears Picture Book, Routledge (London), [1876]
. . . . £125

The Sleeping Beauty in the Wood, Routledge (London), 1876 . . . . £175

Walter Crane's Painting Book, Frederick Warne (London), [1895] £175

Walter Crane's Picture Books Vol. 1: The Little Pig: His Picture Book, John Lane (London), 1895 . . £175

Walter Crane's Picture Books Vol. 2: Mother Hubbard: Her Picture Book, John Lane (London), 1897 . £175

Walter Crane's Picture Books Vol. 3: Cinderella's Picture Book, John Lane (London), 1897 . . . £175

Walter Crane's Picture Books Vol. 4: Red Riding Hood's Picture Book, John Lane (London), 1898 . . £175

Beauty and the Beast Picture Book, John Lane: Large Series Vol. 1 (London), 1901 . . . . . £175

Goody Two Shoes Picture Book, John Lane: Large Series Vol. 2 (London), 1901 . . . . . £175

The Song of Sixpence Picture Book, John Lane: Large Series Vol. 3 (London), 1909 . . . . . £175

The Buckle My Shoe Picture Book, John Lane: Large Series Vol. 4 (London), 1910 . . . . . £175

Puss in Boots and *The Forty Thieves*, John Lane (London), 1914 . . . . £75

The Sleeping Beauty and *Bluebeard*, John Lane (London), 1914 . . . . £75

The Three Bears and *Mother Hubbard*, John Lane (London), 1914 . . . . £75

Books Written by Mary Molesworth, Illustrated by Crane

Tell Me A Story, Macmillan (London), 1875 . . . £85

Carrots, Macmillan (London), 1876 . . . . £75

The Cuckoo Clock, Macmillan (London), 1877 . . £65

Grandmother Dear, Macmillan (London), 1878 . . £50

The Tapestry Room, Macmillan (London), 1879 . . £50

A Christmas Child, Macmillan (London), 1880 . . £50

The Adventures of Herr Baby, Macmillan (London), 1881 .
. . . . £65

Rosy, Macmillan (London), 1882 . . . . . £50

Two Little Waifs, Macmillan (London), 1883 . . . £50

Christmas-Tree Land, Macmillan (London), 1884 . . £45

Us, An Old Fashioned Story, Macmillan (London), 1885 .
. . . . £45

Four Winds Farm, Macmillan (London), 1886 . . £45

Little Miss Piggy, Macmillan (London), 1887 . . £40

A Christmas Posy, Macmillan (London), 1888 . . £40

The Rectory Children, Macmillan (London), 1889 . £35

The Children of the Castle, Macmillan (London), 1890 £35

Studies and Stories, A.D. Innes, 1893 . . . . £35

Other Titles Illustrated by Crane

The New Forest: Its History and Scenery, by John de Capel Wise, Smith & Elder (London), 1863 . . . £150

A Merrie Heart, by Cassell (London), 1871 . . £165

Mrs Mundi at Home, by Walter Crane, Marcus Ward (London), 1875 . . . . £135

The Quiver of Love: A Collection of Valentines, Marcus Ward (London), 1876 (with Kate Greenaway) . £500

The Baby's Opera: Old Rhymes with New Dresses, by Walter Crane, Routledge (London), 1877 . . £135

The Baby's Bouquet, by Walter Crane, Routledge (London), 1878 . . . . £135

The Necklace of Princess Fiorimonde, by Mary de Morgan, Macmillan (London), 1880 . . . . . £100

The First of May: A Fairy Masque, by John R Wise, Henry Southeran (London), 1881 (300 copies, signed by Crane) .
. . . . £750

ditto, Henry Southeran (London), 1881 (folio edition, 200 copies, signed by Crane) £1,000

Household Stories, by the Brothers Grimm, Macmillan (London), 1882 . . . . £100

ditto, Crowell (New York), 1897 . . . . . £100

Art and the Formation of Taste, by Lucy Crane, Macmillan (London), 1882 . . . . £75

Pan Pipes: A Book of Old Songs, by Theodore Marzials, Routledge (London), 1883 . . . . . £165

The Golden Primer, Parts 1 & 2, by Professor J.M.D. Meiklejohn, William Blackwood (Edinburgh/London), 1884-5 (2 vols) £75

Folk and Fairy Tales, by Mrs Burton Harrison, Ward & Downey (London), 1885 . . . . . . £75

Slateandpencilvania: Being the Adventures of Dick on a Desert Island, by Walter Crane, Marcus Ward (London), 1885 . . . . £200

Little Queen Annie, by Walter Crane, Marcus Ward (London), 1886 . . . . £200

Pothooks and Perseverance, by Walter Crane, Marcus Ward (London), 1886 . . . . £200

A Romance of the Three Rs, by Walter Crane, Marcus Ward (London), 1886 . . . . £150

The Sirens Three: A Poem, by Walter Crane, Macmillan (London), 1886 . . . . £150

Legends for Lionel in Pen and Pencil, by Walter Crane, Cassell (London), 1887 . . . . . . £150

The Baby's Own Aesop, by Walter Crane, Routledge (London), 1887 . . . . £150

Echoes of Hellas, Parts 1 & 2, by Professor George C. Warr, Marcus Ward (London), 1887-88 (2 vols) . . £175

The Happy Prince and Other Tales, by Oscar Wilde, David Nutt (London), 1888 . . . . . . £1,500

ditto, David Nutt (London), 1888 (75 signed copies, large handmade paper edition) £6,000

The Book of Wedding Days, Compiled by K.E.J. Reid, Longmans (London), 1889 . . . . . £125

Flora's Feast: A Masque of Flowers, by Walter Crane, Cassell (London), 1889 . . . . . . £125

Queen Summer: or the Tourney of the Lily and the Rose, by Walter Crane, Cassell (London), 1891 . . £125

ditto, by Walter Crane, Cassell (London), 1891 (250 large paper copies) £650

Society for the Encouragement of Arts, Manufacture and Commerce: Lectures by Walter Crane, Trounce (London), 1891 . . . . £75

Renascence: A Book of Verse, by Walter Crane, Elkin Mathews (London), 1891 (350 numbered copies) . £75

ditto, by Walter Crane, Elkin Mathews (London), 1891 (25 signed, numbered copies on Japanese vellum) . £1,000

The Claims of Decorative Art, by Walter Crane, Lawrence & Bullen (London), 1892 . . . . . . £125

A Wonder Book for Boys and Girls, by Nathaniel Hawthorne, Osgood McIlvaine (Boston), 1892 . £175

Columbia's Courtship, by Walter Crane, Prang & Co. (Boston), 1893 . . . . £175

The Old Garden and Other Verses, by Margaret Delane, Osgood McIlvaine (Boston), 1893 . . . . £75

The Tempest, by William Shakespeare, Dent (London), 1893 . . . . £75

Eight Illustrations to Shakespeare's The Tempest, Dent (London), 1893 (600 signed portfolios) . . £450

The Story of the Glittering Plain, by William Morris, Kelmscott Press (Hammersmith, London), 1894 (250 copies) £2,250

ditto, by William Morris, Kelmscott Press (Hammersmith, London), 1894 (7 copies on vellum) . . . £6,000

The History of Reynard the Fox, by F.S. Ellis, David Nutt (London), 1894 . . . . £100

The Merry Wives of Windsor, by William Shakespeare, George Allen (London), 1894 . . . . . £75

Two Gentlemen of Verona, by William Shakespeare, Dent (London), 1894 . . . . . . £75

The Faerie Queen, by Edmund Spenser, George Allen (London), 1894-97 (issued in 19 parts) . £750 the set

ditto, George Allen (London), 1897 (6 vols, 1,000 sets) . . . . £1,250 the set

A Book of Christmas Verse, Methuen (London), 1895 . £75

Cartoons for the Cause, Twentieth Century Press (London), 1896 . . . . £650

Of the Decorative Illustration of Books Old and New, by Walter Crane, Bell (London), 1896 . . . £100

The Work of Walter Crane, Virtue & Co. (London), 1898 . . . . £125

A Floral Fantasy in an Old English Garden, by Walter Crane, Harper (New York), 1898 . . . £150

The Shepherd's Calendar, by Edmund Spenser, Harper (New York), 1898 . . . . . . £100

The Bases of Design, by Walter Crane, Bell (London), 1898 . . . . £100

Triplets, by Walter Crane, Routledge (London), 1899 (500 numbered copies) £300

The Walter Crane Infant Reader, by Nellie Dale, Dent (London), 1899 . . . . . . £60

The Walter Crane Reader: First Primer, by Nellie Dale, Dent (London), 1899 . . . . . £60

The Walter Crane Reader: Second Primer, by Nellie Dale, Dent (London), 1899 . . . . . £60

Don Quixote, translated by Judge Parry, Blackie (London), 1900 . . . . £65

Line and Form, by Walter Crane, Bell (London), 1900 £50

Walter Crane's Picture Book, Frederick Warne (London), 1900 (750 copies, bound in vellum) . . . £400

A Masque of Days, Cassell (London), 1901 . . £150

The Art of Walter Crane, by Paul George Konody, Bell (London), 1902 . . . . . . £250

A Flower Wedding, by Walter Crane, Cassell (London), 1905 . . . . £100

Flowers from Shakespeare's Garden, by Walter Crane, Cassell (London), 1906 . . . . . £150

India Impressions, by Walter Crane, Methuen (London), 1907 . . . . £100

An Artists Reminiscences, by Walter Crane, Methuen (London), 1907 . . . . . . £75

A Child's Socialist Reader, by A.A. Watts (New York), Methuen (London), 1907 . . . . £65

The Rosebud and Other Tales, by Arthur Kelly, Fisher & Unwin (London), 1909 . . . . . £65

King Arthur's Knights, by H. Gilbert, T.C. & E.C. Jack (Edinburgh and London), 1911 . . . £65

William Morris to Whistler, by Walter Morris, Bell (London), 1911 (350 copies) £250

Rumbo Rhymes, by A. Calmour, Harper (New York), 1911 . . . . £125

Robin Hood, by H. Gilbert, T.C. & E.C. Jack (Edinburgh and London), 1912 . . . . £65

The Story of Greece, by M. MacGregor, T.C. & E.C. Jack (Edinburgh and London), 1913 . . . £65

Michael Mouse Unfolds His Tale, by Walter Crane, Yale Univ Press (New Haven, CT), 1956 (300 copies, slipcase) . . . . £150/£125

ditto, by Walter Crane, Merrimack/Yale Univ Press (New Haven, CT), 1956 (wraps) £30

JOHN CREASEY
(b.1908 d.1973)

A British author whose output was prodigious, Creasey is best known for his detective fiction, written under many pseudonyms. His principal characters include Gideon of Scotland Yard, The Toff, Inspector Roger West, and The Baron. He died in Tucson, Arizona in the U.S.

'Inspector West' Novels
Inspector West Takes Charge, Stanley Paul (London), 1942 . . . . £250/£30

ditto, Scribner's (New York), 1972 . . . £20/£5

Inspector West Leaves Town, Stanley Paul (London), 1943 . . . . £225/£25

ditto, as *Go Away To Murder*, Lancer (New York), 1972 (pbk) £5

Inspector West at Home, Stanley Paul (London), 1944. . . . . £200/£20

ditto, Scribner's (New York), 1973 . . . £15/£5

Inspector West Regrets, Stanley Paul (London), 1945 . . . . £150/£20

ditto, Lancer (New York), 1971 (pbk) . . . £5

Holiday for Inspector West, Stanley Paul (London), 1946 . . . . £135/£15

Battle for Inspector West, Stanley Paul (London), 1948 . . . . £125/£15

Triumph for Inspector West, Stanley Paul (London), 1948 . . . . £100/£10

ditto, as *The Case Against Paul Raeburn*, Harper (New York), 1958 . . . . . . £35/£5

Inspector West Kicks Off, Stanley Paul (London), 1949 . . . . £75/£10

ditto, as *Sport for Inspector West*, Lancer (New York), 1971
(pbk) £5
Inspector West Alone, Evans (London), 1950 . . £75/£10
ditto, Scribner's (New York), 1975 . . . £15/£5
Inspector West Cries Wolf, Evans (London), 1950. £75/£10
ditto, as *The Creepers*, Scribner's (New York), 1952 . .
. . . . £65/£10
A Case for Inspector West, Evans (London), 1951. £65/£10
ditto, as *The Figure in the Dusk*, Harper (New York), 1952
. . . . £45/£5
Puzzle for Inspector West, Evans (London), 1951 . £45/£5
ditto, as *The Dissemblers*, Scribner's (New York), 1967
. . . . £15/£5
Inspector West at Bay, Evans (London), 1952 . £40/£5
ditto, as *The Blind Spot*, Harper (New York), 1954 £35/£5
A Gun for Inspector West, Hodder & Stoughton (London),
1953 . . . . £35/£5
ditto, as *Give A Man A Gun*, Harper (New York), 1954 .
. . . . £25/£5
Send Inspector West, Hodder & Stoughton (London), 1953.
. . . . £35/£5
ditto, as *Send Superintendent West*, Scribner's (New York),
1976 . . . . £20/£5
A Beauty for Inspector West, Hodder & Stoughton
(London), 1954 . . . . . . £30/£5
ditto, as *The Beauty Queen Killer*, Harper (New York), 1956
. . . . £20/£5
ditto, as *So Young, So Cold, So Fair*, Dell (New York),
1958 (pbk) £10
Inspector West Makes Haste, Hodder & Stoughton
(London), 1955 . . . . . . £30/£5
ditto, as *The Gelignite Gang*, Harper (New York), 1956 .
. . . . £30/£5
Two for Inspector West, Hodder & Stoughton (London),
1955 . . . . £30/£5
ditto, as *Murder: One, Two, Three*, Scribner's (New York),
1960 . . . . £20/£5
Parcels for Inspector West, Hodder & Stoughton (London),
1956 . . . . £25/£5
ditto, as *Death of a Postman*, Harper (New York), 1957 .
. . . . £25/£5
A Prince for Inspector West, Hodder & Stoughton
(London), 1956 . . . . . . £25/£5
ditto, as *Death of an Assassin*, Scribner's (New York), 1960
. . . . £20/£5
Accident for Inspector West, Hodder & Stoughton (London),
1957 . . . . £25/£5
ditto, as *Hit and Run*, Scribner's (New York), 1959 £20/£5
Find Inspector West, Hodder & Stoughton (London), 1957
. . . . £20/£5
ditto, as *The Trouble at Saxby's*, Harper (New York), 1959
. . . . £20/£5
Murder, London-New York, Hodder & Stoughton (London),
1958 . . . . £20/£5
ditto, Scribner's (New York), 1961 . . . £15/£5
Strike for Death, Hodder & Stoughton (London), 1958 .
. . . . £20/£5
ditto, as *The Killing Strike*, Scribner's (New York), 1961 .
. . . . £15/£5
Death of a Racehorse, Hodder & Stoughton (London), 1959
. . . . £20/£5
ditto, Scribner's (New York), 1962 . . . £10/£5
The Case of the Innocent Victims, Hodder & Stoughton
(London), 1959 . . . . . . £20/£5

ditto, Scribner's (New York), 1966 . . . . £10/£5
Murder on the Line, Hodder & Stoughton (London), 1960 .
. . . . £20/£5
ditto, Scribner's (New York), 1963 . . . £15/£5
Death in Cold Print, Hodder & Stoughton (London), 1961 .
. . . . £20/£5
ditto, Scribner's (New York), 1962 . . . £15/£5
The Scene of the Crime, Hodder & Stoughton (London),
1961 . . . . £20/£5
ditto, Scribner's (New York), 1963 . . . £15/£5
Policeman's Dread, Hodder & Stoughton (London), 1962 .
. . . . £20/£5
ditto, Scribner's (New York), 1964 . . . £15/£5
Hang the Little Man, Hodder & Stoughton (London), 1963
. . . . £15/£5
ditto, Scribner's (New York), 1963 . . . £15/£5
Look Three Ways at Murder, Hodder & Stoughton
(London), 1964 . . . . . . £15/£5
ditto, Scribner's (New York), 1965 . . . £15/£5
Murder, London-Australia, Hodder & Stoughton (London),
1965 . . . . £15/£5
ditto, Scribner's (New York), 1965 . . . £15/£5
Murder, London-South Africa, Hodder & Stoughton
(London), 1966 . . . . . . £15/£5
ditto, Scribner's (New York), 1966 . . . £15/£5
The Executioners, Hodder & Stoughton (London), 1967 .
. . . . £15/£5
ditto, Scribner's (New York), 1967 . . . £15/£5
So Young to Burn, Hodder & Stoughton (London), 1968 .
. . . . £15/£5
ditto, Scribner's (New York), 1968 . . . £15/£5
Murder, London-Miami, Hodder & Stoughton (London),
1969 . . . . £15/£5
ditto, Scribner's (New York), 1969 . . . £15/£5
A Part for a Policeman, Hodder & Stoughton (London),
1970 . . . . £15/£5
ditto, Scribner's (New York), 1970 . . . £15/£5
Alibi, Hodder & Stoughton (London), 1971 . £15/£5
ditto, Scribner's (New York), 1971 . . . £15/£5
A Splinter of Glass, Hodder & Stoughton (London), 1972 .
. . . . £15/£5
ditto, Scribner's (New York), 1972 . . . £15/£5
The Theft of Magna Carter, Hodder & Stoughton (London),
1973 . . . . £15/£5
ditto, Scribner's (New York), 1973 . . . £15/£5
The Extortioners, Hodder & Stoughton (London), 1974 .
. . . . £15/£5
ditto, Scribner's (New York), 1975 . . . £15/£5
A Sharp Rise in Crime, Hodder & Stoughton (London),
1978 . . . . £15/£5

'The Toff' Novels
Introducing The Toff, John Long (London), 1938 . £250/£35
The Toff Goes On, John Long (London), 1939 . £200/£25
The Toff Steps Out, John Long (London), 1939 . £175/£20
Here Comes The Toff, John Long (London), 1940. £175/£20
ditto, Walker (New York), 1967 . . . . £20/£5
The Toff Breaks In, John Long (London), 1940 . £175/£20
Salute the Toff, John Long (London), 1941 . . £175/£20
ditto, Walker (New York), 1971 . . . . £20/£5
The Toff Proceeds, John Long (London), 1941 . £175/£20
ditto, Walker (New York), 1968 . . . . £15/£5
The Toff Goes to Market, John Long (London), 1942 . .
. . . . £150/£20

ditto, Walker (New York), 1967 .   .   .   .   £15/£5
The Toff is Back, John Long (London), 1942 . . £125/£20
ditto, Walker (New York), 1974 .   .   .   .   £15/£5
The Toff Among the Millions, John Long (London), 1943 .
.   .   .   . £125/£15
ditto, Walker (New York), 1976 .   .   .   .   £20/£5
Accuse the Toff, John Long (London), 1943 .   . £125/£15
ditto, Walker (New York), 1975 .   .   .   .   £20/£5
The Toff and the Curate, John Long (London), 1944   .   .
.   .   .   . £100/£15
ditto, Walker (New York), 1969 .   .   .   .   £15/£5
The Toff and the Great Illusion, John Long (London), 1944
.   .   .   . £100/£10
ditto, Walker (New York), 1967 .   .   .   .   £15/£5
Feathers for the Toff, John Long (London), 1945 . £75/£10
ditto, Walker (New York), 1970 .   .   .   .   £15/£5
The Toff and the Lady, John Long (London), 1946   £50/£5
ditto, Walker (New York), 1975 .   .   .   .   £15/£5
The Toff on Ice, John Long (London), 1946   .   .   £45/£5
ditto, as **Poison for The Toff**, Pyramid (New York), 1965
(pbk) £5
Hammer the Toff, John Long (London), 1947   .   £40/£5
The Toff in Town, John Long (London), 1948   .   £30/£5
ditto, Walker (New York), 1977 .   .   .   .   £10/£5
The Toff Takes Shares, John Long (London), 1948   £30/£5
ditto, Walker (New York), 1972 .   .   .   .   £10/£5
The Toff and Old Harry, John Long (London), 1949   £30/£5
ditto, Walker (New York), 1970 .   .   .   .   £10/£5
The Toff on Board, John Long (London), 1949   .   £30/£5
ditto, Walker (New York), 1973 .   .   .   .   £10/£5
Fool The Toff, Evans (London), 1950   .   .   £30/£5
ditto, Walker (New York), 1966 .   .   .   .   £15/£5
Kill The Toff, Evans (London), 1950.   .   .   £30/£5
ditto, Walker (New York), 1966 .   .   .   .   £15/£5
A Knife for The Toff, Evans (London), 1951   .   £30/£5
ditto, Pyramid (New York), 1965 (pbk)   .   .   . £5
The Toff Goes Gay, Evans (London), 1951   .   £30/£5
ditto, as **A Mask for The Toff**, Walker (New York), 1966 .
.   .   .   .   £15/£5
Hunt The Toff, Evans (London), 1952   .   .   £30/£5
ditto, Walker (New York), 1969 .   .   .   .   £10/£5
Call The Toff, Hodder & Stoughton (London), 1953 £30/£5
ditto, Walker (New York), 1969 .   .   .   .   £10/£5
The Toff Down Under, Hodder & Stoughton (London), 1953
.   .   .   .   £30/£5
ditto, Walker (New York), 1969 .   .   .   .   £10/£5
The Toff at Butlins, Hodder & Stoughton (London), 1954 .
.   .   .   .   £30/£5
ditto, Walker (New York), 1976 .   .   .   .   £10/£5
The Toff at the Fair, Hodder & Stoughton (London), 1954.
.   .   .   .   £25/£5
ditto, Walker (New York), 1968 .   .   .   .   £10/£5
A Six for The Toff, Hodder & Stoughton (London), 1955 .
.   .   .   .   £25/£5
ditto, Walker (New York), 1969 .   .   .   .   £15/£5
The Toff and the Deep Blue Sea, Hodder & Stoughton
(London), 1955   .   .   .   .   .   .   £25/£5
ditto, Walker (New York), 1967 .   .   .   .   £10/£5
Make-Up for The Toff, Hodder & Stoughton (London),
1956   .   .   .   .   £25/£5
ditto, Walker (New York), 1967 .   .   .   .   £15/£5
The Toff in New York, Hodder & Stoughton (London), 1956
.   .   .   .   £25/£5
ditto, Pyramid (New York), 1964 (pbk)   .   .   . £5

Model for The Toff, Hodder & Stoughton (London), 1957
.   .   .   .   £25/£5
ditto, Pyramid (New York), 1965 (pbk)   .   .   . £5
The Toff on Fire, Hodder & Stoughton (London), 1957
.   .   .   .   £25/£5
ditto, Walker (New York), 1966 .   .   .   .   £15/£5
The Toff and the Stolen Tresses, Hodder & Stoughton
(London), 1958   .   .   .   .   .   .   £25/£5
ditto, Walker (New York), 1965 .   .   .   .   £15/£5
The Toff on the Farm, Hodder & Stoughton (London), 1958
.   .   .   .   £25/£5
ditto, Walker (New York), 1964 .   .   .   .   £20/£5
ditto, as **Terror for The Toff**, Pyramid (New York), 1965
(pbk) £5
Double for The Toff, Hodder & Stoughton (London), 1959.
.   .   .   .   £25/£5
ditto, Walker (New York), 1965 .   .   .   .   £15/£5
The Toff and the Runaway Bride, Hodder & Stoughton
(London), 1959   .   .   .   .   .   .   £25/£5
ditto, Walker (New York), 1964 .   .   .   .   £15/£5
A Rocket for The Toff, Hodder & Stoughton (London), 1960
.   .   .   .   £20/£5
ditto, Pyramid (New York), 1964 (pbk)   .   .   . £5
The Toff and the Kidnapped Child, Hodder & Stoughton
(London), 1960   .   .   .   .   .   .   £20/£5
ditto, Walker (New York), 1967 .   .   .   .   £15/£5
Follow The Toff, Hodder & Stoughton (London), 1961   .
.   .   .   .   £20/£5
ditto, Walker (New York), 1967 .   .   .   .   £15/£5
The Toff and the Teds, Hodder & Stoughton (London), 1961
.   .   .   .   £20/£5
ditto, as **The Toff and the Toughs**, Walker (New York),
1968   .   .   .   .   £10/£5
A Doll for The Toff, Hodder & Stoughton (London), 1963 .
.   .   .   .   £20/£5
ditto, Walker (New York), 1965 .   .   .   .   £15/£5
Leave it to The Toff, Hodder & Stoughton (London), 1963 .
.   .   .   .   £20/£5
ditto, Pyramid (New York), 1965 (pbk)   .   .   . £5
The Toff and the Spider, Hodder & Stoughton (London),
1965   .   .   .   .   £20/£5
ditto, Walker (New York), 1966 .   .   .   .   £15/£5
The Toff in Wax, Hodder & Stoughton (London), 1966
.   .   .   .   £20/£5
ditto, Walker (New York), 1966 .   .   .   .   £15/£5
A Bundle for The Toff, Hodder & Stoughton (London),
1967   .   .   .   .   £20/£5
ditto, Walker (New York), 1968 .   .   .   .   £15/£5
Stars for The Toff, Hodder & Stoughton (London), 1968 .
.   .   .   .   £20/£5
ditto, Walker (New York), 1968 .   .   .   .   £15/£5
The Toff and the Golden Boy, Hodder & Stoughton
(London), 1969   .   .   .   .   .   .   £20/£5
ditto, Walker (New York), 1969 .   .   .   .   £15/£5
The Toff and the Fallen Angels, Hodder & Stoughton
(London), 1970   .   .   .   .   .   .   £20/£5
ditto, Walker (New York), 1970 .   .   .   .   £10/£5
Vote for The Toff, Hodder & Stoughton (London), 1971   .
.   .   .   .   £15/£5
ditto, Walker (New York), 1971 .   .   .   .   £10/£5
The Toff and the Trip-Trip-Triplets, Hodder & Stoughton
(London), 1972   .   .   .   .   .   .   £15/£5
ditto, Walker (New York), 1972 .   .   .   .   £10/£5

The Toff and the Terrified Taxman, Hodder & Stoughton
(London), 1973 . . . . . . £15/£5
ditto, Walker (New York), 1973 . . . . . £10/£5
The Toff and the Sleepy Cowboy, Hodder & Stoughton
(London), 1975 . . . . . . £15/£5
ditto, Walker (New York), 1975 . . . . . £10/£5
The Toff and the Crooked Copper, Hodder & Stoughton
(London), 1977 . . . . . . £15/£5
ditto, Walker (New York), 1977 . . . . . £10/£5

'The Toff' Short Stories
The Toff on the Trail, Everybody's Books (London), n.d.
[1940s?] (pbk) £10
Murder out of the Past, Barrington Gray (London), 1953
(pbk) £10

'Department Z' Novels
The Death Miser, Melrose (London), 1932 . . £400/£45
Redhead, Hurst & Blackett (London), 1934 . . £350/£40
First Came a Murder, Melrose (London), 1934 . £300/£35
ditto, Popular Library (New York), 1972 (pbk) . . £5
Death Round the Corner, Melrose (London), 1935 £300/£35
ditto, Popular Library (New York), 1972 (pbk) . . £5
The Mark of the Crescent, Melrose (London), 1935 .
. . . . £300/£35
ditto, Popular Library (New York), 1972 (pbk) . . £5
Thunder in Europe, Melrose (London), 1936 . . £250/£30
ditto, Popular Library (New York), 1972 (pbk) . . £5
The Terror Trap, Melrose (London), 1936 . . £250/£30
ditto, Popular Library (New York), 1972 (pbk) . . £5
Carriers of Death, Melrose (London), 1937 . . £200/£30
ditto, Popular Library (New York), 1972 (pbk) . . £5
Days of Danger, Melrose (London), 1937 . . £200/£30
ditto, Popular Library (New York), 1972 (pbk) . . £5
Death Stands By, John Long (London), 1938 . . £150/£25
ditto, Popular Library (New York), 1972 (pbk) . . £5
Menace, John Long (London), 1938 . . . . £150/£25
ditto, Popular Library (New York), 1972 (pbk) . . £5
Murder Must Wait, Melrose (London), 1939 . . £125/£20
ditto, Popular Library (New York), 1972 (pbk) . . £5
Panic!, John Long (London), 1939 . . . . £125/£20
ditto, Popular Library (New York), 1972 (pbk) . . £5
Death By Night, John Long (London), 1940 . £125/£20
ditto, Popular Library (New York), 1972 (pbk) . . £5
The Island of Peril, John Long (London), 1940 . £125/£20
ditto, Popular Library (New York), 1976 (pbk) . . £5
Sabotage, John Long (London), 1941 . . . £125/£20
ditto, Popular Library (New York), 1976 (pbk) . . £5
Go Away Death, John Long (London), 1941 . . £125/£20
ditto, Popular Library (New York), 1976 (pbk) . . £5
The Day of Disaster, John Long (London), 1942 . £100/£15
Prepare for Action, Stanley Paul (London), 1942 . £100/£15
ditto, Popular Library (New York), 1975 (pbk) . . £5
No Darker Crime, Stanley Paul (London), 1943 . £75/£15
ditto, Popular Library (New York), 1976 (pbk) . . £5
Dark Peril, Stanley Paul (London), 1944 . . . £50/£10
ditto, Popular Library (New York), 1975 (pbk) . . £5
The Peril Ahead, Stanley Paul (London), 1946 . £40/£5
ditto, Popular Library (New York), 1974 (pbk) . . £5
The League of Dark Men, Stanley Paul (London), 1947 .
. . . . £30/£5
ditto, Popular Library (New York), 1975 (pbk) . . £5
Department of Death, Evans (London), 1949 . . £30/£5
The Enemy Within, Evans (London), 1950 . . £30/£5

ditto, Popular Library (New York), 1977 (pbk) . . £5
Dead or Alive, Evans (London), 1951 . . . £30/£5
ditto, Popular Library (New York), 1974 (pbk) . . £5
A Kind of Prisoner, Hodder & Stoughton (London), 1954 .
. . . . £20/£5
ditto, Popular Library (New York), 1975 (pbk) . . £5
The Black Spiders, Hodder & Stoughton (London), 1957 .
. . . . £20/£5
ditto, Popular Library (New York), 1975 (pbk) . . £5

'Dr Palfrey' Novels
Traitor's Doom, John Long (London), 1942 . . £125/£20
ditto, Walker (New York), 1970 . . . . £20/£5
The Legion of the Lost, John Long (London), 1943 .
. . . . £100/£15
ditto, Stephen Daye (New York), 1944 . . . £75/£10
The Valley of Fear, John Long (London), 1943 . £75/£10
ditto, as *The Perilous Country*, Walker (New York), 1973 .
. . . . £20/£5
Dangerous Quest, John Long (London), 1944 . . £65/£10
ditto, Walker (New York), 1974 . . . . . £15/£5
Death in the Rising Sun, John Long (London), 1945 .
. . . . £60/£10
ditto, Walker (New York), 1976 . . . . . £15/£5
The Hounds of Vengeance, John Long (London), 1945 .
. . . . £50/£10
Shadow of Doom, John Long (London), 1946 . . £45/£5
The House of the Bears, John Long (London), 1946 £45/£5
ditto, Walker (New York), 1975 . . . . . £15/£5
Dark Harvest, John Long (London), 1947 . . . £35/£5
ditto, Walker (New York), 1977 . . . . . £15/£5
Sons of Satan, John Long (London), 1947 . . . £35/£5
The Wings of Peace, John Long (London), 1948 . £35/£5
ditto, Walker (New York), 1978 . . . . . £15/£5
The Dawn of Darkness, John Long (London), 1949 £35/£5
The League of Light, Evans (London), 1949 . . £30/£5
The Man Who Shook the World, Evans (London), 1950 .
. . . . £30/£5
The Prophet of Fire, Evans (London), 1951 . . £30/£5
The Children of Hate, Evans (London), 1952 . . £30/£5
ditto, as *The Killers of Innocence*, Walker (New York),
1971 . . . . £20/£5
The Touch of Death, Hodder & Stoughton (London), 1954.
. . . . £25/£5
ditto, Walker (New York), 1969 . . . . £20/£5
The Mists of Fear, Hodder & Stoughton (London), 1955 .
. . . . £25/£5
ditto, Walker (New York), 1977 . . . . . £15/£5
The Flood, Hodder & Stoughton (London), 1956 . £25/£5
ditto, Walker (New York), 1969 . . . . . £20/£5
The Plague of Silence, Hodder & Stoughton (London), 1958
. . . . £20/£5
ditto, Walker (New York), 1968 . . . . . £15/£5
The Drought, Hodder & Stoughton (London), 1959 £20/£5
ditto, Walker (New York), 1967 . . . . . £15/£5
The Terror, Hodder & Stoughton (London), 1962 . £20/£5
ditto, Walker (New York), 1966 . . . . . £15/£5
The Depths, Hodder & Stoughton (London), 1963 . £20/£5
ditto, Walker (New York), 1967 . . . . . £20/£5
The Sleep, Hodder & Stoughton (London), 1964 . £20/£5
ditto, Walker (New York), 1968 . . . . . £20/£5
The Inferno, Hodder & Stoughton (London), 1965 £20/£5
ditto, Walker (New York), 1966 . . . . . £15/£5
The Famine, Hodder & Stoughton (London), 1967 £20/£5

ditto, Walker (New York), 1968 . . . . . £20/£5
The Blight, Hodder & Stoughton (London), 1968 . £20/£5
ditto, Walker (New York), 1968 . . . . . £20/£5
The Oasis, Hodder & Stoughton (London), 1970 . £20/£5
ditto, Walker (New York), 1970 . . . . . £20/£5
The Smog, Hodder & Stoughton (London), 1970 . £20/£5
ditto, Walker (New York), 1971 . . . . . £20/£5
The Unbegotten, Hodder & Stoughton (London), 1971. .
. . . . £20/£5
ditto, Walker (New York), 1972 . . . . . £15/£5
The Insulators, Hodder & Stoughton (London), 1972 . .
. . . . £15/£5
ditto, Walker (New York), 1973 . . . . . £15/£5
The Voiceless One, Hodder & Stoughton (London), 1973 .
. . . . £15/£5
ditto, Walker (New York), 1974 . . . . . £10/£5
The Thunder-Maker, Hodder & Stoughton (London), 1976
. . . . £10/£5
ditto, Walker (New York), 1976 . . . . . £10/£5
The Whirlwind, Hodder & Stoughton (London), 1979 . .
. . . . £10/£5

'Sexton Blake' Titles

The Case of the Murdered Financier, Amalgamated Press
(London), 1937 (pbk). £25
The Great Air Swindle, Amalgamated Press (London), 1939
(pbk) £25
The Man from Fleet Street, Amalgamated Press (London),
1940 (pbk) £25
The Case of the Mad Inventor, Amalgamated Press
(London), 1942 (pbk). £25
Private Carter's Crime, Amalgamated Press (London), 1943
(pbk) £25

Other Novels

Seven Times Seven, Melrose (London), 1932 . . £350/£45
Men, Maids and Murder, Melrose (London), 1933 £300/£40
Four of the Best, Hodder & Stoughton (London), 1955 .
. . . . £25/£5
The Mountain of the Blind, Hodder & Stoughton (London),
1960 . . . . £20/£5
The Foothills of Fear, Hodder & Stoughton (London), 1961
. . . . £20/£5
The Masters of Bow Street, Hodder & Stoughton (London),
1972 . . . . £20/£5
ditto, Simon & Schuster (New York), 1974 . . £15/£5

Children's Titles

Ned Cartwright, Middleweight Champion, Mellifont
(London), 1935 (pseud 'James Marsden'; pbk) . . £30
The Men Who Died Laughing, D.C. Thomson (Dundee/
London), 1935 (pbk) £20
The Killer Squad, Newnes (London), 1936 (pbk) . . £20
Our Glorious Term, Sampson Low (London), [n.d.] .
. . . . £175/£25
The Captain of the Fifth, Sampson Low (London), [n.d.] .
. . . . £175/£25
Blazing the Air Trail, Sampson Low (London), 1936 . .
. . . . £175/£25
The Jungle Flight Mystery, Sampson Low (London), 1936.
. . . . £175/£25
The Mystery 'Plane, Sampson Low (London), 1936 . .
. . . . £175/£25

Murder by Magic, Amalgamated Press (London), 1937 (pbk)
. . . . £20
The Mysterious Mr Rocco, Mellifont (London), 1937 (pbk)
. . . . £20
The S.O.S. Flight, Sampson Low (London), 1937 . £150/£25
The Secret Aeroplane, Sampson Low (London), 1937 . .
. . . . £150/£25
The Treasure Flight, Sampson Low (London), 1937 . .
. . . . £150/£25
The Air Marauders, Sampson Low (London), 1937 . .
. . . . £150/£25
The Black Biplane, Sampson Low (London), 1937 £150/£25
The Mystery Flight, Sampson Low (London), 1937 . .
. . . . £150/£25
The Double Motive, Mellifont (London), 1938 . £150/£25
The Double-Cross of Death, Mellifont (London), 1938 (pbk)
. . . . £20
The Missing Hoard, Mellifont (London), 1938 (pbk) . £20
Mystery at Manby House, North News Syndicate, 1938
(pbk) £20
The Fighting Flyers, Sampson Low (London), 1938 . .
. . . . £150/£20
The Flying Stowaways, Sampson Low (London), 1938 .
. . . . £150/£20
The Miracle 'Plane, Sampson Low (London), 1938 . .
. . . . £150/£20
Dixon Hawke, Secret Agent, D.C. Thomson (Dundee/
London), 1939 (pbk) £15
Documents of Death, Mellifont (London), 1939 (pbk) . £15
The Hidden Hoard, Mellifont (London), 1939 (pbk) . £15
Mottled Death, D.C. Thomson (Dundee/London), 1939
(pbk) £15
The Blue Flyer, Mellifont (London), 1939 (pbk) . . £15
The Jumper, Northern News Syndicate, 1939 (pbk) . £15
The Mystery of Blackmoor Prison, Mellifont (London),
1939 (pbk) £15
The Sacred Eye, D.C. Thomson (Dundee/London), 1939 .
. . . . £150/£25
The Ship of Death, D.C. Thomson (Dundee/London), 1939
(pbk) £10
Peril By Air, Newnes (London), 1939 (pbk) . . . £10
The Flying Turk, Sampson Low (London), 1939 . £150/£25
The Monarch of the Skies, Sampson Low (London), 1939 .
. . . . £125/£20
The Fear of Felix Corder, Fleetway (London), [n.d.] (pbk).
. . . . £10
John Brand, Fugitive, Fleetway (London), [n.d.] (pbk) £10
The Night of Dread, Fleetway (London), [n.d.] (pbk) . £10
Dazzle - Air Ace No. 1, Newnes (London), 1940 (pbk) . £10
Dazzle and the Red Bomber, Newnes (London), n.d. (pbk) .
. . . . £10
Five Missing Men, Newnes (London), 1940 (pbk) . . £10
The Poison Gas Robberies, Mellifont (London), 1940 (pbk)
. . . . £10
The Cinema Crimes, Pemberton (London), 1945 (pbk). £10
The Missing Monoplane, Sampson Low (London), 1947 .
. . . . £35/£10

Novels Written as 'J.J. Marric'

Gideon's Day, Hodder & Stoughton (London), 1955 . .
. . . . £65/£10
ditto, Harper (New York), 1955 . . . . . £65/£10
Gideon's Week, Hodder & Stoughton (London), 1956 . .
. . . . £45/£10

ditto, Harper (New York), 1956 . . . £45/£5
Gideon's Night, Hodder & Stoughton (London), 1957 . .
. . . . . £35/£5
ditto, Harper (New York), 1957 . . . . £35/£5
Gideon's Month, Hodder & Stoughton (London), 1958 .
. . . . . £25/£5
ditto, Harper (New York), 1958 . . . . £25/£5
Gideon's Staff, Hodder & Stoughton (London), 1959 . .
. . . . . £25/£5
ditto, Harper (New York), 1959 . . . . £25/£5
Gideon's Risk, Hodder & Stoughton (London), 1960 £25/£5
ditto, Harper (New York), 1960 . . . £25/£5
Gideon's Fire, Hodder & Stoughton (London), 1961 £20/£5
ditto, Harper (New York), 1961 . . . . £20/£5
Gideon's March, Hodder & Stoughton (London), 1962 .
. . . . . £20/£5
ditto, Harper (New York), 1962 . . . £20/£5
Gideon's Ride, Hodder & Stoughton (London), 1963 £20/£5
ditto, Harper (New York), 1963 . . . . £15/£5
Gideon's Vote, Hodder & Stoughton (London), 1964 £15/£5
ditto, Harper (New York), 1964 . . . . £15/£5
Gideon's Lot, Harper (New York), 1964 . . £15/£5
ditto, Hodder & Stoughton (London), 1965 . . £15/£5
Gideon's Badge, Harper (New York), 1965 . . £15/£5
ditto, Hodder & Stoughton (London), 1966 . . £15/£5
Gideon's Wrath, Hodder & Stoughton (London), 1967. .
. . . . . £15/£5
ditto, Harper (New York), 1967 . . . . £15/£5
Gideon's River, Hodder & Stoughton (London), 1968 . .
. . . . . £15/£5
ditto, Harper (New York), 1968 . . . . £15/£5
Gideon's Power, Hodder & Stoughton (London), 1969. .
. . . . . £15/£5
ditto, Harper (New York), 1969 . . . . £10/£5
Gideon's Sport, Hodder & Stoughton (London), 1970 . .
. . . . . £15/£5
ditto, Harper (New York), 1970 . . . . £10/£5
Gideon's Art, Hodder & Stoughton (London), 1971 £15/£5
ditto, Harper (New York), 1971 . . . . £10/£5
Gideon's Men, Hodder & Stoughton (London), 1972 £15/£5
ditto, Harper (New York), 1972 . . . . £10/£5
Gideon's Press, Hodder & Stoughton (London), 1973 . .
. . . . . £10/£5
ditto, Harper (New York), 1973 . . . . £10/£5
Gideon's Fog, Hodder & Stoughton (London), 1975 £10/£5
ditto, Harper (New York), 1975 . . . . £10/£5
Gideon's Drive, Hodder & Stoughton (London), 1976 . .
. . . . . £10/£5
ditto, Harper (New York), 1976 . . . . £10/£5

Novels Written as 'Anthony Morton'
Meet the Baron, Harrap (London), 1937 . . . £250/£30
ditto, Harrap (London), 1937 (12 presentation copies) . £450
ditto, as ***The Man In The Blue Mask***, Lippincott
(Philadelphia, PA), 1937 . . . . . £250/£25
The Baron Returns, Harrap (London), 1937 . . £250/£25
ditto, as ***The Return of The Blue Mask***, Lippincott
(Philadelphia, PA), 1937 . . . . . £225/£25
The Baron Again, Sampson Low (London), 1938 . £200/£30
ditto, as ***Salute Blue Mask***, Lippincott (Philadelphia, PA),
1938 . . . . £200/£25
The Baron At Bay, Sampson Low (London), 1938 £200/£25
ditto, as ***Blue Mask at Bay***, Lippincott (Philadelphia, PA),
1938 . . . . £200/£25

Alias the Baron, Sampson Low (London), 1939 . £175/£20
ditto, as ***Alias Blue Mask***, Lippincott (Philadelphia, PA),
1939 . . . . £175/£20
The Baron at Large, Sampson Low (London), 1939 . .
. . . . £165/£20
ditto, as ***Challenge Blue Mask!***, Lippincott (Philadelphia,
PA), 1939 . . . . £165/£20
Versus the Baron, Sampson Low (London), 1940 . £145/£20
ditto, as ***The Blue Mask Strikes Again***, Lippincott
(Philadelphia, PA), 1940 . . . . . £145/£20
Call for the Baron, Sampson Low (London), 1940 £145/£20
ditto, as ***Blue Mask Victorious***, Lippincott (Philadelphia,
PA), 1940 . . . . £145/£20
The Baron Comes Back, Sampson Low (London), 1943 .
. . . . £100/£15
Mr Quentin Investigates, Sampson Low (London), 1943 .
. . . . £65/£10
Introducing Mr Brandon, Sampson Low (London), 1944 .
. . . . £60/£5
A Case for the Baron, Sampson Low (London), 1945 . .
. . . . £50/£10
ditto, Duell (New York), 1949 . . . . £25/£5
Reward for the Baron, Sampson Low (London), 1945 . .
. . . . £50/£10
Career for the Baron, Sampson Low (London), 1946 . .
. . . . £45/£5
ditto, Duell (New York), 1950 . . . . £25/£5
The Baron and the Beggar, Sampson Low (London), 1947
. . . . £35/£5
ditto, Duell (New York), 1950 . . . . £20/£5
Blame the Baron, Sampson Low (London), 1948 . £35/£5
ditto, Duell (New York), 1951 . . . . £20/£5
A Rope for the Baron, Sampson Low (London), 1948 . .
. . . . £35/£5
ditto, Duell (New York), 1949 . . . . £30/£5
Books for the Baron, Sampson Low (London), 1949 £35/£5
ditto, Duell (New York), 1952 . . . . £20/£5
Cry for the Baron, Sampson Low (London), 1950. £30/£5
ditto, Walker (New York), 1970 . . . . £15/£5
Trap the Baron, Sampson Low (London), 1950 . £30/£5
ditto, Walker (New York), 1971 . . . . £15/£5
Attack the Baron, Sampson Low (London), 1951 . £30/£5
Shadow the Baron, Sampson Low (London), 1951 £25/£5
Warn the Baron, Sampson Low (London), 1952 . £25/£5
The Baron Goes East, Sampson Low (London), 1953 . .
. . . . £25/£5
The Baron in France, Hodder & Stoughton (London), 1953
. . . . £25/£5
ditto, Walker (New York), 1976 . . . . £10/£5
Danger for the Baron, Hodder & Stoughton (London), 1953
. . . . £25/£5
ditto, Walker (New York), 1974 . . . . £10/£5
The Baron Goes Fast, Hodder & Stoughton (London), 1954
. . . . £25/£5
ditto, Walker (New York), 1972 . . . . £10/£5
Nest-Egg for the Baron, Hodder & Stoughton (London),
1954 . . . . £25/£5
ditto, as ***Deaf, Dumb and Blonde***, Doubleday (New York),
1961 . . . . £15/£5
Help from the Baron, Hodder & Stoughton (London), 1955
. . . . £25/£5
ditto, Walker (New York), 1977 . . . . £10/£5
Hide the Baron, Hodder & Stoughton (London), 1956 . .
. . . . £25/£5

ditto, Walker (New York), 1978 . . . . . £10/£5
Frame the Baron, Hodder & Stoughton (London), 1957 .
. . . . £25/£5
ditto, as **The Double Frame**, Doubleday (New York), 1961.
. . . . £15/£5
Red Eye for the Baron, Hodder & Stoughton (London),
1958 . . . . £25/£5
ditto, as **The Double Frame**, Doubleday (New York), 1960.
. . . . £15/£5
Black for the Baron, Hodder & Stoughton (London), 1959 .
. . . . £25/£5
ditto, as **If Anything Happens to Hester**, Doubleday (New
York), 1962 . . . . £15/£5
Salute for the Baron, Hodder & Stoughton (London), 1960.
. . . . £25/£5
ditto, Walker (New York), 1973 . . . . . £10/£5
A Branch for the Baron, Hodder & Stoughton (London),
1961 . . . . £25/£5
ditto, as **The Baron Branches Out**, Scribner's (New York),
1967 . . . . £15/£5
Bad for the Baron, Hodder & Stoughton (London), 1962 .
. . . . £25/£5
ditto, as **The Baron and the Stolen Legacy**, Scribner's (New
York), 1967 . . . . £15/£5
A Sword for the Baron, Hodder & Stoughton (London),
1963 . . . . £25/£5
ditto, as **The Baron and the Mogul Swords**, Scribner's (New
York), 1966 . . . . £15/£5
The Baron on Board, Hodder & Stoughton (London), 1964
. . . . £25/£5
ditto, Walker (New York), 1968 . . . . . £10/£5
The Baron and the Chinese Puzzle, Hodder & Stoughton
(London), 1965 . . . . . £20/£5
ditto, Scribner's (New York), 1966 . . . £20/£5
Sport for the Baron, Hodder & Stoughton (London), 1966 .
. . . . £20/£5
ditto, Walker (New York), 1969 . . . . £15/£5
Affair for the Baron, Hodder & Stoughton (London), 1967.
. . . . £20/£5
ditto, Walker (New York), 1968 . . . . £15/£5
The Baron and the Missing Old Masters, Hodder &
Stoughton (London), 1968 . . . £15/£5
ditto, Walker (New York), 1969 . . . . £15/£5
The Baron and the Unfinished Portrait, Hodder &
Stoughton (London), 1969 . . . £15/£5
ditto, Walker (New York), 1970 . . . . £15/£5
Last Laugh for the Baron, Hodder & Stoughton (London),
1970 . . . . £15/£5
ditto, Walker (New York), 1971 . . . . £15/£5
The Baron Goes A-Buying, Hodder & Stoughton (London),
1971 . . . . £10/£5
ditto, Walker (New York), 1972 . . . . £10/£5
The Baron and the Arrogant Artist, Hodder & Stoughton
(London), 1972 . . . . . £10/£5
ditto, Walker (New York), 1973 . . . . £10/£5
Burgle the Baron, Hodder & Stoughton (London), 1973 .
. . . . £10/£5
ditto, Walker (New York), 1974 . . . . £10/£5
The Baron, King-Maker, Hodder & Stoughton (London),
1975 . . . . £10/£5
ditto, Walker (New York), 1975 . . . . £10/£5
Love for the Baron, Hodder & Stoughton (London), 1976 .
. . . . £10/£5

Novels Written as 'Gordon Ashe'
Death on Demand, John Long (London), 1939 . £125/£25
The Speaker, John Long (London), 1939 . . . £125/£25
ditto, as **The Croaker**, Holt (New York), 1973 . £15/£5
Terror by Day, John Long (London), 1940 . £125/£20
Secret Murder, John Long (London), 1940 . £125/£20
Who Was the Jester?, Newnes (London), 1940 . £125/£20
'Ware Danger, John Long (London), 1941 . £125/£20
Murder Most Foul, John Long (London), 1942 . £100/£20
There Goes Death, John Long (London), 1942 . £100/£20
Death in High Places, John Long (London), 1942 . £100/£20
Death in Flames, John Long (London), 1943 . . £75/£15
Two Men Missing, John Long (London), 1943 . £75/£15
Rogues Rampant, John Long (London), 1944 . £50/£10
Death on the Move, John Long (London), 1945 . £50/£10
Invitation to Adventure, John Long (London), 1945 £45/£10
Here is Danger, John Long (London), 1946 . . £40/£5
Give Me Murder, John Long (London), 1947 . . £30/£5
Murder Too Late, John Long (London), 1947 . . £30/£5
Dark Mystery, John Long (London), 1948 . . £30/£5
Engagement With Death, John Long (London), 1948 . .
. . . . £30/£5
A Puzzle in Pearls, John Long (London), 1949 . £30/£5
Kill or Be Killed, Evans (London), 1949 . . £30/£5
The Dark Circle, Evans (London), 1950 . . . £30/£5
Murder With Mushrooms, Evans (London), 1950 . £25/£5
ditto, Holt (New York), 1974 . . . . £15/£5
Death in Diamonds, Evans (London), 1951 . . £25/£5
Missing or Dead?, Evans (London), 1951 . . £25/£5
Death in a Hurry, Evans (London), 1952 . . . £25/£5
The Long Search, Evans (London), 1953 . . . £25/£5
ditto, as **Drop Dead**, Ace (New York), 1954 (pbk) . . £10
Sleepy Death, Evans (London), 1953 . . . £25/£5
Double for Death, Evans (London), 1954 . . . £20/£5
ditto, Holt (New York), 1969 . . . . £15/£5
Death in the Trees, Evans (London), 1954 . . £20/£5
The Kidnapped Child, Evans (London), 1955 . . £20/£5
ditto, Holt (New York), 1971 . . . . £15/£5
The Man Who Stayed Alive, John Long (London), 1955 .
. . . . £20/£5
Day of Fear, John Long (London), 1956 . . . £20/£5
ditto, Holt (New York), 1978 . . . . £15/£5
No Need to Die, John Long (London), 1956 . £20/£5
ditto, as **You've Bet Your Life**, Ace (New York), 1957 (pbk)
. . . . £10
Wait for Death, John Long (London), 1957 . . £20/£5
ditto, Holt (New York), 1972 . . . . £15/£5
Come Home to Death, John Long (London), 1958 . £20/£5
ditto, as **The Pack of Lies**, Doubleday (New York), 1959 .
. . . . £20/£5
Elope to Death, John Long (London), 1959 . . £20/£5
ditto, Holt (New York), 1977 . . . . £15/£5
Don't Let Him Kill, John Long (London), 1960 . £15/£5
ditto, as **The Man Who Laughed At Murder**, Doubleday
(New York), 1960 . . . . . £15/£5
The Crime Haters, John Long (London), 1961 . £15/£5
ditto, Doubleday (New York), 1960 . . . . £15/£5
Rogues Ransome, John Long (London), 1962 . £15/£5
ditto, Doubleday (New York), 1961 . . . . £15/£5
Death from Below, John Long (London), 1963 . £15/£5
ditto, Holt (New York), 1968 . . . . £15/£5
The Big Call, John Long (London), 1964 . . . £15/£5
ditto, Holt (New York), 1975 . . . . £15/£5
A Promise of Diamonds, John Long (London), 1965 £15/£5

ditto, Dodd (New York), 1964 . . . . . £15/£5
A Taste of Treasure, John Long (London), 1966 . £15/£5
ditto, Holt (New York), 1966 . . . . £15/£5
A Clutch of Coppers, John Long (London), 1967 . £15/£5
ditto, Holt (New York), 1969 . . . . £15/£5
A Shadow of Death, John Long (London), 1968 . £15/£5
ditto, Holt (New York), 1976 . . . . £15/£5
A Scream of Murder, John Long (London), 1970 . £15/£5
ditto, Holt (New York), 1970 . . . . £15/£5
A Nest of Traitors, John Long (London), 1970 . £15/£5
ditto, Holt (New York), 1971 . . . . £15/£5
A Rabble of Rebels, John Long (London), 1971 . £15/£5
ditto, Holt (New York), 1972 . . . . £15/£5
A Herald of Doom, John Long (London), 1973 . £15/£5
ditto, Holt (New York), 1975 . . . . £15/£5
A Blast of Trumpets, John Long (London), 1975 . £10/£5
ditto, Holt (New York), 1976 . . . . £10/£5
A Plague of Demons, John Long (London), 1976 . £10/£5

Novels Written as 'M.E. Cooke'
Fire of Death, Fiction House (New York), 1934 (pbk) . £10
The Black Heart, Gramol (London), 1935 (pbk) . . £10
The Casino Mystery, Mellifont (London), 1935 (pbk) . £10
The Crime Gang, Mellifont (London), 1935 (pbk) . . £10
The Death Drive, Mellifont (London), 1935 (pbk) . . £10
No 1's Last Crime, Fiction House (New York), 1935 (pbk) .
. . . . £10
The Stolen Formula Mystery, Mellifont (London), 1935
(pbk) £10
The Big Radium Mystery, Mellifont, 1936 (pbk) . £10
The Day of Terror, Mellifont (London), 1936 (pbk) . £10
The Dummy Robberies, Mellifont (London), 1936 (pbk) £10
The Hypnotic Demon, Fiction House (New York), 1936
(pbk) £10
The Moat Farm Mystery, Fiction House (New York), 1936
(pbk) £10
The Secret Formula, Fiction House (New York), 1936 (pbk)
. . . . £10
The Successful Alibi, Mellifont (London), 1936 (pbk) . £10
The Hadfield Mystery, Mellifont (London), 1937 (pbk) . £10
The Moving Eye, Mellifont (London), 1937 (pbk) . . £10
The Raven, Fiction House (New York), 1937 (pbk) . £10
For Her Sister's Sake, Fiction House (New York), 1938
(pbk) £10
The Mountain Terror, Mellifont (London), 1939 (pbk) . £10
The Verrall Street Affair, Newnes (London), 1940 (pbk) .
. . . . £10

Paperbacks Written as 'Margaret Cooke'
For Love's Sake, Northern News Syndicate, 1934 (pbk) £5
Troubled Journey, Fiction House (New York), 1937 (pbk) .
. . . . £5
False Love or True, Northern News Syndicate, 1937 (pbk) .
. . . . £5
Fate's Playthings, Fiction House (New York), 1938 (pbk) .
. . . . £5
Web of Destiny, Fiction House (New York), 1938 (pbk) £5
Whose Lover?, Fiction House (New York), 1938 (pbk) £5
A Mannequin's Romance, Fiction House (New York), 1938
(pbk) £5
Love Calls Twice, Fiction House (New York), 1938 (pbk) £5
The Road to Happiness, Fiction House (New York), 1938
(pbk) £5
The Turn of Fate, Fiction House (New York), 1939 (pbk) £5

Love Triumphant, Fiction House (New York), 1939 (pbk) .
. . . . £5
Love Comes Back, Fiction House (New York), 1939 (pbk) .
. . . . £5
Crossroads of Love, Mellifont (London), 1939 (pbk) . £5
Love's Journey, Fiction House (New York), 1940 (pbk) £5

Novels Written as 'Henry St John Cooper'
The Golconda Necklace, Sampson Low (London), 1926 .
. . . . £75/£15
The Splendid Love, Sampson Low (London), 1932 £50/£10
Dangerous Paths, Sampson Low (London), 1933 . £50/£10
Call of Love, Sampson Low (London), 1936 . £45/£10
Chains of Love, Sampson Low (London), 1937 . £30/£5
Love's Pilgrim, Sampson Low (London), 1937 . £30/£5
The Tangled Legacy, Sampson Low (London), 1938 £30/£5
The Greater Desire, Sampson Low (London), 1938 £30/£5
Love's Ordeal, Sampson Low (London), 1939 . £25/£5
The Lost Lover, Sampson Low (London), 1940 . £25/£5

Novels Written as 'Norman Deane'
Secret Errand, Hurst & Blackett (London), 1939 . £125/£20
ditto, McKay (New York), 1974 (published as by 'John
Creasey') . . . . £15/£5
Dangerous Journey, Hurst & Blackett (London), 1939 .
. . . . £125/£20
ditto, McKay (New York), 1974 (published as by 'John
Creasey') . . . . £15/£5
Unknown Mystery, Hurst & Blackett (London), 1940 . .
. . . . £125/£20
ditto, McKay (New York), 1972 (published as by 'John
Creasey') . . . . £15/£5
The Withered Man, Hurst & Blackett (London), 1940 . .
. . . . £125/£20
ditto, McKay (New York), 1974 (published as by 'John
Creasey') . . . . £15/£5
I Am the Withered Man, Hurst & Blackett (London), 1941 .
. . . . £100/£15
ditto, McKay (New York), 1973 (published as by 'John
Creasey') . . . . £15/£5
Where is the Withered Man?, Hurst & Blackett (London),
1942 . . . . £100/£15
ditto, McKay (New York), 1974 (published as by 'John
Creasey') . . . . £15/£5
Return to Adventure, Hurst & Blackett (London), 1943 .
. . . . £75/£10
Gateway to Escape, Hurst & Blackett (London), 1944 . .
. . . . £50/£5
Come Home to Crime, Hurst & Blackett (London), 1945 .
. . . . £50/£5
Play for Murder, Hurst & Blackett (London), 1946 £40/£5
The Silent House, Hurst & Blackett (London), 1947 £30/£5
Why Murder?, Hurst & Blackett (London), 1948 . £30/£5
Intent to Murder, Hurst & Blackett (London), 1948 £30/£5
The Man I Didn't Kill, Hurst & Blackett (London), 1950 .
. . . . £30/£5
Double for Death, Hurst & Blackett (London), 1950 £30/£5
Golden Death, Hurst & Blackett (London), 1952 . £25/£5
Look at Murder, Hurst & Blackett (London), 1952 £25/£5
Murder Ahead, Hurst & Blackett (London), 1953 . £25/£5
Death in the Spanish Sun, Hurst & Blackett (London), 1954
. . . . £25/£5
Incense of Death, Hurst & Blackett (London), 1954 £25/£5

Paperbacks Written as 'Elise Felcamps'
Love or Hate?, Fiction House (New York), 1936 (pbk) . £25
True Love, Fiction House (New York), 1937 (pbk)   . £25
Love's Triumph, Fiction House (New York), 1937 (pbk) £25

Novels Written as 'Robert Caine Frazer'
Kilby Takes a Risk, Pocket (New York), 1962 (pbk)   . £10
R.I.S.C., Collins (London), 1962   .   .   .   . £20/£5
The Secret Syndicate, Collins (London), 1963   . £20/£5
The Hollywood Hoax, Collins (London), 1964   . £20/£5
The Miami Mob and *Mark Kilby Stands Alone*, Collins
   (London), 1965   .   .   .   . £15/£5

Paperbacks Written as 'Patrick Gill'
The Fighting Footballers, Mellifont (London), 1937 (pbk).
   .   .   .   . £20
The Laughing Lightweight, Mellifont (London), 1937 (pbk)
   .   .   .   . £20
The Battle for the Cup, Mellifont (London), 1939 (pbk) £20
The Fighting Tramp, Mellifont (London), 1939 (pbk) . £20
The Mystery of the Centre-Forward, Mellifont (London),
   1939 (pbk) £20
The £10,000 Trophy Race, Mellifont (London), 1939 (pbk)
   .   .   .   . £20
The Secret Super-Charger, Mellifont (London), 1940 (pbk)
   .   .   .   . £20

Novels Written as 'Michael Halliday'
Three For Adventure, Cassell (London), 1937   . £125/£15
Four Find Danger, Cassell (London), 1937   . £100/£15
Two Meet Trouble, Cassell (London), 1938   . £75/£15
Murder Comes Home, Stanley Paul (London), 1940 £65/£10
Heir to Murder, Stanley Paul (London), 1940.   . £60/£10
Murder By the Way, Stanley Paul (London), 1940. £50/£10
Who Saw Him Die?, Stanley Paul (London), 1941.   £50/£5
Foul Play Suspected, Stanley Paul (London), 1942   £45/£5
Who Died at the Grange, Stanley Paul (London), 1942   .
   .   .   .   . £45/£5
Five to Kill, Stanley Paul (London), 1943.   .   . £45/£5
Murder at King's Kitchen, Stanley Paul (London), 1943   .
   .   .   .   . £35/£5
No Crime More Cruel, Stanley Paul (London), 1944 £35/£5
Who Said Murder, Stanley Paul (London), 1944   . £35/£5
Crime With Many Voices, Stanley Paul (London), 1945   .
   .   .   .   . £30/£5
Murder Makes Murder, Stanley Paul (London), 1946 .   .
   .   .   .   . £30/£5
Mystery Motive, Stanley Paul (London), 1947.   . £25/£5
ditto, McKay (New York), 1974 (published as by 'Jeremy
   York')   .   .   .   . £10/£5
Lend a Hand to Murder, Stanley Paul (London), 1947.   .
   .   .   .   . £25/£5
First a Murder, Stanley Paul (London), 1948 .   . £25/£5
ditto, McKay (New York), 1972 (published as by 'Jeremy
   York')   .   .   .   . £10/£5
No End to Danger, Stanley Paul (London), 1948 . £25/£5
Who Killed Rebecca?, Stanley Paul (London), 1949 £25/£5
The Dying Witness, Evans (London), 1949   .   . £25/£5
Dine With Murder, Evans (London), 1950   .   . £25/£5
Murder Weekend, Evans (London), 1950.   .   . £25/£5
Quarrel With Murder, Evans (London), 1951.   . £25/£5
Take a Body, Evans (London), 1951 .   .   .   . £25/£5
ditto, World (New York), 1972 (published as by 'John
   Creasey')   .   .   .   . £10/£5

Lame Dog Murder, Evans (London), 1952   .   . £25/£5
ditto, World (New York), 1972 (published as by 'John
   Creasey')   .   .   .   . £10/£5
Murder in the Stars, Hodder & Stoughton (London), 1953 .
   .   .   .   . £25/£5
Man on the Run, Hodder & Stoughton (London), 1953   .
   .   .   .   . £25/£5
ditto, World (New York), 1972 (published as by 'John
   Creasey')   .   .   .   . £10/£5
Death out of Darkness, Hodder & Stoughton (London),
   1954   .   .   .   . £25/£5
ditto, World (New York), 1979 (published as by 'John
   Creasey')   .   .   .   . £10/£5
Out of the Shadows, Hodder & Stoughton (London), 1954 .
   .   .   .   . £25/£5
ditto, World (New York), 1971 (published as by 'John
   Creasey')   .   .   .   . £10/£5
Cat and Mouse, Hodder & Stoughton (London), 1955 .   .
   .   .   .   . £25/£5
ditto, as *Hilda, Take Heed*, Scribner's (New York), 1957
   (published as by 'Jeremy York')   .   .   . £20/£5
Murder at End House, Hodder & Stoughton (London), 1955
   .   .   .   . £25/£5
Death of a Stranger, Hodder & Stoughton (London), 1957 .
   .   .   .   . £25/£5
ditto, as *Come Here and Die*, Scribner's (New York), 1959
   (published as by 'Jeremy York')   .   .   . £20/£5
Runaway, Hodder & Stoughton (London), 1957   . £25/£10
ditto, World (New York), 1971 (published as by 'John
   Creasey')   .   .   .   . £10/£5
Murder Assured, Hodder & Stoughton (London), 1958   .
   .   .   .   . £25/£10
Missing from Home, Hodder & Stoughton (London), 1959 .
   .   .   .   . £25/£5
ditto, as *Missing*, Scribner's (New York), 1960 (published as
   by 'Jeremy York')   .   .   .   .   .   . £20/£5
Thicker Than Water, Hodder & Stoughton (London), 1959
   .   .   .   . £25/£5
ditto, Doubleday (New York), 1962 (published as by 'Jeremy
   York')   .   .   .   . £20/£5
Go Ahead with Murder, Hodder & Stoughton (London),
   1960   .   .   .   . £25/£5
ditto, as *Two For The Money*, Doubleday (New York), 1962
   (published as by 'Jeremy York')   .   .   . £20/£5
How Many to Kill?, Hodder & Stoughton (London), 1960 .
   .   .   .   . £25/£5
ditto, as *The Girl With The Leopard-Skin Bag*, Scribner's
   (New York), 1961   .   .   .   .   .   . £20/£5
The Edge of Terror, Hodder & Stoughton (London), 1961 .
   .   .   .   . £25/£5
ditto, Macmillan (New York), 1963 (published as by 'Jeremy
   York')   .   .   .   . £15/£5
The Man I Killed, Hodder & Stoughton (London), 1961   .
   .   .   .   . £20/£5
ditto, Macmillan (New York), 1963 (published as by 'Jeremy
   York')   .   .   .   . £15/£5
Hate to Kill, Hodder & Stoughton (London), 1962.   £20/£5
The Quiet Fear, Hodder & Stoughton (London), 1963 .   .
   .   .   .   . £20/£5
ditto, Macmillan (New York), 1968 (published as by 'Jeremy
   York')   .   .   .   . £15/£5
The Guilt of Innocence, Hodder & Stoughton (London),
   1964   .   .   .   . £20/£5

Cunning as a Fox, Hodder & Stoughton (London), 1965 .
.   .   .   .   £20/£5
ditto, Macmillan (New York), 1965 (published as by 'Kyle
Hunt') .   .   .   .   £20/£5
Wicked as the Devil, Hodder & Stoughton (London), 1966 .
.   .   .   .   £20/£5
ditto, Macmillan (New York), 1966 (published as by 'Kyle
Hunt') .   .   .   .   £20/£5
Sly as a Serpent, Hodder & Stoughton (London), 1967.   .
.   .   .   .   £20/£5
ditto, Macmillan (New York), 1967 (published as by 'Kyle
Hunt') .   .   .   .   £15/£5
Cruel as a Cat, Hodder & Stoughton (London), 1968 £20/£5
ditto, Macmillan (New York), 1969 (published as by 'Kyle
Hunt') .   .   .   .   £15/£5
Too Good to be True, Hodder & Stoughton (London), 1969
.   .   .   .   £20/£5
ditto, Macmillan (New York), 1969 (published as by 'Kyle
Hunt') .   .   .   .   £15/£5
A Period of Evil, Hodder & Stoughton (London), 1970 .
.   .   .   .   £15/£5
ditto, World (New York), 1971 (published as by 'Kyle
Hunt') .   .   .   .   £10/£5
As Lonely as the Damned, Hodder & Stoughton (London),
1971   .   .   .   .   £15/£5
ditto, World (New York), 1972 (published as by 'Kyle
Hunt') .   .   .   .   £10/£5
As Empty as Hate, Hodder & Stoughton (London), 1972 .
.   .   .   .   £15/£5
ditto, World (New York), 1972 (published as by 'Kyle
Hunt') .   .   .   .   £10/£5
As Merry as Hell, Hodder & Stoughton (London), 1973 .
.   .   .   .   £15/£5
ditto, World (New York), 1974 (published as by 'Kyle
Hunt') .   .   .   .   £10/£5
This Man Did I Kill?, Hodder & Stoughton (London), 1974
.   .   .   .   £10/£5
ditto, Stein (New York), 1974 (published as by 'Kyle Hunt')
.   .   .   .   £10/£5
The Man Who Was Not Himself, Hodder & Stoughton
(London), 1976 .   .   .   .   .   .   £10/£5

Novels Written as 'Kyle Hunt'
Kill Once, Kill Twice, Simon & Schuster (New York), 1956
.   .   .   .   £30/£5
ditto, Barker (London), 1957 .   .   .   .   £30/£5
Kill a Wicked Man, Simon & Schuster (New York), 1957 .
.   .   .   .   £25/£5
ditto, Barker (London), 1958 .   .   .   .   £25/£5
Kill My Love, Simon & Schuster (New York), 1958 £25/£5
ditto, Boardman (London), 1959.   .   .   .   £25/£5
To Kill a Killer, Random House (New York), 1960 £20/£5
ditto, Boardman (London), 1960.   .   .   .   £20/£5

Novels Written as 'Peter Manton'
Murder Manor, Wright & Brown (London), 1937 . £125/£20
The Greyvale School Mystery, Wright & Brown (London),
1937   .   .   .   . £125/£20
Stand By For Danger, Wright & Brown (London), 1937 .
.   .   .   . £125/£20
The Circle of Justice, Wright & Brown (London), 1938 .
.   .   .   . £100/£15
Three Days' Terror, Wright & Brown (London), 1938.   .
.   .   .   . £100/£15

The Crime Syndicate, Wright & Brown (London), 1939 .
.   .   .   . £75/£10
Death Looks On, Wright & Brown (London), 1939 £65/£10
Murder in the Highlands, Wright & Brown (London), 1939
.   .   .   . £50/£10
The Midget Marvel, Mellifont (London), 1940 (pbk) . £25
Policeman's Triumph, Wright & Brown (London), 1948 .
.   .   .   .   £30/£5
Thief in the Night, Wright & Brown (London), 1950 £30/£5
No Escape from Murder, Wright & Brown (London), 1953
.   .   .   .   £25/£5
The Crooked Killer, Wright & Brown (London), 1954 .
.   .   .   .   £25/£5
The Charity Killers, Wright & Brown (London), 1954 £25/£5

Novels Written as 'Richard Martin'
Keys to Crime, Earl (Bournemouth, Dorset), 1947 .   £30/£5
Vote to Murder, Earl (Bournemouth, Dorset), 1948   £30/£5
Adrian and Jonathan, Hodder & Stoughton (London), 1954
.   .   .   .   £25/£5

Novels Written as 'Jeremy York'
By Persons Unknown, Bles (London), 1941 .   . £75/£15
Murder Unseen, Bles (London), 1942 .   .   . £65/£10
No Alibi, Melrose (London), 1943 .   .   . £50/£10
Murder in the Family, Melrose (London), 1944 . £45/£10
ditto, McKay (New York), 1976 (published as by 'John
Creasey')   .   .   .   .   .   .   £15/£5
Yesterday's Murder, Melrose (London), 1945.   .   £35/£5
Find the Body, Melrose (London), 1945.   .   . £35/£5
ditto, Macmillan (New York), 1967 .   .   .   £15/£5
Murder Came Late, Melrose (London), 1946 .   £35/£5
ditto, Macmillan (New York), 1969 .   .   .   £15/£5
Run Away To Murder, Melrose (London), 1947 .   £35/£5
ditto, Macmillan (New York), 1970 .   .   .   £15/£5
Let's Kill Uncle Lionel, Melrose (London), 1947 .   £30/£5
ditto, McKay (New York), 1976.   .   .   .   £10/£5
Close the Door on Murder, Melrose (London), 1948 £30/£5
ditto, McKay (New York), 1973 .   .   .   .   £10/£5
The Gallows Are Waiting, Melrose (London), 1949 £30/£5
ditto, McKay (New York), 1973 .   .   .   .   £10/£5
Death to My Killer, Melrose (London), 1950 .   £30/£5
ditto, Macmillan (New York), 1966 .   .   .   £15/£5
Sentence of Death, Melrose (London), 1950 .   £30/£5
ditto, Macmillan (New York), 1964 .   .   .   £15/£5
Voyage With Murder, Melrose (London), 1952 . £25/£5
Safari With Fear, Melrose (London), 1953 .   £25/£5
So Soon to Die, Stanley Paul (London), 1955 .   £25/£5
ditto, Scribner's (New York), 1957 .   .   .   £25/£5
Seeds of Murder, Stanley Paul (London), 1956 . £25/£5
ditto, Scribner's (New York), 1958 .   .   .   £25/£5
Sight of Death, Stanley Paul (London), 1958 .   £25/£5
ditto, Scribner's (New York), 1959 .   .   .   £25/£5
My Brother's Killer, Stanley Paul (London), 1958.   £20/£5
ditto, Scribner's (New York), 1959 .   .   .   £20/£5
Hide and Kill, John Long (London), 1959 .   £20/£5
ditto, Scribner's (New York), 1960 .   .   .   £15/£5
To Kill or to Die, John Long (London), 1960 .   £15/£5
ditto, as *To Kill or Die*, Macmillan (New York), 1965 .
.   .   .   .   £10/£5

Novels Written as 'Ken Ranger'
One Shot Marriott, Sampson Low (London), 1938 £125/£20
Roaring Guns, Sampson Low (London), 1939 . £125/£20

Novels Written as 'William K. Reilly'
Range War, Stanley Paul (London), 1939   .   .£100/£15
Two-Gun Texan, Stanley Paul (London), 1939 . £100/£15
Gun Feud, Stanley Paul (London), 1940 .   . .£100/£15
Stolen Range, Stanley Paul (London), 1940   .   £75/£15
War on Lazy K, Stanley Paul (London), 1941 .   £75/£10
Outlaw's Vengeance, Stanley Paul (London), 1941 £65/£10
Guns Over Blue Lake, Jenkins (London), 1942   . £50/£10
Riders of Dry Gulch, Jenkins (London), 1943 .   £45/£10
Long John Rides the Range, Jenkins (London), 1944 .
     .   .   .   .   £40/£5
Miracle Range, Jenkins (London), 1945 .   .   .   £30/£5
Secret of the Range, Jenkins (London), 1946 .   .   £30/£5
Outlaws Guns, Earl (Bournemouth, Dorset), 1949 .   £25/£5
Range Vengeance, Ward Lock (London), 1953   .   £20/£5

Novels Written as 'Tex Riley'
Two-Gun Girl, Wright & Brown (London), 1938 . £125/£20
Gun-Smoke Range, Wright & Brown (London), 1938 .   .
     .   .   .   .£100/£15
Gunshot Mesa, Wright & Brown (London), 1939 . £100/£15
The Shootin' Sheriff, Wright & Brown (London), 1940   .
     .   .   .   .£75/£10
Masked Riders, Wright & Brown (London), 1940 . £75/£10
Rustler's Range, Wright & Brown (London), 1940 £75/£10
Death Canyon, Wright & Brown (London), 1941 . £65/£10
Guns on the Range, Wright & Brown (London), 1942 .
     .   .   .   .£45/£5
Range Justice, Wright & Brown (London), 1943 . £40/£5
Outlaw Hollow, Wright & Brown (London), 1944 . £35/£5
Hidden Range, Earl (Bournemouth, Dorset), 1946. £25/£5
Forgotten Range, Earl (Bournemouth, Dorset), 1947 £20/£5
Trigger Justice, Earl (Bournemouth, Dorset), 1948 £20/£5
Lynch Hollow, Earl (Bournemouth, Dorset), 1949 . £20/£5

Other Pseudonymous Fiction
The Dark Shadow, Fiction House (New York), [n.d.] (pseud
     'Rodney Mattheson'; pbk) £25
The House of Ferrars, Fiction House (New York), [n.d.]
     (pseud 'Rodney Mattheson'; pbk)   .   .   .   £20
Four Motives for Murder, Newnes (London), 1938 (pseud
     'Brian Hope'; pbk) £20
Triple Murder, Newnes (London), 1940 (pseud 'Colin
     Hughes'; pbk) £15
Murder on Largo Island, Selwyn & Blount (London), 1944
     (pseud 'Charles Hogarth', with Ian Bowen) .   £40/£10
Danger Woman, Pocket Books (New York), 1966 (pseud
     'Abel Mann'; pbk) £10

Non-Fiction
Fighting Was My Business, by Jimmy Wilde, Joseph
     (London), 1935 (ghosted by Creasey)   .   .   £75/£15
Log of a Merchant Airman, Stanley Paul (London), 1943
     (with John H. Lock)   .   .   .   .   .   £45/£10
*Heroes of the Air: A Tribute to the Courage, Sacrifice and
     Skill of the Men of the R.A.F.*, Dorset Wings for Victory
     Committee (Dorchester, Dorset), 1943 (stapled wraps) £25
*The Printer's Devil: An Account of the History and Objects
     of the Printers' Pension, Almshouse and Orphan Asylum
     Corporation*, Hutchinson (London), 1943 (with Walter
     Hutchinson) .   .   .   .   £45/£10
Man in Danger, Stanley Paul (London), 1950 (pseud
     'Credo'; pbk) £10

Round the World in 465 Days, Hale (London), 1953 (with
     Jean Creasey)   .   .   .   .   .   .   £25/£10
Let's Look at America, Hale (London), 1956 (with Jean
     Creasey)   .   .   .   .   £25/£10
*They Didn't Mean to Kill: The Real Story of Road
     Accidents*, Hodder & Stoughton (London), 1960.   £15/£5
Optimists in Africa, Timmins (Cape Town, South Africa),
     1963 (with Jean, Martin and Richard Creasey)   £20/£5
African Holiday, Timmins (Cape Town, South Africa), 1963
     .   .   .   .   £20/£5
*Good, God and Man: An Outline of the Philosophy of
     Selfism*, Hodder & Stoughton (London), 1967   .   £25/£5
Evolution to Democracy, Hodder & Stoughton (London),
     1969   .   .   .   .   £15/£5

HARRY CREWS
(b.1935)

Harry Crews is a prolific American novelist whose outland-
ish characters come from a strange, violent but often darkly
humorous white American South. His autobiography, *A
Childhood* is about growing up poor in rural south Georgia
and is very highly regarded.

Novels
The Gospel Singer, William Morrow (New York), 1968   .
     .   .   .   .£400/£65
Naked In Garden Hills, William Morrow (New York), 1969
     (first issue d/w with reviews of *The Gospel Singer* on back)
     .   .   .   .£150/£25
ditto, William Morrow (New York), 1969 (second issue d/w
     with reviews of *Naked in Garden Hills* on back) .   £65/£25
ditto, Charisma Books (London), 1973 (pbk)   .   .   £20
This Thing Don't Lead to Heaven, William Morrow (New
     York), 1970 .   .   .   .   £100/£20
Karate is a Thing of the Spirit, William Morrow (New
     York), 1971   .   .   .   .   £100/£20
ditto, Secker & Warburg (London), 1972 .   .   £75/£15
Car, William Morrow (New York), 1972 .   .   £125/£20
ditto, Secker & Warburg (London), 1973 .   .   £60/£10
The Hawk is Dying, Knopf (New York), 1973   .   £60/£10
ditto, Secker & Warburg (London), 1974 .   .   £50/£10
The Gypsy's Curse, Knopf (New York), 1974.   £50/£10
ditto, Secker & Warburg (London), 1975 .   .   £45/£10
A Feast of Snakes, Atheneum (New York), 1976 . £60/£10
ditto, Secker & Warburg (London), 1977 .   .   £45/£10
All We Need of Hell, Harper & Row (New York), 1987   .
     .   .   .   .   £25/£10
The Knockout Artist, Harper & Row (New York), 1988   .
     .   .   .   .   £15/£5
Body, Poseidon Press (New York), 1990 .   .   £10/£5
ditto, Poseidon Press (New York), 1990 (signed on tipped-in
     leaf)   .   .   .   .   £30/£20
ditto, Poseidon Press/Ultramarine Press (New York), 1990
     (40 signed, numbered copies; paper boards and leather
     spine) £100
ditto, Poseidon Press/Ultramarine Press (New York), 1990
     (10 signed, lettered copies; full leather binding) .   £200
Scar Lover, Poseidon Press (New York), 1992   .   £10/£5
The Mulching of America, Simon & Schuster (New York),
     1995   .   .   .   .   £10/£5

The Gospel Singer and *Where Does One Go When There's No Place to Go*, Gorse (London), 1995 (pbk) . . £25

Where Does One Go When There's No Place to Go, Blood & Guts Press (Los Angeles, CA), 1998 (400 signed, numbered copies; in d/w) . . . . . £50/£30

ditto, Blood & Guts Press (Los Angeles, CA), 1998 (26 lettered copies signed by Crews and Ralph Steadman; d/w and slipcase) . . . . . . £175/£125

ditto, Blood & Guts Press (Los Angeles, CA), 1998 (5 specially numbered copies signed by Crews and double-signed byRalph Steadman; d/w only) . . £200/£150

Celebration, Simon & Schuster (New York), 1998. £10/£5

An American Family: The Baby with the Curious Markings, Blood & Guts Press (Los Angeles, CA), 2006 .

. . . . £10/£5

ditto, Blood & Guts Press (Los Angeles, CA), 2006 (300 signed, numbered copies; slipcase) . . . £50/£30

ditto, Blood & Guts Press (Los Angeles, CA), 2006 (26 signed lettered copies; slipcase) . . . £175/£125

Autobiography

A Childhood: The Biography of a Place, Harper & Row (New York), 1978 . . . . . . £50/£10

ditto, Secker & Warburg (London), 1979 . . . £45/£10

Non-Fiction

Blood and Grits, Harper & Row (New York), 1979 £45/£10

Florida Frenzy, Univ Press of Florida (Gainesville, FL), 1982 (pbk) £25

Two By Crews, Lord John Press (Northridge, CA), 1984 (200 signed, numbered copies; no d/w) . . . £75

ditto, Lord John Press (Northridge, CA), 1984 (26 signed, lettered copies; no d/w) £125

Madonna At Ringside, Lord John Press (Northridge, CA), 1991 (275 signed, numbered copies; no d/w) . . £65

ditto, Lord John Press (Northridge, CA), 1991 (26 signed, lettered copies; no d/w) £125

Others

Jefferson Davis is Alive and Well and Trading in Atlanta, William Morrow (New York), 1971 (galleys of *Karate is a Thing of the Spirit*, printed rectos only; plain covers with label) £800

The Enthusiast, Palaemon Press (Winston-Salem, NC), 1981 (150 signed, numbered copies; no d/w; essentially the first chapter of *All We Need of Hell*) £65

ditto, Palaemon Press (Winston-Salem, NC), 1981 (50 signed, numbered copies; no d/w) £100

Blood Issue: A Drama in Two Acts, no publisher (no place), 1988 (bound photocopied sheets) £65

Classic Crews: A Harry Crews Reader, Poseidon Press (New York), 1993 (pbk; contains *Car*, *The Gypsy's Curse*, *A Childhood*, and essays) £10

ditto, Gorse (London), 1993 (wraps) £5

Getting Naked With Harry Crews, Univ Press of Florida (Gainesville, FL), 1993 (interviews) . . . £10/£5

MICHAEL CRICHTON
(b.1942 d.2008)

An author whose interest in science and its effects on society is at the fore in his most successful work, *Jurassic Park*. He won an Edgar Award in 1980 for *The Great Train Robbery*, and has also won an Emmy, a Peabody, and a Writer's Guild of America Award for the television series *ER*.

Novels

The Andromeda Strain, Knopf (New York), 1969. £100/£15

ditto, Cape (London), 1969 . . . . . . £85/£10

The Terminal Man, Knopf (New York), 1972 . £75/£20

ditto, Cape (London), 1972 . . . . . . £65/£20

The Great Train Robbery, Knopf (New York), 1975 . .

. . . . £50/£10

ditto, Cape (London), 1975 . . . . . . £40/£10

Eaters of the Dead, Knopf (New York), 1976 . £40/£10

ditto, Cape (London), 1976 . . . . . . £30/£5

Congo, Knopf (New York), 1980 . . . . £35/£10

ditto, Franklin Library (Franklin Centre, PA), 1980 (signed, limited edition) £45

ditto, Allen Lane (London), 1981 . . . . £30/£5

Sphere, Knopf (New York), 1987 . . . . £25/£5

ditto, Macmillan (London), 1987 . . . . £25/£5

Jurassic Park, Knopf (New York), 1990 . . . £30/£5

ditto, Franklin Library (Franklin Centre, PA), 1990 (signed, limited edition) £200

ditto, Century (London), 1991 . . . . . £30/£5

Rising Sun, Knopf (New York), 1992 . . . £15/£5

ditto, Century (London), 1992 . . . . . £15/£5

ditto, Franklin Library (Franklin Centre, PA), 1992 (signed, limited edition) £35

Disclosure, Franklin Library (Franklin Centre, PA), 1993 (signed, limited edition) £40

ditto, Knopf (New York), 1994 . . . . . £15/£5

ditto, Century (London), 1994 . . . . . £15/£5

The Lost World, Knopf (New York), 1995 . . £15/£5

ditto, Century (London), 1995 . . . . . £15/£5

Airframe, Knopf (New York), 1996 . . . . £15/£5

ditto, Knopf (New York), 1996 (50 signed deluxe copies of 250, aluminium slipcase) . . . . . £150/£100

ditto, Knopf (New York), 1996 (200 signed copies of 250, slipcase, no d/w) . . . . £45/£25

ditto, Franklin Library (Franklin Centre, PA), 1996 (signed, limited edition) £75

ditto, Century (London), 1996 . . . . . £15/£5

Timeline, Knopf (New York), 1999 . . . . £15/£5

ditto, Franklin Library (Franklin Centre, PA), 1999 (signed, limited edition) £60

ditto, Century (London), 1999 . . . . . £15/£5

Prey, Knopf (New York), 2002 . . . . . £15/£5

ditto, Harper Collins (London), 2002 . . . . £15/£5

State of Fear, Harper Collins (New York), 2004 . £15/£5

ditto, Harper Collins (London), 2004 . . . . £15/£5

Next, Harper Collins (New York), 2006 . . . £10/£5

ditto, Harper Collins (London), 2006 . . . £10/£5

Novels Written as 'John Lange'

Odds On, New American Library/Signet (New York), 1966 (pbk) £50

Scratch One, New American Library/Signet (New York), 1967 (pbk) £65
Easy Go, New American Library/Signet (New York), 1968 (pbk) £65
ditto, Sphere, 1972 (pbk) £5
ditto, as *The Last Tomb*, Bantam (New York), 1974 (by Michael Crichton; pbk) £5
The Venom Business, World (New York), 1969 . £125/£25
Zero Cool, New American Library/Signet (New York), 1969 (pbk) £50
ditto, Sphere, 1972 (pbk) £5
Grave Descend, New American Library/Signet (New York), 1970 (pbk) £50
Drug of Choice, New American Library/Signet (New York), 1970 (pbk) £40
ditto, as *Overkill*, Sphere, 1972 (pbk) . . . £5
Binary, Knopf (New York), 1972 . . . £45/£10
ditto, Heinemann (London), 1972 . . . £45/£10

Novels Written as 'Jeffery Hudson'
A Case of Need, World (New York), 1968 . . £200/£35
ditto, Heinemann (London), 1968 . . . £10/£20

Novels Written as 'Michael Douglas'
Dealing, Knopf (New York), 1971 . . . £40/£10
ditto, Talmy Franklin (London), 1971 . . £40/£10

Screenplays
Westworld, Bantam (New York), 1974 (pbk) . . £10

Non-Fiction
Five Patients: The Hospital Explained, Knopf (New York), 1970 . . . . £45/£15
ditto, Cape (London), 1971 . . . . . £40/£10
Jasper Johns, Abrams (New York), 1977 . £45/£20
ditto, Thames & Hudson (London), 1977 . . £45/£20
Electronic Life: How to Think About Computers, Knopf (New York), 1983 . . . . . £45/£10
ditto, Heinemann (London), 1983 . . . £40/£10
Travels, Knopf (New York), 1988 . . . £35/£10
ditto, Franklin Library (Franklin Centre, PA), 1988 (signed, limited edition) £40
ditto, Macmillan (London), 1988 . . . . £25/£5

EDMUND CRISPIN
(b.1921 d.1978)

Robert Bruce Montgomery will be remembered as a successful author of detective fiction written under the pseudonym of Edmund Crispin. His novels feature a professor of English language and literature, the Oxford don Gervase Fen. Montgomery was also a composer (he wrote scores for the *Carry On* films) and a prolific editor of detective and science fiction anthologies.

Novels
The Case of the Gilded Fly, Gollancz (London), 1944 (green cloth lettered in gilt; d/w priced at 7/6) . . £600/£75
ditto, as *Obsequies at Oxford*, Lippincott (Philadelphia, PA), 1945 . . . . £100/£25
Holy Disorders, Gollancz (London), 1946 (blue cloth lettered in gilt; d/w priced at 7/6) . . . £250/£25

ditto, Lippincott (Philadelphia, PA), 1946. . . £65/£15
The Moving Toyshop, Gollancz (London), 1946 (blue cloth lettered in gilt; d/w priced at 7/6) . . . £200/£35
ditto, Lippincott (Philadelphia, PA), 1946. . . £50/£10
Swan Song, Gollancz (London), 1947 (blue cloth lettered in gilt). . . . . £100/£20
ditto, as *Dead and Dumb*, Lippincott (Philadelphia, PA), 1947 . . . . £75/£20
Love Lies Bleeding, Gollancz (London), 1948 (blue cloth lettered in gilt) . . . . . . £75/£20
ditto, Lippincott (Philadelphia, PA), 1948. . . £50/£15
Buried for Pleasure, Gollancz (London), 1948 (blue cloth lettered in gilt) . . . . . . £75/£20
ditto, Lippincott (Philadelphia, PA), 1948. . . £50/£15
Frequent Hearses, Gollancz (London), 1950 (red cloth lettered in black) . . . . £75/£15
ditto, as *Sudden Vengeance*, Dodd, Mead (New York), 1950 . . . . £50/£10
The Long Divorce, Gollancz (London), 1951 (red cloth lettered in black) . . . . £75/£15
ditto, Dodd, Mead (New York), 1951 . . . £40/£10
ditto, as *A Noose for Her*, Spivak (New York), 1952 £40/£10
The Glimpses of the Moon, Gollancz (London), 1977 (red cloth lettered in gilt) . . . . . £25/£10
ditto, Walker (New York), 1978 . . . . £10/£5

Short Stories
Beware of the Trains: 16 Stories, Gollancz (London), 1953 . . . . £75/£15
ditto, Walker (New York), 1962 . . . . £35/£5
Fen Country: 26 stories, Gollancz (London), 1979 £20/£5
ditto, Walker (New York), 1979 . . . . £15/£5

FREEMAN WILLS CROFTS
(b.1879 d.1957)

Crofts was born in Dublin, Ireland, and is acknowledged as one of the first authors of detective fiction to methodically report police procedure. He also wrote a religious book, *The Four Gospels in One Story*, several short stories, and short plays for the BBC. He was elected a fellow of the Royal Society of Arts in 1939.

'Inspector French' Novels
Inspector French's Greatest Case, Collins (London), 1924 (blue cloth lettered in red) . . . . . £1,250/£125
ditto, Seltzer (New York), 1925 . . . . £350/£35
Inspector French and the Cheyne Mystery, Collins (London), 1926 (blue cloth lettered in red; d/w price 7/6) . . . . £1,250/£125
ditto, as *The Cheyne Mystery*, Boni (New York), 1926 . . . . £300/£30
Inspector French and the Starvel Tragedy, Collins (London), 1927 (blue cloth lettered in red; d/w price 7/6) . . . . £1,250/£100
ditto, as *The Starvel Hollow Tragedy*, Harper (New York), 1927 . . . . £300/£30
The Sea Mystery, Collins (London), 1928 (black cloth lettered in gilt; d/w price 7/6) . . . £1,250/£100
ditto, Harper (New York), 1928 . . . . £300/£30

The Box Office Murders, Collins (London), 1929 (black cloth lettered in red; d/w price 7/6) . . . £1,250/£100

ditto, as *The Purple Sickle Murders*, Harper (New York), 1929 . . . . £300/£30

Sir John Magill's Last Journey, Collins Crime Club (London), 1930 (orange/red cloth lettered in black; d/w price 7/6) . . . . . . £1,000/£75

ditto, Harper (New York), 1930 . . . . £250/£25

Mystery in the Channel, Collins Crime Club (London), 1931 (orange/red cloth lettered in black; d/w price 7/6) . . . . £1,000/£75

ditto, as *Mystery in the English Channel*, Harper (New York), 1931 . . . . £300/£30

Sudden Death, Collins Crime Club (London), 1932 (orange/red cloth lettered in black; d/w price 7/6) . .

. . . . £1,000/£75

ditto, Harper (New York), 1932 . . . . £225/£25

Death on the Way, Collins Crime Club (London), 1932 (orange/red cloth lettered in black; d/w price 7/6) .

. . . . £1,000/£75

ditto, as *Double Death*, Harper (New York), 1932 . £225/£25

The Hog's Back Mystery, Hodder & Stoughton (London), 1933 (blue cloth lettered in black; d/w price 7/6) . .

. . . . £1,000/£75

ditto, as *The Strange Case of Dr Earle*, Dodd, Mead (New York), 1933 . . . . £200/£25

The 12.30 from Croydon, Hodder & Stoughton (London), 1934 (blue cloth lettered in black; d/w price 7/6) . .

. . . . £1,000/£75

ditto, as *Wilful and Premeditated*, Dodd (New York), 1934

. . . . £200/£25

Mystery on Southampton Water, Hodder & Stoughton (London), 1934 (blue cloth lettered in black; d/w price 7/6)

. . . . £1,000/£75

ditto, as *Crime on the Solent*, Dodd (New York), 1934. .

. . . . £200/£25

Crime at Guildford, Collins Crime Club (London), 1935 (orange/red cloth lettered in black; d/w price 7/6) .

. . . . £1,000/£75

ditto, as *The Crime at Nornes*, Dodd (New York), 1935 .

. . . . £200/£25

The Loss of the 'Jane Vosper', Collins Crime Club (London), 1936 (orange/red cloth lettered in black; d/w price 7/6) . . . . . . £1,000/£75

ditto, Dodd (New York), 1936 . . . . £200/£25

Man Overboard!, Collins Crime Club (London), 1936 (orange/red cloth lettered in black; d/w price 7/6) .

. . . . £1,000/£75

ditto, Dodd (New York), 1936 . . . . £200/£25

ditto, as *Cold-Blooded Murder*, Avon (New York), 1947 (abridged; pbk) £20

Found Floating, Hodder & Stoughton (London), 1937 (blue cloth lettered in black; d/w price 7/6) . . £1,000/£75

ditto, Dodd (New York), 1937 . . . . £200/£25

The End of Andrew Harrison, Hodder & Stoughton (London), 1938 (blue cloth lettered in black; d/w price 7/6) .

. . . . £850/£65

ditto, as *The Futile Alibi*, Dodd (New York), 1938 £200/£25

Antidote to Venom Hodder & Stoughton (London), 1938 (blue cloth lettered in black; d/w price 7/6) . £850/£65

ditto, Dodd (New York), 1939 . . . . £200/£25

Fatal Venture, Hodder & Stoughton (London), 1939 (blue cloth lettered in gilt; d/w price 7/6) . . . £850/£65

ditto, as *Tragedy in the Hollow*, Dodd (New York), 1939 .

. . . . £200/£25

Golden Ashes, Hodder & Stoughton (London), 1940 (blue cloth lettered in black; d/w price 8/3) . . £850/£65

ditto, Dodd (New York), 1940 . . . . £200/£25

James Tarrant, Adventurer, Hodder & Stoughton (London), 1941 (blue cloth lettered in black; d/w price 8/3). £850/£65

ditto, as *Circumstantial Evidence*, Dodd (New York), 1941

. . . . £200/£25

The Losing Game, Hodder & Stoughton (London), 1941 (blue cloth lettered in black; d/w price 8/6) . £600/£50

ditto, as *A Losing Game*, Dodd (New York), 1941. £200/£25

Fear Comes to Chalfont, Hodder & Stoughton (London), 1942 (blue cloth lettered in black; d/w price 8/6). £400/£45

ditto, Dodd (New York), 1942 . . . . £150/£15

The Affair at Little Wokeham, Hodder & Stoughton (London), 1943 (blue cloth lettered in black; d/w price 8/6)

. . . . £350/£35

ditto, as *Double Tragedy*, Dodd (New York), 1943 £150/£15

Enemy Unseen, Hodder & Stoughton (London), 1945 (maroon cloth lettered in white; d/w price 8/6) . £200/£20

ditto, Dodd (New York), 1945 . . . . £125/£15

Death of a Train, Hodder & Stoughton (London), 1946 (maroon cloth lettered in white; d/w price 8/6) . £200/£20

ditto, Dodd (New York), 1947 . . . . £100/£15

Young Robin Brand, Detective, Univ of London Press (London), 1947 (juvenile; blue cloth lettered in black) .

. . . . £100/£20

ditto, Dodd (New York), 1948 . . . . £50/£15

Silence for the Murderer, Dodd (New York), 1948 (green cloth lettered in black; d/w price 8/6) . . £100/£15

ditto, Hodder & Stoughton (London), 1949 . £200/£20

Dark Journey, Dodd (New York), 1951 . . £100/£15

ditto, as *French Strikes Oil*, Hodder & Stoughton (London), 1952 (maroon cloth lettered in black; d/w price 12/6). .

. . . . £200/£20

Anything to Declare?, Hodder & Stoughton (London), 1957 (blue cloth lettered in gilt; d/w price 12/6) . £200/£20

Other Novels

The Cask, Collins (London), 1920 (red cloth lettered in black) . . . . £3,000/£400

ditto, Seltzer (New York), 1924 . . . . £750/£65

The Ponson Case, Collins (London), 1921 (red cloth lettered in black). . . . . . . £1,500/£200

ditto, Boni (New York), 1927 . . . . £750/£65

The Pit-Prop Syndicate, Collins (London), 1922 (blue cloth lettered in red) . . . . . £1,500/£200

ditto, Seltzer (New York), 1925 . . . . £750/£65

The Groote Park Murder, Collins (London), 1923 (blue cloth lettered in red) . . . . . £1,250/£125

ditto, Seltzer (New York), 1925 . . . . £750/£65

Short Stories

The Hunt Ball Murder, Todd (London), 1943 (pbk) . £300

Mr. Sefton, Murderer, Vallancey Press (London), 1944 (red cloth) £300

Murderers Make Mistakes, Hodder & Stoughton (London), 1947 (maroon cloth lettered in white; d/w price 8/6) . .

. . . . £250/£25

Many a Slip, Hodder & Stoughton (London), 1955 (maroon cloth lettered in black) . . . . £300/£25

The Mystery of the Sleeping Car Express, Hodder & Stoughton (London), 1956 (green cloth lettered in black; d/w price 11/6) . . . . . . £300/£25

Collaborations (Chapters by Crofts and Others)
The Floating Admiral, Hodder & Stoughton (London), [1931] . . . . £1,500/£100
ditto, Doubleday (New York), 1932 . . . . £500/£30
Six against the Yard, Selwyn & Blount (London), 1936 (six stories by members of 'The Detection Club', one by Crofts) . . . . £1,500/£100
ditto, as *Six against Scotland Yard*, Doubleday (Garden City, NY), 1936 . . . . . . £500/£35
Double Death, Gollancz, 1940 . . . £800/£150
The Scoop and *Behind the Screen*, Gollancz (London), 1983 . . . . £25/£10

Other
Four Gospels in One Story, Longmans, Green and Co (London),1949 (yellow cloth lettered in red). . £25/£10

RICHMAL CROMPTON
(b.1890 d.1969)

Richmal Crompton Lamburn began writing short stories for magazines while working as a teacher. When these were first collected together as *Just William*, the book was an immediate success. Crompton tried to repeat her winning formula with other audiences: her 'Jimmy' books were aimed at younger children, and *Enter—Patricia* was written for girls.

'William' Titles
Just William, Newnes (London), [1922] (red cloth lettered in black; measuring 7" x 4.25"; 4pps of adverts at the end of the book) . . . . . . £1,750/£165
More William, Newnes (London), 1922 (red cloth) . . . . £1,500/£125
William Again, Newnes (London), 1923 (red cloth) . . . . £1,250/£45
William the Fourth, Newnes (London), 1924 (red cloth) . . . . £1,000/£35
Still William, Newnes (London), 1925 (red cloth) . £750/£35
William the Conqueror, Newnes (London), 1926 (red cloth) . . . . £750/£35
William the Outlaw, Newnes (London), 1927 (red cloth) . . . . £750/£35
William in Trouble, Newnes (London), 1927 (red cloth) . . . . £650/£35
William the Good, Newnes (London), 1928 (red cloth). . . . . £650/£35
William, Newnes (London), 1929 (blue cloth). £1,000/£175
William the Bad, Newnes (London), 1930 (blue cloth) . . . . £1,000/£175
William's Happy Days, Newnes (London), 1930 (blue cloth) . . . . £1,000/£150
William's Crowded Hours, Newnes (London), 1931 (blue cloth) . . . . . . £1,000/£150
William the Pirate, Newnes (London), 1932 (blue cloth) . . . . £1,000/£150
William the Rebel, Newnes (London), 1933 (blue cloth) . . . . £1,000/£150
William the Gangster, Newnes (London), 1934 (blue cloth) . . . . £1,000/£150
William the Detective, Newnes (London), 1935 (brown cloth) . . . . £1,000/£150

Sweet William, Newnes (London), 1936 (green cloth) . . . . £1,000/£75
William the Showman, Newnes (London), 1937 (green cloth) . . . . £1,000/£75
William the Dictator, Newnes (London), 1938 (green cloth) . . . . £1,000/£75
William and A.R.P., Newnes (London), 1939 (green cloth; title later changed to *William's Bad Resolution*) . . . . £1,000/£75
Just William, The Story of the Film, Newnes, 1939 (green cloth) . . . . £100/£15
William and the Evacuees, Newnes (London), 1940 (green cloth; title later changed to *William the Film Star*) . . . . £1,250/£150
William Does His Bit, Newnes (London), 1941 (green cloth) . . . . £650/£150
William Carries On, Newnes (London), 1941 (green cloth). . . . . £650/£75
William and the Brains Trust, Newnes (London), 1945 (green cloth). . . . . . . £175/£45
Just William's Luck, Newnes (London), 1948 (green cloth) . . . . £100/£10
William the Bold, Newnes (London), 1950 (green cloth) . . . . £100/£15
William and the Tramp, Newnes (London), 1952 (green cloth) . . . . £100/£15
William and the Moon Rocket, Newnes (London), 1954 (green cloth). . . . . . . £75/£10
William and the Space Animal, Newnes (London), 1956 (green cloth) . . . . . . £75/£10
William's Television Show, Newnes (London), 1958 (green cloth) . . . . £75/£10
William the Explorer, Newnes (London), 1960 (green cloth) . . . . £75/£10
William's Treasure Trove, Newnes (London), 1962 (green cloth) . . . . £75/£10
William and the Witch, Newnes (London), 1964 (green cloth) . . . . £75/£15
William and the Ancient Briton, Armada (London), 1965 (pbk) £5
William and the Monster, Armada (London), 1965 (pbk) £5
William the Globetrotter, Armada (London), 1965 (pbk) £5
William the Cannibal, Armada (London), 1965 (pbk) . £5
William and the Pop Singers, Newnes (London), 1965 (green cloth). . . . . . . £75/£15
William and the Masked Ranger, Newnes (London), 1966 (green cloth). . . . . . . £75/£15
William the Superman, Newnes (London), 1968 (green cloth) . . . . £200/£45
William the Lawless, Newnes (London), 1970 (red cloth) . . . . £1,000/£200

'Jimmy' Titles
Jimmy, Newnes (London), 1949 . . . . £75/£15
Jimmy Again, Newnes (London), 1951 . . £65/£15
Jimmy the Third, Armada (London), 1965 (pbk) . £10

Other Novels
The Innermost Room, Melrose (London), 1923 . £250/£50
The Hidden Light, Hodder & Stoughton (London), [1924] . . . . £200/£40
Anne Morrison, Jarrolds (London), 1925 . . £175/£35
The Wildings, Hodder & Stoughton (London), [1925] . . . . £150/£30

David Wilding, Hodder & Stoughton (London), [1926] . . . . £150/£30
The House, Hodder & Stoughton (London), [1926] . . . . £250/£35
ditto, as *Dread Dwelling*, Boni & Liveright (New York), 1926 . . . . £250/£35
Millicent Dorrington, Hodder & Stoughton (London), [1927] . . . . £125/£25
Leadon Hill, Hodder & Stoughton (London), [1927]. . . . . £125/£25
The Thorn Bush, Hodder & Stoughton (London), [1928] . . . . £125/£25
Roofs Off!, Hodder & Stoughton (London), [1928] £100/£20
The Four Graces, Hodder & Stoughton (London), [1929] . . . . £175/£35
Abbot's End, Hodder & Stoughton (London), [1929] . . . . £175/£35
Blue Flames, Hodder & Stoughton (London), [1930] . . . . £100/£20
Naomi Godstone, Hodder & Stoughton (London), [1930] . . . . £100/£20
Portrait of a Family, Macmillan (London), 1931 . £100/£20
The Odyssey of Euphemia Tracy, Macmillan (London), 1932 . . . . £100/£20
Marriage of Hermione, Macmillan (London), 1932 £65/£20
The Holiday, Macmillan (London), 1933 . . . £65/£20
Chedsy Place, Macmillan (London), 1934 . . £65/£20
The Old Man's Birthday, Macmillan (London), 1934 . . . . £65/£20
Quartet, Macmillan (London), 1935 . . . £65/£20
Caroline, Macmillan (London), 1936 . . £65/£20
There are Four Seasons, Macmillan (London), 1937 . . . . £50/£15
Journeying Wave, Macmillan (London), 1938 . £65/£20
Merlin Bay, Macmillan (London), 1939 . . £65/£20
Steffan Green, Macmillan (London), 1940 . £65/£20
Narcissa, Macmillan (London), 1941 . . £65/£20
Mrs Frensham Describes a Circle, Macmillan (London), 1942 . . . . £45/£15
Weatherley Parade, Macmillan (London), 1943 . £25/£5
Westover, Hutchinson (London), [1946] . . £25/£5
The Ridleys, Hutchinson (London), [1947] . £25/£5
Family Roundabout, Hutchinson (London), [1948] £25/£5
Frost at Morning, Hutchinson (London), 1950 . £25/£5
Linden Rise, Hutchinson (London), 1952 . £25/£5
The Gypsy's Baby, Hutchinson (London), 1954 . £50/£15
Four in Exile, Hutchinson (London), 1955 . £30/£5
Matty and the Dearingroydes, Hutchinson (London), 1956 . . . . £25/£5
Blind Man's Buff, Hutchinson (London), 1957 . £25/£5
Wiseman's Folly, Hutchinson (London), 1959 . £25/£5
The Inheritor, Hutchinson (London), 1960 . £15/£5

Other Short Story Collections
Kathleen and I, and, Of Course, Veronica, Hodder & Stoughton (London), [1926] . . . £125/£25
Enter—Patricia, Newnes (London), [1927] . £65/£15
A Monstrous Regiment, Hutchinson (London), [1927]. . . . . £150/£40
Mist and Other Stories, Hutchinson (London), [1928] . . . . £200/£45
The Middle Things, Hutchinson (London), [1928]. £175/£45
Felicity Stands By, Newnes (London), [1928]. £100/£25
Sugar and Spice, Ward Lock (London), 1929 . £100/£25

Ladies First, Hutchinson (London), [1929] . . £175/£45
The Silver Birch, Hutchinson (London), [1931] . £175/£45
The First Morning, Hutchinson (London), [1936] . £175/£45

HARRY CROSBY
(b.1898 d.1929)

Crosby was born into a rich New England banking family and was heir to a great fortune. He volunteered as an ambulance driver in France during the First World War and was deeply affected by his experiences: his later extravagant lifestyle and experimental poetry can be seen as a reaction to those events. Although his poetic ambition exceeded his ability, the books he published under the Black Sun Press with his wife, Caresse, are things of great beauty.

Sonnets for Caresse, Herbert Clarke (Paris), 1925 (17 copies) £2,500
ditto, Herbert Clarke (Paris), 1926 (second edition, 27 copies) £1,500
ditto, Albert Messein (Paris), 1926 (third edition, 108 copies; maroon printed wraps; hand-painted veined vellum binding). £750
ditto, Editions Narcisse (Paris), 1927 (fourth edition, 44 copies; cream wraps printed red & black; cellophane d/w; gold foil board chemise with ribbon tie). . . . £600
Red Skeletons, Editions Narcisse (Paris), 1927 (illustrated by Alastair ; ordinary edition of 337 copies, 9 illustrations) £600
ditto, Editions Narcisse (Paris), 1927 (33 copies on Imperial Japon paper, 9 illustrations) £1,000
Chariot of the Sun, At the Sign of the Sundial (Paris), 1928 (48 copies) £1,500
Shadows of the Sun, The Black Sun Press (Paris), 1928 (44 copies) £1,250
ditto, Second Series, The Black Sun Press (Paris), 1929 (44 copies) £1,000
ditto, Third Series, The Black Sun Press (Paris), 1930 (44 copies) £1,000
Transit of Venus, The Black Sun Press (Paris), 1928 (44 copies) £1,750
ditto, The Black Sun Press (Paris), 1929 (200 numbered copies) £350
Six Poems, Latterday Pamphlets (New York), 1928 (225 copies; wraps) £350
Mad Queen: Tirades, The Black Sun Press (Paris), 1929 (100 of 141 copies, printed wraps and glassine in gold foil folder with ties) . . . . . £600/£400
ditto, The Black Sun Press (Paris), 1929 (20 copies on Japan paper, bound in 2/4 morocco) £2,250
The Sun, The Black Sun Press (Paris), 1929 (100 copies) £1,250
Sleeping Together, The Black Sun Press (Paris), 1929 (77 copies) £1,500
Aphrodite in Flight, The Black Sun Press (Paris), 1930 (27 copies) £2,500
The Collected Poems, Black Sun Press (Paris), 1931 (500 copies, 4 wrappered vols in box: *Chariot of the Sun*, Introduction by D.H. Lawrence, *Transit of Venus*, With a Preface by T.S. Eliot, *Sleeping Together*, With a Memory of the Poet by Stuart Gilbert, *Torchbearer*, With Notes by Ezra Pound) £1,250

War Letters, The Black Sun Press (Paris), 1932 (as Henry Grew Crosby, 125 copies, preface by Henrietta Crosby) .
.   .   .   . £600

Shadows of the Sun: The Diaries of Harry Crosby, Black Sparrow Press (Santa Barbara, CA), 1977 (edited by Edward Germain, 200 numbered copies)   .   .   . £65

ditto, Black Sparrow Press (Santa Barbara, CA), 1977 (1,300 hardback copies, acetate jacket)   .   .   .   . £25/£15

ditto, Black Sparrow Press (Santa Barbara, CA), 1977 (pbk)
.   .   .   . £10

Devour the Fire, Twowindows Press (Berkeley, CA), 1983 (200 numbered copies) £100

As Editor

Anthology, Maurice Darantiere (Paris), 1924 (edited by 'Henry Grew Crosby') £400

47 Unpublished Letters From Marcel Proust to Walter Berry, Black Sun Press (Paris), 1930 (edited and translated by Harry and Caresse Crosby, 50 numbered copies on Japon; wraps) £300

ditto, Black Sun Press (Paris), 1930 (200 numbered copies on velin d'Arches; wraps) £200

ALEISTER CROWLEY

(b.1875 d.1947)

The notorious British occultist and author of interminable magical works, Crowley's other interests and accomplishments were wide-ranging (he was a chess master, mountain climber, poet, painter, astrologer and social critic). The special copies of his books on Japanese vellum etc were usually for presentation and will vary in value depending upon to whom they were inscribed.

Poetry

Aceldama, A Place to Bury Strangers In, privately printed by Leonard Smithers (London), 1898 (88 copies, pseud 'a gentleman of the Univ of Cambridge'; wraps)   . £1,500

ditto, privately printed by Leonard Smithers (London), 1898 (10 large paper copies, pseud 'a gentleman of the University of Cambridge'; wraps)   .   .   . £2,500

The Tale of Archais: a Romance in Verse, Kegan Paul & Co (London), 1898 (250 copies, pseud 'a gentleman of the University of Cambridge'). £500

Jezebel, privately printed at the Chiswick Press (London), 1898 (40 copies; wraps) £1,000

ditto, privately printed at the Chiswick Press (London), 1898 (10 copies on Japanese vellum; wraps)   .   .   . £2,500

Songs of the Spirit, Kegan Paul & Co (London), 1898 (200 copies) £500

ditto, Kegan Paul & Co (London), 1898 (50 signed, numbered copies) £1,250

Jephthah, and other mysteries, lyrical and dramatic, Kegan Paul & Co (London), 1899   .   .   .   . £300

An Appeal to the American Republic, Kegan Paul & Co (London), 1899 (500 copies; wraps)   .   .   . £300

The Mother's Tragedy, privately printed (London), 1901 (500 copies) £350

The Soul of Osiris, Kegan Paul & Co (London), 1901 (500 copies) £450

ditto, Kegan Paul & Co (London), 1901 (6 copies on india paper) £2,000

Carmen Saeculare, Kegan Paul & Co (London), 1901 (450 copies, pseud 'St. E. A. of M. and S'; wraps)   .   . £600

Tannhäuser, Kegan Paul & Co (London), 1902   .   . £250

The God-Eater, A Tragedy of Satire, Watts & Co (London), 1903 (300 copies; wraps) £300

Summa Spes, privately printed (London), 1903   .   . £300

Ahab and Other Poems, privately printed at the Chiswick Press (London), 1903 (150 copies) £650

ditto, privately printed at the Chiswick Press (London), 1903 (10 copies on Japanese vellum)   .   .   . £1,500

ditto, privately printed at the Chiswick Press (London), 1903 (2 copies on vellum) £2,500

Alice: an Adultery, privately printed, 1903 (100 copies; wraps) £500

The Star and the Garter, Watts & Co (London), 1903 (50 copies; wraps) £750

The Sword of Song, Society for the Propagation of Religious Truth (Benares), 1904 (100 copies; wraps)   .   . £750

The Argonauts, Society for the Propagation of Religious Truth (Boleskin, Foyer, Inverness), 1904 (200 copies; wraps) £350

In Residence: The Don's Guide to Cambridge, Elijah Johnson (Cambridge), 1904 (wraps; with detachable entry form for a £100 essay on 'The Works of Aleister Crowley') £250

ditto, Elijah Johnson (Cambridge), 1904 (wraps; without entry form) £200

Why Jesus Wept, A study of society and of the grace of God, privately printed (London), 1904 (wraps)   . £300

Oracles, The Biography of an Art, Society for the Propagation of Religious Truth (Boleskin, Foyer, Inverness), 1905 (wraps) £375

Orpheus, A Lyrical Legend, Society for the Propagation of Religious Truth (Boleskin, Foyer, Inverness), 1905 (2 vols, various coloured boards) £450

Rosa Mundi, A poem, Renouard and Carr (Paris/London), 1905 (pseud 'H.D. Carr') £325

Collected Works of Aleister Crowley, Society for the Propagation of Religious Truth (Boleskin, Foyer, Inverness), 1905, 1906 & 1907 (3 vols; wraps)   . £500

ditto, Society for the Propagation of Religious Truth (Boleskin, Foyer, Inverness), 1907 (1 vol.)   .   . £300

Gargoyles: being strangely wrought images of life and death, Society for the Propagation of Religious Truth (Foyers), 1906 (300 copies) £450

ditto, Society for the Propagation of Religious Truth (Foyers), 1906 (50 copies on handmade paper)   . £600

Rosa Coeli, Chiswick Press (London), 1907 (pseud 'H.D. Carr') £275

Rosa Inferni, Chiswick Press (London), 1907 (pseud 'H.D. Carr') £275

Rodin in Rhyme, Seven Lithographs by Clot from the Water-Colours of Auguste Rodin, with a chaplet of verse by Aleister Crowley, privately printed at the Chiswick Press (London), 1907 (488 copies) .   .   . £500

Amphora, privately printed, 1908   .   .   .   . £700

ditto, Burns & Oates (London), 1908.   .   .   . £600

Clouds Without Water, 'Privately printed for circulation among ministers of religion' (London), 1909 (pseud 'the Rev. C. Verey'; wraps) £300

The World's Tragedy, privately printed (Paris), 1910 (100 copies) £450

The Winged Beetle, privately printed (London), 1910 (50 signed copies) £2,000

ditto, privately printed (London), 1910 (250 unsigned copies)
. . . . £450
Ambergris, Elkin Mathews (London), 1910 . . .£250
Hail Mary, Wieland & Co (London), [1911] . . .£225
The High History of Good Sir Palamedes..., Wieland & Co.
(London), 1912 . . . .£125
Household Gods, A Comedy, privately printed (Pallanza),
1912 . . . .£150
Chicago May, privately printed (New York), 1914 .£850
Songs for Italy, privately printed (Tyrol [Tunis]), 1923
(single folded sheet) £65
England, Stand Fast!, privately issued by the O.T.O.
(London), 1939 (single sheet folded) £45
Temperance, A Tract for the Times, privately issued by the
O.T.O. (London), 1939 (100 copies; wraps) . . .£250
Thumbs Up! A Pentagram—a Pentacle to Win the War,
O.T.O. (London), 1941 (100 copies; wraps) . . .£250
La Gauloise-Song of the Fighting French, privately printed,
1942 (single sheet folded) £45
Fun of the Fair, O.T.O. (California/London), 1942
(containing errata slip and mimeographed poem 'Landed
gentry') £275
The City of God, A Rhapsody, O.T.O. (London), 1943 (200
copies; wraps) £275
Olla, An Anthology of Sixty Years of Song, etc., O.T.O.
(London), [1946] (500 copies) . . . £250/£175
ditto, O.T.O. (London), [1946] (20 copies on handmade
paper) £750

Novels, Plays etc
Mortadello, or the Angel of Venice, Wieland & Co
(London), 1912 . . . .£200
The Diary of a Drug Fiend, Collins (London), 1922 . .
. . . . £2,000/£350
ditto, Dutton (New York), 1923 . . . . £1,350/£175
Moonchild: A Prologue, Mandrake Press (London), 1929
(d/w illustration by Beresford Egan) . . £1,250/£200
The Stratagem and Other Stories, Mandrake Press
(London), [1929]. . . . .£175/£75
ditto, Temple Press (Brighton), 1990 . . . £30/£10

Erotica
White Stains, privately printed (Amsterdam), 1898 (100
copies on handmade paper, pseud 'George Archibald
Bishop'). £3,000
Snowdrops From A Curate's Garden, privately printed
(Paris), [c.1904] £2,250
*Bagh-I-Muattar, The Scented Garden of Abdullah the
Satirist of Shiraz*, privately printed (London), 1910 (100
copies, pseud 'the late Major Lutiy and another'; wraps) .
. . . . £1,750

Magical Titles
*Berashith – An Essay in Ontology with some remarks on
Ceremonial Magic by Abhavananda*, privately printed for
the Sangha of the West (Paris), 1903 (200 copies, pseud
'Abhavananda'; wraps) £300
The Book of the Goetia of Solomon the King, Society for
the Propagation of Religious Truth (Boleskin, Foyer,
Inverness), 1904 ('Translated into the English tongue by a
dead hand' etc, 200 copies) £400
ditto, Society for the Propagation of Religious Truth
(Boleskin, Foyer, Inverness), 1904 (10 copies on Japanese
vellum) £1,000

Konx om Pax, Essays in Light, Walter Scott Publishing Co.
for The Society for the Propagation of Religious Truth
(Boleskin/New York), 1907 (500 copies on handmade
paper) £600
ditto, Walter Scott Publishing Co. for The Society for the
Propagation of Religious Truth (Boleskin/New York), 1907
(10 copies on Japanese vellum) £1,250
777, Walter Scott Publishing Co. for The Society for the
Propagation of Religious Truth (London), 1909 (500 copies
on handmade paper) £1,500
The Holy Books, privately printed (London), [c.1909] (3
vols) £1,250
The Rites of Eleusis, [The Equinox:] (London), [1910]
(wraps) £100
Book Four, Part One, Wieland & Co (London), 1911 (pseud
'Frater Perdurabo', with 'Soror Virakam') . . .£175
Book Four, Part Two, Wieland & Co (London), 1912 (pseud
'Frater Perdurabo', with 'Soror Virakam') . . .£200
Liber CCCXXXIII, The Book of Lies, Wieland & Co.
(London), 1913 . . . .£400
Liber II, The Message of the Master Therion, privately
printed by the O.T.O. (California), 1916 . . .£100
The Law of Liberty, A tract of Therion, that is a Magus,
O.T.O. (London), 1917 (single folded sheet) . . £75
Book Four, Part Three, Magick, in Theory and Practice,
Lecram Press (Paris), 1929 (four parts, pseud 'Master
Therion'; wraps) £600
ditto, Lecram Press for Subscribers (Paris), 1929 [1930] .
. . . . £500/£175
The Book of the Law, O.T.O. (London), 1938 . .£275
ditto, O.T.O., 1938 (wraps) £175
The Heart of the Master, O.T.O. (London), 1938 (pseud
'Khaled Khan') £325
Little Essays Towards Truth, etc., privately issued by the
O.T.O. (London), [1938] £325
Liber XXI, Khing Kang King, the Classic of Purity, O.T.O.
(London), 1939 . . . .£900
Eight Lectures on Yoga, O.T.O. (London), 1939 (pseud
'Mahatma Guru Sri Parahamsa Shivaji') . £600/£400
*The Book of Thoth, A short essay on the Tarot of the
Egyptians*, O.T.O. (London), 1944 (200 signed copies,
pseud 'Master Therion') £3,250

Others
The Spirit of Solitude, Mandrake Press (London), 1929 (2
vols) . . . . £1,000 the set
The Confessions of Aleister Crowley, Mandrake Press
(London), 1929 (800 copies, 2 vols) £350
ditto, Cape (New York), 1969 . . . . £30/£10
ditto, Hill & Wang (New York), 1970 . . . £30/£10
*The Banned Lecture—Gilles de Rais—to have been
delivered before the Oxford University Poetry Society*,
etc., Stephensen (London), [1930.] £225
The Scientific Solution of the Problem of Government,
O.T.O. (London), [c.1937] (pseud 'Comte de Fénix') £90
The Last Ritual, privately printed, [1947] (wraps) . .£125

Translation
Little Poems in Prose by Baudelaire, Titus (Paris), 1928
(800 copies, with 12 copper plate engravings from the
original drawings by Jean de Bosschere) . . .£400
The Key of the Mysteries, by Eliphas Levi, Rider & Co.
(London), 1959 . . . . £75/£30

JAMES CRUMLEY
(b.1939)

Crumley is an American author of violent hardboiled crime novels and short stories, as well as essays and published and unpublished screenplays. His novel *The Mexican Tree Duck* won the 1994 Dashiell Hammett Award, given by the North American Branch of the International Association of Crime Writers for the best literary crime novel.

Novels
One to Count Cadence, Random House (New York), 1969 .
. . . . £175/£30
ditto, Picador (London), 1994 (pbk) £10
The Wrong Case, Random House (New York), 1975 . .
. . . . £300/£40
ditto, Hart-Davis, MacGibbon (London), 1976 . £145/£30
The Last Good Kiss, Random House (New York), 1978 .
. . . . £45/£10
ditto, Granada (London), 1978 . . . . . £30/£5
Dancing Bear, Random House (New York), 1983 . £30/£5
ditto, Penguin (Harmondsworth, Middlesex), 1987 (pbk) £5
James Crumley: The Collection, Picador (London), 1991 (contains *The Wrong Case*, *The Last Good Kiss* and *Dancing Bear*) . . . . . . £20/£5
ditto, Picador (London), 1991 (pbk) £5
The Mexican Tree Duck, Mysterious Press (New York), 1993 (advance reading copy; pbk) £20
ditto, James Cahill Publishing (Huntington Beach, CA), 1993 (150 signed, numbered copies; slipcase; Mysterious Press sheets with additional title page . . . £30/£20
ditto, Mysterious Press (New York), 1993 . . £10/£5
ditto, Scorpion Press (Bristol, UK), 1993 (75 signed, numbered copies; quarter imitation morocco; glassine d/w; uses Picador sheets) . . . . . . £75/£65
ditto, Scorpion Press (Bristol, UK), 1993 (15 signed, lettered copies) . . . . £200/£190
ditto, Picador (London), 1993 . . . . . £10/£5
Bordersnakes, Dennis McMillan (Tucson, AZ), 1996 (300 signed, numbered copies; slipcase) . . . £75/£65
ditto, Dennis McMillan (Tucson, AZ), 1996 (26 signed, lettered copies; quarter morocco with paper boards; d/w and slipcase). . . . . . . £125/£150
ditto, Mysterious Press (New York), 1996 . . £10/£5
ditto, HarperCollins (London), 1997 . . . . £10/£5
The Final Country, Dennis McMillan (Tucson, AZ), 2001 (400 signed, numbered copies; slipcase) . . £50/£40
ditto, Dennis McMillan (Tucson, AZ), 2001 (52 signed, lettered copies; quarter morocco with paper boards; d/w and slipcase). . . . .£100/£75
ditto, Dennis McMillan (Tucson, AZ), 2001 (10 signed, numbered artist's presentation copies in slipcase; quarter morocco with paper boards) . . . . £150/£125
ditto, Mysterious Press (New York), 2001 . . £10/£5
ditto, HarperCollins (London), 2002 . . . . £10/£5
The Right Madness, Viking (New York), 2005 . £10/£5
ditto, HarperCollins (London), 2005 . . . . £10/£5

Short Stories
Whores, Dennis McMillan (Missoula, MT), 1988 (pbk) £10
ditto, Dennis McMillan (Missoula, MT), 1988 (475 signed, numbered copies) . . . . £80/£50

ditto, Dennis McMillan (Missoula, MT), 1988 (26 signed, lettered copies bound in full goatskin morocco) . . £300
ditto, Dennis McMillan (Missoula, MT), 1988 (13 signed, unlettered copies bound in full goatskin morocco) . £175
The Mexican Pig Bandit, A.S.A.P. (Royal Oak, MI/Mission Viejo, CA), 1998 (300 signed, numbered copies; no d/w)
. . . . £30
ditto, A.S.A.P. (Royal Oak, MI/Mission Viejo, CA), 1998 (50 signed, numbered copies in clamshell slipcase with signed and numbered lithograph drawing by Phil Parks) .
. . . . £85
ditto, A.S.A.P. (Royal Oak, MI/Mission Viejo, CA), 1998 (12 signed copies bound in full leather stamped in blind) .
. . . . £450
ditto, A.S.A.P. (Royal Oak, MI/Mission Viejo, CA), 1998 (20 signed, numbered copies; manuscript proof loosely bound with each page in its own plastic sleeve) in a binder with laid-in preface by publisher, tipped-in colour photo of Crumley, and two consecutive original typescript pages.) .
. . . .£250

Short Fiction and Essays
The Muddy Fork, A Work in Progress, Lord John Press (Northridge, CA), 1984 (200 signed, numbered copies; no d/w) £65
ditto, Lord John Press (Northridge, CA), 1984 (50 signed, numbered delux copies) £175
Muddy Fork and Other Things, Clark City Press (Livingston MT), 1991 (pbk) £10
ditto, Clark City Press (Livingston MT), 1991 (125 signed, numbered copies; slipcase) . . . . .£125/£75

Screenplay
Pigeon Shoot, Neville (Santa Barbara, CA), 1987 (350 signed, numbered copies in clear acetate d/w) . £50/£45
ditto, Neville (Santa Barbara, CA), 1987 (26 signed, lettered copies in slipcase) . . . . . £200/£150
ditto, Neville (Santa Barbara, CA), 1987 (6 signed, unnumbered presentation copies; no slipcase) . .£250

Others
Kent Anderson's Sympathy for the Devil, Pride of Tacoma Press (no place), 1996 (150 copies in stapled wraps) . £30

COUNTEE CULLEN
(b.1903 d.1946)

Countee Cullen, born Countee LeRoy Porter, was an American Romantic poet, associated with the generation of black poets of the Harlem Renaissance. For a number of years following his death Cullen was considered the most celebrated African American writer.

Poetry
Color, Harper & Brothers (New York/London), 1925 (advance 'sample' copy containing two-page 'Synopsis', followed by 3 'samples from the text') . . . £1,250
ditto, Harper & Brothers (New York/London), 1925 . .
. . . . £600/£100
Copper Sun, Harper & Brothers (New York/London), 1927 (slipcase) . . . . £200/£150

ditto, Harper & Brothers (New York/London), 1927 (100 signed, numbered copies; glassine d/w and slipcase) . . . . £500/£400

The Ballad of the Brown Girl, Harper & Brothers (New York/London), 1927 (slipcase and cobweb design glassine d/w) . . . . £125/£100

ditto, Harper & Brothers (New York/London), 1927 (500 numbered copies; slipcase; no d/w). . . £150/£125

ditto, Harper & Brothers (New York/London), 1927 (unknown number of lettered 'dedication' copies) £1,500

The Black Christ and Other Poems, Harper & Brothers (New York/London), 1929 . . . . £175/£35

ditto, Harper & Brothers (New York/London), 1929 (128 signed, numbered copies; slipcase) . . £450/£400

ditto, G.P. Putnam's (London), 1929 . . . £125/£25

The Medea, And Some Other Poems, Harper & Brothers (New York), 1935 . . . . . . £125/£20

Christus Natus Est, privately printed (no place), 1943 (broadside; printed 'Ida and Countee Cullen, Christmas, 1943'; folded to form a Christmas card). . . . £175

On These I Stand, An Anthology of the Best Poems, Harper & Brothers (New York), 1947 . . . . £65/£10

My Soul's High Song, The Collected Writings..., Doubleday (New York), 1991 . . . . . . £10/£5

Prose

One Way to Heaven, Harper & Brothers (New York), 1932. . . . . £250/£40

The Lost Zoo, Harper & Brothers (New York), 1940 (written with 'Christopher Cat') . . . . £150/£35

My Lives and How I Lost Them, Harper & Brothers (New York), 1942 . . . . £150/£35

E.E. CUMMINGS
(b.1894 d.1962)

An innovative American poet, much influenced by slang and jazz, whose work is characterised by unconventional punctuation and typography. It seems that the presentation of his name as 'e.e. cummings' was employed by his publishers without his endorsement. Despite his fascination with avant garde style, much of his work is traditional in its form and themes.

Poetry

Eight Harvard Poets, Gomme (New York), 1917 (dark red lettering to grey boards and tan spine) . . . £145

Tulips and Chimneys, Seltzer (New York), 1923 . . . . £1,350/£175

&, privately printed (New York), 1925 (111 of 333 signed copies, green gold-flecked boards, slipcase) . £1,000/£750

ditto, privately printed (New York), 1925 (222 of 333 signed copies, slipcase) . . . . . £750/£500

XLI Poems, Dial Press (New York), 1925 . £600/£40

Is 5, Boni & Liveright (New York), 1926 (orange gold-flecked boards) . . . . . . £300/£100

ditto, Boni & Liveright (New York), 1926 (77 signed copies, slipcase). . . . . £1,000/£750

[Untitled], Covici Friede (New York), 1930 (491 signed copies) £300

CIOPW, Covici Friede (New York), 1931 (391 signed, numbered copies) £450

W [ViVa], Liveright Inc. (New York), 1931 . £450/£200

ditto, Liveright Inc. (New York), 1931 (95 signed, numbered copies, glassine d/w) £600

No Thanks, Golden Eagle Press (Mt Vernon, NY), 1935 (90 signed copies) £650

ditto, Golden Eagle Press (Mt Vernon, NY), 1935 (9 signed copies with manuscript page) £2,000

ditto, Golden Eagle Press (Mt Vernon, NY), 1935 (900 copies) . . . . £200/£75

Tom, Arrow Editions (Mt Vernon, NY), 1935 (1,500 copies, glassine d/w). . . . . . £250/£75

1/20, Roger Roughton (London), 1936 (tissue d/w) . . . . £125/£100

Collected Poems, Harcourt Brace (New York), 1938 . . . . £125/£35

50 Poems, Duell, Sloane and Pearce (New York), 1940 . . . . £225/£50

ditto, Duell, Sloane and Pearce (New York), 1940 (150 signed copies, glassine d/w slipcase) . £1,250/£1,000

1 x 1, Holt (New York), 1944 . . . . £100/£25

ditto, Horizon (London), 1947 . . . £45/£15

XAIPE: Seventy-One Poems, O.U.P. (New York), 1950 . . . . £65/£20

Poems, 1923-1954, Harcourt Brace (New York), 1954 . . . . £25/£5

95 Poems, Harcourt Brace (New York), 1958 (300 signed copies, slipcase) . . . . . £400/£250

ditto, Harcourt Brace (New York), 1958 . . £25/£10

100 Selected Poems, Grove Press (New York), 1959 (pbk) £20

Selected Poems, 1923-1958, Faber (London), 1960 £25/£10

73 Poems, Harcourt (New York), 1963 . . £45/£15

ditto, Faber (London), 1963 . . . . £40/£10

Complete Poems, MacGibbon & Kee (London), 1968 (150 numbered sets; 2 vols in d/ws and slipcase) . £300/£175

Complete Poems: 1913-1935, MacGibbon & Kee (London), 1968 . . . . . . £45/£15

Complete Poems: 1936-1962, MacGibbon & Kee (London), 1968 . . . . . . £45/£15

Complete Poems 1913-1962, Harcourt Brace (New York), 1972 . . . . £30/£10

Poems 1905-1962, Marchim Press (London), 1973 (225 numbered copies) £250

Hist Whist and Other Poems for Children, Evans (London), 1975 . . . . £25/£10

ditto, Liveright (New York), 1983 . . . £25/£10

Complete Poems 1910-1962, Granada (London), 1981 (2 vols in slipcase) . . . . . £50/£25

Etcetera: The Unpublished Poems, Liveright (New York), 1983 . . . . £45/£15

In Just-Spring, Little, Brown (Boston), 1988 . £35/£10

Complete Poems 1904-1962, Liveright (New York), 1991 . . . . £20/£10

Fiction

The Enormous Room, Boni & Liveright (New York), 1911 (word 'shit' in last line on page 219) . £2,000/£1,000

ditto, Boni & Liveright (New York), 1911 (word 'shit' in last line on page 219 inked out) . . . £1,000 /£500

ditto, Cape (London), 1928 . . . £250/£50

Eimi, Covici Friede (New York), 1933 (1,381 signed, numbered copies) . . . . . £400/£150

Plays

Him, Boni & Liveright (New York), 1927 . . £100/£25

ditto, Boni & Liveright (New York), 1927 (160 signed, numbered copies, slipcase) . . . £250/£150

Anthropos, Golden Eagle Press (Mt Vernon, NY), 1944 (222 copies, slipcase) . . . . . . £175/£150

Santa Claus, Holt (New York), 1946 (250 signed copies, glassine d/w). . . . . . £200/£150

ditto, Holt (New York), 1946 . . . . £125/£35

Others

Puella Mea, Golden Eagle Press (Mt Vernon, NY), 1949 (17 drawings by Cummings, Paul Klee, Picasso, Modigliani, and Kurt Roesch. Contains poem originally in *Tulips and Chimneys*) . . . . £50/£25

i: Six Nonlectures, Harvard Univ Press (Cambridge, MA), 1953 . . . . £60/£15

ditto, Harvard Univ Press (Cambridge, MA), 1953 (350 signed copies) . . . . . £350/£250

A Miscellany, Argophile Press (New York), 1958 (900 copies) . . . . £75/£25

ditto, Argophile Press (New York), 1958 (75 signed, numbered copies, glassine d/w) . . . £250/£200

Adventures in Value, Harcourt, Brace & World (New York), 1962 (50 photographs by Marion Morehouse, with text by Cummings) . . . . . . £76/£25

Fairy Tales, Harcourt Brace (New York), 1965 . £25/£10

Selected Letters, Harcourt Brace (New York), 1969 £25/£10

ditto, Deutsch (London), 1972 . . . . £20/£5

ROALD DAHL

(b.1916 d.1990)

Principally a children's writer, although his short stories for adults are also well known. In the past Dahl's books for children often met with disapproval due to the unpleasant ends met by some of his characters—but this seems to be precisely what children enjoy about them.

Children's Titles

The Gremlins, Random House (New York), [1943] . . . . £1,500/£750

ditto, Collins (London), [1944] (boards, no d/w) . £750

James and the Giant Peach, Knopf (New York), 1961 (first issue bound by the Wolff Press; first issue d/w without numbers on the back panel) . . . £1,200/£200

ditto, Knopf (New York), 1961 (second issue stating on colophon at rear bound by The Book Press; numbers on the back panel) . . . . . . £400/£100

ditto, Allen & Unwin (London), 1967 (boards, no d/w). £300

Charlie and the Chocolate Factory, Knopf (New York), 1964 (first issue with six lines of publishing information on last page) . . . . . £1,500/£500

ditto, Knopf (New York), 1964 (second issue with five lines of publishing information on last page) . . £250/£50

ditto, Allen & Unwin (London), 1967 (boards, no d/w). £250

The Magic Finger, Harper (New York), 1966 (trade edition first printing with $2.50 on the upper front flap, with the lower flap clipped of its library price) . . . £100/£20

ditto, Harper (New York), 1966 (library edition first printing with $2.57 on the lower front flap, with the upper flap clipped of its trade price) . . . . . £100/£20

ditto, Allen & Unwin (London), 1968 (boards, no d/w). £150

Fantastic Mr Fox, Knopf (New York), 1970 . . £75/£25

ditto, Allen & Unwin (London), 1970 (boards, no d/w) £75

Charlie and the Great Glass Elevator, Knopf (New York), 1972 . . . . £75/£20

ditto, Allen & Unwin (London), 1973 (boards, no d/w). £125

Danny, The Champion of the World, Cape (London), 1975 . . . . £100/£25

ditto, Knopf (New York), 1975 . . . . £35/£15

The Wonderful Story of Henry Sugar and Six More, Cape (London), 1977 . . . . . . £75/£15

ditto, Knopf (New York), 1977 . . . . . £35/£15

The Enormous Crocodile, Cape (London), 1978 (no d/w) £65

ditto, Knopf (New York), 1978 . . . . £30/£10

The Twits, Cape (London), 1980 . . . . £50/£10

ditto, Knopf (New York), 1981 . . . . . £35/£10

George's Marvellous Medicine, Cape (London), 1981 . . . . £50/£20

ditto, Knopf (New York), 1982 . . . . . £25/£5

Roald Dahl's Revolting Rhymes, Cape (London), 1982 (no d/w) £65

ditto, Knopf (New York), 1983 . . . . £35/£10

The BFG, Cape (London), 1982. . . . . £45/£10

ditto, Farrar Straus (New York), 1982 . . . £25/£5

Dirty Beasts, Cape (London), 1983 (no d/w) . . . £45

ditto, Farrar Straus (New York), 1983 . . . £25/£10

The Witches, Cape (London), 1983 . . . . £60/£10

ditto, Farrar Straus (New York), 1983 . . . £30/£10

The Giraffe, the Pelly and Me, Cape (London), 1985 (no d/w) £45

ditto, Farrar Straus (New York), 1985 (no d/w) . . £25

Matilda, Cape (London), 1988 . . . . . £60/£10

ditto, Viking Kestrel (New York), 1988 . . . £30/£10

Rhyme Stew, Cape (London), 1989 . . . . £35/£5

ditto, Viking (New York), 1990 . . . . . £25/£5

Esio Trot, Cape (London), 1990 . . . . . £35/£5

ditto, Viking (New York), 1990 . . . . . £25/£5

Roald Dahl's Guide to Railway Safety, British Rail (no place), 1991 (stapled wraps) £10

The Vicar of Nibbleswicke, Random Century (London), 1991 . . . . £30/£5

ditto, Viking (New York), 1991 . . . . . £20/£5

The Minpins, Cape (London), 1991 . . . . £25/£5

ditto, Viking (New York), 1991 . . . . . £15/£5

My Year, Cape (London), 1993 . . . . . £15/£5

ditto, Viking (New York), 1993 . . . . . £10/£5

The Mildenhall Treasure, Cape (London), 1999 . £15/£5

ditto, Knopf (New York), 2000 . . . . . £10/£5

Adult Novels

Sometime Never, Scribner's (New York), 1948 . £125/£25

ditto, Collins (London), 1949 . . . . . £125/£25

My Uncle Oswald, Joseph (London), 1979 . . £30/£5

ditto, Knopf (New York), 1980 . . . . . £30/£5

Short Stories

Over to You, Reynal & Hitchcock (New York), 1946 . . . . £175/£35

ditto, Hamish Hamilton (London), 1946 . . £150/£30

Someone Like You, Knopf (New York), 1953. . £75/£20

ditto, Secker & Warburg (London), 1954 (less 2 stories) . . . . £75/£20

ditto, Michael Joseph (London), 1961 (revised and expanded) . . . . £45/£15
Kiss Kiss, Knopf (New York), 1960 . . . £75/£15
ditto, Joseph (London), 1960 . . . . £65/£15
A Roald Dahl Selection, Longmans (New York), 1960 (pbk)
. . . . £5
Selected Short Stories, Modern Library (New York), 1968 (pbk) £5
Twenty Nine Kisses from Roald Dahl, Joseph (London), 1969 . . . . £25/£5
Switch Bitch, Knopf (New York), 1974 . . . £35/£10
ditto, Joseph (London), 1974 . . . £35/£10
Tales of the Unexpected, Joseph (London), 1979 . £35/£10
ditto, Random/Vintage (New York), 1979 (pbk) . . £5
Taste and Other Tales, Longman/Penguin (London), 1979 (pbk) £5
More Tales of the Unexpected, Joseph (London), 1980 .
. . . . £25/£5
The Best of Roald Dahl, Joseph (London), 1983 . £15/£5
Completely Unexpected Tales, Penguin (Harmondsworth, Middlesex), 1986 (pbk) £5
Two Fables, Viking (London), 1986 . . . £25/£10
ditto, Viking (London), 1986 (300 signed copies) . . £450
ditto, Farrar Straus (New York), 1987 . . £25/£10
Taste a 1934 Chateau Branaire-Ducru Tainted!, Redpath Press (Minneapolis, MN), 1986 (pbk) . . . £5
Ah! Sweet Mystery of Life, Joseph (London), 1989 £15/£5
ditto, Knopf (New York), 1989 . . . . . £10/£5
The Collected Short Stories of Roald Dahl, Cape (London), 1991 . . . . £20/£5
ditto, Viking (New York), 1991 . . . . £15/£5
The Great Automatic Grammatizator, Viking, 1996 £15/£5
ditto, as *The Umbrella Man and Other Stories*, Viking (New York), 1996 . . . . . . £15/£5
Skin, Viking (London), 2000 . . . . £10/£5

Autobiography
Boy: Tales of Childhood, Cape (London), 1984 . £25/£5
ditto, Farrar Straus (New York), 1984 (200 signed copies) .
. . . . £350
ditto, Farrar Straus (New York), 1984 . . . £25/£5
Going Solo, Cape (London), 1986 . . . £15/£5
ditto, Farrar Straus (New York), 1986 . . . £15/£5

THE DANDY

This British children's comic first issued in December 1937 is currently the longest running comic in the world. A successful rival to *The Beano*, *The Dandy* sported Korky the Cat on its front cover for almost 50 years. In September 2004 a first issue of *The Dandy*, with free gift, sold for a record £20,350, the highest price ever paid for a British comic at an auction.

Comics
No.1, D.C. Thomson, 1937 (with 'Express Whistler' free gift)
. . . . £20,000
ditto, D.C. Thomson, 1937 (without free gift) . . £7,500
No.2, D.C. Thomson (with 'Jumping Frog' free gift), 1937.
. . . . £3,500
ditto, D.C. Thomson (without free gift), 1937. . £1,000
Nos 3-10, D.C. Thomson, 1937 . . . . .£500 each

1938-39	£100 each
1940	£50 each
1941-45	£35 each
1946-50	£20 each
1950-60	£5 each
1961-71	£2 each
1971-80	£1 each
1981-90	50p each
1991-to today	25p each

Dandy Monster Comic
1939, D.C. Thomson £3,000
1940, D.C. Thomson £1,250
1941, D.C. Thomson £1,000
1942, D.C. Thomson £750
1943, D.C. Thomson £600
1944, D.C. Thomson £500
1945, D.C. Thomson £450
1946, D.C. Thomson £400
1947, D.C. Thomson £325
1948, D.C. Thomson £250
1949, D.C. Thomson £200
1950, D.C. Thomson £150
1951, D.C. Thomson £100
1952, D.C. Thomson £75

Dandy Books
1953-1960, D.C. Thomson £50
1961-65, D.C. Thomson £65
1966-69, D.C. Thomson £25

CHARLES DARWIN
(b.1809 d.1882)

Darwin was an English naturalist who achieved fame by explaining that different species originate through evolutionary change, proposing the theory that natural selection is the mechanism by which this change occurs. He first co-published this theory with Alfred Russell Wallace who had independently arrived at the same theory. Darwin's book on the subject, *On the Origin of Species*, established evolution by common descent as the dominant scientific explanation of diversification in nature.

Extracts from Letters Addressed to Professor Henslow by C. Darwin, Esq., Cambridge Philosophical Society (Cambridge [Univ Press]), [1835] (pale grey wraps) . .
. . . . £200,000
The Zoology of the Voyage of H.M.S. Beagle, edited by C. Darwin, Smith Elder (London), 1838-43 (issued in 19 numbers making 5 parts; buff printed boards) . £50,000
Narrative of the Surveying Voyages of His Majesty's Ships Adventure and Beagle, Henry Colburn (London), 1839 (4 vols; blue cloth; edited by Robert Fitzroy; includes Darwin's 'Journal and Remarks 1832-1836' as vol. III) .
. . . . £25,000
Journal of Researches into the Geology and Natural History of the Various Countries Visited by H.M.S. Beagle, Henry Colburn (London), 1839 (blue or purple cloth) £10,000
Journal of Researches into the Natural History and Geology of the Countries Visited During the Voyage of

H.M.S. Beagle, John Murray (London), 1845 (3 parts; grey-buff card of the Colonial and Home Library series) .

. . . . £10,000

ditto, John Murray (London), 1845 (1 vol in red morocco or red cloth of the Colonial and Home Library series, or red cloth) £2,000

ditto, Harper & Brothers (New York), 1846 (black cloth of Harper's New Miscellany series) £500

The Structure and Distribution of Coral Reefs, Smith Elder (London), 1842 (blue or purple cloth) . . . £5,000

Geological Observations on the Volcanic Islands Visited, Smith Elder (London), 1844 (blue or purple cloth) £2,500

Geological Observations on South America, Smith Elder (London), 1846 (blue or purple cloth) . . . £3,500

Geological Observations on Coral Reefs, Volcanic Islands, and on South America, Smith Elder (London), 1851 (3 above vols bound together in 1 vol; blue or purple cloth) .

. . . . £3,500

A Monograph of the Sub-Class Cirripedia, Palaeontographical Society (London), 1851-54 (2 vols; blue cloth; [Vol. II: The Lepadidae or Pedunculated Cirripedes]) £1,500

A Monograph of the Fossil Lepadidae, Ray Society (London), 1851-54 (2 vols; [Vol II: A Monograph of the Fossil Balanidae and Verrucidae of Great Britain]) £1,000

'On the tendency of species to form varieties, and on the perpetuation of varieties and species by natural means of selection, by Charles Darwin ... and Alfred Russell Wallace', Journal of the Proceedings of the Linnean Society of London, Vol. III, no 9, Longman (London), 1858 (blue printed wraps; pps 46-52 in first pagination) .

. . . . £25,000

ditto, Journal of the Proceedings of the Linnean Society of London, Vol. III, no 9, Longman (London), 1858 (as above but pps 45-62 in the journal as issued to fellows who only took the zoological parts; pink printed wraps) . £20,000

ditto, as *The Darwin Wallace*, (offprint of above; buff printed wraps) £4,000

On the Origin of Species by Means of Natural Selection, John Murray (London), 1859 (green cloth; first edition with 2 quotes on p.ii) £50,000

ditto, Appleton, 1860 (first edition with 2 quotes on p.ii) .

. . . . £4,000

On the Various Contrivances by Which British and Foreign Orchids are Fertilised by Insects, John Murray (London), 1862 (plum cloth) £1,500

ditto, Appleton, 1877 . . . . £150

On the Movements and Habits of Climbing Plants, Journal of the Linnean Society, vol. IX, nos. 33 & 34, 1865 (green printed wraps) £1,500

ditto, Longman (London), 1865 (green printed wraps) . .

. . . . £1,500

ditto, Taylor and Francis (London), 1865 (plain buff wraps)

. . . . £3,000

ditto, Appleton, 1876 . . . . £150

The Variation of Animals and Plants Under Domestication, John Murray (London), 1868 (2 vols; green cloth) £1,000

ditto, Orange Judd (New York), 1868 (2 vols; green cloth) .

. . . . £300

The Descent of Man and Selection in Relation to Sex, John Murray (London), 1870-71 (2 vols; green cloth) . £7,500

ditto, Appleton, 1871 (2 vols; brown cloth) . . £500

The Expression of the Emotions in Men and Animals, John Murray (London), 1872 (green cloth) . . . £750

ditto, Appleton, 1873 (brown cloth) £500

Insectivorous Plants, John Murray (London), 1875 (green cloth) £1,000

ditto, Appleton, 1875 (brown cloth) £300

The Effects of Cross and Self-Fertilisation in the Vegetable Kingdom, John Murray (London), 1876 (green cloth). £750

ditto, Appleton, 1877 (brown cloth) £250

The Different Forms of Flowers on Plants of the Same Species, John Murray (London), 1877 (green cloth) . £750

ditto, Appleton, 1877 (brown cloth) £250

The Power of Movement in Plants, John Murray (London), 1880 (green cloth) £750

ditto, Appleton, 1881 (brown cloth) £250

The Formation of Vegetable Mould Through the Action of Worms, John Murray (London), 1881 (green cloth) . £500

ditto, Appleton, 1882 (brown cloth) £250

ROBERTSON DAVIES
(b.1913 d.1995)

Robertson Davies was Canada's best-known novelist, playwright, critic and journalist. Canadian critics however, have been divided in their assessment of his work, with some believing that his subtly humorous, sometimes fantastical work is rather too eccentric, informed as it is by his varied interests, from Jungian analysis to the legends of King Arthur.

Fictional Essays

The Diary of Samuel Marchbanks, Clarke, Irwin (Toronto), 1947 (integral title page with unclear type and no disclaimer) . . . . £300/£75

ditto, Clarke, Irwin (Toronto), 1947 (title page mounted on stub; no disclaimer) . . . . . £145/£50

ditto, Clarke, Irwin (Toronto), 1947 (disclaimer slip tipped-in on Table of Contents page) . . . . £100/£20

ditto, Clarke, Irwin (Toronto), 1966 (pbk) . . . £5

The Table Talk of Samuel Marchbanks, Clarke, Irwin (Toronto), 1949 (first issue in dull red cloth) . £75/£15

ditto, Clarke, Irwin (Toronto), 1947 (second issue in bright red cloth) . . . . £65/£15

ditto, Chatto & Windus (London), 1951 . . £75/£15

ditto, as *The Table Talk of Samuel Marchbanks* and *The Diary of Samuel Marchbanks*, Chatto & Windus (London), 1951 (2 vols; red slipcase with spine label) .

. . . . £125/£35

Samuel Marchbanks' Almanack, McClelland and Stewart (Toronto/Montreal), 1967 . . . . . £60/£10

The Papers of Samuel Marchbanks, Viking (New York), 1986 (containing *The Diary*, *The Table Talk* and *A Garland of Miscellanea*, with additions) . . . . £10/£5

Criticism

Shakespeare's Boy Actors, Dent (London), 1939 (pseud 'W. Robertson Davies') . . . . . £1,250/£200

ditto, Wm. Salloch (New York), 1941 . . £750/£175

Shakespeare for Young Players: A Junior Course, Clarke, Irwin (Toronto), 1942 (no d/w) £200

Renown at Stratford, Clarke, Irwin (Toronto), 1953 (with Tyrone Guthrie) . . . . . . £40/£10

Twice Have the Trumpets Sounded, Clarke, Irwin (Toronto), 1954 (with Tyrone Guthrie) . . . . £25/£5 *ditto*, Blackie & Sons (London), 1955 . . £25/£5

ditto, J. Garnet Miller (London), 1955 . . £25/£5

Thrice the Brindled Cat Hath Mew'd, Clarke, Irwin (Toronto), 1955 (with Tyrone Guthrie, Boyd Neel and Tanya Moiseiwitsch) . . . . . . £25/£5

A Voice From the Attic, Knopf (New York), 1960. £50/£10

ditto, McClelland & Stewart (Toronto), 1960 . £75/£15

ditto, as ***The Personal Art: Reading to Good Purpose***, Secker & Warburg (London), 1961 . . . £65/£10

Stratford Papers on Shakespeare, W.J. Gage (Toronto), 1961 (pbk) £15

Literature and Medicine, Canadian Medical Association Journal (Peterborough, Ontario) £100

Stephen Leacock, McClelland and Stewart (Toronto), 1970 (pbk) £10

ditto, as ***Feast of Stephen***, McClelland & Stewart (Toronto), 1970 . . . . £40/£5

One Half of Robertson Davies, Macmillan (Toronto), 1977 . . . . £30/£5

ditto, Viking Press (New York), 1978 . . £30/£5

The Enthusiasms of Robertson Davies, McClelland and Stewart (Toronto), 1979 (edited by Judith Skelton) £20/£5

ditto, Viking Press (New York), 1990 . . £15/£5

The Well-Tempered Critic, McClelland and Stewart (Toronto), 1981 (edited by Judith Skelton Grant). £15/£5

The Mirror of Nature, Univ of Toronto Press (Toronto/Buffalo/London), 1983 (pbk) £10

The Merry Heart, McClelland & Stewart (Toronto), 1996 . . . . £10/£5

ditto, Viking Press (New York), 1997 . . £10/£5

ditto, Viking Press (London), 1997 . . . £10/£5

Happy Alchemy, M[cClelland] & S[tewart] (Toronto), 1997 . . . . £10/£5

ditto, Viking Press (London), 1997 . . . £10/£5

ditto, Viking Press (New York), 1998 . . £10/£5

The Merry Heart [with] ***Happy Alchemy***, McClelland & Stewart (Toronto), 1996, 1997 (special issue two-volume set binding first edition sheets later in uniform dark brown paper boards; no d/ws; slipcase) . . . £15/£5

Novels
The Salterton Trilogy
Tempest-Tost, Clarke, Irwin (Toronto), 1951 . £200/£30

ditto, Rinehart (New York), 1952 . . . £175/£25

ditto, Chatto & Windus (London), 1952 . . £100/£15

Leaven of Malice, Clarke, Irwin (Toronto), 1954 . £125/£25

ditto, Charles Scribner's (New York), 1955 . £100/£20

ditto, Chatto & Windus (London), 1955 . . £65/£10

A Mixture of Frailties, Weidenfeld & Nicolson (London), 1958 . . . . £65/£10

ditto, Chatto & Windus (London), 1955 . . £65/£10

ditto, Charles Scribner's (New York), 1958 . £50/£10

ditto, Macmillan (Toronto), 1958 . . . £75/£15

The Deptford Trilogy
Fifth Business, Macmillan (Toronto), 1970 (first state with pps 172 and 122 reversed in table of contents; first issue d/w with no number at foot of spine and no mention of book club selection; nb Book Club ed with same error on contents page) . . . . . . £65/£10

ditto, Macmillan (Toronto), 1970 (second issue with corrected text, number at foot of spine and book club mention) . . . . £25/£5

ditto, Viking (New York), 1970 . . . . £40/£5

ditto, Macmillan (London), 1971 . . . . £30/£5

The Manticore, Viking (New York), 1972 . . £30/£5

ditto, Macmillan (Toronto), 1972 (first issue d/w without number in lower corner of back panel) . . . £65/£10

ditto, Macmillan (Toronto), 1972 (second issue d/w with '7330' in lower corner of back panel) . . . £25/£10

ditto, Macmillan (London), 1973 . . . . £25/£5

World of Wonders, Macmillan (Toronto), 1975 . £45/£10

ditto, Viking Press (New York), 1976 . . £30/£5

ditto, W.H. Allen (London), 1977 . . . £10/£5

The Deptford Trilogy, Macmillan (Toronto), 1985 (omnibus) . . . . £20/£5

ditto, Viking Press (London), 1987 . . . £20/£5

The Cornish Trilogy

The Rebel Angels, Macmillan (Toronto), 1981 . £25/£5

ditto, Viking Press (New York), 1981 . . £20/£5

ditto, Allen Lane (London), 1982 . . . £20/£5

What's Bred in the Bone, Macmillan (Toronto), 1985 . .
. . . . £25/£5

ditto, Viking Press (New York), 1981 . . £20/£5

ditto, Viking Press (London), 1981 . . . £20/£5

The Lyre of Orpheus, Macmillan (Toronto), 1988 . £10/£5

ditto, Viking Press (London), 1988 . . . £10/£5

ditto, London Limited Editions/Viking Press (London), 1988 (150 signed, numbered copies; glassine d/w) . . £65

ditto, Franklin Library (Franklin Centre, PA), 1988 (signed, limited edition) £30

ditto, Viking Press (New York), 1989 . . £10/£5

The Toronto Trilogy
(final, incomplete, trilogy)
Murther & Walking Spirits, M[cClelland] & S[tewart] (Toronto), 1991 . . . . £10/£5

ditto, Sinclair-Stevenson (London, 1991 . . . £10/£5

ditto, Sinclair-Stevenson Ltd./London Limited Editions (London, 1991 (150 signed, numbered copies; glassine d/w) £60

ditto, Franklin Library (Franklin Centre, PA), 1991 (signed, limited edition) £30

ditto, Viking Press (New York), 1991 . . £10/£5

The Cunning Man, M[cClelland] & S[tewart] (Toronto), 1994 . . . . £10/£5

ditto, Viking Press (New York), 1994 . . £10/£5

ditto, Viking Press (London), 1994 . . . £10/£5

Short Stories
High Spirits, A Collection of Ghost Stories, Penguin Books (Markham, Ontario), 1982 (pbk) £10

ditto, Penguin Books (London), 1982 (pbk) . . £10

ditto, Viking Press (New York), 1983 . . £30/£5

A Gathering of Ghost Stories, Penguin Books (New York etc), 1995 (pbk) £5

Plays
Overlaid: A Comedy, Samuel French (Toronto), 1948 (wraps) £250

ditto, Samuel French (Toronto), 1952 (wraps) . . £50

Eros at Breakfast and Other Plays, Clarke, Irwin (Toronto), 1949 . . . . £200/£65

Fortune My Foe, Clarke, Irwin (Toronto), 1949 (pbk with d/w) . . . . £150/£30

At My Heart's Core, Clarke, Irwin (Toronto), 1950 £100/£20

ditto, Clarke, Irwin (Toronto), 1950 (pbk with d/w) £150/£30

ditto, Chatto & Windus (London), 1952 . . . £75/£15
ditto, Rinehart (New York), 1952 . . . £75/£15
A Masque of Aesop, Clarke, Irwin (Toronto), 1952 £100/£20
A Jig for the Gypsy, Clarke, Irwin (Toronto), 1954 £100/£20
A Masque of Mr Punch, A Victorian Extravaganza for the Boys of U.C.C. Prep, no publisher (Toronto), 1962 (35-50 copies; mimeo-graphed rectos only; wraps bound in blue card folder with typed label) £250
ditto, O.U.P. (Toronto), 1963 . . . . £65/£15
ditto, O.U.P. (Toronto), 1963 (pbk) £10
At My Heart's Core and *Overlaid*, Clarke, Irwin (Toronto), 1966 (pbk) £25
Question Time, Macmillan (Toronto), 1975 (pbk) . . £30
Brothers in the Black Art, Alcuin Society (Vancouver, B.C.), 1981 (100 numbered copies; wraps) . . . £100
ditto, Alcuin Society (Vancouver, B.C.), 1981 (26 signed, lettered copies; wraps) £200

Libretti
Jezebel: The Golden Tale of Naboth & His Vineyard, and Of King Ahab & His Wicked Queen, McClelland & Stewart (Toronto), 1993 (wraps) £30
The Golden Ass, Pendragon/Canadian Opera Company (Toronto), 1999 (500 numbered copies; wraps) . . £10

Letters
For Your Eye Alone: Letters 1975-1995, McClelland & Stewart (Toronto), 1999 . . . . . £10/£5
ditto, Viking Press (New York), 2001 . . . £10/£5
Discoveries: Letters 1938-1975, McClelland & Stewart (Toronto), 2002 (edited by Judith Skelton Grant). £10/£5

Collections
Conversations with Robertson Davies, Univ Press of Missis-sippi (Jackson, MI/London), 1989 . . . . £15/£5

Miscellaneous
The Heart of a Merry Christmas, Macmillan (Toronto), 1970 (printed card cover wraps) £75
ditto, Macmillan (London), 1970 (wraps) . . . £65
ditto, Poole Hall Press (Grimsby, Ontario), 1979 (110 numbered copies in gold foil boards with purple spine; no d/w) £100
What Do You See In The Mirror? A Footnote to the Psychedelic Revolution, Book Society of Canada (Agincourt, Ontario), 1970 (pbk, with 'Commentary' laid in) £75
The Harper of the Stones, Toronto Library (Toronto), no date (wraps; a ghost story for narrator and chamber ensemble) £45
'*Canadian Nationalism in Arts and Science*', off-print from Transactions of the Royal Society of Canada Series IV, Vol. XIII, 1975 (wraps; pages numbered (15)-24) . £75
The McFiggin Fragment, Massey College Press (Toronto), 1979 (75 numbered copies; sewn wraps; written as if by Stephen Leacock) £150
ditto, Massey College Press (Toronto), 1979 (5 copies; as above but spoof with college emblem upside down; 75 crossed out and 5 written in) £300
On Being a Professional, Ontario College of Art Press, 1981 (first 20 copies on beige handmade paper; cloth spine, marbled paper boards) £250
ditto, Ontario College of Art Press, 1981 (20 copies on speckled handmade paper; Cloth spine, plum coloured paper boards) £200

Thirty Years at Stratford, Stratford Festival (no place), 1982 (stapled wraps) £5
Encounters and Explorations, Canadian Writers and European Critics, Konigshausen & Neumann, 1986 (off-print of *What is Canadian About Canadian Literature?*; wraps; pages numbered 127-132) £75
Opera and Humour, Aldeburgh Foundation (Suffolk, UK), 1991 (wraps). £20
A Return to Rhetoric, Poole Hall Press (Grimsby, Ontario), 1993 (80 copies; front cover three-quarter boards with one-quarter green cloth, back cover green cloth, paper label on front cover) £50
Reading and Writing, Univ of Utah Press (Salt Lake City, UT), 1993 (no d/w) £5
An Introduction to the Twenty-First Toronto Antiquarian Book Fair, Letters/Coach House Press (Toronto), 1993 (stapled wraps) £5
ditto, Letters/Coach House Press (Toronto), 1993 (100 signed, numbered copies; sewn wraps) . . . £125
ditto, Letters/Coach House Press (Toronto), 1993 (26 signed, lettered copies; sewn wraps) £200
ditto, Letters/Coach House Press (Toronto), 1993 (10 copies lettered A-J; issued hors commerce; sewn wraps) . £100
Why I Do Not Intend to Write an Autobiography, Harbour-front Reading Series (Toronto), 1993 (350 copies; stapled wraps, erratum slip laid in) £20
ditto, Harbourfront Reading Series (Toronto), 1993 (150 signed, numbered copies; stapled wraps; erratum slip laid in) £40
The Dignity of Literature, Harbourfront (Toronto), 1994 (stapled wraps) £5
ditto, Harbourfront (Toronto), 1994 (50 signed, numbered copies; stapled wraps) £65

W.H. DAVIES
(b.1871 d.1940)

W.H. Davies was a Welshman who became one of the most popular poets of his day, despite living as a tramp for much of his life. *The Autobiography of a Super-Tramp* is his account of his years in America. Returning to England, he paid for his first poetry to be published, and sent copies to influential people asking for payment or to return the slim volume. In 1923 he married an ex-prostitute, thirty years younger than himself, and his frank account of their relationship was published in 1980.

Poetry
The Soul's Destroyer, privately printed by the author (London), 1905 (wraps) £150
ditto, Alston Rivers (London), 1907 (wraps) . . . £30
New Poems, Elkin Mathews (London), 1907 . . . £20
Nature Poems and Others, A.C. Fifield (London), 1908 £15
Farewell to Poesy, A.C. Fifield (London), 1910 . . £10
Song of Joy, A.C. Fifield (London), 1910 . . . £15
Foliage, Elkin Mathews (London), 1913 . . . . £10
The Bird of Paradise, Methuen (London), 1914 . . £10
Child Lovers and Other Poems, A.C. Fifield (London), 1916 . . . . £10
Collected Poems, A.C. Fifield (London), 1916 . . £10
ditto, Knopf (New York), 1916 . . . . . £10
Forty New Poems, A.C. Fifield (London), 1918 . . £10

Raptures: A Book of Poems, Beaumont Press (London), 1918 (250 numbered copies) £50

ditto, Beaumont Press (London), 1918 (22 signed, numbered copies on Japanese vellum) £200

The Song of Life and Other Poems, A.C. Fifield (London), 1920 . . . . £35/£10

The Captive Lion, Yale Univ Press (New Haven, CT), 1921 . . . . £45/£25

The Hour of Magic, Jonathan Cape (London), 1922 £35/£10

ditto, Jonathan Cape (London), 1922 (110 signed copies) £75

ditto, Harper (New York), 1922 . . . . £35/£10

Collected Poems: Second Series, Jonathan Cape (London), 1923 . . . . £25/£10

ditto, Jonathan Cape (London), 1923 (100 signed copies; no d/w) £75

Selected Poems, Jonathan Cape (London), 1923 . £20/£5

Secrets: Poems, Jonathan Cape (London), 1924 . £20/£5

ditto, Jonathan Cape (London), 1924 (100 signed, numbered copies) . . . . £65/£50

A Poet's Alphabet, Jonathan Cape (London), 1925 £20/£5

ditto, Jonathan Cape (London), 1925 (125 signed, numbered copies) . . . . £65/£50

The Song of Love, Jonathan Cape (London), 1926. £15/£5

ditto, Jonathan Cape (London), 1926 (125 signed, numbered copies) . . . . £75/£45

A Poet's Calendar, Jonathan Cape, 1927 . . . £15/£5

ditto, Jonathan Cape (London), 1927 (125 signed, numbered copies) . . . . £50/£35

Forty-Nine Poems, Medici Society (London), 1928 £20/£5

ditto, Medici Society (London), 1928 (110 signed, numbered copies; slipcase) . . . . . . £75/£45

The Collected Poems of W.H. Davies, Jonathan Cape, 1928 £20/£5

ditto, Cape and Smith (New York) 1929 . . £20/£5

Moss and Feather, Faber & Gwyer, 1928 . £15/£5

ditto, Faber & Gwyer, 1928 (500 signed, numbered copies). . . . . £45/£30

Selected Poems, Gregynog Press, 1928 (285 copies) . £175

ditto, Gregynog Press, 1928 (25 copies) . . . £300

Ambition, Jonathan Cape (London), 1929 . . £15/£5

ditto, Jonathan Cape (London), 1929 (210 signed copies) . . . . £45/£20

In Winter, Fytton Armstrong (London), 1931 (290 signed copies) £25

ditto, Fytton Armstrong (London), 1931 (15 copies on fine paper signed by Davies and the illustrator Carrick) . £100

Poems 1930-31, Jonathan Cape (London), 1932 . £10/£5

ditto, Jonathan Cape (London), 1932 (150 signed, numbered copies) . . . . £50/£40

The Lover's Songbook, Gregynog Press, 1933 . . £200

The Poems of W.H. Davies: A Complete Collection, Jonathan Cape (London), 1934. . . . £15/£5

ditto, O.U.P. (New York), 1935 . . . £15/£5

Love Poems, Jonathan Cape (London), 1935 . £10/£5

ditto, O.U.P. (New York), 1935 . . . . £10/£5

The Birth of Song: Poems, 1935-36, Jonathan Cape (London), 1936 . . . . . . £15/£5

The Loneliest Mountain, Jonathan Cape (London), 1939 . . . . £10/£5

Common Joys, Jonathan Cape (London), 1941 . £10/£5

The Poems of W.H. Davies, 1940, Jonathan Cape, 1940 £10

Fiction

A Weak Woman, Duckworth (London),1911 . . £30

Dancing Mad, Jonathan Cape (London), 1927 . . £20

Non-Fiction

The Autobiography of a Super-Tramp, Fifield (London), 1908 . . . . £65

ditto, Knopf (New York), 1917 . . . . . £10

Beggars, Duckworth (London), 1909 . . . £20

The True Traveller, Duckworth (London), 1912 . £20

Nature, Batsford (London), 1914 . . . . £20

A Poet's Pilgrimage, Melrose (London), 1918 . . £15

True Travellers: A Tramps' Opera, Jonathan Cape (London), 1923 . . . . £75/£20

ditto, Harcourt, Brace (New York), 1923 . . . £75/£20

Later Days, Jonathan Cape: 'Travellers' Library' (London), 1925 . . . . £15/£5

ditto, Jonathan Cape (London), 1925 (125 signed, numbered copies) . . . . £45/£30

ditto, Doran (New York), 1926 . . . . . £15/£5

The Adventures of Johnny Walker, Tramp, Jonathan Cape (London), 1926 . . . . £50/£15

My Birds, Jonathan Cape (London), 1933 . . £15/£5

My Garden, Jonathan Cape (London), 1933 . £15/£5

Young Emma, Jonathan Cape (London), 1980 . £10/£5

ditto, Brazilier (New York), 1981 . . . . £10/£5

LINDSEY DAVIS
(b.1949)

Davis became a professional writer after being a runner-up in the Georgette Heyer Historical Novel Prize, at first writing romantic serials for a British women's magazine. An interest in history led to *The Course of Honour*, for which she failed to find a publisher, but with her next novel about the Roman 'detective' Falco, she found success. She was the first to win the Crime Writers Association Ellis Peters Historical Dagger.

The 'Falco' Series

The Silver Pigs, Sidgwick & Jackson (London), 1989 . . . . £400/£35

ditto, Crown (New York), 1989 . . . . . £30/£10

Shadows in Bronze, Sidgwick & Jackson (London), 1990 . . . . £100/£15

ditto, Crown (New York), 1990 . . . . . £20/£5

Venus in Copper, Hutchinson (London), 1991 . £50/£10

ditto, Crown (New York), 1991 . . . . £20/£5

The Iron Hand of Mars, Hutchinson (London), 1992 . . . . £100/£15

ditto, Crown (New York), 1992 . . . . £20/£5

Poseidon's Gold, Century (London), 1993 . . £20/£5

ditto, Century (London), 1993 (400 signed, numbered proof copies; wraps) £45

ditto, Crown (New York), 1993 . . . . £20/£5

Last Act in Palmyra, Century (London), 1994 . £15/£5

ditto, Mysterious Press (New York), 1994 . . £15/£5

Time To Depart, Century (London), 1995 . . £15/£5

ditto, Scorpion Press (Blakeney, Glos), 1995 (99 signed, numbered copies) £35

ditto, Scorpion Press (Blakeney, Glos), 1995 (15 signed, lettered copies) £300

ditto, Mysterious Press (New York), 1997 . . £10/£5

A Dying Light in Corduba, Century (London), 1996 £15/£5

ditto, Scorpion Press (Blakeney, Glos), 1996 (99 signed, numbered copies) £35
ditto, Scorpion Press (Blakeney, Glos), 1996 (15 signed, lettered copies) £250
ditto, Mysterious Press (New York), 1998 . £15/£5
Three Hands in the Fountain, Century (London), 1997 . . . . £15/£5
ditto, Mysterious Press (New York), 1999 . £10/£5
Two For the Lions, Century (London), 1998 . £10/£5
ditto, Mysterious Press (New York), 1999 . £10/£5
One Virgin Too Many, Century (London), 1999 £10/£5
ditto, Mysterious Press (New York), 2000 . £10/£5
Ode to a Banker, Century (London), 2000 . £10/£5
ditto, Mysterious Press (New York), 2001 . £10/£5
A Body in the Bath House, Century (London), 2001 £10/£5
ditto, Mysterious Press (New York), 2002 . £10/£5
The Jupiter Myth, Century (London), 2002 . £10/£5
ditto, Mysterious Press (New York), 2002 . £10/£5
The Accusers, Century (London), 2003 . . £10/£5
ditto, Mysterious Press (New York), 2004 . £10/£5
Scandal Takes a Holiday, Century (London), 2004 £10/£5
ditto, Mysterious Press (New York), 2004 . £10/£5
See Delphi and Die, Century (London), 2005 . £10/£5
ditto, St Martin's Minotaur, New York, 2006 . £10/£5
Saturnalia, Century (London), 2007 . . £10/£5
ditto, St Martin's Minotaur, New York, 2007 . £10/£5
Alexandria, Century (London), 2009. . . £10/£5
ditto, St Martin's Minotaur, New York, 2009 . £10/£5

Other Novels
The Course of Honour, Century (London), 1997 . £10/£5
ditto, Mysterious Press (New York), 1998 . £10/£5
Rebels and Traitors, Century (London), 2009. . £10/£5

C. DAY LEWIS

(b.1904 d.1972)

An Anglo-Irish poet and critic, Cecil Day Lewis worked as a school-teacher for several years before he became a full-time writer, supplementing his income by penning detective novels under the pseudonym 'Nicholas Blake'. He was director and senior editor at Chatto & Windus and Professor of Poetry at Oxford from 1951-56. He was appointed Poet Laureate in 1968.

Poetry
Beechen Vigil and Other Poems, Fortune Press (London), 1925 (green wraps) £150
Country Comets, Martin Hopkinson (London), 1928 (green paper boards, printed label on upper cover) . . . £30
Transitional Poems, Hogarth Press (London), 1929 . £35
From Feathers to Iron, Hogarth Press (London), 1931. £40
The Magnetic Mountain, Hogarth Press (London), 1932 £25
ditto, Hogarth Press (London), 1932 (100 signed, numbered copies) £100
Collected Poems 1929-33, Hogarth Press (London), 1935 . . . . £75/£20
ditto, Random House (New York), 1935 . . £40/£20
A Time to Dance and Other Poems, Hogarth Press (London), 1935 . . . . £45/£15
Noah and the Waters, Hogarth Press (London), 1936 . . . . £40/£10

ditto, Hogarth Press (London), 1936 (100 signed, numbered copies) . . . . £150/£75
A Time to Dance, Noah and the Waters, Random House (New York), 1936 . . . . . £30/£10
Overtures to Death and Other Poems, Cape (London), 1938 . . . . £35/£10
ditto, as *Short is the Time*, Poems 1936-1943, O.U.P. (New York), 1945 (with *Word Over All*) . . . £25/£10
Child of Misfortune, Cape (London), 1939 . £35/£10
Poems in Wartime, Cape (London), 1940 (250 copies; wraps) £75
Selected Poems, Hogarth Press (London), 1940 . £45/£15
Word Over All, Cape (London), 1943 . . £40/£10
The Augustan Poets, Eyre and Spottiswoode (London), 1943 (wraps) £10
Poems 1943-47, Cape (London), 1948 . . £25/£10
ditto, O.U.P. (New York), 1948 . . . . £25/£10
Collected Poems 1929-1946, Hogarth Press (London), 1948 . . . . £20/£5
Selected Poems, Penguin (Harmondsworth, Middlesex), 1951 . . . . £5
An Italian Visit, Cape (London), 1953 . . £25/£10
ditto, Harper (New York), 1953 . . . . £25/£10
Collected Poems, Cape/Hogarth Press (London), 1954 . . . . £35/£10
Christmas Eve, Faber (London), 1954 (illustrated by Edward Ardizzone; sewn orange wraps) £5
Pegasus and Other Poems, Cape (London), 1957 . £20/£5
ditto, Harper (New York), 1958 . . . . £20/£5
The Buried Day, Chatto & Windus (London), 1960 £25/£10
ditto, Harper (New York), 1960 . . . . £20/£10
The Gate and Other Poems, Chatto & Windus (London), 1962 . . . . £10/£5
Requiem for the Living, Harper (New York), 1964 £10/£5
The Room and Other Poems, Cape (London), 1965 £10/£5
Selected Poems, Harper (New York), 1967 . £15/£5
The Abbey That Refused To Die, Dolmen Press (Dublin), 1967 (wraps). £10
The Whispering Roots, Cape (London), 1970. . £10/£5
ditto, Harper (New York), 1970 . . . . £10/£5
Going My Way, Poem-of-the-Month-Club (London), 1970 (broadside) £5
Posthumous Poems, Whittington Press (Andoversford, Gloucestershire), 1979 (250 copies signed by Jill Balcon, the author's widow, slipcase) . . . . £125/£75
Complete Poems of C. Day Lewis, Stanford Univ Press (Stanford, CT), 1992 . . . . . . £20/£10

Detective Fiction Written as 'Nicholas Blake'
A Question of Proof, Collins Crime Club (London), 1935 . . . . £1,250/£65
ditto, Harper (New York), 1935 . . . £400/£20
Thou Shell of Death, Collins Crime Club (London), 1936 . . . . £1,000/£65
ditto, as *Shell of Death*, Harper (New York), 1936. £200/£20
There's Trouble Brewing, Collins Crime Club (London), 1937 . . . . £1,000/£50
ditto, Harper (New York), 1937 . . . . £200/£20
The Beast Must Die, Collins Crime Club (London), 1938 . . . . £1,000/£50
ditto, Harper (New York), 1938 . . . . £200/£20
The Smiler with the Knife, Collins Crime Club (London), 1939 . . . . £850/£45
ditto, Harper (New York), 1939 . . . . £200/£20

Malice in Wonderland, Collins Crime Club (London), 1940
.   .   .   .   £600/£45
ditto, as *The Summer Camp Mystery*, Harper (New York),
1940   .   .   .   .   £200/£20
ditto, as *Malice with Murder*, Pyramid (New York), 1964
(pbk) £10
ditto, as *Murder with Malice*, Carroll & Graf (New York),
1987   .   .   .   .   £15/£5
The Case of the Abominable Snowman, Collins Crime Club
(London), 1941   .   .   .   .   .   £300/£35
ditto, as *The Corpse in the Snowman*, Harper (New York),
1941   .   .   .   .   £100/£20
Minute for Murder, Collins Crime Club (London), 1947 .
.   .   .   .   £125/£35
ditto, Harper (New York), 1948   .   .   .   £45/£15
Head of a Traveller, Collins Crime Club (London), 1949 .
.   .   .   .   £85/£20
ditto, Harper (New York), 1949   .   .   .   £30/£10
The Dreadful Hollow, Collins Crime Club (London), 1953 .
.   .   .   .   £65/£15
ditto, Harper (New York), 1953   .   .   .   £30/£10
The Whisper in the Gloom, Collins Crime Club (London),
1954   .   .   .   .   £50/£15
ditto, Harper (New York), 1954   .   .   .   £25/£10
ditto, as *Catch and Kill*, Bestseller (New York), 1955
(abridged)   .   .   .   .   .   .   £20/£5
A Tangled Web, Collins Crime Club (London), 1956 £45/£10
ditto, Harper (New York), 1956   .   .   .   £20/£5
ditto, as *Death and Daisy Bland*, Dell (New York), 1960
(pbk) £5
End of Chapter, Collins Crime Club (London), 1957 .
.   .   .   .   £45/£10
ditto, Harper (New York), 1957   .   .   .   £20/£5
A Penknife in My Heart, Collins Crime Club (London),
1958   .   .   .   .   £45/£10
ditto, Harper (New York), 1959   .   .   .   £20/£5
The Widow's Cruise, Collins Crime Club (London), 1959 .
.   .   .   .   £40/£10
ditto, Harper (New York), 1959   .   .   .   £20/£5
The Worm of Death, Collins Crime Club (London), 1961 .
.   .   .   .   £40/£10
ditto, Harper (New York), 1961   .   .   .   £20/£5
The Deadly Joker, Collins Crime Club (London), 1963   .
.   .   .   .   £40/£10
The Sad Variety, Collins Crime Club (London), 1964 .   .
.   .   .   .   £40/£10
ditto, Harper (New York), 1964   .   .   .   £20/£5
The Morning After Death, Collins Crime Club (London),
1966   .   .   .   .   £40/£10
ditto, Harper (New York), 1966   .   .   .   £20/£5
The Nicholas Blake Omnibus, Collins Crime Club
(London), 1966   .   .   .   .   .   £25/£10
The Private Wound, Collins Crime Club (London), 1968   .
.   .   .   .   £35/£10
ditto, Harper (New York), 1968   .   .   .   £20/£5

Other Novels
The Friendly Tree, Cape (London), 1936.   .   £30/£10
ditto, Harper (New York), 1937   .   .   .   £30/£10
Starting Point, Cape (London), 1937.   .   .   £30/£10
ditto, Harper (New York), 1938   .   .   .   £30/£10

Children's Titles
Dick Willoughby, Blackwell (Oxford), 1933 .   £400/£100

ditto, Random House (New York), 1938 .   .   .   £75/£20
The Otterbury Incident, Putnam (London), 1948 .   £45/£15
ditto, Viking (New York), 1949   .   .   .   .   £20/£5

Others
A Hope for Poetry, Blackwell (Oxford), 1934.   .   £30/£10
ditto, Random House (New York), 1935 .   .   .   £25/£10
Revolution in Writing, Hogarth Press (London), 1935
(wraps) £25
Imagination and Thinking, British Institute of Adult
Education (London), 1936 (wraps)   .   .   .   £15
*We're Not Going to do Nothing: A Reply to Mr Aldous
Huxley's Pamphlet*, The Left Review (London), 1936
(stapled wraps) £35
ditto, The Left Review (London), 1936 (50 signed, numbered
copies; stapled wraps) £100
Poetry for You, Blackwell (Oxford), 1945   .   £40/£10
ditto, O.U.P. (New York), 1947   .   .   .   £40/£10
The Poetic Image, Cape (London), 1947 .   .   £30/£10
ditto, O.U.P. (New York), 1947   .   .   .   £30/£10
The Colloquial Element In English Poetry, Literary Soc. of
Newcastle (Newcastle, UK), 1947 (stapled wraps)   .   £10
Enjoying Poetry, C.U.P. (Cambridge, UK), 1947 (stapled
wraps) £10
The Poet's Task, O.U.P. (Oxford), 1951 (sewn wraps) .   £10
Notable Images of Virtue, Ryerson Press (Toronto, Canada),
1954   .   .   .   .   £20/£5
The Poet's Way of Knowledge, C.U. P. (Cambridge, UK),
1957   .   .   .   .   £10/£5
The Lyric Impulse, Harvard Univ Press (Cambridge, MA),
1965   .   .   .   .   £15/£5
ditto, Chatto & Windus (London), 1965   .   .   £10/£5
A Need for Poetry, Univ of Hull (Hull, UK), 1968 (stapled
wraps) £10

LOUIS DE BERNIÈRES
(b.1954)

Louis de Bernières was influenced in the writing of his first
three books by his experiences in Colombia, as well as by
the work of Gabriel García Márquez. In 1993 de Bernières
was selected as one of the 20 Best of Young British
Novelists by *Granta* magazine. The following year his
fourth novel, *Captain Corelli's Mandolin*, was published
and became an international bestseller.

Novels
The War of Don Emmanuel's Nether Parts, Secker &
Warburg (London), 1990   .   .   .   .   £150/£25
ditto, Morrow (New York), 1990   .   .   .   £20/£5
Señor Vivo and the Coca Lord, Secker & Warburg
(London), 1991   .   .   .   .   .   £125/£25
ditto, Morrow (New York), 1991   .   .   .   £20/£5
The Troublesome Offspring of Cardinal Guzman, Secker &
Warburg (London), 1992   .   .   .   .   £75/£15
ditto, Morrow (New York), 1994   .   .   .   £20/£5
Captain Corelli's Mandolin, Secker & Warburg (London),
1994 (presumed first issue: white boards)   .   £350/£100
ditto, Secker & Warburg (London), 1994 (black boards)   .
.   .   .   .   £250/£50
ditto, as *Corelli's Mandolin*, Pantheon (New York), 1994 .
.   .   .   .   £25/£10

Red Dog, Secker & Warburg (London), 2001 .	£10/£5
ditto, Secker & Warburg (London), 2001 (100 signed copies)
.	.	.	.	.	.	.	.	.	£85/£65
ditto, Morrow (New York), 1991	.	.	.	£10/£5
Birds Without Wings, Secker & Warburg (London), 2004 .
.	.	.	.	.	.	.	.	£10/£5
ditto, Secker & Warburg (London), 2004 (100 signed, numbered copies, slipcase)	.	.	.	£175/£125
ditto, Secker & Warburg (London), 2004 (1,000 signed, numbered copies, slipcase)	.	.	.	.	£40/£30
ditto, Knopf (New York), 2004	.	.	.	£10/£5
A Partisan's Daughter, Harvill Secker (London), 2008	.
.	.	.	.	.	.	.	.	£10/£5
ditto, Blackwell Collectors' Library/Harvill Secker, London, 2008 (100 numbered, signed copies; slipcase)	£125/£100
ditto, Knopf (New York), 2008 .	.	.	.	£10/£5

Others
Labels, One Horse Press (London), 1993 (2,000 signed copies; wraps)	.	.	.	.	.	.	£25
A Day Out for Mehmet Erbil, Belmont Press (London), 1999 (26 signed, lettered copies of 276) .	.	.	£250
ditto, Belmont Press, 1999 (100 signed, numbered copies of 276)	.	.	.	.	.	.	.	£150
ditto, Belmont Press (London), 1999 (150 signed, numbered copies of 276)	.	.	.	.	.	.	£90
ditto, Secker & Warburg (London), 2004 (pbk)	.	£5
Günter Weber's Confession, Tartarus Press (Carlton-in-Coverdale, Yorkshire), 2001 (26 signed, numbered hardback copies of 300; slipcase; extra print signed by artist)	.	.	.	.	.	.	£175
ditto, Tartarus Press (Carlton-in-Coverdale, Yorkshire), 2001 (74 signed copies of 300; sewn wraps)	.	.	£75
ditto, Tartarus Press (Carlton-in-Coverdale, Yorkshire), 2001 (200 unsigned copies of 300; sewn wraps)	.	.	£25
Sunday Morning at the Centre of the World: A Play for Voices, Vintage (London), 2001 (pbk)	.	.	.	£5
A Night Out for Prudente de Moraes, Hay Festival Press (Hay on Wye, Herefordshire), 2004 (no d/w)	.	£20
ditto, Hay Festival Press (Hay on Wye, Herefordshire), 2004 (100 signed, numbered copies, no d/w)	.	.	£85
A Walberswick Goodnight Story, Tartarus Press (Carlton-in-Coverdale, Yorkshire), 2006 (200 signed, numbered copies)	.	.	.	.	.	.	.	£25
Notwithstanding, Harvill Secker (London), 2009 .	£10/£5

WALTER DE LA MARE

(b.1873 d.1956)

De la Mare began writing when employed by an oil company, but after being awarded a Civil List pension in 1908 he was able to concentrate on writing full time. An author, poet and critic, his delicate and lyrical poems of fantasy and childhood are still much admired today, as are his subtle psychological horror stories, of which 'Seaton's Aunt' is a noteworthy example.

Poetry
Songs of Childhood, Longmans (London), 1902 (pseud 'Walter Ramal')	.	.	.	.	.	.	.	£400
ditto, Longmans (London), 1923 (enlarged and revised)	.
.	.	.	.	.	.	.	.	£75/£30

ditto, Longmans (London), 1923 (310 signed copies)	.	.
.	.	.	.	.	.	.	£150/£100
Poems, Murray (London), 1906 .	.	.	.	£40
The Listeners and Other Poems, Constable (London), 1912
.	.	.	.	.	.	.	.	£35
ditto, Holt (New York), 1916	.	.	.	.	£35
A Child's Day, A Book of Rhymes, Constable (London), 1912	.	.	.	.	.	.	.	.	£75
ditto, Dutton (New York), [1912]	.	.	.	.	£50
Peacock Pie, A Book of Rhymes, Constable (London), 1913
.	.	.	.	.	.	.	.	£35
ditto, Constable (London), 1916 (illustrated by W. Heath Robinson)	.	.	.	.	.	.	.	£75
ditto, Holt (New York), 1920 (illustrated by W. Heath Robinson)	.	.	.	.	.	.	.£125/£20
ditto, Constable (London), 1924 (250 signed copies, illustrated by C. Lovat Fraser)	.	.	.	.	.£125
ditto, Holt (New York), 1924 (500 signed copies, illustrated by C. Lovat Fraser)	.	.	.	.	.	.£125
ditto, Faber (London), 1946 (illustrated by Ardizzone)	.	.
.	.	.	.	.	.	.	£70/£25
The Old Men, Flying Fame (London), 1913 (broadside)	£25
The Sunken Garden and Other Poems, Beaumont Press (London), 1917 (250 signed, numbered copies on handmade paper)	.	.	.	.	.	.	.	£65
ditto, Beaumont Press (London), 1917 (20 signed, numbered copies on Japanese vellum)	.	.	.	.	£250
Motley and Other Poems, Constable (London), 1918 .	£30
ditto, Holt (New York), 1918	.	.	.	.	£30
Flora: A Book of Drawings, by Pamela Bianco, Heinemann (London), 1919 (with 27 poems by de la Mare) .	£35
ditto, Lippincott (Philadelphia, PA), 1919.	.	.	£35
Poems, 1901 to 1918, Constable (London), 1920 (2 vols)
.	.	.	.	.	.	.	.	£60/£25
ditto, Constable (London), 1920 (210 signed, numbered sets)
.	.	.	.	.	.	.	.£100/£45
The Veil and Other Poems, Constable (London), 1921.	.
.	.	.	.	.	.	.	£45/£10
ditto, Constable (London), 1921 (250 signed, numbered copies)	.	.	.	.	.	.	.	.	£60
ditto, Holt (New York), 1922	.	.	.	£45/£10
Down-Adown-Derry, A Book of Fairy Poems, Constable (London), 1922	.	.	.	.	.	.£100/£45
ditto, Constable (London), 1922 (325 signed, numbered copies)	.	.	.	.	.	.	.	.£200
ditto, Holt (New York), 1922	.	.	.	.	£65/£25
Thus Her Tale, A Poem, Porpoise Press (Edinburgh), 1923 (50 numbered copies; sewn wraps)	.	.	.	.	£25
A Ballad of Christmas, Selwyn & Blount (London), 1924 (100 copies) .	.	.	.	.	.	.	£35
Before Dawn, Selwyn & Blount (London), 1924 (100 copies)	.	.	.	.	.	.	.	.	£35
The Hostage, Selwyn & Blount (London), 1925 (100 copies)
.	.	.	.	.	.	.	.	£35
St Andrews, A & C Black (London), 1926 (with Kipling) .
.	.	.	.	.	.	.	.	£40/£15
Alone, Faber (London), 1927 (Ariel Poem No.4; wraps)	£10
Selected Poems, Holt (New York), 1927 .	.	£20/£5
Stuff and Nonsense and So On, Constable (London), 1927.
.	.	.	.	.	.	.	.	£30/£10
ditto, as *Stuff and Nonsense*, Faber (London), 1946 (enlarged and revised edition of above) .	.	£15/£5
The Captive and Other Poems, Bowling Green Press (New York), 1928 (600 signed copies, glassine wraps) .	£35/£20

Self to Self, Faber (London), 1928 (Ariel Poem No. 11; wraps) £10

ditto, Faber (London), 1928 (500 signed large paper copies) £35

A Snowdrop, Faber (London), 1929 (Ariel Poem No. 20; wraps) £10

ditto, Faber (London), 1929 (500 signed large paper copies) £35

News, Faber (London), 1930 (Ariel Poem No. 31; wraps) £10

Poems for Children, Constable (London), 1930 . £25/£10

ditto, Constable (London), 1930 (133 signed, numbered copies) £165

ditto, Holt (New York), 1930 (300 signed copies, slipcase) . . . . £100/£50

To Lucy, Faber (London), 1931 (Ariel Poem No. 33; wraps) £10

The Sunken Garden and Other Verses, Birmingham School of Printing (Birmingham, UK), 1931 (different selection to 1917 edition) £20

Two Poems, privately printed, 1931 (100 copies; wraps) £45

Old Rhymes and New, Constable (London), 1932 (2 vols) . . . . £45/£15

The Fleeting and Other Poems, Constable (London), 1933 . . . . £25/£10

ditto, Constable (London), 1933 (150 signed copies) . £50

Poems, 1919 to 1934, Constable (London), 1935 . £25/£5

This Year, Next Year, Faber (London), 1937 . . £150/£50

ditto, Faber (London), 1937 (100 signed, numbered copies). . . . . £300/£150

ditto, Holt (New York), 1937 . . . . £125/£65

Poems, Corvinus Press (London), 1937 (40 copies; no d/w). £155

Memory and Other Poems, Constable (London), 1938 . . . . £25/£5

ditto, Holt (New York), 1938 . . . . £35/£5

Two Poems by Walter de la Mare and - but! - Arthur Rogers, privately printed (Newcastle-on-Tyne), 1938 (200 copies, single sheet folded) . . . £25

Haunted: A Poem, Linden Broadsheet No. 4, 1939 . £20

Bells and Grass, a book of rhymes, Faber (London), 1941 . . . . £35/£10

ditto, Viking (New York), 1942 . . . £35/£10

Collected Poems, Faber (London), 1942 . . £25/£10

Time Passes and Other Poems, Faber (London), 1942 . . . . £20/£5

Collected Rhymes and Verses, Faber (London), 1944 £20/£5

The Burning-Glass and Other Poems, Faber (London), 1945 . . . . £20/£5

ditto, Viking (New York), 1945 . . . . £20/£5

The Traveller, Faber (London), 1946 . . . £35/£10

Two Poems, Dropmore Press (London), 1946 . . £20

Rhymes and Verses, Collected Poems for Children, Holt (New York), 1947 . . . . . . £20/£5

Inward Companion, Faber (London), 1950 . £20/£5

Winged Chariot, Faber (London), 1951 . . £20/£5

ditto, Viking (New York), 1951 . . . . £15/£5

O Lovely England and Other Poems, Faber (London), 1953 . . . . £20/£5

The Winnowing Dream, Faber (London), 1954 (Ariel Poem; wraps) £10

Selected Poems, Faber (London), 1954 . . £10/£5

The Morrow, privately printed, 1955 (50 copies; sewn wraps) £25

Poems, Puffin (London), 1962 (pbk) £5

Children's Stories

The Three Mulla-Mulgars, Duckworth (London), 1910 (with tipped-in errata slip) £35

ditto, Knopf (New York), 1919 . . . . £30

ditto, as *The Three Royal Monkeys*, Faber (London), 1935 . . . . £15/£5

ditto, as *The Three Mulla-Mulgars*, Selwyn & Blount (London), 1924 (250 signed copies) . . . £45

Broomsticks and Other Tales, Constable (London), 1925 (278 signed copies, slipcase) . . . . £125/£75

ditto, Constable (London), 1925 . . . . £65/£20

ditto, Knopf (New York), 1930 . . . . £50/£15

Miss Jemima, Blackwell (Oxford), 1925 . . . £25

Lucy, Blackwell (Oxford), 1925 . . . . £25

Old Joe, Blackwell (Oxford), 1925 . . . . £25

Readings: Traditional Tales, told by de la Mare, Blackwell (Oxford), 1925-28 (set of 6 vols) £100

Told Again: Traditional Tales, Blackwell (Oxford), 1927 . . . . £50/£10

ditto, Blackwell (Oxford), 1927 (260 signed copies) . £75

ditto, Knopf (New York), 1927 . . . £25/£10

Stories from the Bible, Faber (London), 1929 . £45/£10

ditto, Faber (London), 1929 (300 signed copies) . £65

ditto, Faber (London), 1961 (illustrated by Ardizzone) . . . . £40/£10

ditto, Knopf (New York), 1961 . . . . £40/£10

Desert Islands and Robinson Crusoe, Faber (London), 1930 . . . . £35/£10

ditto, Faber/Fountain Press (London), 1930 (650 signed copies) £45

ditto, Farrar & Rinehart (New York), 1930 . £35/£10

The Dutch Cheese and The Lovely Myfanwy, Knopf (New York), 1931 . . . . £50/£25

The Lord Fish and Other Tales, Faber (London), 1933 . . . . £50/£15

ditto, Faber (London), 1933 (60 signed copies, d/w, slipcase) £200

Animal Stories, Faber (London), 1939 . . £15/£5

Mr Bumps and His Monkey, J.C. Winston (Philadelphia, PA), 1942 . . . . £45/£10

The Old Lion and Other Stories, Faber (London), 1942 . . . . £15/£5

The Magic Jacket and Other Stories, Faber (London), 1943 . . . . £15/£5

Collected Rhymes and Verses, Faber (London), 1944 £10/£5

The Scarecrow and Other Stories, Faber (London), 1945 . . . . £15/£5

The Dutch Cheese and Other Stories, Faber (London), 1946 . . . . £15/£5

Collected Stories for Children, Faber (London), 1947 . . . . £15/£5

Rhymes and Verses, Holt (New York), [1947] . £10/£5

Jack and the Beanstalk, Hulton Press (London), 1951 . . . . £15/£5

Dick Whittington, Hulton Press (London), 1951 . £15/£5

Snow White, Hulton Press (London), 1952 . £15/£5

Cinderella, Hulton Press (London), 1952 . . £15/£5

Selected Stories and Verse, Puffin (London), 1952 (wraps) £5

The Story of Joseph, Faber (London), 1958 (illustrated by Ardizzone) . . . . . . £25/£10

Story of Moses, Faber (London), 1959 (illustrated by Ardizzone) . . . . £25/£10

The Story of Samuel and Saul, Faber (London), 1960 (illustrated by Ardizzone) . . . . . £35/£10
A Penny a Day and Other Stories, Knopf (New York), 1960
. . . . £10/£5

Novels

Henry Brocken, Murray (London), 1904 (first issue without gilding to top edge of book block, and no final bracket after 'Walter Ramal' on title-page) £50
ditto, Murray (London), 1904 (second issue with top edge gilt, including final bracket on title-page) . . . £35
ditto, Collins (London), 1924 (250 signed copies) . . £50
ditto, Knopf (New York), 1924 . . . . £50/£15
The Return, Arnold (London), 1910 . . . . . £75
ditto, Putnam's (New York), 1911 . . . . £65
ditto, Collins (London), 1922 (250 signed copies) . . £45
Memoirs of a Midget, Collins (London), 1921 . £40/£10
ditto, Collins (London), 1921 (210 signed, numbered copies)
. . . . £50
The Walter de la Mare Omnibus, Collins (London), 1933 .
. . . . £20/£5

Short Stories

Story and Rhyme, Dent (London), 1921 . . . £35/£10
Lispet, Lispet and Vaine, Bookman's Journal (London), 1923 (Vine Books No.3, 200 signed copies) . . . £65
The Riddle and Other Stories, Selwyn & Blount (London), 1923 . . . . £65/£10
ditto, Selwyn & Blount (London), 1923 (310 signed copies)
. . . . £50
ditto, Knopf (New York), 1923 . . . . £40/£10
Ding Dong Bell, Selwyn & Blount (London), 1924 £40/£10
ditto, Selwyn & Blount (London), 1924 (300 signed copies)
. . . . £45/£30
ditto, Knopf (New York), 1924 . . . . . £40/£10
ditto, Dobson (London), 1957 (illustrated by Edward Ardizzone) . . . . £65/£25
ditto, Dover (New York), 1969 (illustrated by Edward Ardizzone) . . . . £30/£10
Two Tales: 'The Green Room' and 'The Connoisseur', Bookman's Journal (London), 1925 (200 signed copies) .
. . . . £65
The Connoisseur and Other Stories, Collins (London), 1926
. . . . £75/£20
ditto, Collins (London), 1926 (250 signed copies) . . £65
ditto, Knopf (New York), 1926 . . . . £75/£20
Seaton's Aunt, Faber (London), 1927 (wraps). . . £75
At First Sight, Crosby Gaige (New York), 1928 (650 signed copies) £35
On the Edge, Faber (London), 1930 . . . £50/£20
ditto, Faber (London), 1930 (211 signed copies) . . £100
ditto, Knopf (New York), 1931 . . . . £50/£20
Seven Short Stories, Faber (London), 1931 . . £75/£25
ditto, Faber (London), 1931 (100 signed copies) . . £250
A Froward Child, Faber (London), 1934 . . . £20/£5
The Wind Blows Over, Faber (London), 1936. . £75/£20
ditto, Macmillan (New York), 1936 . . . £65/£20
The Nap and Other Stories, Nelson Classics (London), 1938
. . . . £20/£5
Stories, Essays and Poems, Dent, Everyman's Library (London), 1938 . . . . £20/£5
The Picnic and Other Stories, Faber (London), 1941 £20/£5
Best Stories of Walter de la Mare, Faber (London), 1942 .
. . . . £20/£5

The Almond Tree, Todd (London), 1943 . . . £20/£5
The Orgy, Todd (London), 1943 . . . . £20/£5
The Collected Tales of Walter de la Mare, Knopf (New York), 1950 . . . . £25/£5
A Beginning and Other Stories, Faber (London), 1955 .
. . . . £50/£15
Ghost Stories, Folio Society (London), 1956 (slipcase). .
. . . . £10/£5
Walter de la Mare: A Selection from his Writings, Faber (London), 1956 . . . . £10/£5
Some Stories, Faber (London), 1962 . . . . £10/£5
Eight Tales, Arkham House (Sauk City, WI), 1971 £25/£5
Strangers and Pilgrims, Tartarus Press (Carlton-in-Coverdale), 2007 . . . . £35/£10

Miscellaneous

M.E. Coleridge: An Appreciation, The Guardian, 1907 (limited edition) £40
Rupert Brooke and the Intellectual Imagination, Sidgwick & Jackson (London), 1919 . . . . . . £20
Some Thoughts on Reading, Yellowsands Press (Bembridge, Isle of Wight), 1923 (340 copies) . . £25
The Printing of Poetry, C.U.P. (Cambridge, UK), 1931 (limited to 90 copies) £100
Lewis Carroll, Faber (London), 1932 . . . £45/£10
Poetry in Prose, Humphrey Milford (London), 1936 £25/£5
ditto, O.U.P. (New York), 1937 . . . . . £25/£5
Arthur Thompson: A Memoir, privately printed, 1938 . £15
An Introduction to Everyman, Dent (London), 1938 (400 copies) £30
Pleasures and Speculations, Faber (London), 1940 £25/£5
Private View, Faber (London), 1953 . . . . £20/£5

DON DELILLO
(b.1936)

Don DeLillo is an American novelist who won the National Book Award for Fiction in 1985 for *White Noise*, the PEN/Faulkner Award in 1992 for *Mao II*, the Jerusalem Prize in 1999, the William Dean Howells Medal, and the American Academy and Institute of Arts and Letters in 2000 for *Underworld*.

Novels

Americana, Houghton Mifflin (Boston), 1971. . £350/£50
ditto, Penguin Books (London), 1990 (pbk) . . . £10
End Zone, Houghton Mifflin (Boston), 1972 . £200/£45
ditto, Andre Deutsch (London), 1973. . . . £100/£20
Great Jones Street, Houghton Mifflin (Boston), 1973 . .
. . . . £150/£25
ditto, Andre Deutsch (London), 1974. . . . £65/£10
Ratner's Star, Knopf (New York), 1976 . . £100/£10
Players, Knopf (New York), 1977 . . . . £100/£10
ditto, Vintage (London), 1991 (pbk) £10
Running Dog, Knopf (New York), 1978 . . . £75/£15
ditto, Gollancz (London), 1978 . . . . . £40/£10
Amazons, Holt Rinehart (New York), 1980 (pseud 'Cleo Birdwell') . . . . £50/£10
ditto, Granada (London), 1980 . . . . . £25/£10
The Names, Knopf (New York), 1982 (with wrap-around band) . . . . £125/£10
ditto, Knopf (New York), 1982 (without band) . £45/£10

ditto, Harvester (Brighton, Sussex), 1983 . . . £20/5

White Noise, Viking (New York), 1985 . . . £45/£10

ditto, Picador (London), 1985 . . . . £45/£10

Libra, Viking (New York), 1988 . . . £20/£5

ditto, Viking (London), 1988 . . . . £15/£5

Mao II, Viking (no place [New York]), 1991 . . £20/£5

ditto, Jonathan Cape (London), 1991 . . . £15/£5

Underworld, Scribner (New York), 1997 . . £15/£5

ditto, Scribner (New York), 1997 (300 uncorrected Proof-Special Advance Reader's Copies; pbk). . . £75

ditto, Scribner (New York), 1997 (approx 300 advance promotional copies signed on special bound in page; 'Special Signed Copy; Not For Sale' printed on back panel of d/w; no price on front flap) . . . £125/£100

ditto, Picador (London), 1998 (first state, intended for export to Australia, without the Salman Rushdie quote on d/w; priced £17.99) . . . . . £25/£5

ditto, Picador (London), 1998 (later state with the Salman Rushdie quote on d/w; priced £18.00) . . £15/£5

The Body Artist, Scribner (New York), 2001 . . £10/£5

ditto, Scribner (New York), 2001 (signed by the author on a tipped in leaf) . . . . . . £50/£45

ditto, Picador (London), 2001 . . . . £10/£5

Cosmopolis, Scribner (New York), 2003 . . £10/£5

ditto, Picador (London), 2003 . . . . £10/£5

Falling Man, Scribner (New York), 2007 . . £10/£5

ditto, Picador (London), 2007 . . . . £10/£5

Plays

The Day Room, American Theatre (New York), 1986 (pbk)
. . . . £20

ditto, Knopf (New York), 1987 . . . . £20/£5

Valparaiso, A Play In Two Acts, Scribner (New York), 1999
. . . . £10/£5

Love-Lies-Bleeding, Scribner (New York), 2005 (pbk). £10

Others

'Master Leads the Chant...', Black Oak Books (Berkeley, CA), 1991 (broadside excerpt from *Mao II*) . . . £25

Pafko at the Wall, Harper's (New York), 1992 (pbk; 32-page insert in the October 1992 issue of Harper's magazine; prologue to *Underworld*) £10

ditto, Scribner (New York), 1997 . . . £10/£5

ditto, as ***The Triumph of Death***, Picador (London), 1998 (pbk) £10

THOMAS DE QUINCEY

(b.1785 d.1859)

De Quincey was an English author famous for *Confessions of an English Opium-Eater*, which first appeared in 1821 in the *London Magazine*. He greatly influenced his American contemporary Edgar Allan Poe, later Charles Baudelaire, and even into the 20th century writers such as Jorge Luis Borges have claimed to be partly influenced by his work.

Confessions of an English Opium Eater, Taylor & Hessey (London), 1822 (first issue with advertisement page at end)
. . . . £2,500

ditto, Taylor & Hessey (London), 1822 (second issue without advertisment page at end) £1,500

ditto, E. Little and S. Siegfried (Philadelphia, PA), 1823 .
. . . . £250

The Stranger's Grave, Longman, Hurst, Rees, Orme, Brown and Green (London), 1823 . . . . . . £200

Walladmor, Taylor and Hessey (London), 1825 (2 vols) .
. . . . £300

Klosterheim, or The Masque, Blackwood (Edinburgh)... Cadell (London), 1832 . . . . . . £200

ditto, Whittemore, Niles and Hall (New York), 1855 . £125

Selections Grave and Gay, from Writings Published and Unpublished, James Hogg (London), 1853-1860 (14 vols)
. . . . £750

ditto, Ticknor, Reed and Fields (Boston), 1851-1859 (20 vols) £750

Thomas De Quincey: His Life and Writings, John Hogg (London), 1890 . . . . £35

De Quincey Memorials, Heinemann (London), 1891 (2 vols)
. . . . £40

Posthumous Works of Thomas De Quincey, Heinemann (London), 1891 (2 vols) £25

Masters of Literature: De Quincey, G. Bell and Sons Ltd (London), 1911 . . . . £10

A Diary of Thomas De Quincey, 1803, Noel Douglas (London), 1927 (1,500 numbered copies) . . £65/£10

ditto, Payson & Clarke (New York), 1927 (1,500 numbered copies) . . . . £65/£10

Recollections of the Lake Poets, Lehmann (London), 1948.
. . . . £20/£5

New Essays: His Contributions to the Saturday Post and the Edinburgh Evening Post 1827-1828, Princeton Univ Press (Princeton, NJ), 1966 . . . . . £25/£10

Collected Editions

The Collected Writings of Thomas De Quincey, A. and C. Black (London), 1889-1890 (14 vols) £500

Works of Thomas De Quincey, Pickering and Chatto (London), 2002 (21 vols) £1,500

DANIEL DEFOE

(b.1660 d.1730)

Defoe is regarded as the father of the English novel, of modern journalism and the art of political propaganda. His political and pamphleting activities (particularly the publication of *The Shortest Way With Dissenters*) caused him to be arrested and put in the pillory, although the public are reported to have thrown flowers at him. He was locked up in Newgate Prison but released after agreeing to carry out espionage work for the government.

'Robinson Crusoe'

The Life and Strange Surprizing Adventures of Robinson Crusoe, W. Taylor (London), 1719 (first edition, first issue, anonymous) £15,000

ditto, W. Taylor (London), 1719 (anonymous, later impressions) £2,000

ditto, Etchells & Macdonald (London), 1929 (illustrated by E. McKnight Kauffer, limited edition, 525 copies) . £450

ditto, Basilisk Press, 1979 (illustrated by Edward Gordon Craig, limited edition, 500 copies, slipcase) . . . £500

The Farther Adventures of Robinson Crusoe, W. Taylor (London), 1719 (anonymous) £10,000

Serious Reflections During the Life and Surprising Adventures of Robinson Crusoe, W. Taylor (London), 1720 (anonymous) £6,000

ditto, W. Mears/T. Woodward (London), 1726 (2 vols made up of the abridged seventh edition of *The Life and Strange Adventures of Robinson Crusoe* and the fifth edition of *The Farther Adventures of Robinson Crusoe*) . £1,250

The Life and Strange Surprising Adventures of Robinson Crusoe, John Stockdale (London), 1790 (together with 'The Life of Daniel De Foe' and a bibliography of his writings by George Chalmers. 2 vols) . . . £1,250

The Life and Adventures of Robinson Crusoe, sold by J. Walter (London), 1790 (first joint edition of Parts I, II and III, printed at the Logographic Press, includes 'The True-Born Englishman, A Satire' and 'The Original Power of the People of England examined and asserted', 3 vols) £1,000

ditto, Constable (London) Press, 1925 (reissued with facsimiles of Stothard's plates, as *The Life and Strange Surprising Adventures of Robinson Crusoe*, with an introduction by Charles Whibley. 3 vols, limited edition, 775 copies) £500

The Life and Adventures of Robinson Crusoe, John Major (London), 1831 (illustrated by George Cruikshank and Thomas Stothard, with introductory verses by Bernard Barton. 2 vols) £500

ditto, Dent (London), 1903 (illustrated by J. Ayton Symington) £50

Other Fiction

The Life ... of Captain Singleton, J. Brotherton (London), 1720 (anonymous) £750

Memoirs of a Cavalier, A. Bell (London), 1720 . . £750

Moll Flanders, W. Chetwood/T. Edling (London), [1722] (anonymous). £15,000

A Journal of the Plague Year, E. Nutt (London), 1722 (anonymous). £750

The History ... of Col. Jacque, Commonly Call'd Col. Jack, J. Brotherton (London), 1722 (anonymous) . . £650

The Fortunate Mistress, or ... Roxana, T. Werner (London), 1724 (anonymous) £750

Non-Fiction

The Shortest-Way With Dissenters, published anon, MDCCII [1702] £3,000

The History of the Union of Great Britain, Heirs and Successors of Andrew Anderson (Edinburgh) 1709 (in 6 parts) £500

The Family Instructor [Vol I], Emanuel Matthews/J. Button (London/Newcastle Upon Tyne), 1715 (anonymous) . £300

The Family Instructor [Vol II], Emanuel Matthews (London), 1718 (2 parts) (anonymous) . . . £300

ditto, Thos. Longman (London), 1741 (first combined edition, 2 vols) £300

The Compleat English Tradesman [Vol I], Charles Rivington (London), 1726 [1725] (anonymous) . . £300

Conjugal Lewdness: or, Matrimonial Whoredom, T. Warner (London), 1727 . . . . . £2,500

ditto, as *A Treatise Concerning the Use and Abuse of the Marriage Bed*, London, T. Warner (London), 1727 (second issue of the above with new title on cancel title page). £1,500

The Compleat English Tradesman [Vol II], Charles Rivington (London), 1732 (2 parts, anonymous) . £300

ditto, C. Rivington (London), 1732 (first combined edition, 2 vols) £300

A Tour Thro' the Whole Island of Great Britain, G. Strahan (London), 1724-27 [1726] (3 vols, anonymous) . £2,500

ditto, Peter Davis (London), 1927 (abridged version, 2 vols, limited edition, 1,000 copies) £300

A System of Magick, Roberts (London), 1727. . £1,500

LEN DEIGHTON
(b.1929)

Len Deighton worked as an illustrator until his first novel was published in 1962. He is best known for his popular thrillers and spy novels, the first four of which featured an unnamed hero who became 'Harry Palmer', portrayed by Michael Caine when the books were filmed. Deighton also published a series of cookery books and drew a weekly illustrated cooking guide in *The Observer*.

Novels

The Ipcress File, Hodder & Stoughton (London), 1962 . . . . £450/£45

ditto, Simon & Schuster (New York), 1963 . . £100/£20

ditto, Franklin Library (Franklin Centre, PA), 1988 (signed, limited edition) £65

Horse under Water, Cape (London), 1963 (with loose crossword competition) . . . . . . £200/£75

ditto, Cape (London), 1963 (without loose crossword competition). . . . . £75/£15

ditto, Putnam (New York), 1968. . . . . £65/£15

Funeral in Berlin, Cape (London), 1964 . . . £85/£10

ditto, Putnam (New York), 1965. . . . . £75/£10

Billion Dollar Brain, Putnam (New York), 1966 . £75/£10

ditto, Cape (London), 1966 . . . . . £75/£10

An Expensive Place to Die, Putnam (New York), 1967 (with wallet of documents) . . . . . . £65/£30

ditto, Putnam (New York), 1967 (without wallet of documents) . . . . £45/£5

ditto, Cape (London), 1967 (with wallet of documents). . . . . £65/£30

ditto, Cape (London), 1967 (without wallet of documents) . . . . £45/£5

Only When I Larf, privately printed for the author, 1967 (150 copies in plastic binding) £2,000

ditto, Joseph (London), 1968 (boards) . . £85/£15

ditto, Joseph (London), 1968 (pbk) £5

ditto, as *Only When I Laugh*, The Mysterious Press (New York), 1987 (250 signed copies, slipcase, no d/w) £50/£35

ditto, as *Only When I Laugh*, The Mysterious Press (New York), 1987 . . . . £15/£5

Bomber, Cape (London), 1970 . . . . £35/£10

ditto, Harper & Row (New York), 1970 . . £30/£5

Close-Up, Cape (London), 1972 . . . . £35/£10

ditto, Atheneum (New York), 1972 . . . £25/£5

Spy Story, Cape (London), 1974 . . . . £25/£5

ditto, Harcourt Brace (New York), 1974 . . £20/£5

Yesterday's Spy, Cape (London), 1975 . . . £25/£5

ditto, Harcourt Brace (New York), 1975 . . £20/£5

Twinkle, Twinkle, Little Spy, Cape (London), 1976 £25/£5

ditto, as *Catch a Falling Spy*, Harcourt Brace (New York), 1976 . . . . £20/£5

SS-GB: Nazi-occupied Britain 1941, Cape (London), 1978
. . . . £25/£5
ditto, Knopf (New York), 1979 . . . £20/£5
XPD, Hutchinson (London), 1981 . . . £25/£5
ditto, Knopf (New York), 1981 . . . . £20/£5
Goodbye, Mickey Mouse, Hutchinson (London), 1982 . .
. . . . £25/£5
ditto, Knopf (New York), 1982 . . . . £20/£5
Berlin Game, Hutchinson (London), 1983 . £25/£5
ditto, Knopf (New York), 1984 . . . . £20/£5
Mexico Set, Hutchinson (London), 1984 . . £25/£5
ditto, Knopf (New York), 1985 . . . . £20/£5
London Match, Hutchinson (London), 1985 . £25/£5
ditto, Knopf (New York), 1986 . . . . £20/£5
Winter: A Berlin Family, 1899-1945, Hutchinson (London),
1987 . . . . £25/£5
ditto, Knopf (New York), 1987 . . . . £20/£5
Spy Hook, Hutchinson (London), 1988 . . £25/£5
ditto, Knopf (New York), 1988 . . . . £20/£5
Spy Line, Hutchinson (London), 1989 . . £20/£5
ditto, Knopf (New York), 1989 . . . . £15/£5
Spy Sinker, Hutchinson (London), 1990 . . £20/£5
ditto, HarperCollins (New York), 1990 . . £15/£5
MAMista, Century (London), 1991 . . . £20/£5
ditto, HarperCollins (New York), 1991 . . £15/£5
City of Gold, Century (London), 1992 . . £15/£5
ditto, HarperCollins (New York), 1992 . . £10/£5
Violent Ward, Scorpion Press (Bristol), 1993 (130 signed
copies) £75
ditto, Scorpion Press (Bristol), 1993 (20 deluxe signed
copies) £200
ditto, HarperCollins (London), 1993 . . . £15/£5
ditto, HarperCollins (New York), 1993 . . £10/£5
Faith, HarperCollins (London), 1994 . . £30/£5
ditto, HarperCollins (New York), 1994 . . £10/£5
Hope, Scorpion Press (Blakeney, Glos), 1995 (15 copies of
edition of 114) £250
ditto, Scorpion Press (Blakeney, Glos), 1995 (99 copies of
edition of 114, glassine d/w) £65
ditto, HarperCollins (London), 1995 . . . £30/£5
ditto, HarperCollins (New York), 1995 . . £10/£5
ditto, Franklin Library (Franklin Centre, PA), 1996 (signed,
limited edition) £50
Charity, HarperCollins (London), 1996 . . £25/£5
ditto, HarperCollins (New York), 1996 . . £10/£5
ditto, Franklin Library (Franklin Centre, PA), 1996 (signed,
limited edition) £50

Omnibus Editions
Game, Set and Match, Hutchinson (London), 1986 £35/£10
ditto, Knopf (New York), 1989 . . . . £30/£10
ditto, Hutchinson (London), 1986 (presentation set of 3 first
editions with ***The Len Deighton Companion***, in slipcase).
. . . . £85/£75
Hook, Line and Sinker, Hutchinson (London), 1991 £10/£5
ditto, Hutchinson (London), 1991 (presentation set of 3 first
editions, in slipcase) . . . . . . £85/£75

Short Stories
Declarations of War, Cape (London), 1971 (short stories) .
. . . . £40/£10
ditto, as ***Eleven Declarations of War***, Harcourt Brace (New
York),1971 . . . . £35/£10

Cookery Titles
Action Cook Book, Len Deighton's Guide to Eating, Cape
(London), 1965 (printed boards, clear d/w) . £85/£30
ditto, as ***Cookstrip Cookbook***, Bernard Geis (New York),
1966 . . . . £10/£5
Où Est le Garlic or Len Deighton's French Cook Book,
Penguin (Harmondsworth, Middlesex), 1965 (pbk) . £25
ditto, as ***Où Est le Garlic or French Cooking in 50 Lessons***,
Harper & Row (New York), 1977 . . . . £20/£5
ditto, as ***Basic French Cooking***, Cape (London), 1979 .
. . . . £40/£10
ditto, as ***Basic French Cookery Course***, Century Hutchinson
(London), 1990 . . . . . . £10/£5
ABC of French Food, Century (London), 1989 . £10/£5

Others
The Assassination of President Kennedy, Cape/Jackdaw
(London), 1967 (Portfolio containing 12 reproductions, 1
cut-out model and 5 broadsides, with Rand and Loxton) .
. . . . £250
Len Deighton's London Dossier, Cape (London), 1967 .
. . . . £50/£20
Len Deighton's Continental Dossier, Joseph (London),
1968 (no d/w) £40
Fighter: The True Story of the Battle of Britain, Cape
(London), 1977 . . . . £45/£10
ditto, Knopf (New York), 1978 . . . . £10/£5
Airshipwreck, Cape (London), 1978 (6 postcards laid in,
with record) . . . . . . £175/£75
ditto, Cape (London), 1978 (no postcards or record) £40/£15
ditto, Holt Rinehart (New York), 1979 . . £30/£10
Blitzkrieg: From the Rise of Hitler to the Fall of Dunkirk,
Cape (London), 1979 . . . . . . £30/£5
ditto, Knopf (New York), 1980 . . . . £30/£5
Battle of Britain, Cape (London), 1980 . . £30/£5
ditto, Coward, McCann & Geoghegan (New York), 1980 .
. . . . £30/£5
The Orient Flight: L.Z. 127 – Graf Zeppelin, German
Philatelic Society (Westminster, MD), 1980 (as Cyril
Deighton, with Fred F. Blau, no d/w) . . £200
The Egypt Flight: L.Z. 127 – Graf Zeppelin, German
Philatelic Society (Westminster, MD), 1981 (as Cyril
Deighton, with Fred F. Blau, wraps) . . . £175
***Blood, Tears and Folly: In the Darkest Hour of the Second
World War***, Cape (London), 1993 . . . £25/£5
ditto, as ***Blood, Tears and Folly: An Objective Look at
World War II***, HarperCollins (New York), 1993 . £25/£5
Pests, A Play in Three Acts, Chris Martin (Mansfield
Woodhouse, Notts), 1994 (50 signed, numbered copies of
226, slipcase) . . . . £75/£50
ditto, Chris Martin (Mansfield Woodhouse, Notts), 1994
(150 numbered copies of 226) . . . . £30/£15
ditto, Chris Martin (Mansfield Woodhouse, Notts), 1994 (26
signed, lettered copies of 226) . . . £200/£150

ANITA DESAI
(b.1937)

Desai was born and educated in India, but today lives in
New York State, spending time in India and the United
Kingdom. She is a Fellow of the Royal Society of
Literature and has been shortlisted for the Booker Prize
three times. *In Custody* was filmed by Merchant Ivory in
1993. Her daughter is Kiran Desai.

Novels
Cry, the Peacock, Peter Owen (London), 1963   £750/£100
Voices in the City, Peter Owen (London), 1965   £750/£100
Bye-Bye, Blackbird, Hind Pocket Books (Delhi, India), 1971
(pbk) £5
Where Shall We Go This Summer?, Vikas (New Delhi),
1975 (pbk) £10
Fire on the Mountain, Heinemann (London), 1977   £30/£5
ditto, Harper & Row (New York), 1977 . . . £25/£5
Clear Light of Day, Heinemann (London), 1980 . £30/£5
ditto, Harper & Row (New York), 1980 . . £25/£5
In Custody, Heinemann (London), 1984 . . . £20/£5
ditto, Harper & Row (New York), 1984 . . . £15/£5
Baumgartner's Bombay, Heinemann (London), 1988 £15/£5
ditto, Knopf (New York), 1989 . . . . . £15/£5
Journey to Ithaca, Heinemann (London), 1995 . £10/£5
ditto, Knopf (New York), 1995 . . . . . £10/£5
Fasting, Feasting, Chatto & Windus (London), 1999 £10/£5
ditto, Houghton Mifflin (New York), 2000 . . £10/£5
The Zigzag Way, Chatto & Windus (London), 2004   £10/£5
ditto, Houghton Mifflin Co. (Boston, MA), 2004 . £10/£5

Short Story Collections
Games At Twilight & Other Stories, Heinemann (London),
1978 . . . . £30/£10
ditto, Harper & Row (New York), 1978 . . . £25/£5
Scholar and Gypsy, Pheonix (London), 1996 (pbk) . £5
Diamond Dust: And Other Stories, Chatto & Windus
(London), 2000 . . . . £10/£5

Children's Books
The Peacock Garden, Heinemann (London), 1979 £450/£45
The Village by the Sea: An Indian Family Story,
Heinemann (London), 1982 . . . . . £20/£5

Non-Fiction
Peasant Struggles in India, O.U.P. (Bombay, India), 1979 .
. . . . £35/£10

KIRAN DESAI
(b.1971)

Kiran Desai is an Indian author who is also a permanent
resident of the United States. Her novel *The Inheritance of
Loss* won the 2006 Man Booker Prize and the National
Book Critics Circle Fiction Award. She is the daughter of
the noted author Anita Desai.

Hullabaloo in the Guava Orchard, Faber (London), 1998 .
. . . . £10/£5
ditto, as Atlantic Monthly Press (New York), 1998   £10/£5

The Inheritance of Loss, Hamish Hamilton (London), 2006
. . . . £40/£5
ditto, as Atlantic Monthly Press (New York), 2006   £40/£5

MAURICE & EDWARD DETMOLD
(b.1883 d.1908, b.1883 d.1957)

Maurice and Edward Detmold were brothers who collaborated in illustrating, exhibiting at the Royal Academy in
1897 when they were only 13 years old. They worked
together until the suicide of Maurice, aged only 24. Edward
continued illustrating books until the late 1920s, commit-
ting suicide himself in 1957.

Books Illustrated by Maurice and Edward Detmold
Pictures from Birdland, Dent (London), 1899 (24 coloured
lithographs) £500
*Sixteen Illustrations of Subjects from Kipling's 'Jungle
Book'*, Macmillan (London), 1903 (portfolio) . £3,000
The Jungle Book, Macmillan (London), 1908 (16 colour
illustrations) £175
ditto, Century (New York), 1913 (16 colour illustrations) .
. . . . £150

Books Illustrated by Edward Detmold
The Fables of Aesop, Hodder & Stoughton (London), 1909
(23 colour plates). £250
ditto, Hodder & Stoughton (London), 1909 (750 signed
copies, 25 colour plates) £1,000
ditto, Hodder & Stoughton (New York), 1909 (23 colour
plates) £250
Birds and Beasts, by Camille Lemonnier, Allen (London),
1911 (6 colour plates). £45
The Book of Baby Beasts, by Florence E. Dugdale,
Frowde/Hodder & Stoughton (London), [1911] (19 colour
plates) £75
The Life of the Bee, by Maurice Maeterlinck, Allen
(London), 1911 (13 colour plates) £100
ditto, as *The Children's Life of the Bee*, Dodd, Mead (New
York), 1919 (5 colour plates) £25
Hours of Gladness, by Maurice Maeterlinck, Allen
(London), 1912 (20 colour plates) £250
ditto, as *News of Spring*, Dodd, Mead (New York), 1913 (20
colour plates) £200
The Book of Baby Birds, by Florence E. Dugdale,
Frowde/Hodder & Stoughton (London), [1912] (19 colour
plates) £150
ditto, Hodder & Stoughton (New York), [1912] (19 colour
plates) £150
The Book of Baby Pets, by Florence E. Dugdale,
Frowde/Hodder & Stoughton (London), [1915] (19 colour
plates) £125
ditto, Hodder & Stoughton (New York), [1915] (19 colour
plates) £100
The Book of Baby Dogs, by Charles J. Kaberry,
Frowde/Hodder & Stoughton (London), [1915] (colour
plates) £125
ditto, Hodder & Stoughton (New York), [1915] (colour
plates) £100

Twenty-Four Nature Pictures, Dent (London), [1919]
(portfolio) £600
Birds in Town and Village, by W.H. Hudson, Dent
(London), 1919 (8 colour plates) . . . £35
ditto, Dutton (New York), 1920 . . . . . £75/£25
Our Little Neighbours, by Charles J. Kaberry, Humphrey
Milford/O.U.P. (London), 1921, [1921] (11 colour plates)
. . . . £200/£75
Fabre's Book of Insects, by J.H.C. Fabre, Hodder &
Stoughton (London), [1921] (12 colour plates) £300/£100
ditto, Dodd, Mead (New York), 1921 (12 colour plates) .
. . . . £250/£100
Rainbow House for Boys and Girls, by Arthur Vine Hall,
Cape (London), 1923 (6 colour plates) . . . £50/£20
*The Arabian Nights - Tales from the Thousand and One
Nights*, Hodder & Stoughton (London), [1924] (12 colour
plates) £250
ditto, Hodder & Stoughton (London), [1924] (100 signed
copies, 12 colour plates) £3,000
ditto, Dodd, Mead (New York), 1925 (12 colour plates,
glassine d/w and slipcase). . . . £400/£150
The Fantastic Creatures of Edward Julius Detmold, Pan
(London), 1976 (pbk). £15
ditto, Peacock Press/Bantam Books (New York), 1976 (pbk)
. . . . £10
ditto, Scribner's (New York), 1976 . . . . £25/£10

COLIN DEXTER

(b.1930)

Colin Dexter began writing his first detective novel in 1972
during a family holiday, and in 1975 *Last Bus to
Woodstock* was published, introducing Inspector Morse,
the irritable Oxford detective with penchants for real ale,
Wagner, crosswords and English literature. Dexter has won
several Crime Writers Association Golden Dagger awards,
and in 2000 was awarded the O.B.E. for services to literature.

Novels
Last Bus to Woodstock, Macmillan (London), 1975 . .
. . . . £850/£65
ditto, St Martin's Press (New York), 1975 . £650/£45
Last Seen Wearing, Macmillan (London), 1976 . £850/£65
ditto, St Martin's Press (New York), 1976 . £500/£45
The Silent World of Nicholas Quinn, Macmillan (London),
1977 . . . . £600/£50
ditto, St Martin's Press (New York), 1977 . £250/£35
Service of All the Dead, Macmillan (London), 1979 . .
. . . . £350/£30
ditto, St Martin's Press (New York), 1980 . £150/£15
The Dead of Jericho, Macmillan (London), 1981 . £200/£20
ditto, St Martin's Press (New York), 1981 . £150/£15
The Riddle of the Third Mile, Macmillan (London), 1983 .
. . . . £150/£15
ditto, St Martin's Press (New York), 1983 . £100/£10
The Secret of Annexe 3, Macmillan (London), 1986 . .
. . . . £100/£10
ditto, St Martin's Press (New York), 1987 . £75/£10
The Wench Is Dead, Macmillan (London), 1989 . £25/£5
ditto, St Martin's Press (New York), 1990 . . £15/£5

The Jewel That Was Ours, Scorpion Press (Bristol), 1991
(150 signed copies, quarter leather). . . . £75
ditto, Scorpion Press (Bristol), 1991 (20 signed deluxe
copies) £250
ditto, Macmillan (London), 1991 . . . . £25/£5
ditto, Crown (New York), 1992 . . . . . £10/£5
The Way through the Woods, Macmillan (London), 1992 .
. . . . £15/£5
ditto, Scorpion Press (Bristol), 1992 (150 signed copies,
quarter leather) £75
ditto, Scorpion Press (Bristol), 1992 (20 signed deluxe
copies) £225
ditto, Crown (New York), 1993 . . . . £10/£5
The Daughters of Cain, Macmillan (London), 1994 £10/£5
ditto, Crown (New York), 1994 . . . . . £10/£5
Death Is Now My Neighbour, Macmillan (London), 1996 .
. . . . £10/£5
ditto, as *Death Is Now My Neighbor*, Crown (New York),
1997 . . . . £10/£5
The Remorseful Day, Macmillan (London), 1999 . £10/£5
ditto, Crown (New York), 1999 . . . . . £10/£5

Short Stories
Morse's Greatest Mystery and Other Stories, Macmillan
(London), 1993 . . . . £10/£5
ditto, Scorpion Press (Bristol), 1993 (99 signed copies,
quarter leather) £85
ditto, Scorpion Press (Bristol), 1993 (20 signed deluxe
copies) £225
ditto, Crown (New York), 1993 . . . . . £10/£5
The Inside Story, Macmillan (London), 1993 (for American
Express; pbk) £10
Neighbourhood Watch, Moorhouse/Sorenson, 1993 (150
numbered copies; wraps) £65
ditto, Moorhouse/Sorenson, 1993 (50 signed, numbered
copies; wraps) £100
ditto, Moorhouse/Sorenson, 1993 (26 signed, numbered
copies) £200
As Good as Gold, Kodak/Pan, 1994 (pbk) . . . £5

Omnibus Editions
An Inspector Morse Omnibus, Macmillan (London), 1991 .
. . . . £25/£5
The Second Inspector Morse Omnibus, Macmillan
(London), 1992 . . . . £15/£5
The Third Inspector Morse Omnibus, Macmillan (London),
1993 . . . . £15/£5
The Fourth Inspector Morse Omnibus, Macmillan
(London), 1996 . . . . £15/£5

Non-Fiction
Liberal Studies: An Outline Course, Pergamon Press
(Oxford), 1964 (written as N.C. Dexter, with E.G. Rayner,
2 vols) . . . . £20/£5 (the set)
Guide to Contemporary Politics, Pergamon Press (Oxford),
1966 (written as N.C. Dexter, with E.G. Rayner). £15/£5

MICHAEL DIBDIN
(b.1947 d.2007)

A popular crime writer, Dibdin was the author of the
internationally best-selling 'Aurelio Zen' series, set in Italy.
These detective novels provide a penetrating insight into
less obvious aspects of Italian society over the last 20
years.

'Aurelio Zen' Series
Ratking, Faber (London), 1988 . . . . . . £100£10
ditto, Bantam (New York), 1989. . . . . £20/£5
Vendetta, Faber (London), 1990. . . . . £25/£5
ditto, Doubleday (New York), 1991 . . . £15/£5
Cabal, Faber (London), 1992 . . . . £20/£5
ditto, Doubleday (New York), 1993 . . . £15/£5
Dead Lagoon, Faber (London), 1994. . . . £15/£5
ditto, Pantheon (New York), 1994 . . . £10/£5
Cosi Fan Tuti, Faber (London), 1996 . . . £10/£5
ditto, Pantheon (New York), 1996 . . . £10/£5
A Long Finish, Faber (London), 1998 . . . £10/£5
ditto, Pantheon (New York), 1998. . . . £10/£5
Blood Rain, Faber (London), 1999 . . . £10/£5
ditto, Pantheon (New York), 1999. . . . £10/£5
And Then You Die, Faber (London), 2002 . £10/£5
ditto, Pantheon (New York), 2002 . . . £10/£5
Medusa, Faber (London), 2003 . . . . £10/£5
ditto, Pantheon (New York), 2003 . . . £10/£5
Back to Bologna, Faber (London), 2005 . . £10/£5
ditto, Vintage (New York), 2006 (pbk) . . . £5

Other Novels
The Last Sherlock Holmes Story, Cape (London), 1978 .
. . . . £250/£20
ditto, Pantheon (New York), 1978 . . . £20/£5
A Rich Full Death, Cape (London), 1986 . . £45/£10
ditto, Vintage/Black Lizard (New York), 1999 (pbk) . £5
The Tryst, Faber (London), 1989 . . . £25/£5
ditto, Summit (New York), 1990. . . . £20/£5
Dirty Tricks, Faber (London), 1991 . . . £15/£5
ditto, Summit (New York), 1991. . . . £10/£5
The Dying of the Light, Faber (London), 1993 . £15/£5
ditto, Pantheon (New York), 1993 . . . £10/£5
Dark Spectre, Faber (London), 1995. . . £15/£5
ditto, Pantheon (New York), 1995 . . . £10/£5
Thanksgiving, Faber (London), 2000 . . . £10/£5
ditto, Pantheon (New York), 2000 . . . £10/£5

PHILIP K. DICK
(b.1928 d.1982)

An American author of science fiction, often dealing with
the effects of mechanisation, hallucinogenic drugs and
schizophrenic delusions. He won the Hugo Award for *The
Man in the High Castle*, and the John W. Campbell
Memorial Award for *Flow My Tears, the Policeman Said*.
Do Androids Dream of Electric Sheep? was the source
book for the classic science fiction film *Bladerunner*.

Novels
Solar Lottery, Ace Books (New York), 1955 (pbk; bound
with *The Big Jump* by Leigh Brackett) £35

ditto, as *World of Chance*, Rich & Cowan (London), 1956 .
. . . . £1,000/£200
ditto, Gregg Press (Boston, MA), 1979 (no d/w) . . £200
The World Jones Made, Ace Books (New York), 1956 (pbk;
bound with *Agent of the Unknown* by Margaret St Clair) £30
ditto, Sidgwick & Jackson (London), 1968 . £1,250/£150
ditto, Gregg Press (Boston, MA), 1979 (no d/w) . . £65
The Man Who Japed, Ace Books (New York), 1956 (pbk;
bound with *The Space-Born* by E.C. Tubb) . . . £30
ditto, Eyre Methuen (London), 1978 . . . . £125/£25
Eye in the Sky, Ace Books (New York), 1957 (pbk) . £30
ditto, Arrow (London), 1971 (pbk) £10
ditto, Gregg Press (Boston, MA), 1979 . . . . £65
The Cosmic Puppets, Ace Books (New York), 1957 (pbk;
bound with *Sargasso of Space* by Andrew North) . £30
ditto, Severn House (London), 1986 . . . . £25/£10
Time Out Of Joint, Lippincott (Philadelphia, PA), 1959 .
. . . . £450/£65
ditto, Science Fiction Book Club (London), 1961 . £65/£10
Dr Futurity, Ace Books (New York), 1960 (pbk; bound with
Slavers of Space by John Brunner) £20
Vulcan's Hammer, Ace Books (New York), 1960 (pbk;
bound with *The Skynappers* by John Brunner) . . £20
ditto, Gregg Press (Boston, MA), 1979 . . . . £50
The Man in the High Castle, Putnam (New York), 1962 .
. . . . £500/£45
ditto, Penguin (Harmondsworth, Middlesex), 1965 (pbk) £5
ditto, Gollancz (London), 1975 . . . . £150/£20
The Game Players of Titan, Ace Books (New York), 1963
(pbk) £20
ditto, White Lion (London), 1974 . . . . £200/£35
Martian Time-Slip, Ballantine Books (New York), 1964
(pbk) £20
ditto, New English Library (London), 1976 . £75/£15
The Simulacra, Ace Books (New York), 1964 (pbk) . £25
ditto, Eyre Methuen (London), 1977 . . . £400/£45
The Penultimate Truth, Belmont (New York), 1964 (pbk) .
. . . . £20
ditto, Cape (London), 1967 . . . . . . £600/£75
Clans of the Alphane Moon, Ace Books (New York), 1964
(pbk) £20
ditto, Gregg Press (Boston, MA), 1979 (no d/w) . . £75
The Three Stigmata of Palmer Eldritch, Doubleday (New
York), 1965 . . . . £1,500/£150
ditto, Cape (London), 1966 . . . . . £750/£100
Dr Bloodmoney, Ace Books (New York), 1965 (pbk) . £20
ditto, Gregg Press (Boston, MA), 1977 (no d/w) . . £800
Now Wait for Last Year, Doubleday (New York), 1966 .
. . . . £175/£35
The Crack in Space, Ace Books (New York), 1966 (pbk) £20
ditto, Severn House (London), 1989 . . . . £30/£5
The Unteleported Man, Ace Books (New York), 1966 (pbk)
. . . . £15
ditto, Berkley (New York), 1983 (pbk; revised version). £5
ditto, as *Lies Inc.*, Gollancz (London), 1984 (further
revisions) . . . . £25/£5
The Zap Gun, Pyramid (New York), 1967 (pbk) . £20
ditto, Gregg Press (Boston, MA), 1979 . . . . £65
Counter-Clock World, Berkley (New York), 1967 (pbk) £25
ditto, White Lion (London), 1977 . . . . £150/£25
The Ganymede Takeover, Ace Books (New York), 1967
(with Ray Nelson; pbk) £15
ditto, Severn House (London), 1988 . . . . £40/£5
Do Androids Dream of Electric Sheep?, Doubleday (New
York), 1969 . . . . £4,000/£500

ditto, Rapp & Whiting (London), 1969 . . . £500/£65

Ubik, Doubleday (New York), 1969 . . . £600/£65

ditto, Rapp & Whiting (London), 1970 . . . £175/£20

Galactic Pot-Healer, Berkeley (New York), 1969 (pbk) £15

ditto, Berkeley (New York), 1969 (hardback book club edition with '08L' on page 145) . . . £25/£5

ditto, Gollancz (London), 1971 . . . £40/£10

A Maze of Death, Doubleday (New York), 1970 £750/£100

ditto, Gollancz (London), 1972 . . . £450/£50

Our Friends from Frolix 8, Ace Books (New York), 1970 (pbk) £10

ditto, Ace Books (New York), 1971 . . . £35/£10

ditto, Kinnell (London), 1989 . . . £25/£10

A Philip K. Dick Omnibus, Sidgwick & Jackson (London), 1970 . . . . £500/£200

We Can Build You, Daw Books (New York), 1972 (pbk) £10

ditto, Severn House (London), 1988 . . . £35/£5

Flow My Tears, The Policeman Said, Doubleday (New York), 1974 . . . . . . £175/£25

ditto, Gollancz (London), 1974 . . . £175/£25

Deus Irae, Doubleday (New York), 1976 (with Roger Zelazny). . . . . . . £40/£10

ditto, Gollancz (London), 1977 . . . £35/£5

A Scanner Darkly, Doubleday (New York), 1977 . £35/£10

ditto, Gollancz (London), 1977 . . . £25/£10

Valis, Bantam (New York), 1981 (pbk) . . £10

ditto, Kerosina (Worcester Park, Surrey), 1987 £25/£10

ditto, Kerosina (Worcester Park, Surrey), 1987 (limited edition of 250 copies with d/w, in slipcase together with the 325 copy hardcover edition of *Cosmogony and Cosmology*, Kerosina, 1987) £150

ditto, Kerosina (Worcester Park, Surrey), 1987 (25 numbered deluxe copies of above) £1,000

The Divine Invasion, Simon & Schuster/Timescape (New York), 1981 . . . . . . £25/£5

The Transmigration of Timothy Archer, Simon & Schuster (New York), 1982 . . . . £25/£5

ditto, Gollancz (London), 1982 . . . £25/£5

The Man Whose Teeth Were Exactly Alike, Ziesing (Willimantic CT), 1984 . . . . £75/£25

ditto, Paladin (London), 1986 (pbk) . . . £5

In Milton Lumky Territory, Dragon Press (Pleasantville, NY), 1985 . . . . . £30/£5

ditto, Dragon Press (Pleasantville, NY), 1985 (50 signed, numbered copies) £175

ditto, Gollancz (London), 1986 . . . £45/£10

Ubik: The Screenplay, Corroboree Press (Minneapolis, MN), 1985 . . . . . . £100/£45

ditto, Corroboree Press (Minneapolis, MN), 1985 (20 signed copies in leather) £250

Puttering About in a Small Land, Chicago Academy (Chicago), 1985 . . . . . £25/£5

ditto, Paladin/Collins (London), 1987 (pbk) . £10

Radio Free Albemuth, Arbor House (New York), 1985 . . . . £20/£5

ditto, Severn House (London), 1987 . . . £20/£5

Humpty Dumpty in Oakland, Gollancz (London), 1986 . . . . £45/£10

Mary and the Giant, Arbor House (New York), 1987 £20/£5

ditto, Arbor House (New York), 1987 (50 copies bound in quarter leather with signature pasted-in from a cancelled cheque) £150

ditto, Gollancz (London), 1988 . . . £20/£5

Cosmogony and Cosmology, Kerosina (Worcester Park, Surrey), 1987 (no d/w) £65

ditto, Kerosina (Worcester Park, Surrey), 1987 (pbk) . £15

Nick and the Glimmung, Gollancz (London), 1988 £20/£10

ditto, Trafalgar Square (New York), 1988. . . £20/£10

The Broken Bubble, Morrow/Arbor House (New York), 1988 . . . . £15/£5

ditto, Gollancz (London), 1989 . . . . £15/£5

ditto, Ultramarine Press (New York), 1989 (150 copies, quarter leather) £125

ditto, Ultramarine Press (New York), 1989 (26 copies, full leather) £400

The Dark-Haired Girl, Ziesing (Willimantic CT), 1988 . . . . £25/£10

In Pursuit of Valis, Underwood-Miller (Novato, CA), 1991 . . . . £25/£10

ditto, Underwood-Miller (Novato, CA), 1991 (100 numbered copies) £125

ditto, Underwood-Miller (Novato, CA), 1991 (26 lettered copies) £500

Short Stories

A Handful of Darkness, Rich & Cowan (London), 1955 (first issue boards blue, lettered silver, with first issue d/w not listing *World of Chance* on rear panel) . £750/£150

ditto, Rich & Cowan (London), 1955 (second issue, orange boards, lettered black) . . . . £350/£100

ditto, Gregg Press (Boston, MA), 1978 (no d/w) . . £75

The Variable Man and Other Stories, Ace Books (New York.), 1957 (pbk) £30

The Preserving Machine, Ace Books (New York), 1969 (pbk) £25

ditto, Gollancz (London), 1971 . . . . £125/£25

The Book of Philip K. Dick, Daw Books (New York), 1973 (pbk) £10

ditto, as ***The Turning Wheel***, Coronet (London), 1977 (pbk) £10

The Best of Philip K. Dick, Ballantine (New York), 1977 (pbk) £10

The Golden Man, Berkeley (New York), 1980 (pbk) . £10

I Hope I Shall Arrive Soon, Doubleday (New York), 1985 . . . . £40/£10

ditto, Gollancz (London), 1986 . . . £40/£10

Collected Stories, Underwood Miller (Los Angeles, CA), 1987 (5 vols; slipcase, no d/w; includes *Beyond Lies the Wub* (Vol.1), *Second Variety* (Vol.2), *The Father Thing* (Vol.3), *The Days of Perky Pat* (Vol.4) and *The Little Black Box* (Vol.5)) £200

ditto, Underwood Miller (Los Angeles, CA), 1987 (5 vols; 100 sets numbered 1-100, bound in imitation leather with marbled endpapers and inserted limitation leaf with mounted Dick signature cut from cancelled cheque; slipcase; no d/w; with brief synopsis for *The Acts of Paul*) £500

ditto, Underwood Miller (Los Angeles, CA), 1987 (5 vols; 400 sets numbered 101-500; slipcase; no d/w; with brief synopsis for *The Acts of Paul*) £250

ditto, Gollancz (London), 1988-90 (4 vols) . £250/£45

The Collected Stories of Philip K. Dick, Citadel Twilight (New York), 1990 (five vols; pbk; includes *One The Short Happy Life of The Brown Oxford* (Vol.1), *We Can remember It For You Wholesale* (Vol.2), *Second Variety* (Vol.3), *The Minority Report* (Vol.4), *The Eye Of The Sibyl* (Vol.5)) £65

Paycheck: And 24 Other Classic Stories, Gollancz (London), 2003 . . . . £10/£5

Non-Fiction

Confessions of a Crap Artist, Entwhistle Books (New York), 1975 (90 signed copies of 1,000, no d/w)   .   .   . £500

ditto, Entwhistle Books (New York), 1975 (410 copies of 1,000) £100

ditto, Entwhistle Books (New York), 1975 (500 copies of 1,000; pbk) £30

ditto, Magnum (London), 1979 (pbk).   .   .   . £10

What If Our World Is Their Heaven?: The Final Conversations With Phillip K. Dick, Overlook Press (Woodstock, NY), 1987   .   .   .   .   . £30/£10

The Selected Letters of Philip K. Dick 1974, Underwood-Miller (Novato, CA), 1991   .   .   .   . £25/£10

ditto, Underwood-Miller (Novato, CA), 1991 (26 lettered copies) £200

ditto, Underwood-Miller (Novato, CA), 1991 (250 numbered copies) £75

The Selected Letters of Philip K. Dick 1975-1976, Underwood-Miller (Novato, CA), 1992 .   .   . £25/£10

ditto, Underwood-Miller (Novato, CA), 1992 (26 lettered copies) £200

ditto, Underwood-Miller (Novato, CA), 1992 (250 numbered copies) £75

The Selected Letters of Philip K. Dick 1977-1979, Underwood-Miller (Novato, CA), 1992 .   .   . £25/£10

ditto, Underwood-Miller (Novato, CA), 1992 (26 lettered copies) £180

ditto, Underwood-Miller (Novato, CA), 1992 (250 numbered copies) £65

The Selected Letters of Philip K. Dick 1972-1973, Underwood-Miller (Novato, CA), 1993 .   .   . £25/£10

ditto, Underwood-Miller (Novato, CA), 1993 (26 lettered copies) £180

ditto, Underwood-Miller (Novato, CA), 1993 (250 numbered copies) £65

The Shifting Realities of Philip K. Dick: Selected Literary and Philosophical Writings, Pantheon (New York), 1995   .   .   .   . £15/£5

The Selected Letters of Philip K. Dick 1938-1971, Underwood-Miller (Novato, CA), 1996 .   .   . £25/£10

ditto, Underwood-Miller (Novato, CA), 1996 (26 lettered copies) £175

ditto, Underwood-Miller (Novato, CA), 1996 (250 numbered copies) £50

CHARLES DICKENS

(b.1812 d.1870)

Dickens' position as one of the greats of English literature is beyond dispute. His style is florid and poetic, and there is a strong vein of humour and outright social satire in his work. Many of his books were famously first published as 'part works', the values of which vary considerably depending on the completeness of all of the adverts with which they were issued. There is some debate over the first American editions of his books, which were often pirated. American 'part-works' from the British originals required the re-engraving of the illustrations, and sometimes the addition of new illustrations.

Sketches by 'Boz', Illustrative of Every-Day Life, and Every-Day People, John Macrone (London) MDCCCXXXVI 1836 (2 vols, dark green cloth, Preface states 'Furnival's Inn, February 1836', 16 plates by Cruikshank, frontispiece and 7 plates per vol)   . £4,000

ditto, John Macrone (London) MDCCCXXXVI 1836 (the above vols rebound) £1,000

ditto, as *Watkins Tottle, and Other Sketches, Illustrative of Every-Day Life and Every-Day People*, Carey Lea & Blanchard (Philadelphia, PA), 1837 (2 vols; cloth-backed boards, with paper spine label).   .   .   . £450

Sketches by 'Boz': Illustrative of Every-Day Life, and Every-Day People. The Second Series, John Macrone (London) MDCCCXXXVII 1837 (1 vol, pink cloth, Preface states 'December 17, 1836', 10 plates by Cruikshank) £4,000

ditto, John Macrone (London) MDCCCXXXVII 1837 (the above rebound) £800

ditto, as *Sketches by Boz: Illustrative of Every-Day Life and Every-Day People. Being a Continuation of Watkins Tottle, and Other Sketches*, Carey Lea & Blanchard (Philadelphia, PA), 1837 (cloth-backed boards, with paper spine label) £450

Sketches by 'Boz' Illustrative of Every-Day Life, and Every-Day People, Chapman & Hall (London), November 1837-June 1839 (first and second series together, 20 monthly parts, 40 plates by George Cruikshank, 2 per volume, pink wraps) £15,000

ditto, Chapman & Hall (London), 1839 (first 1 vol. edition dated '1837', monthly parts bound with wrapper in glossy brown or purple cloth, with 40 plates by George Cruikshank) £1,000

Sunday Under Three Heads, Chapman & Hall (London), 1836 (pseud 'Timothy Sparks', 3 illustrations plus wrapper by H.K. Browne, first edition the title appears as a heading to Chapter III on p.35 and 'hair' spelt correctly on p.7, line 15, buff wraps) £1,750

ditto, Chapman & Hall (London), 1836 (the above rebound) £750

The Village Coquettes, Richard Bentley (London), 1836 (wraps) £3,000

ditto, Richard Bentley (London), 1836 (the above rebound) £1,000

The Posthumous Papers of the Pickwick Club edited by 'Boz', Chapman & Hall (London), April 1836-Nov 1837 (20 monthly parts in 19. Parts I & II illustrated by Robert Seymour, part III by R. W. Buss and parts IV-XIX/XX by Phiz. Green wraps) £5,000

ditto, Carey Lea & Blanchard (Philadelphia, PA), 1836-7 (5 vols; cloth-backed boards, with paper spine label)   £2,000

ditto, Chapman & Hall (London), 1837 (first book edition, 1 vol, monthly parts bound with or without wraps. 43 illustrations by R. Seymour and Phiz. Slate or purple/black cloth, first issue with 'S Veller' on p.342, line 5).   £4,000

ditto, Chapman & Hall (London), 1837 (the above rebound) £500

The Tuggs's at Ramsgate, by 'Boz,' Together with Other Tales, by Distinguished Writers, Carey Lea & Blanchard (Philadelphia, PA), 1837   .   .   .   .   .   . £350

Tales and Sketches, Carey Lea & Blanchard (Philadelphia, PA), 1837 (2 vols, each containing only one volume by Dickens; vol 1 entitled *Public Life of Mr Tulrumble, etc*; vol 2 entitled *Oliver Twist, etc*, although it contained only the first two chapters of the novel) £300

Oliver Twist; or, The Parish Boy's Progress, Richard Bentley (London), 1838 (pseud 'Boz', 3 vols, illustrated by George Cruikshank, red-brown cloth, first issue with 'Rose

Maylie and Oliver' plate in vol 3 showing them at fireside)
. . . . £4,000
ditto, Richard Bentley (London), 1838 (the above rebound).
. . . . £1,250
ditto, Richard Bentley (London), 1838 (second issue showing them at church) £2,000
ditto, Richard Bentley 1838 (second edition, or third issue, with 'Dickens' on title-page, not 'Boz'). . . £2,000
ditto, Lea & Blanchard (Philadelphia, PA), 1839 (violet cloth titled with a vignette in gilt on the spine) . . £1,000
ditto, Bradbury & Evans, January-October 1846 (10 monthly parts with illustrations by George Cruikshank, green wraps)
. . . . £20,000
ditto, Bradbury & Evans (London), MDCCCXLVI 1846 (first 1 vol. edition, with slate-coloured cloth) . £1,750
ditto, Bradbury & Evans (London), MDCCCXLVI 1846 (the above rebound) £450
Sketches of Young Gentlemen, Chapman & Hall (London), 1838 (anonymous, 6 illustrations and cover by Phiz, blue-green paper boards) £1,500
The Memoirs of Joseph Grimaldi, Richard Bentley (London), 1838 (edited by 'Boz', 2 vols, 12 plates and frontispiece to vol 1 by Cruikshank, first issue pink cloth, without border around final plate 'The Last Song') £1,500
ditto, Richard Bentley (London), 1838 (as above, second issue brown cloth with border around final plate 'The Last Song') £750
ditto, Lea & Blanchard (Philadelphia, PA), 1838 (2 vols; cloth-backed boards, with paper spine labels) . £350
The Life and Adventures of Nicholas Nickleby, Chapman & Hall (London), April 1838-October 1839 (20 monthly parts in 19, illustrated by Phiz; first issue with 'vister' on p.123, line 17; green wraps) £3,000
ditto, Chapman & Hall (London), 1839 (first book edition, monthly parts in 1 vol., illustrated by Phiz, dark olive green cloth) £2,000
ditto, Chapman & Hall (London), 1839 (the above rebound)
. . . . £300
ditto, Lea and Blanchard (Philadelphia, PA), 1838-39 (20 monthly parts in 19, illustrated by Phiz, yellow wraps) .
. . . . £1,500
ditto, Turney (New York), 1838-39 (20 monthly parts in 19, illustrated by Phiz, green wraps) . . . £1,500
ditto, Turney (New York), 1839 (1 vol) £600
ditto, Colyer (New York), 1839 (2 vols) £600
ditto, Lea and Blanchard (Philadelphia, PA), 1841 (cloth-backed boards, with paper spine label) . . . £600
Sketches of Young Couples, Chapman & Hall (London), 1840 ('By the Author of Sketches of Young Gentlemen', 6 illustrations and cover by Phiz, grey-green paper boards) .
. . . . £1,500
Master Humphrey's Clock, Chapman & Hall (London), April 1840-Nov 1841 (by 'Boz', 88 weekly parts, illustrated by G. Cattermole, Phiz & Daniel Maclise, white wraps) £2,000
ditto, Chapman & Hall (London), April 1840-Nov 1841 (20 monthly parts, illustrated as above, green wraps). £1,500
ditto, Chapman & Hall (London), MDCCCXL/MDCCCXLI 1841 (first book edition, 3 vols, weekly or monthly parts, illustrated as above, brown cloth with clock on front pointing to volume numbers) £750
ditto, Chapman & Hall (London), MDCCCXL/MDCCCXLI 1841 (as above but variant cloth, no hands on clock) . £300

ditto, Lea and Blanchard (Philadelphia, PA), 1841-42 (monthly parts) £1,000
The Old Curiosity Shop, Chapman & Hall (London), 1841 (1 vol; original monthly parts from 'Master Humphrey's Clock', cloth binding). £1,250
ditto, Lea and Blanchard (Philadelphia, PA), 1842 (1 vol; original monthly parts from 'Master Humphrey's Clock', black cloth binding) £600
Barnaby Rudge, Chapman & Hall (London), 1841 (original monthly parts from 'Master Humphrey's Clock', cloth binding). £1,750
ditto, Lea and Blanchard (Philadelphia, PA), 1841-42 (19 monthly parts; white wraps) £1,000
ditto, Lea and Blanchard (Philadelphia, PA), 1842 (1 vol) .
. . . . £500
American Notes for General Circulation, 'Extra Number' of *Brother Jonathan*, Wilson (New York), 1842 (wraps) £400
ditto, Chapman & Hall (London), 1842 (2 vols, first issue with prelims misnumbered with p.10 (x) as 'xvi', purple cloth) £1,000
ditto, Chapman & Hall (London), 1842 (as above but prelims corrected) £500
ditto, supplement to *The New World*, Winchester (New York), 1842 (wraps) £350
ditto, Harper & Brothers (New York), 1842 (wraps) . £300
Martin Chuzzlewit, Chapman & Hall (London), Jan 1843-July 1844 (20 monthly parts in 19, illustrated by Phiz, green wraps). £1,500
ditto, Chapman & Hall (London), MDCCCXXLIV 1844 (first book edition made up of unsold monthly parts, Prussian blue cloth binding) £1,000
ditto, Chapman & Hall (London), MDCCCXXLIV 1844 (as above, brown cloth binding) £750
ditto, Chapman & Hall (London), MDCCCXXLIV 1844 (as above rebound) £300
ditto, Harper & Brothers (New York), 1842 (7 parts, blue wraps) £500
A Christmas Carol, Chapman & Hall (London), 1843 ('trial issue' dated MDCCXLIV' with title page printed in red and green, brown cloth, green endpapers, and 'Stave I' on first text page) £20,000
ditto, Chapman & Hall (London), 1843 (first commercial issue as above but with title-page dated 1843 and printed in red and blue; yellow endpapers) £7,500
ditto, Chapman & Hall (London), 1843 (second issue as above but with green endpapers) £6,000
ditto, Chapman & Hall (London), 1843 (third issue with 1844 title pageyellow endpapers) £5,000
ditto, Chapman & Hall (London), 1843 (fourth issue with 'Stave One' on first text page) £2,500
ditto, Lea and Blanchard (Philadelphia, PA), 1844 (blue cloth) £400
ditto, Care & Hart (Philadelphia, PA), 1844 (black cloth) .
. . . . £400
The Chimes, Chapman & Hall (London), 1845 (first issue with publisher's name in title vignette) £500
ditto, Chapman & Hall (London), 1845 (second issue with publisher's name below title vignette) £300
ditto, Lea and Blanchard (Philadelphia, PA), 1845 . £400
ditto, Harper & Brothers (New York), 1845 (wraps) . £400
The Cricket on the Hearth, Bradbury & Evans (London), 1846 (first issue with ad. page [175] without heading 'New Editions of Oliver Twist', red cloth) £500
ditto, Bradbury & Evans (London), 1846 (second issue) £300

ditto, Lea and Blanchard (Philadelphia, PA), 1846 . . £400

ditto, Harper & Brothers (New York), 1846 (wraps)   . £400

The Battle of Life: A Love Story, Bradbury & Evans (London), 1846 (first issue, on engraved title-page 'A Love Story' in heavy type and publisher's name at bottom of page) £30,000

ditto, Bradbury & Evans (London), 1846 (second issue with 'A Love Story' in light type supported by cupids and publisher's name at bottom of page)   . . . £2,000

ditto, Bradbury & Evans (London), 1846 (third issue as above but publisher's name not at bottom of page) £1,000

ditto, Wiley & Putnam (New York) 1847 (wraps) . . £400

ditto, Harper & Brothers (New York), 1847 (wraps)   . £350

Travelling Letters Written on the Road, Wiley & Putnam (New York), 1846 (2 vols; wraps) £500

ditto, as **Pictures from Italy**, Bradbury & Evans (London), 1846 (illustrations by Samuel Palmer, blue cloth)   . £500

ditto, W.H. Colyer (New York) and G.B. Zeiber & co (Philadelphia, PA), 1846 . . . . £100

Dombey and Son, Bradbury & Evans (London), Oct 1846-April 1848 (20 monthly parts in 19, illustrated by Phiz, with 12 line errata slip in part V) £1,500

ditto, Wiley & Putnam (New York) 1847 (20 monthly parts in 19) £1,000

ditto, Bradbury & Evans (London), 1848 (first book edition, monthly parts bound in dark green cloth.)   . . £2,000

ditto, Bradbury & Evans (London), 1848 (as above rebound) £300

ditto, Wiley & Putnam (New York) 1848 (2 vols; red cloth). £400

The Haunted Man and The Ghost's Bargain, Bradbury & Evans (London), 1848 (date on title-page '1848', red cloth with blind-stamped borders) £200

ditto, Bradbury & Evans (London), 1848 (as above but date on title-page 'MDCCCXLVIII') £1,000

ditto, Harper & Brothers (New York), 1849 (wraps)   . £250

The Personal History of David Copperfield, Bradbury & Evans (London), May 1849-Nov 1850 (20 monthly parts in 19, illustrated by Phiz, green wraps) . . . £3,000

ditto, Lea and Blanchard (Philadelphia, PA), 1849-1850 (20 monthly parts in 19, yellow wraps) . . . £2,000

ditto, Wiley/Putnam/Wiley (New York), 1849-1850 (20 monthly parts in 19) £2,000

ditto, Bradbury & Evans (London), 1850 (first book edition, monthly parts bound in dark green cloth) . . £5,000

ditto, Bradbury & Evans (London), 1850 (above rebound) £1,000

ditto, Harper & Brothers (New York), 1852 . . £2,000

A Child's History of England, Bradbury & Evans (London), 1852, 53, 54 (3 vols, first issue of vol. I with ad. page [211] listing 4 books plus 5 Christmas books, and vol. III with ad. page [324] 'Collected and Revised', red cloth) £1,500

ditto, Bradbury & Evans (London), 1852, 53, 54 (3 vols, second issue of vol. I with ad. page [211] listing this book, plus 7 books plus 5 Christmas books, and vol. III with ad page [324] 'Corrected and Revised', red cloth) . . £650

Bleak House, Bradbury & Evans (London), March 1852-Sept 1853 (20 monthly parts in 19, illustrated by Phiz, blue wraps) £1,750

ditto, Harper & Brothers (New York), 1852-1853 (20 monthly parts in 19, illustrated by Phiz). . . £1,000

ditto, Bradbury & Evans (London), 1853 (first book edition, monthly parts bound in cloth) £3,000

ditto, Bradbury & Evans (London), 1853 (the above rebound) £250

ditto, Harper & Brothers (New York), 1853 (wraps)   . £250

Hard Times, Bradbury & Evans (London), 1854 (1 vol., green cloth, with 'Price 5/' on spine) . . . £1,000

ditto, Bradbury & Evans (London), 1854 (1 vol., green cloth, no price on spine) £500

ditto, Harper & Brothers (New York), 1854 (wrps)   . £250

Little Dorrit, Bradbury & Evans (London), Dec 1855-June 1857 (20 monthly parts in 19, illustrated by Phiz; blue wraps; errata slip in part XVI) £1,000

ditto, Bradbury & Evans (London), 1857 (first book edition, monthly parts bound in olive green cloth)   . . £1,750

A Tale of Two Cities, Chapman & Hall (London), June-Dec MDCCCLIX 1859 (8 parts in 7, illustrated by Phiz, first issue page 213 misnumbered '113', blue wraps) . £3,000

ditto, Chapman & Hall (London), 1859 (first book edition, monthly parts bound in red cloth, first issue). . £3,500

ditto, Chapman & Hall (London), 1859 (as above in green cloth, first issue) £3,000

ditto, Chapman & Hall (London), 1859 (as above, rebound) £750

ditto, Chapman & Hall (London), 1859 (second issue with pages correctly numbered, red cloth) . . . £3,000

ditto, Chapman & Hall (London), 1859 (second issue with pages correctly numbered, green cloth) . . . £2,500

ditto, T.B. Peterson & Brothers (Philadelphia, PA), 1859 (2 vols) £2,000

ditto, T.B. Peterson & Brothers (Philadelphia, PA), 1859 (wraps) £650

Great Expectations, Chapman & Hall (London), MDCCCLXI 1861 (3 vols, purple, plum or yellow-green cloth, 32 pages of ads dated May 1861) . . £17,500

ditto, Chapman & Hall (London), MDCCCLXI 1861 (3 vols, rebound) £3,500

ditto, Harper & Brothers (New York), 1861 (2 vols)   £1,000

The Uncommercial Traveller, Chapman & Hall (London), 1861 (ads dated December 1860, red/purple cloth) £1,250

Our Mutual Friend, Chapman & Hall (London), May 1864-May 1865 (20 monthly parts in 19, illustrated by Marcus Stone, green wraps) £1,250

ditto, Chapman & Hall (London), 1865 (first book edition, 2 vols of monthly parts bound in brown cloth). . £1,500

ditto, Chapman & Hall (London), 1865 (the above rebound) £250

ditto, Harper & Brothers (New York), 1864 (1 vol)   £1,000

The Mystery of Edwin Drood, Chapman & Hall (London), April-Sept 1870 (unfinished, six monthly parts, illustrated by Luke Fildes with cover design by Charles Alston Collins, green wraps) £750

ditto, Chapman & Hall (London), 1870 first book edition (monthly parts bound in green cloth, sawtooth border around front cover) £500

ditto, Chapman & Hall (London), 1870 first book edition (monthly parts bound in green cloth, no border around front cover) £200

Mrs Gamp With the Strolling Players, printed for Mr Lowell P. Plamer (New York), 1899 (85 copies) . . . £300

EMILY DICKINSON
(b.1830 d.1886)

Emily Dickinson was a prolific American poet who chose to publish little of her work during her lifetime. Those that were published were often altered by publishers to fit the conventions of the time. Her prodigious output was only realised after her death, but was not recognised as important until the second half of the twentieth century. She is now considered popularly and critically as a major American poet.

Poems, Roberts Brothers (Boston), 1890 (first edition, first printing on calendered paper; sheets bulk 11/16 inch; various binding styles; originally published in d/w and slipcase which are not valued here).   .   .   .   £3,500
ditto, Roberts Brothers (Boston), 1890 (first edition, second printing, first issue; sheets bulk 9/16 inch; various bindings) £1,500
ditto, Roberts Brothers (Boston), 1891 (first edition, second printing, second issue; the title pages a cancel, but looks integral; on the copyright page states: 'SECOND EDITION') £1,000
ditto, Roberts Brothers (Boston), 1891 (first edition, third printing; integral title leaf; copyright page reads 'SECOND EDITION') £350
ditto, Roberts Brothers (Boston), 1891 (first edition, third printing; integral title leaf; copyright page reads 'SECOND EDITION') £350
ditto, Roberts Brothers (Boston), 1891 (first edition, fourth printing; copyright page reads 'THIRD EDITION'; first state with gathering 2 misfolded so that the leaves containing the poem 'This is my letter to the world' and the half-title to the first section appear in the middle of the table of contents). £300
ditto, Roberts Brothers (Boston), 1891 (first edition, fourth printing; copyright page reads 'THIRD EDITION'; second state with the leaves containing the poem 'This is my letter to the world' and the half-title to the first section canceled and pasted to the first leaf of gathering 3)   .   .   £250
ditto, Roberts Brothers (Boston), 1891 (first edition, fourth printing; copyright page reads 'THIRD EDITION'; third state with gathering 2 folded correctly so that the poem 'This is my letter to the world' and the half-title to the first section are integral and in the correct position)   .   .   £200
ditto, Roberts Brothers (Boston), 1891 (first edition, fifth printing; copyright page reads 'FOURTH EDITION') £200
ditto, James R. Osgood, McIlvaine, & Co (London), 1891 (primary binding: pale yellow cloth stamped in gilt; 'McIlvaine & Co.' at base of spine)   .   .   .   £1,000
ditto, James R. Osgood, McIlvaine, & Co (London), 1891 (as above except 'HARPER AND BROTHERS' stamped at base of the spine). £750
Poems . . . Second Series, Roberts Brothers (Boston), 1891 (binding a: three-piece binding with medium yellow-green V cloth spine extending to meet smooth white V cloth on front and back covers; the meeting of the two cloths is marked by a gold-stamped vertical straight rule).   £3,000
ditto, Roberts Brothers (Boston), 1891 (binding b: smooth medium grey or medium olive V cloth; beveled edges)   .
.   .   .   .   £2,500
ditto, Roberts Brothers (Boston), 1891 (binding c: three-piece three-quarter white leather binding with spine leather

extending to meet paper-covered boards of black floral patterns on a dark orange-yellow background)   .   £5,000
ditto, Roberts Brothers (Boston), 1892 (first edition, second printing; binding a: three-piece binding of medium yellow-green shelfback and white covers, both smooth V cloth)   .
.   .   .   .   £1,250
ditto, Roberts Brothers (Boston), 1892 (first edition, second printing; binding b: medium grey or smooth medium olive V cloth with beveled edges) £500
ditto, Roberts Brothers (Boston), 1892 (first edition, second printing; binding c: smooth white V cloth; edges not bevelled) £400
Letters of Emily Dickinson, Roberts Brothers (Boston), 1894 (2 vols; in the first printing Vol I, p.(v), line 4 reads: 'paration to me'; in Vol II there is one footnote on p.370; medium yellow/green buckram stamped in gilt)   .   £350
Poems . . . Third Series, Roberts Brothers (Boston), 1896   .
.   .   .   .   £1,000
The Single Hound, Little, Brown (Boston), 1914   .   £300
The Complete Poems of Emily Dickinson, Little, Brown (Boston), 1924   .   .   .   .   .   £100/£15
ditto, Martin Secker (London), 1924   .   .   .   £100/£15
Selected Poems of Emily Dickinson, Jonathan Cape (London), 1924   .   .   .   .   .   .   £60/£15
Emily Dickinson, Simon & Schuster (New York), 1927 (pbk). £5
Further Poems of Emily Dickinson, Little, Brown (Boston), 1929   .   .   .   .   £200/£40
ditto, Little, Brown (Boston), 1929 (465 numbered copies; glassine d/w; in a paper-covered cardboard box open at one end and with pink spine label printed in green; this limited issue is the second printing)   .   .   .   £500/£300
ditto, Little, Brown (Boston), 1929 (15 lettered copies, lettered A-O; glassine d/w and box as above)   £1,000/£750
ditto, Martin Secker (London), 1929   .   .   .   £125/£20
The Poems of Emily Dickinson, Little, Brown (Boston), 1930   .   .   .   .   £60/£10
Face to Face, Unpublished Letters With Notes, Houghton Mifflin (Boston/New York)   .   .   .   .   £75/£15
Unpublished Poems of Emily Dickinson, Little, Brown (Boston), 1935 (525 numbered copies; glassine d/w and grey/white paper-covered box (open at one end) with light pink, paper spine label printed in green).   .   £300/£200
ditto, Little, Brown (Boston), 1935 (second printing, first trade issue)   .   .   .   .   £65/£10
Bolts of Melody, Harper & Brothers (New York), 1945   .
.   .   .   .   £75/£15
ditto, Jonathan Cape (London), 1945 .   .   .   £65/£10
Emily Dickinson's Letters to Dr and Mrs Josiah Gilbert Holland, Harvard Univ Press (Cambridge, MA), 1951   .
.   .   .   .   £45/£10
Poems of Emily Dickinson, The Limited Editions Club (New York), 1952 (1,500 numbered copies signed by illustrator Helen Sewell; full leather; glassine d/w and slipcase).   .   .   .   .   £100/£65
Riddle Poems, The Gehenna Press (no place), 1957 (200 numbered copies signed by Esther and Leonard Baskin; bound in leather and numbered in Roman numerals)   .   £100
ditto, The Gehenna Press (no place), 1957 (200 numbered copies signed by Esther and Leonard Baskin; bound in boards and numbered in Arabic) £75

ISAK DINESEN
(b.1885 d.1962)

Isak Dinesen was the pseudonym of Danish-born writer Karen Blixen, née Dinesen. She began publishing fiction in various Danish periodicals in 1905 under the pen name 'Osceola', and under the pseudonym of 'Pierre Andrezel' wrote a novel entitled *The Angelic Avengers*. She is perhaps best known for her autobiographical *Out of Africa*, although her Gothic short stories are also highly regarded.

Seven Gothic Tales, Putnam (London), 1934 .   . £400/£50
ditto, Putnam (London), 1934 (with *Evening Standard* wrap-
   around band) £650
ditto, Smith & Haas (New York), 1934 (by Dinesen) £125/£25
ditto, Smith & Haas (New York), 1934 (1010 numbered
   copies, with slipcase, no d/w)   .   .   .   . £100/£50
Out of Africa, Putnam (London), 1937 (by Blixen)
   .   .   .   . £1,000/£150
ditto, Random House (New York), 1938 .   . £175/£45
Winter's Tales, Putnam (London), 1942 (by Blixen) £175/£25
ditto, Random House (New York), 1942 .   . £150/£20
The Angelic Avengers, Putnam (London), 1946 (pseud
   'Pierre Andrézel')   .   .   .   .   . £75/£15
ditto, Random House (New York), 1947 .   . £75/£15
Last Tales, Putnam (London), 1957 (by Dinesen) . £65/£15
ditto, Random House (New York), 1957 .   . £35/£10
Anecdotes of Destiny, Joseph (London), 1958 (by Dinesen)
   .   .   .   . £40/£10
ditto, Random House (New York), 1958 .   . £40/£10
Shadows on the Grass, Joseph (London), 1961 (by Dinesen)
   .   .   .   . £30/£5
ditto, Random House (New York), 1961 .   . £30/£5
On Mottoes of my Life, Ministry of Foreign Affairs
   (Copenhagen), 1962 (no d/w) £20
Ehrengard, Joseph (London), 1963 (by Dinesen) . £40/£10
ditto, Random House (New York), 1963 .   . £30/£10
Carnival: Entertainments and Posthumous Tales, Univ of
   Chicago Press (Chicago), 1977   .   .   . £20/£5
ditto, Heinemann (London), 1978   .   .   . £20/£5
Daguerreotypes and Other Essays, Heinemann (London),
   1979   .   .   .   . £20/£5
ditto, Univ of Chicago Press (Chicago), 1979 .   . £20/£5
Letters from Africa: 1914-1931, Univ of Chicago Press
   (Chicago), 1981   .   .   .   .   .   . £35/£10
ditto, Weidenfeld & Nicolson (London), 1981.   . £35/£10

BENJAMIN DISRAELI
(b.1804 d.1881)

Benjamin Disraeli was a British 19th-century statesman, imperialist, Tory leader, Prime Minister (twice) and con-fidante of Queen Victoria. He was also a novelist. After the controversial *Vivian Grey*, the novel *Henrietta Temple* was his only popular success.

Fiction
Vivian Grey, Colburn (London), 1826-27 (5 vols,
   anonymous; grey boards and printed paper labels)   £1,000
The Voyage of Captain Popanilla, Colburn (London), 1828
   (1 vol; boards with paper label) £500

The Young Duke, Colburn (London), 1831 (3 vols)   . £750
ditto, J. & J. Harper (New York), 1831 (1 vol).   . £300
Contarini Fleming: A Pyschological Autobiography,
   Murray (London), 1832 (4 vols) £500
ditto, J. & J. Harper (New York), 1832 (2 vols)   . £300
ditto, as *The Young Venetian*, Murray (London), 1834. £250
The Wondrous Tale of Alroy, and *The rise of Iskander*,
   Saunders & Otley (London), 1833 (3 vols) .   . £500
A Year at Hartlebury, or The Election, Saunders & Otley
   (London), 1834 (pseud 'Cherry' and 'Fair Star', with Sarah
   Disraeli, 2 vols) £450
Henrietta Temple, Colburn (London), 1836 (3 vols) . £450
ditto, Carey & Hart (Philadelphia, PA), 1837 (2 vols) . £100
Venetia, or The Poet's Daughter, Colburn (London), 1837
   (3 vols) £450
Coningsby, or The New Generation, Colburn (London),
   1844 (3 vols) £400
Sybil, or The Two Nations, Colburn (London), 1845 (3 vols)
   .   .   .   . £400
Tancred, or The New Crusade, Colburn (London), 1847 (3
   vols) £300
Lothair, Longman (London), 1870 (3 vols)   . £200
ditto, Appleton (New York), 1870   .   .   . £150
Endymion, Longman (London), 1880 (3 vols).   . £250
ditto, Appleton (New York), 1880   .   .   . £75
Ixion in Heaven, Cape (London), 1925 (illustrated by John
   Austen) .   .   .   . £30/£10
ditto, Holt (New York), 1925   .   .   .   . £25/£10
The Infernal Marriage, William Jackson (London), 1929
   (850 numbered copies)   .   .   .   . £60/£35
Falconet, Peter Davies, 1927 (with *Endymion*; vol XII of the
   Bradenham Edition of Disraeli's works)   . £20/£10

Poetry
The Revolutionary Epick, Moxon (London), 1834 (2 vols) .
   .   .   .   . £300

Collected Editions
Uniform Edition of the Novels, David Bryce (London), 1853
   (10 vols) £250
Hughenden Edition of the Novels and Tales, Longmans
   (London), 1870-71 (11 vols) £250
Bradenham Edition of the Novels and Tales, Peter Davies
   (London), 1926-27 (12 vols)   .   .   . £500/£200

E.L. DOCTOROW
(b.1931)
Doctorow is the American author of a number of critically acclaimed novels which combine history and social criticism. His breakthrough was the publication of *The Book of Daniel* in 1971 but his next book, *Ragtime*, was his first real commercial and critical success.

Welcome to Hard Times, Simon & Schuster (New York),
   1960 .   .   .   . £300/£60
ditto, as *Bad Man from Bodie*, Andre Deutsch (London),
   1961 .   .   .   . £200/£40
Big As Life, Simon & Schuster (New York), 1966 . £250/£40
The Book of Daniel, Random House (New York), 1971   .
   .   .   .   . £40/£5
ditto, Random House (New York), 1971 (complimentary
   copy with no front endpaper and previous titles printed on
   front pastedown)   .   .   .   .   .   . £40/£20

ditto, Macmillan, (London), 1972 . . . . £20/£5

Ragtime, Random House (New York), 1975 (first issue d/w without review on back flap) . . . . . £45/£5

ditto, Random House (New York), 1975 (second issue d/w with review on back flap) . . . . . . £25/£5

ditto, Random House (New York), 1975 (signed on tipped-in leaf) . . . . £75/£50

ditto, Random House (New York), 1975 (150 signed, numbered copies; white cloth; slipcase, no d/w) £150/£100

ditto, Random House (New York), 1975 (2,000 copies 'For friends of the author'; plain acetate d/w) . . £65/£50

ditto, Macmillan (London), 1976 (decorated red and gold cloth; silver lettering on spine) . . . . £30/£5

ditto, Macmillan (London), 1976 (green cloth.) . £35/£10

ditto, Easton Press (Norwalk, CT), no date (full leather signed limited edition) £75

Drinks Before Dinner, A Play, Random House (New York), 1979 . . . . £30/£5

ditto, Macmillan (London), 1980 . . . . £10/£5

Loon Lake, Random House (New York), 1980 . £15/£5

ditto, Random House (New York), 1980 (350 signed, numbered copies; slipcase, no d/w) . . . £50/£35

ditto, Random House (New York), 1980 (signed by the author on tipped-in leaf) . . . . . £25/£15

ditto, Random House (New York), 1980 (signed presentation edition in black cloth; no d/w) £25

ditto, Random House (New York), 1980 (unsigned presentation edition in black cloth; no d/w) . . £10

ditto, Franklin Press (Franklin Center, PA), 1980 (full leather limited edition) £20

ditto, Macmillan (London), 1980 . . . . £10/£5

American Anthem, Stewart, Tabori & Chang (New York), 1982 (no d/w) £10

American Anthem, Stewart, Tabori & Chang (New York), 1982 (1,000 signed, numbered copies; in clear plastic d/w and slipcase). . . . . £65/£50

Essays and Conversations, Ontario Review Press (Princeton, NJ), 1983 . . . . £35/£5

ditto, Ontario Review Press (Princeton, NJ), 1983 (pbk) £5

Lives of the Poets, Random House (New York), 1984 £10/£5

ditto, Random House (New York), 1984 (350 signed, numbered copies; slipcase, no d/w). . . . £45/£30

ditto, Michael Joseph (London), 1985 . . £10/£5

World's Fair, Random House (New York), 1985 . £10/£5

ditto, Random House (New York), 1985 (300 signed, numbered copies; blue cloth; slipcase, no d/w) . £40/£20

ditto, Random House (New York), 1985 (signed on a tipped-in leaf) . . . . £25/£10

ditto, Michael Joseph (London), 1986 . . . £10/£5

Billy Bathgate, Random House (New York), 1989 . £10/£5

ditto, Random House (New York), 1989 (300 signed, numbered copies; blue cloth; slipcase, no d/w) . £65/£40

ditto, Random House (New York), 1989 (signed on a tipped-in leaf) . . . . £25/£10

ditto, Franklin Press (Franklin Center, PA), 1989 (full leather limited edition) £35

ditto, Michael Joseph (London), 1989 . . . £15/£5

ditto, from *Billy Bathgate*, Univ of Central Florida [no place], 1991 (broadside; 50 signed copies) . . £60

Scenes and Sequences, Peter Blum Editions (New York), 1989 (oblong folio in cloth-backed boards; slipcase; text by Doctorow and 58 illustrations by Eric Fischl) . £75/£50

ditto, Peter Blum Editions (New York), 1989 (55 signed, numbered copies in slipcase with an original signed monotype by Fischl) . . . . .£2,500/£2,250

An Open Letter to the President, Midwest Booksellers for Social Responsibility (St Paul, MN), [1991] (single sheet folded to make four pages) £45

The People's Text, A Citizen Reads the Constitution, Nouveau Press (Jackson, MI), 1992 (200 signed, numbered copies) £50

ditto, Nouveau Press (Jackson, MI), 1992 (40 signed, numbered (roman numerals) copies; bound in quarter morocco; extra signed frontispiece wood engraving laid in) £100

ditto, Nouveau Press (Jackson, MI), 1992 (15 signed copies in blue cloth and boards) £65

Selected Essays 1977-1992, Random House (New York), 1993 . . . . £10/£5

The Waterworks, Macmillan (London), 1994 . £15/£5

ditto, Franklin Library (Franklin Center, PA), 1994 (signed, full leather limited edition) £30

ditto, Random House (New York), 1994 (first state: binding with cloth backstrip; the pages untrimmed; front panel of d/w with raised lettering and the rear panel with '52300' in the ISBN block) . . . . £15/£5

ditto, Random House (New York), 1994 (150 signed, numbered copies; slipcase, no d/w). . . . £40/£25

ditto, Random House (New York), 1994 (220 numbered copies signed on the title-page; limited edition for booksellers) £50

'Ever since this day I have dreamt sometimes...', Black Oak Books (Berkeley, CA), 1994 (boadside, text from *The Waterworks*). £15

City of God, Random House (New York), 2000 . £10/£5

ditto, Franklin Library (Franklin Center, PA), 2000 (signed, full leather limited edition) £50

ditto, Little, Brown (London), 2000 . . . . £10/£5

Three Screenplays, Johns Hopkins Univ Press (Baltimore, 2003) . . . . £15/£5

Reporting the Universe, Harvard Univ Press (Cambridge, MA), 2003 . . . . £10/£5

Sweet Land Stories, Random House (New York), 2004 . . . . £10/£5

ditto, Abacus (London), 2007 (pbk) £5

The March, Random House (New York), 2005 . £10/£5

ditto, Random House (New York), 2005 (signed by the author on tipped-in leaf) . . . . . . £25/£15

ditto, Little, Brown (London), 2006 (pbk) . . . £5

Creationists: Selected Essays 1993-2006, Random House, 2006 . . . . £10/£5

DAVID DODGE
(b.1910 d.1974)

Dodge's career as a writer began as a bet with his wife Elva when he created the character James 'Whit' Whitney. Dodge became a prolific author of crime novels and travel guides and his most famous novel by far is *To Catch a Thief,* which Alfred Hitchcock filmed in 1955 with Grace Kelly and Cary Grant.

Novels
Death And Taxes, Macmillan (New York), 1941 . £200/£50

ditto, Michael Joseph (London), 1947. . . . £125/£25

Shear The Black Sheep, Macmillan (New York), 1942 . . . . £150/£45

ditto, Michael Joseph (London), 1949. . . .£100/£20
Bullets For The Bridegroom, Macmillan (New York), 1944
. . . . £75/£20
ditto, Michael Joseph (London), 1948. . . £45/£10
It Ain't Hay, Simon & Schuster (New York), 1946 £75/£20
ditto, as **A Drug On The Market**, Michael Joseph (London),
1949 . . . . £35/£10
How Green Was My Father?, Simon & Schuster (New
York), 1947.. . . . . £75/£20
ditto, Home And Van Thal (London), 1951 . £25/£10
How Lost Was My Weekend?, Random House (New York),
1948 . . . . £25/£10
ditto, Home And Van Thal (London), 1949 . £20/£5
The Long Escape, Random House (New York), 1948 . .
. . . . £25/£10
ditto, Michael Joseph (London), 1950 . . £20/£5
The Crazy Glasspecker, Random House (New York), 1949.
. . . . £20/£5
ditto, as **High Life In The Andes**, Barker (London), 1959 .
. . . . £15/£5
Plunder Of The Sun, Random House (New York), 1949 .
. . . . £25/£10
ditto, Michael Joseph (London), 1950 . . £15/£5
The Red Tassel, Random House (New York), 1950 £25/£10
ditto, Michael Joseph (London), 1951 . £15/£5
20,000 Leagues Behind The 8 Ball, Random House (New
York), 1951 . . . . £25/£10
ditto, as **With A Knife And Fork Down The Amazon**, Barker
(London), 1952 . . . . . . £25/£10
To Catch A Thief, Random House (New York), 1952 . .
. . . .£250/£30
ditto, Michael Joseph (London), 1953 . . £75/£20
The Lights Of Skaro, Random House (New York), 1954 .
. . . . £25/£10
ditto, Michael Joseph (London), 1954 . . £15/£5
Angels' Ransom, Random House (New York), 1956 £15/£5
ditto, Michael Joseph (London), 1957 . . £15/£5
Loo Loo's Legacy, Michael Joseph (London) 1960 £15/£5
ditto, Little, Brown & Co (Boston), 1961 . . £15/£5
Carambola, Little, Brown & Co (Boston), 1961 . £15/£5
ditto, White Lion (London), 1972 . . . £15/£5
Hooligan, Macmillan (New York), 1969 . . £15/£5
ditto, as **Hatchetman** Michael Joseph (London), 1970 . .
. . . . £15/£5
Troubleshooter, Macmillan (New York), 1971 . £15/£5
ditto, Michael Joseph (London), 1972 . . . £15/£5
The Last Match, Dorchester Publishing Company/Hard Case
Crime (New York), 2006 . . . . . . £5

Plays
A Certain Man Had Two Sons, Banner Play Bureau (San
Francisco, CA), 1936 (pbk) £30
Shakespeare In Bohemia, The Grabhorn Press [San
Francisco, CA], 1961 (boards; 500 copies) . . £35

Travel Books
The Poor Man's Guide To Europe, Random House (New
York), 1951 . . . . £15/£10
Time Out For Turkey, Random House (New York), 1955 .
. . . . £10/£5
ditto, as **Talking Turkey**, Barker (London), 1955 . £10/£5
The Rich Man's Guide To The Riviera, Little, Brown and
Co (Boston), 1962. . . . . . . £10/£5
ditto, Cassell (London), 1963 . . . . £10/£5

The Poor Man's Guide To The Orient, Simon & Schuster
(New York), 1965. . . . . £10/£5
Fly Down, Drive Mexico, Macmillan (New York), 1968. .
. . . . £10/£5
ditto, as **The Best Of Mexico By Car**, Macmillan (New
York), 1969 . . . . £10/£5

J.P. DONLEAVY
(b.1926)

An American-born novelist and playwright, Donleavy's
first book, *The Ginger Man* was considered controversial
and had at first to be published in Paris. It is one of the
Modern Library 100 best novels. He now lives in Ireland,
having become an Irish citizen in 1967.

Novels
The Ginger Man, Olympia Press (Paris), 1955 (pbk; with
'1500 francs' on rear cover) £450
ditto, Olympia Press (Paris), 1955 (pbk; with new price on
rear cover) £350
ditto, Neville Spearman (London), 1956 (expurgated text) .
. . . .£100/£20
ditto, Olympia Press (Paris), 1958 (d/w with original flaps) .
. . . .£300/£20
ditto, Olympia Press (Paris), 1958 (d/w with new flaps glued
on) . . . . £75/£20
ditto, McDowell Obolensky (New York), 1958 . £40/£10
ditto, Franklin Library (Franklin Centre, PA), 1978 (signed,
limited edition) £25
A Singular Man, Little, Brown (Boston), 1963 . £35/£5
ditto, Bodley Head (London), 1964 [1963] . . £40/£5
The Beastly Beatitudes of Balthazar B, Delacorte (New
York), 1968 . . . . £25/£10
ditto, Eyre & Spottiswoode (London), 1969 . . £25/£10
The Onion Eaters, Delacorte (New York), 1971 . £25/£10
ditto, Eyre & Spottiswoode (London), 1971 . . £25/£10
A Fairy Tale of New York, Delacorte (New York), 1973 .
. . . . £25/£10
ditto, Eyre Methuen (London), 1973 . . . £25/£10
The Destinies of Darcy Dancer, Gentleman, Delacorte (New
York), 1977 . . . . £25/£10
ditto, Franklin Library (Franklin Centre, PA), 1977 (signed,
limited edition) £25
ditto, Allen Lane (London), 1978 . . . £25/£10
Schultz, Delacorte (New York), 1979 . . . £25/£10
ditto, Allen Lane (London), 1980 . . . £25/£10
**Leila: Further in the Destinies of Darcy Dancer,
Gentleman**, Delacorte (New York), 1983 . . £25/£10
ditto, Franklin Library (Franklin Centre, PA), 1983 (signed,
limited edition) £25
ditto, as **Leila: Further in the Life and Destinies of Darcy
Dancer, Gentleman**, Allen Lane (London), 1983 £20/£5
Are You Listening, Rabbi Low, Little, Brown (Boston),
1987 . . . . £20/£5
ditto, Viking (London), 1987 . . . . . £20/£5
That Darcy, That Dancer, That Gentleman, Atlantic
Monthly Press (New York), 1990 . . . . £20/£5
ditto, Viking (London), 1990 . . . . . £20/£5
The Lady Who Liked to Clean Rest Rooms, Thornwillow
Press (New York & West Stockbridge), 1995 (175
numbered copies, slipcase) . . . . .£250/£200

ditto, Little, Brown (London), 1997 . . . £20/£5
ditto, St Martin's Press (New York), 1997 . . £20/£5
Wrong Information Is Being Given Out at Princeton,
Little, Brown (London), 1998 . . . . £20/£5
ditto, St Martin's Press (New York), 1998 . . £20/£5

Short Stories and Novellas
Meet My Maker the Mad Molecule, Little, Brown (Boston),
1964 . . . . £25/£10
ditto, Bodley Head (London), 1965 . . . £25/£10
The Saddest Summer of Samuel S, Delacorte (New York),
1966 . . . . £25/£10
ditto, Eyre & Spottiswoode (London), 1967 . . £25/£10

Plays
The Ginger Man: A Play, Random House (New York), 1961
. . . . £30/£10
ditto, as **What They Did in Dublin With 'The Ginger Man':
A Play**, Macgibbon & Kee (London), 1961 . . £30/£10
Fairy Tales of New York, Random House (New York), 1961
. . . . £30/£10
ditto, Penguin (Harmondsworth, Middlesex), 1961 (pbk) £10
A Singular Man, Bodley Head (London), 1965 . £20/£5
The Plays of J.P. Donleavy, Delacorte (New York), 1972 .
. . . . £30/£10
ditto, Penguin (Harmondsworth, Middlesex), 1974 (pbk) £10

Others
**The Unexpurgated Code: A Complete Manual of Survival
and Manners**, Delacorte (New York), 1975 . . £30/£10
ditto, Wildwood House (London), 1975 . . . £20/£5
De Alfonce Tennis, Dutton (New York), 1984 . £20/£5
ditto, Weidenfeld & Nicolson (London), 1984 . £20/£5
**J.P. Donleavy's Ireland: In All Her Sins and in Some of
Her Graces**, Viking (New York), 1986 . . . £20/£5
ditto, Joseph (London), 1986 . . . . £20/£5
A Singular Country, Ryan Publishing (Peterborough), 1989
. . . . £20/£5
ditto, Norton (New York), 1990 . . . . £20/£5
The History of the Ginger Man, Viking (London), 1994 .
. . . . £25/£10
ditto, Houghton Mifflin (Boston), 1994 . . . £20/£5
An Author and His Image: The Collected Short Pieces,
Viking (London), 1997 . . . . . £25/£10

GUSTAV DORÉ

(b.1832 d.1883)

Doré was a French artist, engraver, illustrator and sculptor.
He illustrated classics by Rabelais, Cervantes, Milton,
Dante and Coleridge. *London: A Pilgrimage*, was a com-
mercial success, but was disliked by many contemporary
critics. His work also appeared in the *Illustrated London
News*. Doré continued to illustrate books until his death in
Paris in 1883.

Les Travaux D'Hercule, Aubert (Paris), [1847] (105
illustrations) £4,000
Trois Artistes – Incompris et Mecontents, Aubert (Paris),
[1851] (155 illustrations) £1,750
Des-Agrements d'un Voyage d'Agrement, Aubert (Paris),
[1851] (175 illustrations) £1,750

Histoire Pittoresque . . . de la Sainte Russia, J. Bry (Paris),
1854 (500 illustrations) £1,250
**Oeuvres de François Rabelais contenant la vie de
Gargantua et celle de Pantagruel**, J. Bry (Paris), 1854
(105 illustrations) £300
ditto, as **The Works of Rabelais,** John Camden Hotten
(London), 1871 (50 illustrations) £100
ditto, Garnier Frers (Paris), 1873 (719 illustrations; 2 vols) .
. . . . £300
ditto, Garnier Frers (Paris), 1873 (719 illustrations; 2 vols;
ltd deluxe edition) £450
ditto, Garnier Frers (Paris), 1875 (674 illustrations; 2 vols;
ltd deluxe edition) £150
Les Differents Publics de Paris, Bur. Jrnl. Amusant (Paris),
[1854] (20 lithographs) £750
Le Menagerie Parisienne, Bur. Jrnl. Rire (Paris), [1854] (24
lithographs) £750
Les Folies Gauloises, Philipon/Aubert (Paris), [1859] (20
lithographs) £750
ditto, as **Historical Cartoon,** John Camden Hotten (London),
[1868] (20 lithographs) £150
Les Contes Drolatiques, by Balzac, Societe Generale de
Libraire (Paris), 1855 (designated 5th edition [of *Les
Contes*]; first edition title page lists 424 instead of 425
illustrations) £400
ditto, as **Droll Stories**, John Camden Hotten (London), 1860
(in French, again claiming 5th edition) . . . £65
Voyage aux Eaux des Pyrenees, by Hippolyte Taine,
Hachette (Paris), 1855 (64 illustrations) . . . £100
ditto, as **Voyage aux Pyrenees**, Hachette (Paris), 1860 (335
illustrations) £200
ditto, as **Cressy & Poictiers**, by J.G. Edgar, Beeton (London),
1865 (24 illustrations from *Voyage aux Eaux des Pyrenees*)
. . . . £65
ditto, as **The Pyrenees**, by H. Blackburn, Sampson Low
(London), 1867 (115 illustrations from *Voyage aux Eaux
des Pyrenees*) £75
ditto, as **The Pyrenees**, by Hippolyte Taine, Holt (New
York), 1874 (258 illustrations) £100
L'Habitation du desert, by Captain Mayne Reid, Hachette
(Paris), 1856 (24 illustrations) £75
ditto, as **Desert Home**, Nelson (Edinburgh), 1869 (24
illustrations) £50
Nouveaux Contes de Fees, by Comtesse de Segur, Hachette
(Paris), 1857 (20 illustrations) £75
ditto, as **French fairy Tales**, Porter/Coates (Philadelpia, PA),
1869 . . . . £50
Le Legende du Juif Errant, Michel Levy (Paris), 1856 (13
illustrations) £400
ditto, as **The Legend of the Wandering Jew**, Addey
(London), 1857 (12 plates) £250
ditto, Belford, Clarke & Company (Chicago), [ca.1890] £100
Les Adventures du Chevalier Jaufre, by Mary Lafon, Lib.
Nouvelle (Paris), 1856 (20 illustrations). . . £150
ditto, as **Jaufry the Knight**, Addey (London), 1856 (20
illustrations) £125
ditto, Wiley/Halstead (New York), 1857 (8 illustrations) £65
Le Page du Duc de Savoie, by Alexandre Dumas, Dufour/
Mulat/Boulanger (Paris), 1856 (12 illsutrations) . £65
Fierbras, Legende Nationale, by Mary Lafon, Lib. Nouvelle
(Paris), 1857 (12 illustrations) £100
Compagnons de Juhu, by Alexandre Dumas, Dufour/Mulat/
Boulanger (Paris), 1858 (8 illsutrations). . . £65

Geographie Universelle, by Victor Malte-Brun, G. Barba (Paris), 1857-9 (108 parts; 324 illustrations). . . £300

ditto, G. Barba (Paris), 1857-9 (6 vols; 324 illustrations) £250

The Tempest, by William Shakespeare, Bell and Daldy (London), [1860] (5 illustrations; cover with ornate lettering) £200

ditto, Bell and Daldy (London), [1860] (5 illustrations; cover with plain lettering) £125

ditto, Appleton (New York), [1861?] (5 illustrations) . £100

L'Enfer, by Dante Alighieri, Hachette (Paris), 1861 (76 engravings) £450

ditto, as *Dante's 'Inferno'*, Cassell (London), 1865 . £150

Le Roi des Montagnes, by Edmond About, Hachette (Paris), 1861 (158 illustrations) £125

Chemin-Ecoliers, by X.-B. Saintine, Hachette (Paris), 1861 (203 illustrations) £175

La Mythologie du Rhin, by X.-B. Saintine, Hachette (Paris), 1862 (165 illustrations) £175

ditto, as *Myths of the Rhine*, Scribner (New York), [1874 or 75] £75

ditto, as *River Legends*, by H. Knatchbull-Hugessen, Daldy Isbister (London), 1875 . . . . . . £45

Contes de Fees, J. Hetzel (Paris), 1862 (42 illustrations) £350

ditto, as *Fairy Realm*, by Tom Hood, Cassell (London), 1865 (24 illustrations) £150

ditto, as *Perrault's 'Fairy Tales'*, Beeton, 1865 . . £150

L'Album de Gustave Dore, Goupil (Paris), 1862 (12 illustrations) £500

Aventures du Baron Munchhausen, by Theophile Gautier, Furne (Paris), n.d. [1862] (158 illustrations) . . £200

ditto, as *The Adventures of Baron Munchausen*, by Raspe, Cassell (London), [1865] (158 illustrations) . . £100

Histoire . . . Intrepide Captain Castagnette, by Ernest L'Epine, Hachette (Paris), 1862 (42 engravings) . . £150

ditto, as *Captain Castaignette: The Man With the Wooden Head*, Beeton, [1866] (42 illustrations) . . . £125

La Legende de Croque-Mitaine, by Ernest L'Epine, Hachette (Paris), 1863 (177 engravings) . . . £150

ditto, as *Legend of Croquemitaine*, Cassell, [1866] (177 illustrations) £125

Atala, by Vicomte de Chateaubriand, Hachette (Paris), 1863 (44 engravings) £400

ditto, Cassell Petter & Galpin (London & New York), [1867] (44 illustrations) £150

L'Ingenieux hidalgo Don Quichotte de la Manche, by Miguel de Cervantes, Hachette (Paris), 1863 (377 engravings; 2 vols) £400

ditto, Cassell Petter & Galpin (London & New York), [1866] (364 illustrations) £100

Les Mille et Une Nuits, by Antoine Galland, Hachette (Paris), 1865 (2 vols; 171 illustrations with 20 by Dore) .
. . . . £200

ditto, as *The Arabian Nights*, Cassell (London), 1868 . £100

Le Capitaine Fracasse, by Théophile Gautier, Charpentier (Paris), 1866 (60 illustrations) £150

Paradise Lost, by John Milton, Cassell (London), [1866] (50 illustrations; earliest printing gives the address of the London and New York publishers) £100

La Sainte Bible, Mame (Tours), 1866 (228 illustrations; 2 vols) £200

ditto, as *The Doré Bible*, Cassell (London), 1866 (238 illustrations; 2 vols) £200

Toilers of the Sea, by Victor Hugo, Sampson Low, 1867 (2 illustrations by Dore) £75

Two Hundred Sketches, Humorous and Grotesque, Warne, 1867 (containing 303 illustrations) £75

Fables, by La Fontaine, Hachette (Paris), 1867 (2 vols; 334 illustrations) £200

ditto, as *La Fontaine's 'Fables'*, Cassell (London), 1868 (329 illustrations) £100

Purgatoire, by Dante Alighieri, Hachette (Paris), 1868 (42 engravings) £200

Paradis, by Dante Alighieri, Hachette (Paris), 1868 (18 engravings) £200

Dante's Il Purgatorio et il Paradiso, Hachette and Co (Paris), 1868 (60). £100

ditto, as *Dante's 'Purgatory' and 'Paradise'*, Cassell (London), 1868 (2 vols) £100

Elaine, Moxon (London), [1866] 1867 (9 illustrations). £125

ditto, Moxon (London), [1866] 1867 (portfolio of photogravures) £300

ditto, Moxon (London), [1866] 1867 (set of India proofs signed by Dore, Tennyson and engraver) . . £1,500

ditto, Cassell (New York), [1866] 1867 (9 illustrations, facsimile letter from Tennyson) £150

ditto, Hachette (Paris), 1867. . . . . . £150

Vivien, Moxon (London), 1867 (9 illustrations) . £125

ditto, Moxon (London), 1867 (portfolio of photogravures) .
. . . . £300

ditto, Moxon (London), 1867 (set of India proofs signed by Dore, Tennyson and engraver). £1,500

ditto, Routledge (New York), 1868 (9 illustrations) . £150

ditto, Hachette (Paris), 1868. . . . . . £150

Guinevere, Moxon (London), 1867 (9 illustrations) . £125

ditto, Moxon (London), 1867 (portfolio of photogravures) .
. . . . £300

ditto, Moxon (London), 1867 (set of India proofs signed by Dore, Tennyson and engraver). £1,500

ditto, Routledge (New York), 1868 (9 illustrations) . £150

ditto, Hachette (Paris), 1868. . . . . . £150

Enid, Moxon (London), 1868 (9 illustrations). . . £125

ditto, Moxon (London), 1868 (portfolio of photogravures) .
. . . . £300

ditto, Moxon (London), 1868 (set of India proofs signed by Dore, Tennyson and engraver). £1,500

ditto, Routledge (New York), 1869 (9 illustrations) . £150

ditto, Hachette (Paris), 1869. . . . . . £150

Vivien and *Guinevere*, Moxon (London), 1867 (18 illustrations). £200

ditto, Moxon (London), 1867 (portfolio of photogravures) .
. . . . £500

Enid and *Elaine*, Cassell (London), 1869 (18 illustrations) .
. . . . £200

Tennyson's 'Idylls of The King', Moxon (London), 1868 (37 illustrations) £200

ditto, Routledge (New York), 1869 (37 illustrations) . £200

ditto, as *Les Idylles du Roi*, Hachette (Paris), 1869 . £100

Thomas Hood's Poetical Works, Moxon, 1870 (9 illustrations) £100

ditto, Moxon, 1870 (portfolio of photogravures) . . £350

ditto, Putnams (New York), 1872 (6 illustrations) . . £75

London: A Pilgrimage, Grant, 1872 (180 illustrations; text by B. Jerrold) . . . .

L'Espagne, by Baron Charles Davillier, Hachette (Paris), 1874 (306 illustrations) £200

ditto, as *Spain*, Sampson-Low (Paris), 1876 (235 illustrations) £75

Coleridge's 'The Rime of the Ancient Mariner', Doré
Gallery (London), 1876 [1875] (42 illustrations)   . £400
ditto, Doré Gallery (London), 1876 [1875] (India proofs; 42
illustrations) £1,250
ditto, Harper (New York), 1876 (42 illustrations) . . £300
The Crusades, by Joseph Michaud, Furne/Jouvet (Paris),
1877 (100 illustrations; 2 vols). £200
ditto, Geo Barrie (New York), [1880?] (2 vols; 100
illustrations) £100
Orlando Furioso, by Ludovico Ariosto, Hachette (Paris),
1874 (618 illustrations) £200
The Raven, by Edgar Allan Poe, Sampson Low (London),
1883 (26 illustrations) £150
ditto, Harper (New York), 1884 . . . . . £150

JOHN DOS PASSOS
(b.1896 d.1970)

John Dos Passos was an American novelist and artist
considered one of the Lost Generation writers (along with
Hemingway, Ezra Pound and others). Some of his most
important work incorporates experimental techniques such
as printing newspaper clippings and mixing autobiography,
biography and fictional realism to depict American culture
in the first decades of the twentieth century.

USA Trilogy
The 42nd Parallel, Harper & Brothers (New York), 1930 .
. . . . £600/£100
ditto, Constable (London), 1930 . . . . . £200/£10
1919, Harcourt, Brace (New York), 1932   . . £300/£50
ditto, Constable (London), 1932 . . . . . £150/£15
The Big Money, Harcourt, Brace (New York), 1936   .
. . . . £300/£50
ditto, Constable (London), 1936 . . . . . £125/£15
USA, Harcourt, Brace (New York), [1938]   . . £75/£10
ditto, Constable (London), 1938 . . . . . £65/£10
ditto, Harcourt, Brace (New York), 1946 (3 vols in slipcase
and paper and glassine d/ws) . . . . . £150/£75
ditto, Harcourt, Brace (New York), 1946 (365 numbered sets
signed by Dos Passos and illustrator Reginald Marsh)   .
. . . . £600/£400

District of Columbia Novels
Adventures of a Young Man, Harcourt, Brace (New York),
1939 . . . . £50/£10
ditto, Constable (London), 1939 (first issue bound in purple
buckram) . . . . £45/£10
Number One, Houghton, Mifflin (Boston), 1943 (date on
title page) . . . . £40/£10
ditto, Constable (London), 1944 . . . . . £25/£10
The Grand Design, Houghton Mifflin (Boston), 1949 (date
on title page). . . . . £30/£10
ditto, John Lehmann (London), 1949 . . . . £25/£10
District of Columbia, Houghton Mifflin (Boston), 1952   .
. . . . £40/£10

Other Novels
One Man's Initiation, Allen & Unwin (London), 1920 (first
state has a broken 'd' and the word 'flat' lost on p.35, line
32) . . . . £400/£75

ditto, Allen & Unwin (London), 1920 (second state with
perfect 'd' and 'flat' restored) . . . . . £350/£30
ditto, Doran (New York), 1922 (UK sheets; title page is a
cancel on a stub with verso of title page blank; first state as
UK ed) . . . . £350/£65
ditto, Doran (New York), 1922 (second state as UK ed)   .
. . . . £250/£30
ditto, as *First Encounter*, Philosophical Library (New York),
1945 . . . . £25/£5
Three Soldiers, Doran (New York), 1921 (first state with
three blank integral pages at front, none at back and
'signing' for 'singing' p.213, line 31; d/w with publisher's
blurb on front, spine and back). . . . £2,000/£200
ditto, Doran (New York), 1921 (second state with two blank
integral pages at front; d/w with a quotation from the
Brooklyn Daily Eagle as last item on front panel) £300/£50
ditto, Doran (New York), 1921 (third state with three blank
integral pages at front; 'signing' corrected to 'singing'; d/w
with quote from *Brooklyn Daily Eagle* replaced by one
from *Stars and Stripes*) . . . . . £150/£15
ditto, Doran (New York), 1921 (fourth state with two blank
integral pages at front; 'signing' corrected to 'singing'; d/w
with quote from *Stars and Stripes*; price on spine blacked
over) . . . . £125/£15
ditto, Hurst and Blackett (London), 1922 . . . £250/£35
Streets of Night, Doran (New York), 1923   . . £250/£30
ditto, Secker (London), 1923 . . . . . £150/£25
Manhattan Transfer, Harper & Brothers (New York), 1925
. . . . £250/£50
ditto, Constable (London), 1927 . . . . . £125/£20
Orient Express, Harper & Brothers (New York), 1927 (first
state binding in lavender boards and lavender paper label
on shiny blue cloth spine, top-edge trimmed and stained
maroon). . . . . £150/£35
ditto, Harper & Brothers (New York), 1927 (second state
binding blue cloth with paper label on spine) . £125/£20
ditto, Cape (London), 1928 . . . . . £75/£15
In All Countries, Harcourt, Brace (New York), 1934 £75/£15
ditto, Constable (London), 1934 . . . . . £60/£10
Chosen Country, Houghton Mifflin (Boston), 1951   £25/£5
ditto, Houghton Mifflin (Boston), 1951 (400 signed copies;
tipped-in 'Complimentary Edition For the Book-sellers ... '
and Dos Passos' signature) . . . . . £125/£75
ditto, John Lehmann (London), 1952 . . . . £20/£5
Most Likely To Succeed, Prentice-Hall (New York), 1954 .
. . . . £25/£10
ditto, Prentice-Hall (New York), 1954 (1000 signed copies)
. . . . £50/£30
ditto, Robert Hale (London), 1955 . . . . £15/£5
The Theme is Freedom, Dodd Mead (New York), 1956   .
. . . . £25/£10
The Great Days, Sangamore Press (New York), 1958 . .
. . . . £25/£10
ditto, Robert Hale (London), 1959 . . . . £10/£5
Midcentury, Houghton Mifflin (Boston) . . . £20/£5
ditto, Andre Deutsch (London), 1961. . . . £20/£5
Occasions and Protests, Regnery (Chicago), 1964. . £20/£5
Century's Ebb, The Thirteenth Chronicle, Gambit (Boston),
1975 . . . . £15/£5

Plays
The Garbage Man, Harper & Brothers (New York), 1926
(first state binding of chocolate brown boards with paper
labels on front cover and spine) . . . . . £150/£25

ditto, Harper & Brothers (New York), 1926 (second state binding of shiny dark blue cloth with paper label on spine only) . . . . £150/£15
ditto, Constable (London), 1929 . . . . £100/£25
ditto, Constable (London), 1929 (pbk) . . . £45
Airways, Inc, Macaulay Co (New York), 1928 . £150/£30
Three Plays, Harcourt, Brace (New York), 1934 . £100/£30

Others
Rosinante to the Road Again, Doran (New York), 1922 .
. . . . £250/£30
A Pushcart at the Curb, Doran (New York), 1922. £250/£30
Facing the Chair, Sacco Vanzetti Defense Committee (Boston), 1927 (wraps) £100
Metropolis, by Manuel Maples Arce, T.S. Book Co (New York), 1929 (wraps; translation) £65
Panama, or The Adventures of My Seven Uncles, by Blaise Cendrars, Harper & Brothers (New York), 1931 (translation; wraps in glassine d/w) . . . . £60/£50
ditto, Harper & Brothers (New York), 1931 (300 numbered copies signed by Cendrars and Dos Passos; wraps, in slipcase with title, author and copy number on spine). .
. . . . £300/£200
Harlan Miners Speak, Harcourt, Brace (New York), 1932 .
. . . . £100/£20
Culture and Crisis, League of Professional Groups for Foster and Ford (New York), 1932 (wraps) . . £100
The Villages are the Heart of Spain, Esquire-Coronet (Chicago), 1937 (1,200 numbered copies; no d/w) . £75
Journeys Between Wars, Harcourt, Brace (New York), 1938
. . . . £60/£10
ditto, Constable (London), 1938 . . . . £45/£10
Man With A Watch in His Hand, Sherwood and Katharine Grover/Grabhorn Press (San Francisco, CA), 1938 (25 numbered copies; reprinted from *The Big Money* where it was titled The American Plan) £300
The Bitter Drink, A Biography of Thorstein Veblen, Sherwood and Katharine Grover/Grabhorn Press (San Francisco, CA), 1939 (35 numbered copies; reprinted from *The Big Money*) £300
Henry and William Fird and Hearst, Sherwood and Katharine Grover/Grabhorn Press (San Francisco), 1940 (35 copies, wraps; *Tin Lizzie* and *Poor Little Rich Boy* retitled and reprinted from *The Big Money*) . . . £300
The Living Thoughts of Tom Paine, Longmans Green (New York), 1940 . . . . £75/£10
ditto, Cassell (London), 1940 . . . . £45/£10
The Ground We Stand On, Harcourt, Brace (New York), 1941 . . . . £50/£10
ditto, George Routledge (London), 1942 . . . £50/£10
State of the Nation, Houghton, Mifflin (Boston), 1944 . .
. . . . £40/£10
ditto, George Routledge (London), 1945 . . . £40/£10
Tour of Duty, Houghton Mifflin (Boston), 1946 . £40/£10
The Prospect Before Us, Houghton Mifflin, Boston, 1950 .
. . . . £20/£5
ditto, John Lehmann (London), 1951 . . . £20/£5
Life's Picture History of World War II, Time/Simon & Schuster (New York), 1950 (no d.w) . . . £25
The Head and Heart of Thomas Jefferson, Doubleday (Garden City, NY), 1954 . . . . £40/£10
ditto, Robert Hale (London), 1955 . . . £30/£5
The Men Who Made the Nation, Doubleday (Garden City, NY), 1957 . . . . £25/£10

Prospects of a Golden Age, Prentice-Hall (Englewood Cliffs), 1959 . . . . £25/£5
USA: A Dramatic Revue, Samuel French (New York), 1960 (wraps; written with Paul Shyre) £10
Mr Wilson's War, Doubleday (Garden City, NY), 1962 .
. . . . £20/£5
ditto, Hamish Hamilton (London), 1963 . . . £20/£5
Brazil on the Move, Doubleday (Garden City, NY), 1963 .
. . . . £40/£10
ditto, Sidgwick & Jackson (London), 1963 . . £30/£5
Thomas Jefferson: The Making of a President, Houghton Mifflin (Boston), 1964 . . . . . £75/£15
The Shackles of Power: Three Jeffersonian Decades, Doubleday (Garden City, NY), 1966 . . £20/£5
World in a Glass, Houghton Mifflin (Boston), 1966 £20/£5
The Best of Times: An Informal Memoir, New American Library (New York), 1966. . . . . £15/£5
ditto, Andre Deutsch (London), 1968. . . . £15/£5
The Portugal Story: Three Centuries of Exploration and Discovery, Doubleday (Garden City, NY), 1969 . £20/£5
ditto, Robert Hale (London), 1970 . . . £20/£5
An Interview With John Dos Passos, Union College Press (Schenectady, NY), 1969 (wraps) £50
Easter Island: Island of Enigmas, Doubleday (Garden City, NY), 1971 . . . . £15/£5
The Fourteenth Chronicle: Letters and Diaries of John Dos Passos, Gambit (Boston), 1973 (wraps; advance sampler). £10
ditto, Gambit (Boston), 1973 . . . £15/£5
ditto, Gambit (Boston), 1973 (300 numbered copies signed by editor with facsimile of a Dos Passos signed note). .
. . . . £50/£35
ditto, Andre Deutsch (London), 1974. . . £15/£5
The Major Nonfictional Prose, Wayne State Press (Detroit, MI), 1988 (wraps) £10
Afterglow and Other Undergratuate Writings, Omnigraphics (Detroit, MI), 1990 (no d/w) . . . £45
John Dos Passos' Correspondence with Arthur K. McComb, or 'Learn to Sing the Carmagnole', Univ Press of Colorado (Boulder, CO), 1991 . . . £10/£5
Travel Books and Other Writings: 1916-1941, Library of America (New York), 2003 . . . . £10/£5

LORD ALFRED DOUGLAS
(b.1870 d.1945)

Lord Alfred Douglas is notorious for his affair with Oscar Wilde which, when discovered by the former's father, the Marquess of Queensberry, instigated Wilde's public downfall. Douglas was a poet of some merit, and his 1892 poem 'Two Loves' was used against Wilde at the latter's trial. It ends with the line that refers to homosexuality as 'the Love that dare not speak its name'.

Poetry
Poèmes, Mercur de France (Paris), 1896 . . . £300
ditto, Mercur de France (Paris), 1896 (20 copies on Holland paper) £1,500
ditto, Mercur de France (Paris), 1896 (50 deluxe copies) .
. . . . £1,000
ditto, Mercur de France (Paris), 1896 (25 grande deluxe copies) £2,000

Perkin Warbeck and Some Other Poems, Chiswick Press (London), 1897 (50 copies) £750

Tails With a Twist: Animal Nonsense Verse, Arnold (London), 1898 (pseud 'The Belgian Hare') . . . £150

The City of the Soul, Grant Richards (London), 1899 . £65

ditto, as *The City of the Soul, and Other Sonnets*, Little Blue Book No. 789, E. Haldeman-Julius (Girard, KS), 1925(wraps) £40

The Duke of Berwick, Smithers (London), [1899] . . £75

The Placid Pug and Other Rhymes By the Belgian Hare, Duckworth (London), 1906 . . . . . £65

The Pongo Papers and the Duke of Berwick, Greening (London), 1907 . . . . £45

Sonnets, W.H. Smith & Son/Academy Publishing Company (London), 1909 . . . . £65

ditto, Arden Press (London), 1909 (large paper edition) £150

Collected Poems, Martin Secker (London), 1919 . . £65

ditto, Martin Secker (London), 1919 (200 signed copies) £300

In Excelsis, Martin Secker (London), 1924 . . £150/£35

ditto, Martin Secker (London), 1924 (100 signed copies) £225

The Duke of Berwick and Other Rhymes, Secker (London), 1925 . . . . £65/£25

ditto, Knopf (New York), 1925 . . . . £65/£25

Nine Poems, privately printed for A.J.A. Symons (London), 1926 (50 copies) £500

Selected Poems, Martin Secker, New Adelphi Library, (London), 1926 . . . . £25/£10

Lord Alfred Douglas ['*Selected Poems*'], Ernest Benn, 'Augustan Books of Modern Poetry' (London), [1926] (wraps) £5

Collected Satires, The Fortune Press (London), 1926 (550 copies) £50

ditto, The Fortune Press (London), 1926 (250 signed, numbered copies) £400

Complete Poems and Light Verse, Martin Secker (London), 1928 . . . . £125/£35

Lyrics, Rich & Cowan (London), 1935 . . . £75/£25

ditto, Rich & Cowan (London), 1935 (50 signed copies; cloth slipcase) £250

ditto, Richards Press (London), 1943 . . . £25/£10

Sonnets, Rich & Cowan (London), 1935 . . . £75/£25

ditto, Rich & Cowan (London), 1935 (50 signed copies, slipcase) £250

ditto, Richards Press (London), 1943 . . . £25/£10

Sonnets, Richards Press (London), 1943 (pocket edition) . . . . £15/£5

Prose

Oscar Wilde and Myself, Long (London), 1914 . . £100

ditto, Duffield (New York), 1914 . . . . £75

The Autobiography of Lord Alfred Douglas, Martin Secker (London), 1929 . . . . £125/£25

ditto, as *My Friendship With Oscar Wilde*, Coventry House (New York), 1932 . . . . £75/£25

The True History of Shakespeare's Sonnets, Secker (London), 1933 . . . . £75/£25

Without Apology, Secker (London), 1938 . . £50/£20

Oscar Wilde: A Summing Up, Duckworth (London), 1940 . . . . £75/£20

Ireland and The War Against Hitler, Richards Press (London), 1940 . . . . £75/£20

The Principles of Poetry, Richards Press (London), 1943 (1,000 copies; wraps) £20

Others

New Preface to 'The Life and Confessions of Oscar Wilde', The Fortune Press (London), 1925 (with Frank Harris) . . . . £125/£45

ditto, The Fortune Press (London), 1925 (225 signed, numbered copies) £250

Songs of Cell, by Horatio Bottomley, Southern (London), 1928 (introduction by Douglas) . . . £45/£15

The Pantomime Man, by Richard Middleton, Rich & Cowan (London), 1933 (introduction by Douglas) . . £75/£25

Bernard Shaw, Frank Harris and Oscar Wilde, by Robert Harborough Sherard, Werner Laurie (London), 1937 (preface by Douglas) . . . . . . £45/£15

Brighton Aquatints, by John Piper, Duckworth (London), 1939 (introduction by Douglas, 200 copies with uncoloured plates) £600

ditto, by John Piper, Duckworth (London), 1939 (55 copies with hand-coloured prints) £2,000

Wartime Harvest, by Marie Carmichael Stopes, De la Mare Press, 1944 (preface by Douglas) . . . £45/£10

Salome: A Tragedy in One Act, by Oscar Wilde, Heritage Press (New York), 1945 (translated by Douglas, with Sandglass booklet) £25

NORMAN DOUGLAS

(b.1868 d.1952)

Born in Scotland, Norman Douglas was in the diplomatic service in Russia from 1894: he resigned in 1896. Also a travel writer and essayist, his best known work is the satirical novel *South Wind*, set on the fictional Mediterranean island of Nepenthe, based on Capri. The pseudonym 'Normyx', used for *Unprofessional Tales*, may indicate joint authorship with his wife Elizabeth FitzGibbon.

Novels

South Wind, Martin Secker (London), 1917 (first issue with two lines transposed on p. 325) £100

ditto, Dodd, Mead (New York), 1918 . . . . £150

ditto, Martin Secker (London), 1922 (150 signed copies, on blue paper) £400

ditto, Argus Books (Chicago), 1929 (2 vols, illustrated by John Austen; slipcase) . . . . . £65/£45

ditto, Argus Books (Chicago), 1929 (2 vols, 40 signed copies containing original Austen drawing; slipcase) . . £600

ditto, Limited Editions Club (New York), 1932 (illustrated and signed by Carlotta Petrina) £50

They Went, Chapman & Hall (London), 1920 . . £125/£45

ditto, Dodd, Mead (New York), 1921 . . . £125/£45

In the Beginning, privately printed (Florence), 1927 (700 signed, numbered copies; slipcase) . . . £200/£50

ditto, Chatto & Windus (London), 1928 . . £45/£15

ditto, John Day (New York), 1928 . . . . £50/£20

Short Stories

Unprofessional Tales, T. Fisher Unwin (London), 1901 (pseud 'Normyx') £350

Nerinda, G. Orioli (Florence), 1929 (475 signed, numbered copies, slipcase) . . . . . . £100/£45

ditto, John Day (New York), 1929 . . . . £50/£20

Travel/Belles Lettres

Siren Land, J.M. Dent (London), 1911 . . . . £200
ditto, Durton (New York), 1911 . . . . . . £200
Fountains in the Sand, Martin Secker (London), 1912. £75
ditto, James Pott (New York), 1912 . . . . . £25
Old Calabria, Martin Secker (London), 1915 . . . £350
ditto, Houghton Mifflin (Boston), 1915 . . . . £125
Alone, Chapman & Hall (London), 1921 (with derogatory
reference to the Hotel Excelsior on page 140 and erratum
slip tipped in at page 157) . . . . . £150/£45
ditto, McBride (New York), 1922 . . . . £150/£35
Together, Chapman & Hall (London), 1923 . . £75/£25
ditto, Chapman & Hall (London), 1923 (275 signed copies).
. . . . £100
ditto, McBride (New York), 1923 . . . . £65/£25
One Day, Hours Press (Paris), 1929 (300 copies) . . £100
ditto, Hours Press (Paris), 1929 (200 signed copies) . £200
Summer Islands, Desmond Harmsworth (London), 1931 .
. . . . £45/£15
ditto, Desmond Harmsworth (London), 1931 (500 numbered
copies) . . . . £100/£40
ditto, Colophon (New York), 1931 . . . . . £25
ditto, Colophon (New York), 1931 (550 signed copies).£100
ditto, Corvinus Press (London), 1942 [1944] (45 copies,
various papers and bindings) £250
Footnote on Capri, Sidgwick & Jackson (London), 1952 .
. . . . £20/£5
ditto, McBride (New York), 1952 . . . £20/£5

Capri Monographs

The Blue Grotto and its Literature, privately printed
(Napoli, Italy), 1904 (100 copies) £250
The Forestal Conditions of Capri, privately printed (Napoli,
Italy), 1904 (100 copies) £250
Fabio Giordano's Relation of Capri, privately printed
(Napoli, Italy), 1906 (250 copies) £200
Three Monographs, privately printed (Napoli, Italy), 1906
(250 copies) £200
The Life of the Venerable Suor Serafina Di Dio, privately
printed (Napoli, Italy), 1907 (100 copies) . . £250
Some Antiquarian Notes, privately printed (Napoli, Italy),
1907 (250 copies) £200
Dislecta Membra, privately printed, 1915 (100 copies). £250
Index, privately printed, 1915 (100 copies) . . £250

Pamphlets

Zur Fauna Santorins, Zoologischa Anzeiger (Leipzig),
1892 (c.50 copies, no wraps) £500
Contributions to an Avifauna of Baden, The Zoologist
(London), 1894 (c.50 copies; no wraps; pseud 'G. Norman
Douglass') £500
On the Herpetology of the Grand Duchy of Baden, The
Zoologist (London), 1894 (c.50 copies, pseud 'G. Norman
Douglass') £500
The Beaver in Norway, The Zoologist (London), [n.d.]
(pseud 'G. Norman Douglass') £200
Report on the Pumice Stone Industry of the Lipari Islands,
H.M.S.O. (London), 1895 (c.125 copies) . . . £350
ditto, Hours Press (Paris), 1928 (80 copies) . . . £350
On the Darwinian Hypothesis of Sexual Selection, privately
printed (London), 1895 (25 copies, pseud 'G. Norman
Douglass') £350

Others

London Street Games, St Catherine's Press (London), 1916
. . . . £125

ditto, Chatto & Windus (London), 1931 . . . £35/£10
ditto, Chatto & Windus (London), 1931 (110 signed copies)
. . . . £75
*D.H. Lawrence and Maurice Magnus: A Plea for Better
Manners*, privately printed (Florence), 1924 (wraps) . £35
Experiments, privately printed (Florence), 1925 (300 signed,
numbered copies) . . . . . . £165/£100
ditto, Chapman & Hall (London), 1925 . . . £75/£25
ditto, McBride (New York), 1925 . . . . £75/£25
Birds and Beasts of the Greek Anthology, privately printed
(Florence), 1927 (500 signed, numbered copies) £200/£100
ditto, Chapman & Hall (London), 1928 . . . £45/£20
ditto, Cape & Smith (New York), 1929 . . . £35/£10
Some Limericks, privately printed (Florence), 1928 (110
signed, numbered copies) £500
ditto, privately printed (Florence), 1928 (750 unnumbered
copies) £100
ditto, privately printed by Guy d'Isere for David Moss
(Boston), 1928 (750 numbered copies) . . . £50
How About Europe?, privately printed (Florence), 1929 (550
signed, numbered copies) . . . . . £150/£75
ditto, Chatto & Windus (London), 1930 . . . £50/£15
The Angel of Manfredonia, The Windsor Press (San
Francisco, CA), 1929 (225 numbered copies, slipcase, no
d/w) . . . . £75/£45
Three of Them, Chatto & Windus (London), 1930. £35/£10
Capri: Materials for a Description of the Island, G. Orioli
(Florence), 1930 (525 signed, numbered copies) . . £300
ditto, G. Orioli (Florence), 1930 (103 signed copies) . £500
Paneros, G. Orioli (Florence), 1930 (250 signed copies) .
. . . . £200/£150
ditto, Chatto & Windus (London), 1931 (650 numbered
copies) . . . . £100/£50
ditto, McBride (New York), 1932 (750 copies, slipcase) .
. . . . £65/£45
Looking Back, Chatto & Windus (London), 1933 (2 vols,
535 signed, numbered sets) . . . . £200/£125
ditto, Harcourt, Brace (New York), 1933 (1 vol.) . £100/£25
ditto, Chatto & Windus (London), 1934 (1 vol.) . £45/£15
An Almanac, privately printed (Lisbon), 1941 (25 [c.50]
signed, numbered copies) £400
ditto, Secker & Warburg (London), 1945 . . . £25/£10
Late Harvest, Lindsay Drummond (London), 1946 £20/£5
Venus in the Kitchen, Heinemann (London), 1952 £25/£5
ditto, Viking (New York), 1953 . . . . . £25/£5

ERNEST DOWSON

(b.1867 d.1900)

Dowson was among the best of the Decadent poets of the
1890s. His most widely known poem is probably 'Non Sum
Qualis Eram Bonae sub Regno Cynarae', with its refrain, 'I
have been faithful to thee, Cynara! in my fashion'. Dowson
also prepared translations and wrote short stories. He died
of tuberculosis at the age of thirty-two.

Poetry

Verses, Leonard Smithers (London), 1896 (300 copies,
cream coloured parchment boards, lettered in gold and with
a design in gold on front by Aubrey Beardsley) . . £650
ditto, Smithers (London), 1896 (30 copies on Japanese
vellum) £2,500

The Pierrot of the Minute, Leonard Smithers (London), 1897 (illustrated by Aubrey Beardsley, 300 copies printed on handmade paper, green cloth lettered in gold, designs in gold to front and back covers, top edge gilt) . . . £350

ditto, Smithers (London), 1897 (30 copies on Japanese vellum) £2,000

ditto, Grolier Club (New York), 1923 (300 copies printed on Dutch antique paper, slipcase) . . . . £100/£75

Decorations, in Verse & Prose, Leonard Smithers (London), 1899 (cream coloured parchment boards lettered in gold) .
. . . . £350

The Poems of Ernest Dowson, Thomas Mosher (Portland, ME), 1902 (600 copies on Van Gelder hand-made paper).
. . . . £35

ditto, Thomas Mosher (Portland, ME), 1902 (50 numbered copies on Japan vellum signed by the publisher) . . £200

The Poems of Ernest Dowson, John Lane (London), 1905 (edited and with a memoir by Arthur Symons. Illustrated by Aubrey Beardsley. Green cloth lettered in gold, top edge gilt). £100

ditto, John Lane (New York), 1905 . . . . . £100

Cynara: A Little Book of Verse, Thomas Mosher (Portland, ME), 1907 (950 copies; glassine d/w; slipcase) . £35/£25

ditto, Thomas Mosher (Portland, ME), 1907 (100 copies on Japan vellum; glassine d/w; slipcase) . . . £100/£75

Poetical Works of Ernest Dowson, Cassell/John Lane (London), 1934 (edited by Desmond Flower) . £25/£10

ditto, Cassell's Pocket Library (London), 1950 . £10/£5

The Poems of Ernest Dowson, The Unicorn Press (London), 1946 . . . . £15/£5

The Poems of Ernest Dowson, Univ of Pennsylvania Press (Pennsylvania), 1962 (edited by Mark Longaker) £20/£5

Prose

A Comedy of Masks, Heinemann (London), 1893 (with Arthur Moore, 3 vols, green cloth lettered in gold, with ornament on front cover in black) £300

Dilemmas, Elkin Matthews (London), 1895 (blue cloth, lettered in black) £150

Adrian Rome, Methuen (London), 1899 (with Arthur Moore, blue cloth lettered in gold). £125

Ernest Dowson, 1888-1897, Reminiscences and Unpublished Letters and Marginalia, Elkin Mathews (London), 1914 (red cloth lettered in gold) . £25/£10

The Stories of Ernest Dowson, Univ of Pennsylvania (Pennsylvania), 1947 (grey cloth, lettered in gold) £25/£10

ditto, W.H. Allen (London), [1949] (edited by Mark Longaker) . . . . £15/£5

The Letters of Ernest Dowson, Fairleigh Dickinson Univ Press, 1967 (collected and edited by Desmond Flower & Henry Maas). . . . . £30/£20

ditto, Cassell (London), 1967 . . . . . £30/£20

New Letters from Ernest Dowson, Whittington Press (Andoversford, Gloucestershire), 1984 (220 copies, signed by Desmond Flower, cloth-backed patterned paper boards)
. . . . £75

A Bouquet, Whittington Press (Andoversford, Gloucestershire), 1991 (95 numbered copies; slipcase) . . . £125

Translations

Majesty, by Louis Couperus, T. Fisher Unwin (London), 1894 (translated with A. Teixera de Mattos, light blue cloth floriated in brown, lettered in gold). £50

La Terre, by Emile Zola, Lutetian Society (London), 1895 (2 vols, dark green cloth lettered in gold, top edges gilt, 300 copies of 310) £150

ditto, Lutetian Society (London), 1895 (as above but 10 sets on Japanese vellum) £750

The History of Modern Painting, by Richard Muther, Henry and Co. (London), 1895 (only the first of the three volume set was translated by Dowson, blue cloth lettered in gold).
. . . . £65

La Fille aux Yeux d'Or, by Honoré de Balzac, Leonard Smithers (London), 1896 (illustrated by Charles Conder, yellow/gold cloth, lettered in brown) £200

ditto, Leonard Smithers (London), 1896 (purple cloth, lettered in gold) £75

Les Liaisons Dangereuses, by Pierre Choderlos de Laclos, privately printed [by Leonard Smithers], 1898 (360 numbered copies, 2 vols, blue boards with white linen back, lettered in gold). £250

ditto, as *Dangerous Acquaintances*, Nonesuch Press (London), 1940 (illustrated by Charles Laborde, blue spine, stamped in gilt, fleur-de-lis decorated boards, slipcase) .
. . . . £50/£35

ditto, as *Les Liaisons Dangereuses*, Black Sun Press (Paris), 1929 (2 vols, edition of 15 sets on Japon paper, 7 illustrations) £2,500

ditto, Black Sun Press (Paris), 1929 (ordinary edition of 1005 sets, 7 illustrations; bound in card wraps with french-fold printed d/w; slipcase) . . . . . £3000/£200

ditto, privately printed for William Godwin (New York), 1933 (as *Dangerous Acquaintances*, a very poor reprint of Vol. 1 of above edition) £10

La Pucelle D'Orléans, by Voltaire, Lutetian Society (London), 1899 (500 numbered sets, 2 vols, cream cloth backed with blue linen) £125

Memoirs of Cardinal Dubois, Leonard Smithers (London), 1899 (2 vols, purple cloth lettered in gold) . . . £50

ditto, privately printed for subscribers, Art Studio Press (New York), 1929 (2 vols; 1,500 copies; illustrated by Lui Trugo) . . . . £25/£10

The Confidantes of a King, by Edmond & Jules de Goncourt, T.N. Foulis (London), 1907 (2 vols, scarlet cloth lettered in gold) £45

The Story of Beauty and the Beast, John Lane (London), 1908 [1907] (illustrated by Charles Conder, green ribbed cloth, lettered in gold, top edge gilt. Issued with an orange d/w) £125

ARTHUR CONAN DOYLE

(b.1859 d.1930)

Doyle was born and educated in Edinburgh, and received his medical degree there in 1881. He is best known for his creation of the detective, Sherlock Holmes, who first appeared in print in 1887. In 1890 Doyle abandoned his medical practice and devoted himself to writing, preferring historical fiction to the exploits of his famous detective. He was knighted in 1902.

'Sherlock Holmes' Titles

A Study in Scarlet, 28th Beeton's Christmas Annual (London), 1887 (story contained in first 95pps; wraps) £50,000

ditto, 28th Beeton's Christmas Annual (London), 1887 (rebound) . . . . £20,000 *ditto*, Ward Lock (London), 1888 (first book edition, first issue with 'younger' spelt correctly in preface; wraps) £30,000

ditto, Ward Lock (London), 1888 (first book edition, first issue with 'younger' spelt correctly in preface; rebound) £10,000

ditto, Ward Lock (London), 1888 (second issue with 'youunger'; wraps) £17,500

ditto, J.B. Lippincott Company (Philadelphia, PA), 1890 (wraps) £5,000

ditto, J.B. Lippincott Company (Philadelphia, PA), 1890 (cloth) £4,000

ditto, J.B. Lippincott Company (Philadelphia, PA), 1890 (rebound) £2,000

The Sign of Four, Lippincott's Magazine (London), February 1890 (pp.147-223; wraps) . . . £2,500

ditto, Lippincott's/Ward Lock (London), 1890, in *Six Complete Novels by Famous Authors* £750

ditto, Spencer Blackett (London), 1890 (first book edition, first issue) £7,500

ditto, Spencer Blackett (London), 1890 (second issue, remainder sheets issued by Griffith Farran, with 'Griffith Farran and Co' at foot of spine) £4,000

ditto, Lippincott's/Ward Lock (London), 1891, in *Five Complete Novels by Famous Authors* £400

ditto, Spencer Blackett (London), 1892 (third issue, remainder sheets issued by Newnes (London), with 'Griffith Farran and Co' on cover) £1,500

ditto, Collier (New York), 1891 . . . . £3,000

ditto, J.B. Lippincott Company (Philadelphia, PA), 1893 (cloth) £1,000

ditto, J.B. Lippincott Company (Philadelphia, PA), 1893 (wraps) £1,500

ditto, J.B. Lippincott Company (Philadelphia, PA), 1893 (rebound) £400

The Adventures of Sherlock Holmes, George Newnes (London), 1892 (first issue with Southampton Street at the base of the spine and no street name on the vignette picture of The Strand) £3,000

ditto, Harper (New York), 1892 (first issue with 'if had' on page 65, line 4) £500

ditto, Harper (New York), 1892 (second issue with 'if he had') £250

The Memoirs of Sherlock Holmes, George Newnes (London), 1894 [1893] £1,250

ditto, Harper (New York), 1894 . . . . . £500

The Hound of the Baskervilles, George Newnes (London), 1902 . . . . £2,500

ditto, McClure, Phillips (New York), 1902 (first issue without 'Published 1902' on copyright page) . £750

ditto, McClure, Phillips (New York), 1902 (second issue with 'Published 1902') £250

ditto, McClure, Phillips (New York), 1902 (third issue with tipped-in title-page with 'Illustrated') . . . £200

ditto, McClure, Phillips (New York), 1902 (fourth issue, as third but integral title-page) £150

The Return of Sherlock Holmes, McClure, Phillips (New York), 1905 (black cloth) £500

ditto, McClure, Phillips (New York), 1905 ('special edition', dark blue cloth) £250

ditto, George Newnes (London), 1905 . . . £1,500

The Valley of Fear, Doran (New York), 1914. . £250

ditto, Smith Elder (London), 1915 . . . . £300

His Last Bow, Murray (London), 1917 . . . £300

ditto, Doran (New York), 1917 (orange cloth). . . £135

ditto, Doran (New York), 1917 (red cloth) . . . £100

The Case-Book of Sherlock Holmes, Murray (London), 1927 . . . . £4,500/£350

ditto, Doran (New York), 1927 . . . . £1,250/£125

Other Novels

The Mystery of Cloomber, Ward and Downey (London), 1889 [1888] (wraps) £750

ditto, Munro (New York), 1893 (wraps) . . . £400

Micah Clarke, Longmans Green (London), 1889 (publisher's catalogue dated June 1888). . . £250

ditto, Harper (New York), 1889 . . . . . £75

The Firm of Girdlestone, Chatto & Windus (London), 1890 (publisher's catalogue dated January 1890) . . . £250

ditto, Chatto & Windus (London), 1890 (publisher's catalogue dated later) £200

ditto, John Lovell Co (New York), 1890 . . . £125

The White Company, Smith Elder (London), 1891 (3 vols) £3,000

ditto, Smith Elder (London), 1892 (1 vol.) . . . £75

ditto, John Lovell Co (New York), 1891 (tan wraps) . £500

ditto, Lovell, Coryell & Co. (New York), 1892 (white pictorial wraps) £300

The Doings of Raffles Haw, Lovell (New York), 1891. £175

ditto, Cassell (London), 1892 . . . . . £250

The Great Shadow, Arrowsmith's Christmas Annual (Bristol), 1892 (pictorial wraps) £400

ditto, Arrowsmith's Christmas Annual (Bristol), 1892 (cloth, brown endpapers) £150

Beyond the City, Rand McNally (New York), [1892] . £125

The Great Shadow, and Beyond the City, Arrowsmith (London), [1893]. £75

ditto, Harper (New York), 1893 . . . . . £75

The Refugees, Longmans Green (London), 1893 (3 vols) £2,500

ditto, Longmans Green (London), [August] 1893 (1 vol) £100

ditto, Harper (New York), 1893 . . . . . £100

The Parasite, Constable (London), 1894 . . . £150

ditto, Constable (London), 1894 (wraps) . . . £150

ditto, Harper (New York), 1895 . . . . . £100

Rodney Stone, Smith Elder (London), 1896 . . . £100

ditto, Appleton (New York), 1896 . . . . . £75

Uncle Bernac, Horace Cox (New York), 1896 [Jan 1897] (wraps; copyright edition: Chapters 1-10 only) . £1,500

ditto, Smith Elder (London), 1897 . . . . £125

ditto, Appleton (New York), 1897 . . . . . £100

A Desert Drama, being the tragedy of the Korosko, Lippincott (Philadelphia, PA), 1898 . . . £100

ditto, as **The Tragedy of Korosko**, Smith Elder (London), 1898 . . . . £100

Sir Nigel, Smith Elder (London), 1906 . . . £30

ditto, McClure, Phillips (New York), 1906 . . . £30

The Lost World, Hodder & Stoughton (London), [1912] £600

ditto, Hodder & Stoughton (London), [1912] (large paper edition, 190 of 1,000 copies comprise the first issue) £1,500

ditto, Henry Frowde/Hodder & Stoughton (London), [1912] (large paper edition, 810 of 1,000 copies comprise the second issue) £400

ditto, Doran (New York), 1912 . . . . . £400

The Poison Belt, Hodder & Stoughton (London), 1913. £100

ditto, Hodder/Doran (New York),1913 . . . . £100
The Land Of Mist, Hutchinson (London), [1926] . .

. . . . £2,000/£200
ditto, Doran (New York),1926 . . . . . £650/£50
The Maracot Deep, Murray (London), 1929 (novel and 3
  short stories). . . . . . . £750/£75
ditto, Doran (New York),1929 . . . . £400/£45

Short Stories
Mysteries and Adventures, Walter Scott (London), [1890] .

. . . . £1,000
ditto, Walter Scott (London), [1890] (wraps) . £1,000
ditto, as **The Gully of Bluemansdyke and Other Stories**,
  Walter Scott (London), [1892] (wraps) £100
ditto, as **My Friend the Murderer**, Lovell (New York), 1893
. . . . £100
The Captain of the Polestar, Longmans (London), 1890 .
. . . . £300
ditto, Munro (New York), [1894] £65
Round the Red Lamp, Methuen (London), 1894 . . £150
ditto, Appleton (New York), 1894 . . . . . £125
The Exploits of Brigadier Gerard, Newnes (London), 1896
  (advertisements dated 10/2/96). £125
ditto, Newnes (London), 1896 (later advertisements) . £75
ditto, Appleton (New York), 1896 . . . . . £65
The Green Flag, Smith Elder (London), 1900 . . £100
ditto, McClure, Phillips (New York), 1900 . . . £75
Adventures of Gerard, Newnes (London), 1903 . . £75
ditto, McClure, Phillips (New York), 1903 . . . £45
The Croxley Master, A Great Tale of the Prize Ring,
  McClure, Phillips (New York), 1907 . . . . £50
ditto, McClure, Phillips (New York), 1907 . . . £30
Round the Fire Stories, Smith Elder (London), 1908 . £30
ditto, McClure, Phillips (New York), 1908 . . . £30
The Last Galley, Smith Elder (London), 1911 . . £50
ditto, Doubleday (New York), 1911 . . . . . £30
Danger, Murray (London), 1918. . . . . . £30
ditto, Doran (New York), 1918 . . . . . . £30

Writings on the Paranormal
The New Revelation, Hodder & Stoughton (London), 1918.
. . . . £200/£35
ditto, Doran (New York), 1918 . . . . £100/£20
A Full Report of a Lecture on Spiritualism, Worthing
  Gazette Co. (Worthing, Sussex), [1919] (pamphlet) £1,000
ditto, Rupert Books (Cambridge, UK), 1997 (400 copies
  signed by Richard L. Green; wraps) £10
The Vital Message, Hodder & Stoughton (London), [1919].
. . . . £200/£35
ditto, Doran (New York), [1919]. . . . £100/£20
The New Revelation and **The Vital Message**, Psychic Press
  (London), 1938 . . . . . . £100/£15
Verbatim Report of a Public Debate, Watts (London), 1920
. . . . £300/£100
ditto, Watts (London), 1920 (wraps) £125
Our Reply to the Cleric, Spiritualist's National Union
  (Halifax, UK), 1920 . . . . £250
ditto, Rupert Books (Cambridge, UK), 1998 (400 copies;
  wraps) £10
Spiritualism and Rationalism, Hodder & Stoughton
  (London), [1920] (wraps) £200
ditto, Rupert Books (Cambridge, UK), 2001 (400 copies;
  wraps) £10

The Wanderings of a Spiritualist, Hodder & Stoughton
  (London), [1921]. £200
ditto, Rupert Books (Cambridge, UK), 2001 (400 copies;
  wraps) £10
The Coming of Fairies, Hodder & Stoughton (London),
  1922 . . . . £500/£200
ditto, Doran (New York), 1922 . . . . £450/£150
The Case for Spirit Photography, Hutchinson (London),
  1922 (by Doyle and others; no d/w) . . . £150
ditto, Hutchinson (London), 1922 (wraps) . . £150
ditto, Doran (New York), 1923 (nod/w) . . . £150
Our American Adventure, Hodder & Stoughton (London),
  [1923] . . . . £300/£75
ditto, Doran (New York), 1923 . . . . £250/£65
The Spiritualists' Reader, Two Worlds (Manchester, UK),
  1924 (compiled by Doyle; cloth binding) . . . £75
ditto, Two Worlds (Manchester, UK), 1924 (leather binding)
. . . . £100
The Early Chrstian Church and Modern Spiritualism,
  Psychic Bookshop and Library, [1925] (wraps) . £250
Psychic Experiences, Putnam's (London), 1925 (wraps) .
. . . . £125
The History of Spiritualism, Cassell (London), 1926 (2 vols)
. . . . £400/£150 the set
ditto, Doran (New York), 1926 (2 vols) . £400/£150 the set
Phineas Speaks, Psychic Press (London), [1927] . £165/£75
ditto, Psychic Press (London), [1927] (wraps). . . £75
A Word of Warning, Psychic Press (London), 1928 (wraps)
. . . . £250
What Does Spiritualism Actually Teach and Stand For,
  Psychic Press (London), 1928 (wraps) . . . £250
The Roman Catholic Church: A Rejoinder, Psychic Press
  (London), 1929 (wraps) £250
Our African Winter, John Murray (London), 1929 £250/£75
An Open letter to Those of My Generation, Psychic Press
  (London), [1929] (wraps) £250
The Edge of the Unknown, John Murray (London), 1930 .
. . . . £250/£75
ditto, Putnam's (New York), 1930 . . . £200/£50
The New Revelation, Rupert Books (Cambridge, UK), 1997
  (400 copies signed by Richard L. Green; wraps) . . £10

Others
Jane Annie, Or the Good Conduct Prize, Chappell
  (London), 1893 (with J.M. Barrie; wraps) . . . £750
Waterloo, French (London), 1907 . . . . £150
Through the Magic Door, Smith Elder (London), 1907 £50
ditto, McClure (New York), 1908 . . . . . £40
The Guards Came Through and Other Poems, Murray
  (London), 1919 (wraps) £85
ditto, Doran (New York),1920 (wraps) £45

Collected Edition
**The Crowborough Edition of the Works of Sir Arthur
  Conan Doyle**, Doubleday, Doran (New York), 1930 (24
  volumes, 760 signed sets) £4,000

RODDY DOYLE
(b.1958)

Irish novelist, dramatist and screenwriter Doyle achieved recognition when *The Commitments* was filmed in 1991, the same year that *The Van* was shortlisted for the Booker Prize. *Paddy Clarke Ha Ha Ha* won the Booker Prize for 1993, establishing Doyle as a leading comic writer and earning him comparisons with those other Irish humorists Sean O'Casey and Brendan Behan.

The 'Barrytown' Trilogy
The Commitments, King Farouk (Dublin), 1987 (pbk) . £650
ditto, Heinemann (London), 1988 (pbk)   .   .   . £45
ditto, Vintage (New York), 1989 (pbk)   .   .   . £20
The Snapper, Secker (London), 1990   .   . £225/£35
ditto, Penguin (New York), 1992 (pbk)   .   .   . £10
The Van, Secker (London), 1991   .   .   . £65/£15
ditto, Viking (New York), 1992 .   .   .   . £15/£5
The Barrytown Trilogy, Secker (London), 1992 (contains *The Commitments*, *The Snapper*, and *The Van*)   . £65/£10

'Last Roundup'
A Star Called Henry, Cape (London), 1999   .   . £20/£5
ditto, Viking (New York), 1999.   .   .   . £15/£5
Oh, Play That Thing, Cape (London), 2004   . £20/£5
ditto, Viking (New York), 2004.   .   .   . £15/£5

Other Novels
Paddy Clarke, Ha Ha Ha, Secker (London), 1993. £40/£10
ditto, Viking (New York), 1994 (first state d/w, with 'Clark' on the spine).   .   .   .   .   .   . £25/£5
The Woman Who Walked Into Doors, Cape (London), 1996
.   .   .   . £20/£5
ditto, Viking (New York), 1996.   .   .   . £15/£5
Paula Spencer, Cape (London), 2006   .   . £15/£5
ditto, Viking (New York), 2007 .   .   .   . £15/£5

Drama
War, Passion Machine (Dublin), 1989 (pbk)   .   . £65
ditto, Penguin (New York), 1992 (pbk)   .   .   . £10
Brownbread and War, Secker (London), 1992 (pbk)   . £20
ditto, Penguin (New York), 1994 (pbk)   .   .   . £10

Children's Titles
Not Just For Christmas, New Island Books (Dublin), 1999 (pbk) £5
The Giggler Treatment, Scholastic Press (London), 2000 .
.   .   .   . £20/£5
ditto, Levine/Scholastic (New York), 2000   . £20/£5
Roger Saves Christmas, Scholastic Press (London), 2001 .
.   .   .   . £15/£5
ditto, Levine/Scholastic (New York), 2001   . £15/£5
The Meanwhile Adventures, Scholastic Press (London), 2004   .   .   .   . £15/£5
ditto, Levine/Scholastic (New York), 2004   . £15/£5
Wilderness, Scholastic Press (London), 2007 .   . £15/£5
ditto, Levine/Scholastic (New York), 2007   . £15/£5
Her Mother's Face, Levine/Scholastic (New York), 2008 .
.   .   .   . £15/£5

Collaborative Novels
Yeats Is Dead, Cape (London), 2001 (with fourteen other Irish writers).   .   .   .   .   .   . £15/£5
ditto, Knopf (New York), 2001 .   .   .   . £15/£5

Finbar's Hotel, Picador (London), 2002 (with six other Irish writers; pbk). £5
ditto, Picador (London), 2002 (with publisher's printed bookplate signed by all contributors)   .   .   . £25

Others
Rory and Ita, Cape (London), 2002   .   .   . £15/£5
ditto, Viking (New York), 2002 .   .   .   . £15/£5
The Deportees and Other Stories, Cape (London), 2007   .
.   .   .   . £10/£5
ditto, Viking (New York), 2008 .   .   .   . £10/£5

MARGARET DRABBLE
(b.1939)

Drabble's novels often explore the struggle of the individual against convention or repression. She has also written screenplays, plays and biographies as well as commentaries on several literary classics, and she edited the *Oxford Companion to English Literature* in 1987 and 2000. In 1980 Drabble was made a C.B.E. for services to English literature.

Novels
A Summer Bird-Cage, Weidenfeld & Nicolson (London), 1963   .   .   .   . £250/£40
ditto, Morrow (New York), 1964   .   .   . £65/£10
The Garrick Year, Weidenfeld & Nicolson (London), 1964.
.   .   .   . £65/£20
ditto, Morrow (New York), 1965   .   .   . £45/£10
The Millstone, Weidenfeld & Nicolson (London), 1965   .
.   .   .   . £75/£20
ditto, Morrow (New York), 1966   .   .   . £45/£10
ditto, as *Thank You All Very Much*, New American Library (New York), 1969 (pbk) £10
Jerusalem the Golden, Weidenfeld & Nicolson (London), 1967   .   .   .   . £30/£10
ditto, Morrow (New York), 1967   .   .   . £25/£5
The Waterfall, Weidenfeld & Nicolson (London), 1969   .
.   .   .   . £25/£5
ditto, Knopf (New York), 1969   .   .   .   . £25/£5
The Needle's Eye, Weidenfeld & Nicolson (London), 1972.
.   .   .   . £30/£5
ditto, Knopf (New York), 1972   .   .   .   . £25/£5
The Realms of Gold, Weidenfeld & Nicolson (London), 1975   .   .   .   . £20/£5
ditto, Knopf (New York), 1975   .   .   .   . £20/£5
The Ice Age, Weidenfeld & Nicolson (London), 1977 .   .
.   .   .   . £20/£5
ditto, Knopf (New York), 1977   .   .   .   . £20/£5
The Middle Ground, Weidenfeld & Nicolson (London), 1980   .   .   .   . £15/£5
ditto, Knopf (New York), 1980   .   .   .   . £15/£5
The Radiant Way, Weidenfeld & Nicolson (London), 1987.
.   .   .   . £15/£5
ditto, Knopf (New York), 1987   .   .   .   . £15/£5
A Natural Curiosity, Viking (London), 1989 .   . £15/£5
ditto, London Limited Editions (London), 1989 (150 signed copies, glassine d/w)   .   .   .   . £65/£45
ditto, Viking (New York), 1989 .   .   .   . £15/£5
The Gates of Ivory, Viking (London), 1991   . £10/£5
ditto, Viking (New York), 1992 .   .   .   . £10/£5

The Witch of Exmoor, Viking (London), 1996   .   £10/£5
ditto, Harcourt Brace (New York), 1996 .   .   .   £10/£5
The Peppered Moth, Viking (London), 2000 .   £10/£5
ditto, Harcourt Brace (New York), 2001 .   .   .   £10/£5
The Seven Sisters, Viking (London), 2002   .   £10/£5
ditto, Harcourt Brace (New York), 2002 .   .   £10/£5
The Red Queen: A Transcultural Tragicomedy, Viking (London), 2004 .   .   .   .   .   .   £10/£5
ditto, Harcourt Brace (New York), 2004 .   .   .   £10/£5

Non-Fiction
Wordsworth, Evans (London), 1966 .   .   .   .   £45/£10
ditto, Arco (New York), 1969 (no d/w)   .   .   .   £20
Virginia Woolf: A Personal Debt, Aloe Editions (New York), 1973 (110 signed, numbered copies; wraps)   .£100
Arnold Bennett: A Biography, Weidenfeld & Nicolson (London), 1974 .   .   .   .   .   .   £25/£5
ditto, Knopf (New York), 1974 .   .   .   .   £25/£5
A Brief History of My Addiction, Warren Editions (London), 1974 (150 copies, wraps) £200
A Writer's Britain: Landscape in Literature, Thames & Hudson (London), 1979 (photographs by Jorge Lewinski)
  .   .   .   .   £25/£10
ditto, Knopf (New York), 1979 .   .   .   .   £20/£10
Wordsworth's Butter Knife, Catawba Press (Northampton, MA) 1980 (wraps; 150 copies). £20
Hassan's Tower, Sylvester & Orphanos (Los Angeles), 1980 (300 signed, numbered copies, glassine d/w and slipcase) .
  .   .   .   .   £80
The Tradition of Women's Fiction: Lectures in Japan, O.U.P. (Tokyo), 1982 .   .   .   .   .   £25/£5
Case for Equality, Fabian Society (London), 1988.   .   £10
Stratford Revisited: A Legacy of the Sixties, Celandine Press (Shipston-on-Stour, Warks), 1989 (150 signed copies; wraps) £25
Safe As Houses: An Examination of Home Ownership and Mortgage Tax Relief, Chatto & Windus (London), 1990 .
  .   .   .   .   £5
Angus Wilson: A Biography, Secker & Warburg (London), 1995 .   .   .   .   £15/£5
ditto, St Martin's Press (New York), 1996   .   .   £10/£5

Children's Title
For Queen and Country: Britain in the Victorian Age, Deutsch (London), 1978 .   .   .   .   .   £15/£5
ditto, Seabury Press (New York), 1979   .   .   £10/£5

THEODORE DREISER

(b.1871 d.1945)

Considered by many to be the first exponent of Naturalism in American writing, Dreiser dealt with social problems and characters struggling to survive in the modern world. His style is distinguished by its long sentences and attention to detail. In *Sister Carrie*, his sympathetic treatment of a 'loose' woman was branded immoral and he suffered for it, principally at the hands of his own publishers.

Novels
Sister Carrie, Doubleday (New York), 1900   .   £3,500
ditto, Heinemann (London), 1901   .   .   .   .£600
ditto, Dodge (New York), 1907   .   .   .   .   .£75

Jennie Gerhardt, Harper (New York), 1911 (first issue, 'is' for 'it' on page 22, line 30, 'Theodore Dreiser' on spine, mottled light blue cloth) £125
ditto, Harper (New York), 1911 (second issue, text corrected, 'Dreiser' on spine) £75
The Financier, Harper (New York), 1912 (first issue with 'Published October, 1912' and 'K-M' on title-page) .   £75
ditto, Constable (London), 1927 .   .   .   .   £65/£15
The Titan, John Lane/Bodley Head (New York), 1914 .   £75
The 'Genius', John Lane (New York), 1915 (first issue, 1¾ inches thick, p.497 correctly numbered).   .   .£150
ditto, John Lane (London), 1915 (first issue as above) .£150
ditto, John Lane (New York), 1915 (second issue, 1½ inches thick, p.497 unnumbered) £75
ditto, John Lane (London), 1915 (second issue as above) £75
Twelve Men, Boni & Liveright (New York), 1919 .   .   £65
ditto, Constable (London), 1931 .   .   .   .   £45/£10
An American Tragedy, Boni & Liveright (New York), 1925 (2 vols, first issue, black cloth, white endpapers, slipcase).
  .   .   .   .   £750/£150
ditto, Boni & Liveright (New York), 1925 (2 vols, second issue, blue cloth, slipcase).   .   .   .   £700/£100
ditto, Boni & Liveright (New York), 1925 (795 signed copies, 2 vols, slipcase)   .   .   .   .   £750/£300
ditto, Constable (London), 1926 .   .   .   .   £65/£15
A Gallery of Women, Horace Liveright (New York), 1929 (560 signed copies, 2 vols, slipcase)   .   £200/£100
ditto, Boni & Liveright (New York), 1929 (2 vols). £100/£45
ditto, Constable (London), 1930 .   .   .   .   £50/£15
The Bulwark, Doubleday (New York), 1946 .   .   £50/£15
ditto, Constable (London), 1947 .   .   .   .   £45/£10
The Stoic, Doubleday (New York), 1947 .   .   .   £50/£15

Short Stories
Free and Other Stories, Boni & Liveright (New York), 1918
  .   .   .   .   £65
Chains: Lesser Novels and Stories, Boni & Liveright (New York), 1927 (440 signed, numbered copies, slipcase) .
  .   .   .   .   £150/£75
ditto, Boni & Liveright (New York), 1927   .   £100/£20
ditto, Constable (London), 1928 .   .   .   .   £65/£15
Fine Furniture, Random House (New York), 1930 (issued with five other titles by Sherwood Anderson and others, limited to 875 copies, slipcase).   .   .   .   £75/£50

Poetry
Moods: Cadenced and Declaimed, Boni & Liveright (New York), 1926 (550 signed, numbered copies).   .£150/£75
ditto, Boni & Liveright (New York), 1928   .   £100/£25
ditto, Constable (London), 1929 .   .   .   .   £50/£15
ditto, as *Moods: Philosophic and Emotional, Cadenced and Declaimed*, Simon & Schuster (New York), 1935 £40/£10
The Aspirant, Random House (New York), 1929 (475 copies; wraps) £30
Epitaph, Heron Press (New York), 1929 (200 signed full leather copies, slipcase) .   .   .   .   £200/£145
ditto, Heron Press (New York), 1929 (200 signed copies bound in silk, slipcase, glassine d/w)   .   £200/£145
ditto, Heron Press (New York), 1929 (700 signed copies bound in cloth, slipcase, glassine d/w)   .   .£150/£75

Others
A Traveller at Forty, Century (New York), 1913 .   .   £35
ditto, Grant Richards (London), 1914   .   .   .   £30

Plays of the Natural and the Supernatural, John Lane (New York/London), 1916 (first issue without 4 page essay by Dreiser at end of text). £85
ditto, John Lane (New York/London), 1916 (second issue with essay) £50
A Hoosier Holiday, John Lane (New York/London), 1916 (first state with 'The war! The war! They were chasing' in the last paragraph on p173) £75
The Hand of the Potter: A Tragedy in Four Acts, Boni & Liveright (New York), 1918 (pre-publication copy with no adverts on verso of half title) £65
ditto, Boni & Liveright (New York), 1918 (first edition with adverts, first issue with the last word on p.191 'that'). £50
ditto, Boni & Liveright (New York), 1918 (first edition with adverts, second issue with the last word on p.191 'it'). £35
ditto, Constable (London), 1931 . . . . . £50/£15
Hey, Rub-a-Dub-Dub: A Book of the Mystery and Wonder and Terror of Life, Boni & Liveright (New York), 1920 . . . . £250/£45
ditto, Constable (London), 1931 . . . . £50/£15
A Book About Myself, Boni & Liveright (New York), 1922 . . . . £250/£50
ditto, Constable (London), 1929 . . . . . £65/£15
ditto, as *Newspaper Days*, Boni & Liveright (New York), 1931 . . . . £100/£35
ditto, as *A History of Myself: Dawn*, Boni & Liveright (New York), 1931 (275 signed copies, slipcase) . £200/£125
ditto, as *A History of Myself: Dawn*, Horace Liveright (New York), 1931 . . . . £75/£25
ditto, as *A History of Myself: Dawn*, Constable (London), 1931 . . . . £50/£15
ditto, as *Autobiography*, Boni & Liveright (New York), 1965 (2 vols) . . . . £50/£15
The Color of a Great City, Boni & Liveright (New York), 1923 . . . . £200/£35
ditto, Constable (London), 1930 . . . . . £50/£15
Dreiser Looks at Russia, Boni & Liveright (New York), 1928 . . . . £75/£25
ditto, Constable (London), 1929 . . . . . £50/£15
The Carnegie Works at Pittsburgh, privately printed (Chelsea, New York), 1929 (150 numbered copies) . £200
Tragic America, Horace Liveright (New York), 1931 . . . . £100/£25
ditto, Constable (London), 1932 . . . . . £50/£15
America is Worth Saving, Modern Age Books (New York), 1941 . . . . £75/£15
Letters of Theodore Dreiser: A Selection, Univ of Pennsylvania Press (Philadelphia, PA), 1959 (3 vols, slipcase). . . . . . £65/£30 the set
Letters to Louise: The Correspondence of Theodore Dreiser and H.L. Menken, 1907-1945, Univ of Pennsylvania Press (Philadelphia, PA), 1959 . . . . . . £50/£20
Notes on Life, Univ of Alabama Press (Alabama), 1974 . . . . £30/£10
Dreiser-Menken Letters: The Correspondence of Theodore Dreiser and H.L. Menken, 1907-1945, Univ of Pennsylvania Press (Philadelphia, PA), 1986 . . £25/£10

EDMUND DULAC
(b.1882 d.1953)

Dulac was a successful illustrator during the 'Golden Age of Illustration' (the first quarter of the 20th Century), but after World War One deluxe illustrated books were no longer in vogue and Dulac's book illustrating had to be supplemented by newspaper caricatures, portraiture, theatre costume and set design, and even postage stamp design.

Written and Illustrated by Dulac
Lyrics Pathetic and Humorous From A to Z, Warne (London), 1908 (24 colour plates) £600
ditto, Warne (London), 1908 [1909] (portfolio of 24 plates, cloth-covered box) £2,500
A Fairy Garland: Being Fairy Tales from the Old French, Cassell (London), 1928 (12 colour plates) . £300/£150
ditto, Cassell (London), 1928 (deluxe edition, 1,000 signed copies, slipcase and glassine d/w, 12 colour plates) . . . . £400/£200
ditto, Scribner's (New York), 1929 (12 colour plates) . . . . £300/£150

Illustrated by Dulac
The Novels of the Brontë Sisters, by The Brontës, Dent (London), 1905 (10 vols, 6 colour plates in each) . . . . £650 the set
Fairies I Have Met, by Mrs R. Stawell, John Lane (London), [1907] (8 colour plates) £450
ditto, Hodder & Stoughton (London), [1910] (8 colour plates) £100
ditto, as *My Days With the Fairies*, Hodder & Stoughton (London), [1913] (8 colour plates) . . £300
Stories from The Arabian Nights, retold by Laurence Housman, Hodder & Stoughton (London), 1907 (50 colour plates) £350
ditto, Hodder & Stoughton (London), 1907 (deluxe edition, 350 signed copies, 50 colour plates) . . . £1,750
ditto, Scribner's (New York), 1907 . . . . £325
The Tempest, by William Shakespeare, Hodder & Stoughton (London), [1908] (40 colour plates) . . £250
ditto, Hodder & Stoughton (London), [1908] (deluxe edition, 500 signed copies, 40 colour plates) . . £1,250
The Rubaiyat of Omar Khyyam, by Edward Fitzgerald, Hodder & Stoughton (London), [1909] (20 colour plates) £250
ditto, Hodder & Stoughton (London), [1909] (deluxe edition, 750 signed copies, 20 colour plates) . . £1,000
The Sleeping Beauty, retold by Sir Arthur Quiller-Couch, Hodder & Stoughton (London), [1910] (30 colour plates) £350
ditto, Hodder & Stoughton (London), [1910] (deluxe edition, 1,000 signed copies, 30 colour plates) . . . £1,500
Stories from Hans Andersen, Hodder & Stoughton (London), 1911 (28 colour plates) £500
ditto, Hodder & Stoughton (London), 1911 (deluxe edition, 750 signed copies, 28 colour plates) . . £1,750
ditto, Hodder & Stoughton (London), 1911 (deluxe edition, 100 signed copies, morocco binding, 28 colour plates) £3,000
The Bells and Other Poems, by Edgar Allan Poe, Hodder & Stoughton (London), [1912] (28 colour plates) . £200
ditto, Hodder & Stoughton (London), [1912] (deluxe edition, 750 signed copies, 28 colour plates) . . . £1,000

Princess Badoura: A Tale from The Arabian Nights, retold by Laurence Housman, Hodder & Stoughton (London), [1913] (10 colour plates) £250

ditto, Hodder & Stoughton (London), [1913] (deluxe edition, 750 signed copies, 10 colour plates) . . . £1,250

Sinbad the Sailor and Other Stories from the Arabian Nights, Hodder & Stoughton (London), [1914] (23 colour plates) £450

ditto, Hodder & Stoughton (London), [1914] (deluxe edition, 500 signed copies, 23 colour plates) . . £2,500

Edmund Dulac's Picture-Book for the French Red Cross, Hodder & Stoughton (London), [1915] (20 colour plates) £75

The Dreamer of Dreams, by Queen Marie of Roumania, Hodder & Stoughton (London), [1915] (6 colour plates) £100

The Stealers of Light, by Queen Marie of Roumania, Hodder & Stoughton (London), 1916 (2 colour plates) . .£100

Edmund Dulac's Fairy-Book, Hodder & Stoughton (London), [1916] (15 colour plates) . . .£125

ditto, Hodder & Stoughton (London), [1916] (deluxe edition, 350 signed copies, 15 colour plates) . . £1,500

ditto, Hodder & Stoughton (London), 1919 (16 colour plates) £100

Contes et Legendes Des Nations Alliees, H. Piazza (Paris), 1917 (1,000 signed copies; 15 colour plates). . .£350

Tanglewood Tales, by Nathaniel Hawthorne, Hodder & Stoughton (London), [1918] (14 colour plates) . .£150

ditto, Hodder & Stoughton (London), [1918] (deluxe edition, 500 signed copies, 14 colour plates) £500

The Kingdom of the Pearl, by Leonard Rosenthal, Piazza (Paris), 1920 (1,500 copies, 10 colour plates) . .£500

ditto, Nisbet (London), [1920] (675 copies, 10 colour plates) . . . . £600/£300

ditto, Nisbet (London), [1920] (100 signed copies, 10 colour plates) £1,500

ditto, Brentano's (New York), 1920 (675 numbered copies, 10 colour plates) . . . . . . £600/£300

ditto, Brentano's (New York), 1920 (100 signed copies, 10 colour plates) £1,000

Four Plays for Dancers, by W.B. Yeats, Macmillan (London), 1921 (7 illustrations) . . .£350/£50

ditto, Macmillan (New York), 1921 . . . .£200/£35

The Green Lacquer Pavilion, by Helen Beauclerk, Collins (London), 1926 (9 illustrations) . . . £40/£20

ditto, Doran (New York), 1926 (9 illustrations) . £40/£20

Treasure Island, by Robert Louis Stevenson, Benn (London), 1927 (12 colour plates) . . . £500/£350

ditto, Benn (London), 1927 (deluxe edition, 50 signed copies, 12 colour plates) £5,000

ditto, Doran (New York), [1927] (12 colour plates) £450/£300

Gods and Mortals in Love, by Hugh Ross Williamson, Country Life (London), [1936] (9 colour plates) .£200/£75

The Daughters of the Stars, by Mary C. Crary, Hatchard (London), 1939 (2 colour plates) . . . £60/£30

ditto, Hatchard (London), 1939 (deluxe edition, 500 copies signed by author and artist, 2 colour plates) . . .£175

The Golden Cockerel, by Alexander Pushkin, Limited Editions Club (New York), [1950] (1,500 signed, numbered copies, slipcase) . . . . .£125/£75

The Marriage of Cupid and Psyche, by Walter Pater, Limited Editions Club (New York), [1951] (1,500 signed, numbered copies, slipcase) . . . .£125/£75

The Masque of Comus, by John Milton, Limited Editions Club (New York), 1954 (1,500 numbered copies, slipcase) . . . .£125/£75

DAPHNE DU MAURIER
(b.1907 d.1989)

Dame Daphne Du Maurier was the daughter of the actor-manager Gerald du Maurier, and granddaughter of the writer George Du Maurier. She was the author of a number of tense romances set in Cornwall, the county in which she lived for most of her life. Her best known work, *Rebecca*, was the inspiration for the Oscar-winning film, starring Laurence Olivier.

Novels

The Loving Spirit, Heinemann (London), 1931   £1,000/£65

ditto, Doubleday (New York), 1931 . . . . £500/£35

I'll Never Be Young Again, Heinemann (London), 1932 . . . . £1,000/£65

ditto, Doubleday (New York), 1932 . . . . £500/£35

The Progress of Julius, Heinemann (London), 1933 . . . . £750/£45

ditto, Doubleday (New York), 1933 . . . . £500/£35

Jamaica Inn, Gollancz (London), 1936 . . £2,750/£200

ditto, Doubleday (New York), 1936 . . £2,250/£200

Rebecca, Gollancz (London), 1938 . . £2,750/£300

ditto, Doubleday (New York), 1938 . . . £1,500/£150

Frenchman's Creek, Gollancz (London), 1941 . £100/£20

ditto, Doubleday (New York), 1942 . . . . £75/£15

Hungry Hill, Gollancz (London), 1943 . . . £30/£5

ditto, Doubleday (New York), 1943 . . . . £25/£5

The King's General, Gollancz (London), 1946 . £35/£5

ditto, Doubleday (New York), 1946 . . . . £35/£5

The Parasites, Gollancz (London), 1949 . . £40/£5

ditto, Doubleday (New York), 1950 . . . . £25/£5

My Cousin Rachel, Gollancz (London), 1951 . £50/£10

ditto, Doubleday (New York), 1952 . . . £40/£5

Mary Anne, Gollancz (London), 1954 . . £25/£5

ditto, Doubleday (New York), 1954 . . . £20/£5

The Daphne du Maurier Omnibus, Gollancz (London), 1956 (contains *Rebecca, Jamaica Inn* and *Frenchman's Creek*) . . . . £15/£5

The Scapegoat, Gollancz (London), 1957 . . £25/£5

ditto, Doubleday (New York), 1957 . . . £20/£5

Castle Dor, Gollancz (London), 1962 (begun by Sir Arthur Quiller-Couch) . . . . £15/£5

ditto, Doubleday (New York), 1962 . . . £15/£5

The Glassblowers, Gollancz (London), 1963 . . £20/£5

ditto, Doubleday (New York), 1963 . . . £15/£5

The Daphne du Maurier Tandem, Gollancz (London), 1964 (contains *Mary Anne* and *My Cousin Rachel*) . £15/£5

The Flight of the Falcon, Gollancz (London), 1965 £15/£5

ditto, Doubleday (New York), 1965 . . . £15/£5

The House on the Strand, Gollancz (London), 1969 £15/£5

ditto, Doubleday (New York), 1969 . . . £15/£5

Rule Britannia, Gollancz (London), 1972 . . £15/£5

ditto, Doubleday (New York), 1972 . . . £15/£5

Three Famous Daphne du Maurier Novels, Gollancz (London), 1982 (contains *The Flight of the Falcon, The House on the Strand* and *The King's General*) . £10/£5

Four Great Cornish Novels, Gollancz (London), 1982
(contains *Jamaica Inn*, *Rebecca*, *Frenchman's Creek* and
My Cousin Rachel)   .   .   .   .   .   .   £10/£5

Short Stories
Happy Christmas, Doubleday (New York), 1940 . £40/£10
ditto, Todd Publishing Co. (London), c.1943 (illustrated
boards without d/w) £35
ditto, Todd Publishing Co. (London), 1952 (hardback with
d/w)   .   .   .   .   £35/£10
Come Wind, Come Weather, Heinemann (London), 1940
(stapled wraps) £10
ditto, Doubleday (New York), 1941 (stapled wraps)   . £10
Consider the Lilies, Polybooks/Todd Publishing Co.
(London), 1943 (stapled wraps)   .   .   .   £15
Escort, Polybooks/Todd Publishing Co. (London), 1943
(stapled wraps) £20
Nothing Hurts for Long and *Escort*, Polybooks/Todd
Publishing Co. (London), 1943 (stapled wraps)   .   . £15
Spring Picture, Todd Publishing Co. (London), 1944 (no
d/w) £25
Leading Lady, Polybooks/Vallancey Press (London), 1945
(stapled wraps) £15
London and Paris, Polybooks/Vallancey Press (London),
1945 (stapled wraps) £15
The Apple Tree, Gollancz (London), 1952 (later published as
The Birds)   .   .   .   .   .   .   £150/£15
Early Stories, Todd (London), 1955 (stapled wraps)   . £35
The Breaking Point, Gollancz (London), 1959 (later
published as *The Blue Lenses*)   .   .   .   £30/£5
ditto, Doubleday (New York), 1959   .   .   .   £25/£5
The Treasury of du Maurier Short Stories, Gollancz
(London), 1960 (contains *The Apple Tree* and *The
Breaking Point*)   .   .   .   .   .   .   £10/£5
The Lover, Ace (New York), 1961 (pbk)   .   .   . £5
Not After Midnight, Gollancz (London), 1971 (later
published as *Don't Look Now*)   .   .   .   £40/£10
Echoes from the Macabre, Gollancz (London), 1976   .   .
   .   .   .   .   £40/£10
ditto, Doubleday (New York), 1976   .   .   .   £35/£10
The Rendezvous, Gollancz (London), 1980   .   £15/£5
Classics of the Macabre, Gollancz (London), 1987   £25/£5
ditto, Gollancz (London), 1987 (250 signed copies in
slipcase)   .   .   .   .   .   .   £175/£150
ditto, Doubleday (New York), 1987   .   .   .   £25/£5

Plays
Rebecca, Gollancz (London), 1940   .   .   .   £125/£35
ditto, Gollancz (London), 1940 (wraps)   .   .   £25
The Years Between, Gollancz (London), 1945   .   £45/£10
ditto, Doubleday (New York), 1946   .   .   £30/£10
September Tide, Gollancz (London), 1946   .   £45/£10
ditto, Doubleday (New York), 1950   .   .   £25/£10
The Little Photographer, French (London), 1979 (adapted
by Derek Hoddinott; wraps) £5
My Cousin Rachel, French (London), 1979 (adapted by
Diana Morgan; wraps) £5

Biographies
Gerald: A Portrait, Gollancz (London), 1934 .   . £50/£10
The du Mauriers, Gollancz (London), 1937   .   £65/£15
ditto, Doubleday (New York), 1937   .   .   £65/£15
The Infernal World of Branwell Brontë, Gollancz
(London), 1960   .   .   .   .   .   .   £20/£5

ditto, Doubleday (New York), 1961   .   .   .   £15/£5
The Golden Lads, Gollancz (London), 1975   .   £20/£5
ditto, Doubleday (New York), 1975   .   .   £15/£5
The Winding Stair: Francis Bacon, His Rise And Fall,
Gollancz (London), 1976   .   .   .   .   £20/£5
ditto, Doubleday (New York), 1977   .   .   .   £15/£5
Growing Pains: The Shaping of a Writer, Gollancz
(London), 1977   .   .   .   .   .   .   £20/£5
The Rebecca Notebook & Other Memories, Doubleday
(New York), 1980   .   .   .   .   .   £15/£5
ditto, Gollancz (London), 1981   .   .   .   £15/£5

Miscellaneous
Vanishing Cornwall, Gollancz (London), 1967   . £20/£5
ditto, Doubleday (New York), 1967   .   .   .   £15/£5
ditto, Gollancz (London), 1981 (colour edition)   . £15/£5
ditto, Doubleday (New York), 1981   .   .   .   £10/£5

GEORGE DU MAURIER
(b.1834 d.1896)

Born in Paris, George du Maurier was a British novelist
and critic. He studied art in Paris, and became a member of
the staff of *Punch* in 1865, drawing two cartoons per week
for the magazine. He was forced to retire because of
worsening eyesight and wrote three novels, the second of
which, *Trilby,* brought him fame. He also wrote humorous
verse.

Novels
Peter Ibbetson, Harper (New York), 1891   .   . £60
ditto, Osgood, McIlvaine (London), 1892 (2 vols)   . £60
Trilby, Osgood, McIlvaine (London), 1894 (3 vols)   . £400
ditto, Harper (New York), 1894 (1 vol)   .   .   £75
ditto, Osgood, McIlvaine (London), 1895 (250 signed copies,
1 vol) £300
ditto, Harper (New York), 1894 (600 numbered copies) £25
The Martian, Harper (New York), 1897   .   .   £25
ditto, Harper (New York), 1897 (500 numbered copies) £75
ditto, Harper (London), 1898   .   .   .   .   £25
ditto, Harper (London), 1898 (250 numbered large paper
copies) £100
Svengali, W.H. Allen (London), 1982 (first unexpurgated
edition of *Trilby*)   .   .   .   .   .   £10/£5

Others
Gauwaine Hys Penance: A Legend of Camelot, Bradbury &
Evans (London), 1866 (wraps) £500
English Society at Home, Bradbury, Agnew & Co.
(London), 1880   .   .   .   .   .   . £100
ditto, Osgood (Boston), 1881   .   .   .   .   £75
Society Pictures, Bradbury, Agnew & Co. (London), 1890-
91 (2 vols) £100
English Society, Osgood, McIlvaine (London), 1897   . £50
ditto, Harper (New York), 1897   .   .   .   .   £50
Social Pictorial Satire, Harper (London), 1898   .   £35
ditto, Harper (New York), 1898   .   .   .   .   £35
A Legend of Camelot, Bradbury, Agnew & Co. (London),
1898.   .   .   .   .   £45
ditto, Harper (New York), 1898   .   .   .   .   £45
The Young du Maurier: A Selection of his Letters, Peter
Davies (London), 1951   .   .   .   .   £25/£10

LORD DUNSANY

(b.1878 d.1957)

Lord Dunsany was educated at Eton and Sandhurst, and served in the army during the Boer War and World War One. A keen sportsman and huntsman, he was at one time chess and pistol champion of Ireland. A versatile writer, Dunsany is read and appreciated today for his contributions to the genre of heroic fantasy.

Short Stories

The Gods of Pegana, Elkin Mathews (London), 1905 (grey boards with white cloth spine; drummer stamped in dark blue on front cover; 8 illustrations by Sidney Sime) . £400
ditto, Elkin Mathews (London), 1905 (grey boards with white cloth spine; drummer blind-stamped on front cover) £350
ditto, Elkin Mathews (London), 1905 (brown boards with white cloth spine; no drummer) £200
ditto, Luce (Boston), [1916]. £125
Time and the Gods, Heinemann (London), 1906 (brown boards with green cloth spine; 10 full page illustrations by Sidney Sime and one monochrome inlaid illustration on front cover) £250
ditto, Luce (Boston), 1913 . . . . . £75
ditto, Putnam's (New York), 1922 [1923] (250 copies signed by Dunsany and Sime) £350
The Sword of Welleran, George Allen (London), 1908 (10 full page illustrations by Sidney Sime'; first issue with 'GEORGE ALLEN/& SONS' at base of spine; top edge gilt) £125
ditto, George Allen (London), 1908 (second issue with 'GEORGE ALLEN' at base of spine; top edge gilt) . £100
ditto, George Allen (London), 1908 (third issue with 'GEORGE ALLEN' at base of spine; top edge plain). £90
ditto, George Allen (London), 1908 (fourth issue with 'GEORGE ALLEN/& UNWIN LTD' at base of spine; first line 3.2cm; top edge plain) £80
ditto, George Allen (London), 1908 (fifth issue with 'GEORGE ALLEN/& UNWIN LTD' at base of spine; first line 2.8cm; top edge plain) £75
ditto, Luce (New York), [no date] . . . £75
A Dreamer's Tales, George Allen (London), 1910 (9 full page illustrations by Sidney Sime) £125
ditto, Luce (New York), 1911 . . . . . £75
The Fortress Unvanquishable, Save for Sacnoth, School of Arts Press (Sheffield, UK), 1910 (30 numbered copies; blue boards with cloth spine) £500
Selections from the Writings of Lord Dunsany, Cuala Press (Dublin), 1912 (boards with cloth spine; 250 copies, Introduction by W.B. Yeats) £200
The Book of Wonder, Heinemann (London), 1912 (10 full page illustrations by Sidney Sime; light brown boards with green cloth spine; inlaid illustration on front cover) . £75
ditto, Luce (Boston), 1912 . . . . . £45
Fifty-One Tales, Elkin Mathews (London), 1915 . £75
ditto, Mitchell Kennerly (New York), 1915 . . £45
Tales of Wonder, Elkin Mathews (London), 1916 (six full page illustrations by Sidney Sime) £75
ditto, as *The Last Book of Wonder*, Luce (Boston), 1916 £60

Tales of War, Talbot Press/T. Fisher Unwin (London), 1918 . . . . £30
ditto, Little, Brown (Boston), 1918 . . . . £25
Unhappy Far Off Things, Little, Brown (Boston), 1919 £25
ditto, Elkin Mathews (London), 1919 . . . £25
Tales of Three Hemispheres, Luce (Boston), 1919 . £35
ditto, T. Fisher Unwin (London), 1920 . . £200/£35
The Travel Tales of Mr. Joseph Jorkens, Putnam's (London), 1931 . . . . . . £175/£35
ditto, Putnam's (New York), 1931 . . . £165/£35
Jorkens Remembers Africa, Longmans (New York), 1934 . . . . £150/£30
ditto, as *Mr Jorkens Remembers Africa*, Heinemann (London), 1934 . . . . . . £175/£35
Jorkens Has A Large Whiskey, Putnam (London), 1940 . . . . £175/£35
The Fourth Book of Jorkens, Jarrolds (London), [1947] (first binding black cloth) . . . . . £100/£25
ditto, Jarrolds (London), [1947] (second binding blue cloth) . . . . £65/£15
ditto, Arkham House (Sauk City, WI), 1948 . £45/£15
The Man Who Ate the Phoenix, Jarrolds (London), [1949]. . . . . £100/£20
The Little Tales of Smethers, Jarrolds (London), 1952 (first binding black cloth) . . . . . . £75/£25
ditto, Jarrolds (London), 1952 (second binding green cloth). . . . . £65/£15
Jorkens Borrows Another Whiskey, Joseph (London), 1954 . . . . £75/£15
The Edge of the World, Ballantine Adult Fantasy (New York), 1970 (pbk) £5
Beyond the Fields We Know, Ballantine Adult Fantasy (New York), 1972 (pbk) £5
Gods, Men and Ghosts: The Best Supernatural Fiction of Lord Dunsany, Dover (New York), 1972 (pbk) . . £5
Over the Hills and Far Away, Ballantine Adult Fantasy (New York), 1974 (pbk) £5

Novels

The Chronicles of Rodriguez, Putnam's (London), 1922 (frontispiece by Sidney Sime; 500 copies numbered and signed by Dunsany and Sime) . . . . £400/£200
ditto, as *Don Rodriguez, Chronicles of Shadow Valley*, Putnam's (New York), 1924 . . . . . £125/£35
The King of Elfland's Daughter, Putnam's (London), 1924 (frontispiece by Sidney Sime; 250 copies numbered and signed by Dunsany and Sime) . . . . £500/£350
ditto, Putnam's (New York), 1924 . . . . £200/£25
The Charwoman's Shadow, Putnam's (London), 1926. . . . . £200/£30
ditto, Putnam's (New York), 1926 . . . . £200/£25
The Blessing of Pan, Putnam's (London), 1927 (frontispiece by Sidney Sime) . . . . . £250/£50
ditto, Putnam's (New York), 1928 . . . £250/£50
The Curse of the Wise Woman, Heinemann (London), 1933 . . . . £150/£30
ditto, Longman's (New York), 1933 . . . . £100/£25
Up in the Hills, Heinemann (London), 1935 . £75/£15
ditto, Putnam's (New York), 1935 . . . . £65/£15
Rory and Bran, Heinemann (London), 1936 . £75/£15
ditto, Putnam's (New York), 1937 . . . . £65/£15
My Talks with Dean Spanley, Heinemann (London), 1936 (frontispiece by Sidney Sime) . . . . . £75/£15
ditto, Putnam's (New York), 1936 . . . . £65/£15

The Story of Mona Sheehy, Heinemann (London), 1939   .
.   .   .   . £100/£25
ditto, Harper (New York), 1940   .   .   .   £50/£20
Guerrilla, Heinemann (London), 1944   .   .   £35/£10
ditto, Bobbs-Merrill (Indianapolis, IN), 1944   .   £25/£5
The Strange Journeys of Colonel Polders, Jarrolds
   (London), 1950   .   .   .   .   .   £50/£20
ditto, Jarrolds (New York), 1950.   .   .   £50/£20
The Last Revolution, Jarrolds (London), 1951   .   £50/£20
His Fellow Men, Jarrolds (London), 1952   .   . £50/£20

Plays
Five Plays, Grant Richards (London), 1914   .   .   £30
ditto, Little, Brown (Boston), 1914   .   .   .   £25
Plays of Gods and Men, Talbot Press (Dublin), 1917 . £30
ditto, Luce (Boston), 1917   .   .   .   .   £25
If, Putnam's (London), 1921   .   .   .   . £45/£15
ditto, Putnam's (London), 1921 (large paper issue).   £35
ditto, Putnam's (New York), 1921   .   .   . £40/£15
The Laughter of the Gods, Putnam's (London), 1922 (from
   Plays of Gods and Men; wraps)   .   .   .   £25
The Tents of the Arabs, Putnam's (London), [1922] (from
   Plays of Gods and Men; wraps)   .   .   .   £25
The Queen's Enemies, Putnam's (London), 1922 (from
   Plays of Gods and Men; wraps)   .   .   .   £25
A Night at an Inn, Putnam's (London), 1922 (from *Plays of
   Gods and Men*; wraps) £25
Plays of Near and Far, Putnam's (London), 1922 (500
   copies) £25
ditto, Putnam's (London), 1923   .   .   . £40/£15
ditto, Putnam's (New York), 1923   .   .   . £40/£15
The Gods of the Mountain, Putnam's (London), 1923 (from
   Five Plays; wraps) £15
The Golden Dome, Putnam's (London), 1923 (from *Five
   Plays*; wraps) £15
King Argimenes and the Unknown Warrior, Putnam's
   (London), 1923 (from *Five Plays*; wraps)   .   . £15
The Glittering Gate, Putnam's (London), 1923 (from *Five
   Plays*; wraps) £15
The Lost Silk Hat, Putnam's (London), 1923 (from *Five
   Plays*; wraps) £15
The Compromise of the King of the Golden Isles, Putnam's
   (London), [1923] (from *Plays of Near and Far*; wraps)   .
.   .   .   .   £15
The Flight of the Queen, Putnam's (London), [1923] (from
   Plays of Near and Far; wraps).   .   .   .   £15
Cheezo, Putnam's (London), [1923] (from *Plays of Near and
   Far*; wraps) £15
A Good Bargain, Putnam's (London), [1923] (from *Plays of
   Near and Far*; wraps). £15
If Shakespeare Lived To-day, Putnam's (London), [1923]
   (from *Plays of Near and Far*; wraps)   .   .   £15
Fame and the Poet, Putnam's (London), [1923] (from *Plays
   of Near and Far*; wraps) £15
Alexander and Three Small Plays, Putnam's (London), 1925
.   .   .   .   £35/£15
ditto, Putnam's (London), 1925 (250 copies)   .   .   £45
ditto, Putnam's (New York), 1923   .   .   . £35/£15
Alexander, Putnam's (London), 1925 (from *Alexander, and
   Three Small Plays*; wraps). £15
The Old King's Tale, Putnam's (London), 1925 (from
   Alexander, and Three Small Plays; wraps)   .   . £15
The Evil Kettle, Putnam's (London), 1925 (from *Alexander,
   and Three Small Plays*; wraps).   .   .   .   £15

The Amusements of Khan Kharuda, Putnam's (London),
   1925 (from *Alexander, and Three Small Plays*; wraps) £15
Seven Modern Comedies, Putnam's (London), 1928   .
.   .   .   .   £25/£10
ditto, Putnam's (London), 1928 (250 copies)   .   .   £35
ditto, Putnam's (New York), 1929   .   .   . £25/£10
Atlanta in Wimbledon, Putnam's (London), 1928 (from
   Seven Modern Comedies; wraps)   .   .   .   £10
The Raffle, Putnam's (London), 1928 (from *Seven Modern
   Comedies*; wraps) £10
The Journey of the Soul, Putnam's (London), 1928 (from
   Seven Modern Comedies; wraps)   .   .   .   £10
In Holy Russia, Putnam's (London), 1928 (from *Seven
   Modern Comedies*; wraps). £10
His Sainted Grandmother, Putnam's (London), 1928 (from
   Seven Modern Comedies; wraps)   .   .   .   £10
The Hopeless Passion of Mr Bunyon, Putnam's (London),
   1928 (from *Seven Modern Comedies*; wraps)   .   . £10
The Jest of Hahalaba, Putnam's (London), 1928 (from
   Seven Modern Comedies; wraps)   .   .   .   £10
The Old Folk of the Centuries, Elkin Mathews & Marrot
   (London), 1930 (100 signed copies of 900)   . £125/£75
ditto, Elkin Mathews & Marrot (London), 1930 (800
   unsigned copies of 900)   .   .   .   . £35/£20
Lord Adrian, Golden Cockerel Press (Waltham St Lawrence,
   Berks), 1933 (325 copies, glassine d/w; seven wood
   engravings by Robert Gibbings)   .   . £150/£100
Mr Faithful, French (London), [1935] (wraps)   .   . £15
Plays for Earth and Air, Heinemann (London), 1937   .
.   .   .   .   £35/£10

Poetry
Fifty Poems, Putnam's (London), 1929 (250 numbered
   copies)   .   .   .   .   .   .   £125/£35
ditto, Putnam's (London), 1929   .   .   . £50/£20
Mirage Water, Putnam's (London), 1938.   . £45/£15
War Poems, Hutchinson (London), [1941]   .   £45/£15
Wandering Songs, Hutchinson (London), [1943] . £45/£15
A Journey, Macdonald (London), [1944] (250 copies,
   initialled 'D', leather-bound in slipcase, no d/w)   £75/£50
ditto, Macdonald (London), [1944] (trade edition) . £30/£10
The Year, Jarrolds (London), 1946   .   .   £30/£10
To Awaken Pegasus, George Ronald (Oxford, UK), 1949   .
.   .   .   .   £25/£10

Autobiography
Patches of Sunlight, Heinemann (London), 1938   . £40/£15
ditto, Reynal & Hitchcock (New York), 1938   .   £40/£15
While the Sirens Slept, Jarrolds (London), [1944]. £30/£10
The Sirens Wake, Jarrolds (London), 1945   .   £25/£10

Miscellaneous
If I Were Dictator, Methuen (London), 1934   .   £40/£10
My Ireland, Jarrolds (London), 1937.   .   £30/£10
ditto, Funk & Wagnalls (New York), 1937   .   £30/£10
ditto, Jarrolds (London), 1950 (revised edition)   £20/£5
The Donnellan Lectures, 1943, Heinemann (London), 1945
.   .   .   .   £40/£15
A Glimpse from the Watch Tower, Jarrolds (London), 1946
.   .   .   .   £30/£10
The Ghosts of the Heaviside Layer and other Phantasms,
   Owlswick Press (Philadelphia, PA), 1980   .   £20/£10

FRANCIS DURBRIDGE

(b.1912 d.1998)

Durbridge's sleuth, Paul Temple, started his career as a radio detective, but moved into film, TV and even comic strips. Temple is a crime novelist as well as a detective, and, along with his wife Steve, a Fleet Street journalist, solves many crimes in the glamorous world of the leisured upper middle classes. Durbridge's other books are similarly fast-paced thrillers with twisting plots.

'Paul Temple' Books

Send for Paul Temple, John Long (London), 1938 (with John Thewes) . . . . £150/£25
Paul Temple and the Front Page Men, John Long (London), 1939 (with Charles Hatton) . . . £150/£25
News of Paul Temple, John Long (London), [1940] (with Charles Hatton) . . . . . . £125/£25
Paul Temple Intervenes, John Long (London), [1944] (with Charles Hatton) . . . . . £125/£25
Send for Paul Temple Again!, John Long (London), [1948] (with Charles Hatton) . . . . . £125/£25
Paul Temple and the Kelby Affair, Hodder & Stoughton (London), 1970 (pbk) £25
Paul Temple and the Harkdale Robbery, Hodder & Stoughton (London), 1970 (pbk) £25
The Geneva Mystery, Hodder & Stoughton (London), 1971 (pbk) £25
The Curzon Case, Hodder & Stoughton (London), 1971 . . . . £100/£20
Paul Temple and the Margo Mystery, Hodder & Stoughton (London), 1986 . . . . . £100/£20
Paul Temple and the Madison Case, Hodder & Stoughton (London), 1988 . . . . . £75/£20

Other Books

Back Room Girl, John Long (London), [1950] . £125/£25
Beware of Johnny Washington, John Long (London), 1951 . . . . £100/£25
Design For Murder, John Long (London), 1951 . £75/£20
The Tyler Message, Hodder & Stoughton (London), 1957 (pseud 'Paul Temple', with James Douglas Rutherford MacConnell). . . . . £75/£20
The Other Man, Hodder & Stoughton (London), [1958] . . . . £75/£20
East of Algiers, Hodder & Stoughton (London), [1959] (pseud 'Paul Temple', with James Douglas Rutherford MacConnell). . . . . . . £75/£20
A Time of Day, Hodder & Stoughton (London), [1959] . . . . £75/£20
The Scarf, Hodder & Stoughton (London), [1960]. £75/£20
ditto, as *The Case of the Twisted Scarf*, Dodd, Mead (New York), 1961 . . . . £65/£20
The World of Tim Frazer, Hodder & Stoughton (London), 1962 . . . . £50/£15
ditto, Dodd, Mead (New York), 1962 . . . £50/£15
Portrait of Alison, Hodder & Stoughton (London), 1962 . . . . £65/£20
ditto, Dodd, Mead (New York), 1962 . . . £50/£15
My Friend Charles, Hodder & Stoughton (London), 1963 . . . . £75/£20
Tim Frazer Again, Hodder & Stoughton (London), 1964 . . . . £45/£15

Another Woman's Shoes, Hodder & Stoughton (London), 1965 . . . . £65/£20
The Desperate People, Hodder & Stoughton (London), [1966] . . . . £50/£15
Dead to the World, Hodder & Stoughton (London), [1967] . . . . £50/£15
My Wife Melissa, Hodder & Stoughton (London), 1967 . £50/£15
The Pig-Tail Murder, Hodder & Stoughton (London), 1969 . . . . £45/£15
A Man Called Harry Brent, Hodder & Stoughton (London), 1970 . . . . £40/£10
Bat Out Of Hell, Hodder & Stoughton (London), 1972. . £40/£10
A Game of Murder, Hodder & Stoughton (London), 1975 . . . . £40/£10
The Passenger, Hodder & Stoughton (London), 1977 . £40/£10
Tim Frazer Gets the Message, Hodder & Stoughton (London), 1978 . . . . £35/£10
Breakaway, Hodder & Stoughton (London), 1981 . £35/£10
The Doll, Hodder & Stoughton (London), 1982 . £35/£10

Plays

Suddenly at Home, French (London), 1973 (wraps) . £15
The Gentle Hook, French (London), 1975 (wraps). . £10
Murder With Love, French (London), 1977 (wraps) . £10
House Guest, French (London), 1982 (wraps). . £5
Deadly Nightcap, French (London), 1986 (wraps) . £5
A Touch of Danger, French (London), 1989 (wraps) . £5
Small Hours, French (London), 1991 (wraps). . £5
Sweet Revenge, French (London), 1993 (wraps) . £5

GERALD DURRELL

(b.1925 d.1995)

Brother of Lawrence, Gerald Durrell wrote popular travel and natural history books based on his animal-collecting expeditions. He was also a naturalist, zookeeper, television presenter, and founder of the Jersey Zoological Park in the Channel Islands. Durrell received the O.B.E. in 1982.

Non-Fiction

The Overloaded Ark, Faber & Faber (London), 1953 . . . . £45/£10
ditto, Viking (New York), 1953 . . . . £20/£5
Three Singles to Adventure, Hart Davis (London), 1954 . . . . £35/£10
The Bafut Beagles, Hart Davis (London), 1954 . £35/£10
ditto, Viking (New York), 1954 . . . . £25/£5
The Drunken Forest, Hart Davis (London), 1956 . £25/£5
ditto, Viking (New York), 1956 . . . . £25/£5
My Family and Other Animals, Hart Davis (London), 1956 . . . . £100/£15
ditto, Viking (New York), 1957 . . . . £75/£10
Encounters with Animals, Hart Davis (London), 1958 . . . . £15/£5
A Zoo in My Luggage, Hart Davis (London), 1960 £35/£5
ditto, Viking (New York), 1956 . . . . £20/£5
The Whispering Land, Hart Davis (London), 1961 £15/£5
ditto, Viking (New York), 1962 . . . . £10/£5

Menagerie Manor, Hart Davis (London), 1964 . £15/£5
ditto, Viking (New York), 1964 . . . . . £10/£5
Two in the Bush, Collins (London), 1966 . £15/£5
ditto, Viking (New York), 1966 . . . . . £10/£5
Birds, Beasts & Relatives, Collins (London), 1969 £15/£5
ditto, Viking (New York), 1969 . . . . . £10/£5
Fillets of Plaice, Collins (London), 1971 . . £15/£5
ditto, Viking (New York), 1971 . . . . . £10/£5
Catch Me a Colobus, Collins (London), 1972 . £15/£5
ditto, Viking (New York), 1972 . . . . . £10/£5
Beasts in My Belfry, Collins (London), 1973 . £15/£5
The Stationary Ark, Collins (London), 1976 . £15/£5
ditto, Simon & Schuster (New York), 1976 . £10/£5
Golden Bats and Pink Pigeons, Collins (London), 1977 .
   . . . . £15/£5
ditto, Simon & Schuster (New York), 1977 . £10/£5
The Garden of the Gods, Collins (London), 1978 . £15/£5
The Amateur Naturalist, Hamish Hamilton (London), 1982
   . . . . £15/£5
ditto, as *A Practical Guide for the Amateur Naturalist*,
   Knopf (New York), 1983 . . . . . £10/£5
How to Shoot an Amateur Naturalist, Collins (London),
   1982 . . . . £10/£5
ditto, Little, Brown (Boston), 1984 . . . £10/£5
Durrell in Russia, McDonald (London), 1986 (with Lee
   Durrell) . . . . £10/£5
ditto, Simon & Schuster (New York), 1986 . £10/£5
Ark's Anniversary, Collins (London), 1990 . £10/£5
ditto, Arcade (New York), 1991 . . . . £10/£5
Gerald Durrell's Army, J. Murray (London), 1992. £10/£5
Best of Durrell, HarperCollins (London), 1996 . £10/£5

Novels
Rosy Is My Relative, Collins (London), 1968 . £35/£5
ditto, Viking (New York), 1968 . . . . £15/£5
The Mockery Bird, Collins (London), 1981 . £15/£5
ditto, Simon & Schuster (New York), 1981 . £10/£5

Short Stories
The Picnic & Suchlike Pandemonium, Collins (London),
   1979 . . . . £15/£5
ditto, as *The Picnic & Other Inimitable Stories*, Simon &
   Schuster (New York), 1980 . . . . £15/£5

Children's Titles
The New Noah, Collins (London), 1955 . . £30/£10
ditto, Viking (New York), 1964 . . . . £20/£5
Island Zoo, Collins (London), 1961 . . £30/£10
ditto, MacRae Smith (Philadelphia, PA), 1963. £15/£5
Look at Zoos, Collins (London), 1961 . . £25/£5
My Favourite Animal Stories, Collins (London), 1962. .
   . . . . £15/£5
The Donkey Rustlers, Collins (London), 1968 . £25/£5
ditto, Viking (New York), 1968 . . . . £25/£5
The Talking Parcel, Collins (London), 1974 . £25/£5
ditto, Lippincott (Philadelphia, PA), 1975. . £25/£5
Fantastic Flying Journey, Conran Octopus (London), 1987
   . . . . £15/£5
ditto, Simon & Schuster (New York), 1987 . £15/£5
Animal Family Adventures with Gerald Durrell, Price Stern
   Sloan (New York), 1988 . . . . . £10/£5
Fantastic Dinosaur Adventure, Conran Octopus (London),
   1989 . . . . £10/£5
ditto, Simon & Schuster (New York), 1989 . £10/£5

Toby the Tortoise, M. O'Mara Books (London), 1991 .
   . . . . £10/£5
ditto, Little, Brown (Boston), 1991 . . . £10/£5

LAWRENCE DURRELL
(b.1912 d.1990)

Lawrence Durrell was the older brother of the naturalist
Gerald. A novelist, poet, dramatist and travel writer,
Lawrence was born in India, and at the age of eleven was
sent home to attend school in England. However, he was
never happy there and left as soon as he could. Much of
Durrell's work owes a debt to the Mediterranean, where he
spent most of the rest of his life.

Poetry
Quaint Fragment, privately printed by the Cecil Press
   (London), 1931 (red boards) . . . £12,500
ditto, Cecil Press (London), 1931 (blue wraps) . £10,000
Ten Poems, Caduceus Press (London), 1932 (wraps) £2,000
ditto, Caduceus Press (London), 1932 (12 signed copies in
   cloth) £5,000
Ballade of Slow Decay, privately printed, 1932 (single sheet,
   folded) £1,500
Transition, Caduceus Press (London), 1934 (no d/w) £1,500
A Private Country, Faber (London), 1943 . £125/£25
Cities, Plains and People, Faber (London), 1946 . £45/£10
On Seeming to Presume, Faber (London), 1948 . £45/£10
Deus Loci, privately printed (Ischia, Italy), 1950 (200 signed
   copies; stapled wraps) £200
The Tree of Idleness, Faber (London), 1955 . £30/£10
Selected Poems, Faber (London), 1956 . . £25/£10
ditto, Faber (London), 1956 (wraps) £5
ditto, Grove Press (New York), 1956. . . £25/£10
Collected Poems, Faber (London), 1960 . . £35/£10
ditto, Dutton (New York), 1960 . . . . £35/£10
Beccafico Le Becfigue, La Licorne (Montpellier, France),
   1963 (150 signed copies; stapled wraps) . . £100
La Descente du Styx, La Murène (France), 1964 (250 signed
   copies; wraps) £75
ditto, as *Down the Styx*, Capricorn Press (Santa Barbara,
   CA), 1971 (200 of 1,000 copies) £75
ditto, as *Down the Styx*, Capricorn Press (Santa Barbara,
   CA), 1971 (800 of 1,000 copies; wraps). . . £10
Selected Poems, 1935-1963, Faber (London), 1964 (pbk) £5
The Ikons, Faber (London), 1966 . . . £25/£10
ditto, Dutton (New York), 1967 . . . . £20/£5
Nothing Is Lost, Sweet Self, Turret (London), 1967 (100
   signed copies; white wraps with gree d/w) . £100/£65
In Arcadia, Turret (London), 1968 (100 signed copies; grey
   wraps with d/w illustrated in blue and purple) . £100/£65
The Red Limbo Lingo: A Poetry Notebook, Faber (London),
   1971 (500 numbered copies of 1,200, glassine d/w,
   slipcase). . . . . £50/£35
ditto, Faber (London), 1971 (100 signed, glassine d/w,
   slipcase) . . . . £75/£50
ditto, Dutton (New York), 1971 (500 numbered copies,
   glassine d/w, slipcase) . . . . . £50/£35
ditto, Dutton (New York), 1971 (100 signed, numbered
   copies, glassine d/w, slipcase) . . . . £75/£50

On the Suchness of the Old Boy, Turret (London), 1972
(226 signed copies; wraps) £75
Vega and Other Poems, Faber (London), 1973 . £25/£5
ditto, Overlook Press (Woodstock, NY), 1973. . £25/£5
Lifelines - Four Poems, Tragara Press (Edinburgh), 1974
(15 signed copies of 115; wraps) £250
ditto, Tragara Press (Edinburgh), 1974 (100 copies of 115;
wraps) £75
ditto, Tragara Press (Edinburgh), 1974 (25 'extra' author's
copies, usually inscribed) £250
Selected Poems, Faber (London), 1977 . . . £25/£10
Collected Poems: 1931-1974, Faber (London), 1980 £25/£10
ditto, Faber (London), 1980 (26 signed copies, with signed
etching by Henry Moore, slipcase) £750
ditto, Viking (New York), 1980 . . . . £20/£10

Parody
Bromo Bombasts, Caduceus Press (London), 1933 (pseud
'Gaffer Peeslake', 100 copies; black boards with paper
label) £2,000

Novels
Pied Piper of Lovers, Cassell (London), 1935. £2,000/£450
Panic Spring, Faber (London), 1937 (pseud 'Charles
Norden') . . . . £2,000/£750
ditto, Covici Friede (New York), 1937 . £1,000/£250
The Black Book: An Agon, Obelisk Press (Paris), 1938
(pbk) £400
ditto, Obelisk Press (Paris), 1959 (pbk with d/w) . £65/£25
ditto, Dutton (New York), 1960 . . . . £40/£10
ditto, Faber (London), 1973 . . . . . £20/£5
Cefalû, Editions Poetry (London), 1947 . . . £125/£30
ditto, as *The Dark Labyrinth*, Ace (New York), 1958 (pbk)
. . . . £10
ditto, as *The Dark Labyrinth*, Faber (London), 1961 £25/£10
Justine, Faber (London), 1957 . . . . . £750/£65
ditto, Dutton (New York), 1957 . . . . £250/£25
White Eagles over Serbia, Faber (London), 1957 . £50/£25
ditto, Criterion (New York), 1957 . . . . £50/£25
Balthazar, Faber (London), 1958 . . . . £200/£25
ditto, Dutton (New York), 1958 . . . . £65/£10
Mountolive, Faber (London), 1958 . . . . £175/£25
ditto, Dutton (New York), 1959 . . . . £45/£10
Clea, Faber (London), 1960. . . . . . £125/£20
ditto, Dutton (New York), 1960 . . . . £35/£5
The Alexandria Quartet, Faber (London), 1962 . £75/£25
ditto, Faber (London), 1962 (500 signed copies, slipcase) .
. . . . £500/£400
ditto, Dutton (New York), 1962 . . . . £65/£20
ditto, Dutton (New York), 1962 (199 signed, numbered
copies; slipcase) . . . . . . £300/£250
Tunc, Faber (London), 1968 . . . . . £25/£5
ditto, Dutton (New York), 1968 . . . . £20/£5
Nunquam, Faber (London), 1970 . . . . £25/£5
ditto, Dutton (New York), 1970 . . . . £15/£5
The Revolt of Aphrodite, Faber (London), 1973 . £25/£10
Monsieur or The Prince of Darkness, Faber (London), 1974
. . . . £20/£5
ditto, Viking (New York), 1974 . . . . £15/£5
Livia or Buried Alive, Faber (London), 1978 . . £15/£5
ditto, Viking (New York), 1979 . . . . £10/£5
Constance or Solitary Practices, Faber (London), 1982 .
. . . . £10/£5
ditto, Viking (New York), 1982 . . . . £15/£5

Sebastian or Ruling Passions, Faber (London), 1983 £15/£5
ditto, Viking (New York), 1984 . . . . £15/£5
Quinx or The Ripper's Tale, Faber (London), 1985 £15/£5
ditto, Viking (New York), 1985 . . . . £10/£5
The Avignon Quintet, Faber (London), 1992 . . £15/£5

Plays
Sappho, Faber (London), 1950 . . . . . £45/£10
ditto, Dutton (New York), 1958 . . . . £20/£5
An Irish Faustus: A Morality in Nine Scenes, Faber
(London), 1963 . . . . £20/£5
ditto, Dutton (New York), 1964 . . . . £15/£5
ditto, Delos (Birmingham, UK), 1987 (75 signed, numbered
copies, no d/w) £65
Acte, Faber (London), 1965 . . . . . £15/£5
ditto, Dutton (New York), 1965 . . . . £15/£5

Short Stories
Zero and Asylum in the Snow, privately printed (Rhodes),
1946 (50 copies; wraps) £650
ditto, as *Two Excursions into Reality*, Circle Editions
(Berkeley, CA), 1947 . . . . . . £25/£10
Esprit de Corps: Sketches from Diplomatic Life, Faber
(London), 1957 . . . . £35/£10
ditto, Dutton (New York), 1958 . . . . £25/£10
Stiff Upper Lip, Faber (London), 1958 . . . £35/£10
ditto, Dutton (New York), 1959 . . . . £30/£10
Sauve Qui Peut, Faber (London), 1966 . . . £20/£5
ditto, Dutton (New York), 1967 . . . . £15/£5
The Best of Antrobus, Faber (London), 1974 . . £15/£5
Antrobus Complete, Faber (London), 1985 . . £15/£5

Non-Fiction
*Prospero's Cell: A Guide to the Landscape and Manners of
the Island of Corcyra*, Faber (London), 1945 . £75/£15
ditto, Dutton (New York), 1960 . . . . £35/£10
Key to Modern Poetry, Nevill (London), 1952 . £35/£10
Reflections on a Marine Venus, Faber (London), 1953 .
. . . . £75/£15
ditto, Dutton (New York), 1960 . . . . £35/£5
Bitter Lemons, Faber (London), 1957 . . . £75/£10
ditto, Dutton (New York), 1958 . . . . £60/£10
Art and Outrage, Putnam (London), 1959 . £49/£10
ditto, Dutton (New York), 1960 . . . . £35/£10
*Lawrence Durrell and Henry Miller: A Private
Correspondence*, Dutton (New York), 1963 . . £25/£10
ditto, Faber (London), 1963 . . . . . £25/£10
Spirit of Place: Letters and Essays on Travel, Faber
(London), 1969 . . . . £30/£10
ditto, Dutton (New York), 1969 . . . . £30/£10
Le Grand Suppositoire, Editions Pierre Belfond (Paris),
1972 . . . . £15/£5
ditto, as *The Big Supposer*, Abelard-Schuman (London),
1973 (English translation) . . . . . £15/£5
ditto, as *The Big Supposer*, Grove Press (New York), 1974.
. . . . £15/£5
Blue Thirst, Capra Press (Santa Barbara, CA), 1975 (250
signed copies, glassine d/w) . . . . £65/£45
ditto, Capra Press (Santa Barbara, CA), 1975 (10 signed,
lettered copies, glassine d/w) . . . . £300/£250
ditto, Capra Press (Santa Barbara, CA), 1975 (pbk) . £5
Sicilian Carousel, Faber (London), 1977 . . £15/£5
ditto, Viking (New York), 1977 . . . . £15/£5
The Greek Islands, Faber (London), 1978 . . £15/£5

ditto, Viking (New York), 1978 . . . . . £15/£5

A Smile in the Mind's Eye, Wildwood House (London),
1980 . . . . £15/£5

*Literary Lifelines: The Richard Aldington-Lawrence
Durrell Correspondence*, Faber (London), 1981 . £15/£5

ditto, Viking (New York), 1981 . . . . . £15/£5

The Durrell-Miller Letters: 1935-80, New Directions
(Norfolk, CT), 1988 . . . . . . £20/£5

ditto, Faber (London), 1988 . . . . . . £20/£5

Letters to Jean Fanchette, 1958-1963, Editions Two Cities
(Paris), 1988 (1,800 of 2,000 copies; wraps) . . £15

ditto, Editions Two Cities (Paris), 1988 (200 signed copies of
2,000; wraps) £150

Caesar's Vast Ghost: Aspects of Provence, Faber (London),
1990 . . . . £10/£5

ditto, Arcade (New York), 1990 . . . . . £10/£5

UMBERTO ECO
(b.1932)

Eco is an Italian semiotician with an interest in the philosophical and aesthetic theories of the Middle Ages. He is
best known, however, for two novels, *The Name of the
Rose* and *Foucault's Pendulum*. His novels are often dense
and intricate, with references to arcane historical characters
and texts, but they have nevertheless become bestsellers
and have been translated into many languages.

Novels

The Name of the Rose, Secker & Warburg (London), 1984.
. . . . £300/£35

ditto, Harcourt Brace (New York), 1984 . . £75/£15

Foucault's Pendulum, Secker & Warburg (London), 1989 .
. . . . £25/£10

ditto, Harcourt Brace (New York), 1989 . . £25/£10

ditto, Franklin Library (Franklin Centre, PA), 1989 (signed,
limited edition) £100

The Island of the Day Before, Harcourt Brace (New York),
1994 . . . . £10/£5

ditto, Harcourt Brace (New York), 1994 (250 signed copies,
slipcase). . . . . £75/£50

ditto, Secker & Warburg (London), 1995 . . £10/£5

Baudolino, Harcourt Brace (New York), 2002 . £10/£5

ditto, Secker & Warburg (London), 2002 . . £10/£5

The Mysterious Flame of Queen Loana, Harcourt Brace &
World (Orlando, FL), 2004 . . . . £10/£5

ditto, Secker & Warburg (London), 2005 . . . £10/£5

Children's Titles (with Eugenio Carmi)

The Three Astronauts, Secker & Warburg (London), 1989 .
. . . . £25/£10

ditto, Harcourt Brace (New York), 1989 . . £25/£10

The Bomb and the General, Secker & Warburg (London),
1989 . . . . £25/£10

ditto, Harcourt Brace (New York), 1989 . . £25/£10

Academic and Other Titles

The Picture History of Inventions, Macmillan (New York),
1963 (with G.B. Zorzoli) . . . . . £40/£10

The Bond Affair, Macdonald (New York), 1966 (with Oreste
del Buono) . . . . £75/£20

ditto, Macdonald (London), 1966 . . . £75/£20

A Theory of Semiotics, Indiana Univ Press (Bloomington,
IN), 1976 . . . . £45/£15

*The Role of the Reader Explorations in the Semiotics of
Texts*, Indiana Univ Press (Bloomington, IN), 1979 . .
. . . . £30/£10

The Sign of Three: Dupin, Holmes, Peirce, Indiana Univ
Press (Bloomington, IN), 1983 (edited by Eco and Thomas
A. Sebeok) . . . . £25/£10

Reflections on The Name of the Rose, Secker & Warburg
(London), 1983 . . . . £20/£5

ditto, as *Postscript to The Name of the Rose*, Harcourt Brace
(New York), 1984 . . . . . . £20/£5

Semiotics and the Philosophy of Language, Indiana Univ
Press (Bloomington, IN), 1984. . . . £25/£10

Travels in Hyperreality, Harcourt Brace (New York), 1986.
. . . . £25/£5

Art and Beauty in the Middle Ages, Yale Univ Press (New
Haven, CT), 1986 . . . . . . £25/£10

How to Travel With A Salmon, Harcourt Brace (New York),
1989 . . . . £15/£5

The Open Work, Hutchinson Radius (London), 1989 (wraps)
. . . . £10

Limits of Interpretation, Indiana Univ Press (Bloomington,
IN), 1990 . . . . £30/£10

Misreadings, Harcourt Brace (New York), 1993 (wraps) £20

ditto, Cape (London), 1993 . . . . . £25/£10

Apocalypse Postponed, Indiana Univ Press (Bloomington,
IN), 1994 . . . . £30/£10

Six Walks in the Fictional Woods, Harvard Univ Press
(Bloomington, IN), 1994 . . . . . £25/£10

The Search for the Perfect Language, Blackwell (Oxford),
1995 . . . . £40/£10

Serendipities: Language and Lunacy, Univ of Columbia
Press (New York), 1998 . . . . . £15/£5

ditto, Weidenfeld & Nicolson (London), 1999. . £15/£5

Talking of Joyce, Univ College Dublin Press (Dublin), 1998
(Lectures delivered by Eco and Liberato Santoro-Brienza)
. . . . £10

*Kant and the Platypus: Essays on Language and
Cognition*, Secker & Warburg (London), 1999 . £20/£5

ditto, Harcourt Brace (New York), 2000 . . £20/£5

Experiences in Translation, Univ Of Toronto Press
(Toronto, Canada), 2001 . . . . . £25/£10

History of Beauty, Rizzoli International Publications (New
York), 2004 (edited by Eco) . . . . £20/£10

ditto, as *On Beauty: A History of a Western Idea*, Secker &
Warburg (London), 2004 . . . . . £20/£10

On Literature, Harcourt Brace (New York), 2004 . £20/£10

Mouse or Rat?: Translation as Negotiation, Weidenfeld &
Nicolson, London, 2003 . . . . . £10/£5

On Ugliness, Rizzoli International Publications (New York),
2007 (edited by Eco) . . . . . . £10/£5

ditto, Harvill Secker (London), 2007. . . . £10/£5

Turning Back the Clock: Hot Wars and Media, Harcourt
Brace (New York), 2006 . . . . . £10/£5

ditto, Harvill Secker (London), 2007. . . . £10/£5

BERESFORD EGAN

(b.1905 d.1984)

Egan has been described as 'the 1920s Aubrey Beardsley'. As an artist, his wickedly satirical black-and-white line drawings were at their most effective in *The Sink of Solitude*, a lampoon of Radclyffe Hall's *The Well of Loneliness* and the outraged reactions to her book.

Written and Illustrated by Egan

The Sink of Solitude: A Broadside, preface by P.R. Stevensen, lampoons by various hands, Hermes Press (London), 1928 (250 numbered, signed copies) . . £175
ditto, Hermes Press (London), 1928 (wraps) . . . £45
Policeman of The Lord: A Political Satire, Sophistocles Press (London), 1929 (500 numbered copies) . . £175
ditto, Sophistocles Press (London), 1929 (wraps) . . £45
Pollen, Denis Archer (London), 1933 (patterned boards, printed glassine d/w) . . . . . . £60/£30
ditto, Denis Archer (London), 1933 (orange boards, printed glassine d/w). . . . . £50/£20
No Sense in Form: A Tragedy of Manners, Denis Archer (London), 1933 . . . . £145/£45
But The Sinners Triumph, Fortune Press (London), 1934 .
. . . . £125/£35
Epitaph, A Double Bedside Book for Singular People, Fortune Press (London), [1943] . . . £75/£25
Epilogue, A Potpourri of Prose, Verse and Drawings, Fortune Press (London), [1946] . . . £75/£20
Bun-Ho!, Floris Bakeries Ltd (London), 1959 (edited and decorated by Egan) £50
Storicards, Barrigan Press (London), 1960 (5 cards) . .
. . . . £50 the set

Illustrated by Egan

Les Fleurs du Mal, In Pattern and Prose, by Baudelaire, translated by C. Bower Adcock, Sophistocles Press and T. Werner Laurie (London), 1929 (500 signed copies) . £150
ditto, Godwin (New York), 1933 (pirated edition) . £40/£15
ditto, as *Flowers of Evil*, Sylvan Press (New York), 1947 (1,499 numbered copies) . . . . . £40/£25
ditto, as *Flowers of Evil*, Sylvan Press (New York), 1947 (unnumbered copies) £20
Aphrodite, by Pierre Loüys, The Fortune Press (London), 1928 [1929] (1,075 copies) . . . . £100/£40
Cyprian Masques, by Pierre Loüys, The Fortune Press (London), 1929 . . . . £125/£65
De Sade, by Beresford Egan and Brian de Shane, The Fortune Press (London), 1929 (1,600 copies) £200/£100
ditto, by Beresford Egan and Brian de Shane, The Fortune Press (London), 1929 (100 numbered and signed copies bound in morocco, with one different plate) . . £300
The Adventures of King Pausole, by Pierre Loüys, Fortune Press (London), 1929 [1931] (1,200 copies) . £125/£65
ditto, Godwin (New York), 1933 (pirated edition) . £35/£20
Income and Outcome: A Study in Personal Finance, by Nigel Balchin, Hamish Hamilton (London), 1936 . £40
Pobottle Stories, by Nigel Balchin, Heavy Duty Alloys Ltd, 1935-39 (advertising, 7 booklets; wraps) . £150 the set

Others

Moonchild: A Prologue, by Aleister Crowley, Mandrake Press (London), 1929 (d/w design by Egan) . £1,250/£200

Beast or Man?, by Sean M'Guire, Palmer (London), c.1930 (d/w design by Egan) . . . . . £65/£10
This Modern Stuff, by Gerald Abraham, Denis Archer (London), 1933 (d/w design by Egan) . . . £50/£5
Beresford Egan: An Introduction to His Work, by Paul Allen, Scorpion Press (London), 1966 (limited edition) .
. . . . £30/£15
ditto, Scorpion Press (London), 1966 (25 signed copies, with extra plate) . . . . £100/£75
Beresford Egan, by Adrian Woodhouse, Tartarus Press (Carlton-in-Coverdale, Yorkshire), 2005 (750 copies) .
. . . . £45/£15

GEORGE ELIOT

(b.1819 d.1880)

George Eliot was the pseudonym of Mary Anne Evans, novelist, critic and poet. Her great achievement is her detailed depiction of character and motivation in middle-class provincial society. Evans used a male pseudonym to ensure that her work was taken seriously, for although Victorian women writers published freely under their own names, she did not want to be thought of as a writer of romances.

Novels

Adam Bede, Blackwood (Edinburgh/London), 1859 (3 vols, original orange/brown cloth) £3,000
ditto, Blackwood (Edinburgh/London), 1859 (3 vols, rebound) £800
ditto, Harper (New York), 1859 . . . . . £300
The Mill on the Floss, Blackwood (Edinburgh/London), 1860 (3 vols, original orange/brown cloth) . . £1,250
ditto, Blackwood (Edinburgh/London), 1860 (3 vols, rebound) £300
ditto, Harper (New York), 1860 . . . . £200
Silas Marner, The Weaver of Raveloe, Blackwood (Edinburgh/London), 1861 (original orange/brown cloth) .
. . . . £600
ditto, Blackwood (Edinburgh/London), 1861 (rebound) £150
ditto, Harper (New York), 1860 (boards) . . . £100
ditto, Harper (New York), 1860 (wraps) . . . £200
Romola, Smith, Elder & Co. (London), 1863 (3 vols, first issue with 2 pages of ads at end of vol. 2, original green cloth) £1,000
ditto, Blackwood (Edinburgh/London), 1863 (3 vols, rebound) £200
ditto, Smith, Elder & Co. (London), 1863 (3 vols, second issue) £750
ditto, Harper (New York), 1863 . . . . . £125
Felix Holt, The Radical, Blackwood (Edinburgh/London), 1866 (3 vols, original brown cloth). . . . £750
ditto, Harper (New York), 1866 . . . . . £75
Middlemarch, A Study of Provincial Life, Blackwood (Edinburgh/London), 1871-1872 (8 parts, pictorial green wraps) £3,000
ditto, Blackwood (Edinburgh/London), 1871-1872 (8 parts bound together as vols) £2,000
ditto, Harper (New York), 1872 (2 vols) . . . £50
ditto, Blackwood (Edinburgh/London), 1874 (4 vols in blue cloth) £2,000

Daniel Deronda, Blackwood (Edinburgh/London), 1874-
1876 (8 parts, with erratum slip in part 3, blue/grey wraps)
. . . . £2,500
ditto, Blackwood (Edinburgh/London), 1874-1876 (8 parts,
without erratum slip in part 3, blue/grey wraps) . £2,000
ditto, Blackwood (Edinburgh/London), 1874-1876 (8 parts
bound together as 1 vol.) £1,250
ditto, Blackwood (Edinburgh/London), 1876 (4 vols in dark
maroon cloth) £1,250
ditto, Harper (New York), 1876 (2 vols) £125

Short Stories

Scenes of Clerical Life, Blackwood (Edinburgh/London),
1858 (2 vols, original dark maroon cloth) . . £7,500
ditto, Blackwood (Edinburgh/London), 1858 (2 vols, rebound) £1,000
ditto, Harper (New York), 1858 . . . . . £150

Essays

Impressions of Theophrastus Such, Blackwood (Edinburgh/
London), 1879 (original grey/brown cloth) . . . £175
ditto, Harper (New York), 1879 . . . . . £75
Essays and Leaves from a Note-Book, Blackwood
(Edinburgh/London), 1884 (original brown cloth) . £150

Poetry

The Spanish Gypsy, Blackwood (Edinburgh/London), 1868
(original blue cloth) £200
ditto, Ticknor & Fields (Boston), 1868 . . . £75
The Legend of Jubal and Other Poems, Blackwood
(Edinburgh/London), 1874 . . . . . £125
ditto, Osgood (New York), 1874. . . . . £35

Translations

The Life of Jesus, Critically Examined by D.F. Strauss,
Chapman (London), 1846 (3 vols, lilac or green cloth;
anonymous 'Translated from the Fourth German Edition')
. . . . £3,500
Feuerbach's Essence of Christianity, Chapman (London),
1854 (3 vols, black cloth; translated by Marian Evans) .
. . . . £1,500
ditto, Chapman (London), 1854 (3 vols, purple cloth) £1,000

T.S. ELIOT

(b.1888 d.1965)

The American-born poet, critic and dramatist lived most of
his adult life in England, although he spent a great deal of
time in the 1920s with other writers and artists in
Montparnasse, Paris. In 1948 Eliot was awarded the Order
of Merit by King George VI, and the Nobel Prize for
Literature for 'remarkable achievements as a pioneer within
modern poetry'.

Poetry

Prufrock and Other Observations, Egoist Ltd (London),
1917 (wraps). £10,000
Poems, Hogarth Press (Richmond, Surrey), 1919 (early
copies of 250 with 'aestival' for 'estivale' on p.13; sewn
wraps) £7,500
ditto, Hogarth Press (Richmond, Surrey), 1919 (later copies
of 250 with misprints corrected p.13; sewn wraps) £3,500

Ara Vus Prec (sic), Ovid Press (London), 1920 (30 signed,
numbered copies) £5,000
ditto, Ovid Press (London), 1920 (220 numbered copies) .
. . . . £2,000
ditto, Ovid Press (London), 1920 (10 unnumbered copies,
although there were probably more) . . . £1,000
ditto, as *Poems*, Knopf (New York), 1920 . £1,250/£200
The Waste Land, Boni & Liveright (New York), 1922
(approx 500 of 1,000 numbered copies with flexible black
cloth, with 'mountain' spelt correctly on p. 41, line 339)
. . . . £4,000
ditto, Boni & Liveright (New York), 1922 (later copies,
approx 500 of 1,000 numbered copies, with stiff black
cloth and 'a' dropped from 'mountain' on p. 41, line 339).
. . . . £2,500
ditto, Hogarth Press (Richmond, Surrey), 1923 (blue marbled
paper boards, white paper label to upper board printed in
black) £4,000
ditto, Faber (London), [1962] (300 numbered, signed copies)
. . . . £2,000
Homage to John Dryden, Hogarth Press (London), 1924
(sewn wraps) £75
Poems, 1909-1925, Faber & Gwyer (London), 1925 . .
. . . . £1,000/£250
ditto, Faber & Gwyer (London), 1925 (85 numbered and
signed copies) £4,000
ditto, Harcourt Brace (New York), 1932 . . . £250/£40
Journey of the Magi, Faber & Gwyer (London), 1927 (sewn
wraps) £35
ditto, Faber & Gwyer (London), 1927 (350 copies with
glassine d/w). . . . . . . £200/£175
ditto, Rudge (New York), 1927 (27 copies, copyright edition)
. . . . £1,250
A Song for Simeon, Faber & Gwyer (London), 1928 (sewn
wraps) £25
ditto, Faber & Gwyer (London), 1928 (500 numbered, signed
large paper copies) . . . . . . £400/£300
Animula, Faber (London), [1929] (wraps) . . . £25
ditto, Faber (London), [1929] (400 numbered, signed copies,
slipcase). . . . . £400/£300
Ash-Wednesday, Faber (London), 1930 . . £200/£65
ditto, Faber/Fountain Press (London), 1930 (600 signed
copies, glassine d/w with white paper flaps, slipcase). .
. . . . £1,500/£750
ditto, Putnam (New York), 1930. . . . . £150/£20
Marina, Faber (London), [1930] (wraps) . . . £50
ditto, Faber (London), [1930] (400 numbered, signed copies)
. . . . £265
Triumphal March, Faber (London), 1931 (wraps). . £45
ditto, Faber (London), 1931 (300 numbered, signed copies,
no d/w) £275
Collected Poems, 1909-1935, Faber (London), 1936 . .
. . . . £45/£15
ditto, Harcourt Brace (New York), 1936 . . . £25/£10
Old Possum's Book of Practical Cats, Faber (London), 1939
. . . . £1,500/£75
ditto, Harcourt Brace (New York), 1939 . . . £750/£75
The Waste Land and Other Poems, Faber (London), 1940 .
. . . . £35/£10
ditto, Harcourt Brace (New York), 1955 . . . £25/£10
East Coker, New English Weekly (London), 1940 (stapled,
unbound supplement). £1,000
ditto, New English Weekly (London), 1940 (reprint,
identified as such on cover, of 500 copies) . . £400

ditto, Faber (London), 1940 (yellow wraps) . . . £150
Burnt Norton, Faber (London), 1941 (wraps) . . £75
The Dry Salvages, Faber (London), 1941 (wraps) . £125
Little Gidding, Faber (London), 1942 (wraps) . . £100
Four Quartets, Harcourt Brace (New York), 1943 (first issue states 'First American edition') . . . £1,250/£150
ditto, Harcourt Brace (New York), 1943 (second issue does not state 'First American edition') . . . £350/£150
ditto, Faber (London), 1944 . . . . . £200/£45
ditto, Faber (London), 1960 (290 signed copies) . £2,000
A Practical Possum, Harvard Univ Printing Office (Cambridge, MA), 1947 (80 numbered copies; wraps) . £1,500
Selected Poems, Penguin (Harmondsworth, Middlesex), 1948 (wraps). £10
ditto, Harcourt Brace (New York), 1967 . . . £25/£10
The Undergraduate Poems, Harvard Advocate (Cambridge, MA), 1949 (unauthorised publication, 1,000 copies; wraps) £35
Poems Written in Early Youth, privately printed (Stockholm), 1950 (12 copies only) . . . £2,000
ditto, Faber (London), 1967 . . . . . £50/£15
ditto, Farrar Straus (New York), 1967 . . . £30/£10
The Complete Poems and Plays, *1909-1950*, Harcourt Brace (New York), 1952 . . . . . £65/£25
The Cultivation of Christmas Trees, Faber (London), 1954 (wraps & envelope) . . . . . . £30/£20
ditto, Farrar Straus (New York), 1956 (no d/w) . £20
Collected Poems, *1909-1962*, Faber (London), 1963 £35/£10
ditto, Farrar Straus (New York), 1963 . . . £35/£10
The Complete Poems and Plays, Faber (London), 1968 . . . . £65/£20
The Waste Land: A Facsimile and Transcript, Faber (London), 1971 . . . . . . £35/£10
ditto, Faber (London), 1971 (500 copies, in slipcase) . . . . £100/£65
ditto, Harcourt Brace (New York), 1971 . . . £35/£10

Prose

Ezra Pound: His Metric and Poetry, Knopf (New York), 1917 . . . . £225
The Sacred Wood, Methuen (London), 1920 (first issue with 3mm 'Methuen' on spine and d/w without subtitle on front) . . . . £1,000/£150
ditto, Methuen (London), 1920 (second issue with 3.5mm 'Methuen' at foot of spine and d/w with subtitle on front and 'Books by A. Clutton-Brock' on back) . £400/£100
ditto, Methuen (London), 1920 (third issue with 8pps of ads after p.156) . . . . £300/£50
ditto, Knopf (New York), 1921 . . . . £1,000/£150
Shakespeare and the Stoicism of Seneca, O.U.P. (Oxford, UK), 1927 (sewn wraps) £150
For Lancelot Andrewes, Faber & Gwyer (London), 1928 . . . . £150/£25
ditto, Doubleday (New York), 1929 . . . . £125/£15
Dante, Faber (London), 1929 (grey d/w) . . £150/£35
ditto, Faber (London), 1929 (125 numbered, signed copies, glassine d/w). . . . . . . £750/£700
Thoughts After Lambeth, Faber (London), 1931 (sewn wraps) £25
ditto, Faber (London), 1931 (boards). . . £125/£25
Charles Whibley: A Memoir, O.U.P. (Oxford, UK), 1931 (sewn wraps) £15
John Dryden: The Poet, the Dramatist, the Critic, Holliday (New York), 1931 . . . . . £125/£20

ditto, Holliday (New York), 1931 (110 signed, numbered copies) £500
Selected Essays, *1917-1931*, Faber (London), 1932 £250/£20
ditto, Faber (London), 1932 (115 numbered, signed copies, cellophane d/w) . . . . . £1,500/£1,400
ditto, Harcourt Brace (New York), 1932 . . . £125/£20
The Use of Poetry and the Use of Criticism, Faber (London), 1933 . . . . £225/£20
ditto, Harvard Univ Press (Cambridge, MA), 1933. £175/£15
After Strange Gods: A Primer of Modern Heresey, Faber (London), 1934 . . . . £200/£25
ditto, Harcourt Brace (New York), 1934 . . . £125/£20
Elizabethan Essays, Faber (London), 1934 (first issue with misprint 'No.21' for 'No.23' on half title) . £100/£35
ditto, Faber (London), 1934 (second issue with error corrected, spine blocked in gold) . . . £85/£25
ditto, Faber (London), 1934 (third issue 18cm high, error corrected, spine blocked in silver) . . . £65/£20
Essays Ancient and Modern, Faber (London), 1936 £65/£20
ditto, Harcourt Brace (New York), 1936 . . £50/£15
The Idea of a Christian Society, Faber (London), 1939 . . . . £35/£10
ditto, Harcourt Brace (New York), 1940 . . . £25/£5
Points of View, Faber (London), 1941 . . . £25/£5
The Classics and the Man of Letters, O.U.P. (Oxford, UK), 1942 (sewn wraps) £25
The Music of Poetry, Jackson and Co. (Glasgow), 1942 (stapled wraps) £30
Reunion by Destruction, Vacher & Sons, 1943 . £45
What is a Classic?, Faber (London), 1945 (Virgil Society issue, with statement of aims; stapled wraps) . £150
ditto, Faber (London), 1945 (Virgil Society issue, without statement of aims; stapled wraps) . . . £75
ditto, Faber (London), 1945 . . . . . £45/£20
On Poetry, Concord (Concord, MA), 1947 (750 copies, not for sale; wraps) £75
Milton, Cumberlege (London), 1947 (500 copies; sewn wraps) £35
A Sermon, C.U.P. (Cambridge, UK), 1948 (300 copies; wraps) £175
Notes Towards the Definition of Culture, Faber (London), 1948 . . . . £45/£15
ditto, Harcourt Brace (New York), 1949 . . . £35/£10
From Poe to Valéry, Harcourt Brace (New York), 1948 (1,500 copies, not for sale, boards and envelope). £65/£25
The Aims of Poetic Drama, Poets' Theatre Guild (London), 1949 (stapled wraps) £45
Poetry and Drama, Harvard Univ Press (Cambridge, MA), 1951 . . . . £50/£15
ditto, Faber (London), 1951 . . . . . £45/£10
The Value and Use of Cathedrals in England Today, Chichester Cathedral (Chichester, UK), 1952 (stapled wraps). £25
An Address to the Members of the London Library, Queen Anne Press (London), 1952 (500 copies; sewn wraps) £25
Selected Prose, Penguin (Harmondsworth, Middlesex), 1953 (pbk) £5
ditto, as **Selected Prose by T.S. Eliot**, Faber (London), 1975 . . . . £25/£10
American Literature and the American Language, Washington Univ (St Louis, MO), 1953 (500 copies; stapled wraps) £100
The Three Voices of Poetry, National Book League (London), 1953 (stapled wraps) £25

ditto, C.U.P. (New York), 1954 . . . . £60/£15
Religious Drama: Mediaeval and Modern, House of Books
(New York), 1954 (300 numbered copies, glassine d/w) .
. . . . £450/£350
ditto, House of Books (New York), 1954 (26 lettered and
signed copies) £1,250
The Literature of Politics, Conservative Political Centre
(London), 1955 (stapled wraps) £20
The Frontiers of Criticism, Univ of Minnesota (Minneapo-
lis, MN), 1956 (10,050 copies, not for sale; stapled wraps)
. . . . £15
On Poetry and Poets, Faber (London), 1957 . £40/£10
ditto, Farrar Straus (New York), 1957 . . £25/£5
Geoffrey Faber, 1889-1961, Faber (London), 1961 (100
hardback copies, not for sale) . . . £400/£300
George Herbert, Longmans (London), 1962 (stapled wraps)
. . . . £10
*Knowledge and Experience in the Philosophy of F.H.
Bradley*, Faber (London), 1964 . . . £35/£10
ditto, Farrar Straus (New York), 1964 . . £25/£10
To Criticize the Critic and Other Writings, Faber (London),
1965 . . . . £30/£10
ditto, Farrar Straus (New York), 1965 . . £25/£5
The Letters of T.S. Eliot, Vol. 1, 1898-1922, Faber
(London), 1988 (edited by Valerie Eliot) . . £25/£10
ditto, Faber (London), 1988 (250 copies signed by Valerie
Eliot, slipcase) . . . . . . £75/£50
ditto, Harcourt Brace (New York), 1988 . . £25/£10
ditto, Harcourt Brace (New York), 1988 (250 signed by
editor, slipcase) . . . . . . £75/£50
Eeldrop and Appleplex, Foundling Press (Tunbridge Wells,
Kent) 1992 (500 numbered copies; sewn wraps) . . £35

Drama

Sweeney Agonistes, Faber (London), 1932 . £75/£10
The Rock, Faber (London), 1934 (sewn wraps) . . £35
ditto, Faber (London), 1934 (hardback) . . £75/£15
ditto, Harcourt Brace (New York), 1934 . . £50/£10
Murder in the Cathedral, Goulden (Canterbury, Kent), 1935
(750 copies, wraps) £200
ditto, Faber (London), 1935 (first complete edition) £125/£15
ditto, Harcourt Brace (New York), 1935 . . £100/£15
The Family Reunion, Faber (London), 1939 . £75/£15
ditto, Harcourt Brace (New York), 1939 . . £65/£10
The Cocktail Party, Faber (London), 1950 (misprint 'here'
for 'her' on page 29, line 1) . . . . £65/£25
ditto, Faber (London), 1950 (misprint corrected) . £45/£15
ditto, Harcourt Brace (New York), 1950 (copies with pp.35-
36 on uncancelled leaf) . . . . £450/£400
ditto, Harcourt Brace (New York), 1950 (copies with pp.35-
36 on cancel leaf) . . . . . £45/£10
The Confidential Clerk, Faber (London), 1954 (first issue
with 'Ihad' on p.7) . . . . . . £60/£20
ditto, Faber (London), 1954 (second issue with 'I had' on p.7)
. . . . £45/£10
ditto, Harcourt Brace (New York), 1954 . . £30/£10
The Elder Statesman, Faber (London), 1959 . £40/£10
ditto, Farrar Straus (New York), 1959 . . £30/£10
Collected Plays, Faber (London), 1962 . . £25/£10

BRET EASTON ELLIS
(b.1964)

Bret Easton Ellis is an American author whose flat, glossy
surface style has attracted extremely polarised reviews. He
has described himself as a moralist, although some consider
him a nihilist. Simon & Schuster gave Ellis a $300,000 ad-
vance for *American Psycho* but then refused to publish the
novel after women's groups and women employees within
the company protested.

Novels
Less Than Zero, Simon & Schuster (New York), 1985 . .
. . . . £25/£5
ditto, Picador (London), 1986 (pbk) £20
Rules of Attraction, Simon & Schuster (New York), 1987 .
. . . . £25/£5
ditto, Picador (London), 1988 (pbk) £20
American Psycho, Vintage (New York), 1991 (pbk) . £20
ditto, Picador (London), 1991 (pbk) £20
The Informers, Knopf (New York), 1994. . . £20/£5
ditto, Picador (London), 1994 . . . . £20/£5
Glamorama, Knopf (New York), 1999 . . . £15/£5
ditto, Picador (London), 1999 . . . . £15/£5
Lunar Park, Knopf (New York), 2005 . . . £10/£5
ditto, Picador (London), 2005 . . . . £10/£5

Novella
Water from the Sun and Discovering Japan, Picador
(London), 2005 (pbk £5

RALPH ELLISON
(b.1913 d.1994)

Ralph Ellison's groundbreaking novel *Invisible Man* is
written from the perspective of an unnamed black man in
New York City and explores the theme of man's search for
identity and place in society. He is 'invisible' in the sense
that people refuse to see him. The novel also deals with
previously taboo subjects such as incest and white
America's perceptions of black sexuality. Ellison's second
novel, *Juneteenth* is a 368-page condensation of over 2000
pages written over a period of forty years.

Novels
Invisible Man, Random House (New York), 1952 . . .
. . . . £1,500/£350
ditto, Gollancz (London), 1953 . . . . £400/£50
Juneteenth, Random House (New York), 1999 . £10/£5
ditto, Hamish Hamilton (London), 1999 . . . £10/£5

Others
Shadow and Act, Random House (New York), 1964 £40/£10
ditto, Secker & Warburg, 1967 . . . . £15/£5
The Writer's Experience, Library of Congress (Washington,
D.C.), 1964 (with Karl Shapiro; stapled wraps) . . £20
The City in Crisis, A. Philip Randolph Educational Fund
(New York), [between 1966 and 1970] (with others;
stapled wraps) £40
Going to the Territory, Random House (New York), 1986 .
. . . . £10/£5

The Collected Essays of Ralph Ellison, Modern Library (New York), 1995 (edited, with an introduction by John F. Callahan; Preface by Saul Bellow) . . . . £10/£5

Flying Home and Other Stories, Random House (New York), 1996 (edited, with an introduction by John F. Callahan) . . . . £10/£5

Trading Twelves: The Selected Letters of Ralph Ellison and Albert Murray, Modern library (New York), 2000 £10/£5

JAMES ELLROY
(b.1948)

The American James Ellroy is one of the world's best-selling crime writers and essayists. His writing style, omitting words and often featuring sentence fragments, is noted for its dark humour and relentlessly pessimistic world-view. His work is densely plotted and has been successfully filmed.

Lloyd Hopkins Novels
Blood on the Moon, Mysterious Press (New York), 1984 . . . . £75/£10
ditto, Allison & Busby (London), 1985 . . £40/£10
Because the Night, Mysterious Press (New York), 1984 . . . . £75/£10
ditto, Mysterious Press (London), 1987 . . £75/£10
Suicide Hill, Mysterious Press (New York), 1986 . £20/£5
ditto, Mysterious Press (London), 1987 (pbk) . . . £5
L.A. Noir, Mysterious Press (New York), 1998 . £10/£5
ditto, Arrow (London), 1997 (pbk) £5

L.A. Quartet Novels
Black Dahlia, Mysterious Press (New York), 1987 £35/£10
ditto, Mysterious Press (London), 1988 . . £75/£10
The Big Nowhere, Mysterious Press (New York), 1988 . . . . £25/£5
ditto, Ultramarine Press (New York), 1988 (350 signed, numbered copies; slipcase . . . . . £75/£45
L.A. Confidential, Mysterious Press (New York), 1990 . . . . £40/£5
ditto, Mysterious Press (New York), 1990 (100 signed, numbered copies) . . . . . £400/£200
ditto, Mysterious Press (New York), 1990 (26 signed, lettered copies) . . . . . . £200/£45
ditto, Mysterious Press (London), 1990 . . £100/£15
White Jazz, Knopf (New York), 1992 . . . £15/£5
ditto, Century (London), 1992 . . . . £25/£10
The Dudley Smith Trio, Arrow (London), 1999 (pbk) . £5

Underworld U.S.A. Novels
American Tabloid, Knopf (New York), 1995 . . £10/£5
ditto, Century (London), 1995 . . . . £10/£5
The Cold Six Thousand, Knopf (New York), 2001 £10/£5
ditto, Century (London), 2001 . . . . £10/£5
Blood's a Rover, Random House (New York), 2009 £10/£5
ditto, Century (London), 2009 . . . . £10/£5

Other Novels
Brown's Requiem, Avon (New York), 1981 (pbk) . . £30
ditto, Allison & Busby (London), 1984 . . . £125/£20
Clandestine, Avon (New York), 1982 (pbk) . . . £20
ditto, Allison & Busby (London), 1984 . . . £100/£15

Silent Terror, Avon (New York), 1986 (pbk; aka *Killer on the Road*) £5
ditto, Blood & Guts Press (US), 1987 (350 signed numbered copies) . . . . £100/£15
ditto, Blood & Guts Press (US), 1987 (26 signed, lettered copies) . . . . £250/£40
ditto, Arrow (London), 1990 (pbk) £5

Short Stories
Hollywood Nocturnes, Otto Penzler (New York), 1994 . . . . £10/£5
Dick Contino's Blues and Other Stories, Arrow (London), 1994 (pbk) £10
Crime Wave, Vintage (New York), 1999 (pbk) . . £5
ditto, Century (London), 1999 . . . . £10/£5
Destination Morgue!, Vintage (New York), 2004 (pbk) £5
ditto, Century (London), 2004 . . . . . £10/£5

Non-Fiction
My Dark Places, Knopf (New York), 1996 . . £10/£5
ditto, Century (London), 1996 . . . . £10/£5
ditto, Scorpion Press (London), 1996 (85 signed, numbered copies) £75
ditto, Scorpion Press (London), 1996 (15 signed, lettered copies) £200

ANNE ENRIGHT
(b.1962)

Anne Enright is an Irish author whose first collection of stories, *The Portable Virgin*, won the Rooney Prize. Her novel *What Are You Like?* was shortlisted for the Whitbread Novel Award and won the Encore Award. *The Gathering* won the 2007 Booker Prize.

Novels
The Wig My Father Wore, Cape (London), 1995 . £100/£10
ditto, Grove (New York), 2001 (pbk). £10
What Are You Like?, Cape (London), 2000 (pbk) . . £10
ditto, Atlantic Monthly Press (New York), 2000 . £15/£5
The Pleasure of Eliza Lynch, Cape (London), 2002 £10/£5
ditto, Atlantic Monthly Press (New York), 2002 . £10/£5
The Gathering, Cape (London), 2007 . . . £60/£10
ditto, Grove/Black Cat (New York), 2007 (pbk) . £15

Collections
The Portable Virgin, Secker & Warburg (London), 1991 . . . . £200/£25
Taking Pictures, Cape (London), 2008 . . . £10/£5
ditto, as *Yesterday's Weather*, Grove (New York), 2008 (pbk) £5

Non-Fiction
Making Babies: Stumbling Into Motherhood, Cape (London), 2004 . . . . £10/£5

JOHN MEADE FALKNER

(b.1858 d.1932)

A British industrialist and antiquarian, Falkner also turned his hand to novel writing and local history. In *The Lost Stradivarius* he created an enduring tale of the supernatural and in *Moonfleet* a classic novel of smuggling and adventure. His third novel, *The Nebuly Coat*, a mystery and a romance, was much admired by Thomas Hardy.

Novels

The Lost Stradivarius, Blackwood (Edinburgh/London), 1895 . . . . £400
ditto, Appleton (New York), 1896 . . . . . £125
ditto, Tartarus Press (Carlton-in-Coverdale, Yorkshire), 2000 (with 'A Midsummer's Marriage' and 'Charalampia') . £40/£10
Moonfleet, Arnold (London), 1898 . . . . . £350
ditto, Little, Brown (Boston), 1951 . . . £35/£10
The Nebuly Coat, Arnold (London), 1903 . . £200
ditto, O.U.P. (Oxford, UK), 1954 . . . £35/£10
ditto, Ash-Tree Press (Ashcroft, Canada), 2003 (500 copies) . . . . £25/£10

Others

Handbook for Travellers in Oxfordshire, Murray (London), 1894 (anonymous) £85
A History of Oxfordshire, Elliot Stock (London), 1899 £65
Handbook for Berkshire, Edward Stanford (London), 1902 . . . . £30
Bath in History and Social Tradition, Murray (London), 1918 (anonymous) £20
A History of Durham Cathedral Library, Durham Country Advertiser (Durham), 1925 (red cloth) . . . £40
ditto, Durham Country Advertiser (Durham), 1925 (green wraps) £30
Poems, Westminster Press (London), [c.1935] (wraps) . £50

G.E. FARROW

(b.1862 d. c.1920?)

Farrow was an author of children's stories somewhat in the tradition of Lewis Carroll. All that is known about him is that he was born in Ipswich, the son of a cement manufacturer, was educated in Britain and America, and later lived for a time in London. Farrow is collected today as much for the artists who illustrated his books as for his own writing.

Fiction

The Wallypug of Why, Hutchinson (London), [1895] (illustrated by Harry Furniss, vignettes by Dorothy Furniss) £125
ditto, Dodd, Mead (New York), 1896 . . . £65
The King's Gardens: An Allegory, Hutchinson (London), 1896 (illustrated by A.L. Bowley) £45
The Missing Prince, Hutchinson (London), 1896 (illustrated by Harry Furniss, vignettes by Dorothy Furniss) . . £45
ditto, Dodd, Mead (New York), 1897 . . . £35
The Wallypug in London, Methuen (London), 1898 [1897] (illustrated by Alan Wright) £75

Adventures in Wallypug-land, Methuen (London), 1898 (illustrated by Alan Wright) £65
ditto, Burt (New York), 1900 . . . . . £65
The Little Panjandrum's Dodo, Skeffington (London), 1899 (illustrated by Alan Wright) £45
ditto, Stokes (New York), 1899 . . . . . £45
ditto, as *Dick, Marjorie and Fidge: The Adventures of Three little People*, Burt (New York), 1901 . . . £40
The Mandarin's Kite, or Little Tsu-Foo and Another Boy, Skeffington (London), 1900 (illustrated by Alan Wright) £35
Baker Minor and the Dragon, Pearson (London), 1902 [1901] (illustrated by Alan Wright) £35
The New Panjandrum, Pearson (London), 1902 [1901] (illustrated by Alan Wright) £35
ditto, Dutton (New York), 1902 . . . . . £35
In Search of the Wallypug, Pearson (London), 1903 [1902] (illustrated by Alan Wright) £65
Professor Philanderpan, Pearson (London), 1904 [1903] £35
All About the Wallypug, Raphael Tuck (London), [1904] £45
The Cinematograph Train and Other Stories, Johnson (London), 1904 (illustrated by Alan Wright) . . £65
Pixie Pickles: The Adventures of Pixene and Pixette in their Woodland Haunts, Skeffington (London), [1904] (illustrated by H.B. Neilson) £65
ditto, Warne (New York), 1906 . . . . . £45
The Wallypug Birthday Book, Routledge (London), 1904 (illustrated by Alan Wright) £45
The Wallypug in Fogland, Pearson (London), 1904 (illustrated by Alan Wright) £65
ditto, Lippincott (Philadelphia), 1904 . . . £45
Ruff and Ready, The Fairy Guide by May Byron and G.E. Farrow, Cooke (London), [1905] (illustrated by John Hassall) £40
The Mysterious 'Mr Punch', A School Story, Christian Knowledge Society (London), [1905] £30
The Wallypug Book, Traherne (London), [1905] . £50
The Wallypug in the Moon, or His Badjesty, Pearson (London), 1905 (illustrated by Alan Wright). . . £50
ditto, Lippincott (Philadelphia), 1905 . . . £45
The Adventures of Ji, Partridge (London), [1906] (illustrated by G.C. Tresidder) £40
Essays in Bacon, An Autograph Book, Treherne (London), [1906] £40
The Escape of the Mullingong, A Zoological Nightmare, Blackie (London), 1907 [1906] (illustrated by Gordon Browne). £35
The Adventures of a Dodo, Unwin (London), [1907] (illustrated by Willy Pogány) £65
ditto, Wessels (New York), 1908 . . . . . £45
ditto, as *A Mysterious Voyage, or The Adventures of a Dodo*, Partridge (London), [1910] (illustrated by K.M. Roberts). £35
The Dwindleberry Zoo, Blackie (London), 1909 [1908] (illustrated by Gordon Browne) £35
Zoo Babies, Frowde/Hodder & Stoughton (London), 1913 (illustrated by Cecil Aldin) £125
ditto, Stokes (New York), 1908 . . . . . £85
The Mysterious Shin Shira, Hodder & Stoughton (London), [1915] £25
Don't Tell, Cooke (London), [no date] (illustrated by John Hassall) £40
ditto, Stokes (New York), [no date] £85
Ten Little Jappy Chaps, Treherne (London), [no date] (illustrated by John Hassall) £30

Poetry

An A.B.C. of Every-day People, Dean (London), [1902]
  (illustrated by John Hassall) £65
Absurd Ditties, Routledge (London), 1903 (illustrated by
  John Hassall) £50
ditto, Dutton (New York), 1903 . . . . . £45
Wallypug Tales, Raphael Tuck (London), [1904] . £45
Round the World A.B.C., Nister (London), [1904]
  (illustrated by John Hassall) £55
ditto, Dutton (New York), 1904 . . . . . £45

Others

Lovely Man, Being the Views of Mistress A. Crosspatch,
  Skeffington (London), 1904 . . . . £40
Food of the Dogs, Johnson (London), 1904 . . . £40

WILLIAM FAULKNER

(b.1897 d.1962)

A respected American novelist who often pushed the boundaries of narrative convention, Faulkner won the Nobel Prize for Literature in 1949. There is some uncertainty as to which is the first issue d/w for *The Sound and the Fury*: the price of *Humanity Uprooted* (another book advertised) may have been raised for the second issue of the jacket, or lowered due to the stock market crash.

Novels

Soldier's Pay, Boni & Liveright (New York), 1926 . .
  . . . . £15,000/£250
ditto, Chatto & Windus (London), 1930 . . £900/£200
Mosquitoes, Boni & Liveright (New York), 1927 (no
  publisher on spine, d/w printed in red on green with
  mosquito) . . . . £4,500/£250
ditto, Boni & Liveright (New York), 1927 (publisher's name
  on spine, d/w with card players on yacht) . £2,000/£200
ditto, Chatto & Windus (London), 1964 . . £45/£20
Sartoris, Harcourt Brace (New York), 1929 . £2,500/£250
ditto, Chatto & Windus (London), 1932 (top edge stained
  blue) . . . . £1,250/£300
ditto, Chatto & Windus (London), 1932 (top edge unstained)
  . . . . £950/£75
The Sound and the Fury, Cape & Smith (New York), 1929
  (unpriced d/w with *Humanity Uprooted* at $3.00 on rear
  panel) . . . . . . £17,500/£2,000
ditto, Cape & Smith (New York), 1929 (*Humanity Uprooted*
  priced $3.50 on rear panel) . . £15,000/£2,000
ditto, Chatto & Windus (London), 1931 (black cloth, top
  edge stained red) . . . . . . £1,250/£250
ditto, Chatto & Windus (London), 1931 (mustard cloth
  stamped in red, top edge unstained) . . £1,000/£150
As I Lay Dying, Cape & Smith (New York), 1930 (first
  issue with capital 'I' on p.11, line 1 not correctly aligned,
  stamping to boards complete and unbroken) . £6,000/£600
ditto, Cape & Smith (New York), 1930 (second issue with
  capital 'I' correctly aligned) . . . . £3,500/£250
ditto, Chatto & Windus (London), 1935 . £1,000/£250
Sanctuary, Cape & Smith (New York), 1931 . £2,500/£250
ditto, Chatto & Windus (London), 1931 (cloth stamped in
  gold, four pages of ads) . . . . £850/£350
ditto, Chatto & Windus (London), 1931 (cloth stamped in
  black, no ads) . . . . . . £650/£150

Idyll in the Desert, Random House (New York), 1931 (400
  signed, numbered copies, glassine d/w) . £1,250/£1,000
Miss Zilphia Gant, Book Club of Texas (Dallas, TX), 1932
  (300 numbered copies) £1,000
Light in August, Smith & Haas (New York), 1932 (tan cloth
  stamped in blue and orange, glassine d/w over paper d/w).
  . . . . £1,250/£150
ditto, Smith & Haas (New York), 1932 (stamped in blue
  only, glassine d/w over paper d/w) . . £650/£150
ditto, Chatto & Windus (London), 1933 . . £750/£75
Pylon, Smith & Haas (New York), 1935 . . £750/£75
ditto, Smith & Haas (New York), 1935 (310 signed,
  numbered copies, slipcase, no d/w) . . £1,750/£750
ditto, Chatto & Windus (London), 1935 (top edge stained
  red, bottom edge untrimmed) . . . . £1,250/£65
ditto, Chatto & Windus (London), 1935 (top edge unstained,
  bottom edge trimmed) . . . . . £250/£75
Absalom, Absalom!, Random House (New York), 1936 .
  . . . . £1,000/£200
ditto, Random House (New York), 1936 (300 signed,
  numbered copies, slipcase and d/w) . £4,000/£3,000
ditto, Chatto & Windus (London), 1937 (glassine d/w with
  glued-on front flaps) . . . . . £400/£100
The Unvanquished, Random House (New York), 1938. .
  . . . . £750/£150
ditto, Random House (New York), 1938 (250 signed,
  numbered copies) £2,500
ditto, Chatto & Windus (London), 1938 (clear d/w with
  paper flaps) . . . . £350/£75
The Wild Palms, Random House (New York), 1939
  (stamped in gold and green on spine) . . £750/£50
ditto, Random House (New York), 1939 (stamped in brown
  and green on spine) . . . . . . £500/£50
ditto, Random House (New York), 1939 (250 signed,
  numbered copies, glassine d/w) . . £1,450/£1,350
ditto, Chatto & Windus (London), 1939 . . £750/£75
The Hamlet, Random House (New York), 1940 (d/w with
  ads for other books) . . . . . £1,500/£150
ditto, Random House (New York), 1940 (d/w with reviews
  of this book) . . . . . . £1,000/£150
ditto, Random House (New York), 1940 (250 signed,
  numbered copies) £3,000
ditto, Chatto & Windus (London), 1940 . . £650/£75
Intruder in the Dust, Random House (New York), 1948 .
  . . . . £300/£45
ditto, Chatto & Windus (London), 1949 . . £200/£30
Notes on a Horsethief, Levee Press (Greenville, MS), 1950
  [1951] (975 signed, numbered copies, tissue d/w) . .
  . . . . £750/£650
Requiem for a Nun, Random House (New York), 1951 .
  . . . . £75/£30
ditto, Random House (New York), 1951 (750 signed,
  numbered copies; glassine d/w) . . . £850/£750
ditto, Chatto & Windus (London), 1953 . . £45/£20
A Fable, Random House (New York), 1954 . £125/£20
ditto, Random House (New York), 1954 (1,000 signed,
  numbered copies, glassine d/w, slipcase) £1,250/£1,000
ditto, Chatto & Windus (London), 1955 . . £60/£25
The Town, Random House (New York), 1957 (first issue red
  cloth, top edge stained grey, threaded grey endpapers, d/w
  with '5/57' on front flap) . . . . £750/£200
ditto, Random House (New York), 1957 (later issues with
  various cloths, endpapers etc) . . . £50/£20
ditto, Random House (New York), 1957 (450 signed,
  numbered copies, acetate d/w) . . £1,250/£1,000

ditto, Chatto & Windus (London), 1958 . . . £45/£15
The Mansion, Random House (New York), 1959 . £50/£20
ditto, Random House (New York), 1959 (500 signed, numbered copies, acetate d/w, no slipcase) . £750/£500
ditto, Chatto & Windus (London), 1961 . . . £40/£15
The Reivers, Random House (New York), 1962 . £100/£20
ditto, Random House (New York), 1962 (500 signed, numbered copies, acetate d/w) . . . . £600/£500
ditto, Chatto & Windus (London), 1962 . . . £75/£15

Short Stories

These 13, Cape & Smith (New York), 1931 . £750/£200
ditto, Cape & Smith (New York), 1931 (299 signed, numbered copies, plain tissue d/w) . . £2,000/£1,500
ditto, Chatto & Windus (London), 1933 . . £1,000/£75
Doctor Martino and Other Stories, Smith & Haas (New York), 1934 . . . . . . £600/£250
ditto, Smith & Haas (New York), 1934 (360 signed, numbered copies; glassine d/w) . . £1,250/£1,000
ditto, Chatto & Windus (London), 1934 . . . £500/£50
Go Down, Moses and Other Stories, Random House (New York), 1942 . . . . £500/£75
ditto, Random House (New York), 1942 (100 signed, numbered copies) £12,500
ditto, Chatto & Windus (London), 1942 . . . £200/£45
A Rose for Emily and Other Stories, Editions for the Armed Services (New York), 1942 (pbk; first issue with floorplan on the verso of the title page) £165
Knight's Gambit, Random House (New York), 1949 . . . . £125/£25
ditto, Chatto & Windus (London), 1951 . . . £100/£15
Collected Stories, Random House (New York), 1950 . . . . £200/£25
ditto, Chatto & Windus (London), 1951 . . £125/£25
Mirrors of Chartres Street, Faulkner Studies (Minneapolis, MN), 1953 (1,000 numbered copies) . £200/£100
Big Woods, Random House (New York), 1955 . £200/£35
Jealousy and Episode, Faulkner Studies (Minneapolis, MN), 1955 (500 copies, no d/w) £200
Uncle Willy and Other Stories: Volume 1 of The Collected Short Stories, Chatto & Windus (London), 1958 . £75/£20
These Thirteen: Volume 2 of The Collected Short Stories, Chatto & Windus (London), 1958 . . . . £75/£20
Dr Martino and Other Stories: Volume 3 of The Collected Short Stories, Chatto & Windus (London), 1958 . £75/£20
Selected Short Stories, Random House Modern Library (New York), 1962 . . . . . . £35/£10
Uncollected Stories, Franklin Library (Franklin Centre, PA), 1979 . . . . £25
ditto, Random House (New York), 1979 . . . £25/£5
ditto, Chatto & Windus (London), 1980 . . . £25/£5

Play

The Marionettes, Univ of Virginia Press (Charlottesville, VA), 1975 . . . . £20/£5
ditto, Univ of Virginia Press (Charlottesville, VA), 1975 (26 lettered copies, unbound in box) £300
ditto, Univ of Virginia Press (Charlottesville, VA), 1975 (100 numbered copies unbound in slipcase) . . . £125
ditto, as **The Marionettes: A Play in One Act**, Yoknapatawpha Press (Oxford, MS), 1975 (10 lettered copies in a box) £300
ditto, as **The Marionettes: A Play in One Act**, Yoknapatawpha Press (Oxford, MS), 1975 (500 numbered copies) £75

Poetry

Vision in Spring, privately printed (U.S.), 1921 . £20,000
The Marble Faun, Four Seas (Boston), 1924 . . . . £15,000/£7,500
This Earth: A Poem, Equinox (New York), 1932 (string-tied wraps; in original envelope) . . . . . £100/£75
A Green Bough, Smith & Haas (New York), 1933 . . . . £400/£150
ditto, Smith & Haas (New York), 1933 (360 signed copies, no d/w) £1,000

Others

Sherwood Anderson and Other Famous Creoles, Pelican Bookshop Press (New Orleans), 1926 (50 copies signed by caricaturist Spratling) £3,000
ditto, Pelican Bookshop Press (New Orleans), 1926 (200/250 numbered copies) £1,000
ditto, Pelican Bookshop Press (New Orleans), 1926 (label pasted over original limitation stating 'Second Issue 150 copies January 1927') £1,000
Salmagundi, Casanova Press (Milwaukee, WI), 1932 (first 26 numbered copies of 525 with top edge level with boards and bottom edge untrimmed, slipcase) . . £1,000/£950
ditto, Casanova Press Press (Milwaukee, WI), 1932 (499 of 525 numbered copies in slipcase) . . . £250/£200
An Address by William Faulkner, Delta State Teachers College (Cleveland, MS), 1952 (wraps) . . . £1,500
Faulkner's Country: Tales of Yoknapatawpha County, Chatto & Windus (London), 1955 . . . . £45/£15
New Orleans Sketches, Hokuseido Press (Tokyo), 1955 . . . . £175/£75
ditto, Hokuseido Press (Tokyo), 1955 (pbk) . . . £75
ditto, Rutgers Univ Press (New Brunswick, NJ), 1958 . . . . £45/£15
ditto, Sidgwick and Jackson (London), 1959 . . £35/£10
Early Prose and Poetry, Little, Brown (Boston), 1962 . . . . £35/£10
ditto, Cape (London), 1963 . . . . . . £35/£10
Essays, Speeches, and Public Letters, Random House (New York), 1966 . . . . £35/£10
ditto, Chatto & Windus (London), 1966 . . . £35/£10
Selected Letters, Franklin Library (Franklin Centre, PA), 1976 . . . . £45
ditto, Random House (New York), 1977 . . . £25/£5
ditto, Scolar Press (London), 1977 . . . . £25/£5

SEBASTIAN FAULKS
(b.1953)

Sebastian Faulks was a journalist for 14 years before becoming a full-time writer in 1991. He is the author of the celebrated bestseller about the horror and passion of the First World War, *Birdsong*, and was named Author of the Year in the British Book Awards of 1995. He lives with his wife and two children in London.

Novels

A Trick of the Light, Bodley Head (London), 1984 . . . . £400/£25
The Girl at the Lion d'Or, Hutchinson (London), 1989 . . . . £450/£65
ditto, Vintage (New York), 1999 (pbk) £5

A Fool's Alphabet, Hutchinson (London), 1992   .   £35/£5
ditto, Little, Brown (Boston), 1992   .   .   .   £20/£5
Birdsong, Hutchinson (London), 1993   .   .   .£350/£40
ditto, Random House (New York), 1996   .   .   . £35/£10
Charlotte Gray, Hutchinson (London), 1998   .   £15/£5
ditto, Random House (New York), 1999   .   .   . £10/£5
On Green Dolphin Street, Hutchinson (London), 2001 .   .
    .   .   .   .   £10/£5
ditto, Random House (New York), 2002   .   . £10/£5
Human Traces, Hutchinson (London), 2005   .   £10/£5
ditto, Hutchinson (London), 2005 (1,000 signed, numbered
    copies; slipcase)   .   .   .   .   .   £35/£25
ditto, Random House (New York), 2005   .   £10/£5
Engleby, Hutchinson, London 2007   .   .   .   .   £10
ditto, Hutchinson, London 2007 (1,500 signed, numbered
    copies; slipcase) £30
ditto, Random House (New York), 2007 .   .   £10/£5
Devil May Care, Penguin (London), 2008   .   £10/£5
ditto, Doubleday (New York), 2008 .   .   .   £10/£5
ditto, Penguin (London), 2008 (500 signed copies with cover
    artwork printed directly on boards; no d/w; in a red velvet
    box with hinged opening) £250
ditto, Doubleday (New York), 2008 (300 leatherbound
    'Bentley' copies with steel engine plate; pages die-cut with
    a car-shaped silhouette to house 1:43 scale model Bentley;
    plexiglass slip-case) £1,500
A Week in December Hutchinson, London 2009 .   £10
ditto, Hutchinson, London 2009 (1,00 signed copies;
    slipcase).   .   .   .   .   £60/£40

Non-Fiction
The Fatal Englishman: Three Short Lives, Hutchinson
    (London), 1996   .   .   .   .   .   £10/£5
ditto, Vintage (New York), 2002 (pbk)   .   .   .   £5
Pistache, Hutchinson (London), 2006   .   .   £10/£5

ELIZABETH FERRARS

(b. 1907 d.1995)

Elizabeth Ferrars was the pseudonym of Morna Brown, and
she is known as E.X. Ferrars in the United States. Often
considered a successor to Agatha Christie, she writes
elegant mysteries with traditional, English middle-class
settings.

'Toby Dyke' Novels
Give a Corpse a Bad Name, Hodder & Stoughton (London),
    1940   .   .   .   .£125/£30
Remove the Bodies, Hodder & Stoughton (London), 1940 .
    .   .   .   .£125/£30
ditto, as ***Rehearsals for Murder***, Doubleday (New York), 1941
    .   .   .   .   £75/£20
Death in Botanist's Bay, Hodder & Stoughton (London),
    1941   .   .   .   .£125/£25
ditto, as ***Murder of a Suicide***, Doubleday (New York), 1941
    .   .   .   .   £75/£20
Don't Monkey with Murder, Hodder & Stoughton (London),
    1942   .   .   .   .   £75/£20
ditto, as ***The Shape of a Stain***, Doubleday (New York), 1942
    .   .   .   .   £75/£25
Your Neck in a Noose, Hodder & Stoughton (London), 1942
    .   .   .   .   £75/£25

ditto, as ***Neck in a Noose***, Doubleday (New York), 1943   .
    .   .   .   .   £50/£15

'Felix and Virginia Freer' Novels
Last Will and Testament, Collins Crime Club (London),
    1978   .   .   .   .   .   .   £10/£5
ditto, Doubleday (New York), 1978   .   .   .   £10/£5
Frog in the Throat, Collins Crime Club (London), 1980   .
    .   .   .   .   £10/£5
ditto, Doubleday (New York), 1980 .   .   .   £10/£5
Thinner than Water, Collins Crime Club (London), 1981 .
    .   .   .   .   £10/£5
ditto, Doubleday (New York), 1982 .   .   .   £10/£5
Death of a Minor Character, Collins Crime Club (London),
    1983   .   .   .   .   .   .   £10/£5
ditto, Doubleday (New York), 1983 .   .   .   £10/£5
I Met Murder, Collins Crime Club (London), 1985   £10/£5
ditto, Doubleday (New York), 1985 .   .   .   £10/£5
Woman Slaughter, Collins Crime Club (London), 1989
    .   .   .   .   £10/£5
ditto, Doubleday (New York), 1990 .   .   .   £10/£5
Sleep of the Unjust, Collins Crime Club (London), 1990   .
    .   .   .   .   £10/£5
ditto, Doubleday (New York), 1991 .   .   .   £10/£5
Beware of the Dog, Collins Crime Club (London), 1992   .
    .   .   .   .   £10/£5
ditto, Bantam (New York), 1993.   .   .   .   £10/£5

'Professor Andrew Basnett' Novels
Something Wicked, Collins Crime Club (London), 1983   .
    .   .   .   .   £10/£5
ditto, Doubleday (New York), 1984 .   .   .   £10/£5
Root of All Evil, Collins Crime Club (London), 1984 £10/£5
ditto, Doubleday (New York), 1984 .   .   .   £10/£5
The Crime and the Crystal, Collins Crime Club (London),
    1985   .   .   .   .   .   .   £10/£5
ditto, Doubleday (New York), 1985 .   .   .   £10/£5
The Other Devil's Name, Collins Crime Club (London),
    1986   .   .   .   .   .   .   £10/£5
ditto, Doubleday (New York), 1987 .   .   .   £10/£5
A Murder Too Many, Collins Crime Club (London), 1988 .
    .   .   .   .   £10/£5
ditto, Doubleday (New York), 1989 .   .   .   £10/£5
Smoke Without Fire, Collins Crime Club (London), 1990 .
    .   .   .   .   £10/£5
ditto, Doubleday (New York), 1991 .   .   .   £10/£5

Other Crime Novels
I, Said the Fly, Hodder & Stoughton (London), 1945   .   .
    .   .   .   .   £75/£20
ditto, Doubleday (New York), 1945   .   .   .   £35/£10
Murder Among Friends, Collins Crime Club (London), 1946
    .   .   .   .   £75/£20
ditto, as ***Cheat the Hangman***, Doubleday (New York), 1946
    .   .   .   .   £35/£10
With Murder in Mind, Collins Crime Club (London), 1948.
    .   .   .   .   £40/£15
The March Hare Murders, Collins Crime Club (London),
    1949   .   .   .   .   .   .   £45/£15
ditto, Doubleday (New York), 1949   .   .   .   £35/£10
Hunt the Tortoise, Collins Crime Club (London), 1950   .
    .   .   .   .   £35/£10
ditto, Doubleday (New York), 1950 .   .   .   £25/£10
Milk of Human Kindness, Collins Crime Club (London),
    1950   .   .   .   .   .   .   £30/£10

The Clock that Wouldn't Stop, Collins Crime Club (London), 1952 . . . . . £25/£10
ditto, Doubleday (New York), 1952 . . . £20/£5
Alibi for a Witch, Collins Crime Club (London), 1952 . . . . £25/£10
ditto, Doubleday (New York), 1952 . . . £20/£5
Murder in Time, Collins Crime Club (London), 1953 . . . . £25/£10
The Lying Voices, Collins Crime Club (London), 1954 . . . . £25/£10
Enough to Kill a Horse, Collins Crime Club (London), 1955 . . . . £20/£5
ditto, Doubleday (New York), 1955 . . . £10/£5
Always Say Die, Collins Crime Club (London), 1956 £20/£5
ditto, as *We Haven't Seen Her Lately*, Doubleday (New York), 1956 . . . . £10/£5
Murder Moves In, Collins Crime Club (London), 1956 . . . . £20/£5
ditto, as *Kill or Cure*, Doubleday (New York), 1956 £10/£5
Furnished for Murder, Collins Crime Club (London), 1957 . . . . £20/£5
Count the Cost, Doubleday (New York), 1957 . £20/£5
ditto, as *Unreasonable Doubt*, Collins Crime Club (London), 1958 . . . . £20/£5
Depart This Life, Doubleday (New York), 1958 . £20/£5
ditto, as *A Tale of Two Murders*, Collins Crime Club (London), 1959 . . . £20/£5
Fear the Light, Collins Crime Club (London)1960 £20/£5
ditto, Doubleday (New York), 1960 . . . £10/£5
The Sleeping Dogs, Collins Crime Club (London), 1960 . . . . £20/£5
ditto, Doubleday (New York), 1960 . . . £10/£5
The Busy Body, Collins Crime Club (London), 1962 £20/£5
ditto, as *Seeing Double*, Doubleday (New York), 1962 . . . . £10/£5
The Wandering Widows, Collins Crime Club (London), 1962 . . . . . £20/£5
ditto, Doubleday (New York), 1962 . . . £10/£5
The Doubly Dead, Collins Crime Club (London), 1963 . . . . £20/£5
ditto, Doubleday (New York), 1963 . . . £10/£5
The Decayed Gentlewoman, Doubleday (New York), 1963 . . . . £15/£5
ditto, as *A Legal Fiction*, Collins Crime Club (London), 1964 . . . . £10/£5
Ninth Life, Collins Crime Club (London), 1965 . £15/£5
No Peace for the Wicked, Collins Crime Club (London), 1966 . . . . £15/£5
ditto, Harper (New York), 1966 . . . £10/£5
Zero at the Bone, Collins Crime Club (London), 1967 . . . . £15/£5
ditto, Walker (New York), 1968 . . . . £10/£5
The Swaying Pillars, Collins Crime Club (London), 1968 . . . . . £15/£5
ditto, Walker (New York), 1969 . . . . £10/£5
Skeleton Staff, Collins Crime Club (London), 1969 £15/£5
ditto, Walker (New York), 1969 . . . . £10/£5
The Seven Sleepers, Collins Crime Club (London), 1970 . . . . . . £15/£5
ditto, Walker (New York), 1970 . . . . £10/£5
A Stranger and Afraid, Collins Crime Club (London), 1971 . . . . . £15/£5
ditto, Walker (New York), 1971 . . . . £10/£5
Breath of Suspicion, Collins Crime Club (London), 1972 . . . . . . £15/£5
ditto, Doubleday (New York), (New York) 1972 . £10/£5

Foot in the Grave, Doubleday (New York) 1972 . £10/£5
ditto, Collins Crime Club (London), 1973. . . £10/£5
The Small World of Murder, Collins Crime Club (London), 1973 . . . . . . £10/£5
ditto, Doubleday (New York), 1973 . . . £10/£5
Hanged Man's House, Collins Crime Club (London), 1974 . . . . £10/£5
ditto, Doubleday (New York), 1974 . . . £10/£5
Alive and Dead, Collins Crime Club (London), 1974 £10/£5
ditto, Doubleday (New York), 1975 . . . £10/£5
Drowned Rat, Collins Crime Club (London), 1975 £10/£5
ditto, Doubleday (New York), 1975 . . . £10/£5
The Cup and the Lip, Collins Crime Club (London), 1975 . . . . £10/£5
ditto, Doubleday (New York), 1976 . . . £10/£5
Blood Flies Upwards, Collins Crime Club (London), 1976 . . . . £10/£5
ditto, Doubleday (New York), 1977 . . . £10/£5
The Pretty Pink Shroud, Collins Crime Club (London), 1977 . . . . . £10/£5
ditto, Doubleday (New York), 1977 . . . £10/£5
Murders Anonymous, Collins Crime Club (London), 1977 . . . . £10/£5
ditto, Doubleday (New York), 1978 . . . £10/£5
In at the Kill, Collins Crime Club (London), 1978. £10/£5
ditto, Doubleday (New York), 1979 . . . £10/£5
Witness Before the Fact, Collins Crime Club (London), 1979 . . . . . £10/£5
ditto, Doubleday (New York), 1980 . . . £10/£5
Experiment with Death, Collins Crime Club (London), 1981 . . . . . £10/£5
ditto, Doubleday (New York), 1981 . . . £10/£5
Skeleton in Search of a Cupboard, Collins Crime Club (London), 1982 . . . £10/£5
ditto, as *Skeleton in Search of a Closet*, Doubleday (New York), 1982 . . . . £10/£5
Come and Be Killed, Collins Crime Club (London), 1987 . . . . £10/£5
ditto, Doubleday (New York), 1987 . . . £10/£5
Trial by Fury, Collins Crime Club (London), 1989 £10/£5
ditto, Doubleday (New York), 1989 . . . £10/£5
Danger from the Dead, Collins Crime Club (London), 1991 . . . . . . £10/£5
ditto, Bantam (New York) 1992 . . . . £10/£5
Answer Came There None, Collins Crime Club (London), 1992 . . . . . £10/£5
ditto, Doubleday (New York), 1993 . . . £10/£5
Thy Brother Death, Collins Crime Club (London), 1993 . . . . £10/£5
ditto, Doubleday (New York), 1993 . . . £10/£5
A Hobby of Murder, Collins Crime Club (London), 1994 . . . . £10/£5
ditto, Doubleday (New York), 1994 . . . £10/£5
Seeing is Believing, Collins Crime Club (London), 1994 . . . . £10/£5
ditto, Doubleday (New York), 1996 . . . £10/£5
A Choice of Evils, Collins Crime Club (London), 1995 . . . . £10/£5
ditto, Doubleday (New York), 1997 . . . £10/£5
A Thief in the Night, Collins Crime Club (London), 1995 . . . . £10/£5

Short Story Collections
Designs on Life, Collins Crime Club (London), 1980 . . . . £15/£10

ditto, Doubleday (New York), 1980 . . . . £10/£5
Sequence of Events Eurographica (Helsinki), 1989 (350
   copies; wraps) £50

Collaboration
No Flowers by Request & Crime on the Coast, Gollancz
   (London), 1984 (chain novel; chapters by Ferrars and
   others) . . . . £10/£5

Novels as 'Morna Doris Mactaggart'
Turn Single, Nicholson (London), 1932 . . . £35/£10
Broken Music, Ivor Nicholson & Watson (London), 1934 .
   . . . . £25/£10
ditto, Dutton (New York), 1934 . . . . £25/£10

HENRY FIELDING
(b.1707 d.1754)

Fielding's reputation rests on his novels, especially his
classic *Tom Jones*, a carefully constructed picaresque
which tells the complicated and comic story of how a
foundling comes into a fortune. Fielding also wrote plays,
poetry and other works, and contributed to Tory periodicals
under the name 'Captain Hercules Vinegar'.

*The History and the Adventures of Joseph Andrews and his
   friend Mr Abraham Adams*, Millar (London), 1742 (2
   vols, anon.) £3,000
Miscellanies, privately printed by subscription, 1743 (3 vols)
   . . . . £600
ditto, privately printed by subscription, 1743 (250 large
   paper or 'royal' paper copies, 3 vols) . . . £900
The History of Tom Jones, A Foundling, Millar (London),
   1749 (6 vols, with errata leaf in vol. 1) . . £2,500
Amelia, A. Millar (London), 1752 [1751] (4 vols) . . £750
The Life of Mr Jonathan Wild the Great, A. Millar
   (London), 1754 (first separate edition, originally printed in
   Vol 3 of *Miscellanies*) £300
The Works of Henry Fielding, Millar (London), 1762 (4
   vols) £500

RONALD FIRBANK
(b.1886 d.1926)

Firbank was an eccentric Roman Catholic author of witty
and artificial novels. Some critics have dismissed these as
trivial, while others consider them comic and innovative.
Writers such as E.M. Forster, Evelyn Waugh and Simon
Raven have championed him and in 1961 the poet W.H.
Auden praised him highly in a radio broadcast.

Novels
Vainglory, Grant Richards (London), 1915 (coloured
   frontispiece by Felicien Rops) £125
ditto, Brentano's (New York), 1925 . . . £125/£25
Inclinations, Grant Richards (London), 1916 . . . £45
Caprice, Grant Richards (London), 1917 . . . £75
Valmouth, Grant Richards (London), 1919 . . £45
ditto, New Directions (Norfolk, CT), 1966 . . £25/£10

The Flower Beneath the Foot, Grant Richards (London),
   1923 . . . . £200/£45
ditto, Brentano's (New York),1924 . . . £150/£25
Prancing Nigger, Brentano's (New York), 1924 . £200/£25
ditto, as *Sorrow in Sunlight*, Brentano's (London), 1924
   (1,000 numbered copies) . . . . . £150/£75
Concerning the Eccentricities of Cardinal Pirelli, Grant
   Richards (London), 1926 . . . . . £200/£30
ditto, as *Extravaganzas*, Coward-McCann (New York), 1935
   (with *The Artificial Princess*) . . . . £45/£15
The Artificial Princess, Duckworth (London), 1934 £75/£25
ditto, Centaur Press (London), 1934 (60 copies) £400/£300
Three Novels, Duckworth (London), 1950 (contains
   Vainglory, *Inclinations* and *Caprice*) . . . £35/£15
ditto, New Directions (Norfolk, CT), [1951] . £35/£15

Short Stories
Odette d'Antrevernes and A Study in Temperament, Elkin
   Mathews (London), 1905 (pink or sea-green wraps) . £300
ditto, Elkin Mathews (London), 1905 (10 copies on Japanese
   vellum) £1,500
ditto, as *Odette: A Fairy Tale for Weary People*, Grant
   Richards (London), 1916 (wraps) £65
Santal, Grant Richards (London), 1921 (wraps) . £75
ditto, Bonacio & Saul with Grove Press (New York), 1955 .
   . . . . £45/£10
Two Early Stories, Albondocani Press (New York), 1971
   (226 numbered copies; marbled wraps; illustrated by
   Edward Gorey) £200

Others
The Princess Zoubaroff - A Play, Grant Richards (London),
   1920 . . . . £200/£45
A Letter from Arthur Ronald Firbank to Madame Albani,
   Centaur Press (London), 1934 (50 facsimile copies of
   letter, issued in envelope) . . . . £250/£175
The New Rythum and Other Pieces, Duckworth (London),
   1962 . . . . £20/£10
ditto, New Directions (Norfolk, CT),1963 . £20/£10
The Wind and the Roses, Alan Clodd (London), 1966 (poem
   limited to 50 copies; wraps) £100
Far Away, Typographical Lab Univ of Iowa (Iowa City, IA),
   1966 (100 copies) £100
An Early Flemish Painter, The Enitharmon Press/Miriam L.
   Benkowitz (London), 1969 (300 copies; wraps) . £35
When Widows Love and *A Tragedy in Green*, The
   Enitharmon Press (London), 1980 (300 copies) . £45/£25

Collected Editions
The Works of Ronald Firbank, Duckworth (London), 1929
   (235 numbered sets, 5 vols) £200
Rainbow Edition, Duckworth (London), 1929-1930 (8 vols)
   . . . . £80
The Complete Ronald Firbank, Duckworth (London), 1961
   (1 vol.) . . . . £25/£10

MARY FITT
(b.1897 d.1959)

'Mary Fitt' was the pseudoym under which British classical scholar Kathleen Freeman wrote a number of popular detective novels. Her books on classical subjects were written for non-specialist readers.

Crime Novels

Three Sisters Flew Home, Nicholson & Watson (London), 1936 (blue cloth with blue lettering; d/w price 7/6) .   .
.   .   .   .£500/£50
ditto, Doubleday, Doran (New York), 1936 .   . £200/£20
Murder Mars the Tour, Nicholson & Watson (London), 1936 (red cloth with gilt lettering; d/w price 7/6). £500/£50
ditto, Doubleday, Doran (New York), 1936 .   . £200/£20
Bulls Like Death, Nicholson & Watson (London), 1937 (red cloth with blue lettering; d/w price 7/6) .   . £450/£45
The Three Hunting Horns, Nicholson & Watson (London), 1937 (light blue cloth with black lettering; d/w price 7/6) .
.   .   .   . £450/£45
Expected Death, Nicholson & Watson (London), 1938 (written with Mallett and Fitzbrown; green cloth with black lettering; d/w price 7/6) .   .   .   . £400/£40
Sky-Rocket, Nicholson & Watson (London), 1938 (written with Mallett; light blue cloth with brown lettering; d/w price 7/6) .   .   .   .   .   . £400/£40
Death at Dancing Stones, Nicholson & Watson (London), 1939 (orange cloth with black lettering; d/w price 7/6) .
.   .   .   . £400/£40
Murder of a Mouse, Nicholson & Watson (London), 1939 (fawn brown cloth with black lettering; d/w price 7/6) .
.   .   .   . £350/£35
Death Starts a Rumour, Nicholson & Watson (London), 1940 (blue cloth with black lettering; d/w price 7/6) .
.   .   .   . £300/£30
Death and Mary Dazill, Michael Joseph (London), 1941 (black cloth with silver lettering; d/w price 7/6) . £250/£25
ditto, as *Aftermath of Murder*, Doubleday, Doran (New York), 1941 .   .   .   . £100/£20
Death on Heron's Mere, Michael Joseph (London), 1941 (fawn cloth with green lettering; d/w price 8/-) . £250/£25
ditto, as *Death Finds a Target*, Doubleday, Doran (New York), 1942 .   .   .   . £65/£15
Requiem for Robert, Michael Joseph (London), 1942 (red cloth with silver lettering; d/w price 8/6) .   . £250/£24
Clues to Christabel, Michael Joseph (London), 1944 (black cloth with silver lettering; d/w price 9/6) .   . £250/£25
ditto, Doubleday, Doran (New York), 1944 .   . £65/£15
Death and the Pleasant Voices, Michael Joseph (London), 1946 (black cloth with silver lettering; d/w price 9/6) .
.   .   .   . £85/£25
ditto, Putnam (New York), 1946.   .   .   . £40/£10
A Fine and Private Place, Macdonald (London), 1947 (black cloth with gilt lettering; d/w price 8/6) .   . £65/£20
ditto, Putnam (New York), 1947.   .   .   . £40/£10
Death and the Bright Day, Macdonald (London), 1948 (black cloth with gilt lettering; d/w price 8/6) .   . £65/£15
The Banquet Ceases, Macdonald (London), 1949 (black cloth with gilt lettering; d/w price 8/6) .   .   . £65/£15
Pity for Pamela, Macdonald (London), 1950 (black cloth with yellow lettering; d/w price 8/6) .   .   . £65/£15
ditto, Harper (New York), 1951 .   .   .   . £35/£10

An Ill Wind, Macdonald (London), 1951 (black cloth with yellow lettering; d/w price 9/6) .   .   .   . £65/£15
Death and the Shortest Day, Macdonald (London), 1952 (black cloth with yellow lettering; d/w price 9/6). £65/£15
The Night Watchman's Friend, Macdonald (London), 1953 (black cloth with yellow lettering; d/w price 9/6). £65/£15
Love from Elizabeth, Macdonald (London), 1954 (black cloth with yellow lettering; d/w price 9/6) .   . £65/£15
Sweet Poison, Macdonald (London), 1956 (black cloth with yellow lettering; d/w price 10/6) .   .   . £65/£15
The Late Uncle Max, Macdonald (London), 1957 (black cloth with yellow lettering) .   .   .   .   . £40/£10
Case for the Defence, Macdonald (London), 1958 (black cloth with yellow lettering; d/w price 12/6) .   . £25/£5
ditto, British Book Centre (New York), 1958 .   . £15/£5
Mizmaze, Michael Joseph (London), 1959 (black cloth with gilt lettering; d/w price 13/6) .   .   .   . £25/£5
ditto, British Book Centre (New York), 1959 .   . £15/£5
There Are More Ways of killing, Michael Joseph (London), 1960 (black cloth with gilt lettering; d/w price 13/6) £25/£5
ditto, British Book Centre (New York), 1960 .   . £15/£5

Short Stories

The Man Who Shot Birds, Macdonald (London), 1954 (black cloth with yellow lettering) .   .   .   . £65/£15

Pseudonymous Crime Novels

Gown and Shroud, Macdonald (London), 1947 (pseud 'Kathleen Freeman'; blue cloth with orange lettering; d/w price 8/6) .   .   .   . £65/£20
And Where's Mr Bellamy, Hutchinson (London), 1948 (pseud 'Mary Wick'; brown cloth with gilt lettering) .   .
.   .   .   . £65/£20

Children's Books

The Island Castle, Nelson (London), 1953 .   . £15/£5
Annabella at the Lighthouse, Nelson (London), 1955 £15/£5
Annabella Takes a Plunge, Nelson (London), 1955 . £15/£5
Annabella to the Rescue, Nelson (London), 1955 . £15/£5
Pomeroy's Postscript, Nelson (London), 1955 .   . £15/£5
The Turnip Watch, Nelson (London), 1956 .   . £15/£5
Annabella and the Smugglers, Nelson (London), 1957 .
.   .   .   . £15/£5
Man of Justice: The Story of Solon, Nelson (London), 1957
.   .   .   . £10/£5
Vendetta, Nelson (London), 1957 .   .   .   . £10/£5
Alfred the Great, Nelson (London), 1958.   .   . £10/£5
The Shifting Sands, Nelson (London), 1958 .   . £10/£5
The Great River, Nelson (London), 1959 .   .   . £10/£5

Novel as Stuart 'Mary Wick'

The Statue and the Lady, Hodder & Stoughton (London), 1950 .   .   .   . £15/£10

Novels as 'Kathleen Freeman'

Martin Hanner: A Comedy, Jonathan Cape (London), 1926
.   .   .   .£100/£15
ditto, Harcourt Brace (New York), 1926 .   .   . £75/£15
Quarelling, Jonathan Cape (London), 1928 .   . £65/£15
This Love, Jonathan Cape (London), 1928 .   . £65/£15
The Huge Shipwreck, Dent (London), 1934 .   . £65/£15
Adventure from the Grave, Davies (London), 1936 £50/£10
Gown and Shroud, Macdonald (London), 1947 (blue cloth with orange lettering; d/w price 8/6) .   .   . £65/£20

Short Stories as 'Kathleen Freeman'

The Intruder and Other Stories, Jonathan Cape (London), 1926 . . . . £125/£25

Other Books

The Work and Life of Solon, Univ of Wales Press (Cardiff, Wales), 1926 (no d/w) £15
It Has All Happened Before: What the Greeks thought of their Nazis, Muller (London), 1941 (wraps) . . . £20
Voices of Freedom, Muller (London), 1943 . . £30/£10
What They Said at the Time, Muller (London), 1945 £15/£5
The Pre-Socratic Philosophers, Blackwell (Oxford), 1946 . . . . £25/£10
The Murder of Herodes, Macdonald (London), 1946 £10/£5
ditto, Norton (New York), 1963 . . . . . £10/£5
Greek City States, Macdonald (London), 1950 . £10/£5
ditto, Norton (New York), 1950 . . . . . £10/£5
God, Man and State, Macdonald (London), 1952 . £10/£5
ditto, Beacon Press (New York), 1952 . . . £10/£5
The Paths of Justice, Lutterworth (London), 1954 . £10/£5
ditto, Roy (New York), [1957] . . . . . £10/£5
T' Other Miss Austen, Macdonald (London), 1956 £10/£5
If Any Man Build, Hodder & Stoughton (London), 1965 . . . . £10/£5
Parson Mansell's Daughter, Hale (London), 1983 £10/£5

F. SCOTT FITZGERALD
(b.1896 d.1940)

Fitzgerald is considered one of the 20th century greats of American writing. His novels and short stories are synonymous with the Jazz Age, and Fitzgerald himself was a self-styled spokesman of the 'Lost Generation' (Americans born in the 1890s who came of age during World War One). His writing is laden with the themes of youth, despair and old age. *The Great Gatsby* is his enduring classic.

Novels

This Side of Paradise, Scribner's (New York), 1920 ('Published April, 1920' on copyright page) . £20,000/£1,750
ditto, Collins (London), 1921 . . . . . £2,500/£350
The Beautiful and Damned, Scribner's (New York), 1922 ('Published March, 1922' on copyright page, first issue d/w title in white outlined in black) . . . £5,000/£300
ditto, Scribner's (New York), 1922 (second printing, d/w with front title letters in black) . . . . £4,000/£100
ditto, Collins (London), 1922 . . . . £1,500/£200
The Great Gatsby, Scribner's (New York), 1925 (first issue with 'chatter' not 'echolalia' on p.60, line 16, 'northern' not 'southern' on p.119, line 22 etc, and d/w with 'jay Gatsby' on back blurb, line 14) . £50,000/£3,000
ditto, Scribner's (New York), 1925 (second issue with 'echolalia' on p.60, line 16, 'southern' on p.119, line 22 etc, and d/w with 'Jay Gatsby' on back blurb, line 14) . . . . £15,000/£500
ditto, Chatto & Windus (London), 1926 (original binding) . . . . £3,500/£500
ditto, Chatto & Windus (London), 1926 [1927] (cheap edition) . . . . £1,500/£100
ditto, as *The Great Gatsby: A Facsimile of the Manuscript*, Microcard Editions Books (Washington, DC), 1973 (2,000 numbered copies, slipcase) . . . . £200/£150

Tender is the Night, Scribner's (New York), 1934 (first issue jacket with review blurbs by T.S. Eliot, Mencken and Rosenfeld on front flap) . . . . £15,000/£400
ditto, Scribner's (New York), 1934 (second issue jacket) . . . . £3,000/£400
ditto, Chatto & Windus (London), 1934 (original binding) . . . . £1,000/£250
ditto, Chatto & Windus (London), 1934 [1936] (cheap edition) . . . . £350/£15
ditto, Scribner's (New York), 1951 . . £100/£30
ditto, Grey Walls Press (London), 1953 . . £125/£30
The Last Tycoon, Scribner's (New York), 1941 (unfinished) £1,000/£100
ditto, Grey Walls Press (London), 1949 . . £200/£25

Short Stories

Flappers and Philosophers, Scribner's (New York), 1920 ('Published September, 1920' on copyright page) . . . . £25,000/£400
ditto, Collins (London), 1922 . . . . £2,000/£125
Tales of the Jazz Age, Scribner's (New York), 1922 ('Published September, 1922' on copyright page) . . . . £4,000/£200
ditto, Collins (London), 1923 . . . . £2,000/£100
All the Sad Young Men, Scribner's (New York), 1926 . . . . £2,500/£200
John Jackson's Arcady, Baker (Boston), 1928 (wraps) £1,000
Taps at Reveille, Scribner's (New York), 1935 (first state, no printed price on d/w, 'Oh, catch it-Oh catch it...' on p.351, lines 29-30) . . . . £2,500/£250
ditto, Scribner's (New York), 1935 (second state, printed price on d/w, 'Oh, things like that happen...' on p.351, lines 29-30) . . . . £1,750/£125
The Stories of F. Scott Fitzgerald, Scribner's (New York), 1951 . . . . £75/£20
ditto, Franklin Library (Franklin Centre, PA), 1977 (full leather edition) £25
Borrowed Time, Grey Walls Press (London), 1951 £125/£35
Afternoon of an Author, privately printed, Princeton Univ Press (Princeton, NJ), 1957 . . . . . £100/£25
ditto, Scribner's (New York), 1958 . . . . £75/£10
ditto, Bodley Head (London), 1958 . . . . £75/£20
The Mystery of Raymond Mortgage, Random House (New York), [1960] (750 copies; stapled wraps) . . . £100
The Pat Hobby Stories, Scribner's (New York), 1962 . . . . £75/£20
ditto, Penguin (Harmondsworth, Middlesex), 1967 (pbk) £5
Dearly Beloved, Windhover Press of the Univ of Iowa (Iowa City, IA), 1969 (300 numbered copies, no d/w) . £75
The Basil and Josephine Stories, Scribner's (New York), 1973 . . . . £40/£10
Bits of Paradise: 21 Uncollected Stories, Bodley Head (London), 1973 (with Zelda Fitzgerald) . . £35/£10
ditto, Scribner's (New York), 1973 . . . £35/£10
The Price Was High, Harcourt Brace (New York), 1979 . . . . £30/£5
ditto, Quartet (London), 1979 . . . . £25/£5

Others

The Evil Eye, A Comedy in Two Acts, John Church Company (Cincinnati, Ohio)/Triangle Club (Princeton, NJ), 1915 (wraps; written with Edmund Wilson) . £1,250
The Vegetable: From President to Postman, Scribner's (New York), 1923 . . . . . . £2,000/£100

The Crack-Up, New Directions (Norfolk, CT), 1945 (first issue title-page printed in red/brown and black, edited by Edmund Wilson) . . . . £250/£45

ditto, New Directions (Norfolk, CT), 1945 ('British Empire' issue) . . . . £125/£35

ditto, Grey Walls Press (London), 1947 . . . £45/£15

The Bodley Head F. Scott Fitzgerald, Volume 1-6, Bodley Head (London), 1958-1963 . . . . . £65/£20

The Letters of F. Scott Fitzgerald, Scribner's (New York), 1963 . . . . £50/£15

ditto, Bodley Head (London), 1964 . . . £40/£15

The Apprentice Fiction of F. Scott Fitzgerald, Rutgers Univ Press (New Brunswick, NJ), 1965 . . . £35/£10

Thoughtbook of Francis Scott Key Fitzgerald, Princeton Univ Press (Princeton, NJ), 1965 (glassine d/w) . £35/£30

F. Scott Fitzgerald in His Own Time, Kent State Univ Press (Kent, OH), 1971 . . . . £30/£10

Dear Scott/Dear Max: The Fitzgerald-Perkins Correspondence, Scribner's (New York), 1971 . . . £30/£10

ditto, Cassell (London), 1973 . . . . . £25/£10

As Ever, Scott Fitz: Letter Between F. Scott Fitzgerald and His Literary Agent Harold Ober, Lippincott (Philadelphia, PA), 1972 . . . . £25/£10

ditto, Woburn (London), 1973 . . . . £25/£10

F. Scott Fitzgerald's Preface to This Side of Paradise, Windhover Press (Iowa City, IA), 1975 (150 copies) . £125

The Notebooks of F. Scott Fitzgerald, Harcourt Brace (New York), 1978 . . . . £30/£10

The Correspondence of F. Scott Fitzgerald, Random House (New York), 1980 . . . . . . £30/£10

PENELOPE FITZGERALD

(b.1916 d.2000)

Penelope Fitzgerald is an English poet, novelist and biographer who was first published at 60. Her first book was a biography of Edward Burne-Jones and she has also written a life of Charlotte Mew. In 1978 she was shortlisted for the Booker Prize for *The Bookshop*, and the following year she won the prize with *Offshore*. Her novels are humorous, understated and often painfully revealing.

Novels

The Golden Child, Duckworth (London), 1977 . £200/£30

ditto, Scribner's (New York), 1977 . . . £100/£15

The Bookshop, Duckworth (London), 1978 . £100/£15

ditto, as **The Book Shop**, Houghton Mifflin (Boston), 1997 (pbk) £5

Offshore, Collins (London), 1979 . . . £40/£5

ditto, Henry Holt (New York), 1979 . . . £25/£5

Human Voices, Collins (London), 1980 . . . £25/£5

ditto, Houghton Mifflin (Boston), 1999 (pbk) . . £5

At Freddie's, Collins (London), 1982 . . £15/£5

ditto, Godine (Boston), 1985 . . . . £15/£5

Innocence, Collins (London), 1986 . . . £10/£5

ditto, Holt (New York), 1987 . . . . . £10/£5

The Beginning of Spring, Collins (London), 1988. £10/£5

ditto, Holt (New York), 1989 . . . . £10/£5

The Gate of Angels, Collins (London), 1990 . £10/£5

ditto, Doubleday (New York), 1992 . . . £10/£5

The Blue Flower, Flamingo (London), 1995 . . £10/£5

ditto, Houghton Mifflin (Boston), 1997 . . . £10/£5

Others

Edward Burne-Jones: A Biography, Joseph (London), 1975 . . . . £65/£15

The Knox Brothers, Macmillan (London), 1977 . £30/£5

ditto, Coward-McCann (New York), 1977 . £15/£5

Charlotte Mew and Her Friends, Collins (London), 1984 . . . . £15/£5

ditto, as **Charlotte Mew and Her Friends: With a Selection of Her Poems**, Addison-Wesley (Reading, MA), 1988 . . . . £15/£5

The Means of Escape: Stories, Flamingo/HarperCollins (London), 2000 . . . . £10/£5

ditto, Houghton Mifflin (Boston), 2000 . . £10/£5

JAMES ELROY FLECKER

(b.1884 d.1915)

A poet and dramatist greatly influenced at Oxford by the last flowering of the Aesthetic movement under J.A. Symonds, Flecker followed a career in the Consular Service in the Eastern Mediterranean. His play *Hassan* was lavishly and successfully produced in London in 1923-24.

Poetry

The Bridge of Fire, Elkin Mathews (London), 1907 (wraps; first issue with no quote) £100

ditto, Elkin Mathews (London), 1907 (wraps; with quote from *Sunday Times*) £35

Thirty-Six Poems, Adelphi Press (London), 1910 . £75

Forty-Two Poems, Dent (London), 1911 . . . £20

The Golden Journey to Samarkand, Goschen (London), 1913 . . . . £75

ditto, Goschen (London), 1913 (50 signed, numbered copies) £750

The Old Ships, Poetry Bookshop (London), [n.d.] (wraps; first issue illustration of a ship with a mermaid on front cover) £65

ditto, Poetry Bookshop (London), [n.d.] (wraps; second issue illustration without mermaid on front cover) . . £40

God Save the King, privately printed for Clement Shorter (London), [1915] (20 copies; wraps) . . . £150

The Burial in England, privately printed for Clement Shorter (London), [1915] (20 copies; wraps) . . £150

The Collected Poems of James Elroy Flecker, Secker (London), [1916] £25

ditto, Doubleday (New York), 1916 . . . . £25

Fourteen Poems, Poetry Bookshop (London), 1921 (50 copies; wraps) £150

Collected Poems, Secker (London), 1923 (500 numbered copies) . . . . £100/£25

Unpublished Poems and Drafts, Keepsake Press (London), 1971 (30 copies in cloth) . . . £75/£25

ditto, Keepsake Press (London), 1971 (sewn wraps) . £10

Drama

Hassan: The Story of Hassan of Bagdad and how he came to make the Golden Journey to Samarkand - A Play in Five Acts, Heinemann (London), 1922 . . . £50/£20

ditto, Knopf (New York), 1922 . . . . . £50/£20

ditto, Heinemann (London), 1923 (380 copies on handmade paper) . . . . £75/£20
ditto, Heinemann (London), 1924 (illustrated by Thomas Mackenzie) . . . .£125/£65
Don Juan, Heinemann (London), 1925 . . . £20/£10
ditto, Heinemann (London), 1925 (380 copies) . £35/£15
ditto, Knopf (New York), 1922 . . . . . £20/£10

Fiction

The Last Generation: A Story of the Future, The New Age Press (London), 1908 (wraps) £75
The King of Alsander, Goschen (London), 1914 (first issue in scarlet buckram) £75
ditto, Goschen (London), 1914 (second issue in yellow cloth) £45
ditto, Putnam's (New York), 1914 . . . . £40

Others

The Best Man, Holywell Press (Oxford, UK), 1906 (wraps) £250
The Grecians; A Dialogue on Education, Dent (London), 1910 . . . . £25
The Scholar's Italian Book, etc., Nutt (London), 1911. £25
Collected Prose, Bell (London), 1920 . . . £25/£10
The Letters of J.E. Flecker to Frank Savery, Beaumont Press (London), 1926 (80 numbered copies signed by the editor, the artists and publisher of 390) . . .£175
ditto, Beaumont Press (London), 1926 (310 numbered, unsigned copies) £45
Some Letters from Abroad, Heinemann (London), 1930 . . . . £45/£15

IAN FLEMING

(b.1908 d.1964)

Fleming was an English author famous for writing the Bond novels and the children's story, *Chitty Chitty Bang Bang*. In 1939 he was recruited as the Director of Naval Intelligence's personal assistant, his intelligence work forming the background and experience for writing the James Bond books. The condition of the early Bond books is of paramount importance in determining their value.

'James Bond' Titles

Casino Royale, Cape (London), 1953 (black cloth with red lettering & heart on front board; copyright page states 'First Published 1953'; d/w priced at 10s.6d; rear panel has pencil drawing of Ian Fleming, with blurb about Fleming's life below; front flap has blurb with jacket credit immediately below; the first issue does *not* have a *Times* review; rear flap is blank but for title, author, Cape & price in bottom left corner; 4,728 copies were bound, a large number of which went to public libraries) £17,500/£2,000
ditto, Macmillan (New York), 1954 (dark green glazed cloth lettered and blocked in red; copyright page states first printing; d/w priced at $2.75; first issue d/w with complete square-cut front flap corners) . . . £2,000/£125
ditto, Macmillan (New York), 1954 (as above but second issue d/w with angle-clipped corners) . £1,750/£125
Live and Let Die, Cape (London), 1954 (black cloth with gilt lettering and gilt medallion on front board; copyright page states 'First Published 1954'; d/w priced at 10s.6d; first

state d/w with no credit for jacket design on front flap) . . . . £7,000/£350
ditto, Cape (London), 1954 (second state d/w with two-line credit positioned midway between blurb end and price) . . . . £3,000/£350
ditto, Cape (London), 1954 (third state d/w with two-line credit positioned directly under the blurb) . £2,500/£350
ditto, Macmillan (New York), 1955 (dark navy blue cloth pattern paper over boards with a yellow 'Cock Robin Thriller' square logo printed on the lower right corner of the front board; author's surname, title and publisher printed in yellow on the spine; copyright page states first printing; d/w priced at $3.00) . . . . .£400/£45
Moonraker, Cape (London), 1955 (black cloth with silver lettering; copyright page states 'First Published 1955'; text block measures either 15mm or 19mm; d/w priced at 10s.6d) . . . . £5,000/£350
ditto, Macmillan (New York), 1955 (light green cloth blocked and lettered in dark green; copyright page states first printing; d/w priced at $2.75) . . .£500/£35
Diamonds are Forever, Cape (London), 1956 (black cloth with silver lettering; copyright page states 'First Published 1956'; d/w priced at 12s.6d) . . . .£1,500/£200
ditto, Macmillan (New York), 1956 (grey cloth lettered in red and green-black; copyright page states first printing; d/w priced at $2.75) . . . .£400/£65
From Russia, with Love, Cape (London), 1957 (black cloth with central vignette of customised Smith & Wesson .38 with a rose blocked in silver and bronze-red imitating jacket artwork, with silver Cape logo at foot of spine; copyright page states 'First Published 1957'; d/w priced at 13s.6d) . . . .£850/£50
ditto, Cape (London), 1957 (Book Club edition, bound from rejected Cape first printing sheets; some but not all copies still state 'First Published 1957; bound in light blue, orange or green cloth with black lettering on spine) . . £75/£20
ditto, Macmillan (New York), 1957 (cream cloth lettered in black; copyright page states first printing; d/w priced at $3.50) . . . .£200/£20
Dr No, Cape (London), 1958 (black cloth with brown silhouette of dancing girl on front board; copyright page states 'First Published 1958'; d/w jacket priced at 13s.6d). . . . .£750/£45
ditto, Cape (London), 1958 (as above without silhouette) . . . . £1,000/£250
ditto, Cape (London), 1958 (presumed trial binding in red cloth lettered in silver in different font with 'Jonathan/Cape' at foot of spine with logo; top edge stained blue) . . . . £1,500/£750
ditto, Cape (London), 1958 (variant proof/advance readers copy; pictorial paper self wraps, with dancing girl design identical to the hardback d/w) £1,500
ditto, Macmillan (New York), 1958 (black cloth lettered in red on upper board and spine; copyright page states first printing; d/w priced at $3.50) . . . . .£200/£20
Goldfinger, Cape (London), 1959 (black cloth with gilt lettering and skull embossed on front board with gilt-stamped coins in eye-sockets; copyright page states 'First Published 1959'; d/w priced at 15s) . . .£750/£35
ditto, Macmillan (New York), 1959 (black cloth with gilt lettering and skull embossed on front board; copyright page states 'First Published 1959'; d/w priced at $3.00) £200/£15
For Your Eyes Only, Cape (London), 1960 (short stories; black cloth with gilt lettering and eye design on front

board; copyright page states 'First Published 1960'; d/w
priced at 15s) . . . . £700/£50
ditto, Viking (New York), 1960 (copyright page does not
state printing; d/w priced at $3.50) . . . £150/£25
Thunderball, Cape (London), 1961 (black cloth with gilt
lettering and a skeletal hand on front board; copyright page
states 'First Published 1961'; d/w priced at 15s) . £375/£20
ditto, Viking (New York), 1961 (yellow cloth with Viking
logo stamped in red on front board and spine lettered in
red; copyright page shows no indication of first printing
though later printings would be noted; d/w priced at $3.95)
. . . . £125/£15
The Spy Who Loved Me, Cape (London), 1962 (black cloth
with silver lettering and dagger on the front board;
copyright page states 'First Published 1962'; d/w wrapper
priced at 15s; rare copies with a quad mark between the E
& M of Fleming on title page) . . . . £500/£75
ditto, Cape (London), 1962 (as above but without a quad
mark between the E & M of Fleming on title page) . .
. . . . £450/£20
ditto, Viking (New York), 1962 (light brown cloth lettered
and stamped in dark brown; copyright page shows no
indication of first printing though later printings would be
noted; d/w priced at $3.95) . . . . £75/£15
On Her Majesty's Secret Service, Cape (London), 1963
(black cloth lettered in silver with a track design on front
board; copyright page states 'First Published 1963'; d/w
priced at 16s) . . . . £200/£25
ditto, Cape (London), 1963 (250 signed copies, clear glassine
d/w) . . . .£5,000/£4,750
ditto, New American Library (New York), 1963 (black cloth-
backed blue paper boards with upper board stamped in
black with Fleming's signature, spine lettered and ruled in
gilt; copyright page states 'First printing, September,
1963'; d/w priced at $4.50) . . . . . £100/£15
You Only Live Twice, Cape (London), 1964 (black cloth
with silver lettering and Japanese lettering on front board;
copyright page states 'First Published 1964' on first state of
first impression) . . . . £175/£50
ditto, Cape (London), 1964 (copyright page states 'First
Published March 1964' on second state of first impression)
. . . . £145/£20
ditto, New American Library (New York), 1964 (yellow
cloth blocked with Fleming autograph in black on upper
board, spine ruled and lettered in red; copyright page states
first printing; d/w priced at $4.50) . . . . £65/£15
The Man with the Golden Gun, Cape (London), 1965 (black
cloth with gold blocked revolver on front cover, spine
lettered in gilt; copyright page states 'First Published
1965'; d/w priced at 18s) . . . . .£3,000/£2,900
ditto, Cape (London), 1965 (as above but without gold
blocked revolver on front cover) . . . . £75/£15
ditto, New American Library (New York), 1965 (black cloth
with gun stamped in gilt over front spine and back covers,
spine lettered in white and red, spine lettered in red;
copyright page states first printing; d/w priced at $4.50) .
. . . . £50/£10
Octopussy and **The Living Daylights**, Cape (London), 1966
(short stories; black cloth with gilt lettering; copyright page
states 'First Published 1966'; d/w priced at 10s.6d) £50/£5
ditto, New American Library (New York), 1966 (black cloth
with stylised rifle stamped in gilt on upper board, spine
lettered in red; copyright page states first printing; d/w
priced at $3.50) . . . . £45/£5

see also **The Ivory Hammer: The Year at Sotherby's**,
Longman (London), 1963 (Contains Bond story 'The
Property of a Lady') . . . . . . £65/£20
ditto, Holt, Rinehart & Winston (New York), 1964   £40/£15

Non-Fiction
The Diamond Smugglers, Cape (London), 1957 (first issue
with the spine lettered in white rather than gold) . £125/£35
ditto, Cape (London), 1957 (second issue with the spine
lettered in gold) . . . . £100/£20
ditto, Macmillan (New York), 1958 . . . . £45/£20
Thrilling Cities, Cape (London), 1963 . . . £30/£15
ditto, New American Library (New York), 1964   £20/£10
Ian Fleming Introduces Jamaica, Deutsch (London), 1965
. . . . £20/£10
ditto, Hawthorne (New York), 1965 . . . . £15/£10

Children's Titles
Chitty Chitty Bang Bang, Cape (London), 1964-65 (3
books) . . . . £100/£20 each, £750/£100 the set
ditto, Random House (New York), 1964 . . . £30/£5

W. RUSSELL FLINT
(b.1880 d.1969)

Flint was a British artist and illustrator, generally of elegant
nudes. Although never highly regarded by critics, the
genteel sensuality of his illustrations has always been very
popular with the public. He was elected a full member of
the Royal Academy in 1933, and in 1962, aged 82, was
accorded the rare honour of a retrospective exhibition. He
received a knighthood in 1947.

King Solomon's Mines, by H. Rider Haggard, Cassell
(London), 1905 (32 b&w plates) £125
Through the Magic Door, by A. Conan Doyle, Smith Elder
(London), 1907 (6 b&w plates) £50
Of The Imitation of Christ, by Thomas à Kempis, Chatto &
Windus (London), 1908 (8 colour plates) . . . £45
Savoy Operas, by W.S. Gilbert, Bell (London), 1909 (32
colour plates) £150
The Song of Songs, Warner/Riccardi/Medici (London), 1909
(500 copies, 10 colour plates, boards) . . . £150
ditto, Warner/Riccardi/Medici (London), 1909 (limp vellum)
. . . . £200
ditto, Warner/Riccardi/Medici (London), 1909 (17 copies,
vellum, extra set of plates). £1,000
ditto, Warner/Riccardi/Medici (London), 1913 . . £45
Iolanthe and Other Operas, by W.S. Gilbert, Bell (London),
1910 (32 colour plates) £100
The Thoughts of The Emperor Marcus Aurelius Antonius,
Warner/Riccardi/Medici (London), 1910 (500 copies,
boards) £125
ditto, Warner/Riccardi/Medici (London), 1910 (limp vellum)
. . . . £150
ditto, Warner/Riccardi/Medici (London), 1912 . . £75
The Scholar Gipsy and Thyrsis, by Matthew Arnold,
Warner/Riccardi/Medici (London), 1910 (10 colour plates)
. . . . £125
Le Morte d'Arthur, by Sir Thomas Malory, Warner/
Riccardi/Medici (London), 1910-11 (4 vols, 500 numbered
copies, boards) £500

ditto, Warner/Riccardi/Medici (London), 1910-11 (limp vellum) £750

ditto, Warner/Riccardi/Medici (London), 1910-11 (12 copies, vellum, extra set of plates). £2,500

ditto, Warner/Riccardi/Medici (London), 1912 . . £100

Iolanthe, or The Peer and the Peri, by W.S. Gilbert, Bell (London), 1911 (8 colour plates) £50

The Mikado, by W.S. Gilbert, Bell (London), 1911 (8 colour plates) £100

ditto, Macmillan (London), 1928 (8 colour plates by Flint, plus b&w drawings by C.E. Brock). . . £50/£15

Patience, by W.S. Gilbert, Bell (London), 1911 (8 colour plates) £40

The Pirates of Penzance, by W.S. Gilbert, Bell (London), 1911 (8 colour plates). £45

Songs and Lyrics, by Robert Burns, Warner/Riccardi/Medici (London), 1911 . . . . . . £100

The Heroes, or Greek Fairy Tales for My Children, by Charles Kingsley, Warner/Riccardi/Medici (London), 1912 (500 copies, boards) £250

ditto, Warner/Riccardi/Medici (London), 1912 (limp vellum binding). £500

ditto, Warner/Riccardi/Medici (London), 1912 (12 copies printed on vellum) £2,000

ditto, Warner/Riccardi/Medici (London), 1914 . . £75

Princess Ida, by W.S. Gilbert, Bell (London), 1912 (8 colour plates) £50

Ruddigore, by W.S. Gilbert, Bell (London), 1912 (8 colour plates) £55

The Gondoliers, by W.S. Gilbert, Bell (London), 1912 (8 colour plates) £65

The Yeomen of the Guard, by W.S. Gilbert, Bell (London), 1912 (8 colour plates). £65

ditto, Macmillan (London), 1929 (8 colour plates by Flint, plus b&w drawings by C.E. Brock). . . £50/£15

The Canterbury Tales, by Geoffrey Chaucer, Warner/Riccardi/Medici (London), 1913 (3 vols, 500 copies, boards) £400

ditto, Warner/Riccardi/Medici (London), 1913 (limp vellum) £600

Rabbi Ben Ezra, Foulis (London), 1913 . . . £30

The Watercolours of W. Russell Flint, The Studio (London), 1920 . . . . £45

The Idyls of Theocritus, Bion and Moschus, Warner/Riccardi/Medici (London), 1922 (2 vols, 500 copies, boards) £150

ditto, Warner/Riccardi/Medici (London), 1922 (limp vellum) £250

The Odyssey, by Homer, Warner/Riccardi/Medici (London), 1924 (500 copies, boards) £125

ditto, Warner/Riccardi/Medici (London), 1924 (limp vellum) £200

Judith, Haymarket Press (London), 1928 (875 numbered copies) . . . . £65/£40

ditto, Haymarket Press (London), 1928 (100 signed, numbered copies, parchment, in slipcase) . £200/£150

ditto, Haymarket Press (London), 1928 (12 signed copies, on vellum, extra set of 4 plates, in slipcase) . £1,000/£800

W. Russell Flint, Famous Water-Colour Painters No. 2, The Studio (London), 1928 . . . . . £45

The Book of Tobit and *History of Susanna*, Haymarket Press (London), 1929 (875 numbered copies) . £50/£25

ditto, Haymarket Press (London), 1929 (100 signed, numbered copies, parchment, in slipcase) . £200/£150

ditto, Haymarket Press (London), 1929 (12 signed copies, on vellum, extra set of 4 plates, in slipcase) . £1,000/£800

W. Russell Flint, Modern Masters of Etching No.27, The Studio (London), 1931 . . . . . £50

Drawings, Collins (London), 1950 . . . £125/£75

ditto, Collins (London), 1950 (500 signed copies, with separate signed mounted print, in slipcase) . £450/£400

ditto, Collins (London), 1950 (125 signed copies, with a titled and initialled pencil drawing, in slipcase) . £1,250/£1,000

Models of Propriety, Joseph (London), 1951 . £50/£30

ditto, Joseph (London), 1951 (500 signed copies) . £100

Minxes Admonished, Golden Cockerel Press (Waltham St Lawrence, Berks), 1955 (400 copies, quarter morocco, in slipcase). £400

ditto, Golden Cockerel Press (Waltham St Lawrence, Berks), 1955 (150 copies, scarlet morocco, with 8 extra plates, in slipcase). . . . . £650/£500

One Hundred and Eleven Poems, by Robert Herrick, Golden Cockerel Press (Waltham St Lawrence, Berks), 1955 (450 copies, slipcase) . . . £400/£350

ditto, Golden Cockerel Press (Waltham St Lawrence, Berks), 1955 (100 signed copies, 8 extra plates, slipcase) . . . . £650/£550

Memoirs of Madame du Barry, by M.F. Pidansat de Mairobert, Folio Society (London), 1956 . . £15

Etchings and Dry Points, Catalogue Raisonne, Coinaghi, 1957 (135 signed copies, buckram). . . . £150

ditto, Coinaghi, 1957 (half morocco) . . . £200

Pictures From An Artist's Studio, Royal Academy of Arts (London), 1962 (wraps) £30

ditto, Royal Academy of Arts (London), 1962 (cloth) . £45

Shadows in Arcady, Skilton (London), 1965 (500 signed copies, slipcase) . . . . . £250/£200

The Lisping Goddess, Stanbrook Abbey Press, 1968 (275 signed copies in slipcase) . . . . £250/£200

Breakfast in Perigord, Skilton (London), 1968 (525 signed copies, in slipcase) . . . . £250/£200

An Autobiography: In Pursuit, Medici Society (London), 1970 (150 of 1050 numbered copies in full morocco, slipcase). . . . . £250/£200

ditto, Medici Society (London), 1970 (remaining copies in quarter morocco, slipcase). . . . . £125/£100

FORD MADOX FORD
(b.1873 d.1939)

A novelist and editor born Ford Hermann Hueffer, although, unless noted otherwise, titles listed below were published as by either Ford Madox Ford, Ford Madox Hueffer or F. Madox Hueffer. Despite his Victorian roots (his grandfather was the Pre-Raphaelite painter Ford Madox Brown), Ford was always a champion of new literature and literary experimentation. He was founder of *The Transatlantic Review*.

Novels

The Shifting of the Fire, T. Fisher Unwin (London), 1892 (pseud 'H. Ford Hueffer') £275

The Benefactor, Brown, Langham & Co. (London), 1905 . . . . £200

The Fifth Queen, Alston Rivers (London), 1906 . . £100

ditto, Vanguard Press (New York), [c.1963] . . £20/£5
Privy Seal, Alston Rivers (London), 1907. . . . £75
An English Girl, Methuen & Co. (London), 1907 . . £100
The Fifth Queen Crowned, Eveleigh Nash (London), 1908
. . . . £65
Mr Apollo, Methuen & Co. (London), 1908 . . . £145
The Half Moon, Eveleigh Nash (London), 1909 . . £65
ditto, Doubleday Page (New York), 1909 . . . £60
A Call: The Tale of Two Passions, Chatto & Windus
(London), 1910 . . . . £75
The Portrait, Methuen & Co. (London), 1910. . . £200
The Simple Life Limited, John Lane (London), 1911 (pseud
'Daniel Chaucer') £125
Ladies Whose Bright Eyes, Constable (London) & Co., 1911
. . . . £75
ditto, Doubleday Page (New York), 1912 . . . . £75
The Panel, Constable (London) & Co., 1912 . . . £125
ditto, as **Ring For Nancy**, Bobbs-Merrill (Indianapolis, IN),
1913 (revised edition). £65
The New Humpty-Dumpty, John Lane (London), 1912
(pseud 'Daniel Chaucer'). £150
ditto, John Lane (New York), 1912 . . . . . £150
Mr Fleight, Howard Latimer (London), 1913 . . . £100
The Young Lovell, Chatto & Windus (London), 1913 . £250
The Good Soldier, John Lane (London), 1915. . £1,500
ditto, John Lane (New York), 1915 . . . . . £750
ditto, Albert & Charles Boni (New York), 1927 (300 signed,
numbered copies) £800
Zeppelin Nights: A London Entertainment, John Lane/
Bodley Head (London), 1915 (with Violet Hunt). . £125
The Marsden Case, Duckworth (London), 1923 . £250/£75
Some Do Not, Duckworth (London), 1924 . . £250/£75
ditto, Seltzer (New York), 1925 . . . . . £100/£30
No More Parades, Duckworth (London), 1925 . £250/£75
ditto, Boni (New York), 1925 . . . . . £100/£25
A Man Could Stand Up, Duckworth (London), 1926 . .
. . . . £125/£25
ditto, Boni (New York), 1926 . . . . . . £75/£15
The Last Post, The Literary Guild of America (New York),
1928 . . . . £75/£15
ditto, as **Last Post**, Duckworth (London), 1928 . £75/£15
A Little Less Than Gods, Duckworth (London), [1928] .
. . . . £75/£20
ditto, Viking (New York), 1928 . . . . . £75/£20
When the Wicked Man, Horace Liveright (New York), 1931
. . . . £75/£20
ditto, Cape (London), 1932 . . . . . . £50/£20
The Rash Act, Long & Smith (New York), 1933 . £50/£15
ditto, Cape (London), 1933 . . . . . . £50/£15
Henry for Hugh, Lippincott (Philadelphia, PA), 1934 . .
. . . . £50/£15
Vive le Roy, Lippincott (Philadelphia, PA), 1936 . £45/£15
ditto, George Allen & Unwin (London), 1937 . £45/£15

Titles Written with Joseph Conrad
The Inheritors, McClure, Phillips & Co. (New York), 1901
(dedicated to Boys & Christina) . . . £3,000
ditto, McClure, Phillips & Co. (New York), 1901 (dedicated
to Borys & Christina) £200
ditto, Heinemann (London), 1901 (top edge untrimmed, 32
pages adverts, publisher's device on spine with initials) .
. . . . £600
ditto, Heinemann (London), 1901 (top edge trimmed, no
catalogue, publisher's device on spine with initials) . £350

ditto, Heinemann (London), 1901 (without initials in
publisher's device) £300
ditto, Heinemann (London), 1901 (remainder issue, non-
pictorial cloth) £150
Romance, Smith Elder (London), 1903 . . . . £150
ditto, McClure (New York), 1904 . . . . . £125
The Nature of a Crime, Duckworth (London), 1924 . .
. . . . £125/£25
ditto, Doubleday (New York), 1924 . . . . £125/£25

Verse
**The Questions at the Well, with Sundry Other Verses for
Notes of Music**, Digby & Co (London), 1893 (pseud 'Fenil
Haig') £250
Poems for Pictures and for Notes of Music, Macqueen
(London), 1900 . . . . £175
**The Face of the Night: A Second Series of Poems for
Pictures**, Macqueen (London), 1904 . . . £175
From Inland and Other Poems, Alston Rivers (London),
1907 (wraps). £175
Songs from London, Elkin Mathews (London), 1910 (wraps)
. . . . £75
High Germany: Eleven Sets of Verse, Duckworth (London),
1911 . . . . £125
Collected Poems, Max Goschen (London), 1914 . . £125
ditto, Secker (London), 1915 (Goschen sheets with cancel
Secker title-page). £100
Antwerp, The Poetry Bookshop (London), 1914 (wraps) .
. . . . £300
On Heaven, and Poems Written on Active Service, John
Lane, The Bodley Head (London), 1918 . . . £65
A House, The Poetry Bookshop (London), 1921 (sewn
wraps) £35
New Poems, Rudge (New York), 1927 (325 signed copies,
glassine d/w). . . . . £225/£175
Collected Poems, O.U.P. (New York), 1936 . . £75/£25
Buckshee, Pym-Randall Press (Cambridge, MA), 1966 .
. . . . £75/£25
ditto, Pym-Randall (Cambridge, MA), 1966 (50 numbered
copies) . . . . £175/£100
Selected Poems, Pym-Randall Press (Cambridge, MA), 1971
(1,000 copies) . . . . £45/£20
ditto, Pym-Randall (Cambridge, MA), 1971 (50 copies) .
. . . . £125/£75

Children's Books
The Brown Owl: A Fairy Story, Unwin (London), 1892
[1891] (as Ford H. Hueffer) £350
ditto, Stokes (New York), 1891 . . . . . £350
The Feather, Unwin (London), 1892. . . . . £300
Christina's Fairy Book, The Pinafore Library (London),
1906 . . . . £250

Others
Ford Madox Brown: A Record of His Life and Work,
Longmans Green (London), 1896 . . . . £150
The Cinque Ports: A Historical and Descriptive Record,
Blackwood (Edinburgh/London), 1900 . . . £350
Rossetti: A Critical Essay on His Art, Duckworth (London),
[1902] £30
ditto, Dutton (New York), 1902 . . . . . . £25
The Soul of London: A Survey of a Modern City, Alston
Rivers (London), 1905 . . . . . . £65

The Heart of the Country: A Survey of a Modern Land,
Duckworth (London), 1906 . . . . . £45
England and the English: An Interpretation, McClure,
Phillips (New York), 1907 . . . . . £40
The Pre-Raphaelite Brotherhood: A Critical Monograph,
Duckworth (London), 1907 . . . . . £150
Ancient Lights and Certain New Reflections, Chapman &
Hall (London), 1911 . . . . . £65
ditto, as *Memories and Impressions: A Study in
Atmospheres*, Harper (New York), 1911 . . £50
The Critical Attitude, Duckworth (London), 1911 (pseud
'Ford Madox Hueffer') £40
This Monstrous Regiment of Women, Women's Freedom
League (London), 1913 . . . . . £100
The Desirable Alien: At Home in Germany, Chatto and
Windus 1913 (with Violet Hunt) £65
Henry James: A Critical Study, Secker (London), 1913 £65
ditto, Dodd Mead (New York), 1916 . . . . £50
*Between St. Dennis and St. George: A Sketch of Three
Civilizations*, Hodder & Stoughton (London), 1915 . £45
*When Blood Is Their Argument: An Analysis of Prussian
Culture*, Hodder & Stoughton (London), 1915 . £45
ditto, Hodder & Stoughton (New York), 1915. . £45
Thus to Revisit: Some Reminiscences, Chapman & Hall
(London), 1921 . . . . . . £100/£45
Women and Men, Three Mountains Press (Paris), 1923 (300
numbered copies; wraps) £400
*Mister Bosphorus and the Muses; or, A Short History of
Poetry in Britain*, Duckworth (London), 1923 £250/£100
ditto, Duckworth (London), 1923 (70 copies signed by artist)
. . . . £500/£300
Joseph Conrad: A Personal Remembrance, Duckworth
(London), 1924 . . . . . . £75/£25
ditto, Little, Brown (Boston), 1924 . . . £75/£25
A Mirror to France, Duckworth (London), 1926 . £75/£25
New York is Not America, Duckworth (London), 1927. .
. . . . £125/£20
ditto, Boni (New York), 1927 . . . . £75/£20
New York Essays, Rudge (New York), 1927 (750 signed
copies) £200
No Enemy, Macaulay (New York), 1929 . . £150/£35
The English Novel, Lippincott (Philadelphia, PA), 1929 .
. . . . £50/£15
ditto, Constable (London), 1930 . . . . £45/£15
Return of Yesterday, Gollancz (London), 1931 . £65/£20
It Was the Nightingale, Lippincott (Philadelphia, PA), 1933
. . . . £50/£15
ditto, Heinemann (London), 1934 . . . £45/£15
Provence, from Minstrels to the Machine, Allen & Unwin
(London), 1935 . . . . . £40/£15
ditto, Lippincott (Philadelphia, PA), 1935. . £40/£15
Great Trade Route, O.U.P. (New York), 1937 . £35/£15
Portraits from Life: Memories and Criticisms, Houghton
Mifflin (Boston), 1937 . . . . . £65/£20
ditto, as *Mightier Than the Sword*, Unwin (London), 1938 .
. . . . £50/£15
The March of Literature from Confucius to Modern Times,
Dial Press (New York), 1938 . . . £65/£25
Critical Writings, Univ of Nebraska Press (Lincoln, NE)
[1964] 1964 . . . . . . £25/£10
Your Mirror to My Times, Holt Rinehart & Winston (New
York), 1971 . . . . . . £15/£5

Translation
The Trail of the Barbarians, by Pier Loti, Longmans
(London), 1917 (stapled wraps) £250
Perversity, by Francis Carco, Covici (New York), 1928
(translation credited to Ford but in fact by Jean Rhys) .
. . . . £250/£40

C.S. FORESTER
(b.1899 d.1966)

'Cecil Scott Forester' was the pen name of Cecil Smith,
best remembered for his novels of adventure with military
themes, notably the 'Horatio Hornblower' series about
naval warfare during the Napoleonic era. The 'Hornblower'
series is rivalled only by the 'Aubrey–Maturin' series of
seafaring novels by Patrick O'Brian. Forester is also remembered for *The African Queen*, the American and English editions of which have different endings.

'Hornblower' Novels
Beat to Quarters, Little, Brown (Boston), 1937 . £500/£75
ditto, as *The Happy Return*, Joseph (London), 1937 . .
. . . . £1,450/£100
A Ship of the Line, Little, Brown (Boston), 1938 . £400/£45
ditto, as *Ship of the Line* Joseph (London), 1938 . £600/£65
Flying Colours, Joseph (London), 1938 (includes *A Ship of
the Line*) . . . . . . £500/£65
ditto, Little, Brown (Boston), 1939 . . . £350/£40
Commodore Hornblower, Little, Brown (Boston), 1945 .
. . . . £45/£15
ditto, as *The Commodore*, Joseph (London), 1945 . £100/£20
Lord Hornblower, Little, Brown (Boston), 1946 . £50/£15
ditto, Joseph (London), 1946 . . . . £65/£15
Mr Midshipman Hornblower, Little, Brown (Boston), 1950
. . . . £45/£10
ditto, Joseph (London), 1950 . . . . £45/£10
Lieutenant Hornblower, Little, Brown (Boston), 1952. .
. . . . £45/£10
ditto, Joseph (London), 1952 . . . . £45/£10
Hornblower and the Atropos, Little, Brown (Boston), 1953
. . . . £45/£10
ditto, Joseph (London), 1953 . . . . £45/£10
Admiral Hornblower in the West Indies, Little, Brown
(Boston), 1958 . . . . . £40/£10
ditto, as *Hornblower in the West Indies*, Joseph (London),
1958 . . . . £40/£10
Hornblower and the Hotspur, Little, Brown (Boston), 1962
. . . . £35/£10
ditto, Joseph (London), 1962 . . . . £35/£10
Hornblower and the Crisis: An Unfinished Novel, Joseph
(London), 1967 . . . . . . £35/£10
ditto, as *Hornblower During the Crisis*, Little, Brown
(Boston), 1967 . . . . . . £35/£10

'Hornblower' Omnibus Editions
Captain Horatio Hornblower, Little, Brown (Boston), 1939
(3 vols in slipcase, no d/ws) . . . . £100/£45
Captain Hornblower R.N., Joseph (London), 1939 £350/£50
Hornblower Takes Command, Little, Brown (Boston), 1953
. . . . £35/£10
Young Hornblower, Little, Brown (Boston), 1960 . £30/£10
ditto, Joseph (London), 1964 . . . . £20/£5

The Indominatable Hornblower, Little, Brown (Boston),
1963 . . . . £25/£10
Admiral Hornblower, Joseph (London), 1968. . £25/£5

Other Novels
A Pawn Among Kings, Methuen (London), 1924 . . .
. . . . £4,000/£750
Payment Deferred, Bodley Head (London), 1926 . .
. . . . £3,500/£450
ditto, Little, Brown (Boston), 1942 . . £100/£15
Love Lies Dreaming, Bodley Head (London), 1927 . .
. . . . £750/£100
ditto, Bobbs-Merrill (Indianapolis, IN), 1927 (first issue
binding with 'C.E. Forester' on cover) . . . £400/£50
The Wonderful Week, Bodley Head (London), 1927 . .
. . . . £1,000/£175
ditto, as *One Wonderful Week*, Bobbs-Merrill (Indianapolis,
IN), 1927 . . . . £1,000/£175
The Shadow of the Hawk, Bodley Head (London), 1928 .
. . . . £400/£75
ditto, as *The Daughter of the Hawk*, Bobbs-Merrill
(Indianapolis, IN), 1928 . . . . . £300/£40
Brown on Resolution, Bodley Head (London), 1929 . .
. . . . £2,000/£145
ditto, as *Single-Handed*, Putnam (New York), 1929 . .
. . . . £400/£50
Plain Murder, Bodley Head (London), 1930 . . £400/£75
ditto, Dell (New York), 1954 (pbk) £15
Death to the French, Bodley Head (London), 1932 .
. . . . £300/£75
ditto, as *Rifleman Dodd*, Little, Brown (Boston), 1943 . .
. . . . £45/£15
The Gun, John Lane (London), 1933. . . . £650/£75
ditto, as *Rifleman Dodd and the Gun*, Little, Brown
(Boston), 1933 . . . . £350/£40
The Peacemaker, Heinemann (London), 1934 . £500/£65
ditto, Little, Brown (Boston), 1934 . . . £250/£40
The African Queen, Heinemann (London), 1935 . .
. . . . £10,000/£750
ditto, Little, Brown (Boston), 1935 . £2,500/£400
The General, Little, Brown (Boston), 1936 . £250/£35
ditto, Joseph (London), 1936 . . . . £600/£75
The Captain from Connecticut, Joseph (London), 1941 .
. . . . £200/£20
ditto, Little, Brown (Boston), 1941 . . . £175/£15
The Ship, Joseph (London), 1943 . . . £65/£10
ditto, Little, Brown (Boston), 1943 . . . £65/£10
The Bedchamber Mystery, S.J. Reginald Saunders (Toronto,
Canada), 1944 . . . . . . £125/£20
The Sky and the Forest, Joseph (London), 1948 . £50/£15
ditto, Little, Brown (Boston), 1948 . . £45/£10
Randall and the River of Time, Little, Brown (Boston),
1950 . . . . £25/£10
ditto, Joseph (London), 1951 . . . . £30/£10
The Good Shepherd, Joseph (London), 1955 . . £25/£5
ditto, Little, Brown (Boston), 1955 . . . £25/£5

Short Stories
The Paid Piper, Methuen (London), 1924 (first issue with
ads dated September 1923) . . . £2,500/£400
ditto, Methuen (London), 1924 (second issue with ads dated
May 1925) . . . . £2,000/£300
Two-and-Twenty, Bodley Head (London), 1931 £1,750/£175
ditto, Appleton-Century Co. (New York), 1931 . £600/£75

The Nightmare, Little, Brown (Boston), 1954. . £50/£10
ditto, Joseph (London), 1954 . . . . £50/£10
The Man in the Yellow Raft, Joseph (London), 1969 . .
. . . . £30/£10
ditto, Little, Brown (Boston), 1969 . . . £30/£10
Gold From Crete, Little, Brown (Boston), 1970 . £20/£5
ditto, Joseph (London), 1971 . . . . £20/£5

Plays
U 97, John Lane (London), 1931 . . . £300/£100
Nurse Cavell, John Lane (London), 1933. . . £300/£40
Payment Deferred, French (London), 1934 (wraps) . £100

Children's Titles
Marionettes At Home, Joseph (London), 1936 (first issue,
sienna cloth). . . . . £300/£75
ditto, Joseph (London), 1936 (second issue orange cloth,
jacket with '3/6 net' on spine) . . . £250/£45
Poo-Poo and the Dragons, Joseph (London), 1942 £350/£45
ditto, Little, Brown (Boston), 1942 . . £250/£40
The Barbary Pirates, Random House (New York), 1953 .
. . . . £45/£10
ditto, Macdonald (London), 1953 . . . £45/£10
Hornblower Goes to Sea, Joseph (London), 1954 . £25/£10
ditto, Little, Brown (Boston), 1965 . . . £25/£10
Hornblower's Triumph, Joseph (London), 1955 . £25/£10
ditto, Little, Brown (Boston), 1965 . . . £25/£10

Non-Fiction
Napoleon and His Court, Methuen (London), 1924 . .
. . . . £650/£75
ditto, Dodd, Mead (New York), 1924 . . £450/£100
Josephine, Napoleon's Empress, Methuen (London), 1925.
. . . . £650/£85
ditto, Methuen (London), 1925 (but with ads dated 1928) .
. . . . £650/£65
ditto, Dodd, Mead (New York), 1924 . . £350/£50
Victor Emmanuel II and the Union of Italy, Methuen
(London), 1927 . . . . . . £250/£50
ditto, Dodd, Mead (New York), 1927 . . £225/£45
Louis XIV, King of France and Navarre, Dodd, Mead (New
York), 1928 . . . . £250/£45
ditto, Methuen (London), 1928 . . . . £250/£45
Nelson, John Lane (London), 1929 . . . £250/£50
ditto, as *Lord Nelson*, Bobbs-Merrill (Indianapolis, IN),
1929 . . . . £200/£50
The Voyage of the Annie Marble, John Lane (London),
1929 . . . . £400/£75
The Annie Marble in Germany, John Lane (London), 1930
. . . . £400/£75
The Earthly Paradise, Joseph (London), 1940 . £100/£20
ditto, as *To the Indies*, Little, Brown (Boston), 1940 . .
. . . . £100/£20
The Naval War of 1812, Joseph (London), 1957 . £50/£20
ditto, as *The Age of Fighting Sail: The Story of the Naval
War of 1812*, Doubleday (New York), 1956. . £45/£15
Hunting the Bismarck, Joseph (London), 1959 . £50/£15
ditto, as *The Last Nine Days of the Bismarck*, Little, Brown
(Boston), 1959 . . . . . . £45/£15
ditto, as *Sink the Bismarck!*, Bantam (New York), 1959
(pbk) £5
The Hornblower Companion, Joseph (London), 1964 . .
. . . . £150/£30
ditto, Little, Brown (Boston), 1964 . . . £125/£25

Long Before Forty, Joseph (London), 1967 . . £30/£10
ditto, Little, Brown (Boston), 1967 . . . . £25/£10

Edited by Forester
The Adventures of John Wetherell, Joseph (London), 1954
. . . . £45/£10
ditto, Doubleday (New York), 1954 . . . . £35/£10

E.M. FORSTER
(b.1879 d.1970)

A novelist and essayist, Forster's writings often reflect his loathing of public schools, imperialism, and the repression of civil liberties. In 1901 at Cambridge University he was involved with a set, many members of which went on to form the Bloomsbury Group. His novels *A Passage to India* and *Howard's End* explore the irreconcilability of class, while *Maurice* considers the possibility of ameliorating such differences by means of a homosexual relationship.

Novels
Where Angels Fear to Tread, Blackwood (Edinburgh/ London), 1905 (first issue with this title not mentioned in ads at rear) £2,000
ditto, Blackwood (Edinburgh/London), 1905 (second issue with this title mentioned in ads) £650
ditto, Knopf (New York), 1920 . . . . £500/£100
The Longest Journey, Blackwood (Edinburgh/London), 1907 . . . . £600
ditto, Knopf (New York), 1922 . . . . £350/£65
A Room with a View, Arnold (London), 1908 . . £1,250
ditto, Putnam (New York), 1911 . . . . . £250
Howard's End, Arnold (London), 1910 (first issue with 4 pages of integral ads) £1,000
ditto, Arnold (London), 1910 (second issue with 8 pages of inserted ads) £750
ditto, Putnam (New York), 1910 (first issue without title to the front cover and two pages of ads at rear) . . £600
ditto, Putnam (New York), 1910 (second issue with title added to the front cover and three pages of ads at rear) .
. . . . £500
A Passage to India, Arnold (London), 1924 . £3,500/£250
ditto, Arnold (London), 1924 (200 numbered, signed copies, fawn paper boards, grey slipcase) . . .£3,000/£2,000
ditto, Harcourt Brace (New York), 1924 . . £1,000/£150
ditto, as *The Manuscripts of A Passage to India*, Arnold (London), 1978 (1,500 copies) . . . . £35/£15
Maurice, Arnold (London), 1971 . . . . £25/£10
ditto, Norton (New York), 1971 . . . . £20/£5
Arctic Summer and Other Fiction, Holmes and Meir (New York), 1981 (unfinished writings; The Abinger Edition of E.M. Forster, Volume 9) . . . . . £20/£5

Short Stories
The Celestial Omnibus and Other Stories, Sidgwick & Jackson (London), 1911 . . . . . .£150
ditto, Knopf (New York), 1923 . . . . £200/£35
The Story of the Siren, Hogarth Press (Richmond, Surrey), 1920 (first state with 'The Story/of the Siren' on front label; marbled paper-covered sewn wraps) . . £500

ditto, Hogarth Press (Richmond, Surrey), 1920 (other states; wraps) £300
The Eternal Moment, Sidgwick & Jackson (London), 1928 (first issue cloth stamped in gold) . . . £350/£75
ditto, Sidgwick & Jackson (London), 1928 (second issue cloth stamped in black) . . . . . £325/£50
ditto, Harcourt Brace (New York), 1928 . . £200/£40
The Collected Tales, Knopf (New York), 1947 . £25/£10
ditto, as *The Collected Short Stories*, Sidgwick & Jackson (London), [1948] . . . . . . £25/£10
The Life to Come, Arnold (London), 1972 . . £25/£10
ditto, Norton (New York), 1973 . . . . . £25/£10
The New Collected Short Stories, Sidgwick & Jackson (London), 1985 . . . . £25/£10

Essays
Pharos and Pharillon, Hogarth Press (Richmond, Surrey), 1923 (900 copies, no d/w) £100
ditto, Knopf (New York), 1923 . . . . . £75/£25
Anonymity: An Enquiry, Hogarth Press (London), 1925 (boards) £65
ditto, Hogarth Press (London), 1925 (swen wraps) . £65
A Letter to Madan Blanchard, Hogarth Press (London), 1931 (sewn wraps) £35
ditto, Harcourt Brace (New York), 1932 (sewn wraps) . £25
Sinclair Lewis Interprets America, privately printed, 1932 (100 copies signed by publisher; stapled wraps) . . £45
Pageant of Abinger, privately printed, 1934 (wraps) . £75
Abinger Harvest, Arnold (London), 1936 (first issue with 'A Flood in the Office', cream d/w decorated orange) .
. . . . £300/£75
ditto, Arnold (London), 1936 (second issue without 'A Flood in the Office') . . . . . . £150/£20
ditto, Harcourt Brace (New York), 1936 . . . £75/£25
What I Believe, Hogarth Press (London), 1939 (sewn wraps)
. . . . £30
Nordic Twilight, Macmillan (London), 1940 (wraps) . £15
Two Cheers for Democracy, Arnold (London), 1951 . .
. . . . £35/£10
ditto, Harcourt Brace (New York), 1951 . . . £35/£10

Others
The Government of Egypt, Labour Research Dept. (London), [1920] (stapled wraps) £175
Alexandria, A History and a Guide, Whitehead Morris (Alexandria, Egypt), 1922 (no d/w) £400
ditto, Whitehead Morris (Alexandria, Egypt), 1922 (revised edition with maps and plans) £200
ditto, Whitehead Morris (Alexandria, Egypt), 1922 (250 signed copies) £500
ditto, Doubleday (New York), 1961 . . . . £25/£10
Aspects of the Novel, Arnold (London), 1927 . .£225/£40
ditto, Harcourt Brace (New York), 1927 . . . £75/£20
Goldsworthy Lowes Dickinson, Arnold (London), 1934 .
. . . . £150/£30
ditto, Harcourt Brace (New York), 1934 . . .£100/£25
Reading as Usual, Tottenham Public Libraries (London), 1939 (wraps) £200
England's Pleasant Land, Hogarth Press (London), 1940 .
. . . . £60/£15
Virginia Woolf, C.U.P. (Cambridge, UK), 1942 (sewn wraps) £30
ditto, Harcourt Brace (New York), 1942 . . . £50/£20

*The Development of English Prose Between 1918 and
1930*, Jackson (Glasgow), 1945 (stapled wraps) .   . £20
A Room with a View: A Play, Arnold (London), 1951
(adapted by Stephen Tait and Kenneth Allott)   . £45/£10
Desmond McCarthy, Mill House Press (Stanford Dingley,
Berkshire), 1952 (64 copies) £350
ditto, Mill House Press (Stanford Dingley, Berkshire), 1952
(8 copies) £1,000
The Hill of Devi, Arnold (London), 1953.   .   . £30/£5
ditto, Harcourt Brace (New York), 1953   .   . £20/£5
I Assert There is an Alternative to Humanism, The Ethical
Union (London), 1955   .   .   .   . £65
Battersea Rise, privately printed (Harcourt Brace, New
York), 1955 .   .   .   . £25
Marianne Thornton, Arnold (London), 1956 .   . £30/£10
ditto, Arnold (London), 1956 (200 signed copies, slipcase) .
.   .   .   . £250/£200
ditto, Harcourt Brace (New York), 1956 .   .   . £30/£5
Tourism vs Thuggism, privately printed, 1957 (wraps). £35
E.K. Bennett, privately printed, 1958 (wraps) .   .   . £75
A View Without a Room, Albondocani Press (New York),
1973 (200 numbered copies; stapled wraps)   .   . £75
Letters to Donald Windham, Campbell (Verona, Italy), 1975
(300 copies) £75
Commonplace Book, Scolar Press (London), 1978
(facsimile, 350 numbered copies, boxed)   .   . £100/£65
Selected Letters, Vol. 1: 1879-1920, Collins (London), 1983
.   .   .   . £25/£10
ditto, Harvard Univ Press (Cambridge, MA), 1983 £25/£10
Selected Letters, Vol. 2: 1921-1970, Collins (London), 1985
.   .   .   . £25/£10
ditto, Harvard Univ Press (Cambridge, MA), 1984 £25/£10

ditto, Bantam (New York), 1991.   .   .   .   . £10/£5
The Fist of God, Bantam (London), 1994.   .   . £10/£5
ditto, Bantam (New York), 1994.   .   .   .   . £10/£5
Icon, Bantam (London), 1996   .   .   .   .   . £10/£5
ditto, Bantam (New York), 1996.   .   .   .   . £10/£5
The Phantom of Manhattan, Bantam (London), 1999 .
.   .   .   . £10/£5
ditto, St Martins Press (New York), 1999 .   .   . £10/£5
ditto, Franklin Library (Franklin Centre, PA), 1999 (signed,
limited edition) £40
Avenger, Bantam (London), 2003   .   .   .   . £10/£5
ditto, St Martin's Press (New York), 2003   .   . £10/£5
The Afghan, Bantam (London), 2006   .   .   . £10/£5
ditto, Putnam's (New York), 2006   .   .   .   . £10/£5

Short Stories
No Comebacks: Collected Short Stories, Hutchinson
(London), 1982   .   .   .   . £15/£5
ditto, Viking (New York), 1982 .   .   .   .   . £15/£5
ditto, Eurographica (Helsinki), 1986 (350 signed copies;
wraps with d/w) .   .   .   . £75/£45
The Veteran and Other Stories, Bantam (London), 2001   .
.   .   .   . £10/£5
ditto, St Martin's Press (New York), 2001   .   . £10/£5

Non-Fiction
The Biafra Story, Penguin (Harmondsworth, Middlesex),
1969 (pbk) £30
ditto, as *The Biafra Story: The Making of an African
Legend*, Penguin (Harmondsworth, Middlesex), 1977
(wraps) £5
ditto, as *The Biafra Story, The Making of an African
Legend*, Severn House (London), 1983 .   .   . £20/£5
Emeka, Spectrum Books (Ibadan, Nigeria), 1982 (pbk)   £20

FREDERICK FORSYTH
(b.1938)

Forsyth is a British writer and occasional political commentator. He is the author of the phenomenally successful
The Day of the Jackal and a number of other bestsellers
which have been turned into box office blockbusters. Forsyth's forte is the tense thriller, and while he eschews
psychological complexity in favour of meticulous plotting,
his stories are based on detailed factual research.

Novels
The Day of the Jackal, Hutchinson (London), 1971 £75/£10
ditto, Viking (New York), 1971 .   .   .   .   . £35/£10
The Odessa File, Hutchinson (London), 1972.   .   . £25/£5
ditto, Viking (New York), 1972 .   .   .   .   . £25/£5
The Dogs of War, Hutchinson (London), 1974   . £25/£5
ditto, Viking (New York), 1974 .   .   .   .   . £20/£5
The Shepherd, Hutchinson (London), 1975   .   . £10/£5
ditto, Viking (New York), 1976 .   .   .   .   . £10/£5
The Devil's Alternative, Hutchinson (London), 1979 £15/£5
ditto, Viking (New York), 1980 .   .   .   .   . £15/£5
The Fourth Protocol, Hutchinson (London), 1984.   . £15/£5
ditto, Viking (New York), 1984 .   .   .   .   . £15/£5
The Negotiator, Bantam (London), 1989 .   .   . £10/£5
ditto, London Limited Editions (London), 1989 (150 signed
copies, glasssine d/w).   .   .   .   .   .   . £35/£30
ditto, Bantam (New York), 1989.   .   .   .   . £10/£5
The Deceiver, Bantam (London), 1991   .   .   . £10/£5

DION FORTUNE
(b.1890 d.1946)

Dion Fortune was born Violet Mary Firth Evans. A British
occultist, her novels and short stories explore various
aspects of magic and mysticism, as does her non-fiction. Although some of her writings may appear dated to contemporary readers, they are nevertheless considered to have a
clarity absent from the work of most dabblers in the occult.

Novels Written as 'Dion Fortune'
The Demon Lover, Noel Douglas (London), [1927]   .   .
.   .   .   . £250/£75
The Winged Bull, Williams & Norgate (London), 1935   .
.   .   .   . £200/£45
The Goat-Foot God, Williams & Norgate (London), 1936 .
.   .   .   . £250/£50
The Sea Priestess, published by the author (London), 1938 .
.   .   .   . £200/£45
Moon Magic, Aquarian Press (London), 1956.   . £75/£20

Short Stories Written as 'Dion Fortune'
The Secrets of Dr Taverner, Noel Douglas (London), 1926
.   .   .   . £250/£65
ditto, Ash-Tree Press (Ashcroft, Canada), 2000 (500 copies)
.   .   .   . £20/£5

Non-Fiction Written as 'Dion Fortune'
The Esoteric Philosophy of Love and Marriage, Rider (London), 1923 . . . . . £125/£35
Esoteric Orders and Their Work, Rider (London), 1928 . . . . £85/£20
Sane Occultism, Rider (London), 1929 . . . £100/£20
The Training and Work of an Initiate, Rider (London), 1930 . . . . £100/£20
Mystical Meditations Upon the Collects, Rider (London), 1930 . . . . . . £75/£20
Spiritualism in the Light of Occult Science, Rider (London), 1931 . . . . . . £100/£20
Psychic Self-Defence, Rider (London), 1931 . £125/£35
Through the Gates of Death, Inner Light (London), 1932 . . . . £100/£20
The Mystical Qabalah, Williams & Norgate (London), 1935 . . . . £125/£25
Practical Occultism in Daily Life, Williams & Norgate (London), 1935 . . . . £100/£20
The Cosmic Doctrine, Inner Light (London), 1949. £60/£10
Applied Magic, Aquarian Press (London), 1962 . £30/£10
Aspects of Occultism, Aquarian Press (London), 1962 . . . . £30/£10
The Magical Battle of Britain, Golden Gates Press (Bradford on Avon, Wilts), 1993 (pbk) . . . £15
An Introduction to Ritual Magic, Thoth Publications (Loughborough, Leics), 1997 . . . £15/£5
ditto, Thoth Publications (Loughborough, Leics), 1997 (pbk) £5
The Circuit of Force, Thoth Publications (Loughborough, Leics), 1998 (pbk) . . . £5
Principles of Hermetic Philosophy, Thoth Publications (Loughborough, Leics), 1999 (pbk) . . £5
Principles of Esoteric Healing, Sun Chalice Books (Oceanside, CA), 2000 (pbk) . . . £5

Novels Written as 'V.M. Steele'
The Scarred Wrists, Stanley Paul (London), [1935] . . . . £125/£30
Hunters of Humans, Stanley Paul (London), [1936] . . . . £125/£30
Beloved of Ishmael, Stanley Paul (London), [1937] . . . . £125/£30

Non-Fiction Written as 'Violet M. Firth'
Machinery of the Mind, Allen & Unwin (London), 1922 . . . . £150/£45
ditto, Dodd, Mead (New York), 1922 . . £150/£45
The Psychology of the Servant Problem, C.W. Daniel (London), 1925 . . . . . £75/£20
The Soya Bean, C.W. Daniel (London), 1925. . £75/£20
The Problem of Purity, Rider (London), [1928] . £100/£25
Avalon of the Heart, Muller (London), 1934 . £100/£25

Poetry Written as 'Violet M. Firth'
Violets, Mendip Press, [1904] (no d/w) . . . £75
More Violets, Jarrold (London), [1906] (no d/w) . £75

JOHN FOWLES
(b.1926 d.2005)

The international success of Fowles' novel *The Collector* ended his teaching career and began his literary vocation. An English novelist and essayist, Fowles became both a popularly and critically acclaimed modern literary figure. His success was due to his experimental style and the broad humanist content of his novels.

Novels
The Collector, Cape (London), 1963 (rust-coloured papered boards, matching top edge stain, first issue d/w) . £350/£25
ditto, Cape (London), 1963 (charcoal-black papered boards, no top edge stain, first issue d/w without reviews quoted) . . . . £400/£50
ditto, Cape (London), 1963 (later issue d/w with reviews) . . . . . . £75/£25
ditto, Little, Brown (Boston), 1963 . . . £75/£25
The Magus, Little, Brown (Boston), 1965 . £150/£25
ditto, Cape (London), 1966 . . . . . £150/£25
ditto, Cape (London), 1977 (revised edition) . £20/£10
ditto, Little, Brown (Boston), 1978 (revised edition) £20/£10
The French Lieutenant's Woman, Cape (London), 1969 . . . . £150/£20
ditto, Little, Brown (Boston), 1969 . . £125/£15
The Ebony Tower, Cape (London), 1974 (novellas) £50/£10
ditto, Little, Brown (Boston), 1974 . . . £35/£5
ditto, Little, Brown (Boston), 1974 (signed issue, with a special tipped-in leaf signed by John Fowles) £125/£100
Daniel Martin, Little, Brown (Boston), 1977 . . £25/£5
ditto, Cape (London), 1977 . . . . . £25/£5
Mantissa, Cape (London), 1982 . . . . £20/£5
ditto, Little, Brown (Boston), 1982 . . . £20/£5
ditto, Little, Brown (Boston), 1982 (500 signed copies, slipcase). . . . . £50/£35
A Maggot, Cape (London), 1985 . . . . £25/£5
ditto, Cape/London Limited Editions (London), 1985 (500 signed copies, glassine d/w) . . . . £35/£20
ditto, Little, Brown (Boston), 1985 . . . £20/£5
ditto, Little, Brown (Boston), 1985 (360 signed copies, slipcase). . . . . £30/£15

Other Titles
The Aristos, Little, Brown (Boston), 1964 . £50/£15
ditto, Cape (London), 1965 . . . . . £250/£35
My Recollections of Kafka, Univ of Manitoba Press (Winnipeg, Canada), 1970 (25 copies; stapled wraps) £150
Poems, Ecco Press (New York), 1973 . . . £35/£10
Cinderella, by Charles Perrault, adapted by John Fowles, Cape (London), 1974 . . . . . £40/£10
ditto, Little, Brown (Boston), 1974 . . . £40/£10
Shipwreck, Cape (London), 1974 (photographs by the Gibsons of Scilly, with text by John Fowles) . £30/£10
ditto, Little, Brown (Boston), 1975 . . . £15/£5
Ourika, W. Thomas Taylor (Austin, TX), 1977 (500 signed copies) £75
Islands, Cape (London), 1978 (photographs by Fay Godwin with text by John Fowles). . . . . £15/£5
ditto, Little, Brown (Boston), 1978 . . . £10/£5
Conditional, Lord John Press (Northridge, CA), 1979 (broadside, 150 numbered, signed copies) . . £125
The Tree, Aurum Press (London), 1979 (photographs by Frank Horvat with text by John Fowles). . £30/£10

ditto, Little, Brown (Boston), 1980 . . . . £25/£10

A Letter from Charles I Concerning Lyme and *Kings Order for Lyme Siege*, Lyme Regis Museum (Lyme Regis, Dorset), 1980 (100 signed sets of 2 printed sheets) . £100

The Enigma of Stonehenge, Cape (London), 1980 (photographs by Barry Brukoff with text by John Fowles) £20/£5

ditto, Summit (New York), 1980 . . . . £20/£5

A Brief History of Lyme, Friends of the Lyme Regis Museum (Lyme Regis, Dorset), 1981 (stapled wraps). £15

The Screenplay of the French Lieutenant's Woman, Cape (London), 1981 (by Harold Pinter, foreword by John Fowles) . . . . £20/£5

ditto, Little, Brown (Boston), 1981 . . . . £20/£5

ditto, Little, Brown (Boston), 1981 (360 signed, numbered copies, slipcase) . . . . £100/£65

Photographs of Lyme Regis, Skelton Press (Lyme Regis, Dorset), 1982 (25 sets; portfolio of 15 mounted, signed black-and-white photographs by Paul Penrose, accompanied by a broadside written and signed by Fowles; in box with lid) £1,000

A Short History of Lyme Regis, Dovecote Press (Lyme Regis, Dorset), 1982 . . . . £25/£10

ditto, Little, Brown (Boston), 1983 . . . . £10/£5

Of Memoirs and Magpies, W. Thomas Taylor (Austin, TX), 1983 (200 copies; sewn wraps) £65

Land, Heinemann (London), 1985 (photographs by Fay Godwin) . . . . £25/£10

ditto, Little, Brown (Boston), 1985 . . . . £25/£10

ditto, Little, Brown (Boston), 1985 (160 signed, numbered copies, slipcase) . . . . . . £150/£125

Poor Koko, Eurographica (Helsinki), 1987 (350 signed, numbered copies; wraps) £65

The Enigma, Eurographica (Helsinki), 1987 (350 signed, numbered copies; wraps) £50

Behind the Magus, Colophon Press (London), 1994 (200 signed copies; wraps). £125

ditto, Colophon Press (London), 1994 (26 signed, lettered copies bound in goatskin) £350

ditto, Colophon Press (London), 1994 (6 signed, roman numeralled copies bound in goatskin) . . . £1,250

ditto, privately printed by the author (Lyme Regis, Dorset), 1995 (wraps). £125

The Nature of Nature and The Tree, Yolla Bolly Press (Covelo, CA), 1995 (140 signed copies, boards, slipcase) .
. . . . £350/£250

ditto, Yolla Bolly Press (Covelo, CA), 1995 (275 signed copies; wraps) £40

Wormholes, Cape (London), 1998 . . . . £15/£5

ditto, Colophon Press (London), 1998 (75 signed, numbered copies, slipcase) . . . . . . £65/£45

ditto, Colophon Press (London), 1998 (10 signed, roman-numbered copies bound in goatskin, slipcase) £400/£350

ditto, Colophon Press (London), 1998 (15 signed, numbered copies for presentation, slipcase) . £150/£100

ditto, Holt (New York), 1998 . . . . £15/£5

ditto, Holt (New York), 1998 (150 signed copies, slipcase) .
. . . . £65/£45

The Journals: Volume One 1949-1965, Cape (London), 2003 . . . . £15/£5

ditto, Knopf (New York), 2005 . . . . . £15/£5

The Journals: Volume Two 1966-1990, Cape (London), 2006 . . . . £15/£5

ditto, Knopf (New York), 2006 . . . . . £15/£5

DICK FRANCIS
(b.1920 d.2010)

A former steeplechase jockey, Francis became a highly popular and collectable thriller writer, often setting his novels in the world of horse racing. He won the Crime Writers' Association's Cartier Diamond Dagger for his contribution to the genre, and in 1996 he was made a Mystery Writers of America Grand Master for a lifetime's achievement. In 2000 he received a C.B.E. in the Queen's Birthday Honours list.

Novels

Dead Cert, Joseph (London), 1962 . . . £3,500/£450

ditto, Holt Rinehart (New York), 1962 . . £800/£100

ditto, Armchair Detective Library (New York), 1989 (100 signed, numbered copies, slipcase) . . . £100/£65

ditto, Armchair Detective Library (New York), 1989 (26 signed, lettered copies, slipcase) . . . £150/£100

Nerve, Joseph (London), 1964 . . . . . £850/£50

ditto, Harper (New York), 1964 . . . . . £250/£35

ditto, Armchair Detective Library (New York), 1990 (100 signed, numbered copies, slipcase) . . . . £50/£35

ditto, Armchair Detective Library (New York), 1990 (26 signed, lettered copies, slipcase) . . . . £65/£50

For Kicks, Joseph (London), 1965 . . . . £500/£40

ditto, Harper (New York), 1965 . . . . . £125/£15

ditto, Armchair Detective Library (New York), 1991 (100 signed, numbered copies, slipcase) . . . . £50/£35

ditto, Armchair Detective Library (New York), 1991 (26 signed, lettered copies, slipcase) . . . . £65/£50

Odds Against, Joseph (London), 1965 . . . £350/£15

ditto, Harper (New York), 1966 . . . . . £100/£10

ditto, Armchair Detective Library (New York), 1991 (100 signed, numbered copies, slipcase) . . . . £50/£35

ditto, Armchair Detective Library (New York), 1991 (26 signed, lettered copies, slipcase) . . . . £65/£50

Flying Finish, Joseph (London), 1966 . . . £225/£25

ditto, Harper (New York), 1967 . . . . . £75/£10

ditto, Armchair Detective Library (New York), 1991 (100 signed, numbered copies, slipcase) . . . . £50/£35

ditto, Armchair Detective Library (New York), 1991 (26 signed, lettered copies, slipcase) . . . . £65/£50

Blood Sport, Joseph (London), 1967 . . . £200/£25

ditto, Harper (New York), 1968 . . . . . £65/£10

ditto, Armchair Detective Library (New York), 1992 (100 signed, numbered copies, slipcase) . . . . £50/£35

ditto, Armchair Detective Library (New York), 1992 (26 signed, lettered copies, slipcase) . . . . £65/£50

Forfeit, Joseph (London), 1968 . . . . . £100/£15

ditto, Harper (New York), 1969 . . . . . £40/£5

Enquiry, Joseph (London), 1969 . . . . £75/£10

ditto, Harper (New York), 1969 . . . . . £25/£5

Rat Race, Joseph (London), 1970 . . . . £75/£10

ditto, Harper (New York), 1971 . . . . . £25/£5

Bonecrack, Joseph (London), 1971 . . . . £50/£5

ditto, Harper (New York), 1972 . . . . . £15/£5

Smokescreen, Joseph (London), 1972 . . . £45/£5

ditto, Harper (New York), 1972 . . . . . £15/£5

Slay-Ride, Joseph (London), 1973 . . . . £40/£5

ditto, Harper (New York), 1974 . . . . . £15/£5

Knock Down, Joseph (London), 1974 . . . £35/£5

ditto, Harper (New York), 1975 . . . . . £15/£5

High Stakes, Joseph (London), 1975 . . . . £35/£5
ditto, Harper (New York), 1976 . . . . £15/£5
In The Frame, Joseph (London), 1976 . . . £25/£5
ditto, Harper (New York), 1977 . . . . £15/£5
Risk, Joseph (London), 1977 . . . . £25/£5
ditto, Harper (New York), 1978 . . . . £15/£5
Trial Run, Joseph (London), 1978 . . . £20/£5
ditto, Harper (New York), 1979 . . . . £15/£5
Whip Hand, Joseph (London), 1979 . . . £20/£5
ditto, Harper (New York), 1980 . . . . £15/£5
Reflex, Joseph (London), 1980 . . . . £15/£5
ditto, Putnam (New York), 1981 . . . . £15/£5
Twice Shy, Joseph (London), 1981 . . . £15/£5
ditto, Putnam (New York), 1982 . . . . £15/£5
Banker, Joseph (London), 1982 . . . . £15/£5
ditto, Putnam (New York), 1983 . . . . £10/£5
The Danger, Joseph (London), 1983 . . . £10/£5
ditto, Putnam (New York), 1984 . . . . £10/£5
Proof, Joseph (London), 1984 . . . . £10/£5
ditto, Putnam (New York), 1985 . . . . £10/£5
Break In, Joseph (London), 1985 . . . £10/£5
ditto, Putnam (New York), 1986 . . . . £10/£5
Bolt, Joseph (London), 1986 . . . . £10/£5
ditto, Putnam (New York), 1987 . . . . £10/£5
Hot Money, Joseph (London), 1987 . . . £10/£5
ditto, Putnam (New York), 1988 (250 signed copies,
  slipcase) . . . . £75/£50
ditto, Putnam (New York), 1988 . . . . £10/£5
The Edge, Joseph (London), 1988 . . . £10/£5
ditto, Putnam (New York), 1989 . . . . £10/£5
Straight, Joseph (London), 1989 . . . . £10/£5
ditto, Joseph (London), 1989 (500 signed copies, bound in
  quarter leather, in slipcase) . . . . £125/£100
ditto, Putnam (New York), 1989 . . . . £10/£5
Longshot, Joseph (London), 1990 . . . £10/£5
ditto, Putnam (New York), 1990 . . . . £10/£5
Comeback, Joseph (London), 1991 . . . £10/£5
ditto, Putnam (New York), 1991 . . . . £10/£5
Driving Force, Joseph (London), 1992 . . £10/£5
ditto, Putnam (New York), 1992 . . . . £10/£5
Decider, Joseph (London), 1993 . . . . £10/£5
ditto, Putnam (New York), 1993 . . . . £10/£5
Wild Horses, Joseph (London), 1994 . . . £10/£5
ditto, Scorpion Press (Blakeney, Glos), 1994 (99 signed,
  numbered copies, bound in quarter leather) . . £175
ditto, Scorpion Press (Blakeney, Glos), 1994 (20 signed,
  lettered copies, deluxe binding) £350
ditto, Putnam (New York), 1994 . . . . £10/£5
Come to Grief, Joseph (London), 1995 . . . £10/£5
ditto, Putnam (New York), 1995 . . . . £10/£5
To the Hilt, Joseph (London), 1996 . . . £10/£5
ditto, Scorpion Press (Blakeney, Glos), 1996 (99 signed,
  numbered copies, bound in quarter leather) . . £125
ditto, Scorpion Press (Blakeney, Glos), 1996 (15 signed,
  lettered copies, deluxe binding) £350
ditto, Putnam (New York), 1996 . . . . £10/£5
10lb Penalty, Joseph (London), 1997 . . . £10/£5
ditto, Putnam (New York), 1997 . . . . £10/£5
Second Wind, Joseph (London), 1999 . . . £10/£5
ditto, Putnam (New York), 1999 . . . . £10/£5
ditto, Scorpion Press (Blakeney, Glos), 1999 (110 signed,
  numbered copies, bound in quarter leather) . . £65
ditto, Scorpion Press (Blakeney, Glos), 1999 (16 signed,
  lettered copies, deluxe binding) £250
Shattered, Joseph (London), 2000 . . . £10/£5

ditto, Putnam (New York), 2000 . . . . £10/£5
Under Orders, Joseph (London), 2006 . . . £10/£5
ditto, Putnam (New York), 2006 . . . . £10/£5
Dead Heat, Joseph (London), 2007 (with Felix Francis) .
  . . . . £10/£5
ditto, Putnam (New York), 2007 . . . . £10/£5
Silks, Joseph (London), 2008 (with Felix Francis) . £10/£5
ditto, Putnam (New York), 2008 . . . . £10/£5
Even Money, Joseph (London), 2009 (with Felix Francis) .
  . . . . £10/£5
ditto, Putnam (New York), 2009 . . . . £10/£5

Early Omnibus Editions
Three To Show, Harper (New York), 1970 (contains *Dead
  Cert, Nerve* and *Odds Against*). . . . . £20/£5
Across the Board, Harper (New York), 1975 (contains
  Flying Finish, Blood Sport and *Enquiry*) . . £35/£5
Three Winners, Joseph (London), 1977 (contains *Dead Cert,
  Nerve* and *For Kicks*) . . . . . . £15/£5
Three Favourites, Joseph (London), 1978 (contains *Odds
  Against, Flying Finish* and *Blood Sport*) . . £10/£5
Three To Follow, Joseph (London), 1979 (contains *Forfeit,
  Enquiry* and *Rat Race*) . . . . . £10/£5
Two by Francis, Harper (New York), 1983 (contains *Forfeit*
  and *Slay Ride*) . . . . £10/£5

Short Stories
Field of 13, Joseph (London), 1998 . . . £10/£5
ditto, Putnam (New York), 1998 . . . . £10/£5

Miscellaneous
The Sport of Queens, Joseph (London), 1957 (autobiography) . . . . £400/£65
ditto, second edition (revised), Joseph (London), 1968 .
  . . . . £15/£5
ditto, Harper & Row (New York), 1969 . . £45/£10
ditto, Armchair Detective Library (New York), 1993 (100
  signed, numbered copies, slipcase) . . . £50/£35
ditto, Armchair Detective Library (New York), 1993 (26
  signed, lettered copies, slipcase) . . . £65/£50
Best Racing and Chasing Stories, Faber (London), 1966
  (edited, with an introduction by Dick Francis and John
  Welcome) . . . . £25/£5
The Racing Man's Bedside Book, Faber (London), 1969
  (edited by Dick Francis and John Welcome) . £20/£5
Best Racing and Chasing Stories Two, Faber (London),
  1972 (edited, with an introduction by Dick Francis and
  John Welcome) . . . . £15/£5
Lester: The Official Biography, Joseph (London), 1986 .
  . . . . £10/£5
ditto, Joseph (London), 1986 (500 signed copies, in slipcase)
  . . . . £50/£45
Great Racing Stories, Bellew (London), 1989 (edited by
  Dick Francis) . . . . £10/£5
ditto, Bellew (London), 1989 (deluxe 75 numbered copies,
  signed by Dick Francis and John Welcome; bound in full
  leather) £225
ditto, Bellew (London), 1989 (standard limited 175
  numbered copies, signed by Dick Francis and John
  Welcome; bound in quarter leather) . . . £300
Classic Lines: More Great Racing Stories, Bellew
  (London), 1991 (edited by Dick Francis with John
  Welcome) . . . . £10/£5

ANNE FRANK
(b.1929 d.1945)

Anne Frank's memorable diary, the most famous journal of
modern times, is a moving testament to the endurance of
the human spirit. Frank was a German Jewish girl and the
diary was kept while she was in hiding with her family and
four friends in Amsterdam during the German occupation
of the Netherlands in World War Two. She died at Bergen-
Belsen concentration camp in 1945, but her diary survived
the war and liberation.

The Diary of a Young Girl
Het Achterhuis, Contact (Amsterdam), 1947 (in Dutch) .   .
.   .   .   .£5,000/£1,500
ditto, as **Anne Frank: The Diary of a Young Girl**,
Doubleday (New York), 1952 (translated by B.M.
Mooyaart-Doubleday, with an Introduction by Eleanor
Roosevelt) .   .   .   . £400/£50
ditto, as **Anne Frank: The Diary of a Young Girl**,
Constellation Books (London), 1952 (translated by B.M.
Mooyaart-Doubleday) .   .   .   .   . £400/£50
Diary of a Young Girl/Het Achterhuis, Pennyroyal Press
(West Hatfield, MA), 1985 (2 vols; folio; slipcase; signed
by artist and Barry Moser). £1,250
The Diary of Anne Frank: Critical Edition, Doubleday
(New York), 1989 .   .   .   .   .   . £15/£5
ditto, Viking (London), 1989 .   .   .   . £15/£5
The Diary of a Young Girl: Definitive Edition, Doubleday
(New York), 1995 .   .   .   .   .   . £15/£5
ditto, Viking (London), 1997 .   .   .   . £15/£5

Other Works by Anne Frank
The Works of Anne Frank, Doubleday (New York), 1959 .
.   .   .   . £125/£25
*Tales from the House Behind: Fables, Personal
Reminiscences and Short Stories*, The World's Work
(Kingswood, Surrey), 1962 .   .   .   .   . £35/£10
Anne Frank's Tales from the Secret Annexe, Doubleday
(New York), 1984 .   .   .   .   .   . £15/£5
ditto, Viking (London), 1985 .   .   .   . £10/£5

GEORGE MACDONALD FRASER
(b.1925 d.2008)

Fraser is a novelist and historian of Scottish descent who
worked as a journalist and served in the British army in
World War Two. His 'Flashman' books have made an unlikely hero out of the school bully who appeared originally
in T. Hughes' *Tom Brown's Schooldays*. The books are presented as 'packets' of memoirs written by the eponymous
hero who looks back on his days in the British army during
the 19th Century. Fraser was awarded an O.B.E. in 1999.

Novels
Flashman, Herbert Jenkins (London), 1969 .   . £150/£25
ditto, World Publishing Co./New American Library (New
York), 1969 .   .   .   . £75/£15
Royal Flash, Barrie & Jenkins (London), 1970 . £165/£20

ditto, Knopf (New York), 1970 .   .   .   . £50/£15
Flash for Freedom, Barrie & Jenkins (London), 1971 .
.   .   .   .£100/£15
ditto, Knopf (New York), 1972 .   .   .   . £35/£10
Flashman at the Charge, Barrie & Jenkins (London), 1973
.   .   .   . £100/£15
ditto, Knopf (New York), 1973 .   .   .   . £45/£15
Flashman in the Great Game, Barrie & Jenkins (London),
1975 .   .   .   . £100/£15
ditto, Knopf (New York), 1975 .   .   .   . £45/£15
Flashman's Lady, Barrie & Jenkins (London), 1977 £65/£15
ditto, Knopf (New York), 1978 .   .   .   . £45/£15
Flashman and the Redskins, Collins (London), 1982 .
.   .   .   . £40/£10
ditto, Knopf (New York), 1982 .   .   .   . £30/£10
Flashman and the Dragon, Collins (London), 1985 £20/£5
ditto, Knopf (New York), 1986 .   .   .   . £10/£5
Flashman and the Mountain of Light, Collins Harvill
(London), 1990 .   .   .   .   .   . £15/£5
ditto, Knopf (New York), 1991 .   .   .   . £10/£5
Flashman and the Angel of the Lord, Harvill (London),
1994 .   .   .   . £10/£5
ditto, Scorpion Press (Blakeney, Glos), 1994 (99 signed,
numbered copies, acetate d/w) .   .   . £150/£125
ditto, Scorpion Press (Blakeney, Glos), 1994 (20 signed,
lettered copies, acetate d/w) .   .   . £275/£250
ditto, Knopf (New York), 1995 .   .   .   . £10/£5
*Flashman and the Tiger, and Other Extracts from the
Flashman Papers*, HarperCollins (London), 1999 £10/£5
ditto, Knopf (New York), 2000 .   .   .   . £10/£5
Flashman on the March, HarperCollins (London), 2005 .
.   .   .   . £10/£5
ditto, Knopf (New York), 2005 .   .   .   . £10/£5
ditto, Scorpion Press (Blakeney, Glos), 2005 (100 signed,
numbered copies; acetate d/w) .   .   . £100/£85
ditto, Scorpion Press (Blakeney, Glos), 2005 (20 signed,
lettered copies, acetate d/w) .   .   . £275/£250

Short Stories
The General Danced at Dawn, Barrie & Jenkins (London),
1970 .   .   .   .£175/£25
ditto, Knopf (New York), 1973 .   .   .   . £75/£10
McAuslan in the Rough, Barrie & Jenkins (London), 1974 .
.   .   .   . £45/£15
ditto, Knopf (New York), 1974 .   .   .   . £25/£10
The Sheik and the Dustbin and Other McAuslan Stories,
Collins Harvill (London), 1988 .   .   . £25/£10
The Complete McAuslan, HarperCollins (London), 2000
(pbk) £5

Others
The Steel Bonnets, Barrie & Jenkins (London), 1971 .   .
.   .   .   .£250/£45
ditto, Knopf (New York), 1972 .   .   .   . £65/£15
Mr American, Collins (London), 1980 .   .   . £20/£5
ditto, Simon & Schuster (New York), 1980 .   . £15/£5
The Pyrates, Collins (London), 1983.   .   .   . £20/£5
ditto, Knopf (New York), 1984 .   .   .   . £15/£5
The Hollywood History of the World, Joseph (London),
1988 .   .   .   . £20/£5
ditto, Beech Tree/Morrow (New York), 1988 .   . £20/£5
*Quartered Safe Out Here: A Recollection of the War in
Burma*, Collins Harvill (London), 1992.   .   . £85/£15
The Candlemass Road, Harvill (London), 1993 .   £10/£5

Black Ajax, HarperCollins (London), 1997   .   .   £10/£5
ditto, Carroll & Graf (New York), 1998   .   .   .   £10/£5
**The Light's on at Signpost: Memoirs of the Movies, among
  Other Matters**, HarperCollins (London), 2002   .   £10/£5
The Reavers, HarperCollins (London), 2007   .   £10/£5
ditto, HarperCollins (London), 2007 (1,000 signed,
  numbered copies; d/w and slipcase)   .   .   .   £50/£40

R. AUSTIN FREEMAN
(b.1862 d.1943)

In his best known character, Dr Thorndyke, Freeman cre-
ated a forensic detective who must surely rival Doyle's
Sherlock Holmes. The collection of adventures written by
Freeman and his friend Dr John James Pitcairn, published
as *The Adventures of Romney Pringle*, was described by
Ellery Queen as 'the rarest book in detective fiction'.

'Dr Thorndyke' Novels
The Red Thumb Mark, Collingwood Bros (London), [1907]
  .   .   .   .   £800
ditto, Collingwood Bros (London), [1907] (pbk)   .   £600
ditto, Hodder & Stoughton (London), 1911   .   .   £100
ditto, Donald Newton (New York), 1911   .   .   .   £100
The Eye of Osiris, Hodder & Stoughton (London), [1911] .
  .   .   .   .   £200
ditto, Hodder & Stoughton (London), [1911] (Egyptian
  binding, 150 copies) £250
ditto, as **The Vanishing Man**, Dodd, Mead (New York),
  1912   .   .   .   .   £75
The Mystery of 31 New Inn, Hodder & Stoughton (London),
  1912   .   .   .   .   £125
ditto, John C. Winston (Philadelphia, PA), 1913 (4 plates
  not in U.K. edition) £125
A Silent Witness, John C. Winston (Philadelphia, PA), 1913
  .   .   .   .   £100
ditto, Hodder & Stoughton (London), [1914]   .   .   £150
Helen Vardon's Confession, Hodder & Stoughton (London),
  [1922]   .   .   .   .   £1,250/£125
The Cat's Eye, Hodder & Stoughton (London), [1923].   .
  .   .   .   .   £1,000/£150
ditto, Dodd, Mead (New York), 1927   .   .   .   £500/£75
The Mystery of Angelina Frood, Hodder & Stoughton
  (London), [1924].   .   .   .   .   .   £750/£100
ditto, Dodd, Mead (New York), 1925   .   .   .   £500/£75
The Shadow of the Wolf, Hodder & Stoughton (London),
  [1925]   .   .   .   .   £750/£100
ditto, Dodd, Mead (New York), 1925   .   .   .   £500/£75
The D'Arblay Mystery, Hodder & Stoughton (London),
  [1926]   .   .   .   .   £750/£100
ditto, Dodd, Mead (New York), 1926   .   .   .   £400/£50
A Certain Dr Thorndyke, Hodder & Stoughton (London),
  [1927]   .   .   .   .   £750/£100
ditto, Dodd, Mead (New York), 1928   .   .   .   £300/£45
As A Thief in the Night, Hodder & Stoughton (London),
  [1928]   .   .   .   .   £750/£75
ditto, Dodd, Mead (New York), 1928   .   .   .   £300/£45
Mr Pottermack's Oversight, Hodder & Stoughton (London),
  [1930]   .   .   .   .   £500/£60
ditto, Dodd, Mead (New York), 1930   .   .   .   £250/£45
Dr Thorndyke Investigates, Univ of London Press (London),
  1930   .   .   .   .   £250/£40

Pontifex, Son & Thorndyke, Hodder & Stoughton (London),
  1931   .   .   .   .   £500/£35
ditto, Dodd, Mead (New York), 1931   .   .   .   £200/£25
When Rogues Fall Out, Hodder & Stoughton (London),
  1932   .   .   .   .   £350/£35
ditto, as **Dr Thorndyke's Discovery**, Dodd, Mead (New
  York), 1932   .   .   .   .   £200/£25
Dr Thorndyke Intervenes, Hodder & Stoughton (London),
  1933   .   .   .   .   £350/£35
ditto, Dodd, Mead (New York), 1933   .   .   .   £200/£25
For the Defence: Dr Thorndyke, Hodder & Stoughton
  (London), 1934   .   .   .   .   .   .   £350/£35
ditto, Dodd, Mead (New York), 1934   .   .   .   £200/£25
The Penrose Mystery, Hodder & Stoughton (London), 1936
  .   .   .   .   £300/£30
ditto, Dodd, Mead (New York), 1936   .   .   .   £200/£25
Felo de Se?, Hodder & Stoughton (London), 1937 £300/£30
ditto, as **Death at the Inn**, Dodd, Mead (New York), 1937 .
  .   .   .   .   £200/£25
The Stoneware Monkey, Hodder & Stoughton (London),
  1938   .   .   .   .   £300/£30
ditto, Dodd, Mead (New York), 1939   .   .   .   £200/£25
Mr Polton Explains, Hodder & Stoughton (London), 1940 .
  .   .   .   .   £300/£30
ditto, Dodd, Mead (New York), 1940   .   .   .   £200/£25
Dr Thorndyke's Crime File, Dodd, Mead (New York), 1941
  .   .   .   .   £200/£25
The Jacob Street Mystery, Hodder & Stoughton (London),
  1942   .   .   .   .   £200/£25
ditto, as **The Unconscious Witness**, Dodd, Mead (New
  York), 1942   .   .   .   .   £175/£20

'Thorndyke' Story Collections
John Thorndyke's Cases, Chatto & Windus (London), 1909
  .   .   .   .   £500
ditto, as **Dr Thorndyke's Cases**, Dodd, Mead (New York),
  1931   .   .   .   .   £300/£45
The Singing Bone, Hodder & Stoughton (London), 1912   .
  .   .   .   .   £250
ditto, Dodd, Mead (New York), 1923   .   .   .   £350/£75
The Great Portrait Mystery, Hodder & Stoughton (London),
  [1918] £250
Dr Thorndyke's Case-Book, Hodder & Stoughton (London),
  [1923]   .   .   .   .   £1,000/£100
ditto, as **The Blue Scarab**, Dodd, Mead (New York), 1923 .
  .   .   .   .   £500/£45
The Puzzle Lock, Hodder & Stoughton (London), [1925]   .
  .   .   .   .   £1,000/£100
ditto, Dodd, Mead (New York), 1926   .   .   .   £500/£45
The Magic Casket, Hodder & Stoughton (London), [1927] .
  .   .   .   .   £1,000/£75
ditto, Dodd, Mead (New York), 1927   .   .   .   £400/£35
The Famous Cases of Dr Thorndyke, Hodder & Stoughton
  (London), [1929].   .   .   .   .   .   .   £200/£25
ditto, as **The Dr Thorndyke Omnibus**, Dodd, Mead (New
  York), 1932   .   .   .   .   £125/£20
The Best Dr Thorndyke Short Stories, Dover (New York),
  1973 (pbk) £10
Dead Hand, Highfield Press (Aldershot, Hants), [1994]   £5

Story Collections Written as 'Clifford Ashdown'
(written with J.J. Pitcairn)
The Adventures of Romney Pringle, Ward Lock (London),
  1902   .   .   .   .   £1,500

ditto, Oswald Train (Philadelphia, PA), 1968 . . £25/£10
The Further Adventures of Romney Pringle, Oswald Train
(Philadelphia, PA), 1975 . . . . . £30/£10
ditto, Oswald Train (Philadelphia, PA), 1969 . £25/£10
From a Surgeon's Diary, Ferret Fantasy (London), 1975
(stapled wraps) £10
ditto, Oswald Train (Philadelphia, PA), 1977 . £25/£10
The Queen's Treasure, Oswald Train (Philadelphia, PA),
1975 . . . . £25/£10

Other Titles
The Golden Pool, Cassell (London), 1905 . . £300
The Unwilling Adventurer, Hodder & Stoughton (London),
[1913] £200
The Uttermost Farthing, John C. Winston (Philadelphia,
PA), 1914 . . . . £75
ditto, as ***A Savant's Vendetta***, Pearson (London), [1920] .
. . . . £750/£75
The Exploits of Danby Croker, Duckworth (London), 1916
. . . . £150
The Surprising Experiences of Mr Shuttlebury Cobb,
Hodder & Stoughton (London), [1927] . £1,000/£75
Flighty Phyllis, Hodder & Stoughton (London), [1928] .
. . . . £750/£50

Non-Fiction
Travels and Life in Ashant and Jaman, Constable
(London), 1898 . . . . £250
ditto, Stokes (New York), 1898 . . . . . £250
Social Decay and Regeneration, Constable (London), 1921
. . . . £100/£25

ROBERT FROST

(b.1874 d.1963)

Frost was an American poet with the distinctive voice of
his own country, whose poetry often addresses the
problems of a solitary character attempting to make sense
of the world. He is considered by many to be the greatest
American poet of the 20th Century and one of the greatest
poets writing in English. Frost was awarded four Pulitzer
Prizes for his work.

[Twilight] Five Poems, [Lawrence, MA, 1894] . £35,000
A Boy's Will, David Nutt (London), 1913 ('A' binding,
bronze cloth). £4,000
ditto, David Nutt (London), 1913 ('B' binding, cream-
coloured vellum-paper boards stamped in red cloth) £2,000
ditto, David Nutt (London), 1913 ('C' binding, cream-
coloured linen-paper wraps stamped in black, and 8-
petalled flowers) £1,250
ditto, David Nutt (London), 1913 ('D' binding, cream-
coloured linen-paper wraps stamped in black, and 4-
petalled flowers) £750
ditto, David Nutt (London), 1913 (135 signed, numbered
copies, cream wraps) £1,450
ditto, David Nutt (London), 1913 (second issue, cream
wraps) £450
ditto, Holt (New York), 1915 ('Aind' for 'And' on last line,
p.14) £450
ditto, Holt (New York), 1915 (with 'And') . . £145

North of Boston, David Nutt (London), 1914 (first issue,
binding 'A', with coarse green cloth) . . . £1,500
ditto, David Nutt (London)/Holt (New York), 1914 (first
issue, binding 'B', UK sheets with Holt title-page) £1,250
ditto, David Nutt (London), 1914 (first issue, binding 'C',
with fine green cloth) £1,000
ditto, David Nutt (London), 1914 (first issue, binding 'D',
with blue cloth) £750
ditto, David Nutt (London), 1914 (first issue, binding 'E',
with coarse green cloth, measuring 200x145mm, tall edges
trimmed, rubber stamp p.iv) £650
ditto, David Nutt (London), 1914 (first issue, binding 'F',
with coarse green cloth, measuring 195x150mm, top edge
trimmed and others rough cut, rubber stamp p.iv). £1,000
Mountain Interval, Holt (New York), 1916 (first state, p.88,
lines 6 and 7 repeated, p.63 line 6 from bottom 'Come' for
'Gone') . . . . £1,250/£300
ditto, Holt (New York), 1916 (errors corrected) £650/£100
Selected Poems, Holt (New York), 1923 . . £650/£100
ditto, Heinemann (London), 1923 . . . £400/£50
New Hampshire, Holt (New York), 1923 . . £500/£125
ditto, Holt (New York), 1923 (350 signed, numbered copies,
slipcase). . . . . . . £1,250/£1,000
ditto, Grant Richards (London), 1924 . . £1,000/£300
ditto, The New Dresden Press (Hanover, NH), 1955 (750
signed, numbered copies, semi-transparent d/w) £400/£300
West-Running Brook, Holt (New York), 1928 (without
'First Edition' statement) . . . . £250/£100
ditto, Holt (New York), 1928 (with 'First Edition' statement)
. . . . £150/£50
ditto, Holt (New York), 1928 (1,000 signed, numbered
copies, slipcase, glassine d/w) . . . £400/£350
A Way Out: A One Act Play, Harbor Press (New York),
1929 (485 signed, numbered copies, glassine d/w) .
. . . . £250/£225
The Lovely Shall Be Choosers, Random House (New York),
1929 (475 copies; wraps) £65
The Cow's in the Corn: A One-Act Irish Play in Rhyme,
Slide Mountain Press (Gaylordsville), 1929 (91 signed,
numbered copies) £1,000
Collected Poems of Robert Frost, Random House (New
York), 1930 (1,000 signed, numbered copies) . £500
ditto, Holt (New York), 1930 (first trade edition) . £225/£30
ditto, Longmans Green (London), 1930 . . £175/£25
The Lone Striker, Knopf (New York), 1933 (sewn wraps in
envelope) . . . . £40/£30
A Further Range, Holt (New York), 1936 . . £125/£15
ditto, Spiral Press (New York), 1936 (800 signed, numbered
copies in slipcase, no d/w). £350
ditto, Cape (London), 1937 . . . . . £75/£10
Selected Poems, Cape (London), 1936 . . £100/£15
From Snow to Snow, Holt (New York), 1936 (no d/w). £100
Collected Poems of Robert Frost, Holt (New York), 1939 .
. . . . £175/£25
ditto, Longmans Green (London), 1939 . . £175/£25
A Witness Tree, Holt (New York), 1942 . . £150/£20
ditto, Spiral Press (New York), 1942 (735 signed, numbered
copies, slipcase) . . . . . £300/£250
ditto, Cape (London), 1943 . . . . £100/£15
Come in and Other Poems, Holt (New York), 1944 £50/£15
ditto, Cape (London), 1944 . . . . . £30/£10
ditto, as ***The Pocket Book of Robert Frost's Poems***, Pocket
Books (New York), 1946 (pbk) £10

ditto, as *The Road Not Taken*, Holt (New York), 1951 .   .
.   .   .   .   £15/£5
A Masque of Reason, Holt (New York), 1945 .   . £50/£15
ditto, Holt (New York), 1945 (800 signed, numbered copies,
slipcase, no d/w) .   .   .   .   .   £250/£200
ditto, Cape (London), 1948 .   .   .   .   . £30/£10
Steeple Bush, Holt (New York), 1947   .   .   . £75/£15
ditto, Holt (New York), 1947 (750 signed, numbered copies,
slipcase, no d/w) .   .   .   .   .   £250/£200
A Masque of Mercy, Holt (New York), 1947 .   . £65/£15
ditto, Holt (New York), 1947 (751 signed, numbered copies,
slipcase).   .   .   .   .   .   .   £250/£200
The Complete Poems, Holt (New York), 1949 (500 signed,
numbered copies, slipcase, no d/w) .   .   £500/£400
ditto, Limited Editions Club (New York), 1950 (signed, 2
vols in slipcase) .   .   .   .   .   £450/£350
ditto, Cape (London), 1951 .   .   .   .   . £100/£20
Hard Not to Be King, House of Books (New York), 1951
(300 signed, numbered copies). £300
A Cabin in the Clearing, Blumenthal/Spiral Press (New
York), 1951 (wraps) £25
Aforesaid, Holt (New York), 1954 (650 signed, numbered
copies, slipcase, no d/w) .   .   .   .   £500/£400
My Objection to Being Stepped On, Blumenthal/Spiral Press
(New York), 1957 (wraps). £25
You Come Too: Favourite Poems for Young Readers, Holt
(New York), 1959 .   .   .   .   .   . £25/£10
ditto, Bodley Head (London), 1964 .   .   . £25/£10
A Wishing Well, Blumenthal/Spiral Press (New York), 1959
(wraps) £25
In the Clearing, Holt (New York), 1962 .   .   . £45/£10
ditto, Blumenthal/Spiral Press (New York), 1962 (1,500
signed, numbered copies, slipcase) .   .   £200/£150
The Prophets Really Prophecy as Mystics, Blumenthal/
Spiral Press (New York), 1962 .   .   .   . £25
The Letters of Robert Frost to Louis Untermeyer, Holt
(New York), 1963 .   .   .   .   .   £20/£5
ditto, Cape (London), 1964 .   .   .   .   £15/£10
*Robert Frost and John Bartlett: The Record of a
Friendship*, Holt (New York), 1963   .   .   £20/£5
Selected Letters of Robert Frost, Holt (New York), 1964 .
.   .   .   .   £20/£5
Interviews with Robert Frost, Holt (New York), 1966 .   .
.   .   .   .   £20/£5
ditto, Cape (London), 1967 .   .   .   .   £15/£5
Selected Prose of Robert Frost, Holt (New York), 1966   .
.   .   .   .   £20/£5
The Poetry of Robert Frost, Holt (New York), 1969   £20/£5
ditto, Cape (London), 1971 .   .   .   .   £15/£5
Family Letters of Robert Frost and Elinor Frost, State Univ
of New York Press (New York), 1972 .   .   £20/£5
Robert Frost: Poetry and Prose, Holt (New York), 1972   .
.   .   .   .   £20/£5

WILLIAM GADDIS
(b.1922 d.1998)

Gaddis was a novelist who, after several years of critical
neglect, is now acknowledged as one of the greatest of
American post-War novelists. He has influenced such
writers as Don DeLillo and Thomas Pynchon, and many
others have admitted their debt to him, and in particular
The Recognitions.

The Recognitions, Harcourt Brace (New York), 1955 (first
issue d/w with price of $7.50 and publisher's address '383
Madison Avenue') .   .   .   . £450/£75
ditto, Harcourt Brace (New York), 1955 (second issue d/w
with price of $8.50 and publisher's address '757 Third
Avenue') .   .   .   . £50/£10
ditto, MacGibbon & Kee (London), [1962]   . £175/£30
J R, Knopf (New York), 1975) .   .   .   . £150/£25
ditto, Cape (London), 1976 (first issue d/w without 'condom'
crossed out on front flap) .   .   .   . £100/£15
ditto, Cape (London), 1976 (wraps) £10
Carpenter's Gothic, Viking (New York), 1985   . £15/£5
ditto, Andre Deutsch (London), 1986.   .   .   . £15/£5
A Frolic of His Own, Poseidon (New York), 1994.   £10/£5
ditto, Viking (London), 1994   .   .   .   .   . £10/£5
Agapé Agapé, Viking (New York), 2002 .   .   . £15/£5
ditto, Atlantic Books (London), 2002.   .   .   £10/£5

Others
Reader's Guide to William Gaddis's The Recognitions,
Univ of Nebraska Press (Lincoln, NE), 1982   . £20/£5
*The Rush for Second Place: Essays and Occasional
Writings*, Penguin Books (New York), 2002 (wraps) .   £5

GABRIEL GARCÍA MÁRQUEZ
(b.1928)

A Colombian novelist and short story writer, Márquez
began his career as a journalist. He is Latin America's pre-
eminent man of letters and is thought by many to be one of
the greatest writers of the 20th century. He is often
considered the foremost writer of 'magic realism', but
while much of his writing contains elements associated
with this genre, his style is too diverse to be so simply
categorised. He was awarded the Nobel Prize for Literature
in 1982.

Novels
La mala hora, ESSO Columbiana (Columbia), 1962 (pbk) .
.   .   .   .   £2,000
ditto, ESSO Columbiana (Columbia), 1962 (pbk; 170
numbered copies) £3,000
ditto, as *In Evil Hour*, Harper & Row (New York), 1979   .
.   .   .   .   £50/£10
ditto, as *In Evil Hour*, Cape (London), 1980 .   . £25/£5
Cien años de soledad, Sudamericana (Argentina), 1967
(pbk) £2,750
ditto, as *One Hundred Years of Solitude*, Harper & Row
(New York), 1970 (no number row on last leaf of book,

first issue d/w with an exclamation mark at the end of the first paragraph of text on the front flap) .   . £1,450/£125

ditto, as **One Hundred Years of Solitude**, Harper & Row (New York), 1970 (second issue d/w without exclamation mark)   .   .   .   . £1,000/£125

ditto, as **One Hundred Years of Solitude**, Cape (London), 1970   .   .   .   . £345/£45

El otoño del patriarca, Plaza y Janes (Spain), 1975   .   .
.   .   .   . £200/£25

ditto, as **The Autumn of the Patriarch**, Harper & Row (New York), 1976 (number row ends in '5'!)   .   . £75/£15

ditto, as **The Autumn of the Patriarch**, Cape (London), 1977
.   .   .   . £30/£5

Crónica de una muerte anunciada, Editorial La Oveja Negra (Columbia), 1981   .   .   .   . £35/£5

ditto, as **Chronicle of a Death Foretold**, Cape (London), 1982   .   .   .   . £25/£5

ditto, as **Chronicle of a Death Foretold**, Knopf (New York), 1983 (first issue jacket cites *One Hundred Days of Solitude*)   .   .   .   . £25/£5

El Amor en los tiempos del colera, Editorial La Oveja Negra (Columbia), 1985 (yellow d/w)   .   .   . £25/£5

ditto, Editorial La Oveja Negra (Columbia), 1985 (deluxe edition, blue and white d/w)   .   .   .   . £35/£15

ditto, Editorial La Oveja Negra (Columbia), 1985 (1,000 signed, unnumbered copies)   .   .   . £65/£30

ditto, as **Love in the Time of Cholera**, Knopf (New York), 1988   .   .   .   . £25/£5

ditto, as **Love in the Time of Cholera**, Knopf (New York), 1988 (350 signed copies)   .   .   . £300/£250

ditto, as **Love in the Time of Cholera**, Cape (London), 1988
.   .   .   . £25/£5

El general en su laberinto, Editorial La Oveja Negra (Columbia), 1989.   .   .   .   .   . £35/£5

ditto, **The General in His Labyrinth**, Knopf (New York), 1990   .   .   .   . £25/£5

ditto, **The General in His Labyrinth**, Knopf (New York), 1990 (350 signed, numbered copies, slipcase) £250/£200

ditto, **The General in His Labyrinth**, Cape (London), 1991.
.   .   .   . £25/£5

Del Amor y Otros Demonios, Grupo Editorial Norma (Columbia), 1994.   .   .   .   .   . £15/£5

ditto, as **Of Love and Other Demons**, Knopf (New York), 1995   .   .   .   . £15/£5

ditto, as **Of Love and Other Demons**, Cape (London), 1995
.   .   .   . £15/£5

Memoria De Mis Putas Tristes, Knopf (New York), 2004 (text in Spanish)   .   .   .   .   . £10/£5

ditto, as **Memories of My Melancholy Whores**, Knopf (New York), 2005   .   .   .   .   .   . £10/£5

ditto, as **Memories of My Melancholy Whores**, Cape (London), 2005   .   .   .   .   .   . £10/£5

Short Stories
La hojarasca, Ediciones S.L.B. (Columbia), 1955 (pbk)   .
.   .   .   . £2,750

ditto, as **Leaf Storm and Other Stories**, Harper & Row (New York), 1972 .   .   .   .   .   . £65/£10

ditto, as **Leaf Storm and Other Stories**, Cape (London), 1972
.   .   .   . £40/£10

El coronel no tiene quien le escribe, Aguirre Editor (Columbia), 1961 (pbk) £1,450

ditto, as **No One Writes to the Colonel and Other Stories**, Harper & Row (New York), 1968 .   .   . £200/£25

ditto, as **No One Writes to the Colonel and Other Stories**, Cape (London), 1971 .   .   .   . £175/£20

Los funerales de la mama grande, Univ of Veracruz (Mexico), 1962 (pbk) £1,000

La increible y triste historia de la candid Eréndira y su abuela Desalmada, Sudamericana (Argentina), 1972 (pbk)
.   .   .   . £100

ditto, as **Innocent Eréndira and Other Stories**, Harper & Row (New York), 1978 .   .   .   . £25/£5

ditto, as **Innocent Eréndira and Other Stories**, Cape (London), 1979 .   .   .   .   . £20/£5

Collected Stories, Harper & Row (New York), 1984 £30/£5

ditto, Cape (London), 1991 .   .   .   . £15/£5

Collected Novellas, HarperCollins (New York), 1990 £10/£5

Strange Pilgrims, Knopf (New York), 1993 .   . £15/£5

ditto, Cape (London), 1993 .   .   .   . £15/£5

Others
El Olor de la Guayaba: Conversaciones con Plinio Apuleyo Mendoza, Editorial La Oveja Negra (Columbia), 1982 (wraps) £20

ditto, as **Fragrance of Guava**, Verso (London), 1982 .   .
.   .   .   . £10/£5

La aventura de Miguel Littin clandestino en Chile, Editorial La Oveja Negra (Columbia), 1986 .   .   . £35/£5

ditto, as **Clandestine in Chile, The Adventures of Miguel Littin**, Holt (New York), 1987 .   .   .   . £30/£5

The Story of a Shipwrecked Sailor, Knopf (New York), 1986 .   .   .   . £25/£5

ditto, Cape (London), 1986 .   .   .   .   . £20/£5

Noticia de un Secuestro, Grupo Editorial Norma (Columbia), 1996.   .   .   .   .   . £10/£5

ditto, as **News of a Kidnapping**, Knopf (New York), 1997 .
.   .   .   . £10/£5

ditto, as **News of a Kidnapping**, Cape (London), 1997 .   .
.   .   .   . £10/£5

Living to Tell the Tale, Knopf (New York), 2003 . £10/£5

ditto, Cape (London), 2003 .   .   .   .   . £10/£5

ERLE STANLEY GARDNER
(b.1889 d.1970)

Gardner was an American lawyer and author of detective stories, best-known for his crime-solving lawyer 'Perry Mason'. His 'D.A. Doug Selby' novels present a series lawyer, A.B. Carr, whose clients are always guilty. Under the pseudonym A.A. Fair he also wrote a series of novels about private detectives Bertha Cool and Donald Lam.

'Perry Mason' Novels
The Case of the Velvet Claws, Morrow (New York), 1933 .
.   .   .   . £3,000/£400

ditto, Harrap (London), 1933 .   .   .   . £600/£45

The Case of the Sulky Girl, Morrow (New York), 1933 .
.   .   .   . £2,500/£250

ditto, Harrap (London), 1934 .   .   .   . £600/£45

The Case of the Lucky Legs, Morrow (New York), 19334 .
.   .   .   . £1,500/£175

ditto, Harrap (London), 1934 .   .   .   . £450/£40

The Case of the Howling Dog, Morrow (New York), 1934 .
. . . . £1,250/£65
ditto, Cassell (London), 1935 . . . . . £450/£40
The Case of the Curious Bride, Morrow (New York), 1934
. . . . £1,000/£45
ditto, Cassell (London), 1935 . . . . . £400/£35
The Case of the Counterfeit Eye, Morrow (New York), 1935
. . . . £750/£30
ditto, Cassell (London), 1935 . . . . . £350/£35
The Case of the Caretaker's Cat, Morrow (New York), 1935
. . . . £750/£30
ditto, Cassell (London), 1936 . . . . . £300/£30
The Case of the Sleepwalker's Niece, Morrow (New York),
1936 . . . . £600/£40
ditto, Cassell (London), 1936 . . . . . £300/£30
The Case of the Stuttering Bishop, Morrow (New York),
1936 . . . . £500/£30
ditto, Cassell (London), 1937 . . . . . £250/£25
The Case of the Dangerous Dowager, Morrow (New York),
1937 . . . . £250/£25
ditto, Cassell (London), 1937 . . . . . £200/£20
The Case of the Lame Canary, Morrow (New York), 1937.
. . . . £250/£20
ditto, Cassell (London), 1937 . . . . . £200/£20
The Case of the Substitute Face, Morrow (New York), 1938
. . . . £250/£20
ditto, Cassell (London), 1938 . . . . . £150/£15
The Case of the Shoplifter's Shoe, Morrow (New York),
1938 . . . . £200/£20
ditto, Cassell (London), 1939 . . . . . £150/£15
The Case of the Perjured Parrot, Morrow (New York), 1939
. . . . £150/£15
ditto, Cassell (London), 1939 . . . . . £150/£15
The Case of the Rolling Bones, Morrow (New York), 1939
. . . . £150/£15
ditto, Cassell (London), 1940 . . . . . £150/£15
The Case of the Baited Hook, Morrow (New York), 1940 .
. . . . £100/£15
ditto, Cassell (London), 1940 . . . . . £75/£10
The Case of the Silent Partner, Morrow (New York), 1940
. . . . £75/£10
ditto, Cassell (London), 1941 . . . . . £65/£10
The Case of the Haunted Husband, Morrow (New York),
1941 . . . . £75/£10
ditto, Cassell (London), 1942 . . . . . £50/£10
The Case of the Empty Tin, Morrow (New York), 1941 .
. . . . £75/£10
ditto, Cassell (London), 1943 . . . . . £50/£10
The Case of the Drowning Duck, Morrow (New York),
1942 . . . . £75/£10
ditto, Cassell (London), 1944 . . . . . £50/£10
The Case of the Careless Kitten, Morrow (New York), 1942
. . . . £75/£10
ditto, Cassell (London), 1944 . . . . . £50/£10
The Case of the Buried Clock, Morrow (New York), 1943 .
. . . . £75/£10
ditto, Cassell (London), 1945 . . . . . £50/£10
The Case of the Drowsy Mosquito, Morrow (New York),
1943 . . . . £65/£10
ditto, Cassell (London), 1946 . . . . . £50/£10
The Case of the Crooked Candle, Morrow (New York),
1944 . . . . £65/£10
ditto, Cassell (London), 1947 . . . . . £50/£10

The Case of the Black-Eyed Blonde, Morrow (New York),
1944 . . . . £65/£10
ditto, Cassell (London), 1948 . . . . . £50/£10
The Case of the Golddigger's Purse, Morrow (New York),
1944 . . . . £65/£10
ditto, Cassell (London), 1948 . . . . . £50/£10
The Case of the Half-Wakened Wife, Morrow (New York),
1945 . . . . £65/£10
ditto, Cassell (London), 1949 . . . . . £50/£10
The Case of the Borrowed Brunette, Morrow (New York),
1946 . . . . £40/£10
ditto, Cassell (London), 1951 . . . . . £35/£5
The Case of the Fandancer's Horse, Morrow (New York),
1947 . . . . £50/£10
ditto, Heinemann (London), 1952 . . . . £35/£5
The Case of the Lazy Lover, Morrow (New York), 1947 .
. . . . £40/£10
ditto, Heinemann (London), 1954 . . . . £35/£5
The Case of the Lonely Heiress, Morrow (New York), 1948
. . . . £35/£5
ditto, Heinemann (London), 1952 . . . . £35/£5
The Case of the Vagabond Virgin, Morrow (New York),
1948 . . . . £35/£5
ditto, Heinemann (London), 1952 . . . . £30/£5
The Case of the Dubious Bridegroom, Morrow (New York),
1949 . . . . £35/£5
ditto, Heinemann (London), 1954 . . . . £30/£5
The Case of the Cautious Coquette, Morrow (New York),
1949 . . . . £35/£5
ditto, Heinemann (London), 1955 . . . . £30/£5
The Case of the Negligent Nymph, Morrow (New York),
1950 . . . . £35/£5
ditto, Heinemann (London), 1956 . . . . £30/£5
The Case of the One-Eyed Witness, Morrow (New York),
1950 . . . . £35/£5
ditto, Heinemann (London), 1957 . . . . £30/£5
The Case of the Fiery Fingers, Morrow (New York), 1951.
. . . . £35/£5
ditto, Heinemann (London), 1957 . . . . £30/£5
The Case of the Angry Mourner, Morrow (New York), 1951
. . . . £35/£5
ditto, Heinemann (London), 1958 . . . . £30/£5
The Case of the Moth-Eaten Mink, Morrow (New York),
1952 . . . . £35/£5
ditto, Heinemann (London), 1958 . . . . £30/£5
The Case of the Grinning Gorilla, Morrow (New York),
1952 . . . . £35/£5
ditto, Heinemann (London), 1958 . . . . £30/£5
The Case of the Hesitant Hostess, Morrow (New York),
1953 . . . . £35/£5
ditto, Heinemann (London), 1959 . . . . £30/£5
The Case of the Green-Eyed Sister, Morrow (New York),
1953 . . . . £30/£5
ditto, Heinemann (London), 1959 . . . . £25/£5
The Case of the Fugitive Nurse, Morrow (New York), 1954
. . . . £30/£5
ditto, Heinemann (London), 1959 . . . . £25/£5
The Case of the Runaway Corpse, Morrow (New York),
1954 . . . . £30/£5
ditto, Heinemann (London), 1960 . . . . £25/£5
The Case of the Restless Redhead, Morrow (New York),
1954 . . . . £30/£5
ditto, Heinemann (London), 1960 . . . . £25/£5

The Case of the Glamorous Ghost, Morrow (New York),
1955 . . . . £25/£5
ditto, Heinemann (London), 1960 . . . £20/£5
The Case of the Sun-Bather's Diary, Morrow (New York),
1955 . . . . £25/£5
ditto, Heinemann (London), 1961 . . . £20/£5
The Case of the Nervous Accomplice, Morrow (New York),
1955 . . . . £25/£5
ditto, Heinemann (London), 1961 . . . £20/£5
The Case of the Terrified Typist, Morrow (New York), 1956
. . . . £25/£5
ditto, Heinemann (London), 1961 . . . £20/£5
The Case of the Demure Defendant, Morrow (New York),
1956 . . . . £25/£5
ditto, Heinemann (London), 1962 . . . £20/£5
The Case of the Gilded Lily, Morrow (New York), 1956 .
. . . . £25/£5
ditto, Heinemann (London), 1962 . . . £20/£5
The Case of the Lucky Loser, Morrow (New York), 1957 .
. . . . £25/£5
ditto, Heinemann (London), 1962 . . . £20/£5
The Case of the Screaming Woman, Morrow (New York),
1957 . . . . £25/£5
ditto, Heinemann (London), 1963 . . . £20/£5
The Case of the Daring Decoy, Morrow (New York), 1957
. . . . £25/£5
ditto, Heinemann (London), 1963 . . . £20/£5
The Case of the Long-Legged Models, Morrow (New York),
1958 . . . . £25/£5
ditto, Heinemann (London), 1963 . . . £20/£5
The Case of the Foot-Loose Doll, Morrow (New York),
1958 . . . . £25/£5
ditto, Heinemann (London), 1964 . . . £20/£5
The Case of the Calendar Girl, Morrow (New York), 1958
. . . . £25/£5
ditto, Heinemann (London), 1964 . . . £20/£5
The Case of the Deadly Toy, Morrow (New York), 1959 .
. . . . £25/£5
ditto, Heinemann (London), 1964 . . . £20/£5
The Case of the Mythical Monkeys, Morrow (New York),
1959 . . . . £25/£5
ditto, Heinemann (London), 1965 . . . £20/£5
The Case of the Singing Skirt, Morrow (New York), 1959 .
. . . . £25/£5
ditto, Heinemann (London), 1965 . . . £20/£5
The Case of the Waylaid Wolf, Morrow (New York), 1960.
. . . . £25/£5
ditto, Heinemann (London), 1965 . . . £20/£5
The Case of the Duplicate Daughter, Morrow (New York),
1960 . . . . £25/£5
ditto, Heinemann (London), 1965 . . . £20/£5
The Case of the Shapely Shadow, Morrow (New York),
1960 . . . . £25/£5
ditto, Heinemann (London), 1966 . . . £20/£5
The Case of the Spurious Spinster, Morrow (New York),
1961 . . . . £25/£5
ditto, Heinemann (London), 1966 . . . £20/£5
The Case of the Bigamous Spouse, Morrow (New York),
1961 . . . . £25/£5
ditto, Heinemann (London), 1967 . . . £20/£5
The Case of the Reluctant Model, Morrow (New York),
1962 . . . . £25/£5
ditto, Heinemann (London), 1967 . . . £20/£5

The Case of the Blonde Bonanza, Morrow (New York),
1962 . . . . £25/£5
ditto, Heinemann (London), 1967 . . . £20/£5
The Case of the Ice-Cold Hands, Morrow (New York), 1962
. . . . £25/£5
ditto, Heinemann (London), 1968 . . . £20/£5
The Case of the Mischievous Doll, Morrow (New York),
1963 . . . . £25/£5
ditto, Heinemann (London), 1968 . . . £20/£5
The Case of the Stepdaughter's Secret, Morrow (New
York), 1963 . . . . £25/£5
ditto, Heinemann (London), 1968 . . . £20/£5
The Case of the Amorous Aunt, Morrow (New York), 1963
. . . . £25/£5
ditto, Heinemann (London), 1969 . . . £20/£5
The Case of the Daring Divorcee, Morrow (New York),
1964 . . . . £20/£5
ditto, Heinemann (London), 1969 . . . £15/£5
The Case of the Phantom Fortune, Morrow (New York),
1964 . . . . £20/£5
ditto, Heinemann (London), 1970 . . . £15/£5
The Case of the Horrified Heirs, Morrow (New York), 1964
. . . . £20/£5
ditto, Heinemann (London), 1971 . . . £15/£5
The Case of the Troubled Trustee, Morrow (New York),
1965 . . . . £20/£5
ditto, Heinemann (London), 1971 . . . £15/£5
The Case of the Beautiful Beggar, Morrow (New York),
1965 . . . . £20/£5
ditto, Heinemann (London), 1972 . . . £15/£5
The Case of the Worried Witness, Morrow (New York),
1966 . . . . £20/£5
ditto, Heinemann (London), 1972 . . . £15/£5
The Case of the Queenly Contestant, Morrow (New York),
1967 . . . . £20/£5
ditto, Heinemann (London), 1973 . . . £15/£5
The Case of the Careless Cupid, Morrow (New York), 1968
. . . . £20/£5
ditto, Heinemann (London), 1973 . . . £15/£5
The Case of the Fabulous Fake, Morrow (New York), 1969
. . . . £15/£5
ditto, Heinemann (London), 1974 . . . £10/£5
The Case of the Fenced-In Woman, Morrow (New York),
1972 . . . . £15/£5
ditto, Heinemann (London), 1976 . . . £10/£5
The Case of the Postponed Murder, Morrow (New York),
1973 . . . . £15/£5
ditto, Heinemann (London), 1977 . . . £10/£5

'Perry Mason' Short Stories
The Case of the Crimson Kiss, Morrow (New York), 1970 .
. . . . £20/£5
ditto, Heinemann (London), 1975 . . . £15/£5
The Case of the Crying Swallow, Morrow (New York), 1971
. . . . £15/£5
ditto, Heinemann (London), 1974 . . . £10/£5
The Case of the Irate Witness, Morrow (New York), 1972 .
. . . . £15/£5
ditto, Heinemann (London), 1975 . . . £10/£5

D.A. Novels
The D.A. Calls it Murder, Morrow (New York), 1937 .
. . . . £250/£35
ditto, Cassell (London), 1937 . . . . £150/£20

The D.A. Holds a Candle, Morrow (New York), 1938 .   .
.   .   .   . £150/£20
ditto, Cassell (London), 1939   .   .   .   . £125/£15
The D.A. Draws a Circle, Morrow (New York), 1939 .   .
.   .   .   . £100/£15
ditto, Cassell (London), 1940   .   .   .   . £75/£15
The D.A. Goes to Trial, Morrow (New York), 1940 £75/£15
ditto, Cassell (London), 1941   .   .   .   . £65/£10
The D.A. Cooks a Goose, Morrow (New York), 1942 .   .
.   .   .   . £75/£15
ditto, Cassell (London), 1943   .   .   .   . £65/£10
The D.A. Calls a Turn, Morrow (New York), 1944 £45/£10
ditto, Cassell (London), 1947   .   .   .   . £35/£10
The D.A. Breaks a Seal, Morrow (New York), 1946 .   .
.   .   .   . £40/£10
ditto, Cassell (London), 1950   .   .   .   . £30/£5
The D.A. Takes a Chance, Morrow (New York), 1948.   .
.   .   .   . £25/£10
ditto, Heinemann (London), 1956   .   .   .   . £20/£5
The D.A. Breaks an Egg, Morrow (New York), 1949 .
.   .   .   . £35/£10
ditto, Heinemann (London), 1957   .   .   . £20/£5

Novels Written as 'A.A. Fair'
The Bigger They Come, Morrow (New York), 1939   .
.   .   .   . £500/£45
ditto, as **Lam to the Slaughter**, Hamish Hamilton (London),
1939   .   .   .   . £250/£25
Turn on the Heat, Morrow (New York), 1940 . £400/£40
ditto, Hamish Hamilton (London), 1940 .   . £200/£25
Gold Comes in Bricks, Morrow (New York), 1940 £200/£35
ditto, Robert Hale (London), 1942   .   .   . £125/£20
Spill the Jackpot, Morrow (New York), 1941 . £200/£35
ditto, Robert Hale (London), 1948   .   .   . £75/£10
Double or Quits, Morrow (New York), 1941 . £75/£15
ditto, Robert Hale (London), 1949   .   .   . £50/£10
Owls Don't Blink, Morrow (New York), 1942 . £150/£25
ditto, Robert Hale (London), 1951   .   .   . £35/£10
Bats Fly at Dusk, Morrow (New York), 1942 . £100/£15
ditto, Robert Hale (London), 1951   .   .   . £35/£10
Cats Prowl at Night, Morrow (New York), 1943 . £75/£15
ditto, Robert Hale (London), 1949   .   .   . £45/£10
Give 'Em the Axe, Morrow (New York), 1944   . £50/£10
ditto, as **An Axe to Grind**, Heinemann (London), 1951 .   .
.   .   .   . £45/£10
Crows Can't Count, Morrow (New York), 1946   . £50/£10
ditto, Heinemann (London), 1953   .   .   . £25/£5
Fools Die on Friday, Morrow (New York), 1947 . £50/£10
ditto, Heinemann (London), 1955   .   .   . £20/£5
Bedrooms Have Windows, Morrow (New York), 1949.   .
.   .   .   . £35/£10
ditto, Heinemann (London), 1956   .   .   . £20/£5
Top of the Heap, Morrow (New York), 1952 .   . £35/£10
ditto, Heinemann (London), 1957   .   .   . £20/£5
Some Women Won't Wait, Morrow (New York), 1953   .
.   .   .   . £30/£10
ditto, Heinemann (London), 1958   .   .   . £20/£5
Beware the Curves, Morrow (New York), 1956 . £25/£10
ditto, Heinemann (London), 1957   .   .   . £15/£5
You Can Die Laughing, Morrow (New York), 1957   .
.   .   .   . £25/£10
ditto, Heinemann (London), 1958   .   .   . £15/£5
Some Slips Don't Show, Morrow (New York), 1957   .
.   .   .   . £25/£10

ditto, Heinemann (London), 1959   .   .   . £15/£5
The Count of Nine, Morrow (New York), 1958   . £25/£10
ditto, Heinemann (London), 1959   .   .   . £15/£5
Pass the Gravy, Morrow (New York), 1959   . £25/£10
ditto, Heinemann (London), 1960   .   .   . £15/£5
Kept Women Can't Quit, Morrow (New York), 1960   .   .
.   .   .   . £25/£10
ditto, Heinemann (London), 1961   .   .   . £15/£5
Bachelors Get Lonely, Morrow (New York), 1961 £25/£10
ditto, Heinemann (London), 1962   .   .   . £15/£5
Shills Can't Count Chips, Morrow (New York), 1961 .
.   .   .   . £25/£10
ditto, as **Stop at the Red Light**, Heinemann (London), 1962.
.   .   .   . £20/£5
Try Anything Once, Morrow (New York), 1962 . £25/£10
ditto, Heinemann (London), 1963   .   .   . £15/£5
Fish Or Cut Bait, Morrow (New York), 1963.   . £20/£5
ditto, Heinemann (London), 1964   .   .   . £10/£5
Up For Grabs, Morrow (New York), 1964   .   . £20/£5
ditto, Heinemann (London), 1965   .   .   . £10/£5
Cut Thin to Win, Morrow (New York), 1965 .   . £20/£5
ditto, Heinemann (London), 1966   .   .   . £10/£5
Widows Wear Weeds, Morrow (New York), 1966 . £20/£5
ditto, Heinemann (London), 1966   .   .   . £10/£5
Traps Need Fresh Bait, Morrow (New York), 1967 £15/£5
ditto, Heinemann (London), 1968   .   .   . £10/£5
All Grass Isn't Green, Morrow (New York), 1970. £15/£5
ditto, Heinemann (London), 1970   .   .   . £10/£5

Other Novels
The Case of the Forgotten Murder, Morrow (New York),
1935 (as 'Carleton Kendrake') .   .   . £1,000/£45
ditto, Cassell (London), 1935   .   .   .   . £400/£45
This Is Murder, Morrow (New York), 1935 (written as
'Charles J. Kenny)   .   .   .   .   . £750/£30
ditto, Cassell (London), 1936   .   .   .   . £350/£35
Murder Up My Sleeve, Morrow (New York), 1937   .
.   .   .   . £500/£40
ditto, Cassell (London), 1938   .   .   .   . £250/£35
The Case of the Turning Tide, Morrow (New York), 1941 .
.   .   .   . £100/£15
ditto, Cassell (London), 1942   .   .   .   . £65/£10
The Case of the Smoking Chimney, Morrow (New York),
1943   .   .   .   . £75/£10
ditto, Cassell (London), 1945   .   .   .   . £50/£10
The Case of the Backward Mule, Morrow (New York),
1946   .   .   .   . £40/£10
ditto, Heinemann (London), 1955   .   .   . £20/£5
Two Clues, Morrow (New York), 1947   .   . £50/£10
ditto, Cassell (London), 1951   .   .   .   . £25/£5
The Case of the Musical Cow, Morrow (New York), 1950 .
.   .   .   . £35/£5
ditto, Heinemann (London), 1957   .   .   . £20/£5

Short Stories
Over the Hump, Gordon Martin (London), 1945 . £30/£10
The Case of the Murderous Bride, Morrow (New York),
1969   .   .   .   . £25/£10
The Amazing Adventures of Lester Leith, Dial (New York),
1980   .   .   .   . £10/£5
The Human Zero, Morrow (New York), 1981   . £10/£5
*Whispering Sands: Stories of Gold Fever and the Western
Desert*, Morrow (New York), 1981 .   .   . £10/£5

Pay Dirt and other Whispering Sands Stories, Morrow (New York), 1983 . . . . . . £10/£5
Adventures of Paul Pry, Mysterious Press (New York), 1989 (pbk) £5
Dead Men's Letters, Carroll & Graf (New York), 1990 .
. . . . £10/£5
The Blonde in Lower Six, Carroll & Graf (New York), 1990
. . . . £10/£5
Honest Money, Carroll & Graf (New York), 1991 . £10/£5

Other Title
The President's Mystery Story, Farrar & Rinehart (New York), 1935 (with Franklin D. Roosevelt, Rupert Hughes, Samuel Hopkins Adams, Rita Weiman, S.S. Van Dine, John Erskine and Eanthony Abbot) . . . £45/£10
ditto, Bodley head (London), 1936 . . . £45/£10

Non-Fiction/Law
The Court of Last Resort, Sloane (New York), 1952 £35/£10
Cops on Campus and Crime in the Streets, Morrow (New York), 1970 . . . . . . £20/£5

Non-Fiction/Nature
The Land of Shorter Shadows, Morrow (New York), 1948.
. . . . £50/£20
Neighborhood Frontiers, Morrow (New York), 1954 . .
. . . . £30/£10
Hunting the Desert Whale, Morrow (New York), 1960 .
. . . . £30/£10
Hovering Over Baja, Morrow (New York), 1961 . £25/£10
The Hidden Heart of Baja, Morrow (New York), 1962 .
. . . . £25/£10
The Desert is Yours, Morrow (New York), 1963 . £25/£10
The World of Water, Morrow (New York), 1964 . £25/£10
Hunting Lost Mines by Helicopter, Morrow (New York), 1965 . . . . £25/£10
Off the Beaten Track in Baja, Morrow (New York), 1967 .
. . . . £25/£10
Gypsy Days on the Delta, Morrow (New York), 1967 . .
. . . . £25/£10
Mexico's Magic Square, Morrow (New York), 1968 . .
. . . . £20/£5
Drifting Down the Delta, Morrow (New York), 1969 £20/£5
Host With the Big Hat, Morrow (New York), 1969 £20/£5

JOHN GARDNER
(b.1933 d.1982)

John Gardner was an American academic specialising in medieval literature. His fiction often incorporated fantasy elements, most notably in *Grendel* (in which the *Beowulf* story is told from the monster's point of view). His first novel, *The Old Men*, was not properly published but was submitted as his University thesis. A prolific author, Gardner also wrote children's books, libretti, non-fiction and plays. His work is often confused in databases and bookshelves with that of his namesake.

Novels and Plays
The Resurrection, New American Library (New York), 1966
. . . . £350/£45
ditto, Ballantine (New York), 1974 (restored text; pbk). £10

The Wreckage of Agathon, Harper & Row (New York), 1970
. . . . £85/£10
Grendel, Knopf (New York), 1971 (illustrated by Emil Antonucci) . . . . £150/£15
ditto, Deutsch (London), 1972 . . . . £75/£10
The Sunlight Dialogues, Knopf (New York), 1972 (illustrations by John Napper) . . . . £45/£10
ditto, Cape (London), 1973 . . . . . £25/£5
Nickel Mountain: A Pastoral Novel, Knopf (New York), 1973 (illustrated with etchings by Thomas O'Donohue) .
. . . . £25/£10
ditto, Cape (London), 1974 (no illustrations) . £25/£5
October Light, Knopf (New York), 1976 (illustrated by Elaine Raphael and Don Bolognese) . . . £25/£10
ditto, Cape (London), 1977 (no illustrations) . £25/£5
Freddy's Book, Knopf (New York), 1980 (illustrated by Daniel Biamonte) . . . . . . £25/£5
ditto, Secker & Warburg (London), 1981 (no illustrations) .
. . . . £25/£5
Mickelsson's Ghosts, Knopf (New York), 1982 (illustrated with photographs by Joel Gardner) . . . £25/£5
ditto, Secker & Warburg (London), 1982 (no illustrations) .
. . . . £25/£5
Stillness and Shadows, Knopf (New York), 1986 . £20/£5
ditto, Secker & Warburg (London), 1987 . . . £20/£5

Collections
The King's Indian: Stories and Tales, Knopf (New York), 1974 (illustrated by Herbert L. Fink) . . . £25/£10
ditto, Cape (London), 1975 (no illustrations) . £20/£5
Gudgekin the Thistle Girl and Other Tales, Knopf (New York), 1976 (illustrated by Michael Sporn) . £25/£5
The King of the Hummingbirds and Other Tales, Knopf (New York), 1977 (illustrated by Michael Sporn) £25/£5
In the Suicide Mountains, Knopf (New York), 1977 (illustrated by Joe Servello) . . . . £20/£5
The Art of Living, and Other Stories, Knopf (New York), 1981 (illustrated with woodcuts by Mary Azarian) £20/£5
ditto, Secker & Warburg (London), 1983 (no illustrations) .
. . . . £15/£5

Children's
Dragon, Dragon, privately published by the author (no place), 1965 (c.15 copies) £1,500
The Miller's Mule and Six Other Tales, privately published by the author (No Place), 1965 (c.30 copies). . £1,250
Dragon, Dragon and Other Tales, Knopf (New York), 1975 (illustrated by Charles Shields). . . . £25/£5

Poetry
Jason and Medeia, Knopf (New York), 1973 . . £25/£10
A Child's Bestiary, Knopf (New York), 1977 (with Lucy Gardner and Eugene Rudzewicz) . . . £25/£5
Poems, Lord John Press (Northridge, CA), 1978 (300 signed, numbered copies) £50
ditto, Lord John Press (Northridge, CA), 1978 (26 signed, lettered copies) £250

Others
Vlemk the Box-Painter, Lord John Press (Northridge, CA), 1979 . . . . £25/£10
ditto, Lord John Press (Northridge, CA), 1979 (300 signed, numbered copies) £65

ditto, Lord John Press (Northridge, CA), 1979 (100 signed deluxe copies with an original drawing by Gardner bound in) £100

Libretti
Rumpelstiltskin, New London Press (Dallas, TX), 1978 (signatures stapled; c.1,000 copies). . . . £125
ditto, New London Press (Dallas, TX), 1979 (750 copies) £25
ditto, New London Press (Dallas, TX), 1979 (250 signed, numbered copies) £50
ditto, New London Press (Dallas, TX), 1979 (26 signed, lettered copies) £75
Frankenstein, New London Press (Dallas, TX), 1979 (750 copies) £25
ditto, New London Press (Dallas, TX), 1979 (250 signed, numbered copies) £50
ditto, New London Press (Dallas, TX), 1979 (26 signed, lettered copies) £75
William Wilson, New London Press (Dallas, TX), 1979 (750 copies) £25
ditto, New London Press (Dallas, TX), 1979 (250 signed, numbered copies) £50
ditto, New London Press (Dallas, TX), 1979 (26 signed, lettered copies) £75
The Temptation Game, New London Press (Dallas, TX), 1980 (300 signed, numbered copies) £60
ditto, New London Press (Dallas, TX), 1980 (26 signed, lettered copies) £75

Scholarly and Critical Books
The Forms of Fiction, Random House (New York), 1962 (edited by Gardner with Lennis Dunlap) . . £100/£30
The Complete Works of the Gawain-Poet, Univ of Chicago Press (Chicago), 1965 (translation and commentary by Gardner; woodcuts by Fritz Kredel) . . £75/£15
The Gawain-Poet: Notes, Cliff's Notes (Lincoln, NE), 1967 (stapled wraps) £40
ditto, as *Sir Gawain and the Green Knight*, Cliff's Notes (Lincoln, NE), 1967 (stapled wraps) . . . £5
Le Morte D'arthur: Notes, Cliff's Notes (Lincoln, NE), 1967 (stapled wraps) £25
The Alliterative Morte Arthure: The Owl and the Nightingale and Five Other Middle English Poems in Modernized Versions, Southern Illinois Univ Press/Feffer & Simon (Carbondale, IL/London), 1971 (translation and commentary by Gardner) . . . . . £75/£15
The Construction of the Wakefield Cycle, Southern Illinois Univ Press/Feffer & Simon (Carbondale, IL/London), 1974 . . . . £30/£10
The Construction of Christian Poetry in Old English, Southern Illinois Univ Press/Feffer & Simon (Carbondale, IL/London), 1975 . . . . . £30/£10
The Poetry of Chaucer, Southern Illinois Univ Press/Feffer & Simon (Carbondale, IL/London), 1977 . £30/£10
The Life and Times of Chaucer, Knopf (New York), 1977 (ornamented by J. Wolf) . . . . . £25/£5
ditto, Cape (London), 1977 (ornamented by J. Wolf) £20/£5
On Moral Fiction, Basic Books (New York), 1978 £20/£5
On Becoming a Novelist, Harper & Row (New York), 1983 . . . . £15/£5
The Art of Fiction: Notes on Craft for Young Writers, Knopf (New York), 1984 . . . . . £15/£5

On Writers and Writing, Addison-Wesley (Reading, MA), 1994 . . . . £10/£5
Lies! Lies! Lies!: A College Journal of John Gardner, Univ of Rochester Libraries (Rochester, NY), 1999 (pbk) . £5
ditto, Univ of Rochester Libraries (Rochester, NY), 1999 (200 numbered hardback copies signed by Thomas Gavin) £25

JOHN GARDNER
(b.1926 d.2007)

John Gardner was a well-respected British thriller writer whose writing resulted in him being given the rights to continue Ian Fleming's James Bond series of novels. His own series characters include Big Herbie Kruger, and *Maestro* was the New York Times Book of the Year. A graduate of Cambridge University, Gardner previously worked as a stage magician, an officer in the Royal Marines, a theatrical journalist, a lecturer in Shakespearean production and a priest in the Church of England.

'James Bond' Novels
Licence Renewed, Cape/Hodder & Stoughton (London), 1981 (d/w priced at £6.50 although many jackets are unpriced) . . . . £35/£5
ditto, Cape/Hodder & Stoughton (London), 1981 (d/w price clipped and repriced with sticker at £6.95) . . £20/£5
ditto, Marek (New York), 1981 . . . . £20/£5
For Special Services, Cape/Hodder & Stoughton (London), 1982 (d/w priced at £6.95 although many appear unpriced) . . . . £25/£5
ditto, Cape/Hodder & Stoughton (London), 1982 (d/w with Cape price stickers of £7.95 or £8.95) . . £20/£5
ditto, Coward, McCann & Geoghegan, New York, 1982 . . . . £20/£5
Icebreaker, Cape/Hodder & Stoughton (London), 1983 . . . . £30/£5
ditto, Putnam's, New York, 1983 . . . £10/£5
Role of Honour, Cape/Hodder & Stoughton (London), 1984 . . . . £25/£5
ditto as *Role of Honor*, Putnam's, New York, 1984 £20/£5
Nobody Lives Forever, Cape/Hodder & Stoughton (London), 1986 . . . . £25/£5
ditto, Putnam's, New York, 1986 . . . £20/£5
No Deals, Mr Bond, Cape/Hodder & Stoughton (London), 1987 . . . . £45/£10
ditto, Putnam's, New York, 1987 . . . £15/£5
Scorpius, Hodder & Stoughton (London), 1988 . £20/£5
ditto, Putnam's, New York, 1988 . . . £15/£5
Win, Lose Or Die, Hodder & Stoughton (London), 1989 (pbk) £5
ditto, Hodder & Stoughton (London), 1989 . £45/£10
ditto, Putnam's, New York, 1989 . . . £10/£5
Licence to Kill, Hodder & Stoughton (London), 1989 (pbk) £10
ditto, Armchair Detective Library (New York), 1990 (with or without tipped-in title page) . . . . £250/£35
ditto, Armchair Detective Library (New York), 1990 (100 signed, numbered copies) £750
ditto, Armchair Detective Library (New York), 1990 (26 signed, lettered copies) £1,000

Brokenclaw, Hodder & Stoughton (London), 1990   £10/£5
ditto, Putnam's, New York, 1990   .   .   .   £10/£5
The Man from Barbarossa, Hodder & Stoughton (London),
1991   .   .   .   .   £10/£5
ditto, Putnam's, New York, 1991   .   .   .   £10/£5
Death Is Forever, Hodder & Stoughton (London), 1992   .
.   .   .   .   £10/£5
ditto, Putnam's, New York, 1992   .   .   .   £10/£5
Never Send Flowers, Hodder & Stoughton (London), 1993.
.   .   .   .   £10/£5
ditto, Putnam's, New York, 1993   .   .   .   £10/£5
Seafire, Hodder & Stoughton (London), 1994.   .   £35/£5
ditto, Putnam's, New York, 1994   .   .   .   £10/£5
Goldeneye, Coronet (London), 1995 (pbk)   .   .   £10
ditto, Boulevard (New York), 1995 (pbk).   .   .   £5
ditto, Hodder & Stoughton (London), 1996   .   .£500/£75
Cold, Hodder & Stoughton (London), 1996   .   .£200/£45
ditto as *Cold Fall*, Putnam's, New York, 1996   .   £10/£5

'Boysie Oakes' Novels
The Liquidator, Frederick Muller (London), 1964.   £40/£10
ditto, Viking (New York), 1964.   .   .   .   £30/£10
Understrike, Frederick Muller (London), 1965   .   £35/£10
ditto, Viking (New York), 1965.   .   .   .   £25/£10
Amber Nine, Frederick Muller (London), 1966   .   £35/£5
ditto, Viking (New York), 1966.   .   .   .   £30/£5
Madrigal, Frederick Muller (London), 1967   .   .   £35/£5
ditto, Viking (New York), 1968.   .   .   .   £30/£5
Founder Member, Frederick Muller (London), 1969   £25/£5
Traitor's Exit, Frederick Muller (London), 1970   .   £25/£5
The Airline Pirates, Hodder & Stoughton, 1970   .   £25/£5
ditto as *Air Apparent*, Putnam's, New York, 1994.   £20/£5
Killer for a Song, Hodder & Stoughton, 1975.   .   £25/£5

'Derek Torry' Novels
A Complete State of Death, Frederick Muller (London),
1969   .   .   .   .   £25/£5
ditto, Viking (New York), 1969.   .   .   .   £20/£5
Corner Men, Michael Joseph (London), 1974.   .   £10/£5
ditto, Doubleday (New York), 1976.   .   .   £10/£5

Professor Moriarty
Return of Moriarty, Weidenfeld & Nicolson (London) 1974
.   .   .   .   £25/£5
ditto, Putnam's (New York), 1974   .   .   .   £20/£5
Revenge of Moriarty, Weidenfeld & Nicolson (London)
1975   .   .   .   .   £25/£5
ditto, Putnam's (New York), 1975   .   .   .   £20/£5

'Herbie Kruger' Novels
The Nostradamus Traitor, Hodder & Stoughton, 1979.   .
.   .   .   .   £25/£5
ditto, Doubleday (New York), 1979   .   .   .   £20/£5
Garden of Weapons, Hodder & Stoughton, 1980   .   £15/£5
ditto, McGraw-Hill (New York), 1981   .   .   £15/£5
Quiet Dogs, Hodder & Stoughton, 1982   .   .   £10/£5
Maestro, Otto Penzler Books (New York), 1993   .   £10/£5
ditto, Bantam (London), 1993   .   .   .   £10/£5
Confessor, Hodder & Stoughton, 1995   .   .   £10/£5
ditto, Otto Penzler Books (New York), 1995   .   £10/£5

Secret Trilogy
Secret Generations, Heinemann (London), 1985   .   £10/£5
ditto, Putnam's, New York, 1985   .   .   .   £10/£5

The Secret Houses, Putnam's, New York, 1987   .   £10/£5
ditto, Bantam (London), 1988   .   .   .   .   £10/£5
The Secret Families, Bantam (London), 1989.   .   £10/£5
ditto, Putnam's, New York, 1989   .   .   .   £10/£5

'Detective Sergeant Suzie Mountford' Novels
Bottled Spider, Severn House (London), 2002   .   £10/£5
The Streets of Town, Severn House (London), 2003   £10/£5
Angels Dining at the Ritz, Severn House, 2004   .   £10/£5
Troubled Midnight, Allison & Busby (London) 2005 £15/£5

Other Novels
The Censor, New English Library (London), 1970 (pbk)   £5
Every Night's a Bullfight, Michael Joseph (London), 1971.
.   .   .   .   £20/£5
To Run a Little Faster, Michael Joseph (London), 1976   .
.   .   .   .   £35/£10
The Werewolf Trace, Hodder & Stoughton, 1977.   £10/£5
ditto, Doubleday (New York), 1977   .   .   .   £10/£5
The Dancing Dodo, Hodder & Stoughton, 1978   .   £25/£5
Golgotha, W.H. Allen (London), 1980   .   .   £10/£5
Flamingo, Hodder & Stoughton, 1983   .   .   £10/£5
Blood of the Fathers, Orion (London), 1992 (pseud
'Edmund McCoy')   .   .   .   .   .   £10/£5
ditto, as *Unknown Fears*, Severn House (London) 2004   .
.   .   .   .   £10/£5
Day of Absolution, Scribners (New York), 2000   .   £10/£5
ditto, Severn House (London), 2002   .   .   .   £10/£5

Collections
Hideaway, Corgi (London), 1972 (pbk)   .   .   .   £5
Assassination File, Corgi (London), 1974 (pbk)   .   £5

Miscellaneous
Spin The Bottle: The Autobiography of an Alcoholic,
Frederick Muller (London), 1964   .   .   .   £75/£15

ALAN GARNER

(b.1934)

Many of Alan Garner's novels for children, a mix of myth,
fantasy and reality, are set in his native Cheshire, and are
inspired by his interest in history and archaeology. His
early books have become children's favourites, but it was
The Owl Service that brought him the most attention, winning The Guardian Award and the Carnegie Medal. It was
made into a TV serial by Granada Television.

'Alderley' Novels
The Weirdstone of Brisingamen: A Tale of Alderley,
Collins (London), 1960   .   .   .   .   .£400/£45
ditto, Watts (New York), 1961   .   .   .   .£165/£30
The Moon of Gomrath, Collins (London), 1963   .£175/£30
ditto, Walck (New York), 1967   .   .   .   .   £35/£10

'Stone Book' Novels
The Stone Book, Collins (London), 1976 (illustrated by
Michael Foreman)   .   .   .   .   .   £35/£10
ditto, Collins (New York), 1976   .   .   .   .   £20/£5
Granny Reardun, Collins (London), 1977 (illustrated by
Michael Foreman)   .   .   .   .   .   £30/£5
ditto, Collins (New York), 1978   .   .   .   .   £20/£5

Tom Fobble's Day, Collins (London), 1977 (illustrated by
Michael Foreman) . . . . . . £25/£5
ditto, Collins (New York), 1979 . . . . £15/£5
The Aimer Gate, Collins (London), 1978 (illustrated by
Michael Foreman) . . . . . . £25/£5
ditto, Collins (New York), 1979 . . . . £15/£5
The Stone Book Quartet, Collins (London), 1983 . £20/£5

Other Novels
Elidor, Collins (London), 1965 (illustrated by Charles
Keeping) . . . . £150/£15
ditto, Walck (New York), 1967 . . . . £25/£10
The Old Man of Mow, Collins (London), 1967 (photographs
by Roger Hill) . . . . . . £25/£10
ditto, Doubleday (New York), 1967 . . . £25/£10
The Owl Service, Collins (London), 1967. . £135/£25
ditto, Walck (New York), 1968 . . . . £100/£15
Red Shift, Collins (London), 1973 . . . £65/£10
ditto, Macmillan (New York), 1973 . . . £35/£10
The Lad of the Gad, Collins (London), 1980 . £15/£5
ditto, Philomel (New York), 1981 . . . £15/£5
Strandloper, Harvill Press (London), 1996 . £10/£5
Thursbitch, Harvill Press (London), 2003 . £10/£5

Short Stories
The Guizer: A Book of Fools, Hamish Hamilton (London),
1975 . . . . £20/£5
ditto, Greenwillow (New York), 1976 . . £20/£5

Fairy Tales
Fairy Tales of Gold, Collins (London), 1979 (4 vols) . .
. . . . £35/£10
ditto, Philomel (New York), 1980 (1 vol.) . £20/£5
Book of British Fairy Tales, Collins (London), 1984 £15/£5
ditto, Delacorte Press (New York), 1984 . . £15/£5
A Bag of Moonshine, Collins (London), 1986 (illustrated by
Patrick Lynch) . . . . . . £15/£5
ditto, Delacorte Press (New York), 1986 . . £15/£5
Jack and the Beanstalk, HarperCollins (London), 1992 .
. . . . £10/£5
Once Upon a Time, Dorling Kindersley (London/New
York), 1993 . . . . . . £10/£5
Little Red Hen, Dorling Kindersley (London/New York),
1997 . . . . £10/£5
The Well of the Wind, Dorling Kindersley (London/New
York), 1998 . . . . . . £10/£5

Miscellaneous
Holly from the Bongs: A Nativity Play, Collins (London),
1966 . . . . £65/£15
Potter Thompson, O.U.P. (Oxford, UK), 1975 . £25/£5
The Breadhorse, Collins (London), 1975 (illustrated by
Albin Trowski) . . . . . . £45/£15
The Voice That Thunders: Essays and Lectures, Harvill
(London), 1998 . . . . . . £20/£5

DAVID GARNETT
(b.1892 d.1981)

Principally a novelist, whose early works have a light,
fantastic touch, Garnett was also a publisher and a
prominent member of the Bloomsbury Group. During the
1920s he ran a bookshop near the British Museum with
Francis Birrell, and with Francis Meynell he founded the
Nonesuch Press. His *Aspects of Love* was recently turned
into a stage musical.

Novels
Dope-Darling: A Story of Cocaine, Werner Laurie
(London), [1919] (pseud 'Leda Burke'; wraps) . £2,500
Lady Into Fox, Chatto & Windus (London), 1922 . £125/£20
ditto, Knopf (New York), 1923 . . . . £100/£15
A Man in the Zoo, Chatto & Windus (London), 1924 . .
. . . . £40/£10
ditto, Chatto & Windus (London), 1924 (110 signed,
numbered copies) £50
ditto, Knopf (New York), 1924 . . . . £30/£10
The Sailor's Return, Chatto & Windus (London), 1925 .
. . . . £35/£10
ditto, Chatto & Windus (London), 1925 (160 signed,
numbered copies) £50
ditto, Knopf (New York), 1925 . . . . £25/£5
Go She Must!, Chatto & Windus (London), 1927 . £35/£10
ditto, Chatto & Windus (London), 1927 (160 signed,
numbered copies) £45
ditto, Knopf (New York), 1927 . . . . £20/£5
No Love, Chatto & Windus (London), 1929 . £35/£10
ditto, Chatto & Windus (London), 1929 (160 signed,
numbered copies) £50
ditto, Knopf (New York), 1929 . . . . £20/£5
The Grasshoppers Come, Chatto & Windus (London), 1931
. . . . £25/£5
ditto, Chatto & Windus (London), 1931 (210 signed,
numbered copies) £40
ditto, Brewer, Warren & Putnam (New York), 1931 £20/£5
A Rabbit in the Air, Chatto & Windus (London), 1932. .
. . . . £25/£5
ditto, Chatto & Windus (London), 1932 (110 signed,
numbered copies) £50
ditto, Brewer, Warren & Putnam (New York), 1932 £15/£5
Pocahontas, or the Nonpareil of Virginia, Chatto & Windus
(London), 1933 . . . . . . £30/£5
ditto, Chatto & Windus (London), 1933 (550 signed,
numbered copies) £50
ditto, Harcourt, Brace (New York), 1933 . . £20/£5
Beany-Eye, Chatto & Windus (London), 1935 . £25/£5
ditto, Chatto & Windus (London), 1935 (110 signed,
numbered copies) £45
ditto, Harcourt, Brace (New York), 1935 . . £15/£5
Aspects of Love, Chatto & Windus (London), 1955 £30/£10
ditto, Harcourt, Brace (New York), 1955 . . £25/£5
A Shot in the Dark, Longmans (London), 1958 . £15/£5
ditto, Little, Brown (Boston), 1958 . . . £15/£5
A Net for Venus, Longmans (London), 1959 . £25/£10
Two By Two: A Story of Survival, Longmans (London),
1963 . . . . £10/£5
ditto, Atheneum (New York), 1964 . . . £10/£5
Ulterior Motives, Longmans (London), 1966 . £10/£5
ditto, Harcourt, Brace (New York), 1967 . . £10/£5

A Clean Slate, Hamish Hamilton (London), 1971 . £10/£5
The Sons of the Falcon, Macmillan (London), 1972 £10/£5
Plough Over the Bones, Macmillan (London), 1973 £10/£5
Up She Rises, Macmillan (London), 1977 . £10/£5
ditto, St Martin's Press (New York), 1977 . . £10/£5

Short Stories
The Old Dovecote and Other Stories, Elkin Mathews & Marrot (London): No.8 in the Woburn Books series, 1928 (530 signed copies) . . . . . . £35/£20
A Terrible Day, William Jackson: No.9 in the Furnival Books series (London), 1932 (550 signed copies). . £35
First 'Hippy' Revolution, San Marcos Press (New Mexico), 1970 (wraps). £25
Purl and Plain, Macmillan (London), 1973 . . £10/£5

Autobiography
The Golden Echo, Chatto & Windus (London), 1953 £10/£5
ditto, Harcourt, Brace (New York), 1954 . . . £10/£5
The Flowers of the Forest, Chatto & Windus (London), 1955 . . . . £10/£5
ditto, Harcourt, Brace (New York), 1956 . . £10/£5
Familiar Faces, Chatto & Windus (London), 1962 £10/£5
ditto, Harcourt, Brace (New York), 1962 . . £10/£5

Miscellaneous
Never Be a Bookseller, Knopf (New York), 1929 (2,000 copies, none for sale) £75
ditto, The Fleece Press (Denby Dale, UK), 1995 (400 copies, card covers with marbled d/w) . . . £20/£10
War in the Air: September 1939 to May 1941, Chatto & Windus (London), 1941 . . . . . £30/£10
ditto, Doubleday (New York), 1941 . . . £25/£10
The Battle of Britain, Puffin Picture Book No.21 (London), 1941 (wraps). £15
The Campaign in Greece and Crete, Chatto & Windus (London), 1942 (wraps) £15
A Historical Pageant of Huntingdonshire in Celebration of the Coronation of Her Majesty Elizabeth II, privately printed (Huntingdon, UK), 1953 (souvenir programme) £20
The White/Garnett Letters, Cape (London), 1968 . £15/£5
ditto, Viking (New York), 1968 . . . . £15/£5
The Master Cat: The True and Unexpurgated Story of Puss in Boots, Macmillan (London), 1974 . . . £10/£5
Sir Geoffrey Keynes: A Tribute, privately printed (UK), 1978 . . . . £10
Great Friends: Portraits of Seventeen Writers, Macmillan (London), 1979 . . . . £25/£10
ditto, Atheneum (New York), 1980 . . . . £25/£10

EVE GARNETT
(b.1900 d.1991)

An author and illustrator, principally of books for children, Garnett is best known for the adventures of the family from One End Street. The first book in this series about a loveable working-class family was awarded the Carnegie medal in 1936, beating Tolkien's *The Hobbit*.

Written and Illustrated by Garnett
The Family from One End Street, and Some of Their Adventures, Muller (London), 1937 . . . £125/£25

ditto, Vanguard (New York), 1939 . . . £85/£20
In and Out and Roundabout: Stories of a Little Town, Muller (London), 1948 . . . . . £65/£20
Further Adventures of The Family from One End Street, Heinemann (London), 1956 . . . . .£100/£20
ditto, Vanguard (New York), 1956 . . . .£45/£10
Holiday at the Dew Drop Inn, Heinemann (London), 1962 . . . . £50/£10
ditto, Vanguard (New York), 1962 . . . £45/£10
Mr Crundell's Cow, Nelson (London), 1966 . £25/£10
To Greenland's Icy Mountains: The Story of Hans Egede–Explorer, Coloniser, Missionary, Heinemann (London), 1968 . . . . £35/£10
ditto, Roy (New York), 1968 . . . . £25/£5
Lost and Found: Four Stories, Muller (London), 1974 . . . . £25/£10
First Affections: Some Autobiographical Chapters of Early Childhood, Muller (London), 1982. . . . £20/£5

Other Titles Illustrated by Garnett
The London Child, by Evelyn Sharp, John Lane (London), 1927 . . . . £45/£15
The Bad Barons of Crashbania, by Norman Hunter, Blackwell (Oxford), 1932 . . . . . . £50
Is It Well With the Child?, Muller (London), 1938 £65/£10
A Child's Garden of Verses, by Robert Louis Stevenson, Penguin (Harmondsworth, Middlesex), 1948 . . £5
A Book of the Seasons: An Anthology, O.U.P (Oxford, UK), 1952 . . . . £35/£10
A Golden Land: Stories, Poems, Songs New and Old, Constable (London), 1958 (with illustrations by others) . . . . £15/£5

JONATHAN GASH
(b.1933)

Gash is the pseudonym of John Grant. His 'Lovejoy' novels have been adapted for television with great success, although some feel that his hero has lost his edge in the transition to the small screen. *Streetwalker*, published anonymously, has been widely reported as Gash's first publication, although he strenuously denies this.

'Lovejoy' Novels
The Judas Pair, Collins Crime Club (London), 1977 . . . . £250/£25
ditto, Harper & Row (New York), 1977 . . £75/£10
Gold from Gemini, Collins Crime Club (London), 1978 . . . . £85/£15
ditto, as *Gold By Gemini*, Harper & Row (New York), 1978 . . . . £35/£10
The Grail Tree, Collins Crime Club (London), 1979 . . . . £100/£15
ditto, Harper & Row (New York), 1979 . £45/£10
Spend Game, Collins Crime Club (London), 1979 . £200/£30
ditto, Ticknor & Fields (New York), 1979 . £25/£10
The Vatican Rip, Collins Crime Club (London), 1981 . . . . £125/£15
ditto, Ticknor & Fields (New York), 1981 . . £25/£10
Firefly Gadroon, Collins Crime Club (London), 1982 . . . . £75/£10
ditto, St Martin's Press (New York), 1982 . . £20/£5

The Sleepers of Erin, Collins Crime Club (London), 1983 .
. . . . £75/£15
ditto, Dutton (New York), 1983 . . . . £20/£5
The Gondola Scam, Collins Crime Club (London), 1984 .
. . . . £65/£10
ditto, St Martin's Press (New York), 1984 . . £15/£5
Pearlhanger, Collins Crime Club (London), 1985 . £25/£5
ditto, St Martin's Press (New York), 1985 . . £15/£5
The Tartan Ringers, Collins Crime Club (London), 1986 .
. . . . £20/£5
ditto, as *The Tartan Sell*, St Martin's Press (New York),
1986 . . . . £15/£5
Moonspender, Collins Crime Club (London), 1986 £20/£5
ditto, St Martin's Press (New York), 1987 . . £15/£5
Jade Woman, Collins Crime Club (London), 1988 £20/£5
ditto, St Martin's Press (New York), 1989 . . £15/£5
The Very Last Gambado, Collins Crime Club (London),
1989 . . . . £15/£5
ditto, St Martin's Press (New York), 1990 . £15/£5
The Great California Game, Century (London), 1991 £15/£5
ditto, St Martin's Press (New York), 1991 . . £15/£5
Lies of Fair Ladies, Scorpion Press (Bristol), 1991 (20
signed, lettered copies) £250
ditto, Scorpion Press (Bristol), 1991 (99 signed, numbered
copies) £60
ditto, Century (London), 1992 . . . . £15/£5
ditto, St Martin's Press (New York), 1992 . . £15/£5
Paid and Loving Eyes, Century (London), 1993 . £15/£5
ditto, St Martin's Press (New York), 1993 . £10/£5
The Sin Within Her Smile, Century (London), 1993 £15/£5
ditto, Viking (New York), 1994 . . . . £10/£5
The Grace in Older Women, Century (London), 1995 . .
. . . . £15/£5
ditto, Viking (New York), 1995 . . . . £10/£5
The Possessions of a Lady, Century (London), 1996 £15/£5
ditto, Viking (New York), 1996 . . . . £15/£5
The Rich and The Profane, Macmillan (London), 1998 .
. . . . £10/£5
ditto, Viking (New York), 1999 . . . . £10/£5
A Rag, a Bone and a Hank of Hair, Macmillan (London),
1999 . . . . £10/£5
ditto, Viking (New York), 2000 . . . . £10/£5
Every Last Cent, Macmillan (London), 2001 . £10/£5
Ten Word Game, Allison & Busby (London), 2003 £10/£5
ditto, St Martin's Press (New York), 2004 . £10/£5
Faces in the Pool, Allison & Busby (London), 2008 £10/£5
ditto, Minotaur (New York), 2009 . . . £10/£5

'Dr Clare Burtonall' Novels
Different Women Dancing, Macmillan (London), 1997 .
. . . . £15/£5
ditto, Viking (New York), 1997 . . . . £15/£5
Prey Dancing, Macmillan (London), 1998 . . £15/£5
ditto, Viking (New York), 1998 . . . . £15/£5
Die Dancing, Macmillan (London), 2000 . . £15/£5
Bone Dancing, Allison & Busby (London), 2002 . £10/£5
Blood Dancing, Allison & Busby (London), 2006 . £10/£5

Sealandings Trilogy written as 'Jonathan Grant'
The Shores of Sealandings, Century (London), 1991 .
. . . . £35/£10
Storms at Sealandings, Century (London), 1992 . £30/£10
Mehala, Lady of Sealandings, Century (London), 1993 .
. . . . £25/£10

Other Novels
The Year of the Woman, Allison & Busby (London), 2004 .
. . . . £10/£5
Finding Davey, Allison & Busby (London), 2005 . £10/£5
ditto, St Martin's Press (New York), 2005 . . £15/£5
Bad Girl Magdalene, Allison & Busby (London), 2007 .
. . . . £10/£5

Other Titles
Streetwalker, Bodley Head (London), 1959 (anonymous) .
. . . . £65/£15
ditto, Viking (New York), 1960 . . . . £30/£10
The Incomer, Collins (London), 1981 (pseud 'Graham
Gaunt') . . . . £300/£35
ditto, Doubleday (New York), 1981 . . . £25/£10

ELIZABETH GASKELL
(b.1810 d.1865)

A Victorian novelist whose work earned the respect of
Dickens, Mrs Gaskell is today remembered as much for her
friendship with Charlotte Brontë and her famous biography
The Life of Charlotte Brontë, as she is for her own realist
novels which are usually set in the North of England.

Novels
Mary Barton, A Tale of Manchester Life, Chapman & Hall
(London), 1848 (anonymous; 2 vols; original maroon cloth)
. . . . £3,000
ditto, Chapman & Hall (London), 1848 (2 volumes rebound)
. . . . £650
ditto, Harper (New York), 1848 (1 vol) . . . £750
The Moorland Cottage, Chapman & Hall (London), 1850 (1
vol) £500
ditto, William Crosby (Boston), 1851 (3 vols) . . £450
ditto, Harper (New York), 1851 (1 vol) . . . £200
Ruth, A Novel, Chapman & Hall (London), 1853 (3 vols) .
. . . . £750
ditto, Ticknor, Reed & Fields (Boston), 1853 (1 vol) . £250
Cranford, Chapman & Hall (London), 1853 (by the author of
'Mary Barton', 'Ruth' etc., 1 volume; original green cloth)
. . . . £1,000
ditto, Harper (New York), 1853 (1 vol) . . . £200
North and South, Chapman & Hall (London), 1855 (2 vols)
. . . . £600
ditto, Harper (New York), 1855 (1 vol) . . . £175
The Sexton's Hero and Christmas Storms and Sunshine,
Chapman & Hall (London), 1855 . . . £100
A Dark Night's Work, Smith Elder (London), 1863 . £375
ditto, Harper (New York), 1863 . . . . £200
Sylvia's Lovers, Smith Elder (London), 1863 (3 vols) . £700
ditto, Dutton (New York), 1863 (1 vol) . . . £300
Wives and Daughters, An Everyday Story, Smith Elder
(London), 1866 (illustrated by George du Maurier, 2 vols)
. . . . £450
ditto, Harper (New York), 1866 (1 vol) . . . £200

Short Stories
Libbie Marsh's Three Eras, A Lancashire Tale, Hamilton,
Adams & Co. (London), 1850 . . . . . £600
The Sexton's Hero, Johnson, Rawson & Co. (Manchester),
1850 . . . . £600

Lizzie Leigh and Other Tales, Smith Elder (London), 1855
[1854] £275
ditto, Hardy (Philadelphia), 1869 . . . . £175
My Lady Ludlow, A Novel, Harper (New York), 1858 . £300
ditto, as *Round the Sofa*, Sampson Low (London), 1859 (2
vols; original green cloth) £450
ditto, as *My Lady Ludlow and Other Tales*, Sampson Low
(London), 1861 (1 vol; original green cloth) . . £275
Right at Last and Other Tales, Sampson Low (London),
1860 . . . . £275
ditto, Harper (New York), 1860 . . . . . £150
Lois the Witch and Other Tales, Tauchnitz (Leipzig,
Germany), 1861 . . . . £35
Cousin Phillis: A Tale, Harper (New York), 1864 . . £200
ditto, as *Cousin Phillis and Other Tales*, Smith Elder
(London), 1865 (illustrated by George du Maurier) . £275
The Grey Woman and Other Tales, Smith Elder (London),
1865 (illustrated by George du Maurier) . . . £275
ditto, Harper, 1882 (New York) £175
The Cage at Cranford and Other Stories, Nelson Classics
(London), [1937]. . . . . . . £10/£5
The Half-Brothers, Gulliver Book Co. (London), [1943] £25
The Squire's Story, Todd Publishing Co. (London), 1943 .
. . . . £10/£5
Mrs Gaskell's Tales of Mystery and Horror, Gollancz
(London), 1978 . . . . . . £10/£5

Miscellaneous
The Life of Charlotte Brontë, Smith Elder (London), 1857
(2 vols; dark brown cloth; vol 1 with portrait frontispiece,
volume 2 with view of Howarth as frontispiece) . . £600
ditto, Appleton (New York), 1857 (2 vols) . . . £125
Letters of Charlotte Brontë, privately printed (London),
1915 (25 copies) £150
My Diary, The Early Years of My Daughter Marianne,
privately printed by Clement Shorter (London), 1923 (50
copies; wraps) £75
*Letters of Mrs Gaskell and Charles Eliot Norton, 1855-
1865*, O.U.P. (Oxford, UK), 1932 . . . . £30/£10
The Letters of Elizabeth Gaskell, Manchester Univ Press
(Manchester, UK), [1966]. . . . . . £30/£10

Collected Editions
The Novels and Tales of Elizabeth Gaskell, Smith Elder
(London), 1878-82 (7 vols) £175
The Works of Elizabeth Gaskell, Smith Elder (London),
1906-1911 (8 vols) £125

ROBERT GIBBINGS

(b.1889 d.1958)

Gibbings was born in County Cork, Ireland, and studied at
the Slade School in London. Along with Eric Gill he is
credited with reviving 20th century wood engraving, and
not just through his own artwork. In 1924 he bought the
Golden Cockerel Press and before he was forced to sell it
in 1933 he had been able to encourage and promote the
works of Eric Ravilious and Blair Hughes-Stanton.

Books Written and Illustrated by Gibbings
The Zoo, The Baynard Press (London), nd [1930-31]
(pamphlet written with Moira Gibbings) . . . £85

Iorana: A Tahitian Journal, Duckworth (London), 1932 .
. . . . £45/£10
Coconut Island, Faber (London), 1936 . . . £65/£15
John Graham, Convict, Faber (London), 1937 . £35/£10
ditto, Barnes (New York), 1957 . . . . . £25/£10
Blue Angels and Whales, Penguin: Pelican Special
(Harmondsworth, Middlesex), 1938 (pbk in d/w) £15/£5
ditto, Dent (London), 1946 . . . . . . £30/£10
ditto, Dutton (New York), 1946 . . . . . £25/£5
Sweet Thames Run Softly, Dent (London), 1940 . £50/£15
ditto, Dutton (New York), 1941 . . . . . £40/£10
ditto, Dent (London), 1946 (196 copies in leather or vellum)
. . . . £125
Coming Down the Wye, Dent (London), 1942 . £30/£10
ditto, Dutton (New York), 1943 . . . . . £30/£10
ditto, Dent (London), 1946 (75 copies bound in morocco) .
. . . . £200
Lovely is the Lee, Dent (London), 1945 [1944] . £25/£10
ditto, Dutton (New York), 1945 . . . . . £20/£5
ditto, Dent (London), 1946 (100 copies bound in morocco) .
. . . . £150
Over the Reefs and Far Away, Dent (London), 1948 .
. . . . £25/£10
ditto, Dent (London), 1948 (75 signed copies bound in
morocco) £200
ditto, Dutton (New York), 1948 . . . . . £20/£5
Sweet Cork of Thee, Dent (London), 1951 . . £15/£5
ditto, Dent (London), 1951 (20 copies bound in morocco) .
. . . . £250
ditto, Dutton (New York), 1951 . . . . . £10/£5
Coming Down the Seine, Dent (London), 1953 . £20/£5
ditto, Dent (London), 1953 (75 copies bound in morocco;
contains signed proof of one engraving on Japanese paper)
. . . . £250
ditto, Dutton (New York), 1953 . . . . . £15/£5
The Perfect Wife, Dolmen Press (Dublin, Ireland), 1955
(hand-printed; 240 copies; sewn wraps) . . . £350
Trumpets from Montparnasse, Dent (London), 1955 . .
. . . . £45/£10
ditto, Dutton (New York), 1955 . . . . . £35/£10
Till I End My Song, Dent (London), 1957 . . £20/£5
ditto, Dutton (New York), 1957 . . . . . £15/£5

Engravings by Gibbings
Twelve Wood Engravings, privately printed by the Baynard
Press (London), 1921 (125 signed, numbered copies,
quarter-bound in canvas, boards covered with paper,
lettered in black on the front) £1,000
The Seventh Man, Golden Cockerel Press (Waltham St
Lawrence, Berks), 1930 (500 signed and numbered copies)
. . . . £300
*Fourteen Wood Engravings, From drawings Made On
Orient Line Cruises*, Orient Line (London), 1932 (sewn
wraps) £250
*A True Tale of Love in Tonga, Told in 23 Engravings and
333 Words*, Faber (London), 1935 . . . . £45/£25
The Wood Engravings of Robert Gibbings, Art and
Technics (London), 1949 . . . . . . £50/£25
The Wood Engravings of Robert Gibbings, Dent (London),
1959 . . . . £75/£20

Other Books Illustrated by Gibbings
Old London Bridge, Findlater, Mackie, Todd & Co
(London), 1921 (wraps) £75

Erewhon, by Samuel Butler, Cape (London), 1923   . £20

The Lives of Gallant Ladies, by Brantome, Golden Cockerel Press (Waltham St Lawrence, Berks), 1924 (2 vols; 626 copies on rag paper) £125

ditto, Golden Cockerel Press (Waltham St Lawrence, Berks), 1924 (2 vols; 75 copies on Dutch hand-made paper) . £200

ditto, Golden Cockerel Press (Waltham St Lawrence, Berks), 1924 (2 vols; 18 copies on English hand-made paper) £350

Songs and Poems, by Henry Carey, Golden Cockerel Press (Waltham St Lawrence, Berks), 1924 (350 numbered copies m quarter parchment boards)   .   . £175/£125

ditto, Golden Cockerel Press (Waltham St Lawrence, Berks), 1924 (30 copies bound in vellum) £300

Where I Lived and What I Lived For, by Henry David Thoreau, Golden Cockerel Press (Waltham St Lawrence, Berks), 1924 (350 numbered copies bound in quarter parchment boards)   .   .   .   . £200/£125

ditto, Golden Cockerel Press (Waltham St Lawrence, Berks), 1924 (30 numbered copies bound in blue morocco) . £300

Miscellaneous Writings of Henry the Eighth, Golden Cockerel Press (Waltham St Lawrence, Berks), 1924 (300 numbered copies bound in quarter parchment boards)   .

.   .   .   . £125/£65

ditto, Golden Cockerel Press (Waltham St Lawrence, Berks), 1924 (65 copies bound in leather) .   .   . £300

Samson and Delilah, Golden Cockerel Press (Waltham St Lawrence, Berks), 1925 (bound m white buckram)   .

.   .   .   . £400/£200

Red Wise, by E. Powys Mathers, Golden Cockerel Press (Waltham St Lawrence, Berks), 1926 (500 numbered copies) .   .   .   .   . £175/£100

Fallodon Papers, by Viscount Grey of Fallodon, Constable (London), 1926 .   .   .   . £45/£15

ditto, Houghton Mifflin (Boston), 1926 .   . £30/£10

Pelagea and Other Poems, by A.E. Coppard, Golden Cockerel Press (Waltham St Lawrence, Berks), 1926 (425 numbered copies).   .   .   .   . £75/£30

The Charm of Birds, by Viscount Grey of Fallodon, Hodder & Stoughton (London), 1927 .   .   . £35/£15

ditto, Hodder & Stoughton (London), 1927 (250 copies on hand-made paper, bound in vellum; slipcase)   . £100/£60

ditto, Stokes (New York), 1927 .   .   . £30/£10

The True Historie of Lucian the Samosatenina, Golden Cockerel Press (Waltham St Lawrence, Berks), 1927 (275 numbered copies) £350

Count Stefan, by A.E. Coppard, Golden Cockerel Press (Waltham St Lawrence, Berks), 1928 (600 signed copies).

.   .   .   . £75/£50

Miscellaneous Poems, by Jonathan Swift, Golden Cockerel Press (Waltham St Lawrence, Berks), 1928 (375 numbered copies) .   .   .   . £150/£100

A Mirror for Witches, by Esther Forbes, Heinemann (London), 1928 .   .   .   .   . £30/£10

ditto, Houghton Mifflin (Boston), 1928 .   . £30/£10

ditto, Houghton Mifflin (Boston), 1928 (220 copies signed by author) £125

Lamia, Isabella & Other Poems, by John Keats, Golden Cockerel Press (Waltham St Lawrence, Berks), 1928 (485 numbered copies, bound in sharkskin by Sangorski and Sutcliffe) £325

ditto, Golden Cockerel Press (Waltham St Lawrence, Berks), 1928 (15 numbered copies on vellum, bound in sharkskin)

.   .   .   . £500

A Circle of the Season, by E. Powys Mathers, Golden Cockerel Press (Waltham St Lawrence, Berks), 1929 (500 numbered copies) £75

The Man from Kilsheelan, by A.E. Coppard, Furnival Books (London), 1930 (550 signed copies) .   . £35

The Hundredth Story, by A.E. Coppard, Golden Cockerel Press (Waltham St Lawrence, Berks), 1931 (1,000 copies) .   .   .   .   .   . £65/£45

Salambo, by Gustave Flaubert, Golden Cockerel Press (Waltham St Lawrence, Berks), 1931 (500 numbered copies) £75

Initiation, translated by J.H. Driberg, Golden Cockerel Press (Waltham St Lawrence, Berks), 1932 (325 numbered copies) £75

Crotty Shinkwin, The Beauty Spot, by A.E. Coppard, Golden Cockerel Press (Waltham St Lawrence, Berks), 1932 (500 numbered copies) .   .   . £50/£25

Rummy, The Noble Game, by A.E. Coppard, Golden Cockerel Press (Waltham St Lawrence, Berks), 1932 (1,000 copies) .   .   .   . £75/£30

ditto, Golden Cockerel Press (Waltham St Lawrence, Berks), 1932 (250 signed copies on handmade paper) . £125/£75

ditto, Houghton Mifflin (Boston), 1933 .   . £25/£10

Lord Adrian, by Lord Dunsany, Golden Cockerel Press (Waltham St Lawrence, Berks), 1933 (325 copies, glassine d/w) .   .   .   .   .   . £150/£100

The Roving Angler, Herbert E. Palmer, Dent (London), 1933

.   .   .   . £25/£10

Glory of Life, by Llewelyn Powys, Golden Cockerel Press (Waltham St Lawrence, Berks), 1934 (277 numbered copies) £500

ditto, Golden Cockerel Press (Waltham St Lawrence, Berks), 1934 (2 copies on vellum) .   .   . £5,000

ditto, John Lane (London), 1938.   .   . £50/£15

The Voyage of the Bounty's Launch, Golden Cockerel Press (Waltham St Lawrence, Berks), 1934 (300 numbered copies) £500

Beasts and Saints, Constable (London), 1934.   . £50/£15

The Journals of James Morrison, Golden Cockerel Press (Waltham St Lawrence, Berks), 1935 (325 numbered copies) £600

Mr Glasspoole and the Chinese Pirates, Golden Cockerel Press (Waltham St Lawrence, Berks), 1935 (315 numbered copies) £100

Narratives of the Wreck of the Whale-Ship Essex, Golden Cockerel Press (Waltham St Lawrence, Berks), 1935 (275 numbered copies) £350

A Bird Diary, by Godfrey Harrison, Dent (London), 1936 .

.   .   .   . £20/£10

The Insect Man, by Eleanor Doorly, W. Heffer & Son (Cambridge, UK), 1936 .   .   . £20/£5

ditto, Appleton-Century (New York), 1937 .   . £20/£5

Le Morte d'Arthur, by Sir Thomas Malory, Limited Editions Club (New York), 1936 (3 vols; slipcase) . £150/£75

The Tale of the Golden Cockerel, by Alexander Pushkin, Golden Cockerel Press (Waltham St Lawrence, Berks), 1936 .   .   .   .   . £30/£15

ditto, Golden Cockerel Press (Waltham St Lawrence, Berks), 1936 (100 numbered copies) .   .   . £250

The Twelve Months, by Llewelyn Powys, Bodley Head (London), 1936 .   .   .   . £45/£10

ditto, Bodley Head (London), 1936 (100 signed copies) £350

A Book of Uncommon Prayer, by George Scott-Moncrieff, Methuen (London), 1937 .   .   .   . £25/£10

Marvels of the Insect World, by Jean-Henri Fabre, Appleton-Century (New York), 1938 . . . £10/£5

The Microbe Man, by Eleanor Doorly, Heffer (Cambridge), 1938 . . . . £15/£5

Othello, Limited Editions Club (New York), 1939 (1,950 numbered copies) £25

The Radium Woman, by Eleanor Doorly, Heinemann (London), 1939 . . . . £10/£5

The Art of Living, by Andre Maurois, English Universities Press (London), 1940 . . . . . . £10/£5

The Midmost Waters, by John Fisher, The Naldrett Press (London), 1952 . . . . . . £10/£5

The Story of Bovril, by Richard Bennett, Bovril Ltd (London), 1953 . . . . £30/£10

An Account of the Discovery of Tahiti, Folio Society (London), 1955 . . . . £10/£5

Journal of Researches, by Charles Darwin, Limited Editions Club (New York), 1956 (1,500 copies; slipcase) . £100/£65

LEWIS GRASSIC GIBBON

(b.1901 d.1935)

'Grassic Gibbon' was the pseudonym used by the Scot James Leslie Mitchell for his best known works, *Sunset Song*, *Cloud Howe* and *Grey Granite*, which together make up the *Scot's Quair* trilogy. Although not generally recognised during the author's lifetime, *A Scot's Quair* and particularly *Sunset Song* are now considered to be among the greatest works of 20th century Scottish literature.

Novels by 'Lewis Grassic Gibbon'

Sunset Song, Jarrolds (London), 1932 . . . £225/£35

ditto, Doubleday, Doran (New York), 1933 . . £200/£30

Cloud Howe, Jarrolds (London), 1933 . . . £200/£35

ditto, Doubleday, Doran (New York), 1934 . . £175/£30

Grey Granite, Jarrolds (London), 1934 . . . £150/£25

ditto, Doubleday, Doran (New York), 1934 . . £150/£25

A Scot's Quair: A Trilogy of Novels, Jarrolds (London), 1946 . . . . £35/£10

The Speak O' The Mearns, Ramsey Head Press (Edinburgh), 1982 (unfinished) . . . . . £10/£5

Others by 'Lewis Grassic Gibbon'

Niger: The Life of Mungo Park, Porpoise Press, (Edinburgh), 1934 . . . . £50/£20

Scottish Scene: Or, The Intelligent Man's Guide to Albyn, Jarrolds (London), 1934 (with Hugh McDiarmid) £45/£15

Nine Against the Unknown: A Record of Geographical Exploration, Jarrolds (London), 1934 (as 'Lewis Grassic Gibbon and J. Leslie Mitchell') . . . . £45/£15

ditto, as *Earth Conquerors: The Lives and Achievements of the Great Explorers*, Simon & Schuster (New York), 1934 (as J. Leslie Mitchell') . . . . . £25/£10

A Scots Hairst: Essays and Short Stories, Hutchinson (London), 1967 . . . . £20/£5

Novels by 'J. Leslie Mitchell'

Stained Radiance: A Fictionist's Prelude, Jarrolds (London), 1930 . . . . £125/£40

The Thirteenth Disciple, Being a Portrait and Saga of Lalcolm Maudslay in His Adventures Through the Dark Corridor, Jarrolds (London), 1931 . . . . £125/£40

Three Go Back, Jarrolds (London), 1932 . . . £125/£40

ditto, Bobbs-Merrill (Indianapolis, IN), 1932 . £75/£25

The Lost Trumpet, Jarrolds (London), 1932 . . £100/£30

ditto, Bobbs-Merrill (Indianapolis, IN), 1932 . £75/£25

Image and Superscription, Jarrolds (London), 1933 . . . . £50/£20

Spartacus, Jarrolds (London), 1933 . . . . £30/£10

Gay Hunter, Jarrolds (London), 1934 . . . £50/£20

Short Stories by 'J. Leslie Mitchell'

The Calends of Cairo, Jarrolds (London), 1931 . £100/£25

ditto, as *Cairo Dawns*, Bobbs-Merrill (Indianapolis, IN), 1932 . . . . £75/£25

Persian Dawns, Egyptian Nights, Jarrolds (London), [1933] . . . . £100/£25

Other Titles by 'J. Leslie Mitchell'

Hanno: Or, The Future of Exploration, Kegan Paul (London), 1928 . . . . £35/£15

The Conquest of the Maya, Jarrolds (London), 1934 . . . . £45/£15

ditto, E.P. Dutton & Company (New York), 1935 . £25/£10

STELLA GIBBONS

(b.1902 d.1989)

Stella Dorothea Gibbons was an English poet and author of many novels. She is collected mainly for her first, the classically humorous *Cold Comfort Farm*. It is said that her own family was not dissimilar to the characterful Starkadder family described in the novel.

Novels

Cold Comfort Farm, Longmans (London), 1932 £3,000/£400

Bassett, Longmans (London), 1934 . . . . £300/£35

Enbury Heath, Longmans (London), 1935 . . £250/£35

Miss Linsey and Pa, Longmans (London), 1936 . £250/£35

Nightingale Wood, Longmans (London), 1938 . £200/£35

My American: A Romance, Longmans (London), 1939 . . . . £125/£35

The Rich House, Longmans (London), 1941 . £75/£25

Ticky, Longmans (London), 1943 . . . . £35/£10

The Bachelor, Longmans (London), 1944 . . £35/£10

Westwood, or, The Gentle Powers, Longmans (London), 1946 . . . . £25/£10

Conference at Cold Comfort Farm, Longmans (London), 1949 . . . . £75/£15

The Matchmaker, Longmans (London), 1949 . £25/£10

The Swiss Summer, Longmans (London), 1951 . £25/£5

Fort of the Bear, Longmans (London), 1953 . £25/£5

The Shadow of a Sorcerer, Hodder & Stoughton (London), 1955 . . . . £25/£5

Here Be Dragons, Hodder & Stoughton (London), 1956 . . . . £25/£5

White Sand and Grey Sand, Hodder & Stoughton (London), [1958] . . . . £25/£5

A Pink Front Door, Hodder & Stoughton (London), [1959] . . . . £20/£5

The Weather at Tregulla, Hodder & Stoughton (London), [1962] . . . . £20/£5
The Wolves Were in the Sledge, Hodder & Stoughton (London), 1964 . . . . . . £20/£5
The Charmers, Hodder & Stoughton (London), 1965 . . . . £20/£5
Starlight, Hodder & Stoughton (London), 1967 . £15/£5
The Snow-Woman, Hodder & Stoughton (London), 1969 . . . . £15/£5
The Woods in Winter, Hodder & Stoughton (London), 1970 . . . . £15/£5

Short Stories
Roaring Tower and Other Short Stories, Longmans (London), 1937 . . . . . . £175/£35
Christmas at Cold Comfort Farm and Other Stories, Longmans (London), 1940 . . . £200/£35
Beside the Pearly Water and Other Stories, Peter Nevill (London), 1954 . . . . . £30/£10

Poetry
The Mountain Beast and Other Poems, Longmans (London), 1930 (wraps) £30
The Priestess and Other Poems, Longmans (London), 1934 (wraps) £25
The Lowland Venus and Other Poems, Longmans (London), 1938 (wraps) £25
Collected Poems, Longmans (London), 1950 . . £15/£5
ditto, The Collector's Book Club (London), 1950 (150 signed copies) £100
ditto, The Collector's Book Club (London), 1950 (5 signed presentation copies) £750

Children's Titles
The Untidy Gnome, Longmans (London), 1935 . £150/£35

MAY GIBBS

(b.1877 d.1969)

May Gibbs was a British-born, Australian children's author, illustrator, and cartoonist. She is best-known for her gumnut babies (also known as 'bush babies' or 'bush fairies'), and the book *Snugglepot and Cuddlepie*. She also drew a long-running newspaper strip featuring two similar characters, Bib and Bub.

Barons and Kings (1215-1485), by Estelle Ross, Harrap (London), 1912 (illustrated by May Gibbs and Stephen Reid) £20
About Us, Nister (London), 1912 . . . . £500
Gum Blossom Babies, Angus & Robertson (Sydney), 1916 (wraps) £175
Gum-Nut Babies, Angus & Robertson (Sydney), 1916 (wraps) £175
Boronia Babies, Angus & Robertson (Sydney), 1917 (wraps) £150
Flannel Flowers and Other Bush Babies, Angus & Robertson (Sydney), 1917 (wraps) . . . £125
Wattle Babies, Angus & Robertson (Sydney), 1918 (wraps) £125
Snugglepot and Cuddlepie: Their Adventures Wonderful, Angus & Robertson (Sydney), 1918 . . £1,000/£300

Little Ragged Blossom and More about Snugglepot and Cuddlepie, Angus & Robertson (Sydney), 1920 . . . . £1,000/£250
Little Obelia and Further Adventures of Ragged Blossom, Snugglepot and Cuddlepie, Angus & Robertson (Sydney), 1921 . . . . £450/£150
Nuttybub and Nittersing, Osboldstone (Melbourne), 1923 . . . . £450/£150
Chucklebud and Wunkydoo, Osboldstone (Melbourne), 1924 . . . . £300/£125
ditto, as *Two Little Gum-Nuts*, Cornstalk (Sydney), 1929 . . . . £250/£75
Bib and Bub: Their Adventures, Cornstalk (Sydney), 1925 (2 vols) . . . . . £450/£200 the set
The Further Adventures of Bib abd Bub, Cornstalk (Sydney), 1927 . . . . . . £400/£200
More Funny Stories About Old Friends, Bib and Bub, Cornstalk (Sydney), 1928 . . . £300/£150
Bib and Bub in Gum-Nut Town, Halstead (Waterloo), 1929 . . . . £300/£150
Gumnuts, Angus & Robertson (Sydney), 1940 . £75/£30
Scotty in Gumnut Land, Angus & Robertson (Sydney), 1941 . . . . £75/£35
Mr and Mrs Bear and Friends, Angus & Robertson (Sydney), 1943 . . . . £50/£20
The Complete Adventures of Snugglepot and Cuddlepie, Angus & Robertson (Sydney), 1946 . . £150/£25
Prince Dande Lion: A Garden Whim-Wham, Ure Smith (Sydney), 1953 . . . . . . £75/£20
Alphabet Frieze, Angus & Robertson (Sydney), 1984 (pictorial wrap portfolio; frieze in four sections) . £15
The May Gibbs Collection: Gumnut Classics, Angus & Robertson (Sydney), 1985 (2 vols; slipcase) . . . . £40/£15 the set

ANTHONY GILBERT

(b.1899 d.1973)

Anthony Gilbert was the pseudoym of British crime author Lucy Malleson. She also wrote crime fiction under other pen-names, and non-crime fiction as 'Anne Meredith'. The best-known character in her fiction is Arthur Crook, a vulgar London lawyer.

Novels by 'Anthony Gilbert'
The Tragedy at Freyne, Collins (London), 1927 . £750/£75
ditto, Dial (New York), 1927 . . . . . £400/£40
The Murder of Mrs Davenport, Collins (London), 1928 . . . . £750/£75
ditto, Dial (New York), 1928 . . . . £250/£25
The Mystery of the Open Window, Gollancz (London), 1929 . . . . £500/£50
ditto, Dodd, Mead (New York), 1930 . . £250/£25
Death at Four Corners, Collins (London), 1929 . £750/£75
ditto, Dial (New York), 1929 . . . . £250/£25
The Night of the Fog, Gollancz (London), 1930 . £500/£45
ditto, Dodd (New York), 1930 . . . . £250/£25
The Case Against Andrew Fane, Collins Crime Club (London), 1931 . . . . . . £750/£75
ditto, Dodd (New York), 1931 . . . . £250/£25
The Body on the Beam, Crime Club (London), 1932 . . . . £750/£75

ditto, Dodd (New York), 1932 . . . . . £250/£25

The Long Shadow, Crime Club (London), 1932 . £750/£75

The Musical Comedy, Crime Crime Club (London), 1933 .

. . . . £750/£75

Death in Fancy Dress, Crime Club (London), 1933 . .

. . . . £750/£75

The Man in Button Boots, Crime Club (London), 1934 .

. . . . £750/£75

ditto, Holt (New York), 1935 . . . . . £200/£20

An Old Lady Dies, Crime Club (London), 1934 . £750/£75

The Man Who Was Too Clever, Crime Club (London), 1935

. . . . £500/£50

Murder by Experts, Crime Club (London), 1936 . £500/£45

ditto, Dial (New York), 1937 . . . . . £150/£20

Courtier to Death, Crime Club (London), 1936 . £500/£45

ditto, as **The Dover Train Mystery**, Dial (New York) 1936 .

. . . . £175/£25

The Man Who Wasn't There, Crime Club (London), 1937 .

. . . . £500/£45

Murder Has No Tongue, Crime Club (London), 1937 . .

. . . . £500/£45

Treason In My Breast, Crime Club (London), 1938 . .

. . . . £350/£35

The Clock in the Hat Box, Crime Club (London), 1939 .

. . . . £350/£35

ditto, Arcadia House (New York), 1943 . . . £25/£10

The Bell of Death, Crime Club (London), 1939 . £250/£25

Dear Dead Woman, Crime Club (London), 1940 . £250/£25

ditto, Arcadia House (New York), 1942 . . £25/£10

ditto, as **Death Takes a Redhead**, Arrow (New York), 1944

(wraps) £5

The Vanishing Corpse, Crime Club (London), 1941 . .

. . . . £200/£20

ditto, as **She Vanished in the Dawn**, Arcadia House (New

York), 1941 . . . . £25/£10

The Woman in Red, Crime Club (London), 1941 . £175/£20

ditto, Smith & Durrell (New York), 1943 . . £25/£10

ditto, as **The Mystery of the Woman in Red**, Quin (New

York), 1944 (wraps) £5

Something Nasty in the Woodshed, Crime Club (London),

1942 . . . . £175/£20

ditto, as **Mystery in the Woodshed**, Smith & Durrell (New

York), 1942 . . . . £25/£10

The Case of the Tea-Cosy's Aunt, Crime Club (London),

1942 . . . . £175/£20

ditto, as **Death in the Blackout**, Smith & Durrell (New

York), 1943 . . . . £25/£10

The Mouse Who Wouldn't Play Ball, Crime Club

(London), 1943 . . . . . . £175/£20

ditto, as **Thirty Days to Live**, Smith & Durrell (New York),

1944 . . . . £25/£10

A Spy for Mr Crook, Barnes (New York), 1944 . £25/£10

He Came By Night, Crime Club (London), 1944 . £150/£15

ditto, as **Death at the Door**, Smith & Durrell (New York),

1945 . . . . £25/£10

The Scarlet Button, Crime Club (London), 1944 . £125/£10

ditto, Smith & Durrell (New York), 1945 . . £25/£10

ditto, as **Murder is Cheap**, Bantam (New York), 1949

(wraps) £5

The Black Stage, Crime Club (London), 1945 . £100/£10

ditto, Barnes (New York), 1946 . . . . £20/£5

ditto, as **Murder Cheats the Bride**, Bantam (New York),

1948 (wraps). £5

Don't Open the Door, Crime Club (London), 1945 £100/£10

ditto, as **Death Lifts the Latch**, Barnes (New York), 1946 .

. . . . £20/£5

The Spinster's Secret, Crime Club (London), 1946 £50/£10

ditto, as **By Hook or Crook**, Barnes (New York), 1947 .

. . . . £20/£5

Death in the Wrong Room, Crime Club (London), 1947 .

. . . . £50/£10

ditto, Barnes (New York) 1947 . . . . £15/£5

Die in the Dark, Crime Club (London), 1947 . £35/£10

ditto, as **The Missing Widow**, Barnes (New York), 1948 .

. . . . £15/£5

Lift up the Lid, Crime Club (London), 1948 . . £35/£10

ditto, as **The Innocent Bottle**, Barnes (New York), 1949 .

. . . . £15/£5

Death Knocks Three Times, Crime Club (London), 1949 .

. . . . £35/£10

ditto, Random House House (New York), 1950 . £15/£5

Murder Comes Home, Crime Club (London), 1950 £35/£10

ditto, Random House (New York), 1951 . . £15/£5

A Nice Cup of Tea, Crime Club (London), 1950 . £20/£5

ditto, as **The Wrong Body**, Random House (New York),

1951 . . . . £20/£5

Lady Killer, Crime Club (London), 1951 . . £35/£10

Miss Pinnegar Disappears, Crime Club (London), 1952 .

. . . . £35/£10

ditto, as **A Case for Mr Crook**, Random House (New York),

1952 . . . . £25/£10

Footsteps Behind Me, Crime Club (London), 1953 £35/£10

ditto, as **Black Death**, Random House (New York) 1953 .

. . . . £15/£5

ditto, as **Dark Death**, Pyramid (New York), 1963 . £5

Snake in the Grass, Crime Club (London), 1954 . £20/£5

ditto, as **Death Won't Wait**, Random House (New York),

1954 . . . . £15/£5

A Question of Murder, Random House (New York), 1955 .

. . . . £25/£5

ditto, as **Is She Dead Too?**, Crime Club (London), 1956 .

. . . . £25/£5

And Death Came Too, Crime Club (London), 1956 £25/£5

ditto, Random House (New York), 1956 . . £15/£5

Riddle of a Lady, Crime Club (London), 1956 . £15/£5

ditto, Random House (New York), 1957 . . £10/£5

Give Death a Name, Crime Club (London), 1957 . £15/£5

Death Against the Clock, Crime Club (London), 1958 . .

. . . . £15/£5

ditto, Random House (New York), 1958 . . £10/£5

Death Takes a Wife, Crime Club (London), 1959 . £15/£5

ditto, as **Death Casts a Long Shadow**, Random House (New

York), 1959 . . . . £10/£5

Third Crime Lucky, Crime Club (London), 1959 . £15/£5

ditto, as **Prelude to Murder**, Random House (New York),

1959 . . . . £10/£5

Out for the Kill, Crime Club (London), 1960 . . £15/£5

ditto, Random House (New York), 1960 . . £10/£5

She Shall Die, Crime Club (London), 1961 . . £15/£5

ditto, as **After the Verdict**, Random House (New York), 1961

. . . . £10/£5

Uncertain Death, Crime Club (London), 1961 . £15/£5

ditto, Random House (New York), 1962 . . £10/£5

No Dust in the Attic, Crime Club (London), 1962 . £15/£5

ditto, Random House (New York), 1963 . . £10/£5

Ring for a Noose, Crime Club (London), 1963 . £15/£5

ditto, Random House (New York), 1964 . . £10/£5

The Fingerprint, Crime Club (London), 1964. . £15/£5

ditto, Random House (New York), 1964 . . . £10/£5
Knock, Knock, Who's There?, Crime Club (London), 1964
. . . . £15/£5
ditto, as **The Voice**, Random House (New York), 1965 . .
. . . . £10/£5
Passenger to Nowhere, Crime Club (London), 1965 £15/£5
ditto, Random House (New York), 1966 . . . £10/£5
The Looking Glass Murder, Crime Club (London), 1966 .
. . . . £15/£5
ditto, Random House (New York), 1967 . . . £10/£5
The Visitor, Crime Club (London), 1967 . . . £15/£5
ditto, Random House (New York), 1967 . . . £10/£5
Night Encounter, Crime Club (London), 1968 . £15/£5
ditto, as **Murder Anonymous**, Random House (New York),
1968 . . . . £10/£5
Missing From Her Home, Crime Club (London), 1969 .
. . . . £15/£5
ditto, Random House (New York), 1969 . . . £10/£5
Death Wears a Mask, Crime Club (London), 1970 £15/£5
ditto, as **Mr Crook Lifts the Mask**, Random House (New
York), 1970 . . . . £10/£5
Tenant for the Tomb, Crime Club (London), 1971 £15/£5
ditto, Random House (New York), 1971 . . . £10/£5
Murder's a Waiting Game, Crime Club (London), 1972 .
. . . . £15/£5
ditto, Random House (New York), 1972 . . . £10/£5
A Nice Little Killing, Crime Club (London), 1974 . £15/£5
ditto, Random House (New York), 1974 . . . £10/£5

Collaborations
No Flowers by Request & *Crime on the Coast*, Gollancz
(London), 1984 (chain novel; chapters by Gilbert and
others) . . . . £10/£5

Novels by 'J. Kilmeny Keith'
The Man Who Was London, Collins (London), 1925 . .
. . . . £800/£100
The Sword of Harlequin, Collins (London), 1927 . . .
. . . . £500/£100

Novels by 'Sylvia Denys Hooke'
Nettle Harvest, Chapman & Hall (London), 1927 . £100/£15
ditto, Doubleday (New York), 1928 . . . £50/£10
Old Stars for Sale, Chapman & Hall (London), 1928 . .
. . . . £100/£15
Aubrey Dene, Longmans Green (London), 1930 . £100/£15
Strange Guest, John Murray (London), 1932 . . £75/£10

Novels by 'Lucy Egerton'
Lady At Large, Cassell (London), 1936 . . . £65/£10
Courage in Gold, Cassell (London), 1938 . . . £65/£10

Novels by 'Anne Meredith'
Portrait of a Murderer, Gollancz (London), 1933 . £200/£35
ditto, Reynal & Hitchcock (New York), 1934 . . £35/£10
The Coward, Gollancz (London), 1934 . . . £125/£20
The Gambler, Gollancz (London), 1937 . . £50/£10
The Showman, Faber & Faber (London), 1938 . £50/£10
The Stranger, Faber & Faber (London), 1939 . £50/£10
The Adventurer, Faber & Faber (London), 1940 . £50/£10
Mrs Boot's Legacy, Samuel French (London), 1941 (wraps)
. . . . £15
There's Always Tomorrow, Faber & Faber (London), 1941 .
. . . . £40/£10

ditto, as **Home is the Heart**, Howell Soskin (New York),
1942 . . . . £20/£5
The Family Man, Faber & Faber (London), 1942 . £35/£10
ditto, Howell Soskin (New York), 1942 . . . £20/£5
Curtain for Mr Greatheart, Faber & Faber (London), 1943
. . . . £35/£10
The Beautiful Miss Burroughs, Faber & Faber (London),
1945 . . . . £25/£5
The Rich Woman, Faber & Faber (London), 1947 . £15/£5
ditto, Random House (New York), 1947 . . . £10/£5
The Sisters, Faber & Faber (London), 1948 . . £15/£5
ditto, Random House (New York), 1949 . . . £10/£5
The Draper of Edgecumbe, Faber & Faber (London), 1950.
. . . . £15/£5
ditto, as **The Unknown Path**, Random House (New York),
1950 . . . . £10/£5
A Fig For Virtue, Faber & Faber (London), 1951 . £15/£5
Call Back Yesterday, Faber & Faber (London), 1952 £15/£5
The Innocent Bride, Hodder & Stoughton (London), 1954 .
. . . . £15/£5
The Day of the Miracle, Hodder & Stoughton (London),
1955 . . . . £15/£5
Impetuous Heart, Hodder & Stoughton (London), 1956 .
. . . . £15/£5
Christine, Hodder & Stoughton (London), 1957 . £10/£5
A Man in the Family, Hodder & Stoughton (London), 1959
. . . . £10/£5
The Wise Child, Hodder & Stoughton (London), 1960 . .
. . . . £10/£5
Up Goes the Donkey, Hodder & Stoughton (London), 1962
. . . . £10/£5

Autobiography by 'Anne Meredith'
Three-A-Penny, Faber & Faber (London), 1940 . £50/£15

GILES' ANNUALS

The distinctive cartoons drawn by Carl Giles, published in
the Daily Express, have been collected together annually.

No. 1, 1946 . . . . £250
ditto, Pedigree Books Limited (London), 1996 (slipcase) .
. . . . £35/£20
No. 2, 1947 . . . . £250
ditto, Pedigree Books Limited (London), 1995 (slipcase) .
. . . . £35/£20
No. 3, 1949 . . . . £200
ditto, Pedigree Books Limited (London), 1997 (slipcase) .
. . . . £35/£20
No. 4, 1950 . . . . £175
No. 5, 1951 . . . . £100
No. 6, 1952 . . . . £85
No. 7, 1953 . . . . £76
No. 8, 1954 . . . . £65
No. 9, 1955 . . . . £40
No. 10, 1956 . . . . £20
No. 11, 1957 . . . . £20
No. 12, 1958 . . . . £15
No. 13, 1959 . . . . £15
No. 14, 1960 . . . . £15
No. 15, 1961 . . . . £15

No. 16, 1962 . . . . £15
No. 17, 1963 . . . . £15
No. 18, 1964 . . . . £15
No. 19, 1965 . . . . £10
No. 20, 1966 . . . . £10
No. 21, 1967 . . . . £10
No. 22, 1968 . . . . £10
No. 23, 1969 . . . . £10
No. 24, 1970 to date . . . . . . £5 each

ERIC GILL

(b.1882 d.1940)

Gill was a sculptor, engraver, typographer, writer and book illustrator. He and his wife formed the nucleus of an artistic community at Ditchling in Sussex. Gill became a Catholic in 1913, joining the Third Order of St Dominic.

Written and Illustrated by Gill

Sculpture, St Dominic Press (Ditchling, Sussex), 1917 (wraps) £215
Birth Control, St Dominic Press (Ditchling, Sussex), 1918 (wraps) £200
Songs Without Clothes, Being a Dissertation on the Song of Solomon and Such-Like Songs, St Dominic Press (Ditchling, Sussex), 1921 (240 copies) £100
Wood Engravings, St Dominic Press (Ditchling, Sussex), 1924 (150 numbered copies) £1,000
Id Quod: A Practical Test of the Beautiful, Golden Cockerel Press (Waltham St Lawrence, Berks), 1926 (150 signed, numbered copies) £300
Christianity and Art, Shakespeare Head Press (Capel-Y-Ffin, Abergavenny), 1928 (200 numbered copies signed by Gill and David Jones). £300
Art and Love, Golden Cockerel Press (Waltham St Lawrence, Berks), 1928 (225 signed, numbered copies) .
. . . . £250
ditto, Golden Cockerel Press (Waltham St Lawrence, Berks), 1928 (35 signed, numbered copies containing extra set of engravings) £1,250
Art and Prudence, Golden Cockerel Press (Waltham St Lawrence, Berks), 1928 (500 numbered copies) . £100
The Future of Sculpture, privately printed (London), 1928 (55 copies printed for private distribution) . . £500
Engravings, Douglas Cleverdon/Fanfare Press (Bristol), 1929 (410 numbered copies) £2,000
ditto, Douglas Cleverdon/Fanfare Press (Bristol), 1929 (80 numbered copies in quarter vellum with extra set of engravings) £3,000
ditto, Douglas Cleverdon/Fanfare Press (Bristol), 1929 (10 signed and numbered copies in full vellum with extra set of engravings) £3,500
Art Nonsense and Other Essays, Cassell/Francis Walterson (London), 1929 . . . . £100/£35
ditto, Cassell/Francis Walterson (London), 1929 (100 signed, numbered copies; slipcase) . . . . £350/£250
Clothing Without Cloth: An Essay on the Nude, Golden Cockerel Press (Waltham St Lawrence, Berks), 1931 (500 numbered copies) £200
An Essay on Typography, Sheed & Ward (London), 1931 (500 copies signed by Gill & Rene Hague) . . . £200

Clothes: An Essay Upon the Nature & Significance of the Natural and Artificial Integuments Worn by Men & Women, Jonathan Cape (London), 1931 . . £100/£50
ditto, Jonathan Cape (London), 1931 (160 signed and numbered copies) £250
Sculpture and the Living Model, Sheed & Ward (London), 1932 (sewn wraps) £30
Unemployment, Faber (London), 1933 (wraps) . £15
Beauty Looks after Herself, Sheed & Ward (London), 1933
. . . . £30/£10
The Lord's Song: A Sermon, Golden Cockerel Press (Waltham St Lawrence, Berks), 1934 (500 numbered copies) £250
Engravings, 1928-1933, Faber (London), 1934 (400 copies)
. . . . £250/£125
Art and a Changing Civilisation, John Lane (London), 1934
. . . . £35/£10
Work and Leisure, Faber (London), 1935 . £35/£10
The Necessity of Belief, Faber (London), 1936 . £50/£15
Trousers and the Most Precious Ornament, Faber (London), 1937 (sewn wraps) £25
Twenty-Five Nudes, Dent (London), 1938 . £200/£100
Unholy Trinity, Dent (London), 1938 (illustrated by Denis Tegetmeier; sewn wraps; in envelope) . . . £40/£30
Drawings from Life, Hague & Gill (London), 1940 £50/£25
Autobiography, Jonathan Cape (London), 1940 . £75/£15
Christianity and the Machine Age, Sheldon Press (London), 1940 . . . . £20/£5
Sacred and Secular, Dent (London), 1940 . . £20/£5
Last Essays, Jonathan Cape (London), 1942 . £30/£10
In a Strange Land, Jonathan Cape (London), 1944 £20/£5
It All Goes Together: Selected Essays, Devin-Adair (New York), 1944 . . . . £35/£10
Letters of Eric Gill, Jonathan Cape (London), 1947 £20/£5
From the Jerusalem Diary of Eric Gill, privately printed (London), 1953 (300 copies; unprinted glassine d/w) . .
. . . . £85/£75
First Nudes, Spearman (London), 1954 . £75/£30
ditto, Spearman (London), 1954 (100 numbered copies signed by Gordian Gill) £250
ditto, Citadel Press (New York), 1954 . . £50/£25
The Engravings of Eric Gill, Christopher Skelton (Wellingborough), 1983 (slipcase) . . . £225/£175
ditto, Christopher Skelton (Wellingborough), 1983 (85 copies; 2 vols & portfolio). £500

Other Books Illustrated by Gill

The Taking of Toll, translated by Ananda Coomaraswamy, The Old Bourne Press (London), 1915 . . . . £125
The Devil's Devices, by Douglas Pepler, The Hampshire House Workshop (London), 1915 (boards) . . . £100
ditto, The Hampshire House Workshop (London), 1915 (wraps) £100
God and the Dragon, by H.D.C.P., St Dominic Press (Ditchling, Sussex), 1917 . . . . £65
The Way of the Cross, by D.P., St Dominic Press (Ditchling, Sussex), 1917 . . . . £65
Woodwork, by A. Romney Green, St Dominic Press (Ditchling, Sussex), 1918 (wraps) £500
Emblems Engraved on Wood, Hampshire House Workshop (London), 1919 . . . . £200
Three Poems, by Ananda Coomaraswamy, St Dominic Press (Ditchling, Sussex), 1920 . . . . . . £75

Autumn Midnight, by Frances Cornford, The Poetry Bookshop (London), 1923 (wraps) £125

Sonnets and Verses, by Enid Clay, Golden Cockerel Press (Waltham St Lawrence, Berks), 1925 (450 numbered copies) £225

Song of Songs, by Solomon, King of Israel, Golden Cockerel Press (Waltham St Lawrence, Berks), 1925 (750 copies signed by Gill and Robert Gibbings) . £1,500

Passio Domini, by St Matthew, Golden Cockerel Press (Waltham St Lawrence, Berks), 1926 (250 numbered copies) £1,500

Cottage Economy, by William Cobbett, Peter Davies (London), 1926 (preface by G.K. Chesterton) . £20/£5

Procreant Hymn, by E. Powys Mathers, Golden Cockerel Press (Waltham St Lawrence, Berks), 1926 (200 numbered copies) £750

Gloria in Profundis, by G.K. Chesterton, Faber & Gwyer (London), 1927 (wraps; in envelope) . . . £50/£35

ditto, by G.K. Chesterton, Faber & Gwyer (London), 1927 (350 copies signed by Gill; glassine wraps) . £150/£125

Troilus and Criseyde, by Geoffrey Chaucer, Golden Cockerel Press (Waltham St Lawrence, Berks), 1927 (219 numbered copies) £2,000

ditto, Golden Cockerel Press (Waltham St Lawrence, Berks), 1927 (6 numbered copies on full vellum) . . £3,000

The Song of the Soul, by St John of the Cross, Francis Walterson (Capel-Y-Ffin, Abergavenny), 1927 (150 signed copies) £250

Canterbury Tales, by Geoffrey Chaucer, Golden Cockerel Press (Waltham St Lawrence, Berks), 1926-1931 (4 vols; 485 sets) . . . . . . £4,000 the set

ditto, Golden Cockerel Press (Waltham St Lawrence, Berks), 1926-1931 (4 vols; 15 copies on vellum) . . £10,000

Leda, by Aldous Huxley, Doubleday (New York), 1929 (361 numbered copies signed by author; slipcase). £125/£100

The Passion of Perpetua and Felicity, The Fleuron (London), 1929 (30 signed, numbered copies) . £1,500

The Story of Amnon, Hague & Gill (London), 1930 . . . . £100/£50

Canticum Canticorum, by Solomon, King of Israel, Cranach Press (Weimar), 1931 (200 numbered copies in quarter vellum) £600

ditto, Cranach Press (Weimar), 1931 (60 numbered copies in levant morocco) £1,250

ditto, Cranach Press (Weimar), 1931 (8 signed, numbered copies on vellum with extra set of engravings) . £3,000

The Four Gospels, Golden Cockerel Press (Waltham St Lawrence, Berks), 1931 (488 copies in quarter pigskin) £3,500

ditto, Golden Cockerel Press (Waltham St Lawrence, Berks), 1931 (12 signed copies bound in full pigskin) . £15,000

Hamlet, by William Shakespeare, Limited Editions Club (London), 1933 (1,500 signed, numbered copies; slipcase) . . . . £250/£200

The Sonnets of William Shakespeare, Cassell, 1933 (500 copies) . . . . £200/£100

The Lost Child, by Mulk Raj Anand, Hague & Gill (London), 1934 (200 copies signed by Anand) . £50

The New Temple Shakespeare, Dent (London), 1934-1936 (40 volumes). . . . . . £600/£400 the set

The Passion of Our Lord, Faber (London), 1934 £200/£125

The Aldine Bible, Dent (London), 1934-36 (4 vols) . . . . £175/£75 the set

The Constant Mistress, by Enid Clay, Golden Cockerel Press (London), 1934 (250 signed copies in green paper boards) £250

ditto, Golden Cockerel Press (London), 1934 (50 signed copies in full red morocco) £700

The Green Ship, Golden Cockerel Press (London), 1936 (134 numbered copies) £200

ditto, Golden Cockerel Press (London), 1936 (62 signed copies with extra set of plates) £750

ditto, Golden Cockerel Press (London), 1936 (4 signed copies with extra set of plates, bound in full levant) £2,000

Morals and Marriage, by T.G. Wayne, Longmans, Green (London), 1936 . . . . £40/£10

Quia Amore Languego, edited by H.S. Bennett, Faber (London), 1937 . . . . £200/£65

Travels and Sufferings of Brebeuf among the Hurons of Canada, translated by Theodore Besterman, Golden Cockerel Press (London), 1938 (300 numbered copies) £200

The Holy Sonnets of John Donne, Dent (London), 1938 (550 copies signed by Gill) . . . . £200/£45

The English Bible; Selections, Ginn & Co. (Boston), [1938] £30

Henry the Eighth, by William Shakespeare, Limited Editions Club New York), 1939 (1,950 numbered copies). £100

Glue and Lacquer, translated by Harold Acton and Lee Yi-hsieh, Golden Cockerel Press (London), 1941 (320 copies in quarter morocco) £250

ditto, Golden Cockerel Press (London), 1941 (30 copies in full morocco) £500

ALLEN GINSBERG

(b.1926 d.1997)

Allen Ginsberg was an American poet born in Newark, New Jersey. He is best known for *Howl*, a long poem about the self-destruction of his friends of the 1950s 'Beat Generation' (a group that had Ginsberg at its centre.) Ginsberg was also associated with 1960s hippies, becoming friends with Timothy Leary, Ken Kesey and Bob Dylan, among others.

Poetry

Howl and Other Poems, City Lights (San Francisco, CA), 1956 (pbk) £1,750

ditto, as *Howl for Carl Solomon*, Grabhorn-Hoyem (San Francisco, CA), 1971 (275 signed copies) . . . £500

ditto, as *Howl: Original Draft Facsimile & Transcripts*, Harper & Row (New York), 1986 . . . £25/£10

ditto, as *Howl: Original Draft Facsimile & Transcripts*, Harper & Row (New York), 1986 (250 signed copies; slipcase). . . . . £200/£165

Kaddish and Other Poems, 1958-1960, City Lights (San Francisco, CA), 1961 (pbk) £75

ditto, as *Kaddish for Naomi Ginsberg, 1894-1956*, Arion Press (San Francisco, CA), 1992 (200 signed copies; lithographs by R.B. Kitaj) £200

Empty Mirror: Early Poems, Totem Press/Corinth Books (New York), 1961 (pbk) £30

Reality Sandwiches: 1953-1960, City Lights (San Francisco, CA), 1963 (pbk) £20

The Change, Writer's Forum (London), 1963 (mimeographed sheets, stapled wraps; first state with name spelt 'Ginsburg') £500

ditto, Writer's Forum (London), 1963 (second state with name spelt correctly) £125

Kral Majales (King of May), Oyez (Berkeley, CA), 1965 (350 copies; broadside) £35

Wichita Vortex Sutra, Coyote Press (San Francisco, CA), 1966 (500 copies; pbk) £65

ditto, Peace News Poetry (London), 1966 . . . . £25

T.V. Baby Poems, Cape Golliard Press (London), 1967 (pbk) £30

ditto, Cape Golliard Press (London), 1967 (100 signed copies) . . . . £200/£125

ditto, Cape Golliard Press (London), 1967 (400 copy case-bound 'Library Edition') . . . . . £50/£30

ditto, Grossman (New York), 1967 (750 unnumbered hardback copies) . . . . . £35/£15

ditto, Grossman (New York), 1967 (pbk) . . . £15

Airplane Dreams: Compositions From Journals, House of Anansi (Toronto, Canada), 1968 . . . £65/£25

ditto, House of Anansi (Toronto, Canada), 1968 (wraps) £20

ditto, City Lights (San Francisco, CA), 1969 (wraps) . £20

Scrap Leaves, Hasty Scribbles, Poet's Press (Millbrook, NY), 1968 (150 signed, numbered copies; stapled wraps) £100

Wales – A Visitation, July 29, 1967, Cape Golliard Press (London), 1968 (200 unsigned copies) . . £45/£25

ditto, Cape Golliard Press (London), 1968 (100 signed, numbered copies with a 45rpm vinyl record) £400/£250

Planet News, City Lights (San Francisco, CA), 1968 (first printing with 'Villiers Publications' on copyright page) £35

ditto, City Lights (San Francisco, CA), 1968 (second printing with 'First American Edition' on copyright page) . £20

ditto, City Lights (San Francisco, CA), 1968 (500 signed copies; slipcase) . . . . . . £75/£50

Ankor Wat, Fulcrum Press (London), 1968 (with photos by Alexandra Lawrence) . . . . . £35/£10

The Moments Return: A Poem, Grabhorn-Hoyem (San Francisco, CA), 1970 (200 copies; paper over boards) £65

New Year Blues, Phoenix Book Shop (New York), 1972 (100 signed, numbered copies; sewn wraps) . . £75

ditto, Phoenix Book Shop (New York), 1972 (26 signed, lettered copies; sewn wraps) £175

Open Head/Open Eye, Sun Books (Melbourne, Australia), 1972 (with Lawrence Ferlinghetti; wraps) . . £25

Bixby Canyon Ocean Path Word Breeze, Gotham Book Mart (New York), 1972 (stapled wraps) . . £25

ditto, Gotham Book Mart (New York), 1972 (100 signed copies; orange cloth) £75

ditto, Gotham Book Mart (New York), 1972 (26 signed, lettered copies; cloth) £200

The Gates of Wrath: Rhymed Poems 1948-1952, Grey Fox (Bolinas, CA), 1972 (wraps) £25

ditto, Grey Fox (Bolinas, CA), 1972 (100 signed copies; yellow boards) £100

Iron Horse, Coach House Press (Toronto, Canada), 1973 (pbk) £35

ditto, Expanded Media Editions (Gottingen, Germany), 1973 (100 signed copies) £75

ditto, City Lights (San Francisco, CA), 1974 (pbk) . £15

The Fall of America: Poems of These States, 1965-1971, City Lights (San Francisco, CA), 1973 (wraps) . £20

Sad Dust Glories: Poems during Work Summer in Woods, Workingman's Press (Berkeley, CA), 1974 (stapled wraps) £15

First Blues: Rags, Ballads and Harmonium Songs, 1971-1974, Full Court Press (New York), 1975 . £25/£10

ditto, Full Court Press (New York), 1975 (100 signed copies) . . . . £85/£45

ditto, City Lights (San Francisco, CA), 1978 (pbk). . £15

Poems All Over the Place: Mostly Seventies, Cherry Valley (Cherry Valley, NY), 1978 (pbk) . . £20

Mostly Sitting Haiku, From Here Press (Patterson, NJ), 1978 (stapled wraps) £30

Careless Love: Two Rhymes, Red Ozier Press (Madison, WI), 1978 (220 hand printed, signed copies; sewn wraps) £50

Plutonische ode/Plutonian ode, Uitgeverij (Heerlen, Holland), 1980 (stapled wraps) £25

ditto, Uitgeverij (Heerlen, Holland), 1980 (100 numbered, signed copies; boards) £150

Plutonian Ode and Other Poems, 1977-1980, City Lights (San Francisco, CA), 1982 (150 numbered, signed copies) . . . . £100/£45

ditto, City Lights (San Francisco, CA), 1982 (pbk). . £10

White Shroud, Kalakshetra Press (Madras, India), 1984 (illustrated by Francesco Clemente; 1,100 copies, acetate dw) . . . . £275/£225

Many Loves, Pequod Press (New York),1984 (500 copies; stapled wraps) £35

Collected Poems, 1947-1980, Harper & Row (New York), 1984 . . . . £35/£10

ditto, Viking (Harmondsworth, Essex), 1985 . £35/£10

White Shroud: Poems, 1980-1985, Harper & Row (New York), 1986 . . . . . . £25/£10

Cosmopolitan Greetings: Poems, 1986-1992, HarperCollins (New York), 1994 . . . . . . £20/£5

Prose, Letters etc

The Yage Letters, City Lights (San Francisco, CA), 1963 (with William Burroughs; pbk) £50

Indian Journals: March 1962 - May 1963, Dave Hazlewood/City Lights (San Francisco, CA), 1970 . . . . £65/£20

ditto, Dave Hazlewood/City Lights (San Francisco, CA), 1970 (pbk) £20

Notes After An Evening With William Carlos Williams, Portents Press, undated [c1970] (300 copies; stapled wraps) £25

Improvised Poetics, Anonym Books (San Francisco, CA), 1971 (pbk) £30

ditto, Anonym Books (San Francisco, CA), 1971 (boards) £50

ditto, Anonym Books (San Francisco, CA), 1971 (100 signed copies; red buckram) £150

The Fall of America Wins a Prize, Gotham Book Mart (New York), 1974 (wraps) £10

ditto, Gotham Book Mart (New York), 1974 (100 signed, numbered copies; wraps) £45

Gay Sunshine Interview: Allen Ginsberg with Allen Young, Grey Fox (Bolinas, CA), 1974 (wraps) . . £20

The Visions of the Great Rememberer, Mulch Press (Amherst, MA), 1974 (illustrated by Basil King; wraps) £25

ditto, Mulch Press (Amherst), 1974 (75 numbered copies signed by Ginsberg and King; wraps) £85

Chicago Trial Testimony, City Lights (San Francisco, CA), 1975 (stapled wraps) £25

Allen Verbatim: Lectures on Poetry, Politics and Consciousness, McGraw-Hill (New York), 1975 £25/£10

The Retreat Diaries: with The Dream of Tibet, The City Moon (New York), 1976 (with William Burroughs; stapled wraps) £30

To Eberhart from Ginsberg: A Letter about Howl, 1956, Penmaen Press (Lincoln MA.), 1976 (pbk) . . £20

ditto, Penmaen Press (Lincoln Ma.), 1976 (300 numbered copies signed by both poets; glassine dw) . . £100/£75

Journals: Early Fifties, Early Sixties, Grove Press (New York), 1977 . . . . £25/£10

As Ever: The Collected Correspondence of Allen Ginsberg and Neal Cassady, Creative Arts (Berkeley, CA), 1977 (pbk) £15

ditto, Creative Arts (Berkeley, CA), 1977 (green boards with white tissue dw) . . . . . £45/£35

Take Care of My Ghost, Ghost Press (n.p. [Berkeley, CA?]), 1977 (with Jack Kerouac; 200 copies; mimeographed sheets) £75

Straight Heart's Delight: Love Poems and Selected Letters with Peter Orlovsky, Gay Sunshine Press (San Francisco, CA), 1980 (wraps) £15

ditto, Gay Sunshine Press (San Francisco, CA), 1980 (50 numbered copies signed by Ginsberg & Orlovsky) . . . . £125/£100

Composed on the Tongue: Literary Conversations, 1967-1977, Grey Fox Press (Bolinas, CA), 1980 (pbk) . . £15

Karel Appell: Street Art, Ceramics, Sculpture, Wood Reliefs, Tapestries, Murals, Villa El Salvador, Abbeville Press (New York), 1985 (with Pierre Restany) . £50/£25

Your Reason and Blake's System, Hanuman Books (Madras and New York), 1989 (wraps in d/w) . . . £20/£10

Journals: Mid-Fifties - 1954-1958, HarperCollins (New York), 1995 . . . . £25/£10

ditto, HarperCollins (New York), 1995 (150 signed, numbered copies; slipcase) . . . . £75/£45

WARWICK GOBLE

(b.1862 d.1943)

Goble was a British illustrator famous in the science fiction genre for the 66 illustrations he provided for the first appearance of H.G. Wells's *The War of the Worlds* in *Pearson's* magazine. He tired of such hack-work and eventually established himself as an illustrator of classic gift books in their heyday before World War One. His work owes a great debt to Chinese and Japanese art.

Children's Books

The Grim House, by Mrs Molesworth, Nisbet (London), 1899 (5 b&w ills inc frontispiece) £35

The Water Babies, by Charles Kingsley, Macmillan (London), 1909 (32 colour plates) £375

ditto, Macmillan (London), 1909 (260 copies). . £1,500

ditto, Macmillan (London), 1910 (16 colour plates) . £50

ditto, Macmillan (London), 1922 (16 colour plates) . £45

Green Willow and Other Japanese Fairy Tales, by Grace James, Macmillan (London), 1910 (40 colour plates) . £400

ditto, Macmillan (London), 1910 (500 copies). . £2,000

ditto, Macmillan (London), 1912 (16 colour plates) . £45

ditto, Macmillan (London), 1923 (16 colour plates) . £40

Peeps at Many Lands - Turkey, by Julius Van Millingen, A. & C. Black (London), 1911 (12 colour plates) . . £30

Stories from the Pentamerone, by Giovanni Battista Basile, Macmillan (London), 1911 (32 colour plates) . . £150

ditto, Macmillan (London), 1911 (150 copies). . £1,250

Folk Tales of Bengal, by Lal Behari Day, Macmillan (London), 1912 (32 colour plates) £225

ditto, Macmillan (London), 1912 (150 copies). . £2,000

The Fairy Book, by D.M. Craik, Macmillan (London), 1913 (32 colour plates). £200

The Book of Fairy Poetry, Dora Owen, ed., Longmans (London), 1920 (16 colour plates and 15 b&w ills) . . . . £450/£250

Treasure Island, by Robert Louis Stevenson, Macmillan (New York), 1923 . . . . £100/£45

Kidnapped, by Robert Louis Stevenson, Macmillan (New York), 1925 (13 b&w full-page illustrations and 3 colour plates) . . . . £100/£45

Others

The Oracle of Baal, by J. Provand Webster, Lippincott (Philadelphia, PA), 1896 . . . . . . £125

Lad's Love, by S.R. Crockett, Bliss Sands & Co. (London), 1897 (100 copies) £200

ditto, Bliss Sands & Co. (London), 1897 . . . . £25

The War of the Worlds, by H.G. Wells, Harper (London), 1898 (15 illustrations by Goble, frontispiece by Cosmo Rowe) £400

ditto, Harper (London), 1898 . . . . . . £400

King for a Summer a Story of Corsican Life and Adventure, Lee and Shepard (Boston), 1902. . . £25

Constantinople, A. & C. Black (London), 1906 (63 colour plates) £100

The Greater Abbeys of England, Chatto & Windus (London), 1908 (60 colour plates) £45

Letters from an Ocean Tramp, by William Morley Punshon McFee, Cassell (London), 1908 . . . . . £65

Irish Ways, by Jane Barlow, Allen & Sons (London), 1909 (16 colour plates). £100

The Complete Poetical Works of Geoffrey Chaucer, Macmillan (New York), 1912 (32 colour plates) . . £100

Indian Myth and Legend, by Donald A. Mackenzie, Gresham (London), 1913 (8 colour plates) . . . £45

Indian Tales of the Great Ones Among Men, Women and Bird-People, by Cornelia Sohrabji, Blackie & Son (Bombay), 1916 (Colour frontispiece, and other b&w ills by Goble) £75

The Cistercians in Yorkshire, by Joseph Smith Fletcher, S.P.C.K. (London), 1919 . . . . . . £65

The Alhambra, by Washington Irving, Macmillan (New York), 1926 (3 colour plates) . . . . . £100/£15

Todd of the Fens, by Elinor Whitney, Macmillan (New York), 1928 . . . . £125/£25

RUMER GODDEN

(b. 1907 d.1998)

Margaret Rumer Godden was born in Sussex, England, but grew up with her three sisters in colonial India, where a number of her novels were set. Although she has been criticised for her portrayal of class, her books for children are highly regarded due to their acute recognition of the problems faced by children growing up.

Adult Novels

Chinese Puzzle, Peter Davies (London), 1936 . . £125/£20
The Lady and the Unicorn, Peter Davies (London), 1937 .
. . . . £150/£30
Black Narcissus, Peter Davies (London), 1939 . £200/£35
ditto, Little, Brown (Boston), 1939 . . . £65/£15
Gypsy, Gypsy, Peter Davies (London), 1940 . £65/£15
ditto, Little, Brown (Boston), 1940 . . . £45/£10
Breakfast with the Nikolides, Peter Davies (London), 1942.
. . . . £30/£10
ditto, Little, Brown (Boston), 1942 . . . £20/£5
A Fugue in Time, Michael Joseph (London), 1945 £25/£5
ditto, Little, Brown (Boston), 1945 . . . £20/£5
The River, Michael Joseph (London), 1946 . . £20/£5
ditto, Little, Brown (Boston), 1946 . . . £15/£5
A Candle for St Jude, Michael Joseph (London), 1947. .
. . . . £15/£5
ditto, Viking (New York), 1948 . . . . £15/£5
A Breath of Air, Michael Joseph (London), 1950 . £15/£5
ditto, Viking (New York), 1951 . . . . £15/£5
Kingfishers Catch Fire, Macmillan (London), 1953 £15/£5
ditto, Viking (New York), 1953 . . . . £15/£5
An Episode of Sparrows, Viking (New York), 1955 £15/£5
ditto, Macmillan (London), 1956 . . . £15/£5
Greengage Summer, Macmillan (London), 1958 . £30/£5
ditto, Viking (New York), 1958 . . . . £15/£5
China Court: The Hours of a Country House, Macmillan (London), 1961 . . . . £10/£5
ditto, Viking (New York), 1961 . . . . £10/£5
The Battle of the Villa Fiorita, Macmillan (London), 1963 .
. . . . £10/£5
ditto, Viking (New York), 1963 . . . . £10/£5
In This House of Brede, Macmillan (London), 1969 £10/£5
ditto, Viking (New York), 1969 . . . . £10/£5
The Peacock Spring, Macmillan (London), 1975 . £10/£5
ditto, Viking (New York), 1976 . . . . £10/£5
Five For Sorrow, Ten For Joy, Macmillan (London), 1979
. . . . £10/£5
ditto, Viking (New York), 1979 . . . . £10/£5
The Dark Horse, Macmillan (London), 1981 . £10/£5
ditto, Viking (New York), 1981 . . . . £10/£5
Thursday's Children, Macmillan (London), 1984 . £10/£5
ditto, Viking (New York), 1984 . . . . £10/£5
Indian Dust, Macmillan (London), 1989 (written with Jon Godden). . . . . £10/£5
Coromandel Sea Change, Macmillan (London), 1991 . .
. . . . £10/£5
ditto, Morrow (New York), 1991 . . . . £10/£5
Pippa Passes, Macmillan (London), 1994 . . £10/£5
ditto, Morrow (New York), 1994 . . . £10/£5
Cromartie vs. the God Shiva, Macmillan (London), 1997 .
. . . . £10/£5
ditto, Morrow (New York), 1997 . . . . £10/£5

Adult Short Stories

Mooltiki, and other stories and poems of India, Macmillan (London), 1957 . . . . £20/£5
ditto, Viking (New York), 1957 . . . . £20/£5
Gone: A Thread of Stories, Macmillan (London), 1968 (written with Jon Godden) . . . . £20/£5
ditto, Viking (New York), 1968 . . . . £15/£5
Swans and Turtles, Macmillan (London), 1968 . £10/£5
Mercy, Pity, Peace, and Love: Stories, Macmillan (London), 1990 (written with Jon Godden) . . . £10/£5
ditto, Morrow (New York), 1990 . . . £10/£5

Non-Fiction

Rungli-Rungliot, Peter Davies (London), 1943 . £35/£10
ditto, as *Thus Far and No Further*, , Macmillan (London), 1961 . . . . £15/£5
Hans Christian Andersen, Hutchinson (London), 1955 .
. . . . £15/£5
ditto, Knopf (New York), 1955 . . . . £15/£5
Two Under the Indian Sun, Macmillan (London), 1966 (written with Jon Godden). . . . . £20/£5
ditto, Knopf/Viking (New York), 1966 . . . £15/£5
Mrs Manders' Cook Book, Macmillan (London), 1968 .
. . . . £10/£5
ditto, Viking (New York), 1968 . . . . £10/£5
The Tale of the Tales: Beatrix Potter Ballet, Warne (London), 1971 . . . . £20/£5
Shiva's Pigeons, Chatto & Windus (London), 1972 (written with Jon Godden) . . . . . . £15/£5
ditto, Viking (New York), 1972 . . . . £15/£5
The Butterfly Lions, Viking (London), 1977 . . £10/£5
ditto, Viking (New York), 1978 . . . . £10/£5
Gulbadan: Portrait of a Rose Princess At the Mughal Court, Macmillan (London), 1980 . . . £10/£5
ditto, Viking (New York), 1981 . . . . £10/£5
A Time to Dance, No Time to Weep, Macmillan (London), 1987 . . . . £10/£5
ditto, Beech Tree / Morrow (New York), 1987 . £10/£5
A House with Four Rooms, Macmillan (London), 1989 .
. . . . £10/£5
ditto, Morrow (New York), 1989 . . . . £10/£5

Children's Books

The Doll's House, Joseph (London), 1947 . . £50/£10
ditto, Viking (New York), 1948 . . . . £35/£10
The Mousewife, Macmillan (London), 1951 . . £25/£5
ditto, Viking (New York), 1951 . . . . £25/£5
Impunity Jane: The Story of a Pocket Doll, , Viking (New York), 1954 . . . . £25/£5
ditto, Macmillan (London), 1955 . . . . £25/£5
The Fairy Doll, Macmillan (London), 1956 . . £25/£5
ditto, Viking (New York), 1956 . . . . £20/£5
The Mouse House, Macmillan (London), 1958 . £25/£5
ditto, Viking (New York), 1957 . . . . £20/£5
The Story of Holly and Ivy, Macmillan (London), 1958 .
. . . . £25/£5
ditto, Viking (New York), 1958 . . . . £20/£5
Candy Floss, Macmillan (London), 1960 . . £25/£5
ditto, Viking (New York), 1960 . . . . £20/£5
Miss Happiness and Miss Flower, Macmillan (London), 1961 . . . . £25/£5
ditto, Viking (New York), 1961 . . . . £20/£5
Little Plum, Macmillan (London), 1963 . . £25/£5
ditto, Viking (New York), 1963 . . . . £20/£5

Home is the Sailor, Macmillan (London), 1964 . £20/£5
ditto, Viking (New York), 1964 . . . . . £20/£5
The Kitchen Madonna, Macmillan (London), 1967 £20/£5
ditto, Viking (New York), 1967 . . . . . £20/£5
Operation Sippacik, Macmillan (London), 1969 . £15/£5
ditto, Viking (New York), 1969 . . . . . £15/£5
The Diddakoi, Macmillan (London), 1972 . . £20/£5
ditto, Viking (New York), 1972 . . . . . £10/£5
ditto, as *Gypsy Girl*, Harper Collins (London), 2002 £10/£5
The Old Woman Who Lived in a Vinegar Bottle, Macmillan
(London), 1972 . . . . £10/£5
ditto, Viking (New York), 1972 . . . . £10/£5
Mr McFadden's Hallowe'en, Macmillan (London), 1975 .
. . . . £15/£5
ditto, Viking (New York), 1975 . . . . . £10/£5
The Rocking Horse Secret, Macmillan (London), 1977 .
. . . . £15/£5
ditto, Viking (New York), 1978 . . . . . £10/£5
A Kindle of Kittens, Macmillan (London), 1978 . £10/£5
ditto, Viking (New York), 1978 . . . . . £10/£5
The Dragon of Og, Macmillan (London), 1981 . £15/£5
ditto, Viking (New York), 1981 . . . . . £10/£5
Four Dolls, Macmillan (London), 1983 . . £10/£5
ditto, Greenwillow Books (New York), 1983 . . £10/£5
The Valiant Chatti-Maker, Macmillan (London), 1983 .
. . . . £10/£5
ditto, Viking (New York), 1983 . . . . . £10/£5
Mouse Time: Two Stories, Macmillan (London), 1984
(laminated boards) £5
Fu-Dog, Macrae (London), 1990 . . . £10/£5
ditto, Viking (New York), 1990 . . . . . £10/£5
Great Grandfather's House, Macrae (London), 1992 £10/£5
ditto, Greenwillow Books (New York), 1993 . . £10/£5
Listen to the Nightingale, Macmillan (London), 1992 £10/£5
ditto, Viking (New York), 1992 . . . . . £10/£5
The Little Chair, Hodder & Stoughton (London), 1996 (pbk)
. . . . £5
Premlata and the Festival of Lights, Macmillan (London),
1996 . . . . £10/£5
ditto, Greenwillow Books (New York), 1996 . . £10/£5

Poetry
In Noah's Ark, Joseph (London), 1949 . . . £25/£5
ditto, Viking (New York), 1949 . . . . . £25/£5
Saint Jerome and the Lion, Macmillan (London), 1961 .
. . . . £25/£5
ditto, Viking (New York), 1961 . . . . . £25/£5

WILLIAM GOLDING
(b.1911 d.1993)

Golding was an English novelist and poet whose novels
often place his characters in extreme situations, facing
moral dilemmas. While there is no obvious single thread
uniting his works, Golding writes principally about evil,
and his world-view has been described as a kind of dark
optimism. He won the Nobel Prize for Literature in 1983,
and was knighted in 1988.

Novels
Lord of the Flies, Faber (London), 1954 . . £2,500/£250
ditto, Coward-McCann (New York), 1955 . £450/£75

The Inheritors, Faber (London), 1955 . . . £350/£45
ditto, Harcourt Brace (New York), 1962 . . £50/£15
Pincher Martin, Faber (London), 1956 . . .£200/£35
ditto, as *The Two Deaths of Christopher Martin*, Harcourt
Brace (New York), 1956 . . . . . £50/£10
Free Fall, Faber (London), 1959 . . . .£100/£20
ditto, Harcourt Brace (New York), 1960 . . £30/£10
The Spire, Faber (London), 1964 . . . . £30/£10
ditto, Harcourt Brace (New York), 1964 . . £15/£5
The Pyramid, Faber (London), 1967 . . . £30/£10
ditto, Harcourt Brace (New York), 1967 . . £15/£5
Darkness Visible, Faber (London), 1979 . . £25/£10
ditto, Farrar Straus (New York), 1979 . . £15/£5
Rites of Passage, Faber (London), 1980 . . £25/£10
ditto, Farrar Straus (New York), 1980 . . £15/£5
The Paper Men, Faber (London), 1984 . . £20/£5
ditto, Farrar Straus (New York), 1984 . . £15/£5
Close Quarters, Faber (London), 1987 . . £15/£5
ditto, Farrar Straus (New York), 1987 . . £10/£5
Fire Down Below, Faber (London), 1989. . £10/£5
ditto, Farrar Straus (New York), 1989 . . £10/£5
Double Tongue, Faber (London), 1995 . . £10/£5
ditto, Farrar Straus (New York), 1995 . . £10/£5

Short Stories
Sometime, Never: Three Tales of Imagination, Eyre &
Spottiswoode (London), 1956 (with John Wyndham and
Mervyn Peake) . . . .£125/£35
ditto, Ballantine (New York), 1956 (pbk) . . . £20
The Ladder and the Tree, Marlborough College Press
(Marlborough, UK), 1961 (c.100 copies; stapled wraps) .
. . . . £2,000
The Scorpion God: Three Short Novels, Faber (London),
1971 . . . . £35/£10
ditto, Harcourt Brace (New York), 1972 . . £25/£10

Collected Editions
To the Ends of the Earth: A Sea Trilogy ('*Rites of Passage*',
'*Close Quarters*' & '*Fire Down Below*'), Faber (London),
1991 . . . . £20/£5
ditto, Faber (London), 1991 (400 signed, numbered copies,
glassine d/w). . . . . . . £125/£100

Others
Poems, Macmillan (London), 1934 (wraps) . . £4,000
The Brass Butterfly, A Play in Three Acts, Faber (London),
1958 . . . .£100/£15
The Hot Gates and Other Occasional Pieces, Faber
(London), 1965 . . . . . . £35/£10
ditto, Harcourt Brace (New York), 1966 . . £30/£5
A Moving Target, Faber (London), 1982 . . £15/£5
ditto, Farrar Straus (New York), 1982 . . £15/£5
Nobel Lecture, Sixth Chamber Press (Leamington Spa, UK),
1983 (500 copies; stapled wraps) £25
ditto, Sixth Chamber Press (Leamington Spa, UK), 1983 (50
signed, numbered copies bound in leather, slipcase) . .
. . . . £250/£200
An Egyptian Journal, Faber (London), 1985 . . £10/£5
ditto, Farrar Straus (New York), 1985 . . £10/£5

NADINE GORDIMER
(b.1923)

Gordimer is a South African writer, political activist and Nobel Prize winner. Her writing was originally concerned with moral and racial issues in apartheid South Africa, and she has recently been active in HIV/AIDS causes. She has received 15 honorary doctorates, and has won literary prizes in many countries.

Short Stories

Face to Face, Silver Leaf Books (Johannesburg, South Africa), 1949 . . . . . £1,000/£100

The Soft Voice of the Serpent and Other Stories, Simon & Schuster (New York), 1952 . . . £125/£20

ditto, Gollancz, London, 1953 . . . . £125/£20

Six Feet of the Country: Fifteen Short Stories, Gollancz (London), 1956 . . . . . £75/£15

ditto, Simon & Schuster (New York), 1956 . . £65/£10

Friday's Footprint and Other Stories, Gollancz (London), 1960 . . . . . . £65/£10

ditto, Viking (New York), 1960 . . . . £45/£10

Not For Publication and Other Stories, Gollancz (London), 1965 . . . . . . £75/£15

ditto, Viking (New York), 1965 . . . . £30/£5

Livingstone's Companions, Viking (New York), 1971 £30/£5

ditto, Cape (London), 1972 . . . . £30/£5

Selected Stories, Cape (London), 1975 . . £30/£5

ditto, Viking (New York), 1976 . . . . £20/£5

Some Monday For Sure, Heinemann (London), 1976 (pbk) £5

A Soldier's Embrace, Cape (London), 1980 . . £25/£5

ditto, Viking (New York), 1980 . . . £15/£5

Town and Country Lovers, Sylvester & Orphanos (Los Angeles, CA), 1980 (300 signed, numbered copies) . £75

ditto, Sylvester & Orphanos (Los Angeles, CA), 1980 (26 signed, lettered copies) £125

ditto, Sylvester & Orphanos (Los Angeles, CA), 1980 (4 signed copies for private distribution) . . . £250

'But Usually People...', Bookslinger Editions/Toothpaste Press/Walker Art Center (Minneapolis, MN), 1982 (broadside; 90 signed, numbered copies) . . £65

Something Out There, Viking (New York), 1984 . £10/£5

ditto, Cape (London), 1984 . . . . £15/£5

A Correspondence Course and Other Stories, Eurographica (Helsinki), 1986 (350 signed, numbered copies) . £65

Why Haven't You Written, Tales for Travellers (Napa, CA), 1987 (single sheet, map-folded) £10

Jump and Other Stories, David Philip (Cape Town, South Africa), 1991 . . . . . . £25/£5

ditto, Bloomsbury (London), 1991 . . . £15/£5

ditto, Franklin Library (Franklin Centre, PA), 1991 (signed limited edition bound in full leather) . . . £35

ditto, Farrar Straus & Giroux (New York), 1991 . £10/£5

Why Haven't You Written: Selected Stories 1950-1972, Penguin (London), 1992 (pbk) £5

Harald, Claudia and Their Son Duncan, Bloomsbury (London), 1996 (pbk; Bloomsbury Quids series) . . £5

Loot and Other Stories, Farrar Straus & Giroux (New York), 2003 . . . . £10/£5

ditto, Bloomsbury (London), 2003 . . . £10/£5

Beethoven Was One-Sixteenth Black, Bloomsbury (London), 2007 . . . . . . £15/£5

ditto, Farrar Straus & Giroux (New York), 2007 . £10/£5

Novels

The Lying Days, Gollancz (London), 1953 . . £100/£20

ditto, Simon & Schuster (New York), 1953 . . £75/£15

A World of Strangers, Gollancz (London), 1958 . £75/£15

ditto, Simon & Schuster (New York), 1958 . . £65/£10

Occasion for Loving, Victor Gollancz (London), 1963 . . . . £75/£15

ditto, Viking (New York), 1963 . . . . £45/£10

The Late Bourgeois World, Victor Gollancz (London), 1966 . . . . £65/£10

ditto, Viking (New York), 1966 . . . . £40/£10

A Guest of Honour, Viking (New York), 1970 . £30/£5

ditto, Cape (London), 1971 . . . . . £30/£5

The Conservationist, Cape (London), 1974 . . £40/£5

ditto, Viking (New York), 1975 . . . . £20/£5

Burger's Daughter, Cape (London), 1979 . . £25/£5

ditto, Viking (New York), 1979 . . . . £15/£5

July's People, Ravan Press/Taurus (Braamfontein/Emmarentia, South Africa), 1981 . . . . . . £65/£15

ditto, Cape (London), 1981 . . . . . £25/£5

ditto, Viking (New York), 1981 . . . . £15/£5

A Sport of Nature, Cape (London), 1987 . . £15/£5

ditto, Knopf (New York), 1987 . . . . £15/£5

My Son's Story, Bloomsbury (London), 1990 . . £15/£5

ditto, Farrar Straus (New York), ... £10/£5

None to Accompany Me, Davis Philip (Cape Town, South Africa), 1994 . . . . . . £15/£5

ditto, Farrar Straus & Giroux (New York), 1994 . £10/£5

ditto, Bloomsbury (London), 1994 . . . £10/£5

The House Gun, Bloomsbury (London), 1998 . £10/£5

ditto, Farrar, Straus and Giroux (New York), 1998 . £10/£5

The Pickup, Farrar Straus and Giroux (New York), 2001 . . . . £10/£5

ditto, Bloomsbury (London), 2001 . . . £10/£5

Get A Life, Farrar Straus and Giroux (New York), 2005 . . . . £10/£5

ditto, Bloomsbury (London), 2005 . . . £10/£5

Others

African Lectures: The Lectures Given on This Theme at The University of Cape Town's Public Summer School February 1972, Univ of Cape Town (Cape Town, South Africa), 1972 (wraps with black cloth tape spine) . £125

On the Mines, C. Struik (Cape Town, South Africa), 1973 (written with David Goldblatt) . . . . . £100/£20

The Black Interpreters, Spro-Cas/Ravan Press (Johannesburg, South Africa), 1973 (pbk; first issue with two passages by Langa on pps 54 and 60 uncensored) . £250

ditto, Spro-Cas/Ravan Press (Johannesburg, South Africa), 1973 (second issue: passages by Langa on pps.54 and 60 obliterated by black triangles) £50

What Happened to Burger's Daughter; or, How South African Censorship Works, Taurus (Emmarentia, South Africa), 1980 (wraps; includes preface and defence of book by Gordimer) £30

Living in the Interregnum, Rhodes Univ (Grahamstown, South Africa), 1983 (pbk) £40

Lifetimes: Under Apartheid, Cape (London), 1986 (photos by David Goldblatt) . . . . . . £30/£5

ditto, Knopf (New York), 1986 . . . . £20/£5

The Essential Gesture, Cape (London), 1988 . . £15/£5

ditto, as *The Essential Gesture: Writing, Politics and Places*, Knopf (New York), 1988 . . . . £20/£5

Conversations With Nadine Gordimer, Univ Press of
Mississippi (Jackson, MI), 1990 .   .   .   .   £15/£5
Crimes of Conscience, Heinemann (Oxford/Portsmouth,
NH), 1991 (pbk) £5
Writing and Being, Harvard Univ Press (Cambridge, MA/
London), 1995 .   .   .   .   £10/£5
Living in Hope and History: Notes from Our Century,
Farrar Straus & Giroux (New York), 1999 .   .   £10/£5
ditto, Bloomsbury (London), 1999 .   .   .   £10/£5

RODERICK GORDON
AND BRIAN WILLIAMS

The children's book *The Highfield Mole* was originally
self-published before being 'discovered', re-titled *Tunnels*,
and proclaimed 'The Next Harry Potter'. Whatever it's
merits, the original edition commands high prices, but
whether from fans or speculators remains to be seen.

The Highfield Mole, Mathew & Sons (London), 2005 (500
hardback copies; no d/w) £750
ditto, Mathew & Sons (London), 2005 ('Remarque' edition;
80 signed, numbered copies from the above edition; no
d/w) £1,750
ditto, Mathew & Sons (London), 2005 ('Colony Leather
Bound Edition'; 10 signed, numbered copies with a hand-
drawn picture by Williams bound into the book) .   £5,000
ditto, Mathew & Sons (London), 2005 (2,000 pbk copies) .
.   .   .   .£100
ditto, as *Tunnels*, Chicken House (Frome, Somerset), 2007
(pbk) £10
ditto, as *Tunnels*, Chicken House (Frome, Somerset), 2007
(hardback) £10
ditto, as *Tunnels*, Scholastic (New York), 2008 (hbk) .   £10
Deeper, Chicken House (Frome, Somerset), 2008 (pbk)   £5

EDWARD GOREY
(b.1925 d.2000)

Edward St John Gorey was an artist appreciated for his
macabre illustrations of his own books, and the works of
others. Comic and ominous, they appear Victorian or
Edwardian. He has long had a cult following, but became
popularly known through his animated introduction to the
PBS series *Mystery!* in 1980, as well as for his designs for
the 1977 Broadway production of *Dracula* (for which he
won a Tony Award for Best Costume Design along with a
nomination for Best Scenic Design.)

The Unstrung Harp; or, Mr Earbrass Writes a Novel,
Duell, Sloan and Pearce/Little, Brown (New York/Boston),
1953 .   .   .   .   £125/£35
The Listing Attic, Sloan and Pearce/Little, Brown and
Company (New York/Boston), 1954 .   .   £125/£35
ditto, as *The Listing Attic* [and] *The Unstrung Harp*,
Abelard (London), 1974 (no d/w) £45
The Doubtful Guest, Doubleday (New York), 1957 £85/£25
ditto, Putnam (London), 1958 .   .   .   .   £45/£20

The Object Lesson, Doubleday (New York), 1958 . £100/£25
ditto, Anthony Blond (London), 1958 .   .   .   £65/£20
The Bug Book, Looking Glass Library (New York), 1959
(600 copies; stapled wraps) £400
ditto, Epstein & Carroll (New York), 1960 .   £200/£100
The Fatal Lozenge: An Alphabet, Ivan Obolensky (New
York), 1960 (wraps; first edition has '$1.25' on front) £40
ditto, as *The Gorey Alphabet*, Constable (London), 1961 (no
d/w) £35
The Hapless Child, Ivan Obolensky (New York), 1961
(wraps; priced at $1.75) £40
ditto, Anthony Blond (London), 1961 (no d/w) .   £30
ditto, Dodd, Mead & Company (New York), 1980 . £35/£10
The Curious Sofa : A Pornographic Work, Ivan Obolensky
(New York), 1961 (pseud 'Ogdred Weary'; wraps; with
spoof limitation stating 'this is copy no 83 of an edition
limited to 212 copies' in every copy) .   .   .   £35
ditto, Dodd Mead and Company (New York), 1980 £30/£10
The Willowdale Handcar; or The Return of the Black Doll,
Bobbs-Merrill (Indianapolis/New York), 1962 (wraps) £30
ditto, Dodd Mead and Company (New York), 1979   £30/£10
The Beastly Baby, The Fantod Press [New York], 1962
(pseud 'Ogdred Weary'; limited to 500 copies; wraps) £350
ditto, Blue Eyed Dog (UK), [1995] (wraps) .   .   £10
The Vinegar Works/Three Volumes of Moral Instruction,
Simon & Schuster (New York), 1963 (three hardback vols
in slipcase comprising: *The Gashlycrumb Tines, or, After
the Outing*, *The Insect God* and *The West Wing*; no
d/ws) .   .   .   .   £175/£100
The Wuggly Ump, J.B. Lippincott (Philadelphia/New York),
1963 .   .   .   .   £45/£15
The Nursery Frieze, The Fantod Press [New York], 1964
(wraps; limited to 500 copies) £300
The Sinking Spell, Ivan Obolensky (New York), 1964
(wraps) £25
The Remembered Visit: A Story Taken from Life, Simon &
Schuster (New York), 1965 .   .   .   .   £45/£15
Three Books from the Fantod Press, The Fantod Press (New
York), 1966 (500 copies; 3 vols in envelope comprising
The Evil Garden, *The Pious Infant* and *The Inanimate
Tragedy*; wraps) £165
The Gilded Bat, Simon & Schuster (New York), 1966 .   .
.   .   .   .   £40/£20
ditto, Jonathan Cape (London), 1967 .   .   .   £30/£15
The Utter Zoo, Meredith Press (New York), 1967 .   £45/£20
Fletcher and Zenobia, by Victoria Chess and Edward Gorey,
Meredith Press (New York), 1967 .   .   .   £40/£15
The Other Statue, Simon & Schuster (New York), 1968 .
.   .   .   .   £25/£15
The Blue Aspic, Meredith Press (New York), 1968 £35/£15
The Very Fine Clock, by Muriel Spark, Knopf (New York),
1968 (drawings by Edward Gorey) .   .   .   £45/£20
ditto, Macmillan (London), 1969 .   .   .   £25/£10
The Iron Tonic, Albondocani Press (New York), 1969 (200
signed, numbered copies; wraps) £200
ditto, Albondocani Press (New York), 1969 (26 signed,
lettered copies; wraps) £300
The Epileptic Bicycle, Dodd, Mead & Company (New
York), 1969 (first edition has '$3' on d/w) .   £40/£15
Why We Have Day and Night, by Peter F. Neumeyer &
Edward Gorey, Young Scott Books (New York), 1970 .
.   .   .   .   £45/£20
Three Books from the Fantod Press [II], The Fantod Press
(New York), 1970 (500 copies; 3 vols in envelope

comprising *The Chinese Obelisks*, *Donald Has a Difficulty* and *The Osbick Bird*) £150
The Sopping Thursday, Gotham Book Mart & Gallery (New York), 1970 (500 signed, numbered copies; wraps) .£200
ditto, Gotham Book Mart & Gallery (New York), 1970 (26 signed, lettered copies, each with an original drawing by Gorey laid in; hardback with slipcase) . . . £1,500
ditto, Capricorn Press (Santa Barbara, CA), 1971 (wraps) .
. . . . £15
Three Books from the Fantod Press [III], The Fantod Press (New York), 1971 (500 copies; 3 vols in envelope comprising *The Deranged Cousins or, Whatever*, *The Eleventh Episode* and *[The Untitled Book]*). . .£150
ditto, The Fantod Press (New York), 1971 (26 signed, lettered copies; slipcase) £300
Story for Sara: What Happened to a Little Girl, by Alphonse Allais, Albondocani Press (New York), 1971 (500 signed, numbered copies; wraps) £200
ditto, Albondocani Press (New York), 1971 (26 signed, lettered copies; wraps) £300
The Salt Herring, by Charles Cros, Gotham Book Mart & Gallery (New York), 1971 (300 signed, numbered copies; wraps) £100
ditto, Gotham Book Mart & Gallery (New York), 1971 (26 signed, lettered copies) £200
Fletcher and Zenobia Save the Circus, Dodd, Mead & Company (New York), 1971 (illustrated by Victoria Chess, text by Edward Gorey) . . . . . £40/£15
Two Early Stories, by Ronald Firbank, Albondocani Press (New York), 1971 (226 numbered copies; marbled wraps)
. . . .£200
Leaves from a Mislaid Album, Gotham Book Mart (New York), 1972 (17 cards laid into a green folder, enclosed in envelope; 500 numbered copies) £175
ditto, Gotham Book Mart (New York), 1972 (18 cards laid into a folding box tied with a black ribbon; 50 signed, Roman-numeraled copies). £225
ditto, Gotham Book Mart (New York), 1972 (26 signed, lettered copies) £300
The Awdrey-Gore Legacy, Dodd, Mead (New York), 1972 .
. . . . £35/£15
Amphigorey, G.P Putnam's (New York), 1972 (no difference between the first-fourth and sixth printings) . £50/£20
ditto, G.P Putnam's (New York), 1972 (50 signed, numbered copies; with an original watercolour and ink drawing; enclosed in a black slipcase) £1,000
The Lavender Leotard: or, Going A Lot to the New York City Ballet, Gotham Book Mart (New York), 1973 (1,000 copies; wraps) £40
ditto, Gotham Book Mart, 1973 (100 signed, numbered copies; slipcase) . . . . . £200/£150
ditto, Gotham Book Mart, 1973 (26 signed, lettered copies; slipcase). . . . . . . £300/£250
The Black Doll: A Silent Film, Gotham Book Mart (New York), 1973 (wraps) £50
ditto, Gotham Book Mart (New York), 1973 (100 signed, numbered copies; slipcase) . . . £150/£125
ditto, Gotham Book Mart (New York), 1973 (26 signed, lettered copies; slipcase) . . . . £300/£250
Fantod IV, Three Books from the Fantod Press, The Fantod Press (New York), 1972 (500 copies; 3 vols in envelope comprising *The Abandoned Sock*, *The Disrespectful Summons* and *The Lost Lions*) £125
ditto, The Fantod Press (New York), 1972 (26 signed, lettered copies; slipcase) £300

A Limerick, Salt-Works Press (US), 1973 (brown or orange wraps) £50
Category: Fifty Drawings, Gotham Book Mart (New York), 1973 (wraps). £40
ditto, Gotham Books Mart (New York), 1973 (100 signed, numbered copies) £150
ditto, Gotham Books Mart (New York), 1973 (26 signed, lettered copies) £200
The Glorious Nosebleed, Fifth Alphabet, Dodd, Mead (New York), 1974 . . . . £35/£10
ditto, Dodd, Mead (New York), 1974 (250 signed, numbered copies) £150
ditto, Dodd, Mead (New York), 1974 (26 signed, lettered copies) £200
L'Heure Bleue, The Fantod Press (New York), 1975 (500 signed, numbered copies; wraps) £100
ditto, The Fantod Press (New York), 1975 (26 signed, lettered copies; slipcase) £150
Amphigorey Too, G.P Putnam's (New York), 1975 £35/£15
Les Passementeries Horribles, Albondocani Press (New York), 1976 (300 signed, numbered copies; wraps) .£150
ditto, Albondocani Press (New York), 1976 (26 signed, lettered copies; wraps) £200
The Broken Spoke, Dodd, Mead (New York), 1976 £35/£15
ditto, Dodd, Mead (New York), 1976 (250 signed, numbered copies) £150
ditto, Dodd, Mead (New York), 1976 (26 signed, lettered copies) £200
ditto, Ernest Benn (London), 1979 . . . £35/£15
The Loathsome Couple, Dodd, Mead (New York), 1977 .
. . . . £35/£15
ditto, Dodd, Mead (New York), 1977 (250 signed, numbered copies) £100
ditto, Dodd, Mead (New York), 1977 (26 signed, lettered copies) £150
Dogear Wryde Postcards: Alms for Oblivion Series, Fantod Press (New York), 1978 (16 postcards in a white envelope)
. . . . £75
The Green Beads, Albondocani Press (New York), 1978 (400 signed, numbered copies; wraps) . . .£225
ditto, Albondocani Press (New York), 1978 (26 signed, lettered copies; wraps) £275
Dracula, A Toy Theatre, Scribner's (New York), 1979 (spiral bound) £40
Gorey Posters, Harry N. Abrams (New York), 1979 (wraps)
. . . . £50
Dogear Wryde Postcards: Interpretive Series, Fantod Press (New York), 1979 (13 postcards in a white envelope). £75
ditto, Fantod Press (New York), 1979 (50 signed, numbered sets) £150
ditto, Fantod Press (New York), 1979 (26 signed, lettered sets hand-painted in watercolours by Gorey). . .£500
Dogear Wryde Postcards: Neglected Murderesses Series, Fantod Press (New York), 1980 (12 postcards in a white envelope; 250 signed, numbered sets) . . .£175
Dancing Cats and Neglected Murderesses, Workman Publishing (New York), 1980 (wraps) £30
ditto, Workman Publishing (New York), 1980 (500 signed, numbered copies; wraps) £125
ditto, Workman Publishing (New York), 1980 (26 signed, lettered copies with a tipped-in colophon leaf and alternate wrapper design; wraps) £200
ditto, Dent (London) 1980 (wraps) £20
Les Urnes Utiles, Halty-Ferguson (Cambridge, MA), 1980 (400 signed, numbered copies; wraps) . . .£175

ditto, Halty-Ferguson (Cambridge, MA), 1980 (26 signed, lettered copies; wraps) £250

F.M.R.A., Andrew Alpern (New York), 1980 (33 unbound leaves of various sizes enclosed in linen clamshell box; 400 signed, numbered copies) £250

Le Melange Funeste, Gotham Book Mart (New York), 1981 (500 signed, numbered copies; wraps) . . . £150

ditto, Gotham Book Mart (New York), 1981 (26 signed, lettered copies; wraps) £200

The Dwindling Party, Random House (New York), 1982 (pop-up book; no d/w) £30

ditto, Heinemann (London), 1982 . . . . . £25

The Water Flowers, Congdon & Weed Inc (New York), 1982 . . . . £30/£10

The Prune People, Albondocani Press (New York), 1983 (400 signed, numbered copies). £200

ditto, Albondocani Press (New York), 1983 (26 signed, lettered copies) £250

The Electric Abecedarium, Anne & David Bromer (New York), 1983 (300 signed copies numbered 101-300; wraps) £125

ditto, Anne & David Bromer (New York), 1983 (100 signed copies numbered 1-100; each drawing hand-painted in watercolours by Gorey; wraps in slipcase) . . £1,000

Amphigorey Also, Congdon & Weed (New York), 1983 . . . . £50/£20

ditto, Congdon & Weed (New York), 1983 (250 signed, numbered copies) £250

ditto, Congdon & Weed (New York), 1983 (26 signed, lettered copies) £300

E.D. Ward: A Mercurial Bear, Gotham Book Mart (New York), 1983 (wraps) £35

The Tunnel Calamity, G.P. Putnam's (New York), 1984 (accordion book, viewable through a clear plastic eye-piece fitted into cover board) £45

Les Echanges Malandreux, Metacom Press (Worcester, MA), 1985 (500 signed, numbered copies; wraps) . £200

ditto, Metacom Press (Worcester, MA), 1985 (26 signed, lettered copies; wraps) £250

The Prune People II, Albondocani Press (New York), 1985 (300 signed, numbered copies). £200

ditto, Albondocani Press (New York), 1985 (26 signed, lettered copies) £250

The Improvable Landscape, Albondocani Press (New York), 1986 (300 signed, numbered copies; wraps) . £200

ditto, Albondocani Press (New York), 1986 (26 signed, lettered copies) £250

The Raging Tide: or, The Black Doll's Imbroglio, Beaufort Books (New York), 1987 . . . . . £35/£10

ditto, Beaufort Books (New York), 1987 (200 signed, numbered copies) . . . . . £200/£150

ditto, Beaufort Books (New York), 1987 (26 signed, lettered copies) . . . . . . £300/£250

Q.R.V., Anne and David Bromer (New York), 1989 (290 signed, numbered copies) £150

ditto, Anne and David Bromer (New York), 1989 (110 signed, numbered deluxe copies with illustrations hand-painted in watercolours by Gorey; slipcase) . . £500

ditto, as **The Universal Solvent**, The Fantod Press (New York), 1990 (wraps) £30

The Dripping Faucet: Fourteen Hundred and Fifty Eight Tiny, Tedious and Terrible Tales, Metacom Press (Worcester, MA), 1989 (500 signed, numbered copies; wraps) £200

ditto, Metacom Press (Worcester, MA), 1989 (26 signed, hand-coloured lettered copies) £500

Dogear Wryde Postcards: Tragedies Topiares Series, no publisher [Fantod Press] (New York), 1989 (12 postcards in a white envelope; 250 signed, numbered sets) . . £200

Dogear Wryde Postcards: Menaced Objects Series, no publisher [Fantod Press] (New York), 1989 (16 postcards in a white envelope; 250 signed, numbered sets) . . £200

The Helpless Doorknob: A Shuffled Story, no publisher [Fantod Press] (New York), 1989 (20 laminated cards in a plastic box; 500 signed, numbered sets). . . . £175

Dogear Wryde Postcards: Whatever Next? Series, no publisher [Fantod Press] (New York), 1990 (12 postcards in a white envelope; 250 signed, numbered sets) . . £200

The Tuning Fork, by Eduard Blutig (translated by Mrs Regera Dowdy), The Fantod Press (New York), 1990 (500 signed, numbered copies; wraps; previously published in **Amphigorey Also**; wraps) £150

The Stupid Joke, by Eduard Blutig (translated by Mrs Regera Dowdy), The Fantod Press (New York), 1990 (500 signed, numbered copies; wraps) £150

The Fraught Settee, The Fantod Press (New York), 1990 (500 signed, numbered copies; wraps) . . . £165

La Ballade Troublante, The Fantod Press (New York), 1991 (wraps) £15

The Grand Passion: A Novel, and **The Doleful Domesticity: Another Novel**, The Fantod Press (New York), 1991 (500 signed, numbered sets issued in a white envelope; wraps) £200

The Betrayed Confidence: Seven Series of Dogear Wryde Postcards, Parnasuss Imprints (Orleans, MA), 1992 (bound volume of seven previously issued 'Dogear Wryde' postcard series; wraps) £60

ditto, Parnasuss Imprints (Orleans, MA), 1992 (250 boxed copies with additional loose plate; wraps; slipcase) . £300

The Pointless Book: or, Nature & Art, by Garrod Weedy, The Fantod Press (New York), 1993 (wraps) . . £20

The Floating Elephant, by Dogear Wryde, and **The Dancing Rock**, by Ogred Weary, The Fantod Press (New York), 1993 (wraps) £20

ditto, The Fantod Press (New York), 1993 (100 signed, numbered copies; wraps) £125

The Twelve Terrors of Christmas, by John Updike, Gotham Book Mart (New York), 1993 (500 copies signed by author and artist; stapled wraps) £150

ditto, Gotham Book Mart (New York), 1993 (50 numbered copies signed by author and artist) £250

ditto, Gotham Book Mart (New York), 1993 (26 lettered copies signed by author and artist) £350

Figbash Acrobate, by Aedwyrd Gore, The Fantod Press (New York), 1994 (500 signed, numbered copies; wraps) £125

ditto, The Fantod Press (New York), 1994 (26 signed, lettered copies; wraps) £150

The Retrieved Locket, , The Fantod Press (New York), 1994 (500 signed, numbered copies; wraps) . . . £125

ditto, The Fantod Press (New York), 1994 (26 signed, lettered copies; wraps) £150

The Unknown Vegetable, The Fantod Press (New York), 1995 (500 signed, numbered copies; wraps) . . £125

The Fantod Pack: Interpreted by Madame Groeda Weyrd, Gotham Book Mart (New York), 1995 (20 laminated printed cards and booklet issued in a grey box; 750 signed, numbered copies) . . . . £75 *ditto*, Gotham Book Mart (New York), 1995 (26 signed, lettered copies) £150

ditto, Owl Press (US), [1996] (pirate edition; 20 cards wrapped in a yellow sheet) £25

Q.R.V. Hikuptah: A Dozen Dogear Wryde Postcards, The Fantod Press (New York), 1996 (12 postcards in a white envelope with pictorial stamping; 500 signed, numbered sets) £75

The Just Dessert: Thoughtful Alphabet XI, The Fantod Press (New York), 1997 (750 signed, numbered copies; wraps) £100

ditto, The Fantod Press (New York), 1997 (26 signed, lettered copies; wraps) £150

The Deadly Blotter: Thoughtful Alphabet XVII, The Fantod Press (New York), 1997 (750 signed, numbered copies; wraps) £100

ditto, The Fantod Press (New York), 1997 (26 signed, lettered copies; wraps) £150

The Haunted Tea-Cosy: A Dispirited and Distasteful Diversion for Christmas, Harcourt Brace (New York), 1997 . . . . £45/£10

ditto, Harcourt Brace (New York), 1997 (500 signed, numbered copies in slipcase, with d/w) . . . £125/£75

ditto, Harcourt Brace (New York), 1997 (26 signed, lettered copies in slipcase, with d/w) . . . £150/£125

The Headless Bust: A Melancholy Meditation on the False Millenium, Harcourt Brace (New York), 1999 . £45/£10

ditto, Harcourt Brace (New York), 1999 (500 signed, numbered copies in slipcase, with d/w) . . . £125/£75

ditto, Harcourt Brace (New York), 1999 (26 signed, lettered copies in slipcase, with d/w; with a Bahhumbug beanbag cloth doll) . . . . £150/£125

ELIZABETH GOUDGE

(b.1900 d.1984)

Elizabeth de Beauchamp Goudge was the author of books for children and adults, whose work uses myth and legend, often with an overtly Christian outlook.

Adult Novels

Island Magic, Duckworth (London), 1934 . . £50/£15
ditto, Coward McCann (New York), 1934 . . £25/£10
The Middle Window, Duckworth (London), 1935 . £50/£15
ditto, Coward McCann (New York), 1939 . . £20/£5
A City of Bells, Duckworth (London), 1936 . . £50/£15
ditto, Coward McCann (New York), 1936 . . £25/£5
Towers in the Mist, Duckworth (London), 1938 . £35/£10
ditto, Coward McCann (New York), 1938) . . £25/£10
The Bird in the Tree, Duckworth (London), 1940 . £35/£10
ditto, Coward McCann (New York), 1940 . . £25/£5
The Castle on the Hill, Duckworth (London), 1941 £35/£10
ditto, Coward McCann (New York), 1941 . . £25/£5
Green Dolphin Country, Hodder & Stoughton (London), 1944 . . . . £25/£5
ditto, as *Green Dolphin Street*, Coward McCann (New York), 1944 . . . . £20/£5
The Herb of Grace, Hodder & Stoughton (London), 1948 . . . . £15/£5
ditto, as Pilgrim's Inn, Coward McCann (New York), 1948 . . . . £15/£5
Gentian Hill, Hodder & Stoughton (London),1949 £15/£5

ditto, Coward McCann (New York), 1949 . . £10/£5
The Heart of the Family, Hodder & Stoughton (London),1953 . . . . £10/£5
ditto, Coward McCann (New York), 1953 . . £10/£5
The Rosemary Tree, Hodder & Stoughton (London), 1956 . . . . £10/£5
ditto, Coward McCann (New York), 1956 . . £10/£5
The White Witch, Hodder & Stoughton (London), 1958 . . . . £10/£5
ditto, Coward McCann (New York), 1958 . . £10/£5
The Dean's Watch, Hodder & Stoughton (London), 1960 . . . . £10/£5
ditto, Coward McCann (New York), 1960 . . £10/£5
The Scent of Water, Hodder & Stoughton (London), 1963 . . . . £10/£5
ditto, Coward McCann (New York), 1963 . . £10/£5
The Child from the Sea, Hodder & Stoughton (London), 1970 . . . . £10/£5
ditto, Coward McCann (New York), 1970 . . £10/£5

Collected Editions

The Eliots of Damerosehay, Hodder & Stoughton (London), 1957 (contains *The Bird in the Tree*, *The Herb of Grace* and *The Heart of the Family*) . . . . . £20/£5
ditto, Coward McCann (New York), 1957 . . £20/£5
Three Cities of Bells, Hodder & Stoughton (London), 1965 (containing *A City of Bells*, *Towers in the Mist* and *The Dean's Watch*) . . . . £20/£5
ditto, Coward McCann (New York), 1965) . £4-£6 (£15-£20)

Adult Short Stories

A Pedlar's Pack and Other Stories, Duckworth (London), 1937 . . . . £25/£10
ditto, Coward McCann (New York), 1937 . . £25/£10
The Golden Skylark and Other Stories, Duckworth (London), 1941 . . . . £35/£10
ditto, Coward McCann (New York), 1941 . . £25/£10
The Ikon on the Wall and Other Stories, Duckworth (London), 1943 . . . . £25/£10
Songs and Verses, Duckworth (London), 1947 . £20/£5
ditto, Coward McCann (New York), 1948 . . £15/£5
The Reward of Faith and Other Stories, Duckworth (London), 1950 . . . . £15/£5
ditto, Coward McCann (New York), 1951 . . £10/£5
White Wings: Collected Short Stories, Duckworth (London), 1952 . . . . £20/£5
A Christmas Book: An Anthology of Christmas Stories, Hodder & Stoughton (London), 1967 . . . £15/£5
ditto, Coward McCann (New York), 1967 . . £15/£5
The Ten Gifts, Hodder & Stoughton (London),1969 (edited by Mary Baldwin) . . . . £10/£5
ditto, Coward McCann (New York), 1969 . . £10/£5
A Pattern of People, Hodder & Stoughton (London), 1978 . . . . £10/£5

Plays

Three Plays: Suomi, The Brontes of Haworth, and Fanny Burney, Duckworth (London), 1939 . . . £35/£10

Children's Books

The Fairies' Baby and Other Stories, Foyles (London), 1919 . . . . £75
Sister of the Angels: A Christmas Story, Duckworth (London),1939 . . . . £25/£10

ditto, Coward McCann (New York), 1939   .   .   £15/£5
Smoky-House, Duckworth (London), 1940   .   £35/£10
ditto, Coward McCann (New York),1940.   .   £25/£10
The Well of the Star, Coward McCann (New York), 1941   .
   .   .   .   .   £35/£10
Henrietta's House, Univ of London Press Press/Hodder &
   Stoughton (London), 1942   .   .   .   .   £35/£10
ditto, as *The Blue Hills*, Coward McCann (New York), 1942
   .   .   .   .   £25/£10
The Little White Horse, Univ of London Press (London),
   1946   .   .   .   .   £75/£25
ditto, Coward McCann (New York), 1947   .   £35/£10
Make-Believe, Duckworth (London), 1949   .   £35/£10
ditto, Bentley (New York) 1953 .   .   .   .   £15/£5
The Valley of Song, Univ of London Pres (London), 1951   .
   .   .   .   .   £35/£10
ditto, Coward McCann (New York), 1952   .   £25/£10
Linnets and Valerians, Brockhampton Press (London), 1964
   .   .   .   .   £35/£10
ditto, Coward McCann (New York), 1964   .   £25/£10
ditto, as *The Runaways*, Hodder & Stoughton (London),
   1996 (pbk) £5
I Saw Three Ships, Brockhampton Press, 1969   .   £35/£10
ditto, Coward McCann (New York), 1969   .   £25/£10
The Lost Angel, Hodder & Stoughton (London), 1971 .   .
   .   .   .   .   £25/£10
ditto, Coward McCann (New York), 1971   .   £15/£5

Others
The Elizabeth Goudge Reader, Coward McCann (New
   York), 1946 (edited by Rose Dobbs) .   .   .   £20/£5
ditto, as *At the Sign of the Dolphin: An Elizabeth Goudge
   Anthology*, Hodder & Stoughton (London), 1947   £15/£5
God So Loved the World: A Life of Christ, Hodder &
   Stoughton (London), 1951   .   .   .   .   £10/£5
ditto, Coward McCann (New York), 1951   .   £10/£5
Saint Francis of Assisi, Duckworth (London),1959   £10/£5
ditto, as *My God and My All: The Life of Saint Francis of
   Assisi*, Coward McCann (New York), 1959 .   .   £10/£5
The Joy of the Snow; An Autobiography, Hodder &
   Stoughton (London), 1974   .   .   .   .   £25/£10
ditto, Coward McCann (New York), 1974   .   £20/£5

SUE GRAFTON
(b.1940)

Sue Taylor Grafton is an American author of detective
fiction whose best known works are her 'alphabet' novels,
featuring the credible female private detective Kinsey
Millhone. They are set in and around the fictional town of
Santa Teresa, which is based on the author's primary city
of residence, Santa Barbara, California. Grafton has also
written for television and films.

'Alphabet' Novels
A is for Alibi, Holt (New York), 1982   .   .   £850/£75
ditto, Macmillan (London), 1986   .   .   .   £225/£25
B is for Burglar, Holt (New York), 1985 .   .   £500/£45
ditto, Macmillan (London), 1986   .   .   .   £200/£20
C is for Corpse, Holt (New York), 1986 .   .   £350/£40
ditto, Macmillan (London), 1987   .   .   .   £200/£20
D is for Deadbeat, Holt (New York), 1987 .   .£150/£20

ditto, Macmillan (London), 1987   .   .   .   £75/£10
E is for Evidence, Holt (New York), 1988   .   £90/£15
ditto, Macmillan (London), 1988   .   .   .   £50/£10
F is for Fugitive, Holt (New York), 1989.   .   £35/£10
ditto, Macmillan (London), 1989   .   .   .   £25/£5
G is for Gumshoe, Holt (New York), 1990   .   £25/£5
ditto, Macmillan (London), 1990   .   .   .   £20/£5
H is for Homicide, Holt (New York), 1991   .   £20/£5
ditto, Macmillan (London), 1991   .   .   .   £15/£5
I is for Innocent, Holt (New York), 1992.   .   £15/£5
ditto, Macmillan (London), 1992   .   .   .   £15/£5
J is for Judgment, Holt (New York), 1993   .   £15/£5
ditto, Macmillan (London), 1993   .   .   .   £15/£5
K is for Killer, Holt (New York), 1994 .   .   £15/£5
ditto, Macmillan (London), 1994   .   .   .   £15/£5
L is for Lawless, Holt (New York), 1995 .   .   £15/£5
ditto, Macmillan (London), 1995   .   .   .   £15/£5
M is for Malice, Holt (New York), 1996 .   .   £15/£5
ditto, Macmillan (London), 1997   .   .   .   £15/£5
N is for Noose, Holt (New York), 1998   .   .   £15/£5
ditto, Macmillan (London), 1998   .   .   .   £15/£5
O is for Outlaw, Macmillan (London), 1999   .   .£200/£50
ditto, Easton Press (Norfolk, Ct) 1999 (1,000 signed copies,
   no d/w) £85
ditto, Holt (New York), 1999   .   .   .   .   £15/£5
P is for Peril, Putnam (New York), 2001 .   .   £10/£5
ditto, Macmillan (London), 2001   .   .   .   £10/£5
Q is for Quarry, Putnam (New York), 2002   .   £10/£5
ditto, Macmillan (London), 2002   .   .   .   £10/£5
R is for Ricochet, Putnam (New York), 2004 .   £10/£5
ditto, Macmillan (London), 2004   .   .   .   £10/£5
S is for Silence, Putnam (New York), 2005   .   £10/£5
ditto, Macmillan (London), 2006   .   .   .   £10/£5
T is for Trespass, Putnam (New York), 2007 .   £10/£5
ditto, Macmillan (London), 2008   .   .   .   £10/£5
U is for Undertow, Putnam (New York), 2009   .   £10/£5

Short Stories
Kinsey and Me, Bench Press (Santa Barbara, CA), 1991 (300
   signed, numbered copies, slipcase) .   .   .   £400/£350
ditto, Bench Press (Santa Barbara, CA), 1991 (26 signed,
   lettered copies, slipcase) £1,000

Other Novels
Keziah Dane, Macmillan (New York), 1967 .   .£400/£35
ditto, Owen (London), 1968.   .   .   .   .£300/£25
The Lolly Madonna War, Owen (London), 1969 .£400/£25

KENNETH GRAHAME
(b.1859 d.1932)

A Scottish novelist, Grahame was successful as an essayist
before he turned to short stories and then the classic
children's novel *The Wind in the Willows*. The book was
originally written for his son, who is reputed to have shared
the waywardness and bluster of Toad of Toad Hall.

'Wind in the Willows' Titles
Wind in the Willows, Methuen (London), 1908   .   £5,000
ditto, Scribner's (New York), 1908   .   .   .   .£125
ditto, Bodley Head (London), 1931 (illustrated by E.H.
   Shepard)   .   .   .   .   £500/£200

ditto, Bodley Head (London), 1931 (illustrated by E.H. Shepard, 200 copies signed by author and artist) .　.　.
.　.　.　.　.　.　.　.　. £4,000/£3,000

ditto, Limited Editions Club (New York), 1940 (16 colour plates by Arthur Rackham, deluxe 2,020 copies, signed by the designer Bruce Rogers, cloth-backed patterned boards, slipcase)　.　.　.　.　.　. £650/£500

ditto, Heritage Press (New York), 1940 (12 colour plates and 14 line drawings by Arthur Rackham, blue-mauve cloth) .
.　.　.　.　.　.　.　.　. £175/£75

ditto, Methuen (London), 1950 (illustrated by Arthur Rackham, green cloth)　.　.　.　.　. £175/£75

ditto, Methuen (London), 1951 (illustrated by Arthur Rackham, deluxe 500 copies, full white calf)　. £1,250

First Whisper of 'The Wind in the Willows', Methuen (London), 1944 .　.　.　.　.　.　. £25/£10

ditto, Lippincott (Philadelphia, PA), 1945.　.　. £25/£10

Sweet Home, Methuen (London), 1946　.　.　. £30/£10

Toad Goes Caravanning, Methuen (London), 1947 £30/£10

Bertie's Escapade, Methuen (London), 1949 (illustrated by E.H. Shepard)　.　.　.　.　.　.　. £75/£20

ditto, Lippincott (Philadelphia, PA), 1949.　.　. £75/£20

Other Titles

The Pagan Papers, Mathews & Lane (London), 1894 [1893] (450 [615] copies, frontispiece by Aubrey Beardsley). £100

The Golden Age, John Lane (London), 1895 .　.　. £125

ditto, Stone and Kimball (Chicago), 1895 .　.　.　. £65

ditto, Bodley Head (London), 1900 [1899] (illustrated by Maxfield Parrish, first issue with 16 pages of ads at back dated 1895) .　.　.　.　.　.　.　.　. £100

ditto, Bodley Head (London), 1928 (illustrated by E.H. Shepard)　.　.　.　.　.　.　. £75/£45

ditto, Bodley Head (London), 1928 (illustrated by E.H. Shepard, 275 copies signed by author and artist; slipcase).
.　.　.　.　.　.　.　.　. £400/£300

ditto, Dodd, Mead (New York), 1929 (illustrated by E.H. Shepard)　.　.　.　.　.　.　. £65/£35

Dream Days, John Lane (New York), 1899 [1898] (first issue with 15 pages of ads at back dated 1898)　.　. £125

ditto, John Lane/Bodley Head (London), 1902 (illustrated by Maxfield Parrish).　.　.　.　.　.　. £125

ditto, Bodley Head (London), 1930 (illustrated by E.H. Shepard)　.　.　.　.　.　.　. £125/£35

ditto, Bodley Head (London), 1930 (illustrated by E.H. Shepard, 275 copies signed by author and artist) £400/£300

ditto, Dodd, Mead (New York), 1930 (illustrated by E.H. Shepard)　.　.　.　.　.　.　. £65/£35

The Headswoman, John Lane/Bodley Head (London), 1898 (wraps) .　.　.　.　.　.　.　.　.　. £45

ditto, Dodd. Mead (New York), 1921　.　.　. £75/£25

Fun o' the Fair, Dent (London), 1929 (wraps)　.　. £15

The Kenneth Grahame Book, Methuen (London), 1932　.
.　.　.　.　.　.　.　.　.　. £40/£10

The Reluctant Dragon, Garden City Pub. Co. (New York), 1941 .　.　.　.　.　.　.　.　.　. £150/£75

ditto, Holiday House (New York), 1953 (illustrated by E.H. Shepard)　.　.　.　.　.　.　. £65/£15

ditto, Holt, Rinehart & Winston (New York), 1983 (illustrated by Michael Hague).　.　.　. £25/£10

ditto, Methuen (London), 1983 (illustrated by Michael Hague)
.　.　.　.　.　.　.　.　.　. £25/£10

GÜNTER GRASS
(b.1927)

Günter Wilhelm Grass is a Nobel Prize-winning author and playwright born in Gdańsk, Poland who has lived in West Germany since 1945. He is best known for his first novel, *The Tin Drum*, a key text in European magic realism. His works frequently have a strong left wing political dimension, but in 2006 Grass caused controversy with his belated disclosure of Waffen-SS service during the final months of World War II.

Novels

Die Blechtrommel, Luchterhand (Darmstadt, Germany), 1959 .　.　.　.　.　.　.　.　. £300/£35

ditto, as ***The Tin Drum***, Secker & Warburg (London), 1962 (translated by Ralph Manheim)　.　.　. £65/£10

ditto, Pantheon Books (New York), 1962 .　.　. £65/£10

Katz und Maus, Luchterhand (Neuwied/Berlin), 1961 .　.
.　.　.　.　.　.　.　.　.　. £100/£15

ditto, as ***Cat and Mouse***, Secker & Warburg (London), 1963 (translated by Ralph Manheim)　.　.　. £45/£10

ditto, Harcourt Brace and World (New York), 1963 £45/£10

Hundejahre, Luchterhand (Neuwied/Berlin), 1963. £45/£10

ditto, as ***Dog Years***, Secker & Warburg (London), 1965 (translated by Ralph Manheim)　.　.　. £45/£10

ditto, Harcourt Brace and World (New York), 1965 £45/£10

Örtlich Betäubt, Luchterhand (Neuwied/Berlin), 1969 .
.　.　.　.　.　.　.　.　.　. £20/£5

ditto, as ***Local Anaesthetic***, Secker & Warburg (London), 1970 (translated by Ralph Manheim)　.　. £15/£5

ditto, Harcourt Brace and World (New York), 1970 £15/£5

Der Butt, Luchterhand (Darmstadt, Germany), 1977 £10/£5

ditto, as ***The Flounder***, Harcourt Brace Jovanovich (New York) 1978 (translated by Ralph Manheim) .　. £10/£5

ditto, Secker & Warburg (London), 1978 .　.　. £10/£5

ditto, The Limited Editions Club (New York), 1985 (1,000 signed copies; grey linen boards and backed with genuine eelskin; slipcase).　.　.　.　.　. £300/£250

Das Treffen in Telgte, Luchterhand (Darmstadt, Germany), 1979 .　.　.　.　.　.　.　.　.　. £10/£5

ditto, as ***The Meeting at Telgte***, Harcourt Brace Jovanovich (New York) 1981 (translated by Ralph Manheim) £10/£5

ditto, Secker & Warburg (London), 1981 .　.　. £10/£5

ditto, Franklin Library (Franklin Centre, PA), 1981 (full leather limited edition.　.　.　.　.　.　. £10

Die Rättin, Luchterhand (Darmstadt, Germany), 1986 £10/£5

ditto, as ***The Rat***, Harcourt Brace Jovanovich (New York) 1986 (translated by Ralph Manheim)　.　. £10/£5

ditto, Secker & Warburg (London), 1987 .　.　. £10/£5

Unkenrufe, Steidl Verlag (Gottingen), 1992 .　. £10/£5

ditto, as ***The Call of the Toad***, Harcourt Brace Jovanovich (New York) 1992 (translated by Ralph Manheim) £10/£5

ditto, Secker & Warburg (London), 1992 .　.　. £10/£5

Ein weites Feld, Steidl (Göttingen), 1995 .　. £10/£5

ditto, as ***Too Far Afield***, Harcourt Brace & Co (New York), 2000 (translated by Krishna Winston)　.　.　. £10/£5

ditto, Faber (London), 2000 .　.　.　.　.　. £10/£5

Mein Jahrhundert, Steidl (Göttingen), 1999 .　. £10/£5

ditto, as ***My Century***, Harcourt Brace & Co (New York), 1999 (translated by Michael Henry Heim)　.　. £10/£5

ditto, Faber (London), 1999 .　.　.　.　.　. £10/£5

Im Krebsgang, Steidl (Göttingen), 2002 .　.　. £10/£5

ditto, as **Crabwalk**, Harcourt Brace & Co (New York), 2002 (translated by Krishna Winston) . . . £10/£5
ditto, Faber (London), 2003 . . . . . £10/£5

Plays
Die Plebejer proben den Aufstand, Luchterhand (Neuwied/Berlin), 1966 . . . . . . £20/£5
ditto, as **The Plebeians Rehearse the Uprising**, Harcourt Brace and World (New York), 1966 (translated by Ralph Manheim) . . . . . . £20/£5
ditto, Secker & Warburg (London), 1967 . . . £20/£5
Four Plays, Harcourt, Brace & World (New York), 1967 .
. . . . £15/£5
ditto, Secker & Warburg (London), 1968 . . . £15/£5

Poetry
Selected Poems, Harcourt, Brace & World (New York), 1966 (translated by Michael Hamburger and Christopher Middleton) . . . . £15/£5
ditto, Secker & Warburg (London), 1966 . . £15/£5
Ausgefragt, Luchterhand (Berlin), 1967 (pbk). . . £20
ditto, as **New Poems**, Harcourt, Brace & World (New York), 1968 (translated by Michael Hamburger) . . £15/£5
Poems of Günter Grass, Penguin (Harmondsworth, Middlesex), 1969 (pbk; translated by Michael Hamburger and Christopher Middleton) £10
In the Egg and Other Poems, Harcourt Brace Jovanovich (New York) 1977 (translated by Michael Hamburger and Christopher Middleton) . . . . . £10/£5
ditto, Secker & Warburg (London), 1978 . . £10/£5
Novemberland: Selected Poems, Harcourt Brace & Co, (New York) 1996 . . . . . £10/£5
Selected Poems 1956-93, Faber (London), 1999 (pbk) . £5

Non-Fiction
Über das Selbstverständliche. Reden - Aufsätze - Offene Briefe - Kommentare, Luchterhand (Neuwied/Berlin), 1968 . . . . £20/£5
ditto, as **Speak Out! Speeches, Open Letters, Commentaries**, Secker & Warburg (London), 1969 (translated by Ralph Manheim) . . . . . . £15/£5
ditto, Harcourt Brace and World (New York), 1969 £15/£5
Aus dem Tagebuch einer Schnecke, Luchterhand (Neuwied/Berlin), 1972 . . . . . £15/£5
From the Diary of a Snail, Harcourt Brace Jovanovich (New York) 1973 (translated by Ralph Manheim) . . £10/£5
ditto, Secker & Warburg (London), 1974 . . . £10/£5
Kopfgeburten oder Die Deutschen sterben aus, Luchterhand (Darmstadt, Germany), 1980 . . . £10/£5
ditto, as **Headbirths, or, the Germans are Dying Out**, Harcourt Brace Jovanovich (New York) 1982 (translated by Ralph Manheim) . . . . . £10/£5
ditto, Secker & Warburg (London), 1982 . . . £10/£5
Zunge zeigen. Ein Tagebuch in Zeichnungen, Luchterhand (Darmstadt, Germany), 1988 . . . . £10/£5
ditto, as **Show Your Tongue**, Harcourt Brace Jovanovich (New York) 1989 (translated John E. Woods) . £10/£5
ditto, Secker & Warburg (London), 1989 . . . £10/£5
Two States One Nation?, Harcourt Brace Jovanovich (New York) 1990 (translated Rishna Winston with A.S. Wensinger) . . . . £10/£5
ditto, Secker & Warburg (London), 1990 . . . £10/£5
Beim Häuten der Zwiebel, Steidl (Göttingen), 2006 £10/£5

ditto, as **Peeling the Onion**, Harcourt Brace & Co (New York), 2007 (translated by Michael Henry Heim) £10/£5
ditto, Harvill Secker (London), 2007 . . . £10/£5

Others
Kinderlied, Lord John Press (Northridge, CA), 1982 (300 signed copies) £50
ditto, Lord John Press (Northridge, CA), 1982 (50 signed deluxe copies) £75
Drawings and Words 1954-1977: Graphics and Writing, Harcourt Brace Jovanovich (New York) 1983 . £25/£10
ditto, Secker & Warburg (London), 1983 . . . £25/£10
ditto, Secker & Warburg (London), 1983 (250 signed copies with original etching) £200
Etchings and words, 1972-1982, Harcourt Brace Jovanovich (New York) 1985 . . . . . . £25/£10
The Günter Grass Reader, Harcourt Brace & Co (New York), 2004 . . . . £10/£5

SHIRLEY ANN GRAU
(b.1929)

Shirley Ann Grau is an award-winning American novelist and short story writer whose work is set primarily in the deep South, exploring issues of race and gender. *The Keepers of the House* was awarded the 1965 Pulitzer Prize for Fiction.

Short Stories
The Black Prince, and Other Stories, Knopf (New York), 1955 (first issue d/w without reviews) . . . £75/£15
ditto, Knopf (New York), 1955 (second issue d/w with reviews). . . . . . . £50/£15
ditto, Heinemann (London), 1956 . . . . £45/£10
The Wind Shifting West, Knopf (New York), 1973 £20/£5
ditto, Chatto & Windus (London), 1974 . . £15/£5
Nine Women, Knopf (New York), 1986 . . . £10/£5
ditto, Franklin Library (Franklin Centre, PA), 1986 (limited edition bound in full leather) £15
Selected Stories, Louisiana State Univ Press (Baton Rouge, LA), 2003 . . . . £10/£5

Novels
The Hard Blue Sky, Knopf (New York), 1958 . £30/£10
ditto, Heinemann (London), 1959 . . . . £25/£10
The House on Coliseum Street, Knopf (New York), 1961 .
. . . . £45/£10
ditto, Heinemann (London), 1961 . . . . £10/£5
The Keepers of the House, Knopf (New York), 1964 . .
. . . . £50/£10
ditto, Longmans (London), 1964. . . . £25/£10
ditto, Franklin Library (Franklin Centre, PA), 1977 (limited edition bound in full leather) £15
The Condor Passes, Knopf (New York), 1971 . £20/£5
ditto, Longmans (London), 1972. . . . £15/£5
Evidence of Love, Knopf (New York), 1977 . . £10/£5
ditto, Franklin Library (Franklin Centre, PA), 1977 (limited edition bound in full leather) £15
ditto, Hamish Hamilton (London), 1977 . . . £10/£5
Roadwalkers, Knopf (New York), 1994 . . . £10/£5

ROBERT GRAVES
(b.1895 d.1985)

Graves was an English poet and novelist. The horror of his experiences in World War One had a profound effect upon him and this is reflected in his first volume of verse, *Over The Brazier*. In 1929 he published his autobiography, *Goodbye to All That*. It was a success, but cost him many of his friends, including Siegfried Sassoon. Graves lived on Majorca for most of his life.

Poetry

Over the Brazier, The Poetry Bookshop (London), 1916 (wraps) £750
ditto, The Poetry Bookshop (London), 1917 (wraps) . £300
ditto, The Poetry Bookshop (London), 1920 . . £125/£35
Goliath and David, Chiswick Press (London), 1916 (200 copies; sewn wraps) £1,500
Fairies and Fusiliers, Heinemann (London), 1917 . . . . £750/£125
ditto, Knopf (New York), 1918 . . . . . £250/£75
Treasure Box, [Chiswick Press (London), 1919] (200 copies; sewn wraps) £750
ditto, [Chiswick Press (London), 1919] (200 copies, boards and d/w). . . . . . . £1,250/£850
Country Sentiment, Secker (London), 1920 . . £200/£40
ditto, Knopf (New York), 1920 . . . . £175/£35
The Pier-Glass, Secker (London), 1921 . . . £300/£75
ditto, Knopf (New York), 1921 (green cloth) . £250/£45
ditto, Knopf (New York), 1921 (orange paper-covered boards) . . . . £250/£45
Whipperginny, Heinemann (London), 1923 . £225/£45
ditto, Knopf (New York), 1923 . . . . £150/£35
The Feather Bed, Hogarth Press (Richmond, Surrey), 1923 (250 copies, signed by the author) £500
Mock Beggar Hall, Hogarth Press (London), 1923 (no d/w) £400
Welchman's Hose, The Fleuron (London), 1925 (525 copies, glassine d/w). . . . . . £175/£125
Poems, Benn (London), 1925 (stapled wraps) . . £40
The Marmosite's Miscellany, Hogarth Press (London), 1925 (pseud 'John Doyle') £400
ditto, Pharos Press (Victoria, BC, Canada), 1975 (80 signed, numbered copies on Strathmore's Grandee paper, slipcase) . . . . £85/£50
ditto, Pharos Press (Victoria, BC, Canada), 1975 (670 signed, numbered copies on Rolland's Zephyr Book paper, slipcase) . . . . £65/£45
Poems, 1914-1926, Heinemann (London), 1927 . £165/£65
ditto, Doubleday, Doran (New York), 1929 . £165/£65
Poems, 1914-1927, Heinemann (London), 1927 (115 signed, numbered copies, slipcase and d/w) . £500/£300
Poems, 1929, Seizin Press (London), 1929 (225 signed, numbered copies) £300
Ten Poems More, Hours Press (Paris), 1930 (200 signed copies) £250
Poems, 1926-1930, Heinemann (London), 1931 (first issue with misbound title-page) . . . . £100/£25
To Whom Else?, Seizin Press (Majorca), 1931 (200 signed copies, glassine d/w) . . . . £250/£200
Poems, 1930-1933, Barker (London), 1933 (no d/w) . £150
Collected Poems, Cassell (London), 1938 . £100/£20
ditto, Random House (New York), 1939 . . £100/£10

No More Ghosts: Selected Poems, Faber (London), 1940 . . . . £50/£15
Poems, Eyre & Spottiswoode (London), 1943 (wraps) . £30
Poems, 1938-1945, Cassell (London), 1946 . £35/£10
ditto, Creative Age Press (New York), 1946 . £35/£10
Collected Poems, 1914-1947, Cassell (London), 1948 . . . . £50/£15
Poems and Satires, Cassell (London), 1951 . £35/£10
Poems, 1953, Cassell (London), 1953 . . . £35/£10
ditto, Cassell (London), 1953 (250 signed, numbered copies, tissue d/w) . . . . . £200/£150
Collected Poems, 1955, Doubleday (New York), 1955 . . . . £35/£10
Poems Selected by Himself, Penguin (Harmondsworth, Middlesex), 1957 (pbk) £5
The Poems of Robert Graves, Doubleday (New York), 1958 . . . . £25/£5
Collected Poems, 1959, Cassell (London), 1959 £75/£35
More Poems, 1961, Cassell (London), 1961 . £20/£5
Collected Poems, Doubleday (New York), 1961 . £35/£10
New Poems, 1962, Cassell (London), 1962 . £25/£5
The More Deserving Cases: Eighteen Old Poems for Reconsideration, Marlborough College Press (Marlborough, VT), 1962 (350 signed copies bound in blue buckram) £100
ditto, Marlborough College Press (Marlborough, VT), 1962 (400 signed copies, bound in morocco) . . . £100
Man Does, Woman Is, Cassell (London), 1964 £25/£10
ditto, Cassell (London), 1964 (175 copies, signed by the author) . . . . . . £100/£65
ditto, Doubleday (New York), 1964 . . . £25/£10
Love Respelt, Cassell (London), 1965 (250 signed copies) . . . . £125/£75
ditto, Doubleday (New York), 1966 . . . £25/£10
Collected Poems, 1965, Cassell (London), 1965 £20/£5
Seventeen Poems Missing From 'Love Respelt', privately printed at the Stellar Press (London), 1966 (330 copies, signed by the author) . . . . . £60/£40
Colophon to 'Love Respelt', privately printed at the Stellar Press (London), 1967 (386 copies, signed by the author) . . . . £75/£50
Poems, 1965-1968, Cassell (London), 1968 . £15/£5
Poems About Love, Cassell (London), 1969 . £25/£10
Love Respelt Again, Doubleday (New York), 1969 (1,000 numbered copies, signed by the author) . . £50/£25
Beyond Giving, privately printed at the Stellar Press for Bertram Rota (London), 1969 (536 copies, signed by the author, card covers, d/w) . . £65/£45
Poems, 1968-1970, Cassell (London), 1970 . £20/£10
Advice from a Mother, Poem-of-the-Month-Club (London), 1970 (broadsheet) £25
The Green-Sailed Vessel, privately printed at the Stellar Press for Bertram Rota (London), 1971 (536 copies) . . . . £65/£45
Poems: Abridged for Dolls and Princes, Cassell (London), 1971 . . . . £25/£10
Poems, 1970-1972, Cassell (London), 1972 . £25/£10
Deya: A Portfolio, Motif Editions (London), 1972 (75 signed copies) £225
Timeless Meeting: Poems, privately printed at the Stellar Press for Bertram Rota (London), 1973 (536 signed, numbered copies) . . . . . . £60/£45
At the Gate, privately printed at the Stellar Press for Bertram Rota (London), 1974 (536 copies) . . £50/£35

Collected Poems, 1975, Cassell (London), 1975 . £25/£10
New Collected Poems, Doubleday (New York), 1977 . .
. . . . £25/£10
Across the Gulf, Late Poems, The New Seizin Press (Majorca), 1992 (175 copies) £75

Fiction
My Head! My Head!, Secker (London), 1925 (500 copies).
. . . . £250/£150
ditto, Knopf (New York), 1925 . . . . £200/£50
The Shout, Mathews & Marrot (London), 1929 (530 signed, numbered copies) . . . . . £125/£100
No Decency Left, Cape (London), 1932 (pseud 'Barbara Rich', with Laura Riding) . . . . £3,000/£500
The Real David Copperfield, Barker (London), 1933 (spine stamped in gold) . . . . . £225/£65
ditto, Barker (London), 1933 (spine stamped in black) .
. . . . £150/£35
ditto, as *David Copperfield*, Harcourt Brace (New York), 1934 (abridged version condensed by Robert Graves) .
. . . . £45/£15
I, Claudius, Barker (London), 1934 (black cloth) £750/£150
ditto, Barker (London), 1934 (remainder copies, orange cloth) . . . . £700/£100
ditto, Smith & Haas (New York), 1934 . . £450/£25
Claudius the God and his Wife Messalina, Barker (London), 1934 . . . . . . £250/£75
ditto, Smith & Haas (New York), 1935 (first word on back jacket flap 'suddenly', blue cloth blind stamped on front) .
. . . . £150/£25
ditto, Smith & Haas (New York), 1935 (first word on back jacket flap 'At', dark blue cloth stamped in gold) £100/£25
Antigua, Penny, Puce, Seizin Press (Majorca)/Constable (London), 1936 (first issue with 'ytyle' instead of 'style' (page 100, line 11), 'being' instead of 'been' (page 103, line 15) and a lowered l as the last letter on page 293) .
. . . . £250/£75
ditto, as *The Antigua Stamp*, Random House (New York), 1937 . . . . £200/£35
Count Belisarius, Cassell (London), 1938 . £200/£25
ditto, Random House (New York), 1938 . . £65/£10
Sergeant Lamb of the Ninth, Methuen (London), 1940. .
. . . . £75/£10
ditto, Random House (New York), 1941 . . £25/£10
Proceed, Sergeant Lamb, Methuen (London), 1941 £75/£25
ditto, Random House (New York), 1941 . . £65/£20
Wife to Mr Milton: The Story of Mary Powell, Cassell (London), 1943 . . . . . £40/£15
ditto, Creative Age Press (New York), 1944 . £25/£10
The Golden Fleece, Cassell (London), 1944 . £45/£15
ditto, as *Hercules, My Shipmate*, Creative Age Press (New York), 1945 . . . . . . £35/£15
King Jesus, Creative Age Press (New York), 1946 £25/£10
ditto, Cassell (London), 1946 . . . . £25/£10
Watch the North Wind Rise, Creative Age Press (New York), 1949 . . . . £40/£15
ditto, as *Seven Days in New Crete*, Cassell (London), 1949 .
. . . . £35/£10
The Islands of Unwisdom, Doubleday (New York), 1949 .
. . . . £25/£10
ditto, as *The Isles of Unwisdom*, Cassell (London), 1950 .
. . . . £25/£10
Homer's Daughter, Cassell (London), 1955 . . £35/£10
ditto, Doubleday (New York), 1955 . . . £25/£10

Catacrok! Mostly Stories, Mostly Funny, Cassell (London), 1956 . . . . £30/£10
They Hanged My Saintly Billy, Cassell (London), 1957 .
. . . . £25/£10
ditto, Doubleday (New York), 1957 . . . £25/£10
Collected Short Stories, Doubleday (New York), 1964. .
. . . . £30/£10
ditto, Cassell (London), 1965 . . . . £25/£10

Plays
John Kemp's Wager: A Ballad Opera, Blackwell (Oxford), 1925 (100 signed, numbered copies) £450
ditto, Blackwell (Oxford), 1925 (750 unsigned copies) . £55
ditto, French (New York), 1925 (250 copies) . . . £100

Children's Books
The Penny Fiddle: Poems for Children, Cassell (London), 1960 (illustrated by Edward Ardizzone). . . £125/£50
ditto, Doubleday (New York), 1960 . . £40/£10
The Big Green Book, Crowell-Collier (New York), 1962 (illustrated by Maurice Sendak) . . . £35/£10
ditto, Kestrel (London), 1962 . . . . £35/£10
Ann at Highwood Hall: Poems for Children, Cassell (London), 1964 (illustrated by Edward Ardizzone) £60/£20
ditto, Doubleday (New York), 1964 . . . £45/£15
Two Wise Children, Quist (New York), 1967 . . £35/£10
The Poor Boy Who Followed His Star, Cassell (London), 1968 . . . . £35/£10
ditto, Doubleday (New York), 1969 . . . £35/£10
An Ancient Castle, Peter Owen (London), 1980 . £20/£5
ditto, Kesend (New York), 1981 . . . . £15/£5

Translations
Almost Forgotten Germany, by George Schwarz, Constable (London)/Seizin Press (Majorca), 1936 (with Laura Riding)
. . . . £900/£200
The Transformations of Lucius, Otherwise Known as the Golden Ass, by Lucius Apuleius, Penguin (Harmondsworth, Middlesex), 1950 (2,000 signed, numbered copies, slipcase). . . . . . . £75/£45
ditto, Penguin (Harmondsworth, Middlesex), 1950 (pbk) £5
ditto, Farrar, Straus, Giroux (New York), 1951 . £20/£5
The Cross and the Sword from 'Enriquillio', by Manuel de Jesus Galvan, Univ Press: Bloomington (Bloomington, IN), 1954 . . . . £40/£10
ditto, Gollancz (London), 1956 . . . £40/£10
The Infant with the Globe from 'El Nino do la Bola', by Pedro de Alarcon, Trianon Press (London), 1955. £30/£5
ditto, Yoseloff (New York), 1959 . . . £30/£5
Winter in Majorca, by George Sand, Cassell (London), 1956
. . . . £20/£5
ditto, Valldemosa Edition (Mallorca), 1959 (pbk) . £10
Pharsalia, by Lucan, Penguin (Harmondsworth, Middlesex), 1956 (pbk) £5
ditto, Penguin (New York), 1957 . . . £15/£5
The Twelve Caesars, by Suetonius, Penguin (Harmondsworth, Middlesex), 1957 (pbk). £5
The Anger of Achilles: Homer's Iliad, Homer, Doubleday (New York), 1959 . . . . . . £35/£10
ditto, Cassell (London), 1960 . . . . £25/£10
The Rubaiyat of Omar Khayyam, by Omar Khayyam, Cassell (London), 1967 (with Omar Ali-Shah) . £20/£5
ditto, Doubleday (New York), 1968 . . . £20/£5

The Song of Songs, Clarkson Potter (New York), 1973 .
. . . . £20/£5
ditto, Collins (London), 1973 . . . . £20/£5

Others

On English Poetry, Knopf (New York), 1922. .£200/£30
ditto, Heinemann (London), 1922 (first issue yellow cloth) .
. . . .£200/£35
ditto, Heinemann (London), 1922 (second issue decorated boards with label) . . . .£175/£20
The Meaning of Dreams, Cecil Palmer (London), 1924 .
. . . . £100/£35
ditto, Greenberg (New York), 1925 . . . £50/£20
Poetic Unreason and Other Studies, Cecil Palmer (London), 1925 . . . . . . £75/£25
Contemporary Techniques of Poetry: A Political Analogy, Hogarth Press (London), 1925 (wraps) . . . £50
Another Future of Poetry, Hogarth Press (London), 1926 .
. . . .£100
Impenetrability, or the Proper Habit of English, Hogarth Press (London), 1927. . . . .£150
The English Ballad: A Short Critical Survey, Benn (London), 1927 . . . . .£100/£25
ditto, as **English and Scottish Ballads**, Heinemann (London), 1957 (revised edition) . . . £25/£10
Lars Porsena, or 'The Future of Swearing and Improper Language', Kegan Paul, Trench, Trubner (London), 1927
. . . . £200/£30
ditto, Dutton (New York), 1927. . . .£175/£25
ditto, as **The Future of Swearing and Improper Language**, Kegan Paul, Trench, Trubner (London), 1936 (revised edition) . . . . . .£25/£10
ditto, as **The Future of Swearing and Improper Language**, Martin Brian & O'Keefe (London), 1972 (100 signed copies) £125
A Survey of Modernist Poetry, Heinemann (London), 1927 (with Laura Riding) . . . .£75/£20
ditto, Doubleday, Doran & Co (Garden City, NY), 1928 .
. . . . £50/£15
Lawrence and the Arabs, Cape (London), 1927 .£200/£30
ditto, as **Lawrence and the Arabian Adventure**, Doubleday (New York), 1928 . . . .£175/£25
A Pamphlet Against Anthologies, Cape (London), 1928 (with Laura Riding) . . . .£125/£25
ditto, Doubleday (New York), 1928 . . .£100/£20
Mrs Fisher, or The Future of Humour, Kegan Paul, Trench, Trubner (London), 1928 . . .£65/£20
ditto, Dutton (New York), 1928 . . .£65/£20
Goodbye to All That: An Autobiography, Cape (London), 1929 (first issue with Sassoon poem pps. 341-343) .
. . . . . .£1,250/£750
ditto, Cape (London), 1929 (second issue, poem replaced by asterisks) . . . . . .£600/£45
ditto, Cape & Smith (New York), 1930 . .£300/£35
But it Still Goes On: An Accumulation, Cape (London), 1930 (first impression with 'the child she bare' first para. on p.157) . . . . .£250/£100
ditto, Cape (London), 1930 (second impression with 'child she bare' deleted). . . . .£150/£20
ditto, Cape & Smith (New York), 1931 . .£125/£20
The Seizin Press, Seizin Press (Mallorca), 1931 (broadside prospectus written with Laura Riding, containing a Graves poem) £100

The Seizin Press, Seizin Press (Mallorca), 1931 (broadside advertising *No Trouble*, *Though Gently* and *To Whom Else?* as printed and *Laura and Francisca* to be published in the summer of 1931; written with Laure Riding) .£125
The Long Weekend (with Alan Hodge), Faber (London), 1940 . . . .£40/£10
ditto, Macmillan (New York), 1941 . . .£35/£10
The Reader Over Your Shoulder (with Alan Hodge), Cape (London), 1943 . . . . .£40/£10
ditto, Macmillan (New York), 1943 . . .£35/£10
The White Goddess, Faber (London), 1948 .£75/£20
ditto, Creative Age Press (New York), 1948 .£65/£15
The Common Asphodel: Collected Essays on Poetry, 1922-1949, Hamish Hamilton (London), 1949 .£40/£10
Occupation: Writer, Creative Age Press (New York), 1950.
. . . . £35/£10
ditto, Cassell (London), 1951 . . . £25/£10
The Nazarene Gospel Restored (with Joshua Podro), Cassell (London), 1953 . . . .£125/£30
ditto, Doubleday (New York), 1954 . .£100/£25
The Greek Myths, Penguin (Harmondsworth, Middlesex), 1955 (2 vols; pbk) £10
ditto, Cassell (London), 1958 . . . £20/£10
The Crowning Privilege: The Clark Lectures, 1954-5, Cassell (London), 1955 . . . £25/£10
ditto, Doubleday (New York), 1956 . . £20/£5
Adam's Rib, Trianon Press (London), 1955 (illustrated by James Metcalf) . . . . £50/£15
ditto, Trianon Press (London), 1955 (26 signed, numbered copies, slipcase) . . . £250/£200
ditto, Trianon Press (London), 1955 (250 signed, numbered copies, slipcase) . . .£150/£100
ditto, Yoseloff (New York), 1955 . . .£45/£15
ditto, Yoseloff (New York), 1955 (100 signed copies) . .
. . . .£125/£100
Jesus in Rome (with Joshua Podro), Cassell (London), 1957
. . . . £45/£20
Steps, Cassell (London), 1958 . . . £25/£10
5 Pens in Hand, Doubleday (New York), 1958 .£30/£10
Food for Centaurs, Doubleday (New York), 1960.£45/£15
Greek Gods and Heroes, Doubleday (New York), 1960
. . . . £25/£10
ditto, as **Myths of Ancient Greece**, Cassell (London), 1961 .
. . . . £25/£10
Selected Poetry and Prose, Hutchinson (London), 1961 (edited by James Reeves) . . . £10/£5
Oxford Addresses on Poetry, Cassell (London), 1962 £20/£5
ditto, Doubleday (New York), 1962 . . .£20/£5
The Siege and Fall of Troy, Cassell (London), 1962 (illustrated by Walter Hodges) . . .£15/£5
ditto, Doubleday (New York), 1962 . . £15/£5
Hebrew Myths: The Book of Genesis, Doubleday (New York), 1964 (with Raphael Patai) . . £30/£10
ditto, Cassell (London), 1964 . . . £30/£10
Majorca Observed, Cassell (London), 1965 . £15/£5
ditto, Doubleday (New York), 1965 . . £15/£5
Mammon and the Black Goddess, Cassell (London), 1965 .
. . . . £20/£5
ditto, Doubleday (New York), 1965 . . £20/£5
Poetic Craft and Principle, Cassell (London), 1967 £15/£5
Greek Myths and Legends, Cassell (London), 1968 £10/£5
The Crane Bag, Cassell (London), 1969 . . £10/£5
On Poetry: Collected Talks and Essays, Doubleday (New York), 1969 . . . . . £20/£5

Difficult Questions, Easy Answers, Cassell (London), 1972
.   .   .   .   .   .   £15/£5
ditto, Doubleday (New York), 1973 .   .   .   £15/£5
Selected Letters, Hutchinson (London), 1982 and 1984 (vol
1: *In Broken Images, 1914 – 1946*, vol 2: *Between Moon
and Moon, 1946 - 1972*) .   .   .   .   £30/£10

As Editor

Oxford Poetry, 1921, Blackwell (Oxford), 1921 (with Alan
Porter and Richard Hughes) £75
ditto, Appleton (New York), 1922 .   .   . £100/£25
John Skelton (Laureate), Benn (London), 1927 (stapled
wraps) £30
The Less Familiar Nursery Rhymes, Benn (London), 1927
(stapled wraps) £45
Focus I, no publisher (no place), 1935 (wraps; 12pps
magazine published with Laura Riding). .   .   .£150
Focus II, no publisher (no place), 1935 (wraps; 24pps
magazine published with Laura Riding). .   .   .£150
Focus III, no publisher (no place), 1935 (wraps; 40pps
magazine published with Laura Riding). .   .   .£150
Epilogue… Volume I, Seizin Press/Constable (Majorca/
London), 1935 (edited by Laura Riding with Robert Graves
as Associate Editor) £150
Focus IV, no publisher (no place), 1935 (wraps; 64pps
magazine published with Laura Riding). .   .   .£125
T.E. Lawrence to His Biographers, Faber (London), 1938 (2
vols, 500 copies signed by Graves and Liddell Hart, with
d/ws, in slipcase). .   .   .   .   £450/£200
ditto, Doubleday Doran (New York), 1938 (2 vols, 500
copies signed by Graves and Liddell Hart, with d/ws, in
slipcase). .   .   .   .   .   £450/£200
The Comedies of Terence, Doubleday (New York), 1962 .
.   .   .   .   £30/£10
ditto, Cassell (London), 1963 .   .   .   .   £30/£10

ALASDAIR GRAY
(b.1934)

An inventive Scottish writer of bizarre tales strangely written, Alasdair Gray is also an artist. His most acclaimed
work is *Lanark*, reputedly written over a 30-year period.
His work combines realism, fantasy and science fiction, a
clever use of typography, and his own illustrations. He also
writes on politics, supporting socialism and Scottish independence.

Novels

Lanark, Canongate (Edinburgh), 1981 .   .   . £250/£30
ditto, Harper Colophon (New York), 1981 (pbk) .   . £10
ditto, Canongate (Edinburgh), 1985 (1,000 signed copies) .
.   .   .   . £100/£45
ditto, Braziller (New York), 1985 .   .   .   £15/£5
1982 Janine, Cape (London), 1984 .   .   .   £15/£5
ditto, Viking (New York), 1984 .   .   .   .   £10/£5
The Fall of Kelvin Walker, Canongate (Edinburgh), 1985 .
.   .   .   .   £15/£5
ditto, Braziller (New York), 1986 .   .   .   . £10/£5
Something Leather, Cape (London), 1990 .   . £10/£5
ditto, Random House (New York), 1990 .   .   . £10/£5

McGrotty and Ludmilla, Dog and Bone (Glasgow), 1990
(pbk) £10
Poor Things, Bloomsbury (London), 1991 .   . £10/£5
ditto, Harcourt (New York), 1992 .   .   .   . £10/£5
History Maker, Canongate (Edinburgh), 1994. .   £10/£5
ditto, Canongate (Edinburgh), 1994 (250 signed copies) .
.   .   .   . £45/£20
ditto, Harcourt (New York), 1996 .   .   .   . £10/£5
Old Men in Love, Bloomsbury (London), 2007 .   £10/£5

Short Stories

The Comedy of the White Dog, Print Studio Press
(Glasgow), 1979 (600 numbered copies; wraps) .   .£200
Unlikely Stories, Mostly, Canongate (Edinburgh), 1983 .
.   .   .   . £50/£10
ditto, Penguin (New York), 1984 .   .   .   . £15/£5
Lean Tales, Cape (London), 1985 (with James Kelman and
Agnes Owens) .   .   .   .   .   . £20/£5
Ten Tales Tall and True, Bloomsbury (London), 1993. .
.   .   .   . £10/£5
ditto, Harcourt (New York), 1993 .   .   .   . £10/£5
Mavis Belfrage, Bloomsbury (London), 1996 .   . £10/£5
The Ends of Our Tethers: Thirteen Sorry Stories,
Canongate (Edinburgh), 2003 .   .   .   . £10/£5

Poetry

Old Negatives: Four Verse Sequences, Cape (London),
1989 (500 signed copies) .   .   .   . £60/£25
ditto, Cape (London), 1989 (pbk) £5
The Artist In His World: Prints 1986-1997, by Ian
McCulloch, Argyll Publishing (Glendaruel, Argyll), 1998
(eight poems by Gray) .   .   .   .   . £15/£5
Sixteen Occasional Poems: 1990-2000, McAlpine
(Glasgow), 2000 (wraps) £10
ditto, McAlpine (Glasgow), 2000 (200 signed copies, boards)
.   .   .   . £45

Others

Dialogue, Scottish Theatre Magazine, 1971 .   .   . £30
5 Scottish Artists Retrospective Show, Famedram Publishers
(Gartocharn, Scotland), 1986 (five colour catalogues and
an introduction by Gray) £50
Self-portrait, Saltaire Society (Edinburgh), 1988 (wraps) £10
ditto, Saltaire Society (Edinburgh), 1988 (signed copies; pbk)
.   .   .   . £20
Pierre Lavalle: Paintings 1947-75, Lavalle Retrospective
Group (Glasgow), 1990 (contains an essay by Gray; wraps)
.   .   .   . £10
Why Scots Should Rule Scotland, Canongate (Edinburgh),
1997 (pbk) £5
Working Legs: A Two Act Play for Disabled Performers,
Dog and Bone (Glasgow), 1998 (pbk) £5
The Book of Prefaces, Bloomsbury (London), 2000 £10/£5
ditto, Bloomsbury (New York), 2001. .   .   . £10/£5

ANNA KATHERINE GREEN
(b.1846 d.1935)

Anna Katherine Green was one of the first writers of detective fiction in America, credited with developing the idea of a series detective. Her main detective was Ebenezer Gryce of the New York Metropolitan Police Force, but in certain novels he is assisted by Amelia Butterworth, a prototype for Miss Marple etc. She also created the 'girl detective' with the character of Violet Strange

Novels

The Leavenworth Case, Putnam (New York), 1878 ('F' missing from 'fresh' last line p.215) . . . £2,000
ditto, Routledge (London), 1884. . . . . £250
A Strange Disappearance, Putnam (New York), 1880 . £200
ditto, Routledge (London), 1884 . . . . . £100
The Sword of Damocles, Putnam (New York), 1881 . £75
ditto, Ward Lock (London), 1884 . . . . £60
Hand and Ring, Putnam (New York), 1883 . . . £75
ditto, Putnam (New York), 1883 (wraps) . . . £200
ditto, Ward Lock (London), 1884 . . . . £50
XYZ, Putnam (New York), 1883. . . . . £75
ditto, Ward Lock (London), 1883 . . . . £45
The Mill Mystery, Putnam (New York), 1886 . . £75
ditto, Routledge (London), 1886. . . . . £45
Risifi's Daughter, Putnam (New York), 1887 . . £75
7 to 12, Putnam (New York), 1887 . . . . £75
ditto, Routledge (London), 1887. . . . . £45
Behind Closed Doors, Putnam (New York), 1888 . . £75
ditto, Routledge (London), 1888. . . . . £40
A Matter of Millions, Bonner (New York), 1890 . . £75
ditto, Routledge (London), 1890 . . . . £40
The Forsaken Inn, Bonner (New York), 1890 . . £65
ditto, Routledge (London), 1890. . . . . £35
Cynthia Wakeham's Money, Putnam (New York), 1892 £60
ditto, Ward Lock (London), 1904 . . . . £30
Marked 'Personal', Putnam (New York), 1893 . . £45
ditto, Ward Lock (London), 1904 . . . . £30
Miss Hurd: An Enigma, Putnam (New York), 1894 . £40
The Doctor, His Wife, and the Clock, Putnam (New York), 1895 . . . . £30
ditto, Unwin (London), 1895 . . . . . £20
Doctor Izard, Putnam (New York), 1895 . . . £25
ditto, Cassell (London), 1895 . . . . . £20
That Affair Next Door, Putnam (New York), 1897 . £25
ditto, Nash (London) (London), 1903 . . . £20
Lost Man's Lane, Putnam (New York), 1898 . . £25
The Circular Study, McClure (New York), 1900 . . £25
ditto, Ward Lock (London), 1902 . . . . £20
One of my Sons, Putnam (New York), 1901 . . £20
ditto, Ward Lock (London), 1904 . . . . £15
The Filigree Ball, Bobbs-Merrill (Indianapolis, IN), 1903 . . . . £15
ditto, Unwin (London), 1904 . . . . . £15
The House in the Mist, Bobbs-Merrill (Indianapolis, IN), 1905 . . . . £15
The Millionaire Baby, Bobbs-Merrill (Indianapolis, IN), 1905 . . . . £15
ditto, Chatto & Windus (London), 1905 . . . £15
The Chief Legatee, The Authors and Newspapers Association (New York), 1906. . . . . £15

ditto, as *A Woman of Mystery*, Collier (London), 1909 . £15
The Woman in the Alcove, Bobbs-Merrill (Indianapolis, IN), 1906 . . . . £15
ditto, Chatto & Windus (London), 1906 . . . £15
The Mayor's Wife, Bobbs-Merrill (Indianapolis, IN), 1907 . . . . £15
ditto, London Daily Mail (London), 1909. . . £15
The House of the Whispering Pines, Putnam (New York), 1910 . . . . £15
ditto, Nash (London), 1910 . . . . . £15
Three Thousand Dollars, Badger (Boston), 1910 . . £15
Initials Only, Dodd, Mead (New York), 1911 . . . £15
ditto, Nash (London), 1912 . . . . . £10
Dark Hollow, Dodd, Mead (New York), 1914. . . £15
ditto, Nash (London), 1914 . . . . . £10
To the Minute and Scarlet and Black: Two of Life's Perplexities, Putnam (New York), 1916. . . £15
The Mystery of the Hasty Arrow, Dodd, Mead (New York), 1917 . . . . £15
The Step on the Stair, Dodd, Mead (New York), 1923 . £15
ditto, Bodley Head (London), 1923 . . . . £10

Short Stories

The Old Stone House and Other Stories, Putnam (New York), 1891 . . . . £65
A Difficult Problem and Other Stories, Lupton (New York), 1900 . . . . £65
ditto, Ward Lock (London), 1903 . . . . £45
Masterpieces of Mystery, Dodd, Mead (New York), 1913 . . . . £65
ditto, as *Room Number 3 and Other Stories*, Dodd, Mead (New York), 1919 . . . . . . £45
The Golden Slipper and Other Problems for Violet Strange, Putnam (New York), 1915. . . . . . £65

HENRY GREEN
(b.1905 d.1973)

'Henry Green' was the pseudonym of the novelist Henry Vincent Yorke. Born near Tewkesbury, Gloucestershire, he attended Eton College and Oxford University, although he left the latter in 1926 without taking a degree. He served as a fireman during World War Two. Green is the author of novels of social satire, but in the last 20 years of his life he gave up writing fiction, publishing only essays and reviews for magazines.

Novels

Blindness, Dent (London), 1926 (first state d/w priced 7s. 6d.). . . . . £1,250/£150
ditto, Dutton (New York), 1926 . . . £1,000/£15
Living, Dutton (New York), 1929 . . . £1,250/£165
ditto, Dent (London), 1929 . . . . £1,000/£145
Party Going, Hogarth Press (London), 1939 . . £700/£75
ditto, Longman (Toronto), 1939 . . . . £150/£25
ditto, Viking (New York), 1951 . . . . £100/£15
Caught, Hogarth Press (London), 1943 . . . £200/£40
ditto, Macmillan (Toronto), 1943 . . . . £125/£35
ditto, Viking (New York), 1950 . . . . £65/£15
Loving, Hogarth Press (London), 1945 . . . £200/£40
ditto, Macmillan (Toronto), 1945 . . . . £125/£35
ditto, Viking (New York), 1949 . . . . £75/£15

Back, Hogarth Press (London), 1946 . . . . £150/£40
ditto, Oxford (Toronto), 1946 . . . . . £60/£20
ditto, Viking (New York), 1950 . . . . £25/£5
Concluding, Hogarth Press (London), 1948 . . £50/£15
ditto, Viking (New York), 1950 . . . . £20/£5
Nothing, Hogarth Press (London), 1950 . . . £40/£15
ditto, Viking (New York), 1950 . . . . £15/£5
Doting, Hogarth Press (London), 1951 . . . £40/£15
ditto, Viking (New York), 1952 . . . . £15/£5

Others

Pack My Bag, Hogarth Press (London), 1940 (first state d/w
    priced 7s. 6d.) . . . . £500/£75
ditto, Macmillan (Toronto), 1940 . . . £125/£40
ditto, New Directions (Norfolk, CT), 1993 . . £10/£5
Surviving, The Uncollected Writings of Henry Green,
    Chatto & Windus (London), [1992] . . . £20/£5
ditto, Viking (New York), 1993 . . . . . £15/£5

KATE GREENAWAY

(b.1846 d.1901)

A British author and illustrator whose first success, *Under the Window*, a collection of simple, idyllic verses concerning children who endlessly gather posies, was a bestseller. The illustrations for the book had a major influence on children's fashion of the 1870s.

Infant Amusements, by William Henry Giles Kingston,
    Griffith and Farran (London), [1867] £650
Aunt Louisa's Nursery Favourite, Warne (London), 1870 .
    . . . . £350
Diamonds and Toads, Warne (London), [1871] . £1,000
ditto, McLoughlin Bros (New York), [c.1875]. . . £250
The Children of the Parsonage, by Henry Courtney Selous,
    Griffith and Farran (London), 1874. . . . . £400
Puck and Blossom, by Rosa Mulholland, Marcus Ward
    (London), [1874?] £300
Fairy Gifts, by K. Knox, Griffith and Farran (London),
    [1875] £250
The Fairy Spinner, by Miranda Hill, Marcus Ward
    (London), [1875] (illustrations unattributed). . . £250
ditto, Nelson (New York), 1875 . . . . . . £150
A Cruise in the Acorn, by Alice Jerrold, Marcus Ward
    (London), [1875]. £300
Turnaside Cottage, by Mary Senior Clark, Marcus Ward
    (London), 1875 . . . . £175
ditto, Nelson (New York), 1875 . . . . . . £150
Children's Songs, Marcus Ward (London), [1875] . £150
Melcombe Manor, by F. Scarlet Potter, Marcus Ward
    (London), [1875]. £200
Seven Birthdays, by K. Knox, Griffith and Farran (London),
    1876 . . . . £250
ditto, Dutton (New York), [1876?] £200
A Quiver of Love: A Collection of Valentines, Marcus Ward
    (London), 1876 (with Walter Crane) . . . £500
Two Little Cousins, by Alice Hepburn, Marcus Ward
    (London), 1876 . . . . £175
What Santa Claus Gave Me, Griffith and Farran (London),
    [c.1876] £150
Starlight Stories, by Fanny Lablache, Griffith and Farran
    (London), 1876 . . . . £125

ditto, Pott, Young & Co (New York), 1879 . . . £100
Tom Seven Years Old, by H. Rutherford Russell, Marcus
    Ward (London), [1877] £150
Pretty Stories for Tiny Folks, Cassell (London), 1877 . £150
Woodland Romances, Cassell, Petter & Galpin (London),
    [1877] £175
ditto, as *The 'Little Folks' Painting Book*, Cassell, Petter &
    Galpin (London), [1879] (wraps) £300
Poor Nelly, by Mrs Bonavia Hunt, Cassell (London), 1878 .
    . . . . £150
Topo, by G.E. Brunefille, Marcus Ward (London), 1878 £200
Esther, by Geraldine Butt, Marcus Ward (London), 1878 .
    . . . . £150
A Little Maid and Her Moods, by Elizabeth Stewart Phelps,
    Lothrop (New York), [1878] £150
Under the Window, by Kate Greenaway, Routledge
    (London), [1878]. £250
ditto, Routledge (New York), [1880]. £150
Heartsease, by Charlotte M. Yonge, Macmillan (London),
    1879 . . . . £175
The Heir of Redclyffe, by Charlotte M. Yonge, Macmillan
    (London), 1879 . . . . £175
Amateur Theatricals, by Walter Herries Pollock and Lady
    Pollock, Macmillan (London), 1879 . . . £150
Trot's Journey, Worthington (New York), 1879 . . £125
A Favourite Album of Fun and Fancy, Cassell, Petter &
    Galpin (London), [1879] £175
Christmas Snowflakes, Lothrop (New York), [1879] . £175
Three Brown Boys, Cassell (London), 1879 . . . £175
ditto, Mallory (New York), 1879 . . . . . £125
Art in the Nursery, Lothrop (New York), [1879] . . £100
A Book for Every Jack and Gill, Dodd, Mead (New York),
    [1879] £150
Once Upon a Time, by Emma E. Brown, Lothrop (New
    York), [1879] £150
The Two Gray Girls, Cassell, Petter & Galpin (London),
    [1880] £150
Kate Greenaway's Birthday Book for Children, Routledge
    (London), [1880]. £150
Little Folks Out and About Book, by Chatty Cheerful
    [William Martin], Cassell (London), [1880] . . £150
Illustrated Children's Birthday Book, Mack (London),
    [1880] £125
Freddie's Letter, Routledge (London), 1880 . . . £125
The Youngster, by Cousin Daisy, Lippincott (Philadelphia,
    PA), [1880] £125
Stevie's Visit, Dodd, Mead (New York), 1880. . . £125
The Purse of Gold, Dodd, Mead (New York), [1880] . £125
The Lost Knife, Dodd, Mead (New York), 1880 . . £125
Little Sunbeam Stories, Cassell, Petter & Galpin (London),
    [1880] £150
Pleasant Hours and Golden Days, Lupton (New York),
    [1880] £125
Baby Dido, Lothrop (New York), [1880] (wraps) . £125
Dumpy, by Archie Fell, Lothrop (New York), [1880] £125
The Easy Book for Children, Pictorial Literature Society
    (London), [1880]. £150
ditto, Butler (Philadelphia, PA), [n.d.] £100
Five Mice in a Mousetrap, by Laura E. Richards, Estes
    Lauriat (Boston), [1880] £125
Grandmamma's Surprise Party, Dodd, Mead (New York),
    1880 . . . . £125
The Library, by Andrew Lang, Macmillan (London), 1881 .
    . . . . £125

London Lyrics, by Frederick Locker, Chiswick Press (London), 1881 . . . . £125
ditto, Scribner's (New York), 1882 . . . . £100
A Day in a Child's Life, Routledge (London), [1881] . £200
Mother Goose, or The Old Nursery Rhymes, Routledge (London), [1881] (wraps) £250
ditto, Routledge (London), [1881] (cloth). . . . £125
Elise, Dodd, Mead (New York), [1881] £125
Hide & Seek Illustrated, Dodd, Mead (New York), [1881] .
. . . . £125
King Christmas, Dodd, Mead (New York), [1881]. . £125
Whose Fault Was It?, Dodd, Mead (New York), 1881 . £125
Some Little People, Dodd, Mead (New York), [1881] . £125
Art Hours, McLoughlin Bros (New York), 1882 . . £150
Steps to Art, McLoughlin Bros (New York), 1882 . . £150
Happy Little People, by Olive Patch, Cassell, Petter & Galpin (London), [1882] £150
Little Ann, by Jane and Ann Taylor, Routledge (London), [1882] £150
Flowers and Fancies, by B. Montgomerie Ranking and Thomas K Tully, Marcus Ward (London), 1882 . . £150
The Wonderful Fan, by Aunt Ella, Dutton (New York), 1882 . . . . £150
Tales from the Edda, told by Helen Zimmerman, Swan Sonnenschein (London), [1882] £150
Papa's Little Daughters, by Mary D Brine, Cassell, Petter & Galpin (London), 1882 . . . . . . £150
Little Loving-Hearts Poem-Book, by Margaret Eleanora Tupper, Dutton (New York), 1882 . . . . £150
Little Gatherers, Cassell, Petter & Galpin (London), [1882]
. . . . £150
Greenaway Pictures to Paint, Cassell, Petter & Galpin (London), [1882]. £250
Jingles and Joys, by Mary D. Brine, Cassell (New York), 1883 . . . . £150
Baby Chatterbox, Worthington (New York), 1883. . £150
Art of England, by John Ruskin, George Allen (London), 1883 . . . . £150
Fors Clavigera, by John Ruskin, George Allen (London), 1884 . . . . £150
A Painting Book, Routledge (London), [1884] . £250
Brothers of Pity, by Juliana Horatia Ewing, S.P.C.K. (London), 1884 . . . . £150
Language of Flowers, Routledge (London), [1884] . £150
A Summer at Aunt Helen's, Dodd, Mead (New York), 1880 [1884] £150
Little Castles with Big Wings, Dodd, Mead (New York), 1880 [1884] £150
Baby's Birthday Book, Marcus Ward (London), [1894] £150
Chatterbox Hall, Worthington (New York), [1884] . £150
Children's Birthday Book, Marcus Ward (London), [1894]
. . . . £150
A Painting Book, Routledge (London), [1884] (wraps) £250
Poems of Frederick Locker, White, Stokes & Allen (New York), [1884] £150
Songs for the Nursery, Mack (London), [1884] . £125
English Spelling Book, by William Mavor, Routledge (London), 1885 . . . . £200
Dame Wiggins of Lee and Her Seven Wonderful Cats, George Allen (London), 1885 . . . . . £65
ditto, George Allen (London), 1885 (400 large paper copies)
. . . . £225
Marigold Garden, Routledge (London), [1885] . £125

Kate Greenaway's Album, Routledge (London), [1885?] (8 copies; wraps) £7,500
Kate Greenaway's Alphabet, Routledge (London), [1885] (miniature book, card covers) £100
ditto, as *New Alphabet*, Routledge (New York), [1885] £125
Tick, Tick, Tick and Other Rhymes, Mayer, Merkel & Ottmann (New York), [1885] £150
Mother Truth's Melodies, by Mrs E.P. Miller, Bay State Publishing (Springfield, MA.), 1885. . . . £150
Little Patience Picture Book, Routledge (London), [1885] .
. . . . £125
The Queen of the Pirate Isle, by Bret Harte, Chatto & Windus (London), [1885] £200
ditto, Houghton Mifflin (Boston), 1887 . . . . £200
A Apple Pie, Routledge (London), 1886 . . . . £200
ditto, Routledge (New York), [1886]. £200
Rhymes for the Young Folk, by William Allingham, Cassell (London), [1886]. £200
Bib and Tucker, Lothrop (New York), [1886]. . . £125
Christmas Dreams, by Mary D. Brine, Cassell (New York), [1886] £125
Queen Victoria's Jubilee Garland, Routledge (London), 1887 . . . . £350
Lucy's Troubles, by Laurie Loring, Lothrop (New York), 1887 . . . . £125
Baby's Birthday Book, Marcus Ward (London), [1887] £150
Orient Line Guide, Sampson Low (London), 1888. . £125
Around the House, Worthington (New York), 1888 . £150
Pied Piper of Hamelin, by Robert Browning, Routledge (London), [1888]. £150
The Old Farm Gate, Routledge (London), [1888] . . £150
Miss Rosebud, Lothrop (New York), [1888] . . £125
Kate Greenaway's Painting Book, Warne (New York), [1888] £250
Kate Greenaway's Book of Games, Routledge (London), [1889] £200
The Royal Progress of King Pepito, by Beatrice Cresswell, S.P.C.K. (London), [1889] £125
Our Girls, Belford, Clarke & Co. (Chicago), 1890. . £125
Songs of the Month, by Lucie E. Willeplait, Worthington (New York), 1891 . . . . £125
Soap Bubble Stories, by Fanny Barry, Skeffington (London), 1892 . . . . £125
Doll's Tea Party, Lothrop (New York), [1895] . £125
Every Girl's Stories, by Grace Aguilar, Geraldine Butt and Jane Butt, Routledge (London), 1896 . . . . £125
Stories Witty and Pictures Pretty, Conky (Chicago), 1896 .
. . . . £100
To Pass the Time, McLoughlin (New York), [1897] . £100
Little Folks' Speaker, Lothrop (New York), 1898 . £100
The April Baby's Book of Tunes, by the author of 'Elizabeth and her German Garden', Macmillan (London), 1900. £200
ditto, by the author of 'Elizabeth and her German Garden', Macmillan (New York), 1900 . . . . . £200
Littledom Castle and Other Tales, by Mabel H. Spielmann, Routledge (London), 1903 (illustrated with Rackham, etc)
. . . . £200
ditto, Dutton (New York), 1903 . . . . . £200

Calendars
Calendar of the Seasons, 1876/1877/1881/1882, Marcus Ward (London) . . . . . . £150 each
A Calendar of the Months, Marcus Ward (London), 1884 .
. . . . £150

Kate Greenaway's Calendar, *1884/1897/1899*, Routledge
(London)   .   .   .   .£200 each

Almanacks (assuming original envelope no longer present)
1883, Routledge (London), [1882] £150
1884, Routledge (London), [1883] (wraps)   .   . £150
1885, Routledge (London), [1884] £145
1886, Routledge (London), [1885] £125
1887, Routledge (London), [1886] £100
1888, Routledge (London), [1887] £100
1889, Routledge (London), [1888] £150
1890, Routledge (London), [1889] £100
1891, Routlefield (London), [1890] £100
1892, Routledge (London), [1891] £100
1893, Routledge (London), [1892] £100
1894, Routledge (London), [1893] £100
1895, Routledge (London), [1894] £100
1897, Routledge (London), [1896] (imitation leather binding)
.   .   .   . £500
1924, Warne (London), [1923] £50
1925, Warne (London), [1924] £50
1926, Warne (London), [1925] £50
1927, Warne (London), [1926] £50
1928, Warne (London), [1927] £50
1929, Warne (London), [1928] (imitation leather binding)   .
.   .   .   . £100

GRAHAM GREENE

(b.1904 d.1991)

Famous mainly for his novels, Greene was also an
acclaimed short story writer, playwright, critic and essayist.
From his first real success, *Stamboul Train*, he seems to
have been preoccupied with the themes of guilt, pursuit and
failure, much of which stemmed from his conversion to
Catholicism. He was made a companion of honour in 1966
and was awarded the Order of Merit in 1986.

Novels
The Man Within, Heinemann (London), 1929. £2,750/£250
ditto, Doubleday (New York), 1929   .   .   . £1,250/£100
The Name of Action, Heinemann (London), 1930 (d/w price
7s6d and reviews of *The Man Within* on back) £3,750/£400
ditto, Heinemann (London), 1930 (d/w price 3s6d and
reviews of current book on d/w flap)   .   . £1,500/£400
ditto, Doubleday (New York), 1931   .   .   . £1,500/£175
Rumour at Nightfall, Heinemann (London), 1931 .   .   .
.   .   .   . £15,000/£450
ditto, Doubleday (New York), 1932   .   .   . £1,500/£400
Stamboul Train, Heinemann (London), 1932 (reference to
'Q.C. Savory' on pps 77, 78, 82, 98, 131)   .£4,000/£1,500
ditto, Heinemann (London), 1932 (reference to 'Quin
Savory').   .   .   .   . £2,000/£75
ditto, as *Orient Express*, Doubleday (New York), 1933   .
.   .   .   . £1,250/£150
It's a Battlefield, Heinemann (London), 1934 (d/w price
7s6d)   .   .   .   . £1,500/£100
ditto, Heinemann (London), 1934 (d/w price 3/6)   .   .
.   .   .   . £1,250/£100
ditto, Doubleday (New York), 1934   .   .   .   . £600/£45
England Made Me, Heinemann (London), 1935   .   .   .
.   .   .   . £8,000/£250

ditto, Doubleday (New York), 1935   .   .   .   . £750/£50
This Gun for Hire, Doubleday (New York), 1936 . £750/£50
ditto, as *A Gun for Sale*, Heinemann (London), 1936   .
.   .   .   . £7,500/£250
Brighton Rock, Viking (New York), 1938   . £850/£100
ditto, Heinemann (London), 1938   .   .   . £25,000/£450
The Confidential Agent, Heinemann (London), 1939   .   .
.   .   .   . £4,000/£200
ditto, Viking (New York), 1939   .   .   .   . £750/£65
The Power and the Glory, Heinemann (London), 1940.   .
.   .   .   . £7,000/£450
ditto, as *The Labyrinthine Ways*, Viking (New York), 1940
(first state)   .   .   .   .   .   . £750/£250
ditto, as *The Labyrinthine Ways*, Viking (New York), 1940
(second state with pp.165 and 256 in correct order)   .   .
.   .   .   . £350/£35
The Ministry of Fear, Heinemann (London), 1943   .   .
.   .   .   . £3,500/£75
ditto, Viking (New York), 1943   .   .   .   . £450/£35
The Heart of the Matter, Heinemann (London), 1948   .   .
.   .   .   . £400/£35
ditto, Viking (New York), 1948   .   .   .   . £125/£20
ditto, Viking (New York), 1948 (750 copies 'For Friends of
the Viking Press', acetate d/w)   .   .   . £100/£75
The Third Man, Viking (New York), 1950   . £175/£15
The Third Man and *The Fallen Idol*, Heinemann (London),
1950   .   .   .   . £200/£15
ditto, Eurographica (Helsinki), 1988 (500 signed, numbered
copies)   .   .   .   . £200/£150
The End of the Affair, Heinemann (London), 1951   .   .
.   .   .   . £100/£15
ditto, Viking (New York), 1951   .   .   .   . £45/£10
Loser Takes All, Heinemann (London), 1955 . £100/£15
ditto, Viking (New York), 1957   .   .   .   . £45/£10
The Quiet American, Heinemann (London), 1955 . £100/£15
ditto, Viking (New York), 1956   .   .   .   . £45/£10
Our Man in Havana, Heinemann (London), 1958. £75/£10
ditto, Viking (New York), 1958   .   .   .   . £35/£10
A Burnt Out Case, Heinemann (London), 1961   . £75/£5
ditto, Viking (New York), 1961   .   .   .   . £25/£5
The Comedians, Viking (New York), 1966 (500 advance
copies, acetate d/w)   .   .   .   .   . £75/£50
ditto, Bodley Head (London), 1966   .   .   . £35/£10
ditto, Viking (New York), 1966   .   .   .   . £25/£5
Travels with My Aunt, Bodley Head (London), 1969   .   .
.   .   .   . £35/£10
ditto, Viking (New York), 1970   .   .   .   . £25/£5
The Honorary Consul, Bodley Head (London), 1973   .   .
.   .   .   . £35/£10
ditto, Viking (New York), 1973   .   .   .   . £25/£5
The Human Factor, Bodley Head (London), 1978. £35/£10
ditto, Simon & Schuster (New York), 1978   .   . £25/£5
Dr Fischer of Geneva or The Bomb Party, Bodley Head
(London), 1980   .   .   .   .   .   . £20/£5
ditto, Simon & Schuster (New York), 1980   .   . £15/£5
ditto, Simon & Schuster (New York), 1980 (500 signed
copies, slipcase)   .   .   .   .   .   . £125/£100
How Father Quixote Became a Monsignor, Sylvester &
Orphanos (Los Angeles, CA), 1980 (330 signed, numbered
copies, acetate d/w)   .   .   .   .   . £150/£125
Monsignor Quixote, Lester & Orpen Dennys (Toronto,
Canada), 1982   .   .   .   .   .   . £20/£5
ditto, Bodley Head (London), 1982   .   .   . £20/£5
ditto, Simon & Schuster (New York), 1982   .   . £15/£5

ditto, Simon & Schuster (New York), 1982 (250 signed, numbered copies in slipcase) . . . £125/£100
The Tenth Man, Bodley Head (London), 1985 . £15/£5
ditto, Simon & Schuster (New York), 1985 . . £10/£5
The Captain and the Enemy, Reinhardt (London), 1988 .
. . . . £15/£5
ditto, Viking (New York), 1988 . . . . £10/£5

Short Stories
The Bear Fell Free, Grayson (London), 1935 (285 signed, numbered copies) . . . £950/£500
The Basement Room, Cresset Press (London), 1935 .
. . . . £1,000/£200
ditto, as **24 Short Stories**, Cresset Press (London), 1939 (*The Basement Room* is bound in with collections by James Laver and Sylvia Townsend Warner) . . £750/£125
Nineteen Stories, Heinemann (London), 1947. . £250/£45
ditto, Viking (New York), 1949 . . . . £150/£35
ditto, as **Twenty-One Stories**, Heinemann (London), 1954 (extra stories added) . . . . . . £100/£15
A Visit to Morin, Heinemann (London), [1959] (250 copies)
. . . . £250/£125
A Sense of Reality, Bodley Head (London), 1963 . £50/£15
ditto, Viking (New York), 1963 . . . . £35/£10
May We Borrow Your Husband?, Bodley Head (London), 1967 . . . . £30/£10
ditto, Bodley Head (London), 1967 (500 signed, numbered copies, glassine d/w) . . . . . £150/£125
ditto, Viking (New York), 1967 . . . . £25/£10
The Collected Stories, Bodley Head/Heinemann (London), 1972 . . . . £30/£10
ditto, Viking (New York), 1973 . . . . £15/£5
Shades of Greene, Bodley Head/Heinemann (London), 1975
. . . . £15/£5
The Last Word and Other Stories, Reinhardt (London), 1990 . . . . £10/£5

Plays
The Living Room, Heinemann (London), 1953 . £125/£10
ditto, Viking (New York), 1954 . . . . £100/£10
The Potting Shed, Viking (New York), 1957 . . £150/£20
ditto, Heinemann (London), 1958 . . . £150/£20
The Complaisant Lover, Heinemann (London), 1959 . .
. . . . £150/£20
ditto, Viking (New York), 1961 . . . . £100/£15
Carving a Statue, Bodley Head (London), 1964 . £75/£15
The Return of A.J. Raffles, Bodley Head (London), 1975 (pbk) £10
ditto, Bodley Head (London), 1975 (250 signed, numbered copies) . . . . £250/£150
ditto, Simon & Schuster (New York), 1975 . £25/£5
The Great Jowett, Bodley Head (London), 1981 (525 signed copies, glassine d/w) . . . . £200/£150
Yes & No and For Whom the Bell Chimes, Bodley Head (London), 1983 (775 signed copies, glassine d/w) . .
. . . . £200/£150
Yes & No-A Play in One Act, Eurographica (Helsinki), 1984 (350 signed, numbered copies; wraps) . . . £100

Travel
Journey Without Maps, Heinemann (London), 1936 . .
. . . . £4,500/£150
ditto, Doubleday (New York), 1936 . . . £300/£45

The Lawless Roads, Longman (London), 1939 (red cloth, lettering in gold) . . . . . £1,500/£350
ditto, Longman (London), 1939 (red cloth, lettering in blue)
. . . . £750/£75
ditto, as **Another Mexico**, Viking (New York), 1939 . .
. . . . £250/£50
In Search of a Character: Two African Journals, Bodley Head (London), 1961 . . . . . . £45/£10
ditto, Viking (New York), 1961 (600 advance copies) . £65
ditto, Viking (New York), 1961 . . . . £45/£10

Children's Titles
The Little Train, Eyre & Spottiswoode (London), 1946 (anonymous; illustrated by Dorothy Craigie) £600/£100
ditto, Lothrop (New York), 1958 . . . . £350/£50
ditto, Bodley Head (London), 1973 (illustrated by Ardizzone) . . . . £50/£20
ditto, Doubleday (New York), 1973 (illustrated by Ardizzone) . . . . £50/£20
The Little Fire Engine, Parrish (London), 1950 (illustrated by Dorothy Craigie) . . . . . £500/£45
ditto, as **The Little Red Fire Engine**, Lothrop (New York), 1952. . . . . £200/£35
ditto, Bodley Head (London), 1973 (illustrated by Ardizzone) . . . . £50/£20
ditto, Doubleday (New York), 1973 (illustrated by Ardizzone) . . . . £50/£20
The Little Horse Bus, Parrish (London), 1952 (illustrated by Dorothy Craigie) . . . . . . £325/£45
ditto, Lothrop (New York), 1954 . . . . £150/£30
ditto, Bodley Head (London), 1974 (illustrated by Ardizzone) . . . . £50/£20
ditto, Doubleday (New York), 1974 (illustrated by Ardizzone) . . . . £45/£20
The Little Steam Roller, Parrish (London), 1953 (illustrated by Dorothy Craigie) . . . . . £325/£45
ditto, Lothrop (New York), 1955 . . . . £150/£30
ditto, Bodley Head (London), 1974 (illustrated by Ardizzone) . . . . £50/£20
ditto, Doubleday (New York), 1974 (illustrated by Ardizzone) . . . . £45/£20

Others
Babbling April, Blackwell (Oxford), 1925 . £3,000/£750
The Old School: Essays by Divers Hands, Cape (London), 1934 (edited by Greene) . . . . . £300/£65
To Beg I Am Ashamed, Vanguard Press (New York), 1938 (pseud 'Sheila Cousins', with Ronald Matthews). £125/£25
ditto, Routledge (London), 1938. . . . . £250/£40
Men at Work, Penguin New Writing (Harmondsworth, Middlesex), 1941 (pbk) £20
British Dramatists, Collins (London), 1942 . . £40/£10
Why Do I Write?: An Exchange of Views Between Elizabeth Bowen, Graham Greene, and V.S. Pritchett, Marshall (London), 1948 . . . . . £125/£35
The Lost Childhood, Eyre & Spottiswoode (London), 1951.
. . . . £65/£15
ditto, Viking (New York), 1952 . . . . £35/£10
The Spy's Bedside Book, Hart-Davis (London), 1957 (edited by Graham and Hugh Greene) . . . £75/£15
ditto, Carroll & Graf (New York), 1985 (pbk). . £5
Introductions to Three Novels, Norstedt (Stockholm), 1962 (sewn wraps) £45

The Revenge, An Autobiographical Fragment, Stellar Press (London), 1963 (300 copies; plain card covers in green printed d/w) . . . . . . £350/£200

Victorian Detective Fiction, A Catalogue of the Collection made by Dorothy Glover and Graham Greene, Bodley Head (London), 1966 (500 numbered copies signed by Dorothy Glover, Graham Greene and co-editor John Carter) . . . . . . £300/£150

Collected Essays, Bodley Head (London), 1969 . £20/£5

ditto, Viking (New York), 1969 . . . . £15/£5

Mr Visconti, Bodley Head (London), 1969 (drawing by Edward Ardizzone; 300 copies; d/w over unprinted white wraps) . . . . . . £150/£75

The Collected Edition, volumes 1-22, Heinemann (London) & Bodley Head (London), 1970-1982 (with new introductions by the author) . . . . £300/£75

A Sort of Life, Bodley Head (London), 1971 . . £25/£5

ditto, Simon & Schuster (New York), 1971 . £25/£5

The Pleasure Dome: The Collected Film Criticism, 1935-1940, Secker & Warburg (London), 1972 . . £25/£5

ditto, Simon & Schuster (New York), 1972 . £25/£5

The Virtue of Disloyalty, Bodley Head (London), 1972 (300 copies; wraps) £150

Lord Rochester's Monkey, Bodley Head (London), 1974 . . . . £20/£5

ditto, Viking (New York), 1974 . . . . £15/£5

An Impossible Woman, The Memories of Dottoressa Moor of Capri, Bodley Head (London), 1975 (edited by Greene) . . . . £20/£5

A Wedding among the Owls, Stellar Press (London), 1977 (250 copies; wraps) £200

Ways of Escape, Lester & Orpen Dennys (Toronto, Canada), 1980 . . . . . . £25/£5

ditto, Lester & Orpen Dennys (Toronto, Canada), 1980 (150 signed copies, slipcase) . . . . £275/£225

ditto, Bodley Head (London), 1980 . . . £10/£5

ditto, Simon & Schuster (New York), 1980 . £10/£5

L'Autre et Son Double: Entretiens avec Marie-Françoise Allain, Pierre Belfond (Paris), 1981 (wraps) . . £10

ditto, as *The Other Man: Conversations with Graham Greene by Marie-Françoise Allain*, Bodley Head (London), 1983 . . . . . . £20/£5

ditto, Simon & Schuster (New York), 1983 . £20/£5

J'Accuse: The Dark Side of Nice, Lester & Orpen Dennys (Toronto, Canada), 1982 (wraps and d/w) . £25/£15

ditto, Bodley Head (London), 1982 (wraps and d/w) £25/£15

A Quick Look Behind, Sylvester & Orphanos (Los Angeles, CA), 1983 (300 signed, numbered copies of 330, slipcase) . . . . . . £150/£100

ditto, Sylvester & Orphanos (Los Angeles, CA), 1983 (26 signed, lettered copies, plus 4 presentation copies, of 330, slipcase). . . . . . . £250/£200

One November Day in 1980 the Other Graham Greene Burst through His Shadow, Bodley Head (London), 1983 (with Marie-Françoise Allain, 225 copies; plain white wraps with blue dust jacket printed in black) £150/£100

Getting to Know the General, Bodley Head (London), 1984 . . . . £15/£5

ditto, Simon & Schuster (New York), 1984 . £15/£5

The Monster of Capri, Eurographica (Helsinki), 1985 (500 signed, numbered copies) . . . . £200/£125

Why the Epigraph?, Nonesuch Press (London), 1989 (950 signed, numbered copies, glassine d/w) . . £125/£100

Dear David, Dear Graham, A Bibliophilic Correspondence, The Alembic Press/The Amate Press (Oxford), 1989 (50 of 250 copies, slipcase) . . . . . £175/£125

ditto, The Alembic Press/The Amate Press (Oxford), 1989 (200 of 250 copies) £100

Yours, etc: Letters to the Press, Reinhardt (London), 1989 . . . . £15/£5

ditto, Viking (New York), 1990 . . . . £15/£5

Reflections on Travels with My Aunt, Firsts & Co. (New York), 1989 (250 signed, numbered copies; wraps) . £150

Reflections 1923-1988, Reinhardt (London), 1990. £10/£5

ditto, Viking (New York), 1990 . . . . £10/£5

A World of My Own, Reinhardt (London), 1992 . £10/£5

ditto, Viking (New York), 1994 . . . . £10/£5

ZANE GREY

(b.1872 d.1939)

Zane Grey was an American author best known for his popular 'Westerns', novels and stories that presented an idealised image of the American Old West. His books were often filmed.

Novels

Betty Zane, Charles Francis Press (New York), 1903 £1,250

ditto, Charles Francis Press (New York), 1903 second edition) £400

ditto, Hodder & Stoughton (London), 1920 . . £400/£75

The Spirit of the Border, Burt (New York), 1906 (4pps of ads and Burt's address as '52-58 Duane Street' on each page) £300

ditto, Werner Laurie (London), 1921 . . £300/£65

ditto, Hodder & Stoughton (London), [no date] . £300/£65

Tarpon the Silver King, New York & Cuba Mail Steamship Co (New York), 1906 (wraps; Grey's name on third page at bottom) £1,000

The Last of the Plainsmen, The Outing Publishing Company (New York), 1908 . . . . £150

ditto, Hodder & Stoughton (London), 1908 . . £150

The Last Trail, Burt (New York), 1909 (2pps of ads and Burt's address as '52-58 Duane Street'). . . £250

ditto, Werner Laurie (London), 1920 . . £300/£65

ditto, Hodder & Stoughton (London), [no date] . £300/£65

The Short-Stop, McClure (New York), 1909 . . £700

ditto, Werner Laurie (London), 1920 . . £300/£65

The Heritage of the Desert, Harper & Brothers (New York), 1910 . . . . £175

ditto, Thomas Nelson & Sons (London), [1918] . £40

The Young Forester, Harper & Brothers (New York), 1910 (no code letters on copyright page) £350

ditto, Thomas Nelson & Sons (London), [c.1922] . £250/£40

The Young Pitcher, Harper & Brothers (New York), 1911 (no code letters on copyright page) £300

ditto, Lloyds (London), 1919 . . . . . £75

The Young Lion Hunter, Harper & Brothers (New York), 1911 (no code letters on copyright page) . . . £200

ditto, Lloyds (London), 1919 . . . . . £75

Riders of the Purple Sage, Harper & Brothers (New York), 1912 (no code letters on copyright page) . . £1,000

ditto, Thomas Nelson and Sons (London), [1921] . £300/£50

Ken Ward in the Jungle, Harper & Brothers (New York), 1912 (no code letters on copyright page) . . . £750 *ditto*, Harper & Brothers (New York), 1912 (code letters 'H-M' on copyright page) £200

ditto, Thomas Nelson and Sons (London), 1919 . . £60

Desert Gold, Harper & Brothers (New York), 1913 (code letters 'CN' on copyright page) £125

ditto, Thomas Nelson and Sons (London), [c.1919] £60

The Light of Western Stars, Harper & Brothers (New York), 1914 (code letters 'M-N' on copyright page) . . £125

ditto, Thomas Nelson and Sons (London), 1918 . . £40

The Lone Star Ranger, Harper & Brothers (New York), 1915 (code letters 'M-O' on copyright page) . . £125

ditto, Thomas Nelson and Sons (London), [no date] . £40

The Rainbow Trail, Harper & Brothers (New York), 1915 (code letters 'F-P' on copyright page) £125

ditto, Thomas Nelson and Sons (London), [no date] . £40

The Border Legion, Harper & Brothers (New York), 1916 (code letters 'E-Q' on copyright page) £125

ditto, Thomas Nelson and Sons (London), [no date] . £40

Wildfire, Harper & Brothers (New York), 1917 (code letters 'L-Q' on copyright page) £125

ditto, Thomas Nelson and Sons (London), 1920 . £125/£20

The U.P. Trail, Harper & Brothers (New York), 1918 (code letters 'A-S' on copyright page) £100

ditto, Harper & Brothers (New York), 1918 (the 'Khaki' edition sent overseas to serviceme, in flexible red leatherette) £200

ditto, as **The Roaring U.P. Trail**, Hodder & Stoughton (London), 1918 . . . . £75

The Desert of Wheat, Harper & Brothers (New York), 1919 (code letters 'A-T' on copyright page) £40

ditto, Hodder & Stoughton (London), [1919] . . £30

The Man of the Forest, Harper & Brothers (New York), 1920 (code letters 'A-U' on copyright page). . £300/£65

The Mysterious Rider, Harper & Brothers (New York), 1921 (code letters 'I-U' on copyright page) . . . £600/£65

ditto, Hodder & Stoughton (London), [1921] . £175/£20

To The Last Man, Harper & Brothers (New York), 1921 (code letters 'K-V' on copyright page) . . £350/£35

ditto, Hodder & Stoughton (London), [1922] . . £125/£15

The Day of the Beast, Harper & Brothers (New York), 1922 (code letters 'G-W' on copyright page) . . . £500/£65

The Bonefish Brigade, Zane Grey (Pasadena, CA), 1922 (stiched wraps with tassel). £2,000

Wanderer of the Wasteland, Harper & Brothers (New York), 1923 (code letters 'L-W' on copyright page). . £250/£35

ditto, Hodder & Stoughton (London), [1923] . . £125/£15

Roping Lions in the Grand Canyon, Harper & Brothers (New York), 1924 (code letters 'B-Y' on copyright page) . . . .£450/£75

ditto, Hodder & Stoughton (London), [1924] . . £125/£15

The Thundering Herd, Harper & Brothers (New York), 1925 (code letters 'L-Y' on copyright page) . . £250/£45

ditto, Hodder & Stoughton (London), [1925] . . £65/£15

The Vanishing American, Harper & Brothers (New York), 1925 (code letters 'I-Z' on copyright page) . . £125/£20

ditto, as **The Vanishing Indian**, Hodder & Stoughton (London), [1926]. . . . . . . £65/£10

Under the Tonto Rim, Harper & Brothers (New York), 1926 (code letters 'F-A' on copyright page) . . . £175/£30

ditto, Hodder & Stoughton (London), [1927] . . £50/£10

Forlorn River, Harper & Brothers (New York), 1927 (code letters 'H-B' on copyright page) . . . . £250/£40

ditto, Hodder & Stoughton (London), 1927 . . £225/£40

Nevada, Harper & Brothers (New York), 1928 (code letters 'B-C' on copyright page) . . . . . £150/£30

ditto, Hodder & Stoughton (London), 1928 . . £60/£10

Wild Horse Mesa, Harper & Brothers (New York), 1928 (code letters 'G-C' on copyright page) . . . £150/£30

ditto, Hodder & Stoughton (London), 1928 . . £50/£10

Don, The Story of a Lion Dog, Harper & Brothers (New York), 1928 (code letters 'G-C' on copyright page) . . . . £300/£65

Fighting Caravans, Harper & Brothers (New York/London), 1929 (code letters 'H-D' on copyright page) . £150/£25

ditto, Hodder & Stoughton (London), 1930 . . £100/£15

The Wolf Tracker, Harper & Brothers (New York), 1930 (code letters 'C-E' on copyright page) . . £800/£100

The Shepherd of Guadaloupe, Harper & Brothers (New York), 1930 (code letters 'C-E' on the copyright page) . . . . £175/£30

ditto, Hodder & Stoughton (London), 1930 . . £65/£10

Sunset Pass, Harper & Brothers (New York), 1931 (code letters 'K-F' on copyright page) . . . . £150/£25

ditto, Harper & Brothers (New York), 1931 (code letters 'A-F' on copyright page). . . . . . . £200/£75

ditto, Hodder & Stoughton (London), 1931 . . £150/£25

Arizona Ames, Hodder & Stoughton (London), 1931 . . . . £100/£15

ditto, Harper & Brothers (New York), 1932 (code letters 'I-F' on copyright page). . . . . . . £150/£20

Robber's Roost, Harper & Brothers (New York), 1932 (code letters 'F-G' on copyright page) . . . £150/£20

ditto, Hodder & Stoughton (London), 1932 . . £100/£20

ditto, as **Thieves' Canyon**, World (London), 1965 (pbk) £5

The Drift Fence, Harper & Brothers (New York), 1933 (code letters 'K-G' on copyright page) . . . £200/£25

ditto, Hodder & Stoughton (London), 1933 . . £100/£20

The Hash Knife Outfit, Harper & Brothers (New York), 1933 (code letters 'G-H' on copyright page). . £150/£20

ditto, Hodder & Stoughton (London), 1933 . . £125/£25

The Code of the West, Harper & Brothers (New York), 1934 (code letters 'B-I' on the copyright page) . . £125/£25

ditto, Hodder & Stoughton (London), 1934 . . £75/£15

Thunder Mountain, Harper & Brothers (New York), 1935 (code letters 'B-K' on copyright page) . . . £125/£20

ditto, Hodder & Stoughton (London), 1935 . . £75/£15

ditto, Grosset & Dunlap (New York), no date (signed edition in slipcase) . . . . £200/£100

The Trail Driver, Harper & Brothers (New York), 1936 (code letters 'M-K' on copyright page) . . . £150/£25

ditto, Hodder & Stoughton (London), 1936 . . £75/£15

The Lost Wagon Train, Harper & Brothers (New York), 1936 (code letters 'G-L' on copyright page) . £125/£20

ditto, Hodder & Stoughton (London), 1936 . . £75/£15

West of the Pecos, Harper & Brothers (New York), 1937 (code letters 'C-M' on copyright page) . . . £125/£25

ditto, Hodder & Stoughton (London), 1937 . . £80/£15

Raiders of Spanish Peaks, Harper & Brothers (New York), 1938 (code letters 'D-N' on copyright page). . £125/£25

ditto, Hodder & Stoughton (London), 1938 . . £100/£20

Knights of the Range, Harper & Brothers (New York), 1939 (code letters 'M-N' on copyright page) . . £125/£25

ditto, Hodder & Stoughton (London), 1939 . . £60/£10

Western Union, Harper & Brothers (New York), 1939 (code letters 'I-O' on copyright page) . . . . £150/£20

ditto, Hodder & Stoughton (London), 1939 . . £60/£10

On the Hoof, Harper & Brothers (New York), 1940 (code letters 'G-P' on copyright page) . . . £200/£35

ditto, as *30,000 on the Hoof*, Hodder & Stoughton (London), 1940 . . . . £60/£10

ditto, as *Woman of the Frontier*, Leisure Books (New York), 2000 (pbk; restored text) £5

Twin Sombreros, Harper & Brothers (New York), 1940 (code letters 'C-Q' on copyright page) . . . £100/£20

ditto, Hodder & Stoughton (London), 1942 . . £60/£10

Majesty's Rancho, Harper & Brothers (New York), 1942 (code letters 'C-R' on copyright page) . . . £200/£30

ditto, Hodder & Stoughton (London), 1942 . . £60/£10

Zane Grey Omnibus, Harper & Brothers (New York), 1943 (code letters 'B-S' on copyright page) (no d/w) . £200

ditto, Harper & Brothers (New York), 1943 (code letters 'C-S' on copyright page) £150

ditto, as *Zane Grey Round-Up*, Grosset & Dunlap (New York), 1943 . . . . £75/£10

Stairs of the Sand, Harper & Brothers (New York), 1928 [1943] (code letters 'C-S' on copyright page) . £150/£30

ditto, Hodder & Stoughton (London), 1943 . . £65/£15

The Wilderness Trek, Harper & Brothers (New York), 1944 (code letters 'E-T' on copyright page) . . . £125/£25

ditto, Hodder & Stoughton (London), 1945 . . £50/£10

Shadow on the Trail, Harper & Brothers (New York), 1946 (code letters 'A-V' on copyright page) . . . £75/£15

ditto, Hodder & Stoughton (London), 1947 . . £45/£10

Valley Of Wild Horses, Harper & Brothers (New York), 1947 (code letters 'B-W' on copyright page) . £75/£15

ditto, Hodder & Stoughton (London), 1947 . . £45/£10

King of the Royal Mounted and *Ghost Guns of Roaring River*, Whitman (Racine, WI), 1946 . . . £45/£10

Rogue River Feud, Harper & Brothers (New York), 1930 [1948] (code letters 'C-X' on copyright page) . £150/£25

ditto, Hodder & Stoughton (London), 1949 . . £45/£10

The Deer Stalker, Harper & Brothers (New York), 1925 [1949] (code letters 'D-Y' on copyright page; first issue d/w without Christian Herald announcement) . £60/£10

ditto, Harper & Brothers (New York), 1925 [1949] (second issue d/w with Christian Herald announcement) . £45/£10

ditto, Hodder & Stoughton (London), 1949 . . £45/£10

The Maverick Queen, Harper & Brothers (New York), 1950 (code letters 'D-Z' on copyright page) . . . £60/£10

ditto, Hodder & Stoughton (London), 1950 . . £30/£5

The Dude Ranger, Harper & Brothers (New York), 1951 (code letters 'F-A' on copyright page) . . . £75/£15

ditto, Hodder & Stoughton (London), 1952 . . £30/£5

Captives of the Desert, Harper & Brothers (New York), 1926 [1952] (code letters 'B-B' on copyright page) . £60/£10

ditto, Hodder & Stoughton (London), 1953 . . £30/£5

Zane Grey's Adventures in Fishing, Harper & Brothers (New York), 1952 (code letters 'I-B' on copyright page) .
. . . . £100/£25

Wyoming, Harper & Brothers (New York), 1932 [1953] (code letters 'F-C' on copyright page) . . . £60/£10

ditto, Hodder & Stoughton (London), 1954 . . £20/£5

Lost Pueblo, Harper & Brothers (New York), 1954 (code letters 'H-D' on copyright page) . . . . £45/£10

ditto, Hodder & Stoughton (London), 1955 . . £20/£5

Black Mesa, Harper & Brothers (New York), 1955 (code letters 'H-E' on copyright page) . . . . £50/£10

ditto, Hodder & Stoughton (London), 1956 . . £20/£5

Stranger from the Tonto, Harper & Brothers (New York), 1956 (code letters 'G-F' on copyright page) . . £50/£10

ditto, Hodder & Stoughton (London), 1957 . . £20/£5

The Fugitive Trail, Harper & Brothers (New York), 1957 (no code letters) . . . . £60/£10

ditto, Hodder & Stoughton (London), 1958 . . £20/£5

Arizona Clan, Harper & Brothers (New York), 1958 (code letters 'H-H' on copyright page) . . . . £60/£10

ditto, Hodder & Stoughton (London), 1959 . . £20/£5

Horse Heaven Hill, Harper & Brothers (New York), 1959 (code letters 'F-I' on copyright page) . . . £60/£10

ditto, Hodder & Stoughton (London), 1960 . . £20/£5

Boulder Dam, Harper & Brothers (New York), 1963 (code letters 'G-N' on copyright page) . . . . £60/£10

ditto, Hodder & Stoughton (London), 1965 . . £20/£5

The Adventures of Finspot, D.J. Books (San Bernardino, CA), 1974 (950 [250] numbered copies; tipped-in colour plates; blue leatherette binding) £125

The Trail of the Jaguar, Zane Grey Collector (Williamsport, MD), 1976 (500 copies; stapled wraps) £40

The Westerner, Belmont Tower (New York), 1977 (pkb) .
. . . . £10

The Reef Girl, Harper & Row (New York), 1977 . £30/£5

The Buffalo Hunter, Belmont (New York), 1978 (pbk) £10

The Rustlers of Pecos County and *Silvermane*, Belmont Tower (New York), 1979 (pbk) £10

Blue Feather, Manor Books (New York), 1972 (pbk) . £10

The Big Land, Belmont Tower (New York), 1976 (pbk) £5

Tenderfoot, Belmont Tower (New York), 1977 (pbk) . £5

Lord of Lackawaxen Creek, Lime Rock Press (Salisbury, CT), 1981 (miniature book illustrated and signed by Catryna Ten Eyck) £15

Nonnezoshe, The Rainbow Bridge, publisher? (place?), 1985 (wraps). £5

Zane Grey Fishing Library, Derrydale Press (Lyon, MI), 1990-91 (10 vols signed by Loren Grey) . £300 the set

Avalanche/The Kidnapping of Roseta Uvaldo, Tor (New York), 1990 (pbk) £5

The Kidnapping of Collie Younger/Outlaws of Palouse, Tor (New York), 1991 (pbk) £5

George Washinton, Frontiersman, Univ Press of Kentucky (Lexington, KY), 1994 . . . . . . £15/£5

Last of the Duanes, Leisure Books (New York), 1998 (pbk)
. . . . £5

Short Stories

Tales of Fishes, Harper & Brothers (New York), 1919 (code letters 'F-T' on copyright page) £150

ditto, Harper & Brothers (New York), 1919 (50 copies bound in quarter leather for presentation) £750

ditto, Hodder & Stoughton (London), [1920] . . £300/£75

ditto, as *Great Game Fishing at Catalina*, Santa Catalina Island Co. (Catalina), 1919 (pbk; excerpt only) . £650

The Redheaded Outfield and Other Stories, Grosset & Dunlap (New York), 1920 (without frontispiece; 11 titles listed on first page of ads with the last *The Last of The Great Scouts*; 18 titles on rear of d/w excluding *Tales of Fishes* and *The Man of The Forest*). . . . £750/£75

Tales of Lonely Trails, Harper & Brothers (New York), 1922 (code letters 'G-W' on copyright page) . £500/£65

ditto, Harper & Brothers (New York), 1922 (signed copies bound in quarter leather) £600

ditto, Hodder & Stoughton (London), 1922 . . £125/£15

Tappan's Burro and Other Stories, Harper & Brothers (New York), 1923 (code letters 'I-X' on copyright page) . .
. . . . £250/£35

ditto, Hodder & Stoughton (London), [1923] .   . £125/£15
Call of the Canyon, Harper & Brothers (New York), 1924
    (code letters 'K-X' on copyright page) .   .   . £200/£30
ditto, Hodder & Stoughton (London), [1924] .   . £125/£15
Tales of Southern Rivers, Harper & Brothers (New York),
    1924 (code letters 'H-Y' on copyright page).   . £450/£75
ditto, Harper & Brothers (New York), 1924 (less than 12
    copies bound in quarter leather for presentation) .   . £750
ditto, Hodder & Stoughton (London), [1924] (code letters
    'H-Y' on copyright page) .   .   .   .   . £150/£50
ditto, Hodder & Stoughton (London), [1924] (reset and
    printed in England; blue cloth stamped in black). £150/£50
Tales of Fishing Virgin Seas, Harper & Brothers (New
    York), 1925 (code letters 'K-Z' on copyright page) .   .
    .   .   .   . £300/£50
ditto, Hodder & Stoughton (London), [1926] .   . £200/£45
Tales of Swordfish and Tuna, Harper & Brothers (New
    York), 1927 (code letters 'H-B' on copyright page) .   .
    .   .   .   . £1,000/£200
ditto, Harper & Brothers (New York), 1927 (presentation
    copies bound in quarter morocco with two frontispiece
    paintings) £850
ditto, Hodder & Stoughton (London), 1927 (code letters 'H-
    B' on copyright page).   .   .   .   . £1,000/£200
ditto, Derrydale Press (Lyon, MI), 1991 (2,500 numbered
    copies signed by author's son Loren Grey; full leather)   .
    .   .   .   . £150
Tales of Fresh Water Fishing, Harper & Brothers (New
    York), 1928 (code letters 'F-C' on copyright page)   .   .
    .   .   .   . £500/£75
ditto, Harper & Brothers (New York), 1928 (c.50 present-
    ation copies bound in quarter leather) .   .   . £1,000
ditto, Hodder & Stoughton (London), 1928   .   . £350/£60
Tales of Tahitian Waters, Harper & Brothers (New York),
    1931 (code letters 'I-F' on copyright page) .   £600/£100
ditto, Hodder & Stoughton (London), 1931   .   . £300/£75
The Ranger and Other Stories, Harper & Brothers (New
    York), 1958 [1960] (code letters 'G-K' on copyright page)
    .   .   .   . £60/£10
ditto, Hodder & Stoughton (London), 1963   .   . £20/£5
ditto, Franklin Library (Franklin Centre, PA), 1979 (limited
    edition bound in full leather) £20
Blue Feather and Other Stories, Harper & Brothers (New
    York), 1961 (code letters 'I-L' on copyright page) £60/£10
ditto, Hodder & Stoughton (London), 1962   .   . £20/£5
Zane Grey: Outdoorsman, Prentice-Hall (Englewood Cliffs,
    NJ), 1972 .   .   .   . £30/£10
Zane Grey's Savage Kingdom, Belmont Tower (New York),
    1975 (pbk) £10
Zane Grey's Greatest Animal Stories, Belmont Tower (New
    York), 1975 (pbk) £10
Zane Grey's Greatest Western Stories, Belmont Tower
    (New York), 1975 (pbk) £10
Zane Grey's Greatest Indian Stories, Belmont Tower (New
    York), 1975 (pbk) £10
Round-Up, Manor Books (New York), 1976 (pbk)   . £10
Shark! Zane Grey's Tales of Man-Eating Sharks, Belmont
    Tower (New York), 1976 (pbk) £15
Yaqui and Other Great Indian Stories, Belmont Tower
    (New York), 1976 (pbk) £5
Tales from a Fisherman's Log, Hodder & Stoughton
    (Auckland, New Zealand), 1978 .   .   .   . £50/£10
ditto, Hodder & Stoughton (Auckland, New Zealand), 1978
    (7 copies bound in quarter red morocco)   .   . £1,000

The Camp Robber and Other Stories, Walter J. Black
    (Roslyn, NY), 1979 .   .   .   . £20
Amber's Mirage and Other Stories, Pocket Books (New
    York), 1983 (pbk) £10
The Undiscovered Zane Grey Fishing Stories, Winchester
    Press (no place [Piscataway, NJ]), 1983.   .   . £15/£5
ditto, Winchester Press (no place [Piscataway, NJ]), 1983
    (deluxe edition in pictorial box)   .   .   . £25/£15
The Secret of Quaking Asp Cabin and Other Stories,
    Pocket Books (New York), 1983 (pbk) £5
The Wolf Tracker and Other Stories, Santa Barbara Press
    (Santa Barbara, CA), 1984 (pbk) £5

Others
*Nassau Cuba Yucatan Mexico; A Personal Note of
    Appreciation of these Nearby Foreign Lands*, New York
    and Cuba Mail Steam Ship Co (New York), 1909 (wraps).
    .   .   .   . £400
ditto, Zane Grey Collector (Williamsport, MD), 1976 (500
    copies; stapled wraps; facsimile) £20
Tales of An Angler's Eldorado, Harper & Brothers (New
    York/New Zealand), 1926 (code letters 'G-A' on the
    copyright page) .   .   .   .   .   . £750/£150
ditto, Harper & Brothers (New York/New Zealand), 1926
    (c.100 deluxe uncut copies in quarter red morocco bound
    for author; includes colour frontispiece not in trade edition)
    .   .   .   . £800
ditto, Hodder & Stoughton (London), 1926 (code letters 'G-
    A' on the copyright page) .   .   .   .   £800/£150
ditto, as *Angler's Eldorado, Zane Grey in New Zealand*,
    Walter J. Black (Roslyn, NY), 1982 (enlarged edition)
    .   .   .   . £30/£10
ditto, Walter J. Black (Roslyn, NY), 1982 (pbk)   . £10
ditto, as *Zane Grey in the South Pacific*, Angus &
    Robertson (Sydney), 1982.   .   .   .   . £30/£10
Zane Grey: The Man and His Work, Harper & Brothers
    (New York), 1928 (yellow wraps printed in green)   . £75
ditto, Harper & Brothers (New York), 1928 (gilt stamped
    leatherette) £125
Zane Grey's Book of Camps and Trails, Harper & Brothers
    (New York), 1931 (code letters 'G-F' on copyright page) .
    .   .   .   .   £450/£100
The Great Mako, American Museum of Natural History
    (New York), 1934 (wraps). £100
Fly Fishing, Horrocks-Ibboston (Utica, NY), 1936 (wraps,
    includes essay by Grey) £300
An American Angler in Australia, Harper & Brothers (New
    York), 1937 (code letters 'B-M' on copyright page) .   .
    .   .   .   .   £700/£100
ditto, Harper & Brothers (New York), 1937 (less than 10
    copies bound in quarter morocco for presentation) £1,250
ditto, Hodder & Stoughton (London), [1937] .   £500/£100
The Zane Grey Cookbook, Prentice-Hall (Englewood Cliffs,
    NJ), 1976 .   .   .   . £10/£5
The Western Motion-Picture, Arundel Press (Los Angeles),
    1984 (100 copies, frontispiece signed by D'Ambrosio)   .
    .   .   .   . £125
ditto, Arundel Press (Los Angeles), 1984 (25 numbered large
    paper copies on handmade paper with check signed by
    Grey tipped in back; bound in half morocco)   .   . £300
The Many Faces of Zane Grey, Silver Spruce (Flagstaff),
    1993 (125 numbered copies; slipcase, no d/w)   . £30/£20

JOHN GRISHAM
(b.1955)

U.S. citizen John Grisham is a retired attorney and novelist best known for his modern legal dramas. His reputation was established by his second novel, *The Firm*. In 1990, a year before it was published, Paramount Pictures purchased the film rights for $600,000. *Publishers Weekly* declared Grisham the best-selling novelist of the 1990s, and since then he has become the best-selling American author of all time.

Novels

A Time to Kill, Wynwood (New York), 1989 (first issue d/w with no mention of *The Firm* on d/w) . . £2,000/£100
ditto, Doubleday (New York), 1993 (350 signed, numbered copies, slipcase; 'First edition' statement incorrect) . .
. . . . £650/£500
ditto, Doubleday (New York), 1993 ('First edition' statement incorrect) . . . . . . £35/£10
ditto, Arrow (London), 1992 (wraps) £5
ditto, Century (London), 1993 . . . . £50/£10
The Firm, Doubleday (New York), 1991 . . . £50/£10
ditto, Doubleday (New York), 1991 (350 signed, numbered copies, slipcase) . . . £600/£500
ditto, Century (London), 1991 . . . . £45/£10
The Pelican Brief, Doubleday (New York), 1992 . £35/£5
ditto, Doubleday (New York), 1993 (350 signed, numbered copies, slipcase) . . . . . £275/£200
ditto, Century (London), 1992 . . . . £25/£5
The Client, Doubleday (New York), 1993 . . £35/£5
ditto, Doubleday (New York), 1993 (350 signed, numbered copies, slipcase) . . . . £200/£150
ditto, Century (London), 1993 . . . . £25/£5
The Chamber, Doubleday (New York), 1994 . . £20/£5
ditto, Doubleday (New York), 1994 (350 signed, numbered copies, slipcase) . . . . . £145/£100
ditto, Century (London), 1994 . . . . £20/£5
The Rainmaker, Doubleday (New York), 1995 . £20/£5
ditto, Doubleday (New York), 1995 (350 signed, numbered copies, slipcase) . . . . . £150/£100
ditto, Century (London), 1995 . . . . £15/£5
The Runaway Jury, Doubleday (New York), 1996 £15/£5
ditto, Doubleday (New York), 1996 (350 signed, numbered copies, slipcase) . . . . . £150/£100
ditto, Century (London), 1996 . . . . £15/£5
The Partner, Doubleday (New York), 1997 . . £15/£5
ditto, Doubleday (New York), 1997 (275 signed, numbered copies, slipcase) . . . . £200/£150
ditto, Century (London), 1997 . . . . £15/£5
The Street Lawyer, Doubleday (New York), 1998 . £10/£5
ditto, Doubleday (New York), 1998 (250 signed, numbered copies, slipcase) . . . . £150/£100
ditto, Century (London), 1998 . . . . £10/£5
The Testament, Doubleday (New York), 1999 . £10/£5
ditto, Doubleday (New York), 1999 (500 signed, numbered copies, slipcase) . . . . . £100/£75
ditto, Century (London), 1999 . . . . £10/£5
The Brethren, Doubleday (New York), 2000 (500 signed, numbered copies, slipcase) . . . . £125/£75
ditto, Doubleday (New York), 2000 . . . . £10/£5
ditto, Century (London), 2000 . . . . £10/£5
A Painted House, Doubleday (New York), 2001 (350 signed, numbered copies, slipcase) . . . £150/£125

ditto, Doubleday (New York), 2001 . . . . £10/£5
ditto, Century (London), 2001 . . . . £10/£5
Skipping Christmas, Doubleday (New York), 2001 (350 signed, numbered copies, slipcase) . . . £150/£125
ditto, Doubleday (New York), 2001 . . . . £10/£5
ditto, Century (London), 2001 . . . . £10/£5
The Summons, Doubleday (New York), 2002 (350 signed, numbered copies, slipcase) . . . £125/£100
ditto, Doubleday (New York), 2002 . . . . £10/£5
ditto, Century (London), 2002 . . . . £10/£5
The King of Torts, Doubleday (New York), 2003 (350 signed, numbered copies, slipcase) . . . £125/£100
ditto, Doubleday (New York), 2003 . . . . £10/£5
ditto, Century (London), 2003 . . . . £10/£5
Bleachers, Doubleday (New York), 2003 (350 signed, numbered copies, slipcase) . . . . £125/£100
ditto, Doubleday (New York), 2003 . . . . £10/£5
ditto, Century (London), 2003 . . . . £10/£5
The Last Juror, Doubleday (New York), 2004 (350 signed, numbered copies, slipcase) . . . . £125/£100
ditto, Doubleday (New York), 2004 . . . . £10/£5
ditto, Century (London), 2004 . . . . £10/£5
The Broker, Doubleday (New York), 2005 (350 signed, numbered copies, slipcase) . . . . £125/£100
ditto, Doubleday (New York), 2005 . . . . £10/£5
ditto, Century (London), 2005 . . . . £10/£5
Playing for Pizza, Doubleday (New York), 2007 (250 signed, numbered copies, glassine d/w; slipcase) £125/£100
ditto, Doubleday (New York), 2007 . . . . £10/£5
ditto, Century (London), 2007 . . . . £10/£5
The Appeal, Doubleday (New York), 2008 (350 signed, numbered copies, slipcase) . . . . £150/£100
ditto, Doubleday (New York), 2008 . . . . £10/£5
ditto, Century (London), 2008 . . . . £10/£5
The Associate, Doubleday (New York), 2009 (200 signed, numbered copies, slipcase) . . . . £250/£200
ditto, Doubleday (New York), 2009 . . . . £10/£5
ditto, Century (London), 2009 . . . . £10/£5

Short Stories
Ford County, Doubleday (New York), 2009 . . £10/£5
ditto, Century (London), 2009 . . . . £10/£5

Others
Special Forces: A Guided Tour of U.S. Special Forces, Berkley (New York), 2001 (with Tom Clancy; pbk) . £5
ditto, Sidgwick & Jackson (London), 2001 (pbk) . . £5
The Innocent Man, Doubleday (New York), 2006. £10/£5
ditto, Century (London), 2006 . . . . . £10/£5

GEORGE & WEEDON GROSSMITH
(b.1847 d.1912 and b.1854 d.1919)

The Diary of a Nobody, a comic classic, was their only published book.

The Diary of a Nobody, Arrowsmith (London), 1892 . £300

DAVIS GRUBB
(b.1919 d.1980)

Grubb was an American novelist and short story writer whose first novel, *The Night of the Hunter*, was a bestseller made into a movie considered a classic of *film-noir*.

Short Stories
Twelve Tales of Suspense and the Supernatural, Charles Scribner's (New York), 1964 . . . . £100/£20
ditto, as *One Foot in the Grave*, Arrow (London), 1966 (pbk) £5
The Siege of 318: Thirteen Mystical Stories, Back Fork Books (Webster Springs, WV), 1978 . £25/£5
You Never Believe Me and Other Stories, St Martin's Press (New York), 1989 . . . . . £15/£5

Novels
The Night of the Hunter, Harper (New York), 1953 £125/£25
ditto, Harper (New York), 1953 (signed by author on tipped-in leaf) . . . . . . £225/£125
ditto, Hamish Hamilton (London), 1954 . . £75/£15
A Dream of Kings, Charles Scribner's (New York), 1955 . . . . £65/£10
The Watchman, Charles Scribner's (New York), 1961 . . . . £45/£10
ditto, Michael Joseph (London), 1962 . . . £20/£5
The Voices of Glory, Charles Scribner's (New York), 1962. . . . . £45/£10
ditto, Michael Joseph (London), 1963 . . . £20/£5
A Tree Full of Stars, Mountain State Press (Richwood, WV), 1965 (no d/w) £45
ditto, Charles Scribner's (New York), 1965 . £40/£5
Shadow of My Brother, Holt, Rinehart & Winston (New York), 1966 . . . . £20/£5
ditto, Hutchinson (London), 1966 . . £15/£5
The Golden Sickle: A Tale, World (New York/Cleveland), 1968 . . . . £30/£5
Fool's Parade, World (New York), 1969. . . £20/£5
ditto, Hodder & Stoughton (London), 1971 . £20/£5
The Barefoot Man, Simon & Schuster (New York), 1971 . . . . £20/£5
Ancient Lights, Viking (New York), 1982 . £20/£5

Others
Icey and Walt Approve of Preacher, John Doesn't, Pearl Does, no publisher (no place), no date (broadside; 250 copies signed by Grubb and Lillian Gish) . . . £100

THOM GUNN
(b.1929 d.2004)

English poetry was dominated in the 1960s and early 1970s by Ted Hughes and Thom Gunn, but while the former remained in the public eye until his death in 1998, Thom Gunn's reputation has waned. Born in England, he moved to California in 1958, settling two years later in San Francisco, where he remained until his death in April 2004.

Poetry
Poetry from Cambridge, 1951-1952, Fortune Press (London), 1952 . . . . £300/£65

The Fantasy Poets No. 16, Fantasy Press (Oxford, UK), 1953 (approx 300 copies; stapled wraps) . . . £325
Fighting Terms, Fantasy Press (Oxford, UK), 1954 (first issue with final 't' in 'thought' missed on first line of p.38) £350
ditto, Fantasy Press (Oxford, UK), 1954 (second issue, error corrected) £250
ditto, Hawk's Well Press (New York), 1958 (1,500 copies; wraps with d/w) . . . . . £125/£20
ditto, Faber (London), 1966 . . . . . £25/£5
Poetry from Cambridge, 1952-1954, Fantasy Press (Oxford, UK), 1955 (wraps) £125
The Sense of Movement, Faber (London), 1957 . £75/£10
ditto, Univ of Chicago Press (Chicago), 1959 . . £45/£10
My Sad Captains, Faber (London), 1961 . . . £40/£10
ditto, Univ of Chicago Press (Chicago), 1961 . . £25/£10
Selected Poems, Faber (London), 1962 (with Ted Hughes; pbk) £30
A Geography, Stone Wall Press (Iowa City, IA), 1966 (220 copies; sewn wraps) £125
Positives, Faber (London), 1966 . . . . . £30/£10
ditto, Univ of Chicago Press (Chicago), 1967 . . £30/£10
Touch, Faber (London), [1967] . . . . £25/£5
ditto, Univ of Chicago Press (Chicago), 1968 . . £25/£5
The Garden of the Gods, Pym-Randall Press (Cambridge, MA), [1968] (200 of 226, signed copies; sewn wraps) £45
ditto, Pym-Randall Press (Cambridge, MA), [1968] (26 signed, lettered copies of 226; sewn wraps) . . . £100
The Explorers, Gilbertson (Crediton, Devon), 1969 (6 copies) £200
ditto, Gilbertson (Crediton, Devon), 1969 (deluxe issue of 10 copies) £150
ditto, Gilbertson (Crediton, Devon), 1969 (special issue of 20 copies) £125
ditto, Gilbertson (Crediton, Devon), 1969 (ordinary issue of 64 copies) £50
The Fair in the Woods, Sycamore Press (Oxford, UK), 1969 (broadsheet, 500 copies) £20
Poems 1950-1966: A Selection, Faber (London), 1969 (pbk) £10
Sunlight, Albondocani Press (New York), 1969 (150 signed, numbered copies) £50
Moly, Faber (London), 1971 . . . . . £25/£10
ditto, Farrar Straus (New York), 1973 . . . £20/£5
Last Days at Teddington, Poem-of-the-Month-Club (London), 1971 (broadsheet, 1,000 copies) . . . £10
Poem After Chaucer, Albondocani Press (New York), 1971 (300 copies; stapled wraps; in envelope) . . £30/£20
The Spell, Steane, (Kettering, Northants), 1973 (broadsheet, 500 copies) £20
Songbook, Albondocani Press (New York), 1973 (200 signed copies; sewn wraps) £35
To the Air, Godine (Boston), 1974 (no d/w) . . . £20
Mandrakes, The Rainbow Press (London), [1974] (150 signed copies, slipcase) . . . . . £250/£200
Jack Straw's Castle, Hallman (New York), 1975 (300 copies; stapled wraps with d/w) . . . . £35/£20
ditto, Hallman (New York), 1976 (100 signed hardback copies) . . . . £65/£55
ditto, as *Jack Straw's Castle and Other Poems*, Faber (London), 1976 (750 hardback copies) . . . £40/£10
ditto, Faber (London), 1976 (100 numbered, signed hardback copies) . . . . £100/£45
ditto, Faber (London), 1976 (4,000 copies; pbk) . . £5

ditto, Farrar Straus (New York), 1976 . . . £15/£5

The Missed Beat, Janus Press (Newark, VT), 1976 (50 copies, slipcase) . . . . . . £200/£150

ditto, Gruffyground Press (Sidcot, Somerset), 1976 (approx 170 copies; sewn wraps) £100

Games of Chance, Abattoir (Univ of Nebraska at Omaha, NE), 1979 (220 copies, no d/w) £65

Selected Poems 1950-1975, Faber (London), 1979. £10/£5

ditto, Farrar Straus (New York), 1979 . . . £10/£5

Talbot Road, Helikon Press (New York), 1981 (150 signed, numbered copies of 400; sewn wraps) . . . £25

ditto, Helikon Press (New York), 1981 (250 numbered copies of 400; stapled wraps) £10

The Passages of Joy, Faber (London), 1982 . . £10/£5

ditto, Farrar Straus Giroux (New York), 1982 . . £10/£5

Sidewalks, Albondocani Press (New York), 1985 (200 signed copies; sewn wraps) £25

Lament, Doe Press [Champaign, IL], 1985 (150 signed copies; sewn wraps) £40

ditto, Doe Press [Champaign, IL], 1985 (26 signed copies, hardback, no d/w) £75

The Hurtless Trees, privately printed by Jordan Davies (New York), 1986 (159 signed copies; wraps and d/w) . . . . £50/£35

Night Sweats, Barth (Florence, KY), 1987 (175 signed, numbered copies; wraps) £25

ditto, as **The Man with Night Sweats**, Faber (London), 1992 . . . . £10/£5

ditto, Farrar Straus Giroux (New York), 1992 . . £10/£5

Undesirables, Pig Press (Durham, UK), 1988 (50 signed copies of 550) £25

ditto, Pig Press (Durham, UK), 1988 (500 unsigned copies of 550) £10

At the Barriers, Nadja (New York), 1989 (26 signed copies of 100) £100

ditto, Nadja (New York), 1989 (74 signed copies of 100; wraps with d/w) . . . . £50/£35

Death's Door, Red Hydra Press (Huntsville, AL), 1989 (20 signed, quarter morocco copies) £250

ditto, Red Hydra Press (AL), 1989 (60 signed copies) . £145

My Mother's Pride, DIA Center for the Arts (New York), 1990 (broadside) £10

Unsought Intimacies, Koch (Berkeley, CA), 1991 (130 copies, slipcase) . . . . £150/£125

The Life of the Otter, Tucson Desert Museum (San Francisco, CA), 1991 (50 signed copies, broadside) . £35

Old Stories, Sea Cliff Press (New York), 1992 (100 copies; wraps) £65

Collected Poems, Faber (London), 1993 . . £15/£5

ditto, Faber (London), 1993 (150 signed copies, slipcase) . . . . £125/£100

ditto, Farrar, Straus & Giroux (New York), 1994 . £15/£5

Shelf Life, Univ of Michigan Press (Ann Arbor, MI), 1993 (no d/w) £10

ditto, Faber (London), 1994 . . . . . £15/£5

Arthur In the Twilight Slot, Enitharmon Press (London), 1995 (75 copies, slipcase) . . . . £250/£225

Dancing David, Nadja (New York), 1995 (26 signed, lettered copies) £200

June, Wood Works (Seattle, WA.), 1998 (250 signed copies, broadside) £20

A Green Place, Occasional Works (Menlo Park, CA), 1999 (with Eileen Hogan, 26 signed, lettered copies, slipcase) £225

ditto, Occasional Works (Menlo Park, CA), 1999 (80 signed, numbered copies) £50

ditto, Occasional Works (Menlo Park, CA), 1999 (220 numbered copies) £20

Others

The Occasions of Poetry, Faber (London), 1982 . £10/£5

ditto, North Point Press (New York), 1985 (pbk) . . £10

H. RIDER HAGGARD

(b.1856 d.1925)

Sir Henry Rider Haggard was a successful British writer of heroic Victorian adventure novels. Haggard's strengths are his story-telling abilities and the authentic background to his books (he had some first-hand experience of their exotic locations). While his novels contain many of the obvious prejudices of British colonialism, they are unusual for the sympathy with which native populations are portrayed.

Novels

Dawn, Hurst & Blackett (London), 1884 (3 vols) . £4,000

ditto, Appleton (New York), 1887 (2 vols; wraps) . £1,500

ditto, Harper (New York), 1887 . . . . . £150

The Witch's Head, Hurst & Blackett (London), 1885 [1884] (3 vols) £7,500

ditto, Appleton (New York), 1885 . . . . £1,000

King Solomon's Mines, Cassell (London), 1885 (first issue with 'Bamamgwato' for 'Bamangwato' on line 14, p.10: 'twins to live' for 'twins live' line 27, p.122 and 'wrod' for 'word' line 29, p.307. Ads dated '5G.8.85') . £3,000

ditto, Cassell (London), 1885 (second issue, uncorrected, with ads dated '5G.10.85') £1,500

ditto, Cassell (New York), 1885 (third issue of English sheets, with no ads) £1,250

She, Harper (New York), 1886 (wraps) . . . £1,000

ditto, Longmans (London), 1887 (first issue with 'Godness me' in line 38, p.269) £600

Jess, Smith, Elder, & Co. (London), 1887 . . . £200

ditto, George Munro (New York), 1887 (wraps) . . £150

ditto, Harper (New York), 1887 . . . . . £100

Allan Quartermain, Longmans (London), 1887 (first issue with no footnote on frontispiece) £350

ditto, Longmans (London), 1887 (112 large paper copies) £1,000

ditto, Harper (New York), 1887 . . . . . £175

ditto, Harper (New York), 1887 (wraps) . . . £175

Maiwa's Revenge, Longmans (London), 1888 . £125

ditto, Harper (New York), 1888 . . . . . £100

Mr Meeson's Will, Spencer Blackett (London), 1888 (first issue with 'Johnson' for 'Johnston' in line 1, p.284, catalogue dated October 1888) £300

ditto, Harper (New York), 1888 . . . . . £125

Colonel Quaritch V.C., Longmans (London), 1888 (3 vols) £600

ditto, Lovell (New York), 1888 . . . . . £50

Cleopatra, Longmans (London), 1889 (catalogue dated January 1889) £200

ditto, Longmans (London), 1889 (50 large paper copies) £2,000

ditto, Harper (New York), 1889 (wraps) . . . £175

Allan's Wife, Spencer Blackett (London), 1889 . £125

ditto, Longmans (London), 1889 (100 large paper copies) £2,000

Beatrice, Longmans (London), 1890 . . . . . £70

ditto, George Munro (New York), 1890 . . . . £50

The World's Desire, Longmans (London), 1890 (with Andrew Lang) £35

ditto, Harper (New York), 1890 . . . . . £35

Eric Brighteyes, Longmans (London), 1891 . . £40

ditto, Harper (New York), 1891 . . . . . £35

Nada the Lily, Longmans (London), 1892 . . £40

ditto, Longmans (New York), 1892 . . . . £35

Montezuma's Daughter, Longmans (New York), 1893 £40

ditto, Longmans (London), 1893 . . . . . £35

The People of the Mist, Longmans (London), 1894 . £175

ditto, Longmans (New York), 1894 . . . . £65

Joan Haste, Longmans (London), 1895 . . . £70

ditto, Longmans (New York), 1895 . . . . £40

Heart of the World, Longmans (New York), 1895 . £70

ditto, Longmans (London), 1896 . . . . . £70

The Wizard, Arrowsmith (London), 1896 (wraps) . £60

ditto, Longmans (New York), 1896 . . . . £50

Doctor Therne, Longmans (London), 1898 . . £50

ditto, Longmans (New York), 1898 . . . . £80

Allan the Hunter, Lothrop (Boston), 1898 . . £125

Swallow, Longmans (London), 1899 . . . . £50

ditto, Longmans (New York), 1899 . . . . £80

Black Heart and White Heart, Longmans (London), 1900 . . . . £100

ditto, as **Elissa**, Longmans (New York), 1900 . . £80

Lysbeth, Longmans (London), 1901 . . . . £50

ditto, Longmans (New York), 1901 . . . . £50

Pearl-Maiden, Longmans (London), 1903 . . £40

ditto, Longmans (New York), 1903 . . . . £40

Stella Fregelius, Longmans (New York), 1903 . . £40

ditto, Longmans (London), 1904 . . . . . £40

The Brethren, Cassell (London), 1904 . . . £40

ditto, McClure, Phillips (New York), 1904 . . £40

Ayesha, Ward Lock (London), 1905 . . . . £75

ditto, Doubleday (New York), 1905 . . . . £40

The Way of the Spirit, Hutchinson (London), 1906 £40

Benita, Cassell (London), 1906 . . . . . £40

ditto, as **The Spirit of Bambatse**, Longmans (New York), 1906 . . . . £40

Fair Margaret, Hutchinson (London), 1907 . . £40

ditto, as **Margaret**, Longmans (New York), 1907 . £40

The Ghost Kings, Cassell (London), 1908 . . £40

ditto, as **The Lady of the Heavens**, Lovell (New York), 1908 . . . . £40

The Yellow God, Cupples & Leon (New York), 1908 . £40

ditto, Cassell (London), 1909 . . . . . £40

The Lady of Blossholme, Hodder & Stoughton (London), 1909 . . . . £50

Morning Star, Cassell (London), 1910 . . . £40

ditto, Longmans (New York), 1910 . . . . £30

Queen Sheba's Ring, Eveleigh Nash (London), 1910 . £300

ditto, Doubleday Page & Co (New York), 1910 . £50

Red Eve, Hodder & Stoughton (London), 1911 . £200

ditto, Doubleday (New York), 1911 . . . . £30

The Mahatma and The Hare, Longmans (London), 1911 . . . . £60

ditto, Henry Holt & Co (New York), 1911 . . £30

Marie, Cassell (London), 1912 . . . . . £30

ditto, Longmans (New York), 1912 . . . . £30

Child of Storm, Cassell (London), 1913 . . . £30

ditto, Longmans (New York), 1913 . . . . . £30

The Wanderer's Necklace, Cassell (London), 1914 £50

ditto, Longmans (New York), 1914 . . . . £30

The Holy Flower, Ward Lock (London), 1915 . £30

ditto, as **Allan and The Holy Flower**, Longmans (New York), 1915 . . . . £30

The Ivory Child, Cassell (London), 1916 . . . £40

ditto, Longmans (New York), 1916 . . . . £30

Finished, Ward Lock (London), 1917 . . . £40

ditto, Longmans (New York), 1917 . . . . £30

Love Eternal, Cassell (London), 1918 . . . £30

ditto, Longmans (New York), 1918 . . . . £30

Moon of Israel, Murray (London), 1918 . . . £50

ditto, Longmans (New York), 1918 . . . . £30

When the World Shook, Cassell (London), 1919 . £40

ditto, Longmans (New York), 1919 . . . . £30

The Ancient Allan, Cassell (London), 1920 . . £500/£35

ditto, Longmans (New York), 1920 . . . £450/£35

Smith and the Pharaohs, Arrowsmith (London), 1920 . . . . £300/£75

ditto, Longmans (New York), 1920 . . . £250/£35

She and Allan, Longmans (New York), 1921 . . £200/£45

ditto, Hutchinson (London), 1921 . . . £175/£65

The Virgin of the Sun, Cassell (London), 1922 . £200/£35

ditto, Doubleday (New York), 1922 . . . £150/£25

Wisdom's Daughter, Hutchinson (London), 1923 . £200/£35

ditto, Doubleday (New York), 1923 . . . £200/£35

Heu-Heu, Hutchinson (London), 1924 . . . £150/£45

ditto, Doubleday (New York), 1924 . . . £150/£35

Queen of the Dawn, Doubleday Page (New York), 1925 . . . . £150/£25

ditto, Hutchinson (London), 1925 . . . £150/£35

The Treasure of the Lake, Hutchinson (London), 1926 . . . . £150/£45

ditto, Doubleday (New York), 1926 . . . £125/£25

Allan and the Ice Gods, Doubleday Page (New York), 1927 . . . . £255/£25

ditto, Hutchinson (London), 1927 . . . £350/£25

Mary of Marion Isle, Hutchinson (London), 1929 . £150/£45

ditto, as **Marion Isle**, Doubleday (New York), 1929 £100/£25

Belshazzar, Stanley Paul (London), 1930 . . £400/£55

ditto, Doubleday (New York), 1930 . . . £250/£25

Non-Fiction

Cetywayo and His White Neighbours, Trubner (London), 1882 . . . . £850

An Heroic Effort, 1893 (wraps) £50

Church and State, 1895 (wraps) £45

East Norfolk Representation, 1895 (wraps) . . £45

Lord Kimberly in Norfolk, 1895 (wraps) . . . £45

Speeches of the Earl of Iddesleigh, NSPCC, 1895 (wraps) £45

A Visit to Victoria Hospital, 1897 (wraps) . . £45

A Farmer's Year, Longmans (London), 1899 . . £100

ditto, Longmans (London), 1899 (100 numbered large paper copies) £300

The Last Boer War, Kegan Paul (London), 1899 . £125

ditto, as **A History of The Transvaal**, Kegan Paul (New York), 1899 . . . . £125

A Winter Pilgrimage, Longmans (London), 1901 . £200

Rural England, Longmans (London), 1902 (2 vols) . £175

Rural Denmark, Longmans (London), 1902 . . £200

Rural England, Royal Institution of Great Britain (London), 1903 (wraps) £30

A Gardener's Year, Longmans (London), 1905 . . £100
The Poor and the Land, Longmans (London), 1905 . £125
The Real Wealth of England, Dr Barnados (London), 1908
(wraps) £25
The Royal Commission on Coast Erosion, HMSO
(London), 1907-1911 (3 vols; wraps) £45
Regeneration, Longmans (London), 1910 . . . £30
Letters to the Right Honorable Lewis Harcourt, HMSO
(London), 1913-1914 (2 vols; wraps) £50
A Call to Arms, 1914 (wraps) £25
*The After-War Settlement and Employment of Ex-
Servicemen*, Saint Catherine Press (London), 1916 (wraps)
. . . . £30
The Salvation Army, 1920 (wraps) £30
The Days of My Life, Longmans (London), 1926 (2 vols) .
. . . . £350/£150
ditto, Longmans (New York), 1926 . . . £250/£125
A Note on Religion, Longmans (London), 1927 (wraps) £25
The Private Diaries of Sir H. Rider Haggard 1914-1925,
Cassell (London), 1980 . . . . . £20/£5
ditto, Stein & Day (New York), 1980. . . . £20/£5

KATHLEEN HALE

(b.1898 d.2000)

Kathleen Hale was an artist whose reputation rests on her
books about a ginger tom-cat called Orlando. Her feline
hero lives in the town of 'Owlbarrow' which is a thinly
disguised version of Aldeburgh on the Suffolk coast. Many
of her illustrations feature recognisable landmarks in the
town.

Books Written and Illustrated by Hale
Orlando the Marmalade Cat: A Camping Holiday, Country
Life (London), [1938] (boards with d/w) . £450/£250
ditto, Scribner's (New York), [1938] (boards with d/w) .
. . . . £400/£225
Orlando the Marmalade Cat: A Trip Abroad, Country Life
(London), 1939 (boards with d/w) . . . £350/£200
ditto, Scribner's (New York), [1939] (boards with d/w) .
. . . . £400/£225
Orlando's Evening Out, Puffin (London), [1941] (boards, no
d/w) £75
ditto, Puffin (London), [1941] (pbk) £45
Orlando's Home Life, Puffin (London), [1942] (boards, no
d/w) £75
ditto, Puffin (London), [1942] (pbk) £45
ditto, Coward-McCann (New York), [1953] . . £150/£35
Orlando the Marmalade Cat Buys A Farm, Country Life
(London), 1942 (card covers) £150
Orlando the Marmalade Cat: His Silver Wedding, Country
Life (London), 1944 (card covers) £150
Orlando the Marmalade Cat Becomes A Doctor, Country
Life (London), 1944 (card covers) £150
Orlando's Invisible Pyjamas, Transatlantic Arts (London),
[1947] (pbk) £45
Henrietta the Faithful Hen, Transatlantic Arts (London),
[1947] (boards) . . . . £150/£75
ditto, Coward-McCann (New York), [1953] . £75/£35
Orlando the Marmalade Cat Keeps A Dog, Country Life
(London), [1949]. . . . . . £250/£100
Orlando The Judge, Murray (London), [1950] (pbk) . £75

Orlando's Country Life (London): A Peep Show Book,
Chatto & Windus (London), 1950 . . . . .£150
Puss in Boots: A Peep Show Book, Chatto & Windus
(London), 1951 . . . .£150
ditto, Houghton Mifflin (Boston), [c.1951] . . .£150
Orlando the Marmalade Cat: A Seaside Holiday, Country
Life (London), 1952 . . . . £300/£125
Orlando's Zoo, Murray (London), [1954] (pbk) . . £30
Manda the Jersey Calf, Murray (London), 1952 (boards) £60
ditto, as *Manda*, Coward-McCann (New York), [1953] .
. . . . £75/£35
Orlando the Marmalade Cat: The Frisky Housewife,
Country Life (London), 1956 (boards) . . . £75
Orlando's Magic Carpet, Murray (London), [1958] £75/£35
Orlando the Marmalade Cat Buys A Cottage, Country Life
(London), 1963 (boards) £75
Orlando and the Three Graces, Murray (London), 1965 .
. . . . £75/£25
Orlando the Marmalade Cat Goes to the Moon, Murray
(London), 1968 . . . . . . £65/£25
Orlando the Marmalade Cat and the Water Cats, Cape
(London), 1972 (laminated boards, no d/w) . . . £60
Henrietta's Magic Egg, Allen & Unwin (London), 1973
(laminated boards, no d/w) £65

Other Books Illustrated by Hale
I Don't Mix Much With Fairies, by Molly Harrower, Eyre
& Spottiswoode (London), 1928 . . £75/£35
Plain Jane, by Molly Harrower, Eyre & Spottiswoode
(London), 1929 . . . . . £75/£35
ditto, Coward-McCann (New York), 1929 . £75/£35
Basil Seal Rides Again, by Evelyn Waugh, Chapman & Hall
(London), 1963 (750 numbered copies signed by author,
glassine d/w). . . . . . . £250/£200
ditto, Little, Brown (Boston), 1963 (1,000 numbered copies
signed by author, glassine d/w) . . . £225/£175

RADCLYFFE HALL

(b.1880 d.1943)

Hall's notoriety stems from the publication and subsequent
suppression for obscenity of *The Well of Loneliness* (1928).
The book, a sympathetic study of lesbian love, was not
republished in Britain until 1949. Hall described herself as
a 'congenital invert', a term taken from the writings of
Havelock Ellis. She was generally known by the name
'John'.

Novels
The Forge, Arrowsmith (London), 1924 . . .£250/£75
The Unlit Lamp, Cassell (London), 1924. . . £250/£65
ditto, Cape & Smith (New York), [1929] . . .£100/£20
A Saturday Life, Arrowsmith (London), 1925. . £250/£45
ditto, Cape & Smith (New York), [1930] . . .£100/£25
Adam's Breed, Cassell (London), 1926 . . £250/£45
ditto, Cape & Smith (New York), [1929] . . .£100/£25
The Well of Loneliness, Cape (London), 1928 (first issue
with 'whip', not 'whips', on p. 50, line 13) . £750/£125
ditto, Pegasus Press (Paris), 1928 . . .£150/£45
ditto, Covici Friede (New York), 1928 (500 numbered
copies, glassine d/w, slipcase) . . . . £250/£175

ditto, Covici Friede (New York), 1929 (225 signed copies, 2 vols, slipcase)   .   .   .   .   .   £300/£250

ditto, Cape (London), 1932 (172 signed large paper copies).
.   .   .   .   £250

The Master of the House, Cape (London), 1932   .   £65/£15

ditto, Cape (London), 1932 (172 signed, numbered copies, slipcase).   .   .   .   .   £250/£175

ditto, Cape & Ballou (New York), 1932   .   .   .   £50/£15

The Sixth Beatitude, Heinemann (London), 1936   £45/£10

ditto, Heinemann (London), 1936 (125 signed, numbered copies, slipcase)   .   .   .   .   .   £200/£150

ditto, Harcourt Brace (New York), [c.1936]   .   .   £45/£10

Short Stories
Miss Ogilvy Finds Herself, Heinemann (London), 1934   .
.   .   .   .   £75/£20

ditto, Harcourt Brace (New York), 1934   .   .   £45/£10

Poetry
Twixt Earth and Stars, Bumpus (Oxford, UK), 1906 (wraps)
.   .   .   .   £100

ditto, Bumpus (Oxford, UK), 1906 (cloth)   .   .   £100

ditto, Bumpus (Oxford, UK), 1906 (presentation binding)   .
.   .   .   .   £650

A Sheaf of Verses, Bumpus (Oxford, UK), 1908 (wraps)   £75

ditto, Bumpus (Oxford, UK), 1908 (cloth).   .   .   £75

Poems of Past and Present, Chapman & Hall (London), 1910   .   .   .   .   £100

Songs of Three Counties, Chapman & Hall (London), 1913
.   .   .   .   £45

The Forgotten Island, Chapman & Hall (London), 1915 £40

Others
Your John: The Love Letters of Radclyffe Hall, New York Univ Press (New York), 1997   .   .   .   .   £15/£5

PATRICK HAMILTON
(b.1904 d.1962)

Patrick Hamilton was a typically English playwright and novelist, relishing the art of understatement. *Hangover Square* is his best known work, describing the problems of doomed love, alcoholism and schizophrenia in pre-World War Two Earl's Court. He was highly regarded by contemporary writers such as Graham Greene and J.B. Priestley.

Novels
Monday Morning, Constable (London), 1925.   .   £500/£75

ditto, Houghton Mifflin (Boston), 1925   .   .   £275/£40

Craven House, Constable (London), 1926   .   £400/£50

ditto, Houghton Mifflin (Boston), 1927   .   .   £250/£30

ditto, Constable (London), 1943 (revised edition)   .   £75/£20

Twopence Coloured, Constable (London), 1928   .£400/£50

ditto, Houghton Mifflin (Boston), 1928   .   .   £250/£40

The Midnight Bell: A Love Story, Constable (London), 1929
.   .   .   .   £400/£50

ditto, Little, Brown (Boston), 1930   .   .   .   £200/£30

The Siege of Pleasure, Constable (London), 1932   £300/£45

ditto, Little, Brown (Boston), 1932   .   .   .   £200/£30

The Plains of Cement, Constable (London), 1934 .£300/£45

ditto, Little, Brown (Boston), 1935   .   .   .   £150/£20

Twenty Thousand Streets Under The Sky: A London Trilogy, Constable (London), 1935.   .   .   .£450/£75

Impromptu in Moribundia, Constable (London), 1939.   .
.   .   .   .   £600/£85

Hangover Square, or The Man with Two Minds: A Story of Darkest Earls Court, Constable (London), 1941   .   .   .
.   .   .   .   £1,250/£200

ditto, Random House (New York), 1942   .   .   .   £600/£75

The Slaves of Solitude, Constable (London), 1947. £150/£25

ditto, as **Riverside**, Random House (New York), 1947 £40/£15

The West Pier, Constable (London), 1951   .   .£150/£25

ditto, Doubleday (New York), 1952   .   .   .   £45/£15

Mr Stimpson and Mr Gorse, Constable (London), 1953   .
.   .   .   .   £150/£25

Unknown Assailant, Constable (London), 1955   .£150/£25

Plays
Rope: A Play, with a Preface on Thrillers, Constable (London), 1929   .   .   .   .   .   .   £200/£40

Gas Light: A Victorian Thriller, Constable (London), 1939 (pbk) £65

ditto, as **Angel Street**, French (New York), 1942 (pbk) £25

Money with Menaces and **To The Public Danger: Two Radio Plays**, Constable (London), 1939 (pbk)   .   £20

This Is Impossible, French (London), 1942 (wraps)   £20

The Duke in Darkness, Constable (London), 1943 (wraps).
.   .   .   .   £45

The Man Upstairs, Constable (London), 1954   .   £25/£10

DASHIELL HAMMETT
(b.1894 d.1961)

An American creator of tough detective fiction, Hammett's best known character is the private eye Sam Spade. His work was published primarily in the pulp magazine *Black Mask*. Many of his books were adapted as films, with the original dialogue often incorporated verbatim into the screenplay.

Novels
Red Harvest, Knopf (New York), 1929   .   . £17,500/£450

ditto, Knopf/Cassell (London), 1929 .   .   .   £7,500/£350

The Dain Curse, Knopf (New York), 1929   . £15,000/£250

ditto, Knopf/Cassell (London), 1930 .   .   .   £4,000/£225

The Maltese Falcon, Knopf (New York), 1930 (first issue d/w without reviews for *Maltese Falcon*)   £30,000/£1,250

ditto, Knopf (New York), 1930 (second issue d/w with reviews).   .   .   .   .   .   £10,000/£1,250

ditto, Knopf/Cassell (London), 1930 .   .   £10,000/£300

The Glass Key, Knopf/Cassell (London), 1931   .   .   .
.   .   .   .   £4,000/£325

ditto, Knopf (New York), 1931   .   .   .   £4,000/£300

The Thin Man, Knopf (New York), 1934 (four jacket variants, of no established priority; green or red, with or without blurbs)   .   .   .   .   £2,500/£175

ditto, Barker (London), 1934   .   .   .   £2,000/£150

$106,000 Blood Money, Spivak (New York), 1943 (digest format pbk) £75

ditto, as **Blood Money**, World (New York), 1943   .   £30/£10

ditto, as **The Big Knock-over**, Spivak (New York), 1948 (digest format pbk) £30

Short Stories

The Adventures of Sam Spade and Other Stories, Spivak
(New York), 1944 (digest format pbk) £100

ditto, as *They Can Only Hang You Once*, Spivak (New
York), 1949 (digest format pbk) £75

The Continental Op, Spivak (New York), 1945 (digest
format pbk) £75

The Return of the Continental Op, Spivak (New York),
1945 (digest format pbk) £50

Hammett Homicides, Spivak (New York), 1946 (digest
format pbk) £50

Dead Yellow Women, Spivak (New York), 1947 (digest
format pbk) £50

Nightmare Town, Spivak (New York), 1948 (digest format
pbk) £50

The Creeping Siamese, Spivak (New York), 1950 (digest
format pbk) £35

Woman in the Dark, Spivak (New York), 1951 (digest
format pbk) £35

ditto, Knopf (New York), 1988   .   .   .   . £15/£5

ditto, Headline (London), 1988   .   .   .   . £15/£5

A Man Named Thin and Other Stories, Ferman/Spivak
(New York), 1962   .   .   .   .   .   . £35

The Continental Op, Random House (New York), 1974   .

.   .   .   . £15/£5

ditto, Macmillan (London), 1975   .   .   . £15/£5

Nightmare Town, Knopf (New York),1999   .   . £15/£5

ditto, Picador (London), 2001   .   .   .   . £10/£5

Omnibus Editions

Dashiell Hammet Omnibus, Knopf (New York), 1935.   .

.   .   .   .£450/£50

The Complete Dashiell Hammet, Knopf (New York), 1942.

.   .   .   .£200/£35

Dashiell Hammet's Mystery Omnibus, World (New York),
1944   .   .   .   . £50/£10

The Dashiell Hammet Omnibus, Cassell (London), 1950   .

.   .   .   .£100/£15

The Novels of Dashiell Hammet, Knopf (New York), 1965

.   .   .   . £40/£10

The Big Knockover: Selected Stories and Short Novels,
Random House (New York), 1966 (edited by Lillian
Hellman)   .   .   .   . £10/£5

ditto, as *The Hammet Story Omnibus*, Cassell (London),
1966   .   .   .   . £15/£5

Others

Creeps by Night: Chills and Thrills, John Day (New York),
1931 (selected by Hammett)   .   .   .   . £250/£50

ditto, as *Modern Tales of Horror*, Gollancz (London), 1932

.   .   .   .£250/£50

Secret Agent X-9, Book One, David McKay (Philadelphia),
1943 (may have been at least partly ghost-written, printed
boards, illustrations by Alex Raymond; stapled wraps with
cloth spine) £750

Secret Agent X-9, Book Two, David McKay (Philadelphia),
1943 (may have been at least partly ghost-written, printed
boards, illustrations by Alex Raymond; stapled wraps with
cloth spine) £750

The Battle of the Aleutians, Western Defense Command
(Adak, AK), 1944 (with Robert Colodny and Harry
Fletcher; stapled wraps) £100

Selected Letters of Dashiell Hammett, 1921-1960,
Counterpoint Press (Washington, DC), 2001   . £15/£5

THOMAS HARDY
(b.1840 d.1928)

Acknowledged as one of the great novelists, Hardy was
also a prolific poet. Much of his writing is set in his native
Dorset, fictionalised as 'Wessex'. Hardy's heart was buried
at Stinsford and his ashes interred in Poets' Corner at
Westminster Abbey. He was awarded the Order of Merit in
1910.

Novels

Desperate Remedies, Tinsley Bros. (London), 1871 (3 vols,
red cloth, anonymous) £20,000

ditto, Tinsley Bros. (London), 1874 (1 vol, various coloured
cloths) £1,000

ditto, Holt (New York), 1874 (1 vol.).   .   .   .£400

Under the Greenwood Tree, Tinsley Bros. (London), 1872
(2 vols, green cloth, 'By the author of Desperate
Remedies') £10,000

ditto, Tinsley Bros. (London), 1872 (2 vols, rebound) £1,500

ditto, Tinsley Bros. (London), 1873 (1 vol.)   .   . £1,000

ditto, Holt (New York), 1874 (1 vol.).   .   .   .£400

A Pair of Blue Eyes, Tinsley Bros. (London), 1873 (first
issue, green cloth, 'c' missing in 'clouds' last line p.5,
vol.2, 3 vols). £10,000

ditto, Tinsley Bros. (London), 1873 (second issue, blue cloth,
3 vols) £3,000

ditto, Tinsley Bros. (London), 1873 (3 vols, rebound) £2,000

ditto, Holt (New York), 1873 (1 vol.).   .   .   .£500

ditto, Henry S. King (London), 1877 (1 vol.)   .   .£300

Far from the Madding Crowd, Holt (New York), 1874 (1
vol, cream cloth). £1,250

ditto, Smith, Elder (London), 1874 (2 vols, green cloth)   .

.   .   .   . £15,000

ditto, Smith, Elder (London), 1874 (2 vols, rebound) £3,000

ditto, Smith, Elder (London), 1875 (2 vols)   .   . £1,000

ditto, Smith, Elder (London), 1877 (1 vol.).   .   .£200

The Hand of Ethelberta, Smith, Elder (London), 1876
(red/brown cloth, 2 vols, 11 illustrations by George du
Maurier). £5,000

ditto, Smith, Elder (London), 1876 (2 vols, rebound) £1,000

ditto, Holt (New York), 1876 (1 vol.).   .   .   .£300

ditto, Smith, Elder (London), 1877 (1 vol., 6 illustrations by
George du Maurier) £200

The Return of the Native, Smith, Elder (London), 1878
(brown cloth, 3 vols) £5,000

ditto, Smith, Elder (London), 1878 (3 vols, rebound) £1,000

ditto, Holt (New York), 1878 (1 vol.).   .   .   .£300

ditto, Kegan Paul (London), 1880 [1879] (1 vol.)   .£200

The Trumpet-Major, Smith, Elder (London), 1880
(decorated red cloth, 3 vols) £10,000

ditto, Smith, Elder (London), 1880 (3 vols, rebound) £1,000

ditto, Holt (New York), 1880 (1 vol.).   .   .   .£300

ditto, Samson Low (London), 1881 (1 vol.)   .   .£200

A Laodicean, Holt (New York), 1881 (1 vol.).   .£450

ditto, Samson Low (London), 1881 (first issue without word
'or' on half-title of vol.1, 3 vols, slate cloth).   . £5,000

ditto, Samson Low (London), 1881 (first issue rebound, 3
vols) £750

ditto, Samson Low (London), 1881 (second issue with word
'or' on half-title of vol.1, 3 vols, slate cloth).   . £2,000

ditto, Samson Low (London), 1882 (1 vol)   .   .£150

Two on a Tower, Samson Low (London), 1882   (3 vols, green cloth) £3,000
ditto, Samson Low (London), 1882 (3 vols, rebound) . £750
ditto, Holt (New York), 1882 (1 vol.).   .   .   . £250
ditto, Samson Low (London), 1883 (3 vols)   .   . £1,000
ditto, Samson Low (London), 1883 (1 vol.)   .   . £150
The Mayor of Casterbridge, Smith Elder (London), 1886 (2 vols) £3,500
ditto, Smith Elder (London), 1886 (2 vols rebound)   £1,000
ditto, Holt (New York), 1886 (1 vol.; wraps)   .   . £500
ditto, Samson Low (London), 1887 (1 vol.)   .   . £250
The Woodlanders, Macmillan (London), 1887 (first binding in smooth green cloth with 2 rule border on back, first issue with ad leaf at back of vol.1, 3 vols)   .   .   . £3,000
ditto, Macmillan (London), 1887 (first issue, 3 vols, rebound) £750
ditto, Macmillan (London), 1887 (second binding in pebbled green cloth with 1 rule border on back, second issue without ad leaf at back of vol.1, 3 vols)   .   . £2,000
ditto, Harper (New York), 1887 (1 vol.)   .   .   . £250
ditto, Macmillan (London), 1887 (1 vol.)   .   . £100
Tess of the D'Urbervilles, Osgood McIlvaine (London), 1891 (3 vols; first issue with 'Chapter XXV' for 'Chapter XXXV' on p.199 of vol2) £8,000
ditto, Osgood McIlvaine (London), 1891 (3 vols rebound) .
.   .   .   . £2,500
ditto, Harper (New York), 1892 (1 vol.)   .   .   . £500
ditto, Osgood McIlvaine (London), 1892 (3 vols)   . £1,000
ditto, Osgood McIlvaine (London), 1892 ('fifth' [third] edition, 1 vol.) £250
Jude the Obscure, Osgood McIlvaine (London), 1896 [1895] (Volume VIII in the 'Wessex Novels' series, 1 vol) . £300
ditto, Harper (New York), 1896 (1 vol.)   .   .   . £100
The Well-Beloved, Osgood McIlvaine (London), 1897 (Volume XVII in the 'Wessex Novels' series, 1 vol) . £125
ditto, Harper (New York), 1897 (1 vol.)   .   .   . £125

Short Stories
Fellow-Townsmen, Harper (New York), 1880 (cloth) . £500
ditto, Harper (New York), 1880 (wraps)   .   .   . £500
The Romantic Adventures of a Milkmaid, Munro (New York), 1883 (wraps) £1,000
Wessex Tales, Macmillan (London), 1888 (2 vols).   £1,500
ditto, Macmillan (London), 1889 (1 vol.)   .   .   . £75
A Group of Noble Dames, Osgood McIlvaine (London), 1891   .   .   .   . £350
ditto, Harper (New York), 1891   .   .   .   . £100
Life's Little Ironies, Osgood McIlvaine (London), 1894 £300
ditto, Macmillan (New York), 1894   .   .   .   . £75
A Changed Man and Other Tales, Macmillan (London), 1913   .   .   .   . £50
ditto, Harper (New York), 1913   .   .   .   .   . £75
Old Mrs Chundle, Crosby Gaige (New York), 1929 (755 numbered copies, glassine d/w)   .   .   . £150/£125
Our Exploits at West Poley, O.U.P. (Oxford, UK), 1952   .
.   .   .   . £20/£5
ditto, O.U.P. (Oxford, UK), 1952 (1,050 numbered copies) .
.   .   .   . £100/£65

Collected Editions
Wessex Novels Edition, Osgood McIlvaine (London), 1895-97 (18 vols)   .   .   .   . £2,750 the set, £75 each
The Writings, Autograph Edition, Harper & Bros (New York), [1911] (153 signed copies, 20 vols) . £3,000 the set
Wessex Edition, Macmillan (London), 1912-31 (24 vols; maroon cloth)   .   .   .   . £1,750 the set, £30 each

Mellstock Edition, Macmillan (London), 1919-20 (37 vols, limited to 500 sets, signed by the author)   . £5,000 the set

Magazine Serialisations
A Pair of Blue Eyes, Tinsley's Magazine (London), Sept 1872-July 1873   .   .   .   .   . £450 (for set)
Far From the Madding Crowd, Cornhill Magazine (London), Jan-Sept 1874   .   .   .   . £400 (for set)
The Hand of Ethelberta, Cornhill Magazine (London), July 1875-May 1876   .   .   .   . £400 (for set)
The Return of the Native, Belgravia (London), Jan-December 1878   .   .   .   .   . £400 (for set)
The Trumpet Major, Good Words (London), Jan-December 1880   .   .   .   .   .   . £400 (for set)
A Laodicean, Harper's (New York), December 1880-December 1881   .   .   .   .   . £400 (for set)
Two on a Tower, Atlantic Monthly (New York), May-December 1882   .   .   .   .   . £400 (for set)
The Mayor of Casterbridge, Graphic (London), June 1885-May 1886   .   .   .   .   . £500 (for set)
The Woodlanders, Macmillan's Magazine (London), May 1886-April 1887   .   .   .   .   . £400 (for set)
Tess of the D'Urbervilles, Graphic (London), July-December 1891   .   .   .   .   .   . £600 (for set)
The Well-Beloved, as *The Pursuit of the Well-Beloved*, Illustrated London News (London), October-December 1892   .   .   .   . £250 (for set)
Jude the Obscure, Harper's (New York), December 1894-November 1895 (first instalment as 'The Simpleton', thereafter 'Hearts Insurgent')   .   .   . £300 (for set)

Poetry
Wessex Poems and Other Verses, Harper (New York/London), 1898   .   .   .   .   .   . £500
ditto, Harper (New York/London), 1898 (presentation binding). £1,500
Poems Of The Past And The Present, Harper (New York/London), 1902   .   .   .   .   . £500
ditto, Harper (New York/London), 1902 (presentation binding). £1,500
The Dynasts, Macmillan (London), 1904, 1906 [1905], 1908 (3 vols) £600
ditto, Macmillan (London), 1910 (1 vol.)   .   .   . £150
ditto, Macmillan (London), 1927 (525 signed large paper copies, 3 vols, tissue d/w, slipcase)   .   . £600/£400
Time's Laughingstocks and Other Verses, Macmillan (London), 1909   .   .   .   .   .   . £150
Satires of Circumstance, Lyrics and Reveries, Macmillan (London), 1914   .   .   .   .   .   . £150
Song of the Soldiers, privately printed by Clement Shorter (London), 1914 (single sheet, 12 copies)   . £750
ditto, privately printed at Hove (Sussex) by E. Williams, 1914 (single sheet) £100
The Oxen, privately printed at Hove (Sussex) by E. Williams, 1915 (wraps) £150
Selected Poems, Macmillan (London), 1916   .   . £150
ditto, Warner/Medici/Riccardi (London), 1921   . £100
Moments of Vision and Miscellaneous Verses, Macmillan (London), 1917   .   .   .   .   .   . £100
Collected Poems, Macmillan (London), 1919 .   . £125
Late Lyrics and Earlier with Many Other Verses, Macmillan (London), 1922   .   .   . £125/£50
The Famous Tragedy of the Queen of Cornwall, Macmillan (London), 1923   .   .   .   .   . £200/£75

ditto, Macmillan (London), 1923 (1,000 numberd copies, no d/w) £75
Human Shows, Far Phantasies, Songs, and Trifles, Macmillan (London), 1925 . . . . £150/£65
ditto, Macmillan (New York), 1925 (100 numbered copies, no d/w) £150
ditto, Macmillan (New York), 1925 . . . £100/£45
Yuletide in a Younger World, Faber (London), 1927 (wraps) £250
ditto, Rudge (New York), 1927 (27 copyright copies; wraps) £400
Winter Words In Various Moods and Metres, Macmillan (London), 1928 . . . . . . £75/£35
ditto, Macmillan (New York), 1928 (500 copies, slipcase) . . . . £150/£125
Chosen Poems, Macmillan (London), 1931 . £75/£35

CYRIL HARE
(b.1900 d.1958)

'Cyril Hare' was the main pseudonym of crime novelist Alfred Gordon Clark, who was also an English judge. *Tragedy at Law* is perhaps his best known novel, in which he drew on his legal expertise, and introduced the barrister sleuth, Francis Pettigrew.

Novels
Tenant For Death, Faber (London), 1937 . . £450/£50
ditto, Dodd, Mead (New York), 1937 . . £300/£40
Death Is No Sportsman, Faber (London), 1938 . £250/£35
Suicide Excepted, Faber (London), 1939 . £250/£35
ditto, Macmillan (New York), 1954 . . . £65/£15
Tragedy At Law, Faber (London), 1942 . . £100/£15
ditto, Harcourt (New York), 1943 . . . £75/£15
With a Bare Bodkin, Faber (London), 1946 . £75/£10
When the Wind Blows, Faber (London), 1949 . £65/£10
ditto, as ***The Wind Blows Death***, Little, Brown (Boston), 1950 . . . . £65/£10
An English Murder, Faber (London), 1951 . £65/£10
ditto, Little, Brown (Boston), 1951 . . . £65/£10
ditto, as ***The Christmas Murder***, Spivak (New York), 1953. . . . . £50/£10
The Yew Tree's Shade, Faber (London), 1954 . £40/£10
ditto, as ***Death Walks the Woods***, Little, Brown (Boston), 1954 . . . . £35/£5
He Should Have Died Hereafter, Faber (London), 1958 . . . . £35/£5
ditto, as ***Untimely Death***, Macmillan (New York), 1958 . . . . £35/£5

Short Stories
Best Detective Stories of Cyril Hare, Faber (London), 1959 . . . . £40/£5
ditto, Walker (New York), 1961 . . . . £25/£5
ditto, as ***Death Among Friends***, Perennial (New York), 1984 (pbk) £5

Children's Title
The Magic Bottle, Faber (London), 1946 . . £45/£15

JOEL CHANDLER HARRIS
(b.1845 d.1908)

Harris was an American journalist and author known for his 'Uncle Remus' stories. A folklorist, Harris recorded Brer Rabbit stories from the African-American oral tradition and when he interpreted these in print he garnered both critical and popular acclaim. Although considered controversial in recent years, the 'Uncle Remus' stories are nevertheless an important chapter in the history of literature for children.

Uncle Remus: His Songs and Sayings: The Folk-Lore of the Old Plantation, Appleton (New York), 1881 [1880] (first state with 'presumptive' in last line p.9) . £2,000
ditto, Appleton (New York), 1881 (second state with 'presumptuous' in last line p.9; 'New Books' on unnumbered p.223) £1,000
ditto, Appleton (New York), 1881 (third state with 'presumptuous' in last line p.9; reviews of *Uncle Remus* on unnumbered p.223) £750
ditto, Ward Lock (London), 1883 . . . . £300
Uncle Remus and His Legends of the Old Plantation, Bogue (London), 1881 . . . . . . £300
Uncle Remus, or Mr Fox, Mr Rabbit and Mr Terrapin, Routledge (London), 1881. . . . . . £300
Nights with Uncle Remus: and Legends of the Old Plantation, Osgood (New York), 1883 . . . £500
ditto, Truübner & Co (London), 1883 . . . £200
Mingo and Other Sketches in Black and White, Osgood (New York), 1884 . . . . . . £200
ditto, D. Douglas (Edinburgh), 1884 . . . . £75
Free Joe and Other Georgian Sketches, Scribner's (New York), 1887 . . . . £150
ditto, Routledge (London), 1907. . . . . £45
Daddy Jake the Runaway and Short Stories Told after Dark by 'Uncle Remus', Century (New York), 1889 £500
ditto, T. Fisher Unwin (London), 1890 . . . £200
Balaam and His Master and Other Sketches and Stories, Houghton Mifflin (Boston), 1891 (first state text bulks to 3/4 inch; stamping at bottom of spine 'Houghton/Mifflin-&-Co') £150
ditto, Houghton Mifflin (Boston), 1891 (second state text bulks to 11/16 inch; stamping at bottom of spine 'Houghton / Mifflin & Co') £75
On the Plantation: The Story of a Georgia Boy's Adventures During the War, Appleton (New York), 1892 . . . . £100
ditto, as ***A Plantation Printer***, Osgood, McIlvaine (London), 1892 . . . . £75
Uncle Remus and His Friends: Old Plantation Stories, Songs and Ballads with Sketches of Negro Character, Houghton Mifflin (Boston), 1892 . . . . £200
ditto, Osgood, McIlvaine (London), 1892. . . £150
Little Mr Thimblefinger and His Queer Country: What the Children Saw and Heard There, Houghton Mifflin (Boston), 1894 . . . . £200
ditto, Osgood, McIlvaine (London), 1894. . . £150
Mr Rabbit at Home: A Sequel to Little Mr Thimblefinger and His Queer Country, Houghton Mifflin (Boston), 1895 . . . . £100
ditto, Osgood, McIlvaine (London), 1895. . . £150

The Story of Aaron (So Named): The Son of Ben Ali, Houghton Mifflin (Boston), 1896 . . . . £100
ditto, Osgood, McIlvaine (London), 1896. . . . £75
Stories of Georgia, American Book Company (New York), 1896 . . . . £100
Sister Jane, Her Friends and Acquaintances, Houghton Mifflin (Boston), 1896 . . . . . £65
ditto, A.P. Watt (London), 1896 . . . . . £50
Aaron in the Wildwoods, Houghton Mifflin (Boston), 1897 . . . . £65
Ditto, Harper (London), 1897 . . . . . £50
Tales of the Home Folks in Peace and War, Houghton Mifflin (Boston), 1898 . . . . . £100
ditto, T. Fisher Unwin (London), 1898 . . . £100
Plantation Pageants, Houghton Mifflin (Boston), 1899 £150
ditto, Constable (London), 1899 . . . . . £100
The Chronicles of Aunt Minervy Ann, Scribner's (New York), 1899 . . . . £100
ditto, Dent (London), 1899 . . . . . . £75
On the Wing of Occasions, Doubleday Page (New York), 1900 . . . . £100
ditto, Murray (London), 1899 . . . . . £75
The Making of a Statesman and Other Stories, McClure, Phillips (New York), 1902 . . . . . £45
Gabriel Tolliver: A Story of Reconstruction, McClure, Phillips (New York), 1902 . . . . . £30
Wally Wanderoon and His Story-Telling Machine, McClure, Phillips (New York), 1903 . . . £65
ditto, Grant Richards (London), 1904 . . . £75
A Little Union Scout, McClure, Phillips (New York), 1904.
. . . . £50
ditto, Duckworth (London), 1904 . . . . £50
The Tar-Baby and Other Rhymes of Uncle Remus, Appleton (New York), 1904 . . . . . £200
Told by Uncle Remus: New Stories of the Old Plantation, McClure Phillips (New York), 1905 . . . £100
ditto, Hodder & Stoughton (London), 1906 . . £50
Uncle Remus and Brer Rabbit, Stokes (New York), 1907 .
. . . . £250
The Bishop and the Boogerman, Doubleday Page (New York), 1909 . . . . £25
ditto, John Murray (London), 1909 . . . . £65
The Shadow Between His Shoulder-Blades, Small, Maynard and Co (Boston), 1909 . . . . . £25
Uncle Remus and the Little Boy, Small, Maynard and Co (Boston), 1910 . . . . £25
Uncle Remus Returns, Houghton Mifflin (Boston), 1918 .
. . . . £100
The Witch Wolf: An Uncle Remus Story, Bacon & Brown (Cambridge, MA), 1921 . . . . . £75
Qua: A Romance of the Revolution, The Library of Emory Univ (Atlanta, GA), 1946 (wraps) £25
Seven Tales of Uncle Remus, The Library of Emory Univ (Atlanta, GA), 1946 (wraps) £25
The Complete Tales of Uncle Remus, Houghton, Mifflin (Boston), 1955 . . . . . . £65/£20

ROBERT HARRIS
(b.1957)

The best-selling author of thrillers, whose non-fiction books include *Selling Hitler*, an account of the forging of Adolf Hitler's diaries. Harris worked as a reporter on the BBC's *Newsnight* and *Panorama* programs, was Political Editor of the *Observer*, and has written a column in *The Sunday Times*.

Novels
Fatherland, Hutchinson (London), 1992 . . . £75/£10
ditto, Random House (New York), 1992 . . . £15/£5
Enigma, Hutchinson (London), 1995 . . . £25/£5
ditto, Random House (New York), 1995 . . . £15/£5
Archangel, Hutchinson (London), 1998 . . . £15/£5
ditto, Random House (New York), 1999 . . . £10/£5
Pompeii, Hutchinson (London), 2003 . . . £10/£5
ditto, Random House (New York), 2003 . . . £10/£5
Imperium, Hutchinson (London), 2006 . . . £10/£5
ditto, Hutchinson (London), 2006 (1,500 signed copies; slipcase). . . . . £40/£20
ditto, Simon & Schuster (New York), 2006 . . £10/£5
The Ghost, Hutchinson (London), 2007 . . . £10/£5
ditto, Simon & Schuster (New York), 2007 . . £10/£5
Lustrum, Hutchinson (London), 2009 . . . £10/£5
ditto, Hutchinson (London), 2006 (750 signed copies; slipcase). . . . . £50/£25

Non-Fiction
A Higher Form of Killing, Chatto & Windus (London), 1982 (with Jeremy Paxman) . . . . £25/£5
ditto, Hill & Wang (New York), 1982 . . . £20/£5
Gotcha!: The Media, the Government, and the Falklands Crisis, Faber (London), 1983 (pbk). £10
The Making of Neil Kinnock, Faber (London), 1984 £10/£5
Selling Hitler, Faber (London), 1986. . . . £20/£5
ditto, Pantheon (New York), 1986 . . . £20/£5
Good and Faithful Servant: The Unauthorized Biography of Bernard Ingham, Faber (London), 1990 . . £10/£5

THOMAS HARRIS
(b.1940)

Thomas Harris's work became well known when his *The Silence of the Lambs* was filmed. Anthony Hopkins won an Oscar for his portrayal of psychopathic serial killer Dr Hannibal Lecter. Aficionados of Harris recommend that *Red Dragon* should not be overlooked (it has also been filmed, under the title *Manhunter*). Lecter appears in *Red Dragon* as a minor character.

'Hannibal Lecter' Novels
Red Dragon, Putnam (New York), 1981 . . . £50/£10
ditto, Bodley Head (London), 1982 . . . . £30/£10
The Silence of the Lambs, St Martin's Press (New York), 1988 . . . . £75/£10
ditto, Heinemann (London), 1988 . . . . £50/£10
Hannibal, Delacorte Press (New York), 1999 . . £15/£5
ditto, Heinemann (London), 1988 . . . . £10/£5
Hannibal Rising, Delacorte Press (New York), 2006 £10/£5

ditto, Heinemann (London), 2006   .   .   .   £10/£5

Other Novel
Black Sunday, Putnam (New York), 1975   .   . £145/£15
ditto, Hodder & Stoughton (London), 1975   .   . £100/£15

L.P. HARTLEY
(b.1895 d.1972)

Novelist and short story writer Leslie Poles Hartley's work won a number of awards, but he is best known for *The Go-Between*, an evocative portrayal of a small boy's view of Edwardian England, which won the Heinemann (London) Foundation Award. The opening sentence of the book—'The past is a foreign country; they do things differently there'—has become an oft-quoted axiom.

Novels
Simonetta Perkins, Putnam (London), 1925   .   . £200/£50
ditto, Putnam (New York), 1925.   .   .   . £125/£25
The Shrimp and the Anemone, Putnam (London), 1944   .
.   .   .   . £75/£20
ditto, as ***The West Window***, Putnam (New York), 1945   .
.   .   .   . £40/£10
The Sixth Heaven, Putnam (London), 1946   .   £45/£5
ditto, Doubleday (New York), 1947   .   .   . £35/£5
Eustace and Hilda, Putnam (London), 1947   .   £35/£5
ditto, British Book Centre (New York), 1958   .   £25/£5
The Boat, Putnam (London), 1950   .   .   . £50/£10
ditto, Doubleday (New York), 1950   .   .   . £45/£10
My Fellow Devils, Barrie (London), 1951   .   £30/£5
ditto, British Book Centre (New York), 1959   .   £25/£5
The Go-Between, Hamilton (London), 1953   .   £45/£10
ditto, Knopf (New York), 1954   .   .   .   £30/£5
A Perfect Woman, Hamilton (London), 1955   .   £25/£5
ditto, Knopf (New York), 1956   .   .   .   £25/£5
The Hireling, Hamilton (London), 1957   .   .   £25/£5
ditto, Rinehart (New York), 1958   .   .   . £25/£5
Facial Justice, Hamilton (London), 1960.   .   £45/£10
ditto, Doubleday (New York), 1961   .   .   . £25/£5
The Brickfield, Hamilton (London), 1964   .   £20/£5
The Betrayal, Hamilton (London), 1966   .   .   £15/£5
Poor Clare, Hamilton (London), 1968   .   .   £15/£5
The Love-Adept, Hamilton (London), 1969   .   £15/£5
My Sister's Keeper, Hamilton (London), 1970   .   £15/£5
The Harness Room, Hamilton (London), 1971   .   £15/£5
The Collections, Hamilton (London), 1972   .   £10/£5
The Will and the Way, Hamilton (London), 1973   .   £10/£5

Short Stories
Night Fears and Other Stories, Putnam (London), 1924   .
.   .   .   . £500/£65
The Killing Bottle, Putnam (London), 1931   . £300/£45
The Travelling Grave, Arkham House (Sauk City, WI), 1948
.   .   .   . £50/£15
ditto, Barrie (London), 1951.   .   .   .   £45/£15
A White Wand and Other Stories, Hamilton (London), 1954
.   .   .   . £50/£10
Two for the River, Hamilton (London), 1961   .   £35/£10
The Collected Stories, Hamilton (London), 1968   .   £15/£5
ditto, Horizon Press (New York), 1969   .   .   £15/£5
Mrs Carteret Receives, Hamilton (London), 1971   .   £15/£5

The Collected Macabre Stories, Tartarus Press (Carlton-in-Coverdale, Yorkshire), 2001   .   .   .   .   £40/£10

Others
The Novelist's Responsibility, Hamilton (London), 1967   .
.   .   .   . £25/£5

JOHN HARVEY
(b.1938)

A highly respected British author of crime novels, Harvey is perhaps best known   for the 'Resnick' police proc-edurals. He has also written novels under various pseudo-nyms and is credited with taking an American style, influenced by Elmore Leonard, and transporting it to a British setting. His books show both the sensitive side of police work and its ingrained prejudices.

'Resnick' Novels
Lonely Hearts, Viking (London), 1989   .   . £125/£20
ditto, Holt (New York), 1989   .   .   . £35/£150
Rough Treatment, Viking (London), 1990   .   £25/£10
ditto, Holt (New York), 1990   .   .   .   £25/£10
Cutting Edge, Viking (London), 1991   .   .   £20/£5
ditto, Holt (New York), 1991   .   .   .   £15/£15
Off Minor, Viking (London), 1992   .   .   £40/£5
ditto, Holt (New York), 1992   .   .   .   £15/£5
Wasted Years, Viking (London), 1993   .   .   £20/£5
ditto, Holt (New York), 1993   .   .   .   £15/£5
Cold Light, Heinemann (London), 1994   .   .   £15/£5
ditto, Holt (New York), 1994   .   .   .   £15/£5
Living Proof, Heinemann (London), 1995   .   £15/£5
ditto, Holt (New York), 1995   .   .   .   £15/£5
Easy Meat, Heinemann (London), 1996   .   .   £15/£5
ditto, Holt (New York), 1996   .   .   .   £15/£5
Still Water, Heinemann (London), 1997   .   .   £10/£5
ditto, Holt (New York), 1997   .   .   .   £10/£5
Last Rites, Heinemann (London), 1998   .   .   £10/£5
ditto, Holt (New York), 1999   .   .   .   £10/£5
Cold in Hand, Heinemann (London), 2008   .   £10/£5
ditto, Harcourt (New York), 2008   .   .   . £10/£5

'Resnick' Short Stories
Now's The Time, Slow Dancer Press (Nottingham, UK), 1999 (pbk) £10
ditto, Slow Dancer Press (Nottingham, UK), 1999 (600 hardback copies)   .   .   .   .   .   £25/£5
ditto, Slow Dancer Press (Nottingham, UK), 1999 (400 signed hard-back copies)   .   .   .   . £25/£10
ditto, Heinemann (London), 2002   .   .   . £10/£5

'Scott Mitchell' Novels
Amphetamines and Pearls, Sphere (London), 1976 (pbk) £5
The Geranium Kiss, Sphere (London), 1976 (pbk)   .   £5
Junkyard Angel, Sphere (London), 1977 (pbk)   .   £5
Neon Madman, Sphere (London), 1977 (pbk).   .   £5

'Frank Elder' Novels
Flesh and Blood, Heinemann (London), 2004.   .   £10/£5
ditto, Carroll & Graf (New York), 2004   .   .   £10/£5
Ash and Bone, Heinemann (London), 2005   .   £10/£5
ditto, Harcourt, Brace & World (Orlando, FL), 2005   £10/£5

Darkness And Light, Heinemann (London), 2006 .   £10/£5

Will Grayson and Helen Walker
Gone to Ground, Heinemann (London), 2007.   .   £10/£5
ditto, Harcourt (New York), 2007   .   .   .   £10/£5
Far Cry, Heinemann (London), 2009   .   .   £10/£5

Other Crime Fiction
Frame, Magnum (London), 1979 (pbk)   .   .   .   £10
ditto, Severn House (London), [1995]   .   .   £25/£10
Blind, Magnum (London), 1981 (pbk)   .   .   .   £10
Endgame, New English Library (London), 1982 (pseud 'James Mann'; pbk) £5
Dancer Draws a Wild Card, Hale (London), 1985 (pseud 'Terry Lennox')   .   .   .   .   .   .   £10/£5
In a True Light, Heinemann (London), 2001   .   £10/£5
ditto, Carroll & Graf (New York), 2002   .   .   £10/£5
Trouble in Mind, Crime Express (Nottingham, UK), 2007 (pbk) £5
Nick's Blues, Five Leaves (Nottingham, UK), 2008 (pbk) £5

NATHANIEL HAWTHORNE
(b.1804 d.1864)

A 19th century American novelist and short story writer, before writing *Twice-Told Tales*, Hawthorne published many short stories and sketches anonymously or pseudo-nymously. His rarest work is his first novel, *Fanshawe*, which he attempted to suppress by destroying as many copies as he could lay his hands upon.

Novels
Fanshawe, Marsh & Capen (Boston), 1828 (anonymous, boards, purple cloth spine, paper labels).   .   £25,000
ditto, Marsh & Capen (Boston), 1828 (rebound)   £10,000
The Scarlet Letter, Ticknor, Reed & Fields (Boston), 1850 (first edition with 'reduplicate' instead of 'repudiate' on p.21, line 20 and no preface) £4,000
ditto, Ticknor, Reed & Fields (Boston), 1850 (second edition with preface). £500
ditto, Ticknor, Reed & Fields (Boston), 1850 (third edition with 'Hobart and Robbins' on copyright page instead of 'Metcalf and Co.') £150
ditto, Bohn (London), 1851 .   .   .   .   .   £150
ditto, Routledge (London), 1851.   .   .   .   £150
The House of the Seven Gables, Ticknor, Reed & Fields (Boston), 1851 (first printing with the last letters 't' and 'h' of the last words in lines 1 and 2 on p.149 broken)   £1,500
ditto, Bohn (London), 1851 .   .   .   .   .   £250
ditto, Routledge (London), 1851.   .   .   .   £250
The Blithedale Romance, Chapman & Hall (London), 1852 (2 vols). £350
ditto, Ticknor, Reed & Fields (Boston), 1852 .   .   £125
Transformation, or the Romance of Monte Beni, Smith, Elder (London), 1860 (3 vols) £500
ditto, as *The Marble Faun*, Ticknor & Fields (Boston), 1860 (first printing with 'Preface' preceeding 'Contents', 2 vols) £450
Septimus Felton or the Elixier of Life, Osgood (Boston), 1872 .   .   .   .   £150

ditto, as *Septimus: A Romance*, Henry S King (London), 1872 .   .   .   .   £100
Doctor Grimshawe's Secret, Osgood (Boston), 1883   .£125
ditto, Longmans (London), 1883.   .   .   .   .£100
Hawthorne's Last Phase, Yale Univ Press (New Haven, CT), 1949 .   .   .   .   £40/£10

Short Stories
Twice-Told Tales, American Stationers Co./John B. Russell (Boston), 1837 (first issue with fifth story listed in Contents as at p.78, not p.77, rose cloth)   .   .   £2,500
ditto, American Stationers Co./John B. Russell (Boston), 1837 (first issue rebound). £750
ditto, James Monroe (Boston), 1842 (enlarged edition, 2 vols) £450
ditto, Bohn (London), 1851 .   .   .   .   .   .   £75
The Gentle Boy, Weeks, Jordon/Wiley & Putnam (Boston/New York), 1839 (wraps)   .   .   .   £2,500
The Sister Years, Salem Gazette (Salem, MA), 1839 (anonymous; wraps) £1,500
The Celestial Rail-Road, Wilder (Boston), 1843 (wraps)   .
   .   .   .   .   £4,000
ditto, Fish (Philadelphia), 1843 (wraps)   .   .   £4,000
Mosses from an Old Manse, Wiley & Putnam (New York), 1846 (printer 'R. Craighead's Power Press' verso title-page, 2 vols; wraps) £3,000
ditto, Wiley & Putnam (New York), 1846 (1 vol., cloth)   .
   .   .   .   .   £400
ditto, Wiley & Putnam (London), 1846 (1 vol., cloth, American sheets with London title-page)   .   .£350
The Snow Image and Other Twice-Told Tales, Ticknor, Reed & Fields (Boston), 1852 [1851]   .   .   .£300
ditto, as *The Snow Image and Other Tales*, Bohn (London), 1851   .   .   .   .£150
Pansie, John Camden Hotten (London), [1864] (wraps) £250
The Ghost of Doctor Harris, Tucker (U.S.), 1900 (wraps; 'Balzac Library'). £150
The Snow Image and Other Stories of the Supernatural, Tartarus Press (Carlton-in-Coverdale, Yorkshire), 2009 (300 copies) .   .   .   .   £30/£10

Children's Books
Peter Parley's Universal History, American Stationers Co./ John B. Russell (Boston), 1837 (anonymous, 2 vols)   .
   .   .   .   .   £2,250
Grandfather's Chair, Peabody/Wiley & Putnam (Boston/ New York), 1841 (cloth, paper label)   .   .   .£400
Famous Old People, Peabody (Boston), 1841 (cloth, paper label) £400
Liberty Tree, Peabody (Boston), 1841 (cloth, paper label, first printing with 'Meet in a Con-' on p.25, line 2)   £1,250
ditto, Peabody (Boston), 1841 (second printing with 'Meet in Con-' on p.25, line 2). £400
Biographical Stories for Children, Taffan & Dennet (U.S.), 1842 .   .   .   .£300
Hawthorne's Historical Tales for Youth, Taffan & Dennet (U.S.), 1842 (containing *Grandfather's Chair, Famous Old People, Liberty Tree* and *Biographical Stories for Children*) £350
ditto, as *True Stories from History and Biography*, Ticknor, Reed & Fields (Boston), 1851 (first issue with 'Cambridge: Printed by Bolles & Houghton' verso title-page) .   £250
A Wonder-Book for Girls and Boys, Ticknor, Reed & Fields (Boston), 1852 [1851] (first issue with 'lifed' for 'lifted' on

page 21, line 3; binding with design at top of spine only, not entire spine) £2,000

ditto, Bohn (London), 1852 [1851] £350

ditto, Osgood McIlvaine (Boston), 1892 (illustrated by Walter Crane) £125

ditto, Houghton Mifflin (Boston), 1893 (illustrated by Walter Crane; 250 numbered deluxe copies) . . . £300

ditto, Hodder & Stoughton (London), [1922] (illustrated by Arthur Rackham; 24 colour illustrations and 20 drawings, red cloth) . . . . . . £350/£150

ditto, Hodder & Stoughton (London), [1922] (illustrated by Arthur Rackham; deluxe 600 signed copies, cream buckram) £1,000

ditto, Doran (New York), [1922] (illustrated by Arthur Rackham; orange-red cloth) . . . . £250/£75

Tanglewood Tales, Chapman & Hall (London), 1853 . £650

ditto, Ticknor, Reed & Fields (Boston), 1853 (without 'George C. Rand' imprint on title-page). . . £650

ditto, Hodder & Stoughton (London), [1918] (14 colour plates by Edmund Dulac) £150

ditto, Hodder & Stoughton (London), [1918] (deluxe edition illustrated by Edmund Dulac, 500 signed copies, 14 colour plates) £500

ditto, Unwin, [1909] (illustrated by Willy Pogány). . £50

Other Titles

Journal of an African Cruiser, Wiley & Putnam (New York), 1845 (wraps) £1,000

ditto, Wiley & Putnam (London), 1845 (wraps) . £750

Life of Franklin Pierce, Ticknor, Reed & Fields (Boston), 1852 (wraps). £300

ditto, Ticknor, Reed & Fields (Boston), 1852 (cloth) . £250

ditto, Routledge (London), 1853 . . . . . £75

A Rill from the Town Pump, Cash (London), 1857 (wraps).
. . . . £1,000

Our Old Home, Ticknor & Fields (Boston), 1863 (first issue with publisher's list on leaf opposite p.398) . . £125

ditto, Smith, Elder (London), 1863 (2 vols) . . £125

Passages from the American Note-Books of Nathaniel Hawthorne, Ticknor & Fields (Boston), 1868 (2 vols, green cloth with spine reading 'Ticknor & Co') . £175

ditto, Smith, Elder (London), 1868 (2 vols) . . £125

Passages from the English Note-Books of Nathaniel Hawthorne, Fields, Osgood (Boston), 1870 (2 vols) . £150

ditto, Strahan (London), 1870 (2 vols) . . . £125

Passages from the French and Italian Note-Books of Nathaniel Hawthorne, Strahan (London), 1871 (2 vols). £125

ditto, Osgood (Boston), 1872 (2 vols) . . . £125

Love Letters of Nathaniel Hawthorne 1839-1841 & 1841-1864, Society of Dofobs (Chicago), 1907 (2 vols; 62 sets).
. . . . £500

Letters of Nathaniel Hawthorne to William D. Ticknor, 1851-1864, Carteret Book Club (Newark, NJ), 1910 (2 vols) £150

The American Notebooks by Nathaniel Hawthorne, Yale Univ Press (New Haven, CT), 1941 . . . £50/£10

Hawthorne's Lost Notebook, 1835-1841, Yale Univ Press (New Haven, CT), 1978 . . . . . £25/£5

SEAMUS HEANEY
(b.1939)

Seamus Justin Heaney is an acclaimed Irish poet, writer and lecturer. His poetry has ranged in subject from the natural world to political and cultural issues, and he has become one of the most widely known and important poets working in English. He was awarded the Nobel Prize for Literature in 1995.

Poetry

Eleven Poems, Festival (Belfast), 1965 (first issue, laid paper, red-violet sun; wraps) £1,000

ditto, Festival (Belfast), 1965 (second issue, wove paper, dark-maroon sun; wraps) £800

ditto, Festival (Belfast), 1965 (third issue, grey paper, stiff green wraps). £650

Death of a Naturalist, Faber (London), 1966 . £750/£150

ditto, O.U.P. (New York), 1966 . . . . £500/£50

ditto, Faber (London), 1969 (pbk) £50

A Lough Neagh Sequence, Phoenix Pamphlet, Poets Press (Manchester, UK), 1969 (950 copies; stapled wraps) . £175

ditto, Phoenix Pamphlet, Poets Press (Manchester, UK), 1969 (50 signed copies; wraps) £500

Door into the Dark, Faber (London), 1969 . £350/£45

ditto, O.U.P. (New York), 1969 . . . . £200/£35

ditto, Faber (London), 1972 (pbk) £20

Night Drive: Poems, Gilbertson (Crediton, Devon), 1970 (100 signed copies) £500

ditto, Gilbertson (Crediton, Devon), 1970 (25 of the above containing poem in author's hand) . . . £1,250

A Boy Driving His Father to Confession, Sceptre Press (Farnham, Surrey), 1970 (150 numbered copies; stapled wraps) £450

ditto, Sceptre Press (Farnham, Surrey), 1970 (50 signed copies; stapled wraps) £850

Land, Poem-of-the-Month-Club (London), 1971 (signed broadside) £100

Servant Boy, Red Hanrahan Press (Detroit, MI), 1971 (broadside) £750

Wintering Out, Faber (London), 1972 (pbk) . . £300

ditto, Faber (London), 1973 . . . . . £100/£20

ditto, O.U.P. (New York), 1973 . . . . £100/£20

Stations, Ulsterman Publications (Belfast), 1975 (stapled wraps) £200

North, Faber (London), 1975 . . . . £300/£75

ditto, Faber (London), 1975 (pbk) £45

ditto, O.U.P. (New York), 1976 . . . . £175/£35

Bog Poems, Rainbow Press (London), 1975 (150 signed copies, slipcase) . . . . . £2,500/£2,000

In Their Element, Arts Council of Northern Ireland (Belfast), 1977 (wraps) £45

Ugolino, Carpenter, 1978 (125 signed copies, hardback, no d/w) £1,500

After Summer, Gallery Press (Dublin), 1979 (250 signed copies) . . . . £500/£325

Hedge School: Sonnets from Glanmore, Seluzicki/Janus Press (Salem, OR./Newark, VT), 1979 (illustrated by Claire Van Vliet; 285 numbered copies signed by poet and artist; wraps) £900

Field Work, Faber (London), 1979 . . . £125/£20

ditto, Faber (London), 1979 (pbk) £15

ditto, Farrar Straus (New York), 1979 . . £100/£20

Gravities: A Collection of Poems and Drawings, Charlotte Press (Newcastle Upon Tyne), 1979 (illustrated by Noel Connor; pbk)　.　.　.　.　.　.　.　.　£30
Selected Poems 1965-1975, Faber (London), 1980.　£75/£20
ditto, Faber (London), 1980 (pbk)　.　.　.　.　£15
ditto, as *Poems 1965-1975*, Farrar Straus (New York), 1980
.　.　.　.　.　.　.　.　.　.　£50/£10
Holly, Gallery Press (Dublin), 1981 (121 signed copies; wraps)　.　.　.　.　.　.　.　.　.　£300
Poems and a Memoir, The Limited Editions Club (New York), 1982 (edited and illustrated by Henry Pearson, introduced by Thomas Flanagan, 2,000 numbered copies signed by all three, slipcase)　.　.　.　£300/£225
Verses for a Fordham Commencement, Fordham Univ (New York), 1982 (broadsheet)　.　.　.　.　£300
ditto, Nadja (New York), 1984 (200 signed, numbered copies; wraps)　.　.　.　.　.　.　.　.　£300
ditto, Nadja (New York), 1984 (26 signed, lettered copies on handmade paper, boards)　.　.　.　.　.　£350
An Open Letter, Field Day (Derry, Ireland), 1983 (stapled wraps)　.　.　.　.　.　.　.　.　£25
Station Island, Faber (London), 1984　.　.　£35/£10
ditto, Faber (London), 1984 (pbk)　.　.　.　.　£15
ditto, Farrar Straus (New York), 1985　.　.　£35/£10
Hailstones, Gallery Press (Dublin), 1984 (250 signed copies)
.　.　.　.　.　.　.　.　.　£500/£300
ditto, Gallery Press (Dublin), 1984 (500 unsigned copies; wraps)　.　.　.　.　.　.　.　.　.　£75
From the Republic of Conscience, Amnesty International (Dublin), 1985 (illustrated by John Behan; 2,000 copies; stapled wraps)　.　.　.　.　.　.　.　£25
Towards a Collaboration, Arts Council of Northern Ireland (Belfast), 1986 (wraps)　.　.　.　.　.　£40
The Haw Lantern, Faber (London), 1987.　.　£50/£10
ditto, Faber (London), 1987 (pbk)　.　.　.　.　£10
ditto, Farrar Straus (New York), 1987　.　.　£25/£5
ditto, Farrar Straus (New York), 1987 (250 signed, numbered copies, slipcase)　.　.　.　.　.　£145/£100
An Upstairs Outlook, Linen Hall (Belfast), 1989 (stapled wraps)　.　.　.　.　.　.　.　.　£20
Railway Children, Poems on the Underground (London), 1989 (200 copies, broadside)　.　.　.　.　£125
The Fire Gaze, Cheltenham Festival of Literature (Cheltenham, Gloucestershire), 1989 (broadside 1 of *The Four Elements*)　.　.　.　.　.　.　.　£25
New Selected Poems 1966-1987, Faber (London), 1990　.
.　.　.　.　.　.　.　.　.　£20/£5
ditto, Faber (London), 1990 (25 signed, Roman numeralled copies, slipcase)　.　.　.　.　.　£600/£450
ditto, Faber (London), 1990 (1100 signed, numbered copies, slipcase).　.　.　.　.　.　.　£500/£350
ditto, Faber (London), 1990 (pbk)　.　.　.　.　£10
ditto, as *Selected Poems 1966-1987* (New York), 1990.　.
.　.　.　.　.　.　.　.　.　£15/£5
ditto, Farrar Straus (New York), 1990 (200 signed, numbered copies, slipcase)　.　.　.　.　.　£250/£200
The Tree Clock, Linen Hall (Belfast), 1990 (750 copies)　.
.　.　.　.　.　.　.　.　.　£125/£60
ditto, Linen Hall (Belfast), 1990 (100 signed, numbered copies, slipcase)　.　.　.　.　.　£500/£350
The Earth House, Cheltenham Festival of Literature (Cheltenham, Gloucestershire), 1990 (broadside 2 of *The Four Elements*)　.　.　.　.　.　.　.　£15
Seeing Things, Faber (London), 1991　.　.　£25/£5

ditto, Faber (London), 1991 (250 signed, numbered copies, slipcase).　.　.　.　.　.　.　.　£275/£175
ditto, Faber (London), 1991 (pbk)　.　.　.　.　£10
ditto, Farrar Straus (New York), 1991　.　.　£20/£5
Squarings, Hieroglyph Editions (Dublin), 1991 (100 signed copies in slipcase)　.　.　.　.　.　.　£2,000
ditto, Arion Press (San Francisco, CA), 2003 (400 numbered copies)　.　.　.　.　.　.　.　.　.　£500
The Water Pause, Cheltenham Festival of Literature (Cheltenham, Gloucestershire), 1991 (broadside 3 of *The Four Elements*)　.　.　.　.　.　.　.　£15
Iron Spike, William B. Ewert (Concord, NH), 1992 (100 signed copies, broadside)　.　.　.　.　.　£100
The Air Station, Cheltenham Festival of Literature (Cheltenham, Gloucestershire), 1992 (broadside 4 of *The Four Elements*)　.　.　.　.　.　.　.　£15
The Gravel Walks, Lenoir Rhyne College (Hickory, NC), 1992 (wraps).　.　.　.　.　.　.　.　£100
ditto, Lenoir Rhyne College (Hickory, NC), 1992 (26 lettered copies; wraps)　.　.　.　.　.　.　.　£700
Poet's Chair, William B. Ewert (Concord, NH), 1993 (100 signed, numbered copies, broadside)　.　.　.　£150
Keeping Going, William B. Ewert (Concord, NH), 1993 (50 signed, numbered copies, boards, no d/w)　.　.　£400
ditto, William B. Ewert (Concord, NH), 1993 (150 signed, numbered copies; wraps)　.　.　.　.　.　£125
A Dog Was Crying To-night in Wicklow Also, White Fields Press (Louisville, KY), 1994 (100 signed, numbered copies, broadside)　.　.　.　.　.　.　£40
ditto, White Fields Press (Louisville, KY), 1994 (broadside)
The Spirit Level, Faber (London), 1996　.　.　£15/£5
ditto, Faber (London), 1996 (350 numbered, signed copies, slipcase).　.　.　.　.　.　.　£250/£225
ditto, Farrar Straus (New York), 1996 (200 signed, numbered copies with audio cassette in slipcase)　.　£200/£175
ditto, Farrar Straus (New York), 1996 (with audio cassette in slipcase).　.　.　.　.　.　.　.　£25/£10
Audenesque, Maeght (Paris), 1998 (with 4 lithographs by Max Neumann, 120 numbered copies, signed by author and artist, slipcase)　.　.　.　.　.　.　.　£500
Opened Ground: Poems 1966-1996, Faber (London), 1998
.　.　.　.　.　.　.　.　.　£15/£5
ditto, Faber (London), 1998 (300 signed, numbered copies in slipcase).　.　.　.　.　.　.　£250/£200
ditto, Faber (London), 1998 (25 signed, roman-numeraled copies in slipcase)　.　.　.　.　£450/£350
ditto, Farrar Straus (New York), 1998　.　.　£15/£5
Electric Light, Faber (London), 2001　.　.　£25/£5
ditto, Faber (London), 2001 (300 signed, numbered copies, slipcase).　.　.　.　.　.　.　£225/£175
District and Circle, Faber (London), 2006　.　£20/£5
ditto, Faber (London), 2006 (300 signed, numbered copies; slipcase).　.　.　.　.　.　.　£400/£300
ditto, Farrar Straus (New York), 2006　.　.　£20/£5

Plays
The Cure at Troy: A Version of Sophocles' Philoctetes, Field Day (Derry, Ireland), 1990 (500 signed, numbered copies)　.　.　.　.　.　.　.　£250/£175
ditto, Faber (London), 1990 (pbk)　.　.　.　.　£5
ditto, Farrar Straus (New York), 1991　.　.　£25/£5
The Burial at Thebes: A version of Sophocles, Antigone, Faber (London), 2004.　.　.　.　.　.　£20/£5

ditto, Faber (London), 2004 (250 signed, numbered copies; slipcase). . . . . £300/£200
ditto, Farrar Straus (New York), 2004 . . £10/£5

Translations
Sweeney Praises the Trees, Kelly/Winterton Press (New York), 1981 (110 copies; wraps) £400
Sweeney Astray: A Version from the Irish, Field Day (Derry, Ireland), 1983. . . . . . £65/£25
ditto, Field Day (Derry, Ireland), 1983 (pbk) . . £25
ditto, Faber (London), 1984. . . . . £35/£10
ditto, Faber (London), 1984 (wraps) . . . £10
ditto, Farrar Straus (New York), 1984 . . £30/£10
ditto, Farrar Straus (New York), 1984 (350 signed, numbered copies, slipcase) . . . . . £225/£175
Sweeney's Flight, Faber (London), 1992 (photographs by Rachel Giese) . . . . . . £45/£10
ditto, Farrar Straus (New York), 1992 . . £45/£10
The Midnight Verdict, Gallery Press (Loughcrew, Ireland), 1993 (translations from the Irish of Brian Merriman and from the *Metamorphoses* of Ovid; 925 copies) . £75/£45
ditto, Gallery Press (Dublin), 1993 (75 signed, numbered copies) £400
Laments: Jan Kochanowski (1530-1584), Faber (London), 1995 (with Stanislaw Baranczak) . . . £25/£10
ditto, Farrar Straus (New York), 1995 . . £25/£10
Beowulf, Faber (London), 1999 . . . . £25/£5
ditto, Faber (London), 1999 (300 signed, numbered copies, slipcase). . . . . . . £450/£375
ditto, Farrar Straus (New York), 2000 . . £25/£5
Diary of One Who Vanished, Faber (London), 1999 (song cycle by Leoš Janáček of poems by Ozef Kalda; dark green stapled wraps with yellow printed dustjacket) . £10/£5
ditto, Farrar Straus (New York), 1999 (pbk) . . . £5
Hallaig, by Sorley MacLean, Sorley MacLean Trust (Dunblane, Scotland), 2002 (150 unsigned copies; stapled wraps) £150
ditto, by Sorley MacLean, Sorley MacLean Trust (Dunblane, Scotland), 2002 (50 signed, numbered copies; stapled wraps) £250
Arion, by Alexander Pushkin, Arion Press (San Francisco, CA), 2002 (400 copies; wraps; with a note by Olga Carlisle). £200
The Testament of Cresseid, by Robert Henryson, Enitharmon Press (London), 2004 (illustrated by Hughie O'Donoghue; 350 numbered hardback copies signed by poet & artist; no d/w) £300
Columcille The Scribe, The Royal Irish Academy (Dublin, Ireland), 2004 (150 numbered copies each hand-lettered by Timothy O'Neill on vellum; signed by Heaney and the calligrapher). £1,000
The Testament of Cresseid & Seven Fables, Faber (London), 2009 . . . . £10/£5
ditto, Faber (London), 2009 (110 signed, numbered copies; slipcase). . . . . . . £300/£200

Others
The Fire i' the Flint: Reflections on the Poetry of Gerard Manley Hopkins, British Academy/O.U.P. (Oxford, UK), 1975 (stapled wraps) £25
Robert Lowell: A Memorial Address and Elegy, privately printed by Faber (London), 1978 (wraps) . . . £175

The Makings of a Music: Reflections on the Poetry of Wordsworth and Yeats, Univ of Liverpool (Liverpool), 1978 (stapled wraps) £65
Preoccupations: Selected Prose 1968-1978, Faber (London), 1980 . . . . £75/£15
ditto, Farrar Straus (New York), 1980 . . . £35/£10
A Personal Selection: August 20 – October 24, 1982, Ulster Museum (Belfast), 1982 (wraps) £20
Among Schoolchildren: In Memory of John M. Malone, Queen's Univ (Belfast), 1983 (green wraps). . . £75
ditto, as *Among Schoolchildren: A Lecture Dedicated to the Memory of John Malone*, John Malone Memorial Committee (Belfast), 1983 (stapled blue wraps) . . £20
Place and Displacement: Recent Poetry of Northern Ireland, Dove Cottage (Kendal, Cumbria), 1984 (stapled wraps) £25
The Government of the Tongue: The 1986 T.S. Eliot Memorial Lectures and Other Critical Writings, Faber (London), 1988 . . . . £15/£5
ditto, as *The Government of the Tongue: Selected Prose 1978-1987*, Farrar Straus (New York), 1989. . £15/£5
The Sounds of Rain, Emory Univ (Atlanta, GA), 1988 (300 copies, sewn wraps) £175
The Place of Writing, Scholars Press (Atlanta, GA), 1989 . . . . £45/£10
ditto, Scholars Press (Atlanta, GA), 1989 (60 signed, numbered copies) . . . . . . £750/£700
The Redress of Poetry: An Inaugural Lecture Delivered before the University of Oxford on 24 October 1989, Clarendon Press (Oxford, UK), 1990 (stapled wraps). £15
ditto, as *The Redress of Poetry: Oxford Lectures*, Faber (London), 1995 (expanded edition). . . . £20/£5
ditto, Farrar Straus (New York), 1995 . . . £10/£5
Dylan the Durable? On Dylan Thomas, Bennington College (Bennington, VT), 1992 (1,000 numbered copies; stapled wraps) £30
Joy or Night, Univ College of Swansea (Swansea, UK), 1993 (stapled wraps) £20
Extending the Alphabet: On Christopher Marlowe's Hero and Leander, Memorial Univ of New Foundland (St John's, NL), 1994 (stapled wraps) £20
Crediting Poetry: The Nobel Lecture, Gallery Books (Loughcrew, Ireland), 1995 (wraps) . . . £25
ditto, Faber (London), 1995 (500 copies, wraps) . . £25
ditto, Farrar Straus (New York), 1996 . . £10/£5
Homage to Robert Frost, Farrar Straus (New York), 1996 (with Joseph Brodsky and Derek Walcott) . . £10/£5
ditto, Faber (London), 1997 (pbk) £5
Commencement Address, Univ of North Carolina (Chapel Hill, NC), 1998 (100 signed, numbered copies of 500; wraps) £350
ditto, Univ of North Carolina (Chapel Hill, NC), 1998 (400 unsigned copies of 500; wraps) £45
Finders Keepers Selected Prose 1971-2001, Faber (London), 2002 . . . . £15/£5
ditto, Farrar Straus (New York), 2002 . . . £15/£5

LAFCADIO HEARN
(b.1850 d.1904)

Hearn is best known as the author of books on Japan, and especially his collections of Japanese ghost stories and legends. He was also known as Koizumi Yakumo after gaining Japanese citizenship.

Fiction

Stray Leaves from Strange Literature: Stories Reconstructed, James R. Osgood (Boston), 1884 (first issue in blue cloth) £450
ditto, James R. Osgood (Boston), 1884 (second issue yellow-green cloth) £250
ditto, Kegan, Paul, Trench, Trübner (London), 1903 . £250
Some Chinese Ghosts, Roberts Brothers (Boston), 1887 .
. . . . £350
ditto, Kegan, Paul, Trench, Trübner (London), 1907 . £100
Chita: A Memory of a Last Land, Harper (New York), 1889 (brown cloth) £125
ditto, Harper (New York), 1889 (orange cloth) . . £75
Youma: The Story of a West-Indian Slave, Harper (New York), 1890 (blue-and-white cloth binding) . . . £125
ditto, Harper (New York), 1890 (red cloth) . . . £75
Two Years in the French West Indies, Harper (New York), 1890 (green cloth) £175
ditto, Harper (New York), 1923 (with illustrations from photographs by A.W. Rushmore and drawings by Marie Royle) . . . . £65/£25
Glimpses of Unfamiliar Japan, Houghton Mifflin (Boston), 1894 (2 vols; green cloth) £200
ditto, Houghton Mifflin (Boston), 1894 (2 vols; black cloth)
. . . . £165
ditto, Osgood McIlvaine (London), 1894 (2 vols) . . £165
Out of the East: Reveries and Studies in New Japan, Houghton Mifflin (Boston), 1895 (yellow cloth) . £175
ditto, Osgood McIlvaine (London), 1895 . . . . £145
Kokoro: Hints and Echoes of Japanese Inner Life, Gay and Bird (London), 1895 . . . . £50
ditto, Houghton Mifflin (Boston), 1896 (olive green cloth) .
. . . . £125
Gleanings in Buddah-Fields: Studies of Hand and Soul in the Far East, Houghton Mifflin (Boston) 1897 (blue cloth)
. . . . £125
ditto, Kegan Paul Trench Trübner (London), 1903 . . £75
ditto, Jonathan Cape: Traveller's Library' (London), 1927 .
. . . . £30/£10
Exotics and Retrospectives, Little, Brown (Boston), 1898 (green cloth) £75
ditto, Sampson Low (London), 1898 . . . . . £65
In Ghostly Japan, Little, Brown (Boston), 1899 (blue cloth)
. . . . £125
ditto, Sampson Low (London), 1899 . . . . . £100
Shadowings, Little, Brown (Boston), 1900 (blue cloth). .
. . . . £200
ditto, Sampson Low (London), 1900 . . . . . £100
A Japanese Miscellany, Little, Brown (Boston), 1901 (green cloth). £75
ditto, Sampson Low (London), 1901 . . . . . £65
Kotto: Being Japanese Curios, With Sundry Cobwebs, Macmillan (New York), 1902 (illustrated by Genjiro Yeto)
. . . . £200
ditto, Macmillan (London), 1902 . . . . . £150

Kwaidan: Stories and Studies of Strange Things, Houghton Mifflin (Boston), 1904 (blue-green binding). . . £65
ditto, Houghton Mifflin (New York), 1904 (black binding) .
. . . . £50
ditto, Kegan Paul Trench Trübner (London), 1904 . . £45
Japan: An Attempt at Interpretation, Macmillan (New York), 1904 (brown cloth; no appendix) . . . £75
ditto, Macmillan (New York), 1904 (olive cloth; no appendix) £65
ditto, Macmillan (New York), 1904 (olive cloth; with additional appendix by Herbert Spencer) . . . £50
The Romance of the Milky Way and Other Studies and Stories, Houghton Mifflin (Boston), 1905 (grey cloth stamped in yellow) £125
ditto, Constable (London), 1905 . . . . . . £100
ditto, Bernhard Tauchnitz (Leipzig), 1910 (pbk) . . £10
Nightmare-Touch, Tartarus Press (Carlton-in-Coverdale), 2010 . . . . £30/£10

Children's Books Translated by Hearn
The Boy Who Drew Cats, T. Hasegawa (Tokyo), 1898 ('Japanese Fairy Tales' series No 23; crepe book) . £100
The Goblin Spider, T. Hasegawa (Tokyo), 1899 ('Japanese Fairy Tales' Second Series; crepe book) . . . £100
The Old Woman Who Lost Her Dumpling, T. Hasegawa (Tokyo), 1902 ('Japanese Fairy Tales' series No 24; crepe book; boxed) £100
Chin Chin Kobakama, T. Hasegawa (Tokyo), 1903 ('Japanese Fairy Tales' series No 25; crepe book; spine sewn with blue silk; boxed) £100
The Boy Who Drew Cats and Other Tales, Collier-Macmillan (New York), 1963 (introduced by Pearl S. Buck) . . . . £50/£10

Other Books Translated by Hearn
One of Cleopatra's Nights, by Theophile Gautier, Worthington (New York), 1882 . . . . £200
ditto, as ***Tales from Theophile Gautier***, Brentano (New York), 1888 (translated by Hearn and Myndart Verelst) .
. . . . £100
ditto, John Lane/Bodley Head (London), 1938 (500 copies; red cloth) £100
Clarimonde and Other Stories, Brentano (New York), 1899
. . . . £100
ditto, T.C. & E.C. Jack (London), 1903 ('The World's Storytellers'). £75
The Temptation of St Anthony, by Gustave Flaubert, Alice Harriman (New York), 1910 (introduction by Elizabeth Bisland). £50
ditto, Grant Richards (London), 1911 . . . . £45
Japanese Lyrics, Houghton Mifflin (New York), 1915 (1,000 copies; green wraps) £35
ditto, Constable (London), 1915 (1,500 copies; wraps) . £30
Saint Anthony and Other Stories by Guy de Maupassant, A. & C. Boni (New York), 1924 . . . . . . £65
Stories from Emile Zola, by Emile Zola, Hokuseido (Tokyo), 1935 (edited and prefaced by Albert Mordell; blue/black cloth stamped in red) £200

Miscellaneous
La Cuisine Creole: A Collection of Culinary Recipes, Will H. Coleman (New York), 1885. . . . . . £125
ditto, F.F. Hansell & Bros (New York), 1922 . . £100
'Gombo Zhebes'; A Little Dictionary of Creole Proverbs, Will H. Coleman (New York), 1885 . . . . £175

Letters from the Raven: Being the Correspondence of Lafcadio Hearn with Henry Watkin, Constable (London), 1908 (edited by Milton Bronner) £40

The Japanese Letters of Lafcadio Hearn, Houghton Mifflin (New York), 1910 (edited by Elizabeth Bisland) . . £20

ditto, Constable (London),1910 (blue cloth) . . . £20

Interpretations of Literature, Heinemann (London), 1916 (edited by John Erskine; 2 vols) . . . £50 the set

Appreciations of Poetry, Dodd Mead (New York), 1916 (edited by John Erskine) £30

ditto, Heinemann (London), 1919 . . . . £25

Life and Literature, Dodd Mead (New York), 1917 (edited by John Erskine) £25

ditto, Heinemann (London), 1920 . . . . £20

Karma and Other Stories & Essays, Boni & Liveright (New York), 1918 . . . . £45

ditto, Harrap (London), 1921 ('Harrap Library' series, Volume 21) . . . . £40/£15

Books and Habits, Heinemann (London), 1922 (edited by John Erskine) . . . . . . £45/£15

The Writings of Lafcadio Hearn, Houghton Mifflin (Boston), 1922 (16 vols; 750 numbered sets) . £1,250/£750 the set

Pre-Raphaelite and Other Poets, Dodd, Mead (New York), 1922 (edited by John Erskine) . . . £65/£20

ditto, Heinemann (London), 1923 . . . £45/£15

Essays in European and Oriental Literature, Dodd Mead (New York), 1923 (edited by Albert Mordell; red cloth) .
. . . . £65/£20

ditto, Heinemann (London), 1923 . . . £45/£15

An American Miscellany, Dodd Mead (New York), 1924 (edited by Albert Mordell; 2 vols) . . £75/£25 the set

ditto, as *Miscellanies: Articles and Stories, Now First Collected*, Heinemann (London), 1924 (2 vols) £75/£25 the set

Occidental Gleanings: Sketches and Essays, Now First Collected, Dodd Mead (New York), 1925 (edited by Albert Mordell; 2 vols) . . . . £85/£25

ditto, Heinemann (London),1925 (2 vols) . . £75/£20

Lectures on Shakespeare, Hokuseido Press (Tokyo), 1928 (edited by Iwao Inagaki) . . . . . .£150/£75

Lectures on Tennyson, Hokuseido Press (Tokyo), 1941 (edited by by S. Kishi) . . . . . £75/£25

Ye Giglampz: A Weekly Illustrated Journal of Art, Literature and Satire, Crossroads Books/Public Library of Cincinnati and Hamilton County (US),1983 (edited by J.C. Hughes; 100 copies; slipcase; no d/w) . . . £125/£75

ROBERT A. HEINLEIN
(b.1907 d.1988)

An influential and controversial American science fiction writer, Heinlein was first published in *Astounding SF* magazine in 1939. He was the first science fiction writer to break into the mainstream, becoming the author of best-selling novels in the 1960s. He won seven Hugo awards and the first Grand Master Award awarded by the Science Fiction Writers of America.

Novels

Beyond This Horizon, Fantasy Press (Reading, PA), 1948 .
. . . . £200/£45

ditto, Fantasy Press (Reading, PA), 1948 (500 signed, numbered copies) . . . . . . £500/£300

Sixth Column, Gnome Press (New York), 1949 . £300/£35

ditto, as *The Day After Tomorrow*, Signet (New York), 1962 (pbk) £10

ditto, as *Sixth Column*, Mayflower (London), 1962 (pbk) .
. . . . £10

The Puppet Masters, Doubleday (New York), 1951 . .
. . . . £300/£75

ditto, Museum Press (London), 1953 . . . . £175/£35

Universe, Dell Books (New York), 1951 (pbk) . . £30

Double Star, Doubleday (New York), 1956 . £1,500/£300

ditto, Joseph (London), 1958 . . . . £200/£40

The Door into Summer, Doubleday (New York), 1957 .
. . . . £325/£45

ditto, Panther (London), 1960 (pbk) £5

ditto, Gollancz (London), 1967 . . . . . £100/£20

Methuselah's Children, Gnome Press (New York), 1958 .
. . . . £300/£35

ditto, Gollancz (London), 1963 (abridged version) . £75/£20

Stranger in a Strange Land, Putnam (New York), 1961 (first issue with 'C22' on p. 408 and d/w priced $4.50) .
. . . . £1,750/£300

ditto, New English Library (London), 1965 . £300/£25

Orphans of the Sky, Gollancz (London), 1963 . £400/£75

ditto, Putnam (New York), 1964 . . . . £300/£45

Glory Road, Putnam (New York), 1963 . . £350/£50

ditto, New English Library (London), 1965 . £150/£20

Farnham's Freehold, Putnam (New York), 1964 . £250/£40

ditto, Dobson (London), 1965 . . . . £100/£25

The Moon is a Harsh Mistress, Putnam (New York), 1966 .
. . . . £1,500/£150

ditto, Dobson (London), 1967 . . . . £200/£20

I Will Fear No Evil, Putnam (New York), 1970 . £100/£15

ditto, New English Library (London), 1971 . £65/£15

Time Enough For Love, Putnam (New York), 1973 . .
. . . . £200/£45

ditto, New English Library (London), 1974 . £125/£35

Destination Moon, Gregg Press (Boston, MA), 1979 (no d/w) £100

The Number of the Beast, New English Library (London), 1980 . . . . £100/£15

ditto, Fawcett (Columbine, NY), 1980 (pbk) . . £10

Friday, Holt Rinehart (New York), 1982 . . . £30/£5

ditto, Ballantine/Del Ray (New York), 1984 (500 signed, numbered copies, slipcase, no d/w) . . £200/£125

ditto, New English Library (London), 1982 . £30/£5

Job, Ballantine/Del Ray (New York), 1984 . £15/£5

ditto, Ballantine/Del Ray (New York), 1984 (750 signed, numbered copies, slipcase) . . . . . £100/£75

ditto, Ballantine/Del Ray (New York), 1984 (26 signed deluxe copies, slipcase) £700

ditto, New English Library (London), 1984 . £20/£5

The Cat Who Walks Through Walls, Putnam (New York), 1985 (first state with line missing on p.300, erratum sheet laid in) . . . . £25/£5

ditto, Putnam (New York), 1984 (350 signed, numbered copies, slipcase) . . . . . . £200/£150

ditto, New English Library (London), 1986 . £20/£5

To Sail Beyond the Sunset, Ace/Putnam (New York), 1987.
. . . . £20/£5

ditto, Joseph (London), 1987 . . . . . £15/£5

Omnibus Editions

The Robert Heinlein Omnibus, Science Fiction Book Club (London), 1958 . . . . £50/£15

Three by Heinlein, Doubleday (New York), 1965 . £75/£25
ditto, as *A Heinlein Triad*, Gollancz (London), 1966 . .
. . . . £45/£10
A Robert Heinlein Omnibus, Sidgwick & Jackson (London),
1966 . . . . £30/£10

Short Stories
The Man Who Sold the Moon, Shasta (Chicago), 1950 .
. . . . £200/£40
ditto, Shasta (Chicago), 1950 (subscriber's copy signed on
tipped-in page) . . . . . £600/£400
ditto, Sidgwick & Jackson (London), 1953 . £125/£25
Waldo and Magic Inc., Doubleday (New York), 1950 .
. . . . £200/£35
The Green Hills of Earth, Shasta (Chicago), 1951. £250/£45
ditto, Shasta (Chicago), 1951 (subscriber's copy signed on
tipped-in page) . . . . . £600/£400
ditto, Sidgwick & Jackson (London), 1954 . £150/£35
Assignment in Eternity, Fantasy Press (Reading, PA), 1953
(500 numbered, signed copies). . . £500/£250
ditto, Fantasy Press (Reading, PA), 1953 . . £200/£75
ditto, Museum Press (London), 1955 . . . £175/£50
Revolt in 2100, Shasta (Chicago), 1953 . . . £150/£25
ditto, Shasta (Chicago), 1953 (subscriber's copy signed on
tipped-in page) . . . . . £500/£250
ditto, Gollancz (London), 1964 . . . . £65/£15
The Menace from Earth, Gnome Press (New York), 1959 .
. . . . £150/£40
ditto, Dobson (London), 1966 . . . . £75/£25
The Unpleasant Profession of Jonathan Hoag, Gnome
Press (New York), 1959 . . . . . £200/£45
ditto, Dobson (London), 1964 . . . . £100/£25
The Worlds of Robert Heinlein, Ace Books (New York),
1966 (pbk) £10
ditto, New English Library (London), 1970 (pbk) . . £10
The Past Through Tomorrow, Putnam (New York), 1967 .
. . . . £200/£50
ditto, New English Library (London), 1977 (2 vols) . .
. . . . £100/£20
Best of Robert Heinlein, Sidgwick & Jackson (London),
1973 . . . . £25/£10
The Notebooks of Lazarus Long, Putnam (New York), 1978
(with D F Vassallo; pbk) £15
Expanded Universe, Grosset & Dunlap (New York), 1980 .
. . . . £50/£15
Grumbles from the Grave, Ballantine (New York), 1989 .
. . . . £10/£5
Requiem, Tor (New York), 1992 . . . . £10/£5
The Fantasies of Robert Heinlein, Tor (New York), 1992 .
. . . . £10/£5

Children's Titles
Rocket Ship Galileo, Scribner's (New York), 1947 (first
state d/w published at $2.00) . . . . £750/£75
ditto, New English Library (London), 1971 (pbk) . . £30
Space Cadet, Scribner's (New York), 1948 (first state d/w
published at $2.50) . . . . . £450/£45
ditto, Gollancz (London), 1966 . . . . £150/£35
Red Planet, Scribner's (New York), 1949 . £125/£35
ditto, Gollancz (London), 1963 . . . £150/£35
Farmer in the Sky, Scribner's (New York), 1950 . £200/£35
ditto, Gollancz (London), 1962 . . . . £125/£25
Between Planets, Scribner's (New York), 1951 . £200/£45
ditto, Gollancz (London), 1968 . . . . £150/£35

The Rolling Stones, Scribner's (New York), 1952. £250/£45
ditto, as *Space Family Stone*, Gollancz (London), 1969 .
. . . . £125/£35
Starman Jones, Scribner's (New York), 1953. . £200/£45
ditto, Sidgwick & Jackson (London), 1954 . . £65/£15
The Star Beast, Scribner's (New York), 1954. . £100/£20
ditto, New English Library (London), 1971 . . £65/£10
Tunnel in the Sky, Scribner's (New York), 1955 . £150/£50
ditto, Gollancz (London), 1965 . . . . £65/£15
Time for the Stars, Scribner's (New York), 1956 . £250/£35
ditto, Gollancz (London), 1963 . . . . £100/£20
Citizen of the Galaxy, Scribner's (New York), 1957 . .
. . . . £200/£50
ditto, Gollancz (London), 1969 . . . . £75/£25
Have Space Suit - Will Travel, Scribner's (New York), 1958
. . . . £300/£50
ditto, Gollancz (London), 1970 . . . . £65/£20
Starship Troopers, Putnam (New York), 1959. £1,000/£250
ditto, New English Library (London), 1961 . . £100/£35
Podkayne of Mars, Putnam (New York), 1963 £500/£125
ditto, New English Library (London), 1969 . . £35/£10

Non-Fiction
The Discovery of the Future, Novacious Press (Los Angeles,
CA), 1941 ('Limited First Edition' [200] on front; stapled
wraps) £1,000
ditto, Novacious Press (Los Angeles, CA), 1941 (adds
'Reprint' (100) under original limitation; stapled wraps) .
. . . . £400
*Take Back Your Government: A Practical Handbook For
The Private Citizen Who Wants Democracy To Work!*,
Baen (Riverdale, NY), 1992 (pbk) £15
Tramp Royale, Ace (New York), 1992 . . . £10/£5

JOSEPH HELLER
(b.1923 d.1999)

Heller is chiefly known for *Catch-22*, a satirical anti-war
novel which drew on his own experiences of military
service. He also wrote stage plays, screenplays, short
stories, articles, memoirs and reviews.

Novels
Catch-22, Simon & Schuster (New York), 1961 (d/w priced
$5.95) . . . . . . £1,500/£200
ditto, Cape (London), 1962 (first issue d/w with blurb about
book on back) . . . . £1,500/£45
ditto, Cape (London), 1962 (second issue d/w with comments
of other authors on back) . . . . £350/£45
ditto, Franklin Library (Franklin Centre, PA), 1978 (signed,
limited edition) £150
ditto, Simon & Schuster (New York), 1994 (750 signed,
numbered copies, slipcase, no d/w). . . £150/£100
Something Happened, Knopf (New York), 1974 . £45/£10
ditto, Knopf (New York), 1974 (350 signed, numbered
copies, d/w and slipcase) . . . . £75/£35
ditto, Cape (London), 1974 . . . . . £25/£10
Good as Gold, Franklin Library (Franklin Centre, PA), 1979
(signed, limited edition) £40
ditto, Simon & Schuster (New York), 1979 . . £25/£5
ditto, Simon & Schuster (New York), 1979 (500 signed
copies, acetate d/w, slipcase) . . . £40/£20

ditto, Cape (London), 1979 . . . . . £25/£5

God Knows, Knopf (New York), 1984 . . £25/£5

ditto, Knopf (New York), 1984 (350 signed copies, d/w and slipcase). . . . . £35/£20

ditto, Cape (London), 1984 . . . . . £20/£5

ditto, Franklin Library (Franklin Centre, PA), 1984 (signed limited edition) £35

Picture This, Putnam (New York), 1988 . . £15/£5

ditto, Putnam (New York), 1988 (250 signed copies, slipcase, no d/w) . . . . . £40/£20

ditto, Macmillan (London), 1988 . . . £15/£5

ditto, Macmillan (London), 1988 (50 proof copies) . £35

Closing Time, Franklin Library (Franklin Centre, PA), 1994 (signed limited edition) £35

ditto, Simon & Schuster (New York), 1994 . £15/£5

ditto, Simon & Schuster (New York), 1994 (750 signed, numbered copies, slipcase, no d/w) . . . £25/£15

ditto, Simon & Schuster (London), 1994 . . £15/£5

Portrait of an Artist as an Old Man, Scribner (New York), 2000 . . . . £15/£5

ditto, Simon & Schuster (London), 2000 . . £15/£5

Plays

We Bombed in New Haven, Knopf (New York), 1968 . .
. . . . £30/£10

ditto, Cape (London), 1969 . . . . . £25/£5

Catch-22: A Dramatization, French (New York), 1971 (pbk)
. . . . £25

Clevinger's Trial, French (New York), 1973 (stapled waps)
. . . . £20

Non-Fiction

No Laughing Matter, Knopf (New York), 1986 (with Speed Vogel) . . . . £25/£5

ditto, Cape (London), 1986 . . . . . £25/£5

Now and Then, From Coney Island to Here, Franklin Library (Franklin Centre, PA), 1994 (signed limited edition) . £40

ditto, Knopf (New York), 1998 . . . . £15/£5

ditto, Simon & Schuster (New York), 1998 . £15/£5

ERNEST HEMINGWAY
(b.1899 d.1961)

One of the most famous and influential American novelists of the 20th century, Hemingway's writing is characterised by a concise minimalism and understatement. His work drew on his own experiences of Europe; especially *A Farewell to Arms*, set during the First World War, and *For Whom the Bell Tolls* with its Spanish Civil War background. He won the Nobel Prize for Literature in 1954.

Novels

The Torrents of Spring, Scribner's (New York), 1926 . .
. . . . £3,500/£350

ditto, Black Sun Press (Paris), 1933 (large paper edition, 125 francs; wraps) £250

ditto, Black Sun Press (Paris), 1933 (small paper edition, 10 francs; wraps) £125

ditto, Cape (London), 1933 . . . . . £500/£50

The Sun Also Rises, Scribner's (New York), 1926 (first issue with 'stoppped' rather than 'stopped' on p.181, line

26, d/w with error 'In Our Times' rather than 'In Our Time') . . . . . . £35,000/£1,250

ditto, Scribner's (New York), 1926 (first issue book with corrected, ie second issue d/w) . . £10,000/£1,250

ditto, Scribner's (New York), 1926 (second issue book and d/w with all errors corrected) . . . £9,000/£250

ditto, as **Fiesta**, Cape (London), 1927 . £25,000/£2,000

A Farewell to Arms, Scribner's (New York), 1929 (510 signed copies, glassine d/w, slipcase) . .£8,000/£5,000

ditto, Scribner's (New York), 1929 (no disclaimer on p.[x]).
. . . . £2,000/£200

ditto, Scribner's (New York), 1929 (with disclaimer on p.[x])
. . . . £750/£100

ditto, Cape (London), 1929 (first issue with 'seriosu' on p.66, line 28) . . . . . £850/£250

ditto, Cape (London), 1929 (second issue with error corrected)
. . . . £400/£50

To Have and Have Not, Scribner's (New York), 1937 . .
. . . . £750/£75

ditto, Cape (London), 1937 . . . . . £250/£30

For Whom the Bell Tolls, Scribner's (New York), 1940 (first issue d/w without photographer's name on back panel) . . . . £800/£45

ditto, Scribner's (New York), 1940 (second issue d/w with photographer's name). . . . . £200/£45

ditto, Cape (London), 1941 . . . . . £250/£30

Across the River and into the Trees, Cape (London), 1950 .
. . . . £175/£25

ditto, Scribner's (New York), 1950 (24 advance copies containing errors) £12,500

ditto, Scribner's (New York), 1950 (first issue d/w with yellow lettering to spine) . . . . £175/£20

ditto, Scribner's (New York), 1950 (second issue d/w with orange lettering to spine) . . . . £125/£20

The Old Man and the Sea, Scribner's (New York), 1952 .
. . . . £250/£75

ditto, Scribner's (New York), 1952 (30 sheets bound in black buckram for presentation, signature blind-stamped on front cover, spine gilt) £10,000

ditto, Cape (London), 1952 . . . . . £125/£15

Islands in the Stream, Scribner's (New York), 1970 £45/£10

ditto, Collins (London), 1970 . . . . £25/£5

The Garden of Eden, Scribner's (New York), 1986 £20/£5

ditto, Hamish Hamilton (London), 1987 . . £15/£5

True at First Light, Heinemann (London), 1999 . £15/£5

Short Stories

Three Stories & Ten Poems, privately printed, Contact Publishing Co. (Paris), 1923 (300 copies; wraps). £25,000

In Our Time, Three Mountains Press (Paris), 1924 (170 copies) £25,000

ditto, Boni & Liveright (New York), 1925 . £4,000/£600

ditto, Cape (London), 1926 . . . . £2,000/£600

ditto, Black Sun Press (Paris), 1932 . . . . £250

Men Without Women, Scribner's (New York), 1927 (first state weighing 15.5 ounces) . . . . £3,500/£500

ditto, Scribner's (New York), 1927 (second state weighing 13.8 ounces). . . . . . £2,000/£100

ditto, Cape (London), 1928 . . . . . £1,000/£75

God Rest You Merry Gentlemen, House of Books (New York), 1933 (300 copies, no d/w) . . . £1,000

Winner Take Nothing, Scribner's (New York), 1933 . .
. . . . £500/£100

ditto, Cape (London), 1934 . . . . . £250/£45

The Fifth Column and The First Forty-Nine Stories,
Scribner's (New York), 1938 . . . . £1,000/£100
ditto, Cape (London), 1939 . . . . . £750/£75
The First Forty-Nine Stories, Cape (London), 1944 £75/£10
ditto, Franklin Library (Franklin Centre, PA), 1977 . £100
Two Christmas Tales, Hart Press (Berkeley, CA), 1959 (150
copies; String-tied pictorial blue wraps). . . . £850
The Snows of Kilamanjaro and Other Stories, Scribner's
(New York), 1961 . . . . . . £30/£10
ditto, Penguin (Harmondsworth, Middlesex), 1963 (pbk) £5
*The Short Happy Life of Francis Macomber and Other
Stories*, Penguin (London), 1963 (pbk) . . . £5
*The Fifth Column and Four Unpublished Stories of the
Spanish Civil War*, Scribner's (New York), 1969 £45/£10
The Nick Adams Stories, Scribner's (New York), 1972 .
. . . . £75/£20
A Divine Gesture, A Fable, Aloe Editions (New York), 1974
(200 copies; wraps) £45

Others

Today is Friday, Stable Publications (Englewood, NJ), 1926
(300 numbered copies; string-tied wraps; envelope) . .
. . . . £1,500/£750
Introduction to Kiki of Montparnasse, Titus (Paris), 1929
(25 copies; wraps) £2,500
Death in the Afternoon, Scribner's (New York), 1932 . .
. . . . £2,000/£200
ditto, Cape (London), 1932 . . . . . £750/£75
Green Hills of Africa, Scribner's (New York), 1935 .
. . . . £1,000/£100
ditto, Cape (London), 1936 . . . . . £500/£45
The Spanish Earth, Savage (Cleveland, OH), 1938 (1,000
numbered copies, some with pictorial endpapers, glassine
d/w) . . . .£1,500/£1,250
ditto, Savage (Cleveland, OH), 1938 (copies of the above
1,000 but with plain endpapers, glassine d/w) £500/£400
The Fifth Column: A Play in Three Acts, Scribner's (New
York), 1940 . . . . . . £1,500/£175
ditto, Penguin (Harmondsworth, Middlesex), 1966 (pbk) £5
ditto, Cape (London), 1968 . . . . . £15/£5
Voyage to Victory, Crowell-Collier (New York), 1944
(wraps with d/w) . . . . . . £45/£20
The Essential Hemingway, Cape (London), 1947 . £25/£5
The Hemingway Reader, Scribner's (New York), 1953 .
. . . . £25/£5
The Collected Poems, Library of Living Poets [Paris],
[c.1955] (pirated; stapled wraps) £50
ditto, Haskell House (New York), 1970 . . £25/£10
Hemingway: The Wild Years, Dell (New York), 1962 (pbk)
. . . . £5
A Moveable Feast, Scribner's (New York), 1964 . £65/£20
ditto, Cape (London), 1964 . . . . . £75/£20
By-Line, Scribner's (New York), 1967 . . £65/£15
ditto, Collins (London), 1968 . . . . £45/£15
*Ernest Hemingway, Cub Reporter: Kansas City Star
Stories*, Univ of Pittsburgh Press (Pittsburgh, PA), 1970
(edited by Matthew J. Bruccoli) . . . . £20/£5
ditto, Univ of Pittsburgh Press (Pittsburgh, PA), 1970 (2000
numbered copies signed by the editor) . . £40/£20
*Ernest Hemingway's Apprenticeship: Oak Park, 1916-
1917*, Microcard (Washington, DC), 1971 . £20/£5
ditto, Microcard (Washington, DC), 1971 (200 copies). .
. . . . £40/£20

Bastard Sheet Note for A Farewell to Arms, House of
Books (New York), 1971 (93 copies, single sheet) . £250
Eighty-Eight Poems, Harcourt Brace (New York), 1980 .
. . . . £25/£10
Selected Letters, 1917-1961, Scribner's (New York), 1981
(edited by Carlos Barker) . . . . . £25/£10
ditto, Scribner's (New York), 1981 (500 copies signed by
editor, glassine d/w, slipcase) . . . . £75/£50
ditto, Granada (London), 1981 . . . . £25/£10
Ernest Hemingway on Writing, Scribner's (New York),
1984 . . . . £20/£5
ditto, Granada (London), 1985 . . . . £15/£5
The Dangerous Summer, Scribner's (New York), 1985 .
. . . . £20/£5
ditto, Hamish Hamilton (London), 1985 . . . £20/£5
Marlin, Big Fish Books (San Francisco, CA), 1992 (1,000
copies, introduction by Gabriel García Márquez). £50/£15

G.A. HENTY
(b.1832 d.1902)

Henty was a popular 19th-century author of patriotic stories
for boys. He had been one of the earliest newspaper war
correspondents, covering the Austro-Italian, Franco-
Prussian and Turko-Serbian Wars in the 1860s, travelling
in Abyssinia and Russia, and witnessing the opening of the
Suez Canal. When his health declined, he turned to
literature.

A Search for a Secret, Tinsley Brothers (London), 1867 (3
vols, blue or green cloth) £2,000
The March to Magdala, Tinsley Brothers (London), 1868
(blue cloth) £2,000
All But Lost, Tinsley Brothers (London), 1869 (3 vols, blue
cloth) £2,000
Out on the Pampas, or The Young Settlers, Griffith &
Farran (London), 1871 [1870] (blue or brown cloth) £1,000
The Young Franc-Tireurs, Griffith & Farran (London),
1872 [1871] (blue, red or green cloth) . . . £1,000
The March to Coomassie, Tinsley Brothers (London), 1874
(blue cloth) £1,000
The Young Buglars, Griffith & Farran (London), 1880
[1879] (adverts dated 1879, red or green cloth) . . £600
Seaside Maidens, Tinsley Brothers (London), 1880 (orange
cloth) £700
The Cornet of Horse, Sampson Low & Marston (London),
1881 (adverts dated January 1881, red cloth) . . £600
In Times of Peril, Griffith & Farran (London), 1881 (adverts
dated October 1881, red or blue cloth) . . . £750
Facing Death, Blackie (London), [1882] (blue or brown
cloth) £600
Winning His Spurs, Sampson Low & Marston (London),
1882 (red cloth) £350
Friends Though Divided, Griffith & Farran (London), 1883
(adverts dated September 1883, red, blue, brown or green
cloth) £400
Jack Archer, Sampson Low & Marston (London), 1883 (red
cloth) £400
ditto, Roberts Bros (Boston), 1884 . . . . £350
ditto, as *The Fall of Sebastopol*, Brown (Boston), 1892 £150
Under Drake's Flag, Blackie (London), 1883 [1882] (green
or brown cloth) £200

ditto, as **Cast Ashore**, Blackie (London), 1906 . . £45

By Sheer Pluck, Blackie (London), 1884 [1883] (adverts dated 'New Series for 1885', red cloth) £300

With Clive in India, Blackie (London), 1884 [1883] (red, brown or blue cloth) £200

ditto, as **The Young Captain**, Blackie (London), 1906 . £50

ditto, as **Charlie Marryat**, Blackie (London), 1906. . £50

The Young Colonists, Routledge (London), 1885 [1884] (blue and gold cloth) £200

True to the Old Flag, Blackie (London), 1885 [1884] (blue, grey, red or green cloth) £200

In Freedom's Cause, Blackie (London), 1885 [1884] (blue, brown or red cloth) £100

ditto, as **A Highland Chief**, Blackie (London), 1906 . £50

St. George For England, Blackie (London), 1885 [1884] (brown, blue or green cloth) £100

The Lion of the North, Blackie (London), 1886 [1885] (brown or green cloth) £175

The Dragon and the Raven, Blackie (London), 1886 [1885] (brown or green cloth) £175

For Name and Fame, Blackie (London), 1886 [1885] (brown or grey cloth) £200

Through the Fray, Blackie (London), 1886 [1885] (brown or red cloth) £150

Yarns on the Beach, Blackie (London), 1886 [1885] (brown or red cloth) £350

The Young Carthaginian, Blackie (London), 1887 [1886] (blue or green cloth) £200

The Bravest of the Brave, Blackie (London), 1887 [1886] (red or blue cloth) £150

A Final Reckoning, Blackie (London), 1887 [1886] (blue or green cloth) £100

ditto, as **Among the Bushrangers**, Blackie (London), 1906 .
. . . . £50

With Wolfe in Canada, Blackie (London), 1887 [1886] (green, blue or red cloth) £200

The Sovereign Reader: Scenes from the Life and Reign of Queen Victoria, Blackie (London), [1887] (red or purple cloth) £175

In the Reign of Terror, Blackie (London), 1888 (red, blue, grey or green cloth) £150

Sturdy and Strong, Blackie (London), 1888 [1887] (red, blue or orange cloth) £150

Orange and Green, Blackie (London), 1888 [1887] (red, blue or orange cloth) £150

ditto, as **Cornet Walter**, Blackie (London), 1906 . . £65

Bonnie Prince Charlie, Blackie (London), 1888 [1887] (brown or red cloth) £125

For the Temple, Blackie (London), 1888 [1887] (brown, red or blue cloth) £200

Gabriel Allen MP, Spencer & Blackett (London), [1888] (red cloth) £250

Captain Bayley's Heir, Blackie (London), 1889 (red, brown or blue cloth) £150

The Cat of Bubastes, Blackie (London), 1889 [1888] (blue, brown, grey or green cloth) £200

The Lion of St Mark, Blackie (London), 1889 [1888] (red, blue or grey cloth) £150

The Curse of Carne's Hold, Spencer & Blackett (London), 1889 (2 vols, blue cloth) £500

The Plague Ship, S.P.C.K. 'Penny Library of Fiction' series (London), 1889 (wraps) £600

By Pike and Dyke, Blackie (London), 1890 [1889] (brown or green cloth) £125

One of the 28th, Blackie (London), 1890 [1889] (red, brown, green or blue cloth) £200

Tales of Daring and Danger, Blackie (London), 1889 [1890] (blue or green cloth) £300

With Lee in Virginia, Blackie (London), 1890 [1889] (brown or blue cloth) £150

Those Other Animals, Henry & Co. (London), [1891] (green cloth) £250

By England's Aid, Blackie (London), 1891 [1890] (blue or brown cloth) £150

By Right of Conquest, Blackie (London), 1891 [1890] (green or brown cloth) £100

Maori and Settler, Blackie (London), 1891 (brown, blue, red or green cloth) £100

A Chapter of Adventures, Blackie (London), 1891 [1890] (blue or grey cloth) £200

A Hidden Foe, Sampson Low & Marston (London), [1891] (2 vols, grey cloth) £2,000

The Dash for Khartoum, Scribner's (New York), 1891 £100

ditto, Blackie (London), 1892 [1891] (brown, red, grey or green cloth) £100

Held Fast for England, Scribner's (New York), 1891 .£100

ditto, Blackie (London), 1892 [1891] (red, grey or brown cloth) £100

Redskin and Cowboy, Scribner's (New York), 1891 .£100

ditto, Blackie (London), 1892 [1891] (red, green or brown cloth) £100

ditto, as **An Indian Raid**, Blackie (London), 1906 . . £50

Beric the Briton, Scribner's (New York), 1891 . .£150

ditto, Blackie (London), 1893 [1892] (blue or brown cloth) .
. . . .£150

The Ranch in the Valley, S.P.C.K. 'Penny Library of Fiction' series (London), 1892 (wraps) £500

Condemned as Nihilist, Scribner's (New York), 1892 .£150

ditto, Blackie (London), 1893 [1892] (brown or blue cloth) .
. . . .£150

In Greek Waters, Scribner's (New York), 1892 . .£100

ditto, Blackie (London), 1893 [1892] (grey, brown or green cloth) £100

Tales from the Works of G.A. Henty, Blackie (London), 1893 (red cloth) £100

Rujub the Juggler, Chatto & Windus (London), 1893 (3 vols, blue cloth) £750

A Jacobite Exile, Scribner's (New York), 1893 . .£200

ditto, Blackie (London), 1894 [1893] (brown, green, grey or blue cloth) £200

Through the Sikh War, Scribner's (New York), 1893 .£100

ditto, Blackie (London), 1894 [1893] (green cloth). .£100

St Bartholomew's Eve, Scribner's (New York), 1893 .£100

ditto, Blackie (London), 1894 [1893] (green, blue or red cloth) £100

A Tale of Waterloo, Worthington (New York), 1894 (tan cloth) £200

Dorothy's Double, Chatto & Windus (London), 1894 (3 vols, blue cloth) £750

When London Burned, Scribner's (New York), 1894 .£200

ditto, Blackie (London), 1895 [1894] (blue cloth) . .£200

Wulf the Saxon, Scribner's (New York), 1894 . . £75

ditto, Blackie (London), 1895 [1894] (green cloth). . £75

In the Heart of the Rockies, Scribner's (New York), 1894 .
. . . .£100

ditto, Blackie (London), 1895 [1894] (grey cloth) . .£100

Cuthbert Hartington and A Woman of the Commune, F.V. White (London), 1895 (red cloth) £200

A Knight of the White Cross, Scribner's (New York), 1895 . £150

ditto, Blackie (London), 1896 [1895] (green cloth). . £150

Through Russian Snows, Scribner's (New York), 1895 £100

ditto, Blackie (London), 1896 [1895] (grey cloth) . . £100

The Tiger of Mysore, Scribner's (New York), 1895 . £100

ditto, Blackie (London), 1896 [1895] (blue cloth) . . £100

Bears and Dacoits, Blackie (London), [1896] (green-brown cloth with five children among flowered vine design on front) . . £300

Surly Joe, Blackie (London), [1896] (wraps) . . £200

White-Faced Dick, Blackie (London), [1896] (limp orange cloth cover) . . £200

On the Irrawaddy, Scribner's (New York), 1896 . £150

ditto, Blackie (London), 1897 [1896] (blue cloth) . £150

At Agincourt, Scribner's (New York), 1896 . . £150

ditto, Blackie (London), 1897 (grey cloth) . . £150

With Cochrane the Dauntless, Scribner's (New York), 1896 . £100

ditto, Blackie (London), 1897 (blue cloth) . £100

The Queen's Cup, Chatto & Windus (London), 1897 (three vols, green or blue cloth) . . £600

Among Malay Pirates, Hurst & Co. (New York), [1897] . £150

With Moore at Corunna, Scribner's (New York), 1897 £100

ditto, Blackie (London), 1898 [1897] (green or blue cloth) . £100

With Frederick the Great, Scribner's (New York), 1897 £100

ditto, Blackie (London), 1898 [1897] (32pps of adverts headed 'Books for Young People' or 'Illustrated Story Books', red cloth) . £100

Colonel Thorndyke's Secret, Chatto & Windus (London), 1898 (pink cloth). . £150

Under Wellington's Command, Scribner's (New York), 1898 . £100

ditto, Blackie (London), 1899 [1898] (blue cloth) . . £100

At Aboukir and Acre, Scribner's (New York), 1898 . £100

ditto, Blackie (London), 1899 [1898] (red cloth) . . £100

Both Sides the Border, Scribner's (New York), 1898 . £75

ditto, Blackie (London), 1899 [1898] (blue cloth) . £75

The Lost Heir, James Bowden (London), 1899 (green cloth) . £150

The Golden Canon, Mershon (New York), 1899 (light brown cloth). . £150

On the Spanish Main, Chambers (London), [1899] (red wraps) . £100

At Duty's Call, Chambers (London), [1899] . . £75

A Roving Commission, Scribner's (New York), 1899 . £100

ditto, Blackie (London), 1900 [1899] (red cloth) . . £100

Won by the Sword, Scribner's (New York), 1899 . £75

ditto, Blackie (London), 1900 [1899] (blue cloth) . £75

No Surrender!, Scribner's (New York), 1899 . . £100

ditto, Blackie (London), 1900 [1899] (red cloth) . . £100

Do Your Duty, Blackie (London), [1900] (blue or green cloth) . £150

With Buller in Natal, Scribner's (New York), 1900 . £65

ditto, Blackie (London), 1901 (blue cloth) . . £65

In the Hands of the Cave Dwellers, Harper (New York), 1900 . £150

ditto, Blackie (London), 1903 [1902]. . £150

In the Irish Brigade, Scribner's (New York), 1900 . £100

ditto, Blackie (London), 1901 [1900] (green cloth). . £100

Out With Garibaldi, Scribner's (New York), 1900. . £65

ditto, Blackie (London), 1901 [1900] (blue cloth) . . £65

The Soul Survivors, Chambers (London), [1901] (red wraps) . £100

John Hawke's Fortune, Chapman & Hall: Young People's Library series (London), 1901 (paper cover). . £65

Queen Victoria, Blackie (London), 1901 (purple cloth). £50

To Herat and Cabul, Scribner's (New York), 1901 . £65

ditto, Blackie (London), 1902 [1901] (blue cloth) . . £65

With Roberts in Pretoria, Scribner's (New York), 1901 £150

ditto, Blackie (London), 1902 [1901] (red cloth) . . £150

At the Point of the Bayonet, Scribner's (New York), 1901 . £65

ditto, Blackie (London), 1902 [1901] (green cloth). . £65

At Duty's Call, Chambers (London), [1902] (red wraps or cloth) . £75

The Treasure of the Incas, Scribner's (New York), 1902 £75

ditto, Blackie (London), 1903 [1902] (green cloth). . £75

With the British Legion, Scribner's (New York), 1902. £75

ditto, Blackie (London), 1903 [1902] (blue or green cloth) . £75

With Kitchener in the Soudan, Scribner's (New York), 1902 . £65

ditto, Blackie (London), 1903 [1902] (red cloth) . . £65

Through Three Campaigns, Scribner's (New York), 1903 . £65

ditto, Blackie (London), 1904 [1903] (red cloth) . . £65

With the Allies to Pekin, Scribner's (New York), 1903. £65

ditto, Blackie (London), 1904 [1903] (green cloth). . £65

By Conduct and Courage, Scribner's (New York), 1904 £100

ditto, Blackie (London), 1905 [1904] (red cloth) . . £100

Gallant Deeds, Chambers (London), 1905 (white or grey cloth) . £65

In the Hands of the Malays, Blackie (London), 1905 (red boards) . £65

A Soldier's Daughter, Blackie (London), 1906 [1905] (red, blue or green boards) . £65

ditto, as *The Two Prisoners*, Blackie (London), 1906 [1905] . £45

FRANK HERBERT
(b.1920 d.1986)

Frank Herbert worked as a reporter and editor before becoming a full-time writer. His first story was published in 1952, but another ten years passed before he achieved fame with *Analog* of 'Dune World' and 'The Prophet of Dune'. These were amalgamated in the novel *Dune* in 1965, and five further 'Dune' novels followed.

'Dune' Chronicles

Dune, Chilton (Philadelphia, PA), 1965 (first edition has no ISBN or number line on title-page; first issue d/w has four lines of publisher's information on rear flap) £3,500/£500

ditto, Chilton (Philadelphia, PA), 1965 (second issue d/w, two lines of publisher's information on rear flap) . £2,000/£500

ditto, Gollancz (London), 1966 . . . . £750/£75

Dune Messiah, Putnam (New York), 1969 . £250/£25

ditto, Gollancz (London), 1971 . . . . £125/£20

Children of Dune, Berkeley (New York), 1976 . £65/£10

ditto, Gollancz (London), 1976 . . . . £30/£10

God Emperor of Dune, Putnam (New York), 1981 £20/£5

ditto, Gollancz (London), 1981 . . . . £15/£5

Heretics of Dune, Putnam (New York), 1984 . . £10/£5
ditto, Gollancz (London), 1984 . . . . £10/£5
Chapterhouse: Dune, Putnam (New York), 1985 . £10/£5
ditto, as *Chapter House: Dune*, Gollancz (London), 1985 .
    .   .   .   .   £10/£5

'Ship' Series
Destination: Void, Berkeley (New York), 1966 (pbk) . £10
ditto, Penguin (Harmondsworth, Middlesex), 1967 (pbk) £5
The Jesus Incident, Putnam (New York), 1979 (with Bill
   Ransom) . . . . £15/£5
ditto, Gollancz (London), 1979 . . . . £15/£5
The Lazarus Effect, Putnam (New York), 1983 (with Bill
   Ransom) . . . . £10/£5
ditto, Gollancz (London), 1983 . . . . £10/£5
The Ascension Factor, Ace/Penguin Putnam (New York),
   1988 (with Bill Ransom) . . . . £10/£5
ditto, Gollancz (London), 1988 . . . . £10/£5

Other Novels
The Dragon in the Sea, Doubleday (New York), 1956 . .
   . . . . £150/£25
ditto, Gollancz (London), 1960 . . . . £75/£15
ditto, as *21st Century Sub*, Avon (New York), [1956] (pbk)
   . . . . £5
ditto, as *Under Pressure*, Ballantine (New York), 1974 (pbk)
   . . . . £5
The Eyes of Heisenberg, Berkeley (New York), 1966 (pbk)
   . . . . £5
ditto, Sphere (London), 1968 (pbk) £5
The Green Brain, Ace (New York), [1966] (pbk) . . £5
ditto, New English Library (London), 1973 (pbk) . . £5
The Santaroga Barrier, Berkeley (New York), 1968 (pbk) £5
ditto, Rapp & Whiting (London), 1970 . . . £25/£5
The Heaven Makers, Avon (New York), [1968] (pbk) . £5
ditto, New English Library (London), 1973 (pbk) . . £5
Whipping Star, Putnam (New York), [1970] . . £30/£5
ditto, New English Library (London), 1972 . . £5
Soul Catcher, Putnam (New York), [1972] . . £25/£5
ditto, New English Library (London), 1972 . . £25/£5
The God Makers, Putnam (New York), [1972] . . £25/£5
ditto, New English Library (London), 1972 . . £25/£5
Hellstrom's Hive, Doubleday (New York), 1973 . £20/£5
ditto, New English Library (London), 1974 . . £20/£5
The Dosadi Experiment, Putnam (New York), [1977] . .
   . . . . £15/£5
ditto, Gollancz (London), 1978 . . . . £15/£5
Direct Descent, Ace (New York), 1980 (pbk) . . £5
The White Plague, Putnam (New York), 1982 . £10/£5
ditto, Putnam (New York), 1982 (500 signed, numbered
   copies) . . . . £40/£15
ditto, Gollancz (London), 1983 . . . . £10/£5
Man of Two Worlds, Putnam (New York), 1986 (with Brian
   Herbert). . . . . £10/£5
ditto, Gollancz (London), 1986 . . . . £10/£5

Collected Short Works
The Worlds of Frank Herbert, New English Library
   (London), 1970 (pbk). £5
ditto, Ace (New York), 1971 (pbk) £5
The Book of Frank Herbert, Daw (New York), 1973 (pbk)
   . . . . £5
The Best of Frank Herbert, Sidgwick & Jackson (London),
   1975 . . . . £20/£5

The Priests of Psi, Gollancz (London), 1980 . . £15/£5
Eye, Berkeley (New York), 1985 (pbk) . . . £5

Poetry
Songs of Muad'dib: The Poetry of Frank Herbert, Ace
   (New York), 1992 (pbk) £5

Non-Fiction
New World or No World, Ace (New York), 1970 (pbk) £5
Threshold: The Blue Angels Experience, Ballantine (New
   York), 1973 . . . . £5
*Without Me, You're Nothing: An Essential Guide to Home
   Computers*, Simon & Schuster (New York), 1980 (with
   Max Barnard) . . . . . . £10/£5
The Maker of Dune, Berkeley (New York), 1987 (edited by
   Timothy O'Reilly; pbk) £5
The Notebooks of Frank Herbert's Dune, Pedigree/Putnam
   (New York), 1988 (edited by Brian Herbert). . £10/£5

JAMES HERBERT
(b.1943)

James Herbert worked as a singer and as the art director of
an advertising agency before turning to writing sensational
horror novels. He is often claimed as the British Stephen
King: while Herbert may not have King's world-wide sales,
his books sell as well as King's in the United Kingdom.

'Rats' Novels
The Rats, New English Library (London), 1974 . £400/£50
ditto, as *Deadly Eyes*, Signet (New York), 1975 (pbk) . £5
ditto, as *The Rats*, New English Library (London), 1985
   (limited edition, limitation unknown) . . £35/£10
Lair, New English Library (London), 1979 . £200/£50
ditto, Signet (New York), 1979 (pbk). . . . £5
ditto, New English Library (London), 1985 (limited edition,
   limitation unknown) . . . . . £100/£25
Domain, New English Library (London), 1984 . £30/£5
ditto, Signet (New York), 1985 (pbk). . . . £5
The City, Pan Macmillan (London), 1994 (pbk) . . £5
ditto, Pan Macmillan (London), 1994 (1,000 copies, signed
   by author and artist in silver, some with flyer) . . £25

Other Novels
The Fog, New English Library (London), 1975 . £150/£45
ditto, Signet (New York), 1975 (pbk). . . . £5
ditto, New English Library (London), 1988 (3,000 copies) .
   . . . . £30/£10
The Survivor, New English Library (London), 1976 £75/£20
ditto, Signet (New York), 1977 (pbk). . . . £5
ditto, New English Library (London), 1988 (2,000 copies) .
   . . . . £30/£10
Fluke, New English Library (London), 1977 . . £65/£15
ditto, Signet (New York), 1978 (pbk). . . . £5
The Spear, New English Library (London), 1978 . £25/£5
ditto, Signet (New York), 1980 (pbk). . . . £5
The Dark, New English Library (London), 1980 . £30/£10
ditto, Signet (New York), 1980 (pbk). . . . £5
ditto, New English Library (London), 1988 (2,000 copies) .
   . . . . £30/£10
The Jonah, New English Library (London), 1981 . £25/£5
ditto, Signet (New York), 1981 (pbk). . . . £5

ditto, New English Library (London), 1985 (limited edition, limitation unknown) . . . . . £25/£5
Shrine, New English Library (London), 1983 . £25/£5
ditto, Signet (New York), 1985 (pbk). £5
Moon, New English Library (London), 1985 . . £20/£5
ditto, Crown (New York), 1985 . . . . . £15/£5
The Magic Cottage, Hodder & Stoughton (London), 1986 . . . . £15/£5
ditto, New American Library (New York), 1987 £15/£5
Sepulchre, Hodder & Stoughton (London), 1987 . £15/£5
ditto, Putnam's (New York), 1988 . . . . £15/£5
Haunted, Hodder & Stoughton (London), 1988 . £15/£5
ditto, Hodder & Stoughton (London), 1988 (250 signed copies, slip-case, no d/w) . . . . . £65/£40
ditto, Putnam's (New York), 1989 . . . . £15/£5
Creed, Hodder & Stoughton (London), 1990 . . £15/£5
Portent, Hodder & Stoughton (London), 1992 . £15/£5
ditto, Hodder & Stoughton (London), 1992 (pre-publication issue, with d/w) . . . . . £35/£10
ditto, Harper Prism (New York), 1996 . . . £15/£5
The Ghosts of Sleath, Harper Collins (London), 1994 (unedited typescript; plastic spiral binding, 500 signed, numbered copies) . . . . . £40/£20
ditto, Harper Collins (London), 1994 . . . . £15/£5
ditto, Harper Prism (New York), 1996 . . . £15/£5
'48, Harper Collins (London), 1996 . . . . £15/£5
ditto, Harper Prism (New York), 1996 . . . £15/£5
Others, Macmillan (London), 1999 . . . . £15/£5
ditto, Forge (New York), 1999 . . . . . £10/£5
Once..., Macmillan (London), 2001 . . . . £10/£5
ditto, Tor (New York), 2002 . . . . . £10/£5
Nobody True, Macmillan (London), 2003 . . £10/£5
ditto, Tor (New York), 2005 . . . . . £10/£5
The Secret of Crickley Hall, Macmillan (London), 2006 . . . . £10/£5
ditto, Macmillan (London), 2006 (1,000 signed, numbered copies; slipcase) . . . . . . £45/£30

Others
James Herbert's Dark Places, Harper Collins (London), 1983 . . . . £35/£10

HERGÉ
(b.1907 d.1983)

Hergé was the pseudonym of the Belgian cartoonist Georges Remi. The first Tintin books were published in black and white, and none were issued with d/ws. The twenty-fourth Tintin adventure, *Tintin and Alph-Art*, is unfinished. Although very much escapist fantasies, the Tintin adventures have always been highly researched and abound in contemporary cultural and political references.

'Tintin' Books
Tintin au Pays de Soviets, Petit Vingtième (Brussels), 1930 . . . . £100
ditto, as ***Tintin in the Land of the Soviets***, Sundancer (London), 1989 . . . . £15
Tintin au Congo, Petit Vingtième (Brussels), 1931 . £75
ditto, as ***Tintin in the Congo***, Casterman (Paris/Tournai), 1982 . . . . £20
ditto, as ***Tintin in the Congo***, Sundancer (London), 1991 £15

Tintin en Amerique, Petit Vingtième (Brussels), 1932 . £65
ditto, as ***Tintin in America***, Methuen (London), 1978 . £20
ditto, as ***Tintin in America***, Little, Brown (Boston), 1979 . . . . £20
Les Cigares du Pharaon, Casterman (Paris/Tournai), 1934 . . . . £60
ditto, as ***Cigars of the Pharoah***, Methuen (London), 1971 . . . . £20
ditto, as ***Cigars of the Pharoah***, Little, Brown (Boston), 1975 . . . . £20
Le Lotus Bleu, Casterman (Paris/Tournai), 1935 . . £60
ditto, as ***The Blue Lotus***, Methuen (London), 1983 . £15
ditto, as ***The Blue Lotus***, Little, Brown (Boston), 1984 . £15
L'Oreille Cassée, Casterman (Paris/Tournai), 1937 . £60
ditto, as ***The Broken Ear***, Methuen (London), 1975 . £20
ditto, as ***The Broken Ear***, Little, Brown (Boston), 1978 £20
L'Isle Noire, Casterman (Paris/Tournai), 1938 . . £60
ditto, as ***The Black Island***, Methuen (London), 1966 . £30
ditto, as ***The Black Island***, Little, Brown (Boston), 1975 £25
Le Sceptre d'Ottokar, Casterman (Paris/Tournai), 1939 £60
ditto, as ***King Ottokar's Sceptre***, Methuen (London), 1958 . . . . £45
ditto, as ***King Ottokar's Sceptre***, Golden Press (New York), 1959 . . . . £45
Le Crabe aux Pinces d'Or, Casterman (Paris/Tournai), 1942 . . . . £50
ditto, as ***The Crab with the Golden Claws***, Methuen (London), 1958 . . . . £45
ditto, as ***The Crab with the Golden Claws***, Golden Press (New York), 1959 . . . . . . £45
L'Etoile Mystérieuse, Casterman (Paris/Tournai), 1943 £50
ditto, as ***The Shooting Star***, Methuen (London), 1961 . £30
Le Secret de la Licorne, Casterman (Paris/Tournai), 1943 . . . . £50
ditto, as ***The Secret of the Unicorn***, Casterman (Paris/Tournai), 1952 . . . . £40
ditto, as ***The Secret of the Unicorn***, Methuen (London), 1959 . . . . £40
ditto, as ***The Secret of the Unicorn***, Golden Press (New York), 1959 . . . . £40
Le Trésor de Rackham le Rouge, Casterman (Paris/Tournai), 1944 . . . . £50
ditto, as ***Red Rackham's Treasure***, Casterman (Paris/Tournai), 1952 . . . . £40
ditto, as ***Red Rackham's Treasure***, Methuen (London), 1959 . . . . £35
ditto, as ***Red Rackham's Treasure***, Golden Press (New York), 1959 . . . . £35
Les Sept Boules de Cristal, Casterman (Paris/Tournai), 1948 . . . . £50
ditto, as ***The Seven Crystal Balls***, Methuen (London), 1962 . . . . £25
ditto, as ***The Seven Crystal Balls***, Little, Brown (Boston), 1975 . . . . £25
Le Temple du Soleil, Casterman (Paris/Tournai), 1949 . £50
ditto, as ***Prisoners of the Sun***, Methuen (London), 1962 £25
ditto, as ***Prisoners of the Sun***, Little, Brown (Boston), 1975 . . . . £25
Tintin au Pays de l'Or Noir, Casterman (Paris/Tournai), 1950 . . . . £45
ditto, as ***The Land of Black Gold***, Methuen (London), 1972 . . . . £20
ditto, as ***The Land of Black Gold***, Little, Brown (Boston), 1975 . . . . £20

Objectif Lune, Casterman (Paris/Tournai), 1953 . . £45
ditto, as **Destination Moon**, Methuen (London), 1959 . £40
ditto, as **Destination Moon**, Golden Press (New York), 1960
. . . . £40
On A Marché sur la Lune, Casterman (Paris/Tournai), 1954
. . . . £45
ditto, as **Explorers on the Moon**, Methuen (London), 1959 .
ditto, as **Explorers on the Moon**, Golden Press (New York),
1960 . . . . £40
L'Affair Tournesol, Casterman (Paris/Tournai), 1954 . £45
ditto, as **The Calculus Affair**, Methuen (London), 1960 £30
ditto, as **The Calculus Affair**, Little, Brown (Boston), 1976
. . . . £30
Coke en Stock, Casterman (Paris/Tournai), 1958 . . £45
ditto, as **The Red Sea Sharks**, Methuen (London), 1960 £30
ditto, as **The Red Sea Sharks**, Little, Brown (Boston), 1976
. . . . £25
Tintin au Tibet, Casterman (Paris/Tournai), 1960 . . £40
ditto, as **Tintin in Tibet**, Methuen (London), 1962 . . £25
ditto, as **Tintin in Tibet**, Little, Brown (Boston), 1975 . £20
Les Bijoux de la Castafiore, Casterman (Paris/Tournai),
1963 . . . . £40
ditto, as **The Castafiore Emerald**, Methuen (London), 1963
. . . . £25
ditto, as **The Castafiore Emerald**, Little, Brown (Boston),
1975 . . . . £20
Vol 714 pour Sydney, Casterman (Paris/Tournai), 1968 £35
ditto, as **Flight 714**, Methuen (London), 1968 . . . £20
ditto, as **Flight 714**, Little, Brown (Boston), 1975 . £20
Tintin et les Picaros, Casterman (Paris/Tournai), 1976 . £30
ditto, as **Tintin and the Picaros**, Methuen (London), 1976 .
. . . . £10
ditto, as **Tintin and the Picaros**, Little, Brown (Boston),
1978 . . . . £10
Tintin et l'Alph-Art, Casterman (Paris/Tournai), 1986 . £20
ditto, as **Tintin and Alph-Art**, Sundancer (London), 1990 £10

'Tintin' Film Books (not by Hergé)
Tintin et le Mystère de la Toison d'Or, Casterman
(Paris/Tournai), 1962 . . . . £35
ditto, as **Tintin and the Golden Fleece**, Methuen (London),
1965 . . . . £30
Tintin et les Oranges Blues, Casterman (Paris/Tournai),
1965 . . . . £35
ditto, as **Tintin and the Blue Oranges**, Methuen (London),
1967 . . . . £25
Tintin et le Lac aux Requins, Casterman (Paris/Tournai),
1973 . . . . £35
ditto, as **Tintin and the Lake of Sharks**, Methuen (London),
1973 . . . . £25
ditto, as **Tintin and the Lake of Sharks**, Little, Brown
(Boston), 1989 . . . . £15

'Making of Tintin' books
The Making of Tintin, Methuen (London), 1983 . . £15
The Making of Tintin II, Methuen (London), 1985 . £15
The Making of Tintin: Mission to the Moon, Methuen
(London), 1989 . . . . £10
*The Making of Tintin: Cigars of the Pharoah/The Blue
Lotus*, Methuen (London), 1995 . . . . £10

'Jo, Zette and Jocko' Books
The Valley of the Cobras, Methuen (London), 1986 . £10

The Stratoship H22. Part One: Mr Pump's Legacy,
Methuen (London), 1987 . . . . . £10
The Stratoship H22. Part Two: Destination New York,
Methuen (London), 1987 . . . . . £10
The Secret Ray, Sundancer (London), 1994 . . . £10

Others
Popol Out West, Methuen (London), 1969 . . . £20
Double Trouble, Mammoth, 1992 (pbk) £5
Two of a Kind, Mammoth, 1992 (pbk) £5

EDWARD HERON-ALLEN
(b.1861 d.1943)

A British scientist and polymath whose writings ranged
from the hard sciences to the occult. He wrote several
works of weird fiction under the pseudonym 'Christopher
Blayre' which are highly sought after by collectors. His
most controversial tale, *The Cheetah-Girl*, is an entertaining
attempt to include as many taboo subjects into one short
story as possible.

Novels
The Princess Daphne, Belford, Clarke & Co. (Chicago),
1888 (with Selina Dolaro). £400
ditto, H.J. Drane (London), 1889 . . . . £250
ditto, Tartarus Press (Carlton-in-Coverdale, Yorkshire), 2001
(300 [150] numbered copies) . . . . £75/£25
The Romance of a Quiet Watering-Place, Belford, Clarke &
Co. (Chicago), 1888 (pseud 'Nora Helen Warddel') . £150
Bella Demonia, Belford, Clarke & Co. (Chicago), [c.1889]
(ghost-written for Selina Dolaro) . . . £125
The Vengeance of Maurice Denalguez, Belford, Clarke & Co.
(Chicago), [c.1889] (ghost written for Selina Dolaro). £125

Short Stories
Kisses of Fate. A Study of Mere Human Nature, Belford,
Clarke & Co. (Chicago), 1888 . . . . £145
A Fatal Fiddle: The Commonplace Tragedy of a Snob,
Belford, Clarke & Co. (Chicago), 1889 . . . £200
The Purple Sapphire and other Posthumous Papers, Allan
(London), 1921 (pseud 'Christopher Blayre', grey paper
boards) £250
ditto, Allan (London), 1921 (10 numbered presentation
copies, grey paper boards). £500
ditto, Allan (London), 1921 (second issue, boards with
purple cloth, gilt lettering). . . . . £250/£100
ditto, Allan (London), 1921 (later issue, purple/grey cloth
with black lettering) . . . . . . £250/£85
ditto, as **The Strange Papers of Dr Blayre**, Allan (London),
1932 . . . . £200/£65
ditto, as **The Strange Papers of Dr Blayre**, Arno Press (New
York), 1976 . . . . £35
The Cheetah-Girl, privately printed (London), 1923 (pseud
'Christopher Blayre', 20 signed copies). . . £1,750
ditto, Tartarus Press (Horam, East Sussex), 1998 (99
numbered copies) . . . . . . £150/£100
Some Women of the University, Sorelle Nessuno, Nubiana
[Stockwell, (London)], 1934 (pseud 'Christopher Blayre',
100 numbered copies). £600
The Collected Strange Papers of Christopher Blayre,
Tartarus Press (Horam, East Sussex), 1998 . . £75/£25

Palmistry

Chiromancy, Or the Science of Palmistry, Routledge &
Sons (London), 1883 . . . . £50
A Manual of Cheirosophy, Ward, Lock & Co. (London),
1885 . . . . £35
*Practical Cheirosophy: A Synoptical Study of the Science
of the Hand, etc.*, G.P. Putnam's & Sons (New York),
1887 . . . . £35

Poetry

The Love-Letters of a Vagabond, H.J. Drane (London),
1889 [1889] £250

Translations and Commentaries

The Ruba'iyat of Omar Khayyam, H.S. Nichols (London),
1898 (1022 copies) £100
*Some Side-lights upon Edward FitzGerald's poem 'The
Ruba'iyat of Omar Khayyam'*, Nichols (London), 1898
(wraps) £45
*The Lament of Baba Tahir: being the Ruba'iyat of Baba
Tahir*, Bernard Quaritch (London), 1902 . . . £45
ditto, Octagon Press (London), 1979 . . . £10/£5

The Violin

Violin-Making, As It Was and Is, Ward, Lock & Co.
(London), 1884 . . . . £200
ditto, Ward, Lock & Co. (London), [1885] . . £65
ditto, Ward, Lock & Co. (London), 1886 (deluxe edition of
25 copies for private circulation) £500

Scientific Titles

*The Foraminifera of the Clare Island District, Co. Mayo,
Ireland*, Clare Island Survey (Dublin), 1913. . . £100
*The Fossil Foraminifera of the Blue Marl of the Côte des
Basques, Biarritz*, Manchester, 1919 . . . £125
Barnacles in Nature and in Myth, Humphrey
Milford/O.U.P. (London), 1928 . . . . £125/£40

Local History

Selsey Bill: Historic and Prehistoric, Duckworth (London),
1911 (2 vols) £250
Journal of the Great War, Phillimore (Chichester, West
Sussex), 2002 . . . . £25/£10

Sette of Odd Volumes titles

*Codex Chiromantiae, Being a compleate Manualle of ye
Science and Arte of Espoundage ye Past, ye Presente, etc*,
Sette of Odd Volumes (London), 1883 (133 copies; wraps)
. . . . £100
*The Ballades of a Blasé Man. To which are added some
Rondeaux of his Rejuvenescence, laboriously constructed
by the Necromancer to the Sette of Odd Volumes*, Sette of
Odd Volumes (London), 1891 (99 copies; wraps) . £100
*Memoranda of Memorabilia, from the Correspondence of
Marquise de Sévigné etc*, Sette of Odd Volumes (London),
1928 (133 signed, numbered copies; parchment over thin
boards) £100
*The Gods of the Fourth World, being Prolegomena towards
a discourse upon the Buddhist Religion and its acquired
Pantheon*, Sette of Odd Volumes (London), 1931 (155
signed, numbered copies; wraps) £100

HERMANN HESSE
(b.1877 d.1962)

One of the greatest literary figures of the German-speaking
world, Hesse's interests in existential, spiritual and
mystical themes, and especially Buddhist and Hindu
philosophy, permeate his fiction. The Nazis banned his
books, and he was awarded the Nobel Prize for Literature
in 1946.

Novels

Peter Camenzind, Fischer (Berlin), 1904 . . . . £300
ditto, Peter Owen/Vision Press (London), 1961 (translated by
W.J. Strachan) . . . . £50/£10
ditto, Farrar Straus & Giroux (New York), 1969 (translated
by Michael Roloff) . . . . . . £50/£10
Unterm Rad, Fischer (Berlin), 1906 . . . . . £250
ditto, as *The Prodigy*, Peter Owen/Vision Press (London),
1957 (translated by W.J. Strachan) . . . £45/£10
ditto, as *Beneath the Wheel*, Farrar Straus & Giroux (New
York), 1968 (translated by Michael Roloff) . £45/£10
Gertrud, Albert Langen (Munchen), 1910 . . . £200
ditto, as *Gertrude*, Peter Owen (London), 1955 (translated by
Hilda Rosner) . . . . £35/£10
ditto, Farrar Straus & Giroux (New York), 1969 £35/£10
Roßhalde, Fischer (Berlin), 1914 . . . . . £150
ditto, as *Rosshalde*, Farrar Straus & Giroux (New York),
1970 (translated by Ralph Manheim) . . . £35/£10
ditto, Cape (London), 1971 . . . . . £35/£10
Knulp: Drei Geschichten aus dem Leben Knulps, Fischer
(Berlin), 1915 . . . . £150
ditto, as *Knulp*, Farrar Straus & Giroux (New York), 1971
(translated by Ralph Manheim) . . . . £40/£10
ditto, Cape (London), 1972 . . . . . £40/£10
Demian, Fischer (Berlin), 1919 . . . . . . £300
ditto, as *In Sight of Chaos*, Seldwyla (Zurich), 1923
(translated by Stephen Hudson, no d/w). . . £350
ditto, as *Demian*, Boni & Liveright (New York), 1923 . .
. . . . £300/£35
ditto, Peter Owen/Vision Press (London), 1960 (translated by
W.J. Strachan) . . . . £65/£20
Klingsor's Letzter Sommer, Fischer (Berlin), 1920 . .
. . . . £750/£150
ditto, as *Klingsor's Last Summer*, Farrar Straus & Giroux
(New York), 1970 (translated by Richard and Clara
Winston) . . . . £20/£5
ditto, Cape (London), 1971 . . . . . £15/£5
Siddhartha, Eine indische Dichtung, Fischer (Berlin), 1922
. . . . £750/£150
ditto, as *Siddhartha*, New Directions (Norfolk, CT), 1951
(translated by Hilda Rosner) . . . . £40/£10
ditto, Peter Owen (London), 1954 . . . . £40/£10
Der Steppenwolf, Fischer (Berlin), 1927 . . £2,500/£250
ditto, as *Steppenwolf*, Secker (London), 1929 (translated by
Basil Creighton) . . . . . . £1,500/£100
ditto, Holt (New York), 1929 . . . . £750/£75
Narziß und Goldmund, Fischer (Berlin), 1930 £1,000/£150
ditto, as *Goldmund*, Peter Owen (London), 1959 (translated
by Geoffrey Dunlop) . . . . . . £65/£10
ditto, as *Narcissus and Goldmund*, Farrar Straus & Giroux
(New York), 1968 (translated by Ursule Molinaro) £50/£10
Die Morgenlandfahrt, Fischer (Berlin), 1932 . £750/£200

ditto, as *The Journey to the East*, Peter Owen (London), 1954 (translated by Hilda Rosner) . . . £65/£15
ditto, Noonday Press (New York), 1957 . . . £45/£10
Das Glasperlenspiel, Fretz & Wasmuth (Zurich), 1943 (2 vols) . . . . £1,500/£75
ditto, as *Magister Ludi*, Holt (New York), 1949 (translated by Mervyn Savill) . . . . . £45/£10
ditto, as *The Glass Bead Game*, Holt (New York), 1969 (translated by Richard and Clara Winston) . £45/£10
ditto, Cape (London), 1970 . . . . . £40/£10

Short Stories
Strange News from Another Star, Farrar Straus & Giroux (New York), 1972 (translated by Denver Lindley) £40/£10
ditto, Cape (London), 1973 . . . . . £40/£10
Stories of Five Decades, Farrar Straus & Giroux (New York), 1975 (translated by Ralph Manheim and Denver Lindley). . . . . . . £30/£10
ditto, Cape (London), 1974 . . . . . £25/£10

Others
Poems, Farrar Straus & Giroux (New York), 1970 (translated by James Wright). . . . . . £30/£10
ditto, Cape (London), 1971 . . . . . £25/£10
If the War Goes On…, Farrar Straus & Giroux (New York), 1971 (translated by Ralph Manheim) . . . £40/£10
ditto, Cape (London), 1972 . . . . . £35/£10
Wandering, Farrar Straus & Giroux (New York), 1972 (translated by James Wright) . . . £50/£15
Autobiographical Writings, Farrar Straus & Giroux (New York), 1972 (translated by Denver Lindley) . £30/£10
ditto, Cape (London), 1973 . . . . . £30/£10
My Belief, Farrar Straus & Giroux (New York), 1974 (translated by Denver Lindley and Ralph Manheim) . .
. . . . £30/£10
ditto, Cape (London), 1976 . . . . . £30/£10
Reflections, Farrar Straus & Giroux (New York), 1974 (translated by Ralph Manheim) . . . £30/£10
ditto, Cape (London), 1972 . . . . . £35/£10
Crisis, Farrar Straus & Giroux (New York), 1975 (translated by Ralph Manheim) . . . . . £30/£10

GEORGETTE HEYER

(b.1902 d.1974)

Georgette Heyer wrote novels in many different genres including historical romance, for which she undertook a great deal of research. Some feel she ignored the bleaker realities of life in her fiction. Her crime novels, mainly country-house murder mysteries set in England between the World Wars, are perhaps the most collectable of her books.

Crime Novels
Footsteps in the Dark, Longmans Green (London), 1932 .
. . . . £600/£65
ditto, Berkeley (New York), 1986 (pbk) . . . £10
Why Shoot a Butler?, Longmans Green (London), 1933 .
. . . . £500/£60
ditto, Doubleday (New York), 1936 . . . £400/£45
The Unfinished Clue, Longmans Green (London), 1934 .
. . . . £400/£45
ditto, Doubleday (New York), 1937 . . . £350/£40

Death in the Stocks, Longmans Green (London), 1935. .
. . . . £400/£45
ditto, as *Merely Murder*, Doubleday (New York), 1935 .
. . . . £350/£40
Behold, Here's Poison, Hodder & Stoughton (London), 1936 . . . . £250/£35
ditto, Doubleday (New York), 1936 . . . £250/£35
They Found Him Dead, Hodder & Stoughton (London), 1937 . . . . £250/£35
ditto, Doubleday (New York), 1937 . . . £250/£35
A Blunt Instrument, Hodder & Stoughton (London), 1938 .
. . . . £250/£35
ditto, Doubleday (New York), 1938 . . . £250/£35
No Wind of Blame, Hodder & Stoughton (London), 1939 .
. . . . £250/£35
ditto, Doubleday (New York), 1939 . . . £250/£35
Envious Casca, Hodder & Stoughton (London), 1941 . .
. . . . £125/£20
ditto, Doubleday (New York), 1941 . . . £125/£20
Penhallow, Heinemann (London), 1942 . . . £50/£10
ditto, Doubleday (New York), 1943 . . . £35/£10
Duplicate Death, Heinemann (London), 1951 . . £50/£5
ditto, Dutton (New York), 1969 . . . . £35/£5
Detection Unlimited, Heinemann (London), 1953 . £50/£5
ditto, Dutton (New York), 1969 . . . . £35/£5

Historical Romances
The Black Moth, Constable (London), 1921 . . £300/£40
ditto, Houghton Mifflin (Boston), 1921 . . £250/£30
The Great Roxhythe, Hutchinson (London), 1922 . £400/£65
ditto, Small Maynard (Boston), 1923 . . . £250/£30
The Transformation of Philip Jettan, Mills & Boon (London), 1923 (as 'Stella Martin'). . . £125/£25
ditto, Doubleday Doran (New York), 1938 . . £75/£10
ditto, as *Powder and Patch*, Heinemann (London), 1930 (under the name Heyer) . . . . . £50/£15
Instead of the Thorn, Hutchinson (London), 1923. £125/£20
ditto, Small Maynard (Boston), 1924 . . . £125/£20
Simon the Coldheart, Heinemann (London), 1925. £125/£20
ditto, Small Maynard (Boston), 1925 . . £125/£20
These Old Shades, Heinemann (London), 1926 . £125/£20
ditto, Small Maynard (Boston), [1926] . . £125/£20
The Masqueraders, Heinemann (London), 1928 . £125/£20
ditto, Longmans Green (New York), 1929 . . £125/£20
Beauvallet, Heinemann (London), 1929 . . £125/£20
ditto, Longmans Green (New York), 1930 . . £125/£20
The Conqueror, Heinemann (London), 1931 . . £125/£20
ditto, Dutton (New York), 1966 . . . . £20/£5
Devil's Cub, Heinemann (London), 1932 . . . £75/£10
ditto, Dutton (New York), 1966 . . . . £20/£5
The Convenient Marriage, Heinemann (London), 1934 .
. . . . £75/£10
ditto, Dutton (New York), 1966 . . . . £20/£5
Regency Buck, Heinemann (London), 1935 . . £75/£10
ditto, Dutton (New York), 1966 . . . . £20/£5
The Talisman Ring, Heinemann (London), 1936 . £75/£10
ditto, Doubleday (New York), 1937 . . . £65/£10
An Infamous Army, Heinemann (London), 1937 . £75/£10
ditto, Doubleday (New York), 1938 . . . £65/£10
Royal Escape, Heinemann (London), 1938 . . £75/£10
ditto, Doubleday (New York), 1939 . . . £65/£10
The Spanish Bride, Heinemann (London), 1940 . £75/£10
ditto, Doubleday (New York), 1940 . . . £65/£10
The Corinthian, Heinemann (London), 1940 . . £75/£10

ditto, as *Beau Wyndham*, Doubleday (New York), 1941   .
.   .   .   .   £65/£10
Faro's Daughter, Heinemann (London), 1941   .   £75/£10
ditto, Doubleday (New York), 1942   .   .   .   £65/£10
Friday's Child, Heinemann (London), 1944   .   .   £50/£5
ditto, Putnam (New York), 1946   .   .   .   .   £45/£5
The Reluctant Widow, Heinemann (London), 1946   £50/£5
ditto, Putnam (New York), 1946   .   .   .   .   £45/£5
The Foundling, Heinemann (London), 1948   .   .   £35/£5
ditto, Putnam (New York), 1948   .   .   .   .   £25/£5
Arabella, Heinemann (London), 1949   .   .   .   £35/£5
ditto, Putnam (New York), 1949   .   .   .   .   £25/£5
The Grand Sophy, Heinemann (London), 1950   .   £25/£5
ditto, Putnam (New York), 1950   .   .   .   .   £25/£5
The Quiet Gentleman, Heinemann (London), 1951   £25/£5
ditto, Putnam (New York), 1951   .   .   .   .   £25/£5
Cotillion, Heinemann (London), 1953   .   .   .   £25/£5
ditto, Putnam (New York), 1953   .   .   .   .   £25/£5
The Toll-Gate, Heinemann (London), 1954   .   .   £25/£5
ditto, Putnam (New York), 1954   .   .   .   .   £20/£5
Bath Tangle, Heinemann (London), 1955   .   .   £25/£5
ditto, Putnam (New York), 1955   .   .   .   .   £20/£5
Spring Muslin, Heinemann (London), 1956   .   .   £25/£5
ditto, Putnam (New York), 1956   .   .   .   .   £20/£5
April Lady, Heinemann (London), 1957   .   .   £20/£5
ditto, Putnam (New York), 1957   .   .   .   .   £20/£5
Sylvester, Heinemann (London), 1957   .   .   .   £20/£5
ditto, Putnam (New York), 1957   .   .   .   .   £20/£5
Venetia, Heinemann (London), 1958   .   .   .   £20/£5
ditto, Putnam (New York), 1958   .   .   .   .   £20/£5
The Unknown Ajax, Heinemann (London), 1959   .   £20/£5
ditto, Putnam (New York), 1960   .   .   .   .   £20/£5
A Civil Contract, Heinemann (London), 1961   .   .   £20/£5
ditto, Putnam (New York), 1961   .   .   .   .   £20/£5
The Nonesuch, Heinemann (London), 1962   .   .   £20/£5
ditto, Putnam (New York), 1963   .   .   .   .   £20/£5
False Colours, Bodley Head (London), 1963   .   .   £20/£5
ditto, Putnam (New York), 1964   .   .   .   .   £15/£5
Frederica, Bodley Head (London), 1965   .   .   £20/£5
ditto, Putnam (New York), 1965   .   .   .   .   £15/£5
Black Sheep, Bodley Head (London), 1966   .   .   £15/£5
ditto, Putnam (New York), 1967   .   .   .   .   £15/£5
Cousin Kate, Bodley Head (London), 1968   .   .   £15/£5
ditto, Putnam (New York), 1968   .   .   .   .   £10/£5
Charity Girl, Bodley Head (London), 1970   .   .   £15/£5
ditto, Putnam (New York), 1970   .   .   .   .   £10/£5
Lady of Quality, Bodley Head (London), 1972   .   £10/£5
ditto, Putnam (New York), 1972   .   .   .   .   £10/£5
My Lord John, Bodley Head (London), 1975   .   .   £10/£5
ditto, Putnam (New York), 1975   .   .   .   .   £10/£5

Other Novels
Helen, Longmans Green (London), 1928   .   .   £100/£25
Pastel, Longmans Green (London), 1929   .   .   £100/£25
Barren Corn, Longmans Green (London), 1930   .   £100/£25

Short Stories
Pistols for Two, Heinemann (London), 1960   .   .   £25/£5
ditto, Dutton (New York), 1964   .   .   .   .   £20/£5

PATRICIA HIGHSMITH
(b.1921 d.1995)

A cult American novelist known mainly for her psychological crime thrillers, Highsmith began writing at the age of 15, initially concocting speech bubbles for comic strips such as *Superman*. Her first novel, *Strangers on a Train*, was filmed by Hitchcock in 1951. She lived in Europe during her later years and died in Switzerland.

Novels
Strangers on a Train, Harper (New York), 1950   .   .   .
.   .   .   .   £1,500/£350
ditto, Cresset Press (London), 1951   .   .   .   £650/£100
The Price of Salt, Coward-McCann (New York), 1952
(pseud 'Claire Morgan')   .   .   .   £2,000/£250
ditto, as *Carol*, Bloomsbury (London), 1990   .   .   £20/£5
The Blunderer, Coward-McCann (New York), 1954   .   .
.   .   .   .   £175/£35
ditto, Cresset Press (London), 1956   .   .   .   .   £150/£35
The Talented Mr Ripley, Coward-McCann (New York),
1955   .   .   .   .   £1,000/£150
ditto, Cresset Press (London), 1957   .   .   .   .   £800/£75
Deep Water, Harper (New York), 1957   .   .   £350/£45
ditto, Heinemann (London), 1958   .   .   .   .   £300/£40
A Game for the Living, Harper (New York), 1958.   £75/£20
ditto, Heinemann (London), 1959   .   .   .   .   £50/£15
This Sweet Sickness, Harper (New York), 1960   .   £65/£15
ditto, Heinemann (London), 1961   .   .   .   .   £45/£10
The Cry of the Owl, Harper (New York), 1962   .   £65/£10
ditto, Heinemann (London), 1963   .   .   .   .   £45/£5
The Two Faces of January, Doubleday (New York), 1964 .
.   .   .   .   £40/£10
ditto, Heinemann (London), 1964   .   .   .   .   £35/£5
The Glass Cell, Doubleday (New York), 1964   .   £45/£10
ditto, Heinemann (London), 1965   .   .   .   .   £45/£10
The Story-Teller, Doubleday (New York), 1965   .   £35/£10
ditto, as *A Suspension of Mercy*, Heinemann (London), 1965
.   .   .   .   £30/£5
Those Who Walk Away, Doubleday (New York), 1967.   .
.   .   .   .   £30/£5
ditto, Heinemann (London), 1967   .   .   .   .   £25/£5
The Tremor of Forgery, Doubleday (New York), 1969   .
.   .   .   .   £20/£5
ditto, Heinemann (London), 1969   .   .   .   .   £25/£5
Ripley Under Ground, Doubleday (New York), 1970   .
.   .   .   .   £85/£10
ditto, Heinemann (London), 1971   .   .   .   .   £35/£10
A Dog's Ransom, Knopf (New York), 1972   .   .   £30/£5
ditto, Heinemann (London), 1972   .   .   .   .   £25/£5
Ripley's Game, Knopf (New York), 1974.   .   .   £50/£10
ditto, Heinemann (London), 1974   .   .   .   .   £35/£10
Edith's Diary, Simon & Schuster (New York), 1977   £20/£5
ditto, Heinemann (London), 1977   .   .   .   .   £20/£5
The Boy Who Followed Ripley, Heinemann (London), 1980
.   .   .   .   £30/£5
ditto, Lippincott (Philadelphia), 1980   .   .   .   £25/£5
The People Who Knock on the Door, Heinemann (London),
1983   .   .   .   .   £15/£5
ditto, Penzler (New York), [1985] (250 signed copies,
slipcase, no d/w)   .   .   .   .   .   .   £40/£30
ditto, Penzler (New York), [1985]   .   .   .   .   £10/£5
Found in the Street, Heinemann (London), 1986   .   £15/£5

ditto, Atlantic Monthly Press (New York), 1986 . £15/£5
Ripley under Water, Bloomsbury (London), 1991 . £25/£5
ditto, London Limited Editions (London), 1991 (150 signed
   copies, glassine d/w) . . . . . . £75/£50
ditto, Knopf (New York), 1992 . . . . £25/£5
Small g: A Summer Idyll, Bloomsbury (London), 1995 .
   . . . . £15/£5
ditto, Norton (New York), 2004 . . . . £10/£5

Short Stories
The Snail-Watcher, Doubleday (New York), 1970 £35/£5
ditto, as *Eleven*, Heinemann (London), 1970 . £25/£5
Kleine Geschichten für Weiberfeinde, Diogenes (Germany),
   1974 . . . . £25/£10
ditto, as *Little Tales of Misogyny*, Heinemann (London),
   1977 . . . . £25/£5
ditto, as *Little Tales of Misogyny*, Penzler (New York),
   [1986] (250 signed copies, slipcase, no d/w). . £30/£20
ditto, as *Little Tales of Misogyny*, Penzler (New York),
   [1986] . . . . . . £10/£5
The Animal-Lover's Book of Beastly Murder, Heinemann
   (London), 1975 . . . . £25/£5
ditto, Penzler (New York), [1986] (250 signed copies,
   slipcase, no d/w) . . . . . £30/£20
ditto, Penzler (New York), [1986] . . . £10/£5
Slowly, Slowly in the Wind, Heinemann (London), 1979 .
   . . . . £20/£5
ditto, Penzler (New York), [1984] (250 signed copies,
   slipcase and d/w). . . . . . £25/£15
ditto, Penzler (New York), [1984] . . . £10/£5
The Black House, Heinemann (London), 1981 . £15/£5
ditto, Penzler (New York), [1988] (250 signed copies,
   slipcase, no d/w) . . . . . £25/£15
ditto, Penzler (New York), [1988] . . . £10/£5
Mermaids on the Golf Course and Other Stories,
   Heinemann (London), 1985 . . . . £15/£5
ditto, Mysterious Press (New York), 1988 . . £10/£5
ditto, Mysterious Press (New York), 1988 (100 signed,
   numbered copies) . . . . . £30/£15
The Man Who Wrote Books in His Head and Other Stories,
   Eurographica (Helsinki), 1986 (350 signed copies; wraps
   and d/w). £125
Tales of Natural and Unnatural Catastrophes, Bloomsbury
   (London), 1987 . . . . . . £15/£5
ditto, Atlantic Monthly Press (New York), 1989 . £10/£5
Where the Action Is and Other Stories, Eurographica
   (Helsinki), 1989 (350 signed copies; wraps and d/w) . £125
Tales of Obsession, Severn House (London), 1994 £10/£5
The Selected Stories of Patricia Highsmith, Norton (New
   York), 2001 . . . . . . £10/£5
*Nothing That Meets the Eye: The Uncollected Stories of
Patricia Highsmith*, Norton (New York), 2002 . £10/£5
ditto, Bloomsbury (London), 2005 . . . £10/£5

Children's Titles
Miranda the Panda Is on the Verandah, Coward-McCann
   (New York), 1958 (with Doris Sanders). . . £50/£15

Miscellaneous
Plotting and Writing Suspense Fiction, Writer (Boston),
   1966 . . . . £25/£10
ditto, Poplar Press (London), 1983 . . . £25/£10

CHARLIE HIGSON
(b.1958)

Charlie, or Charles, Higson is best-known as a British
television comedian who has worked with Paul Whitehouse
and Harry Enfield. As Charles Higson he writes for adults,
but under the name Charlie Higson he has been given
permission by the estate of Ian Fleming to write about the
teenage James Bond.

'Young James Bond' Novels (as Charlie Higson)
Silverfin, Puffin (London), 2005 (first printing with error
   stating at front of book next novel arriving 'October 2005';
   pbk) £10
ditto, Miramax (New York), 2005 . . . . £10/£5
ditto, Puffin (London), 2005 (999 numbered, signed
   hardback copies with d/w; slipcase) . . . £65/£25
BloodFever, Puffin (London), 2006 . . . . . £5
ditto, Miramax (New York), 2006 . . . . £10/£5
ditto, Puffin (London), 2006 (999 numbered, signed
   hardback copies with d/w; slipcase) . . . £65/£25
Double or Die, Puffin (London), 2007 . . . . £5
ditto, Puffin (London), 2007 (999 numbered, signed
   hardback copies with d/w; slipcase) . . . £65/£25
Hurricane Gold, Puffin (London), 2007 . . . £5
ditto, Disney/Hyperion (New York), 2009 . . £10/£5
ditto, Puffin (London), 2007 (1,500 numbered, signed
   hardback copies; no d/w;) £35
By Royal Command, Puffin (London), 2008 (hardback; no
   d/w) £5
ditto, Puffin (London), 2008 (2,000 signed, numbered
   hardback copies; no d/w) £25

Other Novels (as Charles Higson)
King of the Ants, Hamish Hamilton (London), 1992 (pbk
   with d/w) . . . . £10/£5
Happy Now, Hamish Hamilton (London), 1993 (pbk with
   d/w) . . . . £10/£5
Full Whack, Hamish Hamilton (London), 1995 . £10/£5
Getting Rid of Mister Kitchen, Little, Brown (London), 1996
   . . . . £10/£5
The Enemy, Puffin (London), 2009 . . . . £10/£5

JOE HILL
(b. 1972)

Joseph Hillstrom King is an American author of speculative fiction and is the son of horror writer Stephen King.
He chose to write under an abbreviated form of his name in
an attempt to be judged independent of the reputation of his
father, although this had been speculated upon before he
publicly confirmed his identity in 2007. His work has
received a number of awards.

Novel
Heart-Shaped Box, Subterranean Press (Burton, MI), 2007
   (300 signed, numbered copies). . . . £225/£125
ditto, Subterranean Press (Burton, MI), 2007 (200 signed,
   numbered deluxe copies) . . . . . £400/£300
ditto, Subterranean Press (Burton, MI), 2007 (15 signed,
   lettered copies) £1,000

ditto, Subterranean Press (Burton, MI), 2007 (second printing limited to 500 signed copies) . . . £45/£25
ditto, Morrow (New York), 2007 . . . . £10/£5
ditto, Gollancz (London), 2007 . . . . £10/£5
ditto, Gollancz (London), 2007 (1,300 signed, numbered copies; slipcase) . . . . . . £35/£20

Short Stories
20th Century Ghosts, PS Publishing (Hornsea, East Yorkshire), 2005 (500 signed, numbered copies) . . £350
ditto, PS Publishing (Hornsea, East Yorkshire), 2005 (approx 50 signed copies designated 'F-Con') . . . £350
ditto, PS Publishing (Hornsea, East Yorkshire), 2005 (200 deluxe numbered copies signed by Joe Hill and Christopher Golden; slipcase). . . . . . £1,000/£900
ditto, PS Publishing (Hornsea, East Yorkshire), 2005 (pbk; 1,000 unsigned copies) £100
ditto, Morrow/HarperCollins (New York), 2007 . £10/£5
ditto, Gollancz (London), 2007 . . . . £10/£5
Pop Art, Subterranean Press (Burton, MI), 2007 (52 signed, numbered copies) £350
ditto, Subterranean Press (Burton, MI), 2007 (pbk; 150 signed, numbered copies) £75

REGINALD HILL
(b.1936)

A British crime novelist, Hill studied English at Oxford University and worked as a teacher until 1980, when he retired to devote himself to writing. Although he has written a number of books with other characters, often under pseudonyms, Hill is best known for his now televised 'Dalziel (pronounced 'De-al') and Pascoe' novels.

'Dalziel and Pascoe' Novels
A Clubbable Woman, Collins Crime Club (London), 1970 . . . . £750/£75
ditto, Countryman (Woodstock, VT), 1984 . . £45/£5
An Advancement of Learning, Collins Crime Club (London), 1971 . . . . . . £125/£25
ditto, Countryman (Woodstock, VT), 1985 . . £25/£5
Ruling Passion, Collins Crime Club (London), 1973 . . . . £150/£25
ditto, Harper (New York), 1977 . . . . £35/£10
An April Shroud, Collins Crime Club (London), 1975 . . . . £200/£35
ditto, Countryman (Woodstock, VT), 1986 . . £15/£5
A Pinch of Snuff, Collins Crime Club (London), 1978 . . . . £250/£25
ditto, Harper (New York), 1978 . . . . £45/£10
A Killing Kindness, Collins Crime Club (London), 1980 . . . . £150/£20
ditto, Pantheon (New York), 1981 . . . £25/£5
Deadheads, Collins Crime Club (London), 1983 . £65/£10
ditto, Macmillan (New York), 1984 . . . £35/£10
Exit Lines, Collins Crime Club (London), 1984 . £45/£10
ditto, Macmillan (New York), 1985 . . . £25/£5
Child's Play, Collins Crime Club (London), 1987 . £45/£10
ditto, Macmillan (New York), 1987 . . . £25/£5
Under World, Collins Crime Club (London), 1988 £25/£10
ditto, Scribner's (New York), 1988 . . . £20/£5

Bones and Silence, Collins Crime Club (London), 1990 . . . . £15/£5
ditto, Delacorte (New York), 1990 . . . . £15/£5
Recalled to Life, Scorpion Press (Bristol), 1992 (99 signed, numbered copies) £75
ditto, Scorpion Press (Bristol), 1992 (20 signed, lettered copies) £150
ditto, Collins Crime Club (London), 1992. . . £20/£5
ditto, Delacorte (New York), 1992 . . . . £15/£5
Pictures of Perfection, Scorpion Press (Bristol), 1994 (75 signed, numbered copies) £75
ditto, Scorpion Press (Bristol), 1994 (20 signed, lettered copies) £150
ditto, Collins Crime Club (London), 1994. . . £20/£5
ditto, Delacorte (New York), 1994 . . . . £10/£5
The Wood Beyond, Scorpion Press (Blakeney, Glos), 1996 (85 signed, numbered copies) £45
ditto, HarperCollins (London), 1996 . . . . £10/£5
ditto, Delacorte (New York), 1996 . . . . £10/£5
On Beulah Height, Scorpion Press (Blakeney, Glos), 1998 (85 signed, numbered copies) £45
ditto, HarperCollins (London), 1998 . . . . £10/£5
ditto, Delacorte (New York), 1998 . . . . £10/£5
Arms and the Women, HarperCollins (London), 2000 . . . . £10/£5
ditto, Delacorte (New York), 2000 . . . . £10/£5
Dialogues of the Dead, HarperCollins (London), 2001 . . . . £10/£5
ditto, Delacorte (New York), 2001 . . . . £10/£5
Death's Jest Book, HarperCollins (London), 2002 £10/£5
ditto, HarperCollins (New York), 2003 . . . £10/£5
Good Morning, Midnight, HarperCollins (London), 2004 . . . . £10/£5
ditto, HarperCollins (New York), 2004 . . . £10/£5
The Death of Dalziel, HarperCollins (London), 2007 £10/£5
ditto, as ***Death Comes for the Fat Man***, HarperCollins (New York), 2007 . . . . £10/£5
A Cure for All Diseases, HarperCollins (London), 2008 . . . . £10/£5
ditto, as ***The Price of Butcher's Meat***, HarperCollins (New York), 2008 . . . . £10/£5
Midnight Fugue, HarperCollins (London), 2009 . £10/£5
ditto, HarperCollins (New York), 2009 . . . £10/£5

'Joe Sixsmith' Novels
Blood Sympathy, Collins Crime Club (London), 1993 . . . . £25/£5
ditto, St Martin's (New York), 1994 . . . . £15/£5
Born Guilty, HarperCollins (London), 1995 . . £20/£5
ditto, St Martin's (New York), 1995 . . . . £15/£5
Killing the Lawyers, HarperCollins (London), 1997 £15/£5
ditto, St Martin's (New York), 1997 . . . . £10/£5
Singing the Sadness, HarperCollins (London), 1999 £15/£5
ditto, St Martin's (New York), 1999 . . . . £10/£5
The Roar of the Butterflies, HarperCollins (London), 2008. . . . . £15/£5
ditto, Harper (New York), 2008 (pbk) £5

Other Novels
Fell of Dark, Collins Crime Club (London), 1971 . £350/£45
ditto, N.A.L. (New York), 1986 . . . . . £20/£5
A Fairly Dangerous Thing, Collins Crime Club (London), 1972 . . . . £125/£15
ditto, Countryman (Woodstock, VT), 1983 . . £15/£5

A Very Good Hater, Collins Crime Club (London), 1974 .
.   .   .   . £100/£15
ditto, Countryman (Woodstock, VT), 1982   .   . £20/£5
Another Death in Venice, Collins Crime Club (London),
1976   .   .   .   . £100/£15
ditto, NAL (New York), 1987   .   .   .   . £15/£5
The Spy's Wife, Collins (London), 1980 .   .   . £45/£10
ditto, Pantheon (New York), 1980   .   .   . £20/£5
Who Guards a Prince?, Collins (London), 1982   . £40/£5
ditto, as *Who Guards the Prince?*, Pantheon (New York),
1982   .   .   .   . £30/£5
Traitor's Blood, Collins (London), 1983 .   .   . £45/£10
ditto, Countryman (Woodstock, VT), 1986   .   . £25/£5
No Man's Land, Collins (London), 1985 .   .   . £35/£5
ditto, St Martin's Press (New York), 1985   .   . £25/£5
The Collaborators, Collins (London), 1987   .   . £15/£5
ditto, Countryman (Woodstock, VT), 1989   .   . £15/£5
The Stranger House, HarperCollins (London), 2005 £10/£5
ditto, HarperCollins (New York), 2005   .   . £10/£5

Short Stories
Pascoe's Ghost, Collins Crime Club (London), 1979   .   .
.   .   .   . £125/£20
There Are No Ghosts in the Soviet Union, Collins Crime
Club (London), 1987 .   .   .   .   .   . £45/£10
ditto, Countryman (Woodstock, VT), 1988   .   . £15/£5
One Small Step, Collins Crime Club (London), 1990 £40/£5
Brother's Keeper, Eurographica (Helsinki), 1992 (350
signed copies; wraps) £60
Asking for the Moon, HarperCollins (London), 1994 £20/£5
ditto, Countryman (Woodstock, VT), 1996   .   . £15/£5

Novels Written as 'Dick Moorland'
Heart Clock, Faber (London), 1973 .   .   . £125/£25
ditto, as *Matlock's System*, Severn House (Sutton, Surrey),
1996   .   .   .   . £15/£5
Albion! Albion!, Faber (London), 1974 .   .   . £75/£10
ditto, as *Singleton's Law*, Severn House (Sutton, Surrey),
1997   .   .   .   . £10/£5

Novels Written as 'Patrick Ruell'
The Castle of the Demon, John Long (London), 1971 .   .
.   .   .   . £250/£45
ditto, Hawthorn (New York), 1973   .   .   . £30/£5
ditto, as *The Turning of the Tide*, Severn House (Sutton,
Surrey), 1999   .   .   .   . £15/£5
Red Christmas, John Long (London), 1972   .   . £175/£25
ditto, Hawthorn (New York), 1974   .   .   . £50/£10
Death Takes the Low Road, Hutchinson (London), 1974 .
.   .   .   . £150/£25
ditto, Mysterious Press (New York), 1987   .   . £20/£5
Urn Burial, Hutchinson (London), 1975 .   .   . £125/£25
ditto, Countryman (Woodstock, VT), 1987   .   . £15/£5
ditto, as *Beyond the Bone*, Severn House (Sutton, Surrey),
2000   .   .   .   . £15/£5
The Long Kill, Methuen (London), 1986 .   .   . £25/£5
ditto, Countryman (Woodstock, VT), 1988   .   . £20/£5
Death of a Dormouse, Methuen (London), 1987   . £15/£5
ditto, Mysterious Press (New York), 1987   .   . £15/£5
Dream of Darkness, Methuen (London), 1989   .   . £15/£5
ditto, Countryman (Woodstock, VT), 1990   .   . £15/£5
The Only Game, Collins (London), 1991 .   .   . £15/£5
ditto, Countryman (Woodstock, VT), 1993   .   . £15/£5

Novels Written as 'Charles Underhill'
Captain Fantom, Hutchinson (London), 1978.   . £50/£5
ditto, St Martin's Press (New York), 1980   .   . £40/£5
The Forging of Fantom, Hutchinson (London), 1979 .   .
.   .   .   . £100/£25

TONY HILLERMAN
(b.1925)

Tony Hillerman is an American author of detective fiction
whose work has won several awards. In many of his novels
his investigators look into reports of witchcraft or other
supernatural occurances alongside more mundane crimes,
only to discover that the supernatural is staged to cover up
the other crimes.

'Leaphorn & Chee' books
The Blessing Way, Harper & Row (New York), 1970 .   .
.   .   .   . £800/£75
ditto, Macmillan (London), 1970   .   .   . £200/£25
ditto, The Armchair Detective Library (New York), 1990 .
.   .   .   . £10/£5
ditto, The Armchair Detective Library (New York), 1990
(270 copies; no d/w or slipcase) £20
ditto, The Armchair Detective Library (New York), 1990
(100 signed, numbered copies; slipcase)   .   . £40/£30
ditto, The Armchair Detective Library (New York), 1990 (26
signed, lettered copies; slipcase)   .   .   . £225/£175
Dance Hall of the Dead, Harper & Row (New York), 1973.
.   .   .   . £450/£75
ditto, Pluto Press (London/Sydney), 1985.   .   . £60/£10
ditto, The Armchair Detective Library (New York), 1991 .
.   .   .   . £10/£5
ditto, The Armchair Detective Library (New York), 1991
(270 copies; no d/w or slipcase) £20
ditto, The Armchair Detective Library (New York), 1991
(100 signed, numbered copies; slipcase)   .   . £40/£30
ditto, The Armchair Detective Library (New York), 1991 (26
signed, lettered copies; slipcase)   .   .   . £225/£175
Listening Woman, Harper & Row (New York), 1978 (no
blind-stamped square at the lower right hand corner of the
back cover; d/w has printed price)   .   .   . £250/£40
ditto, Macmillan (London), 1979   .   .   . £40/£5
ditto, The Armchair Detective Library (New York), 1994 .
.   .   .   . £10/£5
ditto, The Armchair Detective Library (New York), 1994
(100 signed, numbered copies; slipcase)   .   . £40/£30
ditto, The Armchair Detective Library (New York), 1994 (26
signed, lettered copies; slipcase)   .   .   . £225/£175
People Of Darkness, Harper & Row (New York), 1980 .
.   .   .   . £200/£30
ditto, Gollancz (London), 1982 .   .   .   . £75/£15
ditto, The Armchair Detective Library (New York), 1994 .
.   .   .   . £10/£5
ditto, The Armchair Detective Library (New York), 1994
(100 signed, numbered copies; slipcase)   .   . £40/£30
ditto, The Armchair Detective Library (New York), 1994 (26
signed, lettered copies; slipcase)   .   .   . £225/£175
The Dark Wind, Harper & Row (New York), 1982 £75/£15
ditto, Gollancz (London), 1983 .   .   .   .   . £65/£10
The Ghostway, Dennis McMillan (San Diego, CA) 1984
(300 signed, numbered copies).   .   .   . £400/£300

ditto, Harper & Row (New York), 1985 . . . £75/£15
ditto, Gollancz (London), 1985 . . . . . £50/£10
Skinwalkers, Harper & Row (New York), 1986 . £15/£5
ditto, Michael Joseph (London), 1988 . . . £15/£5
A Thief of Time, Harper & Row (New York), 1988 £10/£5
ditto, Michael Joseph (London), 1989 . . . £10/£5
Talking God, Harper & Row (New York), 1989 . £10/£5
ditto, Harper & Row (New York), 1989 (300 signed, numbered copies; slipcase) . . . . £85/£60
ditto, Michael Joseph (London), 1990 . . £10/£5
Coyote Waits, Harper & Row (New York), 1990 . £10/£5
ditto, Harper & Row (New York), 1990 (500 signed, numbered copies; slipcase) . . . . £65/£30
ditto, Michael Joseph (London), 1991 . . . £10/£5
Sacred Clowns, HarperCollins (New York), 1993 . £10/£5
ditto, HarperCollins (New York), 1993 (500 signed, numbered copies; slipcase, no d/w) . . . £45/£30
ditto, HarperCollins (New York), 1993 (26 signed, lettered copies; slipcase, no d/w) . . . . £200/£175
ditto, Michael Joseph (London), 1993 . . . £10/£5
The Fallen Man, HarperCollins (New York), 1996 £10/£5
ditto, HarperCollins (New York), 1996 (300 signed, numbered copies; slipcase, no d/w) . . . £45/£30
ditto, HarperCollins (New York), 1996 (26 signed, lettered copies; slipcase, no d/w) . . . . £200/£175
ditto, Michael Joseph (London), 1997 . . . £10/£5
The First Eagle, Buffalo Medicine Books (Gallup, NM), 1998 (100 signed, numbered copies with original watercolour by Ernest Franklin; slipcase) . £250/£200
ditto, HarperCollins (New York) 1998 . . . £10/£5
ditto, HarperCollins (New York), 1998 (250 signed, numbered copies; slipcase, no d/w) . . . £45/£30
ditto, HarperCollins (New York), 1998 (26 signed, lettered copies; slipcase, no d/w) . . . £200/£175
ditto, HarperCollins (New York), 1998 (5 signed, numbered copies with an original watercolour by Ed Franklin; slipcase, no d/w) . . . . . £300/£250
ditto, HarperCollins (London), 1998 . . . £10/£5
Hunting Badger, HarperCollins (New York), 1999 £10/£5
ditto, HarperCollins (New York), 1999 (unknown number of trade edition with a full page, signed, original watercolour by Ernest Franklin; signed on title page by Hillerman; slipcase). . . . . . £150/£100
ditto, HarperCollins (London), 1999 . . . £10/£5
The Wailing Wind, HarperCollins (New York), 2002 . .
. . . . £10/£5
The Sinister Pig, HarperCollins (New York), 2003 £10/£5
ditto, HarperCollins (New York), 2003 (signed by the author on a tipped in leaf) . . . . . . £15/£10
ditto, HarperCollins (New York), 2003 (signed by the author; full-page coloured drawing by Ernest Franklin; slipcase and d/w). . . . . £75/£50
Skeleton Man, HarperCollins (New York), 2004 . £10/£5
ditto, HarperCollins (New York), 2004 (signed by the author on a tipped in leaf) . . . . . £15/£10
ditto, HarperCollins (New York), 2004 (signed by the author; full-page coloured drawing by Ernest Franklin; slipcase and d/w). . . . . £75/£50
The Shape Shifter, HarperCollins (New York), 2006 £10/£5
ditto, HarperCollins (New York), 2006 (signed by the author on a tipped in leaf) . . . . . £15/£10
ditto, HarperCollins (New York), 2006 (100 numbered copies signed by the author; full-page coloured drawing by Ernest Franklin; slipcase and d/w) . . . . £75/£50

Other Novels
The Fly On The Wall, Harper & Row (New York), 1972 .
. . . . £700/£100
ditto, The Armchair Detective Library (New York), 1990 .
. . . . £10/£5
ditto, The Armchair Detective Library (New York), 1990 (270 copies; no d/w or slipcase) £20
ditto, The Armchair Detective Library (New York), 1990 (100 signed, numbered copies; slipcase) . . £40/£30
ditto, The Armchair Detective Library (New York), 1990 (26 signed, lettered copies; slipcase) . . . £225/£175
The Boy Who Made Dragonfly, Harper & Row (New York), 1972 (trade issue d/w clipped at base leaving $4.50 issue price) . . . . £300/£50
ditto, Harper & Row (New York), 1972 (library issue d/w with Harpercrest label clipped at top leaving $4.11 issue price; different binding) . . . . . . £300/£40
Finding Moon, HarperCollins (New York), 1995 . £10/£5
ditto, HarperCollins (New York), 1995 (350 signed, numbered copies; slipcase) . . . . £45/£30
ditto, HarperCollins (New York), 1995 (unknown number of signed copies of trade edition with original drawing by Ernest Franklin) . . . . . . £200/£175
ditto, Michael Joseph (London), 1996 . . . £10/£5
Buster Mesquite's Cowboy Band, Buffalo Medicine Books (Gallup, NM), 2001 . . . . . . £10/£5
ditto, Buffalo Medicine Books (Gallup, NM), 2001 (100 signed, numbered copies; slipcase) . . . £100/£65

Non-Fiction
The Great Taos Bank Robbery, Univ of New Mexico Press (Albuquerque, NM), 1973 (first issue yellow-grey cloth with single illustration on back panel of d/w; light yellow-brown endpapers) . . . . . . £200/£40
ditto, Univ of New Mexico Press (Albuquerque, NM), 1973 (second issue grey-yellow cloth with two illustrations on back panel of d/w; yellow-white endpapers) . . £100/£20
New Mexico, Charles H. Belding (Portland, OR), 1974. .
. . . . £65/£25
Rio Grande, Charles H. Belding (Portland, OR), 1975 . .
. . . . £65/£25
Indian Country, Northland Press (Flagstaff, AZ), 1987 .
. . . . £60/£10
Words, Weather and Wolfmen, Southwesterner Books (Gallup, NM), 1989 (350 numbered copies signed by Hillerman, Ernest Franklin and Ernie Bulow; d/w) £70/£40
ditto, Southwesterner Books (Gallup, NM), 1989 (extra-illustrated issues made up from misnumbered and unnumbered copies of above issue; slipcase; original water colour illustrations by Franklin bound in, tipped in, or laid in) . . . . £250/£200
ditto, Southwesterner Books (Gallup, NM), 1989 (26 lettered copies signed by Hillerman, Ernest Franklin and Ernie Bulow; slipcase; original Ernest Franklin pen and ink sketch) . . . . £300/£250
ditto, Southwesterner Books (Gallup, NM), 1989 (26 lettered copies; first issue pale green-yellow cloth; slipcase; rejected copies distributed as advance proof, presentation and review copies) . . . . . . £150/£100
ditto, Southwesterner Books (Gallup, NM), 1989 (16 copies signed by Hillerman, Ernest Franklin and Ernie Bulow for presentation; original watercolour by Franklin tipped in before title page and a small sketch by Franklin in

limitation page where the letters or numbers appear; slipcase).   .   .   .   .   £200/£150

ditto, Southwesterner Books (Gallup, NM), 1989 (10 copies signed by Hillerman, Ernest Franklin and Ernie Bulow; quarter-bound in leather; slipcase)   .   .   .   £300/£250

ditto, Southwesterner Books (Gallup, NM), 1989 (2 copies marked for review; pale green-yellow cloth; slipcase)   .   .   .   .   £125/£75

ditto as **Talking Mysteries: A Conversation With Tony Hillerman**, Univ of New Mexico Press (Albuquerque, NM), 1991   .   .   .   .   £15/£5

Hillerman Country, HarperCollins (New York), 1991 £15/£5

ditto, HarperCollins (New York), 1991 (signed edition)   .   .   .   .   £75/£45

New Mexico, Rio Grande and Other Essays, Graphic Arts Center Publishing Co. (Portland, OR), 1992 .   .   £10/£5

Canyon de Chelley, James Cahill (Aliso Viejo, CA), 1999 (300 copies; pbk). £10

ditto, James Cahill (Aliso Viejo, CA), 1999 (174 signed, numbered copies; slipcase, no d/w).   .   .   £45/£30

ditto, James Cahill (Aliso Viejo, CA), 1999 (26 signed, lettered copies; slipcase, no d/w)   .   .   £125/£100

ditto, James Cahill (Aliso Viejo, CA), 1999 (c.6 signed, lettered copies; slipcase, no d/w)   .   .   .   .£100/£75

Sacred Land..., Buffalo Medicine Books (Gallup, NM), 2000 (150 numbered copies signed by Hillerman, Ernest Franklin, and Ernie Bulow; slipcase; original signed coloured pencil drawing by Ernest Franklin).   £200/£150

Seldom Disappointed, HarperCollins (New York), 2001   .   .   .   .   £10/£5

JAMES HILTON
(b.1900 d.1954)

Hilton achieved literary success early and many of his books were international bestsellers. Although born and brought up in England, he lived and worked in Hollywood from the mid-1930s, and won an Oscar in 1942 for the screenplay of *Mrs Miniver*. He created a much loved character in *Goodbye Mr Chips*. Although the latter can be seen as rather sentimental, many of his other novels have a darker side.

Novels
Catherine Herself, T.F. Unwin (London), 1920   . £700/£75
Storm Passage, T.F. Unwin (London), 1922   .   . £300/£35
The Passionate Year, Thornton Butterworth (London), 1923   .   .   .   . £200/£20

ditto, Little, Brown (Boston), 1924   .   .   .   . £200/£20
The Dawn of Reckoning, Thornton Butterworth (London), 1925   .   .   .   .   £200/£20

ditto, as **Rage in Heaven**, Alfred H. King (New York), 1932   .   .   .   .£150/£15

The Meadows of the Moon, Thornton Butterworth (London), 1926   .   .   .   .£150/£15

ditto, Small, Maynard (Boston), 1927   .   .   .£150/£15
Terry, Thornton Butterworth (London), 1927 .   .£250/£25
The Silver Flame, Thornton Butterworth (London), 1928   .   .   .   .£225/£25

And Now Good-bye, Ernest Benn (London), 1931 .£150/£15
ditto, Morrow (New York), 1932   .   .   .   .£150/£15
Contango, Ernest Benn (London), 1932   .   .£125/£15

ditto, as **Ill Wind**, Morrow (New York), 1932 .   . £75/£10
Knight Without Armour, Ernest Benn (London), 1933 .   .   .   .£300/£20

ditto, as **Without Armor**, Morrow (New York), 1935   .   .   .   .£100/£10

Lost Horizon, Macmillan (London), 1933   . £1,500/£250
ditto, Morrow (New York), 1933   .   .   . £300/£100
Goodbye Mr Chips, Little, Brown (Boston), 1934 . £300/£30
ditto, Hodder & Stoughton (London), 1934   . £250/£25
We Are Not Alone, Macmillan (London), 1934   . £75/£10
ditto, Little, Brown (Boston), 1937   .   .   . £45/£10
To You Mr Chips, Hodder & Stoughton (London), 1938   .   .   .   . £65/£10

Random Harvest, Macmillan (London), 1941 .   . £75/£10
ditto, Little, Brown (Boston), 1941   .   .   . £65/£10
The Story of Dr Wassell, Macmillan (London), 1944 £40/£5
ditto, Little, Brown (Boston), 1943   .   .   .   . £40/£5
So Well Remembered, Little, Brown (Boston), 1945   £15/£5
ditto, Macmillan (London), 1947   .   .   .   . £15/£5
Nothing So Strange, Little, Brown (Boston), 1947   £15/£5
ditto, Macmillan (London), 1948   .   .   .   . £15/£5
Twilight of the Wise, St Hugh's Press, (London), 1949.   .   .   .   . £20/£5

Morning Journey, Macmillan (London), 1951   . £15/£5
ditto, Little, Brown (Boston), 1951   .   .   .   . £15/£5
Time and Time Again, Macmillan (London), 1953   £10/£5
ditto, Little, Brown (Boston), 1953   .   .   .   . £10/£5

Novel Written as 'Glen Trevor'
Murder at School, Ernest Benn (London), 1931 £1,000/£100
ditto, as **Was it Murder?**, Harper (New York), 1931 (sealed mystery).   .   .   .   .   .   . £1,000/£100

CHESTER HIMES
(b.1909 d.1984)

Chester Himes was a famous African American writer whose award-winning work includes a series of Harlem detective novels (featuring Coffin Ed Johnson and Gravedigger Jones) and *If He Hollers Let Him Go*. He moved to France in the 1950s and all of his Harlem crime stories (except *Blind Man with a Pistol*), were originally published in French and then translated for American paperback distribution.

'Coffin Ed Johnson' and 'Grave Digger Jones' Novels
For Love of Imabelle, Fawcett Publications/Gold Medal Book (Greenwich, CT), 1957 (pbk, #717)   .   .   . £50
ditto, as **A Rage In Harlem**, Avon (New York), 1965 (pbk). £15
ditto, as **A Rage In Harlem**, Panther (London), 1969 (pbk) £15
ditto, as **A Rage In Harlem**, Allison & Busby (London/New York), 1985 .   .   .   . £15/£5
The Real Cool Killers, Avon (New York), 1959 (pbk; T-328) £60
ditto, Panther (London), 1969 (pbk) £15
ditto, Allison & Busby (London/New York), 1985.   £25/£10
The Big Gold Dream, Avon (New York), 1960 (pbk)   . £45
ditto, Panther (London), 1968 (pbk) £10
All Shot Up, Avon (New York), 1960 (pbk; T-434)   . £45
ditto, Panther (London), 1969 (pbk) £15

Cotton Comes to Harlem, Putnam's (New York), 1965   .
.   .   .   . £250/£40
ditto, Frederick Muller (London), 1966   .   .   . £100/£20
The Heat's On, Putnam's (New York), 1966 .   . £175/£25
ditto, Frederick Muller (London), 1966   .   .   . £30/£10
ditto, as *Come Back Charleston Blue*, Berkley (New York),
1970 (pbk) £5
ditto, as *The Heat's On*, Allison & Busby (London), 1986 .
.   .   .   . £15/£5
Blind Man With A Pistol, Morrow (New York), 1969 .
.   .   .   . £75/£10
ditto, Hodder & Stoughton (London), 1969   .   . £40/£10
ditto, as *Hot Day, Hot Night*, Dell (New York), 1979 (pbk).
.   .   .   . £5
ditto, as *Blind Man With A Pistol*, Allison & Busby
(London/New York), 1986   .   .   .   . £25/£10
The Crazy Kill, Avon (New York), 1959 (pbk; T-357) . £60
ditto, Panther (London), 1968 (pbk) £10
ditto, Allison & Busby (London/New York), 1984 . £25/£10

Other Novels
If He Hollers Let Him Go, Doubleday (Garden City, NY),
1945   .   .   .   . £300/£65
ditto, Falcon Press (London), 1947   .   .   . £125/£30
Lonely Crusade, Knopf (New York), 1947   . £175/£25
ditto, Falcon Press (London), 1950   .   .   . £75/£15
Cast the First Stone, Coward McCann (New York), 1952 .
.   .   .   . £200/£40
ditto, as *Yesterday Will Make You Cry*, W.W. Norton (New
York), 1988 .   .   .   . £10/£5
The Third Generation, World (Cleveland/New York), 1954 .
.   .   .   . £80/£15
The Primitive, Signet/New American Library (New York),
1956 (pbk) £35
ditto, as *The End of a Primitive*, Allison & Busby (London),
1990   .   .   .   . £25/£10
ditto, as *The End of a Primitive*, W.W. Norton (New York),
1997 (pbk) £5
Pinktoes, Olympia Press (Paris), 1961 (pbk; 'Printed in July
1961' on back page) £150
ditto, Putnam's (New York), 1965   .   .   . £65/£10
ditto, Arthur Barker (London), 1965 .   .   . £25/£5
Run Man Run, G.P. Putnam's Sons (New York), 1966   .
.   .   .   . £100/£15
ditto, Frederick Muller (London), 1967   .   .   . £30/£10
Black on Black, Doubleday (Garden City, NY), 1973 .   .
.   .   .   . £65/£10
ditto, Michael Joseph (London), 1975   .   .   . £25/£5
A Case of Rape, Targ Editions (New York), 1980 (350
signed, numbered copies; glassine d/w) .   .   . £75
ditto, Howard Univ (Washington, D. C.), 1984   . £30/£5
Plan B, Univ Press of Mississippi (Jackson, MI), 1993 .   .
.   .   .   . £20/£5

Collections
The Collected Stories of Chester Himes, Allison & Busby
(London), 1990   .   .   .   .   .   . £30/£5
ditto, Thunder's Mouth Press (New York), 1991 . £30/£5

Autobiography
The Quality of Hurt, Doubleday (Garden City, NY), 1972 .
.   .   .   . £40/£10
ditto, Doubleday (Garden City, NY), 1972 (signed tipped-in
page)   .   .   .   . £200/£150

ditto, Michael Joseph (London), 1973   .   .   . £30/£5
My Life of Absurdity, Doubleday (Garden City, NY), 1976 .
.   .   .   . £30/£10

Interviews and Conversations
Miotte, SMI (Paris), 1977 (no d/w; interviews; text in
English and French) £15
Conversations With Chester Himes, Univ Press of Missis-
sippi (Jackson, MI), 1995 (500 copies) .   .   . £30/£10
ditto, Univ Press of Mississippi (Jackson, MI), 1995 (pbk) £5

WILLIAM HOPE
HODGSON
(b.1877 d.1918)

Hodgson, an English author of horror and fantastic fiction,
spent many of his early years at sea with the Merchant
Navy, and most of his stories have a maritime theme. His
chief achievements are the novels *The House on the
Borderland*, the epic *The Night Land*, and his occult detective Thomas Carnacki, who appeared in several short
stories. Hodgson was killed during World War One in an
artillery bombardment near Ypres in April, 1918.

The Boats of 'Glen Carrig', Chapman & Hall (London),
1907   .   .   .   . £1,250
The House on the Borderland, Chapman & Hall (London),
1908   .   .   .   . £3,000
The Ghost Pirates, Stanley Paul (London), 1909
(frontispiece by Sidney Sime; probable first issue red
boards) £1,750
ditto, Stanley Paul (London), 1909 (frontispiece by Sidney
Sime; green boards) £1,250
The Night Land, Eveleigh Nash (London), 1912 . £2,500
Poems and The Dream of X, R. Harold Paget (New York),
1912 (wraps). £300
Carnacki the Ghost-Finder, Eveleigh Nash (London), 1913
.   .   .   . £1,750
ditto, Mycroft & Moran (Sauk City, WI), 1947 . £100/£30
Men of the Deep Waters, Eveleigh Nash (London), 1914 .
.   .   .   . £1,000
The Luck of the Strong, Eveleigh Nash (London), 1916 .
.   .   .   . £400
Captain Gault, Eveleigh Nash (London), 1917   . £400
ditto, Mcbride & Co. (New York), 1918 .   .   . £200
The Calling of the Sea, Selwyn & Blount (London), 1920 .
.   .   .   . £450/£250
The Voice of the Ocean, Selwyn & Blount (London), 1921 .
.   .   .   . £450/£250
The House on the Borderland and Other Novels, Arkham
House (Sauk City, WI), 1946   .   .   . £225/£50
Deep Waters, Arkham House (Sauk City, WI), 1967 £75/£20
Out of the Storm, Donald Grant (West Kingston, RI), 1975.
.   .   .   . £30/£10
The Dream of X, Donald Grant (West Kingston, RI), 1977 .
.   .   .   . £20/£10
Poems of the Sea, Ferret Fantasy (London), 1977 (50
numbered large paper copies of 500 signed by editor)   .
.   .   .   . £50/£20
ditto, Ferret Fantasy (London), 1977 (450 copies of 500)   .
.   .   .   . £25/£15

The Haunted 'Pampero': Uncollected Fantasies and Mysteries, Donald Grant (West Kingston, RI), 1991 (500 numbered copies signed by editor) . . . . £20/£10
Terrors of the Sea: Unpublished and Uncollected Fantasies, Donald M. Grant (West Kingston, RI), 1996 .
. . . . £20/£10
The Wandering Soul: Glimpses of a Life, A Compendium of Rare and Unpublished Works, PS Publishing/Tartarus Press (North Yorkshire), 2005 (500 copies) . £25/£10
ditto, PS Publishing/Tartarus Press (North Yorkshire), 2005 (150 numbered copies signed by the editor and slipcased with *The Lost Poetry*) . . . . . £175/£125

ALAN HOLLINGHURST
(b.1954)

An award-winning novelist, from 1982 to 1995 Hollinghurst was deputy editor of the *Times Literary Supplement*. *The Swimming Pool Library* won the Somerset Maugham Award in 1989, in 1994, he won the James Tait Black Memorial Prize with *The Folding Star*, but he is best-known for winning the Booker Prize for *The Line of Beauty* in 2004.

Poetry
Isherwood is at Santa Monica, Sycamore Broadsheet 22, Sycamore Press (Oxford, UK), 1975 (two poems, hand-printed on a single folded sheet) £100
Confidential Chats with Boys, Sycamore Press (Oxford, UK), 1982 (purple paper wraps, 6 leaves) . . . £75

Novels
The Swimming Pool Library, Chatto & Windus (London), 1988 . . . . £25/£10
ditto, Random House (New York), 1988 . . . £15/£5
The Folding Star, Chatto & Windus (London), 1994 £10/£5
ditto, Pantheon (New York), 1994 . . . . £10/£5
The Spell, Chatto & Windus (London), 1998 . . £10/£5
ditto, Viking (New York), 1999 . . . . . £10/£5
The Line of Beauty, Picador (London), 2004 . . £10/£5
ditto, Bloomsbury (New York), 2004. . . . £15/£5

Translation
Bazajet by Racine, Chatto & Windus (London), 1991 . £10

NICK HORNBY
(b.1957)

Hornby is a best-selling British author whose themes centre on obsessive male behaviour. He conveys his passions, for example for football and popular music, with humour, to readers who otherwise might remain uninterested in them. In 1999 he received the E.M. Forster Award from the American Academy of Arts and Letters.

Novels
High Fidelity, Gollancz (London), 1995 . . . £35/£5
ditto, Riverhead/Putnam (New York), 1995 . . £25/£5
About a Boy, Gollancz (London), 1998 . . . £15/£5

ditto, Riverhead/Putnam (New York), 1998 . . £10/£5
How to Be Good, Viking (London), 2001. . . £15/£5
ditto, Riverhead/Putnam (New York), 2001 . . £10/£5
A Long Way Down, Viking (London), 2005 . . £10/£5
ditto, Knopf (New York), 2005 . . . . . £10/£5
Slam, Penguin (London), 2007 . . . . . £10/£5
ditto, Putnams (New York), 2007 . . . . £10/£5
Juliet, Naked, Viking (London), 2009 . . . £10/£5
ditto, Penguin/Riverhead (New York), 2009 . . £10/£5

Plays
An Education: The Screenplay, Penguin (London), 2009 (pbk) £5

Non-Fiction
Fever Pitch, Gollancz (London), 1992 . . . £300/£30
ditto, Penguin (New York), 1992 (pbk) . . . £10
ditto, as *Fever Pitch: The Screenplay*, Indigo (London), 1997 (pbk) £5
Contemporary American Fiction, Vision Press/St Martin's Press (London), 1992 . . . . . . £100/£20
Songbook, McSweeney's (New York), 2002 (with 11 track cd, no d/w) . . . . £45/£10
ditto, as *31 Songs*, Viking (London), 2003 . . £10/£5
The Polysyllabic Spree, McSweeney's (New York), 2004 .
. . . . £15/£5
ditto, as *The Complete Polysyllabic Spree*, Viking (London), 2006 . . . . £15/£5
Housekeeping Vs. the Dirt, McSweeney's (New York), 2006 (pbk) £5
Shakespeare Wrote for Money, McSweeney's (New York), 2008 (pbk) £5

E.W. HORNUNG
(b.1866 d.1921)

Ernest William Hornung was the creator of A.J. Raffles, a gentleman thief in late Victorian London. Stories about his character first appeared in *Cassell's Magazine* in 1898, and were disapproved of by contemporary moralists because they glorified the activities of a crook. They have overshadowed his other work which was often in the detection vein.

Raffles Novels
The Amateur Cracksman, Metheun (London), 1899 . £125
ditto, Scribner's (New York), 1899 . . . . . £85
The Black Mask, Grant Richards (London), 1901 . . £100
ditto, as *Raffles: Further Adventures of the Amateur Cracksman*, Scribner's (New York), 1901 . . . £75
A Thief in the Night, Chatto & Windus (London), 1905 £75
ditto, Scribner's (New York), 1905 . . . . . £65
Mr Justice Raffles, Smith Elder (London), 1909 . . £75
ditto, Scribner's (New York), 1909 . . . . . £65

Novels
A Bride from the Bush, Smith Elder (London), 1890 . £50
ditto, United States Book Co. (New York), 1890 . . £45
Tiny Luttrell, Cassell (London), 1893 (2 vols) £100 the set
ditto, Cassell (New York), 1893 . . . . . £45
The Boss of Taroomba, Bliss Sands (London), 1894 . £65
ditto, Scribner's (New York), 1900 . . . . . £45

The Unbidden Guest, Longmans Green (London), 1894 .
. . . . £100
The Rogue's March: A Romance, Cassell (London), 1896 .
. . . . £85
ditto, Scribner's (New York), 1896 . . . . . £45
Irralie's Bushranger, The New Vagabond Library, 1896 .
. . . . £75
ditto, Scribner's (New York), 1896 . . . . . £65
My Lord Duke, Cassell (London), 1897 . . . £65
ditto, Scribner's (New York), 1896 . . . . . £50
Young Blood, Cassell (London), 1898 . . . . £65
ditto, Scribner's (New York), 1898 . . . . . £50
Dead Men Tell No Tales, Metheun (London), 1899 . £65
ditto, Scribner's (New York), 1899 . . . . . £50
Peccavi, Grant Richards (London), 1900 . . . £50
ditto, Scribner's (New York), 1900 . . . . . £45
The Belle of Toorak, Grant Richards (London), 1900 . £50
ditto, as *The Shadow of a Man*, Scribner's (New York),
1900 . . . . £45
The Shadow of the Rope, Chatto & Windus (London), 1902
. . . . £75
ditto, Scribner's (New York), 1902 . . . . . £65
At Large, Scribner's (New York), 1902 . . . £50
No Hero, Smith Elder (London), 1903 . . . . £35
ditto, Scribner's (New York), 1903 . . . . . £30
Denis Dent: A Novel, Ibister (London), 1903 . . £35
ditto, Stokes (New York), 1904 . . . . . £30
Stingaree, Chatto & Windus (London), 1905 . . £45
ditto, Scribner's (New York), 1906 . . . . . £40
The Camera Fiend, Unwin (London), 1911 . . £50
ditto, Scribner's (New York), 1911 . . . . . £45
Fathers of Men, Smith Elder (London), 1912 . . £35
ditto, Scribner's (New York), 1912 . . . . . £30
Witching Hill, Hodder & Stoughton (London), 1913 . £50
ditto, Scribner's (New York), 1913 . . . . . £30
The Thousandth Woman, Eveleigh Nash (London), 1913 .
. . . . £35
ditto, Bobbs-Merrill (Indianapolis, IN), 1913 . . . £35

Short Stories
Under Two Skies, A & C Black, 1892 . . . . £75
Some Persons Unknown, Cassell (London), 1898 . . £65
ditto, Scribner's (New York), 1898 . . . . . £60
The Crime Doctor, Eveleigh Nash (London), 1914 . £65
ditto, Bobbs-Merrill (Indianapolis, IN), 1914 . . . £60
Old Offenders and a Few Old Scores, John Murray
(London), 1923 . . . . £125/£30

Poems
The Ballad of Ensign Joy, Dutton (New York), 1917 . £25
Wooden Crosses, Nisbet (London), 1918 . . . £35
The Young Guard, Constable (London), 1919 . . £40
E.W. Hornung and His Young Guard, 1914, Wellington
College Press (London), 1941 (edited by Shane Chichester;
wraps) £40

Non-Fiction
*Trusty and Well-Beloved: The Little Record of Arthur
Oscar Hornung*, by E.W.H., privately printed, 1915 . £45
Notes of a Camp-Follower on the Western Front, Constable
(London), 1919 . . . . £50

KHALED HOSSEINI
(b.1965)

Khaled Hosseini is an American novelist and physician
originally from Afghanistan. *The Kite Runner* was a bestseller and successfully filmed and the first edition is
currently expensive. It will be fascinating to see how the
value of this title might change over time.

The Kite Runner, Riverhead (New York), 2003 . £200/£25
ditto, Bloomsbury (London), 2003 (with red wrap-around
band) . . . . £200/£25
A Thousand Splendid Suns, Riverhead (New York), 2007 .
. . . . £10/£5
ditto, Bloomsbury (London), 2007 . . . . £15/£5
ditto, Bloomsbury (London), 2007 (limited edition of 1,500
signed copies) . . . . £50/£25

MICHEL HOUELLEBECQ
(b.1958?)

Michel Houellebecq (born Michel Thomas), born on the
French island of Réunion, is a controversial and award-
winning French novelist. He became famous following the
publication of the novel *Extension du domaine de la lutte*
in 1994 (translated as *Whatever*) and won the 1998 Prix
Novembre with *Les Particules élémentaires* (translated as
Atomised) which has been described as a 'nihilistic classic'.

Novels
Extension du domaine de la lutte, M. Nadeau (Paris), 1994
(pbk) £5
ditto, as *Whatever*, Serpent's Tail (London), 1999 (pbk;
translated by Paul Hammond) £5
Les Particules élémentaires, Flammarion (Paris), 1998 .
. . . . £25/£10
ditto, as *Atomised*, Heinemann (London), 2000 (translated by
Frank Wynne) . . . . £50/£10
ditto, as *The Elementary Particles*, Knopf (New York), 2000
. . . . £10/£5
Lanzarote, Flammarion (Paris), 2000 (2 vols; pbk) . £15
ditto, Heinemann (London), 2003 (translated by Frank
Wynne) . . . . £10/£5
Plateforme, Flammarion (Paris), 2001 . . . . £5
ditto, as *Platform*, Heinemann (London), 2002 (translated by
Frank Wynne) . . . . £10/£5
ditto, Knopf (New York), 2003 . . . . . £10/£5
La Possibilité d'une île, Fayard (Paris), 2005 . £10/£5
ditto, as *The Possibility of an Island*, Weidenfeld & Nicholson (London), 2005 (translated by by Gavin Bowd) £10/£5
ditto, Knopf (New York), 2005 . . . . . £10/£5

Other Books
Rester vivant, La Différence (Paris), 1991 (pbk) . £10
H.P. Lovecraft: Contre le monde, contre la vie, éditions du
Rocher (Monaco), 1991 (pbk) £5
ditto, as *H.P. Lovecraft: Against the World, Against Life*,
Believer Books (San Francisco, CA), 2005 (pbk) . £5
ditto, Weidenfeld & Nicolson (London), 2006 (pbk) . £5

La Poursuite du bonheur, La Différence (Paris), 1992 (pbk)
. . . . £5
Le Sens du combat, Flammarion (Paris), 1996 (pbk) . £5
Interventions, Flammarion (Paris), 1998 (pbk) . . £5
Renaissance, Flammarion (Paris), 1999 (pbk) . . . £5

GEOFFREY HOUSEHOLD
(b.1900 d.1988)

'Geoffrey Household' was a pseudonym used by Edward West. He is best known for his second novel, *Rogue Male*, although he wrote 20 other thrillers and adventure stories. 43 years after *Rogue Male* was published, the 82 year old Household wrote the sequel, *Rogue Justice*. His work is characterised by an interest in the psychology of the chase.

Novels
The Third Hour, Chatto & Windus (London), 1937 £125/£25
ditto, Little, Brown (Boston), 1938 . . . . £100/£20
Rogue Male, Chatto & Windus (London), 1939 £2,500/£250
ditto, Little, Brown (Boston), 1939 . . . . £350/£40
Arabesque, Chatto & Windus (London), 1948 . £45/£10
ditto, Little, Brown (Boston), 1948 . . . £35/£5
The High Place, Joseph (London), 1950 . . £30/£5
ditto, Little, Brown (Boston), 1950 . . . £20/£5
A Rough Shoot, Joseph (London), 1951 . . £40/£5
ditto, Little, Brown (Boston), 1951 . . . £20/£5
A Time to Kill, Little, Brown (Boston), 1951 . . £30/£5
ditto, Joseph (London), 1952 . . . . £20/£5
Fellow Passenger, Joseph (London), 1955 . £20/£5
ditto, Little, Brown (Boston), 1955 . . £20/£5
Watcher in the Shadows, Joseph (London), 1960 . £15/£5
ditto, Little, Brown (Boston), 1960 . . £15/£5
Thing to Love, Joseph (London), 1963 . . £15/£5
ditto, Little, Brown (Boston), 1963 . . . £15/£5
Olura, Joseph (London), 1965 . . . . £10/£5
ditto, Little, Brown (Boston), 1965 . . . £10/£5
The Courtesy of Death, Joseph (London), 1967 . £10/£5
ditto, Little, Brown (Boston), 1967 . . . £10/£5
Dance of the Dwarfs, Joseph (London), 1968 . . £10/£5
ditto, Little, Brown (Boston), 1968 . . . £10/£5
Doom's Caravan, Joseph (London), 1971. . £10/£5
ditto, Little, Brown (Boston), 1971 . . £10/£5
The Three Sentinels, Joseph (London), 1972 . . £10/£5
ditto, Little, Brown (Boston), 1972 . . . £10/£5
The Lives and Times of Bernardo Brown, Joseph (London), 1973 . . . . £10/£5
ditto, Little, Brown (Boston), 1974 . . . £10/£5
Red Anger, Joseph (London), 1975 . . . £10/£5
ditto, Little, Brown (Boston), 1976 . . . £10/£5
Hostage: London, Joseph (London), 1977 . £10/£5
ditto, Little, Brown (Boston), 1977 . . £10/£5
The Last Two Weeks of George Rivac, Joseph (London), 1978 . . . . £10/£5
ditto, Little, Brown (Boston), 1978 . . . £10/£5
The Sending, Joseph (London), 1980 . . £10/£5
ditto, Little, Brown (Boston), 1980 . . . £10/£5
Summon the Bright Water, Joseph (London), 1981 £10/£5
ditto, Little, Brown (Boston), 1981 . . . £10/£5
Rogue Justice, Joseph (London), 1982 . . £10/£5
ditto, Little, Brown (Boston), 1983 . . . £10/£5
Face to the Sun, Joseph (London), 1988 . . £10/£5

Short Stories
The Salvation of Pisco Gabar, Chatto & Windus (London), 1938 . . . . £85/£15
ditto, Little, Brown (Boston), 1940 . . . . £65/£5
Tales of Adventurers, Joseph (London), 1952 . . £20/£5
ditto, Little, Brown (Boston), 1952 . . . £15/£5
The Brides of Solomon, Joseph (London), 1958 . £20/£5
ditto, Little, Brown (Boston), 1958 . . . £15/£5
Sabres on the Sand, Joseph (London), 1966 . . £10/£5
ditto, Little, Brown (Boston), 1966 . . . £10/£5
The Europe That Was, David & Charles (London), 1979 . . . . £10/£5
ditto, St Martin's (New York), 1979 . . . £10/£5
Capricorn and Cancer, Joseph (London), 1981 . £10/£5
Arrows of Desire, Joseph (London), 1985 . £10/£5
ditto, Little, Brown (Boston), 1986 . . . £10/£5
The Days of Your Fathers, Joseph (London), 1987 £10/£5
ditto, Little, Brown (Boston), 1987 . . . £10/£5

Children's Titles
The Terror of Villadonga, Hutchinson (London), 1936 . . . . £75/£25
ditto, as *The Spanish Cave*, Little, Brown (Boston), 1936 (revised edition) . . . . £50/£20
The Exploits of Xenophon, Random House (New York), 1955 . . . . £15/£5
ditto, as *Xenophon's Adventure*, Bodley Head (London), 1961 . . . . £10/£5
Prisoner of the Indies, Bodley Head (London), 1967 £10/£5
ditto, Little, Brown (Boston), 1967 . . . £10/£5
Escape Into Daylight, Bodley Head (London), 1976 £10/£5

A.E. HOUSMAN
(b.1859 d.1936)

Housman was a classical scholar and poet, now best known for his cycle of poems *A Shropshire Lad*. Although his output was relatively small, it is very highly regarded. He didn't speak about his poetry publicly until a lecture given in 1933 entitled 'The Name and Nature of Poetry'. In this he argued that it should appeal to the emotions rather than the intellect of the reader.

Poetry
A Shropshire Lad, Kegan Paul, Trench, Trubner & Co. (London), 1896 (first state with 'Shropshire' on the label 33mm wide) £2,500
ditto, Kegan Paul, Trench, Trubner & Co. (London), 1896 (second state with 'Shropshire' on the label 37mm wide) £1,250
ditto, John Lane (New York), 1897 . . . £1,250
Last Poems, Grant Richards (London), [1922] (first issue with comma missing after 'love' and semicolon missing after 'rain' on p.52) . . . . . . £150/£25
ditto, Henry Holt (New York), 1922 . . . £75/£15
A Fragment, privately printed, 1930 (37 copies, two folded leaves) £200
Three Poems, privately printed, Dept of English, Univ College (London), 1935 . . . . . . £100
[*For my Funeral*], C.U.P., 1936 (300 copies, two folded leaves) £100
More Poems, Cape (London), 1936 . . . . £35/£10

ditto, Cape (London), 1936 (379 deluxe copies)   . £100/£65
ditto, Knopf (New York), 1936 .   .   .   .   . £30/£10
Collected Poems, Cape (London), 1939 .   .   . £25/£10
ditto, Henry Holt (New York), 1940 .   .   . £25/£10
Stars, Venice, 1939 (10 copies signed by the artist, F. Prokosch; wraps). £200
The Manuscript Poems of A.E. Housman, O.U.P. (London), 1955   .   .   .   . £30/£10
ditto, Univ of Minnesota (Minneapolis, MN), 1955 £30/£15

Prose
Introductory Lecture, C.U.P. (Cambridge, UK), 1892 (stitched) £350
ditto, privately printed, C.U.P. (Cambridge, UK), 1933 (100 copies; wraps) £100
ditto, C.U.P. (Cambridge, UK), 1937.   .   . £35/£10
ditto, Macmillan & C.U.P. (New York), 1937 .   . £30/£10
The Name and Nature of Poetry, C.U.P. (Cambridge, UK), 1933   .   .   .   . £45/£15
ditto, Macmillan (New York), 1933 .   .   . £45/£15
Jubilee Address to King George V, C.U.P. (Cambridge, UK), 1935 (2 copies of 26 on vellum)   .   .   . £1,250
ditto, C.U.P. (Cambridge, UK), 1935 (24 copies of 26). £600
Letters to E.H. Blakeney, privately printed (18 copies). £200
A.E.H., W.W., privately printed, 1944 (12 copies) .   . £175
Thirty Housman Letters to Witter Bynner, Knopf (New York), 1957 (700 copies) .   .   .   . £45/£20
A Shropshire Lad and Fragment of a Greek Tragedy, including Five Letters to Joseph Ishill, Oriole Press (Berkeley Heights, NJ), 1959 (50 copies)   .   . £25
Selected Prose, C.U.P. (Cambridge, UK), 1961   . £25/£10
Classical Papers, C.U.P. (Cambridge, UK), 1962 (3 vols) £50
The Confines of Criticism, C.U.P. (Cambridge, UK), 1969 .
.   .   .   . £30/£10
The Letters of A.E. Housman, Hart-Davis (London), 1971 .
.   .   .   . £35/£10
ditto, Harvard Univ Press (Cambridge, MA), 1971 £35/£10
Fifteen Letters to Walter Ashburner, Tragara Press (Edinburgh), 1976 (125 copies) £30

ELIZABETH JANE HOWARD
(b.1923)

London-born Howard was an actress and model before becoming an author. She took up writing novels and short stories after spending the War years as an Air Raid Warden in London. In 1951 she won the John Llewellyn Rhys Prize for her first novel, *The Beautiful Visit*. She married the naturalist Sir Peter Scott in 1942, Jim Douglas-Henry in 1958, and was Mrs Kingsley Amis from 1965 to 1983.

Novels
The Beautiful Visit, Cape (London), 1950   .   . £65/£15
ditto, Random House (New York), 1950 .   .   . £45/£5
The Long View, Cape (London), 1956   .   . £25/£5
ditto, Reynal (New York), 1956 .   .   .   . £25/£5
The Sea Change, Cape (London), 1959   .   . £20/£5
ditto, Harper (New York), 1960 .   .   .   . £20/£5
After Julius, Cape (London), 1965 .   .   . £15/£5
ditto, Viking (New York), 1966 .   .   .   . £15/£5

Something in Disguise, Cape (London), 1969.   . £15/£5
ditto, Viking (New York), 1970 .   .   .   . £10/£5
Odd Girl Out, Cape (London), 1972 .   .   . £10/£5
ditto, Viking (New York), 1972 .   .   .   . £10/£5
Getting It Right, Hamish Hamilton (London), 1982 £10/£5
ditto, Viking (New York), 1982 .   .   .   . £10/£5
The Light Years: Volume 1 of the Cazalet Chronicle, Macmillan (London), 1990   .   .   . £10/£5
ditto, Pocket Books (New York), 1990   .   . £10/£5
Marking Time: Volume 2 of the Cazalet Chronicle, Macmillan (London), 1991   .   .   . £10/£5
ditto, Pocket Books (New York), 1992   .   . £10/£5
Confusion: Volume 3 of the Cazalet Chronicle, Macmillan (London), 1993 .   .   .   .   . £10/£5
ditto, Pocket Books (New York), 1994   .   . £10/£5
Casting Off: Volume 4 of the Cazalet Chronicle, Macmillan (London), 1995   .   .   .   . £10/£5
ditto, Pocket Books (New York), 1996   .   . £10/£5
Falling, Macmillan (London), 1999   .   . £10/£5

Short Stories
We Are For the Dark: Six Ghost Stories, Cape (London), 1951 (with Robert Aickman)   .   .   . £325/£125
Mr Wrong, Cape (London), 1975   .   .   . £10/£5
ditto, Viking (New York), 1976 .   .   .   . £10/£5
Three Miles Up, Tartarus Press (Carlton-in-Coverdale, Yorkshire), 2003 .   .   .   .   . £25/£10

Miscellaneous
Bettina: A Portrait, Chatto & Windus (London), 1957 (with Arthur Helps)   .   .   .   .   . £10/£5
ditto, Reynal (New York), [1958]   .   .   . £10/£5
Howard and Maschler on Food, Joseph (London), 1987 (with Fay Maschler) .   .   .   . £10/£5
Slipstream: A Memoir, Macmillan (London), 2002 £10/£5

As Editor
The Lover's Companion, David & Charles (London), 1978
.   .   .   . £15/£5
Green Shades: An Anthology of Plants, Gardens and Gardeners, Aurum (London), 1991.   .   . £10/£5
Marriage, An Anthology, Dent (London), 1997   . £10/£5

ROBERT E. HOWARD
(b.1906 d.1936)

Howard was a Texan writer of pulp fantasy and historical adventures, whose range extended beyond his well known 'Conan the Barbarian' tales through 'Westerns' and sports stories. He also wrote tales of supernatural horror which borrowed heavily from his friend and correspondent H.P. Lovecraft, although he added his own trademarks of quickly-paced action and colourful characters.

'Conan' Novels
Conan the Conqueror, Gnome Press (New York), 1950   .
.   .   .   . £200/£50
ditto, Boardman (London), 1954.   .   .   . £150/£45
The Return of Conan, Gnome Press (New York), 1957 (by L. Sprague de Camp & Bjorn Nyberg)   .   . £125/£45
People of the Black Circle, Grant (West Kingston, RI), 1974
.   .   .   . £35/£15

Red Nails, Grant (West Kingston, RI), 1975 . . £25/£10
A Witch Shall Be Born, Grant (West Kingston, RI), 1975 .
  . . . . £25/£10
The Hour of the Dragon, Grant (West Kingston, RI), 1989.
  . . . . £20/£10

'Conan' Stories
The Sword of Conan: The Hyborean Age, Gnome Press
  (New York), 1952 . . . . . . £150/£45
King Conan: The Hyborean Age, Gnome Press (New York),
  1953 . . . . £175/£45
The Coming of Conan, Gnome Press (New York), 1953 .
  . . . . £150/£65
Conan the Barbarian, Gnome Press (New York), 1954 .
  . . . . £150/£65
Tales of Conan, Gnome Press (New York), 1955 (with L.
  Sprague de Camp) . . . . . . £125/£50
Conan the Adventurer, Lancer (New York), 1966 (pbk) £10
Conan the Warrior, Lancer (New York), 1967 (pbk) . £10
Conan the Usurper, Lancer (New York), 1967 (pbk) . £10
The Tower of the Elephant, Grant (West Kingston, RI),
  1975 . . . . £25/£10
The Devil in Iron, Grant (West Kingston, RI), 1976 £25/£10
Rogues in the House, Grant (West Kingston, RI), 1976 .
  . . . . £25/£10
Queen of the Black Coast, Grant (West Kingston, RI), 1978
  . . . . £25/£10
Black Colossus, Grant (West Kingston, RI), 1979 . £25/£10
Jewels of Gwahlur, Grant (West Kingston, RI), 1979 . .
  . . . . £25/£10
The Pool of the Black One, Grant (West Kingston, RI), 1986
  . . . . £25/£10
The Conan Chronicles, Orbit (London), 1990 (two vols;
  pbk) £10

Other Novels
Almuric, Ace (New York), 1964 (pbk) £10
ditto, New English Library (London), 1971 (pbk) . . £5
ditto, Grant (West Kingston, RI), 1975 . . . £25/£10

Other Short Stories
A Gent from Bear Creek, Herbert Jenkins (London), 1937 .
  . . . .£2,000/£1,000
ditto, Grant (West Kingston, RI), 1965 . . . £35/£10
Skull-Face and Others, Arkham House (Sauk City, WI),
  1946 . . . . £450/£100
ditto, as *Skull-Face Omnibus*, Spearman (London), 1974 .
  . . . . £40/£15
The Dark Man and Others, Arkham House (Sauk City, WI),
  1963 . . . . £125/£45
ditto, as *The Dark Man Omnibus*, Panther (London), 1978
  (two vols; pbk) £10
The Pride of Bear Creek, Grant (West Kingston, RI), 1966.
  . . . . £45/£15
King Kull, Lancer (New York), 1967 (with Lin Carter; pbk)
  . . . . £5
ditto, Bantam (New York), 1978. . . . . . £5
ditto, Grant (West Kingston, RI), 1985 . . . £20/£5
Wolfshead, Lancer (New York), 1968 (pbk) . . . £5
Red Shadows, Grant (West Kingston, RI), 1968 (first state
  with 'first edition' statement and the colour plates
  incorrectly ordered) . . . . . . £75/£30
ditto, Grant (West Kingston, RI), 1968 (second state without
  'first edition' statement and the colour plates correctly
  ordered). . . . . £40/£15

ditto, as *The Savage Tales of Solomon Kane*, Wandering
  Star (London), 1998 (1050 copies) £300
Bran Mak Morn, Dell (New York), 1969 (pbk) . . £5
ditto, Sphere (London), 1976 (pbk) £5
ditto, as *Kull*, Grant (West Kingston, RI), 1985 (revised text)
  . . . . £20/£10
Red Blades of Black Cathay, Grant (West Kingston, RI),
  1971 (with Tevis Clyde Smith). . . . £75/£25
Marchers of Valhalla, Grant (West Kingston, RI), 1972 .
  . . . . £20/£5
ditto, Sphere (London), 1977 (pbk) £5
The Vultures, Fictioneer (Lakemont, GA), 1973 . £20/£10
The Sowers of the Thunder, Grant (West Kingston, RI),
  1973 . . . . £35/£10
ditto, Sphere (London), 1977 (pbk) £5
Worms of the Earth, Grant (West Kingston, RI), 1974 . .
  . . . . £25/£10
ditto, Orbit/Futura (London), 1976 (pbk) £5
The Incredible Adventures of Dennis Dorgan, Fax (West
  Linn, OR), 1974 . . . . £15/£5
The Lost Valley of Iskander, Fax (West Linn, OR), 1974 .
  . . . . £15/£5
ditto, Orbit/Futura (London), 1976 (pbk) £5
Tigers of the Sea, Grant (West Kingston, RI), 1974 £20/£5
ditto, Sphere (London), 1977 (pbk) £5
Black Vulmea's Vengeance and Other Tales of Pirates,
  Grant (West Kingston, RI), 1976 . . . . £15/£5
The Iron Man and Other Tales of the Ring, Grant (West
  Kingston, RI), 1976 . . . . £10/£5
The Swords of Shahrazar, Fax (West Linn, OR), 1976. .
  . . . . £10/£5
ditto, Orbit/Futura (London), 1976 (pbk) £5
Son of the White Wolf, Fax (West Linn, OR), 1977 £10/£5
ditto, Futura (London), 1977 (pbk) £5
Three-Bladed Doom, Futura (London), 1977 (pbk) . £5
Mayhem on Bear Creek, Grant (West Kingston, RI), 1979 .
  . . . . £15/£5
The Road to Azrael, Grant (West Kingston, RI), 1979 . .
  . . . . £15/£5
Lord of the Dead, Grant (West Kingston, RI), 1981 £15/£5
Cthulhu: The Mythos and Kindred Horrors, Baen (New
  York), 1987 . . . . £20/£5
Post Oaks and Sand Roughs, Grant (West Kingston, RI),
  1991 . . . . £15/£5

Poetry
Always Comes Evening, Arkham House (Sauk City, WI),
  1957 . . . . £500/£125
Etchings in Ivory: Poems in Prose, Glenn Lord (Pasadena,
  TX), 1968 (268 copies; wraps). £65
Singers in the Shadows, Grant (West Kingston, RI), 1970
  (500 copies) . . . . £50/£15
Echoes from an Iron Harp, Grant (West Kingston, RI),
  1972 . . . . £45/£15
Rhymes of Death, McHaney (Memphis, TN), 1975 (600
  numbered copies; stapled wraps) £20
Shadows of Dreams, Grant (West Kingston, RI), 1991 . .
  . . . . £20/£10

Essay
The Hyborian Age, LANY Cooperative (Los Angeles), 1938
  (wraps) £750

L. RON HUBBARD
(b.1911 d.1986)

Despite writing a number of very collectable science fiction
titles, L. Ron Hubbard is best known as the founder of
Dianetics and Scientology. Hubbard had many science
fiction, fantasy, adventure and 'Western' stories and
novellas published in pulp magazines in the 1930s. He also
wrote philosophical works, self-help books, business management texts, essays and poetry.

Novels
Buckskin Brigades, Macaulay (New York), 1937 .   .   .
    .   .   .   .   £2,000/£200
ditto, Wright & Brown (London), [1938] .   .   . £650/£65
Final Blackout, Hadley Publishing (Providence, RI), 1948 .
    .   .   .   .   £150/£30
ditto, New Era (Redhill, Surrey), 1989 .   .   . £15/£5
Death's Deputy, Fantasy Publishing (Los Angeles, CA),
1948   .   .   .   . £100/£20
ditto, Fantasy Publishing/Gnome Press (New York), 1959
(sheets rebound by Gnome Press)   .   .   . £50/£15
Slaves of Sleep, Shasta (Chicago), 1948 .   .   . £100/£25
ditto, Shasta (Chicago), 1948 (250 signed copies)   .   .   .
    .   .   .   . £1,250/£500
Triton and *Battle of Wizards*, Fantasy Publishing (Los
Angeles, CA), 1949 .   .   .   .   .   . £100/£25
The Kingslayer, Fantasy Publishing (Los Angeles, CA),
1949   .   .   .   . £75/£20
Typewriter in the Sky and *Fear*, Gnome Press (New York),
1951   .   .   .   . £100/£20
ditto, Cherry Tree (London), 1952   .   .   .   . £20
From Death to the Stars, Fantasy Publishing (Los Angeles,
CA), 1953   .   .   .   . £300/£65
Return to Tomorrow, Ace (New York), 1954 (pbk)   . £10
ditto, Panther (London), 1957 (pbk) £5
Fear and the Ultimate Adventure, Berkley Medallion (New
York), 1970 (pbk) £10
Seven Steps to the Arbiter, Major Books (New York), 1975
(pbk) £10
Battlefield Earth, St Martin's Press (New York), 1982 .   .
    .   .   .   .   £20/£5
ditto, Quadrant (London), 1984 .   .   .   .   . £15/£5
Mission Earth, Bridge Publications (Los Angeles, CA),
1985-87 (ten vols: 'The Invader's Plan', 'Death Quest',
'Black Genesis', 'The Enemy Within', 'An Alien Affair',
'Fortune of Fear', 'Voyage of Vengeance', 'Disaster',
'Villainy Victorious' and 'The Doomed Planet') .   .   .
    .   .   .   . £10/£5 each
ditto, New Era (Redhill, Surrey), 1986-88 (10 vols)   .   .
    .   .   .   . £10/£5 each
ditto, Bridge Publications (Los Angeles, CA), 1987 (special
deluxe set) £200

Short Stories
Ole Doc Methuselah, Theta Press (Austin, TX), 1970 .   .
    .   .   .   .   £50/£15
ditto, New Era (Redhill, Surrey), 1993   .   .   £10/£5
Lives You Wished to Lead but Never Dared, Theta Books
(Austin, TX), 1978   .   .   .   .   .   . £50/£15
ditto, Theta Books (Austin, TX), 1978 (100 leather-bound
copies, no d/w) £250

Dianetics
Dianetics: The Modern Science of Mental Health,
Hermitage House (New York), 1950   .   .   . £250/£50

LANGSTON HUGHES
(b.1902 d.1967)

Langston Hughes was a black American poet, novelist,
short story writer, playwright and lyricist, who, along with
his contemporaries, was often in conflict with the aspirations of the black middle class. He was drawn to Commu-
nism as an answer to segregation in America.

Poetry
The Weary Blues, Knopf (New York), 1926 (first issue d/w
without blurb for *Fine Clothes to the Jew*)   . £4,000/£200
ditto, Knopf (New York), 1926 (second issue d/w with blurb)
    .   .   .   . £2,500/£200
Fine Clothes to the Jew, Knopf (New York), 1927   .   .
    .   .   .   .   £800/£200
Four Negro Poets, Simon & Schuster (New York), [1927]
(stapled wraps; also includes McKay, Toomer and Cullen)
    .   .   .   . £100
The Negro Mother and Other Dramatic Recitations, Golden
Stair Press (New York), 1931 (stapled wraps)   . £450
ditto, Golden Stair Press (New York), 1931 (17 signed,
numbered copies bound in Roma paper for presentation) .
    .   .   .   .   £1,500
The Negro Mother and Other Dramatic Recitations, Golden
Stair Press (New York), 1931 (broadside)   .   . £150
Dear Lovely Death, Troutbeck Press (Amenia, NY), 1931
(100 signed copies; orange printed boards, cloth back) .
    .   .   .   .   £1,250
The Black Clown, Golden Stair Press (New York), 1931
(broadside) £125
Broke, Golden Stair Press (New York), 1931 (broadside) .
    .   .   .   . £125
The Big-Timer, Golden Stair Press (New York), 1931
(broadside) £125
Dark Youth of the USA, Golden Stair Press (New York),
1931 (broadside) £125
Barrel House, Troutbeck Press [Amenia, NY], 1931
(broadside) £125
The Dream Keeper and Other Poems, Knopf (New York),
1932   .   .   .   . £600/£100
Scottsboro Limited: Four Poems and A Play in Verse,
Golden Stair Press, New York, 1932 (wraps)   . £250
ditto, Golden Stair Press (New York), 1932 (30 copies signed
by Hughes and illustrator Prentiss Taylor)   .   £1,000
August 19th; A Poem for Clarence Norris, Communist
Party (Birmingham, AL), 1934 (broadside)   .   . £250
A New Song, International Workers Order (New York), 1938
    .   .   .   . £100
Good-Bye Christ, no publisher (Pasadena, CA), 1940
(broadside) £75
The Negro Speaks of Rivers, no publisher (no place), [1941]
    .   .   .   . £200
Shakespeare in Harlem, Knopf (New York), 1942 £250/£65
Freedom's Plow, Musette Publishers (New York), 1943
(stapled wraps) £125
Jim Crow's Last Stand, Negro Publication Society of
America ([Atlanta, GA]), 1943 (wraps; Race and Culture

Series No. 2; first issue with 'Belt' upside down on contents page) £125

ditto, Negro Publication Society of America ([Atlanta, GA]), 1943 ('Belt' correct) £60

Lament for Dark Peoples and Other Poems, no publisher (Netherlands), 1944 (250 copies; wraps) . . . £200

ditto, no publisher (Netherlands), 1944 (50 numbered copies; wraps) £450

Ballad of the Seven Songs, American Negro Press Association (no place), [c. mid 1940s] (3pps, mimeographed one side only) £125

Fields of Wonder, Knopf (New York), 1947 . £200/£40

Cuba Libre, Ward Ritchie Press (Los Angeles, CA), 1948 (no d/w). £125

One-Way Ticket, Knopf (New York), 1949 . £200/£35

Montage of a Dream Deferred, (Holt, New York), 1951 . . . . £165/£40

Selected Poems of Langston Hughes, Knopf (New York), 1959 . . . . £75/£20

Ask Your Mama: 12 Moods for Jazz, Knopf (New York), 1961 . . . . £150/£30

The Panther and the Lash: Poems of Our Times, Knopf (New York), 1967 . . . . . £75/£15

ditto, Knopf (New York), 1967 (pbk). . . . £25

The Backlash Blues, Broadside Press (Detroit, MI), 1967 (broadside) £30

Is Love, Unicorn Press, [Santa Barbara, CA], [1967] (325 broadside copies). £10

Pair in One, Unicorn Press, [Santa Barbara, CA], [1968] (325 broadside copies) £10

Black Misery, P.S. Erikson (New York), 1969 . £40/£10

The Innocent, Unicorn Press, Santa Barbara, CA, 1969 (broadside) £15

Don't You Turn Back, Knopf (New York), 1969 . £30/£5

Dream Boogie, Poems on the Underground, no publisher (London), 1979 (broadside) £10

The Collected Poems of Langston Hughes, Knopf (New York), 1994 . . . . £15/£5

Let America Be America Again, Black Oak Books (Berkeley, CA), 1990 (200 copies; broadside) . . £25

The Block, Viking/The Metropolitan Museum of Art (New York), 1995 . . . . £10/£5

The Pasteboard Bandit, O.U.P. (New York/Oxford), 1997 (written with Arna Bontemps) . . . . £10/£5

Sunrise Is Coming After While, Limited Editions Club (New York), 1998 200 numbered copies signed by Maya Angelou and by Phoebe Beasley; slipcase) . . £1,000

ditto, Limited Editions Club (New York), 1998 200 numbered copies signed by Maya Angelou and by Phoebe Beasley; slipcase) £2,000

Carol of the Brown King: Nativity Poems, Athenaeum Books (New York), 1998 . . . . . £10/£5

Fiction

Not Without Laughter, Knopf (New York), 1930 £800/£150

ditto, Allen & Unwin (London), 1930 . . £300/£60

The Ways of White Folks, Knopf (New York), 1934 . . . . £600/£125

ditto, Allen & Unwin (London), 1934 . . £250/£60

Simple Speaks His Mind, Simon & Schuster (New York), 1950 . . . . £175/£25

ditto, Gollancz (London), 1951 . . . . £75/£15

Laughing to Keep from Crying, Holt (New York), 1952 . . . . £125/£15

Simple Takes a Wife, Simon & Schuster (New York), 1953 (paper boards; no d/w. £100

ditto, Gollancz (London), 1954 . . . . £100/£20

Sweet Flypaper of Life, Simon & Schuster (New York), 1955 . . . . £450/£75

ditto, Simon & Schuster (New York), 1955 (pbk) . £75

ditto, Gollancz (London), 1958 . . . . £50/£10

Tambourines to Glory, John Day (New York), 1958 . . . . £200/£40

ditto, Gollancz (London), 1959 . . . . £50/£10

The Best of Simple, Hill & Wang, (New York), 1961 . . . . £60/£15

ditto, Hill & Wang (New York), 1961 (pbk) . . £20

Simple's Uncle Sam, Hill & Wang (New York), 1965 . . . . £75/£15

ditto, Hill & Wang (New York), 1965 (pbk) . . £20

ditto, Gollancz (London), 1965 . . . . £45/£10

Something in Common and Other Stories, Hill & Wang (New York), 1963 . . . . . £45/£10

ditto, Hill & Wang (New York), 1963 (pbk) . . £20

The Simple Omnibus, Aeonian Press (Mattiuck, NY), 1978 . . . . £30/£5

Langston Hughes: Laughing to Keep From Crying and 25 Jesse Simple Stories, Franklin Library (Franklin Center, PA), 1981 (full leather limited edition) . . . £30

Short Stories of Langston Hughes, Hill & Wang (New York), 1996 . . . . £10/£5

The Return of Simple, Hill and Wang/Farrar, Straus & Giroux (New York), 1994 . . . . . £10/£5

Plays

Simply Heavenly, Dramatist Play Service (New York), 1957 (stapled wraps) £45

Black Nativity, Dramatic Publishing Company (Woodstock, IL), 1992 (wraps). £5

Five Plays, Indiana Univ Press (Bloomington, IA), 1963 . . . . £80/£20

Mule Bone: A Comedy Of Negro Life, Harper Perennial (New York), 1991 (written with Zora Neale Hurston; no d/w) £65

ditto, Harper Perennial (New York), 1991 (pbk) . £10

Political Plays of Langston Hughes, Southern Illinois Univ Press (Carbondale, IL), 2000 . . . . . £15/£5

Translations

Masters of the Dew, by Jacques Roumain, Reynal & Hitchcock (New York), 1947 . . . . £100/£20

ditto, Heinemann (London), 1978 (pbk) . . . £5

Cuba Libre; Poems, by Nicolas Guillen, Ward Ritchie Press (Los Angeles, CA), 1948 (with Ben Carruthers; no d/w) £125

Selected Poems of Gabriela Mistral, Indiana Univ Press (Bloomington, IN), 1957 . . . . . £50/£10

Blood Wedding and Yerma, by Federico Garcia Lorca, Theatre Communications Group (New York), 1994 (with W.S. Merwin) . . . . £10/£5

Autobiography

The Big Sea, Knopf (New York), 1940 . £300/£75

ditto, Hutchinson (London), 1940 . . . £150/£40

I Wonder as I Wander, Rinehart (New York), 1956 . . . . £100/£20

Books for Children

Popo and Fifina, Macmillan (New York), 1932 (written with
Arna Bontemps) . . . . . . £450/£150
The First Book of Negroes, Franklin Watts (New York),
1952 . . . . £125/£25
ditto, Bailey & Swinfen (London), 1956 . . . £75/£20
The First Book of Rhythms, Franklin Watts (New York),
1954 . . . . £150/£30
ditto, Bailey & Swinfen (London), 1956 . . £75/£20
The First Book of Jazz, Franklin Watts (New York), 1955 .
. . . . £175/£40
ditto, Bailey & Swinfen (London), 1957 . . £75/£20
The First Book of the West Indies, Franklin Watts (New
York), 1956 . . . . £100/£20
ditto, Bailey & Swinfen (London), 1956 . . . £75/£15
First Book of Africa, Franklin Watts (New York), 1960 .
. . . . £75/£15
ditto, Mayflower (London), 1956 . . . £45/£10
Thank You, Ma'am, Creative Education (Mankato, MO),
1991 . . . . £15/£5
The Sweet and Sour Animal Book, O.U.P. (New York),
1994 . . . . £10/£5

Non-Fiction

A Negro Looks At Central Asia, Co-operative Publishing
Society of Foreign Workers in the U.S.S.R. (Moscow/
Leningrad), 1934 (wraps) £250
My Adventures as a Social Poet, Atlanta Univ (Atlanta,
GA), 1947 (offprint in grey wraps printed in red from
Phylon) £175
Famous American Negroes, Dodd, Mead (New York), 1954
. . . . £175/£30
A Pictorial History of the Negro in America, Crown (New
York), 1956 (with Milton Meltzer) . . . £100/£20
ditto, as *A Pictorial History of Black Americans*, Crown
(New York), 1973 (adds C. Eric Lincoln as co-author) .
. . . . £30/£10
*Remarks by Langston Hughes in Acceptance of 45th
Springarn Medal at NAACP 51st Annual Convention*, no
publisher (no place), [1960] (single sheet printed on both
sides) £75
Fight for Freedom: The Story of the NAACP, W.W. Norton
(New York), 1962 . . . . . . £75/£20
The Civil Rights Calendar 1965, Carver Federal Savings &
Loan Association (New York), 1965 (wraps, in envelope).
. . . . £45
A 1966 Calendar of Inventions and Discoveries, Carver
Federal Savings & Loan Association (New York), 1966
(wraps, in envelope) £45
*Black Magic, A Pictorial History of The Negro In
American Entertainment*, Prentice Hall (Englewood
Cliffs, NJ), 1967 . . . . . . £125/£30
*Langston Hughes and the Chicago Defender: Essays on
Race, Politics and Culture, 1942-62*, Univ of Illinois Press
(Urbana, IL), 1995 (pbk) £5

Lyrics/Librettos

Street Scene, Chappell & Co. (New York), 1948 (sewn
wraps) £175
Troubled Island, Leeds Music Co. (New York), 1949
(stapled wraps; opera by William Grant Still) . £175
The Ballad of the Brown King, Sam Fox (New York), 1961
(with Margaret Bond; stapled wraps) . . . £100

Other

The Langston Hughes Reader, Braziller (New York), 1958
. . . . £60/£10
*Good Morning Revolution: Uncollected Social Protest
Writings*, Lawrence Hill (Westport, NY), 1973 . £25/£10
ditto, Lawrence Hill (Westport, NY), 1973 (pbk) . . £10
Arna Bontemps-Langston Hughes Letters 1925-1967,
Dodd, Mead (New York), 1980 . . . . £25/£10
The Collected Works of Langston Hughes, Univ of
Missouri Press (Columbia, MO), 2001-2002 (15 vols) .
. . . . £15/£5 each

RICHARD HUGHES
(b.1900 d.1976)

Richard Arthur Warren Hughes was a British writer of
poems, short stories, novels and plays. He is best known
for *A High Wind in Jamaica*, the story of children kidnapped by pirates. The novel's lack of sentimentality was
considered unusual at the time. Hughes was a Fellow of the
Royal Society of Literature, and was awarded the O.B.E. in
1946.

Novels

The Innocent Voyage, Harper (New York), 1929 . £150/£25
ditto, as *A High Wind in Jamaica*, Chatto & Windus
(London), 1929 . . . . . . £75/£15
ditto, Chatto & Windus (London), 1929 (150 signed copies)
. . . . £250
In Hazard, Chatto & Windus (London), 1938 . . £30/£5
ditto, Harper (New York), 1938 . . . . £30/£5
The Fox in the Attic, Chatto & Windus (London), 1961 .
. . . . £20/£5
ditto, Harper (New York), 1961 . . . . £20/£5
ditto, Harper (New York), 1961 (unknown number of copies
with signature on tipped-in leaf) . . . £30/£15
The Wooden Shepherdess, Chatto & Windus (London),
1973 . . . . £20/£5
ditto, Harper (New York), 1973 . . . . £20/£5

Short Stories

A Moment of Time, Chatto & Windus (London), 1926 . .
. . . . £100/£20
Burial and *The Dark Child*, Chatto & Windus (London),
1930 . . . . £75/£15
In the Lap of Atlas, Chatto & Windus (London), 1979 . .
. . . . £20/£5
ditto, Merrimack (New York), 1980 . . . £20/£5

Plays

The Sister's Tragedy, Blackwell (Oxford), 1922 (wraps) £65
The Sister's Tragedy and Other Plays, Heinemann
(London), 1924 . . . . . . £75/£20
ditto, as *A Rabbit and a Leg, Collected Plays*, Knopf (New
York), 1924 . . . . £45/£10

Poetry

Gipsy-Night and Other Poems, Golden Cockerell Press
(Waltham St Lawrence, Berks), 1922 (750 copies) . .
. . . . £75/£35
ditto, Will Ransom (Chicago), 1922 (63 copies) . . £200

Confessio Juvenis: Collected Poems, Chatto & Windus
(London), 1925 (55 signed, numbered copies)   . £175/£75
ditto, Chatto & Windus (London), 1925 .   .   . £65/£20

Children's Titles
The Spider's Palace, Chatto & Windus (London), 1931 .
.   .   .   . £40/£10
ditto, Chatto & Windus (London), 1931 (110 numbered,
signed copies) £100
ditto, Harper (New York), 1932 .   .   .   . £35/£10
Don't Blame Me and Other Stories, Chatto & Windus
(London), 1940 .   .   .   . £25/£5
ditto, Harper (New York), 1940 .   .   .   . £20/£5
Gertrude's Child, Harlin Quist (New York), 1966 . £25/£10
The Wonder Dog, Chatto & Windus (London), 1977 £20/£5

Others
Richard Hughes: An Omnibus, Harper (New York), 1931 .
.   .   .   . £20/£5
The Administration of War Production, H.M.S.O. (London),
1955 (with J.D. Scott).   .   .   .   .   . £35/£10

TED HUGHES

(b.1930 d.1998)

Ted Hughes is chiefly known for his poetry, which often
depicts the cruelties of the animal world and the malevo-
lence of creatures of his own invention. Hughes was married to the American poet Sylvia Plath from 1956-63.
Considered by many to be the finest poet of his generation,
he was made Poet Laureate in 1984 and awarded the Order
of Merit in 1998.

Poetry
The Hawk in the Rain, Faber (London), 1957.   . £375/£50
ditto, Harper (New York), 1957 .   .   .   . £125/£35
Pike, Gehenna Press (Northampton, MS), 1959 (broadsheet,
150 signed copies) £600
Lupercal, Faber (London), 1960.   .   .   . £250/£45
ditto, Harper (New York), 1960 .   .   .   . £100/£25
Selected Poems, Faber (London), 1962 (with Thom Gunn;
pbk) £30
The Burning of the Brothel, Turret Books (London), 1966
(75 numbered and signed copies; sewn wraps with d/w) .
.   .   .   . £150/£100
ditto, Turret Books (London), 1966 (225 unsigned copies;
sewn wraps with d/w).   .   .   .   .   . £45/£30
Recklings, Turret Books (London), 1966 (150 numbered and
signed copies) .   .   .   .   .   . £250/£200
Scapegoats and Rabies, Poet & Printer (London), 1967
(approx. 400 copies; stapled wraps)   .   .   . £30
ditto, Poet & Printer (London), 1967 (in portfolio with three
other poetry chapbooks published by the press; stapled
wraps) £150
ditto, Poet & Printer (London), 1967 (26 lettered copies for
the poet; stapled wraps) £300
Wodwo, Faber (London), 1967 .   .   .   . £65/£10
ditto, Harper & Row (New York), 1967 .   . £30/£10
Animal Poems, Gilbertson (Crediton, Devon), 1967 (6
signed copies with poems handwritten by Hughes) £1,000
ditto, Gilbertson (Crediton, Devon), 1967 (10 signed copies
with three manuscript poems) £750

ditto, Gilbertson (Crediton, Devon), 1967 (20 signed copies
with one manuscript poem) £500
ditto, Gilbertson (Crediton, Devon), 1967 (63 signed,
numbered copies) £300
Gravestones, Bartholomew (Exeter, Devon), 1967 (set of 6
broadsheets, 40 sets printed) £1,000
ditto, as *Poems*, Bartholomew (Exeter, Devon), 1967 (300
copies). £100
I Said Goodbye to Earth, Turret Books (London), 1969
(broadsheet, 75 signed, numbered copies)   .   . £150
A Crow Hymn, Sceptre Press (Farnham, Surrey), 1970 (21
signed copies for sale) £350
ditto, Sceptre Press (Farnham, Surrey), 1970 (64 unsigned
copies) £175
The Martyrdom of Bishop Farrar, Gilbertson (Crediton,
Devon), 1970 (signed copies; stapled wraps)   . £200
ditto, Gilbertson (Crediton, Devon), 1970 (rejected printing,
lines 15 and 16 of the poem transposed).   .   . £125
A Few Crows, Rougemont Press (Exeter, Devon), 1970 (75
signed, numbered copies) .   .   .   . £250/£150
ditto, Rougemont Press (Exeter, Devon), 1970 (75 unsigned
copies) .   .   .   . £125/£75
Crow: From the Life and Songs of the Crow, Faber
(London), 1970 .   .   .   . £50/£10
ditto, Harper & Row (New York), 1971 (with 7 poems
added) .   .   .   . £30/£10
Fighting for Jerusalem, Northumberland Arts (Ashington),
1970 (poster) £30
Crow Wakes, Poet & Printer (London), 1971 (200 copies)
.   .   .   . £125
Eat Crow, Rainbow Press (London), 1971 (150 signed,
numbered copies, slipcase) .   .   .   . £300/£250
Poems, Rainbow Press, 1971 (with Ruth Fainlight and Alan
Sillitoe, 300 copies, numbered and signed by all three
poets, slipcase) .   .   .   .   .   . £125/£75
In the Little Girl's Angel Gaze, Steam Press (London), 1972
(broadsheet, 50 signed and numbered copies)   . £200
Selected Poems, 1957-1967, Faber (London), 1972 (pbk) £10
ditto, Harper & Row (New York), 1973 .   .   . £50/£15
Prometheus on His Crag, Rainbow Press (London), 1973
(160 copies signed by Hughes and Leonard Baskin,
slipcase).   .   .   .   . £300/£200
Cave Birds, Scolar Press (London), 1975 (10 sheets issued in
box, 125 sets printed). £1,000
ditto, as *Cave Birds: An Alchemical Cave Drama*, Faber
(London), 1978 .   .   .   . £25/£5
ditto, Viking (New York), 1978 .   .   .   . £25/£5
The Interrogator: A Titled Vulturess, Scolar Press
(London), 1975 (250 numbered copies).   .   . £25/£10
The New World, O.U.P. (Oxford, UK), 1975 (six poems by
Hughes set for medium voice and piano by Gordon Crosse)
.   .   .   . £25/£10
Eclipse, Sceptre Press (Knotting, Beds), 1976 (50 signed
copies; stapled wraps) £125
ditto, Sceptre Press (Knotting, Beds), 1976 (200 unsigned
copies; stapled wraps) £20
Gaudete, Faber (London), 1977 .   .   .   . £20/£5
ditto, Harper & Row (New York), 1977 .   .   . £20/£5
Chiasmadon, Janus Press (West Burke, VT), 1977 (120
signed copies; wraps). £250
ditto, Janus Press (West Burke, VT), 1977 (55 roman
numeralled, signed copies; wraps) £300
Sunstruck, Sceptre Press (Knotting, Beds), 1977 (100
signed, numbered copies) £125

ditto, Sceptre Press (Knotting, Beds), 1977 (200 numbered copies) £25

A Solstice, Sceptre Press (Knotting, Beds), 1978 (100 signed, numbered copies; stapled wraps) £125

ditto, Sceptre Press (Knotting, Beds), 1978 (250 numbered copies; stapled wraps) £25

Orts, Rainbow Press (London), 1978 (200 numbered and signed copies, slipcase) . . . . . £250/£150

Moortown Elegies, Rainbow Press (London), 1978 (6 author's copies) £1,000

ditto, Rainbow Press (London), 1978 (26 signed, lettered copies bound in full morocco; slipcase) . . £600/£500

ditto, Rainbow Press (London), 1978 (143 signed, numbered copies; slipcase) . . . . . . £400/£300

Adam and the Sacred Nine, Rainbow Press (London), 1979 (200 numbered and signed copies, slipcase) . £200/£150

Remains of Elmet, Rainbow Press (London), 1979 (with photographs by Fay Godwin; numbered 1-70, signed by Hughes and the photographer, leather-bound) £650/£500

ditto, Rainbow Press (London), 1979 (numbered 71-180, signed by Hughes, ordinary binding) . . £400/£300

ditto, Faber (London), 1979 . . . . . £25/£10

ditto, Harper & Row (New York), 1979 . . £25/£10

The Threshold, Steam Press (London), 1979 (100 copies of 12 leaves, illustrated by Ralph Steadman, and signed by Hughes and Steadman) £500

Night Arrival of Sea-Trout, The Iron Wolf, Puma, Morrigu Press [North Tawton, Devon], 1979 (30 folders with three signed and numbered broadsheets) £500

Brooktrout, Morrigu Press [North Tawton, Devon], 1979 (60 signed, numbered copies, broadsheet) £175

Pan, Morrigu Press [North Tawton, Devon], 1979 (60 signed, numbered copies, broadsheet) £175

Woodpecker, Morrigu Press [North Tawton, Devon], 1979 (60 signed, numbered copies, broadsheet) . . .£175

Moortown, Faber (London), 1979 . . . . £25/£5

ditto, Harper (New York), 1980 . . . . . £20/£5

Wolverine, Morrigu Press [North Tawton, Devon], 1979 (75 signed, numbered copies, broadsheet) £150

Four Tales Told by an Idiot, Sceptre Press (Knotting, Beds), 1979 (450 numbered copies with erratum slip) . . £25

ditto, Sceptre Press (Knotting, Beds), 1979 (100 signed copies with erratum slip) £125

In the Black Chapel, Victoria and Albert Museum (London), 1979 (drawing by Leonard Baskin; poster) . . . £30

ditto, Victoria and Albert Museum (London), 1980 (150 numbered copies signed by Hughes and Baskin) . .£250

Couples under Cover, Rainbow Press (London), 1979 (100 signed, numbered copies; broadsheet) £150

February 17th, Rainbow Press (London), 1979 (100 signed, numbered copies; broadsheet) £150

Ravens, Rainbow Press (London), 1979 (100 signed, numbered copies; broadsheet) £150

Teaching a Dumb Calf, Rainbow Press (London), 1979 (100 signed, numbered copies; broadsheet) £150

Eagle, Morrigu Press [North Tawton, Devon], 1980 (75 signed, numbered copies, broadsheet) £200

Mosquito, Morrigu Press [North Tawton, Devon], 1980 (60 signed, numbered copies, broadsheet) £200

Catadrome, Morrigu Press [North Tawton, Devon], 1980 (75 signed, numbered copies, broadsheet) £200

Caddis, Morrigu Press [North Tawton, Devon], 1980 (75 signed, numbered copies, broadsheet) £200

Visitation, Morrigu Press [North Tawton, Devon], 1980 (75 signed, numbered copies, broadsheet) £200

A Primer of Birds, Gehenna Press (Lurley, Devon), 1981 (250 copies numbered and signed by Hughes and artist, Leonard Baskin) £750

ditto, Gehenna Press (Lurley, Devon), 1981 (25 roman numeralled copies numbered and signed by Hughes and artist, Leonard Baskin, with an extra suite of plates) £1,250

Wolf-Watching, Morrigu Press [North Tawton, Devon], 1981 (75 signed, numbered copies; wraps) . . .£250

Selected Poems, 1957-1981, Faber (London), 1982   £15/£5

ditto, as *New Selected Poems*, Harper (New York), 1982 . . . . £15/£5

River, Faber (London), 1983 . . . . . £25/£5

ditto, Harper (New York), 1984 . . . . . £20/£5

Weasels at Work, Morrigu Press [North Tawton, Devon], 1983 (75 signed copies; wraps) £250

Fly Inspects, Morrigu Press [North Tawton, Devon], 1983 (75 signed copies; wraps) £250

Mice are Funny Little Creatures, Morrigu Press [North Tawton, Devon], 1983 (75 signed copies; wraps). .£250

Flowers and Insects: Some Birds and a Pair of Spiders, Faber (London), 1986. . . . . . . £25/£5

ditto, Knopf (New York), 1986 . . . . . £25/£5

Moortown Diary, Faber (London), 1989 . . . £20/£5

ditto, Faber (London), 1989 (pbk) £5

Wolf-Watching, Faber (London), 1989 . . . £20/£5

ditto, Farrar, Straus and Giroux (New York), 1991. . £20/£5

Rain-Charm for the Duchy, Faber (London), 1992   £15/£5

ditto, Faber (London), 1992 (280 signed copies with loose insert, 'The Unicorn', slipcase) £125

ditto, Faber (London), 1992 (pbk) £5

Three Books: Remains of Elmet, Cave Birds, River, Faber (London), 1993 (pbk). £10

Elmet, Faber (London), 1994 . . . . . £30/£10

Earth Dances, Old Stile Press (Llandogo), 1994 (250 signed copies, slipcase) . . . . . . £250/£200

New Selected Poems, 1957-94, Faber (London), 1995 £15/£5

Ted Hughes Poetry, Collins Educational (London), 1997 . . . . £10/£5

Birthday Letters, Faber (London), 1998 . . £25/£5

ditto, Faber (London), 1998 (300 signed copies) . .£300

ditto, Farrar Straus Giroux (New York), 1998 . . £25/£5

Howls and Whispers, Gehenna Press (Hadley, MA), 1998 (with 11 etchings by Leonard Baskin, 100 numbered copies signed by the poet and the artist) £600

ditto, Gehenna Press (Hadley, MA), 1998 (10 deluxe copies with extra material) £1,250

Collected Poems, Faber (London), 2003 . . £25/£5

ditto, Farrar Straus Giroux (New York), 2003 . . £25/£5

Children's Poetry

Meet My Folks!, Faber (London), 1961 . . .£125/£25

ditto, Bobbs-Merrill (Indianapolis, IN), 1973 . . £35/£10

The Earth-Owl and Other Moon-People, Faber (London), 1963 . . . . £40/£15

ditto, as *Moon-Whales and Other Moon Poems*, Viking (New York), 1976 (combined with *Earth-Moon*) . £25/£5

ditto, as *Moonwhales*, Faber (London), 1988 . . £10/£5

Nessie the Mannerless Monster, Faber (London), 1964 . . . . £75/£15

ditto, as *Nessie the Monster*, Bobbs-Merrill (Indianapolis, IN), 1974 . . . . £25/£5

Five Autumn Songs for Children's Voices, Gilbertson (Bow, Devon), 1968 (9 copies for sale with a verse in manuscript and a watercolour). £450
ditto, Gilbertson (Bow, Devon), 1968 (27 copies with a verse in manuscript; wraps). £250
ditto, Gilbertson (Bow, Devon), 1968 (150 signed copies; wraps) £65
ditto, Gilbertson (Bow, Devon), 1968 (312 numbered copies) £20

Spring Summer Autumn Winter, Rainbow Press (London), 1974 (140 numbered and signed copies) . . . £200
ditto, as *Season Songs*, Viking (New York), 1975 . £20/£5
ditto, Faber (London), 1976 . . . . . £20/£5
Earth-Moon, Rainbow Press (London), 1976 (26 lettered copies for the author) . . . . . £250/£200
ditto, Rainbow Press (London), 1976 (100 signed and numbered copies bound in leather) . . . £200/£150
ditto, Rainbow Press (London), 1976 (100 signed and numbered copies bound in paper-covered boards) . £150
Moon-Bells and Other Poems, Chatto & Windus (London), 1978 . . . . £25/£5
Under the North Star, Faber (London), 1981 . £40/£10
ditto, Viking (New York), 1981 . . . . £35/£5
The Cat and the Cuckoo, Sunstone Press (Bideford, Devon), [1987] (200 sets of 28 loose prints in a grey paper portfolio) £1,000
ditto, Sunstone Press (Bideford, Devon), [1987] (250 signed copies in d/w and slipcase) . . . £200/£150
ditto, Faber (London), 1991 . . . . £15/£5
Under the North Star and Others, Faber (London), 1990 .
. . . . £20/£5
Collected Animal Poems, Faber (London), 1995 (4 vols) .
. . . . £40/£10
ditto, Faber (London), 1996 (1 vol.) . . . £15/£5
The Mermaid's Purse, Faber (London), 1999 . £15/£5
ditto, Knopf (New York), 2000 . . . . £15/£5

Children's Prose
How the Whale Became, Faber (London), 1963 . £65/£15
ditto, Atheneum (New York), 1964 . . . £45/£10
The Iron Man: A Story in Five Nights, Faber (London), 1968 . . . . £400/£150
ditto, as *The Iron Giant*, Harper & Row (New York), 1968 .
. . . . £250/£75
What is the Truth?, Faber (London), 1984 . £25/£5
ditto, Harper (New York), 1984 . . . . £20/£5
Ffangs the Vampire Bat and the Kiss of Truth, Faber (London), 1986 . . . . £20/£5
Tales of the Early World, Faber (London), 1988 . £20/£5
ditto, Farrar, Straus and Giroux (New York), 1991 . £10/£5
The Iron Woman, Faber (London), 1993 . . £15/£5
ditto, Dial (New York), 1995 . . . . £15/£5
Dreamfighter and Other Creation Tales, Faber (London), 1995 . . . . £15/£5
Shaggy and Spotty, Faber (London), 1997 . £15/£5

Others
Poetry in the Making, Faber (London), 1967 (no d/w) . £50
ditto, as *Poetry Is*, Doubleday (Garden City, NY), 1970 .
. . . . £35/£10
Seneca's Oedipus, Faber (London), 1969 (adapted by Hughes). . . . . £25/£5
ditto, Doubleday (Garden City, NY), 1972 . . £20/£5

The Coming of the Kings and Other Plays, Faber (London), 1970 . . . . £25/£5
ditto, as *Tiger's Bones and Other Plays for Children*, Viking (New York), 1974 . . . . . £20/£5
Shakespeare's Poem, Lexham Press (London), 1971 (75 signed copies; sewn wraps) £125
The Coming of the Kings: A Christmas Play in One Act, Dramatic Publishing Company (Chicago), 1972 (stapled wraps) £30
Orpheus, Dramatic Publishing Company (Chicago), 1973 (1,023 copies; stapled wraps) £30
The Story of Vasco: Opera in Three Acts, O.U.P. (London), 1974 (music by Gordon Crosse, libretto by Hughes; stapled wraps) £45
Beauty and the Beast: A Play in One Act, Dramatic Publishing Company (Chicago), 1974 (stapled wraps) £30
Sean, the Fool, the Devil and the Cats, Dramatic Publishing Company (Chicago), 1974 (stapled wraps) . . . £30
The Tiger's Bones, Dramatic Publishing Company (Chicago), 1974 (stapled wraps) £30
Henry Williamson, Rainbow Press (London), 1979 (200 signed, numbered copies; wraps) £100
T.S. Eliot: A Tribute, Faber (London), 1987 (privately printed, 250 copies; wraps) £165
Shakespeare and the Goddess of Complete Being, Faber (London), 1992 . . . . £15/£5
ditto, Farrar Straus Giroux (New York), 1992 . £15/£5
A Dancer to God: Tributes to T.S. Eliot, Faber (London), 1992 . . . . £15/£5
ditto, Farrar, Straus and Giroux (New York), 1993 . £15/£5
Winter Pollen: Occasional Prose, Faber (London), 1994 .
. . . . £20/£5
ditto, Picador (New York), 1995 . . . . £15/£5
Difficulties of a Bridegroom, Faber (London), 1995 £20/£5
ditto, Picador (New York), 1995 . . . . £15/£5
Euripides' Alcestis, Faber (London), 1999 . £20/£5
ditto, Farrar (New York), 1999 . . . . £15/£5

ZORA NEALE HURSTON
(b.1891 d.1960)

Zora Neale Hurston was an American author whose interest in black folklore informs much of her work. As a student of anthropology, however, she experienced some ambivalence in trying to maintain the position of a scientific observer while acknowledging her feelings as an intuitive participant.

Fiction
Jonah's Gourd Vine, Lippincott (Philadelphia, PA), 1934 .
. . . . £3,500/£900
ditto, Duckworth (London), 1934 . £1,250/£250
Their Eyes Were Watching God, Lippincott (Philadelphia, PA) 1937 . . . . £4,000/£400
ditto, Dent (London), 1938 . . . . £2,000/£200
Moses, Man of the Mountains, Lippincott (Philadelphia, PA), 1939 (red/brown cloth) . . . £1,000/£200
ditto, Lippincott (Philadelphia, PA), 1939 (green cloth) .
. . . . £1,000/£150
ditto, as *The Man of the Mountain*, Dent (London), 1941 .
. . . . £450/£75

Seraph on the Suwanee, Charles Scribner's (New York), 1948 . . . . £450/£75

Spunk: The Selected Short Stories of Zora Neale, Turtle Island (Berkeley, CA), 1985 (wraps) . . . £10

The Gilded Six-Bits, Redpath Press (Minneapolis, MN), 1986 (wraps, in envelope). . . . . £15/£10

Spunk: Three Tales by Zora Neale Hurston, Theatre Communications Group (New York), 1991 . . . £10

The Complete Stories of Zora Neale Hurston, HarperCollins (New York), 1995 . . . £10/£5

Zora Neale Hurston Novels and Stories, Library of America (New York), 1995 (subscriber copies in slipcase; no d/w) .

. . . . £10/£5

ditto, Library of America (New York), 1995 (trade copies in d/w) . . . . £10/£5

Bookmarks in the Pages of Life, Limited Editions Club (New York), 2000 (300 numbered copies signed by artist Betye Saar; in slipcase) . . . £1,500/£1,250

What's The Hurry Fox? And Other Animal Stories, HarperCollins (New York), 2004 (laminated pictorial boards; no d/w) £5

Play

Mule Bone: A Comedy Of Negro Life, Harper Perennial (New York), 1991 (written with Langston Hughes; no d/w)

. . . . £65

ditto, Harper Perennial (New York), 1991 (wraps) . . £10

Other Titles

Mules and Men, Lippincott (Philadelphia, PA), 1935 . .

. . . . £1,500/£300

ditto, Kegan, Paul (London), 1936 . . . £600/£100

Tell My Horse, Lippincott (Philadelphia, PA), 1938 . .

. . . . £1,000/£175

ditto, as *Voodoo Gods, An Inquiry Into Native Myths and Magic in Jamaica and Haiti*, Dent (London), 1939 . .

. . . . £500/£100

Dust Tracks on a Road: An Autobiography, Lippincott (Philadelphia, PA), 1942 . . . £600/£150

ditto, Hutchinson (London), [1944] . . . £200/£35

ditto, Virago (London), 1986 (wraps; restored text) . £10

The Sanctified Church, Turtle Island (Berkeley, CA), 1981 (cloth in acetate d/w) . . . . £65/£50

Folklore, Memoirs and Other Writing, Library of America (New York), 1995 (subscriber copies in slipcase; no d/w) .

. . . . £10/£5

ditto, Library of America (New York), 1995 (trade copies in d/w) . . . . £10/£5

Every Tongue Got To Confess, HarperCollins (New York), 2002 . . . . £10/£5

A Life in Letters, Doubleday (New York/London etc), 2002 . . . . £10/£5

Collection

I Love Myself When I'm Laughing, Feminist Press (Old Westbury, NY), 1979 . . . . . . £250/£35

Go Gator and *Muddy the Waters*, W.W. Norton (New York), 1999 . . . . . . £10/£5

FERGUS HUME
(b.1859 d.1932)

Although Hume was born in England his family emigrated to New Zealand, and he later moved to Melbourne, Australia. He self-published his first novel, *The Mystery of a Hansom Cab* (1886), which became the top selling mystery novel of the Victorian era. Hume returned to England in 1888. His mysteries are considered precursors of the popular detective fiction of the 20th century.

Novels

The Mystery of the Hansom Cab, Kemp & Boyce (Melbourne), [1886] (wraps) £3,000

ditto, Hansom Cab Publishing Co (London), [1887] (wraps)

. . . . £1,500

ditto, Munro (New York), 1888 . . . . . £1,000

Professor Brankel's Secret, Baird's Railway Bookstall (Melbourne), [c.1886] (wraps) £1,500

Madame Midas, Hansom Cab Publishing Co (London), 1888 (wraps) £1,000

ditto, Munro (New York), 1888 . . . . . . £500

The Girl from Malta, Hansom Cab Publishing Co (London), [1889] (wraps) £1,000

ditto, Lovell (New York), 1889 . . . . . £500

The Piccadilly Puzzle, F.V. White (London), 1889 . £250

ditto, Lovell (New York), 1889 (with two additional stories)

. . . . £250

The Gentleman Who Vanished, F.V. White (London), 1890

. . . . £250

ditto, as *The Man Who Vanished*, Liberty (New York), 1892

. . . . £225

The Man with a Secret, F.V. White (London), 1890 (3 vols)

. . . . £750

Miss Mephistopheles, F.V. White (London), 1890. . £250

ditto, Lovell (New York), 1890 . . . . . £250

Who God Hath Joined, F.V. White (London), 1891 (3 vols)

. . . . £500

The Year of Miracle, Routledge (London), 1891 . £250

ditto, Lovell (New York), 1891 . . . . . £200

A Creature of the Night, Sampson Low (London), 1891 (wraps) £200

ditto, Lovell (New York), 1891 . . . . . £175

The Fever of Life, Lovell (New York), 1891 . . £175

ditto, Sampson Low (London), 1892 (2 vols) . . £300

Monsieur Judas, Spencer Blackett (London), 1891 . £200

ditto, Waverly (New York), 1891 . . . . . £175

The Island of Fantasy, Griffith & Farran (London), 1892 (3 vols) £500

When I Lived in Bohemia, Arrowsmith (London), [1892] £75

ditto, Tait (New York), 1892 . . . . . . £75

The Chronicles of Faeryland, Griffith & Farran (London), 1892 . . . . £85

ditto, Lippincott (New York), 1893 . . . . £50

The Black Carnation, Gale & Polden (London), 1892 (cloth or wraps) £175

ditto, U.S. Book Co (New York), 1892 . . . £150

Aladdin in London, A & C Black (London), 1892. . £125

ditto, Houghton Mifflin (New York), 1892 . . £100

A Speck of the Motley, Innes (London), 1893 (wraps) . £100

The Harlequin Opal, W.H. Allen (London), 1893 (3 vols) .

. . . . £400

ditto, McNally Rand (New York), 1893 . . . £100

The Chinese Jar, Sampson Low (London), 1893 . . £200	
The Best of Her Sex, W.H. Allen (London), 1894 (2 vols) .	
. . . . £200	
The Gates of Dawn, Sampson Low (London), 1894 . £150	
ditto, Neely (New York), 1894 . . . . . £100	
The Lone Inn, Jarrolds (London), 1894 . . . . £150	
ditto, Cassell (New York), 1895 . . . . . £100	
A Midnight Mystery, Gale & Polden (London), [1894] . £150	
The Mystery of Landy Court, Jarrolds (London), 1894 . £150	
The Crime of 'Liza Jane, Ward Lock (London), 1895 . £150	
The Expedition of Captain Flick, Jarrolds (London), 1895 .	
. . . . £150	
The Masquerade Mystery, Digby Long (London), [1895] .	
. . . . £150	
The Third Volume, Cassell (New York), 1895 . £125	
The Unwilling Bride, Ogilvie (New York), 1895 . . £100	
The White Prior, Warne (London), [1895] . . £100	
The Carbuncle Clue, Warne (London), [1896] . . £100	
A Marriage Mystery, Digby Long (London), [1896] . £100	
Tracked by a Tattoo, Warne (London), 1896 . . £100	
Claude Duval of Ninety Five, Digby Long (London), 1897 .	
. . . . £100	
ditto, Dillingham (New York), 1897 . . . . £100	
The Tombstone Treasure, Daffodil Library (London), 1897	
. . . . £100	
The Clock Struck One, Warne (London), 1898 . £100	
The Devil Stick, Downey (London), [1898] . . £100	
For the Defense, Rand McNally (New York), 1898 . £100	
Lady Jezebel, Pearson (London), 1898 . . . £100	
ditto, Mansfield (New York), 1898 . . . . £100	
The Rainbow Feather, Digby Long (London), 1898 . £100	
ditto, Dillingham (New York), 1898 . . . . £100	
The Indian Bangle, Sampson Low (London), 1899 . £100	
The Red-Headed Man, Digby Long (London), 1899 . £100	
The Silent House in Pimlico, Digby Long (London), 1899 .	
. . . . £100	
ditto, as *The Silent House*, Doscher (New York), 1907 . £75	
The Bishop's Secret, Digby Long (London), 1900 . £75	
ditto, as *Bishop Pendle; or The Bishop's Secret*, Rand	
McNally (New York), 1900 . . . . . £75	
The Crimson Cryptogram, Digby Long (London), 1900 £75	
ditto, New Amsterdam Book Company (New York), 1902 .	
. . . . £75	
Shylock of the River, Digby Long (London), 1900 . £75	
A Traitor in London, Digby Long (London), 1900 . £75	
ditto, Buckles (New York), 1900 . . . . £75	
The Lady from Nowhere, Chatto & Windus (London), 1900	
. . . . £65	
ditto, Brentano's (New York), 1900 . . . . £75	
The Vanishing of Tera, F.V. White (London), 1900 . £75	
The Crime of the Crystal, Digby Long (London), 1901 £75	
The Golden Wang Ho, Digby Long (London), 1901 . £75	
ditto, as *Secret of the Chinese Jar*, Westbrook (New York),	
1928 . . . . £125/£20	
The Mother of Emeralds, Hurst & Blackett (London), 1901	
. . . . £65	
The Millionaire Mystery, Chatto & Windus (London), 1901	
. . . . £65	
ditto, Buckles (New York), 1901 . . . . £65	
A Woman's Burden, Jarrolds (London), 1901 . . £50	
The Pagan's Cup, Digby Long (London), 1902 . £50	
ditto, Dillingham (New York), 1902 . . . . £50	
The Turnpike House, Digby Long (London), 1902 . £50	
Woman the Sphinx, Digby Long (London), 1902 . £50	

The Jade Eye, Digby Long (London), 1903 . . . £50	
The Miser's Will, Treherne (London), 1903 . . . £50	
The Silver Bullet, Digby Long (London), 1903 . £50	
The Guilty House, F.V. White (London), 1903 . £50	
The Yellow Holly, Digby Long (London), 1903 . £50	
ditto, Dillingham (New York), 1903 . . . . £50	
The Coin of Edward VII, Digby Long (London), 1903. £50	
ditto, Dillingham (New York), 1903 . . . . £50	
The Mandarin's Fan, Digby Long (London), 1904 . £50	
ditto, Dillingham (New York), 1904 . . . . £50	
The Lonely Church, Digby Long (London), 1904 . £50	
The Red Window, Digby Long (London), 1904 . £50	
ditto, Dillingham (New York), 1904 . . . . £45	
The Wheeling Light, Chatto & Windus (London), 1904 £50	
The Wooden Hand, F.V. White (London), 1905 . . £50	
The Fatal Song, F.V. White (London), 1905 . . £50	
Lady Jim of Curzon Street, Werner Laurie (London), [1905]	
. . . . £50	
ditto, Dillingham (New York), 1906 . . . . £50	
The White Room, F.V. White (London), 1905. £50	
The Opal Serpent, Digby Long (London), 1905 . £50	
ditto, Dillingham (New York), 1905 . . . . £50	
The Scarlet Bat, F.V. White (London), 1905 . . £50	
The Secret Passage, Digby Long (London), 1905 . £50	
ditto, Dillingham (New York), 1905 . . . . £50	
The Black Patch, Digby Long (London), 1906 . £50	
Jonah's Luck, F.V. White (London), 1906 . . £65	
The Mystery of the Shadow, Cassell (London), 1906 . £50	
ditto, Dodge (New York), 1906 . . . . . £45	
The Purple Fern, Everett (London), 1907 . . . £45	
The Sealed Message, Dillingham (New York), 1907 . £40	
ditto, Digby Long, 1908 . . . . . . £40	
The Yellow Hunchback, F.V. White (London), 1907 . £40	
The Amethyst Cross, Cassell (London), 1908 . . £35	
Flies in the Web, F.V. White (London), 1908 . . £45	
The Crowned Skull, Werner Laurie (London), [1908] . £35	
ditto, as *The Red Skull*, Dodge (New York), 1908 . £45	
The Green Mummy, Digby Long (London), 1908 . £45	
ditto, Dillingham (New York), 1908 . . . . £45	
The Mystery of a Motor Cab, Everett (London), 1908 . £40	
The Sacred Herb, Digby Long (London), 1908 . £40	
ditto, Dillingham (New York), 1908 . . . . £35	
The Devil's Ace, Everett (London), 1909 . . . £40	
The Disappearing Eye, Digby Long (London), 1909 . £40	
ditto, Dillingham (New York), 1909 . . . . £35	
The Top Dog, F.V. White (London), 1909 . . £40	
The Solitary Farm, Ward Lock (London), 1909 . £40	
ditto, Dillingham (New York), 1909 . . . . £35	
The Lonely Subaltern, F.V. White (London), 1910 . £40	
The Mikado Jewel, Everett (London), 1910 . . £40	
The Peacock Jewels, Digby Long (London), 1910. £40	
ditto, Dillingham (New York), 1910 . . . . £35	
The Spider, Ward Lock (London), 1910 . . . £40	
High Water Mark, F.V. White (London), 1911 . £40	
The Jew's House, Ward Lock (London), 1911 . £40	
The Pink Shop, F.V. White (London), 1911 . . £40	
The Rectory Governess, F.V. White (London), 1911 . £35	
Red Money, Dillingham (New York), 1911 . . £35	
ditto, Ward Lock (London), 1912 . . . . £35	
The Steel Crown, Digby Long (London), 1911 . £35	
ditto, Dillingham (New York), 1911 . . . . £35	
Across the Footlights, F.V. White (London), 1912 . £35	
The Blue Talisman, Werner, Laurie (London), 1912 . £35	
ditto, Clode (New York), 1925 . . . . . £65/£15	

A Son of Perdition, Rider (London), 1912 . . £35
Mother Mandarin, F.V. White (London), 1912 . £35
The Mystery Queen, Ward Lock (London), 1912 . £35
ditto, Dillingham (New York), 1912 . . . . £35
The Curse, Werner, Laurie (London), 1913 . . £35
In Queer Street, F.V. White (London), 1913 . . £35
The Thirteenth Guest, Ward Lock (London), 1913 £35
Seen in the Shadow, F.V. White (London), 1913 . £35
The 4 P.M. Express, F.V. White (London), 1914 . £35
Not Wanted, F.V. White (London), 1914 . . £35
The Lost Parchment, Ward Lock (London), 1914 . £35
ditto, Dillingham (New York), 1914 . . . . £35
Answered: A Spy Story, F.V. White (London), 1915 . £35
The Caretaker, Ward Lock (London), 1915 . . £35
The Red Bicycle, Ward Lock (London), 1916 . . £35
The Silent Signal, Ward Lock (London), 1917 . £35
The Grey Doctor, Ward Lock (London), 1917 . £35
The Black Image, Ward Lock (London), 1918 . £35
Heart of Ice, Hurst & Blackett (London), 1918 . £35
Next Door, Ward Lock (London), 1918 . . . £35
Crazy Quilt, Ward Lock (London), 1919 . . . £35
The Master-Mind, Hurst & Blackett (London), [1919] . £30
The Dark Avenue, Ward Lock (London), 1920 . £150/£20
The Other Person, F.V. White (London), 1920 . £150/£20
The Singing Head, Hurst & Blackett (London), [1920] .
. . . . £150/£20
The Woman Who Held On, Ward Lock (London), 1920 .
. . . . £150/£20
Three, Ward Lock (London), 1921 . . £150/£20
The Unexpected, Odhams (London), 1921 . £150/£20
A Trick of Time, Hurst & Blackett (London), [1922] £150/£20
The Moth Woman, Hurst & Blackett (London), [1923] .
. . . . £150/£20
The Whispering Lane, Hurst & Blackett (London), [1924] .
. . . . £150/£20
ditto, Small Maynard (New York), 1925 . . . £150/£20
The Caravan Mystery, Hurst & Blackett (London), [1926] .
. . . . £125/£20
The Last Straw, Hutchinson (London), [1932] . £125/£20
The Hurton Treasure Mystery, Mellifont (London), 1937 .
. . . . £100/£20

Short Stories
The Dwarf's Chamber, Ward Lock (London), 1896 . £125
Hagar of the Pawn Shop, Skeffington (London), 1898. £150
ditto, Buckles (New York), 1898 . . . . £65
The Dancer in Red, Digby Long (London), 1906 . £50

ALDOUS HUXLEY

(b.1894 d.1963)

A British novelist and short story writer, much of Huxley's
work is marked by a certain despair and disgust, none more
so than his great novel of the future, *Brave New World*.
Huxley also published poetry, essays and travel writing.
While his earlier concerns were humanist, he became more
interested in spiritual subjects and mystical philosophy.

Poetry
The Burning Wheel, Blackwell (Oxford), 1916 (wraps) £450
Jonah, Holywell (Oxford), 1917 (approx 50 signed copies;
wraps) £1,500

The Defeat of Youth and Other Poems, Blackwell (Oxford),
1918 (250 copies; decorated stiff wraps; no title-page) £125
Leda, Chatto & Windus (London), 1920 . . £150/£75
ditto, Chatto & Windus (London), 1920 (160 signed,
numbered copies) £75
ditto, Doran (New York), 1920 . . . . . £100/£45
ditto, Doran (New York), 1929 (361 numbered and signed
copies, slipcase) . . . . . . £125/£100
Selected Poems, Blackwell (Oxford), 1925 . . . £35
ditto, Appleton (New York), 1925 . . . £65/£15
ditto, Blackwell (Oxford), 1926 (100 signed copies) . £150
Arabia Infelix, Fountain Press (New York)/Chatto &
Windus (London), 1929 (692 signed, numbered copies,
glassine d/w). . . . . £125/£100
Apennine, Slide Mountain Press (Gaylordsville), 1930 (91
signed, numbered copies, glassine d/w) . £350/£300
The Cicadas and Other Poems, Chatto & Windus (London),
1931 . . . . £45/£15
ditto, Chatto & Windus (London), 1931 (160 signed,
numbered copies) . . . . £100/£85
ditto, Doubleday Doran (New York), 1931 . . £50/£15
Verses and a Comedy, Chatto & Windus (London), 1946 .
. . . . £45/£15
Collected Poetry of Aldous Huxley, Chatto & Windus
(London), 1971 . . . . £20/£5
ditto, Harper (New York), 1971 . . . . £20/£5

Short Stories
Limbo, Chatto & Windus (London), 1920 (6 stories and a
play) . . . . £200/£30
ditto, Doran (New York), 1920 . . . . . £125/£25
Mortal Coils, Chatto & Windus (London), 1922 . £125/£20
ditto, Doran (New York), 1922 . . . . . £65/£15
Little Mexican and Other Stories, Chatto & Windus
(London), 1924 . . . . £100/£35
ditto, as *Young Archimedes*, Doran (New York), 1924 . .
. . . . £75/£25
Two or Three Graces and Other Stories, Chatto & Windus
(London), 1926 . . . . £75/£25
ditto, Doran (New York), 1926 . . . . . £50/£15
Brief Candles, Fountain Press (New York), 1930 (842
signed, numbered copies). £75
ditto, Doubleday Doran (New York), 1930 . £45/£10
ditto, Chatto & Windus (London), 1930 . . £45/£10
Collected Short Stories, Chatto & Windus (London), 1957 .
. . . . £20/£5
ditto, Harper (New York), 1957 . . . . £20/£5

Novels
Crome Yellow, Chatto & Windus (London), 1921 . £500/£65
ditto, Doran (New York), 1922 . . . . . £200/£45
Antic Hay, Chatto & Windus (London), 1923 . . £350/£45
ditto, Doran (New York), 1923 . . . . . £100/£25
Those Barren Leaves, Chatto & Windus (London), 1925 .
. . . . £85/£15
ditto, Doran (New York), 1925 . . . . . £65/£15
ditto, Doran (New York), 1925 (250 signed, numbered
copies) £125
Point Counter Point, Chatto & Windus (London), 1928 .
. . . . £75/£15
ditto, Chatto & Windus (London), 1928 (256 signed,
numbered copies) £250
ditto, Doubleday Doran (New York), 1928 . £75/£15

Brave New World, Chatto & Windus (London), 1932   .   .
.   .   .   .   £2,500/£100
ditto, Chatto & Windus (London), 1932 (324 signed,
numbered copies) £2,000
ditto, Doubleday Doran (New York), 1932   . £1,250/£150
ditto, Doubleday Doran (New York), 1932 (250 signed,
numbered copies) £1,500
Eyeless in Gaza, Chatto & Windus (London), 1936 £150/£25
ditto, Chatto & Windus (London), 1936 (200 signed,
numbered copies) £225
ditto, Harper (New York), 1936   .   .   .   .   £125/£25
After Many a Summer, Chatto & Windus (London), 1939   .
.   .   .   .   £100/£25
ditto, as *After Many a Summer Dies the Swan*, Harper (New
York), 1939   .   .   .   .   £75/£20
Time Must Have a Stop, Chatto & Windus (London), 1944.
.   .   .   .   £40/£10
ditto, Harper (New York), 1945   .   .   .   .   £30/£10
Ape and Essence, Harper (New York), 1948   .   .   £25/£5
ditto, Chatto & Windus (London), 1949   .   .   £30/£5
The Genius and the Goddess, Chatto & Windus (London),
1955   .   .   .   .   £25/£5
ditto, Harper (New York), 1955   .   .   .   .   £20/£5
Island, Chatto & Windus (London), 1962   .   .   £20/£5
ditto, Harper (New York), 1962   .   .   .   .   £20/£5

Drama

The World of Light, Chatto & Windus (London), 1931   .
.   .   .   .   £45/£10
ditto, Chatto & Windus (London), 1931 (160 signed,
numbered copies) £100
ditto, Doubleday Doran (New York), 1931   .   .   £45/£10
The Gioconda Smile, Chatto & Windus (London), 1948   .
.   .   .   .   £35/£5
ditto, Harper (New York), 1948   .   .   .   .   £30/£5

Others

On the Margin, Chatto & Windus (London), 1923 (first
issue with page 'vi' numbered 'v')   .   .   .   £85/£20
ditto, Doran (New York), 1923   .   .   .   .   £75/£15
Along the Road, Chatto & Windus (London), 1925 £65/£20
ditto, Doran (New York), 1925   .   .   .   .   £40/£5
ditto, Doran (New York), 1925 (250 signed, numbered
copies, slipcase and d/w)   .   .   .   .   £150/£100
Essays New and Old, Chatto & Windus (London), 1926 (650
signed, numbered copies)   .   .   .   .   £150/£100
ditto, Doran (New York), 1927   .   .   .   .   £45/£10
Jesting Pilate, Chatto & Windus (London), 1926   . £75/£15
ditto, Doran (New York), 1926   .   .   .   .   £65/£15
Proper Studies, Chatto & Windus (London), 1927. £65/£15
ditto, Chatto & Windus (London), 1927 (260 signed,
numbered copies)   .   .   .   .   .   £100/£85
ditto, Doubleday Doran (New York), 1928   .   £50/£15
Do What You Will, Chatto & Windus (London), 1929   .   .
.   .   .   .   £45/£10
ditto, Chatto & Windus (London), 1929 (260 signed,
numbered copies) £125
ditto, Doubleday Doran (New York), 1929   .   £45/£10
Holy Face and Other Essays, The Fleuron Press (London),
1929 (300 numbered copies, slipcase)   .   .   £100/£75
Vulgarity in Literature, Chatto & Windus (London), 1930,
No. 1 of the 'Dolphin's Books'   .   .   .   £35/£10
ditto, Chatto & Windus (London), 1930 (260 signed,
numbered copies) £125

Music at Night and Other Essays, Chatto & Windus
(London), 1931   .   .   .   .   .   .   £40/£10
ditto, Chatto & Windus (London)/Fountain Press (New
York), 1931 (842 signed, numbered copies) .   .   . £65
ditto, Doubleday Doran (New York), 1931   .   . £35/£10
Rotunda, Chatto & Windus (London), 1932   .   £45/£15
T.H. Huxley as a Man of Letters, Macmillan (London),
1932 (wraps). £75
Texts and Pretexts, Chatto & Windus (London), 1932 (214
signed, numbered copies). £100
ditto, Chatto & Windus (London), 1932   .   .   £25/£5
ditto, Harper (New York), 1933   .   .   .   .   £25/£5
Beyond the Mexique Bay, Chatto & Windus (London), 1934
.   .   .   .   £125/£25
ditto, Chatto & Windus (London), 1934 (210 signed,
numbered copies) £165
ditto, Harper (New York), 1934   .   .   .   .   £75/£10
The Olive Tree and Other Essays, Chatto & Windus
(London), 1936   .   .   .   .   .   .   £50/£15
ditto, Chatto & Windus (London), 1936 (160 signed,
numbered copies) £150
ditto, Harper (New York), 1937   .   .   .   .   £35/£10
*What Are You Going to do About It? The Case for
Constructive Peace*, The Peace Pledge Union (London),
[1935] (stapled wraps) £65
ditto, Chatto & Windus (London), 1936 (stapled wraps) £35
ditto, Harper (New York), 1937 (stapled wraps)   .   . £35
Ends and Means, Chatto & Windus (London), 1937 £50/£15
ditto, Chatto & Windus (London), 1937 (160 signed,
numbered copies) £175
ditto, Harper (New York), 1937   .   .   .   .   £35/£10
The Most Agreeable Vice, Ward Ritchie Press (Los Angeles,
CA), 1938 (500 copies; sewn or stapled wraps)   .   .£125
Beyond the Swarm, Ward Ritchie Press (Los Angeles, CA),
1939 (300 copies; wraps) £200
Words and Their Meanings, Ward Ritchie Press (Los
Angeles, CA), 1940   .   .   .   .   .   .   £50/£30
ditto, Ward Ritchie Press (Los Angeles, CA), 1940 (100
signed copies for Jake Zeitlin)   .   .   .   £250/£200
Grey Eminence: A Study in Religion and Politics, Chatto &
Windus (London), 1941   .   .   .   .   .   £25/£5
ditto, Harper (New York), 1941   .   .   .   .   £25/£5
The Art of Seeing, Harper (New York), 1942   .   .   £25/£5
ditto, Chatto & Windus (London), 1943   .   .   £25/£5
The Perennial Philosophy, Harper (New York), 1945 £25/£5
ditto, Chatto & Windus (London), 1945   .   .   £25/£5
Science, Liberty and Peace, Harper (New York), 1946 £15/£5
ditto, Chatto & Windus (London), 1947   .   .   £20/£5
Prisons, Trianon Press (London), 1949 (1,000 unsigned
copies) £60
ditto, Trianon Press (London)/Grey Falcon Press
(Philadelphia, PA), 1949 (100 signed copies)   .   .£225
ditto, Zeitlin & Ver Brugge (Los Angeles, CA), 1949 (100
signed copies) £200
Themes and Variations, Chatto & Windus (London), 1950.
.   .   .   .   £25/£5
ditto, Harper (New York), 1950   .   .   .   .   £20/£5
The Devils of Loudun, Chatto & Windus (London), 1952   .
.   .   .   .   £25/£5
ditto, Harper (New York), 1952   .   .   .   .   £20/£5
Joyce, the Artificer, Chiswick (London), 1952 (90 copies)   .
.   .   .   .£250
The French of Paris, Harper (New York), 1954 (with
Sanford Roth)   .   .   .   .   £50/£15

The Doors of Perception, Chatto & Windus (London), 1954 . . . . £50/£10
ditto, Harper (New York), 1954 . . . . £45/£10
Heaven and Hell, Chatto & Windus (London), 1956 £30/£10
ditto, Harper (New York), 1956 . . . . £20/£5
Adonis and the Alphabet, Chatto & Windus (London), 1956 . . . . £15/£5
ditto, as *Tomorrow and Tomorrow and Tomorrow*, Harper (New York), 1956 . . . £15/£5
Brave New World Revisited, Chatto & Windus (London), 1958 . . . . . . £30/£5
ditto, Harper (New York), 1958 . . . . £25/£5
Collected Essays, Harper (New York), 1959 . £20/£5
ditto, Chatto & Windus (London), 1960 . . £20/£5
On Art and Artists, Chatto & Windus (London), 1960 £20/£5
ditto, Harper (New York), 1960 . . . . £15/£5
Literature and Science, Chatto & Windus (London), 1960 . . . . £15/£5
ditto, Harper (New York), 1963 . . . . £15/£5
The Crows of Pearblossom, Chatto & Windus (London), 1967 (illustrated by Barbara Cooney) . . . £30/£10
ditto, Random House (New York), 1967 (hardback without d/w) £10
Letters of Aldous Huxley, Chatto & Windus (London), 1969 . . . . £30/£10
ditto, Harper (New York), 1969 . . . . £25/£10

J.K. HUYSMANS
(b.1848 d.1907)

À Rebours, or *Against the Grain* (also translated as *Against Nature*) was a highly sensational and influential novel, which, like Huysmans' early novels was heavily influenced by the writings of Emile Zola. The dates of publication of the English translations of Huysmans' books do not follow the chronology of their original publication in Europe.

Novels
Marthe, Histoire d'une Fille, Gay (Brussels), 1876 . £200
ditto, Dentu (Paris), 1879 . . . . . . £125
ditto, as *Marthe, Story of a Prostitute*, Lear (New York), 1948 . . . . £30/£10
ditto, Fortune Press (London), 1958 . . . £45/£20
Les Soeurs Vatard, Charpentier (Paris), 1879 . . £175
ditto, as *Vatard Sisters*, Univ of Kentucky Press (Lexington, KY), 1983 . . . . £25/£5
En Ménage, Charpentier (Paris), 1881 . . . £150
ditto, as *Living Together*, Fortune Press (London), 1969 . . . . £40/£25
A Vau-l'Eau, Kistemaeckers (Brussels), 1882 (with a portrait by Amédée Lynen) £200
ditto, Tresse et Stock (Paris), 1894 (with a portrait by A. Delâtre) £150
ditto, as *Downstream and Other Works*, Pascal Covici (Chicago), 1927 . . . . . . £100/£35
ditto, Fortune Press (London), 1952 . . . £65/£30
À Rebours, Charpentier (Paris), 1884 . . . £300
ditto, as *Against the Grain*, Lieber & Lewis (New York), 1922 . . . . £65/£20
ditto, Fortune Press (London), 1931 . . . £75/£25
Un Dilemme, Tresse et Stock (Paris), 1887 . . £150
En Rade, Tresse et Stock (Paris), 1887 . . . £125

ditto, as *Becalmed*, Atlas Press (London), 1992 (pbk) . £5
Là-bas, Tresse et Stock (Paris), 1891 . . . . £125
ditto, as *Down There*, Albert & Charles Boni (New York), 1924 . . . . £125/£25
ditto, Fortune Press (London), 1930 . . . £75/£25
En Route, Tresse et Stock (Paris), 1895 . . . £150
ditto, as *En Route*, Kegan Paul (London), 1896 . £75
ditto, Dutton (New York), 1920 . . . . £65/£25
La Cathédrale, Stock (Paris), 1898 . . . £100
ditto, as *The Cathedral*, Kegan Paul (London), 1898 . £50
L'Oblat, Stock (Paris), 1903 . . . . . £100
ditto, as *The Oblate*, Kegan Paul (London), 1924 . £50/£25

Short Story
Knapsack, Collier (London), 1907 . . . . . £25

Essays, Prose Poems etc
Le Drageoir aux Épices, Dentu (Paris), 1874 . . . £250
ditto, as *Pastels in Prose*, Harper (New York), 1890 £40/£15
Croquis Parisiens, Vaton (Paris), 1880 (545 copies with illustrations by Forain and Raffaëlli) . . . £250
ditto, as *Parisian Sketches*, Fortune Press (London), 1962 . . . . £35/£15
Pierrot Sceptique, Rouveyre (Paris), 1881. (a pantomine in collaboration with Léon Hennique) £250
L'Art Moderne, Charpentier (Paris), 1883 . . . £200
Certains, Tresse et Stock (Paris), 1889 . . . £50
La Bièvre: 'Les Vieux Quartiers de Paris', Genonceaux (Paris), 1890 . . . . £100
ditto, as *The Bievre River*, Langtry Press (London), 1986 . . . . £75/£40
La Bièvre et Saint-Séverin, Stock (Paris), 1898 . . £75
La magie en Poitou. Gilles de Rais, Ligugé, 1899 . . £100
Pages Catholiques, Stock (Paris), 1900 . . . £50
La Bièvre. Les Gobelins. Saint-Séverin, Société de propagation des livres d'art (Paris), 1901 (695 copies with illustrations by Auguste Lepère) £65
Sainte Lydwine de Schiedam, Stock (Paris), 1901 . £50
ditto, Stock (Paris), 1901 (1,240 large format copies printed with Gothic type) £75
ditto, as *St. Lydwine of Schiedam*, Kegan Paul (London), 1923 . . . . £75/£35
ditto, Dutton (New York), 1923.. . . . . £65/£25
De Tout, Stock (Paris), 1902 . . . . . . £35
Esquisse Biographique sur Don Bosco, Imprimerie Bologne, 1902 . . . . £30
Le Quartier Notre-Dame, Librairie de la Collection des Dix. A Romagnol (Paris), 1905 . . . . . . £50
Trois Primitifs, Vanier (Paris), 1905 . . . . £65
ditto, as *Grunewald*, Phaidon (London), 1958 . £45/£20
ditto, Dutton (New York), 1976 . . . . £25/£10
Les Foules de Lourdes, Stock (Paris), 1906 . . . £45
ditto, as *The Crowds of Lourdes*, Burns & Oates (London), 1925 . . . . £65/£25
Trois Églises et Trois Primitifs, Plon-Nourrit (Paris), 1908 . . . . £35
Émile Zola and L'Assommoir, Princeton Univ Press (Princeton, NJ), 1963 . . . . . . £25/£10

Letters
The Road from Decadence: From Brothel to Cloister: Selected Letters, Athlone Press (London), 1989 . £20/£5
ditto, Ohio State Univ Press (Columbus, OH), 1989 £20/£5

HAMMOND INNES

(b.1913 d.1998)

Many of Ralph Hammond Innes's early books were published during World War Two while he served in the Royal
Artillery. Demobbed in 1946, he became a full-time writer,
for many years following a regular program of six months
of travel/research followed by six months of writing. His
thrillers have been translated into many languages and
regularly surface in paperback and book club editions.

Novels

The Doppelganger, Jenkins (London), 1936 .   . £750/£65
Air Disaster, Jenkins (London), 1937   .   . £650/£50
Sabotage Broadcast, Jenkins (London), 1938 .   . £650/£50
All Roads Lead to Friday, Jenkins (London), 1939 £650/£50
Wreckers Must Breathe, Collins (London), 1940 . £500/£45
ditto, as *Trapped*, Putnam (New York), 1940 . . £450/£40
The Trojan Horse, Collins (London), 1940 . . £500/£45
Attack Alarm, Collins (London), 1941   .   . £500/£45
ditto, Macmillan (New York), 1942 .   .   . £250/£25
Dead and Alive, Collins (London), 1946 . . £250/£25
The Lonely Skier, Collins (London), 1947   . £125/£15
ditto, as *Fire In The Snow*, Harper (New York), 1947 .   .
.   .   .   . £100/£15
The Killer Mine, Collins (London), 1947.   .   . £75/£10
ditto, Harper (New York), 1947 .   .   . £50/£10
ditto, as *Run By Night*, Bantam (New York), 1951 (pbk) £10
Maddon's Rock, Collins (London), 1948 . . . £50/£10
ditto, as *Gale Warning*, Harper (New York), 1948. £45/£10
The Blue Ice, Collins (London), 1948   .   . £45/£10
ditto, Harper (New York), 1948 .   .   .   . £35/£10
The White South, Collins (London), 1949 . . £45/£10
ditto, as *Survivors*, Harper (New York), 1949 . . £35/£10
The Angry Mountain, Collins (London), 1950 . . £35/£10
ditto, Harper (New York), 1950 .   .   . £35/£10
Air Bridge, Collins (London), 1951 .   . . £45/£10
ditto, Knopf (New York), 1951 .   .   .   . £35/£5
Campbell's Kingdom, Collins (London), 1952 . £35/£5
ditto, Knopf (New York), 1952 .   .   . . £25/£5
The Strange Land, Collins (London), 1954 . . £25/£5
ditto, as *The Naked Land*, Knopf (New York), 1954 £25/£5
The Mary Deare, Collins (London), 1956   . . £25/£5
ditto, as *The Wreck of the Mary Deare*, Knopf (New York),
1956 .   .   .   . £25/£5
The Land God Gave to Cain, Collins (London), 1958 £25/£5
ditto, Knopf (New York), 1958 .   .   .   . £25/£5
The Doomed Oasis, Collins (London), 1960 . . £30/£5
ditto, Knopf (New York), 1960 .   .   . . £25/£5
Atlantic Fury, Collins (London), 1962   . . £15/£5
ditto, Random House (New York), 1962 . . £15/£5
The Strode Venturer, Collins (London), 1965. . £15/£5
ditto, Knopf (New York), 1965 .   .   .   . £15/£5
Levkas Man, Collins (London), 1971   .   . £15/£5
ditto, Knopf (New York), 1971 .   .   . . £15/£5
Golden Soak, Collins (London), 1973   . . £15/£5
ditto, Knopf (New York), 1973 .   .   . . £15/£5
North Star, Collins (London), 1974 .   . . £15/£5
ditto, Knopf (New York), 1975 .   .   . . £15/£5
The Big Footprints, Collins (London), 1977 . . £15/£5
ditto, Knopf (New York), 1977 .   .   . . £15/£5
Solomon's Seal, Collins (London), 1980 . . £15/£5
ditto, Knopf (New York), 1975 .   .   . . £15/£5
The Black Tide, Collins (London), 1982 .   . £15/£5

ditto, Doubleday (New York), 1983 .   .   .   . £15/£5
High Stand, Collins (London), 1985.   .   . £15/£5
ditto, Atheneum (New York), 1986 .   .   . £15/£5
Medusa, Collins (London), 1988   .   . . £15/£5
ditto, Atheneum (New York), 1988 .   .   . £10/£5
Isvik, Chapmans (London), 1991   .   .   . £15/£5
ditto, St Martin's Press (New York), 1992 . . £10/£5
The Delta Connection, Macmillan (London), 1996 £10/£5
ditto, Thorndike Press (Thorndike, ME), 1997. . £10/£5

Children's Titles (pseud 'Ralph Hammond')

Cocos Island, Collins (London), 1950   .   . £75/£15
ditto, as *Cocos Gold*, Harper (New York), 1950 . £75/£15
Isle of Strangers, Collins (London), 1951 . . £75/£15
Saracen's Tower, Collins (London), 1952 . £75/£15
ditto, as *Cruise of Danger*, Westminster Press (Philadelphia,
PA), 1952 .   .   .   .   .   . £75/£15
Black Gold on the Double Diamond, Collins (London),
1953 .   .   .   . £75/£15
ditto, as *Island of Peril*, Westminster Press (Philadelphia,
PA), 1953 .   .   .   .   .   . £75/£15

Non-Fiction

Harvest of Journeys, Collins (London), 1960.   . £25/£5
ditto, Knopf (New York), 1960 .   .   .   . £25/£5
Scandinavia, Time-Life (New York), 1963 (illustrated
boards; no d/w) £15
Sea and Islands, Collins (London), 1967.   . . £20/£5
ditto, Knopf (New York), 1967 .   .   .   . £20/£5
The Conquistadores, Collins (London), 1969 . . £15/£5
ditto, Collins (London), 1969 (deluxe leather-bound edition)
.   .   .   . £200
ditto, Knopf (New York), 1969 .   .   .   . £15/£5
Hammond Innes Introduces Australia, Deutsch (London),
1971 .   .   .   . £10/£5
ditto, McGraw-Hill (New York), 1971 .   . £10/£5
The Last Voyage: Captain Cook's Lost Diary, Collins
(London), 1979 .   .   .   .   .   . £15/£5
ditto, Knopf (New York), 1979 .   .   .   . £10/£5
Hammond Innes' East Anglia, Hodder & Stoughton
(London), 1986 .   .   .   .   . £15/£5

MICHAEL INNES

(b.1906 d.1994)

'Michael Innes' was the pseudonym used by J.I.M. Stewart
for detective novels that range from the ingenious and
urbane through to straightforward adventures. The best
known of Innes' fictional detectives is Sir John Appleby
(originally Inspector John Appleby) of Scotland Yard.

Novels

Death at the President's Lodging, Gollancz (London), 1936
.   .   .   . £1,650/£150
ditto, as *Seven Suspects*, Dodd, Mead (New York), 1937 .
.   .   .   . £600/£45
Hamlet, Revenge!, Gollancz (London), 1937 .   . £500/£75
ditto, Dodd, Mead (New York), 1937.   .   . £250/£40
Lament for a Maker, Gollancz (London), 1938 . £450/£75
ditto, Dodd, Mead (New York), 1938 .   . £250/£40
Stop Press, Gollancz (London), 1939   .   . £450/£75
ditto, as *The Spider Strikes*, Dodd, Mead (New York), 1939
.   .   .   . £250/£45

There Came Both Mist and Snow, Gollancz (London), 1940   . £450/£75

ditto, as *A Comedy of Terrors*, Dodd, Mead (New York), 1940   . £250/£45

The Secret Vanguard, Gollancz (London), 1940 . £300/£25

ditto, Dodd, Mead (New York), 1941   . . £75/£25

Appleby on Ararat, Gollancz (London), 1941 . . £400/£45

ditto, Dodd, Mead (New York), 1941   . . £75/£25

The Daffodil Affair, Gollancz (London), 1942 . £250/£30

ditto, Dodd, Mead (New York), 1942   . . £75/£25

The Weight of the Evidence, Dodd, Mead (New York), 1943   . £125/£25

ditto, Gollancz (London), 1944 .   . £125/£25

Appleby's End, Gollancz (London), 1945.   . £200/£25

ditto, Dodd, Mead (New York), 1945   . . £50/£15

From London Far, Gollancz (London), 1946 . £60/£15

ditto, as *The Unsuspected Chasm*, Dodd, Mead (New York), 1946   . £45/£5

What Happened at Hazelwood, Gollancz (London), 1946 . £50/£15

ditto, Dodd, Mead (New York), 1946   . . £50/£15

A Night of Errors, Dodd, Mead (New York), 1947 £65/£15

ditto, Gollancz (London), 1948 .   . . £50/£10

The Journeying Boy, Gollancz (London), 1949 . £50/£10

ditto, as *The Case of the Journeying Boy*, Dodd, Mead (New York), 1949   . £35/£5

Operation Pax, Gollancz (London), 1951.   . £50/£10

ditto, as *The Paper Thunderbolt*, Dodd, Mead (New York), 1951   . £35/£5

A Private View, Gollancz (London), 1952   . £45/£5

ditto, as *One-Man Show*, Dodd, Mead (New York), 1952 . £35/£5

ditto, as *Murder is an Art*, Avon (New York), 1959 (pbk) £10

Christmas at Candleshoe, Gollancz (London), 1953 £45/£5

ditto, Dodd, Mead (New York), 1953   . . £35/£5

ditto, as *Candleshoe*, Penguin (New York), 1978 (pbk)   £5

The Man from the Sea, Gollancz (London), 1955 . £45/£5

ditto, as *Death by Moonlight*, Dodd, Mead (New York), 1955   . £35/£5

Old Hall, New Hall, Gollancz (London), 1956   £45/£5

ditto, as *A Question of Queens*, Dodd, Mead (New York), 1956   . £35/£5

Appleby Plays Chicken, Gollancz (London), 1956. £45/£5

ditto, as *Death On a Quiet Day*, Dodd, Mead (New York), 1957   . £35/£5

The Long Farewell, Gollancz (London), 1958   £45/£5

ditto, Dodd, Mead (New York), 1958   . £35/£5

Hare Sitting Up, Gollancz (London), 1959   £30/£5

ditto, Dodd, Mead (New York), 1959   . . £25/£5

The New Sonia Wayward, Gollancz (London), 1960 £30/£5

ditto, as *The Case of Sonia Wayward*, Dodd, Mead (New York), 1960 . £25/£5

Silence Observed, Gollancz (London), 1961   . £30/£5

ditto, Dodd, Mead (New York), 1961   . . £25/£5

A Connoisseur's Case, Gollancz (London), 1962   £30/£5

ditto, as *The Crabtree Affair*, Dodd, Mead (New York), 1962   . £25/£5

Money from Holme, Gollancz (London), 1964   £30/£5

ditto, Dodd, Mead (New York), 1965   . . £25/£5

Appleby Intervenes, Dodd, Mead (New York), 1965 £20/£5

The Bloody Wood, Gollancz (London), 1966 . £25/£5

ditto, Dodd, Mead (New York), 1966   . . £20/£5

A Change of Heir, Gollancz (London), 1966 . £25/£5

ditto, Dodd, Mead (New York), 1966   . . £20/£5

Appleby at Allington, Gollancz (London), 1968 . £25/£5

ditto, as *Death by Water*, Dodd, Mead (New York), 1968 . . £20/£5

A Family Affair, Gollancz (London), 1969   . . £25/£5

ditto, as *Picture of Guilt*, Dodd, Mead (New York), 1969 . £20/£5

Death at the Chase, Gollancz (London), 1970   . £25/£5

ditto, Dodd, Mead (New York), 1970   . . £20/£5

An Awkward Lie, Gollancz (London), 1971   . £20/£5

ditto, Dodd, Mead (New York), 1971   . . £15/£5

The Open House, Gollancz (London), 1972   . £20/£5

ditto, Dodd, Mead (New York), 1972   . . £15/£5

Appleby's Answer, Gollancz (London), 1973 . £20/£5

ditto, Dodd, Mead (New York), 1973   . . £15/£5

Appleby's Other Story, Gollancz (London), 1974 . £20/£5

ditto, Dodd, Mead (New York), 1974   . . £15/£5

The Mysterious Commission, Gollancz (London), 1974 . £20/£5

ditto, Dodd, Mead (New York), 1975   . . £15/£5

The Gay Phoenix, Gollancz (London), 1976 . £20/£5

ditto, Dodd, Mead (New York), 1977   . . £15/£5

Honeybath's Haven, Gollancz (London), 1977 . £15/£5

ditto, Dodd, Mead (New York), 1978   . . £10/£5

The Ampersand Papers, Gollancz (London), 1978 £15/£5

ditto, Dodd, Mead (New York), 1979   . . £10/£5

Going It Alone, Gollancz (London), 1980   . £15/£5

ditto, Dodd, Mead (New York), 1980   . . £10/£5

Lord Mullion's Secret, Gollancz (London), 1981 . £15/£5

ditto, Dodd, Mead (New York), 1981   . . £10/£5

Sheikhs and Adders, Gollancz (London), 1982 . £15/£5

ditto, Dodd, Mead (New York), 1982   . . £10/£5

Appleby and Honeybath, Gollancz (London), 1983 £15/£5

ditto, Dodd, Mead (New York), 1983   . . £10/£5

Carson's Conspiracy, Gollancz (London), 1984 . £15/£5

ditto, Dodd, Mead (New York), 1984   . . £10/£5

Appleby and the Ospreys, Gollancz (London), 1986 £15/£5

ditto, Dodd, Mead (New York), 1987   . . £10/£5

Short Stories

Appleby Talking, Gollancz (London), 1954   . £60/£10

ditto, as *Dead Man's Shoes*, Dodd, Mead (New York), 1954   . £40/£10

Appleby Talks Again, Gollancz (London), 1956 . £35/£5

ditto, Dodd, Mead (New York), 1957   . . £25/£5

The Appleby File, Gollancz (London), 1975   . £20/£5

ditto, Dodd, Mead (New York), 1976   . . £15/£5

JOHN IRVING

(b.1942)

John Irving is an American novelist who achieved critical and popular acclaim for *The World According to Garp*. Many of his books have been bestsellers and have been successfully filmed.

Novels

Setting Free The Bears, Random House (New York), 1968 (bottom left rear flap of d/w states '1/69' . £1,000/£200

ditto, Corgi Books (London), 1968 (pbk) .   . . £25

ditto, Bloomsbury Classics (London), 1991   . £15/£5

The Water Method Man, Random House (New York), 1972   . £175/£35

ditto, Corgi Books (London), 1980 (pbk) .   . . £15

The 158-Pound Marriage, Random House (New York), 1974   . £150/£25

ditto, Corgi Books (London), 1980 (pbk) £5
ditto, Bloomsbury Classics (London), 1993   .   £10/£5
The World According to Garp, Dutton (New York), 1978 .
.   .   .   . £150/£25
ditto, Gollancz (London), 1978 .   .   .   . £45/£10
The Hotel New Hampshire, Dutton (New York), 1981 £10/£5
ditto, Dutton (New York), 1981 (550 signed, numbered
copies; full leather in slipcase; no d/w)   .   £150/£100
ditto, Cape (London), 1981 .   .   .   .   . £10/£5
The Cider House Rules, Morrow (New York), 1985 £10/£5
ditto, Morrow (New York), 1985 ('First Trade Edition'
signed by author on a tipped-in leaf)   .   . £50/£40
ditto, Morrow (New York), 1985 ('Special Signed Edition';
beige boards with dark brown cloth spine; glassine d/w)   .
.   .   .   . £125/£100
ditto, Morrow (New York), 1985 (250 signed, numbered
copies; beige and brown cloth; glassine d/w; slipcase)   .
.   .   .   . £200/£150
ditto, Morrow/Book-of-the-Month Club (New York), 1985
(795 signed, numbered copies; dull yellow spine, dark
green boards; glassine d/w; dark green slipcase) £175/£125
ditto, Franklin Library (Franklin, PA), 1985 (signed limited
edition in full leather). £65
ditto, Cape (London), 1985 .   .   .   .   . £10/£5
A Prayer for Owen Meany, Dennys (Toronto), 1989 £50/£10
ditto, Franklin Library (Franklin, PA), 1989 (signed limited
edition in full leather). £150
ditto, Morrow (New York), 1989   .   .   . £40/£10
ditto, Morrow (New York), 1989 (250 signed, numbered
copies; beige and brown cloth; glassine d/w; slipcase)   .
.   .   .   . £650/£500
ditto, Bloomsbury (London), 1989   .   .   . £20/£5
A Son of the Circus, Franklin Library (Franklin Center, PA),
1994 (limited edition in full leather)   .   .   . £65
ditto, Random House (New York), 1994 .   .   £10/£5
ditto, Bloomsbury (London), 1994   .   .   . £20/£5
A Widow for One Year, Bloomsbury (London), 1998
('Special Pre-Publication Limited Edition'; 1,000 copies
numbered on a book plate affixed to the free front
endpaper; no d/w) £60
ditto, Anthos (Amsterdam), 1998   .   .   . £125/£20
ditto, Bloomsbury (London), 1998   .   .   . £15/£5
ditto, Random House (New York), 1998 .   .   £10/£5
ditto, Unicycle Press (Media, PA), 1998 (approx 1,200
signed, numbered copies; bound in full leather)   .   £45
The Fourth Hand, Random House (New York), 2001 £10/£5
ditto, Bloomsbury (London), 2001   .   .   . £15/£5
Until I Find You, Random House (New York), 2005 £10/£5
ditto, Bloomsbury (London), 2005   .   .   . £15/£5

Short Stories
The Pension Grillparzer, Tale Blazer, Perfection Form Co.,
(Logan, IA), 1980 (stapled wraps) £100
Trying to Save Piggy Sneed, Knopf Canada (Toronto), 1993
.   .   .   . £30/£5
ditto, Bloomsbury (London), 1993   .   .   . £20/£5
ditto, Arcade (New York), 1996 .   .   .   . £10/£5

Picture Book
A Sound Like Someone Trying Not To Make A Sound,
Diogenes (Zurich), 2003 (pictorial boards; no d.w)   . £25
ditto, Doubleday (New York), 2004 .   .   . £10/£5

Non-Fiction
How to Spell, International Paper Co. (New York), 1983
(broadside) £35

The Imaginary Girlfriend, Knopf Canada (Toronto), 1996 .
.   .   .   . £30/£5
ditto, Bloomsbury (London), 1996   .   .   . £20/£5
ditto, Ballantine (New York), 2002 (pbk) .   .   . £5
My Movie Business, Bloomsbury (London), 1999 . £10/£5
ditto, Random House (New York), 1999   .   . £10/£5

WASHINGTON IRVING
(b.1783 d.1859)

Washington Irving was an American author perhaps best
known for his short stories, his most famous being 'The
Legend of Sleepy Hollow' and 'Rip van Winkle' (both of
which first appeared in *The Sketch Book of Geoffrey
Crayon*). He and James Fenimore Cooper were probably
the first American writers to earn acclaim in Europe.

Fiction
**Salmagundi; or, The Whim-Whams and Opinions of
Launcelot Lang- staff. Esq, and Others**, David Longworth
(New York), 24th January 1807 to 25th January 1808
(anonymous; with J.K. Paulding and Wil- liam Irving; 2
vols bound from the original 20 parts)   . £1,000 the set
ditto, J.M. Richardson (London), 1811 (2 vols)   £600 the set
**A History of New York, From the Beginnings of the World
to the End of the Dutch Dynasty**, Inskeep & Bradford etc
(New York etc), 1809 (pseud 'Diedrich Knickerbocker'; 2
vols; 1st state with 268 pages in vol. 1)   .   . £1,750
ditto, Inskeep & Bradford etc (New York etc), 1812 (second
[revised] edition; 2 vols) £500
ditto, John Murray (London), 1820   .   .   .   . £500
The Sketch-Book of Geoffrey Crayon, Gent, C.S. Van
Winkle (New York), May 1819 to September 1820 (7
issues: including original first state wraps)   . £6,000 the set
ditto, C.S. Van Winkle (New York), May 1819 to September
1820 (7 issues bound without outer wraps)   .   £1,500
ditto, John Miller (London) (vol.1) and John Murray
(London) (vol.2), 1820 (2 vols) £500
ditto, Bell & Daldy (London), 1865 (Artist's Edition with
120 engravings on wood) £350
ditto, Putnams (New York), 1894 (2 vols, 3 illustrations by
Rackham, many others by various artists, 1,000 numbered
sets, red cloth) £400
ditto, Putnams (New York), [1895] (2 vols, 1 further
illustration by Rackham) £175
Bracebridge Hall, or The Humorists: A Medley, C.S. Van
Winkle (New York), 1822 (pseud 'Geoffrey Crayon', Gent;
2 vols) .   .   .   . £250 the set
ditto, John Murray, 1822 (2 vols) £250
ditto, Macmillan (London), 1877 [1876] (illustrated by
Randolph Caldecott) £45
ditto, Putnams (New York), 1896 (2 vols, 5 illustrations by
Rackham, many others by various artists, dark blue cloth).
.   .   .   . £100
ditto, Putnams (New York), 1896 (2 vols, 100 copies signed
by publishers, light brown full calf)   .   .   . £250
Tales of a Traveller, by Geoffrey Crayon, Gent, H.C. Carey
& I. Lea (New York), 1824 (4 parts; wraps) . £1,500 the set
ditto, by Geoffrey Crayon, Gent, H.C. Carey & I. Lea (New
York), 1824 (4 parts rebound) £150
ditto, John Murray (London), 1824 (2 vols)   . £500 the set

ditto, Putnams (New York), 1895 (illustrated by Arthur Rackham; 2 vols, 5 half-tone illustrations, white or light blue cloth) £100

ditto, Putnams (New York), 1895 (illustrated by Arthur Rackham; 150 copies, light brown full calf)   .   . £200

Letters of Jonathan Oldstyle, Gent, by the Author of 'The Sketch Book', William H. Clayton (New York), 1824 (wraps) £750

ditto, William H. Clayton (New York), 1824 (rebound) £150

ditto, Effingham Wilson (London), 1824 (wraps)   . £600

ditto, Effingham Wilson (London), 1824 (rebound)   . £125

A Chronicle of the Conquest of Granada, Carey, Lea & Carey (Philadelphia, PA), 1829 (pseud 'Fray Antonio Agapida'; 2 vols).   .   .   .   .   . £300 the set

ditto, John Murray (London), 1829 (2 vols)   . £250 the set

The Alhambra: A Series of Tales and Sketches of the Moors and Spaniards, by the Author of 'The Sketch Book', Henry Colburn & Richard Bentley (London), 1832 (2 vols)   .   .   .   .   .   . £450 the set

ditto, Carey & Lea (Philadelphia, PA), 1832 (2 vols)   .   .
.   .   .   . £450 the set

ditto, Macmillan (New York), 1926 (3 colour plates by Warwick Goble)   .   .   .   .   .   . £100/£15

The Crayon Miscellany, Carey, Lea & Blanchard (Philadelphia, PA), 1835 (3 vols: Volume One 'A Tour on the Prairies'; Volume Two 'Abbotsford and Newstead Abbey'; Volume Three 'Legends of the Conquest of Spain')   .   .   .   .   .   . £300 the set

ditto, as *Miscellanies*, John Murray (London), 1835 (3 vols)
.   .   .   . £250 the set

A Book of the Hudson, Collected from the Various Works of Diedrich Knickerbocker, Edited by Geoffrey Crayon, G.P. Putnam (New York), 1849   .   .   .   . £200

Wolfert's Roost and Other Papers, G.P. Putnam (New York), 1855   .   .   .   . £75

ditto, as *Wolfert's Roost and Other Tales*, Henry G. Bohn (London), 1855   .   .   .   . £65

Spanish Papers and Other Miscellanies, Hitherto Unpublished or Uncollected, G.P. Putnam (New York), 1866 (2 vols)   .   .   .   .   .   . £200 the set

ditto, Sampson Low (London), 1866 (2 vols)   . £200 the set

Biographies and Miscellaneous Papers, Bell & Daldy (London), 1867   .   .   .   . £125

Old Christmas, From the Sketchbook of Washington Irving, Macmillan (London), 1876 (illustrated by Randolph Caldecott) £45

ditto, Hodder & Stoughton (London), 1908 (illustrated by Cecil Aldin; 27 colour plates, 6 b/w illustrations)   . £150

Rip van Winkle, by Washington Irving, Heinemann (London), 1905 (illustrated by Arthur Rackham; frontispiece and 50 colour plates, green cloth)   . £650

ditto, Heinemann (London), 1905 (special binding, green leather) £1,250

ditto, Heinemann (London), 1905 (deluxe edition, 250 signed copies, pictorial full vellum) £3,500

ditto, Doubleday (New York), 1905 (trade edition)   . £500

ditto, Heinemann (London), 1916 (only 24 plates, but new drawings added) £250

ditto, Doubleday (New York), 1916   .   .   .   . £250

The Perverse Widow, and *The Widow* by R. Steele, and Washington Irving, Heinemann (London), 1909 (illustrated by Cecil Aldin; 3 colour plates) £25

Wives, and *The Henpecked Man* by Washington Irving, and R. Steele, Heinemann (London), 1909 (illustrated by Cecil Aldin; 3 colour plates) £25

Bachelors, and *Bachelor's Confessions* by Washington Irving, Heinemann (London), 1909 (illustrated by Cecil Aldin; 3 colour plates) £25

Abu Hassan, and *The Wild Huntsman*, Bibliophile Society (Boston), 1924 (2 vols; 455 sets; slipcase)   . £100/£65

An Unwritten Drama of Lord Byron, Charles F. Heartman (New York), 1925 (51 copies) £250

The Legend of Sleepy Hollow, by Washington Irving, Harrap (London), 1928 (illustrated by Arthur Rackham; 8 colour and 30 b&w drawings, green cloth)   . £225/£125

ditto, Harrap (London), 1928 (deluxe 375 signed copies, full vellum) £1,500

ditto, Harrap (London), 1928 (publisher's special binding, grey or brown leather) £250

ditto, McKay (Philadelphia), 1928 (trade edition, brown cloth)   .   .   .   . £225/£125

ditto, McKay (Philadelphia), 1928 (125 signed, numbered copies, full vellum) £1,000

The Bold Dragoon and Other Ghostly Tales, Alfred A. Knopf (New York), 1930   .   .   .   .   . £25/£10

The Ghostly Tales of Washington Irving, John Calder (London), 1979   .   .   .   . £10/£5

The Legend of Sleepy Hollow, Tartarus Press (Carlton-in-Coverdale, Yorkshire), 2009   .   .   .   . £35/£10

History and Biography

Biography of James Lawrence, Esq, Late a Captain in the Navy of the United States, L. Deare (New York), 1813 (anonymous). £1,500

A History of the Life and Voyages of Christopher Columbus, John Murray, 1828 (4 vols)   . £700 the set

ditto, G. & C. Carvill (New York), 1828   .   .   . £600

Voyages and Discoveries of the Companions of Columbus, John Murray (London), 1831   .   .   .   . £250

ditto, Carey & Lea (Philadelphia, PA), 1831   .   . £350

Astoria, or Anecdotes of an Enterprise Beyond the Rocky Mountains, Carey, Lea & Blanchard (Philadelphia, PA), 1836 (2 vols; first state: copyright on verso title page v.I; footnote on p239 of v.II reads '*Bra6.db ury.P.6/*Breckenbridge'; first page of terminal ads has 'Books Published'; terminal ads not boxed)   . £450 the set

ditto, Richard Bentley (London), 1836   .   .   . £350

The Rocky Mountains; or, Scenes, Incidents and Adventures of the Far West etc, Carey, Lea & Blanchard (Philadelphia, PA), 1837 (2 vols)   .   . £350 the set

ditto, as *Adventures of Captain Bonneville, or Scenes Beyond the Rocky Mountains of the Far East*, Richard Bentley (London), 1837 (3 vols)   .   . £300 the set

The Life of Oliver Goldsmith, with Selections from His Writings, Harper & Brothers (New York), 1840 (2 vols)   .
.   .   .   . £250 the set

ditto, as *Oliver Goldsmith: A Biography*, John Murray (London), 1849   .   .   .   . £175

Biography and Poetical Remains of the Late Margaret Miller Davidson, Lea & Blanchard (New York), 1841   .
.   .   .   . £125

ditto, as *Life and Poetical Remains of Margaret M Davidson*, Tilt & Bogus (London), 1843   .   .   . £50

Mahomet and His Successors, George P. Putnam (New York), 1850 (vols XII & XIII of Irving's 'Collected Works').   .   .   .   . £200 for both

ditto, John Murray (London), 1850 (2 vols)   .   . £175

Life of George Washington, G.P. Putnam (New York), 1855-59 (5 vols)   .   .   .   .   .   . £350 the set

ditto, G.P. Putnam (New York), 1855-59 (5 vols; deluxe edition limited to 110 sets) £1,000
ditto, Henry G. Bohn (London), 1855-59 (5 vols) . . £250

Other Titles
Collected Works, G.P. Putnam (New York), 1880-83 (27 vols) . . . . £400 the set
The Letters of Washington Irving to Henry Brevoort, G.P. Putnam's Sons/The Knickerbocker Press (New York), 1915 . . . . £100
ditto, G.P. Putnam's Sons/The Knickerbocker Press (New York), 1915 (255 deluxe sets; 2 vols) . . . £250
The Journals of Washington Irving from July 1815 to July 1842, The Bibliophile Society (Boston), 1919 (3 vols) .
. . . . £200 the set
Notes and Journals of Travel in Europe, 1804-05, The Grolier Club (New York), 1921 (230 sets; 3 vols; slipcase)
. . . . £150 the set
Washington Irving Diary: Spain 1829-29, Hispanic Society of America (New York), 1926 . . . . £50
Notes While Preparing Sketch Book, &c, 1817/Tour in Scotland, 1817, Yale Univ Press (New Haven, CT), 1927 (525 sets; 2 vols; slipcase). . . . . £75/£45
ditto, O.U.P. (London), 1928 (2 vols) . . £75/£45
Letters from Sunnyside and Spain, Yale Univ Press/O.U.P. (New Haven, CT/London), 1928 . . . . £35
The Poems of Washington Irving, New York Public Library (New York), 1931 (wraps). £30
Journal of Washington Irving, 1823-1824, Harvard Univ Press /O.U.P. (Cambridge, MA/London), 1931 . . £35
Washington Irving and the Storrows, 1821-8, Harvard Univ Press/O.U.P. (Cambridge, MA/London), 1933 . . £35
Journal, 1803, O.U.P (London), 1935 . . . £35
Washington Irving and the House of Murray: Geoffrey Crayon Charms the British, 1817-1856, Univ of Tennessee Press (TN), 1969 . . . . . £25

CHRISTOPHER ISHERWOOD

(b.1904 d.1986)

Isherwood was a British-born novelist who moved to Berlin, drawn by its reputation for sexual freedom, and found inspiration there for his best known novels *Mr Norris Changes Trains* and *Goodbye to Berlin*. The latter included the sketch 'Sally Bowles', which was dramatised and turned into the popular musical *Cabaret*. A life-long friend of W.H. Auden: the two travelled first to China in 1938, then emigrated to the U.S. in 1939.

Novels
All the Conspirators, Cape (London), 1928 . £1,750/£175
ditto, New Directions (Norfolk, CT), 1958 . . £50/£10
The Memorial, Hogarth Press (London), 1932 (first binding pink, lettered blue) . . . . . £450/£125
ditto, Hogarth Press (London), 1932 (later bindings, blue or ochre) . . . . £300/£45
ditto, New Directions (Norfolk, CT), 1946 . . £45/£10
Mr Norris Changes Trains, Hogarth Press (London), 1935.
. . . . £2,750/£300

ditto, as **The Last of Mr Norris**, Morrow (New York), 1935
. . . . £250/£45
Sally Bowles, Hogarth Press (London), 1937 . . £500/£65
Goodbye to Berlin, Hogarth Press (London), 1939. . .
. . . . £1,750/£100
ditto, Random House (New York), 1939 . . . £300/£65
Prater Violet, Random House (New York), 1945 . £175/£20
ditto, Methuen (London), 1946 . . . . . £175/£20
The World in the Evening, Random House (New York), 1954 . . . . £45/£10
ditto, Methuen (London), 1954 . . . . . £25/£5
Down There on a Visit, Simon & Schuster (New York), 1962 . . . . £25/£5
ditto, Methuen (London), 1962 . . . . . £15/£5
A Single Man, Simon & Schuster (New York), 1964 £25/£5
ditto, Methuen (London), 1964 . . . . . £15/£5
A Meeting by the River, Simon & Schuster (New York), 1967 . . . . £15/£5
ditto, Methuen (London), 1967 . . . . . £15/£5

Omnibus Editions
The Berlin Stories, New Directions (Norfolk, CT), 1945 .
. . . . £125/£20
ditto, as **The Berlin of Sally Bowles**, Hogarth Press (London), 1975 . . . . £15/£5

Plays
The Dog Beneath the Skin, Faber (London), 1935 (with W.H. Auden) . . . . £165/£25
ditto, Random House (New York), 1935 . . . £165/£25
The Ascent of F6, Faber (London), 1936 (with W.H. Auden)
. . . . £150/£25
ditto, Random House (New York), 1937 (revised) . £125/£25
On The Frontier, Faber (London), 1938 (with W.H. Auden).
. . . . £125/£25
ditto, Random House (New York), 1939 . . . £75/£20

Poetry
People One Ought to Know, Doubleday (New York), 1982 (illustrated by Sylvain Mangeot) . . . . £15/£5
ditto, Macmillan (London), 1982 . . . . £15/£5

Others
Lions and Shadows, Hogarth Press (London), 1938 (blue cloth lettered black) . . . . . £400/£100
ditto, Hogarth Press (London), 1938 (blue cloth lettered gilt)
. . . . £200/£50
ditto, New Directions (Norfolk, CT), 1948 . . £75/£15
Journey to a War, Faber (London), 1939 (with W.H. Auden)
. . . . £175/£45
ditto, Random House (New York), 1939 . . . £100/£20
The Condor and the Cows, Random House (New York), 1949
. . . . £35/£15
ditto, Methuen (London), 1949 . . . . . £35/£10
Ramakrishna and His Disciples, Simon & Schuster (New York), 1965 . . . . £20/£5
ditto, Methuen (London), 1965 . . . . . £20/£5
Exhumations, Simon & Schuster (New York), 1966 £15/£5
ditto, Methuen (London), 1966 . . . . . £15/£5
Kathleen and Frank, Simon & Schuster (New York), 1971.
. . . . £10/£5
ditto, Methuen (London), 1971 . . . . . £10/£5
Frankenstein: The True Story, Avon (New York), 1973 (pbk; screenplay with Don Bachardy) £10

Christopher and His Kind, Farrar, Straus and Giroux (New York), 1976 . . . . £10/£5

ditto, Farrar, Straus/Sylvester & Orphanos (New York/Los Angeles), 1976 (100 signed copies, slipcase)   £300/£225

ditto, Eyre Methuen (London), 1977 . . . . £10/£5

My Guru and His Disciple, Farrar Straus (New York), 1980 . . . . £10/£5

ditto, Eyre Methuen (London), 1980 . . . . £10/£5

October, Twelvetrees Press (Los Angeles, CA), 1980 (150 numbered, signed copies, slipcase) . . . £250/£200

ditto, Twelvetrees Press (Los Angeles, CA), 1980 (26 signed, lettered copies) £350

ditto, Twelvetrees Press (Los Angeles, CA), 1980 (pbk) £15

ditto, Methuen (London), 1982 (1,000 copies; pbk) . £15

Diaries, Volume One: 1939-1960, Methuen (London), 1996 . . . . £15/£5

ditto, HarperCollins (New York), 1997 . . . £15/£5

Lost Years: A Memoir 1945-1951, Chatto & Windus (London), 2000 . . . . £15/£5

ditto, HarperCollins (New York), 2000 . . . £15/£5

KAZUO ISHIGURO
(b.1954)

Kazuo Ishiguro was born in Nagasaki, Japan and his family moved to England when he was five. A graduate of Malcolm Bradbury's creative writing course at the University of East Anglia, Ishiguro's slim, studied novels have brought him success: he won the Whitbread Prize for *An Artist of the Floating World* in 1986, and the Booker Prize in 1989 for *The Remains of the Day*.

Novels

A Pale View of Hills, Faber (London), 1982 . . £750/£50

ditto, Putnam (New York), 1982 . . . . . £90/£15

An Artist of the Floating World, Faber (London), 1986 (first issue, printed by Butler and Tanner) . . . £125/£10

ditto, Faber (London), 1986 (second issue, printed by Richard Clay) . . . . £75/£10

ditto, Putnam (New York), 1986 . . . . . £30/£5

The Remains of the Day, Faber (London), 1989 . £145/£25

ditto, Knopf (New York), 1989 . . . . . £35/£10

The Unconsoled, Faber (London), 1995 . . . £15/£5

ditto, Knopf (New York), 1995 . . . . . £15/£5

When We Were Orphans, Faber (London), 2000 . £15/£5

ditto, Knopf (New York), 2000 . . . . . £15/£5

Never Let Me Go, Faber (London), 2005 . . . £15/£5

ditto, Faber (London), 2005 (130 signed, limited copies) . . . . £150/£25

ditto, Faber (London), 2006 (1,000 signed, limited copies) . . . . £50/£10

ditto, Knopf (New York), 2005 . . . . . £15/£5

Short Stories

Early Japanese Stories, Belmont Press (London), 2000 (illustrated by Eileen Hogan; 50 numbered deluxe copies signed by author and artist; with two separate prints laid in a pocket in back; slipcase) £250

ditto, Belmont Press (London), 2000 (150 signed special with one print) £150

ditto, Belmont Press (London), 2000 (50 signed standard without prints) £100

Nocturnes: Five Stories of Music and Nightfall, Faber (London), 2009 . . . . £10/£5

ditto, Knopf (New York), 2009 . . . . . £15/£5

ditto, Faber (London), 2009 (1,000 signed, un-numbered trade copies in slipcase) . . . . . £45/£20

SHIRLEY JACKSON
(b.1916 d.1965)

Shirley Jackson was a popular American author whose work has influenced such writers as Stephen King. She is best-known now for her *The Haunting of Hill House* which was a classic ghost story updated, and has been filmed. In her day her most famous work was her short story 'The Lottery', which offered an unsettling view of small-town America.

Novels

The Road Through the Wall, Farrar Straus (New York), 1948 . . . . £100/£25

ditto, as *The Other Side of the Street*, Pyramid (New York), 1956 (pbk) £10

Hangsaman, Farrar Straus (New York), 1951 . £45/£15

ditto, Gollancz (London), 1951 . . . . . £75/£15

The Bird's Nest, Farrar Straus (New York), 1954 . £30/£10

ditto, Michael Joseph (London), 1955 . . . £20/£5

ditto, as *Lizzie*, Signet (New York), 1957 (pbk) . . £5

The Sundial, Farrar Straus (New York), 1958 . £45/£10

ditto, Michael Joseph (London), 1958 . . . £25/£5

The Haunting of Hill House, Viking Press (New York), 1959 . . . . £400/£45

ditto, Michael Joseph (London), 1960 . . £300/£35

We Have Always Lived in the Castle, Viking Press (New York), 1962 . . . . £50/£10

ditto, Michael Joseph (London), 1963 . . . £40/£10

Short Stories

The Lottery, or The Adventures of James Harris, Farrar Straus (New York), 1949 . . . . . . £300/£40

ditto, Gollancz (London), 1950 . . . . £200/£25

Come Along With Me, Viking Press (New York), 1968 . . . . £15/£5

ditto, Michael Joseph (London), 1969 . . . £15/£5

Just an Ordinary Day, Bantam (New York), 1996 . £15/£5

ditto, Bantam (New York), 1997 (pbk) £5

Children's

The Witchcraft of Salem Village, Random House (New York), 1956 . . . . £125/£25

The Bad Children: A Play in One Act for Bad Children, Dramatic Publishing Company (New York), 1958 (stapled wraps) £10

9 Magic Wishes, Crowell-Collier (New York), 1963 (no d/w) £75

Famous Sally, Harlin Quist (New York), 1966 . £45/£15

Others

Life Among the Savages, Farrar Straus (New York), 1953 . . . . £25/£10

ditto, Michael Joseph (London), 1954 . . . £20/£5

Raising Demons, Farrar Straus (New York), 1957 . £25/£10

ditto, Michael Joseph (London), 1957 . . . £20/£5
Special Delivery: A Useful Book for Brand-New Mothers,
  Little, Brown (New York), 1960 . . . . £30/£10

W.W. JACOBS
(b.1863 d.1943)

Jacobs was an English author best remembered for his
macabre story 'The Monkey's Paw' (first published in *The
Lady of the Barge*). Most of his writing, however, was
humorous.

Short Stories
Many Cargoes, Lawrence & Bullen (London), 1896 . £100
ditto, Stokes (New York), 1897 . . . . . £50
ditto, Stokes (New York), 1902 (1,000 copies with numbered
  and signed certificate) £45
Sea Urchins, Lawrence & Bullen (London), 1898 . . £25
ditto, as ***More Cargoes***, Stokes (New York), 1898 . . £25
Light Freights, Dodd Mead (New York), 1901 . . £20
ditto, Methuen (London), 1901 . . . . . £25
The Lady of the Barge, Dodd Mead (New York), 1902 £75
ditto, Harpers (London), 1902 . . . . . £35
Odd Craft, Scribners (New York), 1903 . . . £20
ditto, Newnes (London), 1903 . . . . . £25
Captains All, Hurst & Blackett (London), 1907 . . £25
ditto, Scribners (New York), 1907 . . . . £20
Short Cruises, Hurst & Blackett (London), 1907 . . £25
ditto, Scribners (New York), 1907 . . . . £25
Sailors' Knots, Methuen (London), 1909 . . . £20
ditto, Scribners (New York), 1909 . . . . £20
Ship's Company, Hodder & Stoughton (London), 1911 £20
ditto, Scribners (New York), 1911 . . . . £20
Night Watches, Hodder & Stoughton (London), 1914 . £20
ditto, Scribners (New York), 1914 . . . . £20
Deep Waters, Hodder & Stoughton (London), 1919 . £20
ditto, Scribners (New York), 1919 . . . . £20
Sea Whispers, Hodder & Stoughton (London), 1926 £35/£10
ditto, Scribners (New York), 1926 . . . £25/£10
Fifteen Stories, Methuen (London), 1926. . . £15/£5
Snug Harbour, Scribners (New York), 1931 . £30/£10
The Nightwatchmen and Other Longshoremen, Hodder &
  Stoughton (London), 1932 . . . . . £35/£10
Cruises and Cargoes, Methuen (London), 1934 . £30/£10
W.W. Jacobs' Uncollected Cargoes, Hazelwood Press
  (Lancaster, PA), 1996. . . . . . . £20

Novels
The Skipper's Wooing, Pearson (London), 1897 . . £25
ditto, Stokes (New York), 1897 . . . . . £20
A Master of Craft, Stokes (New York), 1900 . . £20
ditto, Methuen (London), 1900 . . . . . £25
At Sunwich Port, Newnes (London), 1902 . . £20
ditto, Scribners (New York), 1902 . . . . £20
Dialstone Lane, Newnes (London), 1904 . . . £20
ditto, Scribners (New York), 1904 . . . . £20
Salthaven, Methuen (London), 1908 . . . . £20
ditto, Scribners (New York), 1908 . . . . £20
The Castaways, Hodder & Stoughton (London), 1916 . £20
ditto, Scribners (New York), 1916 . . . . £20

HENRY JAMES
(b.1843 d.1916)

James is a highly-regarded American (later British) author
of early Modernist fiction, frequently juxtaposing characters from Old World Europe (artistic, corrupting and
alluring) with those of the United States (brash, open and
assertive). The resultant clash of cultures produces a low-
key comedy of manners, and careful psychological insights
into the deeper motivations of his characters. He lived in
Rye, East Sussex, for many years, and was awarded the
Order of Merit in 1916.

Novels
Roderick Hudson, Osgood (Boston), 1876 [1875] (first
  binding with J.R. Osgood & Co. imprint on spine) . £500
ditto, Houghton Mifflin (Boston), 1876 [1875] (second
  binding with Houghton Mifflin imprint on spine) . £300
ditto, Macmillan (London), 1879 (3 vols) . . . £3,500
The American, Osgood (Boston), 1877 (with Osgood imprint
  on spine; without stop after 'Co' on title page) . . £350
ditto, Osgood (Boston), 1877 (as above but with stop on title
  page) £300
ditto, Osgood (Boston), 1877 (with Houghton on spine) £150
ditto, Ward Lock (London), 1877 (pirated UK first edition;
  pictorial boards) £450
ditto, Macmillan (London), 1879 (authorised U.K. first
  edition) £250
Watch and Ward, Houghton Osgood (Boston), 1878 (with
  blank leaf after p.129) £500
ditto, Houghton Osgood (Boston), 1878 (without blank leaf)
  . . . . £200
ditto, Houghton Osgood (London), 1878 (first UK edition
  stamped 'Trübner & Co' on title-page) £350
The Europeans, Macmillan (London), 1878 (2 vols) £1,250
ditto, Houghton Osgood (Boston), 1879 (1 vol) . . £450
Confidence, Chatto & Windus (London), 1880 [1879] (2
  vols) £3,000
ditto, Houghton Osgood (Boston), 1880 (1 vol; first issue
  with 'Houghton, Osgood' on spine) £300
ditto, Houghton Osgood (Boston), 1880 (1 vol; second issue
  with 'Houghton, Mifflin' on spine) £150
***Washington Square; The Pension Beaurepas; A Bundle of
  Letters***, Macmillan (London), 1881 (2 vols, first printing
  with last page numbered 371 and 'H. James Jr.' on spine) .
  . . . . £3,000
ditto, Macmillan (London), 1881 (2 vols, second printing
  with last page numbered 271 and 'Henry/James Jr.' on
  spine, only 250 copies) £2,000
ditto, Harper (New York), 1881 (2 vols, frontispiece and
  illustrations by George Du Maurier) £350
The Portrait of a Lady, Macmillan (London), 1881 (3 vols)
  . . . . £4,000
ditto, Macmillan (London), 1882 (3 vols; second impression)
  . . . . £1,750
ditto, Houghton Mifflin (Boston), 1882 (1 vol; first issue
  with full stop after 'Copyright, 1881') £300
The Bostonians, Macmillan (London), 1886 (3 vols) £3,000
ditto, Macmillan (London/New York), 1886 (1 vol edition;
  orange cloth with maroon spine) £250
ditto, Macmillan (London/New York), 1886 (later binding of
  above in blue/black cloth) £150

The Princess Casamassima, Macmillan (London), 1886 (3 vols) £2,500
ditto, Macmillan (London/New York), 1886 (1 vol) . £200
The Reverberator, Macmillan (London), 1888 (2 vols). £1,250
ditto, Macmillan (London/New York), 1888 (1 vol) . £200
The Tragic Muse, Houghton Mifflin (Boston), 1890 (2 vols) £500
ditto, Macmillan (London), 1890 (3 vols). . . £1,500
The Other House, Heinemann (London), 1896 (2 vols). £500
ditto, Macmillan (New York), 1896 (1 vol) . . . £125
ditto, Heinemann (London), 1897 (1 vol) . . . £125
The Spoils of Poynton, Heinemann (London), 1897 (with four irises on front board) £200
ditto, Heinemann (London), 1897 (nine tulips on front board) £175
ditto, Houghton Mifflin (Boston), 1897 . . . £125
What Maisie Knew, Heinemann (London), 1898 [1897] (tulips on front cover). £400
ditto, Heinemann (London), 1898 [1897] (irises on front cover) £100
ditto, Stone (Chicago), 1897 (probable first issue with pages watermarked 'Stone & Kimball') £175
ditto, Stone (Chicago), 1897 (probable second issue with pages watermarked 'H.S. Stone/Chapbook'). . £100
In the Cage, Duckworth (London), 1898 . . . £100
ditto, Stone (Chicago), 1898 . . . . . £100
The Awkward Age, Harper (New York), 1899 . . £75
ditto, Heinemann (London), 1899 . . . . £75
The Sacred Fount, Scribner's (New York), 1901 (2 vols) £225
ditto, Methuen (London), 1901 (1 vol) . . . £150
The Wings of the Dove, Scribner's (New York), 1902 (2 vols) £200
ditto, Archibald Constable (London), 1902 . . £150
The Ambassadors, Methuen (London), 1903 (scarlet cloth). £300
ditto, Harper (New York), 1903 (blue boards) . . £150
The Golden Bowl, Scribner's (New York), 1905 (2 vols) £200
ditto, Methuen (London), 1905 (1 vol) . . . £125
The Outcry, Methuen (London), 1911 . . . £75
ditto, Scribner's (New York), 1911 . . . . £75
The Ivory Tower, Collins (London), 1917 . . . £75
ditto, Scribner's (New York), 1917 . . . . £75
The Sense of the Past, Collins (London), 1917 (unfinished) £75
ditto, Scribner's (New York), 1917 . . . . £75

Collected Editions
The Collective Edition, Macmillan (London), 1883 (14 vols) £1,000
ditto, Macmillan (London), 1883 (14 vols; wraps) . £750
The New York Edition, Scribner's (New York), 1907-9, 1918 (26 vols) £5,000
ditto, Scribner's (New York), 1907-9 (26 vols, 156 copies on handmade paper). £9,000
ditto, Macmillan (London), 1907-9, 1918 (26 vols, made up from US sheets) £3,500

Short Stories
A Passionate Pilgrim, Osgood (Boston), 1875 (first issue with 'J.R. Osgood & Co' on spine) £750

ditto, Osgood (Boston), 1875 (second issue with 'Houghton Osgood & Co' on spine) £450
ditto, Osgood (Boston), 1875 (third issue with 'Houghton, Mifflin & Co' on spine) £200
ditto, Macmillan (London), 1879 (3 vols) . £1,000
Daisy Miller: A Study, Harper (New York), 1879 (first issue lists 79 titles in Half Hour Series; wraps) . £5,000
ditto, Harper (New York), 1879 (cloth edition, first issue) . £1,500
Daisy Miller: A Study; An International Episode; Four Meetings, Macmillan (London), 1879 (2 vols) . £1,500
An International Episode, Harper (New York), 1879 (first state with line on p.44 repeated as first line on p.45, no.91 in Half Hour Series; wraps) £400
ditto, Harper (New York), 1879 (first state, cloth) . £250
The Madonna of the Future and Other Tales, Macmillan (London), 1879 (2 vols) £3,000
Daisy Miller: A Comedy in Three Acts, privately printed (London), 1882 (18 copies; wraps) . . . £2,500
ditto, Osgood (Boston), 1883 (with 'Osgood' on the spine) £600
ditto, Osgood (Boston), 1883 (with Ticknor monogram on the spine) £250
ditto, Osgood (Boston), 1883 (with 'Houghton Mifflin' on the spine) £200
Tales of Three Cities, Osgood (Boston), 1884. . £150
ditto, Macmillan (London), 1884 . . . . £150
Stories Revived, Macmillan (London), 1885 (3 vols) £1,000
ditto, Macmillan (London), 1885 (2 vol second edition) £250
The Aspern Papers; Louis Pallant, The Modern Warning, Macmillan (London), 1888 (2 vols). . . . £750
ditto, Macmillan (London/New York), 1888 (1 vol) . £150
A London Life; The Patagonia; The Liar; Mrs Temperley, Macmillan (London), 1889 (2 vols). . . . £250
ditto, Macmillan (London/New York), 1889 (1 vol) . £100
The Lesson of the Master; The Marriages; The Pupil; Brooksmith; The Solution; Sir Edmund Orme, Macmillan (New York), 1892 . . . . £125
ditto, Macmillan (London), 1892 . . . . £125
Daisy Miller and An International Episode, Harper (New York), 1892 . . . . £75
ditto, Harper (New York), 1892 (250 copies) . . £150
The Real Thing and Other Tales, Macmillan (London/New York), 1893 (first issue with integral title page) . £2,000
ditto, Macmillan (London/New York), 1893 (second issue with cancel title page). £150
The Private Life; The Wheel of Time; Lord Beaupre; The Visits; Collaboration; Owen Wingrave, Osgood McIlvane (London), 1893 . . . . £150
ditto, Harper (New York), 1893 . . . . . £150
Terminations; The Death of the Lion; The Coxon Fund; The Middle Years; The Altar of the Dead, Heinemann (London), 1895 . . . . £100
ditto, Harper (New York), 1895 . . . . . £75
Embarrassments; The Figure in the Carpet; Glasses; The Next Time; The Way it Came, Heinemann (London), 1896 . . . . £125
ditto, Macmillan (New York), 1896 . . . . £125
The Two Magics: The Turn of the Screw; Covering End, Heinemann (London), 1898 (first issue with four blind-stamped irises on front board) £300
ditto, Heinemann (London), 1898 (later issue with nine blind-stamped tulips on front board) £300
ditto, Macmillan (New York), 1898 . . . . £300

The Soft Side, Methuen (London), 1900 . . . £75
ditto, Macmillan (New York), 1900 . . . . £75
The Better Sort, Methuen (London), 1903 . . £75
ditto, Scribner's (New York), 1903 . . . . £75
The Finer Grain, Scribner's (New York), 1910 . £75
ditto, Methuen (London), 1910 . . . . . £75
The Ghostly Tales of Henry James, Rutgers Univ Press (New Brunswick, NJ), 1948 [1949]. . . . £25/£5
ditto, as *Stories of the Supernatural*, Barrie & Jenkins (London), 1971 . . . . . . £15/£5
The Sense of the Past: The Ghostly Stories of Henry James, Tartarus Press (Carlton-in-Coverdale, Yorkshire), 2006 .
. . . . £35/£10

Plays

Theatricals: Two Comedies—Tenants [and] *Disengaged*, Osgood McIlvaine (London), 1894 . . . . £100
ditto, Harper (New York), 1894 . . . . £100
Theatricals: Second Series—The Album; The Reprobate, Osgood McIlvaine (London), 1895 . . . . £75
ditto, Harper (New York), 1895 [1894] . . . £75
The Complete Plays of Henry James, Lippincott (Philadelphia, PA), 1949 . . . . . £45/£15
ditto, Hart Davis (London), 1949 . . . £45/£15

Non-Fiction

French Poets and Novelists, Macmillan (London), 1878 .
. . . . £300
Hawthorne, Macmillan (London), 1879 (first state with this title listed as 'In Preparation' in adverts at rear) . £100
Hawthorne, Macmillan (London), 1879 (second state with this title listed as 'Now Published' in adverts at rear) . £75
ditto, Harper (New York), 1880 . . . . £65
Portraits of Places, Macmillan (London), 1883 . £100
ditto, Osgood (Boston), 1884 . . . . £100
A Little Tour in France, Osgood (Boston), 1885 (primary binding stamped 'Osgood' on the spine) . . £150
ditto, Osgood (Boston), 1885 (secondary binding stamped 'Houghton Mifflin' on the spine) . . . £100
ditto, Heinemann (London), 1900 . . . £75
ditto, Heinemann (London), 1900 (150 copies; Japanese vellum) £450
Partial Portraits, Macmillan (London/New York), 1888 £75
Essays in London and Elsewhere, Harper (New York), 1893
. . . . £75
ditto, Osgood McIlvaine (London), 1893 . . . £75
William Wetmore Story and His Friends, Blackwood (Edinburgh/London), 1903 (2 vols). . . . £75
ditto, Houghton, Mifflin (Boston), 1903 (2 vols) . . £75
English Hours, Heinemann (London), 1905 . . £50
ditto, Houghton, Mifflin (Boston), 1905 . . £50
ditto, Houghton, Mifflin/Riverside Press (Boston), 1905 (400 large paper copies) £150
The American Scene, Chapman & Hall (London), 1907 £50
ditto, Harper (New York), 1907 . . . . £50
Italian Hours, Heinemann (London), 1909 . . £75
ditto, Houghton, Mifflin (Boston), 1909 . . £75
Notes on Novelists, Dent (London), 1914. . . £50
ditto, Scribner's (New York), 1914 . . . £50
Within the Rim and Other Essays, Collins (London), [1919]
. . . . £65
The Letters of Henry James, Macmillan (London), 1920 (2 vols) . . . . £200/£45
ditto, Scribner's (New York), 1920 (2 vols) . . £200/£45

The Painter's Eye, Hart Davis (London), 1956 . £35/£10
The House of Fiction, Hart Davis (London), 1957. £30/£10
Henry James and Edith Wharton Letters 1900-1915, Scribner's (New York), 1990 . . . . £10/£5

Autobiography

A Small Boy and Others, Macmillan (London), 1913 . £75
ditto, Scribner's (New York), 1913 . . . . £75
Notes of a Son and a Brother, Macmillan (London), 1914 .
. . . . £75
ditto, Scribner's (New York), 1914 . . . . £75
The Middle Years, Collins (London), [1917] . . £75
ditto, Scribner's (New York), 1917 . . . . £75

M.R. JAMES

(b.1862 d.1936)

Montague Rhodes James, Provost of King's College, Cambridge, was a distinguished scholar and academic. He was awarded the Order of Merit in 1930. James had a penchant for the macabre and supernatural, and is best known for his ghost stories, many of which were written as Christmas Eve entertainments and read aloud at gatherings of friends.

Ghost Stories

Ghost Stories of an Antiquary, Edward Arnold (London), [1904] (catalogue dated 1904) £600
ditto, Longmans (New York), 1905 . . . . £400
More Ghost Stories of an Antiquary, Edward Arnold (London), 1911 . . . . £300
A Thin Ghost, Edward Arnold (London), 1919 . £100
A Warning to the Curious, Edward Arnold (London), 1925 .
. . . . £200
ditto, Longmans (New York), 1925 . . . . £175
Wailing Well, Mill House Press (Stanford Dingley, Berkshire), 1928 (157 numbered copies) . . . £550
Collected Ghost Stories, Edward Arnold (London), 1931 .
. . . . £200/£50
ditto, Longmans (New York), 1931 . . . £200/£45
Two Ghost Stories: A Centenary, Ghost Story Press (London), 1993 (200 numbered copies) . . . £115
A Pleasing Terror: The Complete Supernatural Writings, Ash-Tree Press (Ashcroft, Canada), 2001 . £250/£45

Other Titles

Old Testament Legends, Longmans (London), 1913 . £25
The Five Jars, Edward Arnold (London), 1922 £400/£200
ditto, Longmans (New York), 1922 . . . £300/£150
ditto, Ash-Tree Press (Ashcroft, Canada), 1995 . £125/£30
Abbeys, Great Western Railway (London), 1925 . £75/£20
ditto, Doubleday (New York), 1926 . . . £75/£15
Eton and Kings, William & Norgate (London), 1926 .
. . . . £65/£25
ditto, Ash-Tree Press (Ashcroft, Canada), 2005 . £25/£10
Suffolk and Norfolk, Dent (London), 1930 . £45/£15
Letters to a Friend, Edward Arnold (London), 1956 £35/£15

Edited/Translated by M.R. James

The Apocryphal New Testament, Clarendon Press (Oxford, UK), 1924 . . . . £65/£40

Judith, Haymarket Press, 1928 (illustrated by W. Russell Flint, 875 numbered copies) . . . . . £65/£40

ditto, Haymarket Press (London), 1928 (100 copies signed by W. Russell Flint, parchment, in slipcase) . £200/£150

ditto, Haymarket Press (London), 1928 (12 signed copies, on vellum, extra set of 4 plates, in slipcase) . £1,000/£800

The Book of Tobit and *History of Susanna*, Haymarket Press, 1929 (illustrated by W. Russell Flint, 875 numbered copies) . . . . £50/£25

ditto, Haymarket Press (London), 1929 (100 copies signed by W. Russell Flint, parchment, in slipcase) . £200/£150

ditto, Haymarket Press (London), 1929 (12 signed copies, on vellum, extra set of 4 plates, in slipcase) . £1,000/£800

Hans Andersen, Forty Stories, Faber (London), 1930 (illustrated by Christine Jackson) . . . . £65/£25

The Aldine Bible/New Testament, Dent (London), 1934-6 (4 vols, engravings by Eric Gill) . . . £175/£75 the set

P.D. JAMES
(b.1920)

Born in Oxford but educated at Cambridge Girl's High School, Baroness P.D. James worked in the Civil Service and began writing in her 40s. She is famous for her detective fiction, much of which has been successfully televised. She is considered one of the most literate (and conservative) of contemporary crime writers.

'Adam Dalgliesh' Novels

Cover Her Face, Faber (London), 1962 . . £3,000/£400

ditto, Scribner's (New York), 1966 . . . . £300/£30

A Mind to Murder, Faber (London), 1963 . £2,500/£300

ditto, Scribner's (New York), 1967 . . . . £250/£30

Unnatural Causes, Faber (London), 1967 . £2,250/£200

ditto, Scribner's (New York), 1967 . . . . £100/£15

Shroud for a Nightingale, Faber (London), 1971 . £400/£75

ditto, Scribner's (New York), 1971 . . . . £100/£15

The Black Tower, Faber (London), 1975 . . . £175/£15

ditto, Scribner's (New York), 1975 . . . . £75/£10

Death of an Expert Witness, Faber (London), 1977 . .
. . . . £100/£15

ditto, Scribner's (New York), 1977 . . . . £25/£5

A Taste for Death, Faber (London), 1986. . . £35/£5

ditto, Knopf (New York), 1986 . . . . . £15/£5

Devices and Desires, Faber (London), 1989 . . £15/£5

ditto, Franklin Library (Franklin Centre, PA), 1990 (signed, limited edition) £50

ditto, Knopf (New York), 1990 . . . . £10/£5

Original Sin, Faber (London), 1994 . . . £15/£5

ditto, London Limited Editions (London), 1994 (150 signed copies, acetate d/w) . . . . . . £85/£75

ditto, Knopf (New York), 1995 . . . . £10/£5

ditto, Franklin Library (Franklin Centre, PA), 1995 (signed, limited edition) £45

A Certain Justice, Faber (London), 1997 . . . £15/£5

ditto, Knopf (New York), 1997 . . . . £10/£5

Death in Holy Orders, Faber (London), 2001 . . £10/£5

ditto, Knopf (New York), 2001 . . . . £10/£5

The Murder Room, Faber (London), 2003 . . £10/£5

ditto, Knopf (New York), 2003 . . . . £10/£5

The Lighthouse, Faber (London), 2005 . . . £10/£5

ditto, Knopf (New York), 2005 . . . . £10/£5

The Private Patient, Faber (London), 2008 . . £10/£5

ditto, Faber (London), 2008 (1,000 signed, numbered copies; slipcase). . . . . £30/£20

ditto, Knopf (New York), 2008 . . . . . £10/£5

'Cordelia Gray' Novels

An Unsuitable Job for a Woman, Faber (London), 1972 .
. . . . £225/£25

ditto, Scribner's (New York), 1972 . . . £75/£10

The Skull beneath the Skin, Faber (London), 1982 £40/£10

ditto, Scribner's (New York), 1982 . . . . £25/£5

Other Novels

Innocent Blood, Faber (London), 1980 . . . £50/£10

ditto, Scribner's (New York), 1980 . . . . £20/£5

The Children of Men, Faber (London), 1992 . . £20/£5

ditto, Knopf (New York), 1993 . . . . . £10/£5

Omnibus Editions

Murder in Triplicate, Scribner's (New York), 1980 £15/£5

P.D. James Omnibus, Faber (London), 1982 . . £15/£5

The Second P.D. James Omnibus, Faber (London), 1990 .
. . . . £10/£5

Short Stories

Girl Who Loved Graveyards, Penguin (London), 1996 (wraps) £5

Murder in Triplicate, Belmont Press (London), 2001 (50 copies signed by author and illustrator, numbered 1 to 50; bound with leather spine; two extra prints enclosed in rear pocket; slipcase) £225

ditto, Belmont Press (London), 2001 (150 copies signed by author and illustrator, numbered 51-200; bound with leather spine; one extra print enclosed in rear pocket; slipcase). £150

ditto, Belmont Press (London), 2001 (50 copies signed by author and illustrator; bound with a cloth spine and numbered 201 to 250). £200

ditto, Belmont Press (London), 2001 (26 lettered copies signed by author and illustrator; quarter bound in leather; two extra prints enclosed in rear pocket; slipcase) . £250

Non-Fiction

The Maul and the Pear Tree, Constable (London), 1971 (with T.A. Critchley) . . . . . . £50/£20

ditto, Mysterious Press (New York), 1986 . . £15/£5

Bad Language in Church, Prayer Book Society (London), 1988 (wraps). £10

Time to Be in Earnest, A Fragment in Autobiography, Faber (London), 1999. . . . . . . £15/£5

ditto, Knopf (New York), 2000 . . . . . £10/£5

Talking About Detective Fiction, Bodleian Library (London), 2009 . . . . £15/£5

ditto, Bodleian Library (London), 2009 (450 signed, numbered copies) . . . . . . £75/£50

ditto, Knopf (New York), 2009 . . . . . £10/£5

TOVE JANSSON
(b.1914 d.2001)

Tove Jansson was a Swedish-speaking Finnish novelist, illustrator, and comic strip author. She is best-known for her 'Moomin' books about a family of white, round, furry animals with large noses, descended from trolls.

'Moomin' Novels
Finn Family Moomintroll, Ernest Benn (London), 1950 .
. . . . £200/£35
ditto, H.Z. Walck (New York), 1965 . . . £35/£10
Comet in Moominland, Ernest Benn (London), 1951. .
. . . . £100/£25
ditto, H.Z. Walck (New York), 1968 . . . £35/£10
The Exploits of Moominpappa, Ernest Benn (London), 1952 . . . . £100/£25
ditto, H.Z. Walck (New York), 1966 . . . £35/£10
ditto, as *Moominpappa's Memoirs*, Farrar, Straus, Giroux (New York), 1994 . . . . . . £10/£5
Moominsummer Madness, Ernest Benn (London),1955 .
. . . . £100/£20
ditto, H.Z. Walck (New York), 1961 . . . £45/£15
Moominland Midwinter, Ernest Benn (London),1958 .
. . . . £100/£20
ditto, H.Z. Walck (New York), 1962 . . . £40/£10
Moominpappa at Sea, Ernest Benn (London),1966 . .
. . . . £60/£10
ditto, H.Z. Walck (New York), 1967 . . . £35/£10
Moominvalley in November, Ernest Benn (London),1971
. . . . £45/£10
ditto, H.Z. Walck (New York), 1971 . . . £35/£10

'Moomin' Short Stories
Tales from Moominvalley, Ernest Benn (London), 1963 .
. . . . £60/£15
ditto, H.Z. Walck (New York), 1964 . . . £40/£10

'Moomin' Picture Books
The Book about Moomin, Mymble and Little My, Ernest Benn (London), 1953 . . . . . £250/£40
Who Will Comfort Toffle?, Ernest Benn (London), 1969 .
. . . . £100/£20
ditto, H.Z. Walck (New York), 1969 . . . £35/£10
The Dangerous Journey, Ernest Benn (London), 1978 .
. . . . £125/£20

Other Novels
The Summer Book, Hutchinson (London), 1975 £15/£5
ditto, Pantheon Books (New York), 1974 . . £15/£5
Sun City, Hutchinson (London), 1977 . . . £15
ditto, Pantheon Books (New York), 1976 . . £15/£5
The True Deceiver, Penguin (London), 2009 (pbk) . £5
ditto, New York Review of Books (New York), 2009 (pbk)
. . . . £5

Other Short Stories
Sculptor's Daughter, Ernest Benn 1969 . £125/£30
The Fillyjonk Who Believed in Disasters, Creative Education (Mankato, MN), 1989 . . . £10/£5
Fair Play, Sort of Books (London), 2007 (pbk) . £5
A Winter Book, Sort of Books (London), 2006 (pbk) . £5

RICHARD JEFFERIES
(b.1848 d.1887)

Jefferies was a British essayist, novelist, and chronicler of rural life. From his early years he showed a great love of the countryside, but rather than follow his father into farming he worked as a newspaper reporter on the *North Wiltshire Herald*.

Novels
The Scarlet Shawl, Tinsley Brothers (London), 1874 . £400
Restless Human Hearts, Tinsley Brothers (London), 1875 (3 vols) £450
World's End, Tinsley Brothers (London), 1877 (3 vols) £350
Greene Ferne Farm, Smith, Elder & Co. (London), 1880 .
. . . . £200
The Dewy Morn, Bentley (London), 1884 (2 vols). . £250
After London, or Wild England, Cassell & Co. (London), 1885 . . . . £250
Amaryllis at the Fair, Sampson, Low & Co. (London), 1887.
. . . . £75
The Early Fiction of Richard Jefferies, Simpkin, Marshall & Co. (London), 1896 . . . . . £75
ditto, Simpkin, Marshall & Co. (London), 1896 (large paper, 50 numbered copies) £125

Short Story
T.T.T., Arthur Young (London), 1896 (100 copies) . £200

Children's Titles
Wood Magic, A Fable, Cassell, Petter & Galpin (London), 1881 (2 vols) £400
Bevis, The Story of a Boy, Sampson, Low & Co. (London), 1882 (3 vols) £1,000

Non-Fiction
Reporting, Editing and Authorship: Practical Hints for Beginners in Literature, John Snow & Co. (London), [1873] £650
Jack Brass, Emperor of England, Pettit & Co. (London), 1873 . . . . £450
A Memoir of the Goddards of North Wilts Compiled from Ancient Records, Registers and Family Papers, Coate (Swindon), [1873] £500
Suez-cide!! or How Miss Britannia Bought a Dirty Puddle and Lost her Sugar Plums, John Snow (London), 1876 .
. . . . £300
The Gamekeeper at Home, or Sketches of Natural History & Rural Life, Smith, Elder & Co. (London), 1878 (anonymous). £75
Wild Life in a Southern County, Smith, Elder & Co. (London), 1879 (anonymous) £100
The Amateur Poacher, Smith, Elder & Co. (London), 1879 (anonymous). £125
Hodge and His Masters, Smith, Elder & Co. (London), 1880 (2 vols) £100
Round About a Great Estate, Smith, Elder & Co. (London), 1880 . . . . £75
Nature Near London, Chatto & Windus (London), 1883 £75
The Story of My Heart, My Autobiography, Longmans (London), 1883 . . . . £125
Red Deer, Longmans (London), 1884 . . . . £50

The Life of the Fields, Chatto & Windus (London), 1884   .
.   .   .   . £50
The Open Air, Chatto & Windus (London), 1885 .   . £50
Field and Hedgerow, Being the Last Essays of Richard Jefferies Collected by His Widow, Longmans, Green & Co. (London), 1889   .   .   .   . £75
ditto, Longmans, Green & Co. (London), 1889 (large paper, 200 numbered copies). £125
The Toilers of the Field, Longmans, Green & Co. (London), 1892   .   .   .   . £35
ditto, Longmans, Green & Co. (London), 1892 (large paper, 105 numbered copies). £125
Jefferies' Land, A History of Swindon and Its Environs, Simpkin, Marshall & Co. (London), 1896 (350 copies) £75
The Hills and the Vale, Duckworth (London), 1909   . £25
The Nature Diaries and Notebooks of Richard Jefferies, With an Essay 'A Tangle of Autumn' Now Printed for the First Time, Grey Walls Press (London), 1941   . £35/£15
ditto, Grey Walls Press (London), 1941 (large paper, 100 numbered copies) £75
ditto, Grey Walls Press (London), 1941 (large paper, 5 numbered deluxe copies) £450
Chronicles of the Hedges And Other Essays, Phoenix House (London), 1948   .   .   .   .   . £20/£5
The Old House at Coate, Lutterworth Press (London), 1948
.   .   .   . £25/£10
ditto, Harvard Univ Press (Cambridge, MA), 1948   £20/£10
Beauty Is Immortal (Felise of the Dewy Morn), With Some Hitherto Uncollected Essays and Manuscripts, Aldridge Bros (Worthing, Sussex), 1948.   .   .   . £25/£10
Field and Farm, Essays Now Collected With Some From Manuscripts, Phoenix House (London), 1957   . £25/£10
Landscape and Labour, Moonraker Press (Bradford on Avon), 1979 .   .   .   . £15/£5
By the Brook, Eric & Joan Stevens (London), 1981 (170 numbered copies) £35
ditto, Eric & Joan Stevens (London), 1981 (20 leather-bound copies in slipcase) £150
The Birth of a Naturalist, Tern Press (Market Drayton), 1985 (280 numbered copies) £40
ditto, Tern Press (Market Drayton), 1985 (20 leather-bound copies in slipcase)   .   .   .   . £125/£100

JEROME K. JEROME

(b.1859 d.1927)

Jerome Klapka Jerome was first employed as a railway clerk, then an actor. He is best known as a novelist, but was also a successful dramatist and popular journalist. His most enduring work is the humorous travelogue *Three Men in a Boat*. He was born in Walsall, West Midlands, where there is now a museum dedicated to his life and work.

Novels

Three Men in a Boat, Arrowsmith (Bristol, UK), 1889 (first issue, address: 'Quay Street') £125
ditto, Arrowsmith (Bristol, UK), 1889 (second issue, address: '11 Quay Street'). £75
ditto, Holt (New York), 1890   .   .   .   .   . £65
Diary of a Pilgrimage, Arrowsmith (Bristol, UK), 1891   £35
ditto, Holt (New York), 1891   .   .   .   .   . £25

Three Men on the Bummel, Arrowsmith (Bristol, UK), 1900
.   .   .   . £35
ditto, as *Three Men on Wheels*, Dodd, Mead (New York), 1900   .   .   .   . £25
Paul Kelver, Hutchinson (London), 1902.   .   . £35
ditto, Dodd, Mead (New York), 1902   .   .   . £25
Tommy & Co, Hutchinson (London), 1904   .   . £25
ditto, Dodd, Mead (New York), 1904   .   .   . £20
They and I, Hutchinson (London), 1909 .   .   . £20
ditto, Dodd, Mead (New York), 1909   .   .   . £15
All Roads Lead to Calvary, Hutchinson (London), 1919 £15
ditto, Dodd, Mead (New York), 1919   .   .   . £15
Anthony John, Cassell (London), 1923   .   . £40/£15
ditto, Dodd, Mead (New York), 1923   .   . £35/£15

Short Stories

Told After Supper, Leadenhall Press (London), 1891   . £45
ditto, Holt (New York), 1891   .   .   .   .   . £40
John Ingerfield and Other Stories, McClure (London), 1894
.   .   .   . £30
ditto, Holt (New York), 1894   .   .   .   .   . £25
The Observations of Henry, Arrowsmith (London), 1901   .
.   .   .   . £25
ditto, Dodd, Mead (New York), 1901   .   .   . £15
Tea Table Talk, Hutchinson (London), 1903 .   . £15
ditto, Dodd, Mead (New York), 1903   .   .   . £15
The Passing of the Third Floor Back, Hurst & Blackett (London), 1907 .   .   .   . £25
ditto, Dodd, Mead (New York), 1908   .   .   . £25
Malvina of Brittany, Cassell (London), 1916 .   . £15

Plays

Barbara, Lacy (London), 1886 .   .   .   .   . £20
Sunset, French (London), [1888] £20
Fennel, French (London), [1888] £15
Woodbarrow Farm, French (London), [1888].   . £15
The Prude's Progress, French (London), 1895   . £15
Miss Hobbs, French (London), 1902 .   .   .   . £15
Fanny and the Servant Problem, Lacy (London), 1909 £15
The Passing of the Third Floor Back, Hurst & Blackett (London), 1910   .   .   .   . £25
The Master of Mrs Chilvers, Fisher Unwin (London), 1911
.   .   .   . £10
Robina in Search of a Husband, Lacy (London), 1914   £10
The Celebrity, Hodder & Stoughton (London), 1926 £45/£10
The Soul of Nicholas Snyders, Hodder & Stoughton (London), 1927 .   .   .   . £45/£10

Other Works

On Stage-and Off, Field & Tuer (London), 1885 .   . £75
ditto, Leadenhall Press (London), 1891   .   .   . £35
The Idle Thoughts of an Idle Fellow, Field & Tuer (London), 1886 .   .   .   . £100
ditto, Holt (New York), 1890   .   .   .   .   . £50
Stage-Land, Chatto & Windus (London), 1889   . £25
ditto, Holt (New York), 1906   .   .   .   .   . £25
Novel Notes, Leadenhall Press (London), 1893   . £35
ditto, Holt (New York), 1893   .   .   .   .   . £30
Sketches in Lavender, Blue and Green, Longman (London), 1897   .   .   .   . £25
ditto, Holt (New York), 1907   .   .   .   .   . £25
The Second Thoughts of an Idle Fellow, Hurst & Blackett (London), 1898   .   .   .   . £25
ditto, Dodd, Mead (New York), 1898   .   .   . £20

American Wives and Others, Stokes (New York), 1904 £25
Idle Ideas in 1905, Hurst & Blackett (London), 1905 . £15
The Angel and the Author—and Others, Hurst & Blackett (London), 1908 . . . . £15
Thoughts from Jerome K. Jerome, Sesame Booklets (London), 1913 (wraps) £10
A Miscellany of Sense and Nonsense, Arrowsmith (London), 1923 . . . . . . £40/£15
ditto, Dodd, Mead (New York), 1924 . . £40/£15
My Life and Times, Hodder & Stoughton (London), 1926 .
. . . . £35/£15
ditto, Harper (New York), 1926 . . . . . £35/£15

RUTH PRAWER JHABVALA
(b.1927)

Born in Cologne, Germany Ruth Prawer Jhabvala fled with her Polish/Jewish family from the Nazis to England in 1939. She married an Indian architect in 1951 and moved to Delhi. Her first novel was published in 1955. She is also known for her short stories and film scripts written for the Merchant/Ivory partnership.

Novels
To Whom She Will, Allen & Unwin (London), 1955 . .
. . . . £165/£20
ditto, as *Amrita*, Norton (New York), 1956 . . £35/£10
The Nature of Passion, Allen & Unwin (London), 1956 .
. . . . £100/£20
ditto, Norton (New York), 1957 . . . . £25/£5
Esmond in India, Allen & Unwin (London), 1958. £75/£20
ditto, Norton (New York), 1958 . . . . £25/£5
The Householder, Murray (London), 1960 . £45/£20
ditto, Norton (New York), 1960 . . . . £20/£5
Get Ready for Battle, Murray (London), 1962. . £40/£15
ditto, Norton (New York), 1963 . . . . £15/£5
A Backward Place, Murray (London), 1965 . £30/£10
ditto, Norton (New York), 1965 . . . . £15/£5
A New Dominion, Murray (London), 1972 . £25/£10
ditto, as *Travellers*, Harper & Row (New York), 1973 .
. . . . £15/£5
Heat and Dust, Murray (London), 1975 . . £25/£10
ditto, Harper (New York), 1976 . . . £20/£5
In Search of Love and Beauty, Murray (London), 1983 .
. . . . £15/£5
ditto, Morrow (New York), 1983 . . . £10/£5
Three Continents, Murray (London), 1987 . £15/£5
ditto, Morrow (New York), 1987 . . . £10/£5
Poet and Dancer, Murray (London), 1993 . £10/£5
ditto, Doubleday (New York), 1993 . . . £10/£5
Shards of Memory, Murray (London), 1995 . £10/£5
ditto, Doubleday (New York), 1995 . . . £10/£5

Short Stories
Like Birds, Like Fishes and Other Stories, Murray (London), 1963 . . . . . . £35/£10
ditto, Norton (New York), 1964 . . . . £25/£5
A Stronger Climate: Nine Stories, Murray (London), 1968.
. . . . £30/£10
ditto, Norton (New York), 1968 . . . . £15/£5

An Experience of India, Murray (London), 1971 . £30/£10
ditto, Norton (New York), 1972 . . . . £15/£5
How I Became a Holy Mother and Other Stories, Murray (London), 1976 . . . . . £20/£5
ditto, Harper (New York), 1976 . . . . £15/£5
Out of India: Selected Stories, Morrow (New York), 1986 .
. . . . £15/£5
ditto, Murray (London), 1987 . . . . £10/£5
East into Upper East: Plain Tales from New York and New Delhi, Murray (London), 1998. . . . £10/£5
ditto, Counterpoint (Washington, DC), 1998 . £10/£5
My Nine Lives, Chapters of a Possible Past, Murray (London), 2004 . . . . . £10/£5
ditto, Shoemaker & Hoard (Washington, DC), 2004 £10/£5

Screenplays
The Householder: A Screenplay, Ramlochan (Delhi, India), 1963 (pbk) £40
Savages, Shakespeare Wallah: Two Films by James Ivory, Grove Press (New York), 1973 (screenplay of the second film by R.P.J.; wraps). £10
Autobiography of a Princess: Also Being the Adventures of an American Director in the Land of the Maharajas, Harper & Row (New York), 1977 (by James Ivory, screenplay by R.P.J) . . . . . £25/£10

CAPTAIN W.E. JOHNS
(b.1893 d.1968)

William Earle Johns joined the newly-formed Royal Flying Corps in 1916 and remained in the Air Force until 1930. He founded *Popular Flying* magazine, in which Captain James Bigglesworth made his first appearance. Both early and late 'Biggles' books are expensive: the latter were published in small runs as Johns fell out of favour. Two titles published in the 1990s in very small numbers are also much sought after by collectors.

'Biggles' Titles
The Camels Are Coming, Hamilton (London), [1932] (d/w price 3/6) . . . . £4,000/£1,000
The Cruise of the Condor: A Biggles Story, Hamilton (London), [1933] (d/w price 3/6) . . £3,000/£600
'Biggles' of the Camel Squadron, Hamilton (London), [1934] (d/w price 3/6). . . . £2,500/£300
Biggles Flies Again, Hamilton (London), [1934] (d/w price 3/6). . . . . . . £2,500/£300
ditto, Penguin (London), 1941 (Harmondsworth, Middlesex)
. . . . £200
Biggles Learns to Fly, Boys' Friend Library (London), 1935 (price 4d; pbk) £1,150
ditto, Brockhampton Press (Leicester, UK), 1955 (first hardback edition). . . . . £125/£25
The Black Peril: A 'Biggles' Story, Hamilton (London), [1935] (d/w price 3/6). . . . £2,750/£1,000
Biggles Flies East, O.U.P. (Oxford, UK), 1935 (d/w price 3/6). . . . . . . £1,500/£250
Biggles Hits the Trail, O.U.P. (Oxford, UK), 1935 (d/w price 3/6) . . . . . . £1,500/£250
Biggles in France, Boys' Friend Library (London), 1935 (price 4d; wraps) £1,250

Biggles & Co, O.U.P. (Oxford, UK), 1936 (d/w price 3/6) .
.   .   .   . £2,500/£300

Biggles in Africa, O.U.P. (Oxford, UK), 1936 (d/w price
3/6).   .   .   .   .   .   . £1,500/£250

Biggles - Air Commodore, O.U.P. (Oxford, UK), 1937 (d/w
price 3/6).   .   .   .   .   . £1,250/£200

Biggles Flies West, O.U.P. (Oxford, UK), 1937 (d/w price
3/6).   .   .   .   .   .   . £1,250/£200

Biggles Flies South, O.U.P. (Oxford, UK), 1938 (d/w price
3/6).   .   .   .   .   .   . £1,250/£200

Biggles Goes to War, O.U.P. (Oxford, UK), 1938 (d/w price
3/6).   .   .   .   .   .   . £1,250/£200

The Rescue Flight: A 'Biggles' Story, O.U.P. (Oxford, UK),
1939 (d/w price 3/6)   .   .   .   . £1,250/£200

Biggles in Spain, O.U.P. (Oxford, UK), 1939 (d/w price 3/6)
.   .   .   . £1,250/£200

Biggles Flies North, O.U.P. (Oxford, UK), 1939 (d/w price
3/6).   .   .   .   .   .   . £1,250/£200

Biggles - Secret Agent, O.U.P. (Oxford, UK), 1940 (d/w
price 4/-)   .   .   .   .   .   . £1,000/£125

Biggles in the Baltic: A Tale of the Second Great War,
O.U.P. (Oxford, UK), 1940 (d/w price 4/-) . £1,000/£150

Biggles in the South Seas, O.U.P. (Oxford, UK), 1940 (d/w
price 4/-)   .   .   .   .   .   . £1,000/£125

Biggles Defies the Swastika, O.U.P. (Oxford, UK), 1941
(d/w price 4/-)   .   .   .   .   . £1,000/£125

Biggles Sees it Through, O.U.P. (Oxford, UK), 1941 (d/w
price 4/-)   .   .   .   .   .   . £1,000/£125

Spitfire Parade: Stories of Biggles in War-Time, O.U.P.
(Oxford, UK), 1941 (d/w price 4/-) .   . . £1,250/£150

Biggles in the Jungle, O.U.P. (Oxford, UK), 1942 (d/w price
5/-).   .   .   .   . £1,000/£125

Biggles Sweeps the Desert, Hodder & Stoughton (London),
1942 (d/w price 5/-)   .   .   .   .   . £100/£20

Biggles - Charter Pilot, O.U.P. (Oxford, UK), 1943 (d/w
price 5/-)   .   .   .   .   .   . £750/£100

Biggles in Borneo, O.U.P. (Oxford, UK), 1943 (d/w price
5/-) .   .   .   . £750/£75

Biggles 'Fails to Return', Hodder & Stoughton (London),
1943 (d/w price 6/-)   .   .   .   .   . £75/£20

Biggles in the Orient, Hodder & Stoughton (London), 1945
(d/w price 6/-)   .   .   .   .   .   . £90/£20

Biggles Delivers the Goods, Hodder & Stoughton (London),
1946 (d/w price 6/-)   .   .   .   .   . £90/£20

Sergeant Bigglesworth CID, Hodder & Stoughton (London),
1947 (d/w price 6/-)   .   .   .   .   . £90/£20

Biggles' Second Case, Hodder & Stoughton (London), 1948
(d/w price 6/-)   .   .   .   .   .   . £75/£20

Biggles Hunts Big Game, Hodder & Stoughton (London),
1948 (d/w price 6/-)   .   .   .   .   . £65/£15

Biggles Takes a Holiday, Hodder & Stoughton (London),
1949 (d/w price 6/-)   .   .   .   .   . £45/£15

Biggles Breaks the Silence, Hodder & Stoughton (London),
1949 (d/w price 6/-)   .   .   .   .   . £45/£15

Biggles Gets His Men, Hodder & Stoughton (London), 1950
(d/w price 6/-)   .   .   .   .   .   . £45/£15

Biggles - Air Detective, Marks & Spencer, 1951 (price 2/6;
no d/w) £20

Another Job for Biggles, Hodder & Stoughton (London),
1951 (d/w price 6/-)   .   .   .   .   . £40/£10

Biggles Goes to School, Hodder & Stoughton (London),
1951(d/w price 6/-)   .   .   .   .   . £45/£15

Biggles Works It Out, Hodder & Stoughton (London), 1951
(d/w price 7/6)   .   .   .   .   .   . £40/£10

Biggles Takes the Case, Hodder & Stoughton (London),
1952 (d/w price 7/6)   .   .   .   .   . £45/£15

Biggles Follows On, Hodder & Stoughton (London), 1952
(d/w price 7/6)   .   .   .   .   .   . £40/£10

Biggles and the Black Raider, Hodder & Stoughton
(London), 1953 (d/w price 7/6)   .   .   . £45/£15

Biggles in the Blue, Brockhampton Press (Leicester, UK),
1953 (d/w price 7/6)   .   .   .   .   . £50/£15

Biggles in the Gobi, Hodder & Stoughton (London), 1953
(d/w price 7/6)   .   .   .   .   .   . £45/£15

Biggles of the Special Air Police, Thames (London), [1953]
(d/w price 3/6)   .   .   .   .   .   . £25/£10

Biggles Cuts it Fine, Hodder & Stoughton (London), 1954
(d/w price 7/6)   .   .   .   .   .   . £50/£15

*Biggles and the Pirate Treasure and Other Biggles
Adventures*, Brockhampton Press (Leicester, UK), 1954
(d/w price 7/6)   .   .   .   .   .   . £50/£15

Biggles, Foreign Legionnaire, Hodder & Stoughton
(London), 1954 (d/w price 7/6)   .   .   . £50/£15

Biggles, Pioneer Airfighter, Thames (London), [1954] (d/w
price 3/6)   .   .   .   . £25/£10

Biggles in Australia, Hodder & Stoughton (London), 1955
(d/w price 7/6)   .   .   .   .   .   . £50/£15

Biggles' Chinese Puzzle and Other Biggles Adventures,
Brock-hampton Press (Leicester, UK), 1955 (d/w price 7/6)
.   .   .   . £50/£15

Biggles of 266, Thames (London), [1956] (d/w price 3/6) .
.   .   .   . £25/£10

No Rest For Biggles, Hodder & Stoughton (London), 1956
(d/w price 7/6)   .   .   .   .   .   . £60/£15

Biggles Takes Charge, Brockhampton Press (Leicester, UK),
1956 (d/w price 7/6)   .   .   .   .   . £60/£15

Biggles Makes Ends Meet, Hodder & Stoughton (London),
1957 (d/w price 8/6)   .   .   .   .   . £60/£15

Biggles of the Interpol, Brockhampton Press (Leicester,
UK), 1957 (d/w price 8/6).   .   .   .   . £75/£20

Biggles on the Home Front, Hodder & Stoughton (London),
1957 (d/w price 8/6)   .   .   .   .   . £75/£20

Biggles Presses On, Brockhampton Press (Leicester, UK),
1958 (d/w price 8/6)   .   .   .   .   . £50/£15

Biggles on Mystery Island, Hodder & Stoughton (London),
[1958] (d/w price 8/6).   .   .   .   .   . £55/£15

Biggles Buries a Hatchet, Brockhampton Press (Leicester,
UK), 1958 (d/w price 8/6).   .   .   .   . £60/£15

Biggles in Mexico, Brockhampton Press (Leicester, UK),
1959 (d/w price 8/6)   .   .   .   .   . £50/£15

Biggles' Combined Operation, Hodder & Stoughton
(London), [1959] (d/w price 8/6)   .   .   . £50/£15

Biggles at World's End, Brockhampton Press (Leicester,
UK), 1959 (d/w price 8/6).   .   .   .   . £50/£15

Biggles and the Leopards of Zinn, Brockhampton Press
(Leicester, UK), 1960 (d/w price 8/6)   .   . £60/£15

Biggles Goes Home, Hodder & Stoughton (London), [1960]
(d/w price 8/6)   .   .   .   .   .   . £60/£15

Biggles and the Poor Rich Boy, Brockhampton Press
(Leicester, UK), 1961 (d/w price 8/6)   .   . £45/£15

Biggles Forms a Syndicate, Hodder & Stoughton (London),
1961 (d/w price 8/6)   .   .   .   .   . £60/£15

Biggles and the Missing Millionaire, Brockhampton Press
(Leicester, UK), 1961 (d/w price 8/6)   .   . £50/£15

Biggles Goes Alone, Hodder & Stoughton (London), [1962]
(d/w price 8/6)   .   .   .   .   .   . £75/£20

Orchids for Biggles, Hodder & Stoughton (London), 1962
(d/w price 8/6)   .   .   .   .   .   . £65/£15

Biggles Sets a Trap, Hodder & Stoughton (London), 1962
(d/w price 8/6) . . . . . . £75/£20
Biggles Takes it Rough, Brockhampton Press (Leicester,
UK), 1963 (d/w price 8/6) . . . . £75/£20
Biggles Takes A Hand, Hodder & Stoughton (London),
[1963] (d/w price 8/6). . . . . . £75/£15
Biggles' Special Case, Brockhampton Press (Leicester, UK),
1963 (d/w price 8/6) . . . . . £75/£15
*Biggles and the Plane That Disappeared: A Story of the Air
Police*, Hodder & Stoughton (London), 1963 (d/w price
8/6). . . . . £75/£15
Biggles Flies to Work, Dean (London), [1963] (d/w price
2/6). . . . . £25/£10
Biggles and the Lost Sovereigns, Brockhampton Press
(Leicester, UK), 1964 (d/w price 8/6) . . £75/£15
Biggles and the Black Mask, Hodder & Stoughton
(London), 1964 (d/w price 8/6) . . . £100/£20
Biggles Investigates and Other Stories of the Air Police,
Brockhampton Press (Leicester, UK), 1965 (d/w price 8/6)
. . . . £75/£20
Biggles Looks Back: A Story of Biggles and the Air Police,
Hodder & Stoughton (London), 1965 (d/w price 8/6) . .
. . . . £125/£25
Biggles and the Plot That Failed, Brockhampton Press
(Leicester, UK), 1965 (d/w price 8/6) . . £125/£25
Biggles and the Blue Moon, Brockhampton Press (Leicester,
UK), 1965 (d/w price 10/6) . . . £175/£25
Biggles Scores a Bull, Hodder & Stoughton (London), 1965
(d/w price 10/6) . . . . . £150/£35
Biggles in the Terai, Brockhampton Press (Leicester, UK),
1966 (d/w price 10/6). . . . . £200/£40
Biggles and the Gun Runners, Brockhampton Press
(Leicester, UK), 1966 (d/w price 10/6) . . £200/£40
Biggles Sorts It Out, Brockhampton Press (Leicester, UK),
1967 (d/w price 10/6). . . . . £175/£30
Biggles and the Dark Intruder, Knight (London), 1967
(price 3/6; pbk) £20
ditto, Brockhampton Press (Leicester, UK), 1970 . £175/£15
Biggles and the Penitent Thief, Brockhampton Press
(Leicester, UK), 1967 (d/w price 10/6) . . £175/£45
Biggles and the Deep Blue Sea, Brockhampton Press
(Leicester, UK), 1968 (d/w price 10/6) . £350/£100
The Boy Biggles, Dean (London), 1968 (price 3/-). £25/£5
Biggles in the Underworld, Brockhampton Press (Leicester,
UK), 1968 (d/w price 10/6) . . . £200/£50
Biggles and the Little Green God, Brockhampton Press
(Leicester, UK), 1969 (d/w price 12/6) . . £225/£50
Biggles and the Noble Lord, Brockhampton Press (Leicester,
UK), 1969 (d/w price 12/6) . . . £225/£50
Biggles Sees Too Much, Brockhampton Press (Leicester,
UK), 1970 (d/w price 12/6) . . . £225/£50
Biggles of the Royal Flying Corps, Purnell (London), 1978
. . . . £25/£10
Biggles Does Some Homework, Wright/Schofield (Watford,
Herts), 1997 (300 numbered copies; price £18.50; pbk) .
. . . . £450
Biggles Air Ace: The Uncollected Stories, Wright (Watford,
Herts), 1999 (300 numbered copies; price £19.50; pbk) £250

'Biggles' Omnibuses
The Biggles Omnibus, O.U.P. (Oxford, UK), 1938 (d/w
price 3/6) . . . . . £1,500/£165
The Biggles Flying Omnibus, O.U.P. (Oxford, UK), 1940
(d/w price 4/-) . . . . . £1,250/£150

The Third Biggles Omnibus, O.U.P. (Oxford, UK), 1941
(d/w price 4/6) . . . . . £1,000/£150
The First Biggles Omnibus, Hodder & Stoughton (London),
1953 (d/w price 12/6). . . . . £35/£10
The Biggles Air Detective Omnibus, Hodder & Stoughton
(London), 1956 (d/w price 12/6) . . . £40/£15
The Biggles Adventure Omnibus, Hodder & Stoughton
(London), 1965 (d/w price 18/-) . . . £45/£15
The Bumper Biggles Book, Chancellor, 1983 . . £15/£5
The Best of Biggles, Chancellor, 1985 . . . £15/£5

'Worrals' Books
Worrals of the W.A.A.F., Lutterworth Press (London), 1941
(d/w price 3/6) . . . . . . £200/£30
Worrals Carries On, Lutterworth Press (London), 1942 (d/w
price 4/6) . . . . £175/£25
Worrals Flies Again, Hodder & Stoughton (London), 1942
(d/w price 5/-) . . . . . . £150/£25
Worrals On the War-Path, Hodder & Stoughton (London),
1943 (d/w price 5/-) . . . . . £125/£20
Worrals Goes East, Hodder & Stoughton (London), 1944
(d/w price 5/-) . . . . . . £65/£15
Worrals of the Islands: A Story of the War in the Pacific,
Hodder & Stoughton (London), 1945 (d/w price 6/-) . .
. . . . £45/£10
Worrals in the Wilds, Hodder & Stoughton (London), 1947
(d/w price 6/-) . . . . . . £35/£10
Worrals Down Under, Lutterworth Press (London), 1948
(d/w price 6/-) . . . . . . £35/£10
Worrals Goes Afoot, Lutterworth Press (London), 1949 (d/w
price 6/-) . . . . £35/£10
Worrals In the Wastelands, Lutterworth Press (London),
1949 (d/w price 6/-) . . . . . £35/£10
Worrals Investigates, Lutterworth Press (London), 1950
(d/w price 6/-) . . . . . . £35/£10

'Gimlet' Books
King of the Commandos, Univ of London Press (London),
1943 (d/w price 5/-) . . . . . £65/£10
Gimlet Goes Again, Univ of London Press (London), 1944
(d/w price 5/-) . . . . . . £65/£10
Gimlet Comes Home, Univ of London Press (London), 1946
(d/w price 6/-) . . . . . . £50/£10
Gimlet Mops Up, Brockhampton Press (Leicester, UK), 1947
(d/w price 6/-) . . . . . . £50/£10
Gimlet's Oriental Quest, Brockhampton Press (Leicester,
UK), 1948 (d/w price 6/-) . . . . £50/£10
Gimlet Lends a Hand, Brockhampton Press (Leicester, UK),
1949 (d/w price 6/-) . . . . . £50/£10
Gimlet Bores In, Brockhampton Press (Leicester, UK), 1950
(d/w price 6/-) . . . . . . £40/£10
Gimlet Off the Map, Brockhampton Press (Leicester, UK),
1951 (d/w price 6/-) . . . . . £40/£10
Gimlet Gets the Answer, Brockhampton Press (Leicester,
UK), 1952 (d/w price 6/-) . . . . £40/£10
Gimlet Takes a Job, Brockhampton Press (Leicester, UK),
1954 (d/w price 6/-) . . . . . £40/£10

Science Fiction Titles
Kings of Space: A Story of Interplanetary Explorations,
Hodder & Stoughton (London), 1954 (d/w price 7/6). .
. . . . £30/£10
Return to Mars, Hodder & Stoughton (London), 1955 (d/w
price 7/6) . . . . £25/£10

Now to the Stars, Hodder & Stoughton (London), 1956 (d/w price 7/6) . . . . £35/£10
To Outer Space, Hodder & Stoughton (London), 1957 (d/w price 8/6) . . . . £40/£15
The Edge of Beyond, Hodder & Stoughton (London), [1958] (d/w price 8/6) . . . . £40/£15
The Death Rays of Ardilla, Hodder & Stoughton (London), [1959] (d/w price 8/6). . . . . £45/£15
To Worlds Unknown: A Story of Interplanetary Explorations, Hodder & Stoughton (London), [1960] (d/w price 8/6) . . . . £45/£15
The Quest for the Perfect Planet, Hodder & Stoughton (London), 1961 (d/w price 8/6) . . . £25/£10
Worlds of Wonder: More Adventures in Space, Hodder & Stoughton (London), 1962 (d/w price 9/6) . £40/£15
The Man Who Vanished into Space, Hodder & Stoughton (London), [1963] (d/w price 9/6) . . . £35/£10

Other Books Written by Johns
Mossyface, 'The Weekly Telegraph Novel', 1922 (pseud 'William Earle'; pbk) £3,000
ditto, Mellifont (London), 1932 (pbk) . . . £3,000
ditto, Trendler/Wright (Watford, Herts), 1994 (300 numbered copies, no d/w) £100
Modern Boys Book of Aircraft, Amalgamated Press (London), 1931 . . . . £65/£20
Wings: A Book of Flying Adventures, Hamilton (London), [1931] (edited by Johns) . . . . £300/£35
The Pictorial Flying Course, John Hamilton (London), [1932] (by Johns and H.M. Schofield; d/w price 5/-) .
. . . . £300/£75
Fighting Planes and Aces, John Hamilton (London), [1932] (d/w price 5/-) . . . . . . £300/£75
The Spy Flyers, John Hamilton (London), 1933 (d/w price 3/6) . . . . £500/£125
The Raid, John Hamilton (London), [1935] (d/w price 3/6) .
. . . . £400/£75
The Air VC's, John Hamilton (London), [1935] (d/w price 3/6). . . . . £350/£75
Some Milestones in Aviation, John Hamilton (London), [1935] (d/w price 3/6). . . . . £200/£45
Blue Blood Runs Red, Newnes (London), [1936] (pseud 'Jon Early') . . . . . . £2,500/£300
Modern Boy's Book of Adventure Stories, Amalgamated Press (London), 1936 . . . . . £50/£15
Ace High, Ace (London), 1936 . . . . . £100/£30
Air Adventures, Ace (London), 1936. . . . £100/£30
Sky High: A 'Steeley' Adventure, Newnes (London), [1936]
. . . . £500/£100
Steeley Flies Again, Newnes (London), [1936] £500/£100
Flying Stories, John Hamilton (London), 1937 . £100/£25
Murder By Air: A 'Steeley' Adventure, Newnes (London), [1937] (d/w price 3/6). . . . . £500/£100
The Passing Show, My Garden/Newnes (London), 1937 (d/w price 5/-) . . . . . . £100/£20
Desert Night: A Romance, John Hamilton (London), [1938]
. . . . £250/£45
The Murder at Castle Deeping: A 'Steeley' Adventure, John Hamilton (London), [1938] . . . £1,000/£350
Champion of the Main, O.U.P. (Oxford, UK), 1938 (d/w price 5/-) . . . . £400/£75
Wings of Romance: A 'Steeley' Adventure, Newnes (London), 1939 (d/w price 2/6) . . . £500/£100
Modern Boy's Book of Pirates, Amalgamated Press (London), [1939] (d/w price 5/-) . . . £250/£50

The Unknown Quantity, John Hamilton (London), [1940] (with crest on spine of book; d/w price 7/6). £500/£200
Sinister Service: A Tale, O.U.P. (Oxford, UK), 1942 (d/w price 5/-) . . . . £125/£25
Comrades in Arms, Hodder & Stoughton (London), 1947 (d/w price 6/-) . . . . £45/£10
The Rustlers of Rattlesnake Valley, Nelson (London), 1948 (d/w price 5/-) . . . . . . £30/£5
Dr Vane Answers the Call, Latimer House (London), 1950 (d/w price 6/-) . . . . . . £200/£75
Short Sorties, Latimer House (London), 1950 (d/w price 7/6) . . . . £175/£25
Sky Fever and Other Stories, Latimer House (London), [1953] (d/w price 7/6). . . . . £175/£25
Adventure Bound, Nelson (London), 1955 (d/w price 2/6) .
. . . . £15/£5
Adventure Unlimited, Nelson (London), 1957 . £15/£5
No Motive for Murder, Hodder & Stoughton (London), [1958] (d/w price 12/6) . . . . . £175/£40
The Man Who Lost His Way, Macdonald (London), 1959 (d/w price 10/6) . . . . . . £175/£40
The Biggles Book of Heroes, Parrish (London), 1959 .
. . . . £75/£15
Where the Golden Eagle Soars, Hodder & Stoughton (London), [1960] (d/w price 12/6) . . . £40/£5
Adventures of the Junior Detection Club, Parrish (London), [1960] (d/w price 10/6) . . . . . £65/£15
The Biggles Book of Treasure Hunting, Parrish (London), 1962 (d/w price 11/6) . . . . . £75/£15
Steeley and the Missing Page and Other Stories, Norman Wright (Watford, Herts), 2000 (300 numbered copies; pbk; price £19.50) £75
Winged Justice and Other Uncollected Stories, Norman Wright (Watford, Herts), 2001 (300 numbered copies; pbk; price £19.50) £75

Books Illustrated by Johns
Desert Wings, by Covington Clarke, John Hamilton (London), [1931]. . . . . £100/£20
Aces Up, by Covington Clarke, John Hamilton (London), [1931] . . . . £45/£15
For Valour, by Covington Clarke, John Hamilton (London), [1931] . . . . £45/£15

B.S. JOHNSON
(b.1933 d.1973)

A controversial and experimental novelist, Johnson's books were issued with black, blank, and holed pages. *The Unfortunates* was published in loose sections to be shuffled and read in no particular order. He won major awards for his writing but never made a living from it. Johnson committed suicide at 40.

Novels
Travelling People, Constable (London), 1963 . . £250/£50
Albert Angelo, Constable (London), 1964 . . £120/£35
ditto, New Directions (Norfolk, CT), 1987 . . £20/£5
Trawl, Secker & Warburg (London), 1966 . . £100/£30
The Unfortunates, Panther [with Secker & Warburg (London)], 1969 (27 loose sections in box) . . . £125

House Mother Normal, Trigram Press (London), 1971 (26 signed, lettered copies) £350
ditto, Trigram Press (London), 1971 (100 signed, numbered copies) £100
ditto, Collins (London), 1971 . . . . £30/£5
ditto, New Directions (Norfolk, CT), 1986 . . £15/£5
Christie Malry's Own Double Entry, Collins (London), 1973 . . . . £50/£10
ditto, Viking (New York), 1973 . . . . . £20/£5
See the Old Lady Decently, Hutchinson (London), 1975 .
. . . . £25/£5
ditto, Viking (New York), 1975 . . . . . £25/£5

Short Stories
Statement Against Corpses, Constable (London), 1964 (with Zulfikar Ghose) . . . .£150/£25
Aren't You Rather Young to be Writing Your Memoirs?, Hutchinson (London), 1973 . . . . £40/£15
ditto, Hutchinson (London), 1973 (pbk with d/w) . £20/£5
Everyone Knows Somebody Who's Dead, Covent Garden Press (London), 1973 (100 signed, numbered copies of 600; stapled wraps) £65
ditto, Covent Garden Press (London), 1973 (500 copies of 600; stapled wraps) £20

Poetry
Poems, Constable (London), 1964 . . . .£200/£30
ditto, Chilmark Press (New York), 1964 . . .£100/£25
Poems Two, Trigram Press (London), 1972 (26 signed, lettered copies) £250
ditto, Trigram Press (London), 1972 (100 signed, numbered copies, acetate d/w) . . . . . .£100/£75
ditto, Trigram Press (London), 1972 (hardback) . £25/£10
ditto, Trigram Press (London), 1972 (pbk) . . . £10
A Dublin Unicorn, Byron Press (Nottingham, UK), 1975 (25 signed copies of 250; stapled wraps) £225
ditto, Byron Press (Nottingham, UK), 1975 (225 unsigned copies of 250; stapled wraps) £30

Others
Street Children, Hodder & Stoughton (London), 1964 (with photographs by Julia Trevelyan Oman) . . .£125/£25
You're Human Like the Rest of Them, Penguin New English Dramatists (London), 1970 (pbk) . . . £10

JAMES JOYCE
(b.1882 d.1941)

Novelist, poet, short story writer, and father of Modernism, Joyce's *Ulysses* and *Finnegan's Wake* revolutionised narrative form and paved the way for the 20th century novel. Although he spent most of his adult life outside his native Ireland, Joyce's Irish experiences are central to his writing and provide the settings and much of the subject matter of his fiction.

Poetry
Holy Office, privately printed [Austria-Hungary], [1904 or 5] (broadside) £12,500
Chamber Music, Elkin Mathews (London), 1907 (first state 16.2 x 11cm, thick laid endpapers, poems in signature 'c' well centred). £3,750

ditto, Elkin Mathews (London), 1907 (second state 15.8 x 11cm, thick wove endpapers, poems in signature 'c' poorly centred) £2,750
ditto, Elkin Mathews (London), 1907 (third state 15.9 x 10.9cm, thin wove transparent endpapers) . . £1,500
ditto, Cornhill Co. (Boston), 1918 (unauthorised edition) .
. . . .£200
ditto, Huebsch (New York), 1918 (authorised edition) .£200
Gas from a Burner, privately printed [Trieste], [1912] (broadside) £25,000
Pomes Penyeach, Shakespeare and Co. (Paris), 1927 (sage paper covered boards lettered in green, in glassine d/w with author and title in manuscript; with tipped-in errata slip) .
. . . . £350/£250
ditto, privately printed for Sylvia Beach (Princeton Univ Press, Princeton, NJ), 1931 (50 copies, sewn grey wraps) .
. . . . £2,000
ditto, privately printed (Cleveland, OH), 1931 (100 copies) .
. . . . £1,000
ditto, Obelisk Press/Desmond Harmsworth (Paris/London), 1931 (25 signed, numbered copies, green silk portfolio) .
. . . . £30,000
ditto, Faber (London), 1933 (sewn wraps) . . . £65
Collected Poems, Black Sun Press (New York), 1936 (800 copies, glassine d/w) . . . . . . £450/£300
ditto, Black Sun Press (New York), 1936 (50 signed copies, tissue d/w, slipcase) . . . . £4,000/£3,500
ditto, Black Sun Press (New York), 1936 (3 signed, lettered copies, tissue d/w, slipcase) £7,500
ditto, Viking (New York), 1937 . . . . .£250/£65

Short Stories
Dubliners, Grant Richards (London), 1914 . . £5,000
ditto, Huebsch (New York), 1916 . . . . £1,250

Novels
A Portrait of the Artist as a Young Man, Huebsch (New York), 1916 . . . . . . £2,000
ditto, Egoist Ltd (London), 1916 [1917] . . . £1,000
Ulysses, Shakespeare Press (Paris), 1922 (750 numbered copies on handmade paper of 1,000; wraps) . £16,500
ditto, Shakespeare Press (Paris), 1922 (the above 750 copy issue rebound) £5,000
ditto, Shakespeare Press (Paris), 1922 (100 signed, numbered copies of 1,000 on Dutch handmade paper; wraps) . .
. . . .£100,000
ditto, Shakespeare Press (Paris), 1922 (150 numbered copies on verge d'Arches paper of 1,000; wraps) . .£30,000
ditto, Egoist Press (London), 1922 (2,000 numbered copies with errata slip and 4-page leaflet of press notices; wraps)
. . . . £2,500
ditto, Random House (New York), 1934 (first copyright printing, 100 copies) £3,000
ditto, Random House (New York), 1934 (second printing) .
. . . .£2,000/£200
ditto, Bodley Head (London), 1936 (900 copy edition) .
. . . .£2,000/£750
ditto, Bodley Head (London), 1936 (100 signed copies, slipcase). . . . . . .£20,000/£17,500
ditto, Bodley Head (London), 1937 . . . £450/£150
ditto, as *Ulysses; A Facsimile of the Manuscript*, Faber & Rosenbach (London/Philadelphia, PA), 1975 (3 vols, slipcase, no d/w) £125
Finnegan's Wake, Faber (London), 1939. . £2,000/£300

ditto, Viking (New York), 1939 . . . . £1,000/£100

ditto, Faber/Viking (London/New York), 1939 (425 signed copies, glassine d/w, slipcase) . . £7,500/£6,000

ditto, Faber/Viking (London/New York), 1939 (26 signed copies, glassine d/w, slipcase) £12,500

Stephen Hero, Cape (London), 1944 . . . . £250/£75

ditto, New Directions (Norfolk, CT), 1944 . . £200/£75

Fragments

Anna Livia Plurabelle, Crosby Gaige (New York), 1928 (800 signed copies, acetate d/w) . . £2,000/£1,800

ditto, Crosby Gaige (New York), 1928 (50 unsigned copies on green paper) £1,500

ditto, Faber (London), 1930 (tissue d/w) . . £100/£65

ditto, Faber (London), 1930 (sewn wraps) . . . £50

Tales Told of Shem and Shaun, Black Sun Press (Paris), 1929 (500 copies; wraps; slipcase) . . . £750/£600

ditto, Black Sun Press (Paris), 1929 (100 signed copies) .

. . . . £6,000

ditto, Black Sun Press (Paris), 1929 (50 hors de commerce copies) £1,500

ditto, as **Two Tales of Shem and Shaun**, Faber (London), 1932 . . . . £150/£50

Haveth Childers Everywhere, Fountain Press (Paris), 1930 (500 copies of 685; wraps with glassine d/w and slipcase).

. . . . £600/£350

ditto, Fountain Press (Paris), 1930 (75 writer's copies of 685)

. . . . £2,000

ditto, Fountain Press (Paris), 1930 (100 signed copies of 685, glassine d/w, slipcase) £5,000

ditto, Fountain Press (Paris), 1930 (10 signed copies of 685, glassine d/w, slipcase) £6,000

ditto, Faber (London), 1931 (tissue d/w) . . £125/£75

ditto, Faber (London), 1931 (wraps in d/w) . . £75/£45

The Mime of Mick Nick and the Maggies, Servire Press/ Gotham Book Mart (The Hague/New York), 1934 (1000 copies; wraps; slipcase) . . . . £500/£400

ditto, Servire Press/Gotham Book Mart (The Hague/New York), 1934 (29 signed copies; wraps; slipcase) . £7,500

ditto, Faber (London), 1934 . . . . £140/£125

Storiella As She is Syung, Corvinus Press (London), 1937 (150 numbered copies, slipcase) . . £2,500/£2,000

ditto, Corvinus Press (London), 1937 (25 signed copies, slipcase) . . . . . . £8,000/£7,500

Letters

Letters of James Joyce, Faber (London), 1957 (edited by Stuart Gilbert, red d/w) . . . . . £45/£15

ditto, Viking (New York), 1957 . . . . £45/£15

Letters of James Joyce, Volume II, Faber (London), 1966 (edited by Richard Ellmann) . . . £45/£15

ditto, Viking (New York), 1966 . . . . £45/£15

Letters of James Joyce, Volume III, Faber (London), 1966 (edited by Richard Ellmann) . . . £45/£15

ditto, Viking (New York), 1966 . . . . £45/£15

Selected Letters of James Joyce, Faber (London), 1975 .

. . . . £25/£10

ditto, Viking (New York), 1975 . . . . £25/£10

Others

Two Essays, Gerrard Bros (Dublin), 1901 (with F.J.C. Skeffington, pink stapled wraps) . . . £6,000

Exiles, Grant Richards (London), 1918 . . . £450

ditto, Huebsch (New York), 1918 . . . . £175

Introducing James Joyce: A Selection of Joyce's Prose, Faber (London), 1942 (by T.S. Eliot) . . . £25/£10

The Critical Writings, Faber (London), 1959 . £40/£15

ditto, Viking (New York), 1959 . . . . £40/£15

The Cat and the Devil, Dodd, Mead (New York), [1964] .

. . . . £75/£15

ditto, Faber (London), 1965 . . . . . £75/£15

FRANZ KAFKA

(b.1883 d.1924)

Kafka, a Czech author, is one of the major German-language writers of the 20th century. Born in Prague of Jewish descent, his name has become synonymous with the nightmarish, confused struggles of individuals against an incomprehensible system. His work continues to challenge both readers and critics and defies simple classification.

Novels

Der Prozess, Die Schmiede (Berlin, Germany), 1925 . .

. . . . £3,000/£500

ditto, as **The Trial**, Gollancz (London), 1937 (translated by Willa and Edwin Muir) . . £750/£200

ditto, Knopf (New York), 1937 . . . . £300/£75

Das Schloss, Kurt Wolff Verlag (Munich, Germany), 1926 .

. . . . £2,500/£500

ditto, as **The Castle**, Secker (London), 1930 (translated by Willa and Edwin Muir) . . £1,000/£200

ditto, Knopf (New York), 1930 . . . . £750/£175

Amerika, Kurt Wolff Verlag (Munich, Germany), 1927 .

. . . . £2,500/£500

ditto, Kurt Wolff Verlag (Munich, Germany), 1927 (wraps).

. . . . £1,000

ditto, as **America**, Routledge (London), 1938 (translated by Willa and Edwin Muir) . . £500/£100

ditto, New Directions (Norfolk, CT), 1946 . £100/£25

Novellas and Short Stories

Die Verwandlung, Kurt Wolff Verlag (Munich, Germany), 1915 (wraps). £2,500

ditto, as **The Metamorphosis**, Parton Press (London), 1937 (translated by A.L. Lloyd; printed glassine jacket) . .

. . . . £2,500/£500

ditto, Vanguard Press (New York), 1946 . . £225/£35

Beim Bau der Chinesischen Mauer, Gustav Kiepenheuer (Berlin, Germany), 1931 . . . . £2,000/£400

ditto, as **The Great Wall of China**, Secker (London), 1933 (translated by Willa and Edwin Muir) . . £500/£100

ditto, Schocken Books (New York), 1946. . . £75/£20

In The Penal Settlement, Secker & Warburg (London), 1949 (translated by Willa and Edwin Muir) . . . £100/£30

Wedding Preparations in the Country, Secker & Warburg (London), 1954 (translated by Ernst Kaiser and Eithne Wilkins). . . . . £75/£25

Description of a Struggle, Schocken Books (New York), 1958 (translated by Tania & James Stern) . £50/£15

ditto, as **Description of a Struggle** and **The Great Wall of China**, Secker & Warburg (London), 1960 (translated by Tania and James Stern, and Willa and Edwin Muir) . .

. . . . £75/£25

Others

Diaries, 1910-1913, Secker & Warburg (London), 1948
(translated by Joseph Kresh) . . . . £40/£15

ditto, Schocken Books (New York), 1948. . . £35/£15

Diaries, 1914-1923, Secker & Warburg (London), 1949
(translated by M. Greenberg and H. Arendt) . . £40/£15

ditto, Schocken Books (New York), 1949. . . £35/£15

Letters to Milena, Secker & Warburg (London), 1953
(translated by Tania and James Stern) . . £35/£10

ditto, Schocken Books (New York), 1953. . . £30/£10

Letters to Felice, Schocken Books (New York), 1973
(translated by James Stern and Elisabeth Duckworth). .
. . . . £25/£10

ditto, Secker & Warburg (London), 1974 . . . £25/£10

Letters to Friends, Family and Editors, Schocken Books
(New York), 1977 . . . . . . £25/£10

ditto, John Calder (London), 1978 (translated by Richard and
Clara Winton) . . . . . . £25/£10

ERICH KÄSTNER
(b.1899 d.1974)

A German writer in a wide range of genres, Kästner is
collected principally for his children's works, notably *Emil
and the Detectives*. He was a political author; a pacifist
who wrote for children because of his belief in the potential
of each new generation. In his home country his books
were burnt by the Nazis. He was awarded the Hans Christian Andersen Award in 1960 for his lifetime contribution
to children's literature.

Children's Books

Emil and the Detectives, Doubleday (New York), 1930 .
. . . . £150/£35

ditto, Cape (London), 1931 (illustrated by Walter Trier) .
. . . . £150/£35

Annaluise and Anton, Cape (London), 1932 . . £85/£20

ditto, Dodd, Mead (New York), 1933 . . . £75/£20

The 35th of May or Conrad's Ride to the South Seas, Cape
(London), 1933 . . . . . . £45/£15

ditto, as *The 35th of May*, Dodd, Mead (New York), 1934 .
. . . . £65/£25

The Flying Classroom, Cape (London), 1934 . . £75/£20

Emil and the Three Twins, Cape (London), 1935 . £75/£20

ditto, Franklin Watts (New York), 1961 . . . £25/£10

Emil, Cape (London), 1949 (contains *Emil and the Detectives*, *Emil and the Three Twins* and *The 35th of May*). .
. . . . £40/£10

Lottie and Lisa, Cape (London), 1950 . . £65/£20

ditto, Knopf (New York), 1969 . . . . £25/£10

Don Quixote, Messner (New York), [c.1957] . . £20/£5

Baron Munchhausen, Messner (New York), [c.1957] . .
. . . . £20/£5

The Simpletons, Messner (New York), [c.1957] . £20/£5

Till Eulenspiegel the Clown, Messner (New York), [c.1957]
. . . . £25/£10

ditto, Cape (London), 1967 . . . . . £25/£10

Puss in Boots, Messner (New York), [c.1957]. . £25/£10

ditto, Cape (London), 1967 . . . . . £25/£10

The Little Man, Cape (London), 1966 . . £25/£10

ditto, Knopf (New York), 1966 . . . . £25/£10

The Little Man and the Little Miss, Cape (London), 1969 .
. . . . £20/£5

The Little Man and the Big Thief, Knopf (New York), 1969
. . . . £20/£5

Other Novels

Fabian: The Story of a Moralist, Cape (London), 1932 .
. . . . £45/£10

Three Men in the Snow, Cape (London), 1935 . £25/£5

*The Missing Miniature or The Adventures of a Sensitive
Butcher*, Cape (London), 1936. . . . £40/£10

ditto, Knopf (New York), 1937 . . . . £40/£10

The Animals' Conference, D. McKay Co. (New York),
[c.1949] . . . . £65/£10

ditto, Collins (London), 1955 . . . . £45/£15

A Salzburg Comedy, Weidenfeld & Nicolson (London),
1950 . . . . £35/£10

ditto, Frederick Ungar (New York), 1957 . . . £25/£10

Others

When I Was A Little Boy, Cape (London), 1959 . £25/£5

Let's Face It, Cape (London), 1963 . . . . £20/£5

JOHN KEATS
(b.1795 d.1821)

Along with Wordsworth and Coleridge, Keats is one of the
best known and most widely read of the English Romantic
poets. The critics panned his work during most of his short
life and it was some years before it came to be widely
appreciated. His poetry is characterised by his rich, sensuous imagination and exuberant love of language.

Poetry

Poems, Ollier (London), 1817 (original boards with paper
label to spine) £17,500

ditto, Ollier (London), 1817 (rebound) . . . £7,500

Endymion, Taylor & Hessey (London), 1818 (first state with
one line of errata and 2 advert leaves at end, paper covered
boards) £5,000

ditto, Taylor & Hessey (London), 1818 (first state rebound)
. . . . £2,000

ditto, Taylor & Hessey (London), 1818 (second state with 5
lines of errata and 5 advert leaves at end) . . £3,500

ditto, Taylor & Hessey (London), 1818 (second state
rebound) £1,500

ditto, Golden Cockerel Press (Waltham St Lawrence, Berks),
1947 (400 numbered copies, signed by illustrator J.
Buckland Wright) £300

ditto, Golden Cockerel Press (Waltham St Lawrence, Berks),
1947 (100 numbered copies, signed by illustrator J.
Buckland Wright) £400

Lamia, Isabella, The Eve of St Agnes, and Other Poems,
Taylor & Hessey (London), 1820 (with half title and 8
pages of adverts at end) £8,000

ditto, Taylor & Hessey (London), 1820 (rebound) . £2,000

ditto, Golden Cockerel Press (Waltham St Lawrence, Berks),
1928 (485 numbered copies, bound in sharkskin by
Sangorski and Sutcliffe) £325

ditto, Golden Cockerel Press (Waltham St Lawrence, Berks),
1928 (15 numbered copies on vellum, bound in sharkskin)
. . . . £500

Poetical Works of Coleridge, Shelly and Keats, A. & W. Galighasi (Paris), 1829 . . . . £750

ditto, A. & W. Galighasi (Paris), 1829 (rebound) . . £200

Poetical Works, William Smith (London), 1841 . . £100

Poetical Works and Other Writings, Reeves & Turner (London), 1883 (4 vols) . . . . . £350 the set

Ode to a Nightingale, privately printed, 1884 (edited by T.J. Wise, 25 copies; wraps) £300

ditto, privately printed, 1884 (deluxe edition, 4 copies on vellum) £750

Poems, Kelmscott Press (London), 1894 (300 copies, limp vellum binding) £1,750

ditto, Doves Press (London), 1914 (200 copies, limp vellum binding) £450

ditto, Doves Press (London), 1914 (12 copies on vellum) £750

Ode, Sonnets and Lyrics, Daniel Press (Oxford, UK), 1895 (250 copies, mounted photo; wraps) . . . £250

The Collected Sonnets, Halcyon Press (Maastricht), 1930 (376 copies, illustrated by J. Buckland Wright) . . £150

ditto, Halcyon Press (Maastricht), 1930 (35 copies on Japanese vellum) £450

La Belle Dame Sans Merci, Eragny Press, 1946 (210 copies) £500

Miscellaneous

Life, Letters and Literary Remains of John Keats, Moxon (London), 1848 (2 vols) £450

Letters ... to Fanny Brawne, privately printed (London), 1878 (50 copies) £250

ditto, Scribner, Armstrong & Co (New York), 1878 . £75

The Letters of John Keats, Reeves & Turner (London), 1895 . . . . £75

Anatomical and Physiological Notebook, O.U.P. (Oxford, UK), 1934 (350 copies) . . . . . £250/£75

JAMES KELMAN
(b.1946)

James Kelman is the author of novels, short stories, plays and political essays. *A Disaffection* was shortlisted for the Booker Prize and won the James Tait Black Memorial Prize for Fiction. In 1994 he won the Booker Prize for *How Late It Was, How Late*, but it was a controversial award with one of the judges calling the result a 'disgrace'.

Novels

The Busconductor Hines, Polygon Press (Edinburgh), 1984 . . . . £60/£15

A Chancer, Polygon Press (Edinburgh), 1985 . £30/£10

A Disaffection, Secker & Warburg (London), 1989 £15/£5

ditto, Farrar, Straus & Giroux (New York), 1989 . £10/£5

How Late It Was, How Late, Secker & Warburg (London), 1994 . . . . £20/£5

ditto, Norton (New York), 1995 . . . . . £10/£5

Translated Accounts, Secker & Warburg London), 2001 .
. . . . £10/£5

ditto, Doubleday (New York), 2001 . . . . £10/£5

You Have To Be Careful in the Land of the Free, Hamish Hamilton (London), 2004 . . . . . £10/£5

ditto, Harcourt (New York), 2004 . . . . £10/£5

Kieron Smith, Boy, , Hamish Hamilton (London), 2008 .
. . . . £10/£5

ditto, Harcourt (New York), 2008 . . . . . £10/£5

Short Stories

An Old Pub Near the Angel, Puckerbrush Press (Orono, ME), 1973 (pbk) £100

Short Tales from the Nightshift, Print Studio Press (Glasgow), 1978 (500 copies; pbk) £65

Not Not While the Giro, Polygon Press (Edinburgh), 1983 (pbk) £5

Lean Tales, Cape (London), 1985 (with Alasdair Gray and Agnes Owens) . . . . £20/£5

Greyhound for Breakfast, Secker & Warburg (London), 1987 . . . . £20/£5

ditto, Farrar, Straus & Giroux (New York), 1988 . £10/£5

The Burn, Secker & Warburg (London), 1991 . £10/£5

Busted Scotch: Selected Stories, Norton (New York), 1997 . . . . £10/£5

The Good Times, Secker & Warburg (London), 1998 £10/£5

Selected Stories, Canongate (Edinburgh), 2001 (small format pbk) £5

Essays

Some Recent Attacks: Essays Cultural and Political, AK Press (Stirling, Scotland), 1992 (pbk) £10

And the Judges Said ..., Secker & Warburg (London), 2002 . . . . £10/£5

Others

Three Glasgow Writers, Molendinar Press (Glasgow), 1976 (with Alex Hamilton and Tom Leonard; pbk) . . £10

Fighting for Survival: The Steel Industry in Scotland, Clydeside Press (Glasgow), 1990 (stapled wraps) . £15

Hardie and Baird, and Other Plays, Secker & Warburg (London), 1991 . . . . £15/£5

Tantalising Twinkles: Some Thoughts On a First Order Radical Thinker of European Standing, Emergency Eyewash Press (Stenness, Orkney), 1997 (100 copies; wraps) £50

THOMAS KENEALLY
(b.1935)

Thomas Keneally is an Australian novelist whose *Schindler's Ark* won the Booker Prize before being successfully filmed as *Schindler's List*. Many of his novels explore historical material, although they are entirely modern in their style and psychology. He has also written screenplays, memoirs and non-fiction books, several of which reflect his advocacy of Australian Republicanism.

Novels

The Place at Whitton, Cassell (Melbourne), 1964 . £250/£25

ditto, Cassell (London), 1964 . . . . . £200/£25

ditto, Walker (New York), 1964 . . . . £125/£20

The Fear, Cassell (Melbourne), 1965 . . . £100/£15

ditto, Cassell (London), 1965 . . . . . £125/£15

ditto, as *By the Line*, Univ of Queensland Press (St Lucia, Australia), 1989 . . . . £20/£5

ditto, as *By the Line*, Sceptre (London), 1992 (pbk) . £5

Bring Larks and Heroes, Cassell (Melbourne), 1967 . .
. . . . £45/£10

ditto, Cassell (London), 1967 . . . . . £35/£10

ditto, Viking (New York), 1968 . . . . £30/£10
Three Cheers for the Paraclete, Angus & Robertson (London), 1968 . . . . . £30/£10
ditto, Viking (New York), 1969 . . . . £30/£10
The Survivor, Angus & Robertson (London), 1969   £30/£5
ditto, Viking (New York), 1970 . . . . £30/£5
A Dutiful Daughter, Angus & Robertson (London), 1971 .
. . . . £25/£5
ditto, Viking (New York), 1971 . . . £20/£5
The Chant of Jimmie Blacksmith, Angus & Robertson (London), 1972 . . . . . £25/£5
ditto, Viking (New York), 1972 . . . . £20/£5
Blood Red, Sister Rose, Collins (London), 1974 . £25/£5
ditto, Viking (New York), 1974 . . . . £20/£5
Gossip from the Forest, Collins (London), 1975 . £25/£10
ditto, Harcourt Brace (New York), 1976 . . £20/£5
Season in Purgatory, Collins (London), 1976. . £20/£5
ditto, Harcourt Brace (New York), 1977 . . £15/£5
A Victim of the Aurora, Collins (London), 1977 . £15/£5
ditto, Harcourt Brace (New York), 1978 . . £15/£5
Passenger, Collins (London), 1979 . . . £15/£5
ditto, Harcourt Brace (New York), 1979 . . £15/£5
Confederates, Collins (London), 1979 . . £15/£5
ditto, Harper & Row (New York), 1979 . . £15/£5
The Cut-Rate Kingdom, Wildcat Press (Sydney), 1980. £20
ditto, Allen Lane (London), 1984 . . . £15/£5
Schindler's Ark, Hodder & Stoughton (London), 1982. .
. . . . £45/£10
ditto, as **Schindler's List**, Simon & Schuster (New York), 1982 . . . . £35/£5
A Family Madness, Hodder & Stoughton (London), 1985 .
. . . . £15/£5
ditto, Simon & Schuster (New York), 1986 . . £15/£5
The Playmaker, Hodder & Stoughton (London), 1987 . .
. . . . £15/£5
ditto, Simon & Schuster (New York), 1987 . . £15/£5
Act of Grace, Chatto & Windus (London), 1988 (pseud 'William Coyle') . . . . £15/£5
Towards Asmara, Hodder & Stoughton (London), 1989 .
. . . . £15/£5
ditto, as **To Asmara**, Warner (New York), 1989 . £15/£5
Flying Hero Class, Hodder & Stoughton (London), 1991 .
. . . . £15/£5
ditto, Warner (New York), 1991 . . . . £15/£5
Chief of Staff, Chatto & Windus (London), 1991 (pseud 'William Coyle') . . . . £15/£5
Woman of the Inner Sea, Hodder & Stoughton (London), 1992 . . . . £15/£5
ditto, Doubleday (New York), 1993 . . . £10/£5
Jacko, The Great Intruder, Hodder & Stoughton (London), 1994 . . . . £15/£5
A River Town, Hodder & Stoughton (London), 1995 £15/£5
ditto, Franklin Library (Franklin Centre, PA), 1995 (signed, limited edition) £25
ditto, Doubleday (New York), 1995 . . . £10/£5
Bettany's Book, Sceptre/Hodder & Stoughton (London), 2000 . . . . £15/£5
ditto, Doubleday (New York), 2000 . . . £10/£5
An Angel in Australia, Doubleday (New York), 2002 . .
. . . . £10/£5
ditto, as **Office of Innocence**, Sceptre/Hodder & Stoughton (London), 2002 . . . . . . £10/£5
The Tyrant's Novel, Sceptre (London), 2003 . . £10/£5
ditto, Nan A. Talese/Doubleday (New York), 2004   £10/£5

Plays
Halloran's Little Boat, Penguin (Melbourne, Aus), 1975 (with *Stockade* by Kenneth Cook, wraps) . . . £15
Bullie's House, Currency Press (Sydney), 1981 . £20/£5

Others
Moses the Lawgiver, Harper (New York), 1975 . £15/£5
ditto, Collins (London), 1976 . . . . £15/£5
Ned Kelly and the City of the Bees, Cape (London), 1978 (illustrated by Stephen Ryan) . . . . £15/£5
ditto, Godine (Boston), 1981 . . . . £15/£5
Outback, Hodder & Stoughton (London), 1983 (photographs by Gary Hansen and Mark Lang) . . . £15/£5
ditto, Rand McNally & Co. (New York), 1984 . £15/£5
Australia: Beyond the Dreamtime, BBC Books (London), 1987 (with Patsy Adam-Smith and Robyn Davidson) . .
. . . . £15/£5
ditto, Facts on File (New York), 1987 . . £15/£5
Now and in Time to Be: Ireland & the Irish, Ryan Publishing (London), 1991 (photographs by Patrick Prendergast) . . . . £15/£5
ditto, Norton (New York), 1992 . . . . £10/£5
The Place Where Souls are Born, Hodder & Stoughton (London), 1992 . . . . £15/£5
ditto, Simon & Schuster (New York), 1992 . . £15/£5
The Utility Player, The Des Hasler Story, Pan Macmillan (Sydney), 1993 (pbk) £5
Our Republic, Heinemann (Melbourne, Aus), 1993   £10/£5
Memoirs from a Young Republic, Heinemann (London), 1993 . . . . £10/£5
Homebush Boy, A Memoir, Hodder & Stoughton (London), 1995 . . . . £10/£5
The Great Shame, A Story of the Irish in the Old World and the New, Chatto & Windus (London), 1998 . £10/£5
ditto, Doubleday (New York), 1999 . . . £10/£5
American Scoundrel, Chatto & Windus (London), 2002 .
. . . . £10/£5
ditto, Easton Press (Norwalk, CT), 2002 (1150 signed, numbered copies, no d/w) £50
ditto, Doubleday (New York), 2002 . . . £10/£5
Lincoln, Weidenfeld & Nicolson (London), 2003 . £10/£5
ditto, Viking (New York), 2003 . . . . £10/£5

WILLIAM KENNEDY
(b.1928)

William Kennedy is an American author and journalist whose novels frequently feature the fictional Phelan family, set against the backdrop of his hometown of Albany, New York. *Ironweed* was the winner of 1984 Pulitzer Prize for Fiction. Some critics have compared Kennedy's use of Albany as the setting for his novels with that of James Joyce's use of Dublin.

Albany Cycle
Legs, Coward, McCann & Geoghegan (New York), 1975 .
. . . . £75/£15
ditto, Cape (London), 1976 . . . . . £45/£10
Billy Phelan's Greatest Game, Viking (New York), 1978 .
. . . . £60/£10
ditto, Penguin (London), 1984 (pbk) £10
Ironweed, Viking (New York), 1983 . . . . £125/£25

ditto, Viking (London), 1983 (d/w with price of £7.95 added at bottom of front flap, which still has $14.95 on upper corner) .   .   .   .   £40/£10

ditto, Easton Press (Norwalk, CT), 1999 (signed limited edition; full leather) £65

Quinn's Book, Viking (New York), 1988.   .   .   £10/£5

ditto, Viking (New York), 1988 (500 signed, numbered copies; slipcase, no d/w) .   .   .   .   £45/£35

ditto, Cape (London), 1988 .   .   .   .   £10/£5

Very Old Bones, Viking (New York), 1992   .   .   £10/£5

The Flaming Corsage, Viking ([New York]), 1996   £10/£5

ditto, Franklin Library (Franklin Center, PA), 1996 (signed limited edition in full leather) £30

Other Fiction

The Ink Truck, Dial (New York), 1969   .   .   .£300/£50

ditto, Macdonald (London), 1970 .   .   .   .£75/£15

The Cotton Club, St Martin's Press (New York), 1986 (pbk; script by Kennedy and Francis Coppola)   .   .   £10

Charley Malarkey and the Belly Button Machine, Atlantic Monthly Press (Boston), 1986 (written with son Brendan; illustrated by Glen Baxter) .   .   .   .   £10/£5

ditto, Cape (London), 1987 (laminated pictorial boards; no d/w) £15

Charley Malarkey and the Singing Moose, Viking (New York), 1994 .   .   .   .   £10/£5

Roscoe, Viking (New York), 2002   .   .   .   £10/£5

Non-Fiction

Letter to a Would-Be Writer, Fiction II, Empire State College (Saratoga Springs, NY), 1973 (wraps)   .   £10

O Albany, Viking (New York), 1983.   .   .   £30/£5

The Making of Ironweed, Viking (New York). 1988 (pbk) .

.   .   .   .   £15

Riding the Yellow Trolley Car, Viking (New York), 1993 .

.   .   .   .   £10/£5

ditto, Easton Press (Norwalk, CT), 1993 (signed limited edition; full leather) £35

Conversations with William Kennedy, Univ Press of Mississippi (Jackson, MS), 1997 (no d/w).   .   .   .   £15

JACK KEROUAC
(b.1922 d.1969)

Kerouac was a poet, artist, and semi-autobiographical novelist of the 1950s Beat Generation. His writing reflects his rejection of '50s values, especially its growing consumerism, and his desire to break free of society and find a deeper meaning to existence. These aims were the reason for his travels, his experimentation with drugs, and his study of spiritual teachings. He was a major influence on 1960s counterculture.

Fiction

The Town and the City, Harcourt Brace (New York), 1950 (as 'John Kerouac') .   .   .   .   .   .£500/£75

ditto, Eyre & Spottiswoode (London), 1951   .   .£350/£65

On the Road, Viking (New York), 1957 .   .£2,000/£400

ditto, Viking (New York), 1957 (review copy with additional white d/w printed 'This is a copy of the first edition').   .

.   .   .   .   £4,000/£400

ditto, Deutsch (London), 1958 (author photo on rear flap) .

.   .   .   .£800/£100

ditto, Deutsch (London), 1958 (author photo on front flap) .

.   .   .   .£500/£100

The Subterraneans, Grove Press (New York), 1958 (first printing without d/w) £300

ditto, Grove Press (New York), 1958 (second printing with d/w) .   .   .   .£300/£50

ditto, Grove Press (New York), 1958 (100 numbered copies, no d/w) £2,000

ditto, Grove Press (New York), 1958 (pbk)   .   .   £35

ditto, Deutsch (London), 1960   .   .   .   .£225/£50

The Dharma Bums, Viking (New York), 1958   .£200/£50

ditto, Deutsch (London), 1959 (with incorrect '1950' publication date) .   .   .   .   .   .£75/£40

ditto, Deutsch (London), 1959 (with date corrected with sticker) .   .   .   .£75/£25

Doctor Sax: Faust Part Three, Grove Press (New York), 1959   .   .   .   .£400/£75

ditto, Grove Press (New York), 1959 (26 signed, lettered copies) £4,000

ditto, Grove Press (New York), 1959 (4 signed, numbered copies) £5,000

ditto, Evergreen (New York), 1961 (pbk).   .   .   £20

ditto, Deutsch (London), 1977   .   .   .   .£75/£15

Maggie Cassidy, Avon (New York), 1959 (pbk)   .   £35

ditto, Panther (London), 1960 (pbk) £15

ditto, Deutsch (London), 1974   .   .   .   .£125/£20

Excerpts from Visions of Cody, New Directions (Norfolk, CT), 1959 (750 signed, numbered copies, glassine d/w) .

.   .   .   .   £1,250/£1,000

ditto, as **Visions of Cody**, McGraw-Hill (New York), 1972 (full text) .   .   .   .£50/£10

ditto, Deutsch (London), 1973   .   .   .   .£50/£10

Tristessa, Avon (New York), 1960 (pbk) .   .   .   £25

ditto, World Distributors (London), 1963 (pbk)   .   £10

Big Sur, Farrar Straus (New York), 1962 .   .   .£150/£25

ditto, Deutsch (London), 1963   .   .   .   .£100/£20

Visions of Gerard, Farrar Straus (New York), 1963

.   .   .   .£100/£15

ditto, Deutsch (London), 1964 (with **Tristessa**)   .£60/£10

Desolation Angels, Coward-McCann (New York), 1965

.   .   .   .£125/£25

ditto, Deutsch (London), 1966   .   .   .   .£100/£25

Satori in Paris, Grove Press (New York), 1966   .£100/£20

ditto, Deutsch (London), 1967   .   .   .   .£45/£10

Vanity of Duluoz: An Adventurous Education, *1935-46*, Coward-McCann (New York), 1968   .   .   £75/£20

ditto, Deutsch (London), 1969   .   .   .   .£75/£20

Pic, Grove Press (New York), 1971   .   .   .   £25

ditto, as **Pic** and **The Subterraneans**, Deutsch (London), 1973 .   .   .   .£45/£10

Old Angel Midnight, Booklegger/Albion (Brighton), nd [1973] (stapled wraps) £60

ditto, Unicorn Bookshop (Brighton), 1976 (stapled wraps) .

.   .   .   .   £30

ditto, Midnight Press (London?), 1985 (stapled wraps)   £20

Two Early Stories, Oliphant Press/Aloes Editions (New York), 1973 (175 copies; sewn wraps)   .   .   .£100

Take Care of My Ghost, Ghost Press (n.p. [Berkeley, CA?]), 1977 (with Allen Ginsberg; 200 copies; mimeographed sheets) £75

San Francisco Blues, Beat Books (San Francisco. CA), 1983 (500 copies; stapled wraps) £25

ditto, Pacific Red Car (no place, CA), 1991 (pbk) . £25
Two Stories, Pacific Red Car (no place, CA), 1984 (100 copies; wraps) £65
The Great Western Bus Ride, Pacific Red Car (no place, CA), 1984 (100 copies; wraps). £75
Celine and Other Tales, Pacific Red Car (no place, CA), 1985 (100 copies; stapled wraps) . . . £65
The Vision of the Hooded White Angels, Pacific Red Car (no place, CA), 1985 (100 copies; stapled wraps) . £65
Home at Christmas, Pacific Red Car (no place, CA), [no date] (stapled wraps) £65
Good Blonde and Others, Grey Fox (San Francisco, CA), 1993 (50 numbered hardback copies) . . . £100
ditto, Grey Fox (San Francisco, CA), 1993 (pbk) . £15
Book of Blues, Penguin (New York), 1995 (pbk) . . £5
Some of the Dharma, Viking (New York), 1997 . £10/£5
Atop an Underwood: Early Stories and Other Writings, Viking (New York), 1999 . . . . £10/£5

Poetry
Mexico City Blues, Grove Press (New York), 1959 .
. . . . £1,000/£200
ditto, Grove Press (New York), 1959 (26 signed, lettered copies) £4,000
ditto, Grove Press (New York), 1959 (4 signed, numbered copies) £5,000
Hymn-God Pray For Me, Jubilee Magazine, Pax #10 (New York), [1959] (broadsheet) £200
ditto, Caliban Press (Montclair, NJ), 1985 (150 numbered copies; stitched wraps) £50
The Scripture of the Golden Eternity, Totem Press/Corinth Books (New York), 1960 (stapled wraps; first issue with purple illustration on cover) £75
ditto, Totem Press/Corinth Books (New York), 1960 (stapled wraps; second issue with red illustration on cover) . £50
Rimbaud, City Light Books (San Francisco, CA), 1960 (broadsheet, first issue printed in black). . . £100
ditto, City Light Books (San Francisco, CA), 1960 (broadsheet, second issue printed in red) . . £50
'I demand that the human race ceases multiplying its kind...', Jubilee Magazine, Pax #17 (New York), 1962 (broadsheet) £75
A Pun for Al Gepi, Lowell House (Cambridge, MA), 1966 (100 signed, numbered copies, broadsheet) . . £1,650
An Imaginary Portrait of Ulysses S. Grant / Edgar Allan Poe, Portents Press (New York), 1967 (broadsheet, with Hugo Weber, 200 copies) £100
ditto, Portents Press (New York), 1967 (10 copies signed, numbered and dated by Hugo Weber) . . . £750
Someday You'll be Lying, Kriya Press (New York), 1968 (broadsheet, 100 copies) £200
ditto, Kriya Press (New York), 1968 (broadsheet, 26 lettered copies) £300
A Last Haiku, privately printed (U.S.), 1969 (broadsheet) .
. . . . £60
Scattered Poems, City Lights (San Francisco, CA), 1971 (wraps) £50
Trip Trap, Grey Fox Press (Bolinas, CA), 1973 (pbk) . £25
Heaven and Other Poems, Grey Fox Press (Bolinas, CA), 1977 (wraps). £35
Pomes All Sizes, City Lights (San Francisco, CA), 1992 (pbk) £10
Tangier Poem, White Fields Press (Louisville, KY), 1993 (wraps) £35

Others
Lonesome Traveller, McGraw-Hill (New York), 1960 . .
. . . . £125/£20
ditto, Deutsch (London), 1962 . . . . £100/£15
Book of Dreams, City Light Books (San Francisco, CA), 1961 (pbk) £75
Pull My Daisy, Grove Press/Evergreen (New York), 1961 (pbk) £200
Selected Letters, Volume 1: 1940-1956, Viking (New York), 1995 . . . . £15/£5
Selected Letters, Volume 2: 1957-1969, Viking (New York), 1999 . . . . £15/£5

KEN KESEY
(b.1935 d.2001)

In the 1960s Kesey volunteered for U.S. Government experiments on the effects of psychoactive drugs such as L.S.D., psilocybin, mescalin, and IT-290 (AMT). His *One Flew Over the Cuckoo's Nest* draws on his experience of working as an aide on a psychiatric ward in an army veteran's hospital. The novel is considered a link between the 'Beat Generation' of the 1950s and the 'hippy' counter-culture of the 1960s.

Novels
One Flew over the Cuckoo's Nest, Viking (New York), 1962 (first state book with 'that fool Red Cross woman' on page 9, first state d/w with Kerouac blurb on front flap) . . . . £3,750/£400
ditto, Viking (New York), 1962 (second state book with revised text on page 9, second state d/w without Kerouac blurb) . . . . £2,250/£300
ditto, Methuen (London), 1962 . . . . £450/£45
Sometimes a Great Notion, Viking (New York), 1964 (first issue with Viking ship on half title before title-page) . .
. . . . £250/£25
ditto, Viking (New York), 1964 (more scarce second issue with Viking ship on half title after title-page) . £250/£25
ditto, Methuen (London), 1966 . . . . £125/£20
Demon Box, Viking (New York), 1986 . . . £25/£5
ditto, Methuen (London), 1986 . . . . £25/£5
The Further Inquiry, Viking (New York), 1990 . £25/£5
Sailor Song, Viking (New York), 1992 . . . £15/£5
ditto, Black Swan (London), 1993 (pbk) . . . £5
Last Go Round, Viking (New York), 1994 (with Ken Babbs)
. . . . £10/£5
ditto, Black Swan (London), 1995 (wraps) . . . £5

Children's Titles
Little Tricker the Squirrel Meets Big Double the Bear, Viking (New York), 1990 (illustrated by Barry Moser) .
. . . . £25/£10
The Sea Lion: A Story of the Sea Cliff People, Viking (New York), 1991 (illustrated by Neil Waldman) . . £25/£10

Others
Kesey's Garage Sale: Featuring 5 Hot Items, Viking (New York), 1973 (with Neal Cassady, Allen Ginsberg and others) . . . . £35/£10
Kesey, Northwest Review Books (Eugene, OR), 1977 (hardback, no d/w) £75

ditto, Northwest Review Books (Eugene, OR), 1977 (pbk) .
. . . . £15

The Day After Superman Died, Lord John Press (Northridge, CA), 1980 (50 signed deluxe copies of 350) . £165
ditto, Lord John Press (Northridge, CA), 1980 (300 signed
copies of 350) £85
Caverns, as 'O.U. Levon', Penguin (New York), 1990
(collaborative novel written by Kesey and students in his
writing class at the Univ of Oregon; pbk) . . . £5

KEYNOTES

A series of 33 books (34 were advertised) issued by John
Lane between 1893 and 1897. The most collectable are those
with cover, title page and key designs by Aubrey Beardsley
(Nos. 1-21 and 23). The remainder, illustrated by Patten
Wilson, are also collectable, particularly when the con-
tributing authors are themselves of interest.

1. **Keynotes**, by George Egerton, Mathews/Lane (London),
1893 (500 copies in pink wraps) £300
ditto, Mathews/Lane (London), 1893 (600 copies in green
cloth) £75
ditto, Roberts Bros. (Boston), 1893 . . . . £45
2. **The Dancing Faun**, by Florence Farr, Mathews/Lane
(London), 1894 (first issue, light blue cloth, key on spine in
gilt). £175
ditto, Mathews/Lane (London), 1894 (second issue, light
green cloth, key on spine in blue) £150
ditto, Roberts Bros. (Boston), 1894 . . . . . £100
3. **Poor Folk**, by Fedor [sic] Dostoievsky, Mathews/Lane
(London), 1894 . . . . £150
ditto, Roberts Bros. (Boston), 1894 . . . . . £75
4. **A Child of the Age**, by Francis Adams, Lane (London),
1894 . . . . £85
ditto, Roberts Bros. (Boston), 1894 . . . . . £45
5. **The Great God Pan and the Inmost Light**, by Arthur
Machen, Lane (London), 1894 . . . . . . £250
ditto, Roberts Bros. (Boston), 1894 . . . . . £200
6. **Discords**, by George Egerton, Lane (London), 1894 . £100
ditto, Roberts Bros. (Boston), 1894 . . . . . £45
7. **Prince Zaleski**, by M.P. Shiel, Lane (London), 1895. £250
ditto, Roberts Bros. (Boston), 1895 . . . . . £600
8. **The Woman Who Did**, by Grant Allen, Lane (London),
1895 . . . . £100
ditto, Roberts Bros. (Boston), 1895 . . . . . £40
9. **Women's Tragedies**, by H.D. Lowry, Lane (London),
1895 . . . . £100
ditto, Roberts Bros. (Boston), 1895 . . . . . £40
10. **Grey Roses**, by Henry Harland, Lane (London), 1895 .
. . . . £100
ditto, Roberts Bros. (Boston), 1895 . . . . . £40
11. **At the First Corner and Other Stories**, by H.B. Marriott
Watson, Lane (London), 1895 . . . . . £100
ditto, Roberts Bros. (Boston), 1895 . . . . . £40
12. **Monochromes**, by Ella D'Arcy, Lane (London), 1895 .
. . . . £100
ditto, Roberts Bros. (Boston), 1895 . . . . . £40
13. **At the Relton Arms**, by Evelyn Sharp, Lane (London),
1895 . . . . £75
ditto, Roberts Bros. (Boston), 1895 . . . . . £40

14. **The Girl from the Farm**, by Gertrude Dix, Lane
(London), 1895 . . . . £75
ditto, Roberts Bros. (Boston), 1895 . . . . . £40
15. **The Mirror of Music**, by Stanley V. Makower, Lane
(London), 1895 . . . . £75
ditto, Roberts Bros. (Boston), 1895 . . . . . £40
16. **Yellow and White**, by W. Carlton Dawe, Lane (London),
1895 . . . . £75
ditto, Roberts Bros. (Boston), 1895 . . . . . £40
17. **The Mountain Lovers**, by Fiona MacLeod, Lane
(London), 1895 . . . . £65
ditto, Roberts Bros. (Boston), 1895 . . . . . £40
18. **The Woman Who Didn't**, by Victoria Crosse, Lane
(London), 1895 . . . . £65
ditto, Roberts Bros. (Boston), 1895 . . . . . £40
19. **The Three Impostors**, by Arthur Machen, Lane
(London), 1895 . . . . £250
ditto, Roberts Bros. (Boston), 1895 . . . . . £150
20. **Nobody's Fault**, by Netta Syrett, Lane (London), 1896 .
. . . . £65
ditto, Roberts Bros. (Boston), 1895 . . . . . £40
21. **The British Barbarians**, by Grant Allen, Lane (London),
1895 . . . . £100
ditto, Lane/Putnams (New York), 1895 . . . . £40
22. **In Homespun**, E. Nesbit, Lane (London), 1896 . £125
ditto, Roberts Bros. (Boston), 1896 . . . . . £45
23. **Platonic Affections**, by John Smith, Lane (London),
1896 . . . . £65
ditto, Roberts Bros. (Boston), 1896 . . . . . £40
24. **Nets for the Wind**, by Una Taylor, Lane (London), 1896
. . . . £65
ditto, Roberts Bros. (Boston), 1896 . . . . . £40
25. **Where the Atlantic Meets the Land**, by Caldwell
Lipsett, Lane (London), 1896 . . . . . . £65
ditto, Roberts Bros. (Boston), 1896 . . . . . £40
26. **In Scarlet and Grey**, by Florence Henniker (contains
'The Spectre of the Real', by F.H. and Thomas Hardy),
Lane (London), 1896 . . . . £200
ditto, Roberts Bros. (Boston), 1896 . . . . . £80
27. **Maris Stella**, by Marie Clothilde Balfour, Lane
(London), 1896 . . . . £65
ditto, Roberts Bros. (Boston), 1896 . . . . . £40
28. **Day Books**, by Mabel E. Wotton, Lane (London), 1896 .
. . . . £65
ditto, Roberts Bros. (Boston), 1896 . . . . . £40
29. **Shapes in the Fire**, by M.P. Shiel, Lane (London), 1896
. . . . £800
ditto, Roberts Bros. (Boston), 1896 . . . . . £125
30. **Ugly Idol**, by Claud Nicholson, Lane (London), 1896 .
. . . . £65
ditto, Roberts Bros. (Boston), 1896 . . . . . £40
31. **Kakemonos**, by W. Carlton Dawe, Lane (London), 1897
. . . . £65
32. **God's Failures**, by J.S. Fletcher, Lane (London), 1897 .
. . . . £65
33. **A Deliverence**, by Allan Monkhouse. Not published in
Keynotes series although advertised.
34. **Mere Sentiment**, by A.J. Dawson, Lane (London), 1897
. . . . £65

FRANCIS KILVERT
(b.1840 d.1879)

(Robert) Francis Kilvert was a clergyman and diarist. Although many volumes of his diaries were destroyed by his niece after his death, those covering the period 1870-79 were edited by William Plomer and published to great acclaim.

Selections from the Diary of the Rev. Francis Kilvert, Cape (London), 1938-40 (3 vols edited by William Plomer)   .
.   .   .   .   £200/£50 the set
ditto, Macmillan (New York), 1947 (1 vol.)   .   .   £25/£10
Ardizzone's Kilvert, Cape (London), 1976 (illustrated by Edward Ardizzone)   .   .   .   .   .   .   £25/£10

C. DALY KING
(b.1895 d.1963)

Charles Daly King was an American author of detective fiction from its 'Golden Age'. His books are unconventional, enthralling and puzzling. One of his lifelong passions was for psychology and, after writing non-fiction on the subject, he had the idea of using his knowledge of the discipline in detective fiction. The result was his first novel, *Obelists at Sea*.

Novels
Obelists at Sea, Heritage (London), no date [1932] (black cloth lettered in green; d/w price 7/6)   .   . £1,250/£250
ditto, Knopf (New York), 1933   .   .   .   . .£300/£65
ditto, Collins Crime Club (London), [no date] .   . £250/£35
Obelists En Route, Collins Crime Club (London), 1934 (orange cloth lettered in black; d/w price 7/6)   £750/£200
Obelists Fly High, Collins Crime Club (London), 1935 (orange cloth lettered in black; d/w price 7/6)   £750/£200
ditto, Smith & Haas (New York), 1935   .   .   £450/£100
Careless Corpse, Collins Crime Club (London), 1937 (orange cloth lettered in black; d/w price 7/6) £1,000/£200
Arrogant Alibi, Collins Crime Club (London), 1938 (orange cloth lettered in black; d/w price 7/6)   .   £1,000/£150
ditto, Appleton (New York), 1939   .   .   .   £400/£100
Burmuda Burial, Collins Crime Club (London), 1940 (orange cloth lettered in black; d/w price 8/-) £1,000/£150
ditto, Funk (New York), 1941   .   .   .   .   £400/£100

Short Stories
The Curious Mr Tarrant, Collins Crime Club (London), 1935 (orange cloth lettered in black; d/w price 7/6)   .   .
.   .   .   .   £1,250/£150
ditto, Dover (New York), 1977 (pbk).   .   .   .   £10
The Complete Curious Mr Tarrant, Crippen & Landru (Norfolk, VA), 2003   .   .   .   .   .   £25/£10
ditto, Crippen & Landru (Norfolk, VA), 2003 (pbk)   .   £5

STEPHEN KING
(b.1947)

One of the most successful of living writers, King's breakthrough was *Carrie*, which has now sold over 12 million copies. King's horror novels usually involve unremarkable protagonists in increasingly dreadful circumstances. He has also written many non-horror novels, novellas and short stories, such as 'Shawshank Redemption' and *The Green Mile*, both of which have been successfully filmed.

Novels
Carrie, Doubleday (New York), 1974 (inner margin of p.199 has date code 'P6'; d/w price $5.95)   .   .   £750/£100
ditto, New English Library (London), 1974   .   £500/£100
Salem's Lot, Doubleday (New York), 1975 (inner margin of p.439 with date code 'Q37', first state, first issue d/w with Father 'Cody' and price $8.95).   .   .   £1,500/£125
ditto, Doubleday (New York), 1975 (first state, second issue d/w with Father 'Cody' but price clipped and new price of $7.95 added).   .   .   .   .   .   £750/£125
ditto, Doubleday (New York), 1975 (second state d/w with Father 'Callahan' and unclipped price of $7.95) £450/£125
ditto, New English Library (London), 1976   .   .£500/£60
The Shining, Doubleday (New York), 1977   .   .£300/£35
ditto, New English Library (London), 1977   .   .£250/£35
The Stand, Doubleday (New York), 1978 (d/w price $12.95)
.   .   .   .£165/£30
ditto, New English Library (London), 1979   .   .£150/£25
The Dead Zone, Viking (New York), 1979   .   .   £75/£20
ditto, Macdonald & Jane (London), 1979 .   .   .£75/£20
Firestarter, Phantasia Press (Huntington Woods, MI), 1980 (725 copies in d/w and slipcase)   .   .   .   £850/£650
ditto, Phantasia Press (Huntington Woods, MI), 1980 (26 lettered copies, bound in asbestos) £6,000
ditto, Viking (New York), 1980   .   .   .   .   £45/£10
ditto, Macdonald & Jane, 1980   .   .   .   .   £45/£10
Cujo, Viking (New York), 1981 .   .   .   .   £40/£10
ditto, Mysterious Press (New York), 1981 (750 numbered, signed copies)   .   .   .   .   .   .   £500/£350
ditto, Mysterious Press (New York), 1981 (lettered, signed copies) £1,250
ditto, Macdonald (London), 1982 (£6.95 on jacket)   £35/£10
Creepshow, NAL/Plume (New York), 1982 (pbk)   .   .   £25
Christine, Grant (West Kingston, RI), 1983 (lettered, signed edition) £2,000
ditto, Grant (West Kingston, RI), 1983 (1,000 signed copies, slipcase).   .   .   .   .   .   .   £650/£450
ditto, Viking (New York), 1983   .   .   .   .   £35/£5
ditto, Hodder & Stoughton (London), 1983   .   .   £35/£5
Cycle of the Werewolf, Land of Enchantment (Westland, MI), 1983   .   .   .   .£100/£35
ditto, Land of Enchantment (Westland, MI), 1983 (8 presentation copies) £3,000
ditto, Land of Enchantment (Westland, MI), 1983 (250 copies, slipcase)   .   .   .   .   .   £1,250/£950
ditto, Land of Enchantment (Westland, MI), 1983 (100 copies with original drawing, slipcase)   .£1,750/£1,450
ditto, New English Library (London), 1985 (pbk)   .   .   £10
ditto, Signet (New York), 1985 (pbk).   .   .   .   £10
Selected Works, Heinemann (London)/Octopus, 1983 £15/£5
Pet Sematary, Doubleday (New York), 1983   .   .   £35/£5
ditto, Hodder & Stoughton (London), 1984   .   .   £30/£5

The Eyes of the Dragon, Philtrum (Bangor, ME), 1984 (1,000 signed copies numbered in black ink, slipcase, no d/w) . . . . £600/£400

ditto, Philtrum (Bangor, ME), 1984 (250 signed copies numbered in red ink, slipcase, no d/w) . .£1,250/£1,000

ditto, Viking (New York), 1987 . . . . £25/£5

ditto, Macdonald (London), 1987 . . . £25/£5

Silver Bullet, New American Library/Signet (New York), 1985 (pbk) £10

It, Hodder & Stoughton (London), 1986 . . . £25/£5

ditto, Viking (New York), 1986 . . . . . £20/£5

Misery, Viking (New York), 1987 . . . . £25/£5

ditto, Hodder & Stoughton (London), 1987 . £20/£5

The Tommyknockers, Putnam (New York), 1987 . £25/£5

ditto, Hodder & Stoughton (London), 1988 . . £20/£5

The Dark Half, Hodder & Stoughton (London), 1989 £15/£5

ditto, Viking (New York), 1989 . . . . . £15/£5

The Stand, Doubleday (New York), 1990 (complete and uncut edition) . . . . £25/£5

ditto, Doubleday (New York), 1990 (52 signed, lettered copies) £2,000

ditto, Doubleday (New York), 1990 (1,250 signed copies, bound in full leather, in wooden box) . . £1,000/£600

ditto, Hodder & Stoughton (London), 1990 . . £25/£5

Needful Things, Hodder & Stoughton (London), [1991] .
. . . . £15/£5

ditto, Viking (New York), 1991 . . . . . £15/£5

Gerald's Game, Viking (New York), 1992 . . £10/£5

ditto, Hodder & Stoughton (London), 1992 . . £10/£5

Dolores Claiborne, Book Club Associates (London), 1992 .
. . . . £15/£5

ditto, Viking (New York), 1992 . . . . . £15/£5

ditto, Hodder & Stoughton (London), 1992 . . £15/£5

ditto, Hodder & Stoughton (London), 1992 ('Special Limited Christmas Gift Edition', slipcase) . . . £75/£45

Insomnia, Ziesing (Shingletown, CA), 1994 (1,250 signed copies, d/w and case) . . . . . . £350/£250

ditto, Ziesing (Shingletown, CA), 1994 ('Gift edition', d/w and slipcase). . . . . £75/£45

ditto, Viking (New York), 1994 . . . . . £10/£5

ditto, Hodder & Stoughton (London), 1994 . . £10/£5

ditto, Hodder & Stoughton (London), 1994 (200 signed, numbered copies, slipcase, no d/w) . . £300/£200

Rose Madder, Hodder & Stoughton (London), 1994 (three variants; black front-paste-down, rose picture front-paste-down and rose with fabric bookmark) . . £20/£5

ditto, Hodder & Stoughton (London), 1994 (250 signed copies, slipcase, no d/w) . . . . £200/£150

ditto, Viking (New York), 1995 . . . . . £10/£5

The Green Mile, Penguin/Signet (New York), 1996 (six pbks, *The Two Dead Girls*, *The Mouse on the Mile*, *Coffey's Hands*, *The Bad Death of Eduard Delacroix*, *Night Journey*, *Coffey on the Mile*) . . . £15 the set

ditto, Penguin (London), 1996 (six pbks) . . £15 the set

ditto, Penguin/Plume (New York), 1997 (1 vol; slipcase) .
. . . . £10/£5

ditto, Orion (London), 2000 (1 vol) . . . . £25/£10

Desperation, Grant (West Kingston, RI), 1996 (4,000 copy gift edition) . . . . £25/£10

ditto, Grant (West Kingston, RI), 1996 (2,050 signed copies in traycase, no d/w) . . . . . £175/£125

ditto, Viking (New York), 1996 . . . . . £10/£5

ditto, Hodder & Stoughton (London), 1996 . . £10/£5

The Regulators, Dutton (New York), 1996 . . £15/£5

ditto, Dutton (New York), 1996 (pseud 'Richard Bachman'; 500 signed, numbered copies in 'toy box') . . . £800

ditto, Dutton (New York), 1996 (26 signed, lettered copies).
. . . . £2,500

Desperation and *The Regulators*, Hodder Headline (London), 1996 (2 vols with free 'keep you up all night' light) . . . . £35/£10

ditto, Hodder Headline (London), 1996 (250 sets in single slipcase, the former signed, the latter pseud 'Richard Bachman', with free 'keep you up all night' light) .
. . . . £400/£250

Bag of Bones, Simon & Schuster/Scribner's (New York), 1998 . . . . £10/£5

ditto, Hodder & Stoughton (London), 1998 . . £10/£5

ditto, Hodder & Stoughton (London), 1998 (2,000 copies with signed bookplate) . . . . . £200/£175

The Girl Who Loved Tom Gordon, Hodder & Stoughton (London), 1999 . . . . £10/£5

ditto, Scribner's (New York), 1999 . . . . £10/£5

ditto, Simon & Schuster (New York), 2004 (125 signed, pop-up copies) £750

Storm of the Century, Pocket Books (New York), 1999 (pbk) £5

ditto, Book-of-the-Month Club (New York), 1999 . £25/£5

Dreamcatcher, Hodder & Stoughton (London), 2001 £10/£5

ditto, Scribner's (New York), 2001 . . . . £10/£5

From a Buick 8, Cemetery Dance (Baltimore, MD), 2002 (750 signed numbered copies in traycase) . £400/£300

ditto, Cemetery Dance (Baltimore, MD), 2002 (52 signed lettered copies in traycase) . . . .£1,500/£1,250

ditto, Hodder & Stoughton (London), 2002 . . £10/£5

ditto, Scribner's (New York), 2002 . . . . £10/£5

The Colorado Kid, Hard Case Crime (New York), 2005 (pbk) £5

ditto, PS Publishing (Hornsea, UK), 2007 (3 editions with different artwork) . . . . £15/£5

ditto, PS Publishing (Hornsea, UK), 2007 (3 sets of 333 copies signed by one of the artists; slipcase). . £50/£30

ditto, PS Publishing (Hornsea, UK), 2007 (3 sets of 150 copies signed by author and one of the artists; slipcase)
. . . . £225/£175

ditto, PS Publishing (Hornsea, UK), 2007 (99 copies signed by author and all three artists; gilt-edged, leatherbound)
. . . . £1,000

Cell, Scribner's (New York), 2006 . . . . £10/£5

ditto, Hodder & Stoughton (London), 2006 . . £10/£5

Lisey's Story, Scribner's (New York), 2006 . . £10/£5

ditto, Hodder & Stoughton (London), 2006 . . £10/£5

Duma Key, Scribner's (New York), 2008 . . . £10/£5

ditto, Hodder & Stoughton (London), 2008 . . £10/£5

Under the Dome, Scribner's (New York), 2009 (1,000 un-numbered, unsigned copies with 27 cards by Matthew Diffee, 4-colour printed endpapers). £45

ditto, Scribner's (New York), 2009 (1,500 signed, un-numbered copies with 27 cards by Matthew Diffee, 4-colour printed endpapers; slipcase) . . . £350/£300

ditto, Scribner's (New York), 2009 (trade edition) . £10/£5

ditto, Hodder & Stoughton (London), 2009 . . £10/£5

ditto, Hodder & Stoughton (London), 2009 (500 signed, numbered copies with 27 cards; slipcase) . £145/£100

The Plant

The Plant, Philtrum (Bangor, ME), 1982 (200 signed copies; hand-sewn wraps) . . . . £1,000 *ditto*, Philtrum (Bangor, ME), 1982 (26 signed, lettered copies; hand-sewn wraps) £2,000

The Plant - Part Two, Philtrum (Bangor, ME), 1983 (200 copies; hand-sewn wraps) £1,000

ditto, Philtrum (Bangor, ME), 1983 (26 signed, lettered copies; hand-sewn wraps) £2,000

The Plant - Part Three, Philtrum (Bangor, ME), 1985 (200 copies; hand-sewn wraps) £1,000

ditto, Philtrum (Bangor, ME), 1985 (26 signed, lettered copies; hand-sewn wraps) £1,500

'Dark Tower' Series
The Gunslinger, Grant (West Kingston, RI), 1982 . . . . £450/£250

ditto, Grant (West Kingston, RI), 1982 (lettered, signed edition, d/w and slipcase) . . . .£3,000/£2,000

ditto, Grant (West Kingston, RI), 1982 (500 numbered, signed copies, d/w and slipcase) . . . £1,500/£750

ditto, Sphere (London), 1988 (pbk) £10

The Drawing of the Three, Grant (West Kingston, RI), 1987 . . . . £75/£45

ditto, Grant (West Kingston, RI), 1987 (800 signed copies, d/w and slipcase) . . . . . £650/£400

ditto, Grant (West Kingston, RI), 1987 (50 lettered copies, d/w and slipcase) . . . . £1,500/£1,000

ditto, Sphere (London), 1989 (pbk) £10

The Waste Lands, Grant (Hampton Falls, NH), 1991 . . . . £35/£10

ditto, Grant (Hampton Falls, NH), 1991 (1,250 signed copies, d/w and slipcase). . . . . £600/£475

ditto, Sphere (London), 1991 (pbk) £10

Wizard and Glass, Grant (Hampton Falls, NH), 1997 . . . . £40/£10

ditto, Grant (Hampton Falls, NH), 1991 (1,200 signed copies, d/w and slipcase). . . . . £600/£450

ditto, Hodder & Stoughton (London), 1988 (pbk) . . £10

ditto, Hodder & Stoughton (London), 1988 (500 copies, no d/w) £400

Wolves of the Calla, Grant (Hampton Falls, NH), 2003 . . . . £30/£10

ditto, Grant (Hampton Falls, NH), 2003 (two volume edition in d/ws and slipcase, 1,300 copies signed by Stephen King and artist Bernie Wrightson) . . . . £400/£350

ditto, Grant (Hampton Falls, NH), 2003 (artist's edition, 3,500 copies signed by artist Bernie Wrightson) . £100/£50

ditto, Hodder & Stoughton (London), 2003 . . £15/£5

Song of Susannah, Grant (Hampton Falls, NH), 2004 £15/£5

ditto, Grant (Hampton Falls, NH), 2004 (two volume edition in d/ws and slipcase, 1,300 copies signed by Stephen King and artist Darrel Anderson) . . . . £300/£200

ditto, Grant (Hampton Falls, NH), 2004 (artist's edition, 3,500 copies signed by artist Darrel Anderson) . £45/£20

ditto, Hodder & Stoughton (London), 2004 . . £15/£5

The Dark Tower, Grant (Hampton Falls, NH), 2004 £15/£5

ditto, Grant (Hampton Falls, NH), 2004 (two volume edition in d/ws and slipcase, 1,400 copies signed by Stephen King and artist Darrel Anderson) . . . . £325/£200

ditto, Grant (Hampton Falls, NH), 2004 (artist's edition, 5,000 copies signed by artist Darrel Anderson) . £45/£20

ditto, Hodder & Stoughton (London), 2004 . . £15/£5

'Talisman' Series
The Talisman, Viking (New York), 1984 (with Peter Straub) . . . . £30/£5

ditto, Grant (West Kingston, RI), 1984 (70 numbered copies signed by authors and artists, slipcase, 2 vols) . . . .£1,250/£1,000

ditto, Grant (West Kingston, RI), 1984 (1,200 signed, numbered copies, no d/w, slipcase, 2 vols) . £350/£275

ditto, Viking (London), 1984 . . . . . £25/£5

Black House, Random House (New York), 2001 (with Peter Straub) . . . . £10/£5

ditto, HarperCollins (London), 2001 . . . . £10/£5

ditto, Grant (West Kingston, RI), 2002 (1,520 signed copies in traycase) . . . . £250/£200

'Richard Bachman' Novels
Rage, Signet/New American Library (New York), 1977 (pseud 'Richard Bachman'; pbk) £100

ditto, New English Library (London), 1983 (pbk) . . £75

The Long Walk, Signet/New American Library (New York), 1979 (pseud 'Richard Bachman'; pbk) £50

Roadwork, Signet/New American Library (New York), 1981 (pseud 'Richard Bachman'; pbk) £40

ditto, New English Library (London), 1983 (pbk) . . £20

The Running Man, Signet/New American Library (New York), 1982 (pseud 'Richard Bachman'; pbk) . . £45

ditto, New English Library (London), 1983 (pbk) . . £30

Thinner, New American Library (New York), 1984 (pseud 'Richard Bachman'; with yellow wrap-around band) . . . . £40/£10

ditto, New English Library (London), 1985 (pseud 'Richard Bachman'; with yellow wrap-around band) . . £35/£10

The Bachman Books, New American Library (London), 1985 (pseud 'Richard Bachman') . . . . . £75/£10

ditto, New English Library (London), 1986 . . £60/£10

Short Stories
Night Shift, Doubleday (New York), 1978 . .£400/£50

ditto, New English Library (London), 1978 . .£200/£35

Different Seasons, Viking (New York), 1982 . . £65/£15

ditto, Macdonald (London), 1982 . . . £40/£10

Skeleton Crew, Putnam (New York), 1985 . £20/£10

ditto, as **Stephen King's Skeleton Crew**, Scream Press (Santa Cruz, CA), 1985 (1,000 copies numbered in silver ink and signed by author and artist, slipcase) . . £350/£250

ditto, Scream Press (Santa Cruz, CA), 1985 (69 leather-bound, zippered copies) £2,000

ditto, Scream Press (Santa Cruz, CA), 1985 (17 presentation copies) £3,000

ditto, Scream Press (Santa Cruz, CA), 1985 (52 lettered copies) £1,500

ditto, Macdonald (London), 1985 . . . . £25/£5

My Pretty Pony, Whitney Museum of American Art (New York), 1989 (250 signed, numbered copies) . . £1,750

ditto, Knopf (New York), 1989 (slipcase). . . £75/£25

Dolan's Cadillac, Lord John Press (Northridge, CA), 1989 (26 lettered, signed copies) £1,500

ditto, Lord John Press (Northridge, CA), 1989 (100 presentation copies, quarter-bound in leather) . .£500

ditto, Lord John Press (Northridge, CA), 1989 (250 numbered, signed copies, quarter-bound in leather) .£375

ditto, Lord John Press (Northridge, CA), 1989 (1,000 numbered, signed copies, no d/w) £300

Four Past Midnight, Viking (New York), 1990 . £20/£5

ditto, Hodder & Stoughton (London), 1990 . . £15/£5

Nightmares and Dreamscapes, Viking (New York), 1993 . . . . £10/£5

ditto, Hodder & Stoughton (London), 1993 . . £10/£5
ditto, Hodder & Stoughton (London), 1993 (2,000 copy gift issue, slipcase, no d/w) . . . . . £60/£40
Umney's Last Case, Penguin (New York), 1995 (pbk) . £15
Six Stories, Philtrum (Bangor, ME), 1997 (900 [800] signed copies; pbk) £750
Hearts in Atlantis, Hodder & Stoughton (London), 1999 .
. . . . £10/£5
ditto, Scribner's (New York), 1999 . . . £10/£5
Everything's Eventual, Scribner's (New York), 2002 £10/£5
ditto, Hodder & Stoughton, 2002 . . . £10/£5
The Secretary of Dreams, Cemetery Dance (Baltimore, MD), 2006 . . . . £45/£20
ditto, Cemetery Dance (Baltimore, MD), 2006 (750 signed, numbered copies in traycase) . . . £250/£200
Just After Sunset: Stories, Scribner's (New York), 2008 .
. . . . £10/£5
ditto, Hodder & Stoughton, 2008 . . . £10/£5
ditto, Hodder & Stoughton, 2008 (500 numbered copies with DVD and with King's facsimile signature; slipcase) . £45
Stephen King Goes to the Movies, Subterranean Press (Burton, MI), 2009 (2000 unsigned copies) . . £25/£10

Others

Danse Macabre, Everest House (New York), 1981 £65/£20
ditto, Everest House (New York), 1981 (250 signed, numbered copies, slipcase, tissue d/w) . . £600/£500
ditto, Everest House (New York), 1981 (signed, lettered copies, slipcase, tissue d/w) . . . £1,500/£1,000
ditto, Everest House (New York), 1981 (35 publishers copies, no slipcase or d/w). £1,000
ditto, Macdonald Futura (London), 1981 . . £300/£45
Letters from Hell, Lord John Press (Northridge, CA), 1988 (500 signed, numbered copies, broadside in wraps) . .
. . . . £150
ditto, Lord John Press (Northridge, CA), 1988 (26 signed, lettered copies, broadside in wraps). . . . £225
Nightmares in the Sky, Viking (New York), 1988 (with 'f-stop Fitzgerald') . . . . £30/£10
Bare Bones: Conversations on Terror, Underwood-Miller (Los Angeles, CA), 1988 (1,000 numbered copies; slipcase; no d/w) . . . . £50/£35
ditto, Underwood-Miller (Los Angeles, CA), 1988 (52 signed, lettered copies; slipcase) . . . £200/£150
ditto, Underwood-Miller (Los Angeles, CA), 1988 (100 presentation copies; slipcase) . . . £150/£100
ditto, McGraw-Hill (New York), 1989 . . £10/£5
ditto, New English Library (London), 1989 . . £10/£5
Mid-Life Confidential: The Rock Bottom Remainders Tour America With Three Cords and an Attitude, Viking (New York), 1994 (with Dave Barry, Barbara Kingsolver and Amy Tan et al) . . . . £10/£5
On Writing: A Memoir of the Craft, Scribner's (New York), 2000 . . . . £10/£5
ditto, Hodder & Stoughton (London), 2000 . . £15/£5
Secret Windows: Essays and Fiction on the Craft of Writing, Book-of-the-Month Club (New York), 2000 .
. . . . £20/£5
Faithful: Two Diehard Boston Red Sox Fans Chronicle the 2004 Season, Scribner (New York), 2004 (with Stewart O'Nan) . . . . £10/£5

RUDYARD KIPLING
(b.1865 d.1936)

Often considered a poet of British imperialism, Kipling's work has caused much controversy, though poems such as 'If' and his 'Jungle Book' stories remain firmly entrenched in British colonial mythology. Kipling won the Nobel Prize for Literature in 1907, and in 1934 he shared the Gothenburg Prize for Poetry with W.B. Yeats. He turned down offers of a knighthood and the post of Poet Laureate.

Poetry
Schoolboy Lyrics, privately printed at the 'Civil & Military Gazette' Press (Lahore, India), 1881 (approx 25 copies with blank paper wraps and later approx 25 with brown paper wraps). £6,000
Echoes, privately printed (Lahore, India), 1884 (published anonymously, with Alice Kipling; wraps) . . £2,500
Quartette, privately printed at the 'Civil & Military Gazette' Press (Lahore, India), 1885 (published anonymously, with his sister, mother and father; wraps) . . £2,500
Departmental Ditties, Civil and Military Gazette (Lahore, India), 1886 (wraps) £1,500
ditto, Thacker, Spink & Co. (Calcutta, India), 1886 . £400
ditto, as ***Departmental Ditties, Barrack-Room Ballads and Other Verses***, United States Book Company/Lovell (New York), 1890 (first issue with 'Lovell' on spine) . . £100
ditto, Thacker & Co. (London), 1897 (150 large paper copies) £500
Barrack-Room Ballads and Other Verses, Methuen (London), 1892 . . . . £200
ditto, Methuen (London), 1892 (large paper edition, 225 copies) £400
ditto, Methuen (London), 1892 (deluxe edition, 30 copies on half vellum) £1,750
ditto, Thacker, Spink and Co. (Calcutta & Bombay, India) 1892 . . . . £200
The Seven Seas, Appleton (New York), 1896 . . . £35
ditto, Methuen (London), 1896 . . . . . £35
ditto, Methuen (London), 1896 (large paper edition, 150 copies) £200
ditto, Methuen (London), 1896 (deluxe edition, 30 copies on half vellum) £600
An Almanac of Twelve Sports, Heinemann (London), 1898 [1897] (illustrated by William Nicholson) . . £450
ditto, Russell (New York), 1898 . . . . . £450
Early Verse, Macmillan (London), 1900 . . . £60
The Five Nations, Methuen (London), 1903 . . . £45
ditto, Methuen (London), 1903 (large paper edition, 200 copies) £150
ditto, Methuen (London), 1903 (deluxe edition, 30 copies on full vellum) £650
ditto, Doubleday Page (New York), 1903 . . . £45
Collected Verse, Doubleday Page (New York), 1907 (without index) £100
ditto, Doubleday Page (New York), 1907 (with index) . £65
ditto, Doubleday Page (New York), 1910 (9 colour plates by W. Heath Robinson) £150
ditto, Doubleday Page (New York), 1910 (125 signed copies, 9 colour plates by W. Heath Robinson) . . . £750
ditto, Hodder & Stoughton (London), 1912 (500 copies) £125
ditto, Hodder & Stoughton (London), 1912 (deluxe edition, 100 copies on full vellum). £400

A Song of the English, Hodder & Stoughton (London), [c.1909] (30 colour plates illustrated by W. Heath Robinson) £200

ditto, Hodder & Stoughton (London), [c.1909] (deluxe edition, 500 copies signed by the artist, 30 colour plates, full vellum) £600

ditto, Hodder & Stoughton (London), [c.1909] (deluxe edition, 50 copies signed by the artist and author, 30 colour plates, full vellum) £1,000

ditto, Doubleday (New York), [c.1909] (30 colour plates illustrated by W. Heath Robinson) £200

ditto, Doubleday (New York), [c.1909] (deluxe edition, 500 copies signed by the artist, 30 colour plates, full vellum) .
. . . . £600

ditto, Hodder & Stoughton (London), [1912] (12 colour plates) £45

ditto, Hodder & Stoughton/Daily Telegraph (London), [1915] (16 colour plates) £65

ditto, Hodder & Stoughton (London), [1919] (16 colour plates) £45

The Dead King, Hodder & Stoughton (London), 1910 (illustrated by W. Heath Robinson) £65

ditto, Hodder & Stoughton (London), 1910 (illustrated by W. Heath Robinson; wraps) £50

A History of England, Clarendon Press, Henry Frowde and Hodder & Stoughton (Oxford and London), 1911 (quarto, with C.R.L. Fletcher) £25

ditto, O.U.P./Hodder & Stoughton (London), 1911 (octavo edition for schools) £20

ditto, Doubleday (New York), 1911 . . . . £25

Songs from Books, Doubleday (New York), 1912 . . £25

ditto, Macmillan (London), 1913 . . . . £25

Twenty Poems, Methuen (London), 1918 (wraps) . £25

The Irish Guards, privately printed (London), 1918 (100 signed copies; wraps) £200

ditto, Doubleday (New York), 1918 (70 copyright copies; wraps) £200

The Years Between, Methuen (London), 1919 . £25

ditto, Methuen (London), 1919 (large paper edition, 200 copies) £100

ditto, Methuen (London), 1919 (deluxe edition, 30 copies on vellum) £325

Verse: Inclusive Edition 1885-1918, Hodder & Stoughton (London), 1919 (3 vols) £75

ditto, Hodder & Stoughton (London), 1919 (deluxe edition, 100 signed sets on vellum) £1,000

A Kipling Anthology: Verse, Methuen (London), 1922 .
. . . . £20/£5

ditto, Doubleday (New York), 1922 . . . . £30/£5

Songs for Youth, Hodder & Stoughton (London), [1924] .
. . . . £35/£10

ditto, Doubleday (New York), 1925 . . . . £35/£10

A Choice of Songs, Methuen (London), 1925 . £25/£5

ditto, Doubleday (New York), 1925 (stapled wraps) . £25

Sea and Sussex, Macmillan (London), 1926 (illustrated by Donald Maxwell) . . . . . . £45/£10

ditto, Macmillan (London), 1926 (500 copies on half vellum, d/w and slipcase) . . . . . £300/£200

ditto, Doubleday (New York), 1926 . . . £40/£10

Songs of the Sea, Macmillan (London), 1927 (illustrated by Donald Maxwell) . . . . . . £50/£15

ditto, Macmillan (London), 1927 (500 signed copies on half vellum, d/w and slipcase) . . . . £325/£250

ditto, Doubleday (New York), 1927 . . . £45/£15

ditto, Doubleday (New York), 1927 (150 signed copies, d/w and slipcase) . . . . £325/£250

Poems 1886-1929, Macmillan (London), 1929 (3 vols, illustrated by Francis Dodd) . . . . . £50/£20

ditto, Macmillan (London), 1929 (525 signed copies) . .
. . . . £1,750/£750

ditto, Doubleday (New York), 1930 . . . . £50/£20

ditto, Doubleday (New York), 1930 (525 signed copies) .
. . . . £1,750/£750

ditto, Doubleday (New York), 1930 (23 signed presentation copies) £2,250

East of Suez, Macmillan (London), 1931 (illustrated by Donald Maxwell) . . . . . . £45/£15

Selected Poems, Methuen (London), 1931 . £15/£5

Sixty Poems, Hodder & Stoughton (London), 1939 £15/£5

Verse: Definitive Edition, Hodder & Stoughton (London), 1940 . . . . £25/£5

So Shall Ye Reap: Poems For These Days, Hodder & Stoughton (London), 1941 . . . . £15/£5

A Choice of Kipling's Verse, Faber & Faber (London), 1941 (edited by T.S. Eliot) . . . . . . £20/£5

Children's Titles

The Jungle Book, Macmillan (London), 1894. . £1,250

ditto, Century (New York), 1894 . . . . £1,000

The Second Jungle Book, Macmillan (London), 1895 . £350

ditto, Century (New York), 1895 . . . . . £250

'Captains Courageous', a story of the Grand Banks, Macmillan (London), 1897 . . . . . £125

ditto, Century (New York), 1897 . . . . £75

Stalky and Co., Macmillan (London), 1899 . . £125

ditto, Doubleday & McClure (New York), 1899 . £100

Just So Stories for Little Children, Macmillan (London), 1902 . . . . £300

ditto, Doubleday Page (New York), 1902 . . . £250

Puck of Pook's Hill, Macmillan (London), 1906 (illustrated by H.R. Millar) £125

ditto, Doubleday Page (New York), 1906 (4 colour illustrations by Arthur Rackham) £150

Rewards and Fairies, Macmillan (London), 1910 . £45

ditto, Doubleday Page (New York), 1911 . . . £40

Novels

The Light That Failed, Lippincott (Philadelphia), 1890 (12 chapters with happy ending; wraps) . . . £165

ditto, Macmillan (London), 1891 (15 chapters with unhappy ending!) £125

The Naulahka, a story of West and East, Heinemann (London), 1892 (with W. Balestier) £75

ditto, Macmillan (New York), 1892 . . . £65

Kim, Doubleday Page (New York), 1901 . . . £100

ditto, Macmillan (London), 1901 . . . . £85

Short Stories

Plain Tales from the Hills, Thacker Spink (Calcutta, India), 1888 (first issue with 24 pages of adverts at end dated 'Calcutta December 1887') £750

ditto, Thacker Spink (Calcutta, India), 1888 (second issue with 32 pages of adverts at end dated 'Calcutta December 1887') £500

ditto, John W. Lovell Co. (New York), 1889 . . £125

ditto, Macmillan (London), 1890 . . . . . £125

Soldiers Three, A.H. Wheeler (Allahabad, India), 1888 (first state without cross-hatching on barrack doors on cover; wraps) £600

ditto, A.H. Wheeler (Allahabad, India), 1888 (second state with cross-hatching on barrack doors on cover; wraps) £300
ditto, Sampson Low (London), 1890 . . . . . £100
ditto, John W. Lovell Co. (New York), 1890 . . . £100
The Story of the Gadsby's, A.H. Wheeler (Allahabad, India), 1888 (first printing with no date on front cover; wraps) .
. . . . £750
ditto, A.H. Wheeler (Allahabad, India), 1888 (second printing with 1888 date on front cover; wraps) . . £250
ditto, Sampson Low (London), 1890 . . . . . £85
ditto, John W. Lovell Co. (New York), 1890 . . . £85
In Black and White, A.H. Wheeler (Allahabad, India), 1888 (wraps) £600
ditto, Sampson Low (London), 1890 (wraps) . . £300
ditto, John W. Lovell Co. (New York), 1890 . . . £100
Under the Deodars, A.H. Wheeler (Allahabad, India), 1888 (first state without shading around 'No.4' and 'One Rupee'; wraps) £1,000
ditto, A.H. Wheeler (Allahabad, India), 1888 (second state with shading around 'No.4' and 'One Rupee'; wraps) £300
ditto, Sampson Low (London), 1890 (wraps) . . £100
ditto, John W. Lovell Co. (New York), 1890 . . . £100
The Phantom Rickshaw and Other Tales, A.H. Wheeler (Allahabad, India), [1888] (first binding with 'A H Wheeler' and 'Mufid I am Press' below design on front cover; wraps) £1,000
ditto, A.H. Wheeler (Allahabad, India), [1888] (second binding with 'A.H. Wheeler' and 'Mayo School of Art' below design on front cover; wraps) . . . £500
ditto, Sampson Low (London), 1890 (wraps) . . £400
ditto, John W. Lovell Co. (New York), 1890 . . . £100
Wee Willie Winkie and Other Child Stories, A.H. Wheeler (Allahabad, India), 1888 (first issue; wraps) . £1,250
ditto, A.H. Wheeler (Allahabad, India), 1888 (second issue with 'Mayo School of Art' on front wrapper; wraps) . £750
ditto, A.H. Wheeler (Allahabad, India), 1888 (third issue with 96 instead of 104 pages; wraps) . . £250
ditto, Sampson Low (London), 1890 . . . . . £100
ditto, John W. Lovell Co. (New York), 1890 . . . £100
The Courting of Dinah Shad and Other Stories, Harper & Brothers (New York), 1890 . . . . . £150
The City of Dreadful Night and Other Sketches, A.H. Wheeler (Allahabad, India), 1890 (suppressed edition; brown wraps) £3,000
ditto, as *The City of Dreadful Night and Other Places*, A.H. Wheeler (Allahabad, India), 1891 (unsuppressed edition; grey-green pictorial wraps) £350
ditto, Sampson Low (London), 1891 . . . . . £100
ditto, Grosset & Co (New York), 1899 . . . . £100
Life's Handicap, being stories of mine own people, Macmillan (London), 1891 . . . . . £75
ditto, Doubleday & McClure Co (New York), 1899 . £45
Many Inventions, Macmillan (London), 1893 . . £75
ditto, D. Appleton and Company (New York), 1893 . £75
Soldier Tales, Macmillan (London), 1896 (reprints from *The Story of the Gadsbys* and *In Black and White*) . . £75
The Day's Work, Doubleday & McClure (New York), 1898
. . . . £100
ditto, Macmillan (London), 1898 . . . . . £75
The Kipling Reader, Macmillan (London), 1900 . £30
Traffics and Discoveries, Macmillan (London), 1904 . £75
ditto, Doubleday, Page & Company (New York), 1904. £65
They, Macmillan (London), 1905 (from *Traffics and Discoveries*) £50

The Brushwood Boy, Macmillan (London), 1907 (from *The Day's Work*). £30
Actions and Reactions, Macmillan (London), 1909 . £75
ditto, Doubleday, Page & Company (New York), 1909. £65
Abaft the Funnel, Dodge (New York), 1909 . . . £150
A Diversity of Creatures, Macmillan (London), 1917 . £30
ditto, Doubleday, Page & Company (New York), 1917. £25
Land and Sea Tales for Scouts and Guides, Macmillan (London), 1923 . . . . . . £45/£15
ditto, Doubleday, Page & Company (New York), 1923. .
. . . . £45/£15
Debits and Credits, Macmillan (London), 1926 . £40/£15
ditto, Doubleday, Page & Company (New York), 1926. .
. . . . £40/£15
Thy Servant A Dog, Told by Boots, Macmillan (London), 1930 . . . . £40/£15
ditto, Doubleday, Doran & Co (New York), 1930 . £40/£10
Humorous Tales, Macmillan (London), 1931 . . £40/£15
ditto, Doubleday, Doran & Co (New York), 1931 . £40/£10
Animal Stories, Macmillan (London), 1932 . . £40/£15
ditto, Doubleday, Doran & Co (New York), 1938 . £25/£5
Limits and Renewals, Macmillan (London), 1932 . £40/£15
ditto, Doubleday, Doran & Co (New York), 1932 . £40/£10
All The Mowgli Stories, Macmillan (London), 1933 £75/£25
ditto, Doubleday, Doran & Co (New York), 1936 . £25/£5
Collected Dog Stories, Macmillan (London), 1934. £35/£15
ditto, Doubleday, Doran & Co (New York), 1934 . £35/£10
Ham and the Porcupine, Doubleday Doran (New York), 1935 . . . . £40/£15
ditto, Doubleday, Doran & Co (New York), 1935 . £40/£10
The Maltese Cat, Macmillan (London), 1936 (from *The Day's Work*). . . . . £50/£15
Complete Works: The Sussex Edition, Macmillan (London), 1937-1939 (35 vols) . . . . . £2,500 the set
More Selected Stories, Macmillan (London), 1940 £40/£15
Twenty-One Tales, Reprint Society (Montreal, Canada), 1946 . . . . £15/£5
Ten Stories, Pan (London), 1947 (pbk) . . . £5
A Choice of Kipling's Prose, Macmillan (London), 1952 (selected and with an introduction by W. Somerset Maugham) . . . . £15/£5

Others
Something of Myself: For My Friends Known and Unknown, Macmillan (London), 1937 . . . £65/£15
ditto, Doubleday, Doran & Co (New York), 1937 . £50/£10
The Letters of Rudyard Kipling, Volume 1: 1872-1889, Macmillan (London), 1990 . . . . . £15/£5
ditto, Univ of Iowa Press (Iowa City, IA), 1990 . £15/£5
The Letters of Rudyard Kipling, Volume 2: 1890-1899, Macmillan (London), 1990 . . . . . £15/£5
ditto, Univ of Iowa Press (Iowa City, IA), 1990 . £15/£5
The Letters of Rudyard Kipling, Volume 3: 1900-1910, Macmillan (London), 1996 . . . . . £10/£5
ditto, Univ of Iowa Press (Iowa City, IA), 1996 . £10/£5
The Letters of Rudyard Kipling, Volume 4: 1911-1919, Macmillan (London), 1999 . . . . . £10/£5
ditto, Univ of Iowa Press (Iowa City, IA), 1999 . £10/£5
The Letters of Rudyard Kipling, Volume 5: 1920-1930, Palgrave Macmillan (London), 2004 . . £10/£5
ditto, Univ of Iowa Press (Iowa City, IA), 2004 . £10/£5
The Letters of Rudyard Kipling, Volume 6: 1931-1936, Palgrave Macmillan (London), 2004 . . £10/£5
ditto, Univ of Iowa Press (Iowa City, IA), 2004 . £10/£5

C.H.B. KITCHIN
(b.1895 d.1967)

A novelist, poet and musician, it is as the author of a handful of detective novels that Clifford Henry Benn Kitchin is best known. Kitchin led a colourful life, helped along by his being born into wealth and his own lucrative investments on the stock market. He spent his money on various interests including the breeding and racing of greyhounds.

Detective Novels
Death of My Aunt, Hogarth Press (London), 1929 (d/w price 7/6) . . . . £750/£65
ditto, Harcourt Brace (New York), 1930 . . . £250/£20
Crime at Christmas, Hogarth Press (London), 1934 (d/w price 7/6) . . . . £650/£45
Death of His Uncle, Constable (London), 1939 (d/w price 7/6) . . . . £275/£35
ditto, Perennial (New York), 1984 (pbk) £5
The Cornish Fox, Secker & Warburg (London), 1949 . . . . £350/£100

Other Novels
Streamers Waving, Hogarth Press (London), 1925 £250/£65
Mr Balcony, Hogarth Press (London), 1927 . . £200/£45
The Sensitive One, Hogarth Press (London), 1931 . £175/£40
Olive E, Constable (London), 1937 . . . . £65/£15
Birthday Party, Constable (London), 1938 . £65/£15
The Auction Sale, Secker & Warburg (London), 1949 . . . . £45/£15
The Secret River, Secker & Warburg (London), 1956 £25/£5
Ten Pollitt Place, Secker & Werburg (London), 1957 . . . . £25/£10
The Book of Life, Davies (London), 1960 . £25/£10
ditto, Appleton-Century-Crofts (New York), [1961, c1960] . . . . £25/£10
A Short Walk in Williams Park, Chatto & Windus (London), 1971 . . . . . . £15/£5

Short Stories
Jumping Joan and Other Stories, Secker & Warburg (London), 1954 . . . . £35/£10

Poetry
Curtains, Blackwell (Oxford), 1919 (wraps) . . . £100
Winged Victory, Blackwell (Oxford), 1921 (wraps) . £75

ARTHUR KOESTLER
(b.1905 d.1983)

Arthur Koestler was a novelist, political activist and social philosopher. All of his books are more or less an analysis of the turmoil in Europe in the years preceding World War Two. His most famous work, *Darkness at Noon*, is a novel about the purges of the Soviet state during Stalin's era.

Autobiography
Spanish Testament, Gollancz (London), 1937 . £200/£35
ditto, Gollancz (London), 1937 (Left Book Club; pbk) . £35
ditto, as *Dialogue with Death*, Macmillan (New York), 1942 (abridged) . . . . £60/£10
Scum of the Earth, Cape (London), 1941. . . £65/£15
ditto, Macmillan (New York), 1941 . . . . £45/£10
Arrow in the Blue, Collins/Hamilton (London), 1952 . . . . £35/£10
ditto, Macmillan (New York), 1952 . . . . £30/£5
The Invisible Writing, Collins/Hamilton (London), 1954 . . . . £30/£10
ditto, Macmillan (New York), 1954 . . £25/£5
Stranger on the Square, Hutchinson (London), 1984 (unfinished, by Arthur and Cynthia Koestler) . £15/£5
ditto, Random House (New York), 1984 . . . £15/£5

Novels
The Gladiators, Cape (London), 1939 . . . £75/£10
ditto, Macmillan (New York), 1939 . . . . £50/£10
Darkness at Noon, Cape (London), 1940 . . £3,000/£450
ditto, Macmillan (New York), 1941 . . . £75/£15
ditto, Franklin Library (Franklin Centre, PA), 1970 (signed, limited edition) £40
Arrival and Departure, Cape (London), 1943 . . £35/£10
ditto, Macmillan (New York), 1943 . . . £30/£5
Thieves in the Night, Macmillan (London), 1946 . £25/£5
ditto, Macmillan (New York), 1946 . . . . £20/£5
The Age of Longing, Collins (London), 1951 . £20/£5
ditto, Macmillan (New York), 1951 . . . . £20/£5
The Call-Girls, Hutchinson (London), 1972 . £15/£5
ditto, Random House (New York), 1973 . . . £15/£5

Essays
The Yogi and the Commissar, Cape (London), 1945 £25/£5
ditto, Macmillan (New York), 1945 . . . . £15/£5
Insight and Outlook, Macmillan (London), 1949 . £15/£5
ditto, Macmillan (New York), 1949 . . . . £15/£5
The Trail of the Dinosaur, Collins (London), 1955 £15/£5
ditto, Macmillan (New York), 1955 . . . . £15/£5
Reflections on Hanging, Gollancz (London), 1957 £15/£5
ditto, Macmillan (New York), 1957 . . . £15/£5
The Lotus and the Robot, Hutchinson (London), 1960 . . . . £25/£10
ditto, Macmillan (New York), 1961 . . . . £25/£10
Hanged by the Neck, Penguin (Harmondsworth, Middlesex), 1961 (pbk) £5
Drinkers of Infinity: Essays 1955-1967, Hutchinson (London), 1968 . . . . £15/£5
ditto, Macmillan (New York), 1969 . . . . £15/£5
The Lion and the Ostrich, O.U.P. (Oxford, UK), 1973 (stapled wraps) £10
The Heel of Achilles: Essays, Hutchinson (London), 1974 . . . . £15/£5
ditto, Random House (New York), 1975 . . . £15/£5
Janus: A Summing Up, Hutchinson (London), 1978 £10/£5
ditto, Random House (New York), 1978 . . . £10/£5
Bricks to Babel, Hutchinson (London), 1980 . £10/£5
ditto, Random House (New York), 1981 . . . £10/£5

Non-Fiction
Promise and Fulfilment, Macmillan (London), 1949 £25/£5
ditto, Macmillan (New York), 1949 . . . . £20/£5
The Sleepwalkers, Hutchinson (London), 1959 . £20/£5
ditto, Macmillan (New York), 1959 . . . . £15/£5
The Act of Creation, Hutchinson (London), 1964 . £20/£5
ditto, Macmillan (New York), 1964 . . . . £15/£5

The Ghost in the Machine, Hutchinson (London), 1967   .
.   .   .   .   £25/£5
ditto, Macmillan (New York), 1968   .   .   .   £15/£5
The Case of the Midwife Toad, Hutchinson (London), 1971
.   .   .   .   £10/£5
ditto, Random House (New York), 1972   .   .   £15/£5
The Roots of Coincidence, Hutchinson (London), 1972   .
.   .   .   .   £15/£5
ditto, Random House (New York), 1972   .   .   £10/£5
The Challenge of Chance, Hutchinson (London), 1973 (with
Alister Hardy and Robert Harvie)   .   .   .   £10/£5
ditto, Random House (New York), 1975   .   .   £10/£5
The Thirteenth Tribe, Hutchinson (London), 1976   £10/£5
ditto, Random House (New York), 1976   .   .   £10/£5

DEAN KOONTZ

(b.1945)

Koontz's writing career began when, at the age of 20 he
won an *Atlantic Monthly* fiction competition. His breakthrough novel, though, was *Whispers*, published in 1980.
He is renowned for writing page-turners with memorable
characters, original ideas, and an ability to blend horror,
fantasy and humour. His worldwide sales are close to 100
million.

Novels

Star Quest, Ace (New York), 1968 (with *Doom of the Green
Planet* by Emil Petaja; pbk) £45
The Fall of the Dream Machine, Ace (New York), 1969
(with *The Star Venturers*; pbk)   .   .   .   £25
Fear That Man, Ace (New York), 1969 (with *Toyman* by
E.C. Tubb; pbk) £20
Anti-Man, Paperback Library (New York), 1970 (pbk)   £20
Beastchild, Lancer (New York), 1970 (pbk)   .   .   £20
ditto, Charnel House (Lynbrook, NY), 1992 (750 signed,
numbered copies, slipcase, no d/w) .   .   .   £100/£75
ditto, Charnel House (Lynbrook, NY), 1992 (26 signed,
lettered copies, slipcase, no d/w)   .   .   £600/£500
Dark of the Woods and *Soft Come The Dragons*, Ace (New
York), 1970 (pbk) £20
The Dark Symphony, Lancer (New York), 1970 (pbk) .   £20
Hell's Gate, Lancer (New York), 1970 (pbk)   .   .   £20
The Crimson Witch, Curtis (New York), 1971 (pbk)   .   £50
A Darkness in My Soul, Daw (New York), 1972 (pbk).   £15
ditto, Dobson (London), 1979   .   .   .   .   £60/£15
The Flesh in the Furnace, Bantam (New York), 1972 (pbk)
.   .   .   .   £15
Starblood, Lancer (New York), 1972 (pbk)   .   .   £15
Time Thieves, Ace (New York), 1972 (with *Against
Arcturus* by Susan K. Putney; pbk).   .   .   £15
ditto, Dobson (London), 1977   .   .   .   .   £60/£20
Warlock, Lancer (New York), 1972 (pbk)   .   .   £15
A Werewolf Among Us, Ballantine (New York), 1973 (pbk)
.   .   .   .   £15
The Haunted Earth, Lancer (New York), 1973 (pbk) .   £15
Hanging On, M. Evans (New York), 1973   .   .   £65/£15
ditto, Barrie & Jenkins (London), 1974   .   .   £45/£10
Demon Seed, Bantam (New York), 1973 (pbk)   .   £15
ditto, Corgi (London), 1977 (pbk)   .   .   .   £10
ditto, Headline (London), 1977 (revised) .   .   £15/£5

After the Last Race, Athenaeum (New York), 1974   .   .
.   .   .   .   £100/£25
Nightmare Journey, Berkley/Putnam (New York), 1975   .
.   .   .   .   £50/£10
Night Chills, Athenaeum (New York), 1976 .   £60/£15
ditto, W.H. Allen (London), 1977   .   .   .   £50/£10
The Vision, Putnam (New York), 1977   .   .   £50/£15
ditto, Corgi (London), 1980 (pbk) £10
ditto, W.H. Allen (London), 1988   .   .   £45/£10
Whispers, Putnam (New York), 1980   .   .   £200/£50
ditto, W.H. Allen (London), 1981   .   .   £60/£15
Phantoms, Putnam (New York), 1983   .   .   £75/£25
ditto, W.H. Allen (London), 1983   .   .   .   £25/£15
Darkness Comes, W.H. Allen (London), 1984   £75/£20
ditto, as *Darkfall*, Berkeley (New York), 1984 (pbk)   .   £10
Twilight Eyes, Land of Enchantment (Plymouth, MI), 1985.
.   .   .   .   £35/£15
ditto, Land of Enchantment (Plymouth, MI), 1985 (signed,
illustrated collector's edition, 50 copies)   .   .   £350
ditto, Land of Enchantment (Plymouth, MI), 1985 (signed
edition, 200 copies, d/w and slipcase)   .   .   £145/£100
ditto, W.H. Allen (London), 1987   .   .   .   £45/£15
Strangers, Putnam (New York), 1986   .   .   £25/£5
ditto, W.H. Allen (London), 1987   .   .   .   £25/£5
Watchers, Putnam (New York), 1987   .   .   £20/£5
ditto, Headline (London), 1987 .   .   .   .   £20/£5
Lightning, Putnam (New York), 1988   .   .   £20/£5
ditto, Putnam (New York), 1988 (200 signed, numbered
copies) £125
ditto, Putnam (New York), 1988 (26 signed, lettered copies)
.   .   .   .   £300
ditto, Headline (London), 1988 .   .   .   .   £20/£5
Oddkins, Warner (New York), 1988   .   .   .   £25/£10
ditto, Headline (London), 1988   .   .   .   £20/£5
Midnight, Putnam (New York), 1989   .   .   £15/£5
ditto, Headline (London), 1989   .   .   .   £15/£5
Bad Place, Putnam (New York), 1990   .   .   £15/£5
ditto, Putnam (New York), 1990 (250 signed, numbered
copies, d/w and slipcase)   .   .   .   .   £80/£50
ditto, Headline (London), 1990   .   .   .   £15/£5
Cold Fire, Putnam (New York), 1991   .   .   £10/£5
ditto, Putnam (New York), 1991 (750 signed, numbered
copies, d/w and slipcase)   .   .   .   .   £45/£35
ditto, Headline (London), 1991 (200 signed, numbered proof
copies) £125
ditto, Headline (London), 1991   .   .   .   £10/£5
Hideaway, Putnam (New York), 1992   .   .   £10/£5
ditto, Putnam (New York), 1991 (800 signed, numbered
copies, d/w and slipcase)   .   .   .   .   £50/£35
ditto, Headline (London), 1992   .   .   .   £10/£5
ditto, Headline (London), 1992 (100 signed uncorrected
proof copies; pbk) £125
Dragon Tears, Putnam (New York), 1993   .   £10/£5
ditto, Putnam (New York), 1991 (700 signed, numbered
copies, d/w and slipcase)   .   .   .   .   £50/£35
ditto, Headline (London), 1993   .   .   .   £10/£5
Trapped, Eclipse Books (Forestville, CA), 1993 (graphic
novel, adapted by Ed Gorman, illustrated by Anthony
Bilau) .   .   .   .   £10/£5
ditto, Eclipse Books (London), 1993 .   .   £10/£5
Mr Murder, Headline (London), 1993   .   .   £10/£5
ditto, Headline (London), 1993 (200 signed uncorrected
proof copies; pbk) £90
ditto, Putnam (New York), 1993 .   .   .   .   £10/£5

ditto, Putnam (New York), 1993 (600 signed, numbered copies, d/w and slipcase) . . . . . £60/£40
Winter Moon, Headline (London), 1994 . . . £20/£5
ditto, Ballantine (New York), 1994 (pbk) £5
Dark Rivers of the Heart, Charnel House (Lynbrook, NY), 1994 (26 signed, lettered copies, slipcase, no d/w) . .
. . . . £600/£500
ditto, Charnel House (Lynbrook, NY), 1994 (500 signed, numbered copies, slipcase, no d/w) . . £150/£100
ditto, Knopf (New York), 1994 . . . . £10/£5
ditto, Headline (London), 1994 . . . . . £10/£5
Strange Highways, Warner (New York), 1995 . £10/£5
ditto, Headline (London), 1995 . . . . £10/£5
Intensity, Knopf (New York), 1995 . . . . £10/£5
ditto, Headline (London), 1995 . . . . . £10/£5
Ticktock, Headline (London), 1996 . . . . £10/£5
ditto, Ballantine (New York), 1997 (pbk) £5
Santa's Twin, HarperCollins (New York), 1996 . £10/£5
Sole Survivor, Knopf (New York), 1997 . . . £10/£5
ditto, Headline (London), 1997 . . . . £10/£5
Fear Nothing, Headline (London), 1997 . . . £10/£5
ditto, Cemetery Dance (Baltimore, MD), 1998 (52 signed, lettered copies, traycase) . . . . £300/£200
ditto, Cemetery Dance (Baltimore, MD), 1998 (698 signed, numbered copies with d/w and slipcase) . . £70/£45
ditto, Bantam (New York), 1998 . . . . £10/£5
Seize the Night, Headline (London), 1998 . . £10/£5
ditto, Cemetery Dance (Baltimore, MD), 1998 (52 signed, lettered copies) . . . . . £300/£200
ditto, Cemetery Dance (Baltimore, MD), 1998 (698 signed, numbered copies with d/w and slipcase) . . £75/£45
ditto, Bantam (New York), 1999 . . . . £10/£5
False Memory, Headline (London), 1999 . . . £10/£5
ditto, Cemetery Dance (Baltimore, MD), 1999 (52 signed, lettered copies) . . . . . £300/£200
ditto, Cemetery Dance (Baltimore, MD), 1999 (698 signed, numbered copies with d/w and slipcase) . . £75/£45
ditto, Bantam (New York), 1999 . . . . £10/£5
From the Corner of His Eye, Bantam (New York), 2001 .
. . . . £10/£5
ditto, Bantam (New York), 2001 (limited edition–limitation not stated–in faux leather binding, with specially decorated endpapers, without d/w) £50
ditto, Headline (London), 2000 . . . . £10/£5
ditto, Charnel House (Lynbrook, NY), 2001 (500 signed, numbered copies, no d/w, slipcase) . . . £100/£75
ditto, Charnel House (Lynbrook, NY), 2001 (26 signed, lettered copies, no d/w, slipcase) . . .. £400/£275
One Door Away from Heaven, Bantam (New York), 2001 .
. . . . £10/£5
ditto, Headline (London), 2001 . . . . . £10/£5
The Book of Counted Sorrows, Charnel House (Lynbrook, NY), 2001 (1,250 copies, no d/w, slipcase) . £750/£650
ditto, Charnel House (Lynbrook, NY), 2001 (26 lettered copies, no d/w, slipcase) £2,000
By the Light of the Moon, Bantam (New York), 2002 . .
. . . . £10/£5
ditto, Headline (London), 2002 . . . . £10/£5
The Face, Bantam (New York), 2003 . . . £10/£5
ditto, Charnel House (Lynbrook, NY), 2003 (500 signed, numbered copies, slipcase) £200
ditto, Charnel House (Lynbrook, NY), 2003 (26 signed, lettered copies, slipcase) £400
ditto, Headline (London), 2004 . . . . £10/£5

Odd Thomas, Bantam (New York), 2003 . . . £10/£5
ditto, Charnel House (Lynbrook, NY), 2003 (500 signed, numbered copies, slipcase) £150
ditto, Charnel House (Lynbrook, NY), 2003 (26 signed, lettered copies, slipcase) £300
ditto, HarperCollins (London), 2004 . . . . £10/£5
Robot Santa: The Further Adventures of Santa's Twin, HarperCollins (New York), 2004 . . . £10/£5
Life Expectancy, Bantam (New York), 2004 . . £10/£5
ditto, Charnel House (Lynbrook, NY), 2004 (26 signed, lettered copies) £300
ditto, Charnel House (Lynbrook, NY), 2004 (300 signed, numbered copies) £150
ditto, HarperCollins (London), 2005 . . . . £10/£5
The Taking, Bantam (New York), 2004 . . . £10/£5
ditto, Charnel House (Lynbrook, NY), 2004 (26 signed, lettered copies) £300
ditto, Charnel House (Lynbrook, NY), 2004 (300 signed, numbered copies) £150
ditto, HarperCollins (London), 2005 . . . . £10/£5
Forever Odd, Bantam (New York), 2005 . . . £10/£5
ditto, HarperCollins (London), 2005 . . . £10/£5
ditto, Charnel House (Lynbrook, NY), 2006 (26 signed, lettered copies) £300
ditto, Charnel House (Lynbrook, NY), 2006 (500 signed, numbered copies) £150
Velocity, Bantam (New York), 2005 . . . £10/£5
ditto, HarperCollins (London), 2005 . . . . £10/£5
ditto, Charnel House (Lynbrook, NY), 2005 (300 signed, numbered copies) £150
ditto, Charnel House (Lynbrook, NY), 2005 (26 signed, lettered copies) £300
Brother Odd, Bantam (New York), 2006 . . . £10/£5
ditto, HarperCollins (London), 2007 . . . . £10/£5
ditto, Charnel House (Lynbrook, NY), 2007 (300 signed, numbered copies) £150
ditto, Charnel House (Lynbrook, NY), 2007 (26 signed, lettered copies) £300
The Husband, Bantam (New York), 2006 . . £10/£5
ditto, HarperCollins (London), 2006 . . . . £10/£5
ditto, Charnel House (Lynbrook, NY), 2006 (500 signed, numbered copies) £150
ditto, Charnel House (Lynbrook, NY), 2006 (26 signed, lettered copies) £300

Dean Koontz's Frankenstein
Dean Koontz's Frankenstein, The Original Screenplay, Charnel House (Lynbrook, NY), 2005 (750 signed, numbered copies) £80
ditto, Charnel House (Lynbrook, NY), 2005 (26 signed, lettered copies) £300
Dean Koontz's Frankenstein. Book One: Prodigal Son, Bantam (New York), 2005 (with Kevin J. Anderson; pbk)
. . . . £5
ditto, HarperCollins (London), 2005 . . . . £5
Dean Koontz's Frankenstein. Book Two: City of Night, Bantam (New York), 2005 (with Ed Gorman; pbk) . £5
ditto, HarperCollins (London), 2005 . . . . . £5

Poetry
The Paper Doorway: Funny Verse and Nothing Worse, HarperCollins (New York), 2001 . . . . £10/£5
Every Day's a Holiday: Amusing Rhymes for Happy Times, HarperCollins (New York), 2003 . . . . £10/£5

Non-Fiction
Writing Popular Fiction, Writers' Digest Fiction (Cincin-
nati, OH), 1973   .   .   .   . £50/£15
How To Write Best-Selling Fiction, Writers' Digest Books
(Cincinnati, OH), 1981   .   .   .   .   . £50/£15
ditto, Popular Press (London), 1981   .   .   . £35/£10

Titles Written with Gerda Koontz
Bounce Girl, Cameo Press (New York), 1970 (pbk)   . £150
The Underground Lifestyles Handbook, Aware Press (Los
Angeles, CA), 1970 (pbk) £200
The Pig Society, Aware Press (Los Angeles, CA), 1970
(pbk) £200

Written as 'David Axton'
Prison of Ice, Lippincott (Philadelphia), 1976.   . £100/£25
ditto, W.H. Allen (London), 1976   .   .   . £100/£35
ditto, as *Icebound*, Headline (London), 1995 (as 'Dean R.
Koontz')   .   .   .   . £10/£5

Written as 'Brian Coffey'
Blood Risk, Bobbs-Merrill (Indianapolis, IN), 1973   .   .
.   .   .   . £100/£25
ditto, Barker (London), 1974   .   .   .   . £75/£25
Surrounded, Bobbs-Merrill (Indianapolis, IN), 1974   .   .
.   .   .   . £100/£25
ditto, Barker (London), 1975   .   .   .   . £75/£20
The Wall of Masks, Bobbs-Merrill (Indianapolis, IN), 1975
.   .   .   . £100/£25
The Face of Fear, Bobbs-Merrill (Indianapolis, IN), 1977 .
.   .   .   . £125/£30
ditto, Peter Davis (London), 1978 (pseud 'K.R. Dwyer')   .
.   .   .   . £75/£25
The Voice of the Night, Doubleday (New York), 1980 .   .
.   .   .   . £225/£65
ditto, Robert Hale (London), 1981   .   .   . £75/£15

Written as 'Deanna Dwyer'
The Demon Child, Lancer (New York), 1971 (pbk)   . £15
Legacy of Terror, Lancer (New York), 1971 (pbk)   . £15
Children of the Storm, Lancer (New York), 1972 (pbk) £15
The Dark of Summer, Lancer (New York), 1972 (pbk) £15
Dance With the Devil, Lancer (New York), 1972 (pbk) £15

Written as 'K.R. Dwyer'
Chase, Random House (New York), 1972   .   . £100/£30
ditto, Barker (London), 1974   .   .   .   . £75/£20
Shattered, Random House (New York), 1972 .   . £100/£30
ditto, Barker (London), 1974   .   .   .   . £75/£20
Dragonfly, Random House (New York), 1975   . £75/£15
ditto, Peter Davis (London), 1977   .   .   . £75/£15

Written as 'John Hill'
The Long Sleep, Popular Library (New York), 1975 (pbk) .
.   .   .   . £15

Written as 'Leigh Nichols'
The Key to Midnight, Pocket (New York), 1979 (pbk) . £15
ditto, Magnum (London), 1980 (pbk).   .   .   . £10
ditto, Piatkus (London), 1984   .   .   .   . £20/£5
ditto, Dark Harvest (Arlington Heights, IL), 1989 (550
copies, slipcase and d/w; as Dean Koontz)   . £65/£45
ditto, Dark Harvest (Arlington Heights, IL), 1989 (52 signed,
lettered copies, d/w and slipcase; as Dean Koontz)   .   .
.   .   .   . £200/£125

The Eyes of Darkness, Pocket (New York), 1981 (pbk)   £10
ditto, Piatkus (London), 1981   .   .   .   . £25/£5
ditto, Dark Harvest (Arlington Heights, IL), 1988 (400
signed, numbered copies, d/w and slipcase; as Dean
Koontz) .   .   .   . £80/£45
ditto, Dark Harvest (Arlington Heights, IL), 1988 (52 signed,
lettered copies, d/w and slipcase; as Dean Koontz)   .
.   .   .   . £200/£125
The House of Thunder, Pocket (New York), 1982 (pbk) £10
ditto, Fontana (London), 1983 (pbk) £10
ditto, Piatkus (London), 1983   .   .   .   . £20/£5
ditto, Dark Harvest (Arlington Heights, IL), 1988 (550
signed, numbered copies, d/w and slipcase; as Dean
Koontz) .   .   .   . £65/£40
ditto, Dark Harvest (Arlington Heights, IL), 1988 (52 signed,
lettered copies, d/w and slipcase; as Dean Koontz)   .   .
.   .   .   . £200/£125
Twilight, Pocket (New York), 1984 (pbk).   .   . £10
ditto, as *The Servants of Twilight*, Fontana (London), 1985
(pbk) £10
ditto, as *The Servants of Twilight*, Piatkus (London), 1985 .
.   .   .   . £20/£5
ditto, as *The Servants of Twilight*, Dark Harvest (Arlington
Heights, IL), 1988 (450 signed copies, d/w and slipcase; as
Dean Koontz)   .   .   .   .   .   . £100/£65
The Door to December, NAL (New York), 1985 (pseud
'Richard Paige'; pbk) £10
ditto, Fontana (London), 1987 (pseud 'Leigh Nichols'; pbk)
.   .   .   . £10
ditto, Inner Circle (London), 1988 (pseud 'Leigh Nichols') .
.   .   .   . £35/£10
Shadowfires, Pocket (New York), 1987 (pbk).   . £10
ditto, Fontana (London), 1987 (pbk)   .   .   . £10
ditto, Collins (London), 1987   .   .   .   . £50/£15
ditto, Dark Harvest (Arlington Heights, IL), 1990 (600
signed, numbered copies, d/w and slipcase; as Dean
Koontz).   .   .   .   . £65/£40
ditto, Dark Harvest (Arlington Heights, IL), 1990 (52 signed,
lettered copies, d/w and slipcase; as Dean Koontz)   .   .
.   .   .   . £200/£125

Written as 'Owen West'
The Funhouse, Jove (New York), 1980 (pbk).   .   . £10
ditto, Doubleday (New York), 1980   .   .   . £20/£5
ditto, Sphere (London), 1981 (pbk)   .   .   . £10
The Mask, Jove (New York), 1980 (pbk) .   .   . £10
ditto, Coronet/Hodder (London), 1983 (pbk)   .   . £10
ditto, Headline (London), 1989 (as Dean Koontz) £30/£10

Written as 'Anthony North'
Strike Deep, Dial (New York), 1974 .   .   . £450/£100

Written as 'Aaron Wolfe'
Invasion, Laser Books (New York), 1975 (pbk)   . £15

Written as 'Leonard Chris'
Hung, Cameo Press (New York), 1970 (disputed by author;
pbk) £75

MILAN KUNDERA
(b.1929)

Milan Kundera is a Czech writer whose first novel, *The Joke*, was a satirical account of totalitarianism, and which caused his work to be banned by the Soviets. He moved to France where he wrote *The Book of Laughter and Forgetting*, a mixture of novel, short stories, and authorial musing. *The Unbearable Lightness of Being*, his most popular work, laments that only having one life we are unable to experiment with the possibilities of repetition, trial and error.

Novels
The Joke, Coward-McCann (New York), 1969 . £100/£15
ditto, Macdonald (London), 1969 . . . . £85/£10
Life is Elsewhere, Knopf (New York), 1974 . £40/£5
ditto, Faber (London), 1986 . . . . . . £10/£5
The Farewell Party, Knopf (New York), 1976 . £35/£10
ditto, Murray (London), 1976 . . . . . £25/£5
The Book of Laughter and Forgetting, Knopf (New York), 1980 . . . . £25/£5
ditto, Faber (London), 1982 . . . . . . £20/£5
The Unbearable Lightness of Being, Harper (New York), 1984 . . . . £25/£5
ditto, Faber (London), 1984 . . . . . . £25/£5
Immortality, Grove Weidenfeld (New York), 1991 £10/£5
ditto, Faber (London), 1991 . . . . . . £10/£5
Slowness, HarperCollins (New York), 1996 . £10/£5
ditto, Faber (London), 1996 . . . . . . £10/£5
Identity, Harper Flamingo (New York), 1998 . . £10/£5
ditto, Faber (London), 1998 . . . . . . £10/£5
Ignorance, HarperCollins (New York), 2002 . . £10/£5
ditto, Faber (London), 2002 . . . . . . £10/£5

Short Stories
Laughable Loves, Knopf (New York), 1974 . . £30/£10
ditto, Murray (London), 1978 . . . . . £25/£5

PHILIP LARKIN
(b.1922 d.1985)

XX Poems was the first of Larkin's collections of poetry to realise his own distinctive voice, although *The Less Deceived* was his first popular success. He was offered the Poet Laureateship following the death of John Betjeman but declined. Larkin spent his working life as a university librarian in Hull. He was also a novelist and jazz critic. He was made a Companion of Honour in 1985.

Poetry
The North Ship, The Fortune Press (London), 1945 (black cloth) . . . . £1,000/£225
ditto, The Fortune Press (London), 1945 [1965] (unauthorised second edition, red or brown cloth) .
. . . . £145/£30
ditto, Faber (London), 1966 . . . . . . £50/£15
XX Poems, privately printed (Belfast), 1951 (100 copies, not for sale; wraps) £1,250
The Fantasy Poets No. 21, Fantasy Press (Swinford, Oxfordshire), 1954 (300 copies) £500

The Less Deceived, Marvell Press (Hessle, East Yorkshire), 1955 (first issue with flat spine and misprint of 'floor' for 'sea' in the first line of the poem on page 38; d/w priced 6s and rear printed in black only) . . . . £750/£250
ditto, Marvell Press (Hessle, East Yorkshire), 1955 (second issue with rounded spine and d/w priced 7s6d and rear printed in black only) . . . . . . £450/£125
ditto, Marvell Press (Hessle, East Yorkshire), 1955 (wraps with d/w glued on as cover, price 6s) . . . £100
ditto, St Martin's Press (New York), 1960 . £65/£20
The Whitsun Weddings, Faber (London), 1964 . £100/£25
ditto, Random House (New York), 1964 . . . £65/£20
The Explosion, Poem-of-the-Month-Club (London), 1970 (broad-sheet, 1,000 signed copies) £125
High Windows, Faber (London), 1974 . . . £45/£10
ditto, Farrar Straus (New York), 1974 . . . £40/£10
Femmes Damnées, Sycamore Press (Oxford, UK), 1978 (broadsheet) £25
Aubade, Penstemon Press (Salem, OR), 1980 (250 numbered, initialled copies; wraps; in envelope) £250/£175
Collected Poems, Faber (London), 1988 . . . £25/£10
ditto, Farrar Straus (New York), 1988 . . . £20/£5

Novels
Jill, The Fortune Press (London), 1946 . . £1,500/£300
ditto, Faber (London), 1964 . . . . . . £100/£20
ditto, St Martin's Press (New York), 1964 . £50/£15
A Girl in Winter, Faber (London), 1947 . £1,000/£200
ditto, St Martin's Press (New York), 1957 . £75/£20

Recordings
Listen Presents Philip Larkin Reading 'The Less Deceived', Listen/The Marvell Press, 1959 . . . . . £35
ditto, Listen/The Marvell Press, 1959 (100 copies signed by the author) £125
Philip Larkin Reads and Comments on 'The Whitsun Weddings', Listen Records, [1965] £35
British Poets of Our Time, *Philip Larkin 'High Windows': Poems Read by the Author*, Argo (London), [1975] . £30

Others
All What Jazz: A Record Diary, 1961-68, Faber (London), 1970 . . . . £30/£10
ditto, St Martin's Press (New York), 1970 . . £30/£10
Philip Larkin Talks to Eboracum, [Eboracum (York), 1970] (wraps) £125
The Oxford Book of Twentieth Century English Verse, O.U.P. (Oxford, UK), 1973 (edited by Larkin) . £25/£10
Required Writing, Miscellaneous Pieces, 1955-1982, Faber (London), 1983 (pbk) £20
ditto, Farrar Straus (New York), 1983 . . . £20/£5
ditto, Faber (London), 1984 (hardback) . . . £65/£15
Selected Letters of Philip Larkin, 1940-1985, Faber (London), 1992 . . . . £15/£5
ditto, Farrar Straus (New York), 1993 . . . £10/£5
Trouble at Willow Gables and other Fictions, Faber (London), 2002 . . . . £10/£5

STIEG LARSSON
(b.1954 d.2004)

Karl Stig-Erland Larsson was a Swedish journalist and writer, known for his Millennium Trilogy of crime novels which were published after his death. All three titles were translated into English by Reg Keeland

The Girl with the Dragon Tattoo, MacLehose Press (London), 2008 . . . . . . £500/£60
ditto, Knopf (New York), 2008 . . . . £40/£10
The Girl Who Played with Fire, 2009, MacLehose Press (London), 2009 . . . . £10/£5
ditto, Knopf (New York), 2009 . . . . £10/£5
The Girl Who Kicked the Hornets' Nest, MacLehose Press (London), 2009 . . . . . . £10/£5
ditto, Knopf (New York), 2010 . . . . £10/£5

D.H. LAWRENCE
(b.1885 d.1930)

David Herbert Lawrence was a versatile and controversial Modernist writer whose achievements have often been over-shadowed by the various court cases they have provoked, especially the trial of *Lady Chatterly's Lover*. His œuvre includes novels, short stories, poems, plays, essays, travel books, paintings, translations, literary criticism and personal letters.

Novels

The White Peacock, Duffield (New York), 1911 (first issue with integral title-page and copyright date 1910) . £7,500
ditto, Duffield (New York), 1911 (second issue with tipped-in title-page and copyright date 1911) . . . £3,000
ditto, Heinemann (London), 1911 (first issue with windmill device on back cover and pages 227-30 tipped-in) . £800
ditto, Heinemann (London), 1911 (second issue without windmill device, and pages 227-30 integral) . . £325
The Trespasser, Duckworth (London), 1912 (first issue with dark blue cloth) £375
ditto, Duckworth (London), 1912 (second issue with green cloth) £250
ditto, Mitchell Kennerley (New York), 1912 . . £200
Sons and Lovers, Duckworth (London), 1913 (first state without date on title-page or with dated title-page tipped-in) £750
ditto, Duckworth (London), 1913 (second state with dated title-page integral) £500
ditto, Mitchell Kennerley (New York), 1913 . . £200
The Rainbow, Methuen (London), 1915 (blue-green cloth) .
. . . . £1,000
ditto, Methuen (London), 1915 (red or brown cloth) . £650
ditto, Methuen (London), 1915 (pbk) £400
ditto, Huebsch (New York), 1916 . . . . .£300
The Lost Girl, Secker (London), 1920 (first issue, p.256 line 15 reads '...she was taken to her room...' and p.268 reads 'whether she noticed anything in the bedroom, in the beds.') . . . . £1,250/£200
ditto, Secker (London), 1920 (second issue, p.256 line 15 reads '...she let be.' and p.268 deletes 'in the bedroom, in the beds.') . . . . £750/£75

ditto, Seltzer (New York), 1921 (first issue with character's name 'Cicio') . . . . . . £500/£100
ditto, Seltzer (New York), 1921 (second issue with character's name 'Ciccio'). . . . . £500/£65
Women in Love, privately printed (New York), 1920 (16 or 18 signed, numbered copies of 1,250) . . . £7,500
ditto, privately printed (New York), 1920 (1,250 unsigned, numbered, copies; no d/w). £500
ditto, Secker (London), 1921 . . . . £1,000/£250
ditto, Secker (London), 1920 [1922] (from US sheets; 50 signed copies; no d/w) £5,000
ditto, Seltzer (New York), 1922 . . . . £400/£45
Aaron's Rod, Seltzer (New York), 1922 . . £400/£45
ditto, Secker (London), 1922 . . . . £200/£40
Kangaroo, Secker (London), 1923 . . . £200/£25
ditto, Seltzer (New York), 1923 . . . . £175/£25
The Boy in the Bush, Secker (London), 1924 (with M.L. Skinner). . . . . £175/£40
ditto, Seltzer (New York), 1924 . . . . £175/£40
The Plumed Serpent, Secker (London), 1926 . £175/£40
ditto, Knopf (New York), 1926 . . . . £175/£40
Lady Chatterly's Lover, privately printed (Florence), 1928 (1,000 signed, numbered copies, plain protective jacket) .
. . . . £10,000/£5,000
ditto, privately printed (Florence), 1928 (second edition; pbk with glassine d/w) . . . . . £750/£450
ditto, privately printed (Paris), 1929 (pbk) . . .£400
ditto, Secker (London), 1932 (expurgated edition) . £500/£45
ditto, Knopf (New York), 1932 (expurgated edition) .
. . . . £500/£45
ditto, Grove Press (New York), 1959 (unexpurgated edition)
. . . . £45/£15
ditto, Penguin (Harmondsworth, Middlesex), 1960 (unexpurgated edition; pbk) £10
Mr Noon, C.U.P. (Cambridge, UK), 1984 . £15/£5
ditto, Viking (New York), 1985 . . . . £15/£5

Short Stories and Novelettes

The Prussian Officer and Other Stories, Duckworth (London), 1914 (first issue, blue cloth stamped in gold with 20 pages of ads) £350
ditto, Duckworth (London), 1914 (second issue, light blue cloth stamped in dark blue with 16 pages of ads) . £200
ditto, Huebsch (New York), 1916 . . . . .£125
England, My England, Seltzer (New York), 1922 . £250/£75
ditto, Secker (London), 1924 . . . . £250/£75
The Ladybird, The Fox, The Captain's Doll, Secker (London), 1923 . . . . £250/£45
ditto, as *The Captain's Doll*, Seltzer (New York), 1923 .
. . . . £250/£45
St Mawr, Secker (London), 1925 (contents say text begins on p.9). . . . . £175/£65
ditto, Secker (London), 1925 (contents corrected to say text begins on p.7) . . . . £150/£35
ditto, Knopf (New York), 1925 . . . . £150/£35
Glad Ghosts, Ernest Benn (London), 1926 (500 copies; wraps) £75
Sun, E. Archer (London), 1926 (100 copies, expurgated) .
. . . .£400
ditto, Black Sun Press (Paris), 1928 (15 signed copies in glassine d/w and gold slipcase; wraps) . .£2,500/£2,000
ditto, Black Sun Press (Paris), 1928 (150 copies in glassine d/w and gold slipcase; wraps) . . . . £1,000/£500

Rawdon's Roof, Mathews and Marrot (London), 1928 (530 signed, numbered copies) . . . . £325/£225
The Woman Who Rode Away, Secker (London), 1928 .
. . . . £125/£30
ditto, Knopf (New York), 1928 . . . . £125/£30
The Escaped Cock, Black Sun Press (Paris), 1929 (450 numbered copies; wraps, with glassine d/w and slipcase) .
. . . . £450/£200
ditto, Black Sun Press (Paris), 1929 (50 signed copies on Japanese vellum; wraps, with glassine d/w and slipcase) .
. . . . £1,250/£750
ditto, as *The Man Who Died*, Secker (London), 1931 (2,000 copies) . . . . . . £175/£40
ditto, as *The Man Who Died*, Knopf (New York), 1931 .
. . . . £175/£40
The Virgin and the Gypsy, Orioli (Florence), 1930 (810 copies, d/w and slipcase) . . . £200/£100
ditto, Secker (London), 1930 . . . . £100/£25
ditto, Knopf (New York), 1930 . . . . £100/£25
Love Among the Haystacks, Nonesuch Press (London), 1930 (1,600 numbered copies) . . . . £125/£65
ditto, Secker (London), 1930 . . . . £75/£15
ditto, Haldeman Julius (Girard, KS), 1941 (stapled wraps) .
. . . . £25
The Lovely Lady, Secker (London), 1932 [1933] . £75/£25
ditto, Viking (New York), 1933 . . . . £45/£20
The Tales of D.H.Lawrence, Secker (London), 1934 .
. . . . £35/£10
A Modern Lover, Secker (London), 1934. . . £65/£15
ditto, Viking (New York), 1934 . . . . £45/£15

Poetry
Love Poems and Others, Duckworth (London), 1913 (first issue, with 'i' in line 16 on p. xlv) £250
ditto, Mitchell Kennerley (New York), 1913 . . £75
Amores, Duckworth (London), 1916 (first issue with 16pps of ads) £250
ditto, Duckworth (London), 1916 (second issue without ads)
. . . . £150
ditto, Huebsch (New York), 1916 . . . . £50
Look! We Have Come Through!, Chatto & Windus (London), 1917 . . . . £165
ditto, Huebsch (New York), 1918 . . . . £165
New Poems, Secker (London), 1918 (wraps) . . £100
ditto, Huebsch (New York), 1920 (boards) . . £50
Bay, A Book of Poems, Beaumont (London), 1919 . £200
ditto, Beaumont (London), 1919 (30 signed copies) £1,450
Tortoises, Seltzer (New York), 1921 (glassine d/w) .
. . . . £150/£100
Birds, Beasts and Flowers, Seltzer (New York), 1923 . .
. . . . £250/£65
ditto, Secker (London), 1923 . . . . £200/£60
ditto, Cresset Press (London), 1923 (500 copies) . £250
The Collected Poems of D.H. Lawrence, Secker (London), 1928 (2 vols) . . . . . . £250/£65
ditto, Secker (London), 1928 (100 signed 2 vol sets, d/w and slipcase) . . . . . £1,750/£1,250
ditto, Jonathan Cape & Harrison Smith (New York) 1929 .
. . . . £250/£65
Pansies, Secker (London), 1929 . . . . £100/£35
ditto, Secker (London), 1929 (250 signed copies) £450/£350
ditto, Stephenson (London), 1929 (10 signed copies bound in vellum, slipcase) £3,000

ditto, Stephenson (London), 1929 (50 signed copies bound in full leather, glassine d/w and slipcase) . . . £2,000
ditto, Stephenson (London), 1929 (500 signed copies; wraps, glassine d/w and slipcase) . . . . £500/£450
ditto, privately printed [for Frieda Lawrence] (New York), 1954 (750 numbered copies, glassine d/w) . . £45/£30
ditto, privately printed [for Frieda Lawrence] (New York), 1954 (250 numbered copies, signed by Frieda Lawrence, glassine d/w) . . . . . . £85/£65
Nettles, Faber & Faber (London), 1930 (tissue d/w) . .
. . . . £125/£75
ditto, Faber & Faber (London), 1930 (wraps) . . £35
The Triumph of the Machine, Faber (London), [1930] (wraps) £35
ditto, Faber (London), [1930] (400 numbered large paper copies) £150
Last Poems, G. Orioli (Florence), 1932 (750 copies with d/w and slipcase) . . . . . £200/£75
ditto, Secker (London), 1933 . . . . £100/£25
The Ship of Death, Secker (London), 1933 . £125/£60
Poems, Heinemann (London), 1939 (2 vols) . £35/£10
Fire and Other Poems, Book Club of California (San Francisco, CA), 1940 (100 copies) . . £200/£125
The Complete Poems of D.H. Lawrence, Heinemann (London), 1957 (3 vols) . . . . . £50/£25
ditto, Viking (New York), 1964 (2 vols, slipcase) . £40/£20

Plays
The Widowing of Mrs Holroyd, Mitchell Kennerley (New York), 1914 (500 copies) £75
ditto, Duckworth (London), 1914 . . . . £45
Touch and Go, Daniel (London), 1920 . . £175/£35
ditto, Seltzer (New York), 1920 . . . . £150/£35
David, Daniel (London), 1926 . . . . £100/£25
ditto, Knopf (New York), 1926 . . . . £100/£25
The Plays of D.H. Lawrence, Secker (London), 1933 . .
. . . . £75/£15
A Collier's Friday Night, Secker (London), 1934 . £45/£10
The Complete Plays of D.H. Lawrence, Heinemann (London), 1965 . . . . £35/£10
ditto, Viking (New York), 1966 . . . . £35/£10

Miscellaneous
Twilight in Italy, Duckworth (London), 1916 . . £150
ditto, Huebsch (New York), 1916 . . . . £75
Movements in European History, O.U.P. (Oxford, UK), 1921 (pseud 'Lawrence H. Davison') . . £500/£165
Sea and Sardinia, Seltzer (New York), 1921 . £650/£150
ditto, Secker (London), 1923 . . . . £650/£150
Psychoanalysis and the Unconscious, Seltzer (New York), 1921 . . . . £250/£75
ditto, Secker (London), 1923 . . . . £125/£40
Fantasia of the Unconscious, Seltzer (New York), 1922 .
. . . . £250/£65
ditto, Secker (London), 1923 . . . . £125/£35
Studies in Classic American Literature, Seltzer (New York), 1923 . . . . £250/£65
ditto, Secker (London), 1924 . . . . £150/£45
Reflections on the Death of a Porcupine and Further Essays, Centaur Press (Philadelphia), 1925 (925 copies, slipcase). . . . . £85/£50
Mornings in Mexico, Secker (London), 1927 . £200/£50
ditto, Knopf (New York), 1927 . . . . £200/£50

The Paintings of D.H. Lawrence, The Mandrake Press (London), 1929 (500 copies, slipcase) . . £400/£200

ditto, The Mandrake Press (London), 1929 (10 signed copies on Japan paper) £5,000

Pornography and Obscenity, Faber (London), 1929 (wraps) £25

ditto, Faber (London), 1929 (cloth) £75

ditto, Knopf (New York), 1930 . . . £75/£45

The Story of Doctor Manente, by A.F. Grazzini, Orioli (Florence), 1929 (2 signed copies on blue paper, translated and with an Introduction by Lawrence) . . £1,500

ditto, G. Orioli (Florence), 1929 (200 signed copies) . £500

ditto, G. Orioli (Florence), 1929 (1,000 unsigned, numbered copies) . . . . £100/£75

Assorted Articles, Secker (London), 1930 . . £65/£20

ditto, Knopf (New York), 1930 . . . . £65/£20

Apropos of Lady Chatterly's Lover, Mandrake Press (London), 1930 . . . . £40/£15

Apocalypse, Orioli (Florence), 1931 (750 numbered copies) . . . . £150/£75

ditto, Secker (London), 1932 . . . . £30/£10

ditto, Viking (New York), 1932 . . . . £25/£10

The Letters of D.H. Lawrence, Heinemann (London), 1932 (edited by Aldous Huxley) . . . . £65/£30

ditto, Heinemann (London), 1932 (525 numbered parchment bound copies; glassine d/w; slipcase) . . £150/£75

ditto, Viking (New York), 1932 . . . . £65/£30

Etruscan Places, Secker (London), 1932 . . £150/£40

Pornography and So On, Faber (London), 1936 . £75/£25

Phoenix: The Posthumous Papers of D.H. Lawrence, Heinemann (London), 1936 . . . . £35/£15

ditto, Viking (New York), 1936 . . . . £35/£15

The Manuscripts of D.H. Lawrence, Los Angeles Public Library (Los Angeles, CA), 1937 (750 copies; wraps) £25

D.H. Lawrence's Letters to Bertrand Russell, Gotham Book Mart (New York), 1948 (950 copies) . . £50/£20

Sex, Literature and Censorship, Twayne (New York), 1953 . . . . £20/£5

ditto, Heinemann (London), 1955 . . . £20/£5

The Collected Letters of D.H. Lawrence, Heinemann (London), 1962 (2 vols) . . . . £40/£15

ditto, Viking (New York), 1962 (2 vols) . . £30/£10

Phoenix II: Uncollected, Unpublished, and Other Prose Work of D.H. Lawrence, Heinemann (London), 1968 . . . . £30/£10

ditto, Viking (New York), 1968 . . . . £30/£10

Letters to Martin Secker, privately printed, 1970 (500 numbered copies) . . . . . . £45/£15

Letters to Thomas & Adele Seltzer, Black Sparrow Press (Santa Barbara, CA), 1976 (1,000 copies; wraps) . £5

ditto, Black Sparrow Press (Santa Barbara, CA), 1976 (126 numbered copies with an unpublished photograph of Lawrence, acetate d/w) . . . . . £40/£30

ditto, Black Sparrow Press (Santa Barbara, CA), 1976 (26 lettered copies with an unpublished photograph of Lawrence, acetate d/w) . . . . . £125/£100

The Letters of D.H. Lawrence, Volume I: 1901-1913, C.U.P. (Cambridge, UK), 1979 . . . £25/£10

ditto, C.U.P. (New York), 1979 . . . . £25/£10

The Letters of D.H. Lawrence, Volume I: 1913-1916, C.U.P. (Cambridge, UK), 1981 . . . £25/£10

The Letters of D.H. Lawrence, Volume III: 1916-1921, C.U.P. (Cambridge, UK), 1984 . . . £25/£10

The Letters of D.H. Lawrence, Volume IV: 1921-1924, C.U.P. (Cambridge, UK), 1987 . . . £25/£10

The Letters of D.H. Lawrence, Volume V: 1924-1927, C.U.P. (Cambridge, UK), 1989 . . . £25/£10

The Letters of D.H. Lawrence, Volume VI: 1927-1928, C.U.P. (Cambridge, UK), 1991 . . . £25/£10

The Letters of D.H. Lawrence, Volume VII: 1928-1930, C.U.P. (Cambridge, UK), 1993 . . . £25/£10

The Letters of D.H. Lawrence, Volume VIII: Previously Uncollected Letters and General Index, C.U.P. (Cambridge, UK), 2001 . . . . . £25/£10

The Letters of D.H. Lawrence & Amy Lowell, Black Sparrow Press (Santa Barbara, CA), 1985 (500 copies; glassine d/w). . . . . £10/£5

ditto, Black Sparrow Press (Santa Barbara, CA), 1985 (100 copies signed by the editors; glassine d/w) . £15/£10

ditto, Black Sparrow Press (Santa Barbara, CA), 1985 (26 lettered copies signed by the editors; glassine d/w) £35/£20

T.E. LAWRENCE
(b.1888 d.1935)

A soldier and author, Thomas Edward Lawrence is popularly known as 'Lawrence of Arabia', after his account of the First World War Arab Revolt in *The Seven Pillars of Wisdom*. Many Arabs consider him a folk hero for supporting their fight for freedom from Ottoman and European rule, and he is often portrayed in Britain as a war hero, although in some circles he is considered a shameless self-promoter.

The Seven Pillars of Wisdom, Oxford Edition (Oxford, UK), 1922 (8 copies) £32,500

ditto, first proof copy, (London), 1924 (proof of the eight introductory chapters). £4,000

ditto, second proof, (London), 1925 (100 proof copies of seven chapters for subscribers). . . . £3,500

ditto, Cranwell, Subscribers' Edition (London), 1926 (169 copies) £32,500

ditto, Cranwell, Subscribers' Edition (London), 1926 (32 incomplete copies) £16,000

ditto, Doubleday Doran (New York), 1926 (copyright edition, 22 copies) £12,000

ditto, Cape (London), 1935 (750 copies, d/w and slipcase) . . . . £1,500/£1,000

ditto, Cape (London), 1935 . . . . . £250/£25

ditto, Cape (London), 1935 (60 privately issued copies) £650

ditto, Doubleday Doran (New York), 1935 . £100/£25

ditto, Doubleday Doran (New York), 1935 (750 copies, d/w and slipcase). . . . . . . £450/£300

Revolt in the Desert, Cape (London), 1927 . £150/£30

ditto, Cape (London), 1927 (315 large paper copies) . . . . £1,500/£1,000

ditto, Doubleday Doran (New York), 1927 . £150/£25

ditto, Doubleday Doran (New York), 1927 (250 large paper copies, slipcase) . . . . . £1,000/£650

The Mint, Doubleday Doran (New York), 1936 (pseud '352087 A/C Ross', U.S. copyright edition, 50 copies) £16,000

ditto, Cape (London), 1955 (first unexpurgated U.K. edition, 2,000 copies, no d/w, in slipcase) . . . . £85/£60

ditto, Cape (London), 1955 (first U.K. trade edition, expurgated) . . . . £25/£10
ditto, Doubleday Doran (New York), 1955 (1,000 numbered copies, slipcase) . . . . . £85/£60
ditto, Doubleday Doran (New York), 1957. . . £15/£5
Crusader Castles, Golden Cockerel Press (Waltham St Lawrence, Berks), 1936 (2 vols, 1000 copies, no d/w or slipcase). £1,000
ditto, **The Thesis**, Golden Cockerel Press (Waltham St Lawrence, Berks), 1936 (75 unnumbered copies) . £450
ditto, **The Letters**, Golden Cockerel Press (Waltham St Lawrence, Berks), 1936 (35 unnumbered copies) . £450
ditto, Doubleday Doran (New York), 1937 (56 copyright copies; pbk) £1,000
The Diary of T.E. Lawrence MCMXI, Corvinus Press (London), 1937 (30 copies on 'Canute' paper) . £3,500
ditto, Corvinus Press (London), 1937 (40 copies on 'Medway' paper). £2,500
ditto, Corvinus Press (London), 1937 (130 copies on parchment-style paper) £1,750
ditto, Doubleday Doran (New York), 1937 (copyright edition, 50 copies) £2,500
An Essay on Flecker, Corvinus Press (London), 1937 (26 copies, slipcase) . . . . .£2,500/£2,000
ditto, Corvinus Press (London), 1937 (4 copies, vellum) .
. . . . £3,500
ditto, Corvinus Press (London), 1937 (2 copies, leather) .
. . . . £5,000
ditto, Doubleday Doran (New York), 1937 (copyright edition of approx 56 copies; pbk) £1,000
Two Arabic Folk Tales, Corvinus Press (London), 1937 (31 copies) £2,500
Secret Despatches from Arabia, Golden Cockerel Press (Waltham St Lawrence, Berks), 1939 (nos. 1-30, printed on Arnold handmade paper, bound in white pigskin, with supplement) £2,000
ditto, Golden Cockerel Press (Waltham St Lawrence, Berks), 1939 (nos. 31-1,000, printed on Arnold handmade paper, bound in quarter Niger, without supplement; slipcase) .
. . . . £400/£350
Men in Print, Golden Cockerel Press (Waltham St Lawrence, Berks), 1940 (nos. 1-30, bound in full Niger, with supplement; slipcase). . . .£1,750/£1,500
ditto, Golden Cockerel Press (Waltham St Lawrence, Berks), 1940 (nos. 31-500; slipcase) . . . £350/£250
The Essential T.E. Lawrence, Cape (London), 1951 £35/£10
ditto, Dutton (New York), 1951. . . . . £35/£10
Evolution of a Revolt, Early Postwar Writings of T.E. Lawrence, The Pennsylvania State Univ Press (University Park, PA), 1968 . . . . £35/£15

Translations by 'J.H. Ross'
The Forest Giant, by Adrien Le Corbeau, Cape (London), 1924 . . . . £75/£25
ditto, Harper & Bros. (New York), 1924 (first issue with translator incorrectly given as 'L.H. Ross') . £75/£25

Translations by 'T.E. Shaw'
The Odyssey of Homer, Bruce Rogers (London), 1932 (530 copies, slipcase) . . . . . £1,500/£1,000
ditto, O.U.P. (New York), 1932 . . . . .£125/£45
ditto, O.U.P. (New York), 1932 (32 copies) . . £3,000
ditto, O.U.P. (Oxford, UK), 1935 . . . .£125/£45

Letters
Letters from T.E. Shaw to Bruce Rogers, privately printed by Bruce Rogers [New York], 1933 (200 copies, no d/w) .
. . . .£400
More Letters from T.E. Shaw to Bruce Rogers, privately printed by Bruce Rogers [New York], 1936 (300 copies, no d/w) £300
A Letter from T.E. Lawrence to His Mother, Corvinus Press (London), 1936 (30 copies) £1,250
Letter from T.E. Shaw to Viscount Carlow, Corvinus Press (London), 1936 (17 copies) £1,250
The Letters of T.E. Lawrence, Cape (London), 1938 (1st state with 'Baltic' for 'Balkan' on p.182) . . £40/£15
ditto, Doubleday Doran (New York), 1939 . £25/£10
ditto, Dent (London), 1988 (new edition) . . £20/£5
T.E. Lawrence To His Biographers, Faber (London), 1938 (500 copies signed by Robert Graves and Liddell Hart, 2 vols with d/ws, in slipcase) . . . . £250/£125
ditto, Doubleday Doran (New York), 1938 (500 copies signed by Graves and Hart, 2 vols with d/ws, in slipcase) .
. . . . £250/£125
Eight Letters from T.E.L., privately printed [Corvinus Press], 1939 (50 copies) £1,000
Selected Letters of T.E. Lawrence, World Books (London), 1941 . . . . £10/£5
Shaw-Ede: T.E. Lawrence's letters to H.S. Ede, 1927-35, Golden Cockerel Press (Waltham St Lawrence, Berks), 1942 (nos. 1-130, bound in full morocco, with facsimile reproductions of 5 of the letters) . . . £1,000
ditto, Golden Cockerel Press (Waltham St Lawrence, Berks), 1942 (nos. 31-500) £275
The Home Letters of T.E. Lawrence and His Brothers, Blackwell (Oxford), 1954 . . . . .£100/£35
ditto, Macmillan (New York), 1954 . . . £75/£25
From a Letter of T.E. Lawrence, Officina Bodoni (Verona, Italy), 1959 (75 copies) £250
Fifty Letters 1920-1935, Humanities Research Centre at the Univ of Texas (Austin, TX), 1962 (2000 copies, pbk) £25
T.E.L., Five Hitherto Unpublished Letters, privately printed, 1975 (30 copies; wraps) £250
Letters to E.T. Leeds, Whittington Press (Andoversford, Gloucestershire), 1988 (650 numbered copies, slipcase) .
. . . . £125/£100
ditto, Whittington Press (Andoversford, Gloucestershire), 1988 (80 lettered copies with additional proofs of illustrations; slipcase). . . . . £500/£400
ditto, Whittington Press (Andoversford, Gloucestershire), 1988 (20 copies with additional proofs of illustrations and a suite of 12 photographs taken by Lawrence at the excavation of Carchemish; slipcase) . .£1,500/£1,250

Edited by Lawrence
Minorities, Cape (London), 1971 . . . . £40/£15
ditto, Cape (London), 1971 (125 copies signed by C. Day-Lewis) £175
ditto, Doubleday (New York), 1972 . . . . £35/£15

EDWARD LEAR

(b.1812 d.1888)

Popularly known as a nonsense poet, Lear was also an accomplished artist and travel-writer. His first published work featured non-comic illustrations and was issued when he was only 19. In 1846 he published *A Book of Nonsense*, a popular volume of limericks, although it was not until 1867 that his most famous piece of nonsense, *The Owl and the Pussycat*, appeared.

Nonsense Books

A Book of Nonsense, Thomas Maclean (London), 1846 (pseud 'Derry Down Derry', 2 vols, 175 copies; wraps) .
.   .   .   .   £50,000
ditto, Thomas Maclean (London), 1855 (no pseud, 2 vols; wraps) £8,000
ditto, Routledge (London), 1861 (enlarged edition)   . £650
Nonsense Songs, Stories, Botany and Alphabets, Robert John Bush (London), 1871[1870] £750
More Nonsense, Pictures, Rhymes, Botany, Robert John Bush (London), 1872 [1874] £650
Lear's Book of Nonsense, Warne (London), [c.1875] (Juvenile Drolleries series) £125
Laughable Lyrics, A Fourth Book of Nonsense Poems, Songs, Botany, Music, etc., Robert John Bush (London), 1877 [1876] £650
The Jumblies and Other Nonsense Poems, Songs, Botany, Music, Warne (London), 1877 [1876]   .   .   . £200
Nonsense Drolleries, Warne (London), 1889   . £150
A Nonsense Birthday Book, Warne (London), [1894] . £125
Nonsense Songs and Stories, Warne (London), 1895 . £100
Nonsense Songs and Laughable Lyrics, Little, Brown (Boston), 1899   .   .   .   . £100
ditto, Peter Pauper Press (Mt. Vernon, NY.), 1935 (650 copies) £75
The Pelican Chorus and Other Nonsense Verses, Warne (London), 1900   .   .   .   . £125
Queery Leary Nonsense, Mills & Boon (London), 1911 £65
Callico Pie, Warne (London), [1924].   .   . £75/£25
The Owl and the Pussy Cat, Warne (London), [1924] .   .
.   .   .   . £75/£35
Facsimile of A Nonsense Alphabet, Warne (London), 1926 (1,000 numbered copies) £50
The Quangle Wangle's Hat, Hugh Sharp (London), 1933 (50 copies) £250
The Pobble, Hugh Sharpe (London), 1934 (50 copies) .   .
.   .   .   . £250
Edward Lear's Nonsense Songs, Chatto & Windus (London), 1938   .   .   .   .   .   £35/£15
A Book of Lear, Penguin (Harmondsworth, Middlesex), 1939 (wraps with d/w)   .   .   .   . £10/£5
Edward Lear's Nonsense Omnibus, Odhams (London), 1943   .   .   .   . £25/£10
The Complete Nonsense of Edward Lear, Faber (London), 1947   .   .   .   . £25/£10
Edward Lear's Nonsense Alphabet, Collins (London), [1949]   .   .   .   . £25/£15
A Nonsense Alphabet, H.M.S.O. (London), 1952 (wraps) .
.   .   .   .   £10
Teapots and Quails and Other Nonsense, Murray (London), 1953   .   .   .   . £35/£15
ditto, Harvard Univ Press (Cambridge, MA), 1953   £25/£10

Margaret Rutherford Says, How Pleasant to Know Mr Lear!, Icon (London), 1964 (pbk) £25
ABC, Constable (London), 1965.   .   .   .   £15/£5
A Book of Nonsense, Peter Owen (London), 1972 (illustrated by Mervyn Peake)   .   .   .   . £25/£10
Bosh and Nonsense, Allen Lane (London), 1982   . £15/£5

Natural History

Illustrations of the Family Psittacide, or Parrots, R. Ackerman & E. Lear (London), 1832 (42 hand-coloured plates, in original wraps) £75,000
ditto, R. Ackerman & E. Lear (London), 1832 (rebound) .
.   .   .   . £40,000
Gleanings from The Menagerie and Aviary at Knowsley Hall, privately printed (Knowsley, Lancashire), 1846. .
.   .   .   . £18,000
Tortoises, Terrapins and Turtles Drawn from Life, Henry Sotheran & Joseph Baer (London), 1872 (with James de Carle Sowerby) £4,000
The Lear Coloured Bird Book for Children, Mills and Boon (London), [1912]. £60
Edward Lear's Parrots, Duckworth (London), 1949 (12 plates)   .   .   .   . £75/£30
The Birds of Edward Lear, A Selection, Ariel Press (London), 1975 (1000 copies, 12 plates)   . £125/£75

Travel

Views in Rome and Its Environs, Thomas Maclean (London), 1841 (25 plates) £4,000
Illustrated Excursions in Italy, Thomas Maclean (London), 1846 (first series, 30 plates)   .   .   .   £2,000
ditto, Thomas Maclean (London), 1846 (second series, 25 plates) £2,000
Journals of a Landscape Painter in Albania, Richard Bentley (London), 1851 (21 plates).   .   .   £1,000
Journals of a Landscape Painter in Southern Calabria, Richard Bentley (London), 1852 (2 maps, 20 plates) .   .
.   .   .   . £1,000
Views in the Seven Ionian Islands, E. Lear (London), 1863 (20 plates) £5,000
ditto, Hugh Broadbent (Oldham, Lancashire), 1979 (facsimile reprint of 1,000 numbered copies, 20 plates)
.   .   .   . £125/£75
Journals of a Landscape Painter in Corsica, Robert John Bush (London), 1870 (41 plates) £950
Lear in Sicily, Duckworth (London), 1938   .   . £35/£15
Edward Lear's Journals, A Selection, Barker (London), 1952 (4 plates)   .   .   .   .   .   . £45/£20
Edward Lear's Indian Journal, Jarrolds (London), 1953 (9 plates)   .   .   .   . £45/£20
Edward Lear in Southern Italy, Kimber (London), 1964 (20 plates)   .   .   .   . £50/£30
Edward Lear in Greece, Kimber (London), 1965 (20 plates)
.   .   .   . £50/£30
Lear's Corfu, Corfu Travel (Corfu), 1965 (8 illustrations) .
.   .   .   . £25/£10
Edward Lear in Corsica, Kimber (London), 1966 . £50/£30

Letters

The Letters of Edward Lear, T. Fisher Unwin (London), 1907 (20 plates) £50
Letters ... to Chichester Fortescue Lord Carlingford, and Frances Countess Waldegrave, Duffield (New York), [1908] £45

The Later Letters of Edward Lear, T. Fisher Unwin (London), 1911 . . . . £25

A Letter from Edward Lear to George William Curtis, Harvard Printing Office (Cambridge, MA), 1947 (660 copies; wraps) £5

Selected Letters, Clarendon Press (Oxford, UK), 1988 . . . . £25/£10

Others

Three Poems by Tennyson Illustrated by Edward Lear, Bousson, Valadon & Co., Scribner's & Welford (London), 1889 (100 copies signed by Tennyson, 24 illustrations by Lear) £1,500

Edward Lear on My Shelves, privately printed by William Osgood Field (Boston), 1933 . . . . . . £500

JOHN LE CARRÉ
(b.1931)

Le Carré attended the Universities of Berne and Oxford and taught at Eton before spending five years in the British Foreign Service. His thrillers have examined the grey, dubious world of Cold War spying, and as the years have passed his 'fiction' is seen to have been more and more perceptive. It was his third book, *The Spy Who Came In from the Cold*, that secured him a worldwide reputation.

'George Smiley' Novels

Call for the Dead, Gollancz (London), 1961 . £5,000/£350

ditto, Walker (New York), 1962 . . . . . £750/£60

ditto, as *The Deadly Affair*, Signet (New York), 1962 (pbk) £5

ditto, as *The Deadly Affair*, Penguin (London), 1966 (pbk) £5

A Murder of Quality, Gollancz (London), 1962 £3,250/£250

ditto, Walker (New York), 1963 . . . . £500/£100

The Spy Who Came in from the Cold, Gollancz (London), 1963 . . . . £750/£50

ditto, Coward-McCann (New York), 1963 . £100/£20

The Looking-Glass War, Heinemann (London), 1965 . . . . £45/£10

ditto, as *The Looking Glass War*, Coward-McCann (New York), 1965 . . . . £25/£5

Tinker, Tailor, Soldier, Spy, Hodder & Stoughton (London), 1974 . . . . £25/£5

ditto, as *Tinker Taylor Soldier Spy*, Knopf (New York), 1974 . . . . £15/£5

The Honourable Schoolboy, Franklin Library (Franklin Centre, PA), 1977 (signed, limited edition) . . . £30

ditto, Knopf (New York), 1977 . . . . . £20/£5

ditto, Hodder & Stoughton (London), 1977 . £25/£5

Smiley's People, Franklin Library (Franklin Centre, PA), 1979 (signed, limited edition) £40

ditto, Hodder & Stoughton (London), 1980 . £35/£5

ditto, Knopf (New York), 1980 . . . . £20/£5

ditto, Knopf (New York), 1980 (signed sheet tipped-in) . . . . £40/£20

The Secret Pilgrim, Hodder & Stoughton (London), 1991 . . . . £15/£5

ditto, Knopf (New York), 1991 . . . . . £15/£5

ditto, Knopf (New York), 1991 (signed sheet tipped-in) . . . . £40/£20

Other Novels

A Small Town in Germany, Heinemann (London), 1968 . . . . £50/£10

ditto, Coward-McCann (New York), 1968 (500 signed copies, tissue d/w) . . . . £150/£65

ditto, Coward-McCann (New York), 1968 . . £45/£5

The Naive and Sentimental Lover, Hodder & Stoughton (London), 1971 . . . . £30/£5

ditto, Knopf (New York), 1971 . . . . £20/£5

The Little Drummer Girl, Knopf (New York), 1983 £15/£5

ditto, Knopf (New York), 1983 (signed sheet tipped-in) . . . . £65/£40

ditto, Book-of-the-Month Club (New York), 1983 (1,048 signed copies, slipcase) . . . . . £50/£35

ditto, Hodder & Stoughton (London), 1983 . £15/£5

ditto, Pan (London), 1987 (739 signed copies; pbk) . £45

A Perfect Spy, Hodder & Stoughton (London), 1986 £15/£5

ditto, London Limited Editions (London)/Hodder & Stoughton (London), 1986 (250 signed copies, glassine d/w) . . . . £125/£100

ditto, Knopf (New York), 1986 . . . . £15/£5

ditto, Knopf (New York), 1986 (signed sheet tipped-in) . . . . £50/£30

The Russia House, Knopf (New York), 1989 . . £15/£5

ditto, Knopf (New York), 1989 (signed sheet tipped-in) . . . . £60/£30

ditto, Hodder & Stoughton (London), 1989 . £15/£5

ditto, London Limited Editions (London), 1989 (250 signed copies, glassine d/w) . . . . . £125/£75

The Night Manager, Hodder & Stoughton (London), 1993 . . . . £15/£5

ditto, Knopf (New York), 1993 . . . . £15/£5

ditto, Knopf (New York), 1993 (signed sheet tipped-in) . . . . £50/£25

Our Game, Hodder & Stoughton (London), 1995 . £65/£15

ditto, Knopf (New York), 1995 . . . . £10/£5

ditto, Franklin Library (Franklin Centre, PA), 1995 (signed, limited edition) £45

The Tailor of Panama, Hodder & Stoughton (London), 1996 . . . . £10/£5

ditto, Knopf (New York), 1996 . . . . £10/£5

Single and Single, Hodder & Stoughton (London), 1999 . . . . £10/£5

ditto, Scribner's (New York), 1999 . . . £10/£5

ditto, Franklin Library (Franklin Centre, PA), 1999 (signed, limited edition) £45

The Constant Gardener, Hodder & Stoughton (London), 2001 . . . . £10/£5

ditto, Scribner's (New York), 2001 . . . £10/£5

Absolute Friends, Hodder & Stoughton (London), 2003 . . . . £10/£5

ditto, Little, Brown (Boston), 2003 . . . £10/£5

The Mission Song, Hodder & Stoughton (London), 2006 . . . . £10/£5

ditto, Hodder & Stoughton/Waterstones (London), 2006 (1,500 signed copies with le Carré map; slipcase) £45/£25

ditto, Little, Brown (Boston), 2003 . . . £10/£5

A Most Wanted Man, Hodder & Stoughton (London), 2008 . . . . £10/£5

ditto, Hodder & Stoughton (London), 2008 (500 signed, numbered copies; slipcase) . . . . . £100/£65

ditto, Scribners (Boston), 2003 . . . . £10/£5

Collections

The Incongruous Spy, Walker (New York), 1962 (book club
    edition) .   .   .   . £50/£10
ditto, Walker (New York), 1964 .   .   .   . £45/£10
ditto, as *The Le Carré Omnibus*, Gollancz, 1964 . £125/£25
The Quest for Karla, Hodder & Stoughton (London), 1982 .
    .   .   .   . £25/£5
ditto, Knopf (New York), 1982 .   .   .   . £15/£5

Others

The Clandestine Muse, Seluzicki (Portland, OR), 1986 (250
    signed copies; stitched wraps) £175
Nervous Times: An Address Given at the Savoy Hotel...,
    Anglo-Israel Association (London), 1998 (250 signed,
    numbered copies) £80

HARPER LEE
(b.1926)

Lee's one and only novel, *To Kill a Mockingbird*, is a landmark of 20th century American literature and one of the
best-selling novels of all time. She received the Pulitzer
Prize on the strength of the book, and in 1999 it was voted
Best Novel of the Century in a poll conducted by the
Library Journal. Truman Capote, a lifelong friend and
childhood neighbour, was allegedly the inspiration for the
main protagonist of the book.

Novel

To Kill a Mockingbird, Lippincott (Philadelphia), 1960 (first
    issue d/w with author photo by Capote) .   £7,000/£1,500
ditto, Heinemann (London), 1963   .   .   . £750/£75

Other

Romance and High Adventure, Cather & Brown (Birming-
    ham, AL), 1993 (100 signed copies; stapled wraps) £1,000

LAURIE LEE
(b.1914 d.1997)

Lee was primarily a poet, but is best known for his volumes
of autobiography. *Cider with Rosie* is a nostalgic memoir
of his Gloucestershire childhood, and *As I Walked Out One
Midsummer Morning* deals with his leaving home for
London and his first visit to Spain in 1934. *A Moment of
War* charts his return to Spain in December 1937 to join the
Republican forces in the Spanish Civil War.

Autobiography

Cider with Rosie, Hogarth Press (London), 1959 . £100/£15
ditto, as *The Edge of Day*, Morrow (New York), 1960 .   .
    .   .   .   . £40/£10
As I Walked Out One Midsummer Morning, Deutsch
    (London), 1969 .   .   .   .   .   . £20/£5
ditto, Atheneum (New York), 1969 .   .   . £10/£5
A Moment of War, Viking (London), 1991 .   . £10/£5
ditto, New Press (New York), 1991 .   .   . £10/£5
Red Sky at Sunrise, Viking (London), 1992 (collects above
    autobiographical works) .   .   .   .   . £10/£5

Poetry

The Sun My Monument, Hogarth Press (London), 1944   .
    .   .   .   . £75/£25
ditto, Doubleday (New York), 1947 .   .   . £40/£15
The Bloom of Candles, Lehmann (London), 1947 . £40/£15
New Poems, 1954, Joseph (London), 1954 .   . £25/£10
My Many-Coated Man, Deutsch (London), 1955 . £25/£10
ditto, Coward-McCann (New York), 1957 .   . £15/£5
Pocket Poets, Studio Vista (London), 1960 .   .   . £5
15 Poems for William Shakespeare, Trustees and Guardians
    of Shakespeare's Birthplace (Stratford-upon-Avon), 1964
    (sewn wraps, with contributions from Laurie Lee, Derek
    Walcott, Thomas Kinsella, Hugh MacDiarmid, Edmund
    Blunden, Thom Gunn, Roy Fuller, W.D.Snodgrass and
    others) £10
ditto, Trustees and Guardians of Shakespeare's Birthplace
    (Stratford-upon-Avon), 1964 (100 numbered copies;
    papercovered boards with gold gilt embossed Shakespeare
    on front cover) £50
Pergamon Poets 10, Pergamon Press (Oxford, UK), 1970
    (wraps) £5
Selected Poems, Deutsch (London), 1983 (pbk) .   . £5
Fish and Water, Friends of the Cheltenham Festival
    (Cheltenham), [1991] (broadsheet) £15
Boy in Ice, Turret Bookshop (London), [1991] (broadsheet)
    .   .   .   . £40

Plays

Peasant's Priest, Friends of Canterbury Cathedral, H.J.
    Goulden Ltd (Canterbury, Kent), 1947 (wraps) .   £45
The Voyage of Magellan, Lehmann (London), 1948   .   .
    .   .   .   . £100/£15

Others

Land at War, H.M.S.O. (London), 1945 (anonymous;
    stapled wraps) £20
We Made a Film in Cyprus, Longmans, Greene (London),
    1947 (with Ralph Keene) .   .   .   .   . £50/£20
Vassos the Goatherd: A Story of Cyprus, Pilot Press
    (London), 1947 .   .   .   . £45/£15
An Obstinate Exile, privately printed (Los Angeles, CA),
    1951 (glassine d/w) .   .   .   .   . £150/£125
A Rose for Winter: Travels in Andalusia, Hogarth Press
    (London), 1955 .   .   .   . £50/£10
ditto, Morrow (New York), 1956 .   .   .   . £30/£10
Man Must Move, Rathbone (London), 1960 .   . £25/£10
ditto, as *The Wonderful World of Transportation*,
    Doubleday (New York), 1961 (with David Lambert) .   .
    .   .   .   . £20/£5
Atlantic Fairway, Cunard Line (London), [1962] (pbk) . £15
The Firstborn, Hogarth Press (London), 1964.   . £25/£10
ditto, Morrow (New York), 1964 .   .   .   . £15/£5
I Can't Stay Long, Deutsch (London), 1975 .   . £15/£5
ditto, Atheneum (New York), 1976 .   .   . £10/£5
Two Women, Deutsch (London), 1983 .   .   . £10/£5

J. SHERIDAN LE FANU
(b.1814 d.1873)

Joseph Sheridan Le Fanu was an Anglo-Irish writer of mystery, supernatural fiction and historical romances. His atmospheric ghost stories are early examples of the kind of modern horror fiction in which virtue does not always triumph and rational explanations for supernatural occurrences are not always forthcoming. He edited the *Dublin University Magazine* from 1861-1869, including many of his own works in serial form.

Novels

The Cock and Anchor, Curry, Longmans, Fraser (Dublin), 1845 (anonymous, 3 vols, boards) £2,000
ditto, as *Morley Court*, Chapman & Hall (London), 1873 (revised edition) £50
The Fortunes of Colonel Torlogh O'Brien, McGlashan, Orr (Dublin), 1847 (anonymous, 10 monthly parts; wraps) £1,000
ditto, McGlashan, Orr (Dublin), 1847 (anonymous, 1 vol) £400
The House by the Church-Yard, Tinsley (London), 1863 (3 vols, royal blue cloth). £4,500
ditto, Tinsley (London), 1863 (3 vols, green cloth). £2,500
ditto, Carleton (New York), 1866 (1 vol) . . . £1,000
Wylder's Hand, Bentley (London), 1864 (3 vols) . £3,250
ditto, Carleton (New York), 1865 (1 vol) £750
Uncle Silas, Bentley (London), 1864 (3 vols) . . £3,000
ditto, Munro (New York), 1878 (1 vol) £500
Guy Deverell, Bentley (London), 1865 (3 vols) . £3,000
ditto, Harper (New York), 1866 (1 vol) £750
All in the Dark, Bentley (London), 1866 (2 vols, claret cloth) £2,000
ditto, Bentley (London), 1866 (presentation copies, 2 vols, white cloth) £3,000
ditto, Harper (New York), 1866 (1 vol; wraps) . . £750
ditto, Harper (New York), 1866 (1 vol; rebound) . . £350
The Tenants of Malory, Tinsley (London), 1867 (3 vols) £2,500
ditto, Harper (New York), 1867 (1 vol) £750
A Lost Name, Bentley (London), 1868 (3 vols) . £2,750
Haunted Lives, Tinsley (London), 1868 (3 vols) . £2,750
The Wyvern Mystery, Tinsley (London), 1869 (3 vols). £3,000
Checkmate, Hurst & Blackett (London), 1871 (3 vols) £3,000
ditto, Evans (Philadelphia), 1871. . . . . . £650
The Rose and The Key, Chapman & Hall (London), 1871 (3 vols) £2,500
Willing to Die, Hurst & Blackett (London), 1873 (3 vols) £2,000

Short Stories and Collected Editions

Ghost Stories and Tales of Mystery, McGlashan, Orr (Dublin), 1851 (anonymous, red pictorial boards) £5,000
ditto, McGlashan, Orr (Dublin), 1851 (anonymous, with gold blocking to front board) £3,000
ditto, McGlashan, Orr (Dublin), 1851 (anonymous, no gold blocking to front board) £750
Chronicles of Golden Friars, Bentley (London), 1871 (3 vols) £3,000
In A Glass Darkly, Bentley (London), 1872 (3 vols) £5,000

ditto, Peter Davis (London), 1929 (illustrated by Edward Ardizzone, first impression, black cloth, with pictorial d/w) . . . . £250/£125
ditto, Peter Davis (London), 1929 (second impression, orange cloth, plain d/w) . . . . £125/£65
The Purcell Papers, Bentley (London), 1880 (3 vols) £3,000
The Watcher, Downey (London), [1894] £600
The Evil Guest, Downey (London), [1895] . . . £500
Madam Crowl's Ghost, Bell (London), 1923 . £400/£100
Green Tea and Other Ghost Stories, Arkham House (Sauk City, WI), 1945 . . . . £125/£40
A Strange Adventure in the Life of Miss Laura Mildmay, Home & Van Thal (London), 1947 . . . . £25/£10
Best Ghost Stories, Dover (New York), 1964 (pbk) . £5
Ghost Stories and Mysteries, Dover (New York), 1975 (pbk) £5
The Purcell Papers, Arkham House (Sauk City, WI), 1975 . . . . £20/£5
Borrhomeo The Astrologer, Tragara Press (Edinburgh), 1985 (150 numbered copies; sewn wraps) . . . £45
Schalken the Painter and Other Ghost Stories, 1838–61, Ash-Tree Press (Ashcroft, British Columbia), 2002 . . . . £20/£10
The Haunted Baronet and Others, Ghost Stories 1861-70, Ash-Tree Press (Ashcroft, British Columbia), 2003 . . . . £25/£10
Mr Justice Harbottle and Others, Ghost Stories 1870-73, Ash-Tree Press (Ashcroft, British Columbia), 2005 . . . . £20/£10

Poetry
The Poems of Joseph Sheridan Le Fanu, Downey (London), 1896 . . . . £225

RICHARD LE GALLIENNE
(b.1866 d.1947)

Richard Le Gallienne is generally disregarded simply because he survived the 1890s, in which decade any self-respecting poet is expected to have died uncomfortably. Le Gallienne is not overlooked by all collectors of the period, however, for he contributed to *The Yellow Book* and was associated with the Rhymer's Club. At the end of the 1890s he moved to the U.S.

Fiction
The Student and the Body-Snatcher and Other Tales, Elkin Mathews (London), 1890 (with R.K. Leather) . . £50
The Book-Bills of Narcissus, Frank Murray (Derby etc, UK), 1891 (250 small paper copies) £45
ditto, Frank Murray (Derby etc, UK), 1891 (100 large paper copies; wraps; slipcase) . . . . . £65/£45
ditto, Putnam (New York), 1895. . . . . . £20
ditto, John Lane (London), 1895 . . . . . £15
Limited Editions: A Prose Fancy; with, Confessio Amantis: A Sonnet, privately printed for Richard Le Gallienne, Elkin Mathews, John Lane, and their Friends (London), Christmas 1893 (700 copies; wraps) £40
Prose Fancies, Elkin Mathews & John Lane (London), 1894 . . . . £15

ditto, Frank Murray (Derby etc, UK), 1894 (100 large paper
copies; wraps) £75
ditto, Putnam (New York), 1894 . . . . . £25
Prose Fancies: Second Series, John Lane (London), 1896 .
. . . . £15
ditto, Stone (Chicago), 1896 . . . . . £15
The Quest of the Golden Girl, John Lane (London), 1896 .
. . . . £75
The Romance of Zion Chapel, John Lane (London), 1898 .
. . . . £20
Young Lives, A Tale, Arrowsmith (Bristol), 1899 . . £20
ditto, John Lane (New York), 1896 . . . . . £20
The Worshipper of the Image, John Lane (London), 1900 .
. . . . £30
Sleeping Beauty and Other Prose Fancies, John Lane
(London), 1900 . . . . £15
The Life Romantic, Including the Love-Letters of the King,
Hurst & Blackett (London), 1901 . . . . . £35
ditto, as **The Love-Letters of the King, or The Life
Romantic**, Little, Brown (Boston), 1901 . . . £35
Romances of Old France, Baker & Taylor Co (New York),
[1905] £20
Little Dinners with The Sphinx and Other Prose Fancies,
Moffat, Yard (New York), 1907 . . . . . £20
ditto, John Lane (London), 1909 . . . . . £20
Painted Shadows, John Lane (London), 1908 [1907] . £30
ditto, Little, Brown (Boston), 1904 . . . . . £30
**The Maker of Rainbows, with Other Fairy-Tales and
Fables**, Harper (New York), 1912 . . . . . £25
The Highway to Happiness, Morningside Press (New York),
1913 . . . . £25
ditto, T. Werner Laurie (London), [1914] . . . £25
Pieces of Eight, Collins (London), 1918 . . . £10
ditto, Doubleday (New York), 1918 . . . . £10
Old Love Stories Retold, John Lane (London), 1924 £45/£10
ditto, Dodd, Mead and Co. (New York), 1925 . . £45/£10
There Was A Ship, Doubleday (New York), 1930 . £35/£10
ditto, as **The Magic Seas**, H. Toulmin (London), 1930 . .
. . . . £35/£10

Poetry

**My Ladies' Sonnets and Other 'Vain and Amatorious'
Verses, with Some of Graver Mood**, privately printed
[Liverpool, UK], 1887 . . . . . . £125
ditto, privately printed [Liverpool. UK], 1887 (50 signed
copies) £250
Volumes in Folio, Elkin Mathews (London), 1889 . £100
ditto, Elkin Mathews (London), 1889 (250 copies) . £200
ditto, Elkin Mathews (London), 1889 (50 large paper copies)
. . . . £200
English Poems, Elkin Mathews & John Lane (London),
1892 . . . . £35
ditto, Elkin Mathews & John Lane (London), 1892 (150
numbered, signed copies) £65
A Fellowship in Song, Elkin Mathews & John Lane
(London), 1893 (with A. Hayes and N. Gale; wraps) . £30
Robert Louis Stevenson: An Elegy and Other Poems, John
Lane (London), 1895 . . . . . . £10
ditto, Copeland & Day (Boston), 1895 (500 copies) . £20
Holly and Mistletoe, Marcus Ward (London), [1895] (with
E. Nesbit and N. Gale; 200 numbered copies) . £200
Rubaiyat of Omar Khayyam: A Paraphrase, Grant Richards
(London), 1897 (card covers) £30

ditto, John Lane (New York), 1897 (1250 signed, numbered
copies) £45
Odes from the Divan of Hafiz, Duckworth (London), 1903 .
. . . . £40
ditto, Privately Printed, Heintzemann Press (New York),
1903 (300 signed, numbered copies) £75
Omar Repentant, Grant Richards (London), 1908 . . £10
ditto, Mitchell Kennerley (New York), [c.1908] . . £10
New Poems, John Lane (London), 1910 . . . . £10
Orestes: A Tragedy, Mitchell Kennerley (New York), 1910
. . . . £10
The Lonely Dancer and Other Poems, John Lane (New
York), 1914 . . . . £10
The Silk-Hat Soldier and Other Poems, John Lane
(London), 1915 (wraps) £20
The Junk-Man and Other Poems, Doubleday, Page & Co.
(New York), 1920 . . . . £10
**A Jongleur Strayed: Verses on Love and Other Matters,
Sacred and Profane**, Doubleday, Page & Co. (New York),
1922 (1,500 numbered copies) . . . . . £30/£10

Non-Fiction

George Meredith: Some Characteristics, Elkin Mathews
(London), 1890 . . . . £10
The Religion of a Literary Man, Elkin Mathews & John
Lane (London), 1893 . . . . . . £10
ditto, Putnam (New York), 1893 . . . . . £10
Retrospective Reviews: A Literary Log, John Lane
(London), 1896 (2 vols) £15
If I Were God, privately printed by James Bowden
(London), 1897 (wraps) £40
ditto, Crowell & Co. (New York), [c.1897] . . . £30
Rudyard Kipling: A Criticism, John Lane (London), 1900 .
. . . . £10
Travels in England, Grant Richards (London), 1900 . £15
ditto, John Lane (New York), 1900 . . . . . £15
The Beautiful Life of Rome, Simpkin, Marshall, Hamilton,
Kent & Co (London), 1900 . . . . . . £10
An Old Country House, Grant Richards (London), 1902 .
. . . . £15
ditto, Harper (New York), 1902 . . . . . £15
Tristan and Isolde, Stokes (New York), 1909 (translated into
verse by Le Gallienne) £50
October Vagabonds, John Lane (London), 1910 . . £10
ditto, Mitchell Kennerley (New York), 1910 . . . £10
Attitudes and Avowals, John Lane (New York), 1910 . £10
ditto, John Lane (London), 1910 [1911] £10
The Loves of the Poets, Baker & Taylor Co. (New York),
[1911] £15
Vanishing Roads and Other Essays, Putnam (London), 1915
. . . . £10
ditto, Putnam (New York), 1915 . . . . . £10
The Romantic 90s, Doubleday (New York), 1925 . £50/£10
ditto, Putnam (London), 1926 . . . . . £50/£10
The Romance of Perfume, Richard Hudnut (New York),
1928 (boards, glassine d/w, slipcase, brochure in pocket at
rear) . . . . £75/£45
From a Paris Garret, Richards Press (London), 1936 . .
. . . . £25/£10
ditto, Washburn (New York), 1936 . . . . £25/£10
The Cry of the Little Peoples, privately printed (Camden,
NJ), 1941 . . . . £10

URSULA LE GUIN
(b.1929)

An American novelist, poet and critic, Ursula Kroeber Le Guin is admired for her science fiction novels and the 'Earthsea' fantasy books for children. She has received several Hugo and Nebula awards for her science fiction, the Gandalf Grand Master award in 1979 and the Science Fiction and Fantasy Writers of America Grand Master Award in 2003.

'Earthsea' Series
A Wizard of Earthsea, Parnassus Press (Berkeley, CA), 1968 (faint vertical line or smudge on title-page, d/w priced $3.95) . . . . £1,250/£300
ditto, Parnassus Press (Berkeley, CA), 1968 (no line or smudge, unpriced d/w) . . . . . £150/£25
ditto, Penguin Books: Puffin (Harmondsworth, Middlesex), 1971 (pbk, illustrated by Ruth Robbins). . . . £10
ditto, Gollancz (London), 1971 . . . . . £125/£25
The Tombs of Atuan, Atheneum (New York), 1971 (first state book with '1971' only on copyright page; first state d/w without circular silver sticker) . . . . £300/£40
ditto, Atheneum (New York), 1971 (second state book with '1970/1971' on copyright page; second state d/w with sticker) . . . . £200/£25
ditto, Gollancz (London), 1972 . . . . £100/£20
The Farthest Shore, Atheneum (New York), 1972 £100/£20
ditto, Gollancz (London), 1973 . . . . £65/£15
Tehanu, Atheneum (New York), 1990 . . . £10/£5
ditto, Gollancz (London), 1990 . . . . £10/£5
The Other Wind, Harcourt Brace (New York), 2001 £10/£5
ditto, Orion (London), 2002 . . . . . £10/£5
Tales from Earthsea, Harcourt Brace (New York), 2001 .
. . . . £10/£5
ditto, Orion (London), 2002 . . . . . £10/£5

'Hainish' Series
Planet of Exile, Ace (New York), 1966 (pbk) . . . £10
ditto, Tandem (London), 1972 (pbk) £5
ditto, Garland (New York), 1975 (no d/w) . . . £45
ditto, Gollancz (London), 1979 . . . . £15/£5
Rocannon's World, Ace (New York), 1966 (pbk) . . £5
ditto, Tandem (London), 1972 (pbk) £5
ditto, Garland (New York), 1975 (no d/w) . . . £45
ditto, Gollancz (London), 1979 . . . . £15/£5
The Left Hand of Darkness, Ace (New York), 1969 (pbk, no mention of Hugo and Nebula awards) . . . £15
ditto, Walker (New York), 1969 . . . . £500/£65
ditto, Macdonald (London), 1969 . . . £125/£20
City of Illusions, Ace (New York), 1971 (pbk) . . £10
ditto, Gollancz (London), 1971 . . . . £65/£15
ditto, Garland (New York), 1975 (no d/w) . . . £35
The Word for World is Forest, Putnam (New York), 1972 .
. . . . £25/£5
ditto, Gollancz (London), 1977 . . . . £10/£5
The Dispossessed, Harper (New York), [1974] . £100/£20
ditto, Gollancz (London), 1974 . . . . £20/£5

'Adventures in Kroy' Series
The Adventures of Cobbler's Rune, Cheap Street (New Castle, VA), 1982 (26 signed, lettered copies) . . £150

ditto, Cheap Street (New Castle, VA), 1982 (250 signed, lettered copies) £30
Solomon Leviathan's 931st Trip Around the World, Cheap Street (New Castle, VA), 1983 (26 signed, lettered copies) £150
ditto, Cheap Street (New Castle, VA), 1983 (250 signed, lettered copies) £30
ditto, Philomel (New York), 1984 . . . . £10/£5

'Catwings' Series
Catwings, Orchard (New York), 1988 . . . £10/£5
Catwings Return, Orchard (New York), 1989 . £10/£5
Wonderful Alexander And the Catwings, Orchard (New York), 1994 . . . . £10/£5
Jane On Her Own, Orchard (New York), 1999 . £10/£5

Chronicles of the Western Shore
Gifts, Harcourt (Orlando, FL), 2004 . . . . £10/£5
ditto, Gollancz (London), 2004 . . . . £10/£5
Voices, Harcourt (Orlando, FL), 2006 . . . £10/£5
ditto, Orion (London), 2006 . . . . . £10/£5
Powers, Harcourt (Orlando, FL), 2007 . . . £10/£5
ditto, Orion (London), 2007 . . . . . £10/£5

Other Novels
The Lathe of Heaven, Scribner's (New York), 1971 . .
. . . . £200/£30
ditto, Gollancz (London), 1972 . . . . £75/£20
Very Far Away From Anywhere Else, Atheneum (New York), 1976 . . . . £20/£5
ditto, as *A Very Long Way from Anywhere Else*, Gollancz (London), 1976 . . . . £20/£5
Leese Webster, Atheneum (New York), 1979 . . £20/£5
ditto, Gollancz (London), 1981 (laminated boards). . £10
Malafrena, Putnam (New York), 1979 . . . £10/£5
ditto, Gollancz (London), 1980 . . . . £10/£5
The Beginning Place, Harper (New York), 1980 . £15/£5
ditto, as *Threshold*, Gollancz (London), 1980 . . £15/£5
The Eye of the Heron, Harper (New York), 1982 . £10/£5
ditto, Gollancz (London), 1983 . . . . £10/£5
The Visionary, Capra (Santa Barbara CA), 1985 (with *Wonders Hidden* by Scott Saunders; pbk) . . . £5
ditto, Capra (Santa Barbara CA), 1985 (200 signed, numbered copies; pbk) £25
Always Coming Home, Harper (New York), 1985 (hardback in d/w with cassette; slipcase) . . . . £75/£35
ditto, Harper (New York), 1985 (pbk with cassette; slipcase)
. . . . £20/£5
ditto, Gollancz (London), 1986 . . . . £20/£5
ditto, Gollancz (London), 1986 (100 signed copies with cassette in slipcase) . . . . . . £75/£35
Searoad, Harper (New York), 1991 . . . . £10/£5
ditto, Gollancz (London), 1992 . . . . £10/£5
A Ride on the Red Mare's Back, Orchard (New York), 1992
. . . . £10/£5
Blue Moon over Thurman Street, New Sage Press (Portland, OR), 1993 (pbk) £5
Four Ways to Forgiveness, Easton Press (Norwalk, CT), 1995 (signed limited edition) £50
ditto, Harper Prism (New York), 1995 . . . £10/£5
ditto, Gollancz (London), 1996 . . . . £10/£5
The Telling, Easton Press (Norwalk, CT), 2000 (1,100 signed copies; no d/w) £65
ditto, Harcourt Brace (New York), 2000 . . . £10/£5

Tom Mouse, Roaring Brook Press (Brookfield, CT), 2002 .
 .   .   .   . £10/£5
Changing Planes, Harcourt (Orlando, FL), 2003 .   £10/£5
ditto, Gollancz (London), 2004 .   .   .   . £10/£5
Lavinia, Harcourt (Orlando, FL), 2008   .   .   . £10/£5
ditto, Gollancz (London), 2009   .   .   .   . £10/£5

Picture Books
Visit from Dr Katz, Atheneum (New York), 1988 (boards) .
 .   .   .   . £5
ditto, Collins (London), 1988   .   .   .   .   . £5
Fire and Stone, Atheneum (New York), 1989.   .   £10/£5
Fish Soup, Atheneum (New York), 1992 .   .   £10/£5

Short Stories
The Wind's Twelve Quarters, Harper (New York), 1975   .
 .   .   .   . £15/£5
ditto, Gollancz (London), 1976   .   .   . £15/£5
Orsinian Tales, Harper (New York), 1976   .   £15/£5
ditto, Gollancz (London), 1977   .   .   . £10/£5
The Water is Wide, Pendragon Press (Portland, OR), 1976
 (50 signed copies, no d/w). £125
ditto, Pendragon Press (Portland, OR), 1976 (200 signed
 copies; wraps) £15
ditto, Pendragon Press (Portland, OR), 1976 (800 unsigned
 copies; stapled wraps) £5
Gwilan's Harp, Lord John Press (Northridge, CA), 1981 (50
 signed, numbered handbound, cloth copies of 350) . £65
ditto, Lord John Press (Northridge, CA), 1981 (300 signed
 copies of 350; sewn wraps) £25
The Compass Rose, Pendragon Press/Underwood-Miller
 (Portland, OR), 1982 (550 signed copies)   .   £45/£35
ditto, Harper (New York), 1982 .   .   . £15/£5
ditto, Gollancz (London), 1983   .   .   . £15/£5
Buffalo Gals and Other Animal Presences, Capra Press
 (Santa Barbara, CA), 1987   .   .   .   . £10/£5
ditto, Gollancz (London), 1990   .   .   . £10/£5
The Ones Who Walk Away from Omelas, Creative
 Education, Inc. (Mankato, MN), 1991   .   . £10/£5
Nine Lives, Pulphouse (Eugene, OR), 1992 (pbk) .   . £5
ditto, Pulphouse (Eugene, OR), 1992 (100 signed, numbered
 copies) £45
Findings, Ox Head Press (Browerville, MN), 1992 (450
 copies; wraps; slipcase)   .   .   .   . £35/£25
ditto, Ox Head Press (Browerville, MN), 1992 (26 signed,
 lettered copies; no d/w)   .   .   . £125/£100
A Fisherman of the Inland Sea, Harper Prism (New York),
 1994 (526 copies, no d/w) £15
ditto, Harper Prism (New York), 1994 (1,500 advance
 copies) £10
ditto, Harper Prism (New York), 1994   .   . £10/£5
ditto, Gollancz (London), 1994   .   .   . £10/£5
Buffalo Gals: Won't You Come Out Tonight, Pomegranate
 Artbooks (San Francisco, CA), 1994   .   . £10/£5
Unlocking the Air and Other Stories, Harper (New York),
 1996 .   .   .   . £10/£5
The Birthday of the World: And Other Stories,
 HarperCollins (New York), 2002   .   .   . £10/£5
ditto, Gollancz (London), 2002 .   .   .   . £10/£5

Poetry
Wild Angels, Capra Press (Santa Barbara, CA), 1973 (pbk) .
 .   .   .   . £5

ditto, Capra Press (Santa Barbara, CA), 1973 (200 signed,
 numbered hardback copies; no d/w)   .   .   . £25
Hard Words and Other Poems, Harper (New York), 1981 .
 .   .   .   . £20/£5
In The Red Zone, Lord John Press (Northridge, CA), 1983
 (25 signed copies) £100
ditto, Lord John Press (Northridge, CA), 1983 (50 signed
 deluxe copies) £65
ditto, Lord John Press (Northridge, CA), 1983 (150 signed
 copies; slipcase, no d/w) £35
Wild Oats and Fireweed, Harper (New York), 1988   £10/£5
Going Out With Peacocks and Other Poems, Harper (New
 York), 1994 .   .   .   . £10/£5
The Twins, The Dream/Las Gemelas, El Sueño, Arte
 Publico Press (Houston, TX), 1996 (with Diana Bellessi) .
 .   .   .   . £15/£5
Walking in Cornwall: A Poem for the Solstice, Portland
 Press (Portland, OR), 1996 (550 copies; sewn wraps). £25
Sixty Odd: New Poems, Shambhala (Boston, MA), 1999
 (pbk) £10
Incredible Good Fortune: New Poems, Shambhala (Boston,
 MA), 2006 .   .   .   . £10/£5

Screenplay
King Dog, Capra Press (Santa Barbara, CA), 1986 (with Tess
 Gallagher, bound in with *Dostoevsky: A Screenplay* by
 Raymond Carver; pbk) £10
ditto, Capra Press (Santa Barbara, CA), 1985 (200 copies
 signed by all authors; pbk) £85

Non-Fiction
From Elfland to Poughkeepsie, Pendragon Press/Oregon
 Press (Portland, OR), 1973 (26 signed, lettered hardback
 copies, no d/w) £150
ditto, Pendragon Press/Oregon Press (Portland, OR), 1973
 (100 signed, numbered copies; wraps)   .   .   . £50
ditto, Pendragon Press/Oregon Press (Portland, OR), 1973
 (650 trade copies; stapled wraps)   .   .   . £15
Dreams Must Explain Themselves, Algol Press (New York),
 1973 (1,000 numbered copies; stapled wraps)   .   . £10
*Language of the Night: Essays on Fantasy and Science
 Fiction*, Putnam (New York), 1979.   .   . £15/£5
ditto, Women's Press (London), 1989 (revised edition; pbk)
 .   .   .   . £5
*Dancing at the Edge of the World: Thoughts on Words,
 Women and Places*, Grove Press (New York), 1989 £10/£5
ditto, Gollancz (London), 1989 .   .   .   . £10/£5
*The Way of the Water's Going: Images of the Northern
 California Coastal Range*, Harper & Row (New York),
 1989 .   .   .   . £10/£5
Lorenzo Bean, Dozing, Parchment Gallery Graphics
 (Charleston, WV), 1998 (100 signed, numbered copies,
 sketch, broadsheet) £35
*The Wave in the Mind: Talks and Essays on the Writer, the
 Reader, and the Imagination*, Shambhala (Boston, MA),
 2004 (pbk) £10
*Steering the Craft: Exercises and Discussions on Story
 Writing for the Lone Navigator or the Mutinous Crew*,
 Eighth Mountain Pr (Portland, OR), 1998 (pbk) .   . £5
Cheek by Jowl, Aqueduct Press (Seattle, WA), 2009 (pbk) .
 .   .   .   . £5
Lao Tzu: Tao Te Ching, Shambhala (Boston, MA), 1997
 (pbk) .   .   .   . £10/£5

ROSAMOND LEHMANN
(b.1903 d.1990)

Rosamond Lehmann is a British author whose novels often deal with the emotional development of women. She was educated at Girton College, Cambridge, which provided the background for her first novel, *Dusty Answer*. *The Swan in the Evening* is an autobiographical book in which she relates the overwhelming psychic and mystical events that she experienced after the tragic death of her daughter.

Novels
Dusty Answer, Chatto & Windus (London), 1927 . £200/£35
ditto, Holt (New York), 1927 . . . . . £75/£20
A Note in Music, Chatto & Windus (London), 1930 £35/£15
ditto, Chatto & Windus (London), 1930 (260 signed copies)
. . . . £50
ditto, Holt (New York), 1930 . . . . £20/£10
ditto, Holt (New York), 1930 (300 signed copies) . . £30
Invitation to the Waltz, Chatto & Windus (London), 1932 .
. . . . £45/£10
ditto, Holt (New York), 1932 . . . . £30/£10
The Weather in the Streets, Collins (London), 1936 £45/£15
ditto, Reynal & Hitchcock (New York), 1936 . . £25/£5
The Ballad and the Source, Collins (London), 1944 £45/£5
ditto, Reynal & Hitchcock (New York), 1945 . . £30/£5
The Echoing Grove, Collins (London), 1953 . . £25/£5
ditto, Harcourt Brace (New York), 1953 . . £20/£5
A Sea-Grape Tree, Collins (London), 1976 . . £15/£5
ditto, Harcourt Brace (New York), 1977 . . £15/£5

Others
Letter to a Sister, Hogarth Press (London), 1931 (sewn wraps) £20
No More Music, Collins (London), 1939 . . .£125/£45
ditto, Reynal & Hitchcock (New York), 1945 . .£125/£45
The Gipsy's Baby and Other Stories, Collins (London), 1946
. . . . £30/£10
ditto, Reynal & Hitchcock (New York), 1947 . . £25/£10
A Man Seen Afar, Spearman (London), 1965 (with W. Tudor Pole) . . . . £20/£5
The Swan in the Evening: Fragments of an Inner Life, Collins (London), 1967 . . . . . £15/£5
ditto, Harcourt Brace (New York), 1968 . . £15/£5
Letters from Our Daughters, College of Psychic Studies (London), 1972 (with Cynthia Hill Sandys, 2 vols; wraps)
. . . . £25

FRITZ LEIBER
(b.1910 d.1992)

Fritz Leiber Jr was an American author of fantasy, horror and science fiction. *Our Lady of Darkness* won a World Fantasy Award.

Novels
Gather, Darkness, Pellegrini & Cudahy (New York), 1950 .
. . . . £65/£15
ditto, Four Square/New English Library (London), 1966 (pbk) £5
Conjure Wife, Twayne (New York), 1953 . £30/£10

ditto, Penguin (London), 1969 (pbk) £5
The Green Millennium, Abelard Press (New York), 1953 .
. . . . £35/£10
ditto, Abelard-Schuman (London), 1959 . . . £25/£10
The Sinful Ones, Universal Giant (New York), 1953 (pbk; bound with *Bulls, Blood and Passion* by David Williams).
. . . . £30
ditto, Gregg Press (Boston, MA), 1980 (no d/w) . . £45
ditto, as *You're All Alone*, Ace (New York), 1972 (pbk) £10
Destiny Times Three, Galaxy (New York), 1957 (pbk). £10
The Big Time, Ace (New York), 1961 (pbk; bound with Leiber's *The Mind Spider and Other Stories*) . . £10
ditto, Four Square/New English Library (London), 1965 (pbk; without *The Mind Spider*) £5
ditto, Gregg Press (Boston, MA), 1976 (no d/w; without *The Mind Spider*). £250
The Silver Eggheads, Ballantine (New York), 1962 (pbk) .
. . . . £10
ditto, Four Square/New English Library (London), 1966 (pbk) £5
The Wanderer, Ballantine (New York), 1964 (pbk) . £10
ditto, Dobson (London), 1967 . . . . . £75/£20
Tarzan and the Valley of Gold, Ballantine (New York), 1966 (pbk) £10
The Swords of Lankhmar, Ace (New York), 1968 (pbk) .
. . . . £10
ditto, Rupert Hart-Davis (London), 1969 . . .£100/£15
A Specter is Haunting Texas, Walker (New York), 1969 .
. . . . £30/£10
ditto, as *A Spectre is Haunting Texas*, Gollancz (London), 1969 . . . . £30/£10
Our Lady of Darkness, Berkley Putnam (New York), 1977.
. . . . £60/£15
ditto, Millington (London), 1978 (no d/w) . . £25/£10
The Dealings of Daniel Kesserich: A Study of Mass-Insanity at Smithville, Tor (New York), 1997 £10/£5

Short Stories
Night's Black Agents, Arkham House (Sauk City, WI), 1947
. . . .£175/£25
ditto, Spearman (Jersey, Channel Islands [London]), 1975 .
. . . . £35/£10
Two Sought Adventure, Gnome Press (New York), 1927 (first state; black boards) . . . . .£100/£50
ditto, Gnome Press (New York), 1927 (second state; grey boards) . . . . £50/£10
The Mind Spider and Other Stories, Ace (New York), 1961 (pbk; bound with Leiber's *The Big Time*) . . . £10
Shadows With Eyes, Ballantine (New York), 1962 (pbk) .
. . . . £10
A Pail of Air, Ballantine (New York), 1964 (pbk) . . £10
Ships to the Stars, Ace (New York), 1964 (pbk; bound with *The Million Year Hunt* by Kenneth Bulmer) . . £10
The Night of the Wolf, Ballantine (New York), 1966 (pbk).
. . . . £10
ditto, Sphere (London), 1966 (pbk) £5
The Secret Songs, Rupert Hart-Davis (London), 1968 . .
. . . . £65/£15
Swords Against Wizardry, Ace (New York), 1968 (pbk) £10
ditto, Gregg Press (Boston, MA), 1977 (no d/w) . . £40
ditto, Prior (London), 1977 . . . . . £40/£10
Swords in the Mist, Ace (New York), 1968 (pbk) . . £10
ditto, Gregg Press (Boston, MA), 1977 (no d/w) . . £40
ditto, Prior (London), 1977 . . . . . £40/£10

Night Monsters, Ace (New York), 1969 (pbk; bound with
    Leiber's *The Green Millennium*) £10
ditto, Gollancz (London), 1974 (differing contents) £35/£10
Swords Against Death, Ace (New York), 1970 (pbk) . £10
ditto, Gregg Press (Boston, MA), 1977 (no d/w) . . £40
Swords and Deviltry, Ace (New York), 1970 (pbk) . £10
ditto, Gregg Press (Boston, MA), 1977 (no d/w) . . £40
You're All Alone, Ace (New York), 1972 (pbk) . . £10
The Book of Fritz Leiber, DAW (New York), 1974 (pbk) £10
ditto, Gregg Press (Boston, MA), 1980 (no d/w) . . £25
The Best of Fritz Leiber, Sphere (London), 1974 (pbk). £10
ditto, Sidgwick & Jackson (London), 1974 . . £25/£10
The Second Book of Fritz Leiber DAW (New York), 1975
    (pbk) £10
ditto, Gregg Press (Boston, MA), 1980 (no d/w) . . £25
The Worlds of Fritz Leiber, Ace (New York), 1976 (pbk) £10
ditto, Gregg Press (Boston, MA), 1979 (no d/w) . . £10
Swords and Ice Magic, Ace (New York), 1977 (pbk) . £10
ditto, Gregg Press (Boston, MA), 1977 (no d/w) . . £25
ditto, Prior (London), 1977 . . . . £40/£10
Rime Isle, Whispers Press (Chapel Hill, NC), 1977 £25/£10
ditto, Whispers Press (Chapel Hill, NC), 1977 (250 signed,
    numbered copies) £50
ditto, Whispers Press (Chapel Hill, NC), 1977 (26 signed,
    lettered copies) £100
Heroes and Horrors, Whispers Press (Chapel Hill, NC),
    1978 . . . . £25/£10
ditto, Whispers Press (Chapel Hill, NC), 1978 (350 signed,
    numbered copies) £50
ditto, Whispers Press (Chapel Hill, NC), 1978 (26 signed,
    lettered copies) £100
Bazaar of the Bizarre, Grant (West Kingston, RI), 1978
    (1,300 copies signed by author and illustrator) . £25/£10
The Change War, Gregg (Boston), 1978 . . . £25/£10
ditto, as *Changewar*, Ace (New York), 1983 (different
    contents; pbk) £5
Ship of Shadows, Gollancz (London), 1979 . . £10/£5
ditto, Gollancz (London), 1979 (500 signed copies) £40/£15
Ervool, Cheap Street (Roanoke, VA), 1980 (200 signed,
    numbered copies; wraps) £35
ditto, Cheap Street (Roanoke, VA), 1980 (26 signed, lettered
    copies wraps) £125
ditto, Cheap Street (Roanoke, VA), 1980 (62 copies with
    Riches and Power; wraps, slipcase). . . . £65
In the Beginning, Cheap Street (Roanoke, VA), 1983
    (illustrated by Alicia Austin; 128 numbered copies signed
    by author and artist; wraps) £35
ditto, Cheap Street (Roanoke, VA), 1983 (10 lettered copies,
    as above) £100
ditto, Cheap Street (Roanoke, VA), 1983 (32 numbered
    copies, as above, but bound in leather) . . . £100
ditto, Cheap Street (Roanoke, VA), 1983 (7 lettered copies,
    as above, but bound in leather). £125
Quicks Around the Zodiac, Cheap Street (Roanoke, VA),
    1984 (illustrated by Alicia Austin; foreword by Gene
    Wolfe; 99 numbered copies signed buy all three; pbk) £25
ditto, Cheap Street (Roanoke, VA), 1984 (11 lettered copies
    as above) £35
ditto, Cheap Street (Roanoke, VA), 1984 (75 numbered
    copies signed buy all three; slipcase) . . . £65
ditto, Cheap Street (Roanoke, VA), 1984 (15 lettered copies
    as above) £85
The Ghost Light, Berkeley (New York), 1984. . £40/£10
ditto, Berkeley (New York), 1984 (pbk) . . . £10

The Knight and Knave of Swords, Morrow (New York),
    1988 . . . . £30/£10
ditto, Grafton (London), 1990 . . . . . £20/£5
The Leiber Chronicles, Dark Harvest (Arlington Heights,
    IL), 1990 . . . . £15/£10
ditto, Dark Harvest (Arlington Heights, IL), 1990 (500
    signed, numbered copies) . . . . . £35/£15
ditto, Dark Harvest (Arlington Heights, IL), 1990 (52 signed,
    lettered copies) . . . . . . £150/£45
Fafhrd and Me, Wildside Press (Newark, NJ), 1990 (200
    hardback copies) . . . . . . £45/£10
ditto, Wildside Press (Newark, NJ), 1990 (300 pbk copies) .
    . . . . £10
Gummitch and Friends, Donald M. Grant (Hampton Falls,
    NH), 1992 . . . . £10/£5
ditto, Donald M. Grant (Hampton Falls, NH), 1992 (1,000
    numbered hardback copies; slipcase) . . . £35/£20
Kreativity for Kats and Other Feline Fantasies, Wildside
    Press (Newark, NJ), 1992 (200 hardback copies) £45/£10
ditto, Wildside Press (Newark, NJ), 1992 (300 pbk copies) .
    . . . . £10
ditto, Wildside Press (Newark, NJ), 1992 (26 lettered copies
    in leather) £75
The Black Gondolier and Other Stories, Midnight House
    (Seattle, WA), 2000 (450 copies) . . . . £30/£10
Smoke Ghost and Other Apparitions, Midnight House
    (Seattle, WA), 2002 (450 copies) . . . . £25/£10
Dark Day Night Bright, Darkside Press (Seattle, WA), 2002
    (500 copies) . . . . £25/£10
Horrible Imaginings, Midnight House (Seattle, WA), 2004
    (500 copies) . . . . £25/£10

Poetry
The Demons of the Upper Air, Squires (Glendale, CA), 1969
    (275 copies; wraps) £45
Sonnets to Jonquil and All, privately printed (San Francisco,
    CA), 1975 (wraps) £20
ditto, Squires (Glendale, CA), 1978 (265 copies; wraps) £45

Non-Fiction
The Mystery of the Japanese Clock, Montgolfier Press
    (Santa Monica, CA), 1982 (300 copies; wraps) . . £20

PATRICK LEIGH FERMOR

(b.1915)

Sir Patrick 'Paddy' Michael Leigh Fermor D.S.O., O.B.E.
is a British travel writer. His first book, *The Traveller's
Tree* is about his post-War travels in the Caribbean, and it
won the Heinemann Foundation Prize for Literature. *Mani*
and *Roumeli* describe his travels on mule and foot around
remote parts of Greece. *A Time of Gifts* is considered by
many to be one the great travel books in the English
language.

Travel
The Traveller's Tree, John Murray (London), 1950 £175/£25
ditto, Harper (New York), 1950 . . . . .£150/£15
A Time to Keep Silence, Queen Anne Press (London), 1953
    (200 unsigned copies). £200

ditto, Queen Anne Press (London), 1953 (50 signed copies)
. . . . £400
ditto, John Murray (London), 1953 . . . . £125/£20
Mani, John Murray (London), 1958 . . . . £65/£10
Roumeli, John Murray (London), 1966 . . . £35/£5
ditto, Harper (New York), 1966 . . . . . £35/£5
A Time of Gifts, John Murray (London), 1977 . £35/£5
ditto, Harper (New York), 1977 . . . . . £35/£5
Between the Woods and the Water, John Murray (London),
1986 . . . . £20/£5
ditto, Viking (New York), 1986 . . . . . £20/£5
Three Letters from the Andes, John Murray (London), 1991
. . . . £15/£5

Novel
Violins of St Jacques, John Murray/Derek Verschoyle
(London), 1953 . . . . . . £35/£5
ditto, Harper (New York), 1953 . . . . . £35/£5

Translations
Forever Ulysses, by C.P. Rodocanachi, Viking (New York),
1938 . . . . £15/£5
Julie de Carneilhan & Chance Acquaintances, by 'Colette',
Secker & Warburg (London), 1952 . . . £15/£5
The Cretan Runner, by George Psychoundakis, John
Murray (London), 1955 . . . . . £15/£5

Journalism
Words of Mercury, John Murray (London), 2003 . £10/£5

DONNA LEON
(b.1942)

Donna Leon is the American author of a series of crime
novels set in Venice, featuring Guido Brunetti. Her early
career was an academic one, although she now concentrates
on her writing and work in the field of Baroque music. Her
books have been translated into many foreign languages,
although not Italian.

'Guido Brunetti' Series
Death at La Fenice, HarperCollins (New York), 1992 . .
. . . . £65/£10
ditto, Chapmans (London), 1992. . . . £125/£20
Death in a Strange Country, HarperCollins (New York),
1993 . . . . £150/£20
ditto, Chapmans (London), 1993. . . . £175/£25
Dressed for Death, HarperCollins (New York), 1994 . .
. . . . £65/£10
ditto, as *The Anonymous Venetian*, Macmillan (London),
1994 . . . . £75/£10
Death and Judgment, HarperCollins (New York), 1995 .
. . . . £125/£20
ditto, as *A Venetian Reckoning*, Macmillan (London), 1995
. . . . £100/£15
Acqua Alta, HarperCollins (New York), 1996. . £70/£10
ditto, Macmillan (London), 1996 . . . . £70/£10
The Death of Faith, Macmillan (London), 1997 . £100/£15
A Noble Radiance, Heinemann (London), 1998 . £45/£10
ditto, Penguin (New York), 2003 (pbk) . . . £5
Fatal Remedies, Heinemann (London), 1999 . . £45/£10
Friends in High Places, Heinemann (London), 2000 £20/£5

A Sea of Troubles, Heinemann (London), 2001 . £15/£5
Wilful Behaviour, Heinemann (London), 2002 . £15/£5
Uniform Justice, Atlantic Monthly Press (New York), 2003
. . . . £10/£5
ditto, Heinemann (London), 2003 . . . . £10/£5
Doctored Evidence, Atlantic Monthly Press (New York),
2004 . . . . £10/£5
ditto, Heinemann (London), 2004 . . . . £10/£5
Blood from a Stone, Atlantic Monthly Press (New York),
2005 . . . . £10/£5
ditto, Heinemann (London), 2005 . . . . £10/£5
Through a Glass, Darkly, Atlantic Monthly Press (New
York), 2006 . . . . £10/£5
ditto, Heinemann (London), 2006 . . . . £10/£5
Suffer the Little Children, Atlantic Monthly Press (New
York), 2003 . . . . £10/£5
ditto, Heinemann (London), 2003 . . . . £10/£5
The Girl of His Dreams, Atlantic Monthly Press (New
York), 2008 . . . . £10/£5
ditto, Heinemann (London), 2008 . . . . £10/£5
About Face, Atlantic Monthly Press (New York), 2009 .
. . . . £10/£5
ditto, Heinemann (London), 2009 . . . . £10/£5

ELMORE LEONARD
(b.1925)

Elmore John Leonard Jr was born in New Orleans, Louisiana. Gaining early recognition as the writer of 'Westerns',
his crime novels have become more popular in recent years,
in part thanks to Hollywood. Quentin Tarantino directed
Jackie Brown, a film based on Leonard's novel *Rum
Punch*, in 1997.

'Chili Palmer' Novels
Get Shorty, Delacorte (New York), 1990 . . . £15/£5
ditto, Viking (London), 1990 . . . . . £15/£5
Be Cool, Delacorte (New York), 1999 . . . £10/£5
ditto, Viking (London), 1999 . . . . . £10/£5

'Frank Ryan' Novels
Swag, Delacorte (New York), 1976 . . . . £50/£10
ditto, Penguin (London), 1984 (pbk) £5
ditto, as *Ryan's Rules*, Dell (New York), 1978 (pbk) . £5
Unknown Man No. 89, Delacorte (New York), 1977 . .
. . . . £300/£45
ditto, Secker & Warburg (London), 1977 . . . £50/£15

'Raylan Givens' Novels
Pronto, Delacorte (New York), 1993 . . . . £15/£5
ditto, Viking (London), 1993 . . . . . £15/£5
Riding the Rap, Delacorte (New York), 1995 . . £15/£5
ditto, Viking (London), 1995 . . . . . £15/£5

Other Novels
The Bounty Hunters, Houghton, Mifflin (Boston), 1953 .
. . . . £2,250/£300
ditto, Ballantine (New York), 1953 (pbk) . . . £75
ditto, Hale (London), 1956 . . . . . £750/£100
The Law at Randado, Houghton, Mifflin (Boston), 1954 .
. . . . £1,500/£250
ditto, Hale (London), 1957 . . . . . . £600/£65

Escape from Five Shadows, Houghton, Mifflin (Boston), 1956 . . . . £1,250/£175
ditto, Hale (London), 1957 . . . . £500/£65
Last Stand at Saber River, Dell (New York), 1959 (pbk) .
. . . . £20
ditto, as *Lawless River*, Hale (London), 1961 . . £750/£75
Hombre, Ballantine (New York), 1961 (pbk) . . . £50
ditto, Hale (London), 1961 . . . . . £850/£100
ditto, Armchair Detective Library (New York), 1989 (no d/w) £20
ditto, Armchair Detective Library (New York), 1989 (100 numbered, signed copies; slipcase) . . . £150/£100
ditto, Armchair Detective Library (New York), 1989 (26 lettered, signed copies; slipcase) . . . £200/£150
The Big Bounce, Fawcett Gold Medal (Greenwich, CT), 1969 (pbk) £35
ditto, Hale (London), 1969 . . . . . £750/£150
ditto, Armchair Detective Library (New York), 1989 (no d/w) £20
ditto, Armchair Detective Library (New York), 1989 (100 numbered, signed copies; slipcase) . . . £100/£75
ditto, Armchair Detective Library (New York), 1989 (26 lettered, signed copies; slipcase) . . . £125/£85
The Moonshine War, Doubleday (Garden City, NY), 1969 .
. . . . £300/£65
ditto, Hale (London), 1970 . . . . . £250/£30
Valdez is Coming, Hale (London), 1969 . . £300/£40
ditto, Fawcett Gold Medal (Greenwich, CT), 1970 (pbk) £25
Forty Lashes Less One, Bantam (New York), 1972 (pbk) .
. . . . £25
Mr Majestyk, Dell (New York), 1974 (pbk) . . £20
ditto, Penguin (London), 1986 (pbk) £5
Fifty-Two Pickup, Delacorte (New York), 1974 . £100/£15
ditto, Secker & Warburg (London), 1974 . . £75/£10
The Hunted, Dell (New York), 1977 (pbk) . . £20
ditto, Secker & Warburg (London), 1978 . . £75/£20
The Switch, Bantam (New York), 1978 (pbk) . . £20
ditto, Secker & Warburg (London), 1979 . . £75/£20
Gunsights, Bantam (New York), 1979 (pbk) . . £15
City Primeval: High Noon in Detroit, Arbor House (New York), 1980 . . . . £20/£5
ditto, W.H. Allen (London), 1981 . . . £20/£5
Gold Coast, Bantam (New York), 1980 (pbk) . . £15
ditto, W.H. Allen (London), 1982 . . . £25/£10
Split Images, Arbor House (New York), 1981 . . £20/£5
ditto, W.H. Allen (London), 1983 . . . £20/£5
Cat Chaser, Arbor House (New York), 1982 . . £20/£5
ditto, Viking (London), 1986 . . . . £20/£5
Stick, Arbor House (New York), 1983 . . . £20/£5
ditto, Allen Lane (London), 1984 . . . £20/£5
La Brava, Arbor House (New York), 1983 . . £15/£5
ditto, Viking (London), 1984 . . . . £15/£5
Glitz, Viking (London), 1985 . . . . £15/£5
ditto, Arbor House (New York), 1985 . . . £15/£5
ditto, Mysterious Press (New York), 1986 (26 signed, lettered copies, slipcase) . . . . £65/£50
ditto, Mysterious Press (New York), 1986 (500 signed copies, slipcase) . . . . . £25/£10
Bandits, Arbor House (New York), 1987 . . £15/£5
ditto, Mysterious Press (New York), 1987 (26 signed, lettered copies, slipcase) . . . . £65/£50
ditto, Mysterious Press (New York), 1987 (500 signed copies, slipcase) . . . . . £25/£10
ditto, Viking (London), 1987 . . . . £15/£5

Touch, Arbor House (New York), 1987 . . . £15/£5
ditto, Viking (London), 1988 . . . . £15/£5
Freaky Deaky, Arbor House/Morrow (New York), 1988 .
. . . . £15/£5
ditto, Viking (London), 1988 . . . . £15/£5
Killshot, Arbor House/Morrow (New York), 1989 . £10/£5
ditto, Viking (London), 1989 . . . . £10/£5
Maximum Bob, Delacorte (New York), 1991 . . £10/£5
ditto, Viking (London), 1991 . . . . £10/£5
Rum Punch, Delacorte (New York), 1992 . . £20/£5
ditto, Viking (London), 1992 . . . . £20/£5
ditto, as *Jackie Brown*, Dell (New York), 1997 (pbk) . £5
Out of Sight Delacorte (New York), 1996 . . £10/£5
ditto, Viking (London), 1996 . . . . £10/£5
Cuba Libre, Delacorte (New York), 1998 . . £10/£5
ditto, Viking (London), 1998 . . . . £10/£5
Pagan Babies, Delacorte (New York), 2000 . . £10/£5
ditto, Viking (London), 2000 . . . . £10/£5
Tishomingo Blues, Morrow (New York), 2002 . £10/£5
ditto, Viking (London), 2002 . . . . £10/£5
Mr Paradise, Morrow (New York), 2004 . . . £10/£5
ditto, Viking (London), 2004 . . . . £10/£5
A Coyote's in the House, Harper Entertainment (New York), 2004 . . . . £10/£5
ditto, Puffin (London), 2004 . . . . £10/£5
The Hot Kid, Morrow (New York), 2005 . . . £10/£5
ditto, Weidenfeld & Nicolson (London), 2005 . . £10/£5
Up in Honey's Room, Morrow (New York), 2007 . £10/£5
ditto, Weidenfeld & Nicolson (London), 2007 . . £10/£5
Comfort to the Enemy, Weidenfeld & Nicolson (London), 2009 . . . . £10/£5
Road Dogs, Morrow (New York), 2009 . . . £10/£5

Short Stories
The Tonto Woman and other Western Stories, Delacorte (New York), 1998 . . . . . . £15/£5
ditto, Viking (London), 1999 . . . . £15/£5
When the Women Come Out to Dance: And Other Stories, Morrow (New York), 2002 . . . . £10/£5
ditto, Viking (London), 2003 . . . . £10/£5
The Complete Western Stories, Morrow (New York), 2004
. . . . £10/£5
ditto, Weidenfeld & Nicolson (London), 2006 . £10/£5

Collected Editions
Dutch Treat, Arbor House (New York), 1985 (contains *The Hunted*, *Swag* and *Mr Majestyk*) . . . £15/£5
ditto, Mysterious Press (New York), 1985 (350 signed, numbered copies, slipcase, no d/w) . . . £25/£20
Double Dutch Treat, Arbor House (New York), 1985 (contains *The Moonshine War*, *Gold Coast* and *City Primeval*) . . . . £15/£5
The Complete Western Stories of Elmore Leonard, Morrow (New York), 2004 . . . . . . £10/£5
ditto, Weidenfeld & Nicolson, London, 2006 . . £10/£5

Other
Naked Came the Manatee, Putnam's (New York), 1996 (novel written with 12 other writers) . . . £10/£5

GASTON LEROUX
(b.1868 d.1927)

Leroux was celebrated in his lifetime as the author of detective fiction. He worked as a journalist before writing his first novel *Le Mystère de la chambre jaune*. This is an important work in the history of detective fiction; the first 'locked-room puzzle' of the genre. Leroux's posthumous reputation is largely based on *The Phantom of the Opera*, the inspiration for Andrew Lloyd Webber's hugely successful stage musical.

The Mystery of the Yellow Room, Daily Mail Sixpenny Novels (London), 1908 (wraps) £75
ditto, Brentano's (New York), 1908 . . . . £30
ditto, Edward Arnold (London), 1909 . . . £35
The Double Life, Kearney (New York), 1909 . . £45
ditto, Laurie (London), 1910 (wraps). . . . £25
ditto, as *The Man With the Black Feather*, Hurst & Blackett (London), 1912 . . . . £30
ditto, as *The Man With the Black Feather*, Small, Maynard (Boston), 1912 . . . . £30
The Perfume of the Lady in Black, Daily Mail Sixpenny Novels (London), 1909 (wraps) £25
ditto, Brentano's (New York), 1908 . . . . £40
ditto, Eveleigh Nash (London), 1911 . . . . £30
The Phantom of the Opera, Mills & Boon (London), 1911 .
. . . . £1,000
ditto, Bobbs-Merrill (Indianapolis, IN), 1911 (colour plates)
. . . .£250
ditto, Grosset & Dunlap (New York), [1925] (colour plates)
. . . .£250/£35
Balaoo, Hurst & Blackett (London), 1913 . . . £35
The Secret of the Night, Eveleigh Nash (London), 1914 £35
ditto, Macaulay (New York), 1914 . . . . £35
The Bride of the Sun, McBride-Nast (New York), 1915 £45
ditto, Hodder & Stoughton (London), 1918 . . £45
The Man Who Came Back From the Dead, Eveleigh Nash (London), 1916 . . . . £35
The Floating Prison, Laurie (London), 1922 . . £100/£20
ditto, as *Wolves of the Sea*, Macaulay (New York), 1923 .
. . . .£100/£20
The Amazing Adventures of Carolous Herbert, Mills & Boon (London), 1922 . . . . . £100/£20
Cheri-Bibi and Cecily, Laurie (London), 1923 . £100/£20
ditto, as *Missing Men*, Macaulay (New York), 1923 £100/£20
The Veiled Prisoner, Mills & Boon (London), 1923 £85/£15
Cheri-Bibi, Mystery Man, John Long (London), 1924 .
. . . .£100/£15
ditto, as *The Dark Road*, Macaulay (New York), 1924 .
. . . . £75/£15
The Dancing Girl, John Long (London), 1925 . £75/£15
ditto, as *Nomads of the Night*, Macaulay (New York), 1925
. . . . £75/£15
The Burgled Heart, John Long (London), 1925 . £100/£25
ditto, as *The New Terror*, Macaulay (New York), 1926 .
. . . .£100/£25
The Slave Bangle, John Long (London), 1925 . £75/£15
ditto, as *The Phantom Clue*, Macaulay (New York), 1926 .
. . . . £75/£15
The Sleuth Hound, John Long (London), 1926 . £75/£15
ditto, as *The Octopus of Paris*, Macaulay (New York), 1927
. . . . £75/£15

The Adventures of a Coquette, Laurie (London), 1926 . .
. . . . £75/£15
The Masked Man, John Long (London), 1927 . £75/£15
ditto, Macaulay (New York), 1929 . . . . £75/£15
The Son of Three Fathers, John Long (London), 1927. .
. . . . £65/£15
ditto, Macaulay (New York), 1928 . . . . £65/£15
The New Idol, John Long (London), 1928 . . £65/£15
ditto, Macaulay (New York), 1929 . . . . £65/£15
The Midnight Lady, John Long (London), 1930 £65/£15
The Man of a Hundred Masks, Cassell (London), 1930 .
. . . . £65/£15
ditto, as *The Man of a Hundred Faces*, Macaulay (New York), 1930 . . . . £65/£15
The Haunted Chair, Dutton (New York), 1931 . £50/£10
The Missing Archduke, John Long (London), 1931 £50/£10
Lady Helena, Laurie (London), 1931 . . . £50/£10
ditto, Dutton (New York), 1931 . . . . £50/£10
The Kiss That Killed, Macaulay (New York), 1934 £45/£10
The Machine to Kill, Macaulay (New York), 1935 £45/£10
Gaston Leroux's Crime Omnibus Book, Laurie (London), 1935 . . . . £35/£10
The Gaston Leroux Bedside Companion, Gollancz (London), 1980 . . . . £10/£5

DORIS LESSING
(b.1919)

Despite a difficult and unhappy childhood in Southern Rhodesia, Lessing's writings about life in colonial Africa are characterised by a compassion for both the barren lives of British colonists and the plight of local inhabitants. Her first novel is an exploration of a white woman's obsession with her black servant, and is the first of many novels which display a fascination with the private world of the mind.

'Canopus in Argos' Novels
Re: Colonised Planet 5, Shikasta, Cape (London), 1979 .
. . . . £20/£5
ditto, Knopf (New York), 1979 . . . . £15/£5
The Marriages Between Zones Three, Four and Five, Cape (London), 1980 . . . . . . £20/£5
ditto, Knopf (New York), 1980 . . . . £20/£5
The Sirian Experiments, Cape (London), 1981 . £20/£5
ditto, Knopf (New York), 1981 . . . . £20/£5
The Making of the Representative for Planet 8, Cape (London), 1982 . . . . £20/£5
ditto, Knopf (New York), 1982 . . . . £20/£5
Documents Relating to the Sentimental Agents in the Volyen Empire, Cape (London), 1983 . . . £15/£5
ditto, Knopf (New York), 1983 . . . . £15/£5

'Children of Violence' Novels
Martha Quest, Joseph (London), 1952 . . . £75/£20
A Proper Marriage, Joseph (London), 1954 . . £45/£10
A Ripple from the Storm, Joseph (London), 1958 . £40/£10
Children of Violence, Volumes 1 & 2, Simon & Schuster (New York), 1964 (contains *Martha Quest* and *A Proper Marriage*) . . . . £25/£5
Landlocked, MacGibbon & Kee (London), 1965 . £40/£10

Children of Violence, Volumes 3 & 4, Simon & Schuster (New York), 1966 (contains *Ripple from the Storm* and *Landlocked*) . . . . £25/£5
The Four-Gated City, MacGibbon & Kee (London), 1969 .
. . . . £25/£5
ditto, Knopf (New York), 1969 . . . . £20/£5

'Fifth Child' Novels
The Fifth Child, Cape (London), 1988 . . . £15/£5
ditto, Knopf (New York), 1988 . . . . £15/£5
Ben, in the World, Flamingo (London), 2000 . . £10/£5
ditto, HarperCollins (New York), 2000 . . £10/£5

Other Novels
The Grass Is Singing, Joseph (London), 1950 . £250/£45
ditto, Crowell (New York), 1950 . . . £150/£25
Retreat to Innocence, Joseph (London), 1956 . £75/£15
ditto, Liberty Book Club (New York), 1959 (pbk) . . £10
The Golden Notebook, Joseph (London), 1962 . £250/£5
ditto, Simon & Schuster (New York), 1962 . £50/£10
Briefing for a Descent into Hell, Cape (London), 1971 .
. . . . £25/£5
ditto, Knopf (New York), 1971 . . . . £20/£5
The Summer before the Dark, Cape (London), 1973 £25/£5
ditto, Knopf (New York), 1973 . . . . £20/£5
The Memoirs of a Survivor, Octagon Press (London), 1974
. . . . £25/£5
ditto, Knopf (New York), 1975 . . . . £25/£5
The Diary of a Good Neighbour, Cape (London), 1983 (pseud 'Jane Somers') . . . . . £15/£5
ditto, Knopf (New York), 1983 . . . . £15/£5
If the Old Could, Cape (London), 1984 (pseud 'Jane Somers') . . . . £15/£5
ditto, Knopf (New York), 1984 . . . . £15/£5
The Good Terrorist, Cape (London), 1985 . . £15/£5
ditto, Cape (London), 1985 (250 signed, numbered copies; glassine d/w). . . . . £75/£60
ditto, Knopf (New York), 1985 . . . . £15/£5
Playing the Game, HarperCollins (London), 1995 (graphic novel) £10
Love, Again, Flamingo (London), 1996 . . £10/£5
ditto, HarperCollins (New York), 1996 . . £10/£5
Mara and Dann, an Adventure, HarperCollins (London), 1999 . . . . £10/£5
ditto, HarperCollins (New York), 1999 . . £10/£5
The Sweetest Dream, Flamingo (London), 2001 . £10/£5
ditto, HarperCollins (New York), 2002 . . £10/£5
The Story of General Dann and Mara's Daughter, Griot and the Snow Dog, Fourth Estate (London), 2005 £10/£5
ditto, HarperCollins (New York), 2006 . . £10/£5

Short Stories
This Was the Old Chief's Country, Joseph (London), 1951.
. . . . £165/£25
ditto, Crowell (New York), 1952 . . . £65/£15
Five: Short Novels, Joseph (London), 1953 . £45/£10
The Habit of Loving, MacGibbon & Kee (London), 1957 .
. . . . £40/£10
ditto, Crowell (New York), 1957 . . . £35/£5
A Man and Two Women, MacGibbon & Kee (London), 1963 . . . . £40/£10
ditto, Simon & Schuster (New York), 1963 . . £25/£5
African Stories, Joseph (London), 1964 . . £35/£10
ditto, Simon & Schuster (New York), 1965 . £30/£5

The Black Madonna, Panther (London), 1966 (pbk) . £10
Winter in July, Panther (London), 1966 (pbk). . . £10
Nine African Stories, Longman (London), 1968 . £35/£10
The Story of a Non-Marrying Man, Cape (London), 1972 .
. . . . £25/£5
ditto, as *The Temptation of Jack Orkney*, Knopf (New York), 1972 . . . . £25/£5
Collected African Stories, Joseph (London), 1973 (2 vols, *This Was the Old Chief's Country* and *The Sun Between their Feet*) . . . . £25/£5
Collected Stories, Cape (London), 1978 (2 vols, *To Room Nineteen* and *The Temptation of Jack Orkney*) . £20/£5
ditto, as *Stories*, Knopf (New York), 1978 . . £20/£5
The Doris Lessing Reader, Knopf (New York), 1988 £10/£5
ditto, Cape (London), 1989 . . . . . £10/£5
Three Stories, Eurographica (Helsinki), 1988 (350 signed, numbered copies; wraps) £65
London Observed, HarperCollins (London), 1992 . £15/£5
ditto, as *The Real Thing*, HarperCollins (New York), 1992 .
. . . . £15/£5
ditto, as *The Real Thing*, Ultramarine Publishing Company (New York), 1992 (38 signed copies) . . . £75
ditto, Ultramarine Publishing Company (New York), 1992 (12 signed copies in full leather) £125
Spies I Have Known and Other Stories, Cascade/Collins Educational (London), 1995 . . . . . £10/£5
The Grandmothers: Four Short Novels, Flamingo (London), 2003 . . . . £10/£5
ditto, HarperCollins (New York), 2004 . . £10/£5

Others
Going Home, Joseph (London), 1957 (with drawings by Paul Hogarth) . . . . £75/£15
ditto, Ballantine (New York), 1968 . . . . £5
Declaration, MacGibbon & Kee (London), 1957 (essays by Lessing, John Osborne and six others, edited by Tom Maschler) . . . . £20/£5
ditto, Dutton (New York), 1958 . . . . £20/£5
Fourteen Poems, Scorpion Press (Northwood, Middlesex), 1959 (500 copies; wraps) £100
ditto, Scorpion Press (Northwood, Middlesex), 1959 (50 signed copies; wraps). £150
In Pursuit of the English, A Documentary, MacGibbon & Kee (London), 1960 . . . . . . £20/£5
ditto, as *Portrait of the English*, Simon & Schuster (New York), 1961 . . . . £10/£5
Play with a Tiger: A Play in Three Acts, Joseph (London), 1962 . . . . £45/£10
Play with a Tiger and Other Plays, Flamingo (London), 1966 (contains *Play with a Tiger*, *The Singing Door* and *Each His Own Wilderness*; pbk) £5
Particularly Cats, Joseph (London), 1967 . . £25/£5
ditto, Simon & Schuster (New York), 1967 . . £25/£5
ditto, as *Particularly Cats... and Rufus*, Simon & Schuster (New York), 1967 . . . . . . £15/£5
ditto, as *Particularly Cats and More Cats*, Joseph (London), 1989 . . . . £10/£5
ditto, as *Particularly Cats and Rufus the Survivor*, Knopf (New York), 1991 . . . . . . £10/£5
ditto, as *The Old Age of El Magnifico*, Burford Books (Short Hills, NJ), 2000 . . . . . £10/£5
ditto, Flamingo (London), 2000. . . . . £10/£5
A Small Personal Voice: Essays, Reviews, Interviews, Knopf (New York), 1974 . . . . . . £15/£5

ditto, Flamingo (London), 1994 (pbk) . . . £5
Prisons We Choose to Live Inside, C.B.C. (Canada), 1986
(pbk) £10
ditto, Cape (London), 1987 . . . . . £15/£5
ditto, Harper & Row (New York), 1987 . . £15/£5
The Wind Blows Away Our Words, Picador (London), 1987
. . . . £15/£5
ditto, Vintage (New York), 1987. . . £15/£5
African Laughter: Four Visits to Zimbabwe, HarperCollins
(London), 1992 . . . . . £10/£5
ditto, HarperCollins (New York), 1992 . . £10/£5
Conversations, Ontario Review Press (Princeton, NJ), 1994
. . . . £15/£5
ditto, as **Putting the Questions Differently**, Flamingo
(London), 1996 . . . . . . £10/£5
**Under My Skin: Volume One of My Autobiography, to
1949**, HarperCollins (London), 1994 . . £10/£5
ditto, HarperCollins (New York), 1994 . . £10/£5
**Walking in the Shade: Volume Two of My Autobiography,
1949-1962**, HarperCollins (London), 1997 . £10/£5
ditto, HarperCollins (New York), 1997 . . £10/£5
Problems, Myths and Stories, Institute for Cultural Research
(London), 1999 (pbk). £5
On Cats, Flamingo (London), 2002 . . . £10/£5
Time Bites: Views and Reviews, Fourth Estate (London),
2004 . . . . £10/£5
ditto, HarperCollins (New York), 2004 . . £10/£5

IRA LEVIN
(b.1929 d.2007)

Levin was an American novelist, playwright, and songwriter. His novels and plays have often been successfully
filmed.

Novels
A Kiss Before Dying, Simon & Schuster (New York), 1953
. . . . £125/£25
ditto, Joseph (London), 1954 . . . . £65/£10
Rosemary's Baby, Random House (New York), 1967 .
. . . . £200/£35
ditto, Joseph (London), 1967 . . . . £75/£10
This Perfect Day, Random House (New York), 1970 £45/£10
ditto, Joseph (London), 1970 . . . . £25/£10
The Stepford Wives, Random House (New York), 1972 .
. . . . £45/£10
ditto, Joseph (London), 1972 . . . . £25/£10
The Boys from Brazil, Random House (New York), 1976 .
. . . . £45/£10
ditto, Joseph (London), 1976 . . . . £25/£10
Sliver, Bantam Books (New York), 1991 . . £15/£5
ditto, Joseph (London), 1991 . . . . £15/£5
Son of Rosemary, Dutton (New York), 1997 . £10/£5
ditto, Robert hale (London), 1998 . . £10/£5

Plays
No Time For Sergeants, Random House (New York), 1956
. . . . £35/£10
Interlock, Dramatists Play Service [1958] (wraps) . . £5
Critic's Choice, Random House (New York), 1961 £15/£5
ditto, Evans Bothers (London), 1963 (wraps) . . £5
General Seeger, Dramatists Play Service [1968] (wraps) £5

Dr. Cook's Garden, Dramatists Play Service [1968] (wraps)
. . . . £5
Veronica's Room, Random House (New York), 1974 £10/£5
ditto, Joseph (London), 1975 . . . . £10/£5
Deathtrap, Random House (New York), 1979. . £10/£5
Break a Leg: A Comedy in Two Acts, Samuel French
(London), 1981 (wraps) £5
Cantorial, Samuel French (New York), 1990 (wraps) . £5
ditto, Samuel French (London), 1990 (wraps) . . £5

Musicals
Drat! The Cat!, Edwin H. Morris, 1965 (sheet music) . £10

C.S. LEWIS
(b.1898 d.1963)

Clive Staples Lewis is best known for his children's books,
especially the 'The Chronicles of Narnia' series which,
while incorporating Christian themes, borrows from Greek
and Roman mythology and traditional English and Irish
fairy tales. Lewis also wrote a handful of science fiction
novels, and a great number of theological works, and
academic works on medieval literature.

Children's Titles
The Lion, The Witch and The Wardrobe, Bles (London),
1950 . . . . £6,000/£500
ditto, Macmillan (New York), 1950 . . £1,000/£200
Prince Caspian: The Return to Narnia, Bles (London),
1951 . . . . £1,250/£200
ditto, Macmillan (New York), 1951 . . . £400/£50
The Voyage of the 'Dawn Treader', Bles (London), 1952 .
. . . . £1,500/£250
ditto, Macmillan (New York), 1952 . . . £400/£50
The Silver Chair, Bles (London), 1953 . £2,500/£500
ditto, Macmillan (New York), 1953 . . . £400/£50
The Horse and His Boy, Bles (London), 1954 £1,500/£250
ditto, Macmillan (New York), 1954 . . . £400/£50
The Magician's Nephew, Bodley Head (London), 1955 .
. . . . £750/£150
ditto, Macmillan (New York), 1955 . . . £250/£50
The Last Battle, Bodley Head (London), 1956 £750/£150
ditto, Macmillan (New York), 1956 . . . £250/£50

Novels
Out of the Silent Planet, Bodley Head (London), 1938. .
. . . . £2,000/£400
ditto, Macmillan (New York), 1943 . . . £125/£35
Perelandra, Bodley Head (London), 1943 . £400/£75
ditto, Macmillan (New York), 1944 . . . £125/£20
**That Hideous Strength: A Modern Fairy-Tale for Grown-
Ups**, Bodley Head (London), 1945 . . £250/£45
ditto, Macmillan (New York), 1946 . . . £100/£25
Till We Have Faces: A Myth Retold, Bles (London), 1956 .
. . . . £75/£25
ditto, Harcourt Brace & Co (New York), 1957 . £35/£10

Short Stories
The Dark Tower and Other Stories, Collins (London), 1977
. . . . £35/£10
ditto, Harcourt, Brace (New York), 1977 . . £30/£10

Poetry

Spirits in Bondage, Heinemann (London), 1919 (pseud 'Clive Hamilton') . . . . . £6,000/£2,500
Dymer, Dent (London), 1926 (pseud 'Clive Hamilton') .
. . . . £7,500/£4,000
ditto, Dutton (New York), 1926 . . . . £2,000/£250
Poems, Bles (London), 1964 . . . . £50/£15
ditto, Harcourt, Brace (New York), 1965 . . . £25/£10
Narrative Poems, Bles (London), 1969 . . . £50/£15
The Collected Poems of C.S. Lewis, HarperCollins (London), 1994 . . . . £20/£5

Academic Titles

The Allegory of Love: A Study in Medieval Tradition, O.U.P. (Oxford, UK), 1936 . . . £600/£200
Rehabilitations and Other Essays, O.U.P. (Oxford, UK), 1939 . . . . £500/£150
The Personal Heresy: A Controversy, O.U.P. (Oxford, UK), 1939 (with E.M.W. Tillyard) . . . £400/£150
A Preface to Paradise Lost, O.U.P. (Oxford, UK), 1942 .
. . . . £175/£65
Hamlet, the Prince or the Poem, British Academy (London), 1942 (wraps) £60
Arthurian Torso, O.U.P. (Oxford, UK), 1948 (with Charles Williams) . . . . . . £125/£45
ditto, O.U.P. (New York), 1948 . . . . £125/£45
English Literature in the Sixteenth Century, Excluding Drama, O.U.P. (Oxford, UK), 1954 . . £45/£15
ditto, O.U.P. (New York), 1954 . . . . £45/£15
Studies in Words, C.U.P. (Cambridge, UK), 1960 . £20/£5
ditto, Macmillan (New York), 1960 . . . £20/£10
An Experiment in Criticism, C.U. P. (Cambridge, UK), 1961 . . . . £20/£10
ditto, Macmillan (New York), 1961 . . . . £20/£10
They Asked for a Paper, Bles (London), 1962 . £20/£10
The Discarded Image, C.U. P. (Cambridge, UK), 1964. .
. . . . £30/£10
ditto, C.U. P. (New York), 1964 . . . . £25/£10
Of Other Worlds, Bles (London), 1966 . . £20/£10
ditto, Harcourt Brace (New York), 1967 . . £20/£10
Studies in Mediaeval and Renaissance Literature, C.U.P. (Cambridge, UK), 1966 . . . . £25/£10
Spenser's Images of Life, C.U.P. (Cambridge, UK), 1961 .
. . . . £25/£10
Selected Literary Essays, C.U. P. (Cambridge, UK), 1969 .
. . . . £25/£10

Christian Titles

The Pilgrim's Regress: An Allegorical Apology for Christianity, Reason and Romanticism, Dent (London), 1933 . . . . £600/£75
ditto, Sheed & Ward (New York), 1935 . . £200/£35
The Problem of Pain, Centenary Press/Bles (London), 1940 . . . . £50/£10
ditto, Macmillan (New York), 1943 . . . £25/£5
The Screwtape Letters, Bles (London), 1942 . £1,500/£200
ditto, Macmillan (New York), 1943 . . . £250/50
The Weight of Glory, S.P.C.K. (London), 1962 (stapled wraps) £45
ditto, Macmillan (New York), 1949 . . . £45/£15
Broadcast Talks: Right and Wrong: A Clue to the Meaning of the Universe, and What Christians Believe, Bles (London), 1942 . . . . £75/£15
Christian Behaviour: A Further Series of Broadcast Talks, Bles (London), 1943 . . . . . . £35/£15
ditto, Macmillan (New York), 1945 . . . £20/£5

The Abolition of Man: or Reflections on Education with Special Reference to the Teaching of English in the Upper Forms of Schools, O.U.P. (Oxford, UK), 1943 (wraps) £75
ditto, Macmillan (New York), 1947 . . . £65/£20
Beyond Personality: The Christian Idea of God, Centenary Press/Bles (London), 1944 . . . . £50/£10
ditto, Macmillan (New York), 1945 . . . £40/£15
The Great Divorce: A Dream, Centenary Press/Bles (London), 1945 [1946] . . . . £35/£10
ditto, Macmillan (New York), 1946 . . . £30/£5
Miracles: A Preliminary Study, Centenary Press/Bles (London), 1947 . . . . . . £30/£10
ditto, Macmillan (New York), 1947 . . . £30/£5
Vivisection, The National Anti-Vivisection Society (London), [1947] (wraps) £50
Transposition and Other Addresses, Bles (London), 1949 .
. . . . £35/£15
ditto, as *The Weight of Glory and Other Addresses*, Macmillan (New York), 1949 . . . . £35/£10
Mere Christianity, Bles (London), 1952 . . £40/£15
ditto, Macmillan (New York), 1952 . . . £35/£10
Reflections on the Psalms, Bles (London), 1958 . £35/£15
ditto, Harcourt Brace (New York), 1958 . . £25/£10
Shall We Lose God in Outer Space?, S.P.C.K. (London), 1959 (wraps). £50
The Four Loves, Bles (London), 1960 . . . £35/£15
ditto, Harcourt Brace (New York), 1960 . . £25/£15
The World's Last Night, Harcourt Brace (New York), 1960
. . . . £30/£10
Beyond the Bright Blur, Harcourt Brace (New York), 1963 (c.350 copies; glassine d/w) . . . . £65/£45
Letters to Malcolm Chiefly on Prayer, Bles (London), [1964] . . . . £35/£15
ditto, Harcourt Brace (New York), 1964 . . £25/£15
Screwtape Proposes a Toast and Other Pieces, Bles (London), 1965 . . . . . . £25/£15
Christian Reflections, Bles (London), 1967 . £35/£15
ditto, Eerdmans (Grand Rapids, MI), 1967 . £25/£15
Letters to an American Lady, Eerdmans (Grand Rapids, MI), 1967 . . . . £25/£15
ditto, Hodder & Stoughton (London), 1969 . £25/£15
The Joyful Christian, Macmillan (New York), 1977 £20/£10
God in the Dock, Eerdmans (Grand Rapids, MI), 1970 . .
. . . . £25/£10
ditto, as *Undeceptions*, Bles (London), 1971 . £20/£10
Fern-Seed and Elephants, Collins/Fontana (London), 1975 (pbk) £5

Autobiography

Surprised by Joy, Bles (London), 1955 . . . £35/£15
ditto, Harcourt Brace (New York), 1956 . . £30/£10
A Grief Observed, Faber (London), 1961 (pseud 'N.W. Clerk') . . . . £50/£15
ditto, Seabury (Greenwich, CT), 1963 . . . £25/£10

Letters

The Letters of C.S. Lewis, Bles (London), 1966 . £40/£15
The Collected Letters, Volume I: Family Letters 1905-1931, HarperCollins (London), 2000 . . . . £20/£5
ditto, HarperSanFrancisco (San Francisco, CA), 2004 £20/£5
The Collected Letters, Volume II: Books, Broadcasts and the War 1931-1949, HarperCollins (London), 2004 £20/£5
ditto, HarperSanFrancisco (San Francisco, CA), 2004 £20/£5
The Collected Letters, Volume III, Narnia, Cambridge and Joy 1950-1963, HarperCollins (London), 2006 . £20/£5
ditto, HarperSanFrancisco (San Francisco, CA), 2007 £20/£5

MATTHEW GREGORY LEWIS
(b.1775 d.1818)

London-born Lewis was destined for a diplomatic career but while working in the Hague as an attaché to the British embassy he wrote *Ambrosio, or the Monk*, in just ten weeks. It was an immediate but controversial success, and a court order meant that a number of passages were removed from subsequent editions. Despite a parliamentary career Lewis continued to compose dramas for the stage, some of which were published, and undertook translations. Various episodes from *The Monk* were published separately.

Fiction

The Monk, J. Bell (London), [March] 1796 (first issue with 'In Three Volumes' *above* quotation on title-page, 3 vols)
. . . . £3,000 the set
ditto, J. Bell (London), [April] 1796 (second issue with 'In Three Volumes' *below* quotation on title-page, 3 vols) .
. . . . £2,000 the set
ditto, W Cobbett (Philadelphia, PA), 1798 . . . £650
The Bravo of Venice: A Romance, J.F. Hughes (London), 1804 [1805] £400
ditto, as *Abaellino, The Bravo of Venice*, Warner & Hanna (Baltimore, MD), 1809 . . . . . . £150
Feudal Tyrants; or, The Counts of Carlsheim and Sargans: a Romance, J.F. Hughes (London), 1806 (4 vols)
. . . . £2,000 the set
Romantic Tales, Longman, Hurst, Rees & Orme (London), 1808 (4 vols) . . . . . £1,000 the set

Drama

The Castle Spectre; A Drama, J. Bell (London), 1798 . £600
One O'Clock! Or, The Knight and the Wood Daemon, Lowndes & Hobbs (London), 1811 . . . . £400

Poems and Ballads

The Love of Gain: A Poem Imitated from the Thirteenth Satire of Juvenal, J. Bell (London), 1799 . . . £250
Tales of Wonder, W. Bulmer/J. Bell (London), 1801 (2 vols)
. . . . £300 the set
Poems, Hatchard, 1812 . . . . £150
The Isle of Devils, 'Advertiser' (Jamaica), 1827 . £1,000
ditto, George T. Juckes (London), 1912 (250 numbered copies) £65

Non-Fiction

Journal of a West India Proprietor, Kept During a Residence in the Island of Jamaica, John Murray (London), 1834 . . . . £200
Journal of a West India Proprietor, 1815-17, Routledge (London), 1929 . . . . . . £35/£15

NORMAN LEWIS
(b.1908 d.2003)

Norman Lewis was a prolific British travel-writer and novelist, hailed by Graham Greene as one of the best writers of the 20th century. Lewis was fascinated by cultures untouched by the modern world, and by the impact of missionary activity on tribal societies. Another interest on display in his writings is the culture and society of Sicily.

Travel

Spanish Adventure, Gollancz (London), 1935 . £250/£35
ditto, Holt (New York), 1935 . . . . . £125/£20
Sand and Sea in Arabia, Routledge (London), 1938 . .
. . . . £150/£25
A Dragon Apparent, Travels In Indo-China, Cape (London), 1951 . . . . £75/£20
ditto, Scribner's (New York), 1951 . . . . £50/£10
Golden Earth, Travels In Burma, Cape (London), 1952 .
. . . . £50/£20
ditto, Scribner's (New York), 1952 . . . £35/£10
The Changing Sky, The Travels of a Novelist, Cape (London), 1959 . . . . £45/£15
ditto, Pantheon (New York), 1959 . . . £40/£10
The Honoured Society, The Mafia Conspiracy Observed, Collins (London), 1964 . . . . . . £45/£15
ditto, Putnam's (New York), 1964 . . . £40/£10
Naples '44, Collins (London), 1978 . . . £45/£15
ditto, Pantheon (New York), 1978 . . . £40/£10
Voices of the Old Sea, Hamish Hamilton (London), 1984 .
. . . . £25/£5
ditto, Viking (New York), 1985 . . . . . £20/£5
A Goddess in the Stones, Travels In India, Cape (London), 1991 . . . . £20/£5
ditto, Holt (New York), 1992 . . . . . £20/£5
An Empire of the East, Travels In Indonesia, Cape (London), 1993 . . . . £15/£5
ditto, Holt (New York), 1993 . . . . . £15/£5

Novels

Samara, Cape (London), 1949 . . . . . £145/£20
Within the Labyrinth, Cape (London), 1950 . £100/£15
ditto, Carroll & Graf (New York), 1986 . . £35/£10
A Single Pilgrim, Cape (London), 1953 . . £40/£10
ditto, Rinehart & Co. (New York), 1953 . . £35/£5
The Day of the Fox, Cape (London), 1955 . £35/£5
ditto, Rinehart & Co. (New York), 1955 . . £25/£5
The Volcanoes Above Us, Cape (London), 1957 . £15/£5
ditto, Pantheon (New York), [1957] . . . £15/£5
Darkness Visible, Cape (London), 1960 . . £35/£5
ditto, Pantheon (New York), 1960 . . . £25/£5
The Tenth Year of the Ship, Collins (London), 1962 £25/£5
ditto, Harcourt, Brace (New York), 1962 . . £20/£5
A Small War Made to Order, Collins (London), 1966 £15/£5
ditto, Harcourt, Brace (New York), 1966 . . £15/£5
Every Man's Brother, Heinemann (London), 1967 £20/£5
ditto, Morrow (New York), 1968 . . . . £15/£5
Flight from a Dark Equator, Collins (London), 1972 £25/£5
ditto, Putnam (New York), 1972 . . . . . £25/£5
The Sicilian Specialist, Random House (New York), 1974 .
. . . . £25/£5
ditto, Collins (London), 1975 . . . . . £20/£5

The German Company, Collins (London), 1979 .   £25/£5
The Cuban Passage, Collins (London), 1982 .   .   £15/£5
ditto, Pantheon (New York), 1982   .   .   .   .   £10/£5
A Suitable Case for Corruption, Hamish Hamilton
(London), 1984   .   .   .   .   £15/£5
ditto, as *The Man in the Middle*, Pantheon (New York),
1984   .   .   .   .   £10/£5
The March of the Long Shadows, Secker & Warburg
(London), 1987   .   .   .   .   £15/£5

Miscellaneous
Jackdaw Cake, Hamish Hamilton (London), 1985 .   £20/£5
ditto, as *I Came, I Saw*, Picador (London), 1994 (enlarged
edition) .   .   .   .   £10/£5
A View of the World, Eland (London), 1986 .   £15/£5
The Missionaries, Secker & Warburg (London), 1988 £15/£5
ditto, McGraw-Hill (New York), 1988   .   .   .   £15/£5
To Run Across the Sea, Cape (London), 1989 .   £10/£5
The World, The World, Cape (London), 1996.   .   £10/£5
ditto, Holt (New York), 1997   .   .   .   .   £10/£5
The Happy Ant-Heap and Other Pieces, Cape (London),
1998   .   .   .   .   £10/£5

SINCLAIR LEWIS
(b.1885 d.1951)

Sinclair Lewis was an American novelist and playwright
who became, in 1930, the first American to win the Nobel
Prize in Literature, 'for his vigorous and graphic art of
description and his ability to create, with wit and humour,
new types of characters'. He was also awarded the Pulitzer
Prize in 1926 for *Arrowsmith*, but rejected it. His works
provide a critical insight into American society and
capitalist values, and while his style can be droll and
satirical, his characters are always sympathetically drawn.

Novels
Hike and the Aeroplane, Stokes (New York), 1912 (pseud
'Tom Graham') £2,000
*Our Mr. Wrenn: The Romantic Adventures of a Gentle
Man*, Harper (New York), 1914 (first issue with M-N on
copyright page) £85
ditto, Cape (London), 1923 .   .   .   .   .   £300/£25
*The Trail of the Hawk: A Comedy of the Seriousness of
Life*, Harper (New York), 1915 (first issue with H-P on
copyright page) £125
ditto, Cape (London), 1923 .   .   .   .   .   £300/£35
The Job: An American Novel, Harper (New York), 1917
(first issue with B-R on copyright page).   .   .   £75
ditto, as *The Job*, Cape (London), 1926 .   .   £250/£35
The Innocents: A Story for Lovers, Harper (New York),
1917 (first issue with F-R on copyright page)   .   £400
Free Air, Harcourt, Brace & Howe (New York), 1919 . £100
ditto, Cape (London), 1924 .   .   .   .   .   £250/£35
Main Street: The Story of Carol Kennicott, Harcourt, Brace
& Howe (New York), 1920 (first issue with perfect folio on
p.54; d/w without review of this title on front flap)   .   .
.   .   .   .   £10,000/£300
ditto, Harcourt, Brace and Howe (New York), 1920 (first
issue book; d/w with review of this title on front flap)   .
.   .   .   .   £6,000/£300
ditto, Cape (London), 1926 .   .   .   .   .   £250/£45

ditto, Limited Editions Club (Chicago), 1937 (1500
numbered copies illustrated and signed by Grant Wood;
slipcase).   .   .   .   .   £250/£200
Babbitt, Harcourt, Brace & Howe (New York), 1922 (first
state with 'Purdy' instead of 'lyte' on page 49, line 4)   .
.   .   .   .   £1,000/£75
ditto, Cape (London), 1922 .   .   .   .   .   £250/£60
Arrowsmith, Harcourt, Brace & Co (New York), 1925 (states
second printing (first trade edition, January, 1925) although
simultaneous with below) .   .   .   .   .   £1,250/£50
ditto, Harcourt, Brace & Co (New York), 1925 (500 signed,
numbered copies; slipcase; no d/w).   .   .   £300/£200
ditto, as *Martin Arrowsmith*, Cape (London), 1925 £300/£25
Mantrap, Harcourt, Brace & Co (New York), 1926   .   .
.   .   .   .   £800/£100
ditto, Cape (London), 1926 .   .   .   .   .   £200/£25
Elmer Gantry, Harcourt, Brace & Co (New York), 1927
(spine reads 'Elmer Cantry')   .   .   .   .   £750/£125
ditto, Harcourt, Brace & Co (New York), 1927 (spine
lettered correctly)   .   .   .   .   .   .   £650/£25
ditto, Cape (London), 1927 .   .   .   .   .   £300/£35
The Man Who Knew Coolidge, Harcourt, Brace & Co (New
York), 1928 .   .   .   .   £200/£35
ditto, Cape (London), 1928 .   .   .   .   .   £100/£15
Dodsworth, Harcourt, Brace & Co (New York), 1929 (900
advance review copies in orange cloth and cream lettering;
tipped-in sheet; states 'Published, March 1929'; no d/w) .
.   .   .   .   £65
ditto, Harcourt, Brace & Co (New York), 1929 (states
'Published, March 1929'; blue cloth lettered in orange;
first-issue d/w with no reviews on the front flap) .   .   .
.   .   .   .   £1,000/£65
ditto, Cape (London), 1929 .   .   .   .   .   £75/£10
Ann Vickers, Doubleday (New York), 1933 .   £85/£15
ditto, Cape (London), 1933 .   .   .   .   .   £75/£10
Work of Art, Doubleday (New York), 1934 .   .   £75/£10
ditto, Cape (London), 1934 .   .   .   .   .   £75/£10
It Can't Happen Here, Doubleday (New York), 1935 .   .
.   .   .   .   £45/£10
ditto, Cape (London), 1935 .   .   .   .   .   £45/£10
The Prodigal Parents, Doubleday (New York), 1938 .   .
.   .   .   .   £45/£10
ditto, Cape (London), 1938 .   .   .   .   .   £45/£10
Bethel Merriday, Doubleday (New York), 1940   .   £40/£10
ditto, Cape (London), 1940 .   .   .   .   .   £40/£10
Gideon Planish, Random House (New York), 1943 £40/£10
ditto, Cape (London), 1943 .   .   .   .   .   £40/£10
Cass Timberlane: A Novel of Husbands and Wives,
Random House (New York), 1945 (first state d/w black on
blue) .   .   .   .   £45/£10
ditto, Random House (New York), 1945 (second state d/w
black on orange) .   .   .   .   .   .   £40/£10
ditto, Random House (New York), 1945 (third state d/w
black on green) .   .   .   .   .   .   £35/£10
ditto, Cape (London), 1946 .   .   .   .   .   £40/£5
Kingsblood Royal, Random House (New York), 1947 .   .
.   .   .   .   £65/£10
ditto, Random House (New York), 1947 (1,050 signed,
numbered copies; slipcase, no d/w).   .   .   £125/£65
ditto, Cape (London), 1948 .   .   .   .   .   £40/£5
The God-Seeker, Random House (New York), 1949 £50/£10
ditto, Heinemann (London), 1949   .   .   .   £30/£10
World So Wide, Random House (New York), 1951   £45/£5
ditto, Heinemann (London), 1951   .   .   .   £30/£5

Others

Tennis As I Play It, by Maurice E. McLoughlin, Doran (New York), 1915 (probably ghost-written by Lewis)   £75

John Dos Passos' Manhattan Transfer, Harper (New York), 1926 (975 numbered copies; no d/w) .   .   . £35

Keep Out Of The Kitchen, Cosmopolitan (New York), 1929 (no d/w) £100

Cheap and Contented Labor, United Textile Workers Press (New York), 1929 (stapled wraps; first issue, lacking quotation mark at the beginning of 'Dodsworth' on the title page) £200

ditto, United Textile Workers Press (New York), 1929 (stapled wraps; second issue with quotation mark)   . £50

Sinclair Lewis on the Valley of the Moon, Harvard Press (Cambridge MA), 1932 (100 numbered copies signed by Harvey Taylor) £75

Launcelot, Harvard Press (Cambridge MA), 1932 (100 numbered copies signed by Harvey Taylor) .   .   . £75

Jayhawker: A Play in Three Acts, Doubleday (New York), 1935 (with Lloyd Lewis) .   .   .   .   . £30/£10

Selected Short Stories of Sinclair Lewis, Doubleday (New York), 1935 .   .   .   . £25/£10

It Can't Happen Here: A New Version, Dramatists Play Service (New York), 1938 (wraps) £15

From Main Street to Stockholm; Letters of Sinclair Lewis, 1919-1930, Harcourt, Brace (New York), 1952   £25/£10

The Man from Main Street: Selected Essays and Other Writings, 1904-1950, Random House (New York), 1953 .   .   .   . £25/£10

ditto, Heinemann (London), 1954   .   .   . £25/£10

I'm a Stranger Here Myself and Other Stories, Dell (New York), 1962 (pbk) £10

Storm in the West, Stein & Day (New York), 1963 (written with Dore Schary) .   .   .   .   . £25/£10

ditto, Sidgwick & Jackson (London), 1964   . £25/£10

Letters from Jack London containing an Unpublished Correspondence between London and Sinclair Lewis, Odyssey Press (New York), 1965 .   .   .   . £25/£10

ditto, MacGibbon & Kee (London), 1966 .   . £25/£10

WYNDHAM LEWIS

(b.1882 d.1957)

Considered one of the most versatile writers of his time, Lewis was also a painter. He co-founded the Vorticist movement, editing their journal, *BLAST*. World War One saw the end of the Vorticists, and Lewis was posted to the Western Front, serving as an official war artist. His first novel, *Tarr*, is considered one of the key Modernist texts.

Novels

Tarr, Knopf (New York), 1918 (red cloth)   .   . £200

ditto, Knopf (New York), 1918 (blue cloth)   .   . £100

ditto, Egoist Press (London), 1918   .   .   .   . £125

The Childermass: Section 1, Chatto & Windus (London), 1928 .   .   .   . £100/£30

ditto, Chatto & Windus (London), 1928 (231 signed copies) .   .   .   . £350/£125

ditto, Covici Friede (New York), [1928] .   . £75/£25

The Apes of God, The Arthur Press (London), 1930 (750 signed copies) .   .   .   .   .   . £300/£125

ditto, Nash & Grayson (London), 1931   .   . £125/£25

ditto, Robert McBride (New York), 1932 .   .   . £125/£25

Snooty Baronet, Cassell (London), 1932 .   .   . £300/£75

ditto, Haskell House (New York), 1971 .   .   .   . £15

The Revenge for Love, Cassell (London), 1937 . £300/£75

ditto, Regnery (Chicago, IL), 1952 .   .   .   . £40/£10

The Vulgar Streak, Robert Hale (London), 1941 . £300/£75

ditto, Jubilee Books (New York), 1973 .   .   . £20/£5

Self Condemned, Methuen (London), 1954   . £75/£25

ditto, Regnery (Chicago, IL), 1955 .   .   .   . £40/£10

The Human Age, Methuen (London), 1955-56 (2 vols) .   .   .   . £75/£20

The Red Priest, Methuen (London), 1963 .   .   . £45/£15

The Roaring Queen, Secker & Warburg (London), 1973 . .   .   . £25/£10

ditto, Secker & Warburg (London), 1973 (130 copies signed by Mrs Wyndham Lewis) .   .   .   .   . £125/£40

ditto, Liveright (New York), 1973 .   .   .   . £25/£10

Mrs Dukes' Millions, Coach House Press (Toronto, Canada), 1977 (in box) .   .   .   .   .   . £20/£5

ditto, George Prior (London), 1980 .   .   .   . £20/£5

Short Stories

The Wild Body, Chatto & Windus (London), 1927. £200/£45

ditto, Chatto & Windus (London), 1927 (85 signed copies) . .   .   . £500/£350

ditto, Harcourt, Brace (New York), [1928]   . £150/£35

Rotting Hill, Methuen (London), 1951 .   .   . £75/£25

ditto, Regnery (Chicago, IL), 1952 .   .   . £40/£10

Unlucky for Pringle, Vision Press (London), 1973   £25/£10

ditto, David Lewis (New York), [1973] .   .   . £20/£5

Artwork

Timon of Athens, Benmar & Co (London), 1913 (portfolio of 16 loose plates) £3,000

Fifteen Drawings, Ovid Press (London), 1920 (15 mounted plates with printed titles laid within printed portfolio) £2,000

Thirty Personalities and a Self-Portrait, Harmsworth (London), 1932 (200 signed sets, portfolio with 31 loose plates) £750

Wyndham Lewis The Artist, From 'Blast' to Burlington House, Laidlaw & Laidlaw (London), 1939 .   . £150/£40

Others

The Ideal Giant, privately printed for the London Office of the *Little Review* (London), 1917 .   .   .   . £1,000

The Caliph's Design, Egoist Press (London), 1919   . £125

ditto, Black Sparrow Press (Santa Barbara, CA), 1986 (150 copies, acetate d/w) £25

ditto, Black Sparrow Press (Santa Barbara, CA), 1986 (26 lettered copies, acetate d/w) £35

The Art of Being Ruled, Chatto & Windus (London), 1926. .   .   .   . £200/£65

ditto, Harper (New York), 1926 .   .   .   . £175/£50

The Lion and the Fox, Grant Richards (London), 1927 . .   .   . £200/£35

ditto, Harper (New York), [1927]   .   .   . £125/£30

Time and Western Man, Chatto & Windus (London), 1927 .   .   .   . £125/£35

ditto, Harcourt, Brace (New York), 1928 .   .   . £50/£15

Paleface: The Philosophy of the 'Melting-Pot', Chatto & Windus (London), 1929 .   .   .   .   . £165/£35

Hitler, Chatto & Windus (London), 1931 .   . £750/£150

The Diabolical Principle and the Dithyrambic Spectator, Chatto & Windus (London), 1931 .   .   . £150/£30

Doom of Youth, Robert McBride (New York), 1932 . .
. . . . £200/£30
ditto, Chatto & Windus (London), 1932 . . £500/£250
Filibusters in Barbary, Grayson (London), 1932 . £250/£65
ditto, National Travel Club (New York), [1927] . £100/£25
Enemy of the Stars, Harmsworth (London), 1932 . £175/£35
The Old Gang and the New Gang, Harmsworth (London), 1933 . . . . £125/£40
ditto, Haskell House (New York), 1972 . . . £10
One-Way Song, Faber (London), 1933 . . £65/£20
ditto, Faber (London), 1933 (40 signed copies) . £1,000
Men Without Art, Cassell (London), 1934 . £200/£30
ditto, Russell & Russell (New York), 1964 . £25/£10
Left Wings Over Europe, Cape (London), 1936 . £125/£25
ditto, Gordon Press (New York), 1972 . . £20/£5
Count Your Dead: They Are Alive!, Lovat Dickson (London), 1937 . . . . £300/£45
ditto, Gordon Press (New York), 1972 . . £20/£5
Blasting and Bombadiering, Eyre & Spottiswoode (London), 1937 . . . . . . £125/£25
ditto, Univ of California Press (Berkeley, CA), 1967 £25/£5
The Mysterious Mr Bull, Robert Hale (London), 1938 . .
. . . . £165/£25
The Jews, Are They Human, Allen & Unwin (London), 1939 . . . . £150/£30
ditto, Gordon Press (New York), 1972 . . £20/£5
The Hitler Cult, Dent (London), 1939 . . £350/£100
ditto, Gordon Press (New York), 1972 . . £20/£5
America, I Presume, Howell & Soskin (New York), 1940 .
. . . . £45/£15
Anglosaxony: A League That Works, Ryerson Press (Toronto, Canada), 1941 (wraps) £750
America and Cosmic Man, Nicholson & Watson (London), 1948 (first state binding green cloth stamped in red on spine) . . . . £85/£35
ditto, Nicholson & Watson (London), 1948 (second state binding light blue cloth stamped in black on spine) £75/£20
ditto, Doubleday (New York), 1949 . . . £65/£15
Rude Assignment, Hutchinson (London), [1950] . £100/£25
ditto, Black Sparrow Press (Santa Barbara, CA), 1984 (26 lettered copies; acetate d/w) . . . £35/£25
ditto, Black Sparrow Press (Santa Barbara, CA), 1984 (200 numbered copies; acetate d/w) . . . . £25/£15
The Writer and the Absolute, Methuen (London), 1952 .
. . . . £50/£10
ditto, Greenwood Press (Westport, CT), 1975 . £15/£5
The Demon of Progress in the Arts, Methuen (London), 1954 . . . . £30/£10
ditto, Regnery (Chicago, IL), 1955 . . . £25/£10
The Letters, Methuen (London), 1963 . . £35/£10
ditto, New Directions (Norfolk, CT), [1927] . £25/£10
A Soldier of Humour and Selected Writings, New American Library (New York), 1966 (pbk) £10
Wyndham Lewis on Art, Thames & Hudson (London), 1969
. . . . £30/£10
ditto, Funk & Wagnalls (New York), 1969 . £25/£10
Wyndham Lewis: An Anthology of His Prose, Methuen (London), 1969 . . . . £25/£10
Enemy Salvoes: Selected Literary Criticism, Vision Press (London), 1976 . . . . . . £25/£10
ditto, Barnes & Noble (New York), 1976 . . £45/£15
Imaginary Letters, Wyndham Lewis Society (Glasgow, Scotland), 1977 (300 copies; wraps) £35

THOMAS LIGOTTI
(b.1953)

Thomas Ligotti is a cult writer of horror stories who has been highly praised and is very collectable. *The Washington Post* called him 'the best kept secret in contemporary horror fiction'.

Books, Pamphlets and Broadsides
Songs of a Dead Dreamer, Silver Scarab Press (Albuquerque, NM), 1985 (300 copies; pbk) £200
ditto, Robinson (London), 1989 (revised and expanded pbk)
. . . . £10
ditto, Carroll & Graf (New York) 1990 . . £25/£10
ditto, Carroll & Graf (New York) 1991 (pbk) . . £5
Grimscribe: His Lives and Works, Robinson (London), 1991 . . . . £10/£5
ditto, Carroll & Graf (New York) 1991 . . £10/£5
ditto, Jove (New York), 1994 (pbk) . . . £5
Noctuary, Robinson (London), 1994 . . . £20/£5
ditto, Carroll & Graf (New York) 1994 . . £20/£5
ditto, Carroll & Graf (New York) 1995 (pbk) . . £5
The Agonizing Resurrection of Victor Frankenstein & Other Gothic Tales, Silver Salamander Press (Eugene, OR) 1994 (1,000 signed pbks) £100
ditto, Silver Salamander Press (Eugene, OR) 1994 (140 hardback copies) . . . . . . £200/£100
ditto, Silver Salamander Press (Eugene, OR) 1994 (40 black leather copies) £300
ditto, Silver Salamander Press (Eugene, OR) 1994 (10 presentation copies in red leather) £400
The Nightmare Factory, Raven (London), 1996 (pbk) . £40
ditto, Carroll & Graf (New York) 1996 (pbk) . . £40
In a Foreign Town, In a Foreign Land, Durtro (London), 1997 (1,000 copies; shrink-wrapped hardcover with CD by Current 93) . . . . £60/£40
ditto, Durtro (London), 1997 (60 copies with marbled end-papers, and a small card autographed by Ligotti, artist Steven Stapleton, and musicians David Tibet and Cristoph Heemann) . . . . £100/£80
ditto, Durtro (London), 2002 [reissued as a digipack with booklet] £15
I Have a Special Plan for This World, Durtro (London), 2000 (sewn wraps; 125 numbered copies signed by author and artist) £150
This Degenerate Little Town, Durtro (London), 2001 (sewn wraps; 160 copies signed by author and artist David Tibet; includes cd with a reading of the text by the author) . £100
ditto, Durtro (London), 2001 (as above, but one of 40 copies on Zerkall paper) £125
What Good Is Your Head?, [Jason Van Hollander] ([Merion Station, PA]), 2002 (350 copies numbered and signed by author and illustrator; broadside) £50
My Work Is Not Yet Done: Three Tales of Corporate Horror, Mythos Books (Poplar Bluff, MO), 2002 (1,000 unnumbered copies; issued with a tipped-in adhesive printed label signed by the author and the artist) . £60/£30
ditto, Mythos Books (Poplar Bluff, MO), 2004 (540 copies)
. . . . £40/£15
ditto, Mythos Books (Poplar Bluff, MO), 2004 (52 lettered copies, bound in black leather, signed by Ligotti and artist on a bound signature page; colour print of the frontispiece, a business card and a ribbon business card holder, a

presentation pen, two paper bookmarks, a notepad and special coupon, all in leather traycase) . . . £125

Crampton, Durtro (London), 2002 [2003] (with Brandon Trenz; pbk; 510 copies issued with a CD 'The Unholy City' written and recorded by Ligotti) . . £50/£35

Sideshow and Other Stories, Subterranean Press (Burton, MI), 2003 (350 signed, numbered copies; pbk) . . £45

ditto, Subterranean Press (Burton, MI), 2003 (52 signed, lettered copies; hardback) £150

Death Poems, Durtro Press (London), 2004 (333 copies; issued with a 'Carpe Diem' badge) . . . £75/£50

The Shadow at The Bottom of The World, Cold Spring Press (Cold Spring Harbor, NY), 2005 (pbk) . . £10

ditto, Subterranean Press (Burton, MI), 2005 (400 signed, numbered copies) . . . . . . £20/£10

ditto, Subterranean Press (Burton, MI), 2005 (26 signed, lettered copies) £150

Teatro Grottesco, Durtro (London), 2006 (500 copies; no d/w) £75

ditto, Durtro (London), 2006 (150 copies printed in purple ink; tipped-in leaflet with limitation signed by author and publisher; no d/w) £150

ditto, Mythos Books (Poplar Bluff, MO), 2007 . £10/£5

DAVID LINDSAY
(b.1878 d.1945)

Lindsay was a Scottish novelist whose curious meta-physical writings remain largely unknown. Among devotees, however, he is considered highly original and interesting. *A Voyage to Arcturus* is an epic philosophical fantasy that sold so badly when it was first published that is now very difficult to find in its first edition.

Novels
A Voyage to Arcturus, Methuen (London), 1920 (first binding, 8 page catalogue at rear) . . £2,500/£1,250

ditto, Methuen (London), 1920 (second binding without catalogue at rear). . . . . £2,250/£1,000

ditto, Gollancz (London), 1946 . . . . £50/£25

ditto, Macmillan (New York), 1963 . . . £45/£20

The Haunted Woman, Methuen (London), 1922 . . . . £1,250/£450

ditto, Gollancz (London), 1947 . . . . £50/£20

ditto, Newcastle (Hollywood, CA), 1975 (pbk) . . £10

ditto, Tartarus Press (Carlton-in-Coverdale), 2004 (300 copies) . . . . £25/£10

Sphinx, John Long (London), 1923 . . £1,250/£450

Adventures of M. De Mailly, Melrose (London), 1926 . . £450/£150

ditto, as *A Blade for Sale*, McBride (New York), 1927 . . £300/£100

Devil's Tor, Putnam (London), 1932 . . £1,500/£500

The Violet Apple and The Witch, Chicago Review Press (Chicago, IL), 1975 . . . . . £100/£25

The Violet Apple, Sidgwick & Jackson (London), [1978] . . . . £125/£25

DAVID LODGE
(b.1935)

David Lodge is a British author and literary critic. He taught English at the University of Birmingham from 1960 until 1987, when he retired to become a full-time writer. His novels, often satirising academia and especially the humanities, are his most keenly sought titles. Many of his characters are Roman Catholics.

Novels
The Picturegoers, MacGibbon & Kee (London), 1960 . . . . £250/£45

Ginger, You're Barmy, MacGibbon & Kee (London), 1962 . . . . £300/£40

ditto, Doubleday (Garden City, NY), 1965 . £50/£15

The British Museum Is Falling Down, MacGibbon & Kee (London), 1965 . . . . . £250/£45

ditto, Holt Rinehart (New York), 1967 . . . £35/£10

Out of the Shelter, Macmillan (London), 1970 £1,000/£450

Changing Places; A Tale of Two Campuses, Secker & Warburg (London), 1975 . . . . . £100/£15

ditto, Viking (New York), 1979 . . . . £25/£10

How Far Can You Go?, Secker & Warburg (London), 1980 . . . . . £50/£10

ditto, as *Souls and Bodies*, Morrow (New York), 1982. . . . . £15/£5

Small World: An Academic Romance, Secker & Warburg (London), 1984 . . . . . £25/£10

ditto, Macmillan (New York), 1985 . . . £15/£5

Nice Work, Secker & Warburg (London), 1988 . £15/£5

ditto, Viking (new York), 1989 . . . . £15/£5

Paradise News, Secker & Warburg (London), 1991 £10/£5

ditto, Viking (New York), 1992 . . . . £10/£5

Therapy, Secker & Warburg (London), 1995 . . £10/£5

ditto, Viking (New York), 1995 . . . . £10/£5

Thinks..., Bridgewater Press (London), 2001 (XII signed, Roman-numbered copies of 138) £125

ditto, Bridgewater Press (London), 2001 (26 signed, lettered copies of 138) £65

ditto, Bridgewater Press (London), 2001 (100 signed, numbered copies of 138) £45

ditto, Secker & Warburg (London), 2001 . . £10/£5

ditto, Viking (New York), 2001 . . . . £10/£5

Author, Author, Secker & Warburg (London), 2004 £10/£5

ditto, Viking (New York), 2004 . . . . £10/£5

Short Stories and Novellas
The Man Who Wouldn't Get Up and Other Stories, Bridgewater Press (London), 1998 (XII signed, Roman-numbered copies of 138) £125

ditto, Bridgewater Press (London), 1998 (26 signed, lettered copies) £85

ditto, Bridgewater Press (London), 1998 (100 signed, numbered copies) £50

Home Truths, Colophon Press (London), 1999 (XII signed, Roman-numbered copies of 112) £125

ditto, Colophon Press (London), 1999 (100 signed, numbered copies) £45

ditto, Secker & Warburg (London), 1999 (pbk) . . £5

Plays
The Writing Game, Secker & Warburg (London), 1991 (pbk) £5

Others

About Catholic Authors, St Paul Publications (London), 1958 (pseud 'Fr. Aloysius Brown'). . . £500/£100

The Language of Fiction: Essays in Criticism and Verbal Analysis of the English Novel, Routledge (London), 1966 . . . . £30/£10

ditto, Columbia Univ Press (New York), 1966. . £25/£10

Graham Greene, Columbia Univ Press (New York), 1966 (pbk) £25

The Novelist at the Crossroads and Other Essays on Fiction and Criticism, Routledge (London), 1971 £20/£5

ditto, Cornell Univ Press (Ithaca, NY), 1971 . £20/£5

Evelyn Waugh, Columbia Univ Press (New York), 1971 (pbk) £15

The Modes of Modern Writing: Metaphor, Metonymy and the Typology of Modern Literature, Arnold (London), 1977 . . . . £20/£5

ditto, Cornell Univ Press (Ithaca, NY), 1977 . £20/£5

Modernism, Antimodernism and Postmodernism, Univ of Birmingham (Birmingham, UK), 1977 (no d/w) . £15

Working with Structuralism: Essays and Reviews on Nineteenth and Twentieth Century Literature, Routledge (London), 1981 . . . . . . £15/£5

Write On: Occasional Essays '65-'85, Secker & Warburg (London), 1986 . . . . £15/£5

After Bakhtin: Essays on Fiction and Criticism, Routledge (London), 1990 . . . . . . £10/£5

The Art of Fiction Illustrated from Classics and Modern Texts, Viking (New York), 1992 . . . £10/£5

ditto, Secker & Warburg (London), 1992 . . £10/£5

The Practice of Writing: Essays, Lectures, Reviews and a Diary, Secker & Warburg (London), 1996 . £15/£5

ditto, Allen Lane/Penguin Press (New York), 1996. £10/£5

Consciousness and the Novel: Connected Essays, Secker & Warburg (London), 2002 . . . . . £10/£5

ditto, Harvard Univ Press (Cambridge, MA), 2002. £10/£5

The Year of Henry James: The Story of a Novel, Harvill Secker (London), 2006 . . . . . £10/£5

ditto, Random House (New York), 2006 . . . £10/£5

JACK LONDON

(b.1876 d.1916)

A highly successful writer of many adventure stories, London took part in the Klondike gold rush of 1897 and used this experience as the background for much of his work. *The Call of the Wild* is his best known book, but many consider his strength to have been his short stories. Indeed, it has been noted that his novels are episodic, resembling a series of linked tales

Novels

A Daughter of the Snows, Lippincott (Philadelphia), 1902 . . . . £300

ditto, Isbister (London), 1904 . . . . . £165

The Kempton-Wace Letters, Macmillan (New York), 1903 (with Anna Strunsky, first issue without authors' names on title-page) £250

ditto, Macmillan (New York), 1903 (second issue with authors' names on title-page) £175

ditto, Isbister (London), 1903 . . . . . £100

The Call of the Wild, Macmillan (New York), 1903 . £500

ditto, Heinemann (London), 1903 . . . . . £150

The Sea-Wolf, Macmillan (New York), 1904 (title-page not a cancel, copyright notice dated 1904 only) . . £2,500

ditto, Macmillan (New York), 1904 (title-page is a cancel, copyright notices dated 1903 and 1904). . . . £150

ditto, Heinemann (London), 1904 . . . . . £85

The Game, Macmillan (New York), 1905 (first state with no rubber stamp notice on verso of title) . . . £175

ditto, Macmillan (New York), 1905 (second state with Metropolitan Magazine copyright stamp on verso of title). £125

ditto, Heinemann (London), 1905 . . . . . £85

White Fang, Macmillan (New York), 1906 (first state with title leaf integral). £175

ditto, Macmillan (New York), 1906 (second state with title leaf tipped-in) £75

ditto, Methuen (London), 1907 . . . . . £65

Before Adam, Macmillan (New York), 1907 . . £75

ditto, Macmillan Colonial Library Edition (London), 1907 . . . . £75

ditto, Werner Laurie (London), [1908] . . . £75

The Iron Heel, Macmillan (New York), 1908 . . . £125

ditto, Everett (London), [1908] £60

Martin Eden, Donohoe (Chicago), 1908 . . . £200

ditto, Macmillan (New York), 1909 . . . . £150

ditto, Heinemann (London), 1910 . . . . . £50

Burning Daylight, Macmillan (New York), 1910 (first printing, one blank leaf follows p.374) . . . £200

ditto, Macmillan (New York), 1910 (second printing, three blank leaves follow p.374) £100

ditto, Heinemann (London), 1911 . . . . . £50

Adventure, Nelson (London), [1911] ('First published in 1911' on copyright page) £300

ditto, Nelson (London), [1911] ('Published in March 1911' on copyright page) £125

ditto, Macmillan (New York), 1911 . . . . . £75

The Abysmal Brute, The Century Co. (New York), 1913 . . . . £125

ditto, Newnes (London), [1914] £65

John Barleycorn, The Century Co. (New York), 1913 . £65

ditto, as *John Barleycorn or Alcoholic Memoirs*, Mills & Boon (London), 1914. . . . . . . £50

The Valley of the Moon, Macmillan (New York), 1913 £200

ditto, Mills & Boon (London), 1914 . . . . £50

The Mutiny of the Elsinor, Macmillan (New York), 1914 . . . . £175

ditto, Mills & Boon (London), 1915 . . . . £65

The Scarlet Plague, Macmillan (New York), 1915 . £165

ditto, Mills & Boon (London), 1915 . . . . £75

The Jacket, Mills & Boon (London), 1915 . . . £85

ditto, as *The Star Rover*, Macmillan (New York), 1915 £175

The Little Lady of the Big House, Macmillan (New York), 1916 . . . . £75

ditto, Mills & Boon (London), 1916 . . . . £50

Jerry of the Islands, Macmillan (New York), 1917 . £65

ditto, Mills & Boon (London), 1917 . . . . £50

Michael, Brother of Jerry, Macmillan (New York), 1917 . . . . £65

ditto, Mills & Boon (London), 1918 . . . . £45

Hearts of Three, Mills & Boon (London), 1918 . £100

ditto, Macmillan (New York), 1920 . . . . £800/£75

The Assassination Bureau Ltd, McGraw-Hill (New York), 1963 (completed by Robert L. Fish) . . £35/£10

ditto, Deutsch (London), 1964 . . . . . £30/£10

Short Stories

The Son of the Wolf: Tales of the Far North, Houghton, Mifflin (Boston), 1900 (trial bindings of either grass-green cloth stamped in silver, greenish-black cloth stamped in silver, or white buckram stamped in red)　．　£1,000

ditto, Houghton, Mifflin (Boston), 1900 (first printing, grey cloth stamped in silver, pagination (i-viii); no blank leaf following page 252; collation: (4), 2-22(6))　．　．　£500

ditto, Houghton, Mifflin (Boston), 1900 (second printing, grey cloth stamped in silver, pagination: (i-vi) blank leaf following page 252)　．　．　．　£250

ditto, Houghton, Mifflin (Boston), 1900 (third printing, as second except collation differs: 1-21(6), 22(4))　．　£150

ditto, Watt (London), 1900　．　．　．　．　．£650

ditto, Isbister (London), 1902　．　．　．　．　£250

The God of His Fathers, & Other Stories, McClure, Philips (New York), 1901　．　．　．　．　．　．£225

ditto, Isbister (London), 1902　．　．　．　．　．£125

Children of the Frost, Macmillan (New York), 1902　．£350

ditto, Macmillan (London), 1902　．　．　．　．£125

The Faith of Men, and Other Stories, Macmillan (New York), 1904．　．　．　．　．　．　．£125

ditto, Heinemann (London), 1904　．　．　．　．£125

Tales of the Fish Patrol, Macmillan (New York), 1905 £225

ditto, Heinemann (London), 1906　．　．　．　．£100

Moon-Face, and Other Stories, Macmillan (New York), 1906　．　．　．　．　．　．　．　．£75

ditto, Heinemann (London), 1906　．　．　．　．£50

Love of Life, and Other Stories, Macmillan (New York), 1907　．　．　．　．　．　．　．　．£75

ditto, Everett (London), [1908]　．　．　．　．£65

Lost Face, Macmillan (New York), 1910．　．　．£150

ditto, Mills & Boon (London), [1915]　．　．　．£50

When God Laughs, and Other Stories, Macmillan (New York), 1911．　．　．　．　．　．　．£100

ditto, Mills & Boon (London), 1912　．　．　．　．£45

South Sea Tales, Macmillan (New York), 1911　．£175

ditto, Mills & Boon (London), 1912　．　．　．　．£65

The House of Pride and Other Tales of Hawaii, Macmillan (New York), 1912　．　．　．　．　．　．£75

ditto, Mills & Boon (London), 1914．　．　．　．£45

A Son of the Sun, Doubleday, Page & Co. (New York), 1912　．　．　．　．　．　．　．　．£175

ditto, Mills & Boon (London), 1913　．　．　．　．£65

Smoke Bellew, The Century Co. (New York), 1912　．£65

ditto, Mills & Boon (London), 1913　．　．　．　．£75

The Night-Born, The Century Co. (New York), 1913　．£75

ditto, Mills & Boon (London), 1916　．　．　．　．£65

The Strength of the Strong, Macmillan (New York), 1914．　．　．　．　．　．　．　．　．£150

ditto, Mills & Boon (London), 1917　．　．　．　．£50

The Turtles of Tasman, Macmillan (New York), 1916．£125

ditto, Mills & Boon (London), 1917　．　．　．　．£75

The Human Drift, Macmillan (New York), 1917　．　．£200

ditto, Mills & Boon (London), 1919　．　．　．　．£75

The Red One, Macmillan (New York), 1918　．　．　．£300

ditto, Mills & Boon (London), 1919　．　．　．　．£100

On The Makaloa Mat, Macmillan (New York), 1919　．£100

ditto, as ***Island Tales***, Mills & Boon (London), 1920　．　．　．　．　．　．　．　．　．£500/£75

Dutch Courage, and Other Stories, Macmillan (New York), 1922　．　．　．　．　．　．£1,000/£250

ditto, Mills & Boon (London), 1923　．　．　．£450/£50

Others

The Cruise of the Dazzler, The Century Co. (New York), 1902　．　．　．　．　．　．　．　．£1,000

ditto, Hodder & Stoughton (London), 1906　．　．　．£500

The People of the Abyss, Macmillan (New York), 1903 (grey-blue cloth)　．　．　．　．　．　．£250

ditto, Macmillan (New York), 1903 (dark blue cloth)　．£150

ditto, Isbister (London), 1903　．　．　．　．　．£125

War of the Classes, Macmillan (New York), 1905．　．£200

ditto, Heinemann (London), 1905　．　．　．　．£65

Scorn of Women, Macmillan (New York), 1906 (top edge gilt)．　．　．　．　．　．　．　．　．£1,250

ditto, Macmillan (New York), 1906 (top edge not gilt)　．£750

ditto, Macmillan (London), 1906　．　．　．　．£250

The Road, Macmillan (New York), 1907 (grey cloth stamped in gold)　．　．　．　．　．　．　．　．£200

ditto, Macmillan (New York), 1907 (cream cloth stamped in black)　．　．　．　．　．　．　．　．£150

ditto, Mills & Boon (London), 1914．　．　．　．£100

Revolution, Kerr (Chicago, IL), [1909] (ads on p.32 headed 'A Socialist Success'; wraps)　．　．　．　．£200

ditto, Kerr (Chicago, IL), [1909] (ads on p.32 headed 'Pocket Library of Socialism'; wraps)　．　．　．　．£150

ditto, Kerr (Chicago, IL), [1909] (ads on p.32 headed either 'Socialist periodicals' or 'Study Socialism'; wraps)　．£125

ditto, Kerr (Chicago, IL), [1909] (ads on p.32 headed 'Socialist Literature'; wraps)　．　．　．　．£100

Revolution and Other Essays, Macmillan (New York), 1910 (maroon cloth)　．　．　．　．　．　．£200

ditto, Macmillan (New York), 1910 (brown cloth)　．£150

ditto, Mills & Boon (London), 1920　．　．　．£145/£25

Theft: A Play in Four Acts, Macmillan (New York), 1910　．　．　．　．　．　．　．　．　．　．£500

ditto, Macmillan (London), 1910　．　．　．　．£150

The Cruise of the Snark, Macmillan (New York), 1911 £175

ditto, Mills & Boon (London), 1913　．　．　．　．£50

Jack London By Himself, Macmillan (New York), [1913]　．　．　．　．　．　．　．　．　．£250

ditto, Mills & Boon (London), 1913　．　．　．　．£150

The Acorn-Planter; A California Forest Play, Macmillan (New York), 1916　．　．　．　．　．　．£1,000

ditto, Mills & Boon (London), 1916　．　．　．　．£250

Letters from Jack London Containing an Unpublished Correspondence between London and Sinclair Lewis, Odyssey Press (New York), 1965　．　．　．　£25/£10

ditto, MacGibbon & Kee (London), 1966．　．　£25/£10

Collected Editions

The Works of Jack London, Macmillan (New York), 1919 (21 vols)　．　．　．　．　．　．　．　．£1,000

ANITA LOOS
(b.1893 d.1981)

An American writer, Anita Loos started writing scenarios
and screenplays in 1912 for the pioneer movie director
D.W. Griffith. She later wrote plays and dramatisations of
works by other writers. She is perhaps best known for her
short satirical novel *Gentlemen Prefer Blondes* (1925),
which was dramatised and filmed. *But Gentlemen Marry
Brunettes* was the successful sequel. She also wrote several
volumes of Hollywood reminiscences.

Novels
*'Gentlemen Prefer Blondes': The Illuminating Diary of a
Professional Lady*, Boni & Liveright (New York), 1925
(first issue with 'Divine' for 'Devine' on contents page) .
. . . . £600/£100
ditto, Brentano's (London), 1926 . . . . £65/£20
ditto, Brentano's (London), 1926 (1,000 signed copies) .
. . . . £450/£175
'But Gentlemen Marry Brunettes', Boni & Liveright (New
York), 1928 . . . . £125/£30
ditto, Brentano's (London), 1928 . . . . £75/£20
A Mouse is Born, Doubleday (New York), 1951 . £20/£10
ditto, Cape (London), 1951 . . . . . £15/£5
No Mother to Guide Her, McGraw Hill (New York), 1961 .
. . . . £15/£5
ditto, Arthur Barker (London), 1961 . . . £10/£5

Others
How to Write Photoplays, James A. McCann (New York),
1920 (with John Emerson). . . . . £600/£75
Breaking into the Movies, James A. McCann (New York),
1921 (with John Emerson). . . . . £600/£75
'The Struggle', Griffith (New York), 1931 (with John
Emerson) £400
Happy Birthday: A Play in Two Acts, French (New York),
1947 . . . . £200/£15
Gigi, Random House (New York), 1952 (by Colette,
dramatized by Loos) . . . . . . £40/£15
ditto, as *Gigi: A Comedy in Two Acts*, French (London),
1956 (with Colette; wraps) £10
A Girl Like I, Viking (New York), 1966 . . £10/£5
ditto, Hamish Hamilton (London), 1967 . . £10/£5
Twice Over Lightly: New York Then and Now, Harcourt
Bruce Jovanovich (New York), 1972 (with Helen Hayes) .
. . . . £10/£5
Kiss Hollywood Good-by, Viking (New York), 1974 £10/£5
ditto, as *Kiss Hollywood Good-bye*, W.H. Allen (London),
1974 . . . . £10/£5
Cast of Thousands, Grosset & Dunlap (New York), 1977 .
. . . . £10/£5
The Talmadge Girls, Viking (New York), 1978 . £10/£5
San Francisco: A Screenplay, Southern Illinois Univ Press
(Carbondale, IL), 1979 . . . . . £10/£5
*Fate Keeps on Happening: Adventures of Lorelei Lee and
Other Writings*, Dodd, Mead (New York), 1984 . £10/£5
ditto, Harrap (London), 1985 . . . . £10/£5

E.C.R. LORAC
(b.1894 d.1958)

Edith Caroline Rivett was a British crime writer known for
her 'Golden Age' detective fiction written under the
pseudonyms 'Lorac' (Carol backwards) and 'Carnac'. She
was born in London and studied at the London School of
Arts and Crafts. She was later a member of the Detection
Club.

Novels Written as 'E.C.R. Lorac'
The Murder on the Burrows, Sampson Low (London),
[1931] . . . . £2,000/£275
ditto, Macaulay (New York), 1932 . . . £650/£150
The Affair at Thor's Head, Sampson Low (London), [1932]
. . . . £1,500/£250
The Greenwell Mystery, Sampson Low (London), [1932] .
. . . . £1,500/£250
ditto, Macaulay (New York), 1934 . . . £500/£175
Death on the Oxford Road, Sampson Low (London), [1933]
. . . . £1,500/£250
ditto, Macaulay (New York), 1934 . . . £450/£65
The Case of Colonel Marchand, Sampson Low (London),
[1933] . . . . £1,500/£250
ditto, Macaulay (New York), 1933 . . . £400/£50
Murder in St John's Wood, Sampson Low (London), [1934]
. . . . £1,450/£200
ditto, Macaulay (New York), 1934 . . . £400/£50
Murder in Chelsea, Sampson Low (London), [1934] .
. . . . £1,450/£200
ditto, Macaulay (New York), 1935 . . . £400/£50
The Organ Speaks, Sampson Low (London), [1935] .
. . . . £1,450/£200
The Death of an Author, Sampson Low (London), [1935] .
. . . . £1,450/£200
ditto, Macaulay (New York), 1937 . . . £400/£50
Crime Counter Crime, Collins Crime Club (London), 1936
. . . . £1,250/£165
Post After Post-Mortem, Collins Crime Club (London), 1936
. . . . £1,250/£165
A Pall for a Painter, Collins Crime Club (London), 1936 .
. . . . £1,000/£150
Bats in the Belfry, Collins Crime Club (London), 1937.
. . . . £1,000/£150
ditto, Macaulay (New York), 1937 . . . £400/£50
These Names Make Clues, Collins Crime Club (London),
1937 . . . . £1,000/£150
The Devil and the CID, Collins Crime Club (London), 1938
. . . . £1,000/£125
Slippery Staircase, Collins Crime Club (London), 1938 .
. . . . £1,000/£125
John Brown's Body, Collins Crime Club (London), 1938 .
. . . . £1,000/£125
Black Beadle, Collins Crime Club (London), 1939 . .
. . . . £1,000/£125
Death at Dyke's Corner, Collins Crime Club (London),
1940 . . . . £650/£100
Tryst for a Tragedy, Collins Crime Club (London), 1940 .
. . . . £650/£100
Case in the Clinic, Collins Crime Club (London), 1941 .
. . . . £350/£75
Rope's End, Rogue's End, Collins Crime Club (London),
1942 . . . . £200/£25

The Sixteenth Stair, Collins Crime Club (London), 1942   .
.   .   .   . £175/£30
Death Came Softly, Collins Crime Club (London), 1943   .
.   .   .   . £175/£30
ditto, Mystery House (New York), 1943   .   .   . £75/£15
Checkmate to Murder, Collins Crime Club (London), 1944
.   .   .   . £165/£30
ditto, Mystery House (New York), 1944   .   .   . £65/£15
Fell Murder, Collins Crime Club (London), 1944 . £150/£25
Murder by Matchlight, Collins Crime Club (London), 1945
.   .   .   . £150/£25
ditto, Mystery House (New York), 1946   .   . £45/£10
Fire in the Thatch, Collins Crime Club (London), 1946   .
.   .   .   . £125/£25
ditto, Mystery House (New York), 1946   .   .   . £45/£10
The Theft of the Iron Dogs, Collins Crime Club (London),
1946   .   .   .   . £125/£25
ditto, as *Murderer's Mistake*, Mystery House (New York),
1947   .   .   .   . £35/£10
Relative to Poison, Collins Crime Club (London), 1947   .
.   .   .   . £125/£25
ditto, Doubleday (New York), 1948   .   .   . £35/£10
Death Before Dinner, Collins Crime Club (London), 1948 .
.   .   .   . £125/£25
ditto, as *A Screen for Murder*, Doubleday (New York), 1948
.   .   .   . £30/£10
Part for a Poisoner, Collins Crime Club (London), 1948   .
.   .   .   . £125/£25
ditto, as *Place for a Poisoner*, Doubleday (New York), 1949
.   .   .   . £30/£10
Still Waters, Collins Crime Club (London), 1949 . £125/£25
Policemen on the Precinct, Collins Crime Club (London),
1949   .   .   .   . £125/£25
ditto, as *And Then Put Out the Light*, Doubleday (New
York), 1950   .   .   .   . £30/£10
Accident by Design, Collins Crime Club (London), 1950   .
.   .   .   . £125/£25
ditto, Doubleday (New York), 1951   .   .   . £25/£10
Murder of a Martinet, Collins Crime Club (London), 1951.
.   .   .   . £125/£25
ditto, as *I Could Murder Her*, Doubleday (New York), 1951
.   .   .   . £25/£10
The Dog It Was That Died, Collins Crime Club (London),
1952   .   .   .   . £100/£20
ditto, Doubleday (New York), 1952   .   .   . £25/£10
Murder in the Millrace, Collins Crime Club (London), 1952
.   .   .   . £100/£20
ditto, as *Speak Justly of the Dead*, Doubleday (New York),
1953   .   .   .   . £25/£10
Crook o'Lune, Collins Crime Club (London), 1953   .   .
.   .   .   . £100/£20
ditto, as *Shepherd's Crook*, Doubleday (New York), 1953 .
.   .   .   . £25/£10
Shroud of Darkness, Collins Crime Club (London), 1954   .
.   .   .   . £100/£20
ditto, Doubleday (New York), 1954   .   .   . £25/£10
Let Well Alone, Collins Crime Club (London), 1954   .   .
.   .   .   . £100/£20
Ask a Policeman, Collins Crime Club (London), 1955 .   .
.   .   .   . £100/£20
Murder in Vienna, Collins Crime Club (London), 1956   .
.   .   .   . £100/£20
Picture of Death, Collins Crime Club (London), 1957 .   .
.   .   .   . £100/£20

Dangerous Domicile, Collins Crime Club (London), 1957 .
.   .   .   . £100/£20
Death in Triplicate, Collins Crime Club (London), 1958   .
.   .   .   . £100/£20
ditto, as *People Will Talk*, Doubleday (New York), 1958   .
.   .   .   . £25/£10
Murder on a Monument, Collins Crime Club (London),
1958   .   .   .   . £100/£20
Dishonour Among Thieves, Collins Crime Club (London),
1959   .   .   .   . £75/£20
ditto, as *The Last Escape*, Doubleday (New York), 1959   .
.   .   .   . £25/£10

Novels Written as 'Carol Carnac'
Triple Death, Butterworth (London), [1936]   . £1,250/£175
Murder at Mornington, Skeffington (London), [1937].   .
.   .   .   . £1,000/£175
The Missing Rope, Skeffington (London), [1937] .   .   .
.   .   .   . £1,000/£175
When the Devil Was Sick, Peter Davies (London), 1939   .
.   .   .   . £750/£150
The Case of the First-Class Carriage, Peter Davies
(London), 1939   .   .   .   .   .   . £650/£125
Death in the Diving Pool, Peter Davies (London), 1940   .
.   .   .   . £500/£100
A Double for Detection, Macdonald (London), [1945] .   .
.   .   .   . £125/£25
The Striped Suitcase, Macdonald (London), 1946 . £125/£25
ditto, Doubleday (New York), 1947   .   .   . £35/£10
Clue Sinister, Macdonald (London), 1947   . £125/£25
Over the Garden Wall, Macdonald (London), 1948 £125/£25
ditto, Doubleday (New York), 1949   .   .   . £35/£10
Upstairs, Downstairs, Macdonald (London), 1950. £100/£25
ditto, as *Upstairs and Downstairs*, Doubleday (New York),
1950   .   .   .   . £35/£10
Copy for Crime, Macdonald (London), 1950   . £100/£25
ditto, Doubleday (New York), 1951   .   .   . £25/£10
It's Her Own Funeral, Collins Crime Club (London), 1951
.   .   .   . £100/£25
Crossed Skis, Collins Crime Club (London), 1952. £100/£25
Murder As A Fine Art, Collins Crime Club (London), 1953
.   .   .   . £100/£25
A Policeman at the Door, Collins Crime Club (London),
1953   .   .   .   . £100/£25
ditto, Doubleday (New York), 1954   .   .   . £25/£10
Impact of Evidence, Collins Crime Club (London), 1954   .
.   .   .   . £100/£20
ditto, Doubleday (New York), 1954   .   .   . £25/£10
Murder Among Members, Collins Crime Club (London),
1955   .   .   .   . £100/£20
Rigging the Evidence, Collins Crime Club (London), 1955.
.   .   .   . £100/£20
The Double Turn, Collins Crime Club (London), 1956   .
.   .   .   . £75/£20
ditto, as *The Late Miss Trimming*, Doubleday (New York),
1957   .   .   .   . £25/£10
The Burning Question, Collins Crime Club (London), 1957
.   .   .   . £75/£20
Long Shadows, Collins Crime Club (London), 1958   .   .
.   .   .   . £75/£20
ditto, as *Affair at Helen's Court*, Doubleday (New York),
1958   .   .   .   . £25/£10
Death of a Lady Killer, Collins Crime Club (London), 1959
.   .   .   . £75/£20

Novels written as 'Carol Rivett'
Outer Circle, Hodder & Stoughton (London), 1939 £200/£35
Time Remembered, Hodder & Stoughton (London), 1940 .
. . . . £200/£35

Collaboration as 'E.C.R. Lorac'
No Flowers by Request & *Crime on the Coast*, Gollancz
(London), 1984 (chain novel; chapters by Lorac and others)
. . . . £10/£5

H.P. LOVECRAFT
(b.1890 d.1937)

Howard Phillips Lovecraft was an American author of
horror and fantasy fiction published in his lifetime in pulp
magazines such as *Weird Tales*. His works have steadily
become more influential and critically respected, and very
widely reprinted. Arkham House have issued revised and
corrected editions of all the major Lovecraft stories.
See also the entry for *Weird Tales*.

Fiction

The Shunned House, The Recluse Press (Athol, MA), 1928
(original unbound sheets, distributed by Barlow or later
Arkham House) £5,000
ditto, copies bound by R.H. Barlow (De Land, FA), 1934/35
(c.8 may exist; provenance required) . . £6,500
ditto, Arkham House (Sauk City, WI), 1961 (bound with
Arkham House imprint on spine; 100 copies; no d/w). .
. . . . £2,000
ditto, Arkham House (Sauk City, WI), (counterfeit edition,
1965/66; red half leather; spine stamped in gold). £400
The Battle That Ended the Century, [Barlow (De Land,
FA), 1934] (50 mimeographed copies; wraps) . £1,000
The Cats of Ulthar, Dragon-Fly Press (Cassia, FA), 1935 (42
copies; sewn wraps) £1,000
ditto, Roy A. Squires (Glendale, CA), 1979 (200 numbered
copies; wraps) £25
ditto, Necronomicon Press (West Warwick, RI), 1977 (550
numbered copies; stapled wraps) £15
The Shadow Over Innsmouth, Visionary Publishing
(Everett, PA), 1936 (150-200 copies; d/w and errata sheet
were issued later and sent to customers; yellow d/w has
priority over d/w with green illustration). £2,250/£1,500
A History of the Necronomicon, Rebel Press (Oakman, AL),
1938 (wraps). £500
ditto, Necronomicon Press (West Warwick, RI), 1977 (500
numbered copies; stapled wraps) £15
The Outsider and Others, Arkham House (Sauk City, WI),
1939 . . . . £2,000/£600
Beyond the Wall of Sleep, Arkham House (Sauk City, WI),
1943 . . . . £1,000/£300
The Weird Shadow Over Innsmouth, Bartholomew House
(New York), 1944 (pbk) £20
The Dunwich Horror and Other Weird Tales, Editions for
the Armed Services (New York), [1945?] (pbk) . . £30
Best Supernatural Stories, World Publishing Co (Cleveland,
OH), 1945 . . . . £40/£10
The Dunwich Horror, Bartholomew House (New York),
1945 (pbk) £25
The Lurker at the Threshold, Arkham House (Sauk City,
WI), 1945 (novel mainly written by Derleth) . £100/£30

ditto, Museum Press (London), 1948 . . . . £175/£35
ditto, Gollancz (London), 1968 . . . . . £40/£15
The Lurking Fear and Other Stories, Avon (New York),
1947 (pbk) £15
The Haunter of the Dark, Gollancz (London), 1951 £50/£15
The Case of Charles Dexter Ward, Gollancz (London), 1951
. . . . £75/£35
The Curse of Yig, Arkham House (Sauk City, WI), 1953 (by
Zealia B. Bishop). . . . . . . £75/£25
The Challenge from Beyond, Pennsylvania Dutch Cheese
Press (FAPA) [Washington, DC], 1954 (with Abraham
Merrit, Robert E. Howard, Frank Belknap Long, and C.L.
Moore) £75
The Dream Quest of Unknown Kadath, Shroud (Buffalo,
NY), 1955 (50 copies bound in cloth; numbering is out of
sequence) . . . . £200/£125
ditto, Shroud (Buffalo, NY), 1955 (1,400+ copies in wraps,
with d/w) . . . . £40/£20
ditto, Shroud (Buffalo, NY), 1955 (12 numbered copies
clothbound by Gerry de la Ree in 1972). . . £250
The Survivor and Others, Arkham House (Sauk City, WI),
1957 (completed by Derleth) . . . . £75/£25
The Dunwich Horror and Others, Arkham House (Sauk
City, WI), 1963 . . . . £50/£20
At the Mountains of Madness, Arkham House (Sauk City,
WI), 1964 . . . . £75/£25
ditto, Gollancz (London), 1966 . . . . £50/£20
The Colour Out Of Space, Lancer (New York), 1964 (pbk)
. . . . £10
The Lurking Fear and Other Stories, Panther (London),
1964 (pbk) £10
Dagon and Other Macabre Tales, Arkham House (Sauk
City, WI), 1965 . . . . £50/£15
ditto, Gollancz (London), 1967 . . . . £45/£20
The Dark Brotherhood, Arkham House (Sauk City, WI),
1966 . . . . £50/£20
Three Tales of Horror, Arkham House (Sauk City, WI),
1967 . . . . £75/£25
The Shadow Out of Time, Gollancz (London), 1968 . .
. . . . £60/£20
*The Prose Poems: Ex Oblivione, Memory, Nyarlathotep,
What the Moon Brings*, Squires (Glendale, CA), 1969-
1970 (26 lettered copies of 125, 4 booklets in envelopes) .
. . . . £275
ditto, Squires (Glendale, CA), 1969-1970 (99 numbered
copies of 125, 4 booklets, in envelopes). . . . £200
The Dream Quest of Unknown Kadath, Ballantine (New
York), 1970 (pbk) £10
The Horror in the Museum and Other Revisions, Arkham
House (Sauk City, WI), 1970 . . . . £25/£10
The Doom That Came To Sarnath, Ballantine (New York),
1971 (pbk) £10
The Shadow Over Innsmouth, Scholastic (New York), 1971
(pbk) £5
The Watchers Out of Time and Others, Arkham House
(Sauk City, WI), 1974 (stories completed by Derleth).
. . . . £25/£10
Medusa: A Portrait, Oliphant Press (New York), 1975 (500
numbered copies in wraps) £15
The Statement of Randolph Carter, The Strange Company
(Madison, WI), 1976 (150 copies, unbound holographic
sheets in folder) £25
ditto, The Strange Company (Madison, WI), 1976 (30 copies
signed by editor, unbound holographic sheets in folder) £50

Herbert West: Reanimator, Necronomicon Press (West Warwick, RI), 1977 (1,000 copies; stapled wraps) . £10

The Lurking Fear, Necronomicon Press (West Warwick, RI), 1977 (550 copies; stapled wraps) . . . £15

Collapsing Cosmoses, Necronomicon Press (West Warwick, RI), 1977 (500 copies; stapled wraps) . . . £15

Uncollected Prose and Poetry, Vol I, Necronomicon Press (West Warwick, RI), 1978 (stapled wraps) . . . £10

ditto, Vol II, Necronomicon Press (West Warwick, RI), 1980 (stapled wraps) £10

ditto, Vol III, Necronomicon Press (West Warwick, RI), 1982 (stapled wraps) £10

The Colour Out Of Space, Necronomicon Press (West Warwick, RI), 1982 (400 copies; stapled wraps) . . £15

The Best of H.P. Lovecraft, Del Rey/Ballantine (New York), 1982 (pbk) £5

The Young Folks' Ulysses, Soft Books (Toronto, Canada), 1982 (200 copies; wraps) £10

Ashes and Others, Miskatonic Univ Press (Bloomfield, NJ), 1983 (stapled wraps) £10

Juvenilia:, 1895-1905, Necronomicon Press (West Warwick, RI), 1984 (stapled wraps) £5

The Festival, Necronomicon Press (West Warwick, RI), 1984 (50 copies; stapled wraps) £20

At the Mountains of Madness, Grant (West Kingston, RI), 1990 (1,000 copies signed by artist Fernando Duval, leather binding) £70

The Battle that Ended the Century/Collapsing Cosmoses, Necronomicon Press (West Warwick, RI), 1992 (stapled wraps) £10

Crawling Chaos: Selected Works 1920-1935, Creation Press (London), 1993 (pbk). £10

The Dream Cycle of H.P. Lovecraft, Ballantine/Del Ray (New York), 1995 (pbk) £5

The Transition of H.P. Lovecraft, Ballantine/Del Ray (New York), 1995 (pbk) £5

The Annotated H.P. Lovecraft, Dell (New York), 1997 (pbk) £10

Tales of H.P. Lovecraft, Ecco Press (Hopewell, NJ), 1997 . . . . £20/£5

More Annotated H.P. Lovecraft, Dell (New York), 1999 (pbk) £10

The Ancient Track, Necronomicon Press (West Warwick, RI), 2000 (250 copies) £25

ditto, Necronomicon Press (West Warwick, RI), 2000 (800 copies; stapled wraps) £10

Poetry

The Crime of Crimes, Harris (Llandudno, Wales), [1915] (mimeographed pamphlet). £6,500

A Sonnet – The Lovecrafter, Shepherd & Wollheim [Oakman, AL], 1936 (16 copies) . . . £1,250

H.P.L., Corwin Stickney [Belleville, NJ], [1937] (poetry, limited to 23 copies; stapled wraps) . . . £3,000

Fungi from Yuggoth, Fantasy Amateur Press Association [Washington, DC], 1943 (approx 65 copies; stapled wraps) £750

Collected Poems, Arkham House (Sauk City, WI), 1963 . . . . £100/£25

Antarktos, Fantome Press (Warren, OH), 1977 (150 copies; wraps; in envelope) . . . . . £50/£35

A Winter Wish and Other Poems, Whispers Press (Chapel Hill, NC), 1977 (26 copies signed and lettered in slipcase) . . . . £75/£50

ditto, Whispers Press (Chapel Hill, NC), 1977 (200 signed, numbered copies in slipcase and d/w) . . . £40/£25

ditto, Whispers Press (Chapel Hill, NC), 1977 (trade edition, 2,000 copies) . . . . £20/£10

The Illustrated Fungi from Yuggoth, Dream House (Madison, WI), 1983 (250 numbered copies signed by artist; pbk) £35

Saturnalia and Other Poems, Cryptic Publications (Bloomfield, NJ), 1984 (stapled wraps). . . . £25

Medusa and Other Poems, Cryptic Publications (Bloomfield, NJ), 1986 (stapled wraps) . . . £25

The Fantastic Poetry, Necronomicon Press (West Warwick, RI), 1990 (stapled wraps) £15

Non-Fiction

Exponent of Amateur Journalism, United Amateur Press Association [Elroy, WI.], [c.1916] (mimeographed pamphlet) £1,750

Looking Backward, C.W. Smith (Haverhill, MA), [1920] (c. 40 copies, mimeographed pamphlet) . . . £1,750

The Materialist Today, Driftwind Press (Montpelier, VT), 1926 (15 copies, pamphlet) £2,500

Further Criticism of Poetry, George C. Fetter (Louisville, KY), 1932 (pamphlet) £1,750

Charleston, [H.C. Koenig (New York), 1936] (first state presented as a letter, 20-25 copies, pamphlet) . £1,000

ditto, [H.C. Koenig (New York), 1936] (second state presented as an essay, 30-35 copies, pamphlet) . .£600

Some Current Motives and Practices, R.H. Barlow (De Land, FL), 1936 (50-100 copies, mimeographed pamphlet) £425

Notes and the Commonplace Book, Futile Press (Lakeport, CA), 1938 (no d/w) £1,250

Marginalia, Arkham House (Sauk City, WI), 1944 £175/£45

Supernatural Horror in Literature, Ben Abramson (New York), 1945 (first binding black cloth; first state of text with 'elft' for 'left' on p.66; no d/w) £50

ditto, Ben Abramson (New York), 1945 (second binding red cloth; errors corrected) . . . . . £50/£25

Something About Cats, Arkham House (Sauk City, WI), 1949 . . . .£100/£25

The Lovecraft Collector's Library, S.S.R. Publications (North Tonawanda, NY), 1952-55 (7 vols, 75 copies). . . . . £650 the set

The Shuttered Room and Other Pieces, Arkham House (Sauk City, WI), 1959 . . . . . .£125/£45

Dreams and Fancies, Arkham House (Sauk City, WI), 1962 . . . .£125/£45

Some Notes on a Nonentity, Arkham House (Sauk City, WI), 1963 (stapled wraps). £150

Selected Letters, Volume I, 1911-1924, Arkham House (Sauk City, WI), 1965 . . . . . .£50/£20

Selected Letters, Volume II, 1925-1929, Arkham House (Sauk City, WI), 1968 . . . . . £40/£15

Hail, Klarkash-Ton!, Squires (Glendale, CA), 1971 (89 copies; wraps) £75

Selected Letters, Volume III, 1929-1931, Arkham House (Sauk City, WI), 1971 . . . . . £40/£15

Ec'h-Pi-El Speaks, de la Ree (Saddle River, NJ), 1972 (25 cloth bound copies, no d/w) £100

ditto, de la Ree (Saddle River, NJ), 1972 (475 copies; stapled wraps) £25

Lovecraft at Last, Carrollton Clark (Arlington, VA), 1975 ('Collectors edition', 1,000 copies in slipcase) . £40/£20

ditto, Carrollton Clark (Arlington, VA), 1975 (2,000 copies)
. . . . £25/£10

The Occult Lovecraft, de la Ree (Saddle River, NJ), 1975
(128 numbered cloth bound copies, no d/w) . . . £60

ditto, de la Ree (Saddle River, NJ), 1975 (990 copies; stapled
wraps) £20

First Writings: Pawtuxet Valley Gleaner 1906,
Necronomicon Press (West Warwick, RI), 1976 (500
numbered copies; stapled wraps) . . . £30

Selected Letters, Volume IV, 1932-1934, Arkham House
(Sauk City, WI), 1976 . . . . £25/£10

Selected Letters, Volume V, 1935-1937, Arkham House
(Sauk City, WI), 1976 . . . . £25/£10

The Conservative Complete 1915-1923, Necronomicon
Press (West Warwick, RI), 1976 (400 copies; stapled
wraps) £45

Writings in the United Amateur 1915-1922, Necronomicon
Press (West Warwick, RI), 1976 (500 numbered copies;
stapled wraps) £35

To Quebec and the Stars, Grant (West Kingston, RI), 1976.
. . . . £25/£10

The Californian, Necronomicon Press (West Warwick, RI),
1977 (1,000 numbered copies; stapled wraps) . . £25

Writings in The Tryout, Necronomicon Press (West
Warwick, RI), 1977 (1,000 numbered copies; stapled
wraps) £25

Memoirs of an Inconsequential Scribbler, Necronomicon
Press (West Warwick, RI), 1977 (500 copies; stapled
wraps) £30

Science Versus Charlatanry, Strange Company (Madison,
WI), 1979 (200 numbered copies; wraps) . . . £35

H.P. Lovecraft in The Eyrie, Necronomicon Press (West
Warwick, RI), 1979 (stapled wraps) . . . £5

The H.P. Lovecraft Christmas Book, Necronomicon Press
(West Warwick, RI), 1984 (stapled wraps) . . £5

In Defence of Dagon, Necronomicon Press (West Warwick,
RI), 1985 (1,000 numbered copies; stapled wraps) . £5

Uncollected Letters, Necronomicon Press (West Warwick,
RI), 1986 (stapled wraps) £5

Commonplace Book, Necronomicon Press (West Warwick,
RI), 1987 (2 vols; stapled wraps) £10

Yr Obt Servt., The Strange Company (Madison, WI), 1988
(200 copies; stapled wraps) £25

European Glimpses, Necronomicon Press (West Warwick,
RI), 1988 (stapled wraps) £5

The Vivesector, Necronomicon Press (West Warwick, RI),
1990 (stapled wraps) £5

Letters to Henry Kuttner, Necronomicon Press (West
Warwick, RI), 1990 (stapled wraps) . . . £5

The Conservative, Necronomicon Press (West Warwick, RI),
1990 (stapled wraps) £5

Letters to Richard Searight, Necronomicon Press (West
Warwick, RI), 1992 (stapled wraps) . . . £5

Autobiographical Writings, Necronomicon Press (West
Warwick, RI), 1992 (stapled wraps) . . . £5

Letters to Robert Bloch, Necronomicon Press (West
Warwick, RI), 1993 (stapled wraps) . . . £5

Letters to Robert Bloch Supplement, Necronomicon Press
(West Warwick, RI), 1993 (stapled wraps) . . £5

H.P. Lovecraft in The Argosy, Necronomicon Press (West
Warwick, RI), 1994 (stapled wraps) . . . £5

The H.P. Lovecraft Dream Book, Necronomicon Press
(West Warwick, RI), 1994 (stapled wraps) . . £10

Miscellaneous Writings, Arkham House (Sauk City, WI),
1995 . . . . £20/£5

PETER LOVESEY
(b.1936)

Peter Lovesey is the author of British detective fiction. His
first novel, *Wobble to Death*, introduced two Victorian
policemen and won the Macmillan/Panther award for the
Best First Crime Novel. His more recent books have moved
closer to the modern day, but it is as an historical detective
novelist that he is most appreciated.

'Sergeant Cribb' Mystery Series

Wobble to Death, Macmillan (London), 1970 . . £75/£15

ditto, Dodd, Mead (New York), 1970 . . . £50/£10

The Detective Wore Silk Drawers, Macmillan (London),
1971 . . . . £45/£10

ditto, Dodd, Mead (New York), 1971 . . . £25/£5

Abracadaver, Macmillan (London), 1972. . . £45/£10

ditto, Dodd, Mead (New York), 1972 . . . £20/£5

Mad Hatter's Holiday, Macmillan (London), 1973 £40/£5

ditto, Dodd, Mead (New York), 1973 . . . £20/£5

Invitation to a Dynamite Party, Macmillan (London), 1974
. . . . £25/£5

ditto, as *The Tick of Death*, Dodd, Mead (New York), 1974
. . . . £20/£5

A Case of Spirits, Macmillan (London), 1975 . . £20/£5

ditto, Dodd, Mead (New York), 1975 . . . £15/£5

Swing, Swing Together, Macmillan (London), 1976 £25/£5

ditto, Dodd, Mead (New York), 1976 . . . £15/£5

Waxwork, Macmillan (London), 1978 . . . £20/£5

ditto, Pantheon (New York), 1978 . . . . £10/£5

'Peter Diamond' Mystery Series

The Last Detective, Scorpion Press (Bristol, UK), 1991 (99
signed, numbered copies, acetate d/w) . . . £55/£45

ditto, Scribner's (London), 1991 . . . . £15/£5

ditto, Doubleday (New York), 1991 . . . . £15/£5

Diamond Solitaire, Little, Brown (London), 1992 . £10/£5

ditto, Mysterious Press (New York), 1993 . . £10/£5

The Summons, Little, Brown (London), 1995 . . £10/£5

ditto, Mysterious Press (New York), 1995 . . £10/£5

Bloodhounds, Little, Brown (London), 1996 . . £10/£5

ditto, Mysterious Press (New York), 1996 . . £10/£5

Upon a Dark Night, Little, Brown (London), 1997 £10/£5

ditto, Mysterious Press (New York), 1998 . . £10/£5

The Vault, Little, Brown (London), 1999 . . £10/£5

ditto, Soho Press (New York), 2000 . . . . £10/£5

Diamond Dust, Little, Brown (London), 2002. . £10/£5

ditto, Soho Press (New York), 2002 . . . . £10/£5

The House Sitter, Little, Brown (London), 2003 . £10/£5

ditto, Soho Press (New York), 2003 . . . . £10/£5

'Albert Edward, Prince of Wales' Mystery Series

Bertie and the Tinman, Bodley Head (London), 1987 . .
. . . . £15/£5

ditto, Mysterious Press (New York), 1988 . . £10/£5

Bertie and the Seven Bodies, Mysterious Press/Century
(London), 1990 . . . . £10/£5

ditto, Mysterious Press (New York), 1990 . . £10/£5

Bertie and the Crime of Passion, Little, Brown (London),
1993 . . . . £10/£5

ditto, Mysterious Press (New York), 1993 . . £10/£5

Other Novels

Goldengirl, Cassell (London), 1977 (pseud 'Peter Lear') .
.   .   .   .   £25/£5
ditto, Doubleday (New York), 1977 .   .   .   £20/£5
Spider Girl, Cassell (London), 1980 (pseud 'Peter Lear') .
.   .   .   .   £25/£5
ditto, Viking (New York), 1980 .   .   .   .   £20/£5
The False Inspector Dew, Macmillan (London), 1982 .
.   .   .   .   £15/£5
ditto, Pantheon (New York), 1982   .   .   .   £10/£5
Keystone, Macmillan (London), 1983   .   .   £15/£5
ditto, Pantheon (New York), 1983 .   .   .   £10/£5
The Secret of Spandau, Joseph (London), 1986 (pseud
'Peter Lear') .   .   .   .   £15/£5
Rough Cider, Bodley Head (London), 1986 .   £15/£5
ditto, Mysterious Press (New York), 1987   .   £10/£5
On the Edge, Mysterious Press/Century (London), 1989   .
.   .   .   .   £15/£5
ditto, Mysterious Press/Century (London), 1989 (250 signed,
numbered proof copies; pbk) £20
ditto, Mysterious Press (New York), 1989   .   £10/£5
The Reaper, Little, Brown (London), 2000   .   £10/£5
ditto, Soho Press (New York), 2000   .   .   £10/£5
The Circle, Time Warner/Little, Brown (London), 2005   .
.   .   .   .   £10/£5

Short Stories

Butchers and Other Stories of Crime, Macmillan (London),
1985   .   .   .   .   £15/£5
ditto, Mysterious Press (New York), 1987   .   £15/£5
The Staring Man and Other Stories, Eurographica
(Helsinki), 1988 (350 signed, numbered copies; wraps with
d/w) £65
The Crime Of Miss Oyster Brown, Little, Brown (London),
1994   .   .   .   .   £10/£5
ditto, Little, Brown (New York), 1994   .   .   £10/£5
Do Not Exceed the Stated Dose, Mysterious Press (New
York), 1998 .   .   .   .   £10/£5
ditto, Crippen & Landru (Norfolk, VA), 1998 (250 signed,
numbered copies with booklet).   .   .   £30/£20
ditto, Little, Brown (London), 1998 .   .   .   £10/£5
The Sedgemoor Strangler and Other Stories of Crime,
Crippen & Landru (Norfolk, VA), 2001 (275 signed copies
with pamphlet *The Butler Didn't Do It*)   .   £25/£15

Others

Kings of Distance, Eyre and Spottiswoode (London), 1968 .
.   .   .   .   £250/£50
ditto, as *Five Kings of Distance*, St Martin's Press (New
York), 1981 .   .   .   .   £150/£25
The Black Cabinet, Xanadu (London), 1989 .   £10/£5
ditto, Carroll & Graf (New York), 1989   .   .   £10/£5
The Verdict of us All, Crippen & Landru (Norfolk, VA),
2006 (edited by Lovesey; 300 signed copies with booklet
The Justice Boy by H.R.F. Keating)   .   .   £25/£15
ditto, Allison & Busby (London), 2006   .   .   £10/£5

MALCOLM LOWRY
(b.1909 d.1957)

Few of Malcolm Lowry's books were published in his
lifetime and he left an extensive collection of unfinished
manuscripts. *Under the Volcano* is regarded as his best
work and is widely accepted as one of the great works of
the 20th century. The novel is typical of Lowry's work in
drawing heavily upon his own life and making use of complex and allusive layers of symbolism.

Ultramarine, Cape (London), 1933 .   .   .   £2,250/£300
ditto, Lippincott (Philadelphia), 1962 (revised edition) .   .
.   .   .   .   £35/£10
ditto, Cape (London), 1963 (revised edition) .   .   £35/£10
Under the Volcano, Reynal & Hitchcock (New York), 1947
.   .   .   .   £1,250/£125
ditto, Cape (London), 1947 .   .   .   .   £500/£100
Hear Us O Lord from Heaven Thy Dwelling Place, Lippincott (Philadelphia), 1961   .   .   .   .   £30/£10
ditto, Cape (London), 1962 .   .   .   .   .   £20/£10
Selected Poems of Malcolm Lowry, City Lights (San
Francisco, CA), 1962 (pbk) £15
Selected Letters of Malcolm Lowry, Lippincott (Philadel-
phia), 1965   .   .   .   .   £30/£10
ditto, Cape (London), 1967 .   .   .   .   .   £30/£10
Lunar Caustic, Cape (London), 1968   .   .   £40/£15
ditto, Cape (London), 1968 (pbk in d/w)   .   £25/£15
Dark as the Grave Wherein My Friend is Laid, New
American Library (New York), 1968 .   .   £35/£10
ditto, Cape (London), 1969 .   .   .   .   .   £30/£10
October Ferry to Gabriola, World (New York), 1970 £15/£5
ditto, Cape (London), 1971 .   .   .   .   .   £20/£5
China and Kristbjorg's Story in the Black Hills, Aloe
Editions (New York), 1974 (150 numbered copies; stapled
wraps) £45
Malcolm Lowry, Psalms and Songs, New American Library
(New York), 1975 (pbk) £20
*Notes on a Screenplay for F. Scott Fitzgerald's Tender is
the Night*, Bruccoli (Bloomfield Hills, MI.), 1976 £30/£10
*Sursum Corda! The Collected Letters of Malcolm Lowry,
Volume One: 1926-46*, Cape (London), 1995   .   £20/£5
ditto, Univ of Toronto Press (Toronto, Canada), 1995 .   .
.   .   .   .   £15/£5
*Sursum Corda! The Collected Letters of Malcolm Lowry,
Volume Two: 1946-57*, Cape (London), 1996   .   £20/£5
ditto, Univ of Toronto Press (Toronto, Canada), 1997 .   .
.   .   .   .   £15/£5

ROBERT LUDLUM
(b.1927 d.2001)

Ludlum served in the US Marine Corps from 1945 to 1947,
before going to Wesleyan University. He was then an actor
until 1969 when he became a full-time writer.

The Scarlatti Inheritance, World (New York), 1971 (printed
acetate d/w with price $6.95 on front flap; 'A3696' on back
of d/w; no Book-of-the-Month Club blind stamp on back
cover, right corner)   .   .   .   .   .   £150/£20
ditto, Rupert Hart-Davis (London), 1971 .   .   £65/£10

ditto, Armchair Detective (New York), 1991 . . £10/£5
ditto, Armchair Detective (New York), 1991(100 signed, numbered copies; slipcase, no d/w). . . £150/£100
ditto, Armchair Detective (New York), 1991(26 signed, lettered copies; slipcase, no d/w) . . . £250/£200
The Osterman Weekend, World (New York), 1972 (printed acetate d/w with price $6.95 and 'A 3918' on bottom right corner of back panel) . . . . . . £75/£15
ditto, Rupert Hart-Davis (London), 1972 . . . £45/£10
ditto, Armchair Detective (New York), 1990 . £10/£5
ditto, Armchair Detective (New York), 1990(100 signed, numbered copies; slipcase, no d/w). . . £150/£100
ditto, Armchair Detective (New York), 1990(26 signed, lettered copies; slipcase, no d/w) . . . £250/£200
The Matlock Paper, Dial Press (New York), 1973 . £50/£10
ditto, Hart-Davis MacGibbon (London), 1973 . . £35/£10
Trevayne, Delacorte (New York), 1973 (pseud 'Jonathan Ryder') . . . . £75/£15
ditto, Weidenfeld & Nicolson (London), 1974 . . £50/£10
ditto, Bantam (New York), 1989 (pbk; published as by Robert Ludlum) £10
The Cry of the Halidon, Delacorte (New York), 1974 (pseud 'Jonathan Ryder') . . . . £50/£10
ditto, Weidenfeld & Nicolson (London), 1974 . . £50/£10
The Rhinemann Exchange, Dial Press (New York), 1974 .
. . . . £45/£5
ditto, Hart-Davis MacGibbon (London), 1975 . . £15/£5
The Road to Gandolfo, Dial Press (New York), 1975 (pseud 'Michael Shepherd'; in three d/ws) . . . £50/£5
ditto, Hart-Davis MacGibbon (London), 1976 . . £15/£5
The Gemini Contenders, Dial Press (New York), 1976 .
. . . . £30/£5
ditto, Hart-Davis MacGibbon (London), 1976 . . £15/£5
The Chancellor Manuscript, Dial Press (New York), 1977 .
. . . . £25/£5
ditto, Hart-Davis MacGibbon (London), 1977 . . £15/£5
The Holcroft Covenant, Marek (New York), 1978 . £30/£5
ditto, Hart-Davis, MacGibbon/Granada (London etc) £30/£5
The Matarese Circle, Marek (New York), 1979 . £15/£5
ditto, Granada (London), 1979 . . . . . £15/£5
The Bourne Identity, Marek (New York), 1980 . £30/£5
ditto, Marek (New York), 1980 (signed by author on tipped-in leaf) . . . . £60/£35
ditto, Granada (London), 1980 . . . . . £20/£5
The Parsifal Mosaic, Random House (New York), 1982 .
. . . . £15/£5
ditto, Random House (New York), 1982 (signed by author on tipped-in leaf) . . . . . . £50/£40
ditto, Granada (London), 1982 . . . . . £15/£5
The Aquitaine Progression, Random House (New York), 1984 . . . . £15/£5
ditto, Granada (London), 1984 . . . . . £15/£5
The Bourne Supremacy, Random House (New York), 1986
. . . . £15/£5
ditto, Franklin Press (Franklin Center), 1986 (signed limited edition; full leather) £35
ditto, Grafton (London), 1986 . . . . . £15/£5
The Icarus Agenda, Random House (New York), 1988 .
. . . . £10/£5
ditto, Random House (New York), 1988 (signed by author on tipped-in leaf) . . . . . . £50/£40
ditto, Grafton (London), 1988 . . . . . £10/£5
The Bourne Ultimatum, Random House (New York), 1990
. . . . £10/£5

ditto, Random House (New York), 1990 (350 signed, numbered copies; slipcase, no d/w). . . . £45/£20
ditto, Grafton (London), 1990 . . . . . £10/£5
The Road to Omaha, HarperCollins (London), 1992 £10/£5
ditto, Random House (New York), 1992 . . . £10/£5
The Scorpio Illusion, Bantam (New York), 1993 . £10/£5
ditto, HarperCollins (London), 1993 . . . . £10/£5
The Apocalypse Watch, Bantam (New York), 1995 £10/£5
ditto, HarperCollins (London), 1995 . . . . £10/£5
The Matarese Countdown, Bantam (New York), 1997 . .
. . . . £10/£5
ditto, HarperCollins (London), 1997 . . . . £10/£5
Prometheus Deception, St Martin's Press (New York), 2000
. . . . £10/£5
ditto, Orion (London), 2001 . . . . . . £10/£5
The Sigma Protocol, St Martin's Press (New York), 2001 .
. . . . £10/£5
ditto, Orion (London), 2001 . . . . . . £10/£5
The Jason Directive, St Martin's Press (New York), 2002 .
. . . . £10/£5
ditto, Orion (London), 2002 . . . . . . £10/£5
The Tristan Betrayal, St Martin's Press (New York), 2003 .
. . . . £10/£5
ditto, Orion (London), 2003 . . . . . . £10/£5
The Ambler Warning, St Martin's Press (Gordonsville, VA), 2005 . . . . £10/£5
ditto, Orion (London), 2005 . . . . . . £10/£5
The Bancroft Strategy, St Martin's Press (New York), 2006
. . . . £10/£5
ditto, Orion (London), 2006 . . . . . . £10/£5

'Covert-One' Series
The Hades Factor, St Martin's Griffin (New York), 2000 (pbk; written with Gayle Lynds) £5
ditto, HarperCollins (London), 2001 . . . £10/£5
The Cassandra Compact, St Martin's Griffin (New York), 2001 (pbk; written with Philip Shelby) . . . £5
ditto, HarperCollins (London), 2001 . . . . £10/£5
The Paris Option, St Martin's Griffin (New York), 2002 (pbk; written with Gayle Lynds) £5
ditto, HarperCollins (London), 2002 . . . £10/£5
The Altman Code, St Martin's Press (New York), 2003 (pbk; written with Gayle Lynds). £5
ditto, Orion (London), 2003 . . . . . . £10/£5
The Lazarus Vendetta, St Martin's Press (Gordonsville, VA), 2004 (pbk; written with Patrick Larkin) . . £5
ditto, Orion (London), 2005 . . . . . . £10/£5
The Moscow Vector St Martin's Griffin (New York), 2005 (pbk; written with Patrick Larkin) £5
ditto, Orion (London), 2005 . . . . . . £10/£5
The Arctic Event, Grand Central Publishing (New York), 2007 (pbk; written with James H. Cobb) . . £5
ditto, Orion (London), 2007 . . . . . . £10/£5

ROSE MACAULAY

(b.1881 d.1958)

Dame Rose Macaulay is well-respected as a novelist, combining intelligence with humour and compassion in her books. *Potterism*, which attacked modern journalism and its commercialisation, was her first book to attract popular and critical interest. *Letters to a Sister* includes fragments of an unpublished novel, *Venice Besieged*.

Novels

Abbots Verney, Murray (London), 1906 . . . . £200
The Furnace, Murray (London), 1907 . . . . £100
The Secret River, Murray (London), 1909 . . . £75
The Valley Captives, Murray (London), 1911 . . . £65
Views and Vagabonds, Murray (London), 1912 . . £65
ditto, H. Holt and Co (New York), 1912 . . . . £50
The Lee Shore, Hodder & Stoughton (London), 1912 . £45
ditto, Doran (New York), 1912 . . . . . . £40
The Making of a Bigot, Hodder & Stoughton (London), 1914 . . . . £40
Non-Combatants and Others, Hodder & Stoughton (London), 1916 . . . . £35
What Not: A Prophetic Comedy, Constable (London), 1918 . . . . £25
Potterism: A Tragi-Farcical Tract, Collins (London), 1920 . . . . £200/£45
ditto, Boni & Liveright (New York), [1920] . £125/£30
Dangerous Ages, Collins (London), 1921 . £100/£35
ditto, Boni & Liveright (New York), [1921] . £65/£30
Mystery at Geneva, Collins (London), 1922 . £100/£35
ditto, Boni & Liveright (New York), [1923] . £65/£30
Told By an Idiot, Collins (London), 1923. . £60/£20
ditto, Boni & Liveright (New York), 1923 . £50/£20
Orphan Island, Collins (London), 1924 . . £60/£20
ditto, Boni & Liveright (New York), [1925] . £60/£20
Crewe Train, Collins (London), 1926 . . £40/£15
ditto, Boni & Liveright (New York), 1926 . £45/£15
Keeping Up Appearances, Collins (London), 1928 £45/£15
Staying With Relations, Collins (London), 1930 £40/£15
ditto, Liveright (New York), [1930] . . . £40/£15
They Were Defeated, Collins (London), 1932. . £35/£10
ditto, as *The Shadow Flies*, Harper & Bros (New York), 1934 . . . . £35/£10
Going Abroad, Collins (London), 1934 . . . £40/£10
ditto, Harper & Bros (New York), 1934 . . £35/£10
I Would Be Private, Collins (London), 1937 . £30/£10
ditto, Harper & Bros (New York), 1937 . £30/£10
And No Man's Wit, Collins (London), 1940 . £20/£5
ditto, Little, Brown (Boston), 1940 . . . . £15/£5
The World My Wilderness, Collins (London), 1950 £20/£5
ditto, Little, Brown (Boston), 1950 . . . £15/£5
The Towers of Trebizond, Collins (London), 1956 £20/£5
ditto, Farrar, Straus (New York), 1957 . . £15/£5

Poetry

The Two Blind Countries, Sidgwick & Jackson (London), 1914 . . . . £45
Three Days, Constable (London), 1919 . . . £45
ditto, Dutton (New York), 1919 . . . . . £45

Travel

They Went to Portugal, Cape (London), 1946. . £25/£10
Fabled Shore: From the Pyrenees to Portugal, Hamish Hamilton (London), 1949 . . . . . £25/£10

ditto, Farrar, Straus (New York), 1949 . . . £25/£10
Pleasure of Ruins, Weidenfeld & Nicolson (London), 1953 . . . . £15/£5
ditto, Weidenfeld & Nicolson (London), 1953 (150 numbered, deluxe copies, slipcase) . . . £35/£25
ditto, Walker (New York), [1966] . . . . £10/£5
They Went to Portugal Too, Carcanet (London), 1990 . . . . £15/£5

Others

A Casual Commentary, Methuen (London), 1925 . £35/£10
ditto, Boni & Liveright (New York), 1926 . . £35/£10
Catchwords and Claptrap, Hogarth Press (London), 1926 (no d/w). £45
Some Religious Elements in English Literature, Hogarth Press (London), 1931 . . . . . £35/£10
ditto, Harcourt Brace (New York), [1931] . . £30/£10
Milton, Duckworth (London), 1934 . . £25/£10
ditto, Harper & Row (New York), 1935 . . £20/£10
Personal Pleasures, Gollancz (London), 1935 . £35/£10
ditto, Macmillan (New York), 1936 . . . £25/£10
The Writings of E.M. Forster, Hogarth Press (London), 1938 . . . . £65/£15
ditto, Harcourt Brace (New York), 1938 . . £45/£10
Life Among the English, Collins (London), 1942 . £15/£5
Letters to a Friend: 1950-1952, Collins (London), 1961 . . . . £15/£5
ditto, Atheneum (New York), 1962 . . . £15/£5
Last Letters to a Friend, 1952-1958, Collins (London), 1962 . . . . £15/£5
ditto, Atheneum (New York), 1963 . . . £15/£5
Letters to a Sister, Collins (London), 1964 . £15/£5
ditto, Atheneum (New York), 1964 . . . £15/£5

BETTY MACDONALD

(b.1908 d.1958)

The American Betty Macdonald is known for her books of humorous autobiography, and especially *The Egg and I* which was a bestseller, translated into 20 languages. She also wrote the 'Mrs Piggle-Wiggle' series of children's books.

Autobiography

The Egg and I, Lippincott (Philadelphia, PA), 1945 . . . . £125/£25
ditto, Hammond (London), 1946. . . . . £65/£10
The Plague and I, Lippincott (Philadelphia, PA), 1948 . . . . £65/£15
ditto, Hammond (London), 1948 . . . . £45/£10
Anybody Can Do Anything, Lippincott (Philadelphia, PA), 1950 . . . . £50/£10
ditto, Hammond (London), 1950. . . . . £25/£10
Onions in the Stew, Lippincott (Philadelphia, PA), 1955 . . . . £50/£10
ditto, Hammond (London), 1955 . . . £35/£10
Who, Me?, Lippincott (Philadelphia, PA), 1959 . £50/£10
ditto, Hammond (London), 1960 . . . £25/£10

Children's Books

Mrs Piggle-Wiggle, Lippincott (Philadelphia, PA), 1947 . . . . £100/£15
ditto, Hammond (London), 1946 . . . . £50/£10

Nancy and Plum, Lippincott (Philadelphia, PA), 1948 . .
. . . . £300/£45
ditto, Hammond (London), 1953. . . . .£200/£30
Mrs Piggle-Wiggle's Magic, Lippincott (Philadelphia, PA),
1949 . . . .£100/£15
ditto, Hammond (London), 1949 . . . . £50/£10
Mrs Piggle-Wiggle's Farm, Lippincott (Philadelphia, PA),
1954 . . . .£150/£30
ditto, Hammond (London), 1955 . . . . £75/£20
Hello Mrs Piggle-Wiggle, Lippincott (Philadelphia, PA),
1957 . . . . £50/£15
ditto, as *Hullo Mrs Piggle-Wiggle*, Hammond (London),
1957 . . . . £35/£10

GEORGE MACDONALD

(b.1824 d.1905)

George Macdonald was a Scottish author, poet, and
Christian minister, perhaps best known for his children's
book *At the Back of the North Wind*, and his adult fantasy
Phantastes. His work inspired the admiration of Twain,
Tolkien and C.S. Lewis. G.K. Chesterton claimed that *The
Princess and the Goblin* was a book that had 'made a
difference to my whole existence'.

Children's Titles
Dealings with the Fairies, Strahan (London), 1867 (blue
cloth) £1,500
ditto, Strahan (London), 1867 (green cloth) . £1,000
ditto, George Routledge (New York), 1891 . . .£450
At the Back of the North Wind, Strahan (London), 1871
(first issue binding bright blue pictorial cloth stamped in
gold) £2,500
ditto, Strahan (London), 1871 (second issue binding without
gold frame) £2,000
ditto, George Routledge (New York), [c.1871] . £1,000
Ranald Bannerman's Boyhood, Strahan (London), 1871 .
. . . .£700
ditto, Lippincott (Philadelphia), 1871 . . . .£350
The Princess and the Goblin, Strahan (London), 1872 . .
. . . . £1,500
ditto, George Routledge (New York), 1871 . . £1,000
Gutta Percha Willie, King (London), 1873 . . .£425
The Wise Woman, Strahan (London), 1875 . .£175
The Princess and Curdie, Chatto & Windus (London), 1883
. . . .£750
ditto, Lippincott (Philadelphia), 1883 . . . .£500
Cross Purpose and the Shadows, Blackie (London), 1886 .
. . . . £50
The Light Princess and Other Fairy Tales, Blackie
(London), 1890 . . . .£150
ditto, Putnam (New York), 1893 . . . .£100
The Golden Key, Crowell (New York), [1906] . .£200
ditto, Bodley Head (London), 1972 . . . £40/£10

Poetry
Within and Without: a Dramatic Poem, Longman (London),
1855 . . . . £1,000
ditto, Scribner's, Armstrong (New York), 1872 . .£100
Poems, Longman (London), 1857 . . . .£400
ditto, Dutton (New York), 1887 . . . . .£300
The Disciple and Other Poems, Strahan (London), 1867 £250

ditto, Sunrise Books (Eureka, CA), 1989 . . . £10/£5
A Threefold Cord: Poem, by Three Friends, edited by
MacDonald, privately printed by Hughes (London), [1883]
(with John Hill MacDonald and Greville Ewing Matheson)
. . . .£245
Poetical Works, Chatto & Windus (London), 1893 (2 vols)
. . . . £100 the set

Translations
Twelve of the Spiritual Songs of Novalis, Strahan (London),
1851 . . . .£475
Exotics, Strahan (London), 1851 . . . .£475

Others
Phantastes; a Faerie Romance, Smith, Elder (London),
1858 . . . . £1,500
ditto, Loring (Boston), 1870. . . . . .£165
David Elginbrod, Hurst & Blackett (London), 1863 (3 vols)
. . . . £1,500
ditto, Loring (Boston), [1863] £200
Adela Cathcart, Hurst & Blackett (London), 1864 (3 vols) .
. . . .£750
ditto, Loring (Boston), [1864] £200
The Portent, Smith, Elder (London), 1864 . . .£350
ditto, Loring (Boston), [1864] £175
Alec Forbes of Howglen, Hurst & Blackett (London), 1865
(3 vols) £750
Annals of a Quiet Neighbourhood, Hurst & Blackett
(London), 1867 (3 vols) £750
ditto, Harper (New York), 1867 . . . . .£165
Unspoken Sermons, Strahan (London), 1867. . .£450
ditto, Second series, Longmans (London), 1885 . .£100
ditto, Third series, Longmans (London), 1889 . . .£100
ditto, Sunrise Books (Eureka, CA), 1988 . . £10/£5
Guild Court, Hurst & Blackett (London), 1868 (3 vols) £750
Robert Falconer, Hurst & Blackett (London), 1868 (3 vols)
. . . .£750
ditto, Loring (Boston), [1876] £125
The Seaboard Parish, Tinsley (London), 1868 (3 vols)
. . . . £1,000
ditto, Routledge (New York), 1868 . . . .£100
England's Antiphon, Macmillan (London), [1868] .£100
ditto, Lippincott (Philadelphia), [1868] . . . £75
The Miracles of Our Lord, Strahan (London), 1870 . £75
Works of Fancy and Imagination, Strahan (London), 1871
(10 vols, slipcase) . . . . .£1,500/£1,000
Wilfred Cumbermede, Hurst & Blackett (London), 1872 (3
vols) £1,000
ditto, Scribner's (New York), 1872 . . . .£100
The Vicar's Daughter, Tinsley (London), 1872 (3 vols)
. . . . £1,000
ditto, Roberts (Boston), 1872 . . . . .£100
Malcolm, King (London), 1875 (3 vols) . . £1,000
ditto, Lippincott (Philadelphia), 1877 . . . £75
St George and St Michael, King (London), 1876 (3 vols) .
. . . .£750
ditto, Ford & Co (New York), [1876] £100
Thomas Wingfold, Hurst & Blackett (London), 1876 (3 vols)
. . . . £1,000
ditto, Routledge (New York), 1876 . . . .£150
The Marquis of Losse, Hurst & Blackett (London), 1877 (3
vols) £750
ditto, Lippincott (Philadelphia), 1877 . . . £75
Paul Faber, Hurst & Blackett (London), 1879 (3 vols) . £750

469

GUIDE TO FIRST EDITION PRICES

ditto, Lippincott (Philadelphia), 1879 . . . . £100
Sir Gibbie, Hurst & Blackett (London), 1879 (3 vols) . £650
ditto, Lippincott (Philadelphia), 1879 . . . . £75
A Book of Strife, privately printed (London), 1880 . £500
ditto, privately printed (London), 1882 . . . . £400
ditto, Longman (London), 1889 . . . . . . £200
Mary Marston, Sampson, Low (London), 1881 (3 vols) £600
ditto, Appleton (New York), 1881 . . . . . £100
Warlock O'Glen Warlock, Lothrop (Boston), 1881 . £150
ditto, Harper & Brothers (New York), 1881 (wraps) . £125
ditto, as *Castle Warlock*, Sampson, Low (London), 1882 (3 vols) £1,000
Orts, Sampson Low (London), 1882 . . . . . £150
Weighed and Wanting, Sampson, Low (London), 1882 (3 vols) £600
ditto, Lothrop (Boston), 1882 . . . . . . £75
The Gifts of the Child Christ, Sampson, Low (London), 1882 (2 vols) £75
Donal Grant, Kegan Paul (London), 1883 (3 vols). . £600
ditto, Lothrop (Boston), 1883 . . . . . . £75
What's Mine's Mine, Kegan Paul (London), 1886 (3 vols) £500
ditto, Lothrop (Boston), [1886] £75
Home Again, Kegan Paul (London), 1887 . . . £200
ditto, Appleton (New York), 1888 . . . . . £75
The Elect Lady, Kegan Paul (London), 1888 . . . £200
ditto, Appleton (New York), 1888 . . . . . £75
There and Back, Kegan Paul (London), 1891 (3 vols) . £450
ditto, Lothrop (Boston), [1891] £75
A Rough Shaking, Routledge (New York), 1890 . . £200
ditto, Blackie (London), 1891 . . . . . . £65
The Flight of the Shadow, Kegan Paul (London), 1891 £150
ditto, Appleton (New York), 1891 . . . . . £100
The Hope of the Gospel, Ward, Lock (London), 1892 . £50
ditto, Appleton (New York), 1892 . . . . . £45
Heather and Snow, Chatto & Windus (London), 1893 (2 vols) £250
ditto, Harper (New York), 1893 . . . . . . £65
A Dish of Orts, Sampson Low (London), 1893 . . £75
Lilith, Chatto & Windus (London), 1895 . . . . £275
ditto, Dodd, Mead (New York), 1895 . . . . £145
Salted with Fire, Hurst & Blackett (London), 1897 . £75
ditto, Dodd, Mead (New York), 1897 . . . . £65
Far Above Rubies, Dodd, Mead (New York), 1899 . £75
Fairy Tales, Fifield (London), 1904 (five parts) . . £125
ditto, Fifield (London), 1904 (1 vol.) £70

JOHN D. MacDONALD

(b.1916 d.1986)

A prolific American author, MacDonald started his career writing mystery, sports, Western and science fiction stories for pulp magazines after World War Two. When the market dwindled he wrote novels which were published as paperback originals. His first real success was *The Executioners*, later filmed as *Cape Fear*.

'Travis McGee' Novels
The Deep Blue Good-By, Gold Medal (New York), 1964 (single dot on copyright page; pbk). £20
ditto, as *The Deep Blue Goodbye*, Robert Hale (London), 1965 . . . . £300/£50

ditto, as *The Deep Blue Good-By*, Lippincott (Philadelphia, PA), 1975 . . . . £200/£25
Nightmare in Pink, Gold Medal (New York), 1964 ('k1406' on copyright page; pbk) £15
ditto, Robert Hale (London), 1966 . . . . £200/£25
ditto, Lippincott (Philadelphia, PA), 1976. . . £200/£25
A Purple Place for Dying, Gold Medal (New York), 1964 (pbk) £15
ditto, Robert Hale (London), 1966 . . . . £200/£25
ditto, Lippincott (Philadelphia, PA), 1976. . . £125/£20
The Quick Red Fox, Gold Medal (New York), 1964 (pbk) £15
ditto, Robert Hale (London), 1966 . . . . £200/£25
ditto, Lippincott (Philadelphia, PA), 1974 (copyright date states '1964'; d/w with '374' at top of front flap of d/w) . . . . £125/£20
A Deadly Shade of Gold, Gold Medal (New York), 1965 (pbk) £10
ditto, Robert Hale (London), 1967 . . . . £150/£20
ditto, Lippincott (Philadelphia, PA), 1974. . . £125/£20
Bright Orange for the Shroud, Gold Medal (New York), 1965 (pbk) £10
ditto, Robert Hale (London), 1967 . . . . £150/£20
ditto, Lippincott (Philadelphia, PA), 1972. . . £250/£25
Darker than Amber, Gold Medal (New York), 1966 (pbk) £20
ditto, Robert Hale (London), 1966 . . . . £350/£45
ditto, Lippincott (Philadelphia, PA), 1970 (d/w price $4.95) . . . . £500/£65
One Fearful Yellow Eye, Gold Medal (New York), 1966 (pbk) £10
ditto, Robert Hale (London), 1968 . . . . £100/£15
ditto, Lippincott (Philadelphia, PA), 1977. . . £100/£15
The Last One Left, Doubleday (New York), 1967 . £50/£10
ditto, Robert Hale (London), 1968 . . . . . £65/£10
Three for McGee, Doubleday (New York), 1967 (omnibus) . . . . £65/£15
Pale Gray for Guilt, Gold Medal (New York), 1968 (pbk) £10
ditto, as *Pale Grey for Guilt*, Robert Hale (London), 1969 . . . . £250/£30
ditto, Lippincott (Philadelphia, PA), 1971. . . £250/£30
The Girl in the Plain Brown Wrapper, Gold Medal (New York), 1968 (pbk) £10
ditto, Robert Hale (London), 1969 . . . . £150/£15
ditto, Lippincott (Philadelphia, PA), 1973 ('373' at top of front flap of d/w; price $5.95) . . . . . £200/£15
Dress Her in Indigo, Gold Medal (New York), 1969 (pbk) £10
ditto, Lippincott (Philadelphia, PA), 1971. . . £300/£30
ditto, Robert Hale (London), 1971 . . . . £100/£15
The Long Lavender Look, Gold Medal (New York), 1970 (pbk) £10
ditto, Lippincott (Philadelphia, PA), 1972. . . £200/£15
ditto, Robert Hale (London), 1972 . . . . £100/£15
A Tan and Sandy Silence, Gold Medal (New York), 1972 (pbk) £10
ditto, Robert Hale (London), 1973 . . . . . £65/£10
ditto, Lippincott (Philadelphia, PA), 1979. . . £45/£10
The Scarlet Ruse, Gold Medal (New York), 1973 (pbk) £10
ditto, Robert Hale (London), 1975 . . . . . £45/£10
ditto, Lippincott & Crowell, (New York), 1980 . £45/£10
The Tourquoise Lament, Lippincott (Philadelphia, PA), 1973 . . . . £35/£5

ditto, Gold Medal (New York), 1974 (pbk) . . . £5
ditto, Robert Hale (London), 1975 . . . £35/£5
The Dreadful Lemon Sky, Lippincott (Philadelphia, PA), 1975 . . . . £35/£5
ditto, Gold Medal (New York), 1975 (pbk) . . . £5
ditto, Robert Hale (London), 1976 . . . . £30/£5
The Empty Copper Sea, Lippincott (Philadelphia, PA), 1978 . . . . £15/£5
ditto, Robert Hale (London), 1979 . . . . £15/£5
The Green Ripper, Lippincott (Philadelphia, PA), 1979 .
. . . . £15/£5
ditto, Robert Hale (London), 1980 . . . £15/£5
Free Fall in Crimson, Harper (New York), 1981 . £15/£5
ditto, Robert Hale (London), 1981 . . . . £10/£5
Cinnamon Skin, Harper (New York), 1982 . £10/£5
ditto, Collins (London), 1982 . . . . £10/£5
The Lonely Silver Rain, Knopf (New York), 1985. £10/£5
ditto, Hodder & Stoughton (London), 1985 . £10/£5

Science Fiction Novels
Wine of the Dreamers, Greenberg (New York), 1951 . .
. . . . £65/£15
ditto, as **Planet of the Dreamers**, Robert Hale (London), 1954 . . . . £45/£10
Ballroom of the Skies, Greenberg (New York), 1952 . .
. . . . £65/£15
The Girl, The Gold Watch & Everything, Gold Medal (New York), 1962 (pbk) £10
ditto, Frederick Muller (London), 1964 (pbk) . . . £10
ditto, Robert Hale (London), 1974 . . . £35/£10

Other Novels
The Brass Cupcake, Gold Medal (New York), 1950 (pbk) .
. . . . £45
ditto, Frederick Muller (London), 1955 (pbk) . . . £25
ditto, Robert Hale (London), 1974 . . . £500/£100
Murder for the Bride, Gold Medal (New York), 1951 (pbk)
. . . . £20
ditto, Frederick Muller (London), 1954 (pbk) . . £15
ditto, Robert Hale (London), 1977 . . . £500/£100
Judge Me Not, Gold Medal (New York), 1951 (pbk) . £20
ditto, Frederick Muller (London), 1964 (pbk) . . £10
ditto, Robert Hale (London), 1999 . . . £30/£5
Weep For Me, Gold Medal (New York), 1951 (pbk) . £40
ditto, Frederick Muller (London), 1954 (pbk) . . . £20
ditto, Robert Hale (London), 2003 . . . £25/£5
The Damned, Gold Medal (New York), 1952 (pbk) . £20
ditto, Frederick Muller (London), 1964 (pbk) . . £10
ditto, Robert Hale (London), 2005 . . . £30/£5
Dead Low Tide, Gold Medal (New York), 1953 (pbk) . £15
ditto, Frederick Muller (London), 1955 (pbk) . . £10
ditto, Robert Hale (London), 1976 . . . £35/£10
ditto, Garland (New York), 1982 . . . . £30/£10
The Neon Jungle, Gold Medal (New York), 1953 (pbk) £20
ditto, Frederick Muller (London), 1954 (pbk) . . . £10
Cancel All Our Vows, Appleton Century Crofts (New York), 1953 . . . . £100/£15
ditto, Robert Hale (London), 1955 . . . £75/£15
All These Condemned, Gold Medal (New York), 1954 (pbk)
. . . . £20
ditto, Robert Hale (London), 2001 . . . £35/£10
Area of Suspicion, Dell (New York), 1954 (pbk) . £15
ditto, Robert Hale (London), 1956 . . . £200/£35

Contrary Pleasure, Appleton Century Crofts (New York), 1954 . . . . £50/£10
ditto, Robert Hale (London), 1955 . . . £45/£10
A Bullet for Cinderella, Dell (New York), 1955 (pbk) . £15
ditto, Robert Hale (London), 1960 . . . £200/£35
ditto, as **On the Make**, Dell (New York), 1960 (pbk) . £5
Cry Hard, Cry Fast, Popular Library (New York), 1955 (pbk) £15
ditto, Robert Hale (London), 1969 . . . £200/£35
You Live Once, Popular Library (New York), 1956 (pbk) £15
ditto, Robert Hale (London), 1976 . . . £35/£10
April Evil, Dell (New York), 1956 (pbk) . . . £10
ditto, Robert Hale (London), 1957 . . . £200/£35
Murder in the Wind, Dell (New York), 1956 (pbk) . £10
Border Town Girl, Popular Library (New York), 1956 (pbk)
. . . . £20
ditto, Robert Hale (London), 1970 . . . £150/£25
Death Trap, Dell (New York), 1957 (pbk) . . . £15
ditto, Robert Hale (London), 1958 . . . £200/£35
The Price of Murder, Dell (New York), 1957 (pbk) . £15
ditto, Robert Hale (London), 1958 . . . £200/£35
The Empty Trap, Popular Library (New York), 1957 (pbk).
. . . . £20
ditto, Robert Hale (London), 2000 . . . £30/£10
A Man of Affairs, Dell (New York), 1957 (pbk) . . £15
ditto, Robert Hale (London), 1959 . . . £200/£35
The Deceivers, Dell (New York), 1958 (pbk) . . . £15
ditto, Robert Hale (London), 1958 . . . £175/£30
Clemmie, Gold Medal (New York), 1958 (pbk) . . £20
ditto, Robert Hale (London), 2006 . . . £25/£10
The Executioners, Simon & Schuster (New York), 1958 .
. . . . £350/£50
ditto, Robert Hale (London), 1959 . . . £150/£20
Soft Touch, Dell (New York), 1958 (pbk) . . . £15
ditto, Robert Hale (London), 1960 . . . £175/£30
Deadly Welcome, Dell (New York), 1959 (pbk) . . £15
ditto, Robert Hale (London), 1960 . . . £250/£35
Please Write for Details, Simon & Schuster (New York), 1959 . . . . £125/£25
The Crossroads, Simon & Schuster (New York), 1959 . .
. . . . £75/£15
ditto, Robert Hale (London), 1961 . . . £150/£30
The Beach Girls, Gold Medal (New York), 1959 (pbk) £20
ditto, Robert Hale (London), 1968 . . . £200/£30
Slam the Big Door, Gold Medal (New York), 1960 (pbk) £15
ditto, Robert Hale (London), 1961 . . . £150/£30
ditto, Mysterious Press (New York), 1987 . . £25/£10
The End of the Night, Simon & Schuster (New York), 1960
. . . . £75/£15
ditto, Robert Hale (London), 1964 . . . £45/£10
The Only Girl in the Game, Gold Medal (New York), 1960 (pbk) £15
ditto, Robert Hale (London), 1962 . . . £150/£30
Where is Janice Gentry, Gold Medal (New York), 1961 (pbk) £15
ditto, Robert Hale (London), 1963 . . . £150/£30
One Monday We Killed Them All, Gold Medal (New York), 1961 (pbk) £15
ditto, Robert Hale (London), 1963 . . . £150/£30
A Key to the Suite, Gold Medal (New York), 1962 (pbk) £15
ditto, Robert Hale (London), 1968 . . . £150/£30
ditto, Mysterious Press (New York), 1989 . . £20/£5
A Flash of Green, Simon & Schuster (New York), 1962 .
. . . . £125/£15

ditto, Robert Hale (London), 1971 . . . . £30/£10
I Could Go On Singing, Gold Medal (New York), 1963
  (pbk) £15
ditto, Robert Hale (London), 1964 . . . £125/£25
On The Run, Gold Medal (New York), 1963 (pbk) . £10
ditto, Robert Hale (London), 1965 . . . £150/£30
The Drowner, Gold Medal (New York), 1963 (pbk) . £10
ditto, Robert Hale (London), 1964 . . . £150/£30
Condominium, Lippincott (Philadelphia, PA), 1977 £25/£10
ditto, Lippincott (Philadelphia, PA), 1977 (1,000 signed
  copies) . . . . £100/£50
ditto, Robert Hale (London), 1977 . . . £15/£5
One More Sunday, Knopf (New York), 1984 . . £10/£5
ditto, Hodder & Stoughton (London), 1984 . . £10/£5
Barrier Island, Knopf (New York), 1986. . . £10/£5
ditto, Hodder & Stoughton (London), 1987 . . £10/£5

Short Stories
End of the Tiger and Other Stories, Gold Medal (New
  York), 1966 (pbk) £10
ditto, Robert Hale (London), 1967 . . . £150/£30
S*E*V*E*N, Gold Medal (New York), 1971 (pbk) . £10
ditto, Robert Hale (London), 1974 . . . £25/£10
Other Times, Other Worlds, Gold Medal (New York), 1978
  (pbk) £10
The Good Old Stuff, Harper (New York), 1982 . £15/£5
ditto, Collins (London), 1984 . . . . £10/£5
Two, Carroll & Graf (New York), 1983 (pbk) . . £15
More Good Old Stuff, Knopf (New York), 1984 . £10/£5
The Annex and Other Stories, Eurographica (Helsinki),
  1987 (350 signed copies) . . . . . £75/£45

Non-Fiction
The House-Guests, Doubleday (New York), 1965 . £65/£15
ditto, Robert Hale (London), 1966 . . . £15/£5
No Deadly Drug, Doubleday (New York), 1968 . £35/£10
Nothing Can Go Wrong, Harper (New York), 1981 (with
  John H. Kilpack). . . . . . £50/£15
*A Friendship: The Letters of Dan Roawan and John D.
  MacDonald 1967-1975*, Knopf (New York), 1986 £10/£5
Reading For Survival, Library of Congress (Washington,
  DC), 1987 (pbk) £30

PHILIP MACDONALD

(b.1900 d.1981)

Philip Macdonald was an important figure in the 'Golden
Age' of crime fiction. He was a grandson of George Macdonald, and wrote his first books in collaboration with his
father, also a novelist. *The Rasp* and *The Nursemaid Who
Disappeared* were selected as Haycraft-Queen 'Corner-
stones'.

Crime Novels written as 'Philip Macdonald'
The Rasp, Collins (London), 1924 . . . £2,000/£350
ditto, Dial (New York), 1925 . . . . £1,250/£250
The White Crow, Collins (London), 1928. . £1,500/£300
ditto, Dial (New York), 1928 . . . . £1,000/£250
The Noose, Collins Crime Club (London), 1930 . £750/£65
ditto, Dial (New York), 1930 . . . . £300/£40
The Link, Collins Crime Club (London), 1930 . £450/£45
ditto, Doubleday (New York), 1930 . . . £250/£20

Rynox, Collins (London), 1930 . . . . £450/£45
ditto, as *The Rynox Murder Mystery*, Doubleday (New
  York), 1931 . . . . £150/£20
ditto, as *The Rynox Mystery*, Collins (London), 1933 £20/£5
Persons Unknown, Doubleday (New York), 1931 . £150/£20
ditto, as *The Maze*, Collins Crime Club (London), 1932 .
  . . . . £450/£45
Murder Gone Mad, Collins Crime Club (London), 1931 .
  . . . . £450/£45
ditto, Doubleday (New York), 1931 . . . £150/£20
The Wraith, Doubleday (New York), 1931 . . £150/£20
ditto, Collins Crime Club (London), 1931. . £450/£45
The Choice, Collins Crime Club (London), 1931 . £450/£45
ditto, as *The Polferry Riddle*, Doubleday (New York), 1931
  . . . . £75/£15
ditto, as *The Polferry Mystery*, Collins (London), 1932 .
  . . . . £40/£5
Harbour, Doubleday (New York), 1931 (pseud 'Anthony
  Lawless') . . . . £125/£15
ditto, Collins Crime Club (London), 1931 (as Philip
  Macdonald) . . . . £450/£45
The Crime Conductor, Doubleday (New York), 1931 . .
  . . . . £125/£15
ditto, Collins Crime Club (London), 1932. . £450/£45
Rope to Spare, Collins Crime Club (London), 1932 £450/£45
ditto, Doubleday (New York), 1932 . . . £150/£20
Death on My Left, Collins Crime Club (London), 1933 .
  . . . . £450/£45
ditto, Doubleday (New York), 1933 . . . £150/£20
R.I.P., Collins Crime Club (London), 1933 . £450/£45
ditto, as *Menace*, Doubleday (New York), 1933 . £75/£15
The Nursemaid Who Disappeared, Collins Crime Club
  (London), 1938 . . . . . . £450/£45
ditto, as *Warrant for X*, Doubleday (New York), 1938 . .
  . . . . £250/£45
The Dark Wheel, Collins Crime Club (London), 1948 (with
  A. Boyd Correll) . . . . . . £75/£15
ditto, Morrow (New York), 1948 . . . £25/£10
ditto, as *Sweet and Deadly*, Zenith (New York), 1959 (pbk)
  . . . . £10
Guest in the House, Doubleday (New York), 1955 £35/£10
ditto, Herbert Jenkins (London), 1956 . . £75/£15
ditto, as *No Time for Terror*, Bestseller (New York), 1956
  (pbk) £10
The List of Adrian Messenger, Doubleday (New York),
  1959 . . . . £100/£20
ditto, Herbert Jenkins (London), 1960 . . £100/£20

Crime Novels Written as 'Oliver Fleming'
The Ambrotox and Limping Dick, Ward Lock (London),
  1920 (with Ronald MacDonald) . . £750/£100
The Spandau Quid, Cecil Palmer (London), 1923 (with
  Ronald MacDonald) . . . . . £750/£100

Crime Novels Written as 'Martin Porlock'
Mystery at Friar's Pardon, Collins Crime Club (London),
  1931 . . . . £500/£45
ditto, Doubleday (New York), 1932 (as Philip Macdonald) .
  . . . . £200/£20
Mystery in Kensington Gore, Collins Crime Club (London),
  1931 . . . . £450/£45
ditto, as *Escape*, Doubleday (New York), 1932 (as Philip
  Macdonald) . . . . £150/£20
X v. Rex, Collins Crime Club (London), 1933 . . £450/£45

ditto, as **The Mystery of the Dead Police**, Doubleday (New York), 1933 (as 'Philip Macdonald')   .   .   .£150/£20
ditto, as **The Mystery of Mr X**, Literary Press (London), 1934   .   .   .   .   £30/£5

Short Stories
Something to Hide, Doubleday (New York), 1952. £25/£10
ditto, as **Fingers of Fear**, Collins Crime Club (London), 1953   .   .   .   .£75/£20
The Man Out of the Rain, Doubleday (New York), 1955   .   .   .   .£25/£10
ditto, Herbert Jenkins (London), 1957   .   .   £50/£10
Death and Chicanery, Doubleday (New York), 1962 £20/£5
ditto, Herbert Jenkins (London), 1963   .   .   £30/£10

Other Fiction
Gentleman Bill: A Boxing Story, Herbert Jenkins (London), 1923   .   .   .   .£350/£35
Queen's Mate, Collins (London), 1926   .   .   .£350/£35
Patrol, Collins (London), 1927   .   .   .   .£450/£45
ditto, Harper (New York), 1928   .   .   .   .£400/£40
Likeness of Exe, Collins (London), 1929 .   .   .£350/£45
Moonfisher, Collins (London), 1931 .   .   .   .£350/£45
'Glitter', Collins (London), 1934   .   .   .   .£300/£35
Forbidden Planet, Farrar Straus (New York), 1956 (as 'W.J. Stuart')   .   .   .   .£500/£45
ditto, Corgi (London), 1956 (pbk) £10

ROSS MACDONALD
(b.1915 d.1983)

'Ross Macdonald' is the best known of the many pseudonyms for Kenneth Millar, an American-Canadian author of detective novels, who also wrote under his own name. Macdonald followed in the tradition of Hammett and Chandler but added psychological depth and insight into the motivation of his characters. His plots were complicated and the denouements seldom obvious.

Novels Written as 'Ross Macdonald'
The Barbarous Coast, Knopf (New York), 1956   . £600/£65
ditto, Cassell (London), 1957   .   .   .   .   .£150/£25
The Doomsters, Knopf (New York), 1958   .   .£350/£40
ditto, Cassell (London), 1958   .   .   .   .£100/£15
The Galton Case, Knopf (New York), 1959   .   .£300/£40
ditto, Cassell (London), 1960   .   .   .   .£100/£15
The Ferguson Affair, Knopf (New York), 1960   .£300/£40
ditto, Collins Crime Club (London), 1961.   .   .£100/£15
The Wycherly Woman, Knopf (New York), 1961 .£300/£40
ditto, Collins Crime Club (London), 1961.   .   .£100/£15
The Zebra-Striped Hearse, Knopf (New York), 1962   .   .
.   .   .   .£125/£30
ditto, Collins Crime Club (London), 1963.   .   . £25/£10
The Chill, Knopf (New York), 1964 .   .   .   .£125/£30
ditto, Collins Crime Club (London), 1964.   .   . £40/£10
The Far Side of the Dollar, Knopf (New York), 1965   .   .
.   .   .   . £35/£10
ditto, Collins Crime Club (London), 1965.   .   . £20/£10
Black Money, Knopf (New York), 1966   .   .   . £35/£10
ditto, Collins Crime Club (London), 1966.   .   . £25/£10
The Instant Enemy, Knopf (New York), 1968   . £25/£10
ditto, Collins Crime Club (London), 1968.   .   . £25/£10

The Goodbye Look, Knopf (New York), 1969   . £20/£10
ditto, Collins Crime Club (London), 1969.   .   . £20/£5
The Underground Man, Knopf (New York), 1971.   £20/£5
ditto, Collins Crime Club (London), 1971.   .   . £15/£5
Sleeping Beauty, Knopf (New York), 1973   .   . £20/£5
ditto, Collins Crime Club (London), 1973.   .   . £15/£5
The Blue Hammer, Knopf (New York), 1976.   . £20/£5
ditto, Collins Crime Club (London), 1976.   .   . £15/£5
Lew Archer, Private Investigator, Mysterious Press (New York), 1977   .   .   .   . £20/£5
ditto, Mysterious Press (New York), 1977 (250 numbered, signed copies, acetate d/w and slipcase).   .   .£100/£75

Other Titles Written as 'Ross Macdonald'
On Crime Writing, Capra Press (Santa Barbara, CA), 1973 (250 signed, numbered copies, no d/w) £50
ditto, Capra Press (Santa Barbara, CA), 1973 (pbk)   . £15
Self Portrait, Ceaselessly into the Past, Capra Press (Santa Barbara, CA), 1981   .   .   .   .£15/£5
ditto, Capra Press (Santa Barbara, CA), 1981 (250 signed, numbered copies, no d/w) £75
ditto, Capra Press (Santa Barbara, CA), 1981 (26 signed, lettered copies, no d/w) £125

Novels Written as 'Kenneth Millar'
The Dark Tunnel, Dodd, Mead (New York), 1944   .   .
.   .   .   .£3,000/£400
ditto, as **I Die Slowly**, Lion (London), 1955   . £45/£10
Trouble Follows Me, Dodd, Mead (New York), 1946 .   .
.   .   .   .£1,500/£100
ditto, as **Night Train**, Lion (London), 1955   . £25/£10
Blue City, Knopf (New York), 1947 .   .   .   .£325/£65
ditto, Cassell (London), 1949   .   .   .   .   .£150/£20
The Three Roads, Knopf (New York), 1948   .   .£300/£65
ditto, Cassell (London), 1950   .   .   .   .   .£145/£20

Novels Written as 'John Ross Macdonald'
The Drowning Pool, Knopf (New York), 1950   . £500/£75
ditto, Cassell (London), 1952   .   .   .   .   .£250/£25
The Way Some People Die, Knopf (New York), 1951 .   .
.   .   .   .£600/£65
ditto, Cassell (London), 1953   .   .   .   .   .£225/£20
The Ivory Grin, Knopf (New York), 1952   .   .£600/£65
ditto, Cassell (London), 1953   .   .   .   .   .£225/£20
ditto, as **Marked for Murder**, Pocket Books (New York), 1953 (pbk) £10
Meet Me at the Morgue, Knopf (New York), 1953 £250/£45
ditto, as **Experience with Evil**, Cassell (London), 1954.   .
.   .   .   . £45/£10
Find a Victim, Knopf (New York), 1954 .   .   .£400/£35
ditto, Cassell (London), 1955   .   .   .   .   .£200/£20

Short Stories Written as 'John Ross Macdonald'
The Name is Archer, Bantam (New York), 1955 (pbk). £20

Novels Written as 'John Macdonald'
The Moving Target, Knopf (New York), 1949   £1,000/£75
ditto, Cassell (London), 1951   .   .   .   .   .£400/£45

Omnibus Editions
Archer in Hollywood, Knopf (New York), 1967   . £25/£10
Archer at Large, Knopf (New York), 1970   .   . £25/£10

CORMAC McCARTHY
(b.1933)

Cormac McCarthy is considered by many critics to be one of America's greatest novelists, and is often compared to William Faulkner and Herman Melville. His novels have ranged from Southern Gothic, through Westerns, to post-apocalyptic fiction.

Novels
The Orchard Keeper, Random House (New York), 1965 . . . . £1,750/£200
ditto, André Deutsch (London), 1966. . . . £225/£35
Outer Dark, Random House (New York), 1968 . £600/£75
ditto, André Deutsch (London), 1970. . . . £300/£35
Child of God, Random House (New York), 1973 . £300/£35
ditto, Chatto & Windus (London), 1973 . . . £150/£25
Suttree, Random House (New York), 1979 . £500/£65
ditto, Chatto & Windus (London), 1980 . . . £450/£50
Blood Meridian, Or the Evening Redness in the West, Random House (New York), 1986 . . . £500/£65
ditto, Picador (London), 1989 . . . . £200/£25
No Country for Old Men, Knopf (New York), 2005 £10/£5
ditto, Knopf (New York), 2005 (approx 500 copies signed on tipped-in leaf) . . . . . . £125/£75
ditto, Knopf/Trice (New York), 2005 (75 signed copies; slipcase). . . . . . . £500/£400
ditto, Knopf/Trice (New York), 2005 (325 signed copies; slipcase). . . . . . . £100/£75
ditto, Picador (London), 2005 . . . . £10/£5
The Road, Knopf (New York), 2006 . . . £65/£10
ditto, Picador (London), 2006 . . . £50/£5

'The Border' Trilogy
All the Pretty Horses, Knopf (New York), 1992 . £100/£15
ditto, Knopf (New York), 1992 (200 signed advance reading copies; pbk in slipcase) . . . . £200/£135
ditto, Picador (London), 1993 . . . £35/£10
The Crossing, Knopf (New York), 1994 . . £10/£5
ditto, Knopf (New York), 1994 (1,000 copies signed on tipped-in leaf) . . . . . £125/£75
ditto, Picador (London), 1993 . . . £10/£5
Cities of the Plain, Knopf (New York), 1998 . . £10/£5
ditto, Knopf (New York), 1998 (1,000 copies signed on tipped-in leaf) . . . . . £125/£75
ditto, Knopf/Trice (New York), 1998 (50 signed copies; slipcase). . . . . . . £750/£650
ditto, Knopf/Trice (New York), 1998 (300 signed copies; slipcase). . . . . . . £200/£150
ditto, Picador (London), 1998 . . . . £10/£5

Play/Screenplay
The Stonemason, Ecco Press (Hopewell, NJ), 1994 £10/£5
ditto, Ecco Press (Hopewell, NJ), 1994 (350 copies signed on tipped-in leaf) . . . . . £100/£75
The Gardener's Son, Ecco Press (Hopewell, NJ), 1996 . . . . £10/£5
ditto, Ecco Press (Hopewell, NJ), 1996 (350 copies signed on tipped-in leaf) . . . . . £100/£75
The Sunset Limited, Dramatists Play Services (New York), 2006 (pbk) £5

FRANK McCOURT
(b.1930)

Francis McCourt is a teacher and author who was born in Brooklyn, but whose family returned to their native Ireland in 1934. He received the Pulitzer Prize (1997) and National Book Critics Circle Award (1996) for *Angela's Ashes* which is a memoir of his childhood as a poor Irish Catholic in Limerick.

Memoirs
Angela's Ashes, HarperCollins (London), 1996 . £15/£5
ditto, Scribner (New York), 1996 . . . . £15/£5
ditto, Easton Press (Norwalk, CT), 2003 (signed edition; full leather) £100
'Tis, Flamingo (London), 1996 . . . . . £10/£5
ditto, Scribner (New York), 1996 . . . . £10/£5
ditto, Easton Press (Norwalk, CT), 1999 (1,600 signed, numbered copies; full leather) £75
Teacher Man, Fourth Estate (London), 2005 . . £10/£5
ditto, Scribner (New York), 2005 . . . . £10/£5

Others
Ireland Ever: The Photographs of Jill Freedman, Harry N. Abrams (Boston, MA), 2004 (with Malachy McCourt) . . . . £10/£5
Brotherhood, American Express (New York), 2004 (with Thomas Von Essen, Rudy Giuliani) . . . £10/£5
Angela and the Baby Jesus, HarperCollins (London), 2007 . . . . £10/£5
ditto, Scribner (New York), 2007 (adult edition) . £10/£5
ditto, Simon & Schuster (New York), 2007 (juvenile edition) . . . . £10/£5

CARSON McCULLERS
(b.1917 d.1967)

McCullers was an American writer whose fiction explored the spiritual isolation of misfits and outcasts of the American South. Although some critics have detected tragicomic and political elements in her writing, her work is often described as 'Southern Gothic'.

Prose
The Heart is a Lonely Hunter, Houghton Mifflin (Boston), 1940 . . . . £1,000/£100
ditto, Cresset Press (London), 1943 . . . . £250/£25
Reflections in a Golden Eye, Houghton Mifflin (Boston), 1941 (first issue with cellophane window on front panel of d/w) . . . . £650/£20
ditto, Houghton Mifflin (Boston), 1941 (second issue with printed d/w) . . . . . . £100/£20
ditto, Cresset Press (London), 1942 . . . . £65/£15
The Member of the Wedding, Houghton Mifflin (Boston), 1946 . . . . £250/£35
ditto, Cresset Press (London), 1946 . . . . £75/£20
The Ballad of the Sad Café: The Novels and Short Stories of Carson McCullers, Houghton Mifflin (Boston), 1951 . . . . £75/£15
ditto, Cresset Press (London), 1952 . . . . £40/£10

Clock Without Hands, Houghton Mifflin (Boston), 1961 .
. . . . £40/£10
ditto, Cresset Press (London), 1961 . . . £25/£5
The Mortgaged Heart, Houghton Mifflin (Boston), 1971 .
. . . . £30/£10
ditto, Barrie & Jenkins (London), 1971 . . . £25/£5
Collected Short Stories, Franklin Library (Franklin Center,
PA), 1982 (limited edition) £20
Collected Stories, Houghton Mifflin (Boston), 1987 £20/£5
***Illumination and Night Glare: The Unfinished
Autobigraphy of Carson McCullers***, Univ of Wisconson
Press (Madison, WI), 1999 . . . . . £10/£5

Poetry
Sweet As a Pickle and Clean As a Pig, Houghton Mifflin
(Boston), 1964 . . . . £40/£10
ditto, Cape (London), 1965 . . . . . £40/£10

Plays
The Member of the Wedding, New Directions (New York),
1951 . . . . £25/£10
The Square Root of Wonderful, Houghton Mifflin (Boston),
1958 . . . . £35/£10
ditto, Cresset Press (London), 1958 . . . £25/£5

IAN McEWAN

(b.1948)

Ian McEwan was the first of Malcolm Bradbury's creative
writing students to receive recognition. His early short
stories and novels were often obsessive and explicit and
earned him a certain reputation. More recent novels are
notable for their fine writing and restraint, and in 1998 he
was awarded the Booker Prize for his novella, *Amsterdam*.

Short Stories
First Love, Last Rites, Cape (London), 1975 . . £450/£45
ditto, Random House (New York), 1975 . . . £50/£10
In Between the Sheets, Cape (London), 1978 . . £225/£20
ditto, Simon & Schuster (New York), 1979 . . £20/£5
The Short Stories, Cape (London), 1995 . . . £20/£5

Novels
The Cement Garden, Cape (London), 1978 . . £165/£20
ditto, Simon & Schuster (New York), 1978 . . £25/£5
The Comfort of Strangers, Cape (London), 1981 . £65/£5
ditto, Simon & Schuster (New York), 1981 . . £20/£5
The Child in Time, Cape (London), 1987. . . £20/£5
ditto, London Limited Editions (London), 1987 (150
numbered, signed copies in tissue paper jacket) £125/£100
ditto, Houghton Mifflin (Boston), 1987 . . . £15/£5
The Innocent, Cape (London), 1990 . . . . £20/£5
ditto, Doubleday (New York), 1990 . . . . £15/£5
Black Dogs, Cape (London), 1992 . . . . £15/£5
ditto, London Limited Editions (London), 1992 (150
numbered, signed copies in tissue paper jacket) . £75/£50
ditto, Doubleday (New York), 1992 . . . . £10/£5
Enduring Love, Cape (London), 1997 . . . £10/£5
ditto, Doubleday (New York), 1998 . . . . £10/£5
Amsterdam, Cape (London), 1998 . . . . £10/£5
ditto, Doubleday (New York), 1999 . . . . £10/£5
Atonement, Cape (London), 2001 . . . . £10/£5

ditto, Doubleday (New York), 2002 (500 signed copies) .
. . . . £50/£35
ditto, Cape (London), 2007 (2,000 signed film tie-in copies)
. . . . £30/£20
ditto, Talese/Doubleday (New York), 2002 . . £10/£5
Saturday, Cape (London), 2005 . . . . . £10/£5
ditto, Cape (London), 2005 (1,500 signed copies, slipcase, no
d/w) . . . . £45/£20
ditto, Doubleday (New York), 2005 . . . . £10/£5
On Chesil Beach, Cape (London), 2007. . . . £10/£5
ditto, Doubleday (New York), 2007 . . . . £10/£5
ditto, Cape (London), 2007 (1,200 signed copies, slipcase, no
d/w) £60
ditto, Cape (London), 2007 (5,500 copies dedicated to
Waterstones staff, slipcase, no d/w). . . . £35
ditto, London Review Bookshop, 2007 (100 signed copies,
slipcase, no d/w) £150
ditto, London Review Bookshop, 2007 (26 lettered copies,
slipcase, no d/w) £350

Plays
The Imitation Game: Three Plays for Television, Cape
(London), 1981 . . . . £65/£15
ditto, Houghton Mifflin (Boston), 1982 . . . £45/£10
The Ploughman's Lunch, Methuen (London), 1985 (pbk) .
. . . . £10
Soursweet, Faber (London), 1988 (pbk). . . . £10
The Good Son, Pocket Books (New York), 1993 (with Todd
Strasser; pbk). £5

Children's Titles
Rose Blanche, Cape (London), 1985 (with Roberto
Innocenti) £50
ditto, Creative Education (New York), 1985 . . £20
The Daydreamer, Knopf (Canada), 1994 . . . £15/£5
ditto, Cape (London), 1994 . . . . . £15/£5
ditto, Harper Collins (New York), 1994 . . . £10/£5

Miscellaneous
British Films at the London Film Festival, Filmways, 1979
[1980] (wraps) £25
Or Shall We Die?, Cape (London), 1983 . . . £30/£15
ditto, Cape (London), 1983 (in National Peace Week
wrapper) . . . . £50/£15
A Move Abroad, Picador (London), 1989 (pbk) . . £5
***Other Minds: An Extract from His Forthcoming Novel
'Atonement'***, Bridgewater Press (London), 2001 (100
numbered, signed copies) £50
ditto, Bridgewater Press (London), 2001 (26 lettered, signed
copies) £250
ditto, Bridgewater Press (London), 2001 (12 signed copies
bound in quarter calf) £300
For You, Vintage (London), 2008 (1,000 signed pbk copies)
. . . . £25

JOHN McGAHERN
(b.1934 d.2006)

John McGahern is a novelist and short story writer whose works, wherever they are set, always refer back to his native Ireland. His decision to leave teaching to become a full-time writer seems to have been influenced by the controversy over *The Dark*, which was banned in Ireland. His best known book is *Amongst Women*, a detailed and understanding portrayal of an unsympathetic protagonist.

Novels
The Barracks, Faber (London), 1963 . . . £350/£75
ditto, Macmillan (New York), 1964 . . . £100/£15
The Dark, Faber (London), 1965 . . . £200/£25
ditto, Knopf (New York), 1966 . . . £100/£15
The Leavetaking, Faber (London), 1974 . . . £100/£15
ditto, Little, Brown (Boston), 1974 . . . £50/£10
The Pornographer, Faber (London), 1979 . £40/£10
ditto, Harper & Row (New York), 1979 . . £20/£5
Amongst Women, Faber (London), 1990 . . £10/£5
ditto, Viking (New York), 1990 . . . £10/£5
That They May Face the Rising Sun, Faber (London), 2001
. . . . £10/£5
ditto, as *By the Lake*, Knopf (New York), 2002 . £10/£5

Short Stories
Nightlines, Faber (London), 1970 . . . £175/£25
ditto, Little, Brown (Boston), 1971 . . . £75/£15
Getting Through, Faber (London), 1978 . . £65/£10
ditto, Harper & Row (New York), 1980 . . £15/£5
High Ground, Faber (London), 1985. . . £45/£10
ditto, Viking (New York), 1987 . . . £10/£5
The Collected Stories, Faber (London), 1992 . £25/£10
ditto, Knopf (New York), 1993 . . . . £20/£5
Creatures of the Earth: New and Selected Stories, Faber (London), 2006 . . . . . £10/£5

Play
The Power of Darkness, Faber (London), 1991 (pbk) . £10

Non-Fiction
Memoir, Faber (London), 2005 . . . . . £15/£5
ditto, Faber (London), 2005 (250 signed copies; d/w and slipcase). . . . . . . £250/£200
ditto, as *All Will Be Well; A Memoir*, Knopf (New York), 2006 . . . . £10/£5

ARTHUR MACHEN
(b.1863 d.1947)

A novelist, short story writer and essayist, Machen is often read today for his tales of horror and the supernatural. His work, however, is of a predominantly mystical cast. 'The Bowmen' was the origin of the Angels of Mons myth in the First World War.

Poetry
Eleusinia, privately printed by Joseph Jones (Hereford), 1881 (16pps pamphlet without covers, 100 copies printed but only two or three copies recorded) . . . £25,000

Novels
The Chronicle of Clemendy, Carbonnek [London], 1888 (250 numbered copies, blue-grey boards, parchment spine lettered in gilt with raised bands, frontispiece) . . £200
ditto, privately printed, Carbonnek [New York], 1923 (1,050 numbered, signed copies) . . . . . £125/£25
ditto, Martin Secker (London), 1925 [1926] (100 signed, numbered copies) £85
ditto, Martin Secker (London), 1925 (trade edition) £75/£25
ditto, Knopf (New York), 1926 . . . . £65/£20
The Great God Pan, John Lane (London), 1894 (dark blue cloth with design by Aubrey Beardsley on front board in white, spine decorated in white with gilt lettering, rear board with key in white) £250
ditto, Roberts Bros (Boston), 1894 . . . . £200
The Three Impostors, John Lane (London), 1895 (dark blue cloth with design by Aubrey Beardsley on front board in white, spine decorated in white with gilt lettering, rear board with key in white) £250
ditto, Roberts Bros (Boston), 1895 . . . . £175
ditto, Knopf (New York), 1923 . . . . £60/£20
The Hill of Dreams, Grant Richards (London), 1907 (dark red cloth, spine and front board lettered in gilt, 'E. Grant Richards' on spine, first binding without adverts after text)
. . . . £200
ditto, Grant Richards (London), 1907 (second binding as above but with 20 pages of adverts after text) . . £145
ditto, Grant Richards (London), 1907 (third binding, various cloths, 'Grant Richards' on spine) £135
ditto, Dana Estes & Co (Boston), 1907 . . . £175
ditto, Martin Secker (London), [1922] (150 signed, numbered copies) £200
ditto, Tartarus Press (Horam, Sussex), 1998 (frontispiece, d/w illustration and two further illustrations by Sime; 350 copies) . . . . £100/£25
The Great Return, The Faith Press, (London), 1915 (cream boards lettered in red with design in red by T. Noyes Lewis, first issue with top edge stained red) . . £250
ditto, The Faith Press (London), 1915 (second issue with top edge unstained) £65
The Terror, Duckworth & Co., (London) [1917] (light blue boards lettered in dark blue) £45
ditto, as *The Terror, A Mystery*, McBride (New York), [1917] £40
The Secret Glory, Martin Secker (London), 1922 (black cloth, spine lettered in gilt, top edge trimmed and stained green) . . . . £200/£50
ditto, Knopf (New York), 1923 . . . . £75/£45
ditto, as *Chapters Five and Six of 'The Secret Glory'*, Tartarus Press (Lewes, UK), 1990 (250 numbered copies, blue cloth lettered in gilt, light blue d/w lettered in dark blue) . . . . £30/£10
ditto, Tartarus Press (Horam, UK), 1998 (first edition of all six chapters, green cloth, cream d/w) . . . £65/£25
The Green Round, Ernest Benn (London), 1933 . £250/£60
ditto, Arkham House (Sauk City, WI), 1968 . . £15/£5

Short Stories
The House of Souls, Grant Richards (London), 1906 (grey, brown or blue boards with design by Sidney H. Sime in gilt, yellow and black on front board, 'E. Grant Richards' on spine, frontispiece by Sime) £300
ditto, Grant Richards (London), 1906 (second binding with 'Grant Richards' on spine) £250

ditto, Dana Estes & Co (Boston), 1906 . . . . £200

The Bowmen and Other Legends of the War, Simpkin Marshall (London), 1915 (four stories, slate blue paper covered boards, lettered in dark blue with design of medieval soldier with bow and arrow) £50

ditto, Simpkin Marshall (London), 1915 (second edition, boards as above, but six stories, with silhouette frontispiece by Baron Scotfield) £45

ditto, Simpkin Marshall (London), 1915 (as above but red leather binding with lettering in gilt and illustration blind stamped) £75

ditto, Putnams (New York), 1915 (first issue with blue bowman) £50

ditto, Putnams (New York), 1915 (second issue with brown bowman) £45

The Shining Pyramid, Covici-McGee (Chicago), 1923 (875 numbered copies, frontispiece by Wallace Smith, black cloth, lettered in gilt on front, with paper label on spine) .
. . . . £100

Ornaments In Jade, Knopf (New York), 1924 (1,000 signed, numbered copies, slipcase) . . . . £100/£65

ditto, Tartarus Press/Caermaen Books (Horam, UK), 1997 .
. . . . £25/£10

The Shining Pyramid, Martin Secker (London), 1925 (different from above *Shining Pyramid*). . . £75/£25

ditto, Martin Secker (London), 1925 (250 signed, numbered copies) . . . . £225/£100

ditto, Knopf (New York), 1925 . . . . . £75/£25

The Cosy Room, Rich & Cowan (London), 1936 . . .
. . . . £1,250/£400

The Children of the Pool, Hutchinson & Co. (London), 1936
. . . . £1,000/£300

Tales of Horror and the Supernatural, Knopf (New York), 1948 . . . . £40/£15

ditto, Richards Press (London), 1949 . . . £35/£20

Ritual and Other Stories, Tartarus Press (Lewes, UK), 1992
. . . . £50/£10

Essays

The Grande Trouvaille: A Legend of Pentonville, privately printed for the First Edition Bookshop (London), 1923 (250 signed, numbered copies; wraps, 8pps) . . £100

The Collector's Craft, privately printed for the First Edition Bookshop (London), 1923 (250 numbered copies; wraps, 8pps) £100

ditto, privately printed (London), 1923 (unknown number of the above issue signed) £150

Strange Roads & With the Gods in Spring, The Classic Press (London), 1923 (bound in yapp, various colours noted, lettered in gilt on front cover, top edge gilt, marbled lavendar endpapers) £75

ditto, The Classic Press (London), 1923 (second issue, dark green alligatored smooth cloth) £50

ditto, The Classic Press (London), 1923 (third issue, rough light green cloth, pink endpapers) £35

ditto, The Classic Press (London), 1923 (fourth issue, olive green endpapers). £35

ditto, The Classic Press (London), 1924 (300 signed, numbered copies) £100

Dog and Duck, Knopf (New York), 1924 (yellow cloth, purple paper label on spine lettered in gilt) . £65/£25

ditto, Cape (London), [1924] (900 numbered copies, blue patterned boards, paper label on front cover lettered in black, paper label on spine) . . . . £75/£35

ditto, Cape (London), [1924] (150 of above numbered and signed, gilt cloth spine, top edge gilt) . . £125/£75

The Glorious Mystery, Covici-McGee (Chicago), 1924 (pictorial boards) . . . . £125/£65

Dreads and Drolls, Martin Secker (London), 1926 £65/£25

ditto, Martin Secker (London), 1926 (100 signed, numbered copies) . . . . £125/£75

ditto, Knopf (New York), 1927 . . . . . £65/£25

Notes and Queries, Spurr & Swift (London), 1926 (265 signed, numbered copies) £65

Tom O' Bedlam and His Song, The Appellicon Press (Westport, CT), 1930 (200 signed copies, slipcase) .
. . . . £100/£65

Beneath the Barley, privately printed (London), 1931 (25 signed, numbered copies; wraps) £125

The Glitter of the Brook, Postprandial Press (Dalton, GA), 1932 (10 copies) £300

Bridles and Spurs, The Rowfant Club (Cleveland, OH), 1951 (178 numbered copies, slipcase) . . £125/£100

ditto, The Rowfant Club (Cleveland, OH), 1951 (offprint of the Preface only 25 copies) £100

A Critical Essay, privately printed (Lakewood, OH), 1953 (50 copies) £50

A Note on Poetry, Four Ducks Press (Wichita, KS), 1959 (50 numbered copies) £125

From the London Evening News, Four Ducks Press (Wichita, KS), 1959 (50 numbered copies) . . £125

The Secret of the Sangraal, Tartarus Press (Horam, UK), 1995 (withdrawn edition of 250 copies). . . £200/£65

ditto, Tartarus Press (Horam, UK), 1996 (250 copies) . .
. . . . £45/£15

Autobiography

Far Off Things, Martin Secker (London), 1922 (100 signed, numbered copies, blue boards, paper label on spine) . £125

ditto, Martin Secker (London), 1922 (trade edition, green cloth, spine lettered in gilt) . . . . £75/£30

ditto, Knopf (New York), 1923 . . . . . £50/£15

Things Near and Far, Martin Secker (London), 1923 (100 signed, numbered copies, blue boards, paper label on spine)
. . . . £125

ditto, Martin Secker (London), 1923 (trade edition, green cloth, spine lettered in gilt) . . . . £75/£30

ditto, Knopf (New York), 1923 . . . . . £50/£15

The London Adventure, Martin Secker (London), 1924 .
. . . . £75/£25

ditto, Martin Secker (London), 1924 (200 signed, numbered copies) £100

ditto, Knopf (New York), 1924 . . . . . £50/£15

In the Eighties, privately printed (London), 1931 . . £100

ditto, Twyn Barlwm Press (London), 1933 (50 numbered copies) £50

Translations

The Heptameron, by Queen Margaret of Navarre, privately printed [Dryden Press, London], 1886 . . . . £65

ditto, as ***The Fortunate Lovers***, Redway (London), 1887 (a selection of the above) £30

ditto, Scribner's & Welford (New York), 1887 . . £100

Fantastic Tales, or The Way to Attain, privately printed, Carbonnek (London), 1889 [1890] (500 numbered copies)
. . . . £65

ditto, privately printed, Carbonnek (London), 1889 [1890] (large paper issue, 50 signed, numbered copies) . £200

ditto, privately printed, Carbonnek (New York), 1923 (1,050
numbered, signed copies) . . . . . £75/£25
The Memoirs of Casanova, privately printed (London), 1894
(12 vols, 1,000 copies) £400
ditto, privately printed (London), 1894 (large paper issue, 50
numbered sets) £650
ditto, privately printed (London), 1894 (3 numbered sets,
Japanese vellum) £1,000
Casanova's Escape from the Leads, Casanova Society
[London], 1925 . . . . . . £50/£15
ditto, Knopf (New York), Borzoi Pocket Books No. 28 [1925]
. . . . £35/£10

Others

The Anatomy of Tobacco, George Redway (London), 1884
(pseud 'Leolinus Siluriensis', cream boards lettered in red)
. . . . £250
ditto, Knopf (New York), 1926 . . . . £50/£20
Don Quijote de la Mancha, George Redway (London), [n.d.
1887] (16pps pamphlet without wraps) . . . £750
Thesaurus Incantatus, Marvell (London), [n.d.1888] (blue-
grey wraps) £1,000
Hieroglyphics, Grant Richards (London), 1902 (brown cloth,
paper label to spine) £100
ditto, Mitchell Kennerley (New York), 1913 . . . £75
ditto, Knopf (New York), 1923 . . . . £50/£20
The House of the Hidden Light, privately printed (London),
1904 (written with A.E. Waite, 3 copies printed but not
bound, of which only two copies and a proof set are known
to survive) £5,000
ditto, Tartarus/Ferret, (Carlton-in-Coverdale/London) 2003
(green cloth, cream d/w) . . . . . £100/£35
Dr. Stiggins, Francis Griffiths (London), 1906 (tan boards,
orange cloth spine, illustration of a minister on front board)
. . . . £45
ditto, Knopf (New York), 1925 . . . . £45/£10
Parsifal, General Cinematograph Agencies Ltd (London),
[n.d. 1913] (Machen's name does not appear, dark grey
wraps, lettered in blue) £75
War and the Christian Faith, Skeffington & Son (London),
1918 (grey-brown boards lettered in black) . . £50
Arthur Machen, a novelist of ecstasy and sin, Walter M.
Hill (Chicago), 1918 (250 copies) £125
Precious Balms, Spurr & Swift (London), 1924 (265 signed,
numbered copies) £100
ditto, Spurr & Swift (London), 1924 (15 signed, lettered
copies) £200
The Canning Wonder, Chatto & Windus (London), 1925 .
. . . . £65/£20
ditto, Chatto & Windus (London), 1925 (130 signed,
numbered copies) £75
ditto, Knopf (New York), 1926 . . . . £25/£10
A Preface to Casanova's Escape from the Leads, The
Casanova Society [London], 1925 (25 copies; wraps). £150
A Souvenir of Cadby Hall, J. Lyons and Co. Ltd (London),
1927 . . . . £100
Parish of Amersham, Mason (Amersham), 1930 (wraps) .
. . . . £45
Above the River, by John Gawsworth, Ulysses Bookshop
(London), 1931 (85 numbered copies signed by Gawsworth
and Machen). £125
An Introduction to J.Gawsworth: Above the River, privately
printed (London), 1931 (12 signed, numbered copies;
wraps) £250

A Few Letters from Arthur Machen, The Rowfant Club
(Cleveland, OH), 1932 (170 copies) £50
ditto, Aylesford Press (Aylesford, Kent), 1993 (83 copies of
333, signed by Janet Machen) £20
ditto, Aylesford Press (Aylesford, Kent), 1993 (250 copies of
333; wraps) £15
A.L.S., Four Ducks Press (Wichita, KA), 1956 (50 numbered
copies) £125
Starrett Vs. Machen, Autolycus Press (St Louis, MO), 1977
(500 numbered copies) £25
Dreams and Visions, by Morchard Bishop, Caermaen Books
(Oxford/Northampton, UK), 1987 (stapled wraps) . £15
Selected Letters, The Aquarian Press (Wellingborough,
Northants), 1988 . . . . £10/£5

Collected Edition

The Caerleon Edition, Martin Secker (London), 1923 (9
vols) . . . . £600/£350

COLIN MACINNES

(b.1914 d.1976)

Colin MacInnes is chiefly read today for his 'London
Trilogy' novels, which jauntily catch the changing mood of
1950s and '60s Britain. Although born in London,
MacInnes spent his formative years in Australia and two of
his novels are set there: *June in Her Spring* and *All Day
Saturday*.

Novels

To The Victors The Spoils, MacGibbon & Kee (London),
1950 . . . . £50/£10
June in Her Spring, MacGibbon & Kee (London), 1952 .
. . . . £50/£10
City of Spades, MacGibbon & Kee (London), 1957 £45/£10
ditto, Macmillan (New York), 1958 . . . . £30/£5
Absolute Beginners, MacGibbon & Kee (London), 1959 .
. . . . £100/£15
ditto, Macmillan (New York), 1960 . . . . £65/£10
Mr Love and Justice, MacGibbon & Kee (London), 1960 .
. . . . £35/£10
ditto, Dutton (New York), 1961 . . . . . £20/£5
All Day Saturday, MacGibbon & Kee (London), 1966 £20/£5
Westward to Laughter, MacGibbon & Kee (London), 1969
. . . . £20/£5
ditto, Farrar Straus (New York), 1970 . . . £15/£5
Three Years to Play, MacGibbon & Kee (London), 1970 .
. . . . £15/£5
ditto, Farrar Straus (New York), 1970 . . . £10/£5
Out of the Garden, Hart-Davis MacGibbon (London), 1974
. . . . £10/£5

Collected Editions

Visions of London, MacGibbon & Kee (London), 1969 .
. . . . £15/£5
ditto, as *The London Novels*, Farrar Straus (New York),
1969 . . . . £15/£5

Essays

England, Half English, MacGibbon & Kee (London), 1961
. . . . £30/£10
ditto, Random House (New York), 1962 . . . £20/£5

Posthumous Essays, Brian & O'Keefe (London), 1977   .
.   .   .   .   £15/£5
Out of the Way: Later Essays, Brian & O'Keefe (London),
1980   .   .   .   .   .   .   £15/£5

Others
London: City of Any Dream, Thames & Hudson (London),
1962   .   .   .   .   .   .   £25/£10
Australia and New Zealand, Time (New York), 1966 (with
the editors of *Life*)   .   .   .   .   £15/£5
Sweet Saturday Night: Night Pop Song 1840-1920,
MacGibbon & Kee (London), 1967.   .   .   £20/£5
Loving Them Both: A Study of Bisexuality and Bisexuals,
Brian & O'Keefe (London), 1973   .   .   £25/£10
'No Novel Reader', Brian & O'Keefe (London), 1975 £15/£5

JULIAN MACLAREN-ROSS

(b.1912 d.1964)

MacLaren-Ross was British novelist and short story writer
whose reputation as a bohemian in post-war Fitzrovian
London has helped keep alive interest in his writings. He
was also a frequent contributor to literary magazines such
as *Horizon* and the *London Magazine*. A portrait of
Maclaren-Ross as the novelist X. Trapnel appears in
Anthony Powell's *A Dance to the Music of Time*.

Novels
Bitten by the Tarantula, Allan Wingate (London), 1946   .
.   .   .   .   £250/£65
Of Love and Hunger, Allan Wingate (London), 1947   .   .
.   .   .   .   £300/£150
Until the Day She Dies, Hamish Hamilton (London), 1960 .
.   .   .   .   £250/£100
The Doomsday Book, Hamish Hamilton (London), 1961   .
.   .   .   .   £200/£50
ditto, Ivan Obolensky, 1961.   .   .   .   £125/£25
My Name is Love, The Times Press (London), 1964   .   .
.   .   .   .   £200/£65

Short Stories
The Stuff to Give to the Troops, Jonathan Cape (London),
1944   .   .   .   .   .   .   £300/£65
Better Than A Kick in the Pants, Lawson & Dunn/Hyperion
Press (London), 1945.   .   .   .   .   £150/£60
The Nine Men of Soho, Allan Wingate (London), 1946   .
.   .   .   .   £150/£60

Translations
Pierrot, by Raymond Queneau, John Lehmann (London),
1950   .   .   .   .   .   .   £100/£25
Maigret and the Burglar's Wife, by Georges Simenon,
Hamish Hamilton (London), 1955   .   .   £40/£5

Others
The Weeping and the Laughter, Rupert Hart-Davis
(London), 1953   .   .   .   .   .   £225/£45
The Funny Bone, Elek Books (London), 1956   .   £65/£20
Memoirs of the Forties, Alan Ross (London), 1965   .
.   .   .   .   £125/£35

ALISTAIR MACLEAN

(b.1923 d.1987)

A successful popular novelist, Maclean used his wartime
experiences with the Royal Navy as the background to his
first novel, *HMS Ulysses*. A series of naval and military
thrillers followed, characterised by attention to detail and
compelling plots. MacLean also wrote a series of movie
outlines which were, controversially, completed by others,
and bear little resemblance to Maclean's own style.

Novels
HMS Ulysses, Collins (London), 1955   .   .   .   £50/£10
ditto, Doubleday (New York), 1956 .   .   .   £25/£5
The Guns of Navarone, Collins (London), 1957   .   £50/£10
ditto, Doubleday (New York), 1957 .   .   .   £40/£5
South By Java Head, Collins (London), 1958.   .   £35/£10
ditto, Doubleday (New York), 1958 .   .   .   £30/£5
The Last Frontier, Collins (London), 1959   .   .   £35/£10
ditto, as *The Secret Ways*, Doubleday (New York), 1959   .
.   .   .   .   £30/£10
Night Without End, Collins (London), 1960   .   £35/£10
ditto, Doubleday (New York), 1960 .   .   .   £30/£5
Fear is the Key, Collins (London), 1961   .   .   £35/£10
ditto, Doubleday (New York), 1961 .   .   .   £30/£5
The Dark Crusader, Collins (London), 1961 (pseud 'Ian
Stuart')   .   .   .   .   £30/£5
ditto, as *The Blake Shrike*, Scribner's (New York), 1961   .
.   .   .   .   £25/£5
The Golden Rendezvous, Collins (London), 1962 .   £35/£10
ditto, Doubleday (New York), 1962 .   .   .   £25/£5
The Satan Bug, Collins (London), 1962 (pseud 'Ian Stuart')
.   .   .   .   £100/£15
ditto, Scribner's (New York), 1962 .   .   .   £65/£10
Ice Station Zebra, Collins (London), 1963   .   £60/£10
ditto, Doubleday (New York), 1963 .   .   .   £25/£10
When Eight Bells Toll, Collins (London), 1966   .   £25/£5
ditto, Doubleday (New York), 1966 .   .   .   £15/£5
Where Eagles Dare, Collins (London), 1967 .   .   £35/£10
ditto, Doubleday (New York), 1967 .   .   .   £30/£5
Force 10 from Navarone, Collins (London), 1968.   £35/£10
ditto, Doubleday (New York), 1968 .   .   .   £30/£5
Puppet on a Chain, Collins (London), 1969   .   £20/£5
ditto, Doubleday (New York), 1969 .   .   .   £15/£5
Caravan to Vaccares, Collins (London), 1970   .   £20/£5
ditto, Doubleday (New York), 1970 .   .   .   £15/£5
Bear Island, Collins (London), 1971.   .   .   £20/£5
ditto, Doubleday (New York), 1971 .   .   .   £10/£5
The Way to Dusty Death, Collins (London), 1973 .   £20/£5
ditto, Doubleday (New York), 1973 .   .   .   £15/£5
Breakheart Pass, Collins (London), 1974   .   £20/£5
ditto, Doubleday (New York), 1974 .   .   .   £15/£5
Circus, Collins (London), 1975 .   .   .   £15/£5
ditto, Doubleday (New York), 1975 .   .   .   £15/£5
The Golden Gate, Collins (London), 1976   .   £15/£5
ditto, Doubleday (New York), 1976 .   .   .   £15/£5
Death from Disclosure, Hale (London), 1976 (pseud 'Ian
Stuart')   .   .   .   .   .   .   £15/£5
Flood Tide, Hale (London), 1977 (pseud 'Ian Stuart')   .   .
.   .   .   .   £15/£5
Sand Trap, Hale (London), 1977 (pseud 'Ian Stuart') £15/£5

Seawitch, Collins (London), 1977 . . . £15/£5
ditto, Doubleday (New York), 1977 . . . . £15/£5
Goodbye, California, Collins (London), 1978 . . £10/£5
ditto, Doubleday (New York), 1978 . . . £10/£5
Fatal Switch, Hale (London), 1978 (pseud 'Ian Stuart') .
. . . . £10/£5
A Weekend to Kill, Hale (London), 1978 (pseud 'Ian Stuart')
. . . . £10/£5
Athabasca, Collins (London), 1980 . . . £10/£5
ditto, Doubleday (New York), 1980 . . . £10/£5
River of Death, Collins (London), 1981 . . . £10/£5
ditto, Doubleday (New York), 1982 . . . £10/£5
Partisans, Collins (London), 1982 . . . £10/£5
ditto, Doubleday (New York), 1983 . . . £10/£5
Floodgate, Collins (London), 1983 . . . £10/£5
ditto, Doubleday (New York), 1984 . . . £10/£5
San Andreas, Collins (London), 1984 . . . £10/£5
ditto, Doubleday (New York), 1985 . . . £10/£5
The Lonely Sea, Collins (London), 1985 . . . £10/£5
ditto, Doubleday (New York), 1985 . . . £10/£5
Santorini, Collins (London), 1986 . . . £10/£5
ditto, Doubleday (New York), 1987 . . . £10/£5

Others
All About Lawrence of Arabia, Allen (London), 1962 . .
. . . . £65/£15
ditto, as *Lawrence of Arabia*, Random House (New York),
1961 . . . . £45/£10
Captain Cook, Collins (London), 1971 . . . £15/£5
ditto, Doubleday (New York), 1972 . . . . £15/£5
Alistair MacLean Introduces Scotland, Deutsch (London),
1972 . . . . £10/£5

Novels Based on Plots by Maclean
Hostage Tower, Fontana (London), 1980 (by John Denis;
pbk) £10
Air Force One is Down, Fontana (London), 1981 (by John
Denis; pbk) £10
Death Train, Collins (London), 1989 (by Alistair MacNeill)
. . . . £15/£5
Night Watch, Collins (London), 1989 (by Alistair MacNeill)
. . . . £15/£5
Red Alert, Collins (London), 1991 (by Alistair MacNeill)
. . . . £15/£5
Time of the Assassins, Collins (London), 1992 (by Alistair
MacNeill) . . . . £15/£5
Dead Halt, Collins (London), 1992 (by Alistair MacNeill) .
. . . . £15/£5
The Golden Girl, Chapman (London), 1992 (by Simon
Gandolfi) . . . . £10/£5
Golden Web, Chapman (London), 1993 (by Simon Gandolfi)
. . . . £10/£5
Golden Vengeance, Chapman (London), 1994 (by Simon
Gandolfi) . . . . £10/£5
Codebreaker, Collins (London), 1994 (by Alistair MacNeill)
. . . . £15/£5
Rendezvous, Collins (London), 1995 (by Alistair MacNeill)
. . . . £15/£5

LARRY McMURTRY
(b.1936)

Larry McMurtry is an American novelist and bookseller. His 1985 novel *Lonesome Dove* is set in the historical American West and won the Pulitzer Prize for Fiction for 1986. He is also a prolific essayist and screen writer.

Last Picture Show
The Last Picture Show, Dial (New York), 1966 . £500/£75
ditto, Sphere (London), 1972 (pbk) £65
Texasville, Simon & Schuster (New York), 1987 . £15/£5
ditto, Sidgewick & Jackson (London), 1987 . . £15/£5
Duane's Depressed, Simon & Schuster (New York), 1999 .
. . . . £10/£5
ditto, Orion (London), 1999 . . . . . £10/£5
When the Light Goes, Simon & Schuster (New York), 2007
. . . . £10/£5
ditto, Simon & Schuster (New York), 2007 (100 signed,
numbered copies) . . . . £100/£75

Terms of Endearment
Terms of Endearment, Simon & Schuster (New York), 1975
. . . . £85/£15
ditto, W.H. Allen (London), 1977 . . . £45/£5
The Evening Star, Simon & Schuster (New York), 1992 .
. . . . £10/£5
ditto, Orion (London), 1992 . . . . . £10/£5

Desert Rose
The Desert Rose, Simon & Schuster (New York), 1983 .
. . . . £25/£5
ditto, Simon & Schuster (New York), 1983 (250 signed,
numbered copies; in slipcase, no d/w) . . £150/£125
ditto, W.H. Allen (London), 1985 . . . £25/£5
The Late Child, Simon & Schuster (New York), 1995 . .
. . . . £10/£5
ditto, Orion (London), 1996 . . . . . £10/£5

Lonesome Dove
Lonesome Dove, Simon & Schuster (New York), 1985
(p.621, line 16: 'none' vs. 'done') . . . £150/£15
ditto, Pan Books (London/Sydney), 1986 (pbk) . £30
Streets of Laredo, Simon & Schuster (New York), 1993 .
. . . . £10/£5
Dead Man's Walk, Simon & Schuster (New York), 1995 .
. . . . £10/£5
ditto, Orion (London), 1995 . . . . . £10/£5
Comanche Moon, Simon & Schuster (New York), 1997 .
. . . . £10/£5
ditto, Orion (London), 1997 . . . . . £10/£5

Berrybender Narrative
Sin Killer, Simon & Schuster/Three Dog Books (New York),
2002 (50 signed, numbered copies) . . . £150/£125
ditto, Simon & Schuster/Three Dog Books (New York), 2002
(26 signed, lettered copies; slipcase) . . £250/£200
ditto, Simon & Schuster (New York, etc) 2002 (trade issue)
. . . . £10/£5
The Wandering Hill, Simon & Schuster/Three Dog Books
(New York), 2002 (75 signed, numbered copies) £150/£125
ditto, Simon & Schuster/Three Dog Books (New York), 2002
(26 signed, lettered copies; slipcase) . . £250/£200

ditto, Simon & Schuster (New York, etc), 2003 (trade issue)
. . . . £10/£5
By Sorrow's River, Simon & Schuster/Three Dog Books (New York), 2002 (75 signed, numbered copies) £150/£125
ditto, Simon & Schuster/Three Dog Books (New York), 2002 (26 signed, lettered copies; slipcase) . . £250/£200
ditto, Simon & Schuster (New York, etc), 2003 (trade issue)
. . . . £10/£5
Folly and Glory, Simon & Schuster/Three Dog Books (New York), 2004 (75 signed, numbered copies) . £150/£125
ditto, Simon & Schuster/Three Dog Books (New York), 2004 (26 signed, lettered copies; slipcase) . . £250/£200
ditto, Simon & Schuster (New York, etc), 2004 (trade issue)
. . . . £10/£5

Other Novels
Horseman, Pass By, Harper & Brothers (New York), 1961 .
. . . . £1,250/£250
ditto, as **Hud**, Popular Library (New York), 1961 (pbk) £20
ditto, as **Horseman, Pass By**, Sphere (London), 1971 (pbk).
. . . . £65
Leaving Cheyenne, Harper & Row (New York), 1963 . .
. . . . £1,250/£250
ditto, Sphere (London), 1972 (pbk) £65
Moving On, Simon & Schuster (New York), 1970 . £65/£10
ditto, Weidenfeld & Nicolson (London), 1971. . £45/£10
ditto, Weidenfeld & Nicolson (London), 1971 (variant with Simon & Schuster stamped at base of spine). . £75/£40
All My Friends Are Going To Be Strangers, Simon & Schuster (New York), 1972 . . . . . £75/£15
ditto, Secker & Warburg (London), 1972 . . . £45/£10
Cadillac Jack, Simon & Schuster (New York), 1982 £30/£5
ditto, Simon & Schuster (New York), 1982 (250 signed, numbered copies; in slipcase, no d/w) . £150/£125
ditto, W.H. Allen (London), 1986 . . . . £30/£5
Somebody's Darling, Simon & Schuster (New York), 1987
. . . . £45/£5
Anything for Billy, Simon & Schuster (New York), 1988 .
. . . . £10/£5
ditto, Collins (London), 1989 . . . . . £15/£5
Some Can Whistle, Simon & Schuster (New York), 1989 .
. . . . £10/£5
ditto, Century (London), 1990 . . . . . £15/£5
Buffalo Girls, Simon & Schuster (New York), 1990 £10/£5
ditto, Century (London), 1991 . . . . . £10/£5
Pretty Boy Floyd, Simon & Schuster (New York), 1994 .
. . . . £10/£5
ditto, Orion (London), 1996. . . . . . £10/£5
Zeke and Ned, Simon & Schuster (New York), 1997 (written with Diana Ossana) . . . . . . £10/£5
ditto, Orion (London), 1997. . . . . . £10/£5
Boonie's Lick, Simon & Schuster (New York, etc), 2000 .
. . . . £10/£5
Loop Group, Simon & Schuster/Three Dog Books (New York), 2004 (75 signed, numbered copies) . £150/£125
ditto, Simon & Schuster/Three Dog Books (New York), 2004 (26 signed, lettered copies; slipcase) . . £250/£200
ditto, Simon & Schuster (New York, etc), 2004 (trade issue)
. . . . £10/£5
Telegraph Days, Simon & Schuster/Three Dog Books (New York), 2006 (75 signed, numbered copies) . £150/£125
ditto, Simon & Schuster/Three Dog Books (New York), 2006 (26 signed, lettered copies; slipcase) . . £250/£200
ditto, Simon & Schuster (New York, etc), 2006 (trade issue)
. . . . £10/£5

Others
Daughter of the Tejas, New York Graphic (Greenwich, CT), 1965 (ghostwritten for Orphelia Ray; grey d/w) . £125/£25
ditto, New York Graphic (Greenwich, CT), 1965 (white d/w)
. . . . £100/£25
In A Narrow Grave, Encino Press (Austin, TX), 1968 (with 'skycrapers' on p.105, line 12 and other errors) . . .
. . . . £1,600/£1,500
ditto, Encino Press (Austin, TX), 1968 (errors corrected) .
. . . . £500/£100
ditto, Encino Press (Austin, TX), 1968 (250 signed, numbered copies; slipcase) . . . . £1,000/£800
'Texas Is Rich in Unredeemed Dreams', Texas Library Association (Austin, TX), 1971 (broadside; first issue on white paper) £300
ditto, Texas Library Association (Austin, TX), 1971 (second issue on tan paper) £200
It's Always We Rambled: An Essay on Rodeo, Frank Hallman (New York), 1974 (300 signed, numbered copies; no d/w or slipcase) £350
A Walk in Pasadena with Di-Anne and Mary Alice, [no publisher] ([no place]), [1985] (approx 50 copies; oversize heavy paper wraps) £1,000
Film Flam, Simon & Schuster (New York), 1987 . £30/£10
Cowboys, Wind River Press for the Book Club of Texas (Austin, TX), 1988 (poster, 14x20inches, with a drawing by Barbara Holman) £75
Splendours and Miseries of Being an Author-Bookseller, Antiquarian Booksellers' Association of America (no place), 1995 (750 copies in stapled wraps) . . . £40
Crazy Horse, Lipper/Viking (New York), 1999 . £10/£5
ditto, Weidenfeld & Nicolson (London), 1999. . £10/£5
Walter Banjamin at the Dairy Queen: Reflections at Sixty and Beyond, Simon & Schuster (New York), 1999 £10/£5
Roads, Simon & Schuster (New York, etc), 2000 . £10/£5
ditto, Orion (London), 2000. . . . . . £10/£5
Paradise, Simon & Schuster (New York, etc), 2001 £10/£5
ditto, Simon & Schuster/Three Dog Books (New York), 2001 (50 signed, numbered copies) . . . . £150/£125
Sacagawea's Nickname: Essays on the American West, Simon & Schuster/Three Dog Books (New York), 2001 (75 signed, numbered copies) . . . . £150/£125
ditto, Simon & Schuster (New York, etc), 2001 (trade issue)
. . . . £10/£5
Oh What a Slaughter: Massacres in the American West 1846-1890, Simon & Schuster/Three Dog Books (New York), 2005 (75 signed, numbered copies; slipcase) . .
. . . . £150/£125
ditto, Simon & Schuster/Three Dog Books (New York), 2005 (26 signed, lettered copies; slipcase) . £250/£200
ditto, Simon & Schuster (New York, etc), 2005 (trade issue)
. . . . £10/£5
The Colonel and Little Missie: Buffalo Bill, Annie Oakley, and the Beginnings of Superstardom in America, Simon & Schuster/Three Dog Books (New York), 2005 (75 signed, numbered copies; slipcase) . . . £150/£125
ditto, Simon & Schuster/Three Dog Books (New York), 2005 (26 signed, lettered copies; slipcase) . £250/£200
ditto, Simon & Schuster (New York, etc), 2005 (trade issue)
. . . . £10/£5
Brokeback Mountain: Story to Screenplay, Scribners (New York), 2006 (pbk; with Diana Ossana and Annie Proulx) .
. . . . £5

LOUIS MACNEICE
(b.1907 d.1963)

Frederick Louis MacNeice was a poet and playwright often associated with W.H. Auden and Stephen Spender, although his poetry lacks their preoccupation with politics. MacNeice employed irony and satire in his verse, and often explored a profound sense of loss.

Poetry
Blind Fireworks, Gollancz (London), 1929 (first issue cream cloth with green title label on spine) . . £650/£250
ditto, Gollancz (London), 1929 (second issue black cloth with paper spine label) . . . . £600/£200
Poems, Faber (London), 1935 . . . . £145/£40
Poems, Random House (New York), 1937 . £65/£20
The Earth Compels, Faber (London), 1938 . . £50/£15
Autumn Journal, Faber (London), 1939 . . . £250/£35
The Last Ditch, Cuala Press (Dublin), 1940 (450 copies, tissue d/w) . . . . . . £200/£150
ditto, Cuala Press (Dublin), 1940 (25 signed copies) . £400
Selected Poems, Faber (London), 1940 . . . £25/£10
Poems, 1925-1940, Random House (New York), 1940 . .
. . . . £25/£5
Plant and Phantom, Faber (London), 1941 . . £40/£10
Springboard: Poems, 1941-44, Faber (London), 1944 . .
. . . . £35/£10
ditto, Random House (New York), 1945 . . . £25/£5
Holes in the Sky: Poems, 1944-47, Faber (London), 1948 .
. . . . £30/£10
ditto, Random House (New York), 1949 . . . £25/£5
Collected Poems, 1925-48, Faber (London), 1949 . £35/£10
Ten Burnt Offerings, Faber (London), 1951 . . £35/£10
ditto, O.U.P. (New York), 1953 . . . . £25/£5
Autumn Sequel, Faber (London), 1954 . . £30/£10
The Other Wing, Faber (London), 1954 (wraps) . . £10
Visitations, Faber (London), 1957 . . . . £10/£5
ditto, O.U.P. (New York), 1958 . . . . £10/£5
Eighty-Five Poems, Faber (London), 1959 . . £25/£5
ditto, O.U.P. (New York), 1959 . . . . £10/£5
Solstices, Faber (London), 1961 . . . . £25/£5
ditto, O.U.P. (New York), 1961 . . . . £10/£5
The Burning Perch, Faber (London), 1963 . . £20/£5
ditto, O.U.P. (New York), 1963 . . . . £10/£5
Selected Poems, Faber (London), 1964 . . . £15/£5
Collected Poems, Faber (London), 1966 . . . £20/£5
ditto, O.U.P. (New York), 1967 . . . . £15/£5

Novel
Roundabout Way, Putman (London), 1931 (pseud 'Louis Malone') . . . . £1,500/£750

Translations
The Agamemnon of Aeschylus, Faber (London), 1936. .
. . . . £75/£20
ditto, Harcourt Brace (New York), 1937 . . . £45/£15
Goethe's Faust Parts I & II, Faber (London), 1951 £50/£15
ditto, O.U.P. (New York), 1952 . . . . £35/£15

Plays
Out of the Picture, Faber (London), 1937 . . £60/£15
ditto, Harcourt Brace (New York), 1938. . . £35/£15
Christopher Columbus, Faber (London), 1944 . £30/£10

The Dark Tower, Faber (London), 1947 . . . £50/£15
The Mad Islands and The Administrator, Faber (London), 1964 . . . . £35/£10
One for the Grave, Faber (London), 1968 . . £25/£5
ditto, O.U.P. (New York), 1968 . . . . £25/£5
Persons from Porlock and Other Plays, BBC (London), 1969
. . . . £30/£10

Essays
Modern Poetry: A Personal Essay, O.U.P. (New York), 1938
. . . . £100/£25
The Poetry of W.B. Yeats, O.U.P. (Oxford, UK), 1941 . .
. . . . £45/£15
ditto, O.U.P. (New York), 1941 . . . . £20/£10
Meet the U.S. Army, H.M.S.O. (London), 1943 (anonymous; stapled wraps) £40
Varieties of Parable, C.U.P. (Cambridge, UK), 1965 £15/£5

Children's Titles
The Penny That Rolled Away, Putnam (New York), 1954 .
. . . . £100/£25
ditto, as *The Sixpence That Rolled Away*, Faber (London), 1956 . . . . £100/£25

Autobiography
The Strings are False, Faber (London), 1965 . . £35/£10
ditto, O.U.P. (New York), 1966 . . . . £25/£10

Others
Letters from Iceland, Faber (London), 1937 (with W.H. Auden) . . . . £125/£25
ditto, Harcourt Brace (New York), 1937 . . . £100/£15
Zoo, Joseph (London), 1938 . . . . . £250/£45
I Crossed the Minch, Longman (London), 1938 . £200/£35
Astrology, Aldus (London), 1964 . . . . £30/£10
ditto, Doubleday (New York), 1964 . . . . £15/£5

NORMAN MAILER
(b.1923 d.2007)

An American novelist and journalist, Mailer excels at taking real events and rendering them into fiction. *The Naked and the Dead*, his first novel, was based on his experiences in World War Two and has been hailed as one of the best American novels to come out of the War. He remains a controversial anti-establishment figure.

Novels
The Naked and the Dead, Rinehart (New York), 1948 . .
. . . . £650/£75
ditto, Wingate (London), 1949 (240 numbered copies) . £125
ditto, Wingate (London), 1949 . . . . £100/£30
ditto, Franklin Library (Franklin Centre, PA), 1979 (signed, limited edition) £75
Barbary Shore, Rinehart (New York), 1951 (2 d/ws issued simultaneously in red and black, and green and black) .
. . . . £125/£25
ditto, Cape (London), 1952 . . . . . £75/£20
The Deer Park, Putnam (New York), 1955 . . £125/£20
ditto, Wingate (London), 1957 . . . . £65/£15
An American Dream, Dial Press (New York), 1965 £65/£15
ditto, Deutsch (London), 1965 . . . . £40/£10

Why Are We In Vietnam?, Putnam (New York), 1967 (with no dedication page) . . . . . . £100/£45

ditto, Putnam (New York), 1967 (with tipped-in dedication page) . . . . £65/£10

ditto, Weidenfeld & Nicolson (London), 1969. . £40/£5

A Transit to Narcissus: A Facsimile of the Original Transcript, Howard Fertig (New York), 1978 . £75/£45

Of Women and their Elegance, Simon & Schuster (New York), 1980 . . . . £40/£10

ditto, Hodder & Stoughton (London), 1980 . . £40/£10

Ancient Evenings, Little, Brown (Boston), 1983 £25/£5

ditto, Little, Brown (Boston), 1983 (350 signed, numbered copies, slipcase) . . . . . . £100/£65

ditto, Macmillan (London), 1983 . . . £20/£5

Tough Guys Don't Dance, Random House (New York), 1984 . . . . £20/£5

ditto, Random House (New York), 1984 (350 signed, numbered copies, slipcase, no d/w) . . . £75/£45

ditto, Franklin Library (Franklin Centre, PA), 1984 (signed limited edition) £35

ditto, Joseph (London), 1984 . . . . £20/£5

Harlot's Ghost, Random House (New York), 1991 (red d/w) . . . . £35/£5

ditto, Random House (New York), 1991 (grey d/w) £20/£5

ditto, Random House (New York), 1991 (300 signed, numbered copies, slipcase, no d/w) . . . £75/£45

ditto, Joseph (London), 1991 . . . . £15/£5

The Gospel According to the Son, Little, Brown (Boston), 1997 . . . . £10/£5

ditto, Little, Brown (London), 1997 . . . £10/£5

The Castle in the Forest, Random House (New York), 2007 . . . . £10/£5

ditto, Little, Brown (London), 2007 . . . £10/£5

Collections

Advertisements for Myself, Putnam (New York), 1959 . . . . £75/£15

ditto, Deutsch (London), 1961 . . . £50/£10

The Short Fiction of Norman Mailer, Dell (New York), 1967 (pbk) £10

The Long Patrol: 25 Years of Writing from the Work of Norman Mailer, World (New York), 1971 (edited by Robert F. Lucid) . . . . . . £40/£10

The Time of Our Time, Random House (New York), 1998 . . . . £10/£5

ditto, Little, Brown (London), 1998 . . . £10/£5

The Essential Mailer, New English Library (London), 1982 . . . . £10/£5

Modest Gifts: Poems And Drawings, Random House (New York), 2003 (pbk) £5

Non-Fiction

The White Negro, City Lights Books (San Francisco, CA), 1957 (35 cents cover price; stapled wraps) . . £300

ditto, City Lights Books (San Francisco, CA), 1957 (50 cents cover price; stapled wraps) £35

The Presidential Papers, Putnam (New York), 1963 £75/£15

ditto, Deutsch (London), 1964 . . . £40/£10

Cannibals and Christians, Dial Press (New York), 1966 . . . . £50/£10

ditto, Deutsch (London), 1967 . . . . £30/£10

The Armies of the Night: History As a Novel, the Novel as History, NAL (New York), 1968 (pbk) . . . £15

ditto, NAL (New York), 1968 . . . . £50/£15

ditto, Weidenfeld & Nicolson (London), 1968. . £45/£10

The Idol and the Octopus: Political Writings on the Kennedy and Johnson Administrations, Dell (New York), 1968 (pbk) £25

Miami and the Siege of Chicago: An Informal History of the Republican and Democratic Conventions of 1968, World (New York), 1968 . . . . . . £40/£10

ditto, as *Miami and the Siege of Chicago: An Informal History of the American Political Conventions of 1968*, Weidenfeld & Nicolson (London), 1968 . . £35/£5

Of A Fire on the Moon, Little, Brown (Boston), 1970 £25/£5

ditto, Weidenfeld & Nicolson (London), 1970. . £25/£5

'King of the Hill': On the Fight of the Century, NAL (New York), 1971 (pbk) £20

The Prisoner of Sex, Little, Brown (Boston), 1971 (first edition d/w states $5.95 on front flap) . . . £20/£5

ditto, Weidenfeld & Nicolson (London), 1971. . £20/£5

Existential Errands, Little, Brown (Boston), 1972. £20/£5

St. George and the Godfather, NAL (New York), 1972 £20

ditto, Arbor House (New York), 1983 . . . £20/£5

Marilyn, Grosset & Dunlap (New York), 1973 . £35/£15

ditto, Grosset & Dunlap (New York), 1973 (signed limited edition in slipcase) . . . . . . £100/£65

ditto, Hodder & Stoughton (London), 1973 . . £35/£15

The Faith of Graffiti, Praeger (New York), 1974 . £75/£25

ditto, Praeger (New York), 1974 (350 signed copies, slipcase). . . . . £100/£75

ditto, Praeger (New York), 1974 (pbk) . . . £20

The Fight, Little, Brown (Boston), 1975 . . £20/£5

ditto, Hart-Davis, MacGibbon (London), 1976 £15/£5

Some Honourable Men: Political Conventions 1960-1976, Little, Brown (Boston), 1976 . . . . . £20/£5

Genius and Lust: A Journey Through the Major Writings of Henry Miller, Grove Press (New York), 1976. £30/£10

The Executioner's Song, Little, Brown (Boston), 1979 . . . . £25/£5

ditto, Hutchinson (London), 1979 . . . £20/£5

Of a Small and Modest Malignancy, Wicked and Bristling With Dots, Lord John Press (Northridge, CA), 1980 (300 signed, numbered copies, slipcase, no d/w) . £40/£25

ditto, Lord John Press (Northridge, CA), 1980 (100 deluxe signed, numbered copies, slipcase, no d/w) . £100/£65

Pieces and Pontifications, Little, Brown (Boston), 1982 (pbk) £10

Huckleberry Finn, Alive at 100, Caliban Press (Montclair, NJ), 1985 (50 copies in boards) £125

ditto, Caliban Press (Montclair, NJ), 1985 (200 copies in wraps) £65

Conversations with Norman Mailer, Univ Press of Mississippi (Jackson, MS), 1988 . . . £20/£5

How the Wimp Won the War, Lord John Press (Northridge, CA), 1992 (26 signed, lettered copies, no d/w) . £100

ditto, Lord John Press (Northridge, CA), 1992 (275 signed, numbered copies, no d/w) £35

Oswald's Tale, Franklin Library (Franklin Centre, PA), 1995 (signed limited edition) £40

ditto, Random House (New York), 1995 . . £15/£5

ditto, Little, Brown (London), 1995 . . . £15/£5

Portrait of Picasso As a Young Man: An Interpretive Biography, Atlantic Monthly Press (New York), 1995 £15/£5

ditto, Little, Brown (London), 1996 . . . £10/£5

Into the Mirror: The Life of Robert P. Hanssen, HarperCollins (New York), 2002 (with Lawrence Schiller) . . . . £10/£5

Why Are We at War?, Random House (New York), 2003
(pbk) £5
The Spooky Art: Thoughts on Writing, Random House
(New York), 2003 . . . . . . £10/£5
ditto, Little, Brown (London), 2003 . . . £10/£5

Poetry
Deaths for the Ladies and Other Disasters, Putnam (New
York), 1962 . . . . £125/£20
ditto, Putnam (New York), 1962 (pbk) . . . £25
ditto, Deutsch (London), 1962 (pbk) £15
Gargoyle, Guignol, False Closet, Dolmen Press (Dublin),
1964 (two page broadsheet) £125

Plays
Norman Mailer's The Deer Park: A Play, Dial Press (New
York), 1967 . . . . £75/£25
ditto, Dell (New York), 1967 (pbk) £10
ditto, Weidenfeld & Nicolson (London), 1970. . £35/£10
A Fragment from Vietnam, Eurographica (Helsinki), 1985
(350 signed, numbered copies; wraps with d/w) . £75/£45

Screenplays
Maidstone: A Mystery, NAL (New York), 1971 (pbk) . £20
The Last Night, Targ Editions (New York), 1984 (250
signed copies, tissue d/w) . . . . . . £65/£45

BERNARD MALAMUD
(b.1914 d.1986)

Bernard Malamud was a Jewish-American author and
allegorist who received a National Book Award for *The
Magic Barrel* and a Pulitzer Prize for *The Fixer*. His first
novel, *The Natural*, was about baseball and was adapted
into a film starring Robert Redford.

The Natural, Harcourt Brace (New York), 1952 £3,000/£300
ditto, Eyre & Spottiswode (London), 1963 . . £250/£35
Kim of Korea, Julian Messner (New York), 1955 (pseud
'Peter Lumn', written with Faith Norris) . £250/£40
The Assistant, Farrar Straus & Cudahy (New York), 1957
(reviews of *The Natural* on back panel) . . £250/£40
ditto, Farrar Straus & Cudahy (New York), 1957 (reviews of
The Assistant on back panel) . . . . £150/£40
ditto, Eyre & Spottiswode (London), 1959 . . £75/£15
Magic Barrel and Other Stories, Farrar Straus & Cudahy
(New York), 1958 . . . . . . £75/£10
ditto, Jewish Publication Society (Philadelphia, PA), 1958 .
. . . . £75/£10
ditto, Eyre & Spottiswode (London), 1960 . . £45/£10
ditto, as *Magic Barrel* and *Idiots First*, Franklin Library
(Franklin Center, PA), 1978 (limited edition bound in full
leather) £15
National Book Award Acceptance Speech, privately printed
(New York), 1959 (two mimeographed sheets) . . £65
A New Life, Farrar, Straus & Cudahy (New York), 1961 .
. . . . £45/£10
ditto, Eyre & Spottiswode (London), 1962 . . £25/£10
Idiots First, Farrar, Straus (New York), 1963 . . £25/£10
ditto, Eyre & Spottiswode (London), 1964 . . £25/£10
The Fixer, Farrar, Straus & Giroux (New York), 1966 . .
. . . . £60/£10

ditto, Eyre & Spottiswode (London), 1967 . . £25/£10
ditto, Franklin Library (Franklin Center, PA), 1978 (limited
edition bound in full leather) £15
A Malamud Reader, Farrar, Straus & Giroux (New York),
1967 . . . . £25/£5
Pictures of Fidelman, Farrar Straus & Giroux (New York),
1969 . . . . £25/£5
ditto, Eyre & Spottiswode (London), 1970 . . £20/£5
The Tenants, Farrar Straus & Giroux (New York), 1971
(first binding of orange cloth) . . . . £25/£10
ditto, Farrar Straus & Giroux (New York), 1971 (approx 250
copies with signed tipped in sheet; orange cloth). £100/£75
ditto, Farrar Straus & Giroux (New York), 1971 (second
binding of dark red cloth) . . . . . £20/£5
ditto, Methuen (London), 1972 . . . . £20/£5
Glass Blower of Venice, Bunri Co. (Tokyo), 1972 (wraps;
two passages from *Pictures of Fidelman*; stapled pamphlet
of notes laid in) £100
Rembrandt's Hat, Farrar Straus (New York), 1973 £20/£5
ditto, Eyre & Methuen (London), 1973 . . £15/£5
Two Fables, The Banyon Press (Pawlet, VT), 1978 (320
signed, numbered copies; glassine d/w; excerpt from *The
Magic Barrel*) . . . . £75/£65
Dublin's Lives, Farrar Straus (New York), 1979 (missing last
five words on bottom of p.231 'When he asked her why').
. . . . £100/£85
ditto, Farrar Straus (New York), 1979 (review copies with
the five missing words added by hand) . . £90/£75
ditto, Franklin Library (Franklin Center, PA), 1979 (limited
edition bound in full leather) £15
ditto, Farrar Straus (New York), 1979 (750 copies 'For
friends of...'; glassine d/w; p.231 tipped in) . £25/£20
ditto, Farrar Straus (New York), 1979 (with p.231 tipped in)
. . . . £10/£5
ditto, Chatto & Windus (London), 1979 . . £15/£5
God's Grace, Farrar Straus & Giroux (New York), 1982 .
. . . . £10/£5
ditto, Farrar Straus & Giroux (New York), 1982 (300 signed,
numbered copies; in slipcase, no d/w) . . £30/£15
ditto, Chatto & Windus (London), 1982 . . £15/£5
The Stories, Farrar Straus (New York), 1983 . . £10/£5
ditto, Farrar Straus (New York), 1983 (300 signed, numbered
copies; in slipcase, no d/w) . . . . £75/£50
ditto, Chatto & WindusWindus/Hogarth Press (London),
1984 . . . . £15/£5
On Being Acquainted with Eudora Welty, Stuart Wright (no
place), 1984 (5 signed, numbered copies; wraps) . £250
Long Work, Short Life, Bennington College (Bennington,
VT), 1984 (1,000 numbered copies; stapled wraps) . £10
The People and Other Uncollected Fiction, Farrar Straus
(New York), 1989 . . . . . . £10/£5
ditto, Chatto & Windus (London), 1984 . . £10/£5
Magic Barrell, Tales for Travellers (Napa, CA), 1985 (single
sheet, map-folded) £10
Conversations with Bernard Malamud, Univ Press of
Mississippi (Jackson, MS), 1991 . . . £15/£5
ditto, Univ Press of Mississippi (Jackson, MS), 1991 (pbk) .
. . . . £5
Talking Horse, Columbia Univ Press (New York), 1996 .
. . . . £10/£5
The Complete Stories, Farrar, Straus & Giroux (New York),
1997 . . . . £10/£5

THOMAS MANN

(b.1875 d.1955)

Mann received critical admiration and achieved popular success during his lifetime with his epic novels, which are often highly symbolic, ironic, and noted for their insight into the psychology of the artist and intellectual. He won the Nobel Prize for Literature in 1929.

Novels

Royal Highness, Sidgwick & Jackson (London), 1916 (translated by A. Cecil Curtis) £250
ditto, Knopf (New York), 1916 . . . . . £250
Bashan and I, Collins (London), 1923 (translated by H.G. Scheffauer) . . . . . . £175/£35
ditto, Holt (New York), 1923 . . . . £150/£30
ditto, as *A Man and His Dog*, Knopf (New York), 1930 (translated by Herman George Scheffauer) . . £75/£15
Buddenbrooks, Knopf (New York), 1924 (translated by H.T. Lowe-Porter, 2 vols in d/w, matching slipcase) . £500/£50
ditto, Secker (London), 1924 (2 vols in d/w, slipcase) . .
. . . . £500/£150
The Magic Mountain, Secker (London), 1927 (2 vols). .
. . . . £500/£65
ditto, Knopf (New York), 1927 (translated by H.T. Lowe-Porter, 2 vols, d/ws and slipcase) . . . £500/£65
ditto, Knopf (New York), 1927 (200 signed 2 vol sets, d/ws and slipcase). . . . . . .£2,000/£1,500
The Beloved Returns: Lotte in Weimar, Knopf (New York), 1940 (translated by H.T. Lowe-Porter) . . . £30/£5
ditto, Knopf (New York), 1940 (395 signed copies, d/w and slipcase). . . . . £300/£150
ditto, as *Lotte in Weimar*, Secker & Warburg (London), 1940
. . . . £35/£10
Doctor Faustus, Knopf (New York), 1948 (translated by H.T. Lowe-Porter) . . . . . . £35/£10
ditto, Secker & Warburg (London), 1949 . . £35/£10
The Holy Sinner, Knopf (New York), 1951 (translated by H.T. Lowe-Porter) . . . . . . £25/£10
ditto, Secker & Warburg (London), 1952 . . . £25/£10
Confessions of Felix Krull, Knopf (New York), 1955 (translated by Denver Lindley). . . . £25/£10
ditto, Secker & Warburg (London), 1955 . . . £25/£10

'Joseph and His Brothers'/
'Joseph and His Bretheren' Novels

Book 1: The Tales of Jacob, Knopf (New York), 1934 (translated by H.T. Lowe-Porter) . . . £125/£25
ditto, Secker, 1934 . . . . . . £125/£25
Book 2: The Young Joseph, Knopf (New York), 1935 (translated by H.T. Lowe-Porter) . . . £125/£25
ditto, Secker (London), 1935 . . . . £125/£25
Book 3: Joseph in Egypt, Knopf (New York), 1938 (translated by H.T. Lowe-Porter, 2 vols) . . £100/£35
ditto, Secker (London), 1938 (2 vols). . . £100/£35
Book 4: Joseph the Provider, Knopf (New York), 1944 (translated by H.T. Lowe-Porter) . . . £25/£10
ditto, Secker & Warburg (London), 1945 . . . £25/£10

Novellas and Short Stories

Death in Venice and Other Stories, Knopf (New York), 1925 (translated by Kenneth Burke) . . . £350/£50

Death in Venice, Secker (London), 1928 (translated by H.T. Lowe-Porter) . . . . . . £250/£75
ditto, Knopf (New York), 1930 . . . . . £200/£35
Children and Fools, Knopf (New York), 1928 (translated by H.G. Scheffauer) . . . . . . £150/£35
Early Sorrow, Secker (London), 1929 (translated by H.G. Scheffauer) . . . . £75/£20
ditto, Knopf (New York), 1930 . . . . £75/£20
Mario and the Magician, Secker (London), 1930 (translated by H.T. Lowe-Porter). . . . . £75/£25
ditto, Knopf (New York), 1931 . . . . . £75/£25
Nocturnes, Equinox Cooperative Press (New York), 1934 (1,000 signed copies, translated by H.T. Lowe-Porter, lithographs by Lynd Ward; slipcase) . . £300/£200
Stories of Three Decades, Knopf (New York), 1936 (translated by H.T. Lowe-Porter) . . . £45/£10
ditto, Secker & Warburg (London), 1936 . . . £45/£10
The Transposed Heads, Knopf (New York), 1941 (translated by H.T. Lowe-Porter). . . . . £45/£10
ditto, Secker & Warburg (London), 1941 . . . £45/£10
The Tables of the Law, Knopf (New York), 1945 (translated by H.T. Lowe-Porter). . . . . £45/£10
ditto, Secker & Warburg (London), 1947 . . . £45/£10
The Black Swan, Knopf (New York), 1954 (translated by Willard R. Trask). . . . . . . £25/£10
ditto, Secker & Warburg (London), 1954 . . . £25/£10

Poetry

A Christmas Poem, Equinox Cooperative Press (New York), 1932 (translated by Henry Hart; sewn wraps) . . £145

Non-Fiction

Three Essays, Knopf (New York), 1929 (translated by H.T. Lowe-Porter) . . . . . . £50/£20
ditto, Secker (London), 1932 . . . . . £45/£15
A Sketch of My Life, Harrison (Paris), 1930 (695 numbered trade copies of 760, translated by H.T. Lowe-Porter; slipcase). . . . . £100/£65
ditto, Harrison (Paris), 1930 (15 copies marked 'Not for Sale', slipcase) . . . . . £200/£100
ditto, Harrison (Paris), 1930 (50-75 signed, numbered copies on Japanese Imperial vellum; slipcase; some with unprinted blue d/w) . . . . £500/£350
ditto, Knopf (New York), 1960 . . . . . £25/£10
ditto, Secker & Warburg (London), 1961 . . . £25/£10
Past Masters and Other Papers, Secker (London), 1933 (translated by H.T. Lowe-Porter) . . . £45/£15
ditto, Knopf (New York), 1933 . . . . . £45/£15
An Exchange of Letters, Friends of Europe (London), 1937 (translated by H.T. Lowe-Porter; sewn wraps) . . £20
ditto, Knopf (New York), 1937 (sewn wraps) . . . £20
ditto, Overbrook Press (Stamford, CT), 1938 (350 copies; sewn wraps) £25
Freud, Goethe, Wagner, Knopf (New York), 1937 (translated by H.T. Lowe-Porter and R. Mathias-Reil) .
. . . . £45/£15
The Coming Victory of Democracy, Knopf (New York), 1938 (translated by Agnes E. Meyer) . . £25/£10
ditto, Secker & Warburg (London), 1938 . . . £25/£10
This Peace, Knopf (New York), 1938 (translated by H.T. Lowe-Porter) . . . . . . £30/£10
This War, Knopf (New York), 1940 (translated by Eric Sutton) . . . . £25/£10
ditto, Secker & Warburg (London), 1940 . . . £25/£10

Order of the Day, Knopf (New York), 1942 (translated by H.T. Lowe-Porter, Agnes E. Meyer and Eric Sutton) .
. . . . £25/£10
Listen Germany!, Knopf (New York), 1943 . . £35/£10
Essays of Three Decades, Knopf (New York), 1947 (translated by H.T. Lowe-Porter) . . . . £35/£10
ditto, Secker & Warburg (London), 1947 . . £35/£10
Last Essays, Knopf (New York), 1959 (translated by R. & C. Winston and T. & J. Stern) . . . £25/£10
ditto, Secker & Warburg (London), 1959 . . £25/£10
Letters to Paul Amann, Wesleyan Univ Press (Middletown, CT), 1960 (translated by R. & C. Winston) . £25/£10
ditto, Secker & Warburg (London), 1961 . . £25/£10
The Genesis of a Novel, Knopf (New York), 1961 (translated by R. & C. Winston) . . . £25/£10
ditto, Secker & Warburg (London), 1961 . . £25/£10
The Letters of Thomas Mann, 1889-1955, Secker & Warburg (London), 1970 (translated by R. & C. Winston, 2 vols) . . . . £65/£15
ditto, Knopf (New York), 1971 (2 vols) . . . £65/£15
Letters of Heinrich and Thomas Mann, 1900-1949, Univ of California Press (Berkeley, CA), 1988 (translated by Don Reneau and R. & C. Winston) . . . . £25/£10

OLIVIA MANNING
(b.1908 d.1980)

A British novelist, Manning is best known for *Fortunes of War* which comprises The Balkan Trilogy and The Levant Trilogy which tell the stories of the wartime experiences of a group of English expatriates who, as World War II progresses, move between Romania, Greece, Egypt and Palestine.

The Balkan Trilogy
The Great Fortune, Heinemann (London), 1960 . £65/£10
ditto, Doubleday (Garden City, NY), 1961 . . £25/£5
The Spoilt City, Heinemann (London), 1962 . . £45/£10
ditto, Doubleday (Garden City, NY), 1962 . . £25/£5
Friends and Heroes, Heinemann (London), 1965 . £35/£10
ditto, Doubleday (Garden City, NY), 1966 . . £20/£5

The Levant Trilogy
The Danger Tree, Weidenfeld & Nicolson (London), 1977.
. . . . £20/£5
ditto, Atheneum (New York), 1977 . . . . £15/£5
The Battle Lost and Won, Weidenfeld & Nicolson (London), 1978 . . . . £15/£5
ditto, Atheneum (New York), 1979 . . . £10/£5
The Sum of Things, Weidenfeld & Nicolson (London), 1980
. . . . £15/£5
ditto, Atheneum (New York), 1981 . . . £10/£5

Other Novels
The Wind Changes, Cape (London), 1937 . . £75/£20
ditto, Knopf (New York), 1938 . . . . £45/£10
Artist Among the Missing, Heinemann (London), 1949 .
. . . . £65/£20
School for Love, Heinemann (London), 1951 . £35/£15
A Different Face, Heinemann (London), 1953 . £45/£15
ditto, Abelard-Schuman (New York), 1957 . £20/£5
The Doves of Venus, Heinemann (London), 1955 . £25/£10

ditto, Abelard-Schuman (New York), 1956 . . £20/£5
The Play Room, Heinemann (London), 1969 . . £15/£5
ditto, as *The Camperlea Girls*, Coward-McCann (New York), 1969 . . . . £20/£5
The Rain Forest, Heinemann (London), 1974. . £15/£5

Short Stories
Growing Up, Heinemann (London), 1948 . . £50/£10
My Husband Cartwright: Stories, Heinemann (London), 1956 . . . . £20/£10
A Romantic Hero and Others, Heinemann (London), 1967.
. . . . £15/£10

Non-Fiction
The Remarkable Expedition, Heinemann (London), 1947 .
. . . . £20/£5
ditto, as *The Reluctant Rescue*, Doubleday (Garden City, NY), 1947 . . . . £20/£5
The Dreaming Shore, Evans Bros (London), 1950 £20/£5
Extraordinary Cats, Michael Joseph (London), 1967 £20/£5

KATHERINE MANSFIELD
(b.1888 d.1923)

Katherine Mansfield was the pen-name for Kathleen Mansfield Beauchamp who was born in New Zealand, where her work was first published. She moved to England in 1908 in pursuit of a literary career. Best known for her elegant short stories, she is considered one of the most influential writers working in the medium during the Modernist period. She died of tuberculosis at the age of 35.

Fiction
In a German Pension, Stephen Swift (London), 1911 (green cloth lettered in gold, blind tooled design on front board, orange/ochre d/w) . . . . . .£4,000/£2,000
ditto, Constable (London), 1926 (new edition) . £65/£15
ditto, Knopf (New York), 1926 (green cloth, paper label on spine) . . . . £65/£15
Prelude, Hogarth Press (Richmond, Surrey), 1918 (wraps with design by Fergusson). £1,500
ditto, Hogarth Press (Richmond, Surrey), 1918 (wraps with no design) £1,250
ditto, as *The Aloe*, Constable (London), 1930 (750 copies, revised version, edited by J.M. Murry, brown cloth lettered in gold, top edge gilt, d/w). . . . . £100/£25
ditto, Knopf (New York), 1930 (975 numbered copies, green paper-covered boards, d/w and slipcase) . £100/£25
Je ne Parle pas Francais, Heron Press (Hampstead, London), 1919 (100 copies, green wraps with white paper label on front cover) £1,250
Bliss and Other Stories, Constable (London), 1920 (p.13 numbered '3', red cloth lettered in black, white d/w with author portrait) . . . .£500/£65
ditto, Knopf (New York), 1923 . . . . .£300/£35
The Garden Party and Other Stories, Constable (London), 1922 (first issue, 'sposition' for 'position' on p.103, 25 copies with sky blue cloth lettered dark blue, strawberry coloured d/w) . . . . . .£2,000/£1,000

ditto, Constable (London), 1922 (second issue, as above but orange/ochre lettering)   .   .   .   .   . £1,000/£50
ditto, Knopf (New York), 1922   .   .   .   . £300/£20
ditto, Verona Press (London), 1939 [1947] (alternative selection of stories, lithos by Marie Laurencin, patterned paper boards with leather spine label, slipcase) £1,000/£650
ditto, Verona Press (London), 1939 [1947] (30 copies signed by Laurencin, full green morocco, spine bands ruled in black, red morocco gilt spine label, top edge gilt, marbled slipcase). £2,750
The Doves' Nest and Other Stories, Constable (London), 1923 (first issue, 25 copies with verso of title-page blank, 't' missing from first word line 8, p.64., blue/grey cloth lettered in blue, grey d/w)   .   .   .   . £600/£400
ditto, Constable (London), 1923 (second issue as above but with with date on verso of title-page)   .   . £200/£15
ditto, Knopf (New York), 1923   .   .   . £50/£15
Something Childish and Other Stories, Constable (London), 1924 (first issue, verso of title-page blank, 34 copies, grey cloth lettered blue, grey d/w)   .   . £750/£600
ditto, Constable (London), 1924 (second issue as above but with date on verso of title-page)   .   .   . £200/£25
ditto, as **The Little Girl and Other Stories**, Knopf (New York), 1924   .   .   .   .   .   . £200/£20
The Collected Stories of Katherine Mansfield, Constable (London), 1945 (blue cloth lettered in silver)   . £45/£15
Selected Stories of Katherine Mansfield, O.U.P. World's Classics (London), 1953 (edited and with an introduction by D.M. Davin).   .   .   .   . £15/£5
Thirty-Four Short Stories, Collins (London), 1957 £15/£5
The Stories of Katherine Mansfield, O.U.P. (Oxford, UK), 1985 (edited by A. Alpers)   .   .   . £10/£5

Other Works
Poems, Constable (London), 1923 (brown boards, tan cloth, red leather label in spine lettered in gold, date stamped in gold at foot of spine, cream d/w)   .   . £150/£45
ditto, Knopf (New York), 1924 (quarter turquoise cloth over orange & white patterned boards, paper label on spine)   .
   .   .   .   . £100/£30
ditto, Constable (London), 1930 (enlarged edition, grey boards with maroon lettering)   .   .   . £25/£10
The Journal of Katherine Mansfield, Constable (London), 1927 (grey cloth, printed in blue)   .   . £45/£10
ditto, Knopf (New York), 1927   .   .   . £35/£10
ditto, Constable (London), 1954 (revised and enlarged, edited by J.M. Murry).   .   .   . £25/£10
The Letters of Katherine Mansfield, Constable (London), 1928 (2 vols, edited by J.M. Murry, grey cloth, printed in blue)   .   .   .   .   . £65/£25
ditto, Knopf (New York), 1929   .   .   . £65/£20
Novels and Novelists, Constable (London), 1930 (edited by J.M. Murry).   .   .   .   . £35/£15
ditto, Knopf (New York), 1930   .   .   . £35/£15
Reminiscences of Leonid Andreyev, by Maxim Gorky, Heinemann (London), 1931 (translation with S.S. Koteliansky, 750 numbered copies).   .   . £50/£30
Reminiscences of Tolstoy, Chekhov and Gorky, Hogarth Press (London), 1934 (translation with Virginia Woolf and S.S. Koteliansky).   .   .   .   . £30/£10
To Stanislaw Wyspianski, privately printed (London), 1938 (poem, limited to 100 copies; sewn wraps)   .   . £100
The Scrapbook of Katherine Mansfield, Constable (London), 1939 (edited by J.M. Murry).   .   . £35/£10

ditto, Knopf (New York), 1940   .   .   .   . £25/£10
Katherine Mansfield's Letters to John Middleton Murry, 1913-1922, Constable (London), 1951 (375-376 integral).
   .   .   .   . £30/£10
ditto, Knopf (New York), 1951   .   .   . £30/£10
Katherine Mansfield, Letters and Journals, Allen Lane (London), 1977 (edited and with an introduction by C.K. Stead)   .   .   .   .   . £15/£5
The Urewera Notebook, O.U.P. (Oxford, UK), 1978 (edited by Ian Gordon)   .   .   .   . £15/£5
The Collected Letters of Katherine Mansfield Vol.1, 1903-1917, O.U.P. (Oxford, UK), 1984 (edited by Vincent O'Sullivan and Margaret Scott)   .   .   . £10/£5
ditto, **Vol.2, 1918-1919**, O.U.P. (Oxford, UK), 1987   £10/£5
The Critical Writings of Katherine Mansfield, Macmillan (London), 1986   .   .   .   .   . £10/£5

CAPTAIN FREDERICK MARRYAT
(b.1792 d.1848)

Marryat was successful early in his career with novels drawing on his experiences at sea. These were admired by Conrad and Hemingway, and were models for later works by C.S. Forester and Patrick O'Brian, who also set their fiction in the time of Nelson and told the stories of young officers rising through the ranks. Marryat is perhaps best remembered today for his children's titles, which include *Masterman Ready* and *Children of the New Forest*.

Novels
The Naval Officer, or Scenes and Adventures in the Life of Frank Mildmay, Colburn (London), 1829 (3 vols, anonymous). £750
ditto, Carey & Hart (Philadelphia, PA), 1833 (2 vols)   . £300
The King's Own, Colburn & Bentley (London), 1830 (3 vols, 'by the author of *The Naval Officer*')   .   . £400
ditto, Dana Estes (Boston), 1896.   .   .   .   . £50
Newton Forster, or The Merchant Service, James Cochrane (London), 1832 (3 vols, 'by the author of *The King's Own*') £300
ditto, Lane (New York), 1837 (2 vols)   .   . £200
Peter Simple, Saunders & Otley (London), 1834 (3 vols, 'by the author of *Newton Forster*, *The King's Own*, etc.'). £350
ditto, Lane (New York), 1837 (2 vols)   .   . £200
Jacob Faithful, Saunders & Otley (London), 1834 (3 vols, 'by the author of *Peter Simple*, *The King's Own*, etc.') £400
ditto, Carey & Hart (Philadelphia, PA), 1834 (2 vols)   . £250
Japhet In Search of a Father, Saunders & Otley (London), 1836 (3 vols, 'by the author of *Peter Simple*, *Jacob Faithful*, etc.') £300
ditto, Harper (New York), 1836   .   .   .   . £75
Mr Midshipman Easy, Saunders & Otley (London), 1836 (3 vols, 'by the author of *Japhet In Search of a Father*, *Peter Simple*, *Jacob Faithful*, etc.') £200
ditto, Carey & Hart (Philadelphia, PA), 1836   .   . £100
Snarleyyow, or The Dog Fiend, Colburn (London), 1837 (3 vols, 'by the author of *Peter Simple*, *Frank Mildmay*, etc.')
   .   .   .   . £300
ditto, Carey & Hart (Philadelphia, PA), 1837 (2 vols)   . £200
The Phantom Ship, Colburn (London), 1839 (3 vols) £1,000

ditto, Munro (New York), 1877 . . . . .£150
Poor Jack, Longman etc. (London), Jan-Dec 1840 (12 parts)
. . . .£300
ditto, Longman etc. (London), 1840 . . . .£200
ditto, Munro (New York), 1878 . . . . £50
Masterman Ready, or The Wreck of the Pacific, Longman
etc (London) (3 vols, vol.1 1841, vols 2&3 1842) . £200
ditto, Appleton (New York), 1843 (3 vols) . .£125
Joseph Rushbrook, or The Poacher, Longman etc
(London), 1841 (3 vols, 'by the author of *Peter Simple*
etc.') £200
ditto, Dana Estes (Boston), 1895. . . . . £25
Percival Keene, Colburn (London), 1842 (3 vols) . .£200
ditto, Wilson (New York), 1842 . . . . .£150
Narrative of the Travels and Adventures of Monsieur Violet
in California, Sonora and Western Texas, Longmans etc.
(London), 1843 (3 vols) £400
ditto, as **The Travels and Romantic Adventures of Monsieur**
Violet, among the Snake Indians and Wild Tribes of the
Great Western Prairies, Longman etc (London), 1843 £300
ditto, Harper (New York), 1843 . . . . .£200
The Settlers in Canada, Longman etc (London), 1844 (2
vols) £175
ditto, Dana Estes (Boston), 1898. . . . . £25
The Mission, or Scenes in Africa, Longmans etc (London),
1845 (2 vols) £200
ditto, Appleton (New York), 1845 (1 vol). . .£125
The Privateersman, or One Hundred Years Ago, Longman
etc (London), 1846 (2 vols) £200
ditto, Munro (New York), 1877 . . . . . £50
The Children of the New Forest, Hurst (London), [1847] (2
vols) £1,000
ditto, Dana Estes (Boston), 1898. . . . . £45
The Little Savage, Hurst (London), (2 vols, vol.1 1848,
vol.2 1849) £200
ditto, Munro (New York), 1877 . . . . . £50
Valerie: An Autobiography, Colburn (London), 1849 (2
vols) £175
ditto, Munro (New York), 1881 . . . . . £50

Short Stories
The Pacha of Many Tales, Carey & Hart (Philadelphia, PA),
1834 ('by the author of *Peter Simple, Jacob Faithful*, etc.',
2 vols) £250
ditto, Saunders & Otley (London), 1835 (3 vols) . .£250
The Pirate and The Three Cutters, Longman etc (London),
1836 . . . .£200
ditto, Lane (New York), 1837 . . . . .£150

Others
A Code of Signals for the Use of Vessels Employed in the
Merchant Service, J.M. Richardson (London), 1818 .£250
Suggestions for the Abolition of the Present System of
Impressment in the Naval Service, Richardson (London),
1822 (64 page booklet, withdrawn). . . .£500
Birman Empire: Views Taken At and Near Rangoon,
Kingsbury/Clay (London), 1825-6 (3 parts in portfolio, and
2 booklets) £450
Diary in America: with Remarks on its Institutions,
Longman etc (London), 1839 (3 vols) . . .£200
ditto, Carey & Hart (Philadelphia, PA), 1839 . .£200
A Diary in America: Part Second, Longman etc (London),
1839 (3 vols) £250
Olla Porida, Longman etc (London), 1840 (3 vols 'by the
author of *Peter Simple* etc.') £250

NGAIO MARSH
(b.1899 d.1982)

A Kiwi author of detective fiction, Marsh's novels are
considered amongst the best of the genre, along with those
of Agatha Christie, Margery Allingham and Dorothy L.
Sayers. Her fans would argue that her work offers a greater
depth of characterisation than that of her rivals. Her books
feature British C.I.D. detective Roderick Alleyn and are set
in England, unless Alleyn is on holiday or on secondment
in New Zealand. She was awarded the O.B.E. in 1948 and
made a D.B.E. in 1966.

Novels
A Man Lay Dead, Geoffrey Bles (London), 1934 (red cloth
lettered in black; d/w price 7/6) . . . £1,750/£200
ditto, Sheridan House (New York), 1942 . . . £100/£20
Enter a Murderer, Geoffrey Bles (London), 1935 (red cloth
lettered in black; d/w price 7/6) . . . £1,500/£165
ditto, Pocket Books (New York), 1941 (pbk) . . £10
ditto, Sheridan House (New York), 1942 . . £100/£20
The Nursing Home Murder, Geoffrey Bles (London), 1935
(with Henry Jellett; red cloth lettered in white; d/w price
7/6). . . . . £1,250/£150
ditto, Sheridan House (New York), 1941 . . £100/£20
Death in Ecstasy, Geoffrey Bles (London), 1936 (red cloth
lettered in white; d/w price 7/6) . . . £800/£100
ditto, Sheridan House (New York), 1941 . . £100/£20
Vintage Murder, Geoffrey Bles (London), 1937 (red cloth
lettered in white; d/w price 7/6) . . . £700/£75
ditto, Sheridan House (New York), 1940 . . £100/£20
Artists in Crime, Geoffrey Bles (London), 1938 (red cloth
lettered in white; d/w price 7/6) . . . £700/£75
ditto, Lee Furman (New York), 1938. . . . £150/£20
Death in a White Tie, Geoffrey Bles (London), 1938 (red
cloth lettered in white) . . . . £700/£75
ditto, Lee Furman (New York), 1938. . . £150/£20
Overture to Death, Collins Crime Club (London), 1939
(orange/red cloth lettered in black; d/w price 7/6) £700/£75
ditto, Lee Furman (New York), 1939. . . . £150/£20
Death at the Bar, Collins Crime Club (London), 1940
(orange/red cloth lettered in black; d/w price 8/3) £450/£45
ditto, Little, Brown (Boston), 1940 . . . £75/£15
Death of a Peer, Little, Brown (Boston), 1940 . £75/£25
ditto, as **Surfeit of Lampreys**, Collins Crime Club (London),
1941 (orange/red cloth lettered in black; d/w price 8/6) .
. . . .£400/£40
Death and the Dancing Footman, Little, Brown (Boston),
1941 . . . . £65/£15
ditto, Collins Crime Club (London), 1942 (orange/red cloth
lettered in black; d/w price 8/6) . . . . £500/£50
Colour Scheme, Little, Brown (Boston), 1943 (orange/red
cloth lettered in black; d/w price 8/6) . . £45/£15
ditto, Collins Crime Club (London), 1943. . £150/£25
Died in the Wool, Collins Crime Club (London), 1945
(orange/red cloth lettered in black; d/w price 8/6) £150/£25
ditto, Little, Brown (Boston), 1945 . . . £65/£15
Final Curtain, Collins Crime Club (London), 1947
(orange/red cloth lettered in black; d/w price 8/6) £100/£15
ditto, Little, Brown (Boston), 1947 . . . £50/£15
A Wreath for Rivera, Little, Brown (Boston), 1949 £45/£10

ditto, as *Swing Brother Swing*, Collins Crime Club (London), 1949 (orange/red cloth lettered in black; d/w price 9/6) . . . . . . £75/£10
Opening Night, Collins Crime Club (London), 1951 (orange/red cloth lettered in black; d/w price 9/6) £75/£10
ditto, as *Night at the Vulcan*, Little, Brown (Boston), 1951 .
. . . . £45/£10
Spinsters in Jeopardy, Little, Brown (Boston), 1953 £45/£10
ditto, Collins Crime Club (London), 1954 (orange/red cloth lettered in black; d/w price 10/6) . . . £65/£10
Scales of Justice, Collins Crime Club (London), 1955 (orange/red cloth lettered in black; d/w price 10/6) £50/£10
ditto, Little, Brown (Boston), 1955 . . . . £40/£10
Death of a Fool, Little, Brown (Boston), 1956 . £40/£10
ditto, as *Off With His Head*, Collins Crime Club (London), 1957 (orange/red cloth lettered in black; d/w price 12/6) .
. . . . £40/£10
Singing in the Shrouds, Little, Brown (Boston), 1958 . .
. . . . £40/£10
ditto, Collins Crime Club (London), 1959 (orange/red cloth lettered in black; d/w price 12/6) . . . £40/£10
False Scent, Little, Brown (Boston), 1959 . . £30/£5
ditto, Collins Crime Club (London), 1960 (black cloth lettered in silver; d/w price 12/6) . . . £30/£5
Hand in Glove, Little, Brown (Boston), 1962 . £30/£10
ditto, Collins Crime Club (London), 1962 (orange/red cloth lettered in black; d/w price 15/-) . . £30/£10
Dead Water, Little, Brown (Boston), 1963 . £35/£5
ditto, Collins Crime Club (London), 1964 (orange/red cloth lettered in gilt; d/w price 15/-) . . . . £25/£5
Killer Dolphin, Little, Brown (Boston), 1966 . £15/£5
ditto, as *Death at the Dolphin*, Collins Crime Club (London), 1967 (orange/red cloth lettered in gilt; d/w price 18/-) . . . . £25/£5
Clutch of Constables, Collins Crime Club (London), 1968 (orange/red cloth lettered in gilt; d/w price 21/-) . £10/£5
ditto, Little, Brown (Boston), 1969 . . . . £10/£5
When in Rome, Collins Crime Club (London), 1970 (orange/red cloth lettered in gilt; d/w price 25/-) . £15/£5
ditto, Little, Brown (Boston), 1971 . . . £10/£5
Tied up in Tinsel, Collins Crime Club (London), 1972 (orange/red cloth lettered in gilt; d/w price £1.50) £20/£5
ditto, Little, Brown (Boston), 1972 . . . £10/£5
Black as He's Painted, Collins Crime Club (London), 1974 (black cloth lettered in gilt; d/w price £2.00). . £25/£5
ditto, Little, Brown (Boston), 1974 . . . £15/£5
Last Ditch, Collins Crime Club (London), 1977 (black cloth lettered in gilt; d/w price £3.50) . . . £20/£5
ditto, Little, Brown (Boston), 1977 . . . £15/£5
Grave Mistake, Collins Crime Club (London), 1978 (orange/red cloth lettered in gilt; d/w price £4.50) £20/£5
ditto, Little, Brown (Boston), 1978 . . . £10/£5
Photo-Finish, Collins Crime Club (London), 1980 (orange/red cloth lettered in gilt; d/w price £5.95) £15/£5
ditto, Little, Brown (Boston), 1980 . . . £15/£5
Light Thickens, Little, Brown (Boston), 1982. . £10/£5
ditto, Collins Crime Club (London), 1982 (orange/red cloth lettered in gilt; d/w price £7.50) . . . £10/£5

Others
Yours and Mine: Stories by Young New Zealanders, Thomas Avery (New Plymouth, New Zealand), 1936 (one short story by Marsh) . . . . . . £100/£25
The Christmas Tree, S.P.C.K. (London), 1962 (wraps). £30

New Zealand, Collins (London), 1942 (with Randal Matthew Burdon). . . . . £10/£5
ditto, Hastings House (New York), 1942 . . . £10/£5
A Play Toward: A Note on Play Production, Caxton (Christchurch, New Zealand), 1946 (wraps) . . . £10
Perspectives: The New Zealander and the Visual Arts, Auckland Gallery Associates (Auckland, New Zealand), 1960 (wraps). £10
New Zealand, Macmillan (New York), 1964 (juvenile). .
. . . . £10/£5
Black Beech and Honeydew: An Autobiography, Little, Brown (Boston), 1965 . . . . . £15/£5
ditto, Collins (London), 1966 . . . . . £15/£5
ditto, Collins (London), 1981 (revised and enlarged edition)
. . . . £10/£5

RICHARD MARSH
(b.1857 d.1915)

Marsh was the pseudonym of the British author Richard Bernard Heldmann. Although he first started publishing under his real name, following a curious break of ten years he resumed under the name of 'Richard Marsh'. He is best-known for his supernatural thriller *The Beetle* which was more popular in its day than Bram Stoker's *Dracula*, published in the same year. Many of his other novels and short stories cross the supernatural and detective fiction genres.

Novels as 'Bernard Heldmann'
Dorrincourt: The Story of a Term There, Nisbet (London), 1881 . . . . £25
Boxall School: A Tale of Schoolboy Life, Nisbet (London), 1881 . . . . £25
Expelled: Being the Story of a Young Gentleman, Nisbet (London), 1882 . . . . £25
The Belton Scholarship: A Chapter from the Life of George Denton, Griffith & Farran (London), [1882]. . £25
The Mutiny On Board the Ship 'Leander': A Story of the Sea, Sampson Low (London), 1882 . . . £25
Daintree, Nisbet (London), 1883 . . . . . £25

Novels as 'Richard Marsh'
The Devil's Diamond, Henry (London), 1893 . . . £250
ditto, as *The Ape and the Diamond*, Street (New York), c.1928 . . . . £300/£100
The Mahatma's Pupil, Henry (London), 1893 . £150
Mrs Musgrave and Her Husband, Heinemann (London), 1895 . . . . £45
ditto, Appleton (New York), 1895 . . . . . £35
The Strange Wooing of Mary Bowler, Pearson (London), 1895 . . . . £45
ditto, as *A Strange Wooing*, Street (New York), 1929 £65/£15
The Mystery of Philip Bennion's Death, Ward Lock (London), 1897 . . . . £150
ditto, as *Philip Bennion's Death*, Ward Lock (London), 1899 . . . . £150
The Crime and the Criminal, Ward Lock (London), 1897 .
. . . . £200
The Beetle: A Mystery, Skeffington (London), 1897 £1,750
ditto, Brentano's (New York), 1915 . . . . . £300
The Duke and the Damsel, Pearson (London), 1897 . £100

The House of Mystery, F.V. White (London), 1898 . £250
The Datchet Diamonds, Ward Lock (London), 1898 . £250
ditto, New Amsterdam Book Co. (New York), [1898] . £75
Tom Ossington's Ghost, James Bowden (London), 1898 .
. . . . £300
In Full Cry, F.V. White (London), 1899 . . . £200
ditto, Street (New York), 1928 . . . £250/£65
The Woman With One Hand and *Mr Ely's Engagement*,
James Bowden (London), 1899 . . . . £65
A Second Coming, Grant Richards (London), 1900 . £100
Ada Vernham, Actress, John Long (London), 1900 . £40
ditto, Page (New York), 1900 . . . . . £25
The Goddess: A Demon, F.V. White (London), 1900 . £175
The Chase of the Ruby, Skeffington (London), 1900 . £200
A Hero of Romance, Ward Lock (London), 1900 . . £40
The Joss: A Reversion, F.V. White (London), 1901 . £125
The Twickenham Peerage, Methuen (London), 1902 . £35
The Magnetic Girl, John Long (London), 1903 . . £35
The Death Whistle, Traherne (London), 1903 . . £150
ditto, as *The Whistle of Fate*, Street (New York), 1903. £100
A Metamorphosis, Methuen (London), 1903 . . £125
Miss Arnott's Marriage, John Long (London), 1904 . £35
A Duel, Methuen (London), 1904 . . . . £150
ditto, as *Cuthbert Grahame's Will*, Pearson (London), 1930
. . . . £150/£45
A Spoiler of Men, Chatto & Windus (London), 1905 . £100
The Marquis of Putney, Methuen (London), 1905 . . £25
The Garden of Mystery, John Long (London), 1906 . £125
In the Service of Love, Methuen (London), 1906 . . £25
The Romance of a Maid of Honour, John Long (London),
1907 . . . . £25
The Girl and the Miracle, Methuen (London), 1907 . £25
A Woman Perfected, John Long (London), 1907 . . £75
The Coward Behind the Curtain, Methuen (London), 1908
. . . . £25
The Surprising Husband, Methuen (London), 1908 . £25
The Interrupted Kiss, Cassell (London), 1909. . . £25
A Royal Indiscretion, Methuen (London), 1909 . . £25
Live Men's Shoes, Methuen (London), 1910 . . . £35
The Lovely Mrs Blake, Cassell (London), 1910 . . £25
Twin Sisters, Cassell (London), 1911 . . . £25
Violet Forster's Lover, Cassell (London), 1912 . . £35
A Master of Deception, Cassell (London), 1913 . £125
Justice – Suspended, Chatto & Windus (London), 1913 .
. . . . £125
Margot and Her Judges, Chatto & Windus (London), 1914
. . . . £25
Molly's Husband, Cassell (London), 1914 . . . £25
His Love or His Life, Chatto & Windus (London), 1915 £25
The Woman in the Car, T. Fisher Unwin (London), 1915 £65
The Man With Nine Lives, Ward Lock (London), 1915 £65
Love in Fetters, Cassell (London), 1915 . . . £25
The Flying Girl, Ward lock (London), 1915 . . £65
Sam Briggs, V.C., T. Fisher Unwin (London), 1916 . £100
The Great Temptation, T. Fisher Unwin (London), 1916 £20
ditto, Brentano's (New York), 1916 . . . . £15
Coming of Age, John Long (London), 1916 . . £15
The Deacon's Daughter, John Long (London), 1917 . £15
Orders to Marry, John Long (London), 1918 . . £20
Outwitted, John Long (London), 1919 . . . £15
Apron Strings, John Long (London), 1920 . £45/£10

Short Stories as 'Richard Marsh'
Curios: Some Strange Adventures of Two Bachelors, John
Long (London), 1898 . . . . . . £175

*Frivolities: Especially Addressed to Those Who Are Tired
of Being Serious*, James Bowden (London), 1899 . £125
ditto, as *The Purse Which Was Found and Other Stories*,
Pearson (London), 1918 . . . . . . £45
Marvels and Mysteries, Methuen (London), 1900 . . £250
The Seen and the Unseen, Methuen (London), 1900 . £250
ditto, New Amsterdam Book Co, 1900 . . . £200
An Aristocratic Detective, Digby Long (London), 1900 £250
Amusement Only, Hurst & Blackett (London), 1901 . £45
Both Sides of the Veil, Methuen (London), 1901 . . £250
*The Adventures of Augustus Short: Things Which I Have
Done for Others and Wish I Hadn't*, Traherne (London),
1902 . . . . £35
Between the Dark and the Daylight, Digby Long (London),
1902 . . . . £200
Garnered, Methuen (London), 1904 . . . £30
Confessions of A Young Lady: Her Doings and Misdoings,
John Long (London), 1905 . . . . £25
Under One Flag, John Long (London), 1906 . . £35
The Girl in the Blue Dress, John Long (London), 1909 £25
A Drama of the Telephone and Other Tales, Digby Long
(London), 1910 . . . . £25
Sam Briggs: His Book, John Long (London), 1912 . £35
Judith Lee: Some Pages from Her Life, Methuen (London),
1912 . . . . £125
If It Please You, Methuen (London), 1913 . . £25
The Adventures of Judith Lee, Methuen (London), 1916 £165
On the Jury, Methuen (London), 1918 . . . £25
*The Haunted Chair: Collected Tales of Horror and the
Supernatural of Richard Marsh*, Ash-Tree Press
(London), 1997 . . . . . . £25/£10

PAULE MARSHALL
(b.1929)

Paule Marshall is an American author born in Brooklyn to
Barbadian parents, and although she started out writing
poetry, she later turned to prose. Her career was given a
great boost when Langston Hughes chose her to
accompany him on a world tour during which they both
read their work.

Brown Girl, Brownstones, Random House (New York),
1959 . . . . £250/£45
ditto, W.H. Allen (London), 1960 . . . £150/£25
Soul Clap Hands and Sing, Atheneum (New York), 1961 .
. . . . £100/£15
ditto, W.H. Allen (London), 1962 . . . £50/£10
The Chosen Place, the Timeless People, Harcourt Brace &
World (New York), 1969 . . . . £65/£10
ditto, Longmans (London), 1970. . . . £45/£10
Reena and Other Stories, Feminist Press (Old Westbury,
NY), 1983 (pbk) £15
ditto, as *Merle: A Novella and Other Stories*, Virago
(London), 1985 . . . . £15/£5
Praisesong for the Widow, G.P. Putnam's Sons (New York),
1983 . . . . £15/£5
ditto, Virago (London), 1983 . . . . £20/£5
Daughters, Atheneum (New York), 1991 . . . £10/£5
The Fisher King: A Novel, Scribner's (New York etc), 2000
. . . . £10/£5

YANN MARTEL

(b.1963)

Martel is a Canadian author whose *Life of Pi* won the Man Booker Prize in 2002. The premise of the novel and some aspects of the plot were borrowed from Moacyr Scliar's *Max e os Felinos* (1981), and later editions include an acknowledgement to Scliar in the preface.

Novels

Self, Knopf (Toronto), 1996. .   .   .   .   £15/£5
ditto, Faber (London), 1996 (pbk) £10
Life of Pi, Knopf (Toronto), 2001   .   .   . £10/£5
ditto, Harcourt (New York), 2001   .   .   . £10/£5
ditto, Canongate (Edinburgh), 2002 .   .   . £10/£5

Collections

Seven Stories, Magnum Book Store (Ottawa, Canada), 1993 (26 signed, numbered copies) £200
The Facts Behind the Helsinki Roccamatios, Knopf (Toronto), 1993 (pbk). £20
ditto, Faber (London), 1993 .   .   .   .   . £15/£5
ditto, Canongate (Edinburgh), 2004 (1,000 signed copies; slipcase).   .   .   .   .   .   . £45/£15
ditto, Harcourt (New York), 2004   .   .   . £10/£5

RICHARD MATHESON

(b.1926)

Matheson has had a successful career in several genres including Horror, Science Fiction, Fantasy and Westerns. He wrote a number of episodes for the American TV series *The Twilight Zone*, adapted the works of Edgar Allan Poe for filmmaker Roger Corman and scripted Steven Spielberg's first feature, the TV movie *Duel*. A Grand Master of Horror and past winner of the Bram Stoker Award for Lifetime Achievement, he has also won the Edgar, the Hugo, the Spur, and the Writer's Guild awards.

Novels

Someone Is Bleeding, Lion (New York), 1953 (pbk)   . £50
ditto, Miller (London), 1953 (pbk) £50
Fury on Sunday, Lion (New York), 1953 (pbk)   . £50
I Am Legend, Fawcett/Gold Medal (New York), 1954 (pbk)
.   .   .   . £30
ditto, Corgi (London), 1956 .   .   .   .   .   . £20
ditto, Walker (New York), 1956.   .   .   . £125/£35
ditto, David Bruce & Watson (London), 1974 .   . £100/£30
The Shrinking Man, Fawcett/Gold Medal (New York), 1956 (pbk) £20
ditto, Muller/Gold Medal (London), 1956 (pbk)   . £20
ditto, David Bruce & Watson (London), 1973 .   . £400/£75
ditto, Gregg Press (London), 1979 (no d/w)   .   . £75
A Stir of Echoes, Lippincott (Phildelphia, PA), 1958   .   .
.   .   .   . £125/£25
ditto, David Bruce & Watson (London), 1973 .   . £100/£20
Ride the Nightmare, Ballantine (New York), 1959 (pbk) £20
ditto, Consul (London), 1961 (pbk) £10
The Beardless Warriors, Little, Brown (Boston, MA), 1960
.   .   .   . £65/£15
ditto, Heinemann (London), 1961 [1962] .   . £50/£15

Comedy of Terrors, Lancer (New York), 1964 (pbk; with Elsie Lee) £15
Hell House, Viking (New York), 1971   .   .   . £75/15
ditto, Corgi (London), 1973.   .   .   .   .   . £10
ditto, Severn House (Sutton, Surrey), 2004   .   £20/£5
Bid Time Return, Viking (New York), 1971 .   . £450/£65
ditto, Sphere (London), 1977   .   .   .   .   . £10
ditto, as *Somewhere in Time*, Ballantine (New York), 1975 (pbk) £5
ditto, Sphere (London), 1980   .   .   .   .   . £5
What Dreams May Come, Putnam (New York), 1978 £30/£5
ditto, Joseph (London), 1979   .   .   .   . £30/£5
Earthbound, Playboy Paperbacks (New York), 1982 (pseud 'Logan Swanson'; abridged text) £10
ditto, Robinson (London), 1989 ('by Richard Matheson'; full text)   .   .   .   . £15/£5
ditto, Tor Books (London), 1994 ('by Richard Matheson'; full text).   .   .   .   . £15/£5
Journal of the Gun Years, M. Evans & Co (New York), 1991   .   .   .   . £10/£5
7 Steps to Midnight, Forge (New York), 1993.   . £10/£5
The Gun Fight, Berkeley (New York), 1993 (pbk)   . £5
ditto, M. Evans & Co (New York), 1993   .   . £10/£5
Shadow on the Sun, M. Evans & Co (New York), 1994   .
.   .   .   . £10/£5
Now You See It...., Tor (New York), 1995   .   £10/£5
The Memoirs of Wild Bill Hickok, Jove Books (New York), 1996 (pbk £5
Passion Play, Cemetery Dance (Abingdon, MD), 2000 (1,000 signed, numbered copies)   .   .   . £15/£10
ditto, Cemetery Dance (Abingdon, MD), 2000 (52 signed, lettered copies; traycase) .   .   .   . £125/£100
Hunger And Thirst, Gauntlet (Springfield, PA), 2000 £10/£5
ditto, Gauntlet (Springfield, PA), 2000 (500 signed, numbered copies; slipcase)   .   .   .   . £15/£5
ditto, Gauntlet (Springfield, PA), 2000 (52 signed, lettered copies with audio cd; traycase).   .   . £150/£125
Camp Pleasant, Cemetery Dance (Abingdon, MD), 2001 (1,000 signed, numbered copies)   .   .   . £15/£10
ditto, Cemetery Dance (Abingdon, MD), 2001 (52 signed, lettered copies; traycase) .   .   .   . £125/£100
Abu and the Seven Marvels, Gauntlet (Springfield, PA), 2001   .   .   .   . £10/£5
ditto, Gauntlet (Springfield, PA), 2001 (350 signed, numbered copies; slipcase)   .   .   .   . £15/£5
ditto, Gauntlet (Springfield, PA), 2001 (52 signed, lettered copies; traycase) .   .   .   . £175/£145
Hunted Past Reason, Tom Doherty Associates (New York), 2002   .   .   .   . £10/£5
Come Fygures, Come Shadowes, Gauntlet (Springfield, PA), 2003 (500 signed, numbered copies; slipcase) £15/£5
ditto, Gauntlet (Springfield, PA), 2003 (52 signed, lettered copies; traycase) .   .   .   .   . £175/£145
The Link, Gauntlet (Springfield, PA), 2006 (500 signed, numbered copies; slipcase)   .   .   .   . £15/£5
ditto, Gauntlet (Springfield, PA), 2006 (52 signed, lettered copies; traycase) .   .   .   .   . £175/£145

Omnibus Edition

Noir: Three Novels of Suspense, G&G Books (Delavan, WI), 1997 (500 signed, numbered copies; slipcase) £35/£25
ditto, G&G Books (Delavan, WI), 1997 (52 signed, lettered copies; traycase) .   .   .   .   . £125/£100

Short Stories

Born of Man and Woman, Chamberlain Press (Philadelphia, PA), 1954 . . . . £250/£45

ditto, Max Reinhardt (London), 1956. . . . £75/£10

The Shores of Space, Bantam (London), 1957 (pbk) . £10

ditto, Corgi (London), 1958 (pbk) £5

Shock!: Thirteen Tales to Thrill and Terrify, Dell (New York), 1961 (pbk) £5

ditto, Corgi (London), 1962 (pbk) £5

Shock II, Dell (New York), 1964 (pbk) . . . £5

ditto, Corgi (London), 1965 (pbk) £5

Shock III, Dell (New York), 1966 (pbk) . . . £5

ditto, Corgi (London), 1967 (pbk) £5

Shock Waves, Dell (New York), 1970 (pbk) . . £5

ditto, as ***Shock IV***, Corgi (London), 1980 (pbk) . £5

Richard Matheson: Collected Stories, Dream/Press (Los Angeles, CA), 1989 (350 copy 'Prevue Edition'; pbk) £25

ditto, Dream/Press (Los Angeles, CA), 1989 (500 signed, unnumbered copies; no d/w) £75

ditto, Dream/Press (Los Angeles, CA), 1989 (400 signed, numbered copies; slipcase) . . . . £100/£75

ditto, Dream/Press (Los Angeles, CA), 1989 (100 deluxe numbered copies in traycase) . . . . £200/£150

By the Gun, M. Evans & Co (New York), 1993 . £10/£5

Nightmare at 20,000 Feet, Tom Doherty Associates (New York), 2002 . . . . £10/£5

Duel: Terror Stories by Richard Matheson, Tor (New York), 2003 . . . . £10/£5

Off Beat: Uncollected Stories, Subterranean Press (Burton, MI), 2002 (750 signed, numbered copies) . £20/£10

Pride, Gauntlet (Springfield, PA), 2002 (with Richard Christian Matheson; 52 signed, lettered copies; with audio cd and handwritten page; traycase) . . . £45/£30

Richard Matheson's Kolchak Scripts, Gauntlet (Springfield, PA), 2003 (500 signed, numbered copies; slipcase) £75/£50

ditto, Gauntlet (Springfield, PA), 2003 (52 signed, lettered copies; traycase) . . . . . . £200/£165

Duel & The Distributor, Gauntlet (Springfield, PA), 2004 (500 signed, numbered copies; slipcase) . £30/£10

Darker Places, Gauntlet (Springfield, PA), 2004 (500 signed, numbered copies; slipcase) . . £25/£10

ditto, Gauntlet (Springfield, PA), 2004 (52 signed, lettered copies; traycase) . . . . . £200/£165

Unrealized Dreams: Three Scripts, Gauntlet (Springfield, PA), 2005 (500 signed, numbered copies; slipcase) £25/£10

ditto, Gauntlet (Springfield, PA), 2005 (52 signed, lettered copies; traycase) . . . . . £200/£165

Collected Stories: Volume One, Edge Books (Colorado Springs, CO), 2003 (pbk) £10

Collected Stories: Volume Two, Edge Books (Colorado Springs, CO), 2005 (pbk) £10

Collected Stories: Volume Three, Edge Books (Colorado Springs, CO), 2005 (pbk) £10

Bloodlines: Richard Matheson's Dracula, I Am Legend, and Other Vampire Stories, Gauntlet (Springfield, PA), 2006 (500 signed, numbered copies; slipcase) . £40/£20

Non-Fiction

The Path: A New Look at Reality, Capra Press (Santa Barbara, CA), 1993 (pbk) £10

ditto, Tor (New York), 1999 . . . . . £10/£5

Robert Bloch: Appreciations of the Master, Tor (New York), 1995 . . . . £10/£5

Medium's Rare, Cemetery Dance (Abingdon, MD), 2000 (750 signed, numbered copies) . . . . £20/£10

A Primer of Reality, Gauntlet (Springfield, PA), 2002 (100 signed, numbered copies) . . . . . £25/£10

ditto, Gauntlet (Springfield, PA), 2002 (26 signed, lettered copies; with audio cd; traycase) . . . . £50/£45

PETER MATTHIESSEN
(b.1927)

Matthiessen is an American novelist, naturalist, conservationist and explorer. He is known for writing about Native American issues and history, as in his detailed study of the Leonard Peltier case, *In the Spirit of Crazy Horse*. He founded the *Paris Review* in 1952 with George Plimpton.

Novels

Race Rock, Harper (New York), 1954 . . . £250/£25

ditto, Secker & Warburg (London), 1954 . . . £200/£20

Partisans, Viking (New York), 1955 . . . £75/£15

ditto, Secker & Warburg (London), 1956 . . . £65/£15

Raditzer, Viking (New York), 1961 . . . £75/£15

ditto, Heinemann (London), 1962 . . . . £65/£15

At Play in the Fields of the Lord, Random House (New York), 1965 . . . . £75/£10

ditto, Heinemann (London), 1966 . . . . £65/£15

Far Tortuga, Random House (New York), 1975 . £40/£10

Killing Mister Watson, Random House (New York), 1990 .
. . . . £25/£10

ditto, Collins Harvill (London), 1990. . . . £15/£5

Lost Man's River, Random House (New York), 1997 £20/£5

ditto, Collins Harvill (London), 1998. . . . £10/£5

Bone by Bone, Random House (New York), 1999 . £10/£5

Short Stories

Midnight Turning Gray, Ampersand (Bristol, RI), 1984 (pbk) £20

On the River Styx & Other Stories, Random House (New York), 1989 . . . . £20/£5

ditto, Collins Harvill (London), 1989. . . . £15/£5

For Children

Seal Pool, Douleday (New York), 1972 (illustrated by William Pene du Bois) . . . . . £100/£25

ditto, as ***The Great Auk Escape***, Angus & Robertson (London), 1974 (laminated boards; no d/w) . . £45

Non-Fiction

Wildlife in America, Viking (New York), 1959 . £75/£15

ditto, Deutsch (London), 1959 . . . . £65/£10

The Cloud Forest: A Chronicle of the South American Wilderness, Viking (New York), 1961 . . £75/£15

ditto, Deutsch (London), 1962 . . . . £75/£15

Under the Mountain Wall, Viking (New York), 1962 .
. . . . £100/£20

Oomingmak : The Expedition to the Musk Ox Island in the Bering Sea, Hastings House (New York), 1967 . £35/£10

The Shorebirds of North America, Viking (New York), 1967 . . . . £100/£20

ditto, Viking (New York), 1967 (350 signed, numbered copies; slipcase) . . . . . . £500/£400 ditto, as *The Wind Birds*, Viking (New York), 1973 (smaller format and different illustrations) . . . £35/£10

Sal Si Puedes, Random House (New York), 1969 . £25/£10

Blue Meridian: The Search for the Great White Shark, Random House (New York), 1971 . . . . £30/£10

ditto, Harvill (London), 1995 . . . . . £15/£5

The Tree Where Man was Born: The African Experience, Dutton (New York), 1972 (photos by Peter Porter; brown cloth, not paper-over boards) . . . . £40/£10

ditto, Collins (London), 1972 . . . . £30/£5

The Snow Leopard, The Franklin Library (Franklin Centre, PA), 1978 . . . . £25

ditto, Viking (New York), 1978 . . . . . £30/£10

ditto, Viking (New York), 1978 (199 signed copies) . .
.   .   .   .   £250/£200

ditto, Chatto & Windus (London), 1978 . . . £30/£10

Sand Rivers, Viking (New York), 1981 (photographs by Hugo van Lawick) . . . . . . £25/£10

In the Spirit of Crazy Horse, Viking (New York), 1983 .
.   .   .   .   £30/£10

Indian Country, Viking (New York), 1984 . . £25/£5

ditto, Harvill (London), 1985 . . . . £25/£5

Nine-Headed Dragon River: Zen Journals 1969-1982, Shambala (Boston, MA), 1986 . . . . £20/£5

ditto, Collins Harvill (London), 1986 . . . £20/£5

Men's Lives: The Surfmen and Bayen of the South Fork, Random House (New York), 1986 . . . £15/£5

ditto, Collins Harvill (London), 1988 . . . £15/£5

African Silences, Random House (New York), 1991 £10/£5

ditto, Harvill (London), 1991 . . . . £10/£5

Baikal: Sacred Sea of Siberia, Sierra Club Books (San Francisco, CA), 1992 . . . . . £10/£5

East of Lo Monthang: In the Land of the Mustang, Shambala (Boston, MA), 1995 . . . . £15/£5

Tigers in the Snow, North Point Press (New York), 2000 .
.   .   .   .   £25/£10

The Birds of Heaven: Travels with Cranes, North Point Press (New York), 2001 . . . . £20/£5

ditto, Harvill (London), 2002 . . . . £20/£5

W. SOMERSET MAUGHAM

(b.1874 d.1965)

For many years Maugham was better known as a playwright than a novelist or short story writer, but in all of these endeavours he achieved popular success. He had a very low opinion of his own abilities, but his success caused other authors to be jealous and scornful of his achievements. He is now generally acknowledged as a master of the short story.

Novels

Liza of Lambeth, T. Fisher Unwin (London), 1897 . £750

ditto, Doran (New York), 1921 . . . . £250/£35

ditto, Heinemann (London), 1947 (1,000 signed, numbered copies) . . . . £125/£75

The Making of a Saint, L.C. Page (Boston), 1898 . £125

ditto, T. Fisher Unwin (London), 1898 . . . £125

The Hero, Hutchinson (London), 1901 (with evil eye symbol on front cover upside down) £500

ditto, Hutchinson (London), 1901 (with symbol on front cover correct) £250

Mrs Craddock, Heinemann (London), 1902 . . . £450

ditto, Doran (New York), 1920 . . . . . £250/£45

The Merry-Go-Round, Heinemann (London), 1904 . £450

ditto, Doubleday, Page & Co. (New York), 1904 . . £400

The Bishop's Apron, Chapman & Hall (London), 1906 £350

The Explorer, Heinemann (London), 1908 . . . £450

ditto, Baker and Taylor (New York), 1909 . . . £65

The Magician, Heinemann (London), 1908 . . . £250

ditto, Duffield and Co. (New York), 1909 . . . £150

Of Human Bondage, Doran (New York), 1915 . . £450

ditto, Heinemann (London), 1915 . . . . £450

The Moon and Sixpence, Heinemann (London), 1919 . £175

ditto, Doran (New York), 1919 (name mis-spelled 'Maughan' on cover) £175

The Painted Veil, Doran (New York), 1925 . £500/£40

ditto, Doran (New York), 1925 (50 signed copies of 250) £200

ditto, Doran (New York), 1925 (200 unsigned copies of 250)
.   .   .   .   £300

ditto, Heinemann (London), 1925 . . . . £500/£40

Cakes and Ale, Heinemann (London), 1930 . . £200/£30

ditto, Doubleday (New York), 1930 . . . . £175/£20

ditto, Heinemann (London), [1954] (eightieth birthday edition, 1,000 signed copies; glassine d/w and slipcase) .
.   .   .   .   £250/£150

The Narrow Corner, Heinemann (London), 1932 . £75/£15

ditto, Doubleday (New York), 1932 . . . . £75/£15

Theatre, Doubleday (New York), 1937 . . . £75/£15

ditto, Heinemann (London), 1937 . . . . £50/£10

Christmas Holiday, Heinemann (London), 1939 . £65/£15

ditto, Doubleday (New York), 1939 . . . . £45/£10

Up at the Villa, Doubleday (New York), 1941 . £65/£20

ditto, Heinemann (London), 1941 . . . . £75/£20

The Razor's Edge, Doubleday (New York), 1944 (750 signed, numbered copies, slipcase) . . . £1,000/£750

ditto, Doubleday (New York), 1944 (trade issue) . £125/£30

ditto, Heinemann (London), 1944 . . . . £125/£25

Then and Now, Heinemann (London), 1946 . . £40/£10

ditto, Doubleday (New York), 1946 . . . . £25/£10

Catalina, Heinemann (London), 1948 . . . £35/£10

ditto, Doubleday (New York), 1948 . . . . £35/£10

Short Stories

Orientations, T. Fisher Unwin (London), 1899 . . £200

The Trembling of a Leaf, Doran (New York), 1921 . .
.   .   .   .   £250/£30

ditto, Heinemann (London), 1921 . . . . £250/£30

The Casuarina Tree, Heinemann (London), 1926 . £500/£75

ditto, Doran (New York), 1926 . . . . . £400/£50

Ashenden: or The British Agent, Heinemann (London), 1928 . . . . £2,500/£75

ditto, Doubleday (New York), 1928 . . . . £750/£25

Six Stories Written in the First Person Singular, Doran (New York), 1931 . . . . . . £125/£20

ditto, Heinemann (London), 1931 . . . . £125/£20

Ah King, Heinemann (London), 1933 . . . £100/£15

ditto, Heinemann (London), 1933 (175 signed, numbered copies, slipcase) . . . . . . £300/£200

ditto, Doubleday (New York), 1933 . . . . £75/£10

The Judgement Seat, Centaur Press (London), 1934 (150 copies; glassine d/w) . . . . . £350/£300

Cosmopolitans: Very Short Stories, Doran (New York), 1936 . . . . £150/£25

ditto, Heinemann (London), 1936 . . . . £150/£25

ditto, Heinemann (London), 1936 (175 signed, numbered copies, slipcase) . . . . . . £225/£175

The Mixture as Before, Heinemann (London), 1940 £100/£15

ditto, Doubleday (New York), 1940 . . . . £35/£10

The Unconquered, House of Books (New York), 1944 (300 signed, numbered copies; tissue d/w) . . £250/£225

Creatures of Circumstance, Heinemann (London), 1947 .

. . . . £100/£15

ditto, Doubleday (New York), 1947 . . . . £65/£10

Quartet, Heinemann (London), 1948 . . . . £65/£15

ditto, Doubleday (New York), 1949 . . . . £50/£10

Trio, Heinemann (London), 1950 . . . . £45/£10

ditto, Doubleday (New York), 1950 . . . . £35/£10

Encore, Heinemann (London), 1952 . . . . £35/£10

ditto, Doubleday (New York), 1952 . . . . £30/£10

Seventeen Lost Stories by W. Somerset Maugham, Doubleday (New York), 1969 . . . . . £25/£10

Plays

A Man of Honour, Chapman & Hall (London), 1903 (150 copies; pbk) £500

ditto, Dramatic Publishing Company (Chicago), [1912] (pbk)

. . . . £150

Lady Frederick, Heinemann (London), 1912 . . £175

ditto, Heinemann (London), 1912 (pbk) . . . £75

ditto, Dramatic Publishing Company (Chicago), [1912] (pbk)

. . . . £100

Jack Straw, Heinemann (London), 1912 . . . £125

ditto, Heinemann (London), 1912 (pbk) . . . £65

ditto, Dramatic Publishing Company (Chicago), [1912] (pbk)

. . . . £75

Mrs Dot, Heinemann (London), 1912 . . . . £200

ditto, Heinemann (London), 1912 (pbk) . . . £75

ditto, Dramatic Publishing Company (Chicago), [1912] (pbk)

. . . . £75

Penelope, Heinemann (London), 1912 . . . £150

ditto, Heinemann (London), 1912 (pbk) . . . £65

ditto, Dramatic Publishing Company (Chicago), [1912] (pbk)

. . . . £75

The Explorer, Heinemann (London), 1912 . . £125

ditto, Heinemann (London), 1912 (pbk) . . . £60

ditto, Dramatic Publishing Company (Chicago), [1912] (pbk)

. . . . £75

The Tenth Man, Heinemann (London), 1913 . . £125

ditto, Heinemann (London), 1913 (pbk) . . . £60

ditto, Dramatic Publishing Company (Chicago), [1913] (pbk)

. . . . £75

Landed Gentry, Heinemann (London), 1913 . . £100

ditto, Heinemann (London), 1913 (pbk) . . . £50

ditto, Dramatic Publishing Company (Chicago), [1913] (pbk)

. . . . £75

Smith, Heinemann (London), 1913 . . . . £125

ditto, Heinemann (London), 1913 (pbk) . . . £60

ditto, Dramatic Publishing Company (Chicago), [1913] (pbk)

. . . . £75

The Land of Promise, Bickers & Son (London), 1913 (pbk)

. . . . £750

ditto, Doran (New York), 1923 . . . . . £350

The Unknown, Heinemann (London), 1920 (pbk) . £100

The Circle, Heinemann (London), 1921 (no d/w) . £100

ditto, Heinemann (London), 1921 (pbk) . . . £50

ditto, Doran (New York), [1921]. . . . £125/£30

Caesar's Wife, Heinemann (London), 1922 (no d/w) . £100

ditto, Heinemann (London), 1922 (pbk) £60

ditto, Doran (New York), [1923]. . . . . £100/£35

East of Suez, Heinemann (London), 1922 (no d/w) . £100

ditto, Heinemann (London), 1922 (pbk) . . . £45

ditto, Doran (New York), 1922 . . . . . £75/£30

Our Betters, Heinemann (London), 1923 . . . £75

ditto, Heinemann (London), 1923 (pbk) . . . £45

ditto, Doran (New York), 1924 . . . . . £75/£30

Home and Beauty, Heinemann (London), 1923 . . £100

ditto, Heinemann (London), 1923 (pbk) . . . £45

The Unattainable, Heinemann (London), 1923 . £75

ditto, Heinemann (London), 1923 (pbk) . . . £45

Loaves and Fishes, Heinemann (London), 1924 . £75

ditto, Heinemann (London), 1924 (pbk) . . . £45

ditto, French (New York), 1926 (pbk) . . . £45

The Constant Wife, Doran (New York), 1927 . . £125/£45

ditto, Heinemann (London), 1927 . . . . £125/£45

The Letter, Heinemann (London), 1927 . . . £150/£30

ditto, Doran (New York), 1927 . . . . . £125/£25

The Sacred Flame, Doubleday (New York), 1928 . £125/£30

ditto, Heinemann (London), 1928 . . . . £100/£25

The Bread-Winner, Heinemann (London), 1930 (no d/w) .

. . . . £125

ditto, Heinemann (London), 1930 (pbk) . . . £45

ditto, Doubleday (New York), 1931 . . . . £100/£20

For Services Rendered, Heinemann (London), 1932 . .

. . . . £100/£15

ditto, Doubleday, Doran (New York), 1933 . . £45/£10

Sheppey, Heinemann (London), 1933 . . . £75/£15

ditto, W.H. Baker (Boston), 1949 . . . £75/£15

The Noble Spaniard, Evans Brothers (London), 1953 (pbk)

. . . . £30

Travel

The Land of the Blessed Virgin: Sketches and Impressions in Andalusia, Heinemann (London), 1905 . . . £250

ditto, as *Andalusia: Sketches and Impressions*, Knopf (New York), 1920 . . . . £100/£35

On a Chinese Screen, Doran (New York), 1922 . £150/£25

ditto, Heinemann (London), 1922 . . . . £200/£35

The Gentleman in the Parlour: A Record of a Journey from Rangoon to Haiphong, Heinemann (London), 1930 . .

. . . . £250/£25

ditto, Doubleday (New York), 1930 . . . . £200/£25

Don Fernando, Heinemann (London), 1935 . . £50/£10

ditto, Heinemann (London), 1935 (175 signed, numbered copies, slipcase) . . . . . . £125/£100

ditto, Doubleday (New York), 1935 . . . . £50/£10

Princess September and the Nightingale, O.U.P. (Oxford, UK), 1939 . . . . £100/£25

Essays

Books and You, Heinemann (London), 1940 . . £50/£104

ditto, Doubleday (New York), 1940 . . . . £45/£10

Great Novelists and Their Novels, Winston (Philadelphia), 1948 . . . . £45/£10

ditto, as *Ten Novels and Their Authors*, Heinemann (London), 1954 . . . . £30/£10

The Writer's Point of View, C.U.P. (Cambidge, UK), 1951 (wraps) £10

The Vagrant Mood, Heinemann (London), 1952 . £25/£10

ditto, Heinemann (London), 1952 (500 signed copies, slipcase). . . . . £145/£75

ditto, Doubleday (New York), 1953 . . . . £25/£10

Others

My South Sea Island, [Ben Abramson] (Chicago), 1936 (first issue with name spelt 'Sommerset' on title-page; wraps) £200

ditto, [Ben Abramson] (Chicago), 1936 (second issue with name spelt correctly; wraps) £45

The Summing Up, Heinemann (London), 1938   . £75/£15

ditto, Doubleday (New York), 1938   .   .   .   £45/£10

ditto, Doubleday (New York), 1954 (391 signed, numbered copies; slipcase)   .   .   .   .   . £225/£250

France at War, Heinemann (London), 1940 (pbk)   . £40

ditto, Doubleday (New York), 1940   .   .   . £30/£10

The Inside Story of the French Collapse, Redbook (New York), 1940 (wraps) £15

Strictly Personal, Doubleday (New York), 1941 (515 signed, numbered copies, slipcase)   .   .   .   . £125/£100

ditto, Doubleday (New York), 1941   .   .   . £25/£10

ditto, Heinemann (London), 1942   .   .   . £25/£10

The Hour Before the Dawn, Doubleday (New York), 1942.
.   .   .   . £65/£15

Of Human Bondage, with a Digression on the Art of Fiction, Library of Congress (Washington, DC), 1946 (500 signed copies of 800, hardcover without d/w)   .   . £200

ditto, Library of Congress (Washington, DC), 1946 (300 unsigned copies of 800, hardcover without d/w)   .   . £50

ditto, Library of Congress (Washington, DC), 1946 (wraps)
.   .   .   . £25

A Writer's Notebook, Hearst (New York), 1949 (no d/w) £35

ditto, Heinemann (London), 1949   .   .   .   . £25/£5

ditto, Heinemann (London), 1949 (1,000 signed copies, slipcase).   .   .   .   . £125/£75

ditto, Doubleday (New York), 1949   .   .   . £25/£5

ditto, Doubleday (New York), 1949 (1,000 signed copies, slipcase).   .   .   .   . £125/£75

Points of View, Heinemann (London), 1958   . £25/£10

ditto, Doubleday (New York), 1959   .   .   . £25/£10

Purely For My Pleasure, Heinemann (London), 1962 .   .
.   .   .   . £25/£10

ditto, Doubleday (New York), 1962 (slipcase).   . £25/£10

A Traveller in Romance: Uncollected Writings, 1901-1964, Blond (London), 1984   .   .   .   .   . £15/£5

ditto, Clarkson Potter (New York), 1984   .   .   . £15/£5

WILLIAM MAXWELL
(b.1908 d.2000)

William Maxwell was an American author who spent his working career as a member of the staff of *The New Yorker* magazine.

Bright Centre of Heaven, Harper & Brothers (New York), 1934   .   .   .   . £750/£125

They Came Like Swallows, Harper & Brothers (New York), 1937 (first edition d/w with '1186' at bottom of back panel which is headed 'New Harper Fiction')   .   . £500/£65

ditto, Michael Joseph (London), 1937   .   . £225/£40

The Folded Leaf, Harper & Brothers (New York), 1945   .
.   .   .   . £450/£75

ditto, Faber & Faber (London), 1946.   .   . £125/£20

Heavenly Tenants, Harper & Brothers (New York), 1946 (d/w priced $2.00, with '6317' at bottom of front flap)   .
.   .   .   . £125/£30

Time Will Darken It, Harper & Brothers (New York), 1948
.   .   .   . £200/£20

ditto, Faber & Faber (London), 1949 .   .   . £100/£20

The Writer As Illusionist, Unitelum Press (New York), 1955 (stapled wraps) £75

Stories, Farrar Straus & Cudahy (New York), 1956 (with Cheever, Stafford, and Daniel Fuchs)   .   . £30/£5

The Anxious Man, Pax (New York), 1957 (broadside).   £65

The Chateau, Knopf (New York), 1961 (first state d/w with back cover author photo by Knopf).   .   . £60/£10

ditto, Knopf (New York), 1961 (second state d/w with back cover author photo by Consuelo Kanaga)   .   . £30/£10

The Old Man at the Railroad Crossing, Knopf (New York), 1966   .   .   .   . £45/£10

Ancestors, Knopf (New York), 1971 .   .   .   £20/£5

Over By The River and Other Stories, Knopf (New York), 1977   .   .   .   . £15/£5

So Long, See You Tomorrow, Knopf (New York), 1980   .
.   .   .   . £20/£5

ditto, Secker & Warburg (London), 1989 .   .   . £15/£5

ditto, Vintage (New York), 1996 (pbk; signed keepsake edition in pictorial card slipcase/mailing envelope) £45/£35

Five Tales, Cummington Press (Omaha, OH), 1988 (160 numbered copies) £45

ditto, Cummington Press (Omaha, OH), 1988 (60 numbered copies) £65

The Outermost Dream, Knopf (New York), 1989 .   £10/£5

Billy Dyer and Other Stories, Knopf (New York), 1992   .
.   .   .   . £10/£5

All The Days and Nights; The Collected Stories, Knopf (New York), 1995   .   .   .   .   .   . £10/£5

Mrs MacDonald's Dog Bun and His Home Away from Home, Knopf (New York), 1995   .   .   . £10/£5

The Happiness of Getting It Down Right: Letters of Frank O'Connor and William Maxwell, Knopf (New York), 1996   .   .   .   . £10/£5

The Element of Lavishness: Letters of Sylvia Townsend Warner and William Maxwell, 1938-1978, Counterpoint (Washington, DC), 2001   .   .   .   .   . £15/£5

HERMAN MELVILLE
(b.1819 d.1891)

Moby-Dick, the novel which recounts Captain Ahab's search for a white sperm whale, is a mixture of realism, fantasy and parable. Now considered a classic of American literature, it was not well-received during the author's lifetime, and his lack of success meant that in later years he turned almost exclusively to writing poetry.

Short Stories

The Piazza Tales, Dix, Edwards (New York), 1856   £1,000

ditto, Sampson, Low (London), 1856.   .   .   £1,000

Billy Budd and Other Prose Pieces, Constable (London), 1924 (vol.13 of *The Works of Herman Melville*)   . £100

Novels

Narrative of a Four Months' Residence Among the Natives of a Valley of the Marquesas Islands, John Murray (London), 1846 (1 vol; cloth) £2,500

ditto, John Murray (London), 1846 (2 vols; wraps)   .   .
.   .   .   . £5,000 the set

ditto as ***Typee: A Peep at Polynesian Life***, Wiley & Putnam (New York), 1846 (1 vol; cloth) £1,500

ditto as ***Typee: A Peep at Polynesian Life***, Wiley & Putnam (New York), 1846 (2 vols; wraps) . . . £4,000

ditto, Wiley & Putnam (New York), 1846 (revised with 'The Story of Toby'; 2 vols) . . . . £1,250 (the set)

ditto, John Murray (London), 1846 (2 vols). . . £1,250

The Story of Toby, John Murray (London), 1846 (wraps) .

. . . . £2,500

Omoo, John Murray (London), 1847 (2 vols; wraps) £3,500

ditto, John Murray (London), 1847 (1 vol; cloth) . £1,500

ditto, Harper (New York), 1847 (2 vols; wraps) . £2,500

ditto, Harper (New York), 1847 (1 vol; cloth) . . £1,250

Mardi, Bentley (London), 1849 (3 vols) . . . £4,000

ditto, Harper (New York), 1849 (2 vols) . . . £2,000

Redburn: His Voyage, Bentley (London), 1849 (2 vols) .

. . . . £2,000

ditto, Harper (New York), 1849 . . . . £1,500

ditto, Harper (New York), 1849 (wraps) . . . £2,500

White Jacket; or, The World in a Man-O-War, Bentley (London), 1850 (2 vols £2,000

ditto, Harper (New York), 1850 . . . . £1,000

The Whale, Bentley (London), 1851 (3 vols) . . £65,000

ditto, as ***Moby Dick***, Harper (New York), 1851 (with publisher's circular device blindstamped at centre of sides)

. . . . £30,000

ditto, as ***Moby Dick***, Harper (New York), 1851 (no blindstamped circular device) £16,000

Pierre; or, The Ambiguities, Harper (New York), 1852 .

. . . . £1,250

ditto, Sampson, Low (London), 1852. . . . £800

Israel Potter: His Fifty Years of Exile, Putnam (New York), 1855 . . . . £1,250

ditto, Sampson, Low (London), 1855. . . . £1,000

ditto, Routledge (London), 1855 (pirate edition) . £1,250

The Confidence-Man, Dix, Edwards (New York), 1857 .

. . . . £2,500

ditto, Longman, Brown (London), 1857 . . . £2,500

Poetry

Battle-Pieces and Aspects of the War, Harper (London), 1866 . . . . £750

Clarel: A Poem and Pilgrimage in the Holy Land, Putnam (New York), 1876 (2 vols) £1,000

John Marr and the Other Sailors, De Vinne Press (New York), 1888 (25 copies) £1,500

Timoleon, Caxton Press (New York), 1891 (25 copies) £1,000

Poems, Constable (London), 1924 (vol.16 of *The Works of Herman Melville*) . . . . . £125/£50

John Marr and Other Poems, Princeton Univ Press (Princeton, NJ), 1922 . . . . . . £25

ditto, Princeton Univ Press (Princeton, NJ), 1922 (175 numbered copies) £75

Miscellaneous

The Apple-Tree Table and Other Sketches, Princeton Univ Press (Princeton, NJ), 1922 . . . . . £25

ditto, Princeton Univ Press (Princeton, NJ), 1922 (175 numbered copies) £75

Journal up the Straits, The Colophon (New York), 1935 £45

ditto, as ***Journal of a Visit to Europe and the Levant***, Princeton Univ Press (Princeton, NJ), 1955 . . £40/£20

Journal of a Visit to London and the Continent, Harvard Univ Press (Cambridge, MA), 1948 . . £40/£20

ditto, Cohen & West (London), 1949. . . . £35/£15

The Letters of Herman Melville, Yale Univ Press (New Haven, CT), 1960 . . . . . £65/£25

Correspondence, Northwestern Univ Press/Newberry Library, US, 1993 (volume 14 of the Northwestern-Newberry Edition of *The Writings of Herman Melville*) .

. . . . £30/£15

Journals, Northwestern Univ Press/Newberry Library, US, 1989 (volume 15 of the Northwestern-Newberry Edition of *The Writings of Herman Melville*) . . . . £30/£15

Collected Editions

The Works of Herman Melville, Constable (London), 1922-24 (16 vols) . . . . . . £2,000/£1,000

The Writings of Herman Melville, Northwestern Univ Press/Newberry Library (Chicago), 1968-1993 (15 vols) .

. . . . £650/£250

H.L. MENCKEN
(b.1880 d.1956)

Henry Louis Mencken was an American journalist, essayist and magazine editor. A commentator on American life and culture and a student of American English, he is regarded by many as one of the most influential American writers and prose stylists of the first half of the 20th century.

Fiction
Christmas Story, Knopf (New York), 1946 . . £60/£10

Plays
The Artist; A Drama Without Words, John W. Luce (Boston), 1912 (grey and brown boards lettered in dark brown on front, spine and rear cover blank) . . £150

ditto, as ***The Artist: A Satire in One Act***, John Lane (New York), 1917 (wraps; acting issue) £30

Heliogabalus; A Buffoonery in Three Acts, Knopf (New York), 1920 (written with George Jean Nathan; 60 numbered copies signed by both authors; bound in Japanese boards with parchment back, stamped in gilt) .

. . . . £1,250

ditto, Knopf (New York), 1920 (150-200 copies; light brown wraps printed dark brown). £150

ditto, Knopf (New York), 1920 (2,000 numbered copies bound in black cloth stamped in gilt) . . . £200/£45

Verse
Ventures into Verse, Marshall, Beek Gordon (New York/London, etc), 1903 (85 copies; dark brown paperwraps with white label on front cover) . . £5,000

ditto, Marshall, Beek Gordon (New York/London, etc), 1903 (15 copies with red cloth spine and white label on front cover) £7,000

ditto, Marshall, Beek Gordon [Smith's Book Store], ([Baltimore, MD]), [1960] (250 numbered facsimile copies in brown paperwraps with paper label) £200

Autobiography
Happy Days 1880-1892, Knopf (New York), 1940 £75/£15

ditto, Kegan Paul, Trench, Trubner & Co (London), 1940 .

. . . . £75/£15

Newspaper Days, 1899-1906, Knopf (New York), 1941   .
.   .   .   . £65/£10

ditto, Kegan Paul, Trench, Trubner & Co (London), 1942   .
.   .   .   . £60/£10

Heathen Days, 1890-1936. Knopf (New York), 1943   .   .
.   .   .   . £45/£10

The Days of H.L. Mencken; Happy Days, Newspaper Days,
Heathen Days, Knopf (New York), 1947   .   . £30/£10

Translator

The Antichrist, by F.W. Nietzsche, Knopf (New York), 1920
(translated, introduced and with notes by Mencken; first
binding with printed front cover)   .   .   . £150/£30

ditto, by F.W. Nietzsche, Knopf (New York), 1920 (second
binding with front cover unprinted and spine label dated
'1921')   .   .   .   . £125/£20

ditto, by F.W. Nietzsche, Knopf (New York), 1920 (third
binding with printed front cover and spine label dated
'1921')   .   .   .   . £125/£15

Others

George Bernard Shaw: His Plays, John W. Luce
(Boston/London), 1905 (dark blue cloth with white cover
and spine labels printed black) £125

The Philosophy of Friedrich Nietzshe, Luce & Company
(Boston), 1908   .   .   .   . £200

ditto, T. Fisher Unwin (London), 1908   .   .   . £150

Men Versus the Man . . ., Henry Holt (New York), 1910
(first issue in red ribbed cloth stamped in gilt)   . £250

ditto, Henry Holt (New York), 1910 (second issue in lighter
red, cross-filed cloth stamped in gilt)   .   .   . £200

ditto, Henry Holt (New York), 1910 (remainder binding red
cloth stamped in black) £150

What You Ought to Know About Your Baby, by Leonard
Keene Hirshberg, Butterick Publishing (New York), 1910
(ghostwritten by Mencken) £1,500

The American; His Morals, no publisher (no place), 1913   .
.   .   .   . £200

Europe After 8:15, John Lane/Bell & Cockburn (New
York/Toronto), 1914 (first issue binding yellow cloth
stamped in blue and gilt; written with George Jean Nathan
and Willard Huntington Wright) £100

ditto, John Lane /Bell & Cockburn (New York/Toronto),
1914 (second issue binding yellow cloth stamped in black
and gilt). £65

The Old Sun Ain't What She Used To Be, Baltimore Sun
(Baltimore, MD), 1914 (2 pps). £150

A Note To Authors, The Smart Set (no place), c.1915 (grey
wraps, 8pps) £100

'The Editors regret...', The Smart Set (New York), c.1915
(single leaf) £50

ditto, The Smart Set (New York), c.1915 (two leaves, 4 pps)
.   .   .   . £100

A Little Book in C Major, John Lane (New York), 1916   .
.   .   .   . £150

A Book of Burlesques, John Lane (New York), 1916 (first
binding maroon 'T' cloth stamped in gilt; on spine the
word 'COMPANY' is 13/16 inch wide, and shorter than
'JOHN LANE') £200

ditto, John Lane (New York), 1916 (second binding maroon
'V' cloth stamped in gilt; on spine 'COMPANY' is 15/16
inch wide and the same width as 'JOHN LANE')   . £150

ditto, Knopf (New York), 1920   .   .   .   . £200/£40

ditto, Jonathan Cape (London), 1923.   .   . £150/£30

The Creed of a Novelist, The Smart Set/John Lane (New
York), 1916 (wraps) £145

Pistols For Two, Knopf (New York), 1917 (wraps; written
with George Nathan under the single pseudonym 'Owen
Hatteras') £150

A Book of Prefaces . . . [Opus 13], Knopf (New York), 1917
(first binding dark blue 'V' cloth stamped in gilt; top edges
untrimmed and unstained). £75

ditto, Knopf (New York), 1917 (second binding as above but
but top edges stained orange) £50

ditto, Jonathan Cape (London), 1922.   .   . £125/£20

Ireland; Her Books, John Lane (New York), 1917 (wraps,
8pps) £125

Virtuosi of Virtue, Chicago Sunday Tribune (Chicago), 1917
(8pps) £150

Prohibition and the Mails, New York Mail (New York),
1918 (single sheet) £65

Damn! A Book of Calumny, Philip Goodman Company
(New York), 1918   .   .   .   . £250

ditto, as *A Book of Calumny*, Knopf (New York), 1918   . £75

In Defense of Women, Pplip (sic) Goodman (New York),
1918 (first binding very dark blue 'T' cloth stamped in
yellow) £300

ditto, Pplip (sic) Goodman (New York), 1918 (second
binding light red 'V' cloth stamped in black)   . £250

ditto, Jonathan Cape (London), 1923.   .   . £125/£20

Mr Cabell of Virginia, Robert McBride (New York), 1918
(single sheet folded twice to make 8 pps)   .   .   . £30

Dithyrambs on Alcohol, Allied Printing Trades Council
(New York), 1918 (2 leaves) £75

Review of the New International Encyclopedia, The New
International Encyclopaedia (no place), [c.1918] (2 leaves)
.   .   .   . £75

ditto, The New International Encyclopaedia (no place),
[c.1918] (single sheet folded to make 4pps)   .   . £75

The American Language, Knopf (New York), 1919 (25
signed, numbered copies) £1,250

ditto, Knopf (New York), 1919 (1,475 numbered copies)
.   .   .   . £300

ditto, Jonathan Cape (London), 1922.   .   . £250/£75

Prejudices, First Series, Knopf (New York), 1919 (first
binding; edges uneven and unstained)   .   .   . £100

ditto, Knopf (New York), 1919 (second binding top edges
trimmed and stained orange) £75

ditto, Jonathan Cape (London), 1921.   .   . £250/£65

The Literary Capital of The United States, Chicago Daily
News (Chicago), 1920 (wraps; 6pps)   .   .   . £100

The American Credo, Knopf (New York), 1920   . £350/£35

Prejudices, Second Series, Knopf (New York), 1920 (edges
unevenly trimmed; top edges unstained)   . £600/£225

ditto, Knopf (New York), 1920 (edges trimmed and top
edges stained orange).   .   .   .   .   . £500/£65

ditto, Jonathan Cape (London), 1921.   .   . £225/£25

A Personal Word, The Smart Set (New York), [1921]
(wraps; 16pps) £125

Spiritual Autopsies, Houghton Mifflin (New York/Boston),
[1922] (wraps; single sheet folded to make 6pps)   . £75

Prejudices, Third Series, Knopf (New York), 1922 (edges
unevenly trimmed; top edges unstained)   . £600/£225

ditto, Knopf (New York), 1922 (edges trimmed and top
edges stained orange)   .   .   .   .   . £500/£65

ditto, Jonathan Cape (London), 1923.   .   . £225/£25

Suggestions to Our Visitors, The Smart Set (New York),
[1922] (wraps; 4pps) £75

ditto, Grabhorn-Hoyem/Zamorano Club/Roxburghe Club (no place), 1968 (wraps; 150 copies) £125
Saviors of Civilisation, Baltimore Evening Sun (Baltimore, MD), 1923 . . . . £75
The Nordic Blond Renaissance, Baltimore Evening Sun (Baltimore, MD), [1923?] (single sheet). . . . £75
'The undersigned announce...', [The Smart Set], ([New York]), 1923 (single sheet) £60
Editorial.. from the first issue of The American Mercury, January 1924, no publisher (no place), 1924 (3 mimeographed sheets) £75
Prejudices, Fourth Series, Knopf (New York), 1924 .
. . . . £250/£25
ditto, Knopf (New York), 1924 (100 signed, numbered copies; slipcase; signed errata slip laid in . £450/£300
ditto, Knopf (New York), 1924 (10 signed and lettered copies; slipcase) . . . . . £800/£650
ditto, Jonathan Cape (London), 1925. . . . £200/£25
A Review of Americanism, [privately printed] (no place), c.1924 (wraps) £75
The Rewards of Virtue, Baltimore Evening Sun (Baltimore, MD), 1925 (single sheet folded to make 6 pps) . £65
Mencken on the Nation, Baltimore Evening Sun (Baltimore, MD), 1925 (single sheet) £60
Bryan, Baltimore Evening Sun (Baltimore, MD), 1925 (single sheet) £60
Prejudices Jonathan Cape (London), 1925 (wraps). . £30
ditto, as *Selected Prejudices* Jonathan Cape (London), 1926 . . . . £45/£10
The American Mercury Editorial of December 1925, American Mercury (no place), 1925 (two leaves). . £75
My Dear Mr Walpole, An Open Letter, George H. Doran/The Bookman (New York), 1925 (wraps). . £60
Eye Exercise from Prejudices, Second Series, [E.F. Darling, M.D.] ([New York]), 1925 (heavy grey wraps) . . £100
ditto, [E.F. Darling, M.D.] ([New York]), 1925 (buff wraps) £75
The Friends of the Saloon, Preliminary Announcement, Bull No 1 (Confidential), no publisher (no place), 1926 (one page) £75
To The Friends of the American Mercury, The American Mercury (no place), 16 April 1926 (wraps; 8pps). . £125
Notes on Democracy, Knopf (New York), 1926 . £125/£25
ditto, Knopf (New York), 1926 (200 signed, numbered copies; in publisher's box). . . . £300/£250
ditto, Knopf (New York), 1926 (35 signed. numbered copies printed on Japan vellum, bound in white vellum stamped in gilt; slipcase) . . . . £1,000/£750
ditto, Jonathan Cape (London), 1927. . . £75/£15
What Mencken Thinks of El Paso and Jaurez, El Paso Times (El Paso, TX), [1926?] (two leaves) . . £75
Prejudices, Fifth Series, Knopf (New York), 1926 £125/£25
ditto, Knopf (New York), 1926 (192 signed, numbered copies; slipcase) . . . . . . £300/£250
ditto, Knopf (New York), 1926 (8 signed and lettered copies; slipcase) . . . . . . £800/£650
ditto, Jonathan Cape (London), 1927. . . £65/£10
To Friends of the American Mercury, The American Mercury (New York), 1926 (wraps, 6 pps) . . £150
Chiropractic, Chicago Tribune (Chicago), 1927 (4pps) £75
Editorial, American Mercury (New York), 1927 (wraps, enclosed in a replica of the magazine cover; 8pps) . £100
Saturnalia, Evening Sun (Baltimore, MD), 1927 (single sheet of newsprint) £65

James Branch Cabell, Robert M. McBride & Company, New York, 1927 (wraps) £30
ditto, Robert M. McBride & Company, New York, 1927 (110 numbered copies; glassine d/w) £150
Prejudices, Sixth Series, Knopf (New York), 1927 £125/£20
ditto, Knopf (New York), 1927 (140 signed, numbered copies; slipcase; glassine d/w) . . . . £300/£250
ditto, Knopf (New York), 1927 (50 signed and lettered copies; slipcase) . . . . £800/£650
ditto, Jonathan Cape (London), 1927. . . £65/£10
Selected Prejudices, Second Series Jonathan Cape (London), 1927 . . . . £45/£10
ditto, as *Selected Prejudices* Knopf (New York), 1927 .
. . . . £100/£20
Sterling, John Henry Nash (San Francisco, CA), 1927 (broadside) £100
Menckeniana; A Schimpflexikon, Knopf (New York), 1928 (acetate d/w with text on front and rear flaps) . £200/£35
ditto, Knopf (New York), 1928 (80 signed, numbered copies; slipcase). . . . . . £450/£400
ditto, Knopf (New York), 1928 (230 signed and numbered copies; glassine d/w; slipcase) . . . £250/£200
H.L. Mencken's Essyas, Keibundo (Tokyo), 1928 (no d/w) £175
Editorial . . . the December 1928 Number of The American Mercury, The American Mercury (New York), 1928 (wraps with string tie; 8pps) £75
My View of Companionate Marriage..., [Philadelphia Public Ledger] ([Philadelphia, PA]), c.1928 (broadside) £50
Treatise on the Gods, Knopf (New York), 1929 (wraps, 16pps) £75
Hot Dogs, Oppenheimer Casing Co. ([Baltimore]), 1929 (single sheet) £65
Mr Mencken to the Book Publishers, The American Mercury (New York), 1929 (250 copies; wraps) . £100
Treatise on the Gods, Knopf (New York/London), 1930 .
. . . . £125/£25
ditto, Knopf (New York), 1930 (375 signed, numbered copies; d/w and slipcase) . . . . £400/£250
ditto, Knopf (London/New York), 1930 . . £65/£10
The Editor Reviews His Magazine, The American Mercury ([New York]), [1930] (two leaves) £60
Lo, The Poor Bookseller, Stanley Rose, Ltd./The Picador Press (Hollywood, CA), c.1930 (wraps). . . £200
A Suggestion, [American Mercury (New York)], c.1930 (card) £60
So Far As I Know, The American Mercury (New York), c.1930 (single sheet) £65
The 10,000 Best American Books in Print, Books-Baltimore (Baltimore, MD), 1930 (wraps) £100
A Literary History of the American People By Charles Angoff, Knopf (New York), c.1930 (4pps) . . £45
Making A President, Knopf (New York), 1932 . £150/£25
Project for a Licensing Act for Baltimore City, Evening Sun (Baltimore, MD), 1933 (wraps) £85
Treasise on Right and Wrong, Knopf (New York), 1934 .
. . . . £125/£25
ditto, Kegan Paul, Trench, Trubner & Co (London), 1934 .
. . . . £75/£10
Erez Israel, privately printed by B.P. Safran at The New School (New York), 1935 (25 copies) £500
The Anatomy of Quakery, William Feather (Cleveland, OH), 1935 (single sheet folded five times) £75

The Average American Newspaper...., [Hermitage Press (Greenfield, MA)], c.1935 (single sheet) . . £75

Three Years of Dr Roosevelt, The American Mercury (New York), 1936 (wraps) £100

The Incomprable Physician, School of Medicine, Univ of California/T.W. McDonald (San Francisco, CA), 1936 (wraps) £150

ditto, The Gillick Press (Berkeley, CA), [c.1940] (529 copies, yellow wraps). £125

'Here is one chapter from the fourth edition . . . of The American Language . . .', [Knopf (New York), 1936] (wraps) £100

...The John Hopkins Hospital, The Johns Hopkins Hospital (Baltimore, MD), 1937 (wraps; 96 ppps mimeographed and paginated on rectos only) £125

Notes on a Moral War, Porter Sargent (Boston), 1939 . £50

An American Editor Speaks, The Concord Press (Mt Vernon, WA), c.1940 (wraps) £50

'Generally Political', Columbia Univ (New York), 1940 £65

'Generally Political', Institute of Arts and Sciences, Columbia Univ ([New York)], [1940] (wraps) . . £75

The Triumph of Democracy, Porter Sargent (Boston), 1940 (single sheet) £65

Quickstep to War, Porter Sargent (Boston), 1940 (single sheet) £65

A Girl from Red Lion, no publisher (no place), [c.1941] (wraps) £150

A New Dictionary of Quotations, Knopf (New York), [c.1942?] (single sheet folded twice to make four uncut leaves) £65

Beethoven, R.J. Bucholtz (Baltimore, MD), 1943 (7pps) £75

Notes on American Given-Names, New York Public Library (New York), 1943 (wraps). £150

Stylebook, The Sunpapers (Baltimore, MD), 1944 (wraps) £75

Designations for Colored Folk, American Speech (Baltimore, MD), 1944 (wraps) £200

War Words in England, American Speech (Baltimore, MD), 1944 (wraps). £150

American Profanity, Columbia Univ (New York), 1945 £75

Stare Decisis, A New Yorker Reprint (New York), 1944 (wraps) £75

Supplement I: The American Language, Knopf (New York), 1945 . . . . £50/£10

ditto, Routledge & Kegan Paul Ltd (London), 1948 (English issue of fourth American printing with English publisher imprint over US) . . . . . . £20/£5

'Hon', American Speech (Baltimore, MD), 1946 (wraps) £75

Vachel Lindsay, John S. Mayfield (Washington, DC), 1947 (100 signed, numbered copies; wraps) . . . £450

Names for Americans, American Speech (Baltimore, MD), 1948 (wraps). £100

What the People of American Towns Call Themselves, American Speech (Baltimore, MD), 1948 (wraps) . £75

Supplement II: The American Language, Knopf (New York), 1948 . . . . £50/£10

ditto, Routledge and Kegan Paul Ltd (London), 1948 (English issue of fourth American printing with English publisher imprint over US) . . . £20/£5

Menckiana, A Selection from H.L. Mencken's A Mencken Chrestomathy, Knopf (New York), 1949 (wraps) . £25

Some Approbrious Nicknames, American Speech (Baltimore, MD), 1949 (wraps) £60

A Mencken Chrestomathy, Knopf (New York), 1949 £30/£5

The Birth of New Verbs, [Johns Hopkins Press (Baltimore), 1949] (stapled sheets). £65

The Vintage Mencken, Vintage Books (New York), 1955 (pbk) £10

Minority Report, H.L. Mencken's Notebooks, Knopf (New York), 1956 . . . . £30/£5

A Carnival of Buncombe, The Johns Hopkins Press (Baltimore, MD), 1956 . . . . . . £25/£5

The Bathtub Hoax, And Other Blasts & Bravos From The Chicago Tribune, Knopf (New York), 1958 . £25/£5

Prejudices: A Selection, Vintage Books (New York), 1958 (pbk) £10

On Politics, Vintage Books (New York), 1960 (pbk) . £10

Letters of H.L. Mencken, Knopf (New York), 1961 £25/£10

Mencken on Music, Knopf (New York), 1961 . £35/£10

The American Language Abridged, Knopf (New York), 1963 . . . . £35/£10

ditto, as *One-Volume Abridged Edition: The American Language*, Routledge & Kegan Paul (London), 1963. . . . . £25/£5

In The Footsteps of Gutenberg, Princeton Univ Press (Princeton, NJ), 1964 (pbk) £75

H.L. Mencken; The American Scene; A Reader, Knopf (New York), 1965 . . . . £25/£5

Memorials of Gormandizing, Princeton Univ Press (Princeton, NJ), 1965 (wraps) £65

H.L.Memcken Replies To A Letter. . ., no publisher (no place), c.1965 (broadside) £40

H.L. Mencken's Smart Set Criticism, Cornell Univ Press (Ithaca, NY), 1968 . . . . £25/£5

A Letter from Mencken, Printed at the Sign of the Rolling Stone... (Champaign, IL), 1968 (wraps) . . . £60

What's Ahead for Books and Authors?, Roxburghe/ Zamorano ([San Francisco, CA]), 1972 (wraps) . £50

The Young Mencken: The Best of His Work, The Dial Press (New York), 1973 . . . . £30/£5

Salvos from the Sage of Baltimore, Enoch Pratt Free Library (Baltimore, MD), 1973 (broadside). . . . £40

On Being An American and Other Essays, Kenkyusha (Tokyo), 1973 (wraps; in d.w) . . . . £45/£25

The Mating Game and How To Play It, Hallmark Editions (Kansas City, MO), 1974 . . . . . £20/£5

Mencken's Baltimore, The Sun (Baltimore, MD), 1974 (wraps; newspaper supplement on newsprint) . . £25

Quotations from Chairman Mencken or Poor Henry's Almanack, Institute of Communications Research, Univ of Illinois (Urbana, IL), [1974] (wraps; mimeographed and paginated on rectos only) £30

A Gang of Pecksniffs, Arlington House (New Rochelle, NY), 1975 . . . . £20/£5

Mencken's Last Campaign, New Republic Book Company (Washington, DC), 1976 . . . . . . £20/£5

The New Mencken Letters, The Dial Press (New York), 1977 . . . . £15/£5

A Choice of Days, Knopf (New York), 1980 . £15/£5

H.L. Mencken on Pants-Pressers, Publishers & Editors, Univ of West Florida, John C. Pace Library/Williamsburg Press, Inc., ([Pensacola, FL]), 1980 (200 copies; wraps) £40

Menckeniana, The House of Type (Baltimore, MA), 1980 (70 copies; wraps) £60

Letters from Baltimore; The Mencken-Cleator Correspondence, Fairleigh Dickinson Univ/Associated Univ Presses (Rutherford/Madison etc), 1982 . £25/£5

The Sage of Baltimore, The House of Type (Baltimore, MD), 1984 (wraps) £65

'Ich Kuss Die Hand', The Letters of H.L. Mencken to Gretchen Hood, Univ of Alabama Press (Tuscaloosa, AL), 1986 . . . . £15/£5

Dreiser-Mencken Letters; The Correspondence of Theodore Dreiser & H.L. Mencken 1907-1945, Univ of Pennsylvania Press (Philadelphia, PA), 1986 (2 vols). . . £50/£20

Mencken and Sara: A Life in Letters; The Correspondence of H.L. Mencken and Sara Haardt, McGraw-Hill Book Company (New York/St Louis etc), 1987 . . £10/£5

The Editor, The Bluenose and the Prostitute, Roberts Rinehart (Boulder, CO), 1988 . . . . . £15/£5

ditto, Roberts Rinehart (Boulder, CO), 1988 (250 numbered copies signed by the editor) . . . . £75/£50

Fante/Mencken... A Personal Correspondence 1930-1952, Black Sparrow Press (Santa Barbara, CA), 1989 (26 lettered copies; acetate d/w) . . . £150/£125

ditto, Black Sparrow Press (Santa Barbara, CA), 1989 (150 numbered copies; acetate d/w) . . . . . £100/£75

ditto, Black Sparrow Press (Santa Barbara, CA), 1989 (750 unnumbered copies; acetate d/w) . . . £35/£25

ditto, Black Sparrow Press (Santa Barbara, CA), 1989 (pbk) £10

The Diary of H.L. Mencken, Knopf (New York), 1989 . . . . £10/£5

A Texas Schoolmarm, W. Thomas Taylor (no place), 1989 (750 copies; wraps) £25

Tall Tales and Hoaxes of H.L. Mencken, Franklin Printing (Annapolis, MD), 1990 (wraps) £25

The Gist of H.L. Mencken, Scarecrow Press (Metuchen, NJ/London), 1990 (no d/w) £20

The Impossible H.L. Mencken, A Selection of His Best Newspaper Stories, Doubleday (New York/London etc), 1991 . . . . £15/£5

My Life As Author and Editor, Knopf (New York), 1993 . . . . £15/£5

Thirty-Five Years of Newspaper Work, Johns Hopkins Univ Press (Baltimore, MD/London), 1994 . . £15/£5

A Second Mencken Chrestomathy, Knopf (New York), 1995 . . . . £15/£5

Definitions, Skepticisms . . ., Roxburghe Club/Arion Press (San Francisco, CA), 1995 (wraps) £50

Do You Remember?, Maryland Historical Society (Baltimore, MD), 1996 . . . . £25/£5

ditto, Maryland Historical Society (Baltimore, MD), 1996 (100 numbered copies signed by the editor; no d/w; in box) . . . . £125/£75

From Baltimore to Bohemia, The Letters of H.L. Mencken and George Sterling, Farleigh Dickinson Univ Press/ Associated Univ Presses (Madison/Teaneck/London), 2001 . . . . £15/£5

H.L. Mencken on American Literature, Ohio Univ Press (Athens, OH), 2002 . . . . . . £15/£5

H.L. Mencken on Religion, Prometheus Press (Amherst, NY), 2002 . . . . £10/£5

Mencken's America, Ohio Univ Press (Athens, OH), 2004 . . . . £15/£5

ditto, Ohio Univ Press (Athens, OH), 2004 (pbk) . . £5

Advertising Material

Loudon Park Cemetery Company, 1853-1902, Williams and Wilkins (Baltimore, MD), 1902 (wraps). . . £1,500

Echoes from the Hub, E.B. Read & Son/Charles M. Stieff (Baltimore, MD), [1902] (advertising pamphlet; anonymous) £1,000

Sixtieth Anniversary of Charles M. Steiff..., E.B. Read & Son/Charles M. Stieff (Baltimore, MD), 1902 (advertising pamphlet; anonymous) £1,000

Steiff Pianos, E.B. Read & Son/Charles M. Stieff (Baltimore, MD), 1902 (advertising pamphlet; anonymous) £1,000

Edited by Mencken

... A Doll's House, by Ibsen, John W. Luce (Boston/London), 1909 (edited by Mencken who contributed notes, introduction and co-translated). £150

... Little Eyolf, , by Ibsen, John W. Luce (Boston/London), 1909 (edited by Mencken who contributed notes, introduction and co-translated). £150

The Gist of Nietzsche, John W. Luce (Boston), 1910 . £100

Americana 1925, Martin Hopkinson (London), 1925 . . . . £150/£25

ditto, Knopf (New York), 1925 . . . . £125/£25

ditto, Knopf (New York), 1925 (50 copies signed by the author on free font endpaper; unprinted brown paper d/w) . . . . £300/£250

Americana 1926, Knopf (New York), 1926 . £125/£25

ditto, Knopf (New York), 1925 (50 copies signed by the author on free font endpaper; unprinted brown paper d/w) . . . . £300/£250

ditto, Martin Hopkinson (London), 1926 . . £150/£25

...The Sunpapers of Baltimore, Knopf (New York), 1937 (edited and with chapters by Mencken) . . £40/£5

and edited by Mencken) . . . . . £35/£5

ditto, as *H.L. Mencken's Dictionary of Quotations*, Collins (London), 1982 . . . . £25/£5

ABRAHAM MERRITT

(b.1884 d.1943)

Merritt was first a journalist and then assistant editor of *The American Weekly* from 1912 until 1937, when he was made editor. Fiction was a secondary career, but he was a popular contributor to the pre-World War Two American pulp magazines, writing exotic fantasies often more extreme than those of Edgar Rice Burroughs.

Novels

The Moon Pool, Putnam (New York), 1919 (first printing without advert on p.434, 'Putnam' printed on spine in upper and lower case). . . . . . £1,000/£75

The Ship of Ishtar, Putnam (New York), 1926 £1,000/£75

Seven Footprints to Satan, Boni & Liveright (New York), 1928 . . . . £650/£75

ditto, Richards (London), 1928. . . . . £450/£75

The Face in the Abyss, Liveright (New York), 1931 . . . . £1,000/£85

Dwellers in the Mirage, Liveright (New York), 1932 . . . . £1,000/£65

ditto, Skeffington (London), [1933]. . . . £500/£50

Thru the Dragon Glass, ARRA Printers (Jamaica, NY), 1932 (pbk) £50

ditto, as *Through the Dragon Glass*, Doreal (Sedalia, CO), 1948 (pbk) £40

Burn Witch Burn!, Liveright (New York), 1932 . £750/£75

ditto, Methuen (London), 1934. . . . . £350/£50

Creep, Shadow, Doubleday, Doran (New York), 1934 . .

. . . . £650/£75

ditto, as *Creep, Shadow, Creep!*, Methuen (London), 1935 .

. . . . £200/£25

Three Lines of Old French, Bizarre (Millheim, PA), 1937

(pbk) £85

ditto, Doreal (Sedalia, CO), 1948 (pbk) £40

The Story Behind the Story, privately printed by the

American Weekly (New York), 1942 (no d/w) . . £10

The Metal Monster, Avon (New York), [1946] (pbk) . £10

ditto, Hyperion (Westport, CT), 1974 (no d/w) . . £15

The Fox Woman/The Blue Pagoda, New Collectors (New

York), 1946 (with Hannes Bok, nude woman illustration;

no d/w) £30

ditto, New Collectors (New York), 1946 (with Hannes Bok,

nude man illustration; no d/w) £30

The Black Wheel, New Collectors (New York), 1947

(completed by Hannes Bok) £30

The Drone Man, Doreal (Sedalia, CO), 1948 (pbk) . £45

Rhythm of the Spheres, Doreal (Sedalia, CO), 1948 (pbk) .

. . . . £45

The People of the Pit, Doreal (Sedalia, CO), 1948 (pbk) .

. . . . £45

The Woman of the Wood, Doreal (Sedalia, CO), 1948 (pbk)

. . . . £45

Short Stories, Doreal (Sedalia, CO), 1948 (pbk) . .£200

The Fox Woman & Other Stories, Avon (New York), 1949

(pbk) £20

ditto, Eshbach (Philadelphia, PA), 1949 (300 copies of Avon

sheets bound in black cloth with white d/w) . £200/£100

ditto, Eshbach (Philadelphia, PA), 1949 (bound in light blue

cloth with white d/w) . . . . . £250/£150

Seven Footprints to Satan/Burn Witch Burn!, Liveright

(New York), 1952 . . . . . . £25/£10

Dwellers in the Mirage/The Face in the Abyss, Liveright

(New York), 1953 . . . . . . £25/£10

The Challenge from Beyond, Pennsylvania Dutch Cheese

Press (FAPA) [Washington, DC], 1954, 1954 (with H.P.

Lovecraft, Robert E. Howard, Frank Belknap Long and

C.L. Moore) £75

Reflections in the Moon Pool, Oswald Train (Philadelphia,

PA), 1985 . . . . £15/£5

JAMES MICHENER

(b.1907 d.1997)

James Albert Michener was an American author whose
novels are sweeping family sagas following the lives of
many generations in a particular geographic location. He is
known for meticulous research into the places and histories
which form the background to his work. *Tales of the South
Pacific* won the Pulitzer Prize in 1947 and was adapted into
the popular musical *South Pacific*.

South Pacific and Related Titles

Tales of the South Pacific, Macmillan (New York), 1947 .

. . . . £1,500/£145

ditto, Editions For The Armed Services (New York), 1947

(wraps) £45

ditto, Macmillan (New York), 1950 (1,500 signed copies for
the American Booksellers Association; unprinted glassine
d/w) . . . . £250/£200

ditto, Collins (London), 1951 . . . . .£250/£45

South Pacific: A Musical Play, Random House (New York)
1949 (adaptation by Rodgers and Hammerstein; first
printing includes Joshua Logan on copyright page) . .

. . . .£150/£20

The Tale of Rodgers and Hammerstein's South Pacific,
Lehmann Books (New York), 1958 (pictorial boards; no
d/w) £45

Other Collections

Return to Paradise, Random House (New York), 1951 (no
small BOMC dot bottom right of back cover, and no
reference to BOMC on d/w) . . . . .£150/£20

ditto, Random House (New York), 1951 ('Presentation
Edition' stamped in green on front cover; acetate d/w) .

. . . . £125/£100

ditto, Secker & Warburg (London), 1951 . . .£65/£10

Rascals in Paradise, Random House (New York), 1957
(written with A. Grove Day) . . . . £75/£15

ditto, Secker & Warburg (London), 1957 . . .£65/£10

Selected Writings, Modern Library (New York), 1957 . .

. . . . £35/£5

The Watermen: Selections From Chesapeake, Random
House (New York), 1979 . . . . . £25/£5

*Creatures of the Kingdom, Stories About Animals and
Nature*, Random House (New York), 1993 . £10/£5

ditto, Secker & Warburg (London), 1993 . . £10/£5

South Pacific as told by James A. Michener, Gulliver
Books/Harcourt Brace Jovanovich (New York), 1992 .

. . . . £10/£5

ditto, Gulliver Books/Harcourt Brace Jovanovich (New
York), 1992 (250 numbered copies signed by Michener and
illustrator Michael Hague; slipcase; no d/w) . £150/£125

Novels

The Fires of Spring, Random House (New York), 1949 .

. . . .£500/£65

ditto, Random House (New York), 1949 ('Presentation
Edition' stamped in green on front cover; acetate d/w)

. . . . £250/£200

ditto, Corgi Books (London), 1960 (pbk) £45

ditto, Secker & Warburg (London), 1972 . . . £65/£10

The Voice of Asia, Random House (New York), 1951 . .

. . . . £125/£10

ditto, as *Voices of Asia*, Secker & Warburg (London), 1952

. . . . £65/£10

The Bridges at Toko-Ri, Random House (New York), 1953
(blue endpapers) . . . .£150/£50

ditto, Random House (New York), 1953 (white endpapers) .

. . . .£100/£10

ditto, Secker & Warburg (London), 1953 . . . £65/£10

Sayonara, Random House (New York), 1954 (d/w with
blurb by Pearl S. Buck) . . . . .£100/£15

ditto, Secker & Warburg (London), 1954 . . . £65/£10

Hawaii, Random House (New York), 1959 (top edges
stained pale blue, and without the small BOMC square at
the bottom right of the back cover; d/w priced $6.95).

. . . .£100/£20

ditto, Random House (New York), 1959 (400 signed,
numbered copies; acetate d/w and slipcase) . £350/£300

ditto, Secker & Warburg (London), 1960 . . . £65/£10

A Report of the County Chairman, Random House (New York), 1961 . . . . £25/£5

ditto, Secker & Warburg (London), 1961 . . . £25/£5

Caravans, Random House (New York), 1963 . . £50/£10

ditto, Random House (New York), 1963 (signed by Michener on a tipped in leaf; a card laid in states 'A first edition autographed by the author especially for the members of the First Edition Circle' . . . . . £100/£50

ditto, Companion Book Club (London), 1963 . . £30/£5

ditto, Secker & Warburg (London), 1964 . . . £35/£5

The Source, Random House (New York), 1965 (500 signed, numbered copies; acetate d/w and slipcase) . £350/£300

ditto, Random House (New York), 1965 (300 signed, numbered copies prepared for the Israeli Museum, Jerusalem) . . . . £100/£75

ditto, Random House (New York), 1965 (trade issue with d/w priced $7.95 and 'First Printing' on copyright page without series of numbers; no BOMC indentation on the back cover) . . . . . . £65/£10

ditto, Secker & Warburg (London), 1965 . . . £40/£5

The Quality of Life, Girard Bank (no place), 1970 (with colour paintings by James B. Wyeth; no d/w; slipcase) . . . . £30/£20

ditto, Lippincott (Philadelphia/New York), 1970 . £15/£5

ditto, Secker & Warburg (London), 1971 . . . £15/£5

The Drifters, Random House (New York), 1971 . £25/£5

ditto, Random House (New York), 1971 (500 signed, numbered copies; slipcase; no d/w) . . . £225/£175

ditto, Secker & Warburg (London), 1971 . . . £25/£5

Centennial, Random House (New York), 1974 . £25/£5

ditto, Random House (New York), 1974 (500 signed, numbered copies; slipcase) . . . . £200/£150

ditto, Secker & Warburg (London), 1974 . . . £20/£5

About 'Centennial', Some Notes on the Novel, Random House (New York), 1974 . . . . . . £50/£15

James A Michener: The Source, The Bridges at Toko-Ri, Caravans, Sayonara, Secker & Warburg/Octopus (London), 1976 . . . . £20/£5

Chesapeake, Random House (New York), 1978 . £20/£5

ditto, Random House (New York), 1978 (trade issue signed by the author on a tipped in leaf) . . . . £100/£75

ditto, Random House (New York), 1978 (deluxe edition; slipcase; no d/w) . . . . £45/£30

ditto, Random House (New York), 1978 (presentation edition; slipcase; no d/w) . . . . . £45/£30

ditto, Random House (New York), 1978 (500 signed, numbered copies; slipcase; no d/w) . . . £250/£200

ditto, Secker & Warburg (London), 1978 . . . £25/£5

The Covenant, Random House (New York), 1980 . £25/£10

ditto, Random House (New York), 1980 (trade issue signed by the author on a tipped in leaf) . . . . £100/£75

ditto, Random House (New York), 1980 (500 signed, numbered copies; slipcase, no d/w) . . . £250/£200

ditto, The Franklin Library (Franklin Centre, PA), 1980 £40

ditto, Secker & Warburg (London), 1980 . . . £20/£5

Space, Random House (New York), 1982 . . £15/£5

ditto, Random House (New York), 1982 (leather-bound issue signed by author on a tipped-in leaf) . . £100/£75

ditto, Random House (New York), 1982 (500 signed, numbered copies; slipcase) . . . . £150/£125

ditto, Secker & Warburg (London), 1982 . . . £15/£5

Poland, Random House (New York), 1983 . . £15/£5

ditto, Random House (New York), 1983 (trade issue signed by the author on a tipped in leaf) . . . . £50/£40

ditto, Random House (New York), 1983 (500 signed, numbered copies; slipcase) . . . . £125/£100

ditto, Secker & Warburg (London), 1983 . . . £15/£5

Texas, Random House (New York), 1985 . . £20/£5

ditto, Random House (New York), 1985 (trade issue signed by the author on a tipped in leaf) . . . . £50/£40

ditto, Random House (New York), 1985 (1,000 signed, numbered copies; slipcase) . . . . £125/£100

ditto, Secker & Warburg (London), 1985 . . . £15/£5

ditto, Univ of Texas Press (Austin, TX), 1986 (2 vols; slipcase; no d/ws) . . . . £50/£30

ditto, Univ of Texas Press (Austin, TX), 1986 (400 copies signed by Michener and illustrator Charles Shaw; 2 vols in polished quarter buffalo leather in cloth slipcase; with Shaw's *Impressions of Texas*, 14 colour paintings bound and signed by Shaw on title page) . . . £1,000/£750

Legacy, Random House (New York), 1987 . . £10/£5

ditto, Random House (New York), 1987 (500 signed, numbered copies; slipcase; no d/w) . . . £100/£75

ditto, Secker & Warburg (London), 1987 . . . £15/£5

Alaska, Random House (New York), 1988 . . £10/£5

ditto, Random House (New York), 1988 (1,000 signed, numbered copies; slipcase; no d/w) . . . £100/£75

ditto, Secker & Warburg (London), 1988 . . . £10/£5

Journey, McClelland & Stewart (Toronto), 1988 . £15/£5

ditto, Random House (New York), 1989 . . . £10/£5

ditto, Secker & Warburg (London), 1989 . . . £10/£5

Caribbean, Random House (New York), 1989 . £15/£5

ditto, Random House (New York), 1989 (1,000 signed, numbered copies; slipcase; no d/w) . . . £100/£75

ditto, Secker & Warburg (London), 1989 . . . £10/£5

The Eagle and the Raven, State House Press (Austin, TX), 1990 (first issue without accent on 'Yucatan' on endpaper) . . . . £20/£10

ditto, State House Press (Austin, TX), 1990 (second issue with accent on 'Yucatán' on endpaper) . . . £15/£5

ditto, State House Press (Austin, TX), 1990 (350 numbered copies signed by Michener and illustrator Charles Shaw; slipcase). . . . . £100/£75

ditto, Secker & Warburg (London), 1991 . . . £10/£5

Mexico, Random House (New York), 1992 . . £10/£5

ditto, Random House (New York), 1992 (400 signed, numbered copies; slipcase) . . . . £125/£100

Recessional, Franklin Library (Franklin Center, PA), 1994 (signed, limited edition; full leather) £45

ditto, Random House (New York), 1994 . . . £10/£5

ditto, Random House (New York), 1994 (500 signed, numbered copies; slipcase; no d/w). . . . £85/£65

ditto, Secker & Warburg (London), 1996 . . . £10/£5

Miracle in Seville, Random House (New York), 1995 £10/£5

ditto, Random House (New York), 1995 (500 signed, numbered copies; slipcase; no d/w). . . . £75/£50

ditto, John Fulton Gallery (Seville, Spain), 1995 (26 slettered copies signed by author and illustrator John Fulton; slipcase; includes a page printed with the subscribers' names and two signed, numbered etchings not in the Random House edition; a signed, numbered lithographic portrait of Michener; overlays showing the development of the illustrations; commentary by Michener and Fulton; photographs of Michener and Fulton; a numbered silver matador's sword book marker designed by Fulton) . £500/£400

ditto, John Fulton Gallery (Seville, Spain), 1995 (100 signed, numbered copies as above but without subscribers) . . . . £300/£250

Matecumbe, Univ Press of Florida (Gainsville, FL), 2007
(pbk) £5

Non-Fiction
The Future of the Social Studies, National Council for the
Social Studies (Cambridge, MA), 1939 (wraps; edited and
compiled by Michener) £500
The Unit in the Social Studies, Graduate School of
Education, Harvard Univ (Cambridge, MA), 1940 (wraps;
written with Harold Long). £500
The Floating World, Random House (New York), 1954 .
. . . . £125/£30
ditto, Secker & Warburg (London), 1954 . . £75/£15
'Islam; The Misunderstood Religion', Muslim Sunrise
(Washington, DC), 1955 (stapled wraps) . . .£175
The Bridge At Andau, Random House (New York), 1957 .
. . . . £65/£10
ditto, Random House (New York), 1957 ('Special Deluxe
Edition' with no price on d/w front flap) . . £25/£5
ditto, Secker & Warburg (London), 1957 . . £45/£10
The Hokisai Sketchbooks, Charles E. Tuttle (Rutland,
VT/Tokyo), 1958 (in d/w and decorative corrugated
cardboard slipcase) . . . . . .£200/£45
Japanese Prints From the Early Masters To The Modern,
Tuttle (Rutland, VT/Tokyo), 1959 (55 colour plates tipped
in, while others are integral; in d/w and decorative
corrugated cardboard slipcase). . . . .£200/£40
ditto, Tuttle (Rutland, VT/Tokyo), 1959 (19 signed,
numbered copies) £750
ditto, Tuttle (Rutland, VT), 1972 (51 colour plates tipped in,
while others are integral; in d/w box with illustrated label
printed on box) . . . .£65/£20
The Modern Japanese Print, An Appreciation, Charles E.
Tuttle (Rutland, VT/Tokyo), 1967 (510 signed, numbered
copies; contains 10 original colour Japanese prints signed
by the artist; in wooden slipcase) . . £2,500/£2,000
ditto, Charles E. Tuttle (Rutland, VT/Tokyo), 1968 (first
popular edition; plates integral) . . . £125/£40
The Matador Who Conquered Mexico, College of
Technology (Oxford), [1965-1966] (wraps; approx 50
copies) £250
Adickes, A Portfolio with Critique, DuBose Gallery
(Houston, TX), 1968 (written with Alessandra) .£150/£40
Iberia, Spanish Travels and Reflections, Random House
(New York), 1968 . . . . . . £30/£5
ditto, Random House (New York), 1968 (500 signed,
numbered copies; d/w and slipcase) . . £250/£200
ditto, Secker & Warburg (London), 1968 . . £20/£5
*The Presidential Lottery, The Reckless Gamble in Our
Electoral System*, Random House (New York), 1969 £30/£5
ditto, Secker & Warburg (London), 1969 . . . £20/£5
*America vs America, The Revolution in Middle-Class
Values*, New American Library (New York), 1969 (pbk) £20
Facing East, Maecenas Press/Random House (New York),
1970 (16 lettered copies signed by Michener and Levine;
two parts; contains four original lithographs and one
original woodcut by Levine in leather wallet; clam shell
slipcase) . . . . . . £1,250/£1,000
ditto, Maecenas Press/Random House (New York), 1970
(2,500 numbered copies signed by Michener and Levine
issued as above) . . . . . . £500/£450
Kent State, What Happened and Why, Random
House/Reader's Digest (New York), 1971 (no BOMC
indentation on the back cover) . . . . £20/£5

ditto, Secker & Warburg (London), 1971 . . . £20/£5
*The Sixties, A Collection of Paintings from the James A.
Michener Collection*, Springfield Art Museum (Springfield, MO), 1971 (pbk) £20
A Michener Miscellany, 1950-1970, Random House/
Reader's Digest (New York), 1973 . . . £25/£5
ditto, Corgi Books (London), 1975 (pbk) . . . £10
Sports in America, Random House (New York), 1976 £25/£10
ditto, Random House (New York), 1976 (500 signed copies;
no d/w or slipcase) £150
ditto, as *Michener on Sport*, Secker & Warburg (London),
1976 . . . . £25/£10
*Nothing Is Long Ago, A Documentary History of Colorado
1776/1976*, Denver Public Library (Denver, CO), 1976
(100 numbered copies signed by Michener, Thomas
Hornsby Ferril, the Governor of Colorado and the Mayor of
Denver) . . . . £200/£150
*The James A. Michener Collection: Twentieth Century
American Painting*, Univ of Texas (Austin, TX), 1977 (no
d/w) £45
ditto, Univ of Texas (Austin, TX), 1977 (pbk). . £10
How To Use A Library, International Paper Co. (Elmsford,
NY), 1980 (2pps; advert for series 'The Power of the
Printed Word') £20
James A. Michener's USA, Crown Publishers (New York),
1981 . . . . £25/£5
Collectors, Forgers—And A Writer, A Memoir, Targ
Editions/Random House (New York), 1983 (250 signed
copies; clipcase; no d/w) . . . . £225/£175
Testimony, White Knight Press (Honolulu), 1983 (200
numbered copies; copies signed by Michener; wraps) £250
ditto, White Knight Press (Honolulu), 1983 (200 numbered
copies; copies signed by publisher; wraps) . . .£150
Six Days in Havana, Univ of Texas Press (Austin, TX),
1989 (written with John King) . . . . £20/£5
ditto, Souvenir Press (London), 1990 . . . £15/£5
From the Boundless Deep, Four Seasons Resort (Wailea,
Maui, Hawaii), [1989] (wraps; in slipcase) . £45/£10
ditto, Four Seasons Resort (Wailea, Maui, Hawaii), [1989]
(leather-bound) £75
Pilgrimage, A Memoir of Poland & Rome, Rodale Press
(Emmaus, PA), 1990 . . . . . . £15/£5
James A Michener on the Social Studies, National Council
for the Social Studies (Washington, DC), 1991 (pbk). £15
The Novel, Random House (New York), 1991 . £10/£5
ditto, Secker & Warburg (London), 1991 . . . £10/£5
The World Is My Home, A Memoir, Random House (New
York), 1992 . . . . £10/£5
ditto, Random House (New York), 1992 (maroon cloth
binding with 'JAM: Eighty-fifth birthday edition' in gilt on
front cover; dedication leaf tipped in; no d/w) . . £50
ditto, Random House (New York), 1992 (500 signed,
numbered copies; slipcase) . . . . .£100/£75
ditto, Secker & Warburg (London), 1992 . . . £10/£5
*James A. Michener's Writer's Notebook, Explorations in
Writing and Publishing*, Random House (New York),
1992 (pbk) £10
ditto, Literary Guild (New York), 1992 . . . £10/£5
Lost Mexico, State House Press (Austin, TX), 1992 £10/£5
ditto, State House Press (Austin, TX), 1992 (350 signed,
numbered copies; slipcase) . . . . .£100/£75
*Literary Reflections, Michener on Michener, Hemingway,
Capote, and Others*, State House Press (Austin, TX), 1993
. . . . £10/£5

ditto, State House Press (Austin, TX), 1993 (200 signed, numbered copies in leather and cloth; slipcase)   £125/£100

William Penn, The Pennsbury Society (no place), 1994 (wraps) £5

Ventures in Editing, James Cahill Publishing (Huntington Beach, CA), 1995 (274 [148] signed, numbered copies; slipcase; no d/w) .   .   .   .   .   .   £75/£50

ditto, James Cahill Publishing (Huntington Beach, CA), 1995 (50 copies; signed uncorrected proof; maroon cloth with the colophon of the lettered issue and marked 'proof copy'; no d/w; slipcase) .   .   .   .   £125/£100

ditto, James Cahill Publishing (Huntington Beach, CA), 1995 (26 signed, lettered copies; slipcase; no d/w)   £200/£150

James A, Michener, The Beginning Teacher and His Textbooks, by G.L. Dybald and Joy V. Bliss, The Book Stops Here (Albuquerque, NM), 1995 (800 copies, with notes and reminiscences by Michener) .   .   £25/£5

A Letter to My Neighbours, Barnes & Nobel (Austin, TX), 1996 (poster) £30

James A. Michener, A Bibliography, by David Groseclose, State House Press, Austin (TX), 1996 (no d/w) .   £25

ditto, State House Press, Austin (TX), 1996 (100 numbered copies signed by the author and Michener; Introduction by Michener; slipcase; no d/w) .   .   .   £150/£125

This Noble Land, Random House (New York), 1996 £10/£5

A Century of Sonnets, State House Press (Austin, TX), 1997 .   .   .   .   £10/£5

ditto, State House Press (Austin, TX), 1997 (250 signed, numbered copies; slipcase) .   .   .   £125/£100

Talking With Michener, Univ Press of Mississippi, Jackson, MS) 1999 .   .   .   .   £10/£5

ARTHUR MILLER

(b.1915 d.2005)

A prominent American playwright, essayist and author, Miller is perhaps best known for his plays *The Death of a Salesman*, about unsuccessful shoe salesman Willy Loman, and *The Crucible*, which relates the Salem witch trials to the era of McCarthyism. He was married, briefly, to the Hollywood actress Marilyn Monroe.

Plays

All My Sons: A Play in Two Acts, Reynal & Hitchcock (New York), 1947 .   .   .   .   .   .£250/£40

ditto, Penguin (Harmondsworth, Middlesex), 1961 (pbk) £10

Death of a Salesman: Certain Private Conversations in Two Acts and a Requiem, Viking (New York), 1949 (pictorial orange cloth; first state d/w with photo of Miller on rear flap of d/w) .   .   .   .   £1,000/£45

ditto, Cresset (London), 1949 .   .   .   .   £100/£20

ditto, Limited Editions Club (New York), 1984 (1500 copies signed by Miller & Leonard Baskin, in slipcase) £350/£300

The Crucible: A Play in Four Acts, Viking (New York), 1953 .   .   .   .£300/£30

ditto, Cresset (London), 1956 .   .   .   .£100/£20

A View from the Bridge: Two One-Act Plays, Viking (New York), 1955 .   .   .   .   .   .£30/£10

ditto, Cresset (London), 1957 .   .   .   .£25/£10

A Memory of Two Mondays: A Play in One Act, Dramatists Play Service (New York), 1956 (wraps). .   .   . £10

Collected Plays, Viking (New York), 1957 .   £25/£10

ditto, Cresset (London), 1958 .   .   .   .   .   £25/£10

After the Fall, Viking (New York), 1964 .   .   .   £20/£5

ditto, Viking (New York), 1964 (500 signed copies, glassine d/w and slipcase) .   .   .   .   .   .£125/£65

ditto, Secker & Warburg (London), 1964 .   .   .   £20/£5

Incident at Vichy, Viking (New York), 1965 .   .   £20/£5

ditto, Secker & Warburg (London), 1966 .   .   .   £20/£5

The Price, Viking (New York), 1968. .   .   .   £15/£5

ditto, Secker & Warburg (London), 1968. .   .   £15/£5

ditto, Arion Press (San Francisco, CA), 1999 (300 signed, numbered copies; slipcase) .   .   .   £200/£150

ditto, Arion Press (San Francisco, CA), 1999 (26 signed, lettered copies; slipcase) .   .   .   .   £300/£250

The Portable Arthur Miller, Viking (New York), 1971 (ed. Harold Clurman) .   .   .   .   £25/£10

The Creation of the World and Other Business, Viking (New York), 1973 .   .   .   .   £15/£5

The Archbishop's Ceiling, Dramatists Play Service (New York), 1976 (wraps) £10

ditto, Methuen (London), 1984 .   .   .   .   .   £10/£5

The American Clock, Viking (New York), 1980 .   £15/£5

ditto, Methuen (London), 1983 .   .   .   .   £10/£5

Collected Plays, Franklin Library (Franklin Centre, PA), 1980 (signed limited edition) £75

Collected Plays: Volume II, Viking (New York), 1981.   .   .   .   .   £10/£5

Playing for Time, Bantam (New York), 1981 (pbk)   £5

Elegy for a Lady, Dramatists Play Service (New York), 1984 (wraps) £5

ditto, Methuen (London), 1984 .   .   .   .   £10/£5

Some Kind of Love Story, Dramatists Play Service (New York), 1984 (wraps) £5

Danger: Memory! Two Plays: 'I Can't Remember Anything' and 'Clara', Methuen (London), 1986   £10/£5

ditto, Grove (New York), 1987 .   .   .   .   £10/£5

The Golden Years, Methuen (London), 1989 .   .£10/£5

ditto, Dramatists Play Service (New York), 1990 (wraps) £5

Everybody Wins, Methuen (London), 1990 .   .£10/£5

ditto, Grove Weidenfeld (New York), 1990 (pbk) .   .   £5

The Last Yankee, Dramatists Play Service (New York), 1991 (wraps) £5

ditto, Methuen (London), 1993 (pbk). .   .   .   £5

The Ride Down Mt. Morgan, Viking Penguin (New York), 1992 (pbk) £5

ditto, Stephens (Hastings-on-Hudson, NY), 1991 (200 signed, numbered copies) £45

Broken Glass, Viking Penguin (New York), 1994 (pbk) £5

ditto, Methuen (London), 1994 (pbk). .   .   .   £5

The Last Yankee and **Broken Glass**, Fireside Theatre (New York), 1994 .   .   .   .   £10/£5

Novels

Focus, Reynal & Hitchcock (New York), 1945 .£150/£20

ditto, Gollancz (London), 1949 .   .   .   .£125/£15

The Misfits, Viking (New York), 1961 .   .£150/£25

ditto, Secker & Warburg (London), 1961 .   .£100/£15

Short Stories

I Don't Need You Anymore, Viking (New York), 1967 .   .   .   .   £20/£5

ditto, Secker & Warburg (London), 1967 .   .   .   £20/£5

Homely Girl, A Life, Peter Blum Books (New York), 1992 (100 signed copies of 1,200; 2 vols; slipcase)   £300/£250

ditto, Peter Blum Books (New York), 1992 (1,100 copies of 1,200; 2 vols; slipcase) .   .   .   .   .£100/£75

Homely Girl, A Life, and Other Stories, Viking (New York), 1995 (no d/w) £5
ditto, as *Plain Girl*, Methuen (London), 1995 . . £10/£5

Others
Situation Normal, Reynal & Hitchcock (New York), 1944 .
. . . . £150/£25
An Enemy of the People, Viking (New York), 1951 (adaptation of play by Henrik Ibsen) . . £25/£5
On Social Plays, Viking (New York), 1955 (introduction to *View from the Bridge*; stapled wraps) £75
Jane's Blanket, Crowell-Collier (New York), 1963 (no d/w)
. . . . £75
In Russia, Viking (New York), 1969 (with Inge Morath) .
. . . . £15/£5
ditto, Secker & Warburg (London), 1969 . . . £15/£5
In the Country, Viking (New York), 1977 (with Inge Morath) . . . . . . £15/£5
ditto, Secker & Warburg (London), 1977 . . . £15/£5
The Theater Essays of Arthur Miller, Viking (New York), 1978 (ed. Robert A. Martin) . . . . £10/£5
Chinese Encounters, Farrar, Straus (New York), 1979 (with Inge Morath). . . . . . £10/£5
ditto, Secker & Warburg (London), 1979 . . . £10/£5
Salesman in Beijing, Viking (New York), 1984 . £10/£5
ditto, Methuen (London), 1984 . . . . . .
£10/£5
Timebends: A Life, Franklin Library (Franklin Centre, PA), 1987 (signed limited edition) £20
ditto, Grove (New York), 1987 . . . . . £10/£5
ditto, Methuen (London), 1987 . . . . . £10/£5
Echoes Down the Corridor: Collected Essays 1944-2000, Methuen (London), 2000 (edited by Steven R. Centola) .
. . . . £10/£5
ditto, Viking (New York), 2000 . . . . . £10/£5
On Politics and the Art of Acting, Viking (New York), 2001
. . . . £10/£5

HENRY MILLER
(b.1891 d.1980)

Miller made his name with *The Tropic of Cancer* which describes the promiscuous lifestyle he witnessed while living in the Paris in the 1930s. It led to a series of controversial obscenity trials in the U.S. and was the first of many of his books to be suppressed in both America and England because of their sexual frankness.

Fiction
The Tropic of Cancer, Obelisk Press (Paris), 1934 (first printing, paperback issued in printed green and white wraps) £7,500
ditto, Obelisk Press (Paris), 1934 (second printing, issued in plain wraps with an illustrated d/w). . . £3,500/£750
ditto, Medvsa (New York), 1940 (variant bindings; no d/w).
. . . . £200
ditto, Grove Press (New York), 1961 (100 signed copies, no d/w) £1,750
ditto, Grove Press (New York), 1961. . . . £65/£15
ditto, Calder (London), 1963 . . . . . £45/£10
Black Spring, Obelisk (Paris), 1936 (pbk) . . £1,000
ditto, Grove (New York), 1963 . . . . . £45/£10

ditto, Calder (London), 1965 . . . . . £30/£10
The Tropic of Capricorn, Obelisk Press (Paris), 1939 (60 francs price on spine, errata slip tipped-in; pbk) . . £750
ditto, Grove Press (New York), 1961. . . . £50/£15
ditto, Calder (London), 1964 . . . . . £45/£15
Sexus, Obelisk (Paris), 1949 (2 vols, 3,000 numbered copies, no d/ws). £125
ditto, Grove Press (New York), 1965. . . . £30/£10
ditto, Calder (London), 1969 . . . . . £45/£10
Plexus, Correa (Paris), 1952 (100 numbered copies, in French; tissue d/w) . . . . £1,250/£1,000
ditto, Correa (Paris), 1952 (pbk; in d/w) . . £125/£65
ditto, Olympia (Paris), 1953 (2,000 numbered copies, 2 vols; pbks in d/ws) . . . . . . £125/£65
ditto, Weidenfeld & Nicolson (London), 1963. . £50/£15
ditto, Grove Press (New York), 1965. . . . £25/£10
Nexus, Obelisk (Paris), 1960 (pbk) £50
ditto, Weidenfeld & Nicolson (London), 1964. . £45/£10
ditto, Grove Press (New York), 1965. . . . £25/£10

Plays
Scenario (A Film with Sound), Obelisk (Paris), 1937 (200 signed copies; five gatherings and folded b&w frontispiece by Abraham Rattner loose within printed card wraps). £500
Just Wild About Harry: A Melo Melo in Seven Scenes, New Directions (Norfolk, CT), 1963 . . . . £45/£15
ditto, MacGibbon & Gee (London), 1964. . . £25/£10

Others
What Are You Going to Do About Alf?, Lecram-Servant (Paris), 1935 (stapled wraps) £1,350
ditto, Porter (Berkeley, CA), 1944 (stapled wraps). . £50
ditto, Turret (London), 1971 (100 signed copies of 350) .
. . . . £150/£100
ditto, Turret (London), 1971 (250 unsigned copies of 350) .
. . . . £65/£15
Aller Retour New York, Obelisk (Paris), 1935 (150 signed copies; wraps) £1,500
ditto, privately printed by Ben Abramson (New York), 1945 (500 copies, no d/w) £50
Money and How it Gets that Way, Booster (Paris), 1938 (with author's holograph limitation and copyright note, 495 copies; wraps) £400
ditto, Booster (Paris), 1938 (without author's holograph limitation and copyright note, 495 copies; wraps) . £75
Max and the White Phagocytes, Obelisk (Paris), 1938 (pbk)
. . . . £150
Hamlet, Carrefour (Puerto Rico), 1939 (500 copies; wraps).
. . . . £75
ditto, Carrefour (Puerto Rico), 1939 (25 signed, numbered copies of 500; wraps). £300
The Cosmological Eye, New Directions (Norfolk, CT), 1939 (photo of eye inset on front cover, d/w spine lettered white, priced $2.50) . . . . . . £350/£45
ditto, Editions Poetry (London), 1945 . . £125/£25
The World of Sex, J.H.N. for Friends of Henry Miller (Chicgo), 1940 (250 copies) . . . . £250/£100
ditto, [Abrahamson (New York), between 1946 and 1956?] (no d/w). £75
ditto, Olympia Press (Paris), 1957 (pbk) . . . £45
ditto, as *The World of Sex* and *Max and the White Phagocytes*, Calder (London), 1970 . . . £30/£10
Hamlet, Volume II, Carrefour (Puerto Rico), 1941 (500 copies; wraps) £75

ditto, Carrefour (Puerto Rico), 1941 (25 signed, numbered copies of 500; wraps) £300

The Colossus of Maroussi, Colt (San Francisco, CA), 1941 . . . . £75/£25

ditto, Colt (San Francisco, CA), 1941 (100 signed copies) . . . . £400/£300

ditto, Secker & Warburg (London), 1942 . . . £75/£25

The Wisdom of the Heart, New Directions (Norfolk, CT), 1941 . . . . £200/£30

ditto, Editions Poetry (London), 1947 . . £65/£15

The Angel is My Watermark, Holve-Barrows (Fullerton, CA), 1944 (20 copies, watercolours; wraps with clear celluloid overlay). £4,500

Sunday After the War, New Directions (Norfolk, CT), 1944 . . . . £75/£20

Murder the Murderer, Miller (Big Sur, CA), 1944 (stapled wraps) £50

ditto, Delphic Press (Fordingbridge, Hants), 1946 (wraps; d/w attached) £65

The Plight Of The Creative Artist In The United States Of America, Bern Porter (Houlton, ME), 1944 (950 copies signed by Porter; stapled wraps with plain d/w) . £75/£50

Semblance of a Devoted Past, Bern Porter (Berkeley, CA), 1945 . . . . £125/£75

Henry Miller Miscellanea, Bern Porter (Berkeley, CA), 1945 (500 numbered copies with inscription by Miller or postcard by Miller) . . . . . . £225/£175

Obscenity and the Law of Reflection, Alicat Bookshop (Yonkers, NY), 1945 (750 copies; stapled wraps) . £75

Echolalia, Bern Porter (Berkeley, CA), 1945 (portfolio of 12 prints, 1,000 copies) £75

ditto, Editions Poetry (London), 1945 (portfolio of 12 prints, 1,000 copies) £65

Why Abstract?, New Directions (Norfolk, CT), 1945 . . . . £50/£15

Varda: The Master Builder, Bern Porter (Berkeley, CA), 1945 (wraps). £65

The Amazing and Invariable Beauford Delaney, Alicat Bookshop (Yonkers, NY), 1945 (750 copies; stapled wraps) £65

The Air-Conditioned Nightmare, New Directions (Norfolk, CT), 1945 (tipped-in illustrations; first issue d/w without photo of Miller on rear panel) . . . . £125/£35

ditto, Secker & Warburg (London), 1947 . . £125/£25

Maurizius Forever, Colt Press (San Francisco, CA), 1946 (500 copies, plain brown d/w) . . . £145/£50

ditto, as **Reflections on the Maurizius Case**, Capra Press (Santa Barbara, CA), 1974 (275 signed, numbered copies, no d/w) £65

Patchen: Man of Anger, Padell (New York), 1946 (stapled wraps with d/w) . . . . £65/£35

Into the Night Life, Miller and Schatz (Berkeley, CA), 1947 (800 numbered, signed copies, slipcase). . £600/£400

Remember to Remember, New Directions (Norfolk, CT), 1947 (first state with title-pages divided by frontispiece photograph of author). . . . . . £75/£35

ditto, Grey Walls Press (London), 1952 . . £75/£25

The Smile at the Foot of the Ladder, Duell, Sloan & Pearce (New York), 1948 . . . . £125/£25

ditto, MacGibbon & Kee (London), 1966 . . . £35/£10

The Waters Reglitterized, Kidis (no place), 1950 (1,000 numbered copies; stapled wraps) £30

ditto, Village Press (London), 1973 (pbk). . . . £15

Rimbaud, Mermod (Aigle, France), 1952 (5,000 numbered copies; wraps) £75

ditto, as **The Time of the Assassins: A Study of Rimbaud**, New Directions (Norfolk, CT), 1956 (acetate d/w) . . . . £125/£100

ditto, Spearman (London), 1956 . . . . £125/£30

The Books in My Life, Owen (London), 1952 . £100/£25

ditto, New Directions (Norfolk, CT), 1952 . . £100/£25

Nights of Love and Laughter, Signet/New American Library (New York), 1955 (pbk) £10

A Devil in Paradise, Signet/New American Library (New York), 1956 (pbk) £10

ditto, Signet (London), 1965 (pbk) £10

Quiet Days in Clichy, Olympia (Paris), 1956 (photographs by Brassai; pbk) £500

ditto, Grove (New York), 1965 (pbk). £25

ditto, Calder (London), 1966 . . . . . £30/£10

Big Sur and the Oranges of Hieronymous Bosch, New Directions (Norfolk, CT), 1957 . . . . £85/£20

ditto, Heinemann (London), 1958 . . . £65/£15

The Red Notebook, Williams (Highlands, NC), 1958 (pbk) £15

Reunion in Barcelona, Scorpion Press (Northwood, Middlesex), 1959 (50 signed copies of 500; wraps) . £250

ditto, Scorpion Press (Northwood, Middlesex), 1959 (450 unsigned copies; wraps) £25

The Intimate Henry Miller, Signet (New York), 1959 (pbk) £10

The Henry Miller Reader, New Directions (Norfolk, CT), 1959 (ed. Lawrence Durrell) . . . . £25/£10

ditto, as **The Best of Henry Miller**, Heinemann (London), 1960 . . . . £25/£10

To Paint Is to Love Again, Cambia (Alhambra, CA), 1960 . . . . £35/£10

ditto, Cambia (Alhambra, CA), 1960 (50 signed copies) £250

ditto, Cambia (Alhambra, CA), 1960 (pbk) . . . £10

Journey to an Antique Land, Big Ben Press (Big Sur, CA), 1962 (stapled wraps) £25

ditto, Village Press (London), 1973 (pbk). . . . £15

Hamlet I & II, Carrefour (London), 1962 (wraps) . £45

Stand Still Like Hummingbird, New Directions (Norfolk, CT), 1962 . . . . £30/£10

ditto, Village Press (London), 1974 (pbk). . . . £10

Lawrence Durrell and Henry Miller: A Private Correspondence, Dutton (New York), 1963 . . £25/£10

ditto, Faber (London), 1963 . . . . . £25/£10

Henry Miller on Writing, New Directions (Norfolk, CT), 1964 (pbk) £15

Greece, Viking (New York), 1964 . . . . £25/£10

ditto, Thames and Hudson (London), 1964 . . £25/£10

Henry Miller: Letters to Anais Nin, Putnam (New York), 1965 . . . . £20/£5

ditto, Owen (London), 1965 . . . . . . £20/£5

Order and Chaos Chez Hans Reichel, Loujon Press (New Orleans, LA), 1966 (3 copy Orange Oasis edition, d/w and slipcase). . . . . £1,000/£900

ditto, Loujon Press (New Orleans, LA), 1966 (11 lettered and signed copies of the Black Oasis edition, d/w and slipcase) . . . . £500/£400

ditto, Loujon Press (New Orleans, LA), 1966 (26 lettered and signed copies of the Cork edition, d/w and slipcase) . . . . £400/£300

ditto, Loujon Press (New Orleans, LA), 1966 (99 copy Blue Oasis edition, d/w and slipcase) . . . £300/£200 *ditto*, Loujon Press (New Orleans, LA), 1966 (1,399 copy Cork edition, d/w and slipcase) . . . . £50/£25

Insomnia: Or, the Devil at Large, Loujon Press (Albuquerque, NM), 1971 (385 signed, paper covered wooden box containing 12 colour lithographs; spiral bound book) . . . . £1,250/£750

ditto, Doubleday (New York), 1974 . . . . £25/£10

ditto, Doubleday (New York), 1974 (100 numbered copies in English of 150 with an original signed lithograph by Miller laid in and a signed insert; slipcase) £200/£150

ditto, Editions Stock (New York), 1974 (50 numbered copies in French of 150 with an original signed lithograph by Miller laid in and a signed insert; slipcase) £200/£150

My Life and Times, Playboy (New York), 1971 . £25/£10

ditto, Playboy (New York), 1971 (500 signed, numbered copies; slipcase) . . . . £100/£75

ditto, Pall Mall Press (London), 1972. . . . £25/£10

Reflections on the Death of Mishima, Capra (Santa Barbara, CA), 1972 (200 signed, numbered copies, no d/w) . £100

ditto, Capra (Santa Barbara, CA), 1972 (pbk) . . £15

On Turning Eighty: Journey to an Antique Land: Forward to the 'Angel is My Watermark', Capra (Santa Barbara, CA), 1972 (200 signed, numbered copies, no d/w) . £75

ditto, Capra (Santa Barbara, CA), 1972 (wraps) . £10

ditto, Village Press (London), 1973 (stapled wraps) . £10

First Impressions of Greece, Capra (Santa Barbara, CA), 1973 (250 signed, numbered copies, no d/w) . £65

ditto, Capra (Santa Barbara, CA), 1973 (wraps) . £10

ditto, Village Press (London), 1973 (wraps) . . £10

This is Henry Miller from Brooklyn, Nash (Los Angeles, CA), 1974 (100 signed copies, plexiglass holder) . £250

ditto, Nash (Los Angeles, CA), 1974 (400 unsigned copies, no holder) £30

The Nightmare Notebook, New Directions (Norfolk, CT), 1975 (700 signed, numbered copies) . . £125/£75

Henry Miller's Book of Friends: A Tribute to Friends of Long Ago, Capra (Santa Barbara, CA), 1976 (250 signed, numbered copies) £75

ditto, Capra (Santa Barbara, CA), 1976 (26 signed, numbered copies with original artwork by author) £250

ditto, Capra (Santa Barbara, CA), 1976 . . £15/£5

ditto, W.H. Allen (London), 1978 . . . £15/£5

ditto, as ***The Complete Book of Friends***, Allison & Busby (London), 1988 . . . . . . £15/£5

Gliding Into the Everglades, Lost Pleiade Press (Lake Oswego, OR), 1977 (250 signed, numbered copies, no d/w) £65

ditto, Lost Pleiade Press (Lake Oswego, CA), 1977 (pbk) £10

Mother, China, and the World Beyond, Capra (Santa Barbara, CA), 1977 (250 signed, numbered copies, no d/w) £50

ditto, Capra (Santa Barbara, CA), 1977 (wraps) . £10

Four Visions of America, Capra (Santa Barbara, CA), 1977 (with Jong, Sanchez and Boyle) . . . . £20/£5

ditto, Capra Press (Santa Barbara, CA), 1977 (225 copies signed by all four authors). . . . . £75/£50

ditto, Capra Press (Santa Barbara, CA), 1977 (wraps) . £5

My Bike and Other Friends, Capra (Santa Barbara, CA), 1978 (250 signed, numbered copies) . . £65/£45

ditto, Capra (Santa Barbara, CA), 1978 . . £15/£5

Joey, Capra (Santa Barbara, CA), 1979 (250 signed, numbered copies) . . . . . £50/£30

ditto, Capra (Santa Barbara, CA), 1979 (wraps) . £10

The World of Lawrence: A Passionate Appreciation, Capra (Santa Barbara, CA), 1979 (250 signed, numbered copies) £65

ditto, Capra (Santa Barbara, CA), 1979 (26 signed, lettered copies with photo of Miller) £125

ditto, Capra (Santa Barbara, CA), 1979 . . £15/£5

ditto, John Calder (London), 1980 . . . £15/£5

Notes on Aaron's Rod, Black Sparrow (Santa Barbara, CA), 1980 (250 signed, numbered copies, acetate d/w) . £65

ditto, Black Sparrow (Santa Barbara, CA), 1980 (26 signed, lettered copies) £125

ditto, Black Sparrow (Santa Barbara, CA), 1980 . £15/£5

Reflections, Capra (Santa Barbara, CA), 1981 (pbk) . £10

The Paintings of Henry Miller: Paint as You Like and Die Happy, Capra (Santa Barbara, CA), 1982 (250 numbered copies signed by Lawrence Durrell; slipcase) . £125/£75

ditto, Chronicle Books (San Francisco, CA), 1982 (pbk) £25

Opus Pistorum, Grove (New York), 1983 . £20/£5

ditto, Allen (London), 1984 . . . . . £10/£5

From Your Capricorn Friend, New Directions (Norfolk, CT), 1984 . . . . £15/£5

Dear, Dear Brenda, Morrow (New York), 1986 . £15/£5

Letters from Henry Miller to Hoki Tokuda Miller, Freundlich Books (New York), 1987 . . . £15/£5

ditto, Hale (London), 1990 . . . . . £15/£5

A Literate Passion: Letters of Anaïs Nin and Henry Miller, 1932-1953, Harcourt Brace Jovanovich (New York), 1987 . . . . £10/£5

ditto, Allison & Busby/W.H. Allen (London), 1988 £10/£5

The Durrell-Miller Letters: 1935-80, New Directions (Norfolk, CT), 1988 . . . . . . £20/£5

ditto, Faber (London), 1988 . . . . . . £20/£5

Letters to Emil, New Directions (Norfolk, CT), 1989 £20/£5

ditto, Carcanet (Manchester, UK), 1990 . . . £20/£5

Crazy Cock, Grove Weidenfeld (New York), 1991 £15/£5

ditto, HarperCollins (London), 1992 . . . £15/£5

Moloch: Or This Gentile World, Grove (New York), 1992 . . . . £15/£5

ditto, HarperCollins (London), 1992 . . . £15/£5

The Mezzotints, Jackson (Ann Arbor, MI), 1993 (26 private copies, no d/w) £125

ditto, Jackson (Ann Arbor, MI), 1993 (100 numbered copies) £65

ditto, Jackson (Ann Arbor, MI), 1993 (400 library copies) £10

ditto, Jackson (Ann Arbor, MI), 1993 (100 economy) . £10

ditto, Alyscamps Press (Paris and London), 1993 (50 numbered copies) £65

Writers Three: A Literary Exchange, Jackson (Ann Arbor, MI), 1995 . . . . £15/£5

ditto, Jackson (Ann Arbor, MI), 1995 (100 numbered copies) £35

Henry Miller and James Laughlin: Selected Letters, Norton (New York), 1996 . . . . . . £15/£5

ditto, Constable (London), 1996 . . . . £10/£5

The Colossus of Armenia: G.I. Gurdjieff and Henry Miller with Five Previously Unpublished Miller Letters to Pham Công Thiên, Jackson (Ann Arbor, MI), 1998 (100 numbered copies) £75

Henry Miller and Elmer Gertz: Selected Letters 1965-1975, Jackson (Ann Arbor, MI), 1998 (100 numbered copies) £75

A.A. MILNE
(b.1882 d.1956)

Milne was a freelance journalist in London, then assistant editor of *Punch*, before becoming a full-time writer. He is famous for his plays and children's books, especially *Winnie-the-Pooh*, although he also wrote novels, short stories, poetry and essays. The 'Winnie-the-Pooh' books were originally illustrated by E.H. Shepard who apparently used his own bear, Growler as the model for Pooh.

Children's Titles

Once on a Time: A Fairy Story, Hodder & Stoughton (London), 1917 (illustrated by H.M. Brock) . . . £100
ditto, Putnam (New York), 1922 (illustrated by Charles Robinson) . . . . £125/£35
ditto, Hodder & Stoughton (London), [1925] (illustrated by Charles Robinson) . . . . . . £125/£30
When We Were Very Young, Methuen (London), 1924 (illustrated by E.H. Shepard) . . . £4,000/£1,000
ditto, Methuen (London), 1924 (illustrated by E.H. Shepard, 100 numbered copies, signed by the author and artist) . . . . £6,000/£4,000
ditto, Dutton (New York), 1924 (100 numbered copies signed by the author and artist, of 500) . £2,500/£1,500
ditto, Dutton (New York), 1924 (400 unsigned copies of 500) . . . . £1,250/£650
ditto, Methuen (London), 1974 (300 numbered copies, signed by Christopher Milne) . . . £500/£150
Vespers: A Poem, Methuen, [1924] (illustrated by E.H. Shepard, music by H. Fraser-Simson) . . £250/£65
ditto, Dutton (New York), 1925 . . . . . . £45
Fourteen Songs, Methuen (London), 1924 (illustrated by E.H. Shepard, music by H. Fraser-Simson) . £200/£75
Make-Believe: A Children's Play in a Prologue and Three Acts, Methuen (London), 1925. . . . £100/£25
A Gallery of Children, Stanley Paul, 1925 (illustrated by H. Willebeek le Mair) . . . £500/£100
ditto, Stanley Paul (London), 1925 (500 numbered copies, signed by the author) . . . . . £1,250/£750
ditto, David McKay (Philadelphia, PA), 1925 . £250/£45
The King's Breakfast, Methuen (London), 1925 (illustrated by E.H. Shepard, music by H. Fraser-Simson) . £175/£45
ditto, Methuen (London), 1925 (100 copies signed by Milne, Shepard and Fraser-Simson) £600
ditto, Dutton (New York), 1925 . . . . £75/£35
Winnie-the-Pooh, Methuen (London), 1926 (illustrated by E.H. Shepard; first state d/w with '117th thousand' on advert for *When We Were Very Young* at top of rear flap) . . . . £2,500/£600
ditto, Methuen (London), 1926 (deluxe edition: red, green or blue leather binding, in slipcase) . . £1,500/£1,000
ditto, Methuen (London), 1926 (350 copies, signed by the author and artist, d/w and slipcase) . . £7,500/£3,500
ditto, Methuen (London), 1926 (20 special copies, signed by the author and artist, on Japanese vellum) . . £8,000
ditto, Dutton (New York), 1926 (200 numbered copies, signed by the author and artist). . . £6,500/£3,000
ditto, Dutton (New York), 1926 . . . . £1,000/£300
ditto, Methuen (London), 1973 (illustrated in colour by E.H. Shepard) . . . . £45/£10
ditto, Methuen (London), 1973 (300 copies signed by E.H. Shepard; slipcase) . . . . . £750/£600

ditto, Methuen (London), 1976 (illustrated by E.H. Shepard, 300 numbered copies, signed by Christopher Milne; slipcase). . . . . £500/£300
Teddy Bear and Other Songs From 'When We Were Very Young', Methuen (London), 1926 (illustrated by E.H. Shepard, music by H. Fraser-Simson) . . £200/£45
ditto, Methuen (London), 1926 (100 numbered copies, signed by the author, artist and composer, d/w and slipcase) . . . . £750/£450
ditto, Dutton (New York), 1926 . . . £200/£45
Now We Are Six, Methuen (London), 1927 (illustrated by E.H. Shepard) . . . . . . £750/£125
ditto, Methuen (London), 1927 (deluxe edition: red, blue or green leather binding, in slipcase) . . £1,000/£750
ditto, Methuen (London), 1927 (200 numbered copies, signed by the author and artist). . . £2,250/£1,500
ditto, Methuen (London), 1927 (20 special copies, signed by the author and artist, on Japanese vellum) . . £4,500
ditto, Dutton (New York), 1927 (200 signed copies, acetate d/w) . . . . £2,000/£1,000
ditto, Dutton (New York), 1928 . . . . £450/£75
ditto, Methuen (London), 1976 (300 numbered copies, signed by Christopher Milne) . . . . £400/£175
Songs from 'Now We Are Six', Methuen (London), 1927 (music by H. Fraser-Simson) . . . . . £200/£50
ditto, Methuen (London), 1927 (100 signed copies) . £750
ditto, Dutton (New York), 1927 . . . . . £200/£45
More Very Young Songs, Methuen (London), 1928 . . . . £200/£75
ditto, Methuen (London), 1928 (100 numbered copies, signed by the author, artist and composer, d/w and slipcase) £750
The House at Pooh Corner, Methuen (London), 1928 (illustrated by E.H. Shepard) . . . £750/£250
ditto, Methuen (London), 1928 (350 numbered copies, signed by the author and artist). . . £3,500/£2,500
ditto, Methuen (London), 1928 (20 special copies, signed by the author and artist) £6,000
ditto, Methuen (London), 1928 (deluxe edition: red, green or blue leather binding, in slipcase) . . £600/£400
ditto, Dutton (New York), 1928 (250 numbered copies, signed by the author and artist). . . £2,000/£1,350
ditto, Dutton (New York), 1928 . . . . £450/£75
ditto, Methuen (London), 1974 (illustrated in colour by E.H. Shepard) . . . . £45/£10
The Christopher Robin Calendar 1929, Methuen 'Ephemerides' series (London), [1928] (illustrated by E.H. Shepard) £150
The Christopher Robin Story Book, Methuen (London), 1928 (selections from *When We Were Very Young*, *Now We Are Six*, *Winnie-the-Pooh* and *The House at Pooh Corner*, new preface by the author) . . . . £400/£75
ditto, Methuen (London), 1928 (350 copies signed by Milne & Shepard; unprinted acetate d/w and slipcase) . . . . £1,750/£1,250
ditto, Dutton (New York), 1929 . . . . £350/£65
ditto, Dutton (New York), 1929 (350 copies signed by Milne & Shepard; unprinted acetate d/w and slipcase) . . . . £1,750/£1,250
The Hums of Pooh, Methuen (London), 1929 (illustrated by E.H. Shepard, music by H. Fraser-Simson) . £200/£45
ditto, Methuen (London), 1929 (100 numbered copies, signed by the author and artist and composer, d/w and slipcase). . . . . £1,450/£1,000

ditto, Dutton (New York), 1930 . . . . . £75/£35

Toad of Toad Hall: A Play Taken from Kenneth Grahame's 'The Wind in the Willows', Methuen (London), 1929 . . . .£125/£35

ditto, Methuen (London), 1929 (200 numbered copies, signed by Kenneth Grahame and A. A. Milne) . . .
. . . .£1,250/£1,000

ditto, Scribners (New York), 1929 . . . .£100/£30

Tales of Pooh, Methuen: 'Modern Classics' series (London), [1930] (selections from *Winnie-The-Pooh* and *The House at Pooh Corner*, illustrated by E.H. Shepard) .£200/£65

The Christopher Robin Birthday Book, Methuen (London), 1930 (selections from *When We Were Very Young, Now We Are Six, Winnie-the-Pooh* and *The House at Pooh Corner*, illustrated by E.H. Shepard) . . . .£125/£45

ditto, Dutton (New York), 1931 . . . . .£125/£45

The Christopher Robin Verses, Methuen (London), 1932 (contains *When We Were Very Young* and *Now We Are Six*, illustrated by E.H. Shepard) . . . .£200/£65

ditto, Dutton (New York), 1932 . . . . .£175/£50

Introducing Winnie-the-Pooh, Methuen (London), 1947 .
. . . . £75/£35

ditto, Dutton (New York), 1947 . . . . . £75/£35

The World of Pooh, Methuen (London), 1958 . £75/£35

ditto, Dutton (New York), 1958 . . . . . £75/£35

The World of Christopher Robin, Dutton (New York), 1958.
. . . . £75/£35

ditto, Methuen (London), 1959 . . . . . £75/£35

Prince Rabbit and The Princess Who Could Not Laugh, Ward Lock (London), 1966 (illustrated by Mary Shepard)
. . . . £40/£15

ditto, Dutton (New York), 1966 . . . . . £40/£15

The Pooh Story Book, Dutton (New York), 1965 . £30/£5

ditto, Methuen (London), 1967 . . . . . £30/£5

Adult Novels

Mr Pim, Hodder & Stoughton (London), 1921 . £75/£25

The Red House Mystery, Methuen (London), 1922 .
. . . . £1,250/£65

Chloe Marr, Methuen (London), 1946 . . £45/£10

ditto, Dutton (New York), 1946 . . . . . £45/£10

Adult Short Stories

The Secret and Other Stories, Methuen/Fountain Press (New York), 1929 (742 signed copies, no d/w) . £275

Birthday Party and Other Stories, Dutton (New York), 1948
. . . . £25/£10

ditto, Methuen (London), 1949 . . . . £25/£10

A Table Near the Band, Methuen (London), 1950. £35/£15

ditto, Dutton (New York), 1950 . . . . . £35/£15

Plays

First Plays, Chatto & Windus (London), 1919 (contains 'Wurzel-Flummery', 'The Lucky One', 'The Boy Comes Home', 'Belinda' and 'The Red Feathers') . . £45/£15

Second Plays, Chatto & Windus (London), 1921 (contains 'Make-Believe', 'Mr Pim Passes By', 'The Camberley Triangle', 'The Romantic Age' and 'The Stepmother') .
. . . . £25/£10

Three Plays, Putnam (New York), 1922 (contains 'The Dover Road', 'The Truth about Blayds' and 'The Great Broxopp') . . . . £25/£10

ditto, Chatto & Windus (London), 1923 . . £25/£10

Success, Chatto & Windus (London), 1923 . £25/£10

ditto, Putnam (New York), 1926. . . . . £25/£10

The Man in the Bowler Hat, French (London/New York), 1923 (pbk) £15

Four Plays, Chatto & Windus (London), 1926 (contains 'To Have the Honour, Meet the Prince', 'Ariadne', 'Portrait of a Gentleman in Slippers' and 'Success') . . £25/£10

More Plays, Chatto & Windus (London), 1935 (contains 'The Ivory Doors', 'The Fourth Wall' and 'Other People's Lives') . . . . £20/£5

Four Plays, Penguin (Harmondsworth, Middlesex), 1939 (contains 'To Have the Honour', 'Belinda', 'The Dover Road' and 'Mr Pim Passes By'; pbk) £5

The Ugly Duckling, French (London), 1941 (pbk). . £10

Before the Flood, French (London/New York), 1951 (pbk).
. . . . £5

Poetry

For the Luncheon Interval: Cricket and Other Verses, Methuen (London), 1925 (wraps) £25

Behind the Lines, Methuen (London), 1940 . £30/£10

ditto, Dutton (New York), 1940 . . . . . £30/£10

The Norman Church, Methuen (London), 1948 . £30/£10

Others

Lovers in London, Alston Rivers (London), 1905 . .£250

The Day's Play, Methuen (London), 1910 . . . £35

ditto, Dutton (New York), [1910] £35

The Holiday Round, Methuen (London), 1912 . . £30

Once a Week, Methuen (London), 1914 . . . £25

Happy Days, George H. Doran (New York), 1915 . . £20

Not That It Matters, Methuen (London), 1919 . . £20

ditto, Dutton (New York), 1920 . . . . £35/£15

If I May, Methuen (London), 1920 . . . . £35/£15

ditto, Dutton (New York), 1921 . . . . £35/£15

The Sunny Side, Methuen (London), 1921 . £35/£15

ditto, Dutton (New York), 1922 . . . . £35/£15

The Ascent of Man, Ernest Benn (London), 1928 . £35/£15

By Way of Introduction, Methuen (London), 1929 £30/£15

ditto, Dutton (New York), 1929 . . . . £30/£15

ditto, Dutton (New York), 1929 (166 signed, large paper copies) £250

Those Were the Days, Methuen (London), 1929 . £30/£10

Two People, Methuen (London), 1931 . . . £30/£10

ditto, Dutton (New York), 1931 . . . . £30/£10

Four Days Wonder, Methuen (London), 1933 . £30/£10

Peace with Honour, Methuen (London), 1934 . £25/£10

ditto, Dutton (New York), 1934 . . . . £25/£10

Miss Elizabeth Bennett, Chatto & Windus (London), 1936 .
. . . . £30/£10

It's Too Late Now, Methuen (London), 1939 . £30/£10

War With Honour, Macmillan (London), 1940 . £25/£10

War Aims Unlimited, Methuen (London), 1941 (wraps) £15

The Pocket Milne, Dutton (New York), 1941 . £25/£10

ditto, Methuen (London), 1942 . . . . £20/£5

Year In, Year Out, Methuen (London), 1952 . £25/£10

ditto, Dutton (New York), 1952 . . . . £25/£10

DAVID MITCHELL
(b. 1969)

Mitchell is an English author who has written five novels, two of which were shortlisted for the Booker Prize. His first novel, *Ghostwritten*, won the *Mail on Sunday*/John Llewellyn Rhys Prize and his second, *Number9dream* was shortlisted for the James Tait Black Memorial Prize. He was chosen as one of Granta's 20 Best Young British Novelists 2003.

Novels

Ghostwritten, Sceptre (London), 1999 (pbk)   .   .   . £45
ditto, Random House (New York), 2000   .   .   . £15/£5
Number9dream, Sceptre (London), 2001 (pbk)   .   . £30
ditto, Random House (New York), 2002   .   .   . £15/£5
Cloud Atlas, Sceptre (London), 2004 (with publisher's green
   wrap-around band)   .   .   .   . £65/£5
ditto, Random House (New York), 2004 (pbk)   .   . £10
Black Swan Green, Sceptre (London), 2006   .   . £10/£5
ditto, Sceptre (London), 2006 (1,000 signed copies issued by
   Waterstones in slipcase; no dw)   .   .   . £25/£10
ditto, Random House (New York), 2006   .   .   . £10/£5
The Thousand Autumns of Jacob de Zoet, Sceptre
   (London), 2009 (no d/w) £10
ditto, Sceptre (London), 2009 (500 signed, numbered copies
   in slipcase)   .   .   .   . £75/£45

GLADYS MITCHELL
(b.1901 d.1983)

From the 'Golden Age' of Detective Fiction, Mitchell's unconventional sleuth, Beatrice Adela Lestrange Bradley, was already elderly when she made her first appearance in 1929. Her last case was recorded in 1984, by which time she may have been 125 years old. Mitchell was an early member of the Detection Club, along with G.K. Chesterton, Agatha Christie and Dorothy L. Sayers.

Novels

Speedy Death, Gollancz (London), 1929   .   . £1,500/£200
ditto, Dial Press (New York), 1929   .   .   . £750/£125
The Mystery of a Butcher's Shop, Gollancz (London), 1929
   .   .   .   . £1,250/£150
ditto, Dial Press (New York), 1930   .   .   . £600/£100
The Longer Bodies, Gollancz (London), 1930. £1,250/£150
The Saltmarsh Murders, Gollancz (London), 1932   .   .
   .   .   .   . £1,250/£150
ditto, Macrae-Smith (Philadelphia, PA), 1933 .   . £450/£75
Death at the Opera, Grayson (London), 1934 . £1,250/£150
ditto, as *Death in the Wet*, Macrae-Smith (Philadelphia, PA),
   1934   .   .   .   . £450/£75
The Devil at Saxon Wall, Grayson (London), 1935   .   .
   .   .   .   . £1,250/£150
Dead Men's Morris, Joseph (London), 1936 . £1,000/£125
Come Away Death, Joseph (London), 1937 . £1,000/£125
St Peter's Finger, Joseph (London), 1938   . £1,000/£125
ditto, St Martin's Press (New York), 1987   .   . £15/£5
Printer's Error, Joseph (London), 1939   . £1,000/£125
Brazen Tongue, Joseph (London), 1940   .   . £750/£125
Hangman's Curfew, Joseph (London), 1941 .   . £750/£125

When Last I Died, Joseph (London), 1941   .   . £500/£100
ditto, Knopf (New York), 1942   .   .   .   .   . £125/£15
Laurels are Poison, Joseph (London), 1942   .   . £350/£45
The Worsted Viper, Joseph (London), 1943   .   . £325/£45
Sunset Over Soho, Joseph (London), 1943   .   . £250/£35
My Father Sleeps, Joseph (London), 1944   .   . £200/£35
The Rising of the Moon, Joseph (London), 1945 . £175/£20
ditto, St Martin's Press (New York), 1985   .   . £15/£5
Here Comes a Chopper, Joseph (London), 1946 . £150/£20
Death and the Maiden, Joseph (London), 1947 . £150/£20
The Dancing Druids, Joseph (London), 1948 .   . £125/£15
ditto, St Martin's Press (New York), 1986   .   . £10/£5
Tom Brown's Body, Joseph (London), 1949   .   . £125/£15
Groaning Spinney, Joseph (London), 1950   .   . £100/£10
The Devil's Elbow, Joseph (London), 1951   .   . £100/£10
The Echoing Strangers, Joseph (London), 1952 .   £75/£10
Merlin's Furlong, Joseph (London), 1953   .   .   £75/£10
Faintly Speaking, Joseph (London), 1954   .   .   £75/£10
ditto, St Martin's Press (New York), 1986   .   . £10/£5
Watson's Choice, Joseph (London), 1955   .   .   £50/£10
ditto, McKay-Washburn (New York), 1976   .   . £10/£5
Twelve Horses and The Hangman's Noose, Joseph
   (London), 1956   .   .   .   . £50/£10
ditto, British Book Centre (New York), 1958 .   . £15/£5
ditto, as *Hangman's Noose*, Severn House (London), 1983.
   .   .   .   . £10/£5
The Twenty-Third Man, Joseph (London), 1957 .   £50/£10
Spotted Hemlock, Joseph (London), 1958   .   .   £50/£10
ditto, St Martin's Press (New York), 1985   .   . £10/£5
The Man Who Grew Tomatoes, Joseph (London), 1959   .
   .   .   .   . £50/£10
ditto, British Book Centre (New York), 1959 .   . £15/£5
Say it with Flowers, Joseph (London), 1960   .   . £40/£5
ditto, London House (New York), 1960   .   .   . £20/£5
The Nodding Canaries, Joseph (London), 1961 .   . £40/£5
My Bones Will Keep, Joseph (London), 1962 .   .   £35/£5
ditto, British Book Centre (New York), 1962 .   . £15/£5
Adders on the Heath, Joseph (London), 1963 .   .   £35/£5
ditto, British Book Centre (New York), 1963 .   . £15/£5
Death of a Delft Blue, Joseph (London), 1964 .   . £35/£5
ditto, British Book Centre (New York), 1965 .   . £15/£5
ditto, as *Death in Amsterdam*, Severn House (London), 1990
   .   .   .   . £10/£5
Pageant of a Murder, Joseph (London), 1965.   .   £35/£5
ditto, British Book Centre (New York), 1965 .   . £15/£5
The Croaking Raven, Joseph (London), 1966.   .   £35/£5
Skeleton Island, Joseph (London), 1967   .   .   . £35/£5
Three Quick and Five Dead, Joseph (London), 1968 £20/£5
Dance to Your Daddy, Joseph (London), 1969   .   £30/£5
Gory Dew, Joseph (London), 1970   .   .   .   . £30/£5
Lament for Letto, Joseph (London), 1971   .   .   £25/£5
A Nearse on May-Day, Joseph (London), 1972 .   . £25/£5
The Murder of Busy Lizzie, Joseph (London), 1973   £20/£5
A Javelin for Jonah, Joseph (London), 1974 .   .   £20/£5
Winking at the Brim, Joseph (London), 1975 .   .   £20/£5
ditto, McKay-Washburn (New York), 1977   .   . £10/£5
Convent on Styx, Joseph (London), 1975.   .   .   £20/£5
Late, Late in the Evening, Joseph (London), 1976.   £20/£5
Noonday and Night, Joseph (London), 1977 .   .   £20/£5
Fault in the Structure, Joseph (London), 1977   .   £20/£5
Wraiths and Changelings, Joseph (London), 1978   £20/£5
Mingled with Venom, Joseph (London), 1978.   .   £20/£5
Nest of Vipers, Joseph (London), 1979   .   .   . £20/£5
The Mudflats of the Dead, Joseph (London), 1979   £20/£5

Uncoffin'd Clay, Joseph (London), 1980 . . . £20/£5
ditto, St Martin's Press (New York), 1981 . . £10/£5
The Whispering Knights, Joseph (London), 1980 . £20/£5
The Death-Cap Dancers, Joseph (London), 1981 . £20/£5
ditto, St Martin's Press (New York), 1981 . . £10/£5
Lovers, Make Moan, Joseph (London), 1982 . . £15/£5
Here Lies Gloria Mundy, Joseph (London), 1982 . £15/£5
ditto, St Martin's Press (New York), 1983 . . £10/£5
Death of a Burrowing Mole, Joseph (London), 1982 £15/£5
The Greenstone Griffins, Joseph (London), 1983 . £15/£5
Cold, Lone and Still, Joseph (London), 1983 . . £10/£5
No Winding Sheet, Joseph (London), 1984 . . £10/£5
The Crozier Pharoahs, Joseph (London), 1984 . £10/£5

Novels Written as 'Stephen Hockaby'
Marsh Hay, Grayson (London), 1933 . . . £400/£75
Seven Stars and Orion, Grayson (London), 1934 . £300/£45
Gabriel's Hold, Grayson (London), 1935 . . £300/£45
Shallow Brown, Joseph (London), 1936 . . £250/£40
Grand Master, Joseph (London), 1939 . . £150/£30

Novels Written as 'Malcolm Torrie'
Heavy as Lead, Joseph (London), 1966 . . £35/£10
Late and Cold, Joseph (London), 1967 . . £35/£10
Your Secret Friend, Joseph (London), 1968 . £35/£10
Churchyard Salad, Joseph (London), 1969 . £35/£10
Shades of Darkness, Joseph (London), 1970 . £20/£10
Bismark's Herrings, Joseph (London), 1971 . £30/£10

Collaboration
Ask a Policeman, Barker (London), [1933] (chain novel;
  chapters contributed by Gladys Mitchell, John Rhode,
  Dorothy L. Sayers and others) . . . £1,000/£100
ditto, Morrow (New York), 1933 . . . £500/£65
No Flowers by Request & *Crime on the Coast*, Gollancz
  (London), 1984 (chain novel; chapters by Gladys Mitchell,
  Dorothy L. Sayers, E.C.R. Lorac, John Dickson Carr and
  others) . . . . £10/£5

Children's Titles
Outlaws of the Border, Pitman (London), 1940 (as Stephen
  Hockaby) . . . . £250/£45
*The Three Fingerprints: A Detective Story for Boys and
  Girls*, Heinemann (London), 1940 . . . £125/£30
Holiday River, Evans (London), 1940 . . £125/£30
The Seven Stones Mystery, Evans (London), 1940 £100/£25
The Malory Secret, Evans (London), 1940 . . £85/£20
Pam at Storne Castle, Evans (London), 1940 . £75/£15
Caravan Creek, Blackie (London), 1940 . . £65/£15
On Your Marks, Heinemann (London), 1940 . £75/£15
The Light Blue Hills, The Bodley Head (London), 1940 .
  . . . . £65/£15

MARGARET MITCHELL
(b.1900 d.1949)

Margaret Mitchell was born in Atlanta, Georgia. *Gone With the Wind* was the result of 10 years' work, a distillation of all the American Civil War stories Mitchell had heard. Her 1,000 page novel won the Pulitzer Prize, has sold over 25 million copies and is translated into 27 different languages. It continues to sell over 200,000 copies a year.

Gone With the Wind, Macmillan (New York), 1936 (d/w
with *Gone With the Wind* listed in second column of book
list on back panel) . . . . . £4,500/£200
ditto, Macmillan (New York), 1936 (d/w with *Gone With the
Wind* top of list in first column on back panel) £1,750/£200
ditto, Macmillan (London), 1936 . . . £500/£75

NAOMI MITCHISON
(b.1897 d.1999)

Edinburgh-born Naomi Mitchison was a prolific novelist with a long career spanning several genres. Her works of the 1920s and '30s are held in the highest esteem, especially those which evoke classical Greece and Rome. Mitchison also wrote fiction for children. In 1964 her husband, Dick Mitchison, was created a life peer and Naomi thus became Lady Mitchison.

Novels
The Conquered, Cape (London), 1923 . . . £75/£10
ditto, Harcourt Brace (New York), 1923 . . £50/£10
Cloud Cuckoo Land, Cape (London), 1925 . . £50/£10
ditto, Harcourt Brace (New York), 1926 . . £45/£15
The Corn King and the Spring Queen, Cape (London), 1931
  (illustrated by Z. Stryjenska) . . . . £35/£15
ditto, Harcourt Brace (New York), [n.d.] . . £20/£10
We Have Been Warned, Constable (London), 1935 £35/£15
ditto, The Vanguard Press (New York), [1936] . £25/£10
Beyond this Limit, Cape (London), 1935 (Illustrated by
  Wyndham Lewis) . . . . . . £100/£25
The Blood of the Martyrs, Constable (London), 1939 .
  . . . . £40/£10
ditto, McGraw-Hill (New York), 1939 . . £25/£10
The Bull Calves, Cape (London), 1947 (illustrated by
  Louise Richard Annand) . . . . . £35/£10
Lobsters on the Agenda, Gollancz (London), 1952 £35/£10
Behold Your King, Muller (London), 1957 . . £35/£10
Memoirs of a Spacewoman, Gollancz (London), 1962 .
  . . . . £100/£25
When We Become Men, Collins (London), 1965 . £20/£5
Cleopatra's People, Heinemann (London), 1972 . £15/£5
Solution Three, Dobson (London), 1973 . . £15/£5
ditto, Warner (New York), 1975 (pbk) . . . £5
Not By Bread Alone, Marion Boyars (London), 1983 £15/£5
Early in Orcadia, R. Drew (Glasgow), 1987 . £10/£5

Short Stories
When the Bough Breaks and Other Stories, Cape (London),
  1924 . . . . £50/£15
ditto, Harcourt Brace (New York), 1924 . . £30/£15
Black Sparta, Greek Stories, Cape (London), 1928 £50/£15

ditto, Harcourt Brace (New York), [n.d.] . . . £35/£15
Barbarian Stories, Cape (London), 1929 . . . £30/£10
ditto, Harcourt Brace (New York), 1929 . . . £25/£10
The Powers of Light, Pharos (London), 1932 (illustrations by Eric Kennington) . . . . . . £65/£20
Images of Africa, Canongate (Edinburgh), 1980 . £15/£5
What Do You Think of Yourself? Scottish Short Stories, P. Harris (Edinburgh), 1982 . . . . . £10/£5
Beyond this Limit, Selected Shorter Fiction, Scottish Academic Press (Edinburgh), 1986 . . . £10/£5

Short Stories and Poetry
The Delicate Fire, Cape (London), 1933 . . . £50/£15
ditto, Harcourt Brace (New York), 1933 . . . £50/£15
The Fourth Pig, Constable (London), 1936 . . £35/£10
Five Men and a Swan, Allen & Unwin (London), 1957 . . . . £20/£5

Poetry
The Laburnum Branch, Cape (London), 1926 . £20/£5
ditto, Harcourt Brace (New York), 1926 . . . £20/£5
The Alban Goes Out, Raven Press (no place), 1939 (engravings by Gertrude Hermes; wraps) . . . £150
The Cleansing of the Knife and Other Poems, Canongate (Edinburgh), 1978 . . . . . £15/£5

Plays
The Price of Freedom, Cape (London), 1931 (with Lewis Gielgud) . . . . £35/£10
As It Was in the Beginning, Cape (London), 1939 (with Lewis Gielgud) . . . . . . £15/£5
Spindrift, French (London), 1951 (with Denis Macintosh; pbk) £15

Children's Fiction
The Hostages and Other Stories for Boys & Girls, Cape (London), 1930 . . . . . . £25/£10
ditto, Harcourt Brace (New York), [1931] . . £20/£5
Boys and Girls and Gods, Watts & Co (London), 1931 . . . . £20/£5
The Big House, Faber (London), 1950 . . . £25/£5
Travel Light, Faber (London), 1952 . . . £20/£5
Graeme and the Dragon, Faber (London), 1954 . £20/£5
The Swan's Road, Naldrett Press (London), 1954 . £20/£5
The Land the Ravens Found, Collins (London), 1955 . . . . £20/£5
To The Chapel Perilous, Allen & Unwin (London), 1955 . . . . £20/£5
Little Boxes, Faber (London), 1956 . . . £20/£5
The Far Harbour, Collins (London), 1957 . £15/£5
Judy and Lakshmi, Collins (London), 1959 . £15/£5
The Rib of the Green Umbrella, Collins (London), 1960 (illustrated by Edward Ardizzone) . . . £50/£20
The Young Alexander the Great, Max Parrish (London), 1960 . . . . £15/£5
ditto, Roy (New York), [1961] . . . . £10/£5
Karensgaard: The Story of a Danish Farm, Collins (London), 1961 . . . . £15/£5
The Young Alfred the Great, Max Parrish (London), 1962 . . . . £15/£5
ditto, Roy (New York), [1963] . . . . £10/£5
The Fairy Who Couldn't Tell a Lie, Collins (London), 1963 . . . . £15/£5
Alexander the Great, Longman (London), 1964 . £10/£5

Henry and Crispies, Department of Education (Wellington, New Zealand), 1964 . . . . . . £10/£5
A Mochudi Family, Department of Education (New Zealand), 1965 . . . . £10/£5
Ketse and the Chief, Nelson (London), 1965 . £10/£5
ditto, Nelson (New York), 1967 . . . . £10/£5
Friends and Enemies, Collins (London), 1966 . £10/£5
ditto, John Day Co. (New York), [1968] . . £10/£5
Highland Holiday, Department of Education (New Zealand), 1967 . . . . £10/£5
The Big Surprise, Kaye & Ward (London), 1967 . £10/£5
African Heroes, Bodley Head (London), 1968 . £15/£5
ditto, Farrar Straus Giroux (New York), 1968 . . £15/£5
Don't Look Back, Kaye & Ward (London), 1969 . £10/£5
The Family at Ditlabeng, Collins (London), 1969 . £10/£5
ditto, Farrar, Straus & Giroux (New York), [1970] . £10/£5
Sun and Moon, Bodley Head (London), 1970 . £10/£5
ditto, Dutton (New York), [1973] . . . £10/£5
Sunrise Tomorrow: A Story of Botswana, Collins (London), 1973 . . . . £10/£5
ditto, Farrar, Straus & Giroux (New York), [1973] . £10/£5
The Danish Teapot, Kaye & Ward (London), 1973 £15/£5
Snake, Collins (London), 1976 . . . . £10/£5
The Little Sister, O.U.P. (Cape Town, South Africa), 1976 . . . . £10/£5
The Wild Dogs, O.U.P. (Cape Town, South Africa), 1977 . . . . £10/£5
The Brave Nurse, and Other Stories, O.U.P. (Cape Town, South Africa), 1977 . . . . £10/£5
The Two Magicians, Dobson (London), 1978 (with G.R. Mitchison) . . . . £10/£5
The Vegetable War, Hamish Hamilton (London), 1980 . . . . £10/£5
The Sea Horse, Hamish Hamilton (London), 1980 . £10/£5
A Girl Must Live, R. Drew (Glasgow), 1990 . . £10/£5
The Oath Takers, Balnain Books (Nairn, Scotland), 1991 (pbk) £5
Sea-Green Ribbons, Balnain Books (Nairn, Scotland), 1991 (pbk) £5

Children's Plays
Nix-Nought-Nothing: Four Plays for Children, Cape (London), 1928 . . . . £30/£10
ditto, Harcourt Brace (New York), 1929 . . . £25/£5
Kate Crackernuts: a Fairy Play for Children, Alden Press (London), 1931 (300 numbered, signed copies; wraps) £45
An End and a Beginning and Other Plays, Constable (London), 1937 . . . . £15/£5
ditto, as ***Historical Plays for Schools***, Constable (London), 1939 (2 vols) . . . . . . £15/£5
Nix-Nought-Nothing and Elfin Hill: Two Plays for Children, Cape (London), 1948 . . . . £15/£5

Non-Fiction
Anna Comnena, Howe (London), 1928 . . . £135/£50
Comments on Birth Control, Faber (London), 1930 (tissue d/w) . . . . £30/£15
ditto, Faber (London), 1930 (stapled wraps) . . £15
Naomi Mitchison's Vienna Diary, Gollancz (London), 1934 . . . . £20/£5
ditto, Smith and Haas (New York), 1934 . . . £20/£5
The Home and Changing Civilisation, Bodley Head (London), 1934 . . . . £25/£5

Socrates, Hogarth Press (London), 1937 (with Richard Crossman) . . . . £35/£10
The Moral Basis of Politics, Constable (London), 1938 . . . . £20/£5
ditto, Kennikat Press (Port Washington, N.Y.), [1971] . . . . £10/£5
The Kingdom of Heaven, Heinemann (London), 1939 . . . . £15/£5
Man and Herring, A Documentary, Serif Books (Edinburgh), 1949 (with Denis Macintosh) . . £20/£5
Highlands and Islands, Unity Publishing, 1954 . £20/£5
Other People's Worlds, Secker & Warburg (London), 1958 . . . . £20/£5
A Fishing Village on the Clyde, O.U.P. (Oxford, UK), 1960 (with George Patterson) . . . . . £15/£5
Presenting Other People's Children, Hamlyn (London), 1961 . . . . £10/£5
Return to the Fairy Hill, Heinemann (London), 1966 £10/£5
ditto, John Day Co. (New York), [1966] . . . £10/£5
The Africans, Blond (London), 1970 . . £25/£10
A Life for Africa, Bram Fischer, Merlin Press (London), 1973 . . . . £10/£5
Small Talk, Memories of an Edwardian Childhood, Bodley Head (London), 1973 . . . . . £15/£5
Oil for the Highlands?, Fabian Society (London), 1974 (wraps) £10
All Change Here, Girlhood and Marriage, Bodley Head (London), 1975 . . . . . . £10/£5
Sittlichkeit, Birkbeck College (London), [1975] (wraps) £5
You May Well Ask, A Memoir 1920-1940, Gollancz (London), 1979 . . . . £15/£5
Mucking Around, Five Continents over Fifty Years, Gollancz (London), 1981 . . . . . £10/£5
Margaret Cole, 1883-1980, The Fabian Society (London), 1982 (wraps) £5
Among You Taking Notes, The Wartime Diary of Naomi Mitchison, 1939-1945, Gollancz (London), 1985. £20/£5
Saltaire Self-Portraits, Saltaire Society (Edinburgh), 1986 (wraps) £5

MARY RUSSELL MITFORD

(b.1787 d.1855)

Mary Russell Mitford's early poetry was in the manner of Coleridge and Walter Scott and her plays were successfully produced in London. However, prose appears to have been her strength, and *Our Village* is her classic. She supported her father through her writing after he had ruined the family through his extravagance.

Poetry

Poems, Longman, Hurst, Rees and Orme (London), 1810 . . . . £500
Christina: The Maid of the South Seas - A Poem, Valpy & Rivington (London), 1811 . . . . . .£200
Watlington Hill, A.J. Valpy (London), 1812 (wraps) .£100
Narrative Poems on the Female Character in the Various Relations of Life, Vol.1, Rivington (London), 1813 . £200
Dramatic Scenes, Sonnets and Other Poems, Geo. B Whittaker (London), 1827 . . . .£100

Sketches

Our Village, G. & W.B. Whittaker (London), 1824-32 (5 vols) £750
ditto, E. Bliss (New York), 1826 (3 vols) . . .£250
ditto, Macmillan (London), 1893 (illustrated by Hugh Thomson, 1 vol) £25
ditto, Macmillan (London), 1893 (470 large paper copies, illustrated by Hugh Thomson, 1 vol) £300
Belford Regis, Bentley (London), 1835 (3 vols) . .£200

Novels

Atherton and Other Tales, Hurst & Blackett (London), 1854 (3 vols) £175
ditto, Ticknor and Fields (Boston), 1854 (3 vols) . .£150

Plays

Julian, a tragedy in five acts, W.B. Gilley (New York), 1823 . . . . £60
Foscari, Whittaker (London), 1826 . . . . £50
Foscari and Julian, Whittaker (London), 1827. . . £50
Charles I, John Duncombe (London), 1834 . . . £35
Sadak and Kalasrade, Lyceum Opera House (London), 1835 . . . . £75
Dramatic Works, Hurst & Blackett (London), 1854 (2 vols) £50

Short Stories

American Stories, First Series, Whittaker, Treacher (London), 1831 (3 vols) £125
Country Stories, Saunders & Otley (London), 1837 .£100
ditto, Macmillan (New York), 1896 . . . . . £30

Others

Lights and Shadows of American Life, Colborn & Bentley, Treacher (London), 1832 (3 vols) £200
The Works: Prose and Verse, James Crissy (Philadelphia), 1841 . . . . £45
Recollections of a Literary Life; or, Books, Places, and People, R. Bentley (London), 1852 (3 vols) . . £150
ditto, Harper (New York), 1852 . . . . . £45
The Life of Mary Russell Mitford, related in a selection from her letters to her friends, R. Bentley (London), 1870 (3 vols) £100
Memoirs and Letters of Charles Boner, with letters of Mary Russell Mitford to him..., R. Bentley (London), 1871 (2 vols) £45
Letters of Mary Russell Mitford, Second Series, Bentley (London), 1872 (edited by Henry Chorley, 2 vols) . £75
The Friendships of Mary Russell Mitford, Hurst and Blackett (London), 1882 (2 vols) £50
ditto, Harper & Brothers (New York), 1882 . . £45
Correspondence with Charles Boner and John Ruskin, Unwin (London), 1914 (edited by Elizabeth Lee) . £20
The Letters of Mary Russell Mitford, Bodley head (London), 1925 . . . .£35/£10
Elizabeth Barrett to Miss Mitford; the unpublished letters..., Murray (London), 1954 . . .£25/£10
ditto, Yale Univ Press (New Haven, CT), 1954 . £25/£10

NANCY MITFORD
(b.1904 d.1973)

Nancy Mitford, the eldest daughter of Baron Redesdale, was an English novelist and biographer. She edited and contributed an essay to *Noblesse Oblige* which originated the famous 'U', or upper-class, and 'non-U' classification of linguistic usage and behaviour. Mitford's satirical novels of aristocratic life are her most appreciated works.

Novels
Highland Fling, Hamish Hamilton (London), 1931 £250/£65
Christmas Pudding, Thornton Butterworth (London), 1932 . . . . £250/£50
Wigs on the Green, Thornton Butterworth (London), 1935 . . . . £250/£50
Pigeon Pie: A Wartime Receipt, Hamish Hamilton (London), 1940 . . . . £250/£45
ditto, British Book Centre (New York), 1959 . . £45/£15
The Pursuit of Love, Hamish Hamilton (London), 1945 . . . . £225/£30
ditto, Random House (New York), 1946 . . . £50/£15
Love in a Cold Climate, Hamish Hamilton (London), 1949 . . . . £100/£20
ditto, Random House (New York), 1949 . . £50/£10
The Blessing, Hamish Hamilton (London), 1951 . £40/£15
ditto, Random House (New York), 1951 . . £30/£10
The Nancy Mitford Omnibus, Hamish Hamilton (London), 1956 (contains *The Pursuit Of Love, Love In A Cold Climate* and *The Blessing*). . . . . £10/£5
Don't Tell Alfred, Hamish Hamilton (London), 1960 £25/£10
ditto, Harper (New York), 1960 . . . . £20/£10

Biography
Madame de Pompadour, Hamish Hamilton (London), 1954 . . . . £25/£5
ditto, Random House (New York), 1954 . . £25/£5
ditto, Hamish Hamilton (London), 1968 (revised edition with illustrations) . . . . £10/£5
Voltaire in Love, Hamish Hamilton (London), 1957 £20/£5
ditto, Harper (New York), 1957 . . . . £20/£5
The Sun King: Louis XIV at Versailles, Hamish Hamilton (London), 1966 . . . . . £20/£5
ditto, Harper (New York), 1966 . . . £20/£5
ditto, Arcadia Press (London), 1970 (265 signed, numbered copies, slipcase) . . . . . £125/£75
Frederick the Great, Hamish Hamilton (London), 1970 . . . . £20/£5
ditto, Harper (New York), 1970 . . . . £20/£5

Translation
The Princess of Cleves, by Madame de Lafayette, Hamish Hamilton (London), 1950 . . . £35/£10
The Little Hut, by Alfred Roussin, Hamish Hamilton (London), 1951 . . . . £35/£15
ditto, Random House (New York), 1953 . . £25/£10

Essays
The Water Beetle, Hamish Hamilton (London), 1962 £15/£5
ditto, Harper (New York), 1962 . . . . £10/£5
A Talent to Annoy: Essays, Articles and Reviews 1929-1968, Hamish Hamilton (London), 1986 . £10/£5
ditto, Beaufort Books (New York), 1987 . . £10/£5

Editor
The Ladies of Alderley, Chapman & Hall (London), 1938 . . . . £45/£15
The Stanleys of Alderley: Their Letters Between the Years 1851-1865, Chapman & Hall (London), 1939 £45/£15
Noblesse Oblige: An Inquiry into the Identifiable Characteristics of the English Aristocracy, Hamish Hamilton (London), 1956 . . . . £50/£15
ditto, Harper (New York), 1956 . . . . £30/£10

Letters
Love from Nancy: Letters of Nancy Mitford, Hodder & Stoughton (London), 1993 . . . . £10/£5
ditto, Houghton Mifflin (Wilmington, MA), 1993 . £10/£5
The Letters of Nancy Mitford and Evelyn Waugh, Hodder & Stoughton (London), 1996 . . . £10/£5
ditto, Houghton Mifflin (Boston), 1996 . . £10/£5
The Bookshop at 10 Curzon Street: Letters Between Nancy Mitford and Heywood Hill 1952-1973, Francis Lincoln (London), 2004 . . . . . . £10/£5

NICHOLAS MONSARRAT
(b.1910 d.1979)

Nicholas Monsarrat was a British novelist best known for his sea stories. The one novel still widely read today is *The Cruel Sea*, his first post-World War Two novel, based on his own wartime service. It described life aboard the vital but unglamorous 'small ships' of the War. His other great achievement is his history of seafaring, *Master Mariner*.

Novels
Think of Tomorrow, Hurst & Blackett (London), 1934. . . . . £65/£15
At First Sight, Hurst & Blackett (London), 1935 . £60/£15
The Whipping Boy, Jarrolds (London), 1936 . £45/£10
This is the Schoolroom, Cassell (London), 1939 . £25/£10
ditto, Knopf (New York), 1940 . . . . £25/£10
The Cruel Sea, Cassell (London), 1951 . . £100/£15
ditto, Knopf (New York), 1951 . . . . £45/£10
The Story of Esther Costello, Cassell (London), 1953 . . . . £25/£10
ditto, Knopf (New York), 1951 . . . . £25/£10
Castle Garac, Knopf (New York), 1955 . . £15/£5
ditto, Pan (London), 1968 (pbk) £5
The Tribe That Lost Its Head, Cassell (London), 1956. . . . . £20/£5
ditto, Sloane (New York), 1956 . . . . £15/£5
The Nylon Pirates, Cassell (London), 1960 . £20/£5
ditto, Sloane (New York), 1960 . . . . £15/£5
The White Rajah, Cassell (London), 1961 . £20/£5
ditto, Sloane (New York), 1961 . . . . £15/£5
The Time Before This, Cassell (London), 1962 . £15/£5
ditto, Sloane (New York), 1962 . . . . £15/£5
Smith and Jones, Cassell (London), 1963 . £15/£5
ditto, Sloane (New York), 1963 . . . . £15/£5
A Fair Day's Work, Cassell (London), 1964 . £15/£5
ditto, Sloane (New York), 1964 . . . . £15/£5
Something to Hide, Cassell (London), 1965 . £15/£5
ditto, Sloane (New York), 1966 . . . . £15/£5

The Pillow Fight, Cassell (London), 1965   .   .   £10/£5
ditto, Sloane (New York), 1965 .   .   .   .   £10/£5
Richer Than All His Tribe, Cassell (London), 1968   £10/£5
ditto, Morrow (New York), 1969   .   .   .   £10/£5
The Kapillan of Malta, Cassell (London), 1973   .   £10/£5
ditto, Morrow (New York), 1974   .   .   .   £10/£5
The Master Mariner, Volume 1: Running Proud, Cassell
(London), 1978   .   .   .   .   .   £20/£5
ditto, Morrow (New York), 1979   .   .   .   £20/£5
The Master Mariner, Volume 2: Drunken Ship, Cassell
(London), 1980   .   .   .   .   .   £20/£5
ditto, Morrow (New York), 1981   .   .   .   £20/£5

Short Stories
Depends What You Mean By Love, Cassell (London), 1947
.   .   .   .   £25/£10
ditto, Knopf (New York), 1948 .   .   .   .   £25/£10
ditto, as *HMS Marlborough Will Enter Harbour*, Panther
(London), 1956 (pbk). £5
HMS Marlborough Will Enter Harbour, Cassell (London),
1952   .   .   .   .   £15/£5
The Ship That Died of Shame, Cassell (London), 1959   .
.   .   .   .   £20/£5
ditto, Sloane (New York), 1959 .   .   .   .   £20/£5
Monsarrat At Sea, Cassell (London), 1975   .   .   £15/£5
ditto, Morrow (New York), 1976   .   .   .   £10/£5

Autobiography
H.M. Corvette, Cassell (London), 1942 (pbk) .   .   £15
ditto, Lippincott (Philadelphia), 1943   .   .   £30/£10
East Coast Corvette, Cassell (London), 1943 (pbk)   .   £15
ditto, Lippincott (Philadelphia), 1943   .   .   £35/£10
Corvette Command, Cassell (London), 1944 (pbk)   .   £15
Three Corvettes, Cassell (London), 1945 .   .   £25/£10
H.M. Frigate, Cassell (London), 1948 (pbk)   .   .   £15
My Brother Denys: A Memoir, Cassell (London), 1948   .
.   .   .   .   £30/£10
ditto, Knopf (New York), 1949 .   .   .   .   £25/£10
Canada Coast To Coast, Cassell (London), 1955 .   £20/£5
Life is a Four Letter Word, Volume 1: Breaking In, Cassell
(London), 1966   .   .   .   .   .   £15/£5
Life is a Four Letter Word, Volume 2: Breaking Out,
Cassell (London), 1970   .   .   .   .   £15/£5
Breaking In, Breaking Out, Morrow (New York), 1971   .
.   .   .   .   £15/£5

Other
To Stratford, With Love, McClelland & Stewart (Toronto),
1963 (pbk) £10

L.M. MONTGOMERY
(b.1874 d.1942)

Lucy Maud Montgomery was the Canadian author of the
well-known series of novels which started with the internationally successful *Anne of Green Gables*.

Anne Novels
Anne of Green Gables, L.C. Page & Co (Boston), 1908   .
.   .   .   .   £7,500
ditto, Pitman (London), 1908 .   .   .   .   £3,000
Anne of Avonlea, Page (Boston), 1909   .   .   .   £400

ditto, Pitman (London), 1909   .   .   .   .   .   £175
Anne of the Island, Page (Boston), 1915 .   .   .   £400
ditto, Pitman (London), 1915   .   .   .   .   £125
Anne's House of Dreams, Stokes (New York), 1917   .   £75
ditto, Constable (London), 1917 .   .   .   .   £65
Rainbow Valley, Stokes (New York), 1919   .   .   £100
ditto, Constable (London), 1920 .   .   .   £150/£40
Rilla of Ingleside, Stokes (New York), 1921 .   £250/£75
ditto, Hodder & Stoughton (London), [1921] .   £150/£40
Anne of Windy Poplars, Stokes (New York), 1936 £250/£75
ditto, as *Anne of Windy Willows*, Harrap (London), 1936   .
.   .   .   .   £150/£40
Anne of Ingleside, Stokes (New York), 1939 .   £200/£50
ditto, Harrap (London), 1939 .   .   .   .   £100/£25

Avonlea Short Stories
Chronicles of Avonlea, Page (Boston), 1912 .   .   £200
ditto, Sampson Low (London), 1912 .   .   .   £125
Further Chronicles of Avonlea, Page (Boston), 1920   .   .
.   .   .   .   £150/£50
ditto, Harrap (London), 1925 .   .   .   .   £100/£20

Sara Series
The Story Girl, Page (Boston), 1911 .   .   .   £200
ditto, Pitman (London), 1911 .   .   .   .   £200
The Golden Road, Page (Boston), 1913 .   .   .   £200
ditto, Cassell (London), 1914 .   .   .   .   £200

Emily Series
Emily of New Moon, Stokes (New York), 1923 .   £250/£45
ditto, Hodder & Stoughton (London), [1923] .   £150/£35
Emily Climbs, Stokes (New York), 1925 .   .   £200/£40
ditto, Hodder & Stoughton (London), [1925] .   £150/£35
Emily's Quest, Stokes (New York), 1927.   .   £150/£35
ditto, Hodder & Stoughton (London), [1927] .   £125/£30

Pat Series
Pat of Silver Bush, Stokes (New York), 1933 .   £150/£35
ditto, Hodder & Stoughton (London), [1933] .   £125/£30
Mistress Pat, Stokes (New York), 1935 .   .   £150/£35
ditto, Harrap (London), 1935 .   .   .   .   £125/£30

Juvenile Novels
Kilmeny of the Orchard, Page (Boston), 1910   .   .   £175
ditto, Hodder & Stoughton (London), [1929] .   £150/£30
Magic for Marigold, Stokes (New York), 1929 .   £125/£65
ditto, Harrap (London), 1935 .   .   .   .   £65/£20
Jane of Lantern Hill, Stokes (New York), 1937 .   £100/£25
ditto, Harrap (London), 1937 .   .   .   .   £65/£20

Other Novels
The Blue Castle, Stokes (New York), 1926   .   £200/£65
ditto, Hodder & Stoughton (London), [1926] .   .   £75/£20
A Tangled Web, Stokes (New York), 1931   .   £200/£65
ditto, as *Aunt Betty Began It*, Hodder & Stoughton
(London), [1932] .   .   .   .   .   £75/£20

Other Short Stories
The Road to Yesterday, McGraw-Hill Ryerson (Toronto,
Canada), 1974 .   .   .   .   .   .   £10/£5
ditto, Angus & Robertson (London), 1975   .   .   £10/£5
The Doctor's Sweetheart and Other Stories, McGraw-Hill
(Toronto, Canada), 1979 .   .   .   .   £10/£5
ditto, Harrap (London), 1979 .   .   .   .   £10/£5

Akin to Anne: Tales of Other Orphans, McClelland &
Stewart (Toronto, Canada), 1988 . . . £10/£5
Along the Shore: Tales by the Sea, McClelland & Stewart
(Toronto, Canada), 1989 . . . £10/£5
Among the Shadows: Tales from the Darker Side,
McClelland & Stewart (Toronto, Canada), 1990 . £10/£5
After Many Days: Tales of Time Passed, McClelland &
Stewart (Toronto, Canada), 1991 . . . £10/£5
Against the Odds: Tales of Achievement, McClelland &
Stewart (Toronto, Canada), 1993 . . . £10/£5
At the Altar: Matrimonial Tales, McClelland & Stewart
(Toronto, Canada), 1994 . . .. . £10/£5
Across the Miles: Tales of Correspondence, McClelland &
Stewart (Toronto, Canada), 1995 . .. . £10/£5
Christmas with Anne and Other Holiday Stories,
Delacorte (New York), 1995 . . . . £10/£5

Poetry
The Watchman and Other Poems, McClelland, Goodchild
& Stewart (Toronto, Canada), 1916. . . . .£750
ditto, Constable (London), 1920 . . . . .£200/£50
The Poetry of Lucy Maud Montgomery, Fitzhenry &
Whiteside (Ontario, Canada), 1987 . . . £10/£5

Autobiography
The Alpine Path: The Story of My Career, Fitzhenry &
Whiteside (Ontario, Canada), 1974 . . . £10/£5
The Selected Journals of L.M. Montgomery, O.U.P.
(Toronto, Canada), 1985-2004 (5 vols) . £100/£45 the set

MICHAEL MOORCOCK
(b.1939)

Michael Moorcock is a wide-ranging author writing predominantly in the fields of science fiction and fantasy,
although he has also published a number of literary novels.
As editor of the controversial British science fiction magazine *New Worlds* in the 1960s and '70s Moorcock is
credited with fostering the development of the science
fiction New Wave in Britain and indirectly in the U.S.

'Elric of Melniboné' Titles
The Stealer of Souls, Neville Spearman (London), 1963
(orange boards) . . . . . .£140/£40
ditto, Neville Spearman (London), 1963 (green boards) .
. . . . £70/£20
Stormbringer, Herbert Jenkins (London), 1965 . £175/£50
ditto, DAW (New York), 1977 (revised edition; pbk) . £5
The Sleeping Sorceress, New English Library (London),
1971 . . . . £25/£5
ditto, as *The Vanishing Tower*, DAW (New York), 1977
(pbk) £5
ditto, as *The Vanishing Tower*, Archival Press (Cambridge,
MA), 1981 (no d/w, in illustrated red slipcase) . £50/£30
ditto, as *The Vanishing Tower*, Archival Press (Cambridge,
MA), 1981 (150 signed copies, no d/w, in brown slipcase)
. . . .£150/£90
Elric of Melniboné, Hutchinson (London), 1972 . £50/£10
ditto, as *The Dreaming City*, Lancer (New York), 1972 (cut
text; pbk) £5
ditto, as *Elric of Melniboné*, Blue Star (Hartford, CT), 1977
(no d/w, in red slipcase) . . . . £50/£30

ditto, as *Elric of Melniboné*, Blue Star (Hartford, CT), 1977
(150 signed copies, no d/w, in brown slipcase) . £150/£90
Elric: The Return to Melnibone [sic], Unicorn (Brighton,
UK), 1973 (graphic, illustrated by Philippe Druillet,
outsized pbk) £60
ditto, as *Elric: The Return to Melniboné*, Jayde Design
(London), 1997 (outsized pbk) £25
The Jade Man's Eyes, Unicorn (Brighton, UK), 1973 (pbk)
. . . . £15
The Sailor on the Seas of Fate, Quartet (London), 1976 .
. . . . £25/£5
The Weird of the White Wolf, DAW (New York), 1977
(pbk) £5
The Bane of the Black Sword, DAW (New York), 1977
(pbk) £5
Elric at the End of Time, Paper Tiger (Limpsfield, UK),
1987 (illustrated by Rodney Matthews) . £25/£5
ditto, Paper Tiger (Limpsfield, UK), 1987 (outsized pbk) £15
The Fortress of the Pearl, Gollancz (London), 1989 £20/£5
The Revenge of the Rose, Grafton (London), 1991 £20/£5
The Dreamthief's Daughter, Earthlight (London), 2001 .
. . . . £25/£5
ditto, American Fantasy (Woodstock, IL), 2001 (600 signed
copies, slipcase) . . . . . £85/£30
ditto, American Fantasy (Woodstock, IL), 2003 [dated 2001]
(26 signed copies, no d/w, in traycase) . . £350/£200
The Skrayling Tree: The Albino in America, Warner (New
York), 2003 . . . . . . £20/£5
The White Wolf's Son: The Albino Underground, Warner
(New York), 2005 . . . . . £15/£5
Elric: The Making of a Sorcerer, DC Comics (New York),
2007 (graphic, illustrated by Walter Simonson, outsized
pbk) £15

'Elric'
('Chronicles of the Last Emperor of Melniboné') Titles
Elric: The Stealer of Souls, Del Rey (New York), 2008
(pbk) £15
Elric: To Rescue Tanelorn, Del Rey (New York), 2008
(pbk) £10
Elric: The Sleeping Sorceress, Del Rey (New York), 2008
(pbk) £10
Duke Elric, Del Rey (New York), 2009 (pbk) . . £10
Elric In the Dream Realms, Del Rey (New York), 2009
(pbk) £10

'Kane of Old Mars' Titles
Warriors of Mars, Compact (London), 1965 (pbk, pseud
'Edward P. Bradbury') £15
ditto, as *The City of the Beast*, Lancer (New York), [1970]
(pbk, as Michael Moorcock) £5
ditto, as *City of the Beast or Warriors of Mars*, DAW (New
York), 1979 (pbk, as Michael Moorcock, with new
introduction) £5
Blades of Mars, Compact (London), 1965 (pbk, pseud
'Edward P. Bradbury') £15
ditto, as *The Lord of the Spiders*, Lancer (New York),
[1971] (pbk, as Michael Moorcock) . . . £5
Barbarians of Mars, Compact (London), 1965 (pbk, pseud
'Edward P. Bradbury') £15
ditto, as *Masters of the Pit*, New English Library (London),
1971 (pbk, as Michael Moorcock) £5
*N.B. All 'Bradbury' titles also published as Michael
Moorcock, Ace (New York), 1991 (pbk) . . £5 each*

'The Roads Between the Worlds' Titles

The Fireclown, Compact (London), 1965 (pbk) . . £15

ditto, as *The Winds of Limbo*, Paperback Library (New York), 1969 (pbk) £5

The Twilight Man, Compact (London), 1966 (pbk) . £15

ditto, as *The Shores of Death*, Sphere (London), 1970 (pbk) £5

The Wrecks of Time, Ace (New York), [1967] (cut text, with 'Tramontane' by Emil Petaja; pbk) £5

ditto, as *The Rituals of Infinity*, Arrow (London), 1971 (full text; pbk) £5

ditto, as *The Wrecks of Time*, Roc (London), 1994 (full text; pbk) £5

'Nick Allard'/'Jerry Cornell' Titles

The LSD Dossier, by Roger Harris, Compact (London), 1966 (rewritten by Moorcock; pbk). £55

Somewhere in the Night, Compact (London), 1966 (pbk, pseud 'Bill Barclay') £60

ditto, as *The Chinese Agent*, Macmillan (New York), 1970 (revised edition, as Michael Moorcock) . . . £30/£5

Printer's Devil, Compact (London), 1966 (pbk, pseud 'Bill Barclay') £50

ditto, as *The Russian Intelligence*, Savoy (Manchester, UK), 1980 (revised edition; pbk, as Michael Moorcock, illustrated by Harry Douthwaite) £15

ditto, as *The Russian Intelligence*, New English Library (Sevenoaks, UK), 1983 (revised text, as Michael Moorcock, no illustrations) . . . . £25/£5

'Hawkmoon' ('The History of the Runestaff') Titles

The Jewel in the Skull, Lancer (New York), 1967 (pbk) £10

ditto, White Lion (London), 1973 . . . . £40/£10

ditto, DAW (New York), 1977 (revised edition; pbk) . £5

ditto, as *Hawkmoon: The Jewel in the Skull*, Tor (New York), 2010 (pbk) £10

Sorcerer's Amulet, Lancer (New York), 1968 (pbk) £10

ditto, as *The Mad God's Amulet*, Mayflower (London), 1969 (pbk) £5

ditto, as *The Mad God's Amulet*, White Lion (London), 1973 . . . . £20/£5

ditto, as *The Mad God's Amulet*, DAW (New York), 1977 (revised edition; pbk) £5

ditto, as *Hawkmoon: The Mad God's Amulet*, Tor (New York), 2010 (pbk) £10

Sword of the Dawn, Lancer (New York), 1968 (pbk) . £10

ditto, as *The Sword of the Dawn*, White Lion (London), 1973 . . . . £20/£5

ditto, as *The Sword of the Dawn*, DAW (New York), 1977 (revised edition; pbk) £5

The Secret of the Runestaff, Lancer (New York), 1969 (pbk) £10

ditto, as *The Runestaff*, Mayflower (London), 1969 (pbk) £5

ditto, as *The Runestaff*, White Lion (London), 1974 £20/£5

ditto, as *The Runestaff*, DAW (New York), 1977 (revised edition; pbk). £5

'Jerry Cornelius' Titles

The Final Programme, Avon (New York), 1968 (cut text; pbk) £15

ditto, Allison & Busby (London), 1969 (full text, Mal Dean d/w) . . . . £70/£20

ditto, Gregg Press (Boston, MA), 1976 (full text, with Norman Spinrad introduction, no d/w) £30

ditto, Allison & Busby (London), 1976 (full text, Richard Glyn Jones d/w) . . . . £25/£5

ditto, Fontana (London), 1979 (revised edition; pbk) . £5

A Cure for Cancer, Allison & Busby (London), 1971 (lettered d/w) . . . . £60/£15

ditto, Allison & Busby (London), 1976 [dated 1971] (pictorial d/w) . . . . £30/£10

ditto, Fontana (London), 1979 (revised edition; pbk) . £5

The English Assassin, Allison & Busby (London), 1972 (multiple-figure d/w) . . . . . £70/£20

ditto, Allison & Busby (London), 1976 (single-figure d/w) . . . . £20/£5

ditto, Fontana (London), 1979 (revised edition; pbk) . £5

The Lives and Times of Jerry Cornelius, Allison & Busby (London), 1976 . . . . £30/£5

ditto, Harrap (London), 1987 (expanded edition) . £20/£5

ditto, Grafton (London), 1987 (expanded edition; pbk) . £5

ditto, as *The Lives and Times of Jerry Cornelius: Stories of the Comic Apocalypse*, Four Walls Eight Windows (New York), 2003 (differing content; pbk) £10

The Adventures of Una Persson and Catherine Cornelius in the Twentieth Century, Quartet (London), 1976 £25/£5

ditto, Quartet (London), 1976 (pbk) £10

The Condition of Muzak, Allison & Busby (London), 1977 . . . . £40/£10

ditto, Allison & Busby (London), 1977 (pbk) . . £15

ditto, Allison & Busby (London), 1977 (with blurbs on d/w) . . . . £15/£5

ditto, Gregg Press (Boston, MA), 1978 (with Charles Platt introduction, no d/w) £30

ditto, Fontana (London), 1978 (revised edition [no note of revision]; pbk) £5

The Great Rock 'n' Roll Swindle, Virgin (London), 1980 ('newspaper') £35

ditto, Virgin (London), 1981 (pbk, with new introduction) . £10

The Entropy Tango, New English Library (London), 1981 . . . . £15/£5

Firing the Cathedral, PS Publishing (Harrogate, UK), 2002 (400 signed copies) £40

ditto, PS Publishing (Harrogate, UK), 2002 (500 signed copies; pbk) £15

'Sailing to Utopia' Titles

The Ice Schooner, Sphere (London), 1969 (pbk) . . £5

ditto, Harper & Row (New York), 1977 (revised edition) . . . . £30/£5

ditto, Harrap (London), 1985 (re-revised edition) . £20/£5

The Black Corridor, Ace (New York), 1969 (cut text; pbk). £10

ditto, Mayflower (London), 1969 (full text; pbk) . . £5

ditto, Ace [book club] (New York), 1970 (cut text) £15/£5

The Distant Suns, Unicorn (Carmarthen, UK), 1975 (with pseud. 'Philip James' [Cawthorn]; pbk) £10

ditto, New English Library (Sevenoaks, UK), 1989 (pbk, with new introduction) £5

'Karl Glogauer' Titles

Behold the Man, Allison & Busby (London), 1969 (novel) . . . . £35/£5

ditto, as *Behold the Man: The Thirtieth Anniversary Edition*, Mojo Press (Austin, TX), 1996 (novella) £30/£5

Breakfast in the Ruins: A Novel of Inhumanity, New English Library (London), 1972 . . . . . £30/£5

'The Eternal Champion' Titles

The Eternal Champion, Dell (New York), 1970 (pbk) . £5

ditto, Harper & Row (New York), 1978 (revised edition) .
. . . . £35/£5

Phoenix in Obsidian, Mayflower (London), 1970 (pbk) £5

ditto, as *The Silver Warriors*, Dell (New York), 1973 (pbk)
. . . . £5

The Swords of Heaven, The Flowers of Hell, HM/Simon &
Schuster (New York), 1979 (graphic novel, illustrated by
Howard V. Chaykin, outsized pbk) £50

Das Ewige Schwert, Bastei Lübbe (Germany), 1986 (pbk) .
. . . . £10

ditto, as *The Dragon in the Sword*, Ace (New York), 1986
(cut text) . . . . £20/£5

ditto, as *The Dragon in the Sword*, Grafton (London), 1987
(full text) . . . . £20/£5

'Corum' ('The Coming of Chaos') Titles

The Knight of the Swords, Mayflower (London), 1971 (pbk)
. . . . £5

ditto, Allison & Busby (London), 1977 . . . £15/£5

The Queen of the Swords, Berkley (New York), 1971 (pbk)
. . . . £5

The King of the Swords, Berkley (New York), 1971 (pbk) £5

'A Nomad of the Time Streams' Titles

The Warlord of the Air, Ace (New York), 1971 (pbk) . £10

ditto, New English Library (London), 1971 (censored text) .
. . . . £30/£5

The Land Leviathan, Quartet (London), 1974. . £25/£5

ditto, Quartet (London), 1974 (pbk) £10

The Steel Tsar, Granada (St. Albans, UK), 1981 (pbk) . £5

'The Dancers at the End of Time' Titles

An Alien Heat, MacGibbon & Kee (London), 1972 £40/£10

The Hollow Lands, Harper & Row (New York), 1974 £20/£5

Legends from the End of Time, Harper & Row (New York),
1976 . . . . £25/£5

The End of All Songs, Harper & Row (New York), 1976 .
. . . . £30/£5

The Transformation of Miss Mavis Ming, W.H. Allen
(London), 1977 . . . . £50/£10

ditto, as *A Messiah at the End of Time*, DAW (New York),
1978 (pbk) £5

'Corum' ('The Prince with the Silver Hand') Titles

The Bull and the Spear, Allison & Busby (London), 1973 .
. . . . £35/£5

The Oak and the Ram, Allison & Busby (London), 1973 .
. . . . £35/£5

The Sword and the Stallion, Berkley (New York), 1974
(pbk) £5

ditto, Allison & Busby (London), 1974 . . . £25/£5

'Hawkmoon' ('Count Brass') Titles

Count Brass, Mayflower (St. Albans, UK), 1973 (pbk). £5

The Champion of Garathorm, Mayflower (St. Albans, UK),
1973 (pbk) £5

The Quest for Tanelorn, Mayflower (St. Albans, UK), 1975
(pbk) £5

'The Hawklords' Titles

The Time of the Hawklords, Aidan Ellis [Henley-on-
Thames, UK], 1976 (with Michael Butterworth) . £50/£10

ditto, Collector's Guide Publishing (Burlington, Ontario),
1995 (pbk, as Michael Butterworth only) . . . £10

Queens of Deliria, Star (London), 1977 (by Michael
Butterworth; pbk) £10

Ledge of Darkness, Collector's Guide Publishing (Burlington, Ontario), 1994 (outsized pbk, by Bob Walker
[illustrator] with Michael Butterworth, in four-CD box set
[Griffin Music], *Hawkwind: 25 Years On*) . . . .
. . . . £70 for complete box set

'Colonel Pyat' Titles

Byzantium Endures, Secker & Warburg (London), 1981 .
. . . . £35/£5

The Laughter of Carthage, Secker & Warburg (London),
1984 . . . . £30/£5

Jerusalem Commands, Cape (London), 1992 (buff
endpapers) . . . . £25/£10

ditto, Cape (London), 1992 (white endpapers). . £10/£5

The Vengeance of Rome, Cape (London), 2006 . £20/£5

'Von Bek' Titles

The War Hound and the World's Pain, Timescape (New
York), 1981 . . . . £30/£5

The City in the Autumn Stars, Grafton (London), 1986 .
. . . . £20/£5

'The Second Ether' Titles

Blood: A Southern Fantasy, Millennium (London), 1995 .
. . . . £25/£5

ditto, Millennium (London), 1995 (pbk) . . . £10

Fabulous Harbours, Millennium (London), 1995 . £40/£10

ditto, Millennium (London), 1995 (pbk) . . . £10

The War Amongst the Angels, Orion (London), 1996 £30/£5

ditto, Orion (London), 1996 (pbk) £10

Other Novels

Caribbean Crisis, Fleetway (London), 1962 (pbk, pseud.
'Desmond Reid'). £50

The Sundered Worlds, Compact (London), 1965 (pbk) £15

ditto, as *The Blood Red Game*, Sphere (London), 1970 (pbk)
. . . . £5

ditto, as *The Sundered Worlds*, Roc (London), 1992 (revised
edition; pbk). £5

Gloriana, or The Unfulfill'd Queen, Allison & Busby
(London), 1978 . . . . £45/£10

ditto, as *La Saga di Gloriana*, Mondadori (Italy), 1991
(revised edition, cut text; pbk) £10

ditto, as *Gloriana; or, The Unfulfill'd Queen*, Phoenix
House (London), 1993 (revised text, full; pbk) . £5

ditto, as *Gloriana; or, The Unfulfill'd Queen*, Warner (New
York), 2004 (pbk, 1978 text, with new afterword and
appendices [incl. full 1991 revisions]) £10

The Real Life Mr Newman, A.J. Callow (Worcester, UK),
1979 (500 copies; pbk) £10

The Golden Barge, Savoy (Manchester, UK), 1979 (pbk,
illustrated by James Cawthorn) £15

ditto, New English Library (Sevenoaks, UK), 1983 (no full-
page illustrations) . . . . . . £30/£5

The Brothel in Rosenstrasse, New English Library
(London), 1982 . . . . £30/£5

Mother London, Secker & Warburg (London), 1988 £20/£5

The Birds of the Moon: A Travellers' Tale, Jayde Design
(London), 1995 (pbk) £5

The Adventure of the Dorset Street Lodger, Number Two Dorset Street, [1996] (no d/w, pseud. 'John H. Watson M.D.') £150

Michael Moorcock's Multiverse, DC Comics (New York), 1999 (graphic, with Walter Simonson, Mark Reeve & John Ridgway [illustrators], outsized pbk)   .   .   . £30

King of the City, Scribner (London), 2000   .   . £30/£5
ditto, Scribner (London), 2000 (pbk).   .   .   . £15

Silverheart, Earthlight (London), 2000 (with Storm Constantine) .   .   .   . £25/£5

The Mystery of the Texas Twister, Coppervale (Taylor, AZ), 2003 (pbk, in slipcase with *Argosy Magazine* [Jan/Feb 2004]) £10

Short Stories
The Deep Fix, Compact (London), 1966 (pbk, pseud. 'James Colvin') £20

The Time Dweller, Hart Davis (London), 1969   . £70/£20
The Singing Citadel, Mayflower (London), 1970 (pbk)   £5

The Nature of the Catastrophe (by Moorcock & others), Hutchinson (London), 1971 (edited with Langdon Jones) .
.   .   .   . £70/£20

Moorcock's Book of Martyrs, Quartet (London), 1976 (pbk)
.   .   .   . £5

ditto, as *Dying for Tomorrow*, DAW (New York), 1978 (pbk) £5

Sojan, Savoy (Manchester, UK), 1977 (pbk, ISBN 0-7045-0241-0) £10

ditto, Savoy (Manchester, UK), 1977 (pbk, with variant ISBN 0-352-33000-7 on inside back cover)   .   . £10

My Experiences in the Third World War, Savoy (Manchester, UK), 1980 (pbk) £10

Elric at the End of Time, New English Library (Sevenoaks, UK), 1984 .   .   .   . £30/£5

The Opium General and Other Stories, Harrap (London), 1984 .   .   .   . £20/£5

Casablanca, Gollancz (London), 1989   .   . £15/£5

Elric: Tales of the White Wolf (by Moorcock & others), White Wolf (Stone Mountain, GA), 1994 (edited by Edward E. Kramer & Richard Gilliam)   .   . £15/£5

Lunching with the Antichrist, Mark V. Ziesing (Shingletown, CA), 1995   .   .   .   . £25/£5

ditto, Mark V. Ziesing (Shingletown, CA), 1995 (300 signed copies, in slipcase)   .   .   .   .   . £65/£40

Pawn of Chaos: Tales of the Eternal Champion (by Moorcock & others), White Wolf (Clarkston, GA), 1996 (edited by Edward E. Kramer; pbk)   .   .   . £10

Tales from the Texas Woods, Mojo Press (Austin, TX), 1997 .   .   .   . £15/£5

London Bone, Scribner (London), 2001 (pbk).   . £20

The Metatemporal Detective, Pyr (Amherst, NY), 2007
.   .   .   . £15/£5

The Best of Michael Moorcock, Tachyon (San Francisco, CA), 2009 (pbk) £10

'The Tale of the Eternal Champion' Omnibus Editions
Von Bek, Millennium (London), 1992 (with errata slip)   .
.   .   .   . £60/£15

ditto, Millennium (London), 1992 (pbk, with errata slip) £20
ditto, Millennium (London), 1995   .   .   . £20/£5
ditto, White Wolf (Stone Mountain, GA), 1995 (differing content).   .   .   .   . £40/£10

The Eternal Champion, Millennium (London), 1992   .   .
.   .   .   . £40/£10

ditto, Millennium (London), 1992 (pbk)   .   .   . £20
ditto, White Wolf (Stone Mountain, GA), 1994 (differing content).   .   .   .   . £30/£5

Hawkmoon, Millennium (London), 1992 (revised texts)   .
.   .   .   . £40/£10

ditto, Millennium (London), 1992 (revised texts; pbk) . £15

Corum, Millennium (London), 1992   .   .   . £30/£5
ditto, Millennium (London), 1992 (pbk)   .   .   . £15
ditto, as *Corum: The Coming of Chaos*, Millennium (London), 1996 (pbk). £5

ditto, as *Corum: The Coming of Chaos*, White Wolf (Clarkston, GA), 1997   .   .   .   .   . £25/£5

Sailing to Utopia, Millennium (London), 1993   . £40/£10
ditto, Millennium (London), 1993 (pbk)   .   .   . £20

A Nomad of the Time Streams, Millennium (London), 1993 (revised) .   .   .   . £40/£10

ditto, Millennium (London), 1993 (revised; pbk)   .   . £20

The Dancers at the End of Time, Millennium (London), 1993 (revised edition).   .   .   .   .   . £40/£10

ditto, Millennium (London), 1993 (revised edition; pbk) £20

Elric of Melniboné, Millennium (London), 1993 (revised) .
.   .   .   . £40/£10

ditto, Millennium (London), 1993 (revised; pbk)   .   . £20
ditto, as *Elric: Song of the Black Sword*, White Wolf (Clarkston, GA), 1995   .   .   .   .   . £30/£5

The New Nature of the Catastrophe (by Moorcock & others), Millennium (London), 1993 (edited with Langdon Jones) .   .   .   . £30/£5

ditto, Millennium (London), 1993 (pbk)   .   .   . £20
ditto, Orion (London), 1997 (differing content; pbk)   . £5

The Prince with the Silver Hand, Millennium (London), 1993 .   .   .   . £30/£5

ditto, Millennium (London), 1993 (pbk)   .   .   . £15
ditto, as *Corum: The Prince with the Silver Hand*, White Wolf (Clarkston, GA), 1999   .   .   .   . £40/£10

Legends from the End of Time, Millennium (London), 1993 (revised, cut text).   .   .   .   .   . £20/£5

ditto, Millennium (London), 1993 (revised, cut text; pbk) £15
ditto, Orion (London), 1997 (revised text, full; pbk)   . £5
ditto, White Wolf (Clarkston, GA), 1999 (revised text, full)
.   .   .   . £60/£15

Stormbringer, Millennium (London), 1993 (revised) £40/£10
ditto, Millennium (London), 1993 (revised; pbk)   .   . £20
ditto, as *Elric: The Stealer of Souls*, White Wolf (Clarkston, GA), 1998 (re-revised)   .   .   . £40/£10

Earl Aubec and Other Stories, Millennium (London), 1993
.   .   .   . £40/£10

ditto, Millennium (London), 1993 (pbk)   .   .   . £20
ditto, White Wolf (Clarkston, GA), 1999 (differing content)
.   .   .   . £60/£15

Count Brass, Millennium (London), 1993   .   . £40/£10
ditto, Millennium (London), 1993 (pbk)   .   .   . £20

The Roads Between the Worlds, White Wolf (Clarkston, GA), 1996 (revised)   .   .   .   .   .   . £40/£10

Kane of Old Mars, White Wolf (Clarkston, GA), 1998 £30/£5

Other Omnibus Editions
The Swords Trilogy, Berkley (New York), 1977 (pbk) .   £5
ditto, Gregg Press (Boston, MA), 1980 (with introduction by Richard Gid Powers, no d/w) £30

ditto, as *The Swords of Corum*, Grafton (London), 1986   .
.   .   .   . £20/£5

ditto, as *Corum: The Prince in the Scarlet Robe*, Gollancz (London), 2002 (pbk). £5

The Cornelius Chronicles, Avon (New York), 1977 (pbk) .
. . . . £10

ditto, as *The Cornelius Quartet*, Phoenix House (London), 1993 (revised texts) . . . . . £20/£5

ditto, as *The Cornelius Quartet*, Phoenix House (London), 1993 (revised texts; pbk) £15

The Chronicles of Corum, Berkley (New York), 1978 (pbk)
. . . . £5

ditto, Grafton (London), 1986 . . . . £15/£5

The History of the Runestaff, Granada (St. Albans, UK), 1979 . . . . £40/£10

The Black Corridor/The Adventures of Una Persson and Catherine Cornelius, Dial Press (New York), [1980] (pbk)
. . . . £10

Warrior of Mars, New English Library (London), 1981 .
. . . . £40/£10

The Dancers at the End of Time, Granada (St. Albans, UK), 1981 . . . . £40/£10

The Nomad of Time, Nelson Doubleday [book club] (New York), [1982] . . . . . . £15/£5

The Elric Saga Part One, Nelson Doubleday [book club] (New York), 1984 . . . . . £15/£5

The Elric Saga Part Two, Nelson Doubleday [book club] (New York), 1984 . . . . . £15/£5

The Chronicles of Castle Brass, Granada (London), 1985 .
. . . . £20/£5

The Cornelius Chronicles Vol. II, Avon (New York), 1986 (pbk) £5

The Cornelius Chronicles Vol. III, Avon (New York), 1987 (pbk) £5

The Cornelius Chronicles Book One, Fontana (London), 1988 (revised texts, cut; pbk) £5

The Cornelius Chronicles Book Two, Fontana (London), 1988 (revised texts, cut; pbk) £5

Tales from the End of Time, Guild America [book club] (New York), [1989] . . . . . £15/£5

A Cornelius Calendar, Phoenix House (London), 1993 .
. . . . £20/£5

ditto, Phoenix House (London), 1993 (pbk) . . £15

Behold the Man and Other Stories, Phoenix House (London), 1994 . . . . . . £20/£5

ditto, Phoenix House (London), 1994 (pbk) . . £10

Elric, Gollancz (London), 2001 (pbk) . . . £5

The Elric Saga Part Three, Science Fiction Book Club (New York), 2002 . . . . . £20/£5

Jerry Cornell's Comic Capers, Immanion (Stafford, UK), 2005 (pbk) £15

The Elric Saga Part IV, Science Fiction Book Club (New York), 2005 . . . . . . £20/£5

Boxed Sets

The History of the Runestaff, Mayflower (St. Albans, UK), [1973] (pbk, in slipcase) £10

Mighty Moorcock, Quartet (London), [1974] (pbk, in slipcase). £10

Multi-Dimensional Moorcock, Quartet (London), [1975] (pbk, in slipcase). £15

The Chronicles of Count Brass, Mayflower/Granada (St. Albans, UK), [1977] (pbk, in slipcase) . £10

ditto, as *The Chronicles of Castle Brass*, Granada (St. Albans, UK), [1978] (pbk, in slipcase) . . £10

The Dancers at the End of Time, Mayflower (St. Albans, UK), [1978] (pbk, in slipcase) . . £10

The Jerry Cornelius Quartet, Fontana (London), [1979] (pbk, in slipcase) £25

Six Science Fiction Classics from the Master of Heroic Fantasy, DAW (New York), [1979] (pbk, in box) . £40

The Books of Corum, Granada (St. Albans, UK), [1980] (pbk, in slipcase) £10

Non-Fiction

Epic Pooh, British Fantasy Society (Dagenham, UK), 1978 (500 copies; stapled wraps) £15

The Retreat from Liberty, Zomba (London), 1983 (stapled wraps) £25

Letters from Hollywood, Harrap (London), 1986 . £25/£5

Wizardry and Wild Romance: A Study of Epic Fantasy, Gollancz (London), 1987 . . . . £20/£5

ditto, Gollancz (London), 1987 (pbk). . . . £10

ditto, as *Wizardry & Wild Romance: A Study of Epic Fantasy*, MonkeyBrain (Austin, TX), 2004 (expanded edition; pbk, no illustrations) . . . £10

Fantasy: The 100 Best Books, Xanadu (London), 1988 (with James Cawthorn, plain green boards, white d/w) . £25/£5

ditto, Xanadu (London), 1988 (50 signed copies, decorated green boards, clear d/w) . . . . £80/£20

Death Is No Obstacle, Savoy (Manchester, UK), 1992 (with Colin Greenland). . . . . . £30/£5

Into the Media Web: Selected Short Non-Fiction, 1956–2006, Savoy (Manchester, UK), 2010 . . £50/£10

BRIAN MOORE

(b.1921 d.1999)

Brian Moore was an Irish author of novels which deal with the torments of guilt and sexual obsession in relation to Catholicism. He was born and grew up in Belfast, but emigrated to Canada in 1948 and became a Canadian citizen. Despite moving to the United States in 1959, he maintained his Canadian citizenship. He was shortlisted for the Booker Prize three times.

Novels

Wreath for a Redhead, Harlequin (Toronto), 1951 (pseud 'Michael Bryan'; pbk) £200

ditto, as *Sailor's Leave*, Pyramid Books (New York), 1953 (pbk) £50

The Executioners, Harlequin (Toronto), 1951 (pseud 'Michael Bryan'; pbk) £65

French for Murder, Fawcett (Greenwich, CT), 1954 (pseud 'Bernard Mara'; pbk) £20

ditto, L. Miller & Sons (London), 1954 (pseud 'Bernard Mara'; pbk) £20

A Bullet for My Lady, Fawcett (Greenwich, CT), 1955 (pseud 'Bernard Mara'; pbk) £20

ditto, Muller (London), 1956 (pseud 'Bernard Mara'; pbk) .
. . . . £20

Judith Hearne, Deutsch (London), 1955 . . £225/£35

ditto, as *The Lonely Passion of Judith Hearne*, Little, Brown (Boston), 1955 . . . . £150/£25

ditto, as *Judith Hearne*, McClelland & Stewart (Toronto), 1964 (pbk) £30

This Gun for Gloria, Dell (New York), 1956 (pseud 'Bernard Mara'; pbk) £20

ditto, Muller (London), 1956 (pseud 'Bernard Mara'; pbk) .
. . . . £15

Intent to Kill, Dell (New York), 1956 (pseud 'Michael
Bryan'; pbk) £15

ditto, Eyre & Spottiswoode (London), 1956 (pseud 'Michael
Bryan') . . . . £145/£30

The Feast of Lupercal, Little, Brown (Boston), 1957 . .
. . . . £150/£25

ditto, Deutsch (London), 1958 . . . . £150/£25

ditto, as **A Moment of Love**, Longacre, 1960 . £25/£10

Murder in Majorca, Dell (New York), 1957 (pseud 'Michael
Bryan'; pbk) £20

ditto, Eyre & Spottiswoode (London), 1958 (pseud 'Michael
Bryan') . . . . £125/£25

The Luck of Ginger Coffey, Little, Brown (Boston), 1960 .
. . . . £45/£10

ditto, McClelland & Stewart (Toronto), 1960 . . £45/£10

ditto, Deutsch (London), 1960 . . . . £45/£10

An Answer from Limbo, Little, Brown (Boston), 1962 . .
. . . . £45/£10

ditto, McClelland & Stewart (Toronto), 1962 . £45/£5

ditto, Deutsch (London), 1963 . . . . £35/£5

The Emperor of Ice-Cream, Viking Press (New York), 1965
. . . . £35/£10

ditto, McClelland & Stewart (Toronto), 1965 . £35/£5

ditto, Deutsch (London), 1966 . . . . £30/£5

I Am Mary Dunne, McClelland & Stewart (Toronto), 1968.
. . . . £15/£5

ditto, Viking Press (New York), 1968 . . . £15/£5

ditto, Cape (London), 1968 . . . . £15/£5

Fergus, Holt Rinehart (New York), 1970 . . £20/£5

ditto, McClelland & Stewart (Toronto), 1970 . . £20/£5

ditto, Cape (London), 1971 . . . . £20/£5

The Revolution Script, McClelland & Stewart (Toronto),
1971 . . . . £20/£5

ditto, Holt Rinehart (New York), 1971 . . £20/£5

ditto, Cape (London), 1972 . . . . £20/£5

Catholics, McClelland & Stewart (Toronto), 1972 . £20/£5

ditto, Cape (London), 1972 . . . . £20/£5

ditto, Holt Rinehart (New York), 1973 . . £15/£5

The Great Victorian Collection, Farrar Straus (New York),
1975 . . . . £15/£5

ditto, McClelland & Stewart (Toronto), 1975 . £15/£5

ditto, Cape (London), 1975 . . . . £15/£5

The Doctor's Wife, Farrar Straus (New York), 1976 £15/£5

ditto, McClelland & Stewart (Toronto), 1976 . £15/£5

ditto, Cape (London), 1976 . . . . £15/£5

The Mangan Inheritance, Farrar Straus (New York), 1979 .
. . . . £15/£5

ditto, McClelland & Stewart (Toronto), 1979 . £15/£5

ditto, Cape (London), 1979 . . . . £15/£5

The Temptation of Eileen Hughes, Farrar Straus (New
York), 1981 . . . . £15/£5

ditto, McClelland & Stewart (Toronto), 1981 . £15/£5

ditto, Cape (London), 1981 . . . . £15/£5

Cold Heaven, Holt Rinehart (New York), 1983 £15/£5

ditto, McClelland & Stewart (Toronto), 1983 . £15/£5

ditto, Cape (London), 1983 . . . . £15/£5

Black Robe, Dutton (New York), 1985 . . £15/£5

ditto, McClelland & Stewart (Toronto), 1985 . £15/£5

ditto, Cape (London), 1985 . . . . £15/£5

ditto, Cape (London), 1985 (50 numbered, signed copies,
bound by Kenny's of Galway, slipcase) . . £100/£75

The Color of Blood, Dutton (New York), 1987 £10/£5

ditto, McClelland & Stewart (Toronto), 1987 . . £10/£5

ditto, as **The Colour of Blood**, Cape (London), 1987 £15/£5

Lies of Silence, Bloomsbury (London), 1990 . . £15/£5

ditto, London Limited Editions (London), 1990 (250
numbered, signed copies, acetate d/w) . . . £45/£35

ditto, McClelland & Stewart (Toronto), 1990 . £15/£5

ditto, Doubleday (New York), 1990 . . . . £10/£5

No Other Life, Bloomsbury (London), 1993 . £10/£5

ditto, Knopf (Canada), 1993 . . . . £15/£5

ditto, Doubleday (New York), 1993 . . . . £10/£5

The Statement, Knopf (Canada), 1995 . . £15/£5

ditto, Bloomsbury (London), 1995 . . . . £10/£5

ditto, Dutton (New York), 1996 . . . . £10/£5

The Magician's Wife, Knopf (Canada), 1997 . . £10/£5

ditto, Bloomsbury (London), 1997 . . . . £10/£5

ditto, Dutton (New York), 1998 . . . . £10/£5

Short Stories

Two Stories, Santa Susana Press/California State Univ
(Northridge CA), 1978 (300 signed, numbered copies) .
. . . . £30/£25

ditto, Santa Susana Press/California State Univ (Northridge
CA), 1978 (26 signed, lettered copies) . . . £75/£60

Other Title

Canada, Time Life International (New York), 1965 (no d/w)
. . . . £10

WILLIAM MORRIS
(b.1834 d.1896)

Poet, artist and socialist, William Morris excelled in many
of the artistic fields in which he attempted to combat
ugliness, no more so than in book production through the
Kelmscott Press. In one of his best-known novels, *News
from Nowhere*, Morris espoused the ideal that everyone
should work only for pleasure, and that beautifully hand-
crafted objects should be given away free to those who
appreciate them.

The Defence of Guenevere and Other Poems, Bell & Daldy
(London), 1858 . . . . £650

ditto, Kelmscott Press (London), 1892 (300 copies) £1,500

ditto, Kelmscott Press (London), 1892 (10 copies on vellum)
. . . . £7,000

The Life and Death of Jason, Bell & Daldy (London), 1867
. . . . £200

ditto, Bell & Daldy (London), 1867 (25 large paper copies) .
. . . . £650

ditto, Roberts Bros (Boston), 1867 . . . . £100

ditto, Kelmscott Press (London), 1895 (200 copies) £5,000

The Earthly Paradise, F.S. Ellis (London), 1868-70 (4 parts
- 1 & 2 together - 3 vols) £750

ditto, F.S. Ellis (London), 1868-70 (25 large paper copies) .
. . . . £1,500

ditto, Roberts Bros (Boston), 1868 . . . . £100

ditto, Roberts Bros (Boston), 1871 (4 parts in 3 vols) . £200

ditto, Kelmscott Press (London), 1896-97 (225 copies, 8
vols) £3,000

ditto, Kelmscott Press (London), 1896-97 (6 copies on
vellum, 8 vols) £10,000

The Story of Grettir the Strong, F.S. Ellis (London), 1869 (translated by Morris & Magnusson) . . . £100

ditto, F.S. Ellis (London), 1869 (25 large paper copies). £300

The Story of Volsangs and Niblungs, F.S. Ellis (London), 1870 (translated by Morris & Magnusson) . . . £150

ditto, F.S. Ellis (London), 1870 (25 large paper copies). £350

Love is Enough, Ellis & White (London), 1873 [1872]. £100

ditto, Kelmscott Press (London), 1897 [1898] (300 copies) £3,000

Three Northern Love Stories and Other Tales, Ellis & White (London), 1873 (translated by Morris & Magnusson) £200

ditto, F.S. Ellis (London), 1873 (large paper copies) . £400

ditto, Roberts Bros (Boston), 1873 . . . . £100

The Aenids of Virgil, Done into English Verse, Ellis & White (London), 1876 (translation, 2 vols) . . . £200

ditto, Ellis & White (London), 1876 (25 large paper copies, 2 vols) £500

The Story of Sigurd the Volsung, and the Fall of the Niblungs, Ellis & White (London), 1877 [1876] . . £200

ditto, Ellis & White (London), 1877 [1876] (25 large paper copies) £500

ditto, Roberts Bros (Boston), 1877 . . . . £100

ditto, Kelmscott Press (London), 1898 (160 copies) £2,500

Hopes and Fears for Art, Ellis & White (London), 1882 . . . . £100

ditto, Ellis & White (London), 1882 (large paper copies) £250

ditto, Roberts Bros (Boston), 1882 . . . . £100

Chants for Socialists, Socialist League (London), 1885 (wraps) £100

Pilgrims of Hope, privately printed by H. Buxton Forman (London), 1886 . . . . £250

The Odyssey of Homer, Done into English Verse, Reeves & Turner (London), 1887 (translation, 2 vols) . . £150

The Aims of Art, The Commonweal (London), 1887 (wraps) £75

The Tables Turned, The Commonweal (London), 1887 (wraps) £65

Signs of Change, Reeves & Turner (London), 1888 . £125

True and False Society, Socialist League (London), 1888 (sewn wraps) £45

A Dream of John Ball, and A King's Lesson, Reeves & Turner (London), 1888 . . . . £100

ditto, Reeves & Turner (London), 1888 (large paper copies) £300

ditto, Kelmscott Press (London), 1892 (300 copies) £2,000

ditto, Kelmscott Press (London), 1892 (11 copies on vellum) £8,000

ditto, Roycroft Shop (East Aurora, NY), 1898 . . £100

ditto, Roycroft Shop (East Aurora, NY), 1898 (100 copies on Whatman paper) £200

A Tale of the House of the Wolfings and All the Kindreds of the Mark, Reeves & Turner (London), 1889 . £125

ditto, Reeves & Turner (London), 1888 (100 large paper copies) £300

ditto, Roberts Bros (Boston), 1890 . . . . £100

The Roots of the Mountains, Reeves & Turner (London), 1889 [1890] £125

ditto, Reeves & Turner (London), 1889 [1890] (250 copies on Whatman Paper) £1,500

News From Nowhere, Roberts Bros (Boston), 1890 . £100

ditto, Reeves & Turner (London), 1891 . . . . £100

ditto, Reeves & Turner (London), 1891 (wraps) . £125

ditto, Reeves & Turner (London), 1891 (250 large paper copies) £400

ditto, Kelmscott Press (London), 1892 (300 copies) £1,500

ditto, Kelmscott Press (London), 1892 (10 copies on vellum) £7,500

The Story of Gunnlaug the Worm Tounge, Chiswick Press (London), 1891 (75 copies, translated by Morris & Magnusson) £650

The Story of the Glittering Plain, Reeves & Turner/ Kelmscott Press (London), 1891 (200 copies, slipcase) £2,500

ditto, Kelmscott Press (London), 1891 (6 copies on vellum). £6,000

ditto, Kelmscott Press (London), 1894 (250 copies, illustrated by Walter Crane) £3,000

ditto, Kelmscott Press (London), 1894 (7 copies on vellum). £10,000

ditto, Reeves & Turner (London), 1891 . . . £100

ditto, Roberts Bros (Boston), 1891 . . . . £100

Poems by the Way, Reeves & Turner (London), 1891 . £100

ditto, Reeves & Turner (London), 1891 (100 large paper copies). £225

ditto, Kelmscott Press (London), 1891 (300 copies) £1,500

ditto, Kelmscott Press (London), 1891 (13 copies on vellum) £5,000

The Order of Chivalry & L'Ordene de Chevalerie, Kelmscott Press (London), 1892 [1893] (225 copies, the latter translated by Morris) £2,000

Gothic Architecture, Kelmscott Press (London), 1893 (1,500 copies) £350

A Tale of King Florus and the Fair Jehane, Kelmscott Press (London), 1893 (350 copies, translated by Morris) £1,000

Socialism: It's Growth and Outcome, Swan Sonnenschein (London), 1893 (350 copies, translated by Morris) . £100

Of the Friendship of Amis and Amilie, Kelmscott Press (London), 1894 (500 copies, translated by Morris) . £750

The Tale of the Emperor Coustans and of Oversea, Kelmscott Press (London), 1894 (with E. Belfort Bax, 525 copies) £1,000

The Wood Beyond the World, Kelmscott Press (London), 1894 (350 copies) £1,500

ditto, Kelmscott Press (London), 1894 (8 copies on vellum). £7,500

ditto, Lawrence and Bullen (London), 1895 . . £75

ditto, Roberts Bros (Boston), 1895 . . . . £75

A Tale of Beowulf, Kelmscott Press (London), 1895 (300 copies, translated by Morris) £2,500

Child Christopher and Goldilind the Fair, Kelmscott Press (London), 1895 (600 copies, 2 vols) . . . £850

ditto, Kelmscott Press (London), 1895 (12 copies on vellum) £2,500

Old French Romances, George Allen (London), 1896 (translation) £65

The Well at the World's End, Kelmscott Press (London), 1896 (350 copies) £4,000

ditto, Longman's Green (London), 1896 (2 vols) . £200

ditto, Longman's Green (New York), 1896 (2 vols) . £200

A Note By William Morris on His Aims in Founding the Kelmscott Press, Kelmscott Press (London), 1896 (525 copies) £600

How I Became A Socialist, Twentieth Century Press (London), 1896 (wraps) £75

The Water of the Wondrous Isles, Kelmscott Press
(London), 1897 (250 copies) £2,000
ditto, Kelmscott Press (London), 1897 (6 copies on vellum).
.   .   .   .   £6,000
ditto, Longman's Green (London), 1897 .   .   . £100
ditto, Longman's Green (New York), 1897 .   . £100
The Sundering Flood, Kelmscott Press (London), 1897 (300
copies) £1,000
ditto, Kelmscott Press (London), 1897 (10 copies on vellum)
.   .   .   .   £5,000

ARTHUR MORRISON

(b.1863 d.1945)

Morrisson is perhaps best remembered for his detective
stories which are in the mould of Sherlock Holmes, but
'Martin Hewitt' lacks the eccentricities of the more famous
sleuth. His other detective, 'Horace Dorrington' is perhaps
a little more interesting as a character. Morrison also wrote
a number of mainstream novels, and of note are *The Hole
in the Wall* (a story of theft and murder in the London
slums), and *The Green Eye of Goona* (an adventure story
about a stolen Indian gem).

Detective Short Stories
Martin Hewitt, Investigator, Ward, Lock & Bowden, 1894 .
.   .   .   . £350
ditto, Harper (New York), 1894 .   .   .   . £250
Chronicles of Martin Hewitt, Ward, Lock & Bowden, 1895
.   .   .   . £300
ditto, Appleton (New York), 1896 .   .   .   . £200
Adventures of Martin Hewitt, Ward, Lock, 1896 .   . £300
The Dorrington Deed-Box, Ward Lock, 1897 .   . £300
ditto, New Amsterdam Book Co./Ward-Lock & Co. (New
York), 1900 .   .   .   . £200

Detective Fiction Novel
The Red Triangle, Eveleigh Nash, 1903 (episodic Hewitt
novel) £250
ditto, Page (New York), 1903 .   .   .   .   . £100

Other Short Stories
The Shadows Around Us, Simpkin Marshall (London), 1891
.   .   .   . £350
Tales of Mean Streets, Methuen (London), 1894 .   . £200
ditto, R.F. Fenno & Co (New York), 1895 .   .   £50
Zig-Zags at the Zoo, Newnes (London) [1894] .   . £250
Divers Vanities, Methuen (London), 1905 .   .   . £250
Green Ginger, Hutchinson (London), 1909 .   .   . £250
ditto, Stokes (New York), 1909 .   .   .   .   £50
Fiddle O' Dreams and More, Hutchinson (London), 1933 .
.   .   .   .   £500/£200

Other Novels
A Child of the Jago, Methuen (London), 1896 .   . £200
ditto, Herbert S. Stone (Chicago), 1896 .   .   . £75
To London Town, Methuen (London), 1899 .   .   £150
ditto, Herbert S. Stone (Chicago), 1899 .   .   . £75
Cunning Murrell, Methuen (London), 1900 .   .   £150
ditto, Doubleday Page & Co (New York), 1900 .   £100
The Hole in the Wall, Methuen (London), 1902 .   £150
ditto, McClure (New York), 1902 .   .   .   . £150

The Green Eye of Goona, Eveleigh Nash (London), 1904 .
.   .   .   . £250
ditto, as *The Green Diamond*, Page (New York), 1904 . £250

Plays
That Brute Simmons, Lacy (London), [1904] (with Herbert
C. Sargent) £75
The Dumb-Cake, Lacy (London), [1907] (with Richard
Pryce) £75

Others
Exhibition of Japanese Prints, Fine Art Society (London),
1909 .   .   .   .   £50
Exhibition of Japanese Screens, Yamanata & Co, 1910 £75
Painters of Japan, Jack (London), 1911 (2 vols) .   . £175
ditto, Jack (London), 1911 (150 signed sets, 2 vols) . £400
ditto, Stokes (New York), [1911] £175

TONI MORRISON

(b.1931)

In 1993 Toni Morrison became the first African-American
to win the Nobel Prize for Literature. Through her writing
and other works she has been instrumental in bringing
recognition to the genre of African-American literature.
Many of her books have achieved bestseller status in the
U.S. after their promotion by Oprah Winfrey on her
television Book Club.

Novels
The Bluest Eye, Holt Rinehart & Winston (New York), 1970
.   .   .   .   £3,000/£300
ditto, Chatto & Windus (London), 1979 .   . £100/£20
Sula, Knopf (New York), 1974 .   .   .   . £450/£50
ditto, Allen Lane (London), 1974 .   .   . £100/£25
Song of Solomon, Knopf (New York), 1977 .   £60/£15
ditto, Chatto & Windus (London), 1978 .   . £35/£10
Tar Baby, Franklin Library (Franklin Centre, PA), 1981
(signed, limited edition) £35
ditto, Knopf (New York), 1981 .   .   .   . £20/£5
ditto, Chatto & Windus (London), 1981 .   . £20/£5
A Brief Vignette from Tar Baby, Toothpaste Press (St Paul,
MN), 1982 (broadside, 90 signed copies) .   . £200
Beloved, Knopf (New York), 1987 .   .   .   . £20/£5
ditto, Chatto & Windus (London), 1987 .   . £20/£5
Jazz, Franklin Library (Franklin Centre, PA), 1992 . £70
ditto, Knopf (New York), 1992 .   .   .   . £15/£5
ditto, Chatto & Windus (London), 1992 .   . £15/£5
Paradise, Knopf (New York), 1998 .   .   . £10/£5
ditto, Chatto & Windus (London), 1998 .   . £10/£5
Love, Knopf (New York), 2003 .   .   .   . £10/£5
ditto, Chatto & Windus (London), 2003 .   . £10/£5
A Mercy, Knopf (New York), 2008 .   .   . £10/£5
ditto, Chatto & Windus (London), 2008 .   . £10/£5

Children's Titles with Slade Morrison
The Big Box, Hyperion (New York), 1999 .   . £10/£5
The Book of Mean People, Hyperion (New York), 2002 .
.   .   .   .   £10/£5
Who's Got Game? The Lion or the Mouse?, Scribner (New
York), 2003 .   .   .   . £10/£5

Who's Got Game? The Ant or the Grasshopper?, Scribner (New York), 2003 . . . . . £10/£5
Who's Got Game? Poppy or the Snake?, Scribner (New York), 2004 . . . . . . £10/£5
Peeny Butter Fudge, Simon & Schuster (New York), 2009 . . . . £10/£5
Little Cloud and Lady Wind, Simon & Schuster (New York), 2010 . . . . . . £10/£5

Others

Playing in the Dark, Harvard Univ Press (Cambridge, MA), 1992 . . . . . . £15/£5
ditto, Pan Books (London), 1993 (pbk) . . . £5
Race-Ing Justice, En-gendering Power, Pantheon (New York), 1992 (edited by and with a contribution from Morrison, pbk) £5
Lecture and Speech of Acceptance upon the Award of the Nobel Prize for Literature, Knopf (New York), 1994 (no d/w) £10
ditto, Chatto & Windus (London), 1994 . . £10
The Dancing Mind, Knopf (New York), 1996 . £10/£5
Deep Sightings and Rescue Missions, Pantheon (New York), 1996 (edited by and with a preface from Morrison) . . . . £15/£5
Birth of a Nation 'hood, Pantheon (New York), 1997 (edited by Morrison and Claudia Brodsky Lacour, pbk) . . £5
Remember: The Journey to School Integration, Houghton Mifflin (Boston), 2004 . . . . £10/£5
What Moves at the Margin: Selected Nonfiction, Univ Press of Mississippi (Jackson, MS), 2008 . . . £10/£5
Burn This Book, Harper Studio (New York), 2009 £10/£5

JOHN MORTIMER
(b.1923)

A playwright and barrister, Sir John Mortimer was called to the Bar in 1948 and became a Q.C. in 1966. He started writing by rising early and working before attending court. Rumpole, his fictional, incorrigible barrister, has been successfully and popularly televised. The autobiographical play, *A Voyage Round My Father*, tells of Mortimer's relationship with his blind father.

'Rumpole' Series

Rumpole of the Bailey, Penguin (Harmondsworth, Middlesex), 1978 (pbk) £20
ditto, Penguin (New York), 1980 (pbk) . . £10
ditto, Mysterious Press (New York), 1991 (100 signed copies, slipcase) £125
ditto, Easton Press (Norwalk, CT), 2004 . . £125
The Trials of Rumpole, Penguin (Harmondsworth, Middlesex), 1979 (pbk) £10
ditto, Penguin (New York), 1981 (pbk) . . £10
ditto, Mysterious Press (New York), 1990 . £10/£5
ditto, Mysterious Press (New York), 1990 (100 signed copies, slipcase) £100
Rumpole's Return, Penguin (Harmondsworth, Middlesex), 1981 (pbk) £10
ditto, Penguin (New York), 1982 (pbk) . . £10
ditto, Mysterious Press (New York), 1992 . £10/£5
ditto, Mysterious Press (New York), 1992 (100 signed copies, slipcase) £100

Rumpole for the Defence, Penguin (Harmondsworth, Middlesex), 1982 (pbk) £5
Rumpole and the Golden Thread, Penguin (New York), 1983 (pbk) £10
Rumpole's Last Case, Penguin (London), 1987 (pbk) . £10
ditto, Penguin (New York), 1988 (pbk) . . . £10
Rumpole and the Age of Miracles, Penguin (London), 1988 (pbk) £10
ditto, Penguin (New York), 1989 (pbk) . . . £10
Rumpole à la Carte, Viking (London), 1990 . £15/£5
ditto, Viking (New York), 1990 . . . . £10/£5
Rumpole on Trial, Viking (London), 1992 . £10/£5
ditto, Penguin (New York), 1992 . . . £10/£5
Rumpole and the Angel of Death, Viking (London), 1995 . . . . £10/£5
ditto, Penguin (New York), 1996 . . . £10/£5
Rumpole And the Younger Generation, Penguin (London), 1995 (pbk) £5
ditto, Penguin (New York), 1995 (pbk) . . £5
Rumpole Rests His Case, Viking (London), 2001 . £10/£5
ditto, Viking (New York), 2001 . . . . £10/£5
Rumpole And the Primrose Path, Viking (London), 2002 . . . . £10/£5
ditto, Viking (New York), 2003 . . . . £10/£5
Rumpole and the Penge Bungalow Murders, Viking (London), 2004 . . . . . . £10/£5
ditto, Viking (New York), 2004 . . . . £10/£5
Rumpole and the Reign of Terror, Viking (London), 2006 . . . . £10/£5
ditto, Viking (New York), 2006 . . . . £10/£5
The Anti-social Behaviour of Horace Rumpole, Viking (London), 2007 . . . . . . £10/£5
ditto, Viking (New York), 2007 . . . . £10/£5
Rumpole Misbehaves, Viking (London), 2007 . £10/£5
ditto, Viking (New York), 2007 . . . . £10/£5
Rumpole at Christmas, Viking (London), 2009 . £10/£5
ditto, as *A Rumpole Christmas*, Viking (New York), 2009 . . . . £10/£5

Novels

Charade, Bodley Head (London), 1947 . . . £125/£30
ditto, Viking (London), 1986 . . . . . £15/£5
Rumming Park, Lane (London), 1948 . . . £100/£20
Answer Yes or No, Lane (London), 1950 . . . £65/£15
ditto, as *The Silver Hook*, Morrow (New York), 1950 . . . . £30/£5
Like Men Betrayed, Collins (London), 1953 . . £25/£5
ditto, Lippincott (Philadelphia), 1954 . . £25/£5
The Narrowing Stream, Collins (London), 1954 . £25/£5
ditto, Viking (New York), 1989 . . . . £10/£5
Three Winters, Collins (London), 1956 . . £25/£5
Will Shakespeare: The Untold Story, Hodder & Stoughton (London), 1977 . . . . £20/£5
ditto, Delacorte (New York), 1978 . . . £15/£5
Paradise Postponed, Viking (London), 1985 . . £15/£5
ditto, Viking (New York), 1985 . . . . £15/£5
Summer's Lease, Viking (London), 1988 . . £25/£5
ditto, Viking (New York), 1988 . . . . £20/£5
ditto, Franklin Library (Franklin Centre, PA), 1988 (signed limited edition) £20
ditto, London Limited Editions (London), 1988 (250 signed copies) £35
Titmuss Regained, Viking (London), 1990 . £15/£5
ditto, Viking (New York), 1990 . . . . £10/£5

Dunster, Viking (London), 1992 . . . . £10/£5
ditto, Viking (New York), 1993 . . . . £10/£5
Felix in the Underworld, Viking (London), 1997 . £10/£5
ditto, Viking (New York), 1997 . . . . £10/£5
The Sound of Trumpets, Viking (London), 1998 . £10/£5
ditto, Viking (New York), 1999 . . . . £10/£5
Quite Honestly, Viking (London), 2005 . . £10/£5
ditto, Viking (New York), 2006 . . . . £10/£5

Plays
Three Plays, Elek (London), 1958 . . . . £45/£10
ditto, Grove Press (New York), 1962 . . . £25/£5
The Wrong Side of the Park, Heinemann (London), 1960 .
. . . . £30/£5
Lunch Hour, French (London), 1960 (pbk) . . £10
Lunch Hour and Other Plays, Methuen (London), 1960 .
. . . . £25/£5
Two Stars For Comfort, Methuen (London), 1962. £15/£5
A Flea in Her Ear, French (London), 1967 (pbk) . £5
ditto, French (New York), 1967 (pbk) . . . £5
The Judge, Methuen (London), 1967 . . . £10/£5
Five Plays, Methuen (London), 1970. . . . £10/£5
Come As You Are: Four Short Plays, Methuen (London), 1971 . . . . £10/£5
A Voyage Round My Father, Methuen (London), 1971 .
. . . . £25/£10
Knightsbridge, French (London), 1973 (pbk) . . £5
Collaborations, Methuen (London), 1973 . £10/£5
The Fear of Heaven, French (London), 1978 (pbk) . £5
Heaven and Hell, French (London), 1978 (pbk) . £5
Edwin and Other Plays, Penguin (Harmondsworth, Middlesex), 1984 (pbk) £5
Three Boulevard Farces, Penguin (Harmondsworth, Middlesex), 1985 (pbk) £5

Collected Editions
Rumpole, Allen Lane (London), 1980 . . . £10/£5
Regina v. Rumpole, Allen Lane (London), 1981 . £10/£5
The First Rumpole Omnibus, Penguin (Harmondsworth, Middlesex), 1983. . . . . . . £10/£5
The Second Rumpole Omnibus, Viking (London), 1987 .
. . . . £10/£5
ditto, Penguin (New York), 1988 . . . £10/£5
The Rapstone Chronicles, Viking (London), 1991. £10/£5
The Best of Rumpole, Viking (London), 1993 . £10/£5
The Third Rumpole Omnibus, Viking (London), 1997. .
. . . . £10/£5

Others
With Love and Lizards, Joseph (London), 1957 (written with Penelope Mortimer) . . . . . £30/£10
No Moaning at the Bar, Bles (London), 1957 (pseud 'Geoffrey Lincoln') . . . . . . £35/£10
Clinging to the Wreckage, Weidenfeld & Nicolson (London), 1982 . . . . £15/£5
ditto, Ticknor & Fields (New Haven/New York), 1982 . .
. . . . £15/£5
In Character, Allen Lane (London), 1983 . . £15/£5
Character Parts, Viking (London), 1986 . . £15/£5
The Oxford Book of Villains, O.U.P. (Oxford, UK), 1992 (edited by Mortimer) . . . . . £10/£5
ditto, O.U.P. (New York), 1992 . . . . £10/£5
Murderers and Other Friends, Viking (London), 1994 .
. . . . £10/£5

ditto, Viking (New York), 1994 . . . . . £10/£5
The Summer of a Dormouse: A Year of Growing Old Disgracefully, Viking (London), 2000 . . £10/£5
ditto, Viking (New York), 2001 . . . £10/£5
Where There's a Will, Viking (London), 2003 . £10/£5

KATE MOSSE
(b. 1961)

Kate Mosse is a British author and broadcaster. The Co-Founder of the Orange Prize for Fiction and the Orange Award for New Writers, she is also a former Executive Director of Chichester Festival Theatre. Mosse is a Fellow of the Royal Society of the Arts, won the 2000 European Woman of Achievement Award for her contribution to the Arts, and was awarded an honorary MA from University College, Chichester.

Novels
Eskimo Kissing, Hodder & Stoughton (London), 1996 . .
. . . . £75/£20
Crucifix Lane, Hodder & Stoughton (London), 1998 (pbk) .
. . . . £50
Labyrinth, Orion (London), 2005. . . . . £75/£15
ditto, Orion/Goldsboro Books (London) 2005 (500 signed, numbered copies) . . . . . £30/£10
ditto, Orion (London), 2005 (later printing; 1,000 signed in slipcase). . . . . . £125/£100
ditto, Putnam (New York), 2006 . . . . £10/£5
ditto, Orion (London), 2006 (first illustrated edition; no d/w)
. . . . £30
Sepulchre, Orion (London) 2007. . . . . £10/£5
ditto, Orion/Goldsboro Books (London) 2007 (500 signed, numbered copies; slipcase) . . . . £35/£20
ditto, Putnam (New York), 2008. . . . . £10/£5
The Winter Ghosts, Orion (London) 2009. . . £10/£5

Non-Fiction
Becoming A Mother, Virago (London) 1993 (pbk) . £5
The House, A Season In The Life Of The Royal Opera House, Covent Garden, BBC Books (London) 1995 . .
. . . . £50/£15

PATRICIA MOYES
(b.1923 d.2000)

Patricia Moyes was born in Dublin but educated in England. She became Peter Ustinov's personal assistant and in 1960 wrote the screenplay for the film *School for Scoundrels*. She was the author of nineteen crime novels.

Novels
Dead Men Don't Ski, Collins Crime Club (London), 1959 .
. . . . £65/£10
ditto, Holt (New York), 1960 . . . . . £35/£10
The Sunken Sailor, Collins Crime Club (London), 1961 .
. . . . £50/£10
ditto, as *Down Among the Dead Men*, Holt (New York), 1961 . . . . £30/£5

Death on the Agenda, Collins Crime Club (London), 1962 .
. . . . £40/£10
ditto, Holt (New York), 1962 . . . . £25/£5
Murder a la Mode, Collins Crime Club (London), 1963 .
. . . . £35/£5
ditto, Holt (New York), 1963 . . . . £20/£5
Falling Star, Collins Crime Club (London), 1964 . £45/£10
ditto, Holt (New York), 1964 . . . . £20/£5
Johnny Under Ground, Collins Crime Club (London), 1965
. . . . £45/£10
ditto, Holt (New York), 1966 . . . . £20/£5
Murder Fantastical, Collins Crime Club (London), 1967 .
. . . . £25/£5
ditto, Holt (New York), 1967 . . . . £20/£5
Death and the Dutch Uncle, Collins Crime Club (London),
1968 . . . . £20/£5
ditto, Holt (New York), 1968 . . . . £20/£5
Who Saw Her Die?, Collins Crime Club (London), 1970 .
. . . . £15/£5
ditto, as *Many Deadly Returns*, Holt (New York), 1970 .
. . . . £15/£5
Season of Snows and Sins, Collins Crime Club (London),
1971 . . . . £15/£5
ditto, Holt (New York), 1971 . . . . £15/£5
The Curious Affair of the Third Dog, Collins Crime Club
(London), 1973 . . . . . . £15/£5
ditto, Holt (New York), 1973 . . . . £15/£5
Black Widower, Collins Crime Club (London), 1975 £15/£5
ditto, Holt (New York), 1975 . . . . £15/£5
To Kill a Coconut, Collins Crime Club (London), 1977 .
. . . . £15/£5
ditto, as The Coconut Killings, Holt (New York), 1977. .
. . . . £10/£5
Who Is Simon Warwick?, Collins Crime Club (London),
1978 . . . . £10/£5
ditto, Holt (New York), 1978 . . . . £10/£5
Angel Death, Collins Crime Club (London), 1980 . £10/£5
ditto, Holt (New York), 1980 . . . . £10/£5
A Six-Letter Word for Death, Collins Crime Club (London),
1983 . . . . £10/£5
ditto, Holt (New York), 1983 . . . . £10/£5
Night Ferry to Death, Collins Crime Club (London), 1985 .
. . . . £10/£5
ditto, Holt (New York), 1983 . . . . £10/£5
Black Girl, White Girl, Holt (New York), 1989 . £10/£5
ditto, Collins Crime Club (London), 1990. . . £10/£5
Twice in a Blue Moon, Collins Crime Club (London), 1993
. . . . £10/£5
ditto, Holt (New York), 1993 . . . . £10/£5

Miscellaneous
Time Remembered, Methuen (London), 1955 (translation of
play by Jean Anouilh). . . . . £20/£5
ditto, Coward-McCann (New York), 1958 . . £20/£5
Helter-Skelter, Holt (New York), 1968 . . £15/£5
ditto, Macdonald (London), 1969 . . . £10/£5
After All, They're Only Cats, Curtis (New York), 1973 (pbk)
. . . . £5
How to Talk to Your Cat, Arthur Barker (London), 1978 .
. . . . £15/£5
ditto, Holt (New York), 1978 . . . . £10/£5
*Who Killed Father Christmas And Other Unseasonable
Demises*, Crippen & Landru (Norfolk, VA), 1996 (pbk) £5

ditto, Crippen & Landru (Norfolk, VA), 1996 (350 signed,
numbered hardback copies with tipped-in manuscript page)
. . . . £25/£15

HARUKI MURAKAMI
(b.1949)

Haruki Murakami was born in Kyoto, Japan. He met his
wife, Yoko, at university and they opened a jazz club in
Tokyo called Peter Cat. The massive success of his novel
Norwegian Wood (1987) made him a national celebrity. He
fled Japan and did not return until 1995 when he came to
regard the Kobe earthquake and the Tokyo gas attack as
twin manifestations of a violence just beneath the surface
of Japanese life.

Novels
Pinball 1973, Kodansha (Tokyo, Japan), 1985 (pbk) . £600
Hear The Wind Sing, Kodansha (Tokyo, Japan), 1987 (pbk)
. . . . £600
A Wild Sheep Chase, Kodansha (Cary, NC), 1989 £45/£15
ditto, Hamish Hamilton (London), 1990. . . . £175/£30
Norwegian Wood, Kodansha (Tokyo, Japan), 1989 (pbk; 2
vols) £300
ditto, Harvill Press (London), 2000 (pbk 2 vol boxed set) .
. . . . £45/£10
ditto, Harvill Press (London), 2000 (500 Signed, Numbered
two volume boxed set in a tin box) £275
The Hard Boiled Wonderland And The End Of The World,
Kodansha (Tokyo/New York), 1991. . . £65/£15
ditto, Hamish Hamilton (London), 1991. . . £85/£20
Dance, Dance, Dance, Kodansha (America), 1994 £100/£25
ditto,Hamish Hamilton (London), 1994 (pbk in d/w)
. . . . £125/£65
The Wind Up Bird Chronicle, Knopf (New York) 1997 .
. . . . £75/£25
ditto, Harvill Press (London), 1998 (pbk). . . £30
South Of The Border, West Of The Sun, Knopf (New
York), 1999 . . . . £35/£10
ditto Harvill Press (London), 2005 (pbk) . . £10
Sputnik Sweetheart, Knopf (New York), 2001 . £25/£10
ditto, Harvill Press (London), 1998 (pbk). . . £10
Kafka On The Shore, Harvill Press (London), 2005 £20/£10
ditto Harvill Press (London), 2005 (1000 signed, numbered
copies; slipcase) . . . . . £225/£175
ditto Harvill Press (London), 2005 (100 Signed, numbered
copies bound in leather' slipcase) . . £600/£500
ditto, Knopf (New York), 2005 . . . . £25/£10
After Dark, Knopf (New York), 2007 . . £15/£5
ditto, Harvill Secker (London), 2007. . . £15/£5
ditto, Harvill Secker (London), 2007, (100 signed, numbered
copies bound in leather) . . . £300/£250
ditto, Harvill Secker (London), 2007, (800 unsigned,
unnumbered copies in a slipcase exclusive to Borders) .
. . . . £30/£25

Short Stories
The Elephant Vanishes, Knopf (New York), 1993 £100/£25
After The Quake, Knopf (New York), 2002. . . £25/£5
ditto, Harvill Press (London), 2002 . . . £45/£10
Vintage Murakami, Vintage (New York), 2004 (pbk) . £5

Blind Willow, Sleeping Woman, Harvill Secker (London) ,
2006 . . . . £20/£5
ditto, Harvill Secker (London) , 2006 (1000 signed,
numbered copies; slipcase) . . . . £90/£65
ditto Knopf (New York), 2006. . . . . £10/£5
Tony Takitani, Harvill Press (London), 2007 (pbk) . £5
ditto, Cloverfield Press (Los Angeles, CA), 2006 (1,000
numbered copies; pbk in d/w) . . . £50/£35
Aeroplane, Oundle Festival of Literature Press (Oundle),
2007 (120 signed, numbered hardback copies in acetate
d/w) . . . . £225/£200

Non-Fiction

Underground, Harvill Press (London), 2000 . £20/£5
ditto, Knopf (New York), 2001 (wraps) . . . £5
What I Talk About When I Talk About Running, Knopf
(New York) 2008 . . . . . . £15/£5
ditto, Harvill Secker (London 2008) . . . £15/£5
ditto, Harvill Secker (London), 2008 (75 signed, numbered
copies) . . . . £150/£100

IRIS MURDOCH

(b.1919 d.1999)

An Anglo–Irish novelist and philosopher, Dame Iris
Murdoch employed a blend of Realism and Symbolism in
her highly regarded novels. Her full characterisation and
compelling plotlines usually involve ethical or sexual
themes. *Under the Net* was chosen by the American
Modern Library as one of the 100 best English-language
novels of the 20th century. *The Sea, The Sea* won the 1978
Booker Prize.

Novels

Under the Net, Chatto & Windus (London), 1954 £750/£125
ditto, Viking (New York), 1954 . . . . £75/£20
The Flight from the Enchanter, Chatto & Windus
(London), 1956 . . . . . . £450/£65
ditto, Viking (New York), 1956 . . . . £125/£20
The Sandcastle, Chatto & Windus (London), 1957 £225/£50
ditto, Viking (New York), 1957 . . . £65/£15
The Bell, Chatto & Windus (London), 1958 . £75/£20
ditto, Viking (New York), 1958 . . . £25/£5
A Severed Head, Chatto & Windus (London), 1961 £25/£10
ditto, Viking (New York), 1961 . . . . £15/£5
An Unofficial Rose, Chatto & Windus (London), 1962.
. . . . £20/£5
ditto, Viking (New York), 1962 . . . . £10/£5
The Unicorn, Chatto & Windus (London), 1963 £15/£5
ditto, Viking (New York), 1963 . . . . £10/£5
The Italian Girl, Chatto & Windus (London), 1964 £15/£5
ditto, Viking (New York), 1964 . . . . £10/£5
The Red and the Green, Chatto & Windus (London), 1965 .
. . . . £15/£5
ditto, Viking (New York), 1965 . . . . £10/£5
The Time of the Angels, Chatto & Windus (London), 1966.
. . . . £15/£5
ditto, Viking (New York), 1966 . . . . £10/£5
The Nice and the Good, Chatto & Windus (London), 1968 .
. . . . £15/£5
ditto, Viking (New York), 1968 . . . . £10/£5
Bruno's Dream, Chatto & Windus (London), 1969 £15/£5

ditto, Viking (New York), 1969 . . . . £10/£5
A Fairly Honourable Defeat, Chatto & Windus (London),
1970 . . . . £15/£5
ditto, Viking (New York), 1970 . . . £10/£5
An Accidental Man, Chatto & Windus (London), 1971 .
. . . . £15/£5
ditto, Viking (New York), 1972. . . . . £10/£5
The Black Prince, Chatto & Windus (London), 1973 £15/£5
ditto, Viking (New York), 1973 . . . . £10/£5
The Sacred and Profane Love Machine, Chatto & Windus
(London), 1974 . . . . . £15/£5
ditto, Viking (New York), 1974 . . . . £10/£5
A Word Child, Chatto & Windus (London), 1975 . £15/£5
ditto, Viking (New York), 1975 . . . . £10/£5
Henry and Cato, Chatto & Windus (London), 1976 £20/£5
ditto, Viking (New York), 1977 . . . . £10/£5
The Sea, the Sea, Chatto & Windus (London), 1978 £50/£10
ditto, Viking (New York), 1978 . . . . £35/£10
Nuns and Soldiers, Chatto & Windus (London), 1980 . .
. . . . £10/£5
ditto, Viking (New York), 1981 . . . . £10/£5
The Philosopher's Pupil, Chatto & Windus (London), 1983
. . . . £10/£5
ditto, Viking (New York), 1983 . . . . £10/£5
The Good Apprentice, Chatto & Windus (London), 1985 .
. . . . £10/£5
ditto, London Limited Editions (London), 1985 (250 signed
copies, glassine d/w) . . . . £80/£65
ditto, Viking (New York), 1986 . . . . £10/£5
The Book and the Brotherhood, Chatto & Windus
(London), 1987 . . . . . £10/£5
ditto, Viking (New York), 1988 . . . . £10/£5
ditto, Franklin Library (Franklin Centre, PA), 1988 (signed
limited edition) £20
The Message to the Planet, Chatto & Windus (London),
1989 . . . . £10/£5
ditto, London Limited Editions (London), 1989 (150 signed
copies, glassine d/w) . . . . £85/£65
ditto, Viking (New York), 1990 . . . . £10/£5
The Green Knight, Chatto & Windus (London), 1993 . .
. . . . £10/£5
ditto, Viking (New York), 1994 . . . . £10/£5
Jackson's Dilemma, Chatto & Windus (London), 1995 .
. . . . £10/£5
ditto, Viking (New York), 1995 . . . . £10/£5

Plays

A Severed Head, Chatto & Windus (London), 1964 (with
J.B. Priestley) . . . . . . £40/£10
The Italian Girl, French (London), 1968 (with James
Saunders) £40
The Three Arrows and ***The Servants and the Snow: Two
Plays***, Chatto & Windus (London), 1973 . £65/£10
ditto, Viking (New York), 1974 . . . . £45/£10
Three Plays, Chatto & Windus (London), 1989 (*The Black
Prince, The Three Arrows* and *The Servants and the Snow*)
. . . . £35/£10
The Black Prince, French (London), 1989 . £10
Joanna Joanna, *A Play in Two Acts*, Colophon Press
(London), 1994 (12 signed copies of 143, leather, slipcase)
. . . . £200
ditto, Colophon Press (London), 1994 (125 numbered, signed
copies of 143) £100

ditto, Colophon Press (London), 1994 (6 lettered, signed copies of 143) £350

The One Alone, Colophon Press (London), 1995 (26 lettered, signed copies) £200

ditto, Colophon Press (London), 1995 (6 roman numeralled, signed copies; wraps) £350

ditto, Colophon Press (London), 1995 (200 numbered, signed copies; wraps) £65

Poetry

A Year of Birds, Compton Press (Tisbury, Wiltshire), 1978 (350 signed, numbered copies, 12 plates by Reynolds Stone, no d/w) £165

ditto, Compton Press (Tisbury, Wiltshire), 1978 (50 signed, numbered copies, no d/w, with extra set of proof engravings, box) £400

ditto, Chatto & Windus (London), 1984 . . £40/£15

Something Special, Four Poems and a Story, Eurographica (Helsinki), 1990 (350 signed, numbered copies; wraps in d/w) . . . . £125/£85

ditto, Chatto & Windus (London), 1999 . . £10/£5

ditto, Norton (New York), 2000 . . . . . £10/£5

Others

Sartre: Romantic Rationalist, Bowes & Bowes (Cambridge, UK), 1953 . . . . £125/£20

ditto, Yale Univ Press (New Haven, CT), 1953 . £65/£20

The Sovereignty of Good over Other Concepts, C.U.P. (Cambridge, UK), 1967 (wraps) £65

ditto, as **The Sovereignty of Good**, Routledge & Kegan Paul (London), 1970 (containing extra essays; wraps). £25/£10

ditto, Schocken Books (New York), 1971. . . £15/£5

The Fire and the Sun: Why Plato Banished the Artists, O.U.P. (Oxford, UK), 1977 . . . . . £30/£10

ditto, Viking (New York), 1990 . . . . £25/£10

The Servants: An Opera in Three Acts, O.U.P. (Oxford, UK), 1980 (music by William Mathias, libretto by Murdoch; 125 signed, numbered copies; wraps) . . £750

Reynolds Stone, Warren Editions (London), 1981 (300 signed copies of 750; wraps) £75

ditto, Warren Editions (London), 1981 (unsigned copies of 750; wraps) £25

Acastos: Two Platonic Dialogues, Chatto & Windus (London), 1986 . . . . £15/£5

ditto, Viking (New York), 1987 . . . . £15/£5

The Existentialist Political Myth, Delos Press (Birmingham, West Midlands), 1989 (45 signed copies of 225; wraps, slipcase). £150

ditto, Delos Press (Birmingham, West Midlands), 1989 (180 numbered copies of 225; wraps, slipcase) . . . £45

Metaphysics as a Guide to Morals, Chatto & Windus (London), 1992 . . . . £15/£5

ditto, Allen Lane (New York), 1993 . . . . £10/£5

Existentialists and Mystics, Delos Press (Birmingham, West Midlands), 1993 (100 signed copies of 500; wraps, slipcase) £125

ditto, Delos Press (Birmingham, West Midlands), 1993 (400 numbered copies of 500; wraps) £40

Existentialists and Mystics: Writings on Philosophy and Literature, Chatto & Windus (London), 1997 . £10/£5

ditto, Allen Lane (New York), 1998 . . . . £10/£5

VLADIMIR NABOKOV
(b.1899 d.1977)

A Russian-born naturalised American novelist, short story writer and poet, Nabokov's much admired first published works were written in Russian. However, he rose to international prominence as a masterly prose stylist of novels in English. During the second half of his career he achieved a somewhat notorious success with the novel *Lolita*.

Novels

Camera Obscura, John Long (London), 1936 (pseud 'Vladimir Nabokoff-Sirin', translated by Winifred Roy) .
. . . . £12,000/£2,000

ditto, as **Laughter in the Dark**, Bobbs-Merrill (Indianapolis, IN), 1938 (pseud 'Vladimir Nabokoff', revised edition; first issue in green cloth) . . . . . £1,250/£175

ditto, as **Laughter in the Dark**, Weidenfeld & Nicolson (London), 1961 . . . . £50/£15

Despair, John Long (London), 1937 (pseud 'Vladimir Nabokoff-Sirin') . . . . . £10,000/£1,500

ditto, Putnam (New York), 1966 (revised edition; first issue with title in purple on front flap) . . . £65/£15

ditto, Putnam (New York), 1966 (second issue with title in black on front flap) . . . . . £45/£15

ditto, Weidenfeld & Nicolson (London), 1966 (revised edition) . . . . £45/£10

The Real Life of Sebastian Knight, New Directions (Norfolk, CT), 1941 (woven red burlap, no d/w) . £200

ditto, New Directions (Norfolk, CT), 1941 (smooth red cloth) . . . . £300/£75

ditto, Editions Poetry (London), 1945 . . . £200/£25

Bend Sinister, Holt (New York), 1947 . . £175/£35

ditto, Weidenfeld & Nicolson (London), 1960. . £65/£20

Lolita, Olympia Press (Paris), 1955 (2 vols, 'Francs: 900' on back cover; pbk) £3,000

ditto, Putnam (New York), 1958 (d/w bears only distinction between trade and book club copies) . . . £300/£35

ditto, Weidenfeld & Nicolson (London), 1959. . £175/£35

ditto, as **The Annotated Lolita**, McGraw-Hill (New York), 1970 (edited by Alfred Appel) . . . . £25/£10

ditto, as **The Annotated Lolita**, Weidenfeld & Nicolson (London), 1971 . . . . £25/£10

Pnin, Doubleday (New York), 1957 . . £175/£45

ditto, Heinemann (London), 1957 . . . £125/£35

Invitation to a Beheading, Putnam (New York), 1959 . .
. . . . £45/£10

ditto, Weidenfeld & Nicolson (London), 1960. . £35/£10

Pale Fire, Putnam (New York), 1962 . . . £135/£35

ditto, Weidenfeld & Nicolson (London), 1962. . £100/£15

The Gift, Putnam (New York), 1963 . . . £45/£15

ditto, Weidenfeld & Nicolson (London), 1963. . £40/£15

The Defence, Weidenfeld & Nicolson (London), 1964 . .
. . . . £40/£15

ditto, as **The Defense**, Putnam (New York), 1964 . £40/£15

The Eye, Phaedra (New York), 1965 . . . £35/£15

ditto, Weidenfeld & Nicolson (London), 1966. . £35/£15

King, Queen, Knave, McGraw-Hill (New York), 1968 . .
. . . . £35/£15

ditto, Weidenfeld & Nicolson (London), 1968. . £35/£15

Ada or Ardor: A Family Chronicle, McGraw-Hill (New York), 1969 . . . . £25/£10

ditto, Weidenfeld & Nicolson (London), 1969. . £25/£10
Mary, McGraw-Hill (New York), 1970 . . . £20/£5
ditto, Weidenfeld & Nicolson (London), 1971. . £20/£5
Glory, McGraw-Hill (New York), 1971 . . . £20/£5
ditto, Weidenfeld & Nicolson (London), 1972. . £20/£5
Transparent Things, McGraw-Hill (New York), 1972 £20/£5
ditto, Weidenfeld & Nicolson (London), 1973. . £20/£5
Look at the Harlequins!, McGraw-Hill (New York), 1974 .
. . . . £20/£5
ditto, Weidenfeld & Nicolson (London), 1975. . £20/£5
The Enchanter, Putnam (New York), 1986 . . £20/£5
ditto, Picador (London), 1987 . . . £15/£5

Short Stories
Nine Stories/Direction Two, New Directions (Norfolk, CT), 1947 (pbk) £150
Nabokov's Dozen: A Collection of Thirteen Stories, Doubleday (New York), 1958 . . . . £85/£25
ditto, Heinemann (London), 1959 . . . £75/£15
ditto, as *Spring in Fialta*, Popular Library (New York), 1959 (pbk) £15
Nabokov's Quartet, Phaedra (New York), 1966 . £25/£5
ditto, Weidenfeld & Nicolson (London), 1967. . £25/£5
A Russian Beauty and Other Stories, McGraw-Hill (New York), 1973 . . . . £25/£5
ditto, Weidenfeld & Nicolson (London), 1973. . £25/£5
Tyrants Destroyed and Other Stories, McGraw-Hill (New York), 1975 . . . . £20/£5
ditto, Weidenfeld & Nicolson (London), 1975. . £20/£5
Details of a Sunset and Other Stories, McGraw-Hill (New York), 1976 . . . . £20/£5
ditto, Weidenfeld & Nicolson (London), 1976. . £20/£5
The Stories of Vladimir Nabokov, Knopf (New York), 1995
. . . . £15/£5
ditto, Weidenfeld & Nicolson (London), 1996. . £15/£5

Collected Edition
Nabokov's Congeries, Viking Press (New York), 1968 .
. . . . £20/£5

Poetry
Poems, Doubleday (New York), 1959 . . . £145/£35
ditto, Weidenfeld & Nicolson (London), 1961. . £100/£25
Poems and Problems, McGraw-Hill (New York), 1970. .
. . . . £50/£15
ditto, Weidenfeld & Nicolson (London), 1972. . £45/£10

Plays
The Waltz Invention: A Play in Three Acts, Phaedra (New York), 1966 . . . . £30/£10
Lolita: A Screenplay, McGraw-Hill (New York), 1974. .
. . . . £25/£5
The Man from the USSR and Other Plays, Harcourt Brace (New York), 1984 . . . . £20/£5
ditto, Weidenfeld & Nicolson (London), 1985. . £20/£5

Others
Nikolai Gogol, New Directions (Norfolk, CT), 1944 (first issue, tan cloth with brown lettering, 5 titles listed on verso of half title, d/w with $1.50 price) . . . £100/£35
ditto, New Directions (Norfolk, CT), 1944 (second issue, tan cloth with blue lettering, 14 titles listed on verso of half title, d/w with $2.00 price and 14 titles on rear flap) £75/£15
ditto, Editions Poetry (London), 1947 . . . £100/£20

Three Russian Poets: Selections from Pushkin, Lermontov and Tyutchev, New Directions (Norfolk, CT), 1944 (new translations by Nabokov, grey paper boards, grey d/w with brown lettering, at '$1.00') . . . . . £125/£45
ditto, New Directions (Norfolk, CT), 1944 (tan stapled wraps with blue-grey d/w lettered in brown, at '$.50') . £75/£15
ditto, as *Pushkin, Lermontov and Tyutchev: Poems*, Lindsay Drummond (London), 1947 . . £65/£15
A Hero of Our Time, by Mihail Lermontov, Doubleday (New York), 1958 (translated by Vladimir Nabokov; pbk)
. . . . £15
The Song of Igor's Campaign, Vintage (New York), 1960 (translated by Vladimir Nabokov; pbk) . . . £10
ditto, Weidenfeld & Nicolson (London), 1961. . £30/£10
Eugene Onegin: A Novel in Verse, by Aleksandr Pushkin, Pantheon (New York), 1964 (translation and commentary by Vladimir Nabokov, 4 vols, slipcase) . . £150/£75
ditto, Princeton Univ Press (Princeton, NJ), 1975 (revised edition) . . . . £25/£5
Notes on Prosody From the Commentary to his translation of Pushkin's Eugene Onegin, Routledge (London), 1965
. . . . £25/£5
ditto, Princeton Univ Press (Princeton, NJ), 1969 . £25/£5
Strong Opinions, McGraw-Hill (New York), 1973 £25/£10
ditto, Weidenfeld & Nicolson (London), 1974. . £20/£5
The Nabokov/Wilson Letters, 1940-1971, Harper & Row (New York), 1979 . . . . . . £20/£5
ditto, Weidenfeld & Nicolson (London), 1979. . £20/£5
Lectures on Literature, Harcourt Brace (New York), 1980 .
. . . . £25/£5
ditto, Weidenfeld & Nicolson (London), 1980. . £20/£5
Lectures on Ulysses: A Facsimilie of the Manuscript, Bruccoli Clark (Bloomfield Hills, MI & Columbia, SC), 1980 (500 numbered copies, glassine d/w, slipcase) .
. . . . £150/£100
Lectures on Russian Literature, Harcourt Brace (New York), 1981 . . . . £25/£5
ditto, Weidenfeld & Nicolson (London), 1982. . £20/£5
Lectures on Don Quixote, Harcourt Brace (New York), 1983
. . . . £20/£5
ditto, Weidenfeld & Nicolson (London), 1983. . £15/£5
Nabokov's Butterflies: Unpublished and Uncollected Writings, Beacon Press (Boston), 2000 . . £25/£5
ditto, Beacon Press (Boston), 2000 (240 numbered copies signed by Brian Boyd, Robert Michael Pyle and Dmitri Nabokov, slipcase) . . . . . £125/£85
ditto, Allen Lane (London), 2000 . . . £15/£5

Autobiography
Conclusive Evidence: A Memoir, Harper (New York), 1951
. . . . £150/£45
ditto, as *Speak, Memory: A Memoir*, Gollancz (London), 1951 (first issue blue-green cloth, black stamping, no *Daily Mail* device on spine or at bottom of front flap) . £300/£50
ditto, Gollancz (London), 1951 (second issue blue cloth, gilt stamping, with *Daily Mail* device on spine and at bottom of front flap) . . . . . . £150/£20
ditto, as *Speak, Memory: An Autobiography*, Putnam (New York), 1966 (revised edition) . . . £50/£20
ditto, as *Speak, Memory: An Autobiography*, Weidenfeld & Nicolson (London), 1967 (revised edition) . £25/£10
Selected Letters, 1940-1977, Harcourt Brace (New York), 1989 . . . . £20/£5
ditto, Weidenfeld & Nicolson (London), 1990. . £20/£5

SHIVA NAIPAUL
(b.1945 d.1985)

A Trinidadian novelist, and younger brother of V.S. Naipaul, Shiva Naipaul's three novels effectively mix satire and compassion. *Fireflies*, his first novel, won the Jock Campbell *New Statesman* Award, the John Llewellyn Rhys Prize and the Winifred Holtby Prize. He died in a car accident in 1985, aged only 40, after which the *Spectator* established the Shiva Naipaul Memorial Prize.

Novels
Fireflies, Deutsch (London), 1970 . . . . £65/£15
ditto, Knopf (New York), 1971 . . . . . £35/£10
The Chip-Chip Gatherers, Deutsch (London), 1973 £35/£5
ditto, Knopf (New York), 1973 . . . . . £25/£5
A Hot Country, Hamilton (London), 1983 . . £15/£5
ditto, as *Love and Death in a Hot Country*, Viking (New York), 1984 . . . . £10/£5

Travel
North of South: An African Journey, Deutsch (London), 1978 . . . . £10/£5
ditto, Simon & Schuster (New York), 1979 . . £10/£5
Black and White, Hamilton (New York), 1980 . £10/£5
ditto, as *Journey to Nowhere: A New World Tragedy*, Simon & Schuster (New York), 1981 . . . £10/£5
Beyond the Dragon's Mouth: Stories and Pieces, Hamilton (London), 1984 . . . . . . £10/£5
ditto, Viking (New York), 1985 . . . . . £10/£5
ditto, as *A Man of Mystery and Other Stories*, Penguin (Harmondsworth, Middlesex), 1995 (wraps). . . £5
An Unfinished Journey, Hamilton (London), 1986 £10/£5
ditto, Viking (New York), 1987 . . . . . £10/£5

V.S. NAIPAUL
(b.1932)

A distinguished Trinidadian-born British novelist, Sir V.S. Naipaul uses 20th century uncertainties such as imperialism and colonialism as the motivation for his work. Both his fiction and his travel-writing have been criticised for their allegedly unsympathetic portrayal of the Third World. He won the Nobel Prize for Literature in 2001.

Novels
The Mystic Masseur, Deutsch (London), 1957 . £350/£65
ditto, Vanguard Press (New York), 1959 . . .£100/£15
The Suffrage of Elvira, Deutsch (London), 1958 . £400/£75
A House for Mr Biswas, Deutsch (London), 1961. £450/£75
ditto, McGraw-Hill (New York), 1962 . . .£150/£20
Mr Stone and the Knights Companion, Deutsch (London), 1963 . . . . £75/£20
ditto, Macmillan (New York), 1964 . . . £50/£15
The Mimic Men, Deutsch (London), 1967 . £45/£10
ditto, Macmillan (New York), 1967 . . £35/£10
In a Free State, Deutsch (London), 1971 . . £35/£10
ditto, Knopf (New York), 1971 . . . . £25/£10

Guerrillas, Deutsch (London), 1975 . . . . £20/£5
ditto, Knopf (New York), 1975 . . . . . £15/£5
A Bend in the River, Deutsch (London), 1979. . £20/£5
ditto, Knopf (New York), 1979 . . . . . £15/£5
The Enigma of Arrival, Viking (London), 1987 . £15/£5
ditto, Knopf (New York), 1987 . . . . . £10/£5
A Way in the World: A Sequence, Heinemann (London), 1994 . . . . £15/£5
ditto, Knopf (New York), 1994 (advance copy, signed, in slipcase). . . . . £40/£20
ditto, Knopf (New York), 1994 . . . . . £10/£5
Half a Life, Picador (London), 2001 . . . £10/£5
ditto, Picador (London), 2001 (50 signed, numbered, uncorrected proof copies; pbk). £100
ditto, Knopf (New York), 2001 . . . . . £10/£5
Magic Seeds, Picador (London), 2004 . . . £10/£5
ditto, Knopf (New York), 2004 . . . . . £10/£5

Short Stories
Miguel Street, Deutsch (London), 1959 . . .£300/£50
ditto, Vanguard Press (New York), 1960 . . . £75/£20
A Flag on the Island, Deutsch (London), 1967 . £75/£15
ditto, Macmillan (New York), 1968 . . . £25/£10

Others
The Middle Passage, Deutsch (London), 1962 . £125/£20
ditto, Macmillan (New York), 1963 . . . . £65/£20
An Area of Darkness: An Experience of India, Deutsch (London), 1964 . . . . £65/£20
ditto, Macmillan (New York), 1965 . . . . £50/£15
The Loss of El Dorado, Deutsch (London), 1969 . £35/£10
ditto, Knopf (New York), 1970 . . . . . £25/£10
The Overcrowded Barracoon, Deutsch (London), 1972 .
. . . . £45/£15
ditto, Knopf (New York), 1972 . . . . . £35/£10
India: A Wounded Civilisation, Deutsch (London), 1977 .
. . . . £35/£10
ditto, Knopf (New York), 1977 . . . . . £25/£10
The Return of Eva Peron with *The Killings in Trinidad*, Deutsch (London), 1980 . . . . . . £20/£5
ditto, Knopf (New York), 1980 . . . . . £15/£5
A Congo Diary, Sylvester & Orphanos (Los Angeles, CA, 1980 (300 signed, numbered copies, no d/w) . . £65
Among the Believers: An Islamic Journey, Deutsch (London), 1981 . . . . £20/£5
ditto, Franklin Library (Franklin Centre, PA), 1981 (signed limited edition) £25
ditto, Knopf (New York), 1981 . . . . . £15/£5
Finding the Centre: Two Narratives, Deutsch (London), 1984 . . . . £15/£5
ditto, Knopf (New York), 1984 . . . . . £15/£5
A Turn in the South, Viking (London), 1989 . . £15/£5
ditto, Knopf (New York), 1989 . . . . . £15/£5
ditto, Franklin Library (Franklin Centre, PA), 1989 (signed limited edition) £20
India: A Million Mutinies Now, Heinemann (London), 1990
. . . . £15/£5
ditto, London Limited Editions (London), 1990 (150 signed, numbered copies, glassine d/w) . . . .£100/£75
ditto, Viking (New York), 1991 . . . . . £10/£5
Conversations with V.S. Naipaul, Univ Press of Mississippi (Jackson, MS), 1995 . . . . . . £20/£5
Beyond Belief: Islam Excursions Among the Converted Peoples, Little, Brown (London), 1998 . . . £15/£5

ditto, Random House (New York), 1998 . . . £10/£5
Letters Between a Father and a Son, Little, Brown (London), 1999 . . . . . . £10/£5
ditto, as **Between Father and Son: Family Letters**, Knopf (New York), 2000 . . . . . . £10/£5
Reading and Writing: An Essay, New York Review of Books (New York), 2000 . . . . . £15/£5
The Writer and the World: Essays, Picador (London), 2002 . . . . £10/£5
ditto, Knopf (New York), 2002 . . . . . £10/£5
Two Worlds: Nobel lecture December 7, 2001, Rees & O'Neill (London), 2002 (58 numbered, signed copies, no d/w) £225
ditto, Rees & O'Neill (London), 2002 (12 numbered, signed copies, full leather) £750
Literary Occasions: Essays, Knopf (New York), 2003 . . . . £10/£5
ditto, Picador (London), 2004 . . . . £10/£5

VIOLET NEEDHAM
(b.1876 d.1967)

British-born Violet Needham was 63 when her first book was published. She is credited with writing books for and about children which do not talk down to or patronise their readers. Her novels are old-fashioned, exciting tales of adventure set in romantic, exalted locations, sometimes with a supernatural element.

The Black Riders, Collins (London), 1939 . . £200/£75
The Emerald Crown, Collins (London), 1940 . £150/£45
The Stormy Petrel, Collins (London), 1942 . £150/£45
The Horn of Merlyns, Collins (London), 1943 . £125/£35
The Woods of Windri, Collins (London), 1944 £45/£10
The House of the Paladin, Collins (London), 1945 £35/£10
The Changeling of Monte Lucio, Collins (London), 1946 . . . . £35/£10
The Bell of the Four Evangelists, Collins (London), 1947 . . . . £50/£10
The Boy in Red, Collins (London), 1948 . . £35/£10
The Betrayer, Collins (London), 1950 . . £35/£10
Pandora of Parrham Royal, Collins (London), 1951 . . . . £100/£25
The Avenue, Collins (London), 1952 . . £45/£10
How Many Miles to Babylon?, Collins (London), 1953 . . . . £100/£25
Adventures at Hampton Court, Lutterworth Press (London), 1954 . . . . £125/£25
Richard and the Golden Horse Shoe, Collins (London), 1954 . . . . £150/£25
The Great House of Estraville, Collins (London), 1955 . . . . £150/£25
The Secret of the White Peacock, Collins (London), 1956 . . . . £125/£20
The Red Rose of Ruvina, Collins (London), 1957 . £100/£20
Adventures at Windsor Castle, Lutterworth Press (London), 1957 . . . . £125/£15

EDITH NESBIT
(b.1858 d.1924)

An English author who had aspirations to be a poet, Edith Nesbit is fondly remembered as the author of classic children's novels. She was one of the first writers for children to combine realistic, contemporary characters in recognisable settings with magical objects and adventures.

Books for Children
Doggy Tales, Marcus Ward (London), [1895] . . . £50
Pussy Tales, Marcus Ward (London), [1895] . . . £50
Tales of the Clock, Raphael Tuck (London), 1895 . . £50
Tales Told in the Twilight, Nister (London), 1897 . £165
A Book of Dogs, Dent (London), 1898 . . . . £50
Pussy and Doggy Tales, Dent (London), 1899 . . £50
ditto, Dutton (New York), 1900 . . . . . £35
The Story of the Treasure Seekers, T. Fisher Unwin (London), 1899 . . . . £450
ditto, Stokes (New York), 1899 . . . . . £200
The Book of Dragons, Harper (London), 1901 . £300
Nine Unlikely Tales for Children, T. Fisher Unwin (London), 1901 . . . . £125
ditto, Dutton (New York), 1901 . . . . . £65
The Wouldbegoods, T. Fisher Unwin (London), 1901 . £275
ditto, Harper (New York), 1901 . . . . . £100
The Revolt of the Toys and What Comes of Quarrelling, Nister (London), [1902] £125
ditto, Dutton (New York), 1902 . . . . . £65
Five Children and It, T. Fisher Unwin (London), 1902 £275
ditto, Dodd Mead (New York), 1905 . . . . £165
The Rainbow Queen and Other Stories, Raphael Tuck (London), [1903] £50
Playtime Stories, Raphael Tuck (London), 1903 . £50
The Story of Five Rebellious Dolls, Nister (London), 1904 . . . . £125
Cat Tales, Nister (London), 1904 . . . . £75
ditto, Dutton (New York), 1904 . . . . . £45
The Phoenix and the Carpet, Newnes (London), 1904 . £275
ditto, Macmillan (New York), 1904 . . . . £175
The New Treasure Seekers, T. Fisher Unwin (London), 1904 . . . . £275
ditto, Stokes (New York), 1904 . . . . . £165
Pug Peter, King of Mouseland, Alf Cooke (Leeds), [1905] . £150
Oswald Bastable and Others, Wells Gardner (London), 1905 . . . . £400
ditto, Coward McCann (New York), 1960 . £25/£10
The Railway Children, Wells Gardner Darton (London), 1906 . . . . £750
ditto, Macmillan (New York), 1906 . . . . £250
The Story of the Amulet, T. Fisher Unwin (London), 1906 . £175
ditto, Dutton (New York), 1907 . . . . . £85
The Enchanted Castle, T. Fisher Unwin (London), 1907 . £150
ditto, Harper (New York), 1908 . . . . . £75
The House of Arden, T. Fisher Unwin (London), 1908 . £150
ditto, Dutton (New York), 1909 . . . . . £65
The Old Nursery Stories, Hodder & Stoughton/H. Frowde (London), 1908 . . . . £50
Harding's Luck, Hodder & Stoughton (London), 1909 . £150
ditto, Stokes (New York), 1910 . . . . . £65

The Magic City, Macmillan (London), 1910 . . . £150
ditto, Coward McCann (New York), 1958 . . £25/£10
The Wonderful Garden, Macmillan (London), 1911 . £150
ditto, Coward McCann (New York), 1935 . . £25/£10
The Magic World, Macmillan (London), 1912 . . £150
ditto, Macmillan (New York), 1912 . . . . £250
Wet Magic, T. Werner Laurie (London), [1913] . . £100
ditto, Coward McCann (New York), 1937 . . £25/£10
Children's Stories from English History, Raphael Tuck (London), 1914 . . . . £150
Five of Us, and Madeline, T. Fisher Unwin (London), 1925 . . . . £150
ditto, Adelphi (New York), 1926 . . . . £200/£25
Complete History of the Bastable Family, Ernest Benn (London), 1928 . . . . £50

Poetry for Children
Songs of Two Seasons, Raphael Tuck (London), [1890] £200
The Voyage of Columbus, 1492, Raphael Tuck (London), [1892] £150
Our Friends and All About Them, Raphael Tuck (London), [1892] £125
As Happy as a King, Marcus Ward (London), [1896] . £75
Dinna Forget, Nister (London), 1897 . . . £75
ditto, Dutton (New York), 1898 . . . . . £65
To Wish You Every Joy, Raphael Tuck (London), 1901. £50

Novels for Adults
The Prophet's Mantle, H.J. Drane (London), 1885 (pseud 'Fabian Bland', written with Hubert Bland) . . £150
ditto, Belford, Clarke (Chicago), 1889 . . . £100
The Secret of the Kyriels, Hurst & Blackett (London), 1899 . . . . £100
ditto, Lippincott (Philadelphia), 1899 . . . £65
The Red House, Methuen (London), 1902 . . £125
ditto, Harper (New York), 1902 . . . . . £100
The Incomplete Amorist, Constable (London), 1906 . £50
ditto, Doubleday (New York), 1906 . . . . £35
Daphne in Fitzroy Street, George Allen (London), 1909 £40
ditto, Doubleday (New York), 1909 . . . . £30
Salome and the Head, Alston Rivers (London), 1909 . £50
ditto, as *The House With No Address*, Doubleday (New York), 1909 . . . . £35
Dormant, Methuen (London), 1911 . . . . £50
ditto, Dodd Mead (New York), 1912 . . . . £25
The House With No Address, Newnes (London), [1914] £30
The Incredible Honeymoon, Harper (New York), 1916 £25
ditto, Hutchinson (London), [1921] £25
The Lark, Hutchinson (London), [1922] . . . £25

Short Stories for Adults
Grim Tales, A.D. Innes (London), 1893 . . . £200
Something Wrong, A.D. Innes (London), 1893 . £150
The Butler in Bohemia, H.J. Drane (London), 1894 . £100
In Homespun, John Lane (London), 1896 . . £125
ditto, Roberts Bros. (Boston), 1896 . . . . £45
Thirteen Ways Home, Treherne (London), 1901 . £35
The Literary Sense, Methuen (London), 1903. . £25
ditto, Macmillan (New York), 1903 . . . . £25
Man and Maid, T. Fisher Unwin (London), 1906 . . £25
These Little Ones, George Allen (London), 1909 . £50
Fear, Stanley Paul (London), 1910 . . . . £150
To The Adventurous, Hutchinson (London), [1923] . £25

Edith Nesbit's Tales of Terror, Methuen (London), 1983 (7 stories) . . . . £10/£5
ditto, as *In The Dark: Tales of Terror*, Equation (London), 1988 (14 stories; pbk). £10
ditto, as *In The Dark: Tales of Terror*, Lythway (Bath, UK), 2000 (14 stories) . . . . £25/£10
ditto, as *In The Dark*, Ash-Tree Press (Ashcroft, BC, Canada), 2000 (21 stories, 500 copies) . . £25/£10

Poetry
Lays and Legends, Longman (London), 1886 and 1892 (2 vols) £75
The Lily and the Cross, Griffith Farran (London), 1887 £45
ditto, Dutton (New York), 1887 . . . . . £35
The Star of Bethlehem, Nister (London), 1887 . £125
Leaves of Life, Longman (London), 1888. . . £50
The Message of the Dove, H.J. Drane (London), 1888 . £50
ditto, Dutton (New York), 1888 . . . . . £35
The Better Part and Other Poems, H.J. Drane (London), 1888 . . . . £50
Easter-Tide, H.J. Drane (London), 1888 . . . £50
ditto, Dutton (New York), 1888 . . . . . £35
Landscape and Song, H.J. Drane (London), 1888 . £50
ditto, Dutton (New York), 1888 . . . . . £35
By Land and Sea, H.J. Drane (London), 1888. . £50
The Lilies Round the Cross, Nister (London), [1889] . £125
ditto, Dutton (New York), 1889 . . . . . £45
Corals, Nister (London), [1889] £250
Sweet Lavender, Nister (London), [1892]. . . £125
Flowers I Bring and Songs I Sing, Raphael Tuck (London), [1893] £75
The Girl's Own Birthday Books, H.J. Drane (London), [1894] £30
Holly and Mistletoe, Marcus Ward (London), [1895] (with R. Le Gallienne and N. Gale; 200 numbered copies) . £200
A Pomander of Verse, John Lane (London), 1895 . . £75
ditto, McClurg (Chicago), 1895 . . . . . £35
Rose Leaves, Nister (London), [1895] . . . £125
Songs of Love and Empire, Constable (London), 1898. £50
The Rainbow and the Rose, Longman (London), 1905. £45
Jesus in London, Fifield (London), 1908 . . . £35
Ballads and Lyrics of Socialism, Fabian Society (London), 1908 . . . . £50
Ballads and Verses of the Spiritual Life, Elkin Mathews (London), 1911 . . . . £25
Garden Poems, Collins (London), 1912 . . . £25
Many Voices, Hutchinson (London), [1922] . . £50/£20

Others
Cinderella, Sidgwick & Jackson (London), 1909 . . £35
Wings and the Child, Hodder & Stoughton (London), 1913 . . . . £100
ditto, Doran (New York), 1913 . . . . . £65
Long Ago When I Was Young, Whiting & Wheaton (London), 1966 (illustrated by Ardizzone) . . £50/£20
ditto, Watts (New York), [1966] . . . . . £45/£15

KAY NIELSEN
(b.1886 d.1957)

Kay Nielson was born in Copenhagen and studied in Paris before moving to London in 1911, where he was commissioned to illustrate a series of gift books. After World War One he became involved in theatre design, and in the 1930s was employed by Walt Disney: some of his work was used in sequences of the film *Fantasia*.

In Powder and Crinoline, Old Fairy Tales, retold by Sir Arthur Quiller-Couch, Hodder & Stoughton (London), [1913] (24 colour plates) £750
ditto, Hodder & Stoughton (London), [1913] (large paper edition; 26 colour plates) £1,250
ditto, Hodder & Stoughton (London), [1913] (deluxe edition, 500 signed copies; 26 colour plates) . . £3,000
ditto, as *Twelve Dancing Princesses and Other Fairy Tales*, George H. Doran (New York), [1923] . . £325/£200
East of the Sun and West of the Moon, Old Tales from the North, retold by Peter C. Asbjörnsen and Jorgen Moe, Hodder & Stoughton (London), [1914] (25 colour plates) .
. . . . £1,500
ditto, Hodder & Stoughton (London), [1914] (deluxe edition, 500 signed copies) £12,500
ditto, George H. Doran (New York), [1914] (black boards stamped in gold with gold pictorial paste-on, purple cloth spine) £600
ditto, George H. Doran (New York), [1914] (yellow cloth) .
. . . . £450
Sous le Signe de Rossignol, by Henry Jacques, L'Edition d'Art (Paris/Zurich), 1923 (19 colour plates; 1,500 copies in wraps) £500
Hans Andersen's Fairy Tales, Hodder & Stoughton (London), [1924] (12 colour plates) . . £1,500/£750
ditto, Hodder & Stoughton (London), [1924] (deluxe edition, approx 250 of 500 signed copies, issued with d/w) . .
. . . . £3,500/£1,500
ditto, Hodder & Stoughton (London), [1924] (deluxe edition, approx 250 of 500 signed copies, white vellum binding) .
. . . . £2,500
ditto, Doran (New York), 1924 . . . £1,000/£250
Hansel and Gretel and Other Stories, Hodder & Stoughton (London), [1925] (600 signed copies, cream buckram binding; 12 colour plates) £1,750
ditto, Doran (New York), [1925]. £600
ditto, Doran (New York), [1925] (600 signed copies) £1,750
Red Magic: A Collection of the World's Best Fairy Tales from all Countries, edited by Romer Wilson, Cape (London), 1930 (8 colour plates) . . £1,000/£450

ANAÏS NIN
b.1903 d.1977

Nin was born in Paris, moved to America aged eleven, and returned to Paris a decade later and to study psychoanalysis. She is popularly remembered for her volumes of erotica, including *The Delta of Venus*.

Cities of the Interior Series
Ladders to Fire, Dutton (New York), 1946 . £150/£20

ditto, Peter Owen (London), 1963 . . . . £20/£5
Children of the Albatross, Dutton (New York), 1947 . .
. . . . £75/£10
ditto, Peter Owen (London), 1959 . . . £20/£5
The Four-Chambered Heart, Duell, Sloan & Pearce (New York), 1950 . . . . £45/£10
ditto, Peter Owen (London), 1959 . . . £20/£5
A Spy in the House of Love, The British Book Centre (New York), 1954 . . . . . . £30/£10
ditto, Neville Spearman (London), 1955 . . £30/£10
Cities of the Interior, Alan Swallow (Denver, CO), 1959 (omnibus) . . . . £30/£10
ditto, Peter Owen (London), 1978 . . . £20/£5

Novels
House of Incest, Siana Editions (Paris), 1936 (249 signed, numbered copies) . . . . £750/£650
ditto, Gemor Press [San Francisco], [1947] . £175/£65
ditto, Gemor Press [San Francisco], [1947] (50 signed, numbered copies with three signed prints) . £500/£400
ditto, Peter Owen (London), 1974 (with *Winter of Artifice*).
. . . . £25/£10
Seduction of the Minotaur, Alan Swallow (Denver, CO), 1961 . . . . £20/£5
ditto, Peter Owen (London), 1961 . . . £20/£5
Collages, Swallow Press (Chicago), 1964 (pbk) . £10
ditto, Peter Owen (London), 1964 . . . £20/£5
Delta of Venus, Harcourt Brace Jovanovich (New York), 1969 . . . . £25/£10
ditto, W.H. Allen (London), 1978 . . . £10/£5
Little Birds, Harcourt Brace, Jovanovitch (New York), 1979
. . . . £10/£5
ditto, W.H. Allen (London), 1979 . . . £10/£5

Collections
Winter of Artifice, The Obelisk Press (Paris), 1939 (pbk) .
. . . . £400
ditto, Gemor Press [San Francisco], [1942] (500 copies) £100
ditto, Peter Owen (London), 1974 . . . £20/£5
Under a Glass Bell, Gemor Press [San Francisco], 1944 £65
ditto, Editions Poetry (London), 1947 . . £30/£10
Anaïs Nin Reader, Swallow Press (Chicago), 1973 £10/£5
Waste of Timelessness: And Other Early Stories, Magic Circle Press (Weston, CT), 1977 . . . £10/£5

Diaries/Journals
The Diary of Anaïs Nin 1931-1934, Swallow Press/ Harcourt, Brace & World (New York), 1966 . £15/£5
ditto, as *The Journals of Anaïs Nin: Volume 1, 1931-1934*, Peter Owen (London), 1966 . . . . £15/£5
The Diary of Anaïs Nin 1934-1939, Swallow Press/ Harcourt, Brace & World (New York), 1967 . £15/£5
ditto, as *The Journals of Anaïs Nin: Volume 2, 1934-1939*, Peter Owen (London), 1969 . . . . £10/£5
The Diary of Anaïs Nin 1939-1944, Harcourt Brace Jovanovich (New York), 1969 . . . . £10/£5
ditto, as *The Journals of Anaïs Nin: Volume 3, 1939-1944*, Peter Owen (London), 1970 . . . . £10/£5
The Diary of Anaïs Nin 1944-1947, Harcourt Brace Jovanovich (New York), 1971 . . . . £10/£5
ditto, as *The Journals of Anaïs Nin: Volume 4, 1944-1947*, Peter Owen (London), 1972 . . . . £10/£5
The Diary of Anaïs Nin 1947-1955, Harcourt Brace Jovanovich (New York), 1974 . . . . £10/£5

ditto, as *The Journals of Anaïs Nin: Volume 5, 1947-1955*,
Peter Owen (London), 1974 . . . . £10/£5
The Diary of Anaïs Nin 1955-1966, Harcourt Brace
Jovanovich (New York), 1976 . . . . £10/£5
ditto, as *The Journals of Anaïs Nin: Volume 6, 1955-1966*,
Peter Owen (London), 1977 . . . . £10/£5
Linotte: The Early Diary of Anaïs Nin, 1914-1920,
Harcourt Brace Jovanovich (New York), 1978 . £10/£5
The Diary of Anaïs Nin 1966-1974, Harcourt Brace
Jovanovich (New York), 1980 . . . . £10/£5
ditto, as *The Journals of Anaïs Nin: Volume 7, 1966-1974*,
Peter Owen (London), 1980 . . . . £10/£5
The Early Diary of Anaïs Nin, 1920-1923, Harcourt Brace
Jovanovich (New York), 1982 . . . . £10/£5
The Early Diary of Anaïs Nin, 1923-1927, Harcourt Brace
Jovanovich (New York), 1983 . . . . £10/£5
ditto, as *Journal of a Wife: The Early Diary of Anaïs Nin,
1923-27*, Peter Owen (London), 1984 . . £10/£5
The Early Diary of Anaïs Nin, 1927-1931, Harcourt Brace
Jovanovich (New York), 1985 . . . . £10/£5
ditto, *The Early Diary of Anaïs Nin, 1923-27*, Peter Owen
(London), 1994 . . . . . . £10/£5
*Henry And June: From the Unexpurgated Diary of Anaïs
Nin*, Harcourt Brace Jovanovich (New York), 1986 £10/£5
ditto, W.H. Allen (London), 1986 . . . £10/£5
*Incest: From a Journal of Love: the Unexpurgated Diary
of Anaïs Nin, 1932-1934*, Harcourt Brace Jovanovich
(New York), 1992 . . . . . £10/£5
*Fire: From a Journal of Love The Unexpurgated Diary of
Anaïs Nin 1934-1937*, Harcourt Brace Jovanovich (New
York), 1995 . . . . £10/£5
*Nearer the Moon: From a Journal of Love The
Unexpurgated Diary of Anaïs Nin 1937-1939*, Harcourt
Brace Jovanovich (New York), 1996 . . £10/£5

Letters
*A Literate Passion: Letters of Anaïs Nin and Henry Miller,
1932-1953*, Harcourt Brace Jovanovich (New York), 1987
. . . . £10/£5
ditto, Allison & Busby/W.H. Allen (London), 1988 £10/£5
Letters to a friend in Australia, Nosukumo (Melbourne)
1992 (pbk) £5

Others
D.H. Lawrence: An Unprofessional Study, Edward W. Titus
(Paris), 1932 (550 numbered copies) . . £150/£100
ditto, Neville Spearman (London), 1961 . . £30/£10
The Novel of the Future, Macmillan (New York), 1968 .
. . . . £15/£5
ditto, Peter Owen (London), 1969 . . . £45/£10
ditto, Alan Swallow (Denver, CO), 1964 . . £40/£10
Photographic Supplement to The Diary of Anaïs Nin,
Harcourt Brace Jovanovich (New York), 1974 (pbk) . £5
Paris Revisited, Capra Press (Santa Barbara, CA), 1972
(wraps) £5
ditto, Capra Press (Santa Barbara, CA), 1972 (250 signed,
numbered copies) £100
In Favour of the Sensitive Man and Other Essays W.H.
Allen (London), 1976 . . . . . £10/£5
Aphrodisiac, Crown (New York), 1976 . . . £10/£5
ditto, Quartet Books, London, 1978 . . . £10/£5
*A Woman Speaks: The Lectures, Seminars And Interviews
of Anaïs Nin*, Swallow Press (Chicago IL), 1975 £15/£5
Conversations with Anaïs Nin, Univ Press of Mississippi
(Jackson, MS), 1994 . . . . . £10/£5

PATRICK O'BRIAN
(b.1914 d.2000)

Born in England as Richard Patrick Russ, the author later
changed his name to O'Brian and claimed to be Irish. He is
best known for his 'Aubrey–Maturin' novels about the
Royal Navy during the Napoleonic Wars. They follow the
friendship between Captain Aubrey and the physician,
naturalist and intelligence agent, Maturin. His work is
considered a well-researched and authentic portrayal of
early 19th century life at sea.

'Jack Aubrey' Novels
Master and Commander, Lippincott (Philadelphia), 1969 .
. . . . £750/£65
ditto, Collins (London), 1970 . . . . £650/£60
Post Captain, Collins (London), 1972 . . . £375/£40
ditto, Lippincott (Philadelphia), 1972 . . . £250/£35
H.M.S. Surprise, Collins (London), 1973 . . £350/£45
ditto, Lippincott (Philadelphia), 1973 . . . £250/£35
The Mauritius Command, Collins (London), 1977 £350/£40
ditto, Stein & Day (New York), 1978 . . . £200/£25
Desolation Island, Collins (London), 1978 . . £200/£25
ditto, Stein & Day (New York), 1979 . . . £100/£20
The Fortune of War, Collins (London), 1979 . . £150/£20
ditto, Norton (New York), 1991 (pbk) . . . £20
ditto, Norton (New York), 1994 (hardback) . £20/£5
The Surgeon's Mate, Collins (London), 1980 . £1,000/£75
ditto, Norton (New York), 1992 (pbk) . . . £15
ditto, Norton (New York), 1994 (hardback) . £20/£5
The Ionian Mission, Collins (London), 1981 . . £450/£50
ditto, Norton (New York), 1992 (pbk) . . . £15
ditto, Norton (New York), 1994 (hardback) . £20/£5
Treason's Harbour, Collins (London), 1983 . . £475/£50
ditto, Norton (New York), 1992 (pbk) . . . £15
ditto, Norton (New York), 1994 (hardback) . £20/£5
The Far Side of the World, Collins (London), 1984 .
. . . . £475/£50
ditto, Norton (New York), 1992 (pbk) . . . £15
ditto, Norton (New York), 1994 (hardback) . £20/£5
The Reverse of the Medal, Collins (London), 1986 £350/£45
ditto, Norton (New York), 1992 (pbk) . . . £20
ditto, Norton (New York), 1994 (hardback) . £20/£5
The Letter of Marque, Collins (London), 1988 . £225/£30
ditto, Norton (New York), 1990 . . . . £35/£5
The Thirteen-Gun Salute, Collins (London), 1989 £250/£35
ditto, Norton (New York), 1991 . . . . £25/£5
The Nutmeg of Consolation, Collins (London), 1991 [1990]
. . . . £150/£20
ditto, Norton (New York), 1991 . . . . £25/£5
Clarissa Oakes, Harper Collins (London), 1992 . £75/£20
ditto, as *The Truelove*, Norton (New York), 1992 . £25/£10
The Wine-Dark Sea, Harper Collins (London), 1993 £50/£5
ditto, Norton (New York), 1993 . . . . £15/£5
The Commodore, Harper Collins (London), 1994 . £30/£5
ditto, Norton (New York), 1994 . . . . £15/£5
ditto, Norton (New York), 1994 (200 signed, numbered
copies, slipcase) . . . . . . £275/£200
The Yellow Admiral, Norton (New York), 1996 . £15/£5
ditto, Harper Collins (London), 1997 . . . £20/£5
The Hundred Days, Harper Collins (London), 1998 £20/£5

ditto, Norton (New York), 1998 . . . . £15/£5
Blue at the Mizzen, Norton (New York), 1999 . £15/£5
ditto, Harper Collins (London), 1999 . . . £15/£5

Other Novels

Caesar: The Life Story of a Panda Leopard, Putnam (London), 1930 (pseud 'Richard Patrick Russ', illustrated by Harry Rowntree; with first issue UK d/w priced 5/-) .
. . . . £3,000/£400
ditto, Putnam (London), 1930 (second issue UK d/w with titles listed on the rear panel not published until 1932) .
. . . . £1,500/£400
ditto, Putnam (London), 1930 (US d/w priced at $2) . .
. . . . £1,500/£400
ditto, British Library (London), 1999 (200 signed copies of 1,000, with *Hussein*, no d/ws, 2 vols in slipcase) £175/£145
ditto, British Library (London), 1999 (50 signed copies in three-quarter leather of 1,000, with *Hussein*, no d/ws, 2 vols in slipcase) £1,000
ditto, British Library (New York), 1999 . . . £15/£5
ditto, Norton (New York), 1999 . . . . £10/£5
ditto, HarperCollins (London), 2000 . . . £10/£5
Beasts Royal, Putnam (London), 1934 (pseud 'Patrick Russ', illustrated by Harry Rowntree) . . . £1,350/£250
Hussein: An Entertainment, O.U.P. (London/Oxford), 1938
. . . . £1,000/£125
ditto, British Library (London), 1999 (200 signed copies of 1,000, with *Caesar*, no d/ws, 2 vols in slipcase) £175/£145
ditto, British Library (London), 1999 (50 signed copies in three-quarter leather of 1,000, with *Caesar*, no d/ws, 2 vols in slipcase) £1,000
ditto, British Library (London), 1999 . . . £15/£5
ditto, Norton (New York), 1999 . . . . £10/£5
ditto, HarperCollins (London), 2000 . . . £10/£5
Three Bear Witness, Secker & Warburg (London), 1952 .
. . . . £650/£75
ditto, as **Testimonies**, Harcourt, Brace & Co. (New York), [1952] . . . . £450/£50
ditto, as **Testimonies**, Harper Collins (London), 1994 £20/£5
The Catalans, Harcourt, Brace & Co. (New York), [1953] .
. . . . £650/£50
ditto, as **The Frozen Flame**, Hart Davis (London), 1953 .
. . . . £1,000/£125
Richard Temple, Macmillan (London), 1962 . . £250/£30

Short Stories

The Last Pool and Other Stories, Secker & Warburg (London), 1950 . . . . . . £500/£65
The Walker and Other Stories, Harcourt, Brace & Co. (New York), [1955] . . . . . . £200/£30
ditto, as **Lying in the Sun and Other Stories**, Hart Davis (London), 1956 (slightly different contents) . £350/£45
The Chian Wine and Other Stories, Collins (London), 1974
. . . . £80/£20
Collected Short Stories, Harper Collins (London), 1994 .
. . . . £20/£5
ditto, as **The Rendezvous and Other Stories**, Norton (New York), 1994 . . . . £20/£5

Children's Titles

The Road to Samarcand, Hart Davis (London), 1954 . .
. . . . £250/£35
The Golden Ocean, Hart Davis (London), 1956 . £350/£45
ditto, John Day (New York), 1957 . . . . £300/£35

The Unknown Shore, Hart Davis (London), 1959 . £150/£15
ditto, Norton (New York), 1995 . . . . . £20/£5

Non-Fiction

Men-Of-War, Collins (London), 1974 . . . £60/£15
ditto, Norton (New York), 1995 . . . . . £20/£10
Pablo Ruiz Picasso: A Biography, Collins (London), 1976 .
. . . . £30/£5
ditto, as **Picasso: Pablo Ruiz Picasso: A Biography**, Putnam (New York), [1976] . . . . . £30/£5
Joseph Banks: A Life, Collins Harvill (London), 1987 .
. . . . £50/£10
ditto, Godine (Boston), 1992 . . . . . £25/£5

Translations

The Quicksand War, by Lucian Bodard, Faber (London), 1967 . . . . £75/£20
The Italian Campaign, by Michael Mohart, Weidenfeld & Nicolson (London), 1967 . . . . . £75/£20
The Woman Destroyed, by Simone De Beauvoir, Collins (London), 1969 . . . . . . £25/£5
ditto, Putnam (New York), 1969 . . . . £15/£5
Papillon, by Henri Charrière, Hart-Davis (London), 1970 .
. . . . £40/£10
Banco: The Further Adventures of Papillon, Hart-Davis, MacGibbon (London), 1973 . . . . £25/£10

Editor

A Book of Voyages, Home & Van Thal (London), 1947 .
. . . . £250/£65

EDNA O'BRIEN
(b.1932)

Edna O'Brien is an Irish novelist and short story writer whose work often deals with the position of women in society. Her novels are a blend of bleakness and quiet joy. *A Pagan Place* was about her own childhood in a repressive Irish town. She has received much recognition for her writing, including a Kingsley Amis Award in 1962, and the Los Angeles Times Book Prize for *Lantern Slides* in 1990.

Novels

The Country Girls, Hutchinson (London), 1960 . £80/£15
ditto, Knopf (New York), 1960 . . . . . £50/£10
The Lonely Girl, Cape (London), 1962 . . . £40/£10
ditto, Random House (New York), 1962 . . . £30/£10
ditto, as **The Girl With Green Eyes**, Penguin (Harmondsworth, Middlesex), 1964 (pbk) £5
Girls in Their Married Bliss, Cape (London), 1964 £25/£5
ditto, Houghton Mifflin (Boston), 1968 . . . £15/£5
August is a Wicked Month, Cape (London), 1965 . £25/£5
ditto, Simon & Schuster (New York), 1965 . . £15/£5
Casualties of Peace, Cape (London), 1966 . . £25/£5
ditto, Simon & Schuster (New York), 1967 . . £15/£5
A Pagan Place, Weidenfeld & Nicolson (London), 1970 .
. . . . £20/£5
ditto, Knopf (New York), 1970 . . . . . £15/£5
Night, Weidenfeld & Nicolson (London), 1972 . £15/£5
ditto, Knopf (New York), 1973 . . . . . £15/£5
Johnnie, I Hardly Knew You, Weidenfeld & Nicolson (London), 1977 . . . . £15/£5

ditto, as *I Hardly Knew You*, Doubleday (New York), 1978
.   .   .   .   £10/£5
The High Road, Weidenfeld & Nicolson (London), 1988 .
.   .   .   .   £15/£5
ditto, London Limited Editions (London), 1988 (150 signed
copies, tissue d/w)   .   .   .   .   .   £45/£35
ditto, Farrar Straus (New York), 1988   .   .   £10/£5
Time and Tide, Viking (London), 1992   .   .   £10/£5
ditto, Farrar Straus (New York), 1992   .   .   £10/£5
House of Splendid Isolation, Weidenfeld & Nicolson
(London), 1994   .   .   .   .   .   .   £10/£5
ditto, Farrar Straus (New York), 1994   .   .   £10/£5
Down by the River, Weidenfeld & Nicolson (London), 1995
.   .   .   .   £10/£5
ditto, Farrar Straus (New York), 1997   .   .   £10/£5
Wild Decembers, Weidenfeld & Nicolson (London), 1999 .
.   .   .   .   £10/£5
ditto, Houghton Mifflin (Boston), 2000   .   .   £10/£5
In the Forest, Weidenfeld & Nicolson (London), 2002.   .
.   .   .   .   £10/£5
ditto, Houghton Mifflin (Boston), 2002   .   .   £10/£5

Short Stories
The Love Object, Cape (London), 1968   .   .   £15/£5
ditto, Knopf (New York), 1969   .   .   .   £15/£5
A Scandalous Woman, Weidenfeld & Nicolson (London),
1974   .   .   .   .   £15/£5
ditto, Harcourt Brace (New York), 1974   .   .   £10/£5
Mrs Reinhardt and Other Stories, Weidenfeld & Nicolson
(London), 1978 .   .   .   .   .   .   £15/£5
ditto, as **A Rose in the Heart**, Doubleday (New York), 1979
.   .   .   .   £10/£5
Returning, Weidenfeld & Nicolson (London), 1982   £15/£5
A Fanatic Heart, Franklin Library (Franklin Centre, PA),
1984 (signed, limited edition) £10
ditto, Farrar Straus (New York), 1984   .   .   £10/£5
ditto, Weidenfeld & Nicolson (London), 1985   .   £10/£5
Lantern Slides, Weidenfeld & Nicolson (London), 1990   .
.   .   .   .   £10/£5
ditto, Farrar Straus (New York), 1990   .   .   £10/£5

Collected Editions
The Collected Edna O'Brien, Collins (London), 1978 £15/£5
Some Irish Loving, Weidenfeld & Nicolson (London), 1979
.   .   .   .   £15/£5
ditto, Harper (New York), 1979 .   .   .   .   £10/£5
The Country Girls Trilogy and Epilogue, Farrar Straus
(New York), 1986   .   .   .   .   .   £10/£5
ditto, Cape (London), 1987   .   .   .   .   £10/£5

Children's Titles
The Dazzle, Hodder & Stoughton (London), 1981 (laminated
pictorial boards) £10
Christmas Treat, Hodder & Stoughton (London), 1982
(laminated pictorial boards) £10
Tales for Telling: Irish Folk and Fairy Stories, Pavilion
(London), 1986   .   .   .   .   .   .   £10/£5
ditto, Atheneum (New York), 1986   .   .   .   £10/£5

Plays
A Pagan Place, Faber (London), 1973   .   .   £15/£5
Virginia, Hogarth Press (London), 1981 (pbk)   .   £10
ditto, Harcourt Brace (New York), 1981   .   .   £10/£5

Others
Zee & Co, Weidenfeld & Nicolson (London), 1971   £25/£10
Mother Ireland, Weidenfeld & Nicolson (London), 1976 .
.   .   .   .   £15/£5
ditto, Harcourt Brace (New York), 1976   .   .   £15/£5
Arabian Days, Horizon Press (New York), 1977   .   £10/£5
ditto, Quartet (London), 1977   .   .   .   .   £10/£5
James and Nora, Lord John Press (Northridge, CA), 1981
(26 signed, lettered copies of 276, slipcase)   .   £125/£85
ditto, Lord John Press (Northridge, CA), 1981 (250 signed,
numbered copies of 276)   .   .   .   .   £50/£40
Vanishing Ireland, Cape (London), 1986 (photos by Richard
Fitzgerald)   .   .   .   .   .   .   £25/£10
ditto, Clarkson N. Potter (New York), 1986   .   £25/£10
James Joyce, Weidenfeld & Nicolson (London), 1999 .   .
.   .   .   .   £10/£5
ditto, Viking (New York), 1999   .   .   .   £10/£5

FLANN O'BRIEN
(b.1911 d.1966)

'Flann O'Brien' was the pseudonym of Brian O'Nolan who
also published as 'Myles na gCopaleen'. An Irish novelist
and journalist, his first novel, *At Swim-Two-Birds*, was
hailed by many as a masterpiece in the tradition of Joyce's
Ulysses. O'Brien wrote mainly for newspapers and his
work has only recently begun to receive attention from literary scholars. He is considered a major figure in 20th
century Irish literature.

Novels
At Swim-Two-Birds, Longmans (London), 1939 (black
cloth)   .   .   .   .   £3,250/£850
ditto, Longmans (London), 1939 (second issue, grey-green
cloth)   .   .   .   .   £2,250/£500
ditto, Pantheon (New York), 1939 [1951]   .   £250/£40
An Beal Bocht, An Press Naisiunta (Dublin), 1941 (pseud
'Myles na gCopaleen'; pbk) £400
ditto, translated as **The Poor Mouth**, Hart-Davis MacGibbon
(London), 1973 (illustrated by Ralph Steadman) .   £75/£15
ditto, Hart-Davis MacGibbon (London), 1973 (130 copies
signed by Ralph Steadman with a numbered and signed
print by him laid in) £1,000
ditto, Viking (New York), 1974 .   .   .   .   £45/£10
The Hard Life: An Exegesis of Squalor, MacGibbon & Kee
(London), 1961   .   .   .   .   .   £200/£45
ditto, Pantheon (New York), 1962   .   .   .   £25/£10
The Dalkey Archive, MacGibbon & Kee (London), 1964   .
.   .   .   .   £125/£20
ditto, Macmillan (New York), 1965   .   .   .   £45/£10
The Third Policeman, MacGibbon & Kee (London), 1967 .
.   .   .   .   £350/£50
ditto, Walker & Co (New York), 1967   .   .   £150/£35

Others
Cruiskeen Lawn, Cahill and Co (Dublin), 1943 (pseud
'Myles na gCopaleen'; pbk) £600
Faustus Kelly, Cahill and Co (Dublin), 1943 (pbk)   .   £850
The Best of Myles, a Selection from 'Cruiskeen Lawn',
MacGibbon & Kee (London), 1968.   .   .   £75/£15
ditto, Walker & Co (New York), 1968   .   .   £40/£10

Stories and Plays, Hart-Davis MacGibbon (London), 1973 .
. . . . £50/£10
ditto, Viking (New York), 1976 . . . . £45/£10
Further Cuttings from 'Cruiskeen Lawn', Hart-Davis
MacGibbon (London), 1976 . . . . £25/£5
ditto, Dalkey Archive Press (Normal, IL), 2000 (pbk) . £5
The Various Lives of Keats and Chapman and The
Brother, Hart-Davis MacGibbon (London), 1976 £30/£5
ditto, St Martin's Press (New York), 2005 . . £10/£5
The Hair of the Dogma: A Further Selection from
'Cruiskeen Lawn', Hart-Davis MacGibbon (London),
1977 . . . . £35/£10
A Flann O'Brien Reader, Viking (New York), 1978 £20/£5
Myles Away from Dublin, Granada (London), 1985 £20/£10

TIM O'BRIEN
(b.1946)

Tim O'Brien is an American novelist who has frequently
written about his experiences in the Vietnam War and the
impact of that conflict on its veterans. His first book, *If I*
Die in a Combat Zone was originally classified as non-
fiction, but after revisions to later editions is now classed as
fiction. These boundaries are also blurred in his books
which are marketed as fiction, based as they are on real-life
incidents and experiences.

Non-Fiction
If I Die in a Combat Zone: Box Me Up And Ship Me
Home, Delacorte (New York), 1973 (first issue d/w with
$5.95 price and 0373 code on back flap) . £1,000/£75
ditto, Calder & Boyars (London), 1973 . . . £200/£35

Novels
Northern Lights, Delacorte (New York), 1975 . £425/£65
ditto, Marion Boyars (London), 1976. . . . £100/£15
ditto, Marion Boyars (London), 1976 (pbk) . . . £15
Going After Cacciato, Delacorte (New York), 1978 . .
. . . . £100/£15
ditto, Jonathan Cape (London), 1978 . . . . £25/£10
Nuclear Age, Press-22 (Portland, OR), 1981 (125 numbered
copies; pbk) £100
ditto, Press-22 (Portland, OR), 1985 (26 numbered copies;
boards) . . . . £275/£200
ditto, Knopf (New York), 1985 . . . . . £10/£5
ditto, Collins (London), 1986 . . . . . £10/£5
In the Lake of the Woods, Houghton Mifflin (Boston), 1994
. . . . £10/£5
Tomcat in Love, Broadway Books (New York), 1998 £10/£5
ditto, Franklin Library (Franklin Center, PA), 1998 (signed,
limited edition) £50
ditto, Flamingo (London), 1998 . . . . . £10/£5
July, July, Houghton Mifflin (Boston), 2002 . . £10/£5

Others
Speaking of Courage, Neville (Santa Barbara, CA), 1980
(300 numbered copies) £80
ditto, Neville (Santa Barbara, CA), 1980 (26 lettered copies)
. . . . £500
From How to Tell a True War Story, Minnesota Center for
the Book Arts (no place), 1987 (150 signed, numbered
copies; broadside) £100

The Things They Carried, Houghton Mifflin (Boston), 1990
. . . . £10/£5
ditto, Franklin Library (Franklin Centre), 1990 . £70
ditto, Collins (London), 1990 . . . . . £10/£5

FLANNERY O'CONNOR
(b.1925 d.1964)

O'Connor is considered one of the best American short
story writers of the post war generation. Sixteen years after
her death *Wise Blood* was made into a film directed by
John Huston and the same year she was given an award
from the National Book Award Committee for the writing
she produced in her short career.

Wise Blood, Harcourt Brace (New York), 1952 £2,500/£500
ditto, Neville Spearman (London), 1955 . . . £300/£60
A Good Man Is Hard To Find, Harcourt Brace (New York),
1955 (first issue with 'Tyring' on p.125, line 25; first issue
d/w with *Wise Blood* on rear panel). . . £750/£150
ditto, Harcourt Brace (New York), 1955 (second issue d/w
with *A Good Man Is Hard To Find* on back panel) . .
. . . . £350/£150
ditto, as ***The Artificial Nigger and Other Tales***, Neville
Spearman (London), 1957 . . . . £450/£75
The Violent Bear It Away, Farrar, Straus & Cudahy (New
York), 1960 . . . . £300/£65
ditto, Longmans, Green (London), 1960 . . . £150/£20
Some Aspects of the Grotesque in Southern Fiction,
Wesleyan College (Macon, GA), 1960 (five single-spaced
mimeographed pages from typescript) . . . £1,500
A Memoir of Mary Ann, by the Domincan Nuns of Our
Lady of Perpetual Help Home, Farrar, Straus & Cudahy,
(New York), 1961 (edited and introduced by O'Connor) .
. . . . £50/£10
ditto, as ***Death of a Child***, Burns & Oates (London), 1961 .
. . . . £50/£10
Three By Flannery, New American Library/Signet (New
York), 1964 (pbk) £10
Everything That Rises Must Converge, Farrar, Straus &
Giroux (New York), 1965 . . . . . £150/£20
ditto, Faber & Faber (London), 1966 . . . . £100/£15
ditto, Tales For Travellers (Napa, CA), 1985 (single sheet,
map-folded) £20
The Added Dimension, The Art and The Mind of Flannery
O'Connor, Fordham Univ Press (New York), 1966 . .
. . . . £85/£15
Mystery and Manners, Farrar, Straus & Giroux (New York),
1969 . . . . £75/£15
ditto, Faber & Faber (London), 1972 (first state without
author's name on spine of book) . . . . £75/£15
ditto, Faber & Faber (London), 1972 (second state with
author's name on spine) . . . . . £50/£5
The Complete Stories, Farrar, Straus & Giroux (New York),
1971 . . . . £145/£20
ditto, Franklin Library (Franklin Center, PA), 1980 (full
leather) £35
Three Short Stories, World Today Press (Hong Kong), 1975
(wraps) £50
The Habit of Being, Farrar, Straus & Giroux (New York),
1979 . . . . £40/£10
ditto, Faber & Faber (London), 1980 . . . . £30/£5

Higher Education, Palaemon (Winston-Salem, NC), [c.1980] (100 numbered copies) £25

ditto, Palaemon (Winston-Salem, NC), [c.1980] (26 lettered copies) £45

Home of the Brave, Albondocani (New York), 1981 (200 numbered copies; wraps) £65

ditto, Albondocani (New York), 1981 (26 lettered copies; wraps) £165

The Presence of Grace and Other Book Reviews, Univ of Georgia Press (Athens, GA), 1983 . . £40/£10

The Correspondence of Flannery O'Connor and the Brainard Cheneys, Univ Press of Mississippi (Jackson, MS), 1986 . . . . £15/£5

ditto, Univ Press of Mississippi (Jackson, MS), 1986 (pbk) £5

Revelation, Tales For Travellers (Napa, CA), 1987 (single sheet, map-folded) £15

Collected Works, Library of America (New York), 1988 . . . . £15/£5

ditto, Library of America (New York), 1988 (subscriber copies in slipcase without d/w). . . £15/£5

The Complete Stories, Faber & Faber (London), 1990 (pbk) £10

LIAM O'FLAHERTY

(b.1896 d.1984)

O'Flaherty was a leading Irish novelist and short story writer of the early 20th century. His works are characterised by a powerfully dramatised Realism. *The Informer* was selected as a Haycraft-Queen Cornerstone and was filmed in 1935. O'Flaherty wrote mostly in English, but towards the end of his life he published *Dúil*, a highly-regarded collection of stories in Irish.

Novels

Thy Neighbour's Wife, Cape (London), 1923 . . £300/£35

ditto, Boni & Liveright (New York), 1924 . . £300/£35

The Black Soul, Cape (London), 1924 . . . £100/£25

ditto, Boni & Liveright (New York), 1924 . . £65/£15

The Informer, Cape (London), 1925 . . . £1,500/£145

ditto, Knopf (New York), 1925 . . . . £450/£50

Mr Gilhooey, Cape (London), 1926 . . . £125/£30

ditto, Harcourt Brace (New York), 1927 . . £50/£15

The Assassin, Cape (London), 1928 . . . £125/£25

ditto, Cape (London), 1928 (150 signed, numbered copies) . . . . £250/£175

ditto, Harcourt Brace (New York), 1928 . . . £65/£10

The House of Gold, Cape (London), 1929 . . £75/£15

ditto, Harcourt Brace (New York), 1929 . . £45/£10

Return of the Brute, Mandrake Press (London), 1929 . . . . £150/£30

ditto, Harcourt Brace (New York), 1930 . . £85/£15

The Puritan, Cape (London), 1931 [1932] . . £85/£15

ditto, Harcourt Brace (New York), 1932 . . £50/£20

The Ecstasy of Angus, Joiner & Steele (London), 1931 (365 signed copies, glassine d/w) . . . £125/£100

ditto, Wolfhound Press (Dublin), 1978 . . £25/£10

Skerrett, Gollancz (London), 1932 . . . £75/£10

ditto, Long & Smith (New York), 1932 . . £45/£10

The Martyr, Gollancz (London), 1933 . . £75/£15

ditto, Macmillan (New York), 1933 (expurgated edition) . . . . £45/£10

Hollywood Cemetery, Gollancz (London), 1935 . £200/£30

Famine, Gollancz (London), 1937 . . . £70/£20

ditto, Random House (New York), 1937 . . . £45/£10

Land, Gollancz (London), 1946 . . . . £40/£10

ditto, Random House (New York), 1946 . . . £25/£5

Insurrection, Gollancz (London), 1950 . . . £30/£10

ditto, Little, Brown (Boston), 1951 . . . £20/£5

The Wilderness, Wolfhound Press (Dublin), 1979 (pbk) £5

ditto, Wolfhound Press (Dublin), 1979 (hardback with d/w). . . . . £15/£5

ditto, Wolfhound Press (Dublin), 1979 (50 signed, numbered copies) £75

ditto, Dodd Mead (New York), 1987 . . . £15/£5

Short Stories

Spring Sowing, Cape (London), 1924 . . . £85/£25

ditto, Knopf (New York), 1926 . . . . £50/£15

The Tent, Cape (London), 1926 (blue cloth) . £50/£15

ditto, Cape (London), 1926 (dark green cloth). . £45/£10

The Fairy Goose and Two Other Stories, Crosby Gaige (New York) & Faber & Gwyer (London), 1927 (1,190 signed copies, tissue jacket) . . . . . £50/£35

ditto, Crosby Gaige (New York) & Faber & Gwyer (London), 1928 (12 signed copies on blue handmade paper) £250

ditto, Crosby Gaige (New York) & Faber & Gwyer (London), 1928 (12 signed copies on green handmade paper) £250

Red Barbara and Other Stories, Crosby Gaige (New York) & Faber & Gwyer (London), 1928 (600 signed, numbered copies) £50

ditto, Crosby Gaige (New York) & Faber & Gwyer (London), 1928 (9 signed copies on grey handmade paper) £250

The Mountain Tavern and Other Stories, Cape (London), 1929 . . . . £65/£15

ditto, Harcourt Brace (New York), 1929 . . £45/£15

The Wild Swan and Other Stories, Joiner & Steele: 'Furnival Books' (London), 1932 (550 signed copies) . . . . £75/£45

The Short Stories of Liam O'Flaherty, Cape (London), 1937 . . . . £25/£5

Two Lovely Beasts, Gollancz (London), 1948 . . £40/£10

ditto, Devin-Adair (New York), 1950 . . . £20/£5

Dúil, Sainseal & Dill, 1953 (Gaelic) . . . . £15/£5

The Stories of Liam O'Flaherty, Devin-Adair (New York), 1956 . . . . £15/£5

The Pedlar's Revenge, Wolfhound Press (Dublin), 1976 . . . . £20/£5

Pamphlets

Civil War, E. Archer (London), 1925 (100 signed copies; stapled wraps) £135

The Terrorist, E. Archer (London), 1926 (100 signed copies; stapled wraps) £135

Darkness: A Tragedy in Three Acts, E. Archer (London), 1926 (100 signed copies; stapled wraps) . £150

ditto, E. Archer (London), 1926 (12 copies with cast-list) £350

The Child Of God, E. Archer (London), 1926 (100 signed copies; stapled wraps) £135

ditto, E.Archer (London), 1926 (25 signed large paper copies) £275
A Tourist's Guide to Ireland, Mandrake Press (London), [1929] . . . . £65/£30
Joseph Conrad, E. Lahr: 'Blue Moon Booklet' (London), 1930 (stapled wraps) £45
ditto, E. Lahr: 'Blue Moon Booklet' (London), 1930 (100 large paper copies) £95
A Cure for Unemployment, E. Lahr: 'Blue Moon Booklet' (London), 1931 (stapled wraps) £45
ditto, E. Lahr: 'Blue Moon Booklet' (London), 1931 (100 large paper copies) £95
ditto, E. Lahr/Julian Press (New York), 1931 . . £35

Others

The Life of Tim Healy, Cape (London), 1927 . . £100/£25
ditto, Harcourt Brace (New York), 1927 . . . £65/£15
Two Years, Cape (London), 1930 . . . . £35/£10
ditto, Harcourt Brace (New York), 1930 . . . £35/£10
I Went to Russia, Cape (London), 1931 . . . £30/£10
ditto, Harcourt Brace (New York), 1931 . . . £30/£10
Shame the Devil, Grayson & Grayson (London), 1934 . .
. . . . £30/£10
ditto, Grayson & Grayson (London), 1934 (single page from original manuscript bound in) . . . £150/£125
All Things Come of Age, A Rabbit Story, Wolfhound Press (Dublin), 1977 (laminated pictorial boards) . . £15

JOHN O'HARA
(b.1905 d.1970)

John Henry O'Hara was a U.S. author who made a name for himself initially with his short stories and then his novels. He was a keen recorder of the minutiæ of American life: its social hierarchies and class differences. His work was not highly regarded by the literary establishment, however; his vigorous self-promotion is thought to have antagonised many critics.

Novels

Appointment In Samarra, Harcourt Brace (New York), 1934 . . . . £2,500/£150
ditto, Faber (London), 1935 . . . . . £1,000/£150
Butterfield 8, Harcourt Brace (New York), 1935 . £450/£45
ditto, Cresset Press (London), 1951 . . . £45/£10
Hope of Heaven, Harcourt Brace (New York), 1938 . .
. . . . £250/£35
ditto, Faber (London), 1939 . . . . . £125/£25
A Rage to Live, Random House (New York), 1949 £75/£20
ditto, Random House (New York), 1949 (stamped 'Presentation Edition', glassine d/w) . . . £75/£45
ditto, Cresset Press (London), 1950 . . . £35/£10
The Farmer's Hotel, Random House (New York), 1951 .
. . . . £50/£10
ditto, Cresset Press (London), 1953 . . . £25/£5
Ten North Frederick, Random House (New York), 1955 .
. . . . £50/£10
ditto, Cresset Press (London), 1956 . . . £25/£5
A Family Party, Random House (New York), 1956 £25/£10
ditto, Cresset Press (London), 1957 . . . £15/£5
From The Terrace, Random House (New York), 1958 . .
. . . . £30/£10

ditto, Cresset Press (London), 1959 . . . £15/£5
Ourselves to Know, Random House (New York), 1960.
. . . . £20/£5
ditto, Cresset Press (London), 1960 . . . £10/£5
Sermons and Soda Water, Random House (New York), 1960 (3 vols in slipcase) . . . . . £25/£10
ditto, Random House (New York), 1960 (as above but with signed leaf tipped-in) . . . . . £45/£30
ditto, Cresset Press (London), 1961 (3 vols, slipcase) . .
. . . . £25/£10
ditto, Cresset Press (London), 1961 (525 signed and numbered copies, boxed set) . . . £75/£45
The Big Laugh, Random House (New York), 1962 £10/£5
ditto, Cresset Press (London), 1962 . . . £10/£5
Elizabeth Appleton, Random House (New York), 1963
. . . . £10/£5
ditto, Cresset Press (London), 1963 . . . £10/£5
The Lockwood Concern, Random House (New York), 1965
. . . . £10/£5
ditto, Hodder & Stoughton (London), 1965 . £10/£5
The Instrument, Random House (New York), 1967 £10/£5
ditto, Hodder & Stoughton (London), 1968 . £10/£5
Appointment in Samarra, Hope of Heaven, Butterfield 8, Random House (New York), 1968 . . . £10/£5
The Ewings, Random House (New York), 1972 . £10/£5
ditto, Hodder & Stoughton (London), 1972 . £10/£5
The Second Ewings, Bruccoli Clark (Bloomfield Hills, MI and Columbia, SC), 1977 (500 numbered copies, loose sheets in box) £65

Short Stories

The Doctor's Son and Other Stories, Harcourt Brace (New York), 1935 . . . . £1,000/£75
Files on Parade, Harcourt Brace (New York), 1939 (first state with the foreword on a tipped-in page) . £225/£30
Pal Joey, Duell, Sloan & Pearce (New York), 1940 £225/£30
ditto, Cresset Press (London), 1952 . . . £65/£15
Pipe Night, Duell, Sloan & Pearce (New York), 1945 . .
. . . . £125/£20
ditto, Faber (London), 1946 . . . . . £45/£15
Here's O'Hara, Duell, Sloan & Pearce (New York), 1946 .
. . . . £30/£10
Hellbox, Random House (New York), 1947 . £30/£10
ditto, Faber (London), 1952 . . . . . £15/£5
All The Girls He Wanted, Avon (New York), 1949 (pbk) £5
The Great Short Stories of John O'Hara, Bantam (New York), 1956 (pbk) £5
The Selected Short Stories of John O'Hara, Modern Library (New York), 1956. . . . . £10/£5
Assembly, Random House (New York), 1961 . £20/£5
ditto, Cresset Press (London), 1962 . . . £10/£5
The Cape Cod Lighter, Random House (New York), 1962 .
. . . . £20/£5
ditto, Cresset Press (London), 1963 . . . £10/£5
The Hat on the Bed, Random House (New York), 1963 .
. . . . £10/£5
ditto, Cresset Press (London), 1964 . . . £10/£5
49 Stories, Modern Library (New York), 1963 £10/£5
The Horse Knows the Way, Random House (New York), 1964 . . . . £10/£5
ditto, Cresset Press (London), 1965 . . . £10/£5
Waiting for Winter, Random House (New York), 1966 .
. . . . £10/£5
ditto, Hodder & Stoughton (London), 1967 . £10/£5

And Other Stories, Random House (New York), 1968 .   .
.   .   .   .   £10/£5
ditto, Hodder & Stoughton (London), 1969   .   . £10/£5
Lovey Childs, Random House (New York), 1969 .   £10/£5
ditto, Hodder & Stoughton (London), 1970   .   . £10/£5
The O'Hara Generation, Random House (New York), 1969
.   .   .   .   £10/£5
The Time Element and Other Stories, Random House (New
York), 1972 .   .   .   .   .   . £10/£5
ditto, Hodder & Stoughton (London), 1973   .   £10/£5
The Good Samaritan and Other Stories, Random House
(New York), 1974 .   .   .   .   .   £10/£5
ditto, Hodder & Stoughton (London), 1974   .   £10/£5
Two By O'Hara, Harcourt, Brace, Jovanovich (New York),
1979 .   .   .   . £10/£5
The Collected Stories of John O'Hara, Random House
(New York), 1984 .   .   .   .   . £10/£5

Others
Pal Joey: Libretto and Lyrics, Random House (New York),
1952 .   .   .   . £75/£25
Sweet and Sour, Random House (New York), 1954 £25/£10
ditto, Cresset Press (London), 1955   .   .   . £25/£10
Five Plays, Random House (New York), 1961   . £25/£5
ditto, Cresset Press (London), 1962   .   .   . £25/£5
My Turn, Random House (New York), 1966 .   . £25/£10
An Artist Is His Own Fault, Southern Illinois Univ Press
(Carbondale, IL), 1977   .   .   .   .   . £20/£5
Selected Letters of John O'Hara, Random House (New
York), 1978 .   .   .   .   .   . £10/£5

EUGENE O'NEILL

(b.1888 d.1953)

O'Neill was an American playwright who is credited with
introducing a dramatic Realism to American theatre. His
plays have present marginalised characters who struggle to
maintain their aspirations but finally fall into despair. He
won the Nobel Prize for Literature in 1936.

Plays
Thirst and Other One-Act Plays, Gorham Press (Boston),
1914 .   .   .   .   .   . £1,000/£100
Before Breakfast, Frank Shay (New York), 1916 (wraps) .
.   .   .   .£100
ditto, Cape (London), 1926 .   .   .   . £45/£10
The Moon of the Caribees and Six Other Plays of the Sea,
Boni & Liveright (New York), 1919   .   . £600/£35
ditto, Cape (London), 1923 .   .   .   . £35/£10
Gold, Boni & Liveright (New York), 1920 [1921] . £300/£40
Beyond the Horizon, Boni & Liveright (New York), 1921 .
.   .   .   .   £300/£40
ditto, as *Beyond the Horizon* and *Gold*, Cape (London),
1924 .   .   .   . £150/£20
The Emperor Jones, Diff'rent, The Straw, Boni & Liveright
(New York), 1921 .   .   .   .   . £300/£45
ditto, as *Plays First Series: The Emperor Jones, Diff'rent,
The Straw*, Cape (London), 1922   .   . £200/£25
The Emperor Jones, Stuart Kidd (Cincinnati, OH), 1921
(stapled wraps) £25
ditto, Cape (London), 1925 .   .   .   . £50/£10

ditto, Boni & Liveright (New York), 1928 (775 signed,
numbered copies, illustrated, d/w and slipcase) £250/£175
The Hairy Ape, Anna Christie, The First Man, Boni &
Liveright (New York), 1922 .   .   .   .£350/£45
ditto, as *The Hairy Ape and Other Plays*, Cape (London),
1923 .   .   .   .£125/£25
Anna Christie, Cape (London), 1923.   .   . £200/£25
ditto, Boni & Liveright (New York), 1930 (775 signed,
numbered copies, illustrated, d/w and slipcase) £175/£125
ditto, Boni & Liveright (New York), 1930 (12 signed copies
in morocco with original lithograph)   .   .   .£750
All God's Chillun' Got Wings and *Welded*, Boni &
Liveright (New York), 1924 .   .   .   .£200/£45
ditto, as *All God's Chillun' Got Wings*, *Desire under the
Elms* and *Welded*, Cape (London), 1925   . £150/£20
Desire Under the Elms, Boni & Liveright (New York), 1925
.   .   .   .   £300/£35
ditto, Cape (London), 1925 .   .   .   . £75/£15
*The Great God Brown, The Fountain, The Moon of the
Caribees and Other Plays*, Boni & Liveright (New York),
1926 .   .   .   .   .   .   £150/£25
ditto, Cape (London), 1926 .   .   .   . £75/£20
Marco Millions, Boni & Liveright (New York), 1927 .   .
.   .   .   .   £150/£25
ditto, Boni & Liveright (New York), 1927 (450 signed
copies, slipcase) .   .   .   .   . £200/£150
ditto, Cape (London), 1927 .   .   .   . £75/£15
Lazarus Laughed, Boni & Liveright (New York), 1927 .
.   .   .   .   £100/£15
ditto, Boni & Liveright (New York), 1927 (775 signed
copies, slipcase) .   .   .   . £150/£100
ditto, Cape (London), 1929 .   .   .   . £50/£15
Strange Interlude, Boni & Liveright (New York), 1928 .
.   .   .   .   £100/£20
ditto, Boni & Liveright (New York), 1928 (775 signed
copies, slipcase) .   .   .   . £200/£150
ditto, Cape (London), 1928 .   .   .   . £50/£15
The Hairy Ape, Boni & Liveright (New York), 1929 (775
signed copies, slipcase and d/w)   .   . £200/£125
Dynamo, Boni & Liveright (New York), 1929   . £75/£15
ditto, Boni & Liveright (New York), 1929 (775 signed
copies, slipcase) .   .   .   .   . £150/£100
Mourning Becomes Electra, Boni & Liveright (New York),
1931 .   .   .   . £75/£25
ditto, Boni & Liveright (New York), 1931 (550 signed
copies, slipcase) .   .   .   . £175/£100
ditto, Boni & Liveright (New York), 1931 (50 signed
presentation copies) £300
ditto, Cape (London), 1932 .   .   .   . £65/£15
Ah, Wilderness!, Random House (New York), 1933   .   .
.   .   .   .   £100/£20
ditto, Random House (New York), 1933 (325 signed copies,
slipcase).   .   .   .   .   . £250/£200
Days Without End, Random House (New York), 1934.   .
.   .   .   .   £100/£20
ditto, as *Ah, Wilderness!* and *Days Without End*, Cape
(London), 1934 .   .   .   .   .   . £40/£10
The Iceman Cometh, Random House (New York), 1946 .
.   .   .   .   £100/£25
ditto, Cape (London), 1947 .   .   .   . £45/£15
ditto, Limited Editions Club (New York), 1982 (2,000 copies
illustrated and signed by Leonard Baskin, with lithograph,
slipcase).   .   .   .   .   . £100/£45

Lost Plays of Eugene O'Neill, New Fathoms Press (New York), 1950 . . . . £30/£10

A Moon for the Misbegotten, Random House (New York), 1952 . . . . £75/£15

ditto, Cape (London), 1953 . . . . . . £25/£10

Nine Plays by Eugene O'Neill, Modern Library (New York), 1954 . . . . £75/£15

Long Day's Journey Into Night, Yale Univ Press (New Haven, CT), 1956 . . . . . . £150/£25

ditto, Cape (London), 1956 . . . . . . £30/£10

A Touch of the Poet, Yale Univ Press (New Haven, CT), 1957 . . . . £50/£10

ditto, Cape (London), 1957 . . . . . . £45/£10

Hughie, Yale Univ Press (New Haven, CT), 1959 . £35/£10

ditto, Cape (London), 1962 . . . . . . £25/£5

More Stately Mansions, Yale Univ Press (New Haven, CT), 1964 . . . . £35/£10

ditto, Cape (London), 1965 . . . . . . £25/£5

The Calms of Capricorn – A Preliminary Edition, Volume 1: The Scenario, Volume 2: The Play, Yale Univ Press (New Haven, CT), 1981 (two pbks) . . . £5

ditto, as *The Calms of Capricorn*, Ticknor & Fields (New York), 1982 . . . . £15/£15

Eugene O'Neill: The Unfinished Plays, Continuum (New York), 1988 . . . . £15/£5

The Unknown O'Neill: Unpublished and Unfamiliar Writings of Eugene O'Neill, Yale Univ Press (New Haven, CT), 1988 . . . . £15/£5

Eugene O'Neill: Complete Plays, Library of America (New York), 1988 . . . . £20/£5

Others

A Bibliography of the Works of Eugene O'Neill and The Collected Poems of Eugene O'Neill, Random House (New York), 1931 (limited to 500 copies). . . . £75/£50

Inscriptions: Eugene O'Neill to Carlotta Monterey O'Neill, Yale Univ Press (New Haven, CT), 1960 (500 numbered copies, slipcase) . . . . £75/£50

Poems: 1912-1944, Yale Univ Press (New Haven, CT), 1979 . . . . £20/£5

ditto, Cape (London), 1980 . . . . . . £15/£5

Work Diary: 1924-1943, Yale Univ Press (New Haven, CT), 1981 . . . . £15/£5

Eugene O'Neill At Work: Newly Released Ideas for Plays, Ungar (New York), 1981 . . . . . . £15/£5

The Theatre We Worked For: The Letters of Eugene O'Neill to Kenneth MacGowran, Yale Univ Press (New Haven, CT), 1982 . . . . . . £75/£10

Love, Admiration and Respect: The O'Neill-Commins Correspondence, Duke Univ Press (Durham, NC), 1986 . . . . £50/£10

As Ever, Gene: The Letters of Eugene O'Neill to George Jean Nathan, Fairleigh Univ Press (Rutherford, NJ), 1987 . . . . £15/£5

Selected Letters of Eugene O'Neill, Yale Univ Press (New Haven, CT), 1988 . . . . . . £25/£10

MICHAEL ONDAATJE
(b.1943)

Philip Michael Ondaatje is a Sri Lankan/Canadian novelist and poet. He was made an Officer of the Order of Canada in 1988 and a Foreign Honorary Member of the American Academy of Arts and Letters in 1990. He is best-known for his Booker Prize winning novel *The English Patient* which was adapted into an Academy Award-winning film.

Novels

Coming Through Slaughter, House of Anansi (Toronto, Canada), 1976 . . . . £200/£30

ditto, Norton (New York), 1976 . . . . £50/£10

ditto, Marion Boyars (London), 1979. . . £25/£10

In the Skin of a Lion, McClelland & Stewart (Toronto, Canada), 1987 . . . . £25/£5

ditto, Knopf (New York), 1987 . . . . . £20/£5

ditto, Secker & Warburg (London), 1987 . . . £15/£5

The English Patient, Bloomsbury (London), 1992. £100/£10

ditto, McClelland & Stewart (Toronto, Canada), 1992 £50/£10

ditto, Knopf (New York), 1992 . . . . £25/£10

Anil's Ghost, Bloomsbury (London), 2000 . £15/£5

ditto, McClelland & Stewart (Toronto, Canada), 2000 £15/£5

ditto, Knopf (New York), 2000 . . . . £15/£5

Divisadero, Bloomsbury (London), 2007 . . . £10/£5

ditto, McClelland & Stewart (Toronto, Canada), 2000 £10/£5

ditto, Knopf (New York), 2007 . . . . £10/£5

Poetry

The Dainty Monsters, Coach House Press, Toronto, Canada), 1967 (500 numbered copies) . . £500/£200

ditto, Coach House Press, Toronto, Canada), 1967 (pbk) £40

Rat Jelly, Coach House Press, Toronto, Canada), 1973 . . . . £300/£100

ditto, Coach House Press, Toronto, Canada), 1973 (pbk) £45

The Collected Works of Billy the Kid: Left Handed Poems, House of Anansi (Toronto, Canada), 1976 . £350/£150

ditto, House of Anansi (Toronto, Canada), 1976 (pbk; first issue, without the gilt stamped Governor General Award Winner emblem to upper right of front cover) . £100

ditto, House of Anansi (Toronto, Canada), 1976 (pbk; second issue without Award Winner emblem) £75

ditto, Norton (New York), 1974 . . . . . £50/£10

ditto, Marion Boyars (London), 1981. . . £35/£10

The Broken Ark: Book of Beasts, Oberon Press (Ottawa, Canada), 1971 . . . . £100/£50

There's a Trick with a Knife I'm Learning to Do: Poems 1963-1978, McClelland & Stewart (Toronto, Canada), 1979 . . . . £35/£10

ditto, Knopf (New York), 1979 . . . . . £25/£10

Rat Jelly: And Other Poems 1963-78, Marion Boyars (London), 1980 . . . . £35/£10

Tin Roof, Island Writing Series (Lantzville, Canada), 1982 (50 hardback copies) £300

ditto, Island Writing Series (Lantzville, Canada), 1982 (450 pbk copies) £100

Secular Love: Poems, Coach House Press, Toronto, Canada), 1984 (pbk) £10

ditto, Norton (New York), 1985 . . . . . £20/£5

Two Poems, Perishable Press (n.p.), 1986 (275 copies of a broadside printed oblong and folded three times to make a small booklet) £100

The Cinnamon Peeler: Selected Poems, Picador (London), 1989 (pbk) £5

ditto, McClelland & Stewart (Toronto, Canada), 1991 (pbk)
. . . . £5
ditto, Knopf (New York), 1991 . . . . . £15/£5
Elimination Dance, Nairn Coldstream (Iderton, Ontario),
1978 (stapled wraps) £100
ditto, as **Elimination Dance/La danse eliminatoire** Brick
Books (Ontario, Canada), 1991 (pbk) £10
Handwriting: Poems, McClelland & Stewart (Toronto,
Canada), 1998 . . . . £10/£5
ditto, Bloomsbury (London), 1998 . . . . £10/£5
ditto, Knopf (New York), 2000 . . . . £10/£5
The Story, House of Anansi (Toronto, Canada), 2004
(hardback with wrap-around band; no d/w) . . . £15

Plays
The English Patient: Screenplay, Miramax (New York),
1996 (pbk; with Anthony Minghella) £5

Non-Fiction
Running in the Family, McClelland & Stewart (Toronto,
Canada), 1982 . . . . £65/£10
ditto, Norton (New York), 1982 . . . . . £35/£10
ditto, Gollancz (London), 1983 . . . . . £20/£5
**The Conversations: Walter Murch And the Art of Editing
Film**, Vintage (Canada), 2002 (pbk) £5
ditto, Knopf (New York), 2002 . . . . . £10/£5

JOE ORTON
(b.1933 d.1967)

Joe Orton was a satirical modern British playwright whose
black farces are a skilful blend of the crude and the clever.
He shocked, outraged and amused audiences with his
irreverence and unique ear for comic dialogue. He was
murdered by his partner, Kenneth Halliwell, who then committed suicide. Alan Bennett wrote the screenplay for the
1987 film *Prick Up Your Ears*, based on Orton's diaries.

Plays
Entertaining Mr Sloane, Hamish Hamilton (London), 1964
. . . . £125/£25
ditto, Grove Press (New York), 1965 (pbk) . . . £10
Loot, Methuen (London), 1967 . . . . . £200/£25
ditto, Methuen (London), 1967 (pbk) £10
ditto, Grove Press (New York), 1967 (pbk) . . . £10
Crimes of Passion, Methuen (London), 1967 . . £50/£10
ditto, Methuen (London), 1967 (pbk) £15
ditto, Grove Press (New York), 1968 . . . . £15
What the Butler Saw, Methuen (London), 1969 . £45/£10
ditto, Methuen (London), 1969 (pbk) £10
ditto, Grove Press (New York), 1969 (pbk) . . . £10
Funeral Games and **The Good and Faithful Servant**,
Methuen (London), 1970 . . . . . £45/£10
ditto, Methuen (London), 1970 (pbk) £10
Joe Orton: The Complete Plays, Eyre Methuen (London),
1976 . . . . £30/£10
ditto, Grove Press (New York), 1976 . . . . £10
Fred and Madge and **The Visitors**, Nick Hern (London),
1998 . . . . £10/£5
ditto, as **The Visitors** and **Fred and Madge**, Grove Press
(New York), 1999 (pbk) £5

Screenplay
Up against It: A Screenplay for the Beatles, Eyre Methuen
(London), 1979 (pbk) £15
ditto, Grove Press (New York), 1979 (pbk) . . . £15

Novels
Head to Toe: A Posthumous Novel, Anthony Blond
(London), 1971 . . . . £15/£5
ditto, St Martin's Press (New York), 1987 . . £10/£5
Between Us Girls, Nick Hern (London), 1998 . . £10/£5
The Boy Hairdresser and **Lord Cucumber: Two Novels**,
Nick Hern (London), 1999 (with Kenneth Halliwell) £10/£5

Others
The Orton Diaries, Methuen (London), 1986 . . £10/£5
ditto, Harper & Row (New York), 1986 . . . £10/£5

GEORGE ORWELL
(b.1903 d.1950)

A left-wing novelist, essayist and journalist, Orwell, a
pseudonym for Eric Blair, is famous for his bleak political
satires *Animal Farm* (an allegory of the corruption of the
socialist ideals of the Russian Revolution by Stalinism) and
Nineteen Eighty-Four (a prophetic vision of the consequences of totalitarianism). Orwell is also widely admired
as an essayist.

Novels
Burmese Days, Harper (New York), 1934 . £2,500/£200
ditto, Gollancz (London), 1935 . . . . £3,000/£300
A Clergyman's Daughter, Gollancz (London), 1935 . .
. . . . £3,000/£250
ditto, Harper (New York), 1936 . . . . £2,000/£150
Keep the Aspidistra Flying, Gollancz (London), 1936 . .
. . . . £2,500/£200
ditto, Harcourt Brace (New York), 1956 . . . £75/£15
Coming Up for Air, Gollancz (London), 1939. £2,000/£150
ditto, Harcourt Brace (New York), 1950 . . . £75/£25
Animal Farm, Secker & Warburg (London), 1945. . .
. . . . £1,750/£100
ditto, Harcourt Brace (New York), 1946 . . £100/£20
ditto, Secker & Warburg (London), 1954 (illustrated by Joy
Batchelor & John Halas) . . . . . £100/£15
ditto, Harcourt Brace (New York), 1954 . . . £25/£10
ditto, Secker & Warburg (London), 1995 (illustrated by
Ralph Steadman) . . . . £45/£10
ditto, Harcourt Brace (New York), 1995 . . . £25/£10
Nineteen Eighty-Four, Secker & Warburg (London), 1949
(red d/w) . . . . £1,250/£100
ditto, Secker & Warburg (London), 1949 (green d/w) . .
. . . . £1,000/£100
ditto, Harcourt Brace (New York), 1949 (red d/w) . £250/£25
ditto, Harcourt Brace (New York), 1949 (blue d/w) £125/£25

Non-Fiction
Down and Out in Paris and London, Gollancz (London),
1933 . . . . £3,000/£250
ditto, Harper (New York), 1933 . . . . £1,250/£200
The Road to Wigan Pier, Gollancz (London), 1937 (Left
Book Club Edition) £50
ditto, Gollancz (London), 1937 . . . . £1,000/£125

ditto, Gollancz (London), 1937 (200 copies of the Left Book Club Edition bound separately, without the preface) . £200
ditto, Supplementary Left Book Club Edition (London) (part one only, plus photographs) £200
ditto, Harcourt Brace (New York), 1958 . . . £50/£15
Homage to Catalonia, Secker & Warburg (London), 1938 .
. . . . £2,000/£175
ditto, Harcourt Brace (New York), 1952 . . £75/£15
The Lion and the Unicorn, Secker & Warburg (London), 1941 (Searchlight Books, No.1) . . . . £75/£20
James Burnham and the Managerial Revolution, Socialist Book Centre (London), 1946 (stapled wraps) . . £300

Essays
Inside the Whale, Gollancz (London), 1940 . £1,500/£200
Critical Essays, Secker & Warburg (London), 1946 £75/£15
ditto, as **Dickens, Dali and Others**, Reynal & Hitchcock (New York), 1946 . . . . . . £50/£15
The English People, Collins (London), 1947 . £45/£10
Shooting an Elephant, Secker & Warburg (London), 1950 .
. . . . £45/£10
ditto, Harcourt Brace (New York), 1950 . . . £40/£10
Such, Such Were the Joys, Harcourt Brace (New York), 1953 . . . . £50/£15
ditto, as **England, Your England**, Secker & Warburg (London), 1953 . . . . £45/£15
The Decline of the English Murder and Other Essays, Penguin (Harmondsworth, Middlesex), 1965 (pbk) . £10
The War Broadcasts, BBC/Duckworth (London), 1985 .
. . . . £15/£5
The War Commentaries, BBC/Duckworth (London), 1985 .
. . . . £15/£5

Selected and Collected Editions
The Orwell Reader, Harcourt Brace (New York), 1956 .
. . . . £35/£10
Selected Essays, Penguin (Harmondsworth, Middlesex), 1957 (pbk) £5
Selected Writings, Heinemann (London), 1958 . £15/£5
The Collected Essays, Journalism and Letters of George Orwell, Secker & Warburg (London), 1968 (4 vols) .
. . . . £200/£45
ditto, Harcourt Brace (New York), 1968 (4 vols) . £145/£40
The Penguin Complete Longer Non-fiction of George Orwell, Penguin (Harmondsworth, Middlesex), 1983 (pbk)
. . . . £5

JOHN OSBORNE

(b.1929 d.1994)

Osborne was the author of *Look Back in Anger*, which won the 1956 Evening Standard Award for Best Play. He is best known for his 'kitchen sink' dramas, and was the first of the 'Angry Young Men' of the 1950s. Osborne's work is considered to have made 1950s British theatre artistically respectable again: he subverted existing formal constraints of language, rhetoric and emotional restraint.

Plays
Look Back in Anger, Evans (London), 1957 (pbk) . £50
ditto, Faber (London), 1957 . . . . . £100/£15
ditto, Criterion (New York), 1957 . . . . £40/£10

The Entertainer, Faber (London), 1957 . . . £50/£10
ditto, Criterion (New York), 1958 . . . . £35/£5
Epitaph for George Dillon, Faber (London), 1958 (with Anthony Creighton) . . . . £25/£10
ditto, Criterion (New York), 1958 . . . . £15/£5
The World of Paul Slickey, Faber (London), 1959. £25/£10
ditto, Criterion (New York), 1961 . . . . £15/£5
A Subject of Scandal and Concern: A Play for Television, Faber (London), 1961. . . . . . . £35/£15
Luther, Faber (London), 1961 . . . . £25/£10
ditto, Dramatic Publishing Co. (Chicago), 1961 . £15/£5
Plays for England, Faber (London), 1963 . . £25/£10
ditto, Criterion (New York), 1964 . . . . £15/£5
Inadmissible Evidence, Faber (London), 1965 . £25/£10
ditto, Grove Press (New York), 1965. . . . £15/£5
A Patriot for Me, Faber (London), 1966 . . . £25/£10
ditto, Random House (New York), 1970 . . . £15/£5
Time Present and **Hotel in Amsterdam**, Faber (London), 1968 . . . . £20/£5
The Right Prospectus: A Play for Television, Faber (London), 1970 . . . . £15/£5
Very Like a Whale, Faber (London), 1971 . . £15/£5
West of Suez, Faber (London), 1971 . . . . £15/£5
The Gift of Friendship: A Play for Television, Faber (London), 1972 . . . . £15/£5
A Sense of Detachment, Faber (London), 1973 . £15/£5
The End of Me Old Cigar: A Play and **Jill and Jack: A Play for Television**, Faber (London), 1975 . . . £15/£5
Watch It Come Down, Faber (London), 1975 . . £15/£5
You're Not Watching Me, Mummy and **Try a Little Tenderness: Two Plays for Television**, Faber (London), 1978 . . . . £15/£5
A Better Class of Person and **God Rot Tunbridge Wells**, Faber (London), 1985. . . . . . . £15/£5
Déjà Vu, Faber (London), 1991 . . . . . £10/£5

Autobiography
A Better Class of Person: An Autobiography 1929-1956, Faber (London), 1981. . . . . . . £20/£5
ditto, Dutton (New York), 1981 . . . . . £15/£5
Almost a Gentleman: An Autobiography, Vol II, 1955 - 1966, Faber (London), 1991 . . . . . £15/£5

Translations/Adaptations
A Bond Honoured, Faber (London), 1966 (from Lope de Vega's *La Fianza Satisfecha*) . . . . £20/£5
Hedda Gabler, Faber (London), 1972 (from the play by Henrik Ibsen) . . . . £15/£5
The Picture of Dorian Gray: A Moral Entertainment, Faber (London), 1973 (from the novel by Oscar Wilde) £15/£5
ditto, French (New York), 1973 . . . . . . £5
A Place Calling Itself Rome, Faber (London), 1973 (based on Shakespeare's *Coriolanus*) . . . . £15/£5
Strindberg's 'The Father' and **Ibsen's 'Hedda Gabler'**, Faber (London), 1989. . . . . . . £10/£5

Others
Declaration, MacGibbon & Kee (London), 1957 (essays by Osborne, Doris Lessing and six others, edited by Tom Maschler) . . . . £20/£5
ditto, Dutton (New York), 1958 . . . . . £20/£5
Look Back in Anger, Four Square Books (London), 1960 (novelisation by John Burke; pbk) £5

The Entertainer, Four Square Books (London), 1960 (novelisation by John Burke; pbk) £5
Tom Jones: A Film Script, Faber (London), 1964 . £20/£5
ditto, Grove Press (New York), 1964 . . . £10/£5
Damn You, England: Collected Prose, Faber (London), 1994 . . . . . . £15/£5
ditto, Faber (New York), 1994 . . . . £10/£5

WILFRED OWEN

(b.1893 d.1918)

Wilfred Owen suffered trench fever and concussion in World War One and was diagnosed as 'shell-shocked'. While waiting to return to the front he drafted and revised his best poems, but was killed in action only a week before the Armistice. Most of his poetry was published posthumously.

Poetry
Poems, Chatto & Windus (London), 1920 . £2,500/£350
ditto, Huebsch (New York), n.d. [1921] . . £750/£200
The Poems of Wilfred Owen, Chatto & Windus (London), 1931 . . . . . . £250/£65
ditto, Viking (New York), 1931 . . . . £200/£45
Thirteen Poems, Gehenna Press (Northampton, MA), 1956 (illustrated by Shahn and Baskin, 400 copies signed by Baskin, no d/w, slipcase) . . . . £250/£175
ditto, Gehenna Press (Northampton, MA), 1956 (35 copies with portrait proof, signed by both artists, slipcase) . . . . £1,000/£800
The Collected Poems of Wilfred Owen, Chatto & Windus (London), 1963 . . . . . £40/£15
ditto, New Directions (Norfolk, CT), 1964 . £35/£15
The Complete Poems and Fragments, Chatto & Windus (London), 1983 (2 vols, d/ws and slipcase) . £125/£50
ditto, Norton (New York), 1984 (2 vols, d/ws and slipcase) . . . . £125/£50

Others
Collected Letters, O.U.P. (Oxford, UK), 1967 . £125/£50

ELSIE J. OXENHAM

(b.1880 d.1960)

Born Elsie Jeanette Dunkerley, Oxenham was the author of numerous school novels, the better-known being set in the 'Abbey School', based on Cleeve Abbey in Somerset.

'Abbey' Books Series
The Abbey Girls, Collins (London), [1920] . £850/£200
The Girls of the Abbey School, Collins (London), [1921] . . . . £500/£125
The Abbey Girls Go Back to School, Collins (London), [1922] . . . . . . £500/£125
The New Abbey Girls, Collins (London), [1923] £500/£125
The New Abbey Girls Again, Collins (London), [1924] . . . . £500/£125
The Abbey Girls in Town, Collins (London), [1925] . . . . £500/£125

Queen of the Abbey Girls, Collins (London), [1926] . . . . £500/£125
ditto, as *The Call of the Abbey School*, Collins (London), [1934] (adaptation) . . . . . £125/£35
Jen of the Abbey School, Collins (London), [1927] . . . . £500/£125
ditto, as *The Girls of Rocklands School*, Collins (London), 1929 (adaptation) . . . . . £125/£35
ditto, as *The Second Term at Rocklands*, Collins (London), [1930] (adaptation) . . . . £125/£35
ditto, as *The Third Term at Rocklands*, Collins (London), [1931] (adaptation) . . . . £125/£35
The Abbey Girls Win Through, Collins (London), [1928] . . . . £500/£125
The Abbey Girls at Home, Collins (London), [1929] . . . . £250/£65
The Abbey Girls Play Up, Collins (London), [1930] . . . . £350/£85
The Abbey Girls on Trial, Collins (London), [1931] . . . . £450/£125
Schooldays at the Abbey, Collins (London), 1938 . £250/£75
Secrets of the Abbey, Collins (London), 1939 . £150/£45
Stowaways in the Abbey, Collins (London), 1940 . £150/£45
Maid of the Abbey, Collins (London), 1943 . £75/£35
Two Joans at the Abbey, Collins (London), 1945 . £125/£40
An Abbey Champion, Muller (London), 1946 . £250/£75
Robins in the Abbey, Collins (London), 1947 . £75/£35
A Fiddler for the Abbey, Muller (London), 1948 . £250/£75
Guardians of the Abbey, Muller (London), 1950 . £250/£75
Schoolgirl Jen at the Abbey, Collins (London), [1950] . . . . £75/£35
Strangers at the Abbey, Collins (London), 1951 . £75/£35
Rachel in the Abbey, Muller (London), 1951 . £250/£75
Selma at the Abbey, Collins (London), 1952 . £65/£25
A Dancer from the Abbey, Collins (London), 1953 £65/£25
The Song of the Abbey, Collins (London), 1954 . £65/£25
Tomboys at the Abbey, Collins (London), 1957 . £65/£25
Two Queens at the Abbey, Collins (London), 1959. £65/£25

Other Abbey Books
Girls of the Hamlet Club, Chambers (London), 1914 . £750
Biddy's Secret, Chambers (London), 1932 . £750/£350
Rosamund's Victory, Harrap (London), 1933 . £350/£125
Maidlin to the Rescue, Chambers (London), 1934 £750/£350
Joy's New Adventure: A Romance of the Abbey Girls, Chambers (London), 1935 . . . £750/£350
Maidlin Bears the Torch: An Abbey Story, Religious Tract Society/Girl's Own Paper (London), [1937] . £750/£350
Rosamund's Tuck Shop: School Story, Religious Tract Society/Girl's Own Paper (London), [1937] . £250/£75
Rosamund's Castle, Religious Tract Society/Girl's Own Paper (London), [1938] . . . . £750/£350
Jandy Mac Comes Back, Collins (London), 1941 . £100/£35

Others
Goblin Island, Collins (London), [1907] . . . £175
A Princess in Tatters, Collins (London), [1908] . £175
The Girl Who Wouldn't Make Friends, Nelson (London), [1909] £200
The Conquest of Christina, Collins (London), [1909] . £125
Mistress Nanciebel, Hodder & Stoughton, 1910 [1909] £100
A Holiday Queen, Collins (London), [1910] . . £175
Rosaly's New School, Chambers (London), 1913 . £125

Schoolgirls and Scouts, Collins (London), [1914] . . £150
At School With the Roundheads, Chambers (London), 1915
.   .   .   .   £125
Finding Her Family, SPCK (London), [1916]   . £150
The Tuck-Shop Girl: A School Story of Girl Guides,
Chambers (London), 1916.   .   .   .   .£200
A School Camp Fire, Chambers (London), 1917 . £200
The School of Ups and Downs: The Story of a Summer
Camp, Chambers (London), 1918 .   .   .£200
A Go-Ahead Schoolgirl, Chambers (London), 1919 . £200
Expelled from School, Collins (London), [1919] . £75
The School Torment, Chambers (London), 1920 £500/£225
The Twins of Castle Charming, Swarthmore Press
(London), [1920].   .   .   .   . £750/£400
The Two Form Captains, Chambers (London), 1921 . .
.   .   .   .   . £500/£250
The Captain of the Fifth, Chambers (London), 1922 .
.   .   .   .   . £500/£200
Patience Joan, Outsider, Cassell (London), [1922] .
.   .   .   .   . £400/£150
The Junior Captain, Chambers (London), [1923] £500/£200
'Tickles', or The School That Was Different, Partridge
(London), [1924]. .   .   .   .£200/£45
The School Without a Name, Chambers (London), [1924] .
.   .   .   .   . £850/£300
The Girls of Gwynfa, Warne (London), 1924 . . £450/£75
The Testing of the Torment, Cassell (London), 1925 .
.   .   .   .   . £225/£35
Ven at Gregory's, Chambers (London), [1925] £500/£200
The Camp Fire Torment, Chambers (London), 1926 .
.   .   .   .   . £500/£225
The Troubles of Tazy, Chambers (London), [1926] . .
.   .   .   .   . £500/£250
Patience and Her Problems, Chambers (London), [1927] .
.   .   .   .   . £500/£200
Peggy Makes Good, Partridge (London), [1927] .£200/£45
The Crisis in the Camp Keema, Chambers (London), [1928]
.   .   .   .   . £500/£200
Deb at School, Chambers (London), 1929 . £500/£250
Dorothy's Dilemma, Chambers (London), 1930 £300/£100
Deb of Sea House, Chambers (London), 1931. £500/£250
The Camp Mystery, Collins (London), [1932]. £350/£100
The Reformation of Jinty, Chambers (London), 1933 . .
.   .   .   .   . £500/£225
Jinty's Patrol, Newnes (London), [1934]. . £350/£100
Peggy and the Brotherhood, Religious Tract Society/Girl's
Own Paper (London), [1936] .   .   . £350/£75
Damaris at Dorothy's, SPCK/Sheldon Press (London),
[1937] .   .   .   . £350/£75
Sylvia of Sarn, Warne (London), 1937 . . £150/£45
Damaris Dances, O.U.P. (London), 1940. . . £200/£45
Patch and a Pawn, Warne (London), 1940 . £200/£45
Adventure for Two, O.U.P. (London), 1941 . £200/£45
Pernel Wins, Muller (London), 1942. . . £200/£45
Elsa Puts Things Right, Muller (London), 1944 . £200/£45
Daring Doranne, Muller (London), 1945. . £200/£45
The Secrets of Vairy, Muller (London), 1947 . £200/£45
Margery Meets the Roses, Lutterworth Press (London), 1947
.   .   .   .   . £200/£45
New Girls at Wood End, Blackie/Frederick? (London), 1957
.   .   .   .   . £200/£45
A Divided Patrol, Woodfield (London), 1992 .   . £10
Deb Leads the Dormitory, Woodfield (London), 1993 . £10

SARA PARETSKY
(b.1947)

Paretsky is a contemporary American author whose main
series of novels follow the exploits of V.I. Warshawski, an
unconventional female private investigator. It could be
argued that her main character, and the backgrounds that
Paretski describes, are the key to her success rather than the
crimes and her solutions to them. *Toxic Shock* won the
Crime Writers' Association Silver Dagger Award.

'V.I. Warshawski' Novels
Indemnity Only, Dial (New York), 1982 . . . £650/£75
ditto, Gollancz (London), 1982 .   .   . £65/£10
Deadlock, Dial (New York), 1984 .   . £150/£25
ditto, Gollancz (London), 1984 .   .   . £25/£10
Killing Orders, Morrow (New York), 1985 . £30/£10
ditto, Gollancz (London), 1986 .   .   . £25/£10
Bitter Medicine, Morrow (New York), 1987 . £15/£5
ditto, Gollancz (London), 1987 .   .   . £15/£5
Toxic Shock, Gollancz (London), 1988 . . £15/£5
ditto, as *Blood Shot*, Delacorte (New York), 1988 . £15/£5
Burn Marks, Delacorte (New York), 1990 . £15/£5
ditto, Chatto & Windus (London), 1990 . . £15/£5
Guardian Angel, Delacorte (New York), 1992 . £15/£5
ditto, Hamish Hamilton (London), 1992 . . £10/£5
ditto, Scorpion Press (Bristol), 1992 (99 signed copies). £60
ditto, Scorpion Press (Bristol), 1992 (20 lettered copies) £250
Tunnel Vision, Delacorte (New York), 1994 . £10/£5
ditto, Hamish Hamilton (London), 1994 . . £10/£5
Hard Time, Delacorte (New York), 1999 . . . £10/£5
ditto, Hamish Hamilton (London), 1999 . . £10/£5
Total Recall, Delacorte (New York), 2001 . £10/£5
ditto, Hamish Hamilton (London), 2001 .   . £10/£5
Blacklist, Putnam's (New York), 2003 . . £10/£5
ditto, Hamish Hamilton (London), 2003 . . £10/£5
Fire Sale, Putnam's (New York), 2005 . . £10/£5
ditto, Hodder & Stoughton (London), 2006 . £10/£5
Hardball, Putnam's (New York), 2009 . . £10/£5

Other Novels
Ghost Country, Delacorte (New York), 1998 .   . £10/£5
ditto, Hamish Hamilton (London), 1998 . . £10/£5
Bleeding Kansas, Putnam's (New York), 2008 . £10/£5
ditto, Hodder & Stoughton (London), 2008 . £10/£5

Short Stories
A Taste of Life and Other Stories, Penguin (London), 1995
(small format pbk) £5
Windy City Blues, Delacorte (New York), 1995 . £10/£5
ditto, as *V I for Short*, Hamish Hamilton (London), 1995 .
.   .   .   .   . £10/£5

Non-Fiction
Writing in an Age of Silence, Verso (New York/London),
2007 .   .   .   .   .   . £10/£5

DOROTHY PARKER
(b.1893 d.1967)

An American poet, short story writer and critic, Parker's work is characterised by her sophisticated and sardonic wit. Although she never considered her short, viciously humorous poems to be her most important works, they are still enjoyed today. Most are about the perceived ludicrousness of her many (largely unsuccessful) romantic affairs, and some wistfully consider the appeal of suicide.

Poetry
Enough Rope, Boni & Liveright (New York), 1926 £400/£75
Sunset Gun, Boni & Liveright (New York), 1928 . £165/£15
ditto, Boni & Liveright (New York), 1928 (250 signed, numbered copies) . . . . . £400/£300
Death and Taxes, Viking (New York), 1931 . . £100/£25
ditto, Viking (New York), 1931 (250 signed, numbered copies, slipcase) . . . . . £275/£225
Not So Deep As a Well, The Collected Poems of Dorothy Parker, Viking (New York), 1936 . . . £30/£10
ditto, Viking (New York), 1936 (485 signed copies, glassine d/w, slipcase) . . . . . £250/£175
ditto, Hamish Hamilton (London), 1937 . . £25/£10

Short Stories
Laments for the Living, Viking (New York), 1930 £100/£20
ditto, Longmans (London), 1930. . . . £100/£20
After Such Pleasures, Viking (New York), 1933 . £100/£20
ditto, Viking (New York), 1933 (250 signed copies, slipcase)
. . . . £250/£175
ditto, Longmans (London), 1934. . . . £100/£20
Here Lies: The Collected Stories of Dorothy Parker, Viking (New York), 1939 . . . . . £45/£10
ditto, Longmans (London), 1939. . . . £40/£10

THOMAS LOVE PEACOCK
(b.1785 d.1866)

Although he also wrote poetry, Thomas Love Peacock is remembered as the author of a number of unique, if odd novels each with the same basic premise of characters at a table discussing and criticising the philosophical opinions of the day. His place in literature is pre-eminently that of a satirist. Peacock was a close friend of Percy Bysshe Shelley and they are considered to have influenced each other's work.

Poetry
Palmyra and Other Poems, Richardson (London), 1806 £600
The Genius of the Thames, Hookham (London), 1810 . £350
The Philosophy of Melancholy, Hookham (London), 1812 .
. . . . £300
Sir Hornbook, or Childe Launcelot's Expedition, Sharpe & Hailes (London), 1814 (anonymous) . . . £1,000
The Round Table, or King Arthur's Feast, John Arliss (London), 1817 (anonymous) £1,000
Rhododaphne, or The Thessalian Spell, Hookham (London), 1818 (anonymous) £400

ditto, Carey & Son (Philadelphia, PA), 1818 . . . £125
Paper Money Lyrics, Reynell (London), 1837 (100 copies, anonymous) £600

Novels
Headlong Hall, Hookham (London), 1816 (anonymous) .
. . . . £1,250
Melincourt, Hookham (London), 1817 (anonymous, 3 vols)
. . . . £1,000
Nightmare Abbey, Hookham (London), 1818 ('By the Author of Headlong Hall') £1,500
Maid Marian, Hookham (London), 1822 ('By the Author of Headlong Hall') £700
The Misfortunes of Elphin, Hookham (London), 1829 ('By the Author of Headlong Hall') £500
Crotchet Castle, Hookham (London), 1831 ('By the Author of Headlong Hall') £600
Gryll Grange, Parker, Son, & Bourn (London), 1861 (anonymous) £250

Others
Gl'Ingannati, The Deceived and Aelia Laelia Crispis, Chapman & Hall (London), 1862 (translated by Peacock) . £100
Memoirs of Shelley, Frowde (London), 1909 . . . £50

Collected Editions
The Works of Thomas Love Peacock, Richard Bentley (London), 1875 (3 vols, edited by Henry Cole) . . £250
The Halliford Edition of the Works of Thomas Love Peacock, Constable (London), 1923-24 (675 sets, 10 vols, edited by H.F.B. Brett-Smith and C.E. Jones) . . £500

MERVYN PEAKE
(b.1911 d.1968)

Peake was a British writer, artist, poet and illustrator, best known for the 'Gormenghast' trilogy, an unfinished series of fantasies which follow the character Titus Groan. Peake's strength in both his writing and drawing is the creation of atmosphere through often grotesque detail. Some of his verse is of the Nonsense school.

Novels
Titus Groan, Eyre & Spottiswoode (London), 1946 (first issue book, first issue jacket with no quotes). . £300/£50
ditto, Eyre & Spottiswoode (London), 1946 (second issue book on cheaper paper, with jacket containing quotes from reviews and stating 'Second Impression') . . £175/£35
ditto, Reynal and Hitchcock (New York), 1946 . £100/£20
Gormenghast, Eyre & Spottiswoode (London), 1950 . .
. . . . £200/£45
ditto, Weybright & Talley (New York), 1967 . . £50/£10
Mr Pye, Heinemann (London), 1953 . . . £75/£15
Titus Alone, Eyre & Spottiswoode (London), 1959 £200/£45
ditto, Weybright & Talley (New York), 1967 . . £65/£15
Boy in Darkness, Wheaton (Exeter, Devon), 1976 (pbk) £45
ditto, Hodder (London), 1996 . . . . . £10/£5

Poetry
Shapes and Sounds, Chatto & Windus (London), 1941 . .
. . . . £250/£50
ditto, Transatlantic (New York), 1941 . . . £250/£50

Rhymes Without Reason, Eyre & Spottiswoode (London), 1944 . . . . £200/£45

The Glassblowers, Eyre & Spottiswoode (London), 1950 . . . . £145/£35

The Rhyme of the Flying Bomb, Dent (London), 1962. . . . . £135/£30

Poems and Drawings, Keepsake Press (London), 1965 (150 copies; sewn wraps) £275

A Reverie of Bone, Rota (London), 1967 (320 copies; wraps with d/w) . . . . . £175/£100

Selected Poems, Faber (London), 1972 . . . £30/£10

A Book of Nonsense, Peter Owen (London), 1972. £25/£10

ditto, Dufour (Chester Springs, PA), 1975 . . £15/£5

Swans Die and Towers Fall, Grasshopper Press (Chalfont St Peter), 1973 (100 copies, broadside) £150

Twelve Poems, 1939-1960, Bran's Head (Hayes, Middlesex), 1975 (350 numbered copies; wraps with glassine d/w) . . . . £100/£75

Children's Titles

Captain Slaughterboard Drops Anchor, Country Life (London), 1939 . . . . . £2,000/£1,000

ditto, Eyre & Spottiswoode (London), 1945 . £325/£75

ditto, Macmillan (New York), 1967 . . . £35/£10

Letters from a Lost Uncle from Polar Regions, Eyre & Spottiswoode (London), 1948 (d/w in form of envelope) . . . . £175/£75

Other Books

The Craft of the Lead Pencil, Wingate (London), 1946 (no d/w) £75

The Drawings of Mervyn Peake, Grey Walls Press (London), 1949 . . . . £50/£20

Figures of Speech, Gollancz (London), 1954 . £75/£15

The Inner Landscape, Allison & Busby (London), 1969 (contains three original novellas: 'Boy in Darkness' by Mervyn Peake; 'The Voices of Time' by J.G. Ballard; 'Danger: Religion!' by Brian Aldiss) . . . £20/£5

The Drawings of Mervyn Peake, Davis-Poynter (London), 1974 . . . . £50/£15

Mervyn Peake: Writings and Drawings, Academy (London), 1974 . . . . £20/£10

ditto, St Martin's Press (New York), 1974 . £20/£10

Peake's Progress: Selected Writings and Drawings, John Lane (London), 1979 . . . . . . £20/£10

ditto, Overlook Press (Woodstock, NY), 1981. £20/£10

Sometime, Never: Three Tales of Imagination, Eyre & Spottiswoode (London), 1956 (with John Wyndham and William Golding) . . . . . . £125/£35

ditto, Ballantine (New York), 1956 (pbk) . . . £20

Books Illustrated by Peake

Ride a Cock-Horse, and other nursery rhymes, Chatto & Windus (London), 1940 (first printing without dedication to Peake's son) . . . . . £350/£100

ditto, Chatto & Windus (London), 1940 (second printing with dedication page) . . . . . £250/£45

ditto, Transatlantic (New York), 1944 . . £250/£45

The Hunting of the Snark, An agony in eight fits, by Lewis Carroll, Chatto & Windus (London), 1941 (yellow boards) . . . . £75/£20

ditto, by Lewis Carroll, Chatto & Windus (London), 1941 (large format, pink boards) . . . . . £125/£35

The Adventures of The Young Soldier in Search of The Better World, by C[yril] E[dwin] M[itchinson] Joad, Faber & Faber (London), 1943 . . . . £40/£10

ditto, Acro (U.S.), 1944. . . . . . £40/£10

All This and Bevin Too, by Quentin Crisp, Nicholson & Watson (London), 1943 (stapled wraps). . . £350

ditto, Mervyn Peake Society (London), 1978 (40 hardback copies signed by Crisp; no d/w) £200

The Rime of the Ancient Mariner, by Samuel Taylor Coleridge, Chatto & Windus (London), 1943 . £75/£20

Prayers and Graces, A little book of extraordinary piety, by Allan M. Laing, Gollancz (London), 1944 . £50/£15

Witchcraft in England, by Christina Hole, Batsford (London), 1945 . . . . . . £75/£15

ditto, Scribner's (New York), 1947 . . . . £50/£15

Alice's Adventures in Wonderland and Through the Looking-Glass, by Lewis Carroll, Zephyr Books (Stockholm, Sweden), 1946 (wraps with d/w) £200/£75

ditto, Allan Wingate (London), 1954 . . . . £150/£65

ditto, Schocken (New York), 1979 . . . £25/£10

Quest for Sita, by Maurice Collis, Faber (London), 1946 (500 copies) . . . . . . £350/£200

ditto, John Day (New York), 1947 . . . £45/£15

Household Tales, by Brothers Grimm, Eyre & Spottiswoode (London), 1946 . . . . . . £75/£25

ditto, Schocken (New York), 1979 . . . . £25/£10

Dr Jekyll & Mr Hyde, by Robert Louis Stevenson, The Folio Society (London), 1948 . . . . . £65/£15

ditto, Duchesne (New York), 1948 . . . . £50/£15

Treasure Island, by Robert Louis Stevenson, Eyre & Spottiswoode (London), 1949 . . . £75/£15

ditto, Schocken (New York), 1979 . . . £25/£10

ditto, Schocken (New York), 1979 (pbk) . . . £5

Thou Shalt Not Suffer a Witch and Other Stories, by Dorothy K. Haynes, Methuen (London), 1949 . £75/£25

The Swiss Family Robinson, by Johann R. Wyss, Heirloom Library/Chanticleer Press, [1950] . . . £45/£15

The Wonderful Life & Adventures of Tom Thumb, by Paul Britten Austin, Radiotjänst (Stockholm, Sweden), 1954 (2 vols; pbks) £200

Men: A Dialogue Between Women, by Allegra Sander, Cresset Press (London), 1955 (translated by Vyvyan Holland) . . . . £45/£10

Under the Umbrella Tree, The Oxford English Course for Secondary Schools, by H[enry] B[urgess] Drake, O.U.P. (Oxford, UK), 1957 . . . . £30

More Prayers and Graces, A second little book of unusual piety, by Allan M. Laing, Gollancz (London), 1957 . . . . £40/£15

The Pot of Gold and Two Other Tales, by Aaron Judah, Faber (London), 1959. . . . . . £35/£10

Droll Stories, by Honoré de Balzac, The Folio Society (London), 1961 (translated by Alec Brown, slipcase) . . . . £25/£10

Meryyn Peake/Oscar Wilde, by Oscar Wilde, Gordon, Spilstead (London), 1980 (200 numbered copies, slipcase) . . . . £150/£125

ditto, Sidgwick & Jackson (London), 1980 . . £15/£5

Sketches from Bleak House, Methuen (London), 1983. . . . . £25/£10

WALKER PERCY
(b.1916 d.1990)

Walker Percy was an American author whose interests included philosophy and semiotics. He is best known for his philosophical novels, the first of which, *The Moviegoer*, won the National Book Award for Fiction in 1962. His work explores the moral confusion of man in the modern world and combines existentialism with a deep-rooted Catholic faith.

Symbol As Need, Fordham Univ (New York), 1954 (stapled wraps) £400
Symbol As Hermeneutic in Existentialism, Philosophy and Phenomenological Research (no place), 1956 (wraps) £300
Semiotic and a Theory of Knowledge, Modern Schoolman (no place), 1957 (wraps) £300
Symbol, Consciousness and Intersubjectivity, The Journal of Philosophy (Lancaster, PA), 1958 (wraps) . £300
Culture, The Antimony of the Scientific Method, New Scholasticism (no place), 1958 (wraps) . . . £300
The Message in the Bottle, Thought Magazine (no place), 1959 . . . . £250
Naming and Being, The Personalist (Bruges), 1960 . £250
The Symbolic Structure of the Interpersonal Process, Psychiatry Journal... (Washington, DC), 1961 (wraps) £250
The Moviegoer, Knopf (New York), 1961 . £2,000/£300
ditto, Eyre & Spottiswoode (London), 1963 . . £200/£45
ditto, Franklin Library (Franklin Center, PA), 1980 (signed limited edition; full leather) £75
The Last Gentleman, Farrar Straus & Giroux (New York), 1966 . . . . £125/£10
ditto, Eyre & Spottiswoode (London), 1967 . . £65/£15
Love in the Ruins, Farrar Straus (New York), 1971 £35/£5
ditto, Eyre & Spottiswoode (London), 1971 . . £30/£5
Toward A Triadic Theory of Meaning, Psychiatry Journal... (no place), 1972 (10 leaves with 'Reprinted from...' at top of first page). £200
Lanterns on the Levee, Louisiana State Univ (Baton Rouge, LA), 1973 (wraps) £15
The Message in the Bottle, Farrar Straus (New York), 1975 (top edge stained orange) . . . . . £45/£10
ditto, Farrar Straus (New York), 1975 (top edge unstained) . . . . £40/£5
Lancelot, Farrar Straus (New York), 1977 . . £20/£5
ditto, Secker & Warburg (London), 1977 . . £20/£5
Going Back to Georgia, Univ of Georgia (no place), 1978 (wraps) £100
ditto, Friends of Lucy Cobb & Seney-Stoval (Athens, GA), 1991 (300 numbered copies; wraps) £65
Bourbon, Palaemon Press (Winston-Salem, NC), 1979 (5 signed copies lettered A to E; full green leather) . £350
ditto, Palaemon Press (Winston-Salem, NC), 1979 (50 signed copies numbered with Roman numerals; marbled warbled wraps; d/w) . . . . . . £150/£100
ditto, Palaemon Press (Winston-Salem, NC), 1979 (200 signed, numbered copies; marbled wraps; d/w) £125/£100
ditto, Palaemon Press (Winston-Salem, NC), 1981 (26 signed, lettered copies; cloth spine and boards; no d/w or slipcase). £200
ditto, Palaemon Press (Winston-Salem, NC), 1981 (50 signed copies numbered with Roman numerals; cloth spine and boards; no d/w or slipcase) £100

Questions They Never Asked Me, Lord John Press (Northridge, CA), 1979 (50 signed, numbered copies; full blue leather) £200
ditto, Lord John Press (Northridge, CA), 1979 (300 signed, numbered copies; patterned paper covered boards with blue cloth spine) £100
The Second Coming, Franklin Library (Franklin Center, PA), 1980 (limited first edition in full leather) . . £30
ditto, Farrar Straus (New York), 1980 . . . £10/£5
ditto, Farrar Straus (New York), 1980 (450 signed, numbered copies; slipcase; no d/w) . . . . . £100/£75
ditto, Secker & Warburg (London), 1981 . . . £10/£5
Sewanee, Frederic C. Beil (New York), 1982 (no d/w) . £15
Lost in the Cosmos, Farrar Straus (New York), 1983 (top edge unstained) . . . . £10/£5
ditto, Farrar Straus (New York), 1983 (350 signed, numbered copies; slipcase; no d/w) . . . . £125/£100
ditto, Arrow Books (London), 1984 (pbk) . . . £10
The City of the Dead, Lord John Press (Northridge, CA), 1984 (26 signed, lettered copies; broadside) . . . £125
ditto, Lord John Press (Northridge, CA), 1984 (100 signed, unnumbered copies) £65
Diagnosing the Modern Malaise, Faust Publishing Co (New Orleans, LA), 1985 (50 signed, numbered copies; no d/w or slipcase). £250
ditto, Faust Publishing Co (New Orleans, LA), 1985 (250 signed, numbered copies; no d/w or slipcase) . £150
Conversations With Walker Percy, Univ Press of Mississippi (Jackson, MS), 1985 . . . . . £25/£10
ditto, Univ Press of Mississippi (Jackson, MS), 1985 (pbk) £10
Novel Writing in an Apocalyptic Time, Faust Publishing Co. (New Orleans, LA), 1986 (300 signed and numbered copies) £200
ditto, Faust Publishing Co. (New Orleans, LA), 1986 (100 numbered copies signed by Percy and Eudora Welty). £350
The Thanatos Syndrome, Franklin Library (Franklin Center, PA), 1987 (signed limited edition in full leather) . . £35
ditto, Farrar Straus Giroux (New York), 1987 . . £10/£5
ditto, Farrar Straus Giroux (New York), 1987 (250 signed, numbered copies; slipcase) . . . . £125/£100
ditto, Andre Deutsch (London), 1987. . . . £10/£5
The State of the Novel, Dying Art or New Science, Faust Publishing Co. (New Orleans, LA), 1988 (75 signed, numbered copies) £200
ditto, Faust Publishing Co. (New Orleans, LA), 1988 (250 signed, unnumbered copies) £100
Signposts in a Strange Land, Farrar Straus Giroux (New York), 1991 . . . . £10/£5
More Conversations With Walker Percy, Univ Press of Mississippi (Jackson, MS), 1993 . . . . £20/£10
ditto, Univ Press of Mississippi (Jackson, MS), 1993 (pbk) £10
The Correspondence of Sheldy Foote and Walker Percy, W.W. Norton (New York), 1996 . . . . £10/£5

ELLIS PETERS

(b.1913 d.1995)

Edith Pargeter has written many books under her own name and such pseudonyms as 'Jolyon Carr' and 'John Redfern'. However, it is as 'Ellis Peters' that she is best known, for it was in this guise that she gave to the world a fictional detective who is also a Benedictine monk, the now televised Brother Cadfael.

'Brother Cadfael' Novels by 'Ellis Peters'

A Morbid Taste for Bones: A Mediaeval Whodunnit, Macmillan (London), 1977 . . . . £600/£75
ditto, Morrow (New York), 1978 . . . .£300/£30
One Corpse Too Many, Macmillan (London), 1979 £375/£45
ditto, Morrow (New York), 1980 . . . £85/£10
Monk's Hood, Macmillan (London), 1980 . .£300/£65
ditto, Morrow (New York), 1981 . . . £65/£15
Saint Peter's Fair, Macmillan (London), 1981 .£200/£50
ditto, Morrow (New York), 1981 . . . .£100/£15
The Leper of Saint Giles, Macmillan (London), 1981 . .
. . . .£225/£30
ditto, Morrow (New York), 1982 . . . . £40/£10
The Virgin in the Ice, Macmillan (London), 1982 .£175/£20
ditto, Morrow (New York), 1983 . . . . £40/£10
The Sanctuary Sparrow, Macmillan (London), 1983 .
. . . .£125/£20
ditto, Morrow (New York), 1983 . . . . £25/£10
The Devil's Novice, Macmillan (London), 1983 . £75/£15
ditto, Morrow (New York), 1984 . . . . £25/£10
Dead Man's Ransom, Macmillan (London), 1984 . £65/£15
ditto, Morrow (New York), 1985 . . . . £25/£10
The Pilgrim of Hate, Macmillan (London), 1984 . £75/£15
ditto, Morrow (New York), 1984 . . . . £20/£5
An Excellent Mystery, Macmillan (London), 1985. £50/£15
ditto, Morrow (New York), 1985 . . . . £20/£5
The Raven in the Foregate, Macmillan (London), 1986 .
. . . . £30/£10
ditto, Morrow (New York), 1986 . . . . £20/£5
The Rose Rent, Macmillan (London), 1986 . . £30/£10
ditto, Morrow (New York), 1986 . . . . £20/£5
The Hermit of Eyton Forest, Headline (London), 1987 .
. . . . £30/£10
ditto, Mysterious Press (New York), 1988 . £20/£5
The Confession of Brother Haluin, Headline (London), 1988 . . . . £30/£10
ditto, Mysterious Press (New York), 1989 . £20/£5
The Heretic's Apprentice, Headline (London), 1989 £25/£5
ditto, Mysterious Press (New York), 1990 . £15/£5
The Potter's Field, Headline (London), 1989 . £25/£5
ditto, Mysterious Press (New York), 1990 . £15/£5
The Summer of the Danes, Headline (London), 1991 £25/£5
ditto, Mysterious Press (New York), 1990 . £15/£5
The Holy Thief, Headline (London), 1992 . £20/£5
ditto, Mysterious Press (New York), 1993 . £15/£5
Brother Cadfael's Penance, Headline (London), 1994 £15/£5
ditto, Headline (London), 1994 (97 signed, numbered, uncorrected proof copies; pbk). £100
ditto, Mysterious Press (New York), 1994 . £10/£5

'Brother Cadfael' Short Stories by 'Ellis Peters'

A Rare Benedictine, Headline (London), 1988 . £35/£5
ditto, Mysterious Press (New York), 1989 . £25/£5

The 'Felse' Series by 'Ellis Peters'

Death and the Joyful Woman, Collins Crime Club (London), 1961 . . . . . .£250/£25
ditto, Doubleday (New York), 1961 . . . .£100/£25
Flight of a Witch, Collins Crime Club (London), 1964. .
. . . .£175/£25
ditto, Mysterious Press (New York), 1991 . . £15/£5
A Nice Derangement of Epitaphs, Collins Crime Club (London), 1965 . . . . . .£175/£25
ditto, as *Who Lies Here?*, Morrow (New York), 1966 .
. . . . £65/£15
The Piper on the Mountain, Collins Crime Club (London), 1966 . . . . £75/£15
ditto, Morrow (New York), 1966 . . . . £40/£10
Black is the Colour of My True-Love's Heart, Collins Crime Club (London), 1967 . . . .£100/£15
ditto, Morrow (New York), 1967 . . . . £40/£10
The Grass Widow's Tale, Collins Crime Club (London), 1968 . . . . £65/£10
ditto, Morrow (New York), 1968 . . . . £40/£10
The House of Green Turf, Collins Crime Club (London), 1969 . . . . £75/£10
ditto, Morrow (New York), 1969 . . . . £30/£10
Mourning Raga, Macmillan (London), 1969 . £50/£10
ditto, Morrow (New York), 1970 . . . . £20/£5
The Knocker on Death's Door, Macmillan (London), 1970
. . . . £45/£10
ditto, Morrow (New York), 1971 . . . . £20/£5
Death to the Landlords!, Macmillan (London), 1972 £35/£10
ditto, Morrow (New York), 1972 . . . . £20/£5
City of Gold and Shadows, Macmillan (London), 1973 .
. . . . £30/£10
ditto, Morrow (New York), 1974 . . . . £20/£5
Rainbow's End, Macmillan (London), 1978 . . £30/£10
ditto, Morrow (New York), 1979 . . . . £20/£5

Novels Written as 'Edith Pargeter'

Hortensius, Friend of Nero, Lovat Dickson (London), 1936
. . . .£250/£100
ditto, Lovat Dickson (London), 1936 (125 numbered copies signed by Pargeter and illustrator John Farleigh) . . £500
ditto, Greystone Press (New York), 1937 . . .£225/£35
Iron-Bound, Lovat Dickson (London), 1936 . .£450/£50
The City Lies Foursquare, Heinemann (London), 1939 .
. . . .£175/£25
ditto, Reynall & Hitchcock (New York), 1939. .£125/£25
Ordinary People, Heinemann (London), 1941. .£100/£15
She Goes to War, Heinemann (London), 1942 .£100/£15
The Eighth Champion of Christendom, Heinemann (London), 1945 . . . . . . £75/£15
Reluctant Odyssey, Heinemann (London), 1946 . £75/£15
Warfare Accomplished, Heinemann (London), 1947 £75/£15
By This Strange Fire, Reynal & Hitchcock (New York), 1948 . . . . £50/£15
ditto, as *By Firelight*, Heinemann (London), 1948 . £50/£15
The Fair Young Phoenix, Heinemann (London), 1948. .
. . . . £45/£15
Lost Children, Heinemann (London), 1948 . £45/£15
Fallen into the Pit, Heinemann (London), 1951 . £45/£15
Holiday with Violence, Heinemann (London), 1952 £45/£15
This Rough Magic, Heinemann (London), 1953 . £45/£15
Most Loving Mere Folly, Heinemann (London), 1953 . .
. . . . £40/£10
The Soldier at the Door, Heinemann (London), 1954 £40/£10

A Means of Grace, Heinemann (London), 1956 . £40/£10

The Heaven Tree, Heinemann (London), 1960 . £40/£10

ditto, Doubleday (New York), 1960 . . . £25/£5

The Green Branch, Heinemann (London), 1962 . £35/£10

The Scarlet Seed, Heinemann (London), 1963 £35/£10

A Bloody Field by Shrewsbury, Macmillan (London), 1972
. . . . £35/£10

ditto, Viking (New York), 1973 . . . . . £25/£5

Sunrise in the West, Macmillan (London), 1974 . £35/£10

The Dragon at Noonday, Macmillan (London), 1975 . .
. . . . £35/£10

The Hounds of Sunset, Macmillan (London), 1976 £35/£10

Afterglow and Nightfall, Macmillan (London), 1977 . .
. . . . £35/£10

The Marriage of Meggotta, Macmillan (London), 1979 .
. . . . £35/£10

ditto, Viking (New York), 1979 . . . . . £25/£5

Short Stories Written as 'Edith Pargeter'

The Assize of the Dying, Heinemann (London), 1958 . .
. . . . £100/£20

ditto, Doubleday (New York), 1958 . . . £45/£10

The Lily Hand, Heinemann (London), 1965 . £100/£15

Novels Written as 'Ellis Peters'

Death Mask, Collins Crime Club (London), 1959 . £175/£30

ditto, Doubleday (New York), 1960 . . . £75/£15

The Will and the Deed, Collins Crime Club (London), 1960
. . . . £100/£15

ditto, as *Where There's a Will*, Doubleday (New York),
1960 . . . . £100/£15

Funeral of Figaro, Collins Crime Club (London), 1962 .
. . . . £100/£20

ditto, Morrow (New York), 1964 . . . £45/£10

The Horn of Roland, Macmillan (London), 1974 . £50/£10

ditto, Morrow (New York), 1974 . . . . £35/£5

Never Pick Up Hitchhikers!, Macmillan (London), 1976 .
. . . . £65/£15

ditto, Morrow (New York), 1976 . . . . £35/£5

Short Stories Written as 'Ellis Peters'

The Trinity Cat and Other Mysteries, Crippen & Landru,
2006 (hardback copies) . . . . . £60/£20

ditto, Crippen & Landru, 2006 (pbk) £10

Novels Written as 'Jolyon Carr'

Murder in the Dispensary, Herbert Jenkins (London), 1938
. . . . £450/£100

ditto, Post Mortem Books (London), 1999 (350 numbered
copies signed by the publisher, no d/w) . . . £25

Freedom for Two, Herbert Jenkins (London), 1938 .
. . . . £450/£100

Death Comes by Post, Herbert Jenkins (London), 1940 .
. . . . £450/£100

Masters of the Parachute Mail, Herbert Jenkins (London),
1940 . . . . £450/£100

Novels Written as 'John Redfern'

The Victim Needs a Nurse, Jarrolds (London), 1940 .
. . . . £600/£100

Others

The Coast of Bohemia, Heinemann (London), 1950 (by
Edith Pargeter) . . . . £100/£25

Shropshire, A Memoir of the English Countryside,
Macdonald (London), 1990 (by 'Ellis Peters') . £30/£10

ditto, Mysterious Press (New York), 1993 . . £35/£10

Strongholds and Sanctuaries, Sutton (Stroud, Gloucestershire), 1993 (by 'Ellis Peters') . . . . . £25/£10

DBC PIERRE
(b.1961)

DBC Pierre is the pseudonym of Peter Findlay, who was
born in 1961 in Reynella, Australia. He was brought up in
Mexico and the UK, and now lives in Ireland. His first
novel, *Vernon God Little* is a dark satire set in the aftermath of a Texas high school massacre, and was the winner
of the 2003 Man Booker Prize for Fiction.

Novels

Vernon God Little, Faber (London), 2003 . . £20/£5

ditto, Canongate (New York), 2003 . . . £15/£5

Ludmila's Broken English, Faber (London), 2006 £10/£5

ditto, Norton (New York), 2006 . . . . £10/£5

HAROLD PINTER
(b.1930)

Pinter is an English playwright, actor and theatre director
who has written for theatre, radio, television and film. His
early work is often associated with the Theatre of the Absurd and in his best drama he created a 'comedy of
menace'; claustrophobic situations in which there is an in-
definable threat hanging over the characters. He won the
Nobel Prize for Literature in 2005, and was made a Companion of Honour in 2002.

Plays

The Birthday Party, Encore Publishing (London), [1959]
(stapled wraps) £100

The Birthday Party and Other Plays, Methuen (London),
1960 (*The Dumb Waiter* & *The Room*) . . . £85/£20

The Caretaker, Encore Publishing (London), 1960 (stapled
wraps) £100

ditto, Methuen (London), 1960 . . . . £65/£15

ditto, Methuen (London), 1960 (pbk) £15

ditto, Grove (New York), 1960 . . . . £25/£10

The Black and White, French (London), [1960] (pbk) . £20

A Night Out, French (London), 1961 (pbk) . . £20

The Room, French (London), 1961 (pbk) . . . £20

The Dumb Waiter, French (London), 1961 (pbk) . . £20

A Slight Ache and Other Plays, Methuen (London), 1961 .
. . . . £50/£10

The Birthday Party and The Room, Grove (New York),
1961 . . . . £25/£10

The Collection, French (London), 1962 (pbk) . . . £15

Three Plays, Grove (New York), 1962 (*A Slight Ache, The
Collection* and *The Dwarfs*) . . . . . £25/£5

The Collection and The Lover, Methuen (London), 1963 .
. . . . £35/£10

The Lover, Dramatists Play Service (New York), 1965 (pbk)
. . . . £10

The Dwarfs and Eight Review Sketches, Dramatists Play
  Service (New York), 1965 (pbk) £15
The Homecoming, Methuen (London), 1965 .   . £30/£5
ditto, Grove (New York), 1966   .   .   .   . £25/£5
ditto, as *The Homecoming: Images*, by Harold Cohen,
  Karnac (London), 1968 (175 numbered copies, nine
  lithographs, slipcase)   .   .   .   .   . £200/£150
ditto, Karnac (London), 1968 (25 copies, additional set of
  plates, slipcase)   .   .   .   .   . £375/£325
Tea Party, Methuen (London), 1965 .   .   . £25/£5
ditto, Vanista (Zagreb, Yugoslavia), 1965 (280 numbered
  copies; wraps) £30
ditto, Grove (New York), 1966   .   .   .   . £20/£5
*The Lover, Tea Party, The Basement: Two Plays & A
  Filmscript*, Grove (New York), 1967   .   . £35/£10
Tea Party and Other Plays, Methuen (London), 1967 £20/£5
A Night Out, Night School, Revue Sketches: Early Plays,
  Grove (New York), 1967   .   .   .   . £25/£10
Landscape, Emanuel Wax for Pendragon Press (Ipswich,
  Norfolk), 1968 (2,000 numbered hardback copies, no d/w)
  .   .   .   . £25
Landscape and Silence, Methuen (London), 1969 . £30/£5
ditto, Grove (New York), 1970   .   .   .   . £25/£5
Old Times, Methuen (London), 1971.   .   . £25/£5
ditto, Karnac (London), 1971 (150 signed, numbered
  hardback copies; glassine d/w).   .   . £135/£125
ditto, Grove (New York), 1973 .   .   .   . £20/£5
Monologue, Covent Garden Press (London), 1973. £25/£10
ditto, Covent Garden Press (London), 1973 (100 signed
  copies in slipcase)   .   .   .   .   . £100/£75
No Man's Land, Methuen (London), 1975 .   . £25/£5
ditto, Karnac (London), 1975 (150 signed, numbered copies,
  glassine d/w).   .   .   .   .   . £125/£100
ditto, Grove (New York), 1975 .   .   .   . £20/£5
Betrayal, Methuen (London), 1978 .   .   . £20/£5
ditto, Grove (New York), 1979 .   .   .   . £15/£5
The Hothouse, Methuen (London), 1980 .   . £20/£5
ditto, Grove (New York), 1980 .   .   .   . £15/£5
Family Voices, Next Editions/Faber (London), 1981 (spiral
  bound in wraps) £15
Other Places, Methuen (London), 1982 .   . £15/£5
ditto, Grove (New York), 1983   .   .   .   . £10/£5
One for the Road, Methuen (London), 1985 .   . £15/£5
Mountain Language, Faber (London), 1988 .   . £15/£5
ditto, Grove (New York), 1988 .   .   .   . £10/£5
The Heat of the Day, Faber (London), 1989 .   . £15/£5
ditto, Grove (New York), 1990   .   .   .   . £10/£5
Party Time, Faber (London), 1991 .   . £15/£5
ditto, Grove (New York), 1993 (pbk).   .   . £5
Moonlight, Faber (London), 1993   .   .   . £10/£5
ditto, Grove (New York), 1993 (pbk).   .   . £5
Ashes to Ashes, Faber (London), 1996 (pbk) .   . £5
ditto, Grove (New York), 1997 (pbk).   .   . £5
Celebration and *The Room*, Faber (London), 2000 (pbk) £5
Press Conference, Faber (London), 2002.   .   . £5

Omnibus Editions
Plays 1-4, Methuen (London), 1975-1981 (4 vols). £50/£20
ditto, as *Complete Works, Volumes 1-4*, Grove (New York),
  1977-1981 (4 vols)   .   .   .   .   . £50/£20

Screenplays
Five Screenplays, Methuen (London), 1971 .   . £40/£10
ditto, Methuen (London), 1971 (pbk).   .   . £10

ditto, Karnac (London), 1971 (150 signed, numbered copies,
  no d/w) £150
ditto, Grove (New York), 1973 .   .   .   . £30/£10
The Proust Screenplay, Grove (New York), 1977 . £15/£5
ditto, Methuen (London), 1978 .   .   .   . £15/£5
The Screenplay of the French Lieutenant's Woman, Cape
  (London), 1981   .   .   .   .   .   . £20/£5
ditto, Little, Brown (Boston), 1981 .   .   . £20/£5
ditto, Little, Brown (Boston), 1981 (360 signed, numbered
  copies, slipcase)   .   .   .   .   . £100/£65
The French Lieutenant's Woman and Other Screenplays,
  Methuen (London), 1982 .   .   .   . £20/£5
The Heat of the Day, Faber (London), 1989 .   . £15/£5
The Comfort of Strangers and Other Screenplays, Faber
  (London), 1990   .   .   .   .   .   . £15/£5
The Trial, Faber (London), 1993 (pbk) .   .   . £5
Collected Screenplays, Faber (London), 2000 (3 vols) .   .
  .   .   .   . £20 the set

Poetry
Poems, Enitharmon Press (London), 1968 (wraps, with
  erratum slip). £20
ditto, Enitharmon Press (London), 1968 (200 signed copies,
  no d/w) £75
ditto, Enitharmon Press (London), 1971 (enlarged edition,
  boards) £25
ditto, Enitharmon Press (London), 1971 (pbk).   . £15
ditto, Enitharmon Press (London), 1971 (200 signed copies)
  .   .   .   . £165
Poems and Prose, 1949-1977, Grove Press (New York),
  1978   .   .   .   . £20/£5
ditto, Methuen (London), 1978 .   .   .   . £20/£5
ditto, as *Collected Poems and Prose*, Methuen (London),
  1986   .   .   .   . £15/£5
I Know The Place, Greville Press (Warwick, Staffordshire),
  1979 (500 signed copies, no d/w)   .   .   . £30
10 Early Poems, Greville Press (Warwick, Staffordshire),
  1992 (wraps). £15
ditto, Greville Press (Warwick, Staffordshire), 1992 (50
  signed copies) £150
The Disappeared and Other Poems, Enitharmon Press
  (London), 2002 (75 deluxe numbered copies signed by the
  author and the artist and containing an original etching
  signed and numbered by the artist, slipcase) . £400/£300
ditto, Enitharmon Press (London), 2002 (100 signed copies)
  .   .   .   . £100
War, Faber (London), 2003 .   .   .   .   . £5
Six Poems for A, Greville Press (Warwick, Staffordshire),
  2007 (250 numbered copies; wraps)   .   . £35
ditto, The Greville Press (Warwick, UK), 2007 (50 signed
  copies; wraps) £150

Others
Gorgona 8/Tea Party, Josip Vanista (Zagreb, Yugoslavia)
  1965 (280 numbered copies; wraps)   .   . £150
Mac, Emanuel Wax for Pendragon Press (Ipswich, Norfolk)
  1968 (2,000 numbered copies, no d/w) .   .   . £20
The Dwarfs, Faber (London), 1990 .   . £20/£5
ditto, London Limited Editions (London), 1990 (150 signed
  copies) £75
ditto, Grove (New York), 1990   .   .   .   . £20/£5
Conversations with Pinter, Limelight Editions (New York),
  1994   .   .   .   . £10/£5
ditto, Nick Hern Books (London), 1994 .   . £10/£5

Various Voices - Prose, Poetry, Politics 1948-1998, Faber (London), 1998 . . . . . £15/£5
ditto, Grove Press (New York), 1998 . . . £15/£5
Death etc, Grove Press (New York), 2005 (wraps). . £5

SYLVIA PLATH

(b.1932 d.1963)

Plath was an American poet whose work has an ironic tone and an undercurrent of terror. She suffered from bipolar disorder and while at college made the first of her suicide attempts, described in the semi-autobiographical novel, *The Bell Jar*. She married the poet Ted Hughes in 1956, and committed suicide in 1963. In 1982 she became the first poet to win a Pulitzer Prize posthumously (for *The Collected Poems*).

Poetry
Sculptor, Grecourt Review (Northampton, MS), 1959 (25 copies; wraps) £2,250
A Winter Ship, Tragara Press (Edinburgh), 1960 (anonymous leaflet). £1,750
The Colossus, Heinemann (London), 1960 . £1,500/£200
ditto, as *The Colossus and Other Poems*, Knopf (New York), 1962 . . . . . . £250/£50
Ariel, Faber (London), 1965. . . . . £400/£30
ditto, Harper & Row (New York), 1966 . . £100/£15
Uncollected Poems, Turret Books (London), 1965 (150 copies; wraps) £200
Wreath for a Bridal, Sceptre Press (Farnham, Surrey), 1970 (100 numbered copies, wraps unprinted tissue d/w) . . . . £150/£125
Million Dollar Month, Sceptre Press (Farnham, Surrey), 1971 (150 copies; wraps) £40
Fiesta Melons, Rougemont Press (Exeter, Devon), 1971 (75 copies of 150, signed by Ted Hughes) . £400/£300
ditto, Rougemont Press (Exeter, Devon), 1971 (75 unsigned copies of 150) . . . . . £175/£125
Child, Rougemont Press (Exeter, Devon), 1971 (325 copies; wraps with d/w) . . . . . . £40/£30
Crystal Gazer and Other Poems, Rainbow Press (London), 1971 (300 copies, slipcase) . . . £150/£125
ditto, Rainbow Press (London), 1971 (80 morocco bound copies) £500
ditto, Rainbow Press (London), 1971 (20 vellum bound copies) £750
Lyonesse, Rainbow Press (London), 1971 (300 copies bound in quarter leather, slipcase) . . . £150/£125
ditto, Rainbow Press (London), 1971 (90 copies bound in full calf). £500
ditto, Rainbow Press (London), 1971 (10 bound in vellum) £750
Crossing the Water, Faber (London), 1971 . £65/£15
ditto, as *Crossing the Water: Transitional Poems*, Harper & Row (New York), 1971 . . . . £60/£15
Winter Trees, Faber (London), 1971 . . . £35/£10
ditto, Harper & Row (New York), 1972 . . £25/£5
Pursuit, Rainbow Press (London), 1973 (100 numbered copies, with an etching and drawings by Leonard Baskin, slipcase). . . . . . . £750/£500
Two Poems, Sceptre Press (Knotting, Bedfordshire), [1980] (225 of 300 copies; wraps) £30

ditto, Sceptre Press (Knotting, Bedfordshire), [1980] (75 'especial' of 300 copies; wraps) £75
Two Uncollected Poems, Anvil Press (London), 1980 (450 copies; wraps) £35
Collected Poems, Faber (London), 1981 . . £30/£5
ditto, Harper & Row (New York), 1981 . . £20/£5
Dialogue Over a Ouija Board, Rainbow Press (London), 1981 (140 copies, slipcase) . . . £275/£225
The Green Rock, Embers Handpress (Ely, Cambridgeshire), 1982 (160 numbered copies; wraps, slipcase) £150/£125

Novel
The Bell Jar, Heinemann (London), 1963 (pseud 'Victoria Lucas') . . . . £3,000/£450
ditto, Faber (London), 1966 (as 'Sylvia Plath') . £450/£50
ditto, Harper & Row (New York), 1971 (as 'Sylvia Plath') . . . . £50/£10

Plays
Three Women: A Monologue for Three Voices, Turret Books (London), 1968 (180 copies, glassine d/w) . . . . £250/£200
ditto, no place [Oakland, California], no date [c.1970-75] (wraps) £25

Children's Title
The Bed Book, Faber (London), 1976 (illustrations by Quentin Blake) . . . . £100/£25
ditto, Harper & Row (New York), 1976 . . £75/£15

Others
The Art of Sylvia Plath: A Symposium, Faber (London), 1970 . . . . £50/£15
Letters Home, Harper & Row (New York), 1975 . £25/£5
ditto, Faber (London), 1976 . . . . . £25/£5
Johnny Panic and the Bible of Dreams and Other Writings, Faber (London), 1977 . . . . . £50/£10
ditto, as *Johnny Panic and the Bible of Dreams: Short Stories, Prose and Diary Excerpts*, Harper & Row (New York), 1979 . . . . £40/£10
A Day in June: an Uncollected Short Story, Embers Handpress (Ely, Cambridgeshire), 1981 (160 numbered copies; wraps) £150
The Journals of Sylvia Plath, Dial Press (New York), 1982 . . . . £25/£10
The Magic Mirror: A Study of the Doublein Two of Dostoevsky's Novels, Embers Handpress (Ely, Cambridgeshire), 1989 (50 copies, 'Oxford Hollow' binding, slipcase) . . . . £300/£200
ditto, Embers Handpress (Ely, Cambridgeshire), 1989 (176 copies, in d/w) . . . . . £175/£100
The Journals of Sylvia Plath 1950-1962, Faber (London), 2000 . . . . £15/£5

EDGAR ALLAN POE
(b.1809 d.1849)

An American poet, short story writer, editor and critic, Poe is best known for often anthologised horror tales such as 'The Fall of the House of Usher'. Along with Mary Shelley he is regarded as the foremost proponent of the Gothic strain in literary Romanticism. His 'The Murder in the Rue Morgue' also signalled the birth of the detective fiction genre.

Also see under individual illustrators.

Poetry

Tamerlane and Other Poems, Calvin F.S. Thomas (Boston), 1827 ('by a Bostonian'; wraps) £200,000

ditto, Calvin F.S. Thomas (Boston), 1827 (rebound)   .
  .   .   .   .£100,000

ditto, Redway (London), 1884 (100 copies)   .   .£2,500

Al AAraaf, Tamerlane and Minor Poems, Hatch & Dunning (Baltimore), 1829 (blue or red/tan boards with ivory paper spine) £75,000

ditto, Hatch & Dunning (Baltimore), 1829 (stitched but without covers) £65,000

ditto, Hatch & Dunning (Baltimore), 1829 (rebound) £20,000

Poems, Elam Bliss (New York), 1831 (claims wrongly to be the second edition) £25,000

The Raven and Other Poems, Wiley & Putnam (New York), 1845 (first issue with 'T.B. Smith, Stereotyper' on copyright page; wraps) £65,000

ditto, Wiley & Putnam (London), 1845 (cloth)   .£45,000

ditto, as *The Raven and Other Poems* and *The Tales* Wiley & Putnam (New York), 1845 (2 vols in one, dark blue cloth; first edition of *The Raven* and third edition of *The Tales*) £12,500

Fiction

The Narrative of Arthur Gordon Pym of Nantucket, Harper Bros. (New York), 1838 (anonymous; blue or grey cloth; paper label on spine) £3,000

ditto, Wiley & Putnum (London), 1838 (cloth)   .£2,000

Tales of the Grotesque and Arabesque, Lea & Blanchard (Philadelphia), 1840 (page 213 wrongly numbered, 2 vols)
  .   .   .   .£17,500

ditto, Lea & Blanchard (Philadelphia), 1840 (page 213 correctly numbered, 2 vols) £12,500

ditto, Lea & Blanchard (Philadelphia), 1840 (page 213 correctly numbered, 1 vol.) £7,500

The Prose Romances of Edgar A. Poe, William H. Graham (Philadelphia), 1843 (*Murders in the Rue Morgue, and the Man that was Used Up*; wraps)   .   .   .£15,000

The Tales, Wiley & Putnum (New York), 1845 (wraps)   .
  .   .   .   .£30,000

ditto, Wiley & Putnam (London), 1845   .   .£15,000

Eureka, A Prose Poem, Putnam (New York), 1848   £2,500

Others

The Conchologist's First Book, Haswell, Barrington & Baswell (Philadelphia), 1839 (coloured plates)   .£1,500

ditto, Haswell, Barrington & Baswell (Philadelphia), 1839 (uncoloured plates) £1,000

ditto, Haswell, Barrington & Baswell (Philadelphia), 1840 (second edition) £250

Mesmerism, 'In Articulo Mortis', Short & Co. (London), 1846 (wraps). £1,750

WILLY POGÁNY
(b.1882 d.1955)

Pogány was born in Hungary in 1882 and in 1915 settled in America after spending two years in Paris and ten in London. During that time he had established himself as an illustrator equal to Arthur Rackham and Edmund Dulac. According to Pogány himself, he illustrated over a hundred books, although these have never been fully catalogued.

The Welsh Fairy Book, by W. Jenkyn Thomas, Unwin (London), [1907] (100 illustrations by Pogány)   .   .£200

ditto, Stokes (New York), 1913   .   .   .   .   .£150

The Adventures of a Dodo, by G.E. Farrow, Unwin (London), [1907] (70 illustrations by Pogány)   .   .£65

ditto, Wessels (New York), 1908   .   .   .   .   .£45

Milly and Olly, by Mrs Humphry Ward, Unwin (London), 1907 (48 illustrations by Pogány) £40

Confessions of an English Opium Eater, by Thomas De Quincey, Collins (London), [1908] £35

Faust, J.W. von Goethe, Hutchinson (London), 1908 (30 full-page colour plates) £175

ditto, Hutchinson (London), 1908 (deluxe edition limited to 250 copies, signed by the artist, 31 full-page colour plates)
  .   .   .   .£400

ditto, Dana Estes (Boston), 1908 (500 numbered copies)   .
  .   .   .   .£250

ditto, Dana Estes (Boston), 1908 (trade copies)   .£175

A Treasury of Verse for Little Children, Harrap (London), [1908] £65

ditto, Crowell (New York), 1912   .   .   .   .   .£45

Rubaiyat of Omar Khayyam, Harrap (London), [1909] (24 colour illustrations by Pogány). £100

ditto, Harrap (London), [1909] (525 signed copies)   .£500

ditto, Harrap (London), [1909] (25 deluxe, signed copies)   .
  .   .   .   .£1,500

ditto, Crowell (New York), 1935 (500 signed copies)   .£400

ditto, Crowell (New York), 1935 (trade copies)   .£100

Tanglewood Tales, by Nathaniel Hawthorne, Unwin (London), [1909]. £50

Norse Wonder Tales, by Sir George Dasent, Collins (London), [1909]. £20

Gisli the Outlaw, by Sir George Dasent, Harrap (London), [1909] £20

The Blue Lagoon, by H. de Vere Stacpoole, Unwin (London), 1910   .   .   .   .£65

Folk Tales from Many Lands, by Lilian Gask, Harrap (London), 1910   .   .   .   .£75

ditto, Crowell (New York), 1910   .   .   .   .   .£35

The Witch's Kitchen, by Gerald Young, Harrap (London), [1910] £40

The Rime of the Ancient Mariner, by Samuel Taylor Coleridge, Harrap (London),1910 (20 mounted colour plates) £350

ditto, Harrap (London),1910 (525 signed, numbered copies)
  .   .   .   .£1,250

ditto, Harrap (London),1910 (25 deluxe, signed copies)   .
  .   .   .   .£2,000

ditto, Crowell (New York), 1910   .   .   .   .   .£350

Tannhauser, by T.W. Rolleston (after Richard Wagner), Harrap (London), [1911]   .   .   .   .   .   .£200 *ditto*, Harrap (London), [1911] (525 signed, numbered copies) £750

ditto, Crowell (New York), [1911] £200

Parsifal, by T.W. Rolleston (after Richard Wagner), Harrap (London),1912 . . . . £200

ditto, Harrap (London),1912 (525 signed, numbered copies) £500

ditto, Crowell (New York), 1912 . . . . . £200

The Fairies and the Christmas Child, by Lilian Gask, Harrap (London), [1912] £35

Atta Troll, by Heinrich Heine, Sidgwick & Jackson (London), 1913 . . . . £60

ditto, Huebsch (New York), 1914 . . . . . £50

The Hungarian Fairy Book, by Nandor Pogány, Unwin (London), 1913 . . . . £125

ditto, Stokes (New York), [c.1915] £75

Forty-Four Turkish Fairy Tales, by Ignacz Kunos, Harrap (London), [1913] £100

ditto, Harrap (London), [1913] (leather-bound edition) . £125

ditto, Crowell (New York), [c.1913] £100

The Tale of Lohengrin, by T.W. Rolleston (after Richard Wagner), Harrap (London), [1913] £250

ditto, Harrap (London), [1913] (525 signed, numbered copies) £650

ditto, Crowell (New York), [c.1913] £200

Willy Pogány Children, Harrap (London), [1914] (5 panoramic volumes: *Children at the Pole, Hiawatha, Red Riding Hood, Robinson Crusoe* and *The Three Bears*) . . . . £75 each

ditto, Holt (New York), [c.1914]. . . . £75 each

The Children in Japan, by Grace Bartruse, Harrap (London), [1915]. £100

ditto, McBride (New York), [1915] £100

Cinderella, by E.L. Elias, Harrap (London), [1915] . £100

ditto, McBride (New York), 1915 . . . . . £75

The Gingerbread Man, by Lionel Fable, Harrap (London), [1915] £50

ditto, McBride (New York), 1915 . . . . . £45

Mother Goose, [anon.], Harrap (London), [1915] . £35

More Tales from The Arabian Nights, by Frances J. Olcott, Holt (New York), 1915 . . . . . . £45

Home Book of Verse for Young Children, edited by B.E. Stevenson, Holt (New York), 1915 . . . . £30

Stories to Tell the Little Ones, by Sara Cone Bryant, Houghton Mifflin (Boston), 1916 . . . . £25

ditto, Harrap (London),1918 . . . . . £25

The King of Ireland's Son, by Padraic Colum, Macmillan (New York), 1916 . . . . . . £25

ditto, Harrap (London),1920 . . . . £50/£25

Bible Stories to Read and Tell, by Frances J. Olcott, Houghton Mifflin (Boston), 1916 . . . . £15

Tales of the Persian Genii, by Frances J. Olcott, Houghton Mifflin (Boston), 1917 . . . . . £30

ditto, Harrap (London),1919 . . . . . £25

Gulliver's Travels, by Jonathan Swift, Macmillan (New York), 1917 . . . . £50

ditto, Harrap (London),1919 . . . . . £50

Little Tailor of the Winding Way, by Gertrude Crownfield, Macmillan (New York), 1917 . . . . £20

Polly's Garden, by Helen Ward Banks, Macmillan (New York), 1918 . . . . £30

The Adventures of Odysseus and the Tale of Troy, by Padraic Colum, Macmillan (New York), 1918 . £50

ditto, Harrap (London),1920 . . . . £100/£50

Children's Plays, by Eleanor & Ada Skinner, Appleton (New York), 1919 . . . . . . £20

ditto, Appleton (London), 1919 . . . . . £20

Uncle Davie's Children, by Agnes McClelland Daulton, Macmillan (New York), 1920 . . . £50/£20

The Children of Odin: A Book of Northern Myths, by Padraic Colum, Macmillan (New York), 1920 . £65/£25

ditto, Harrap (London),1922 . . . . £65/£25

The Golden Fleece, and the Heroes Who Lived Before Achilles, by Padraic Colum, Macmillan (New York), 1921 . . . . £65/£25

The Adventures of Haroun el Raschid, by Frances J. Olcott, Holt (New York), 1923 . . . . . £65/£25

The Song of Bilitis, by Pierre Louys, Macy-Massius (New York), 1926 (2,000 copies signed by Pogány) £250/£200

Fairy Flowers, by Isidora Newman, Holt (New York), 1926 . . . . £200/£75

ditto, Humphrey Milford/O.U.P. (London), [1926]. £200/£75

George Washington Goes Around the World, by Margaret L. Thomas, Nelson (New York), 1927 . . £50/£25

ditto, Nelson (London), 1927 . . . . £40/£15

Looking Out For Jimmie, by Helen H. Flanders, Dutton (New York), 1927 . . . . . . £50/£25

ditto, Dent (London), [1928] . . . . £50/£25

Tisza Tales, by Rosika Schwimmer, Doubleday Doran (New York), 1928 . . . . £70/£40

Alice's Adventures in Wonderland, by Lewis Carroll, Dutton (New York), 1929 . . . . . £250/£75

ditto, Dutton (New York), 1929 (200 signed, numbered copies) . . . . . . £750/£500

Willy Pogány's Mother Goose, Nelson (New York), [1929] . . . . £200/£125

ditto, Nelson (New York), [1929] (500 signed copies) . £500

Casanova Jones, by Joseph Anthony, Century (New York), 1930 . . . . £65/£20

Magyar Fairy Tales, by Nandor Pogány, Dutton (New York), 1930 . . . . £100/£65

The Kasidah of Haji Abdu El-Yezdi, McKay (Philadelphia), 1931 . . . . £100/£45

ditto, McKay (Philadelphia), 1931 (250 signed, numbered copies) £225

The Light of Asia, by Edwin Arnold, McKay (Philadelphia), 1932 . . . . £75/£30

The Song Celestial, by Edwin Arnold, McKay (Philadelphia), 1934 . . . . . . £75/£30

My Poetry Book, edited by G.T. Huffard and L.M. Carlisle, Winston (Philadelphia), 1934 . . . . £45/£15

The Wimp and the Woodle, by Helen von Kolnitz Hyer, Suttonhouse (Los Angeles, San Francisco, New York City), 1935 . . . . £75/£35

ditto, Suttonhouse (London), 1935 . . . £75/£35

The Goose Girl of Nurnberg, by H.S. Hawley, Suttonhouse (Los Angeles, San Francisco, New York City), 1936 . . . . £65/£30

Coppa Hamba, by Blanche Ambrose, Suttonhouse (Los Angeles, San Francisco, New York City), 1936 . £65/£30

How Santa Found the Cobbler's Shop, by Margaretta Harmon, Suttonhouse (Los Angeles, San Francisco, New York City), 1936 . . . . . £65/£30

Sonnets from the Portugese, by Elizabeth Barrett Browning, Crowell (New York), 1936 . . . . . £75/£25

The Golden Cockerel, by Alexander Pushkin, Nelson (New York), 1938 . . . . £75/£25

Peterkin, by Elaine and Willy Pogány, McKay (Philadelphia), 1940 . . . . £125/£45
Bookplates, Original Etchings, Castle (New York), 1940 . . . . £200
The Frenzied Prince: Being Heroic Stories of Ancient Ireland, by Padraic Colum, McKay (Philadelphia), 1943 . . . . £45/£20
Running Away with Nebby, by Philis Garrard, McKay (Philadelphia), 1944 . . . . . £35/£10
Willy Pogány's Drawing Lessons, McKay (Philadelphia), 1946 (no d/w) £75
ditto, as *The Art of Drawing*, A.S. Barnes (New York)/Yoseloff (London), 1968 . . . . £35/£15
Willy Pogány's Water-Colour Lessons, McKay (Philadelphia), 1950 . . . . . . £75/£20
Willy Pogány's Oil Painting Lessons, McKay (Philadelphia), 1954 . . . . . . £35/£15

ELEANOR H. PORTER
(b.1868 d.1920)

American author best-known for Pollyanna, a girl who overcomes adversity through her sunny nature.

Children's Titles
Cross Currents, Wilde (Boston), 1907 . . . £20
ditto, Harrap (London), 1928 . . . . . £10
The Turn of the Tide, Wilde (Boston), 1908 . . £20
ditto, Harrap (London), 1928 . . . . . £10
The Sunbridge Girls at Six Star Ranch, Page (Boston), 1913 (pseud 'Eleanor Stuart') £25
ditto, as *Six Star Ranch*, Page (Boston), 1916. . £20
ditto, Stanley Paul (London), 1916 . . . . £10
Pollyanna, Page (Boston), 1913 . . . . £350
ditto, Pitman (London), 1913 . . . . . £150
Pollyanna Grows Up, Page (Boston), 1915 . . £85
ditto, Pitman (London), 1915 . . . . . £50
Dawn, Houghton Mifflin (Boston), 1919 . . . £15

Adult Novels
The Story of Marco, Jennings and Graham, and Eaton and Mains (Cincinnati and New York), 1911 . . £20
ditto, Stanley Paul (London), [1920] £10
Miss Billy, Page (Boston), 1911 . . . . £15
ditto, Stanley Paul (London), 1914 . . . . £10
Miss Billy's Decision, Page (Boston), 1912 . . £15
ditto, Stanley Paul (London), 1915 . . . . £10
Miss Billy—Married, Page (Boston), 1914 . . £15
ditto, Stanley Paul (London), 1915 . . . . £10
Just David, Houghton Mifflin (Boston), 1916. . £20
ditto, Constable (London), 1916 . . . . . £15
The Road to Understanding, Houghton Mifflin (Boston), 1917 . . . . £15
ditto, Constable (London), 1917 . . . . . £10
Oh, Money! Money!, Houghton Mifflin (Boston), 1918 £20
ditto, Constable (London), 1918 . . . . . £15
Keith's Dark Tower, Constable (London), 1919 . £15
Mary Marie, Houghton Mifflin (Boston), 1920 . £20
ditto, Constable (London), 1920 . . . . . £10
Sister Sue, Houghton Mifflin (Boston), 1921 . . £10
ditto, Constable (London), 1921 . . . . . £5

The 'Miss Billy' Stories, Harrap (New York), 1927 (contains: *Miss Billy*, *Miss Billy's Decision* and *Miss Billy—Married*) £15

Adult Short Stories
The Tangled Threads: Just Tales, Houghton Mifflin (Boston), 1919 . . . . £15
Across the Years: Tales of Age, Houghton Mifflin (Boston), 1919 . . . . £15
The Tie That Binds: Tales of Love and Marriage, Houghton Mifflin (Boston), 1919 . . . . £15
Money, Love, and Kate, and *The Story of a Nickel*, Doran (New York), 1923 . . . . . . £20
ditto, Hodder & Stoughton (London), 1924 . . £10
Hustler Joe and Other Stories, Doran (New York), 1924 £15
Little Pardner and Other Stories, Doran (New York), 1926 . . . . £15
ditto, Houghton & Stoughton (London), 1927 . . £10
Just Mother and Other Stories, Doran (New York), 1927 £15
The Fortunate Mary, Doubleday (New York), 1928 . £10

CHARLES PORTIS
(b.1933)

Charles Portis is an American author of Westerns whose work is both inventive and comic, while using the obvious formulas of the genre. His fans have a cult-like devotion to his books, the best-known of which is *True Grit*.

Norwood, Simon & Schuster (New York), 1966 . £300/£50
ditto, Jonathan Cape (London), 1967 . . . . £100/£20
True Grit, Simon & Schuster (New York), 1968 . £125/£25
ditto, Jonathan Cape (London), 1969 . . . . £50/£10
The Dog of the South, Knopf (New York), 1979 . £25/£5
Masters of Atlantis, Knopf (New York), 1985 . £15/£5
Gringos, Simon & Schuster (New York), 1991 . £10/£5

BEATRIX POTTER
(b.1866 d.1943)

A British author and illustrator. *The Tale of Peter Rabbit* was first written down in a letter to the son of one of Potter's governesses. It was later privately printed in an edition of 250 copies, the first of a highly successful series of books for the very young. She stopped writing and drawing in the early 1920s due to poor eyesight.

The Tale of Peter Rabbit, privately printed (London), [1901] (250 copies, flat spine, monochrome plates) . . £75,000
ditto, privately printed (London), [1902] (200 copies, round spine, monochrome plates) £25,000
ditto, Warne (London), [1902] (trade edition, brown paper covered boards, pale grey-blue leaf pattern endpapers, first issue text with 'wept big tears' on p.51, colour plates) £6,500
ditto, Warne (London), 1902 (as above but later green paper covered boards) £5,000
ditto, Warne (London), 1902 (as above but in yellow cloth). £12,000

ditto, Warne (London), 1902 (as above but in olive green cloth) £9,000
The Tailor of Gloucester, privately printed (London), 1902 (500 copies in pink boards). £8,000
ditto, Warne (London), 1903 (trade edition; first issue with same endpapers repeated four times)   .   .   .   £1,000
ditto, Warne (London), 1903 (flower-patterned art cloth binding). £3,500
ditto, Warne (London), 1968 (facsimile of the original manuscript and illustrations, 1,500 numbered copies in box)   .   .   .   .   £50/£35
ditto, Warne (London), 1969 (facsimile of the original manuscript). £35
The Tale of Squirrel Nutkin, Warne (London), 1903 (paper covered boards) £1,000
ditto, Warne (London), 1903 (flower-patterned art cloth binding). £3,500
The Tale of Benjamin Bunny, Warne (London), 1904 (paper covered boards; first issue with 'muffatees' mis-spelled with an 'a' instead of an 'e' on p.15)   .   .   £1,000
ditto, Warne (London), 1904 (cloth binding)   .   £3,500
The Tale of Two Bad Mice, Warne (London), 1904 (paper covered boards) £800
ditto, Warne (London), 1904 (cloth binding)   .   £3,500
The Tale of Mrs Tiggy-Winkle, Warne (London), 1905 (paper covered boards) £750
ditto, Warne (London), 1905 (cloth edition)   .   £4,000
The Pie and the Patty Pan, Warne (London), 1905 (paper covered boards; large format) £250
ditto, Warne (London), 1905 (cloth edition; large format) £1,000
The Tale of Mr Jeremy Fisher, Warne (London), 1906 (paper covered boards) £750
ditto, Warne (London), 1906 (cloth edition)   .   £4,000
The Story of a Fierce Bad Rabbit, Warne (London), 1906 (panorama) £750
The Story of Miss Moppet, Warne (London), 1906 (panorama) £1,000
The Tale of Tom Kitten, Warne (London), 1907 (paper covered boards) £500
ditto, Warne (London), 1907 (cloth edition)   .   £4,000
The Tale of Jemima Puddle-Duck, Warne (London), 1908 (paper covered boards) £750
ditto, Warne (London), 1908 (cloth edition)   .   £5,000
The Roly-Poly Pudding, Warne (London), 1908 (cloth edition; large format) £650
ditto, as **The Tale of Samuel Whiskers**, Warne (London), [1926] (paper covered boards) £200
The Tale of the Flopsy Bunnies, Warne (London), 1909 (paper covered boards) £750
ditto, Warne (London), 1909 (cloth edition)   .   £5,000
Ginger and Pickles, Warne (London), 1909 (paper covered boards; large format) £400
The Tale of Mrs Tittlemouse, Warne (London), 1910 (paper covered boards) £500
ditto, Warne (London), 1910 (cloth edition)   .   £4,000
Peter Rabbit's Painting Book, Warne (London), [1911] £650
The Tale of Timmy Tiptoes, Warne (London), 1911 (paper covered boards) £500
ditto, Warne (London), 1911 (cloth edition)   .   £2,250
The Tale of Mr Tod, Warne (London), 1912 (paper covered boards) £250
The Tale of Pigling Bland, Warne (London), 1913 (paper covered boards) £350

Appley Dapply's Nursery Rhymes, Warne (London), 1917 (paper covered boards) £450
Tom Kitten's Painting Book, Warne (London), 1917   .   £500
The Tale of Johnny Town-Mouse, Warne (London), [1918] (paper covered boards; first issue with 'N' missing from London on title-page). £500
Cecily Parsley's Nursery Rhymes, Warne (London), 1922 (paper covered boards)   .   .   .   £5,000/£500
Jemima Puddle-Duck's Painting Book, Warne (London), [1925] £400
Peter Rabbit's Almanac for 1929, Warne (London), [1928] £750
The Fairy Caravan, McKay (Philadelphia), 1929   .   .   .   .   £1,000/£350
ditto, privately printed (London), 1929 (100 copies)   £3,500
ditto, Warne (London), 1952   .   .   .   .   £100/£50
The Tale of Little Pig Robinson, Warne (London), [1930] (large format)   .   .   .   .   .   £750/£250
ditto, McKay (Philadelphia), 1930   .   .   £750/£250
Sister Anne, McKay (Philadelphia), 1932   .   £750/£250
Wag-By-Wall, Warne (London), [1944] (100 copies)   .   .   .   .   £1,000/£400
ditto, The Horn Book (Boston), 1944.   .   .   £75/£30
Jemima Puddle-Duck's Painting Book, From the Original Designs by B. Potter, Warne (London), [1954]   .   £75
Jeremy Fisher's Painting Book, From the Original Designs by B. Potter, Warne (London), [1954]   .   .   .   £75
Peter Rabbit's Painting Book, From the Original Designs by B. Potter, Warne (London), [1954]   .   .   £75
Tom Kitten's Painting Book, From the Original Designs by B. Potter, Warne (London), [1954]   .   .   .   £75
The Tale of the Faithful Dove, Warne (London), [1955] (100 copies, illustrated by Marie Angel)   .   .   £750
The Sly Old Cat, Warne (London), 1971   .   .   £40/£10
The Tale of Tupenny, Warne (London), 1973 (illustrated by Marie Angel)   .   .   .   .   .   .   £30/£5

Illustrated by Potter
A Happy Pair, by Frederic E. Weatherley, Hildensheimer & Faulkner/Geo C. Whitney (London/New York), [1890] (illustrated by Potter as 'HBP'; pictorial wraps)   .   £18,000

DENNIS POTTER
(b.1935 d.1994)

Best-known for *The Singing Detective*, Potter wrote over forty plays for television. His work often contains elements of fantasy and he drew heavily on popular culture, especially music, for inspiration.

Drama
The Nigel Barton Plays, Penguin (London), 1967 (pbk) £20
Son of Man, Deutsch (London), 1970   .   .   £40/£15
Brimstone and Treacle, Eyre Methuen (London), 1978 (pbk) £10
Sufficient Carbohydrate, Faber (London), 1983 (pbk)   .   £15
Waiting for the Boat, Faber (London), 1984 (pbk).   .   £5
The Singing Detective, Faber (London), 1986 (pbk)   .   £5
Christabel, Faber (London), 1988 (pbk)   .   .   .   £5
Lipstick on Your Collar, Channel 4/Faber (London), 1993 (pbk) £5

Seeing the Blossom, Faber (London) 1994 (pbk) . . £5
Karaoke and Cold Lazarus, Faber (London) 1996 (pbk) £5

Novels
Hide and Seek, Deutsch (London), 1973 . . £35/£10
ditto, Quartet Books (London), 1973 (pbk) . . . £5
Pennies from Heaven, Quartet Books (London), 1981 (pbk)
. . . . £5
Ticket to Ride, Faber (London), 1986 . . . £25/£10
Blackeyes, Faber (London), 1987 . . . . £15/£5

Miscellaneous
The Glittering Coffin, Gollancz (London), 1960 . £50/£15
The Changing Forest: Life in the Forest of Dean Today,
Secker & Warburg (London), 1962 (laminated boards) £40
Potter on Potter, Faber (London), 1993 . . . £15/£5

EZRA POUND
(b.1885 d.1972)

An American poet, musician and critic, Ezra Pound is generally acknowledged as a prime mover of Modernist poetry. He was one of the first to successfully write in free verse in his extended compositions and was the driving force behind several Modernist movements, notably Imagism and Vorticism. His *Cantos* were an inspiration for Allen Ginsberg and other Beat poets of the 1950s and '60s.

Poetry
A Lume Spento, Antonini (Venice, Italy), 1908 (150 copies; green wraps). £30,000
ditto, All'insegna del pesce d'oro (Milano), 1958 (2,000 copies; stiff grey wraps in d/w) . £45/£30
ditto, New Directions (Norfolk, CT), 1965 (acetate d/w)
. . . . £40/£15
ditto, Faber (London), 1965 . . . . . £45/£20
A Quinzane for this Yule, Pollock & Co (London), 1908 (100 copies; wraps) £20,000
ditto, printed for Elkin Mathews (London), 1908 (100 copies; wraps) £12,500
Personae, Elkin Mathews (London), 1909 (500 copies, first issue binding with the five lines of type on spine measuring 2 cm) £600
ditto, Elkin Mathews (London), 1909 (500 copies, second issue binding with type on spine measuring 1.5 cm) . £500
ditto, Boni & Liveright (New York), 1926 . £1,000/£150
Exultations, Elkin Mathews (London), 1909 (500 copies) .
. . . . £400
Provenca, Small Maynard (Boston), [1910] (200 copies, tan boards stamped in dark brown). £500
ditto, Small Maynard (Boston), [1917] (later issue, tan boards stamped in green) £100
Canzoni, Elkin Mathews (London), 1911 (grey cloth, author's name on cover) £400
ditto, Elkin Mathews (London), 1911 (brown boards, without author's name on cover) £200
*Riposte*s, Stephen Swift (London), 1912 . . . £450
ditto, Small Maynard (Boston), 1913 . . . . £300
Lustra, Elkin Mathews (London), [1916] (200 numbered copies, unexpurgated version for private circulation) . .
. . . . £1,250

ditto, Elkin Mathews (London), 1916 (expurgated trade edition) £200
ditto, Knopf (New York), 1917 . . . . . £200
Pavannes and Divisions, Knopf (New York), 1918 (first binding, blue cloth stamped in gold) £75
ditto, Knopf (New York), 1918 (later bindings stamped in green) £45
ditto, Peter Owen (London), 1960 . . . £35/£10
Quia Pauper Amavi, The Egoist (London), [1919] (100 signed copies, handmade paper) . . . £1,500
ditto, The Egoist (London), [1919] (10 signed copies, roman numerals) £4,000
ditto, The Egoist (London), [1919] £200
The Fourth Canto, Ovid Press (London), 1919 (40 copies for private circulation) £6,000
Hugh Selwyn Mauberley, Ovid Press (London), 1920 (165 unsigned copies) £2,500
ditto, Ovid Press (London), 1920 (35 signed copies) £5,000
Umbra, Elkin Mathews (London), 1920 . £600/£300
ditto, Elkin Mathews (London), 1920 (100 signed copies) .
. . . . £2,500
ditto, Elkin Mathews (London), 1920 (signed, lettered copies) £5,000
Poems, 1918-21, Boni & Liveright (New York), 1921 . .
. . . . £500/£175
Indiscretions; Or, Une Revue de Deux Mondes, Three Mountains Press (Paris, France), 1923 (300 numbered copies) £750
ditto, Three Mountains Press (Paris, France), 1923 (300 numbered copies, unbound sheets) £300
A Draft of XVI Cantos, Three Mountains Press (Paris, France), 1925 (90 copies) £1,500
A Draft of Cantos 12-27, Three Mountain Press (Paris, France), 1928 . . . . £500
Selected Poems, Faber (London), 1928 (100 signed copies).
. . . . £2,000
ditto, Faber (London), 1928 . . . . . £250/£75
A Draft of XXX Cantos, Hours Press (Paris, London), 1930 (200 unsigned copies). £2,000
ditto, Hours Press (Paris, London), 1930 (10 signed copies).
. . . . £7,500
ditto, Farrar & Rinehart (New York), 1933 ('shit' on page 62) £1,000
ditto, Farrar & Rinehart (New York), 1933 ('sh-t' on page 62) . . . . £250/£45
ditto, Faber (London), 1933 . . . . . £175/£35
Imaginary Letters, Black Sun Press (Paris, France), 1930 (50 signed copies on Japanese vellum; wraps with glassine d/w and slipcase) . . . . £1,500/£1,000
ditto, Black Sun Press (Paris, France), 1930 (300 copies; wraps with glassine d/w and slipcase) . £425/£250
Eleven New Cantos: XXXI-XLI, Farrar & Rinehart (New York), 1934 . . . . £150/£40
ditto, as *Draft of Cantos XXXI-XLI*, Faber (London), 1935.
. . . . £125/£30
Homage to Sextus Propertius, Faber (London), 1934 . .
. . . . £150/£45
The Fifth Decad of Cantos, Faber (London), 1937 £150/£45
ditto, Farrar & Rinehart (New York), 1937 . £125/£25
ditto, New Directions (Norfolk, CT), 1940 . £100/£20
Cantos LII-LXXI, Faber (London), 1940 . . £200/£45
ditto, New Directions (Norfolk, CT), 1940 (500 copies with envelope and pamphlet) . . . . £200/£65

ditto, New Directions (Norfolk, CT), 1940 (500 copies without envelope and pamphlet) . . . £100/£35

The Pisan Cantos, New Directions (Norfolk, CT), 1948 .
. . . . £250/£65

ditto, Faber (London), 1949 . . . . . £200/£50

Section: Rock-Drill, Pesce d'Oro (Milan, Italy), 1955 . £200

ditto, New Directions (Norfolk, CT), 1956 . . £45/£15

ditto, Faber (London), 1957 . . . . . £45/£15

Diptych Rome-London, New Directions (Norfolk, CT), 1957 (125 signed copies in slipcase) . . . £1,000/£650

ditto, Faber (London), 1957 (50 signed copies in slipcase) .
. . . . . . £1,250/£1,000

ditto, Vanni Scheiwiller (Italy), 1957 (25 signed copies in slipcase) . . . . . . £2,000/£1,750

Thrones, Pesce d'Oro (Milan, Italy), 1959 (300 copies) £300

ditto, New Directions (Norfolk, CT), 1959 . £40/£15

ditto, Faber (London), 1960 . . . . . £40/£15

The Cantos, Faber (London), 1964 (all 109 cantos) £45/£10

Cavalcanti Poems, New Directions (Norfolk, CT), [1966] (200 signed copies, glassine d/w, slipcase) . £1,000/£850

ditto, Faber (London), [1966] (190 signed copies in slipcase) .
. . . . £1,000/£850

Drafts and Fragments of Cantos CX-CXVII, New Directions (Norfolk, CT), 1969 . . . £60/£20

ditto, New Directions/Stone Wall Press (Norfolk, CT/Iowa City, IA), 1969 (1-200 signed, numbered copies of 310, for New Directions, slipcase) . . . £500/£400

ditto, New Directions/Stone Wall Press (Norfolk, CT/Iowa City, IA), 1969 (201-300 signed, numbered copies, of 310, for Faber, slipcase) . . . . £450/£350

ditto, New Directions/Stone Wall Press (Norfolk, CT/Iowa City, IA), 1969 (301-310 signed, numbered copies, of 310, for Stone Wall Press, slipcase) . . . £1,000/£850

ditto, Faber (London), 1970 . . . . £40/£15

Others

The Spirit of Romance, Dent (London), 1910 (first issue top edge gilt) £200

ditto, Dent (London), 1910 (second issue top edge stained green) £165

ditto, Dutton (New York), 1910 . . . £75

Cathay, Elkin Mathews, 1915 (printed tan wraps) . £300

Gaudier-Brzeska, Bodley Head (London), 1916 (with design on front cover) £450

ditto, Bodley Head (London), 1916 (without design on front cover) £250

ditto, Lane (New York), 1916 . . . . . £350

Instigations, Boni & Liveright (New York), 1920 .
. . . . £1,000/£200

Antheil and the Treatise on Harmony, Three Mountains Press (Paris, France), 1924 (360 copies, red wraps) . £500

ditto, Three Mountains Press (Paris, France), 1924 (40 copies, Arches paper, red wraps) £1,000

ditto, Contact Editions/Three Mountains Press (Paris, France), 1924 (unsold copies of above with buff label on title page 'Contact Editions'; wraps) . . . £300

ditto, Pascal Covici (Chicago), 1927 . . . £200/£50

How to Read, Harmsworth (London), 1931 . £225/£40

ABC of Economics, Faber (London), 1933 . . £150/£35

ditto, New Directions (Norfolk, CT), 1940 . £125/£30

ABC of Reading, Routledge (London), 1934 . £100/£30

ditto, Yale Univ Press (New Haven, CT), 1934 . £75/£25

Make it New, Faber (London), 1934 . . . £100/£30

ditto, Yale Univ Press (New Haven, CT), 1935 . £75/£20

Social Credit, Nott (London), [1935 or 37?] (wraps) . £65

Polite Essays, Faber (London), 1937 . . . £150/£35

ditto, New Directions (Norfolk, CT), 1940 . £125/£25

Guide to Kulchur, Faber (London), 1938 . . £150/£30

ditto, as **Culture**, New Directions (Norfolk, CT), 1938 . .
. . . . £145/£30

Patria Mia, Seymour (Chicago), 1950 . . £100/£25

ditto, Peter Owen (London), 1962 . . . £45/£15

The Letters of Ezra Pound, Harcourt Brace (New York), 1950 . . . . £40/£15

ditto, Faber (London), 1951 . . . . . £35/£10

The Translations of Ezra Pound, Faber (London), 1953 .
. . . . £75/£20

ditto, New Directions (Norfolk, CT), 1953 . £65/£15

Literary Essays of Ezra Pound, Faber (London), 1954 . .
. . . . £40/£10

ditto, New Directions (Norfolk, CT), 1954 . £40/£10

Impact, Essays on Ignorance and the Decline of American Civilisation, Regnery (Chicago, IL), 1960 . £35/£10

Pound/Joyce, New Directions (Norfolk, CT), 1967 £25/£10

ditto, Faber (London), 1968 . . . . . £25/£10

Selected Prose, 1909-65, Faber (London), 1973 . £25/£10

ditto, New Directions (Norfolk, CT), 1975 . . £25/£10

An Autobiographical Outline, NADJA (New York), 1980 (200 numbered copies; sewn wraps) £25

ditto, NADJA (New York), 1980 (26 lettered copies) . £50

Pound/Ford, Faber (London), 1982 . . . . £25/£10

The Selected Letters of Ezra Pound to John Quinn, 1915-1924, Duke Univ Press (Durham, NC), 1991 . £25/£10

ANTHONY POWELL

(b.1905 d.2000)

Powell studied at Oxford, where Evelyn Waugh, Henry Green, Graham Greene, and George Orwell were among his contemporaries. He was a regular contributor to and reviewer for various newspapers and was appointed Literary Editor of *Punch* in 1953. As a novelist Powell is best known for the series of novels with the collective title *Dance to the Music of Time*. In 1973 he declined the offer of a knighthood, but was made a Companion of Honour in 1988.

'Dance to the Music of Time' Novels

A Question of Upbringing, Heinemann (London), 1951 .
. . . . £800/£125

ditto, Scribner's (New York), 1951 . . . £250/£45

A Buyer's Market, Heinemann (London), 1952 £800/£125

ditto, Scribner's (New York), 1953 . . . £250/£35

The Acceptance World, Heinemann (London), 1955 . .
. . . . £600/£65

ditto, Farrar Straus (New York), 1956 . . £125/£35

At Lady Molly's, Heinemann (London), 1957 . £125/£20

ditto, Little, Brown (Boston), 1958 . . . . £75/£10

Casanova's Chinese Restaurant, Heinemann (London), 1960
. . . . £75/£15

ditto, Little, Brown (Boston), 1960 . . . £25/£10

The Kindly Ones, Heinemann (London), 1962 . £65/£15

ditto, Little, Brown (Boston), 1962 . . . £30/£5

The Valley of Bones, Heinemann (London), 1964 . £65/£15

ditto, Little, Brown (Boston), 1964 . . . . £25/£5

The Soldier's Art, Heinemann (London), 1966 . £35/£10

ditto, Little, Brown (Boston), 1966 . . . £15/£5
The Military Philosophers, Heinemann (London), 1968 .
. . . . £20/£5
ditto, Little, Brown (Boston), 1969 . . . £10/£5
Books Do Furnish a Room, Heinemann (London), 1971 .
. . . . £30/£10
ditto, Little, Brown (Boston), 1971 . . . £10/£5
Temporary Kings, Heinemann (London), 1973 . £25/£10
ditto, Little, Brown (Boston), 1963 . . . £10/£5
Hearing Secret Harmonies, Heinemann (London), 1975 .
. . . . £15/£5
ditto, Little, Brown (Boston), 1975 . . . £10/£5
All twelve *Dance to the Music of Time* titles as first editions
in very good d/ws £4,000

Other Novels

Afternoon Men, Duckworth (London), 1931 . £3,000/£300
ditto, Holt (New York), 1932 . . . £2,250/£300
Venusberg, Duckworth (London), 1932 . . £2,000/£200
ditto, as *Venusberg & Agents and Patients*, Periscope/
Holliday (New York), 1952 . . . . £25/£5
From a View to a Death, Duckworth (London), 1933 . .
. . . . £1,750/£250
ditto, as *Mr Zouch: Superman*, Vanguard Press (New York),
1934 . . . . £1,000/£100
ditto, Little, Brown (Boston), 1964 . . . £20/£5
Agents and Patients, Duckworth (London), 1936 . . .
. . . . £1,500/£125
What's Become of Waring, Cassell (London), 1939 . .
. . . . £3,000/£350
ditto, Little, Brown (Boston), 1963 . . . £20/£5
O, How the Wheel Becomes It, Heinemann (London), 1983
. . . . £10/£5
ditto, Holt Rinehart (New York), 1983 . . £10/£5
The Fisher King, Heinemann (London), 1985. . £10/£5
ditto, Norton (New York), 1986 . . . . £10/£5

Autobiography

Infants of the Spring, Heinemann (London), 1976 £15/£5
ditto, Holt Rinehart (New York), 1976 . . . £10/£5
Messengers of the Day, Heinemann (London), 1978 £25/£5
ditto, Holt Rinehart (New York), 1978 . . £10/£5
Faces in My Time, Heinemann (London), 1980 . £20/£5
ditto, Holt Rinehart (New York), 1981 . . £10/£5
The Strangers all are Gone, Heinemann (London), 1982 .
. . . . £20/£5
ditto, Holt Rinehart (New York), 1983 . . £10/£5

Others

Caledonia: A Fragment, privately printed (London), 1934
(100 copies; cloth backed tartan boards) . . £2,250
John Aubrey and His Friends, Heinemann (London), 1948
. . . . £45/£10
ditto, Scribner's (New York), 1949 . . . £40/£10
The Garden God and *The Rest I'll Whistle*, Heinemann
(London), 1971 . . . . . . £30/£5
ditto, Little, Brown (Boston), 1971 . . . £20/£5
Under Review, Further Writings on Writers, 1946-1989,
Heinemann (London), 1991 . . . . £20/£5
ditto, Univ of Chicago (Chicago), 1991 . . £20/£5
A Reference for Mellors, Moorhouse and Sorensen
(London), 1994 (26 signed, lettered copies of 326, quarter
goatskin, slipcase) . . . . . £350/£275
ditto, Moorhouse and Sorensen (London), 1994 (100 signed,
numbered copies of 326) £200

ditto, Moorhouse and Sorensen (London), 1994 (200
numbered copies of 326; wraps) £45
Journals, 1982-1986, Heinemann (London), 1995. £20/£5
Journals, 1987-1989, Heinemann (London), 1996. £20/£5
Journals, 1990-1992, Heinemann (London), 1997. £20/£5

JOHN COWPER POWYS
(b.1872 d.1963)

John Cowper Powys was descended from the poet William
Cowper. A novelist, poet and essayist, Powys's romances
are very highly rated by his readers, although he has never
received general literary recognition. His younger brothers
Llewelyn and Theodore also became well-known writers,
and his other brothers and sisters prominent in the arts.

Novels

Wood and Stone, A Romance, G.Arnold Shaw (New York),
1915 . . . . £100
ditto, Heinemann (London), 1915 [1917] . . . £100
Rodmoor, A Romance, G. Arnold Shaw (New York), 1916.
. . . . £125
Ducdame, Doubleday Page (New York), 1925 . £200/£50
ditto, Grant Richards (London), 1925 . . £200/£50
Wolf Solent, Simon & Schuster (New York), 1929 (2 vols,
slipcase). . . . . £75/£30
ditto, Cape (London), 1929 (1 vol.) . . . £150/£25
A Glastonbury Romance, Simon & Schuster (New York),
1932 . . . . £200/£35
ditto, Simon & Schuster (New York), 1932 (204 signed,
numbered copies, no d/w) £500
ditto, John Lane (London), 1933 (1 vol.) . . £200/£35
Weymouth Sands, Simon & Schuster (New York), 1934 .
. . . . £100/£25
ditto, as *Jobber Skald*, John Lane (London), 1935 (revised
text) . . . . £65/£20
ditto, Cape (London), 1963 (unexpurgated version) £25/£5
Maiden Castle, Simon & Schuster (New York), 1936 £75/£15
ditto, Cassell (London), 1937 . . . . £50/£15
Morwyn, or The Vengeance of God, Cassell (London), 1937
. . . . £225/£50
Owen Glendower, Simon & Schuster (New York), 1940 (2
vols) . . . . £125/£35
ditto, John Lane (London), 1941 (1 vol.) . . £65/£15
Porius, Macdonald (London), 1951 . . . £75/£15
ditto, Macdonald (London), 1951 (200 signed copies) . £250
ditto, Philosophical Library (New York), 1952 . £65/£15
The Inmates, Macdonald (London), 1952 . . £75/£35
ditto, Philosophical Library (New York), 1952 . £75/£35
Atlantis, Macdonald (London), 1954. . . . £75/£15
The Brazen Head, Macdonald (London), 1956 . £50/£15
All or Nothing, Macdonald (London), 1960 . . £35/£10
ditto, Colgate Univ Press (Hamilton, NY), 1960 . £35/£10
Real Wraiths, Village Press (London), 1974 (pbk). . £5
You and Me, Village Press (London), 1975 (pbk) . . £5
After My Fashion, Picador (London), 1980 (pbk) . . £5
Three Fantasies, Carcanet (Manchester, UK), 1985 £15/£5

Short Stories

The Owl, the Duck and - Miss Rowe! Miss Rowe!, Black
Archer Press (Chicago), 1930 (250 signed copies, slipcase)
. . . . £125/£100

ditto, Village Press (London), 1975 (pbk). . . . £5
Up and Out, Macdonald (London), 1957 . . . £45/£10
ditto, Village Press (London), 1974 (with *The Mountains of the Moon*; pbk) £5

Poetry
Corinth, privately printed (Oxford), 1891 ('English Verse' on front cover; wraps) £2,000
Odes and Other Poems, Rider & Co. (London), 1896 . £300
Poems, Rider & Co. (London), 1899 . . . . £200
Wolf's-Bane, G. Arnold Shaw (New York), 1916 . . £50
Mandragora, G. Arnold Shaw (New York), 1917 . . £75
Samphire, Thomas Seltzer (New York), 1922 . . £75/£35
Lucifer, A Poem, Macdonald (London), 1956 (560 signed, numbered copies, acetate d/w) . . . . £85/£65
John Cowper Powys: A Selection from His Poems, Macdonald (London), 1964 . . . . . £35/£10
ditto, Colgate Univ Press (Hamilton, NY), 1964 (slipcase) . . . . £35/£10

Others
The War and Culture, G. Arnold Shaw (New York), 1914 (boards) £25
ditto, G. Arnold Shaw (New York), 1914 (pbk) . . £25
ditto, as ***The Menace of German Culture***, Rider & Co. (London), 1915 . . . . £50
Visions and Revisions: A Book of Literary Devotions, G. Arnold Shaw (New York), 1915 . . . . £30
ditto, Macdonald (London), 1955 . . . . £25/£10
Confessions of Two Brothers, Manas Press (Rochester, NY), 1916 (with Llewelyn Powys) £25
One Hundred Best Books, G. Arnold Shaw (New York), 1916 . . . . £20
Suspended Judgements, Essays on Books and Sensations, G. Arnold Shaw (New York), 1916. . . . £20
The Complex Vision, Dodd, Mead (New York), 1920 . . . . £100/£25
The Art of Happiness, Haldeman-Julius (Girard, KS), 1923 (stapled wraps) £35
Psychoanalysis and Morality, Jessica Colbert (San Francisco, CA), 1923 (350 signed, numbered copies of 500) £60
ditto, Jessica Colbert (San Francisco, CA), 1923 (150 unsigned copies of 500) £25
ditto, Village Press (London), 1975 (pbk). . . . £5
The Religion of a Sceptic, Dodd, Mead (New York), 1925 (1,000 copies) . . . . . . £100/£25
ditto, Village Press (London), 1975 (pbk). . . . £5
The Secret of Self-Development, Haldeman-Julius (Girard, KS), 1926 (stapled wraps) £25
The Art of Forgetting the Unpleasant, Haldeman-Julius (Girard, KS), 1928 (stapled wraps) £25
The Meaning of Culture, Norton (New York), 1929 £75/£20
ditto, Cape (London), 1930 . . . . . £75/£20
In Defence of Sensuality, Simon & Schuster (New York), 1930 . . . . £50/£15
ditto, Gollancz (London), 1930 . . . . £45/£10
Debate! Is Modern Marriage a Failure?, Discussion Guild (New York), 1930 (with Bertrand Russell) . £1,250
Dorothy M. Richardson, Joiner & Steele (London), 1931 . . . . £45/£15
ditto, Joiner & Steele (London), 1931 (60 signed, numbered copies) . . . . . . £175/£125

A Philosophy of Solitude, Simon & Schuster (New York), 1933 . . . . £65/£20
Autobiography, Simon & Schuster (New York), 1934 . . . . £75/£20
ditto, Bodley Head (London), 1934 . . . . £75/£20
The Art of Happiness, Simon & Schuster (New York), 1935 (not the 1923 version). . . . . . £45/£10
ditto, Bodley Head (London), 1935 . . . . £45/£10
Enjoyment of Literature, Simon & Schuster (New York), 1938 . . . . £30/£10
ditto, as ***The Pleasures of Literature***, Cassell (London), 1938 (contains one extra essay) . . . £30/£10
Mortal Strife, Cape (London), 1941 . . . £30/£10
The Art of Growing Old, Cape (London), 1944 . £35/£10
Dostoievsky, John Lane (London), 1946 . . £30/£10
Pair Dadeni, or The Cauldron of Rebirth, Druid Press (Carmarthen, Wales), 1946 . . . . £45/£15
Obstinate Cymric, Essays 1935-47, Druid Press (Carmarthen, Wales), 1947 . . . . £45/£15
Rabelais, John Lane (London), 1948 . . . £25/£5
ditto, Philosophical Library (New York), 1951 . £20/£5
In Spite Of, A Philosophy for Everyman, Macdonald (London), 1952 . . . . . . £20/£5
ditto, Philosophical Library (New York), 1953 . £20/£5
The Letters of John Cowper Powys to Louis Wilkinson, 1935-1956, Macdonald (London), 1958. . . £25/£10
Homer and the Aether, Macdonald (London), 1959 £15/£5
Letters to Nicholas Ross, Bertram Rota (London), 1971 . . . . £25/£10
Two & Two, Village Press (London), 1974 (pbk) . £5
Letters to Henry Miller, Village Press (London), 1975 (pbk) £10
Letters to His Brother Llewelyn, 1902-1939, Village Press (London), 1975 (2 vols; pbk) £15

LLEWELYN POWYS
(b.1884 d.1939)

Although he wrote three novels, Llewelyn Powys's reputation rests upon his collected essays, many of which contain his observations of Africa. He contracted tuberculosis while lecturing in the U.S. and afterwards lived in Switzerland, Kenya and Dorset.

Essays
Ebony and Ivory, American Library Service (New York), 1923 . . . . £75/£15
ditto, Grant Richards (London), 1923 . . . £75/£15
Thirteen Worthies, American Library Service (New York), 1923 . . . . £75/£15
ditto, Grant Richards (London), 1924 . . . £65/£15
Honey and Gall, Haldeman-Julius (Girard, KS), 1924 (wraps) £20
Cup Bearers of Wine and Hellebore, Haldeman-Julius (Girard, KS), 1924 (wraps) £20
Black Laughter, Harcourt Brace (New York), 1924 £75/£20
ditto, Grant Richards (London), 1925 . . . £75/£20
The Cradle of God, Harcourt Brace (New York), 1929. . . . . £30/£10
ditto, Cape (London), 1924 . . . . . £30/£10
The Pathetic Fallacy, Longmans Green (London), 1930 . . . . £40/£10

Impassioned Clay, Longmans Green (New York), 1931   .
.   .   .   .   £35/£10
ditto, Longmans Green (London), 1931   .   .   .   £35/£10
Now that the Gods are Dead, Equinox Press (New York),
1932 (400 signed copies; illustrated by Lynd Ward) . £200
Glory of Life, Golden Cockerel Press (Waltham St
Lawrence, Berks), 1934 (277 numbered copies; illustrated
by Robert Gibbings) £500
ditto, Golden Cockerel Press (Waltham St Lawrence, Berks),
1934 (2 copies on vellum).   .   .   .   £5,000
ditto, John Lane (London), 1938.   .   .   .   £50/£10
Earth Memories, John Lane (London), 1934   .   £75/£15
ditto, Norton (New York), 1938   .   .   .   £30/£10
Damnable Opinions, Watts (New York), 1935   .   £30/£10
Dorset Essays, Bodley Head (London), 1935   .   £35/£10
The Twelve Months, Bodley Head (London), 1936
(illustrated by Robert Gibbings)   .   .   .   £45/£10
ditto, Bodley Head (London), 1936 (100 signed copies) £350
Somerset Essays, Bodley Head (London), 1937   £35/£10
Rats in the Sacristy, Watts & Co. (New York), 1937   .   .
.   .   .   .   £25/£10
A Baker's Dozen, Trovillion Press (Herrin, IL), 1940 (493
signed, numbered copies, in slipcase)   .   .   £35/£25
ditto, Bodley Head (London), 1941   .   .   .   £25/£10
Old English Yuletide, Trovillion Press (Herrin, IL), 1940
(202 numbered copies, signed by the printers, in slipcase).
.   .   .   .   £125/£100
Swiss Essays, Bodley Head (London), 1947   .   £25/£10
Glory of Life and *Now that the Gods are Dead*, Bodley
Head (London), 1949 .   .   .   .   .   £15/£5
Somerset and Dorset Essays, Bodley Head (London), 1957.
.   .   .   .   £20/£10

Novel
Apples Be Ripe, Harcourt Brace (New York), 1930 £50/£20
ditto, Longman (London), 1930   .   .   .   .   £50/£20

Autobiography
Skin for Skin, Harcourt Brace (New York), 1925   .   £45/£10
ditto, Cape (London), 1927 (900 signed, numbered copies) .
.   .   .   .   £40/£25
The Verdict of Bridlegoose, Harcourt Brace (New York),
1926   .   .   .   .   £35/£10
ditto, Cape (London), 1927 (900 signed, numbered copies) .
.   .   .   .   £40/£25
Love and Death, Bodley Head (London), 1939   .   £45/£10
ditto, Simon & Schuster (New York), 1941   .   £30/£10

Others
Confessions of Two Brothers, Manas Press (Rochester, NY),
1916 (with John Cowper Powys) £25
Henry Hudson, John Lane (London), 1927 (1000 copies) .
.   .   .   .   £45/£15
ditto, Harper & Brothers (New York), 1928   .   £35/£10
Out of the Past, Grey Bow Press, 1928 (25 copies)   . £225
A Pagan's Pilgrimage, Harcourt Brace (New York), 1931 .
.   .   .   .   £35/£10
The Life & Times of Anthony A. Wood, Wishart & Co.
(London), 1932   .   .   .   .   .   .   £35/£10
The Book of Days, Golden Cockerel Press (Waltham St
Lawrence, Berks), 1937 (300 copies)   .   .   . £300
ditto, Golden Cockerel Press (Waltham St Lawrence, Berks),
1937 (nos. 1-55 bound in red leather & signed by artist)   .
.   .   .   . £400

ditto, Golden Cockerel Press (Waltham St Lawrence, Berks),
1937 (nos. 1-5 on lamb's vellum, bound in red leather &
signed by artist) £1,250
The Letters of Llewelyn Powys, Bodley Head (London),
1943   .   .   .   .   £25/£10
Advice to a Young Poet, **Letters Between Llewelyn Powys
and Kenneth Hopkins**, Bodley Head (London), 1949
(issued as a volume in the Uniform Edition of the Works of
Llewelyn Powys).   .   .   .   .   .   £25/£10
So Wild a Thing, **Letters to Gamel Woolsey**, Ark Press
(Dulverton, Somerset), 1973   .   .   .   .   £30/£15

T.F. POWYS
(b.1875 d.1953)

T.F. Powys was the author of a number of eccentric novels
which offer a highly personal and idiosyncratic view of
God and human nature. Powys was deeply if unconvention-
ally religious, and did most of his writing whilst living in
the small Dorset coastal village of East Chaldon.

Novels
Black Bryony, Chatto & Windus (London), 1923   .   £40/£10
ditto, Knopf (New York), 1923   .   .   .   .   £40/£10
Mark Only, Chatto & Windus (London), 1924   .   £60/£10
ditto, Knopf (New York), 1924   .   .   .   .   £45/£10
Mr Tasker's Gods, Chatto & Windus (London), 1925   .   .
.   .   .   .   £45/£10
ditto, Knopf (New York), 1925   .   .   .   .   £40/£10
Mockery Gap, Chatto & Windus (London), 1925   .   £40/£10
ditto, Knopf (New York), 1925   .   .   .   .   £35/£10
Innocent Birds, Chatto & Windus (London), 1926.   £40/£10
ditto, Knopf (New York), 1926   .   .   .   .   £35/£10
Mr Weston's Good Wine, Chatto & Windus (London), 1927
(660 copies)   .   .   .   .   .   .   £125/£65
ditto, Viking (New York), 1928   .   .   .   .   £40/£10
ditto, Chatto & Windus (London), 1928   .   .   £40/£10
Kindness in a Corner, Chatto & Windus (London), 1930   .
.   .   .   .   £35/£10
ditto, Chatto & Windus (London), 1930 (206 signed,
numbered copies) £80
ditto, Viking (New York), 1930   .   .   .   .   £30/£5
Unclay, Chatto & Windus (London), 1931   .   £40/£10
ditto, Chatto & Windus (London), 1931 (large paper edition
of 160 copies) £75
ditto, Viking (New York), 1932   .   .   .   .   £35/£5
The Market Bell, Brynmill (Doncaster, South Yorkshire),
1990   .   .   .   .   £25/£5

Short Stories
The Left Leg, Chatto & Windus (London), 1923   .   £45/£10
ditto, Knopf (New York), 1923   .   .   .   .   £40/£10
A Stubborn Tree, privately printed by E. Archer (London),
1926 (100 signed, numbered copies; wraps).   .   £200
Feed My Swine, E. Archer (London), 1926 (100 signed,
numbered copies) £75
A Strong Girl, E. Archer (London), 1926 (100 signed,
numbered copies) £100
What Lack I Yet?, E. Archer (London), 1926 (100 signed,
numbered copies) £50
ditto, E. Archer (London), 1926 (25 signed, numbered copies
on Japanese vellum) £200

ditto, The Lantern Press San Francisco, CA), 1927 (stapled wraps; 25 signed, numbered copies) £100
The Rival Pastors, E. Archer (London), 1927 (100 signed, numbered copies) £60
The House with the Echo, Chatto & Windus (London), 1928 . . . . £45/£10
ditto, Chatto & Windus (London), 1928 (206 numbered, signed copies) £50
ditto, Viking (New York), 1929 . . . £40/£10
The Dewpond, Elkin Matthews (London), 1928 (530 signed, numbered copies) . . . . £35/£20
Fables, Viking Press (New York), 1929 . . £35/£10
ditto, Chatto & Windus (London), 1929 (750 signed copies) . . . . £45/£30
Christ in the Cupboard, Blue Moon Booklets no. 5 (London), 1930 (500 numbered, signed copies; stapled wraps) £20
ditto, Blue Moon Booklets no. 5 (London), 1930 (100 small-format copies 'for presentation'; stapled wraps) . £25
The Key of the Field, Furnival Books no.1 (London), 1930 (550 signed copies) £35
The White Paternoster, Chatto & Windus (London), 1930 . . . . £35/£10
ditto, Chatto & Windus (London), 1930 (310 copies) £40
ditto, Viking (New York), 1931 . . . £35/£10
Uriah on the Hill, Minority Press (Cambridge, UK), 1930 (wraps) £15
Uncle Dottery, Douglas Cleverdon (Bristol, Avon), 1930 (350 numbered, signed copies, with engravings by Gill) .
. . . . £100
ditto, Douglas Cleverdon (Bristol, Avon), 1930 (nos. 1-50, containing extra set of engravings in a pocket at the back) £300
The Only Penitent, Chatto & Windus (London), 1931 .
. . . . £20/£10
ditto, Chatto & Windus (London), 1931 (large paper edition of 160 signed, numbered copies) £65
When Thou Wast Naked, Golden Cockerel Press (Waltham St Law-rence, Berks), 1931 (edition of 500 numbered, signed copies) £125
The Tithe Barn, K.S. Bhat (London), 1932 (350 signed, numbered copies) £75
ditto, K.S. Bhat (London), 1932 (50 copies on Japanese vellum, bound in white buckram) . . . £200
The Two Thieves, Chatto & Windus (London), 1932 .
. . . . £50/£15
ditto, Chatto & Windus (London), 1932 (85 signed, numbered copies) £115
ditto, Viking (New York), 1933 . . . £25/£10
No Painted Plumage, Chatto & Windus (London), 1934 .
. . . . £35/£10
Captain Patch, Chatto & Windus (London), 1935 £35/£10
Make Thyself Many, Grayson & Grayson (London), 1935 (285 signed, numbered copies) . . . £45/£25
Goat Green, Golden Cockerel Press (Waltham St Lawrence, Berks), 1937 (150 signed, numbered copies, slipcase) .
. . . . £175/£135
ditto, Golden Cockerel Press (Waltham St Lawrence, Berks), 1937 (wraps). £45
Bottle's Path, Chatto & Windus (London), 1946 . £25/£10
God's Eyes A-Twinkle, Chatto & Windus (London), 1947 .
. . . . £25/£10
Rosie Plum, Chatto & Windus (London), 1966 . £25/£10
Two Stories, Brimmell (Hastings, England), 1967 (525 numbered copies) £30

ditto, Brimmell (Hastings, England), 1967 (25 numbered copies on handmade paper, signed by Reynolds Stone) .
. . . . £200
Three Short Stories, Dud Noman Press (Loughton, Essex), 1971 (120 numbered copies, acetate d/w) . . £35/£25
Three Short Stories, Dud Noman Press (Loughton, Essex), 1971 (30 numbered copies on handmade paper) . . £90
Mock's Curse, Brynmill Press (Denton, Norfolk), 1995 .
. . . . £10/£5

Others
An Interpretation of Genesis, privately printed (London), 1907 (100 copies) £300
ditto, Chatto & Windus (London), 1929 (490 signed copies, slipcase). . . . . . . £75/£50
ditto, Viking (New York), 1929 (260 signed copies, slipcase) . . . . £75/£50
The Soliloquy of a Hermit, G. Arnold Shaw (New York), 1916 . . . . £75
ditto, as **The Soliloquies of a Hermit**, Melrose (London), 1918 . . . . £25

TERRY PRATCHETT
(b.1948)

Pratchett is the author of the hugely successful 'Discworld' novels, which begin with *The Colour of Magic*. By early 2005 he had sold approximately 40 million books worldwide. In 1998 he was given an O.B.E. for services to literature. His reaction was: 'I suspect the "services to literature" consisted of refraining from trying to write any.'

'Discworld' Novels
The Colour of Magic, Colin Smythe (Gerrards Cross, Buckinghamshire), 1983 (with or without alternative reviews pasted on to flap) . . . . £5,000/£500
ditto, St Martin's Press (New York), 1983 . £250/£25
ditto, Colin Smythe (Gerrards Cross, Buckinghamshire), 1989 (new edition) . . . . . . £25/£10
The Light Fantastic, Colin Smythe (Gerrards Cross, Buckinghamshire), 1986 . . £1,750/£250
ditto, NAL/Signet (New York), 1988 (pbk) . . £10
Equal Rites, Gollancz/Colin Smythe (London), 1987 . .
. . . . £600/£75
ditto, NAL/Signet (New York), 1988 (pbk) . . £10
Mort, Gollancz/Colin Smythe (London), 1987 . £250/£25
ditto, NAL/Signet (New York), 1989 (pbk) . . £10
Sourcery, Gollancz/Colin Smythe (London), 1988. £200/£25
ditto, NAL/Signet (New York), 1989 (pbk) . . £10
Wyrd Sisters, Gollancz (London), 1988 . £100/£15
ditto, NAL/Roc (New York), 1990 (pbk) . . . £5
Pyramids, Gollancz (London), 1989 . . £65/£15
ditto, NAL/Roc (New York), 1989 (pbk) . . . £5
Guards! Guards!, Gollancz (London), 1989 . £50/£10
ditto, NAL/Roc (New York), 1991 (pbk) . . . £5
Eric, Gollancz (London), 1990 (large format) . £45/£10
ditto, NAL/Roc (New York), 1995 (pbk) . . . £5
Moving Pictures, Gollancz (London), 1990 . £45/£10
ditto, NAL/Roc (New York), 1992 (pbk) . . . £5
Reaper Man, Gollancz (London), 1991 . . £35/£10
ditto, NAL/Roc (New York), 1992 (pbk) . . . £5
Witches Abroad, Gollancz (London), 1991 . £35/£10

ditto, NAL/Roc (New York), 1993 (pbk) £5
Small Gods, Gollancz (London), 1992   .   .   . £25/£5
ditto, HarperCollins (New York), 1992   .   .   . £10/£5
Lords and Ladies, Gollancz (London), 1992 .   . £25/£5
ditto, HarperPrism (New York), 1995 (pbk)   .   .   . £5
Men at Arms, Gollancz (London), 1993   .   .   . £25/£5
ditto, HarperPrism (New York), 1996   .   .   . £15/£5
Soul Music, Gollancz (London), 1994   .   .   . £20/£5
ditto, HarperPrism (New York), 1995   .   .   . £10/£5
Interesting Times, Gollancz (London), 1994 .   . £15/£5
ditto, HarperPrism (New York), 1997   .   .   . £10/£5
Maskerade, Gollancz (London), 1995   .   .   . £15/£5
ditto, HarperPrism (New York), 1997   .   .   . £10/£5
Feet of Clay, Gollancz (London), 1996   .   .   . £10/£5
ditto, HarperPrism (New York), 1996   .   .   . £10/£5
Hogfather, Gollancz (London), 1996.   .   .   . £10/£5
ditto, HarperPrism (New York), 1998   .   .   . £10/£5
Jingo, Gollancz (London), 1997.   .   .   .   . £10/£5
ditto, HarperPrism (New York), 1998   .   .   . £10/£5
Last Continent, Doubleday (London), 1998   .   . £10/£5
ditto, HarperPrism (New York), 1999   .   .   . £10/£5
Carpe Jugulum, Doubleday (London), 1998 .   . £10/£5
ditto, HarperPrism (New York), 1999   .   .   . £10/£5
The Fifth Elephant, Doubleday (London), 1999 . £10/£5
ditto, HarperCollins (New York), 2000   .   .   . £10/£5
Truth, Doubleday (London), 2000   .   .   . £10/£5
ditto, HarperCollins (New York), 2000   .   .   . £10/£5
Thief of Time, Doubleday (London), 2001   .   . £10/£5
ditto, HarperCollins (New York), 2001   .   .   . £10/£5
The Last Hero, Gollancz (London), 2001 (illustrated by Paul
    Kidby) .   .   .   . £10/£5
ditto, Gollancz (London), 2001 (deluxe edition signed by
    author and artist, no d/w) £35
ditto, HarperCollins (New York), 2001   .   .   . £10/£5
Night Watch, Doubleday (London), 2002.   .   . £10/£5
ditto, HarperCollins (New York), 2002   .   .   . £10/£5
Monstrous Regiment, Doubleday (London), 2003 . £10/£5
ditto, HarperCollins (New York), 2003   .   .   . £10/£5
Going Postal, Doubleday (London), 2004   .   . £10/£5
ditto, HarperCollins (New York), 2004   .   .   . £10/£5
Thud!, Doubleday (London), 2005   .   .   . £10/£5
ditto, Doubleday (London), 2005 (1,000 signed, numbered
    copies; slipcase) .   .   .   .   .   . £100/£75
ditto, HarperCollins (New York), 2005   .   .   . £10/£5
Making Money, Doubleday (London), 2007   .   . £10/£5
ditto, Doubleday (London), 2007 (2,500 signed copies; no
    d/w; slipcase) .   .   .   . £50/£40
ditto, HarperCollins (New York), 2007   .   .   . £10/£5
ditto, HarperCollins (New York), 2007 (signed by author on
    tipped-in page) .   .   .   . £15/£5
Unseen Academicals, Doubleday (London), 2009 . £10/£5
ditto, Doubleday (London), 2009 (3,000 numbered copies;
    slipcase).   .   .   .   . £50/£40
ditto, HarperCollins (New York), 2009   .   .   . £10/£5

Children's 'Discworld' Titles
The Amazing Maurice and His Educated Rodents,
    Doubleday (London), 2001   .   .   .   . £10/£5
ditto, HarperCollins (New York), 2002   .   .   . £10/£5
The Wee Free Men, Doubleday (London), 2003   . £10/£5
ditto, HarperCollins (New York), 2003   .   .   . £10/£5
A Hat Full of Sky, Doubleday (London), 2004   . £10/£5
ditto, HarperCollins (New York), 2004   .   .   . £10/£5
Where's My Cow?, Doubleday (London), 2005   . £10/£5

ditto, HarperCollins (New York), 2005   .   .   . £10/£5
Wintersmith, Doubleday (London), 2006.   .   . £10/£5
ditto, Doubleday (London), 2006 (1,000 signed, numbered
    copies; slipcase) .   .   .   .   .   . £65/£45
ditto, HarperCollins (New York), 2006   .   .   . £10/£5

'Discworld' Related Titles
The Streets of Ankh-Morpork, Corgi (London), 1993 (card
    covers with booklet attached to inside front and fold-out
    map attached to inside rear cover; with Stephen Briggs) .
    .   .   .   . £10
The Discworld Companion, Gollancz (London), 1994 (with
    Stephen Briggs) .   .   .   . £10/£5
The Discworld Mapp, Corgi (London), 1995 (card cover
    with booklet attached to inside front cover; with Stephen
    Briggs) £10
The Pratchett Portfolio, Gollancz (London), 1996 (pbk, with
    Paul Kidby) £10
Discworld's Unseen University Diary, 1998, Gollancz
    (London), 1997 (laminated boards; with Stephen Briggs
    and Paul Kidby) £15
A Tourist Guide to Lancre, Corgi (London), 1998 (with
    Stephen Briggs, Paul Kidby; pbk; first issue with cancel
    page correcting errors) £25
**Terry Pratchett Collector's Edition Discworld 1999 Day-
    To-Day Calendar**, Ink Group (London), 1998 (deskpad
    with plastic holder in box, illustrated by Paul Kidby) . £15
Discworld's Ankh-Korpork City Watch Diary 1999,
    Gollancz (London), 1998 (illustrated matt glazed boards,
    no d/w; with Stephen Briggs and Paul Kidby)   . £45
Death's Domain: A Discworld Mapp, Corgi (London), 1999
    (pbk, with Paul Kidby) £10
The Science of Discworld, Ebury Press (London), 1999
    (with Ian Stewart & Jack Cohen) .   .   .   . £30/£10
Nanny Ogg's Cookbook, Doubleday (London), 1999 (with
    Stephen Briggs, Tina Hannan and Paul Kidby, no d/w) £15
Discworld Assassins' Guild Yearbook and Diary 2000,
    Gollancz (London), 1999 .   .   .   .   .   . £10
The Science of Discworld II, Ebury Press (London), 2002
    (with Ian Stewart & Jack Cohen) .   .   .   . £10/£5
The Discworld Fools' Guild Yearbook and Diary 2001,
    Gollancz (London), 2000 (with Paul Kidby).   .   . £15
The Science of Discworld III: Darwin's Watch, Ebury Press
    (London), 2005 .   .   .   . £10/£5
The Wit and Wisdom of Discworld, Doubleday (London),
    2007   .   .   .   . £10/£5
ditto, HarperCollins (New York), 2007   .   .   . £10/£5
Lu-tse's Yearbook of Enlightenment , Gollancz (London),
    2007 (with Stephen Briggs) .   .   .   .   . £10/£5

The 'Bromeliad' Trilogy
Truckers, Doubleday (London), 1989   .   .   . £20/£5
ditto, Delacorte Press (New York), 1990   .   . £20/£5
Diggers, Doubleday (London), 1990 .   .   .   . £15/£5
ditto, Delacorte Press (New York), 1991   .   . £15/£5
Wings, Doubleday (London), 1990   .   .   . £15/£5
ditto, Delacorte Press (New York), 1991 .   .   . £15/£5

'Johnny Maxwell' Novels
Only You Can Save Mankind, Doubleday (London), 1992 .
    .   .   .   . £20/£5
ditto, HarperCollins (New York), 2004   .   .   . £10/£5
Johnny and the Dead, Doubleday (London), 1993   £15/£5
Johnny and the Bomb, Doubleday (London), 1996   £15/£5

Omnibus editions

The Bromeliad, Delacorte (New York), 1991 (*Truckers*, *Diggers* and *Wings*) .　.　.　.　.　£15/£5

ditto, Doubleday (London), 1998　.　.　.　£15/£5

The Johnny Maxwell Trilogy, Science Fiction Book Club (New York), 1996 (*Only You Can Save Mankind*, *Johnny and the Dead*, *Johnny and the Bomb*, with poster)　£15/£5

ditto, Doubleday (London), 1999　.　.　.　£15/£5

Death Trilogy, Gollancz (London), 1998 (*Mort*, *Reaper Man* and *Soul Music*)　.　.　.　.　.　£10/£5

Rincewind the Wizzard, Science Fiction Book Club (New York), 1999 (*The Colour of Magic*, *The Light Fantastic*, *Sourcery* and *Eric*)　.　.　.　.　.　£10/£5

The City Watch, Gollancz (London), 1999 (*Guards! Guards!*, *Men At Arms* and *Feet of Clay*)　.　£10/£5

The Colour of Magic/The Light Fantastic, Colin Smythe (Gerrards Cross, Buckinghamshire), 1999　.　£10/£5

Gods Trilogy, Gollancz (London), 2000 (*Pyramids*, *Small Gods* and *Hogfather*)　.　.　.　.　.　£10/£5

Collection

Once More with Footnotes, The NESFA Press (Framingham, MA), 2004　.　.　.　.　.　.　£45/£15

Other Novels

The Carpet People, Colin Smythe (Gerrards Cross, Buckinghamshire), 1971　.　.　.　.　.　£450/£60

The Dark Side of the Sun, Colin Smythe (Gerrards Cross, Buckinghamshire), 1976　.　.　.　£450/£60

ditto, St Martin's Press (New York), 1976　.　£200/£30

ditto, Doubleday (London), 1994　.　.　.　£10/£5

ditto, Doubleday (London), 1994 (500 signed copies)　.　.
　.　.　.　.　.　.　.　.　.　£125/£75

STRATA, Colin Smythe (Gerrards Cross, Buckinghamshire), 1981　.　.　.　.　.　.　£250/£100

ditto, St Martin's Press (New York), 1981　.　£50/£10

ditto, Doubleday (London), 1994　.　.　.　£10/£5

ditto, Doubleday (London), 1994 (500 signed copies)　.　.
　.　.　.　.　.　.　.　.　.　£150/£100

The Unadulterated Cat, Gollancz (London), 1989 (pbk)　£15

Good Omens, Gollancz (London), 1990 (with Neil Gaiman)
　.　.　.　.　.　.　.　.　.　£30/£5

ditto, Workman (New York), 1990　.　.　.　£30/£5

Nation, Doubleday (London), 2008　.　.　.　£10/£5

ditto, HarperCollins (New York), 2008　.　.　£10/£5

ANTHONY PRICE

(b.1928)

Anthony Price served in the British Army from 1947 to 1949, then studied at Merton College, Oxford. He became a journalist with the Westminster Press from 1952 to 1988, and was editor of the *Oxford Times* from 1972 to 1988. He is the author of espionage thrillers, winning the Crime Writers Association's Silver Dagger award with his first book, *The Labyrinth Makers*, and later the Gold Dagger with *Other Paths to Glory*.

Novels

The Labyrinth Makers, Gollancz (London), 1970　.　£250/£30

ditto, Doubleday (New York), 1971　.　.　.　£35/£10

The Alamut Ambush, Gollancz (London), 1971　.　£100/£20

ditto, Doubleday (New York), 1972　.　.　.　£25/£5

Colonel Butler's Wolf, Gollancz (London), 1972　.　£85/£20

ditto, Doubleday (New York), 1973　.　.　.　£25/£5

October Men, Gollancz (London), 1973　.　.　£75/£15

ditto, Doubleday (New York), 1974　.　.　.　£25/£5

Other Paths to Glory, Gollancz (London), 1974　.　£75/£15

ditto, Doubleday (New York), 1975　.　.　.　£25/£5

Our Man in Camelot, Gollancz (London), 1975　.　£65/£10

ditto, Doubleday (New York), 1976　.　.　.　£25/£5

War Game, Gollancz (London), 1976　.　.　£65/£10

ditto, Doubleday (New York), 1977　.　.　.　£25/£5

The '44 Vintage, Gollancz (London), 1978　.　£65/£10

ditto, Doubleday (New York), 1979　.　.　.　£20/£5

Tomorrow's Ghost, Gollancz (London), 1979.　.　£45/£10

ditto, Doubleday (New York), 1979　.　.　.　£15/£5

The Hour of the Donkey, Gollancz (London), 1980　£40/£10

Soldier No More, Gollancz (London), 1981　.　£35/£10

ditto, Doubleday (New York), 1982　.　.　.　£15/£5

The Old Vengeful, Gollancz (London), 1982　.　£15/£5

ditto, Doubleday (New York), 1983　.　.　.　£15/£5

Gunner Kelly, Gollancz (London), 1983　.　.　£15/£5

ditto, Doubleday (New York), 1984　.　.　.　£15/£5

Sion Crossing, Gollancz (London), 1984.　.　.　£10/£5

ditto, Mysterious Press (New York), 1985　.　.　£10/£5

ditto, Mysterious Press (New York), 1985 (26 signed, lettered copies, slipcase)　.　.　.　.　.　£20/£10

ditto, Mysterious Press (New York), 1985 (250 signed, numbered copies, slipcase)　.　.　.　.　£10/£5

Here Be Monsters, Gollancz (London), 1985　.　.　£10/£5

ditto, Mysterious Press (New York), 1986　.　.　£10/£5

ditto, Mysterious Press (New York), 1986 (26 signed, lettered copies, slipcase)　.　.　.　.　.　£20/£10

ditto, Mysterious Press (New York), 1986 (250 signed, numbered copies, slipcase)　.　.　.　.　£10/£5

For the Good of the State, Gollancz (London), 1986　£10/£5

ditto, Mysterious Press (New York), 1987　.　.　£10/£5

ditto, Mysterious Press (New York), 1987 (26 signed, lettered copies, slipcase)　.　.　.　.　.　£20/£10

ditto, Mysterious Press (New York), 1987 (250 signed, numbered copies, slipcase)　.　.　.　.　£10/£5

A New Kind of War, Gollancz (London), 1987　.　£10/£5

ditto, Mysterious Press (New York), 1988　.　.　£10/£5

A Prospect of Vengeance, Gollancz (London), 1988　£10/£5

ditto, The Armchair Detective (New York), 1990　.　£10/£5

ditto, The Armchair Detective (New York), 1990 (100 signed copies, slipcase)　.　.　.　.　.　.　£20/£10

The Memory Trap, Gollancz (London), 1989　.　.　£10/£5

ditto, The Armchair Detective (New York), 1991　.　£10/£5

ditto, The Armchair Detective (New York), 1991 (100 signed copies, slipcase)　.　.　.　.　.　.　£20/£10

Non-Fiction

The Eyes of the Fleet, Hutchinson (London), 1990　£10/£5

ditto, Norton (New York), 1996　.　.　.　.　£10/£5

J.B. PRIESTLEY
(b.1894 d.1984)

Priestley was born in Bradford, the son of an elementary schoolmaster, and became a clerk after leaving school. He served with distinction in the West Riding and Devonshire Regiments during the First World War, afterwards studying politics and history at Cambridge. His output was prodigious and included many non-fiction titles. He was awarded the Order of Merit in 1977.

Novels

Adam in Moonshine, Heinemann (London), 1927 . £250/£40
ditto, Harper (New York), 1927 . . . . . £250/£40
Benighted, Heinemann (London), 1927 . . .£225/£45
ditto, as *The Old Dark House*, Harper, 1928 . . £225/£45
Farthing Hall, Macmillan (London), 1929 (with Hugh Walpole) . . . . £45/£10
ditto, Doubleday, Doran (New York), 1929 . . £40/£10
The Good Companions, Heinemann (London), 1929 . .
. . . . £100/£15
ditto, Harper (New York), 1929 . . . . . £65/£15
Angel Pavement, Heinemann (London), 1930 . . £50/£10
ditto, Heinemann (London), 1930 (1,025 signed copies, slipcase) . . . . £100/£50
ditto, Harper (New York), 1930 . . . . . £45/£10
Faraway, Heinemann (London), 1932 . . £40/£10
ditto, Harper (New York), 1932 . . . . . £35/£10
I'll Tell You Everything: A Frolic, Macmillan (New York), 1932 (with Gerald Bullett) . . . . £65/£25
ditto, Heinemann (London), 1933 . . . . £65/£25
Wonder Hero, Heinemann (London), 1933 . . £35/£10
ditto, Heinemann (London), 1933 (175 signed, numbered copies; slip-case) . . . . £75/£45
ditto, Harper (New York), 1933 . . . . . £35/£10
They Walk in the City: The Lovers in the Stone Forest, Heinemann (London), 1936 . . . . £30/£10
ditto, Harper (New York), 1936 . . . . . £30/£10
The Doomsday Men: An Adventure, Heinemann (London), 1938 . . . . £60/£15
ditto, Harper (New York), 1938 . . . . . £40/£10
Let the People Sing, Heinemann (London), 1939 . £25/£10
ditto, Harper (New York), 1940 . . . . . £25/£5
Black-Out in Gretley: A Story of—and for—Wartime, Heinemann (London), 1942 . . . . £45/£15
ditto, Harper (New York), 1942 . . . . . £40/£15
Daylight on Saturday: A Novel about an Aircraft Factory, Heinemann (London), 1943 . . . . £25/£10
ditto, Harper (New York), 1943 . . . . . £25/£10
Three Men in New Suits, Heinemann (London), 1945 £20/£5
ditto, Harper (New York), 1945 . . . . . £20/£5
Bright Day, Heinemann (London), 1946 . . . £20/£5
ditto, Harper (New York), 1946 . . . . . £20/£5
Jenny Villiers: A Story of the Theatre, Heinemann (London), 1947 . . . . £20/£5
ditto, Harper (New York), 1947 . . . . . £20/£5
Festival at Farbridge, Heinemann (London), 1951 £20/£5
ditto, as *Festival*, Harper (New York), 1951 . £20/£5
The Magicians, Heinemann (London), 1954 . . £20/£5
ditto, Harper (New York), 1954 . . . . . £15/£5
Low Notes on a High Level: A Frolic, Heinemann (London), 1954 . . . . £15/£5
ditto, Harper (New York), 1954 . . . . . £15/£5

Saturn Over the Water, Heinemann (London), 1961 £20/£5
ditto, Doubleday (New York), 1961 . . . £20/£5
The Shapes of Sleep: A Topical Tale, Heinemann (London), 1962 . . . . £20/£5
ditto, Doubleday (New York), 1962 . . . . £20/£5
Sir Michael and Sir George, Heinemann (London), 1964 .
. . . . £10/£5
ditto, Little, Brown (Boston), 1965 . . . £10/£5
Lost Empires, Heinemann (London), 1965 . . £20/£5
ditto, Little, Brown (Boston), 1965 . . . £20/£5
Salt is Leaving: A Detective Story, Pan (London), 1966 (pbk) £5
ditto, Harper (New York), 1975 . . . . . £10/£5
It's an Old Country, Heinemann (London), 1967 . £10/£5
ditto, Little, Brown (Boston), 1967 . . . £10/£5
The Image Men, Heinemann (London), 1968-9 (2 vols, *Out of Town* and *London End*) . . . . £20/£10
ditto, Little, Brown (Boston), 1969 (1 vol.) . £10/£5
Found, Lost, Found or The English Way of Life, Heinemann (London), 1976 . . . . . £10/£5
ditto, Hall (Boston), 1976 . . . . . £10/£5

Short Stories

The Town Major of Miraucourt, Heinemann (London), 1930 . . . . £40/£5
ditto, Heinemann (London), 1930 (525 copies signed by the author, in slipcase) . . . . . . £65/£45
Albert Goes Through, Heinemann (London), 1933 £25/£10
ditto, Harper (New York), 1933 . . . . . £25/£5
Going Up, Heinemann (London), 1933 . . . £30/£5
The Other Place, Heinemann (London), 1953 . . £75/£25
ditto, Harper (New York), [1954] . . . . £65/£20
The Thirty-First of June: A tale of true love, enterprise and progress in the Arthurian and ad-atomic ages, Heinemann (London), 1961 . . . . . . £20/£5
ditto, Doubleday (New York), 1962 . . . . £15/£5
Snoggle: A Story for Anybody Between 9 and 90, Heinemann (London), 1971 . . . . £10/£5
ditto, Harcourt Brace (New York), [1972] . £10/£5
The Carfitt Crisis and Two Other Stories, Heinemann (London), 1975 . . . . £10/£5
ditto, Stein & Day (New York), 1976 . . . £10/£5

Plays

The Good Companions, French (London), 1931 (card wraps)
. . . . £20
Dangerous Corner, Heinemann (London), 1932 . £75/£15
ditto, French (New York), 1932 . . . . £65/£15
The Roundabout, Heinemann (London), 1933 . £20/£5
Laburnum Grove, Heinemann (London), 1934 . £20/£5
Eden End, Heinemann (London), 1934 . . . £15/£5
Duet in Floodlight, Heinemann (London), 1935 . £15/£5
Cornelius, Heinemann (London), 1935 . . . £15/£5
Spring Tide, Heinemann (London), 1936 (pseud 'Peter Goldsmith', with George Bilham) . . . . £15/£5
ditto, French (London), 1936 (wraps) . . . £5
Bees on the Boat Deck, Heinemann (London), 1936 £15/£5
Time and the Conways, Heinemann (London), 1937 £15/£5
Mystery at Greenfingers, French (London), 1937 (wraps) £5
I Have Been Here Before, Heinemann (London), 1937 .
. . . . £15/£5
People At Sea, Heinemann (London), 1937 . . £15/£5
When We Are Married, Heinemann (London), 1938 £15/£5
Johnson Over Jordan, Heinemann (London), 1939 £15/£5

The Long Mirror, Heinemann (London), 1940 . £15/£5
Goodnight, Children, Heinemann (London), 1942. £15/£5
Desert Highway, Heinemann (London), 1944 . . £15/£5
How Are They At Home?, Heinemann (London), 1944 . .
. . . . £15/£5
They Came To A City, French (London), 1944 (wraps). £5
Music At Night, French (London), 1947 (wraps) . . £5
An Inspector Calls, Heinemann (London), 1947 . £10/£5
The Rose and Crown, French (London), 1947 (wraps) . £10
The Long Mirror, French, 1947 (wraps) £5
The Linden Tree, Heinemann (London), 1948 . £10/£5
The High Toby, puffin (Harmondsworth, Middlesex), 1948
(Puffin Cut-Out Book No. 5. A play for the Toy Theatre;
16 pages of text and 16 printed single side in colour to be
cut out; stapled) £25
The Golden Fleece, Heinemann (London), 1948 . £10/£5
The Olympians, Novello (London), 1948 (opera libretto,
music by Arthur Bliss) . . . . . . £80/£35
Home is Tomorrow, Heinemann (London), 1949 . £10/£5
Ever Since Paradise, French (London), 1949 (music by
Dennis Arundell; wraps) £10
Summer's Day Dream, Heinemann (London), 1950 £10/£5
Bright Shadow, Heinemann (London), 1950 . . £15/£5
Dragon's Mouth: A Dramatic Quartet in Two Parts, Heine-
mann (London), 1952 (with Jacquetta Hawkes) . £10/£5
ditto, Harpers (New York), 1952. . . . . £10/£5
Private Rooms, French (London), 1953 (wraps) . £10/£5
Treasure on Pelican, Heinemann (London), 1953 . £10/£5
A Glass of Bitter, French (London), 1954 (wraps) . . £5
The Scandalous Affair of Mr Kettle and Mrs Moon,
Heinemann (London), 1955 . . . . . £10/£5
The Glass Cage, Kingswood House (Toronto, Canada), 1957
. . . . £10/£5
ditto, French (London), 1958 (wraps) £5
A Severed Head, Chatto & Windus (London), 1964 (with Iris
Murdoch) . . . . £40/£10

Poetry
The Chapman of Rhymes, Alexander Moring (London),
1918 . . . . £125

V.S. PRITCHETT
(b.1900 d.1997)

A writer and critic, Pritchett's books range widely through
many genres, encompassing travel, essays, short stories,
novels and memoirs. His reputation was established by the
collection of short stories *The Spanish Virgin and Other
Stories*. He received many literary awards and in 1975 was
knighted. He became a Companion of Honour in 1993.

Novels
Clare Drummer, Benn (London), 1929 . . . £300/£65
Shirley Sanz, Gollancz (London), 1932 . . . £250/£35
ditto, as *Elopement into Exile*, Little, Brown (Boston), 1932
. . . . £175/£25
Nothing Like Leather, Chatto & Windus (London), 1935 .
. . . . £250/£35
ditto, Macmillan (New York), 1935 . . . . £150/£25
Dead Man Leading, Chatto & Windus (London), 1937 .
. . . . £350/£35

ditto, Macmillan (New York), 1937 . . . . .£150/£25
Mr Beluncle, Chatto & Windus (London), 1951 . £30/£10
ditto, Harcourt Brace (New York), 1951 . . £25/£5

Short Stories
The Spanish Virgin and Other Stories, Benn (London),
1930 . . . .£300/£45
You Make Your Own Life, Chatto & Windus (London),
1938 . . . .£225/£25
It May Never Happen and Other Stories, Chatto & Windus
(London), 1945 . . . .£35/£10
ditto, Reynal & Hitchcock (New York), 1947 . . £25/£10
Collected Stories, Chatto & Windus (London), 1956 £30/£10
The Sailor, The Sense of Humour and Other Stories, Knopf
(New York), 1956 . . . . £20/£5
When My Girl Comes Home, Chatto & Windus (London),
1961 . . . . £20/£5
ditto, Knopf (New York), 1961 . . . . . £20/£5
The Key to My Heart, Chatto & Windus (London), 1963 .
. . . . £25/£5
ditto, Random House (New York), 1964 . . . £25/£5
The Saint and Other Stories, Penguin (Harmondsworth,
Middlesex), 1966 (pbk) £5
Blind Love and Other Stories, Chatto & Windus (London),
1969 . . . . £15/£5
ditto, Random House (New York), 1970 . . . £15/£5
The Camberwell Beauty and Other Stories, Chatto &
Windus (London), 1974 . . . . . . £15/£5
ditto, Random House (New York), 1974 . . . £15/£5
Selected Stories, Chatto & Windus (London), 1978 £10/£5
ditto, Random House (New York), 1978 . . £10/£5
On the Edge of the Cliff, Random House (New York), 1979
. . . . £15/£5
ditto, Chatto & Windus (London), 1980 . . . £15/£5
Collected Stories, Random House (New York), 1982 £10/£5
ditto, Chatto & Windus (London), 1982 . . . £10/£5
More Collected Stories, Random House (New York), 1983 .
. . . . £10/£5
ditto, Chatto & Windus (London), 1983 . . . £10/£5
The Other Side of the Frontier, A V.S. Pritchett Reader,
Robin Clark (London), 1984 (pbk) £5
A Careless Widow and Other Stories, Chatto & Windus
(London), 1989 . . . . £10/£5
ditto, Random House (New York), 1989 . . . £10/£5
Complete Short Stories, Chatto & Windus (London), 1990 .
. . . . £10/£5
ditto, as *Complete Collected Stories*, Random House (New
York), 1991 . . . . £10/£5

Autobiography
A Cab at the Door, Chatto & Windus (London), 1968 £20/£5
ditto, Random House (New York), 1968 . . . £10/£5
Midnight Oil, Chatto & Windus (London), 1971 . £15/£5
ditto, Random House (New York), 1972 . . . £15/£5
Autobiography, English Association (London), 1977 (pbk).
. . . . £5

Biography
Balzac, Chatto & Windus (London), 1973 . . £15/£5
ditto, Knopf (New York), 1973 . . . . . £15/£5
The Gentle Barbarian, The Life and Work of Turgenev,
Chatto & Windus (London), 1977 . . . . £15/£5
ditto, Random House (New York), 1977 . . . £15/£5

Chekhov: A Spirit Set Free, Hodder & Stoughton (London), 1988 . . . . . . £10/£5
ditto, Random House (New York), 1988 . . £10/£5

Others
Marching Spain, Benn (London), 1928 . . .£250/£65
ditto, Left Book Club (London), 1928 (pbk) . . . £45
In My Good Books, Chatto & Windus (London), 1942 . .
. . . . £40/£15
The Living Novel, Chatto & Windus (London), 1946 . .
. . . . £30/£10
ditto, Reynal & Hitchcock (New York), 1947 . £30/£10
Build the Ships, HMSO (London), 1947 (stapled wraps) £15
Why Do I Write?: An Exchange of Views Between Elizabeth Bowen, Graham Greene, and V.S. Pritchett, Marshall (London), 1948 . . . . . .£125/£35
Books in General, Chatto & Windus (London), 1953 . .
. . . . £20/£5
ditto, Harcourt Brace (New York), 1954 . . £20/£10
The Spanish Temper, Chatto & Windus (London), 1954 .
. . . . £20/£5
ditto, Knopf (New York), 1954 . . . £20/£5
London Perceived, Chatto & Windus (London), 1962 (photographs by Evelyn Hofer) . . . £25/£10
ditto, Harcourt Brace (New York), 1962 . . £25/£10
Foreign Faces, Chatto & Windus (London), 1964 . £15/£5
New York Proclaimed, Chatto & Windus (London), 1965 (photographs by Evelyn Hofer) . . . £20/£5
ditto, Harcourt Brace (New York), 1965 . . £20/£5
The Working Novelist, Chatto & Windus (London), 1965 .
. . . . £15/£5
Dublin, A Portrait, Bodley Head (London), 1967 . £20/£5
ditto, Harper & Row (New York), 1967 (photographs by Evelyn Hofer) . . . . . . £20/£5
George Meredith and English Comedy, Random House (New York), 1969 . . . . . £10/£5
ditto, Chatto & Windus (London), 1970 . . £10/£5
The Myth Makers, Chatto & Windus (London), 1979 £10/£5
ditto, Random House (New York), 1979 . . £10/£5
The Tale Bearers, Chatto & Windus (London), 1980 £10/£5
ditto, Random House (New York), 1980 . . £10/£5
The Turn of the Years, Michael Russell (London), 1982 (illustrated by Reynolds Stone, glassine wraps) . £20/£5
ditto, Michael Russell (London), 1982 (150 copies signed by author and artist) . . . . . . £45/£35
ditto, Random House (New York), 1982 . . £20/£5
ditto, Random House (New York), 1982 (500 copies signed by author and artist, slipcase) . . . . £25/£15
A Man of Letters, Chatto & Windus (London), 1985 £10/£5
ditto, Random House (New York), 1985 . . £10/£5
At Home and Abroad, Chatto & Windus (London), 1989 .
. . . . £10/£5
ditto, North Point Press (San Francisco, CA), 1989 £10/£5
Lasting Impressions, Chatto & Windus (London), 1990 .
. . . . £10/£5
ditto, Random House (New York), 1990 . . £10/£5
Complete Essays, Chatto & Windus (London), 1991 £10/£5
ditto, as *Complete Collected Essays*, Random House (New York), 1991 . . . . . . £10/£5

MARCEL PROUST
(b.1871 d.1922)

Marcel Proust was a French intellectual, novelist, essayist and critic. The subject of his work was his own past, which he recreated through an evocation of its smell, taste and sound.

'À la Recherche du Temps Perdu'
Swann's Way, Chatto & Windus (London), 1922 (translated by C.K. Scott Moncrieff, 2 vols) . . . .£150/£50
ditto, Thomas Seltzer (New York), 1922 (2 vols) . £75/£25
Within a Budding Grove, Chatto & Windus (London), 1924 (translated by C.K. Scott Moncrieff, 2 vols) . .£125/£35
ditto, Thomas Seltzer (New York), 1924 (2 vols) . £75/£25
The Guermantes Way, Chatto & Windus (London), 1925 (translated by C.K. Scott Moncrieff, 2 vols) . .£125/£35
ditto, Thomas Seltzer (New York), 1925 (2 vols) . £75/£25
Cities of the Plain, Knopf (London), 1925 (translated by C.K. Scott Moncrieff, 2,230 numbered copies; 2 vols in slipcase; no d/w) . . . .£100/£40
ditto, Boni (New York), 1927 (2,000 numbered copies; 2 vols in slipcase; no d/w) . . . . . .£100/£40
The Captive, Knopf (London), 1929 (translated by C.K. Scott Moncrieff, 2 vols) . . . . . £75/£20
ditto, Boni (New York), 1929 . . . . £75/£20
The Sweet Cheat Gone, Knopf (London), 1930 (translated by C.K. Scott Moncrieff) . . . . . £50/£15
ditto, Boni (New York), 1930 . . . . £50/£15
ditto, as *Albertine Gone*, Chatto & Windus (London), 1989 (translated by Terence Kilmartin) . . . £15/£5
Time Regained, Chatto & Windus (London), 1931 (1,300 numbered copies, translated by Stephen Hudson) £75/£35
Remembrance of Things Past, Chatto & Windus (London)/ Knopf (New York), 1922-31 (12 vols) . £1,000/£300

Others
47 Lettres Inédites De Marcel Proust à Walter Berry, Black Sun Press (Paris, France), 1930 (edited and translated by Harry and Caresse Crosby, 50 numbered copies on Japon; wraps, glassine d/w, silver foil slipcase). . . .£500
ditto, Black Sun Press (Paris, France), 1930 (200 numbered copies on vélin d'Arches; wraps, glassine d/w, silver foil slipcase). £275
Marcel Proust: A Selection from His Miscellaneous Writings, Allan Wingate (London), 1948 (translated by Gerard Hopkins) . . . . . . £20/£5
Pleasures and Regrets, Crown (New York), 1948 . £25/£10
ditto, Dobson (London), 1950 (translated by Louise Varese)
. . . . £25/£10
Letters to a Friend, The Falcon Press (London), 1949 £25/£10
Letters of Marcel Proust, Random House (New York), 1949 (translated by Mina Curtis) . . . . £25/£10
ditto, Chatto & Windus (London), 1950 . . £25/£10
The Letters of Marcel Proust to Antoine Bibescu, Thames and Hudson (London), [1953] (translated by Gerard Hopkins) . . . . £25/£10
ditto, Thames & Hudson (London), [1953] (500 copies signed by translator) . . . . . £25/£15
Jean Santeuil, Weidenfeld & Nicolson (London), 1955 (translated by Gerard Hopkins) . . . £25/£10
ditto, Simon & Schuster (New York), 1956 . £15/£5
Letters to His Mother, Rider (London), 1956 . . £20/£5

ditto, Citadel (New York), 1957 . . . . £20/£5

By Way of Saint-Beuve, Chatto & Windus (London), 1958 (translated by Sylvia Townsend Warner) . . £35/£10

ditto, as **On Art and Literature, 1896-1919**, Meridian Books (New York), 1958 . . . . . £25/£10

On Reading, Macmillan (New York), 1971 . £15/£5

ditto, Souvenir Press (London), 1972 (translated by Jean Autret and William Burford) . . . . £15/£5

Selected Letters: 1880-1903, Collins (London), 1983 (translated by Ralph Manheim) . . . . £15/£5

ditto, Doubleday (New York), 1983 . . . £15/£5

On Reading Ruskin, Yale Univ Press (New Haven, CT), 1987 . . . . £15/£5

Selected Letters, Volume Two: 1904-1909, Collins (London), 1989 (translated by Terence Kilmartin) £15/£5

ditto, O.U.P. (New York), 1989 . . . . £15/£5

Selected Letters, Volume Three: 1910-1917, HarperCollins (London), 1992 (translated by Terence Kilmartin) £15/£5

Selected Letters, Volume Four: 1918-1922, HarperCollins (London), 2000 (translated by Terence Kilmartin) £15/£5

PHILIP PULLMAN

(b.1946)

Pullman has won the Carnegie Medal, the Guardian Children's Fiction Award, the Smarties Prize and the Children's Book of the Year award. *The Amber Spyglass* gained him wide recognition when it was judged the Whitbread Book of the Year.

'His Dark Materials' Trilogy

Northern Lights, Scholastic (London), 1995 (first printing: no number line on the copyright page; states 'First published by Scholastic Publications Ltd, 1995'. First issue d/w with the word 'POINT' on spine, the address of 7-9 Pratt Street to the rear flap) . . . £2,250/£350

ditto, as **The Golden Compass**, Knopf (New York), 1996 .
. . . . £75/£10

The Subtle Knife, Scholastic (London), 1997 . . £600/£60

ditto, Knopf (New York), 1997 . . . . £65/£10

The Amber Spyglass, Knopf (New York), 2000 . £15/£5

ditto, Scholastic (London), 2000 . . . . £65/£10

Lyra's Oxford, Fickling (Oxford), 2003 (no d/w, laminated boards) £5

ditto, Knopf (New York), 2003 . . . . . £5

'Sally Lockhart' Titles

The Ruby in the Smoke, O.U.P. (Oxford, UK), 1985 . .
. . . . £1,250/£150

ditto, Knopf (New York), 1987 . . . . . £350/£40

The Shadow in the Plate, O.U.P. (Oxford, UK), 1986 . .
. . . . £400/£50

ditto, as **Shadow in the North**, Knopf (New York), 1988 .
. . . . £100/£15

The Tiger in the Well, Knopf (New York), 1990 . £100/£10

ditto, Viking (London), 1991 . . . . . £100/£15

ditto, Viking (London), 1991 (copies with final para on last page missing) . . . . . . £300/£200

The Tin Princess, Puffin/O.U.P. (London/Oxford, UK), 1994 (wraps). £25

ditto, Knopf (New York), 1994 . . . . . £150/£20

Others

The Haunted Storm, New English Library (London), 1972 .
. . . . £2,500/£400

Galatea, Gollancz (London), 1978 . . . . £250/£30

ditto, Dutton (New York), 1979 . . . . £50/£10

Count Karlstein, Chatto & Windus (London), 1982 . .
. . . . £500/£45

ditto, as **Count Karlstein or The Ride of the Demon Huntsman**, Knopf (New York), 1998 . . . £45/£10

How to be Cool, Heinemann (London), 1987 (laminated boards; no d/w) £200

ditto, Heinemann (London), 1987 (wraps) . . £25

Spring-Heeled Jack: A Story of Bravery and Evil, Doubleday (London), 1989 (laminated boards, no d/w) .
. . . . £125

ditto, Knopf (New York), 1991 . . . . £50/£10

The Broken Bridge, Macmillan (London), 1990 (wraps) £10

ditto, Knopf (New York), 1992 . . . . £25/£5

The White Mercedes, Pan Macmillan (London), 1992 . .
. . . . £200/£20

ditto, Knopf (New York), 1993 . . . . £35/£5

The Wonderful Story of Aladdin and the Enchanted Lamp, Deutsch (London), 1993 . . . . £100/£15

Sherlock Holmes and the Limehouse Horror, Nelson (London), 1992 (wraps) £250

The New Cut Gang: Thunderbolt's Waxwork, Viking (London), 1994 (illustrated boards, no d/w) . . £150

The New Cut Gang: The Gas-Fitter's Ball, Viking (London), 1995 (illustrated boards, no d/w) . . £150

The Firework-Maker's Daughter, Doubleday (London), 1995 (illustrated boards, no d/w) . . . £300

ditto, Levine/Scholastic Press (New York), 1999 . £25/£5

Clockwork, or All Wound Up, Doubleday (London), 1996 (illustrated boards, no d/w) £200

ditto, Levine/Scholastic Press (New York), 1998 . £15/£5

Mossycoat, Scholastic Hippo (London), 1998 (wraps, illustrated by Peter Bailey) £5

I Was a Rat: or The Scarlet Slippers, Doubleday (London), 1999 (illustrated boards, no d/w) . . . £200

ditto, Knopf (New York), 2000 . . . . £15/£5

Puss in Boots: or The Ogre, the Ghouls and the Windmill, Doubleday (London), 2000 . . . . £10/£5

ditto, Knopf (New York), 2001 . . . . £10/£5

The Scarecrow And His Servant, Doubleday (London), 2004 . . . . £10/£5

A Word or Two About Myth, Cannongate (Edinburgh), 2005 (wraps) £5

ditto, Cannongate (New York), 2005 . . . £10/£5

ditto, Knopf (Toronto), 2005 . . . . £10/£5

ditto, Cannongate (Edinburgh), 2005 (box set, **Myths**, also containing **Weight** by Jeanette Winterson, **A Short History of Myth** by Karen Armstrong, and an introductory pamphlet, **The Penelopiad: The Myth of Penelope and Odysseus** by Margaret Atwood) £45

ditto, Cannongate (Edinburgh), 2005 (1,500 numbered box sets, as above but each item signed by the authors) . £80

The Good Man Jesus and the Scoundrel Christ, Cannongate (Edinburgh), 2010 (d/w with black or white background) . . . . £15/£5

ditto, Cannongate (Edinburgh), 2010 (400 signed, numbered copies of both d/w variants) . . . . £50/£40

MARIO PUZO

(b.1920 d.1999)

Puzo was a wide-ranging novelist, but will always be thought of as the man who created *The Godfather*, a phenomenally successful novel about the Mafia. *The Sicilian* was his sequel, and *The Last Don* followed some thirty years later.

Novels

The Dark Arena, Random House (New York), 1955 . . . . £100/£15
ditto, Heinemann (London), 1971 . . . . £45/£10
The Fortunate Pilgrim, Atheneum (New York), 1965 . . . . £125/£20
ditto, Heinemann (London), 1965 . . . . £50/£10
The Godfather, Putnam (New York), 1969 . . £750/£75
ditto, Heinemann (London), 1969 . . . £85/£15
Fools Die, Putnam (New York), 1978 . . . £10/£5
ditto, Heinemann (London), 1978 . . . . £10/£5
The Sicilian, Linden Press (New York), 1984 . . £10/£5
ditto, Bantam (London), 1985 . . . . . £10/£5
The Fourth K, Random House (New York), 1990 . £10/£5
ditto, Heinemann (London), 1991 . . . . £10/£5
The Last Don, Random House (New York), 1996 . £10/£5
ditto, Heinemann (London), 1996 . . . . £10/£5
Omerta, Random House (New York), 2000 . . £10/£5
ditto, Heinemann (London), 2000 . . . . £10/£5
The Family, Harper Collins (New York), 2001 (completed by Carol Gino) . . . . £10/£5
ditto, Heinemann (London), 2001 . . . . £10/£5

Children's Book

The Runaway Summer of Davie Shaw, Platt & Munk (New York), 1966 . . . . £30/£10
ditto, World's Work (Kingswood, Surrey), 1976 . £15/£5

Non-Fiction

The Godfather Papers and Other Confessions, Putnam (New York), 1972 . . . . £25/£5
ditto, Heinemann (London), 1972 . . . . £20/£5
Inside Las Vegas, Grosset & Dunlap (New York), 1977 . . . . £10/£5

As Mario Cleri

Six Graves to Munich, Banner (New York), 1967 (pbk) £5

BARBARA PYM

(b.1913 d.1980)

Pym was an English author whose novels are often sad comedies set against a background of middle class church-going. Her literary career included a long hiatus when she was unable to find a publisher. David Cecil and Philip Larkin described her as the most underrated writer of the 20th century in a *TLS* article. Her novel *Quartet in Autumn* was nominated for the Booker Prize.

Novels

Some Tame Gazelle, Cape (London), 1950 . . £300/£75
ditto, Dutton (New York), 1983 . . . . . £15/£5

Excellent Women, Cape (London), 1952 . . . £225/£45
ditto, Dutton (New York), 1978 . . . . £20/£5
Jane and Prudence, Cape (London), 1953 . . £200/£45
ditto, Dutton (New York), 1981 . . . . £10/£5
Less Than Angels, Cape (London), 1955 . . £150/£45
ditto, Vanguard (New York), 1957 . . . . £35/£10
A Glass of Blessings, Cape (London), 1959 . . £175/£40
ditto, Dutton (New York), 1980 . . . . £10/£5
No Fond Return of Love, Cape (London), 1961 . £175/£40
ditto, Dutton (New York), 1982 . . . . £10/£5
Quartet in Autumn, Macmillan (London), 1977 . £75/£15
ditto, Dutton (New York), 1978 . . . . £20/£5
The Sweet Dove Died, Macmillan (London), 1978 . £30/£5
ditto, Dutton (New York), 1979 . . . . £25/£5
A Few Green Leaves, Macmillan (London), 1980 . £25/£5
ditto, Dutton (New York), 1980 . . . . £20/£5
An Unsuitable Attachment, Macmillan (London), 1982 . . . . £25/£5
ditto, Dutton (New York), 1982 . . . . £10/£5
Crampton Hodnet, Macmillan (London), 1985 . £15/£5
ditto, Dutton (New York), 1985 . . . . £10/£5
An Academic Question, Macmillan (London), 1986 £10/£5
ditto, Dutton (New York), 1986 . . . . £10/£5
Civil to Strangers, Macmillan (London), 1987 . £10/£5
ditto, Dutton (New York), 1988.. . . . . £10/£5

Journals

A Very Private Eye, An Autobiography in Diaries and Letters, Macmillan (London), 1984. . . . £20/£5
ditto, Dutton (New York), 1984 . . . . . £10/£5

THOMAS PYNCHON

(b.1937)

Thomas Pynchon, is an American writer known for his avoidance of publicity, resulting in the circulation of numerous rumours about his location and identity. He is appreciated for his dense and complex novels and has been the recipient of the National Book Award. He is regularly cited as a contender for the Nobel Prize in Literature.

Novels

V, Lippincott (Philadelphia), 1963 (first issue d/w with chapter headings on the rear panel, not reviews) . . . . £1,250/£125
ditto, Cape (London), 1963 . . . . . £300/£30
The Crying of Lot 49, Lippincott (Philadelphia), 1966 . . . . £300/£35
ditto, Cape (London), 1967 . . . . . . £200/£25
Gravity's Rainbow, Viking (New York), 1973 . £800/£100
ditto, Viking (New York), 1973 (pbks) . . . £30
ditto, Cape (London), 1973 . . . . . . £650/£75
Vineland, Little, Brown (Boston), 1990 . . £10/£5
ditto, Secker & Warburg (London), 1990 . . £10/£5
Mason and Dixon, Holt (New York), 1997 . . £10/£5
ditto, Cape (London), 1997 . . . . . . £10/£5
Against the Day, Penguin Press (New York), 2006 £10/£5
ditto, Cape (London), 2006 . . . . . . £10/£5
Inherent Vice, Penguin Press(New York), 2009. £10/£5
ditto, Cape (London), 2009 . . . . . . £10/£5

Collections
Slow Learner, Little, Brown (Boston), 1984   .   .   £10/£5
ditto, Cape (London), 1984 .   .   .   .   .   £10/£5

Piracies
Mortality and Mercy in Vienna, Aloes (London), 1976
(stapled wraps; variants noted) £20
Low Lands, Aloes Books (London), 1978 (stapled wraps;
variants noted) £25
The Secret Integration, Aloes Books (London), 1980
(stapled wraps) £15
Entropy, Troy Town [London], 1957 [c.1981] (first issue
green pbk with black stamping) .   .   .   £25
ditto, Troy Town [London], 1957 [c.1983] (second issue pbk
with photo montage) £20
A Journey into the Mind, Mouldwarp (Westminster), 1983
(stapled wraps) £20
The Small Rain, Aloes Books (London), 1989 (stapled
wraps) £10
*Of a Fond Ghoul: Being a Correspondence Between
Corlies M. Smith and Thomas Pynchon*, The Blown Litter
Press (New York), 1990 .   .   .   .   .   £25

ELLERY QUEEN

'Ellery Queen' was the pseudonym for Frederic Dannay
(b.1905 d.1982) and Manfred B. Lee (b.1905 d.1971), as
well as the name of their fictional detective, who also wrote
detective fiction. The pair also penned a handful of
'Barnaby Ross' novels. Some 'Ellery Queen' novels were
ghost written by other writers.

'Ellery Queen' Novels by Dannay and Lee
The Roman Hat Mystery, Stokes (New York), 1929   .   .
.   .   .   .   £4,500/£350
ditto, Gollancz (London), 1929 .   .   .   £1,000/£100
The French Powder Mystery, Stokes (New York), 1930   .
.   .   .   .   £2,750/£175
ditto, Gollancz (London), 1930 .   .   .   .   .£450/£60
The Dutch Shoe Mystery Stokes (New York), 1931   .
.   .   .   .   £1,650/£125
ditto, Gollancz (London), 1931 .   .   .   .   .£300/£40
The Greek Coffin Mystery, Stokes (New York), 1932 .
.   .   .   .   £1,250/£150
ditto, Gollancz (London), 1932 .   .   .   .   .£225/£30
The Egyptian Cross Mystery, Stokes (New York), 1932   .
.   .   .   .   £1,250/£125
ditto, Gollancz (London), 1933 .   .   .   .   .£225/£30
The American Gun Mystery, Stokes (New York), 1933   .
.   .   .   .   £900/£65
ditto, Gollancz (London), 1933 .   .   .   .   .£175/£30
ditto, as *Death at the Rodeo*, Mercury (New York), 1951   .
.   .   .   .   £45/£10
The Siamese Twin Mystery, Stokes (New York), 1933 .   .
.   .   .   .   £900/£65
ditto, Gollancz (London), 1934 .   .   .   .   .£175/£30
The Chinese Orange Mystery, Stokes (New York), 1934   .
.   .   .   .   £900/£65
ditto, Gollancz (London), 1934 .   .   .   .   .£175/£30
The Spanish Cape Mystery, Stokes (New York), 1935 .   .
.   .   .   .   £700/£65
ditto, Gollancz (London), 1935 .   .   .   .   .£175/£30

Halfway House, Stokes (New York), 1936   .   .   .£125/£20
ditto, Gollancz (London), 1936 .   .   .   .   .£125/£20
The Door Between, Stokes (New York), 1937   .£225/£35
ditto, Gollancz (London), 1937 .   .   .   .   .£175/£20
The Devil To Pay, Stokes (New York), 1938 .   .£200/£30
ditto, Gollancz (London), 1938 .   .   .   .   .£125/£20
The Four of Hearts, Stokes (New York), 1938 .   .£300/£35
ditto, Gollancz (London), 1939 .   .   .   .   .£125/£20
The Dragon's Teeth, Stokes (New York), 1939 .   .£200/£30
ditto, Gollancz (London), 1939 .   .   .   .   .£125/£20
ditto, as *The Virgin Heiress*, Pocket Books (New York),
1954 .   .   .   .   £20
Calamity Town, Gollancz (London), 1942   .   .£150/£20
ditto, Little, Brown (Boston), 1942 .   .   .£125/£20
There Was an Old Woman, Little, Brown (Boston), 1943   .
.   .   .   .£225/£20
ditto, Gollancz (London), 1944 .   .   .   .   .£75/£15
ditto, as *The Quick and the Dead*, Pan (London), 1961   £10
The Murderer is a Fox, Little, Brown (Boston), 1945 .   .
.   .   .   .£100/£15
ditto, Gollancz (London), 1945 .   .   .   .   .£60/£10
Ten Days' Wonder, Little, Brown (Boston), 1948 .   £65/£15
ditto, Gollancz (London), 1948 .   .   .   .   .£50/£10
Cat of Many Tails, Little, Brown (Boston), 1949 .   £65/£15
ditto, Gollancz (London), 1949 .   .   .   .   .£50/£10
Double, Double, Little, Brown (Boston), 1950   .£65/£10
ditto, Gollancz (London), 1950 .   .   .   .   .£45/£10
ditto, as *The Case of the Seven Murders*, Pocket (New
York), 1958 (pbk) £10
The Origin of Evil, Little, Brown (Boston), 1951 .   £65/£10
ditto, Gollancz (London), 1951 .   .   .   .   .£45/£10
The Lamp of God, Dell (New York), 1951 (pbk) .   .£25
The King is Dead, Little, Brown (Boston), 1952 .   £50/£10
ditto, Gollancz (London), 1952 .   .   .   .   .£45/£10
The Scarlet Letters, Little, Brown (Boston), 1953 .   £50/£10
ditto, Gollancz (London), 1953 .   .   .   .   .£40/£10
The Glass Village, Little, Brown (Boston), 1954 .   £50/£10
ditto, Gollancz (London), 1954 .   .   .   .   .£50/£10
Inspector Queen's Own Case, Simon & Schuster (New
York), 1956 .   .   .   .   .   .   £50/£10
ditto, Gollancz (London), 1956 .   .   .   .   .£35/£5
The Finishing Stroke, Simon & Schuster (New York), 1958
.   .   .   .   £50/£10
ditto, Gollancz (London), 1958 .   .   .   .   .£35/£5
A Study in Terror, Lancer (New York), 1966 (written with
Paul W. Fairman). £15
ditto, as *Sherlock Holmes Versus Jack the Ripper*, Gollancz
(London), 1967 .   .   .   .   .   .£150/£35
Face to Face, NAL (New York), 1967 .   .   £45/£10
ditto, Gollancz (London), 1967 .   .   .   .   .£35/£5
Cop Out, World (New York), 1969 .   .   .   £45/£10
ditto, Gollancz (London), 1969 .   .   .   .   .£35/£5
The Last Woman in His Life, World (New York), 1970   .
.   .   .   .   £40/£10
ditto, Gollancz (London), 1970 .   .   .   .   .£30/£5
A Fine and Private Place, World (New York), 1971 .   .
.   .   .   .   £35/£5
ditto, Gollancz (London), 1971 .   .   .   .   .£25/£5

Omnibus Editions
The Ellery Queen Omnibus, Grosset & Dunlap (New York),
1932 (contains *The Roman Hat Mystery*, *The French
Powder Mystery*, *The Dutch Shoe Mystery*) .   .   £75/£20

The Ellery Queen Omnibus, Gollancz (London), 1934 (contains *The French Powder Mystery, The Dutch Shoe Mystery* and *The Greek Coffin Mystery*). . . £75/£20

The New York Murders: An Ellery Queen Omnibus, Little, Brown (Boston), 1958 (contains *Cat of Many Tails, The Scarlet Letters* and *The American Gun Mystery*) . £40/£15

'Ellery Queen' Short Stories

The Adventures of Ellery Queen, Stokes (New York), 1934 . . . . £600/£75

ditto, Gollancz (London), 1935 . . . . £175/£30

The New Adventures of Ellery Queen, Stokes (New York), 1940 . . . . £500/£65

ditto, Gollancz (London), 1940 . . . . £150/£25

The Case Book of Ellery Queen, Spivak (New York), 1945 (pbk) £50

The Case Book of Ellery Queen, Gollancz (London), 1949 (different from above) . . . . . £45/£10

Calendar of Crime, Little, Brown (Boston), 1952 . £65/£15

ditto, Gollancz (London), 1952 . . . . £50/£10

QBI: Queen's Bureau of Investigation, Little, Brown (Boston), 1954 . . . . £40/£10

ditto, Gollancz (London), 1955 . . . . £30/£5

Queen's Full, Random House (New York), 1965 . £25/£5

ditto, Gollancz (London), 1966 . . . . £25/£5

QED: Queen's Experiments in Detection, New American Library (New York), 1968. . . . . £25/£5

ditto, Gollancz (London), 1969 . . . . £25/£5

'Ellery Queen' Non-Fiction Titles

Queen's Quorum, Little, Brown (Boston), 1951 . £75/£25

ditto, Gollancz (London), 1953 . . . . £65/£25

In the Queen's Parlour, Simon & Schuster (New York), 1957 . . . . £35/£10

ditto, Gollancz (London), 1957 . . . . £30/£10

'Barnaby Ross' Titles

The Tragedy of X, Viking (New York), 1932 . . £200/£50

ditto, Cassell (London), 1932 . . . . £150/£45

The Tragedy of Y, Viking (New York), 1932 . . £200/£50

ditto, Cassell (London), 1932 . . . . £150/£45

The Tragedy of Z, Viking (New York), 1933 . . £200/£50

ditto, Cassell (London), 1933 . . . . £150/£45

Drury Lane's Last Case, Viking (New York), 1933 £175/£40

ditto, Cassell (London), 1933 . . . . £150/£35

'Ellery Queen' Novels by Other Writers

The Last Man Club, Whitman (Racine, WI), 1940 (pictorial boards; no d/w) £75

ditto, Pyramid (New York), 1968 (with *The Murdered Millionaire*; pbk). £5

Ellery Queen, Master Detective, Grosset & Dunlap (New York), 1941 . . . . £50/£10

ditto, as **The Vanishing Corpse**, Pyramid (New York), 1968 (pbk) £5

The Penthouse Mystery, Grosset (New York), 1941 £50/£10

The Murdered Millionaire, Whitman (Racine, WI), 1942 (pictorial boards; no d/w) £75

The Perfect Crime, Grosset (New York), 1942 . £50/£10

Dead Man's Tale, Pocket Books (New York), 1961 (by Stephen Marlowe; pbk) £10

ditto, Four Square (London), 1967 (pbk) . . . £5

Death Spins the Platter, Pocket Books (New York), 1962 (by Richard Deming; pbk). £10

ditto, Gollancz (London), 1975 . . . . . £40/£10

The Scrolls of Lysis, Simon & Schuster (New York), 1962 . . . . £35/£10

The Player on the Other Side, Random House (New York), 1963 (by Theodore Sturgeon) . . . . £65/£10

ditto, Gollancz (London), 1963 . . . . £45/£10

Murder With a Past, Pocket Books (New York), 1963 (by Talmage Powell; pbk). £10

Kill as Directed, Four Square (London), 1963 (pbk) . £5

Wife or Death, Four Square (London), 1963 (pbk). . £5

And on the Eighth Day, Random House (New York), 1964 (by Avram Davidson). . . . . . £45/£10

ditto, Gollancz (London), 1964 . . . . £35/£5

The Golden Goose, Pocket Books (New York), 1964 (pbk). £10

ditto, Four Square, 1967 (pbk) £5

The Four Johns, Pocket Books (New York), 1964 (by Jack Vance; pbk) £5

ditto, as **Four Men Called John**, Gollancz (London), 1976 . . . . £25/£5

Blow Hot Blow Cold, Pocket Books (New York), 1964 (pbk) £10

The Duke of Chaos, Pocket Books (New York), 1964 (pbk) £10

The Last Score, Pocket Books (New York), 1964 (pbk) £10

The Copper Frame, Pocket Books (New York), 1965 (pbk) £10

ditto, Four Square (London), 1968 (pbk) . . . £5

The Fourth Side of the Triangle, Random House (New York), 1965 (by Avram Davidson) . . . . £45/£10

ditto, Gollancz (London), 1965 . . . . £35/£5

The Killer Touch, Pocket Books (New York), 1965 (pbk) £10

Beware the Young Stranger, Pocket Books (New York), 1965 (pbk) £10

A Room To Die In, Pocket Books (New York), 1965 (by Jack Vance; pbk). £10

ditto, Kinnell (London), 1987 . . . . . £20/£5

The Madman Theory, Pocket Books (New York), 1965 (by Jack Vance; pbk). £10

ditto, Kinnell (London), 1988 . . . . . £20/£5

Why So Dead?, Popular Library (New York), 1966 (pbk) £5

ditto, Four Square (London), 1966 (pbk) . . . £5

Shoot the Scene, Dell (New York), 1966 (pbk) . . £5

Where is Bianca?, Popular Library (New York), 1966 (pbk) £5

ditto, Four Square (London), 1966 (pbk) . . . £5

Who Spies, Who Kills?, Popular Library (New York), 1966 (pbk) £5

ditto, Four Square (London), 1967 (pbk) . . . £5

Losers, Weepers, Dell (New York), 1966 (pbk) . . £5

How Goes the Murder?, Popular Library (New York), 1967 (pbk) £5

Which Way to Die?, Popular Library (New York), 1967 (pbk) £5

The House of Brass, NAL (New York), 1968 (by Theodore Sturgeon) . . . . £45/£10

ditto, Gollancz (London), 1968 . . . . £35/£5

What's In The Dark, Popular Library (New York), 1968 (by Richard Deming; pbk) £5

ditto, as **When Fell the Night**, Gollancz (London), 1970 . . . . £40/£10

Guess Who's Coming to Kill You?, Lancer (New York), 1968 (pbk) £5

The Campus Murders, Lancer (New York), 1969 (pbk)   £5
Kiss and Kill, Dell (New York), 1969 (pbk)   .   .   £5
The Black Hearts Murders, Lancer (New York), 1970 (pbk)
.   .   .   .   £5
The Blue Movie Murders, Lancer (New York), 1972 (by
Edward D. Hoch; pbk) £5
ditto, Gollancz (London), 1973   .   .   .   .   £30/£5

JONATHAN RABAN
(b.1942)

Jonathan Raban is a British author whose early works are
academic titles. However, he now has a considerable
reputation as a travel writer whose accounts often blend the
story of a journey with a full discussion of the history of
the land through which he travels. He is also well regarded
as a novelist. Raban has lived in America since 1990.

Travel Titles
Soft City, Hamish Hamilton (London), 1974   .   .   £30/£5
ditto, Dutton (New York), 1974   .   .   .   .   £20/£5
Arabia Through the Looking Glass, Collins (London), 1979
.   .   .   .   £25/£5
ditto, as *Arabia: A Journey Through the Labyrinth*, Simon
& Schuster (New York), 1979   .   .   .   .   £20/£5
Old Glory: An American Voyage, Collins (London), 1981   .
.   .   .   .   £20/£5
ditto, Simon & Schuster (New York), 1981   .   .   £15/£5
Coasting, Collins (London), 1986   .   .   .   .   £15/£5
ditto, Simon & Schuster (New York), 1987   .   .   £15/£5
Hunting Mr Heartbreak, Collins (London), 1990   .   £10/£5
ditto, Harper Collins (New York), 1991   .   .   £10/£5
Passage to Juneau: A Sea and Its Meanings, Picador
(London), 1999   .   .   .   .   .   .   £10/£5
ditto, Pantheon (New York), 1999   .   .   .   £10/£5

Novels
Foreign Land, Collins (London), 1985   .   .   .   £15/£5
ditto, Viking (New York), 1985   .   .   .   .   £10/£5
Bad Land: An American Romance, Picador (London), 1996
.   .   .   .   £15/£5
ditto, Pantheon (New York), 1996   .   .   .   £10/£5
Waxwings: A Novel of Seattle, Picador (London), 2003   .
.   .   .   .   £10/£5
ditto, Pantheon (New York), 2003   .   .   .   £10/£5
Surveillance, Picador (London), 2006   .   .   £10/£5
ditto, Pantheon (New York), 2006   .   .   .   £10/£5

Academic Titles
The Technique of Modern Fiction, Arnold (London), 1968
.   .   .   .   £100/£25
ditto, Univ of Notre Dame Press (Notre Dame, IN), 1968
(wraps) £10
Huckleberry Finn, Arnold (London), 1968   .   £50/£10
The Society of the Poem, Harrap (London), 1971   .   £25/£10

Others
For Love and Money, Collins (London), 1987   .   £15/£5
ditto, Harper & Row (New York), 1989   .   .   £15/£5
God, Man and Mrs Thatcher, Chatto & Windus (London),
1989 (wraps). £10

ARTHUR RACKHAM
(b.1867 d.1939)

Rackham was a highly successful British book illustrator
whose early gift books are his most sought-after titles. He
won a gold medal at the Milan International Exhibition in
1906 and another at the Barcelona International Exposition
in 1911. His works were shown at many galleries, including the Louvre in Paris in 1914.

To the Other Side, by Thomas Rhodes, George Philip
(London), 1893 (also illustrated by Alfred Bryan; boards).
.   .   .   .   £3,500
ditto, George Philip (London), 1893 (wraps)   .   £3,500
The Dolly Dialogues, by Anthony Hope, Westminster
Gazette Library (London): Volume One, [July] 1894 (4
half-tone illustrations; first issue with 'Dolly' running
head; wraps). £250
ditto, Westminster Gazette Library (London): Volume One,
[July] 1894 (4 half-tone illustrations; second issue with
'The Dolly Dialogues' running head; wraps)   .   £150
ditto, Westminster Gazette Library (London): Volume One,
[August] 1894 (4 half-tone illustrations; cloth edition) £150
ditto, Holt (New York), 1894 (frontispiece illustration only)
.   .   .   .   £125
The Sketch-Book of Geoffrey Crayon, by Washington
Irving, Putnams (New York), 1894 (2 vols; 3 illustrations
by Rackham, many others by various artists; 1,000 numbered sets; red cloth) £400
ditto, Putnams (New York), [1895] (2 vols; 1 further
illustration by Rackham) £175
The Illustrated Guide to Wells-next-the-Sea, by Lingwood
Lemmon, Jarrolds (London), [1894] (49 b&w illustrations;
illustrated wraps). £350
ditto, Jarrolds (London), [1894] (red cloth issue; date on title-
page) £200
Sunrise-Land - Rambles in Eastern England, by Mrs Alfred
Berlyn, Jarrolds (London), 1894 (71 vignette illustrations;
mauve pictorial cloth). £250
ditto, Jarrolds (London), 1894 (cheaper edition; white
pictorial boards). £150
ditto, as *East Coast Health Resorts*, Jarrolds (London), 1894
(14 illustrations reprinted from above; red cloth).   £200
Isis Very Much Unveiled, by Edmund Garrett, Westminster
Gazette (London), 1894 (1 b&w illustration; wraps)   .£150
Souvenir of Sir Henry Irving, Drane (London), 1895 (1 half-
tone drawing by Rackham, many others by various artists;
wraps) £135
The Homes and Haunts of Thomas Carlyle, Westminster
Gazette (London), 1895 (1 sketch by Rackham, many
others by various artists; blue cloth)   .   .   .   £125
The New Fiction and Other Papers, by The Philistine,
Westminster Gazette (London), 1895 (1 b&w illustration).
.   .   .   .   £100
A London Garland, Macmillan (London), 1895 (1 illustration by Rackham, many others by various artists; cream
cloth) £75
ditto, Macmillan (London), 1895 (bound in vellum; slipcase)
.   .   .   .   £300/£200
The Wonderful Visit, by H.G. Wells, Dent (London), 1895
(design on upper board by Rackham; red cloth)   .   £250

Tales of a Traveller, by Washington Irving, Putnams (New York), 1895 (5 half-tone illustrations; 2 vols; white or light blue cloth) £100

ditto, Putnams (New York), 1895 (150 copies; light brown full calf). £200

The Zankiwank and the Bletherwitch, Dent (London), 1896 (17 full page illustrations and 1 double page illustration, plus 24 b&w illustrations; dark green cloth) . . £2,000

ditto, Dutton (New York), 1896 . . . . . . £750

Bracebridge Hall, by Washington Irving, Putnams (New York), 1896 (5 illustrations by Rackham, many others by various artists; 2 vols; dark blue cloth) . . . £100

ditto, Putnams (New York), 1896 (100 copies signed by publishers; 2 vols; light brown full calf). . . . £250

The Money Spinner and Other Character Notes, by Henry Seaton Merriman and S.G. Tallentyre, Smith Elder (London), 1896 (12 half-tone illustrations; red calf) . £150

In the Evening of His Days - A Study of Mr Gladstone in Retirement, Westminster Gazette (London), 1896 (10 b&w illustrations by Rackham, some by other artists; grey/blue cloth) £175

Captain Castle, by Carlton Dawe, Smith Elder (London), 1897 (frontispiece by Rackham; dark blue cloth). . £250

The Grey Lady, by Henry Seaton Merriman, Smith Elder (London), 1897 (12 b&w illustrations; lavender-grey cloth) £200

Two Old Ladies, Two Foolish Fairies and a Tom Cat, The Surprising Adventures of Tuppy and Tue, by Maggie Browne, Cassell (London), 1897 (4 colour, 19 b&w illustrations; various colours of cloth) £500

ditto, as *The Surprising Adventures of Tuppy & Tue*, Cassell (London), 1904 (4 colour illustrations, 10 b&w drawings and 12 drawings in text) £250

Charles O'Malley, The Irish Dragoon, by Charles Lever, Service & Paton (London), 1897 (16 b&w illustrations; maroon cloth) £250

ditto, Putnams (New York), 1897 . . . . . £175

Through A Glass Lightly, by T.T. Greg, Dent (London), 1897 (title-page sketch by Rackham; bound in yellow silk) £175

The Castle Inn, by Stanley J. Wellman, Smith, Elder (London), 1898 (frontispiece by Rackham; dark blue cloth) £150

Evelina, by Frances Burney, George Newnes (London), 1898 (16 b&w illustrations; first issue with one page advert at rear; grey/blue cloth) £150

ditto, George Newnes (London), 1898 (second issue with two page advert at rear) £100

The Ingoldsby Legends, [by R.H. Barham], J.M. Dent (London), 1898 (12 colour, 90 b&w illustrations; gilt lettering on cover and spine; dark green cloth) . £150

ditto, J.M. Dent (London), 1907 (second edition, revised and enlarged; 24 colour plates, 12 tinted illustrations, 66 drawings in text) £200

ditto, J.M. Dent (London), 1907 (560 signed copies) £1,400

ditto, Dutton (New York), 1907 (trade edition) . £150

ditto, Dutton (New York), 1907 (50 signed copies) . £650

East Coast Scenery, by William J. Tate, Jarrolds (London), 1899 (7 b&w illustrations; pictorial eggshell green boards) £150

Feats on the Fjords, by Harriet Martineau, J.M. Dent (London), 1899 (colour frontispiece and 11 b&w illustrations; blue leather edition). £175

ditto, J.M. Dent (London), 1898 (blue cloth edition) . £125

ditto, as *Feats on the Fjord and Merdhin*, Dent: Everyman Library (London), [1910] (3 additional b&w plates) . £50

ditto, J.M. Dent (London), 1914 (plates coloured) . £65

ditto, Dutton (New York), 1914 . . . . . £65

Tales from Shakespeare, by Charles and Mary Lamb, J.M. Dent (London), 1899 (colour frontispiece and 11 b&w illustrations; blue leather edition) £200

ditto, J.M. Dent (London), 1899 (blue cloth edition) . £125

ditto, J.M. Dent (London), 1909 (750 signed, numbered copies; revised and enlarged; 13 colour illustrations, 2 b&w illustrations, 20 chapter headings and 14 tailpieces) £1,000

ditto, J.M. Dent (London), 1909 (trade edition of above, less one colour plate) £200

ditto, Dutton (New York), 1909 . . . . . £150

A World In A Garden, by R Neish, J.M. Dent (London), 1899 (chapter headings and tailpieces by Rackham, and illustrations by Jessie Macgregor; pink cloth) . £100

Gardens Old And New, Newnes (London), 1900 (designs by Rackham in first of two vols; green cloth) . . £125

Gulliver's Travels, by Jonathan Swift, J.M. Dent (London), 1900 (colour frontispiece and 11 b&w illustrations; blue leather edition) £125

ditto, J.M. Dent (London), 1900 (blue cloth edition) . £75

ditto, J.M. Dent (London), 1909 (750 signed, numbered copies with extra plate; revised and enlarged; 13 colour plates, 2 b&w illustrations, 7 chapter heads and tailpieces;) £1,000

ditto, J.M. Dent (London), 1909 (trade edition of above, less one colour plate) £175

ditto, Dutton (New York), 1909 . . . . . £150

Fairy Tales of the Brothers Grimm, Freemantle (London), 1900 (cover design, endpapers, colour frontispiece and 99 b&w illustrations) £300

ditto, Lippincott (Philadelphia), [1902] . . . £250

ditto, Constable (London), 1909 (revised and enlarged; 40 colour plates, 45 b&w illustrations). . . . £1,000

ditto, Constable (London), 1909 (750 signed, numbered copies) £3,000

ditto, Doubleday (New York), 1909 . . . . £1,000

ditto, Doubleday (New York), 1909 (50 signed, numbered copies) £2,750

ditto, as *Hansel & Gretel and Other Tales* by the Brothers Grimm, Constable (London), 1920 (30 stories from the above; 20 colour plates, 28 b&w illustrations; dark blue cloth) . . . . £400/£200

ditto, Dutton (New York), 1920 . . . . £400/£200

ditto, as *Snowdrop and Other Tales*, by the Brothers Grimm, Constable (London), 1920 (30 stories from the above; 20 colour plates, 29 b&w illustrations; dark blue cloth) . . . . £400/£200

ditto, Dutton (New York), 1920 . . . . £400/£200

Animal Antics, Partridge (London), 1901 (1 b&w drawing by Rackham) £75

Queen Mab's Fairy Realm, Newnes (London), 1901 (2 full-page illustrations and three within the text by Rackham, with illustrations by other artists; dark blue cloth). . £250

The Argonauts of the Amazon, by C.R. Kenyon, W. & R. Chambers (London), 1901 (6 half-tone illustrations; light blue cloth) £125

ditto, Dutton (New York), 1901 . . . . . £125

The Life of a Century, Newnes (London), 1901 (12 parts, with 3 line and 3 wash drawings by Rackham in part 4; wraps) £150

Mysteries of Police and Crime, by Major Arthur Griffiths, Cassell (London), 1901 (3 vols; with illustrations by Rackham in vols 1 and 2, along with other artists; green cloth) £125

More Tales of the Stumps, Horace Bleackley, Ward Lock (London), 1902 (11 b&w illustrations; blue cloth) . £300

Faithful Friends, Blackie (London), 1902 (6 colour illustrations by Rackham, with other artists; pictorial boards) £100

Brains and Bravery, Being Stories told by ..., G.A. Henty etc, W. & R. Chambers (London), [1903] (8 half-tone illustrations; red or blue cloth) £300

ditto, W. & R. Chambers (London), 1903 (later edition; green cloth) £150

The Grey House on the Hill, by Hon. Mrs Greene, Thomas Nelson (London), [1903] (8 colour illustrations; pink cloth) £200

Littledom Castle and Other Tales, by Mrs M.H. Speilmann, George Routledge (London), 1903 (9 full-page and 3 text drawings by Rackham, with others; red cloth) . £200

ditto, Dutton (New York), 1903 . . . . . £200

Plays for Little Folks, Cassell (London), 1903 (2 coloured illustrations and 2 b&w drawings by Rackham, with other artists; grey-green cloth) £125

The Greek Heroes, Cassell (London), 1903 (4 colour, 8 b&w illustrations; limp green buckram) £100

Two Years Before the Mast, by Richard Henry Dana, Collins (London), [1904] (8 colour plates; green or pink cloth) £100

ditto, Winston (Philadelphia), 1903 (tan or light blue cloth) £75

Where Flies the Flag, by Henry Harbour, Collins (London), [1904] (6 colour plates; red or blue cloth) . . . £200

Molly Bawn, by Mrs Hungerford, George Newnes (London): Newnes Sixpenny Novels, [1904] (8 b&w illustrations; wraps) £1,000

The Peradventures of Private Pagett, by Major W.P. Drury, Chapman & Hall (London), 1904 (8 b&w illustrations; orange-red cloth) £125

Little Folks Picture Album, by S.H. Hamer (London), Cassell (London) 1904 (1 colour illustration by Rackham, with other artists; green or brown cloth) . . . £100

Red Pottage, by Mary Cholmondeley, George Newnes (London): Newnes Sixpenny Novels, [1904] (8 half-tone illustrations; first issue with 50 titles in Newnes Sixpenny Novels list; wraps) £300

ditto, by Mary Cholmondeley, George Newnes (London): Newnes Sixpenny Novels, [1904] (second issue with 140 titles in Newnes Sixpenny Novels list; wraps) . £150

The Venture, Baillie (London), 1905 [1904] (1 illustration by Rackham, with other artists) £100

The Infants Magazine, (London), 1905 (3 b&w illustrations by Rackham, with other artists; pictorial card boards). £135

The Children's Christmas Treasury, Dent (London), [1905] (2 illustrations by Rackham from *Ingoldsby Legends*, with other artists; white cloth) £125

The 'Old' Water Colour Society, Offices of the Studio (London), 1905 (1 illustration by Rackham, with other artists; green or grey cloth) £125

Rip van Winkle, by Washington Irving, Heinemann (London), 1905 (frontispiece and 50 colour plates; green cloth) £650

ditto, Heinemann (London), 1905 (special binding, green leather) £1,250

ditto, Heinemann (London), 1905 (250 signed copies; pictorial full vellum) £3,500

ditto, Doubleday (New York), 1905 (trade edition) . £500

ditto, Heinemann (London), 1916 (only 24 plates, but new drawings added) £250

ditto, Doubleday (New York), 1916 . . . . . £250

Kingdoms Curious, by Myra Hamilton, Heinemann (London), 1905 (4 b&w illustrations by Rackham, with other artists; tan cloth) £250

The Little Folks Fairy Book, Cassell (London), 1905 (1 full-page and 8 text illustrations by Rackham, with other artists; red or blue boards) £350

Penrose's Pictorial Annual, (London), 1905 (vols 11 and 23 each contain a colour plate by Rackham from *Rip Van Winkle* and *Cinderella*, with other artists; pictorial cloth) . . . . £100 for each of the two relevant volumes

The Children's Hour, Newnes (London), 1906 (1 b&w illustration by Rackham, with other artists; green cloth) . £350

Peter Pan in Kensington Gardens, by J.M. Barrie, Hodder & Stoughton (London), 1906 (frontispiece and 49 colour plates; 500 signed, numbered copies; captioned tissue guards; bound in vellum; gilt titles and decoration to upper board and spine; yellow silk ties, top edge gilt but others untrimmed) £4.000

ditto, Hodder & Stoughton (London), 1906 (trade edition) £750

ditto, Scribner's (New York), 1906 . . . . £600

ditto, Hodder & Stoughton (London), 1910 (24 colour plates) £100

ditto, Hodder & Stoughton (London), 1912 (50 colour plates, 12 drawings) £500

ditto, Hodder & Stoughton (London), 1912 (deluxe edition; unsigned; 50 colour plates, 12 drawings) . . £1,500

Puck of Pook's Hill, by Rudyard Kipling, Doubleday (New York), 1906 (4 colour illustrations; dark green cloth) . £150

The Children and the Pictures, by Pamela Tennant, Heinemann (London), 1907 (title-page illustration by Rackham; pink cloth) £125

Alice's Adventures in Wonderland, by Lewis Carroll, Heinemann (London), [1907] (13 colour plates, 14 b&w illustrations; 1,130 numbered copies; white buckram) £1,750

ditto, Heinemann (London), [1907] (trade edition; green cloth) £300

ditto, Doubleday (New York), [1907] (550 signed, numberd copies; green boards) £1,750

ditto, Doubleday (New York), [1907] (trade edition; red cloth) £300

Tales and Talks About Animals, Blackie (London), 1907 (5 colour plates and 3 text illustrations by Rackham, with other artists; pictorial boards) £125

ditto, as *Faithful Friends*, Blackie (London), 1913 . £65

Good Night, by Eleanor Gates, Crowell (New York), [1907] (5 colour illustrations; grey pictorial cloth) . . £150

Auld Acquaintance, Dent (London), 1907 (2 illustrations from *The Zankiwank* and *Haddon Hall Library*; grey pictorial cloth) £125

The Land of Enchantment, by Alfred E. Bonser, Cassell (London), 1907 (frontispiece and 12 half-tone illustrations, 24 drawings in text, first binding; green cloth) . £200

ditto, Cassell (London), 1907 (second binding, cocoa cloth) £150

Featherweights, Hodder & Stoughton (London), 1908 (frontispiece and mounted cover label by Rackham; wraps) £150

The Cotter's Saturday Night, by Robert Burns, Hewetson (London), 1908 (frontispiece by Rackham; imitation vellum) £75

A Midsummer Night's Dream, by William Shakespeare, Heinemann (London), 1908 (40 colour plates and 30 b&w drawings; tan cloth) £450

ditto, Heinemann (London), 1908 (special binding in brown calf) £600

ditto, Heinemann (London), 1908 (1,000 signed, numbered copies; full vellum) £2,000

ditto, Doubleday (New York), 1908 (trade edition; grey boards) £250

ditto, by William Shakespeare, Limited Editions Club (New York), 1939 (6 new colour illustrations; 1,950 copies) £500

Henry IV, Part II, by William Shakespeare, Harrap (London), 1908 (frontispiece by Rackham) . . . £75

Macbeth, by William Shakespeare, Harrap (London), 1908 (frontispiece by Rackham). £75

The Odd Volume, by Simpkin etc (London), 1908 (1 illustration by Rackham from *Ingoldsby Legends*, with other artists; red wraps) £100

Undine, by De La Motte Fouque, Heinemann (London), 1909 (15 colour plates, 30 b&w drawings; blue cloth) £200

ditto, Heinemann (London), 1909 (1,000 signed, numbered copies; full vellum) £1,250

ditto, Doubleday (New York), 1909 (trade edition; grey boards) £200

ditto, Doubleday (New York), 1909 (250 signed, numbered copies; brown boards) £1,250

The Rainbow Book, by Mrs M.H. Spielmann, Chatto & Windus (London), 1909 (15 coloured illustrations by Rackham, with other artists; coral cloth) . . £200

ditto, Warne (New York), 1909 . . . . . £200

The Book of Betty Barber, by Maggie Browne, Duckworth (London), [1910] (6 colour illustrations, 14 b&w drawings; brown cloth with plate on cover) £500

ditto, Badger (Boston), 1914 . . . . . £200

The Bee-Blowaways, by Agnes Grozier Herbertson, Cassell (London), [1910] (14 b&w illustrations; green cloth) . £400

Stories of King Arthur, by A.L. Haydon, Cassell (London), 1910 (4 colour and 2 b&w illustrations; red cloth) . £75

Children's Treasury of Great Stories, Daily Express (London), 1910 (6 colour and 5 b&w illustrations by Rackham, with other artists; blue and black marbled cloth) £100

The Rhinegold and The Valkyrie, by Richard Wagner, Heinemann (London), 1910 (34 colour and 14 b&w illustrations; brown buckram) £200

ditto, Heinemann (London), 1910 (1,150 signed, numbered copies; full vellum) £1,000

ditto, Doubleday (New York), 1910 (trade edition; grey boards) £200

ditto, Doubleday (New York), 1910 (150 signed, numbered copies; brown boards) £1,000

Siegfried and The Twilight of the Gods, by Richard Wagner, Heinemann (London), 1911 (30 colour and 9 b&w illustrations; brown buckram) £200

ditto, Heinemann (London), 1911 (deluxe binding in limp suede) £750

ditto, Heinemann (London), 1911 (1,150 signed, numbered copies; full vellum) £1,000

ditto, Doubleday (New York), 1911 (trade edition; grey boards) £200

ditto, Doubleday (New York), 1911 (150 signed, numbered copies; brown boards) £1,000

ditto, as *The Ring of the Niblung*, Heinemann (London), 1939 (48 colour illustrations; blue-green cloth) . £175/£75

ditto, as *The Ring of the Niblung*, Doubleday (New York), 1939 . . . . £175/£75

Aesop's Fables, Heinemann (London), 1912 (13 colour plates, 53 drawings; green cloth) £200

ditto, Heinemann (London), 1912 (1,450 signed, numbered copies; white buckram) £1,000

ditto, Doubleday (New York), 1912 (trade edition; green cloth) £200

ditto, Doubleday (New York), 1912 (250 signed, numbered copies; brown boards) £1,000

The Peter Pan Portfolio, Hodder & Stoughton (London), [1912] (500 boxed portfolios of 12 plates numbered 101-600; signed by publishers). £8,000

ditto, Hodder & Stoughton (London), 1912 (approx 20 boxed portfolios signed by the artist) £15,000

ditto, Brentano's (New York), 1912 (300 unsigned boxed portfolios) £2,000

The Little White Bird, by J.M. Barrie, Scribner's (New York), 1912 (2 of 3 colour plates are by Rackham) . £400

Mother Goose: The Old Nursery Rhymes, Heinemann (London), 1913 (13 colour plates, 85 drawings; grey cloth) £450

ditto, Heinemann (London), 1913 (1,130 signed, numbered copies; white cloth) £2,000

ditto, Century (New York), 1913 (black cloth) . £250

Arthur Rackham's Book of Pictures, Heinemann (London), 1913 (44 colour plates and 10 drawings; grey-green cloth) £200

ditto, Heinemann (London), 1913 (1,030 signed, numbered copies; white cloth) £750

ditto, Heinemann (London), 1913 (30 inscribed copies with original drawing). £4,000

ditto, Century Co. (New York), 1913 (trade edition; tan cloth) £200

Princess Mary's Gift Book, Hodder & Stoughton (London), 1914 (1 mounted plate and 5 drawings by Rackham, with other artists; white or blue cloth) £100

ditto, Hodder & Stoughton (London), 1914 (bound in full brown leather) £125

King Albert's Book, Hodder & Stoughton (London), 1914 (1 mounted colour plate by Rackham, with other artists; white cloth) £100

ditto, Hodder & Stoughton (London), 1914 (bound in quarter brown calf) £100

ditto, International News (New York), 1914 . . £100

Imagina, by Julia Ellsworth Ford, Duffield (New York), 1914 (2 colour illustrations; blue cloth). . . £125

A Christmas Carol, by Charles Dickens, Heinemann (London), 1915 (12 colour plates and 20 drawings; olive green cloth) £250

ditto, Heinemann (London), 1915 (special binding in antique brown leather) £450

ditto, Heinemann (London), 1915 (525 signed, numbered copies; full vellum) £1,750

ditto, Lippincott (Philadelphia), 1915 (trade edition; red or lavender cloth) £250

ditto, Lippincott (Philadelphia), 1915 (100 signed, numbered copies; full vellum) £1,750

The Queen's Gift Book, Hodder & Stoughton (London), 1915 (1 colour plate and 2 drawings by Rackham, with other artists; light blue cloth) £100

The Allies' Fairy Book, Heinemann (London), 1916 (12 colour illustrations and 24 drawings; slate blue cloth). £150 *ditto*, Heinemann (London), 1916 (525 signed, numbered copies; blue cloth) £1,000

ditto, Lippincott (Philadelphia), 1916 (green or red cloth) .

. . . . £150

ditto, Lippincott (Philadelphia), 1916 (525 signed, numbered copies; blue cloth) £1,000

ditto, as *A Fairy Book*, Doubleday (New York), 1923 (11 colour illustrations and 20 drawings) £75

Little Brother and Little Sister, by the Brothers Grimm, Constable (London), 1917 (12 colour illustrations, 43 drawings; light green cloth) £350

ditto, Constable (London), 1917 (525 signed, numbered copies, including one extra colour plate laid in and signed; light grey cloth) £2,500

ditto, Dodd, Mead (New York), 1917 (red or blue cloth) £350

The Romance of King Arthur, And his Knights of the Round Table, by Thomas Malory and Alfred Pollard, Macmillan (London), 1917 (16 colour illustrations, 7 full-page drawings, 63 drawings in text; dark blue cloth) . £250

ditto, Macmillan (London), 1917 (500 signed, numbered copies; full vellum) £1,750

ditto, Macmillan (New York), 1917 (trade edition, green cloth) £250

ditto, Macmillan (New York), 1917 (250 signed, numbered copies; full vellum) £1,750

English Fairy Taies, by Flora Annie Steel, Macmillan (London), 1918 (16 colour illustrations and 41 drawings; red cloth) £250

ditto, Macmillan (London), 1918 (500 signed, numbered copies; full vellum) £1,750

ditto, Macmillan (New York), 1918 (trade edition; red cloth)

. . . . £150

ditto, Macmillan (New York), 1918 (250 unsigned, numbered copies; white calf) £650

The Springtide of Life: Poems of Childhood, by Algernon Charles Swinburne, Heinemann (London), 1918 (8 colour plates and 52 drawings; green cloth) £100

ditto, Lippincott (Philadelphia), 1918 (green cloth) . £100

ditto, Heinemann (London), 1918 (publishers special binding of dark green mottled leather) £200

ditto, Heinemann (London), 1918 (765 signed, numbered copies; extra colour plate; vellum-backed cream boards) .

. . . . £500

ditto, Heinemann (London), 1918 [1925] (later issue, as trade edition but top edge not gilt) £50

Cinderella, by Charles Perrault, Heinemann (London), 1919 (colour frontispiece, 16 silhouette illustrations; pictorial boards) £150

ditto, Heinemann (London), 1919 (525 signed, numbered copies on handmade paper; extra silhouette in colour; green boards with tan cloth spine) £500

ditto, Heinemann (London), 1919 (325 signed, numbered copies; printed on Japanese vellum; vellum-backed cream boards) £900

ditto, Lippincott (Philadelphia), 1919 (trade edition) . £150

Snickerty Nick and the Giant, by Julia Ellsworth Ford, Moffat, Yard & Co (New York), 1919 (3 coloured plates and 10 drawings; light blue cloth) £300

ditto, Suttonhouse (Los Angeles, CA), 1933 (new edition, with music by C.A. Ridgeway). £150

Some British Ballads, by various, Constable (London), [1919] (16 colour plates and 24 drawings; light blue cloth)

. . . . £175

ditto, Constable (London), [1919] (575 signed, numbered copies, vellum-backed cream boards) £750

ditto, Dodd Mead (New York), [1919] (trade edition, dark blue cloth) £150

ditto, Constable (London), [1924] (with 'Heinemann (London)' at the foot of the spine) . . . £100/£35

Irish Fairy Tales, by James Stephens, Macmillan (London), 1920 (16 colour illustrations, 21 drawings; green cloth) .

. . . . £500/£250

ditto, Macmillan (London), 1920 (520 signed, numbered copies; vellum-backed white boards) . . . £1,000

ditto, Macmillan (New York), 1920 . . . £500/£250

The Sleeping Beauty, by Charles Perrault, Heinemann (London), 1920 (colour frontispiece, 4 silhouettes, 41 drawings; pictorial boards with red cloth backstrip) . .

. . . . £250/£100

ditto, Heinemann (London), 1920 (625 signed, numbered copies, extra silhouette drawing; vellum-backed cream boards) £750

ditto, Lippincott (Philadelphia), 1920 . . £250/£100

Comus, by John Milton, Heinemann (London), [1921] (24 colour illustrations, 37 drawings; green cloth) £400/£200

ditto, Heinemann (London), [1921] (550 signed, numbered copies; vellum-backed cream boards) £600

ditto, Doubleday (New York), [1921] . . £400/£200

A Dish of Apples, by Eden Phillpotts, Hodder & Stoughton (London), 1921 (3 colour illustrations, 23 drawings; grey cloth) . . . . £250/£100

ditto, Hodder & Stoughton (London), 1921 (500 numbered copies signed by author and artist; cream buckram) . £450

ditto, Hodder & Stoughton (London), 1921 (55 copies on Batchelor's Kelmscott paper) £1,000

A Wonder Book, by Nathaniel Hawthorne, Hodder & Stoughton (London), [1922] (24 colour illustrations and 20 drawings; red cloth) . . . . . £375/£150

ditto, Hodder & Stoughton (London), [1922] (600 signed, numbered copies; cream buckram) £1,000

ditto, Doran (New York), [1922] (orange-red cloth) . .

. . . . £200/£100

Drawings In Pen and Pencil, by George Sheringham, The Studio (London), 1922 (1 illustration with work by others; grey-green cloth). . . . . . . £250/£100

ditto, by George Sheringham, The Studio (London), 1922 (250 numbered copies; full vellum). £250

British Book Illustration, by Malcolm C. Salaman, The Studio (London), 1923 (1 colour and 2 b&w illustrations with work by others; tan cloth). . . . £250/£100

The Windmill, Heinemann (London), 1923 (1 colour picture by Rackham, with other artists; orange boards with brown cloth back) £75

ditto, Heinemann (New York), 1923 (as above but top edge gilt). £75

Annual of Advertising Art, Book Service Co. (New York), 1924 (1 colour picture by Rackham, with other artists; grey boards with tan cloth back) £75

The Book of the Queen's Dolls' House, Methuen (London), 1924 (1,500 copies, containing 1 Rackham illustration, with other artists; 2 vols; blue boards with tan cloth back).

. . . . £200

ditto, Methuen (London), 1924 (1 volume cheap edition; blue boards) £75

Where the Blue Begins, by Christopher Morley, Heinemann (London), [1925] (4 coloured plates, 16 drawings; blue cloth) . . . . £250/£100

ditto, Heinemann (London), [1925] (175 signed, numbered copies; vellum-style boards) £1,000

ditto, Doubleday (New York), 1922 [1925] (blue cloth). .
. . . . £250/£100
ditto, Doubleday (New York), 1922 [1925] (100 signed copies; black cloth) £600
Poor Cecco, by Margery Williams Bianco, George H. Doran (New York), 1925 (105 numbered copies signed by the author, 7 colour plates, 24 drawings; slipcase; vellum-style spine and blue boards) . . . £4,000/£3,500
ditto, George H. Doran (New York), 1925 (first trade issue with pictorial endpapers; blue cloth) . . £375/£200
ditto, George H. Doran (New York), 1925 (second trade issue with plain endpapers) . . . . £250/£100
ditto, Chatto & Windus (London), 1925 [May, 1926] (yellow cloth) . . . . £275/£150
A Road to Fairyland, by Erica Fay, Putnam (London), 1926 (colour frontispiece only; grey cloth with blue lettering) .
. . . . £250/£150
ditto, Putnams (New York), 1926 (red cloth with gilt lettering) . . . . £250/£150
The Tempest, by William Shakespeare, Heinemann (London)/Doubleday (New York), 1926 (21 colour plates, 25 drawings; olive green or grey-black cloth) £300/£150
ditto, Heinemann (London)/Doubleday (New York), 1926 (520 signed, numbered copies; vellum-style boards with vellum spine) £1,000
'Now Then', Pearson (London), 1927 (1 full-page drawing; red pictorial wraps) £100
The Lonesomest Doll, by Abbie Farwell Brown, Houghton Mifflin (Boston), 1928 (4 rose and turquoise, and 26 b&w drawings; tan pictorial cloth) . . . £500/£250
The Legend of Sleepy Hollow, by Washington Irving, Harrap (London), 1928 (8 colour and 30 b&w drawings; green cloth) . . . . . £225/£125
ditto, Harrap (London), 1928 (375 signed, numbered copies; full vellum) £1,500
ditto, Harrap (London), 1928 (publisher's special binding, grey or brown leather) £250
ditto, McKay (Philadelphia), 1928 (trade edition; brown cloth) . . . . . . £225/£125
ditto, McKay (Philadelphia), 1928 (125 signed, numbered copies; full vellum) £1,000
Not All the Truth, by Lewis Melville, Jarrolds (London), 1928 (1 b&w drawing, with other artists; light blue cloth) .
. . . . £250/£100
A New Book of Sense and Nonsense, Dent (London), 1928 (11 b&w drawings, green or orange cloth) . £250/£100
Peter Pan Retold For Little People, Hodder & Stoughton (London), 1929 (6 colour illustrations and 15 drawings within text; green or orange cloth) . . . £125/£50
ditto, Scribner's (New York), 1929 . . . . £125/£50
The Vicar of Wakefield, by Oliver Goldsmith, Harrap (London), 1929 (12 colour and 22 b&w illustrations; dark green cloth) . . . . . . £250/£100
ditto, Harrap (London), 1929 (575 signed, numbered copies; full vellum) £750
ditto, Harrap (London), 1929 (publisher's special binding; olive persian morocco) £250
ditto, McKay (Philadelphia), 1929 . . £250/£100
ditto, McKay (Philadelphia), 1929 (200 signed, numbered copies; full vellum) £750
The Outline of Literature, Newnes (London), 1930 (1 colour plate from Rip Van Winkle, with work by other artists; red or blue half leather) . . . . . . £100/£35

The Sun Princess, Shaw, [c.1930] (1 full-page drawing and 2 in text from *Queen Mab's Fairy Realm*, 1901, with work by other artists; coloured pictorial boards) . . £100/£35
The Chimes, by Charles Dickens, with an introduction by Edward Wagenknecht, Limited Editions Club (London/New York), 1931 (6 full-page and 14 smaller b&w drawings, 1,500 copies signed by the artist; tan buckram in pictorial slipcase) . . . £400/£300
The Night Before Christmas, by Clement C. Moore, Harrap (London), 1931 (4 coloured plates, 17 b&w drawings; wraps with d/w) . . . . £125/£65
ditto, Harrap (London), 1931 (275 signed, numbered copies; limp vellum in slipcase) . . . . . £1,000/£800
ditto, Lippincott (Philadelphia), 1931 (green cloth) £125/£65
ditto, Lippincott (Philadelphia), 1931 (275 signed, numbered copies; limp vellum in slipcase) . £1,000/£800
The Compleat Angler, by Izaak Walton, Harrap (London), 1931 (12 colour and 25 b&w illustrations; dark blue cloth)
. . . . £400/£200
ditto, Harrap (London), 1931 (775 signed, numbered copies; full vellum) £750
ditto, Harrap (London), 1931 (10 signed, numbered copies with signed watercolour; bound in crimson morocco) .
. . . . £17,500
ditto, Harrap (London), 1931 (publisher's special binding; dark green or brown leather) £400
ditto, McKay (Philadelphia), 1931 (grey-blue cloth) . .
. . . . £400/£200
The King of the Golden River, by John Ruskin, Harrap (London), 1932 (4 colour and 15 drawings; wraps with d/w) . . . . £100/£65
ditto, Harrap (London), 1932 (570 signed, numbered copies; limp vellum) £500
ditto, Harrap (London), 1932 (9 signed, numbered copies with original drawing; bound in full green morocco) . .
. . . . £12,500
ditto, Lippincott (Philadelphia), 1932 (red cloth with pictorial panel) . . . . £100/£65
Fairy Tales, by Hans Andersen, Harrap (London), 1932 (8 colour and 19 b&w drawings; rose-red cloth) £300/£150
ditto, Harrap (London), 1932 (525 signed, numbered copies; full vellum) £1,750
ditto, Harrap (London), 1932 (publisher's full morocco binding). £300
ditto, McKay (Philadelphia), 1932 . . . £300/£150
Oxted, Limpsfield and Neighbourhood, Lewis G Fry, editor, printed by Godwin (Oxted, Surrey), 1932 (5 b&w drawings, and head and tailpieces; slate green boards with grey-blue cloth spine) £100
Goblin Market, by Christina Rossetti, Harrap (London), 1933 (4 colour and 19 b&w illustrations; wraps with d/w)
. . . . £200/£65
ditto, Harrap (London), 1933 (400 signed, numbered copies; limp vellum, slipcase) . . . . . £750/£600
ditto, Harrap (London), 1933 (10 numbered copies with original drawing; bound in full green morocco) . £12,500
ditto, Lippincott (Philadelphia), 1933 (red boards with pictorial panel) . . . . . . £150/£65
Raggle-Taggle, by Walter Starkie, John Murray (London), 1933 (title-page drawing and frontispiece; green cloth) .
. . . . £125/£45
ditto, Dutton (New York), 1933 (green cloth) . . £125/£45
The Arthur Rackham Fairy Book, by various, Harrap (London), 1933 (8 colour and 60 b&w illustrations; red cloth) . . . . £250/£125

ditto, Harrap (London), 1933 (450 signed, numbered copies; full vellum; slipcase) . . . . . £1,000/£750

ditto, Harrap (London), 1933 (10 signed, numbered copies with original watercolour; full vellum) . . . £12,500

ditto, Lippincott (Philadelphia), 1933 (red cloth) £250/£125

River & Rainbow, by Walter Carroll, Forsyth (London), 1934 (title-page illustration; pictorial wraps) . . £150

The Old Water-Colour Society's Club, Old Water-Colour Society (London), 1934 (one plate from *The Compleat Angler*; mottled tan boards) . . . . £125/£45

The Pied Piper of Hamelin, by Robert Browning, Harrap (London), 1934 (4 colour and 14 b&w illustrations; wraps with d/w) . . . . . . £125/£50

ditto, Harrap (London), 1934 (400 signed, numbered copies; limp vellum; slipcase). . . . . £1,100/£750

ditto, Harrap (London), 1934 (10 signed, numbered copies with original illustration; full vellum) . . £12,500

ditto, Lippincott (Philadelphia), 1934 (red or green cloth with pictorial panel) . . . . . £125/£50

Spanish Raggle-Taggle, by Walter Starkie, John Murray (London), 1934 (title-page drawing and frontispiece; red cloth) . . . . . £125/£45

ditto, Dutton (New York), 1933 (red cloth) . £125/£45

English Illustration, by James Thorpe, Faber (London), 1935 (1 b&w illustration; purple cloth) . . £125/£60

Tales of Mystery and Imagination, by Edgar Allan Poe, Harrap (London), 1935 (12 colour, 17 full-page b&w and 11 small illustrations; grey-black cloth) . . £400/£250

ditto, Harrap (London), 1935 (460 signed, numbered copies; full vellum; slipcase) . . . . £2,500/£1,500

ditto, Harrap (London), 1935 (10 signed, numbered copies with original illustration; full vellum) . . £20,000

ditto, Harrap (London), 1935 (publisher's special binding; dark blue morocco) £400

ditto, Lippincott (Philadelphia), 1935 (red cloth) £400/£250

Arthur Rackham, A Bibliography, by Sarah Briggs Latimore and Grace Clark Haskell, Suttonhouse (Los Angeles, CA), 1936 (colour frontispiece and 14 b&w illustrations; turquoise cloth) . . . . £100/£60

ditto, Suttonhouse (Los Angeles, CA), 1936 (550 numbered copies; pink cloth; slipcase) . . £175/£125

Don Gypsy, by Walter Starkie, John Murray (London), 1936 (title-page drawing and frontispiece; tan cloth) . £125/£45

Peer Gynt, by Henrik Ibsen, Harrap (London), 1936 (12 colour and numerous b&w text illustrations; orange-brown cloth) . . . . £300/£150

ditto, Harrap (London), 1936 (460 signed, numbered copies; full vellum; slipcase) . . . . £1,000/£500

ditto, Harrap (London), 1936 (10 signed, numbered copies with original illustration; full vellum) . . £12,500

ditto, Harrap (London), 1936 (publisher's special binding; green morocco) £250

ditto, Lippincott (Philadelphia), 1936 (orange cloth) . . . . £300/£150

The Far Familiar, by Percy MacKaye, Richards (London), 1938 (frontispiece by Rackham; blue cloth) . £125/£45

The Wind in the Willows, by Kenneth Grahame, Limited Editions Club (New York), 1940 (16 colour plates; 2,020 copies, signed by the designer Bruce Rogers; cloth-backed patterned boards) . . . . . £650/£500

ditto, Heritage Press (New York), 1940 (12 colour plates and 14 line drawings; blue-mauve cloth) . . £125/£75

ditto, Methuen (London), 1950 (green cloth) . £175/£75

ditto, Methuen (London), 1951 (500 copies; full white calf). £1,250

'Haddon Hall Library' Titles
(illustrated by Rackham and other artists)

Wild Life in Hampshire Highlands, by George A.B. Dewar, Dent (London), 1899 . . . . £50

ditto, Dent (London), 1899 (150 numbered copies) . £125

Fly Fishing, by Sir Edward Grey, Dent (London), 1899 £75

ditto, Dent (London), 1899 (150 numbered copies) . £250

Our Gardens, by S. Reynolds Hole, Dent (London), 1899 £40

ditto, Dent (London), 1899 (150 numbered copies, signed by Hole) £150

Our Forests and Woodlands, by John Nisbet, Dent (London), 1900 . . . . £40

ditto, Dent (London), 1900 (150 numbered copies) . £125

Hunting, by J. Otho Paget, Dent (London), 1900 . £50

ditto, Dent (London), 1900 (150 numbered copies) . £175

Outdoor Games, Cricket & Golf, by Hon R.H. Lyttelton, Dent (London), 1901 . . . . . . £75

ditto, Dent (London), 1901 (150 numbered copies) . £250

Bird Watching, by Edmund Selous, Dent (London), 1901 £50

ditto, Dent (London), 1901 (150 numbered copies) . £125

Shooting, by Alexander Innes Shand, Dent (London), 1902 . . . . £50

ditto, Dent (London), 1902 (150 numbered copies) . £175

Farming, by W.M. Todd, Dent (London), 1903 . £45

ditto, Dent (London), 1903 (150 numbered copies) . £125

ANN RADCLIFFE
(b.1764 d.1823)

Despite her inability to create life-like characters, Radcliffe excelled in her descriptions of scenes of mystery and terror. The best known writer of the Gothic school, without whom there would probably be no *Frankenstein* or *Dracula*, she nevertheless rationalised most of her supernatural manifestations, until her final novel, *Gaston de Blondeville*. Her books spawned many imitators, and, famously, Jane Austen's burlesque of *The Mysteries of Udolpho* in *Northanger Abbey*.

Novels

The Castles of Athlin and Dunbayne, Hookham (London), 1789 (anonymous) £2,500

A Sicilian Romance, Hookham & Carpenter (London), 1790 (anonymous). £3,000

The Romance of the Forest, Hookham (London), 1791 (3 vols, 'By the Authoress of 'A Sicilian Romance,', &c...') £2,500

The Mysteries of Udolpho, a Romance; interspersed with some pieces of poetry, Robinson (London), 1794 (4 vols) £3,000

ditto, Samuel Etheridge (Boston), 1795 (3 vols) . £1,750

The Italian, or the Confessional of the Black Penitents, Cadell & Davies (London), 1797 (3 vols) . . £650

Gaston de Blondeville, and *St Alban's Abbey, A Metrical Tale*, Colburn (London), 1826 (4 vols) . . . £750

The Complete Novels of Ann Radcliffe, Folio Society (London), 1987 (6 vols; slipcase) £45

Poetry

The Poems of Mrs A. Radcliffe, Bounden (London), 1815 . . . . £1,000

The Poems of Mrs Ann Radcliffe, Smith (London), 1816 .
. . . . £750
The Poetical Works of Ann Radcliffe, Colburn & Bentley
(London), 1834 . . . . £500

Travel
A Journey Made in the Summer of 1794..., Robinson
(London), 1795 . . . . £1,000

AYN RAND

(b.1905 d.1982)

Ayn Rand was an American novelist and social critic, born
in Russia. *The Fountainhead* was her first novel to receive
popular attention. Through her later novels and her journal,
The Objectivist, Rand put over her beliefs that people are
rational, self-interested and pledged to individualism. *Atlas
Shrugged* suggests that socialism and even anarchy are the
inevitable results of altruism.

Fiction
We The Living, Macmillan (New York), 1936   £3,000/£350
ditto, Cassell (London), 1936   .   .   .   £1,500/£200
Anthem, Cassell (London), 1938   .   .   £3,000/£300
ditto, Pamphleteers Inc. (New York), 1946   .   .   £350
ditto, Pamphleteers Inc. (New York), 1946 (second state)   .
. . . . £175
ditto, Pamphleteers Inc. (New York), 1946 (author's binding;
50 copies) £1,000
The Fountainhead, Bobbs-Merrill (New York), 1943 (first
state, red cloth; d/w with price of $3.00 with Bobbs Merrill
titles on back) . . . . . . £3,500/£750
ditto, Bobbs-Merrill (New York), 1943 (second state, green
cloth; d/w at $3.00 with photo of author on back and
reviews). . . . . £2,500/£350
ditto, Cassell (London), 1947   .   .   .   £850/£200
Atlas Shrugged, Random House (New York), 1957   .   .
. . . . £1,000/£150
ditto, Random House (New York), 1967 (Tenth anniversary
edition, 2,000 copies signed by author) . . . £500
Night of January 16th, World Publishing Company (New
York), 1968 . . . . £50/£10
The Early Ayn Rand, New American Library (New York),
1984 . . . . £10/£5

Non-Fiction
Pola Negri, Kino-izdatel'stvo RSFSR (Moscow-Leningrad),
1925 . . . . £2,000
Hollywood: American Movie City, Kinopechat (Moscow-
Leningrad), 1926. . . . . . . £2,000
For the New Intellectual, Random House (New York), 1961
. . . . £75/£15
The Virtue of Selfishness, Signet (New York), 1964 (pbk) .
. . . . £35
ditto, New American Library, 1965 . £100/£15
The Objectivist Newsletter: Volumes 1,2,3,4, The Objectivist
Inc. New York), 1965 (first complete volume) . . £50
Capitalism: The Unknown Deal, New American Library
(New York), 1966 . . . . . . £75/£15
ditto, New American Library, 1966 (700 signed
copies) £1,000

The Romantic Manifesto, World Publishing Company
(New York), 1969) . . . . . . £65/£10
The New Left: The Anti-Industrial Revolution, Signet/New
American Library (New York), 1971 (pbk) . . . £10
Introduction to Objectivist Epistemology, Mentor, 1979 £10
ditto, New American Library, 1990 . . . . £40/£10
Philosophy: Who Needs It?, Bobbs-Merrill (New York),
1982 . . . . £50/£10
The Objectivist Newsletter: Volumes 5-10, Intellectual
Activist (New York), 1986 (complete volume) . . £50
The Voice of Reason, New American Library (New York),
1989 . . . . £10/£5
The Ayn Rand Column, Second Renaissance (New York),
1991 . . . . £10/£5
Letters of Ayn Rand, Button (New York), 1995 . £20/£10
Journals of Ayn Rand, Dutton (New York), 1997. £20/£10
The Ayn Rand Reader, Plume (New York), 1999 (pbk) £5
Russian Writings on Hollywood, Ayn Rand Institute Press
(New York), 1999) (pbk) £10
The Art of Fiction, Plume (New York), 2000 (pbk) . £10
The Art of Nonfiction, Plume (New York), 2001 (pbk). £10

IAN RANKIN

(b.1960)

A Scottish crime writer who has lost his cult status as he
has become more successful, Rankin's novels are vivid
portrayals of contemporary Edinburgh life. He has won two
Crime Writers Association Daggers for his short stories and
in 1997 their Gold Dagger for *Black & Blue*. He won the
Edgar in 2004 for *Resurrection Men*. He was awarded an
O.B.E. in 2002.

'Rebus' Novels
Knots & Crosses, Bodley Head (London), 1987 . £850/£75
ditto, Doubleday (Garden City, NY), 1987 . . £400/£40
Hide & Seek, Barrie & Jenkins (London), 1991 .£225/£25
ditto, Barrie & Jenkins (London), 1991 (400 proof copies;
pbk) £100
ditto, Penzler Books (New York), [1994] . . £50/£10
Wolfman, Century (London), 1992 . . . .£275/£50
ditto, Arrow (London), 1993 (pbk) £10
ditto, as *Tooth & Nail*, Orion (London), 1998 (pbk) . £5
Strip Jack, Orion (London), 1992 . . . .£400/£30
ditto, Orion (London), 1992 (500 proof copies; pbk) .£125
ditto, St Martin's Press (New York), 1994 . £200/£25
The Black Book, Orion (London), 1993 . . .£100/£10
ditto, Penzler Books (New York), 1994 . . . £45/£10
Mortal Causes, Orion (London), 1994 . . .£100/£10
ditto, Simon & Schuster (New York), 1995 . . £15/£5
Let It Bleed, Orion (London), 1995 . . . .£400/£50
ditto, Simon & Schuster (New York), 1996 . £65/£10
Black & Blue, Orion (London), 1997 . . .£200/£30
ditto, St Martin's Press (New York), 1997 . £20/£5
The Hanging Garden, Orion (London), 1998. . £5/£5
ditto, Scorpion Press (Blakeney, Glos), 1998 (75 signed,
numbered copies) £75
ditto, Scorpion Press (Blakeney, Glos), 1998 (15 signed,
lettered copies) £250
ditto, St Martin's Press (New York), 1998 . . £10/£5
Dead Souls, Orion (London), 1999 . . . . £15/£5
ditto, St Martin's Press (New York), 1999 . . £10/£5

Set in Darkness, Orion (London), 2000 . . . £10/£5
ditto, St Martin's Press (New York), 2000 . £10/£5
The Falls, Orion (London), 2001 . . . £10/£5
ditto, St Martin's Press (New York), 2001 . £10/£5
Resurrection Men, Orion (London), 2001 . £10/£5
ditto, Little, Brown (Boston), 2003 . . . £10/£5
A Question of Blood, Orion (London), 2003 . £10/£5
ditto, Scorpion Press (Gladestry, Powys), 2003 (90 signed, numbered copies) £75
ditto, Scorpion Press (Gladestry, Powys), 2003 (15 signed, lettered copies) £250
ditto, Little, Brown (Boston), 2003 . . . £10/£5
Fleshmarket Close, Orion (London), 2004 . £10/£5
ditto, Scorpion Press (Gladestry, Powys), 2003 (80 signed, numbered copies) £90
ditto, as *Fleshmarket Alley*, Little, Brown (Boston), 2005 . . . . £10/£5
The Naming of the Dead, Orion (London), 2006 £10/£5
ditto, Scorpion Press (Gladestry, Powys), 2006 (80 signed, numbered copies) £75
ditto, Little, Brown (Boston), 2007 . . . £10/£5
Exit Music, Orion (London), 2007 . . . £10/£5
ditto, Little, Brown (Boston), 2008 . . . £10/£5

Novellas and Short Stories
A Good Hanging & Other Stories, Century (London), 1992 . . . . £90/£20
ditto, St Martin's Press (New York), 2002 . £15/£5
Herbert in Motion & Other Stories, Revolver (London), 1997 (200 numbered, signed copies; pbk) . . £100
Death Is Not the End, Orion (London), 1998 . £10/£5
ditto, St Martin's Press (New York), 2000 . £10/£5
Beggars Banquet, Orion (London), 2002 . . £10/£5
ditto, Scorpion Press (Gladestry, Powys), 2002 (99 signed, numbered copies) £75
Complete Short Stories, Orion (London), 2006 £15/£5

Other Novels
The Flood, Polygon (Edinburgh, Scotland), 1986 . . . . £1,000/£145
ditto, Polygon (Edinburgh, Scotland), 1986 (pbk) . £125
Watchman, Bodley Head (London), 1988 . £450/£30
ditto, Doubleday (New York), 1991 . . . £15/£5
Westwind, Barrie & Jenkins (London), 1990 . £125/£15
Doors Open, Orion (London), 2008 . . . £10/£5
ditto, Scorpion Press (Gladestry, Powys), 2008 (80 signed, numbered copies) £75
ditto, Little, Brown (Boston), 2010 . . . £10/£5
The Complaints, Orion (London), 2009 . . £10/£5

Novels Written as 'Jack Harvey'
Witch Hunt, Headline (London), 1993 . . £300/£35
ditto, Little, Brown (Boston), 2004 . . . £10/£5
Bleeding Hearts, Headline (London), 1994 . £500/£45
ditto, Little, Brown (Boston), 2006 . . . £10/£5
Blood Hunt, Headline (London), 1995 . £600/£50
ditto, Little, Brown (Boston), 2006 . . . £10/£5

Graphic Novel
Dark Entries, Titan (London), 2009 (no d/w) . . . £10
ditto, Vertigo (New York), 2009 (no d/w). . . . £10

ARTHUR RANSOME
(b.1884 d.1967)

Arthur Ransome was the British author of the much loved 'Swallows and Amazons' series of books which tell of the boating adventures of a group of children in their school holidays in the Lake District and the Norfolk Broads. He was the first winner of the Carnegie Medal for children's literature, awarded for *Pigeon Post* in 1936. He also wrote for adults.

'Swallows and Amazons' Titles
Swallows and Amazons, Cape (London), 1930 £5,000/£750
ditto, Cape (London), 1931 (illustrated by Clifford Webb) . . . . £1,250/£75
ditto, Lippincott (Philadelphia), 1931 . . £500/£45
Swallowdale, Cape (London), 1931 . . £2,500/£350
ditto, Lippincott (Philadelphia), 1932 . . £200/£35
Peter Duck, Cape (London), 1932 . . £1,250/£150
ditto, Lippincott (Philadelphia), 1933 . . £200/£35
Winter Holiday, Cape (London), 1933 . £1,250/£150
ditto, Lippincott (Philadelphia), [1934] . . £200/£35
Coot Club, Cape (London), 1934 . . £1,250/£150
ditto, Lippincott (Philadelphia), 1935 . . £200/£35
Pigeon Post, Cape (London), 1936 . . . £500/£75
ditto, Lippincott (Philadelphia), 1937 . . £150/£35
We Didn't Mean to Go to Sea, Cape (London), 1937 . .
. . . . £375/£45
ditto, Macmillan (New York), 1938 . . . £150/£35
Secret Water, Cape (London), 1939 . . . £300/£35
ditto, Macmillan (New York), 1940 . . . £150/£35
The Big Six, Cape (London), 1940 . . . £300/£35
ditto, Macmillan (New York), 1941 . . . £150/£30
Missee Lee, Cape (London), 1941 . . . £300/£35
ditto, Macmillan (New York), 1942 . . . £150/£30
The Picts and the Martyrs, or Not Welcome At All, Cape (London), 1943 . . . . £150/£30
ditto, Macmillan (New York), 1943 . . . £125/£25
Great Northern?, Cape (London), 1947 . . . £150/£30
ditto, Macmillan (New York), 1948 . . . £125/£25

Other Children's Titles
Pond and Stream, Treherne (London), 1906 . . £250
The Child's Book of the Seasons, Treherne (London), 1906
. . . . £250
The Things in Our Garden, Treherne (London), 1906 . £250
Highways and Byways in Fairyland, Alston Rivers, Pinafore Library (London), [1906] £200
The Imp and the Elf and the Ogre, Nisbet (London), 1910 .
. . . . £175
The Hoofmarks of the Faun, Martin Secker (London), 1911
. . . . £150
Old Peter's Russian Tales, T.C. & E.C. Jack (London), 1916
. . . . £150
ditto, Nelson (New York), [1938] . . . . £75/£25
Aladdin and His Wonderful Lamp, Nisbet (London), [1919]
. . . . £250
ditto, Nisbet (London), [1919] (250 signed copies). £1,000
ditto, Brentano's (New York), 1920 . . . £300/£200

Adult Titles
The Souls of the Streets, Brown Langham (London), 1904 .
. . . . £400

The ABC of Physical Culture, Drane (London), 1904
(published as by 'A.M. Ransome') £75
The Stone Lady, Brown Langham (London), 1905. . £125
Bohemia in London, Chapman & Hall (London), 1907. £100
ditto, Dodd, Mead (New York), 1907 . . . . £75
A History of Storytelling, T.C. & E.C. Jack (London), 1909
. . . . £125
Edgar Allan Poe, Secker (London), 1910. . . . £90
ditto, Mitchell Kennerley (New York), 1910 . . . £65
Oscar Wilde, Secker (London), 1912. . . . . £125
ditto, Mitchell Kennerley (New York), 1912 . . . £50
Portraits and Speculations, Macmillan (London), 1913 £20
The Elixir of Life, Methuen (London), 1915 . . . £100
The Truth About Russia, New Republic (London), 1918
(stapled wraps) £100
Six Weeks in Russia in 1919, Allen & Unwin (London),
1919 (wraps). £100
ditto, Huebsch (New York), 1919 (cloth) £35
The Soldier and Death: A Russian Folk Tale Told in
English, J. C. Wilson (London), 1920 (sewn wraps) . £50
ditto, Huebsch (New York), 1922 . . . . £75/£20
The Crisis in Russia, Allen & Unwin (London), 1921 £40/£15
ditto, Huebsch (New York), 1921 . . . . £40/£15
Racundra's First Cruise, Allen & Unwin (London), 1923 .
. . . . £500/£150
ditto, Huebsch (New York), 1923 . . . . £300/£75
The Chinese Puzzle, Allen & Unwin (London), 1927 . .
. . . . £400/£125
ditto, Houghton Mifflin (Boston), 1927 . . £300/£100
Rod and Line, Cape (London), 1929 . . . £500/£145
Mainly About Fishing, A. & C. Black (London), 1959. .
. . . . £85/£30
The Autobiography of Arthur Ransome, Cape (London),
1976 . . . . £25/£5

SIMON RAVEN

(b.1927 d.2001)

Simon Raven was an English novelist, essayist and
dramatist who was said to have had 'the mind of a cad and
the pen of an angel'. He is remembered and collected
principally for his 'Alms for Oblivion' series of novels
which have been compared to Anthony Powell's 'Dance to
the Music of Time' sequence.

Alms for Oblivion
The Rich Pay Late, Blond (London), 1964 . . £65/£10
ditto, Putnam's (New York), 1965 . . . . £25/£10
Friends in Low Places, Blond (London), 1965 . £30/£5
ditto, Putnam's (New York), 1966 . . . . £25/£10
The Sabre Squadron, Blond (London), 1966 . . £25/£5
ditto, Harper & Row (New York), 1967 . . . £20/£5
Fielding Gray, Blond (London), 1967 . . . £30/£10
ditto, Beaufort Books (New York), 1985 . . . £10/£5
The Judas Boy, Blond (London), 1968 . . . £25/£5
Places Where They Sing, Blond (London), 1970 . £75/£15
Sound the Retreat, Blond (London), 1971 . £75/£15
ditto, Beaufort Books (New York), 1986 . . . £10/£5
Come Like Shadows, Blond & Briggs (London), 1972 £15/£5
Bring Forth The Body, Blond & Briggs (London), 1974 .
. . . . £25/£5
The Survivors, Blond & Briggs (London), 1976 . £20/£5

'The First Born of Egypt'
Morning Star, Blond & Briggs (London), 1984 . £15/£5
The Face of the Waters, Blond (London), 1985 . £15/£5
Before the Cock Crow, Muller, Blond and White (London),
1986 . . . . £15/£5
New Seed for Old, Muller (London), 1988 . . £15/£5
Blood of My Bone, Muller (London), 1989 . . £20/£5
In the Image of God, Muller (London), 1990 . . £35/£10
The Troubadour, Hutchinson (London), 1992 . £40/£10

Other Novels
The Feathers of Death, Blond (London), 1959 . £50/£10
ditto, Simon & Schuster (New York), 1960 . . £15/£5
Brother Cain, Blond (London), 1959 . . . £35/£5
ditto, Simon & Schuster (New York), 1960 . . £15/£5
Doctors Wear Scarlet, Blond (London), 1960 . . £35/£5
ditto, Simon & Schuster (New York), 1961 . . £10/£5
Close of Play, Blond (London), 1962 . . . £30/£10
The Roses of Picardie, Blond & Briggs (London), 1980
. . . . £20/£5
An Inch of Fortune, Blond & Briggs (London), 1980 £10/£5
September Castle: A Tale of Love, Blond & Briggs
(London), 1983 . . . . £10/£5
The Islands of Sorrow, The Winged Lion (London), 1994 .
. . . . £25/£5

Short Stories
The Fortunes of Fingel, Blond & Briggs (London), 1976 .
. . . . £20/£5
Remember Your Grammar and Other Haunted Stories, The
Winged Lion (Broze, France), 1997 . . . £30/£10

Others
The English Gentleman, Blond (London), 1961 . £40/£10
Boys Will Be Boys, Blond (London), 1963 . . £35/£10
The Royal Foundation and Other Plays, Blond (London),
1966 . . . . £25/£5
Shadows on the Grass, Blond (London), 1982 . £15/£5
The Old School, Hamilton (London), 1986 . . £10/£5
The Old Gang, Hamilton (London), 1988. . . £10/£5
Bird of Ill Omen, Hamilton (London), 1989 . £15/£5
Is There Anybody There? Said the Traveller, Muller
(London), 1991 . . . . £45/£10

MARJORIE KINNAN
RAWLINGS

(b.1896 d.1953)

Marjorie Kinnan Rawlings was an American author who
wrote novels with rural themes and backgrounds. Her best
known work, *The Yearling*, about a boy who adopts an
orphaned fawn but has to kill it because it destroys the
family's crops. The book became a bestseller and won the
Pulitzer Prize for fiction in 1939. It is now considered a
classic of young-adult fiction.

South Moon Under, Charles Scribner's Sons (New York/
London), 1933. (Scribner's 'A' and seal on copyright page;
first printing p.184, line 20 describes the alligator: 'The big
bull was all of thirty feet'). . . . . £600/£100
ditto, Faber & Faber (London), 1933 . . . . £350/£60

Golden Apples, Charles Scribner's Sons (New York), 1935 (Scribner's 'A' and seal on copyright page) . . £350/£60

ditto, William Heinemann (London/Toronto), 1939 £200/£25

The Yearling, Charles Scribner's Sons (New York), 1938 (Scribner's 'A' and seal on copyright page; first issue d/w does not mention the Pulitzer Prize) . . £350/£45

ditto, William Heinemann (London/Toronto), 1938 £200/£25

ditto, Charles Scribner's Sons (New York), 1939 (770 copies signed by the author and the illustrator N.C. Wyeth; 'Pulitzer Prize Limited Edition'; slipcase) £1,500/£1,250

When the Whippoorwill, Charles Scribner's Sons (New York), 1940 (Scribner's 'A' and seal on copyright page) . . . . £250/£50

ditto, William Heinemann (London/Toronto), 1940 £125/£25

Cross Creek, Charles Scribner's Sons (New York), 1942 (first edition, first printing; Scribner 'A' on copyright page but no Scribner seal; d/w priced $2.50 in red on front flap; no stain on page top edge). . . . . . £350/£75

ditto, Charles Scribner's Sons (New York), 1942 (first edition, second printing (Book-of-the-Month Club issue); as above but no printed price on front flap of d/w) £15/£5

ditto, William Heinemann (London/Toronto), 1942 (first state binding light green calico-textures cloth; light brown/grey uncoated endpapers) . . . £75/£15

ditto, William Heinemann (London/Toronto), 1942 (second state binding light blue/green cloth; light brown uncoated endpapers) . . . . £60/£5

ditto, South Moon Books (Jacksonville, FL), 1992 (1,000 copies signed by Philip S. May, Jr; d/w) . . £30/£20

ditto, South Moon Books (Jacksonville, FL), 1992 (200 numbered copies signed by Norton Baskin, Dessie Smith Prescott, Idella Parker and Jake Glisson; in green cloth box) . . . . £100/£75

ditto, South Moon Books (Jacksonville, FL), 1992 (26 lettered copies signed by Norton Baskin, Dessie Smith Prescott, Idella Parker and Jake Glisson; in green cloth box) . . . . £200/£150

Cross Creek Cookery, Charles Scribner's Sons (New York), 1942 (first edition, first issue; Scribner's 'A' on copyright page, but no Scribner's seal; pictorial calico-textured cloth matching d/w; pictorial endpapers). . . £100/£20

ditto, Charles Scribner's Sons (New York), 1942 (first edition, second issue; tan cloth, white endpapers) £35/£5

ditto, as *The Marjorie Kinnan Rawlings Cookbook: Cross Creek Cookery*, Hammond, Hammond & Co (London), 1960 . . . . £45/£10

Jacob's Ladder, Univ of Miami Press (Coral Gables, FL), 1950 . . . . £500/£100

The Sojourner, Charles Scribner's Sons (New York), 1953 (Scribner's 'A' and seal on copyright page) . . £40/£5

ditto, Charles Scribner's Sons (New York), 1953 (600 numbered copies signed on a tipped-in leaf; d/w) . . . . £300/£250

ditto, William Heinemann (London/Toronto), 1953 £30/£5

Gal Young Un And Other Famous Stories of the Cross Creek Country, Bantam Books (New York), 1954 (pbk) £15

The Secret River, Charles Scribner's Sons (New York), 1955 (Scribner's 'A' on copyright page, but no seal) . £200/£20

The Marjorie Rawlings Reader, Charles Scribner's Sons (New York), 1956 ('A-9.56[H]' on copyright page) . . . . £75/£15

Selected Letters of Marjorie Kinnan Rawlings, Univ of Florida Presses (Gainesville, FL), 1983 . . £45/£10

An Address Delivered by Marjorie Kinnan Rawlings at the Dedication of the New Addition to the University of Florida Library…, Univ of Florida Libraries (Gainesville, FL), 1991 (wraps) £10

Short Stories, Univ of Florida Presses (Gainesville/ Tallahassee etc), 1994 . . . . . £30/£10

ditto, Univ of Florida Presses (Gainesville/Tallahassee etc), 1994 (pbk) £10

Songs of a Housewife: Poems, Univ Press of Florida (Gainesville, FL), 1997 . . . . . £30/£5

Blood of My Blood, Univ Press of Florida (Gainesville, FL), 2002 . . . . £20/£5

FORREST REID

(b.1875 d.1947)

Reid was a novelist, literary critic and translator whose evocations of youth and his native Ulster landscape are tinged with the supernatural. Reid also translated poems from the Greek, and his study of W.B. Yeats has been acclaimed as one of the best critical appreciations of the poet.

Novels

The Kingdom of Twilight, Fisher Unwin (London), 1904 . . . . £300

The Garden God, David Nutt (London), 1905. . . £800

The Bracknels, Edward Arnold (London), 1911 . . £100

ditto, as *Denis Bracknel*, Faber (London), 1947 (revised edition) . . . . £30/£10

Following Darkness, Edward Arnold (London), 1912 . £150

The Gentle Lover, Edward Arnold (London), 1913 . £200

At the Door of the Gate, Edward Arnold (London), 1915 . . . . £150

The Spring Song, Edward Arnold (London), 1916. . £150

ditto, Houghton Mifflin (Boston), 1917 . . . £100

Pirates of the Spring, Talbot Press/Fisher Unwin (London), 1919 [1920] £125

ditto, Houghton Mifflin (Boston), 1920 . . £200/£75

Pender Among the Residents, Collins (London), 1922 . . . . £250/£125

ditto, Houghton Mifflin (Boston), 1923 . . . £200/£75

Demophon, Collins (London), 1927 . . . £200/£75

Uncle Stephen, Faber (London), 1931 . . £65/£20

Brian Westby, Faber (London), 1934. . . £65/£20

The Retreat, Faber (London), 1936 . . . £65/£20

Peter Waring, Faber (London), 1937. . . £65/£20

Young Tom, Faber (London), 1944 . . . £40/£10

Tom Barber, Pantheon (New York), 1955 (contains *Uncle Stephen*, *Young Tom* and *The Retreat*) . . . £25/£5

Short Stories

A Garden by the Sea, Talbot Press/Fisher Unwin (London), 1918 . . . . £60

Others

W.B. Yeats, A Critical Study, Secker (London), 1915 . £75

ditto, Dodd, Mead (New York), 1915 . . . . £65

Apostate, Constable (London), 1926 (50 signed copies) £300

ditto, Constable (London), 1926 . . . . £75/£20

ditto, Houghton Mifflin (Boston), 1926 . . £60/£20

ditto, Faber (London), 1947 (engravings by Reynolds Stone) . . . . £75/£20

Illustrators of the Sixties, Faber & Gwyer (London), 1928 .
.   .   .   .   .   .   £125/£75
Walter de la Mare, A Critical Study, Faber (London), 1929.
.   .   .   .   .   .   £50/£20
ditto, Holt (New York), 1929   .   .   .   £45/£15
Private Road, Faber (London), 1940 .   .   £45/£15
Retrospective Adventures, Faber (London), 1941 . £35/£10
Notes and Impressions, The Mourne Press (Newcastle, Co.
Down), 1942. .   .   .   .   .£150/£50
Poems from the Greek Anthology, Faber (London), 1943 .
.   .   .   .   .   .   £25/£5
The Milk of Paradise, Faber (London), 1946 .   £25/£5
The Suppressed Dedication and Envoy of The Garden God,
D'Arch Smith (London), [1970's?] (105 numbered copies;
wraps) £45

RUTH RENDELL

(b.1930)

A novelist and short story writer, Rendell is popularly
known for the 'Wexford' detective stories and novels. Her
other fiction explores wider issues of criminal maladjust-
ment, while the 'Barbara Vine' books investigate darker
psychological motivation. She has received many awards
for her writing, was made a C.B.E. in 1996 and a life peer
in 1997. She sits in the House of Lords as a Labour baroness.

'Wexford' Novels

From Doon with Death, Long (London), 1964   .   .
.   .   .   .   .   £2,000/£150
ditto, Doubleday (New York), 1965   .   .   .£350/£30
A New Lease of Death, Long (London), 1967 .   .£750/£45
ditto, Doubleday (New York), 1967   .   .   .£150/£15
ditto, as *Sins of the Fathers*, Ballantine (New York), 1970
(pbk) £5
Wolf to the Slaughter, Long (London), 1967 . £2,250/£100
ditto, Doubleday (New York), 1968 .   .   .£150/£15
The Best Man to Die, Long (London), 1969 .   .£600/£40
ditto, Doubleday (New York), 1970 .   .   .£60/£10
A Guilty Thing Surprised, Hutchinson (London), 1970 .
.   .   .   .   .   .£350/£25
ditto, Doubleday (New York), 1970 .   .   .£60/£10
No More Dying, Then, Hutchinson (London), 1971   .
.   .   .   .   .   .£175/£25
ditto, Doubleday (New York), 1972 .   .   .£35/£10
Murder Being Once Done, Hutchinson (London), 1972 .
.   .   .   .   .   .£150/£15
ditto, Doubleday (New York), 1972   .   .   .£35/£10
Some Lie and Some Die, Hutchinson (London), 1973 .
.   .   .   .   .   .£150/£15
ditto, Doubleday (New York), 1973 .   .   .£30/£10
Shake Hands for Ever, Hutchinson (London), 1975   .
.   .   .   .   .   .£125/£15
ditto, Doubleday (New York), 1975 .   .   .£30/£10
A Sleeping Life, Hutchinson (London), 1978 .   £65/£5
ditto, Doubleday (New York), 1978   .   .   £15/£5
Put on by Cunning, Hutchinson (London), 1981   £50/£5
ditto, as *Death Notes*, Pantheon (New York), 1981.   £10/£5
The Speaker of Mandarin, Hutchinson (London), 1983   .
.   .   .   .   .   £30/£5
ditto, Pantheon (New York), 1983   .   .   £10/£5

An Unkindness of Ravens, Hutchinson (London), 1985   .
.   .   .   .   £25/£5
ditto, Pantheon (New York), 1985   .   .   £10/£5
The Veiled One, Hutchinson (London), 1988 .   £20/£5
ditto, Pantheon (New York), 1988   .   .   £10/£5
Kissing the Gunner's Daughter, Hutchinson (London), 1992
.   .   .   .   £15/£5
ditto, Mysterious Press (New York), 1992   .   £10/£5
Simisola, Hutchinson (London), 1994   .   £15/£5
ditto, Crown (New York), 1995 .   .   .   £10/£5
Road Rage, Hutchinson (London), 1997 .   .   £15/£5
ditto, Scorpion Press (Blakeney, Gloucestershire), 1997 (99
signed copies) £65
ditto, Crown (New York), 1997 .   .   .   £10/£5
ditto, Franklin Library (Franklin Centre, PA), 1997 (signed,
limited edition) £40
Harm Done, Hutchinson (London), 1999.   .   £15/£5
ditto, Scorpion Press (Blakeney, Gloucestershire), 1999 (99
signed, numbered copies) £65
ditto, Scorpion Press (Blakeney, Gloucestershire), 1999 (15
signed, lettered copies) £200
ditto, Crown (New York), 1999 .   .   .   £10/£5
Babes in the Wood, Hutchinson (London), 2002 .   £10/£5
ditto, Crown (New York), 2003 .   .   .   £10/£5
End in Tears, Hutchinson (London), 2005   .   £10/£5
ditto, Crown (New York), 2005 .   .   .   £10/£5
Not in the Flesh, Hutchinson (London), 2007.   .   £10/£5
ditto, Crown (New York), 2007 .   .   .   £10/£5
The Monster in the Box, Hutchinson (London), 2009 £10/£5
ditto, Scribner (New York), 2009   .   .   .   £10/£5

Omnibus Editions

Wexford: An Omnibus, Hutchinson (London), 1988 £20/£5
A Second Wexford Omnibus, Hutchinson (London), 1988 .
.   .   .   .   £15/£5
The Third Wexford Omnibus, Hutchinson (London), 1989 .
.   .   .   .   £10/£5
The Fourth Wexford Omnibus, Hutchinson (London), 1990
.   .   .   .   £10/£5
The Fifth Wexford Omnibus, Hutchinson (London), 1991 .
.   .   .   .   £10/£5

Other Novels

To Fear a Painted Devil, Long (London), 1965   .£800/£75
ditto, Doubleday (New York), 1965   .   .   .£150/£15
Vanity Dies Hard, Long (London), 1965 .   .£750/£45
ditto, as *In Sickness and in Health*, Doubleday (New York),
1966   .   .   .   .£250/£45
The Secret House of Death, Long (London), 1968. £650/£45
ditto, Doubleday (New York), 1969 .   .   .£100/£15
One Across, Two Down, Hutchinson (London), 1971 .
.   .   .   .   .£250/£25
ditto, Doubleday (New York), 1971   .   .   .£65/£10
The Face of Trespass, Hutchinson (London), 1974 £150/£15
ditto, Doubleday (New York), 1974   .   .   £25/£10
A Demon in My View, Hutchinson (London), 1976 £75/£10
ditto, Doubleday (New York), 1977   .   .   £25/£10
A Judgement in Stone, Hutchinson (London), 1977   .
.   .   .   .   .£100/£10
ditto, Doubleday (New York), 1978 .   .   .   £25/£5
Make Death Love Me, Hutchinson (London), 1979 £40/£10
ditto, Doubleday (New York), 1979   .   .   £25/£5
The Lake of Darkness, Hutchinson (London), 1980 £25/£10
ditto, Doubleday (New York), 1980 .   .   .   £10/£5

Master of the Moor, Hutchinson (London), 1981 . £20/£5
ditto, Pantheon (New York), 1982 . . . . £10/£5
The Killing Doll, Hutchinson (London), 1984 . £20/£5
ditto, Pantheon (New York), 1984 . . . . £10/£5
The Tree of Hands, Hutchinson (London), 1984 . £20/£5
ditto, Pantheon (New York), 1984 . . . . £10/£5
Live Flesh, Hutchinson (London), 1986 . . £20/£5
ditto, Pantheon (New York), 1986 . . . . £10/£5
A Dark-Adapted Eye, Viking (London), 1986 (pseud 'Barbara Vine') . . . . £20/£5
ditto, Bantam (New York), 1986 . . . . £10/£5
A Fatal Inversion, Viking (London), 1987 (pseud 'Barbara Vine') . . . . £15/£5
ditto, Bantam (New York), 1987 . . . . £10/£5
Heartstones, Hutchinson (London), 1987 (illustrated by George Underwood) . . . . . . £15/£5
ditto, Harper (New York), 1987 . . . . £10/£5
Talking to Strange Men, Hutchinson (London), 1987 £15/£5
ditto, Pantheon (New York), 1987 . . . . £10/£5
The House of Stairs, Viking (London), 1988 (pseud 'Barbara Vine') . . . . . . £15/£5
ditto, Crown (New York), 1989 . . . . £10/£5
The Bridesmaid, Hutchinson (London), 1989 . £15/£5
ditto, Mysterious Press (New York), 1989 . £10/£5
Gallowglass, Viking (London), 1990 (pseud 'Barbara Vine')
. . . . £15/£5
ditto, Crown (New York), 1990 . . . . £10/£5
Going Wrong, Hutchinson (London), 1990 . £15/£5
ditto, Mysterious Press (New York), 1990 . £10/£5
King Solomon's Carpet, Viking (London), 1991 (pseud 'Barbara Vine') . . . . . . £15/£5
ditto, Crown (New York), 1992 . . . . £10/£5
Asta's Book, Viking (London), 1993 (pseud 'Barbara Vine')
. . . . £15/£5
ditto, Scorpion Press (Bristol, UK), 1993 (99 signed, numbered copies) £75
ditto, Scorpion Press (Bristol, UK), 1993 (20 signed, lettered copies) £250
ditto, as *Anna's Book*, Harmony (New York), 1993 £10/£5
The Crocodile Bird, Hutchinson (London), 1993 . £10/£5
ditto, London Limited Editions (London), 1993 (150 signed copies, glassine d/w) . . . . £50/£40
ditto, Crown (New York), 1993 . . . . £10/£5
No Night is Too Long, Viking (London), 1994 (pseud 'Barbara Vine') . . . . . . £10/£5
ditto, Harmony (New York), 1994 . . . . £10/£5
The Brimstone Wedding, Harmony (New York), 1995 (pseud 'Barbara Vine') . . . . £10/£5
ditto, Viking (London), 1996 . . . . £10/£5
The Keys to the Street, Hutchinson (London), 1996 £10/£5
ditto, Crown (New York), 1996 . . . . £10/£5
The Chimney Sweeper's Boy, Viking (London), 1998 (pseud 'Barbara Vine') . . . . £10/£5
ditto, Harmony (New York), 1998 . . . . £10/£5
A Sight for Sore Eyes, Hutchinson (London), 1998 £10/£5
ditto, Crown (New York), 1998 . . . . £10/£5
ditto, Scorpion Press (Blakeney, Gloucestershire, 1998 (99 signed copies) £65
Grasshopper, Harmony (New York), 2000 (pseud 'Barbara Vine') . . . . £10/£5
ditto, Viking (London), 2000 . . . . £10/£5
Adam and Eve and Pinch Me, Hutchinson (London), 2001.
. . . . £10/£5
ditto, Crown (New York), 2001 . . . . £10/£5

The Blood Doctor, Viking (London), 2002 (pseud 'Barbara Vine') . . . . £10/£5
ditto, Shaye Areheart Books (New York), 2002 . £10/£5
The Rottweiler, Hutchinson (London), 2003 . £10/£5
ditto, Crown (New York), 2004 . . . . £10/£5
Thirteen Steps Down, Hutchinson (London), 2004. £10/£5
ditto, Crown (New York), 2005 . . . . £10/£5
The Minotaur, Viking (London), 2005 (pseud 'Barbara Vine') . . . . £10/£5
ditto, Shaye Areheart Books (New York), 2005 . £10/£5
The Water's Lovely, Hutchinson (London), 2006 . £10/£5
ditto, Crown (New York), 2007 . . . . £10/£5
Portobello, Hutchinson (London), 2008 . . £10/£5

Short Stories
The Fallen Curtain and Other Stories, Hutchinson (London), 1976 . . . . £100/£25
ditto, Doubleday (New York), 1976 . . . £50/£15
Means of Evil and Other Stories, Hutchinson (London), 1979 . . . . £65/£10
ditto, Doubleday (New York), 1980 . . . £30/£5
The Fever Tree and Other Stories, Hutchinson (London), 1982 . . . . £40/£10
ditto, Pantheon (New York), 1983 . . . £20/£5
The New Girlfriend and Other Stories, Hutchinson (London), 1985 . . . . £20/£5
ditto, Pantheon (New York), 1986 . . . £10/£5
Three Cases for Chief Inspector Wexford, Eurographica (Helsinki), 1986 (350 signed, numbered copies, wraps) £60
Collected Short Stories, Hutchinson (London), 1987 £10/£5
ditto, as *Collected Stories*, Pantheon (New York), 1988 .
. . . . £10/£5
Unguarded Hours, Pandora Press (London), 1990 (contains 'The Strawberry Tree' by Rendell, and 'Flesh and Grass' by Helen Simpson) . . . . . . £10/£5
The Copper Peacock and Other Stories, Hutchinson (London), 1991 . . . . £15/£5
ditto, Mysterious Press (New York), 1991 . £10/£5
Blood Lines: Long and Short Stories, Hutchinson (London), 1995 . . . . £10/£5
ditto, Crown (New York), 1996 . . . . £10/£5
Piranha to Scurfy and Other Stories, Hutchinson (London), 2000 . . . . £10/£5
ditto, Crown (New York), 2002 . . . . £10/£5
The Thief, Arrow (Londo), 2006 (pbk) . . . £5
Collected Stories 2, Hutchinson (London), 2008 (pbk) . £5

Non-Fiction
Matters of Suspense, Eurographica (Helsinki), 1986 (350 signed, numbered copies, wraps) . . £50
Ruth Rendell's Suffolk, Muller (London), 1989 (photographs by Paul Bowden) . . . . . £25/£5
Undermining the Central Line, Chatto & Windus (London), 1989 (with Colin Ward, signed; pbk) . . . £25
ditto, Chatto & Windus (London), 1989 (unsigned copies) .
. . . . £10

JOHN RHODE/
MILES BURTON

(b.1884 d.1964)

Major Cecil Street wrote detective fiction under the
pseudonyms John Rhode and Miles Burton. As 'Rhode' he
tells how Dr Lancelot Priestley solved some 77 crimes,
usually with sheer brainpower rather than action, and as
'Burton' we follow the exploits of the rather more active
detective Desmond Merrion.

Novels as 'John Rhode'

A.S.F.: The Story of a Great Conspiracy, Bles (London),
1924   .   .   .   .   .   £2,250/£200
ditto, as *The White Menace*, McBride (New York), 1926.   .
.   .   .   .   £350/£75
The Double Florin, Bles (London), 1924   .   £1,750/£150
The Alarm, Bles (London), 1925.   .   .   £1,650/£150
The Paddington Mystery, Bles (London), 1925   £2,500/£250
Dr. Priestley's Quest, Bles (London), 1926   .   £2,650/£250
The Ellerby Case, Bles (London), 1927   .   £2,250/£200
ditto, Dodd, Mead (New York), 1927   .   .   £350/£75
The Murders in Praed Street, Bles (London), [1928]   .   .
.   .   .   .   £2,250/£200
ditto, Dodd, Mead (New York), 1928   .   .   £350/£75
Tragedy at the Unicorn, Bles (London), [1928]   £2,000/£200
ditto, Dodd, Mead (New York), 1928   .   .   £350/£75
The House on Tollard Ridge, Bles (London), 1929.   .
.   .   .   .   £2,000/£200
ditto, Dodd, Mead (New York), 1929   .   .   £250/£65
The Davidson Case, Bles (London), [1929]   .   £2,000/£175
ditto, as *Murder at Bratton Grange*, Dodd, Mead (New
York), 1929   .   .   .   .   .   £250/£65
Peril at Cranbury Hall, Bles (London), 1930   .   £1,500/£100
ditto, Dodd, Mead (New York), 1930   .   .   £250/£65
Pinehurst, Bles (London), 1930   .   .   £1,250/£125
ditto, as *Dr Priestley Investigates*, Dodd, Mead (New York),
1930   .   .   .   .   .   .   £250/£65
Tragedy on the Line, Collins Crime Club 1931   £2,000/£150
ditto, Dodd, Mead (New York), 1931   .   .   £250/£65
The Hanging Woman, Collins Crime Club (London), 1931   .
.   .   .   .   £1,750/£100
ditto, Dodd, Mead (New York), 1931   .   .   £250/£65
Mystery at Greycombe Farm, Collins Crime Club (London),
1932   .   .   .   .   .   .   £1,750/£100
ditto, as *The Fire at Greycombe Farm* **Dodd**, Mead (New
York), 1932   .   .   .   .   .   £150/£50
Dead Men at the Folly, Collins Crime Club (London), 1932.
.   .   .   .   £1,750/£100
ditto, Dodd, Mead (New York), 1932   .   .   £150/£50
The Motor Rally Mystery, Collins Crime Club (London),
1933   .   .   .   .   .   .   £1,750/£100
ditto, as *Dr Priestley Lays a Trap*, Dodd, Mead (New York),
1933   .   .   .   .   .   .   £150/£50
The Claverton Mystery, Collins Crime Club (London), 1933
.   .   .   .   £1,750/£100
ditto, as *The Claverton Affair*, Dodd, Mead (New York),
1933   .   .   .   .   .   .   £150/£50
The Venner Crime, Odhams (London), 1933   .   £50/£10
ditto, Dodd, Mead (New York), 1934   .   .   £15/£5
The Robthorne Mystery, Collins Crime Club (London), 1934
.   .   .   .   £1,750/£100

ditto, Dodd, Mead (New York), 1934   .   .   £150/£45
Poison for One, Collins Crime Club (London), 1934   .
.   .   .   .   £1,750/£100
ditto, Dodd, Mead (New York), 1934   .   .   £150/£45
Shot at Dawn, Collins Crime Club (London), 1934   .
.   .   .   .   £1,750/£100
ditto, Dodd, Mead (New York), 1934   .   .   £150/£45
The Corpse in the Car, Collins Crime Club (London), 1935.
.   .   .   .   £1,750/£100
ditto, Dodd, Mead (New York), 1935   .   .   £150/£45
Hendon's First Case, Collins Crime Club (London), 1935   .
.   .   .   .   £1,750/£100
ditto, Dodd, Mead (New York), 1935   .   .   £150/£45
Mystery at Olympia, Collins Crime Club (London), 1935   .
.   .   .   .   £1,750/£100
ditto, as *Murder at the Motor Show*, Dodd, Mead (New
York), 1936   .   .   .   .   .   £150/£45
Death at Breakfast, Collins Crime Club (London), 1936   .
.   .   .   .   £1,750/£100
ditto, Dodd, Mead (New York), 1936   .   .   £150/£45
In Face of the Verdict, Collins Crime Club (London), 1936.
.   .   .   .   £1,750/£100
ditto, as *In the Face of the Verdict*, Dodd, Mead (New York),
1940   .   .   .   .   .   .   £150/£45
Death in the Hopfields, Collins Crime Club (London), 1937
.   .   .   .   £1,750/£100
ditto, as *The Harvest Murder*, Dodd, Mead (New York),
1937   .   .   .   .   .   .   £150/£45
Death on the Board, Collins Crime Club (London), 1937   .
.   .   .   .   £1,750/£100
ditto, as *Death Sits on the Board*, Dodd, Mead (New York),
1937   .   .   .   .   .   .   £150/£45
Proceed with Caution, Collins Crime Club (London), 1937   .
.   .   .   .   £1,750/£100
ditto, as *Body Unidentified*, Dodd, Mead (New York), 1938.
.   .   .   .   £150/£45
Invisible Weapons, Collins Crime Club (London), 1938   .
.   .   .   .   £1,750/£100
ditto, Dodd, Mead (New York), 1938   .   .   £125/£40
The Bloody Tower, Collins Crime Club (London), 1938   .
.   .   .   .   £1,750/£100
ditto, as *The Tower of Evil*, Dodd, Mead (New York), 1938.
.   .   .   .   £125/£40
Drop to His Death, Heinemann [1939] (with Carter Dickson)
.   .   .   .   £250/£45
ditto, as *Fatal Descent*, Dodd, Mead (New York), 1939.   .
.   .   .   .   £250/£45
Death Pays a Dividend, Collins Crime Club (London), 1939
.   .   .   .   £1,750/£100
ditto, Dodd, Mead (New York), 1939   .   .   £125/£40
Death on Sunday, Collins Crime Club (London), 1939.   .
.   .   .   .   £1,750/£100
ditto, as *The Elm Tree Murder*, Dodd, Mead (New York),
1939   .   .   .   .   .   .   £100/£35
Death on the Boat Train, Collins Crime Club (London),
1940   .   .   .   .   .   .   £1,750/£100
ditto, Dodd, Mead (New York), 1940   .   .   £100/£35
Murder at Lilac Cottage, Collins Crime Club (London),
1940   .   .   .   .   .   .   £1,750/£100
ditto, Dodd, Mead (New York), 1940   .   .   £100/£35
Death at the Helm, Collins Crime Club (London), 1941   .
.   .   .   .   £1,750/£100
ditto, Dodd, Mead (New York), 1941   .   .   £100/£35

They Watched by Night, Collins Crime Club (London), 1941
. . . . £1,750/£100
ditto, as *Signal for Death*, Dodd, Mead (New York), 1941 .
. . . . £100/£35
The Fourth Bomb, Collins Crime Club (London), 1942 .
. . . . £500/£45
ditto, Dodd, Mead (New York), 1942 . . . £75/£25
Night Exercise, Collins Crime Club (London), 1942 . .
. . . . £500/£45
ditto, as *Dead of the Night*, Dodd, Mead (New York), 1942 .
. . . . £75/£25
Dead on the Track, Collins Crime Club (London), 1943 .
. . . . £250/£35
ditto, Dodd, Mead (New York), 1943 . . . £75/£25
Men Die at Cyprus Lodge, Collins Crime Club (London),
1943 . . . . £250/£35
ditto, Dodd, Mead (New York), 1944 . . . £75/£25
Death Invades the Meeting, Collins Crime Club (London),
1944 . . . . £250/£35
ditto, Dodd, Mead (New York), 1944 . . . £75/£25
Vegetable Duck, Collins Crime Club (London), 1944 . .
. . . . £250/£35
ditto, as *Too Many Suspects*, Dodd, Mead (New York), 1945
. . . . £75/£25
Bricklayer's Arms, Collins Crime Club (London), 1945 .
. . . . £200/£35
ditto, as *Shadow of a Crime*, Dodd, Mead (New York), 1945 .
. . . . £45/£15
The Lake House, Bles (London), 1946 . . £100/£25
ditto, as *The Secret of the Lake House*, Dodd, Mead (New
York), 1946 . . . . £35/£10
Death in Harley Street, Bles (London), 1946 . £100/£25
ditto, Dodd, Mead (New York), 1946 . . . £35/£10
Nothing But the Truth, Bles (London), 1947 . £100/£25
ditto, as *Experiment in Crime*, Dodd, Mead (New York),
1947 . . . . £35/£10
Death of an Author, Bles (London), 1947 . £100/£25
ditto, Dodd, Mead (New York), 1948 . . . £35/£10
The Paper Bag, Bles (London), 1948 . . £100/£25
ditto, as *The Links in the Chain*, Dodd, Mead (New York),
1948 . . . . £35/£10
The Telephone Call, Bles (London), 1948 . £100/£25
ditto, as *Shadow of an Alibi*, Dodd, Mead (New York), 1949
. . . . £35/£10
Blackthorn House, Bles (London), 1949 . . £100/£25
ditto, Dodd, Mead (New York), 1949 . . . £35/£10
Up the Garden Path, Bles (London), 1949 . £100/£25
ditto, as *The Fatal Garden*, Dodd, Mead (New York), 1949 .
. . . . £35/£10
The Two Graphs, Bles (London), 1950 . . £100/£25
ditto, as *Double Identities*, Dodd, Mead (New York), 1950 .
. . . . £35/£10
Family Affairs, Bles (London), 1950. . . £100/£25
ditto, as *The Last Suspect*, Dodd, Mead (New York), 1951 .
. . . . £35/£10
Dr Goodwood's Locum, Bles (London), 1951. . £100/£25
ditto, as *The Affair of the Substitute Doctor*, Dodd, Mead
(New York), 1951 . . . . £35/£10
The Secret Meeting, Bles (London), 1951 . . £100/£25
ditto, Dodd, Mead (New York), 1952 . . . £35/£10
Death in Wellington Road, Bles (London), 1952 . £100/£25
ditto, Dodd, Mead (New York), 1952 . . . £35/£10
Death at the Dance, Bles (London), 1952 . £100/£25
ditto, Dodd, Mead (New York), 1953 . . . £35/£10

By Registered Post, Bles (London), 1952 . . . £100/£25
ditto, as *The Mysterious Suspect*, Dodd, Mead (New York),
1953 . . . . £35/£10
Death at the Inn, Bles (London), 1953 . . . £100/£25
ditto, as *The Case of the Forty Thieves*, Dodd, Mead (New
York), 1954 . . . . £35/£10
The Dovebury Murders, Bles (London), 1954. . £100/£25
ditto, Dodd, Mead (New York), 1954 . . . £35/£10
Death on the Lawn, Bles (London), 1954 . . £100/£25
ditto, Dodd, Mead (New York), 1955 . . . £35/£10
The Domestic Agency, Bles (London), 1955 . . £100/£25
ditto, as *Grave Matters*, Dodd, Mead (New York), 1955 .
. . . . £35/£10
Death of a Godmother, Bles (London), 1955 . . £100/£25
ditto, as *Delayed Payment*, Dodd, Mead (New York), 1956 .
. . . . £35/£10
An Artist Dies, Bles (London), 1956 . . . . £100/£25
ditto, as *Death of an Artist*, Dodd, Mead (New York), 1956
. . . . £35/£10
Open Verdict, Bles (London), 1956 . . . . £100/£25
ditto, Dodd, Mead (New York), 1957 . . . £35/£10
Robbery with Violence, Bles (London), 1957 . £100/£25
ditto, Dodd, Mead (New York), 1957 . . £35/£10
Death of a Bridegroom, Bles (London), 1957. . £100/£25
ditto, Dodd, Mead (New York), 1958 . . . £35/£10
Murder at Derivale, Bles (London), 1958 . £100/£25
ditto, Dodd, Mead (New York), 1958 . . . £35/£10
Death Takes a Partner, Bles (London), 1958 . £100/£25
ditto, Dodd, Mead (New York), 1959 . . . £35/£10
Licenced for Murder, Bles (London), 1958 . £100/£25
ditto, Dodd, Mead (New York), 1959 . . . £35/£10
Three Cousins Die, Bles (London), 1959 . . £100/£25
ditto, Dodd, Mead (New York), 1960 . . . £35/£10
Twice Dead, Bles (London), 1960 . . . £100/£25
ditto, Dodd, Mead (New York), 1960 . . . £35/£10
The Fatal Pool, Bles (London), 1960 . . . £100/£25
ditto, Dodd, Mead (New York), 1961 . . . £35/£10
The Vanishing Diary, Bles (London), 1961 . . £100/£25
ditto, Dodd, Mead (New York), 1961 . . . £35/£10

Novels as 'Miles Burton'
The Hardway Diamonds Mystery, Collins Crime Club
(London), 1930 . . . . . . £1,850/£150
ditto, Mystery League (New York), 1930 . . . £150/£35
The Secret of High Eldersham, Collins Crime Club
(London), 1930 . . . . . . £1,750/£150
ditto, Mystery League (New York), 1931 . . £150/£35
ditto, as *The Mystery of High Eldersham*, Collins Crime
Club (London), 1933 . . . . . £250/£45
The Three Crimes, Collins Crime Club (London), 1931 .
. . . . £1,750/£150
The Menace on the Downs, Collins Crime Club (London),
1931 . . . . £1,750/£150
Death of Mr Gantley, Collins Crime Club (London), 1932 .
. . . . £1,750/£150
Murder at the Moorings, Collins Crime Club (London),
1932 . . . . £1,750/£150
Fate at the Fair, Collins Crime Club (London), 1933 . .
. . . . £1,750/£150
Tragedy at the Thirteenth Hole, Collins Crime Club
(London), 1933 . . . . . . £1,750/£150
Death at the Cross Roads, Collins Crime Club (London),
1933 . . . . £1,750/£150

The Charabanc Mystery, Collins Crime Club (London), 1934
. . . . £1,750/£150
To Catch a Thief, Collins Crime Club (London), 1934 . .
. . . . £1,750/£150
The Devereux Court Mystery, Collins Crime Club (London),
1935 . . . . £1,750/£150
The Milk Churn Murder, Collins Crime Club (London),
1935 . . . . £1,750/£150
ditto, as *The Clue of the Silver Brush*, Doubleday (New
York), 1936 . . . . £125/£40
Death in the Tunnel, Collins Crime Club (London), 1936 .
. . . . £1,750/£150
ditto, as *Dark Is the Tunnel*, Doubleday (New York), 1936 .
. . . . £125/£40
Murder of a Chemist, Collins Crime Club (London), 1936 .
. . . . £1,750/£150
Where is Barbara Prentice?, Collins Crime Club (London),
1936 . . . . £1,750/£150
ditto, as *The Clue of the Silver Cellar*, Doubleday (New
York), 1937 . . . . £125/£40
Death at the Club, Collins Crime Club (London), 1937 . .
. . . . £1,500/£150
ditto, as *The Clue of the Fourteen Keys*, Doubleday (New
York), 1937 . . . . £100/£30
Murder in Crown Passage, Collins Crime Club (London),
1937 . . . . £1,500/£150
ditto, as *The Man with the Tattooed Face*, Doubleday (New
York), 1937 . . . . £100/£30
Death at Low Tide, Collins Crime Club (London), 1938 .
. . . . £1,500/£150
The Platinum Cat, Collins Crime Club (London), 1938. .
. . . . £1,500/£150
ditto, Doubleday (New York), 1938 . . . . £100/£30
Death Leaves No Card, Collins Crime Club (London), 1939
. . . . £1,500/£150
Mr Babbacombe Dies, Collins Crime Club (London), 1939 .
. . . . £1,500/£150
Murder in the Coalhole, Collins Crime Club (London), 1940
. . . . £1,500/£150
ditto, as *Written in Dust*, Doubleday (New York), 1940 .
. . . . £100/£30
Mr Westerby Missing, Collins Crime Club (London), 1940 .
. . . . £1,500/£150
ditto, Doubleday (New York), 1940 . . . . £100/£30
Death Takes a Flat, Collins Crime Club (London), 1940 .
. . . . £1,500/£150
ditto, as *Vacancy with Corpse*, Doubleday (New York), 1941
. . . . £100/£30
Death of Two Brothers, Collins Crime Club (London), 1941
. . . . £1,500/£150
Up the Garden Path, Collins Crime Club (London), 1941 .
. . . . £1,250/£125
ditto, as *Death Visits Downspring*, Doubleday (New York),
1941 . . . . £100/£25
This Undesirable Residence, Collins Crime Club (London),
1942 . . . . £1,250/£125
ditto, as *Death at Ash House*, Doubleday (New York), 1942
. . . . £50/£15
Dead Stop, Collins Crime Club (London), 1943 . £350/£45
Murder M.D., Collins Crime Club (London), 1943. £150/£25
ditto, as *Who Killed the Doctor?*, Doubleday (New York),
1943 . . . . £45/£15
Four-ply Yarn, Collins Crime Club (London), 1944 . .
. . . . £150/£25

ditto, as *The Shadow on the Cliff*, Doubleday (New York),
1944 . . . . £45/£15
The Three Corpse Trick, Collins Crime Club (London), 1944
. . . . £125/£20
Not a Leg to Stand On, Collins Crime Club (London), 1945.
. . . . £125/£20
ditto, Doubleday (New York), 1945 . . . . £40/£10
Early Morning Murder, Collins Crime Club (London), 1945
. . . . £100/£15
ditto, as *Accidents Do Happen*, Doubleday (New York), 1946
. . . . £35/£10
The Cat Jumps, Collins Crime Club (London), 1946 . .
. . . . £100/£15
Situation Vacant, Collins Crime Club (London), 1946 . .
. . . . £100/£15
Heir to Lucifer, Collins Crime Club (London), 1947 . .
. . . . £100/£15
A Will in the Way, Collins Crime Club (London), 1947. .
. . . . £100/£15
ditto, Doubleday (New York), 1947 . . . . £35/£10
Death in Shallow Water, Collins Crime Club (London), 1948
. . . . £100/£15
Devil's Reckoning, Collins Crime Club (London), 1948 .
. . . . £100/£15
ditto, Doubleday (New York), 1949 . . . . £35/£10
Death Takes the Living, Collins Crime Club (London), 1949
. . . . £100/£15
ditto, as *The Disappearing Parson*, Doubleday (New York),
1949 . . . . £35/£10
Look Alive, Collins Crime Club (London), 1949 . £100/£15
ditto, Doubleday (New York), 1950 . . . £75/£15
Ground for Suspicion, Collins Crime Club (London), 1950 .
. . . . £75/£15
A Village Afraid, Collins Crime Club (London), 1950 . .
. . . . £75/£15
Beware Your Neighbour, Collins Crime Club (London), 1951
. . . . £75/£15
Murder Out of School, Collins Crime Club (London), 1951.
. . . . £75/£15
Murder on Duty, Collins Crime Club (London), 1952 . .
. . . . £75/£15
Something to Hide, Collins Crime Club (London), 1953 .
. . . . £75/£15
Heir to Murder, Collins Crime Club (London), 1953 £75/£15
Murder in Absence, Collins Crime Club (London), 1954 .
. . . . £75/£15
Unwanted Corpse, Collins Crime Club (London), 1954. .
. . . . £75/£15
Murder Unrecognised, Collins Crime Club (London), 1955 .
. . . . £75/£15
A Crime in Time, Collins Crime Club (London), 1955 . .
. . . . £75/£15
Found Drowned, Collins Crime Club (London), 1956 . .
. . . . £75/£15
Death in a Duffle Coat, Collins Crime Club (London), 1956
. . . . £75/£15
Chinese Puzzle, Collins Crime Club (London), 1957 £75/£15
The Moth Watch Murder, Collins Crime Club (London),
1957 . . . . £75/£15
Bones in the Brickfield, Collins Crime Club (London), 1958
. . . . £75/£15
Death Takes a Detour, Collins Crime Club (London), 1958 .
. . . . £75/£15

Return from the Dead, Collins Crime Club (London), 1959 .
. . . . £75/£15
A Smell of Smoke, Collins Crime Club (London), 1959. .
. . . . £75/£15
Legacy of Death, Collins Crime Club (London), 1960 . .
. . . . £65/£10
Death Paints a Picture, Collins Crime Club (London), 1960
. . . . £65/£10

Novels written as 'Cecil Waye'
Murder at Monk's Barn, Hodder & Stoughton (London),
1931 . . . . £1,500/£125
The Figure of Eight, Hodder & Stoughton (London), 1931 .
. . . . £1,500/£125
ditto, Kinsey (New York), 1933 . . . . . £200/£65
The End of the Chase, Hodder & Stoughton (London), 1932
. . . . £1,500/£125
The Prime Minister's Pencil, Hodder & Stoughton (London),
1933 . . . . £500/£65
ditto, Kinsey (New York), 1933 . . . . . £200/£65

**Novels written as 'John Rhode' with other members
of the Detection Club**
The Floating Admiral, Hodder & Stoughton (London),
[1931] (chain novel; chapters contributed by John Rhode,
G.K. Chesterton, Dorothy L. Sayers, Agatha Christie,
Freeman Wills Crofts and others) . . . £1,500/£100
ditto, Doubleday (New York), 1932 . . . . £500/£30
Ask a Policeman, Barker (London), [1933] (chain novel;
chapters contributed by John Rhode, Gladys Mitchell,
Dorothy L. Sayers and others) . . . £1,000/£100
ditto, Morrow (New York), 1933 . . . . £500/£65

Non-Fiction as 'C.J.C. Street'
The Case of Constance Kent, Bles (London), 1928 £200/£45

JEAN RHYS
(b.1890 d.1979)

Jean Rhys was a novelist noted for her clear and imaginative writing. Her works usually present strong female
characters, although the protagonists are often lonely and
lacking in direction. *Wide Sargasso Sea* brought her
popular and critical acclaim, providing a 'prequel' to
Charlotte Brontë's *Jane Eyre*.

Novels
Postures, Chatto & Windus (London), 1928 . £1,500/£250
ditto, as *Quartet*, Simon & Schuster (New York), 1929
(printed glassine d/w). . . . . . £750/£50
After Leaving Mr Mackenzie, Cape (London), 1931 . .
. . . . £1,000/£200
ditto, Knopf (New York), 1931 . . . . . £250/£40
Voyage in the Dark, Constable (London), 1934 . £400/£65
ditto, Morrow (New York), 1935 . . . . £300/£45
Good Morning, Midnight, Constable (London), 1939 . .
. . . . £500/£75
ditto, Harper & Row (New York), [1970] . . £20/£5
Wide Sargasso Sea, Deutsch (London), 1966 . . £125/£15
ditto, Norton (New York), 1966 . . . . . £85/£15

Short Stories
The Left Bank and Other Stories, Cape (London), 1927 .
. . . . £750/£75
ditto, Harper (New York), 1927 . . . . . £350/£40
Tigers Are Better Looking, Deutsch (London), 1968 £50/£15
ditto, Harper (New York), 1974 . . . . . £25/£10
Sleep It Off Lady, Deutsch (London), 1976 . . £20/£5
ditto, Harper (New York), 1976 . . . . . £20/£5

Translation
Perversity, by Francis Carco, Covici (Chicago), 1928
(translation credited to Ford Madox Ford but in fact Jean
Rhys) . . . . £250/£40

Others
My Day, Three Pieces, Frank Hallman (New York), 1975
(wraps) £10
ditto, Frank Hallman (New York), 1975 (750 copies) £25/£10
ditto, Frank Hallman (New York), 1975 (26 signed, lettered
copies) £450
Smile Please, An Unfinished Biography, Deutsch (London),
1979 . . . . £15/£5
ditto, Harper (New York), 1980 . . . . . £15/£5
Letters, 1931-1966, Deutsch (London), 1984 . . £15/£5
ditto, as *The Letters of Jean Rhys*, Viking (New York), 1984
. . . . £15/£5

ANNE RICE
(b.1941)

Rice is an American author of horror/fantasy stories who
was born and has lived most of her life in New Orleans,
Louisiana. Her subject matter is mainly made up of vam-
pires, mummies and witches. *Interview with the Vampire*
started life as a cult best-seller and found itself two decades
later as a Hollywood film. Her works have been an
influence on recent 'Goth' youth subculture, and she has
published several works with sado-masochistic themes.

The 'Vampire' Chronicles
Interview with the Vampire, Knopf (New York), 1976 . .
. . . . £500/£45
ditto, Macdonald/Raven Books (London), 1976 . £150/£20
The Vampire Lestat, Knopf (New York), 1985 (presumed
first state with purple top stain on top edge) . £100/£30
ditto, Knopf (New York), 1985 (no top edge stain). £40/£10
ditto, Futura Books (London), 1986 (pbk) . . . £5
ditto, Macdonald (London), 1987 (first hardback) . £45/£10
The Queen of the Damned, Knopf (New York), 1988 . .
. . . . £45/£10
ditto, Knopf/Ultramarine Press (New York), 1988 (26 signed,
lettered copies) £650
ditto, Knopf/Ultramarine Press (New York), 1988 (150
signed, numbered copies) £250
ditto, Macdonald (London), 1989 . . . . £45/£10
The Tale of the Body Thief, Knopf (New York), 1992 . .
. . . . £25/£5
ditto, Chatto & Windus (London), 1992 . . . £20/£5
Memnoch the Devil, Knopf (New York), 1995 . £15/£5
ditto, Trice (New Orleans), 1995 (26 signed, lettered copies)
. . . . £250

ditto, Trice (New Orleans), 1995 (50 signed copies in full
  leather) £150
ditto, Trice (New Orleans), 1995 (425 signed, numbered
  copies). £75
ditto, Chatto & Windus (London), 1995 . . . £15/£5
Pandora, Knopf (New York), 1998 . . . . £10/£5
ditto, Trice (New Orleans), 1998 (26 signed, lettered copies,
  bound in full leather) £500
ditto, Trice (New Orleans), 1998 (50 signed, deluxe copies,
  quarterbound in leather) £250
ditto, Trice (New Orleans), 1998 (250 signed, numbered
  copies) £200
ditto, Chatto & Windus (London), 1998 . . . £10/£5
The Vampire Armand, Knopf (New York), 1998 . £10/£5
ditto, Trice (New Orleans), 1998 (26 signed, lettered copies,
  bound in full leather) £500
ditto, Trice (New Orleans), 1998 (50 signed, deluxe copies,
  quarterbound in leather) £250
ditto, Trice (New Orleans), 1998 (250 signed, numbered
  copies) £200
ditto, Chatto & Windus (London), 1998 . . . £10/£5
Vittorio the Vampire, Knopf (New York), 1999 . £10/£5
ditto, Trice (New Orleans), 1999 (250 signed, numbered
  copies) £200
ditto, Franklin Library (Franklin Centre, PA), 1999 (signed
  limited edition) £150
ditto, Chatto & Windus (London), 1999 . . . £10/£5
Merrick, Franklin Library (Franklin Centre, PA), 2000
  (signed limited edition) £75
ditto, Knopf (New York), 2000 . . . . £10/£5
ditto, Chatto & Windus (London), 2000 . . . £10/£5
Blood and Gold, Knopf (New York), 2001 . £10/£5
ditto, Chatto & Windus (London), 2001 . . . £10/£5
Blackwood Farm, Knopf (New York), 2002 . £10/£5
ditto, Chatto & Windus (London), 2002 . . . £10/£5
Blood Canticle, Knopf (New York), 2003 . £10/£5
ditto, Chatto & Windus (London), 2003 . . . £10/£5

The 'Witch' Chronicles
The Witching Hour, Knopf (New York), 1990 . £20/£5
ditto, Chatto & Windus (London), 1991 . . £15/£5
Lasher, Knopf (New York), 1993 . . . £20/£5
ditto, Chatto & Windus (London), 1993 . . £15/£5
Taltos, Lives of the Mayfair Witches, Knopf (New York),
  1994 . . . . £20/£5
ditto, Trice (New Orleans), 1994 (500 signed, numbered
  copies) £75
ditto, Chatto & Windus (London), 1994 . . . £15/£5

Ghost Novels
Servant of the Bones, Knopf (New York), 1996 . £35/£5
ditto, Trice (New Orleans), 1996 (26 signed, lettered copies)
  . . . .£300
ditto, Trice (New Orleans), 1996 (50 signed copies in full
  leather) £250
ditto, Trice (New Orleans), 1996 (425 signed, numbered
  copies) £75
ditto, Chatto & Windus (London), 1996 . . . £30/£5
Violin, Chatto & Windus (London), 1997. . £35/£10
ditto, Trice (New Orleans), 1997 (26 signed, lettered copies)
  . . . .£250
ditto, Trice (New Orleans), 1997 (50 signed copies in full
  leather) £150

ditto, Trice (New Orleans), 1997 (325 signed, numbered
  copies) £65
ditto, Knopf (New York), 1997 . . . . £35/£10

Christ the Lord
Christ the Lord: Out of Egypt, Knopf (New York), 2005 .
  . . . . £10/£5
The Road to Cana, Knopf (New York), 2008 . . £10/£5

Songs of the Seraphim
Angel Time, Knopf (New York), 2009 . . . £10/£5
ditto, Chatto & Windus (London), 2009 . . . £10/£5

Other Historical Novels
The Feast of All Saints, Simon & Schuster (New York),
  1979 . . . . £65/£15
ditto, Penguin (Harmondsworth, Middlesex), 1982 (pbk) £5
Cry to Heaven, Knopf (New York), 1982. . . £60/£10
ditto, Chatto & Windus (London), 1990 . . . £40/£10
The Mummy, or Ramses the Damned, Ballantine Books
  (New York), 1989 . . . . . .£150/£25
ditto, Ballantine Books (New York), 1989 (pbk) . £10
ditto, Chatto & Windus (London), 1989 . . . £75/£15

Novels Written as 'Anne Rampling'
Exit to Eden, Arbor House (New York), 1985. . £40/£10
ditto, Macdonald (London), 1986 . . . . £40/£10
Belinda, Arbor House (New York), 1986. . . £35/£10
ditto, Macdonald (London), 1987 . . . . £35/£10

Novels Written as 'A.N. Roquelaure'
The Claiming of Sleeping Beauty, Dutton (New York), 1983
  . . . . £45/£10
ditto, Futura (London), 1987 (pbk) £5
ditto, Macdonald (London), 1987 . . . . £25/£5
Beauty's Punishment, Dutton (New York), 1984 . £75/£20
ditto, Futura (London), 1987 (pbk) £10
ditto, Macdonald (London), 1987 . . . . £40/£10
Beauty's Release, Dutton (New York), 1985 . .£125/£35
ditto, Futura (London), 1988 (pbk) £10

CRAIG RICE
(b.1908 d.1957)

Rice wrote a number of often humorous mystery novels
under her own name, as well as writing as Michael
Venning and Daphne Saunders, and ghost-writing three
novels. Her books were first published in the US, and UK
editions followed erratically. She is the only mystery writer
to have had the distinction of being featured on the cover
of *Time* magazine.

Novels by Craig Rice
8 faces at 3, Simon & Schuster (New York), 1939 . £175/£25
ditto, Eyre & Spottiswoode (London), 1939 . .£175/£25
ditto, as ***Death at Three***, Cherry Tree (Withy Grove Press),
  London (1941) (pbk) £10
The Corpse Steps Out, Simon & Schuster (New York), 1940
  . . . .£125/£20
ditto, Eyre & Spottiswoode (London), 1940 . .£125/£20
The Wrong Murder, Simon & Schuster (New York), 1940 .
  . . . .£125/£15

ditto, Eyre & Spottiswoode (London), 1942   . £100/£15

The Right Murder, Simon & Schuster (New York), 1941 .

. £125/£15

ditto, Eyre & Spottiswoode (London), 1948 . £75/£10

Trial by Fury, Simon & Schuster (New York), 1941 . .

. £250/£35

ditto, Hammond (London), 1950. . . . £100/£20

The Big Midget Murders, Simon & Schuster (New York), 1942 . . £125/£15

The Sunday Pigeon Murders, Simon & Schuster (New York), 1948 . £75/£10

ditto, Nicholson & Watson (London), 1958 . £45/£5

Telefair, Bobbs Merrill (New York), 1942 . £75/£10

ditto, as **Yesterday's Murder**, Popular Library, 1950 (pbk) .

. £10

Having Wonderful Crime, Simon & Schuster (New York), 1943 . . . . £100/£15

ditto, Nicholson & Watson (London), 1944 . £85/£10

The Thursday Turkey Murders, Simon & Schuster (New York), 1943 . . . . . £65/£5

ditto, Nicholson & Watson (London), 1946 . £45/£5

Home Sweet Homicide, Simon & Schuster (New York), 1944 . . . . £150/£25

The Lucky Stiff, Simon & Schuster (New York), 1945 . .

. £40/£5

The Fourth Postman, Simon & Schuster (New York), 1948

. £30/£5

ditto, Hammond (London), 1951. . . . £30/£5

Innocent Bystander, Simon & Schuster (New York), 1949 .

. £30/£5

ditto, Hammond (London), [1958] . . . £30/£5

My Kingdom for a Hearse, Simon & Schuster (New York), 1957 . . . . £30/£5

ditto, Hammond (London), 1959. . . . £30/£5

Knocked for a Loop, Simon & Schuster (New York), 1957 .

. £30/£5

ditto, as **The Double Frame**, Hammond (London), 1958 .

. £30/£5

The April Robin Murders, Random House (New York), 1958 . . . . £30/£5

ditto, Hammond (London), 1959. . . . £25/£5

But the Doctor Died, Lancer (New York), 1967 (pbk) . £5

Short Stories by Craig Rice

The Name Is Malone, Pyramid (New York), 1958. . £10

ditto, Hammond (London), 1960. . . . £10/£5

People vs Withers and Malone, Simon & Schuster (New York), 1963 (with Stuart Palmer) . . . £50/£10

Once Upon A Train and Other Stories, Gold Penny Press (Canoga Park, CA), 1963 (with Stuart Palmer) . £45/£10

Novels by Michael Venning

The Man Who Slept All Day, Coward-McCann (New York), 1942 . . . . £150/£25

Murder through the Looking Glass, Coward-McCann (New York), 1943 . . . . . . £150/£25

ditto, Nicholson & Watson (London), 1947 . £100/£15

Jethro Hammer, Coward-McCann (New York), 1944 . .

. . . . £100/£15

ditto, Nicholson & Watson (London), 1947 . £75/£15

Novel by Daphne Saunders

To Catch a Thief, Dial (New York), 1943 . £100/£15

Ghost-written Novels

The G-String Murders, Simon & Schuster (New York), 1941 (for Gypsy Rose Lee) . . . . £75/£10

ditto, as **Lady of Burlesque**, Tower, 1942. . . £20/£5

ditto, as **The Strip-Tease Murders**, Bodley Head (London), 1943 . . . . . £75/£10

Mother Finds a Body, Simon & Schuster (New York), 1942 (for Gypsy Rose Lee) . . . . . £50/£10

ditto, Bodley Head (London), 1943 . . . £45/£5

Crime on My Hands, Simon & Schuster (New York), 1944 (for George Sanders) . . . . . £40/£10

ditto, Edwards (London), [1948]. . . . £40/£10

FRANK RICHARDS

(b.1876 d.1961)

Under the pseudonym 'Frank Richards' Charles Hamilton created the everlasting, rotund schoolboy, Billy Bunter. It is estimated that Hamilton wrote over 100 million words and had the equivalent of 1,000 full-length novels published. Most of his fiction, though, appeared in the weekly boys' comics of the time. He used more than 20 different pen-names.

'Billy Bunter' Titles

Billy Bunter of Greyfriars School, Skilton (London), 1947 .

. . . . £125/£25

Billy Bunter's Banknote, Skilton (London), 1948 . £100/£15

Billy Bunter's Barring-Out, Skilton (London), 1948 . .

. . . . £75/£15

Billy Bunter's Christmas Party, Skilton (London), 1949 .

. . . . £75/£15

Billy Bunter in Brazil, Skilton (London), 1949 . £75/£15

Billy Bunter's Benefit, Skilton (London), 1950 . £75/£15

Billy Bunter Among the Cannibals, Skilton (London), 1950

. £65/£15

Billy Bunter's Postal Order, Skilton (London), 1951 . .

. £65/£15

Billy Bunter Butts In, Skilton (London), 1951 . £65/£15

Billy Bunter and the Blue Mauritius, Skilton (London), 1952

. £65/£15

Billy Bunter's Beanfeast, Cassell (London), 1952 . £50/£10

Billy Bunter's Brain-Wave, Cassell (London), 1953 £50/£10

Billy Bunter's First Case, Cassell (London), 1953. £50/£10

Billy Bunter the Bold, Cassell (London), 1954 . £45/£10

Bunter Does His Best, Cassell (London), 1954 . £45/£10

Billy Bunter's Double, Cassell (London), 1955 . £45/£10

Backing Up Billy Bunter, Cassell (London), 1955. £40/£10

Lord Billy Bunter, Cassell (London), 1956 . £40/£5

The Banishing of Billy Bunter, Cassell (London), 1956 .

. £40/£5

Billy Bunter's Bolt, Cassell (London), 1957 . £40/£5

Billy Bunter Afloat, Cassell (London), 1957 . £40/£5

Billy Bunter's Bargain, Cassell (London), 1958 . £40/£5

Billy Bunter the Hiker, Cassell (London), 1958 . £40/£5

Bunter Out of Bounds, Cassell (London), 1959 . £40/£5

Bunter Comes for Christmas, Cassell (London), 1959 . .

. £40/£5

Bunter the Bad Lad, Cassell (London), 1960 . . £40/£5

Bunter Keeps It Dark, Cassell (London), 1960 . £40/£5

Billy Bunter's Treasure-Hunt, Cassell (London), 1961   .
.   .   .   .   £40/£5
Billy Bunter at Butlins, Cassell (London), 1961   .   £35/£5
ditto, Butlins Beaver Club edition (London), 1961 .   £15/£5
Bunter the Ventriloquist, Cassell (London), 1961.   £40/£5
Bunter the Caravanner, Cassell (London), 1962 .   £40/£5
Billy Bunter's Bodyguard, Cassell (London), 1962   £35/£5
Big Chief Bunter, Cassell (London), 1963   .   .   £35/£5
Just Like Bunter, Cassell (London), 1963   .   .   £35/£5
Bunter the Stowaway, Cassell (London), 1964   .   £35/£5
Thanks to Bunter, Cassell (London), 1964   .   .   £35/£5
Bunter the Sportsman, Cassell (London), 1965   .   £35/£5
Bunter's Last Fling, Cassell (London), 1965   .   .   £35/£5

Title Written as 'Hilda Richards'
Bessie Bunter of Cliff House School, Skilton (London),
1949   .   .   .   .   £100/£20

'Jack' Titles
Jack Of All Trades, Mandeville (London), 1930   .   £25/£5
Jack's The Lad, Spring Books (London), 1957   .   £10/£5
Jack of the Circus, Spring Books (London), 1957 .   £10/£5

'Tom Merry' Titles
The Secret of the Study, Mandeville (London), 1949 (pseud
'Martin Clifford')   .   .   .   .   .   £20/£5
Talbot's Secret, Mandeville (London), 1949   .   £20/£5
Tom Merry and Co of St Jim's, Mandeville (London), 1949
(pseud 'Martin Clifford')   .   .   .   .   £20/£5
Rallying Round Gussy, Mandeville (London), 1950 (pseud
'Martin Clifford')   .   .   .   .   .   £15/£5
The Scapegrace of St Jim's, Mandeville (London), 1951
(pseud 'Martin Clifford')   .   .   .   .   £15/£5
The Rivals of Rookwood, Mandeville (London), 1951 (pseud
'Owen Conquest')   .   .   .   .   .   £15/£5
Tom Merry's Secret, Hamilton (London), 1952 (pseud
'Martin Clifford'; pbk) £5
Tom Merry's Rival, Hamilton (London), 1952 (pseud
'Martin Clifford'; pbk) £5
Trouble for Tom Merry, Spring Books (London), 1953 .
.   .   .   .   £10/£5
Down and Out, Spring Books (London), 1953   .   £10/£5
Cardew's Catch, Spring Books (London), 1954   .   £10/£5
The Disappearance of Tom Merry, Spring Books (London),
1954   .   .   .   .   £10/£5
Tom Merry's Own, Mandeville (London), 1954 (pseud
'Martin Clifford')   .   .   .   .   .   £10/£5
Through Thick and Thin, Spring Books (London), 1955   .
.   .   .   .   £10/£5
Tom Merry's Triumph, Spring Books (London), 1956 .   .
.   .   .   .   £10/£5
Tom Merry and Co, Caravanners, Spring Books (London),
1956   .   .   .   .   £10/£5

Other Titles Written as 'Martin Clifford'
The Man from the Past, Hamilton (London), 1952 (pbk)   £5
Who Ragged Railton?, Hamilton (London), 1952 (pbk)   £5
Skimpole's Snapshot, Hamilton (London), 1952 (pbk).   £5
Trouble for Trimble, Hamilton (London), 1952 (pbk) .   £5
D'Arcy in Danger, Hamilton (London), 1952 (pbk)   .   £5
D'Arcy on the Warpath, Hamilton (London), 1952 (pbk)   £5
D'Arcy's Disappearance, Hamilton (London), 1952 (pbk) £5
Darcy the Reformer, Hamilton (London), 1952 (pbk) .   £5
Darcy's Day Off, Hamilton (London), 1952 (pbk)   .   £5

Other Titles
The Secret of the School, Merrett (London), 1946 (pbk) £10
The Black Sheep of Sparshott, Merrett (London), 1946
(pbk) £10
First Man In, Merrett (London), 1946 (pbk)   .   .   £10
Looking After Lamb, Merrett (London), 1946 (pbk)   £10
The Hero of Sparshott, Merrett (London), 1946 (pbk) .   £10
Pluck Will Tell, Merrett (London), 1946 (pbk)   .   .   £10
Top Study at Topham, Matthew (London), 1947 (pbk).   £10
Bunny Binks on the Warpath, Matthew (London), 1947
(pbk) £10
The Dandy of Topham, Matthew (London), 1947 (pbk) £10
Sent to Coventry, Matthew (London), 1947 (pbk)   .   £10
The Lone Texan, Atlantic (London), 1954   .   .   £30/£10

LAURA RIDING
(b.1901 d.1991)

Laura Riding was an American poet, critic, novelist,
essayist and short story writer. Her poem 'The Quids' was
noticed by Nancy and Robert Graves, who then left his
wife for Laura. They moved first to Mallorca, then
America. She later renounced poetry for citrus farming and
did not publish again until the 1970s.

The Close Chaplet, Hogarth Press (London), 1926 (no d/w;
author's name given as Laura Riding Gottschalk)   £2,500
ditto, Adelphi Co (New York), 1926 (tissue d/w)   £500/£400
Anatole France At Home, by Marcel Le Goff, Adelphi Co
(New York), 1926 (translation)   .   .   .   £250/£50
Voltaire, Hogarth Press (London), 1927 (no d/w; author's
last name 'Gottschalk' canceled by double rule)   £1,000
A Survey of Modernist Poetry, Heinemann (London), 1927
(with Robert Graves)   .   .   .   .   .   £75/£20
ditto, Doubleday, Doran & Co (Garden City, NY), 1928   .
.   .   .   .   £50/£15
Contemporaries and Snobs, Jonathan Cape (London), 1928
.   .   .   .   £250/£45
ditto, Doubleday, Doran (Garden City, NY), 1928 . £125/£30
Anarchism Is Not Enough, Jonathan Cape (London), 1928
.   .   .   .   £150/£30
ditto, Doubleday, Doran (Garden City, NY), 1928 . £100/£25
A Pamphlet Against Anthologies, Cape (London), 1928
(with Robert Graves)   .   .   .   .   .   £125/£25
ditto, Doubleday (New York), 1928   .   .   . £100/£20
Love As Love, Death As Death,   Seizin Press (London),
1928 (175 signed, numbered copies; tissue d/w) £300/£250
Poems: A Joking Word, Jonathan Cape (London), 1930   .
.   .   .   .   £300/£60
Four Unposted Letters to Catherine, Hours Press (Paris),
1930 (200 signed, numbered copies; tissue d/w) £225/£200
ditto, Persea Books (New York), 1993   .   .   . £10/£5
Experts Are Puzzled, Jonathan Cape (London), 1930   .   .
.   .   .   .   £300/£50
Though Gently, Seizin Press (Majorca), 1930 (200 signed,
numbered copies; glassine d/w)   .   .   £200/£175
Twenty Poems Less, Hours Press, Paris, 1930 (200 signed,
numbered copies; tissue d/w)   .   .   . £250/£225
The Seizin Press, Seizin Press (Mallorca), 1931 (broadside
prospectus written with and containing a Robert Graves
poem) £100

The Seizin Press, Seizin Press (Mallorca), 1931 (broadside advertising *No Trouble, Though Gently* and *To Whom Else?* as printed and *Laura and Francisca* to be published in the summer of 1931; written with Robert Graves) . £125

Laura and Francisca, Seizin Press (Majorca), 1931 (200 signed, numbered copies; tissue d/w) £200

No Decency Left, Cape (London), 1932 (pseud 'Barbara Rich', with Robert Graves) . . . £3,000/£500

The First Leaf, Seizin Press (Majorca), 1933 (single sheet folded twice, unbound, tied and uncut) . . . £200

Everybody's Letters, Arthur Barker (London), 1933 £150/£20

The Life of the Dead, Arthur Barker (London), [1933] (200 numbered copies signed by Riding and the illustrator John Aldridge; wraps) £250

Poet: A Lying Word, Arthur Barker (London), 1933 £250/£60

Pictures, Seizin Press (London), 1933 (wraps) . £125

14A, Arthur Barker (London), 1934 (written with George Elleridge; suppressed) . . . . . £350/£100

Americans, Primavera (Los Angeles, CA), 1934 (200 numbered copies; no d/w) £350

Focus I, no publisher (no place), 1935 (wraps; 12pps magazine published with Robert Graves) . . £150

Focus II, no publisher (no place), 1935 (wraps; 24pps magazine published with Robert Graves) . . £150

The Second Leaf, Seizin Press (Majorca), 1935 (single sheet folded twice, unbound, tied and uncut) . . . £200

Focus III, no publisher (no place), 1935 (wraps; 40pps magazine published with Robert Graves) . . £150

Epilogue... Volume I, Seizin Press/Constable (Majorca/London), 1935 (Edited by Riding with Robert Graves as Associate Editor) £150

Focus IV, no publisher (no place), 1935 (wraps; 64pps magazine published with Robert Graves) . . £125

Progress of Stories, Seizin & Constable (London), 1935 . . . . £150/£40

Almost Forgotten Germany, by George Schwarz, Constable/Seizin Press (London/Majorca), 1936 (translated with Robert Graves) . . . . £900/£200

The Moon's No Fool, by Tom Matthews, Seizin/Constable (Deya/London), 1936 (ghostwritten by Riding) . £125/£20

Convelescent Conversations, Seizin Press/Constable (Majorca/London), 1936 (pseud 'Madeleine Vara') £300/£100

Epilogue... Volume II, Seizin Press/Constable (Majorca/London), 1936 . . . . £150

Epilogue... Volume III, Seizin Press/Constable (Majorca/London), 1937 . . . . £150

A Personal Letter/With A Request for Reply, no publisher (London), January 1937 (400 copies; mimeographed sheets with facsimile signature) £400

A Trojan Ending, Seizin Press/Constable (Majorca/London), 1937 (folding map at rear) . . . £150/£30

ditto, Random House (New York), 1937 . . £100/£20

Collected Poems, Cassell (London), 1938 . £225/£40

ditto, Random House (New York), 1938 . . £175/£25

The World and Ourselves, Chatto & Windus (London), 1938 (fourth volume of Epilogue Magazine; edited by Riding) . . . . £125/£25

Preliminary Questions, Seizin Press (London), 1938 (anonymous broadside) £300

The Covenant of Literal Morality, Seizin Press (no place), 1938 (paper covers) £400

To The Endorsers of the Covenant of Literal Morality, privately printed (Suffolk), February 1939 (mimeographed sheets) £700

The Left Heresy in Literature and Life, by Harry Kemp, Riding and others, Methuen (London), 1939 . £125/£30

Lives of Wives, Cassell (London), 1939 . . £250/£50

ditto, Random House (New York), 1939 . . £150/£25

Selected Poems: In Five Sets, Faber and Faber (London), 1970 (pbk) £15

ditto, W.W. Norton (New York), 1973 . . £20/£5

ditto, W.W. Norton (New York), 1973 (pbk) . . £5

The Telling, Univ of London/Athlone Press (no place), 1972 (author's name given as 'Laura (Riding) Jackson') £25/£5

ditto, Harper & Row (New York), 1973 . £10/£5

ditto, Harper & Row (New York), 1973 (100 signed copies) . . . . £100/£75

From the Chapter 'Truth' in Rational Meaning: A New Foundation For..., Priapus Press (Berkhamsted), 1975 (45 copies; wraps; author's name given as 'Laura (Riding) Jackson.') £65

It Has Taken Long..., special issue of **Chelsea 35** (New York), 1976 (pbk) £10

ditto, special issue of **Chelsea 35** (New York), 1976 (200 signed, numbered copies; pbk) £45

How A Poem Comes To Be, Lord John Press (Northridge, CA), 1980 (150 signed, numbered copies; broadside). £25

Description of Life, Targ Editions (New York), 1980 (350 signed, numbered copies; glassine d/w) . . £45/£40

Some Communications of Broad Reference, Lord John Press (Northridge, CA), 1983 (125 signed, numbered copies; no d/w) £30

ditto, Lord John Press (Northridge, CA), 1983 (26 signed, lettered copies) £100

First Awakenings, The Early Poems of Laura Riding, Persea Books (New York), 1992 . . . £10/£5

ditto, Carcanet (Manchester), 1992 . . . £10/£5

The Word Woman And Other Related Writings, Persea Books (New York), 1993 . . . . . £10/£5

ditto, Carcanet (Manchester), 1994 . . . £10/£5

Rational Meaning..., Univ of Virginia Press (Charlottesville/London), 1997 (with Schuyler B. Jackson) . £15/£5

Letters to Ken..., Brunswick Press (Cathedral City, CA), 1997 (200 numbered copies; no d/w; letters from Graves and Laura Riding to Wilfrid Kenyon Barrett, 1917-1961; edition suppressed) £1,000

ditto, Brunswick Press (Cathedral City, CA), 1997 (second edition of 50 numbered copies bound in leather). £50

Essays from 'Epilogue' 1935-1937, Carcanet (Manchester), 2001 (pbk) £5

W. HEATH ROBINSON

(b.1872 d.1944)

A British author, illustrator and cartoonist, Robinson did not find his own distinctive style until *The Adventures of Uncle Lubin*. He is popularly known for his illustrations of preposterous inventions: machines created by bespectacled, balding men and powered by steam boilers, kettles or candles, lengths of knotted string and pulleys.

Written and Illustrated by Heath Robinson

The Adventures of Uncle Lubin, Grant Richards (London), 1902 . . . . £1,500

ditto, Brentanos (New York), 1902 . . . . £1,250

ditto, Grant Richards (London), 1925 (new edition) £350/£225

ditto, Stokes (New York), 1925 . . . . £350/£225
The Child's Arabian Nights, Grant Richards (London), 1903
. . . . £850
Bill the Minder, Constable (London), 1912 . . . £300
ditto, Constable (London), 1912 (380 signed copies bound in
vellum) £1,750
ditto, Holt (New York), 1912 . . . . . £300
Some Frightful War Pictures, Duckworth (London), 1915 .
. . . . £300/£100
ditto, Duckworth (London), 1915 (wraps) . . . £135
Hunlikely, Duckworth (London), 1916 . . . £125
The Saintly Hun, Duckworth (London), [1917] (stapled
wraps) £100
Flypapers, Duckworth (London), 1919 (stapled wraps). £200
Get On With It, Duckworth (London), [1920] (with J. Birch;
stapled wraps) £200
A Jamboree of Laughter, Jones (London), [1920] (stapled
wraps) £175
The Home Made Car, Duckworth (London), [1921] (stapled
wraps) £200
Motor Mania, The Motor Owner (London), [1921] (stapled
wraps) £250
Peter Quip in Search of a Friend, S.W. Partridge (London),
[1922] £1,000
Quaint and Selected Pictures, Duckworth (London), [1922]
(with J. Birch; stapled wraps) £200
Humours of Golf, Methuen (London), 1923 (pictorial
boards) . . . . £1,000/£400
ditto, Dodd Mead (New York), 1923 . . . £800/£300
The Heath Robinson Calendar, Delgardo (London), 1933-
36 (tied with a red silk ribbon; in publisher's pictorial box)
. . . . £500 each
Absurdities, Hutchinson (London), [1934] . £350/£125
ditto, Hutchinson (London), [1934] (deluxe edition) . £400
ditto, Hutchinson (London), [1934] (250 signed copies) .
. . . . £1,000
Railway Ribaldry, G.W.R. (London), 1935 (wraps) . £65
My Line of Life, Blackie (London), 1938 . . £150/£50
Let's Laugh, A Book of Humorous Inventions, Hutchinson
(London), [1939]. . . . . . . £75/£25
Heath Robinson at War, Methuen (London), 1942 (wraps in
d/w) . . . . £25/£10
The Penguin Heath Robinson, Penguin (Harmondsworth,
Middlesex), 1966 (pbk) £10
Inventions, Duckworth (London), 1973 . . . £15/£5
The Gentle Art of Advertising, Duckworth (London), 1979.
. . . . £15/£5
Great British Industries, Duckworth (London), 1985 £10/£5

Illustrated by Heath Robinson

Danish Fairy Tales and Legends, by H.C. Andersen, Bliss
Sands & Co. (London), 1897 . . . . £100
ditto, Page & Co (Boston), 1898. . . . . £100
The Life and Exploits of Don Quixote, by Cervantes, Bliss
Sands & Co. (London), 1897 . . . . £100
The Pilgrim's Progress, by John Bunyan, Bliss Sands & Co.
(London), 1897 . . . . £60
The Giant Crab and Other Tales from Old India, by
W.H.D. Rouse, Nutt (London), 1897 . . . £350
The Queen's Story Book, edited by L. Gomme, Constable
(London), 1898 . . . . £60
The Arabian Nights Entertainments, Newnes/Constable
(London), 1899 . . . . £100

Fairy Tales from Hans Christian Andersen, Dent (London),
1899 . . . . £150
The Talking Thrush, by W.H.D. Rouse, Dent (London),
1899 . . . . £300
The Poems of Edgar Allan Poe, Bell (London), 1900 . £300
ditto, Bell (London), 1900 (75 copies on Japanese vellum) .
. . . . £1,000
Tales for Toby, by A.R. Hope, Dent (London), 1900 . £50
The Adventures of Don Quixote, by Cervantes, Dent
(London), 1902 . . . . £50
Mediaeval Stories, by H. Schuck, Sands (London), 1902 £50
**The Surprising Travels and Adventures of Baron
Munchausen**, by R.E. Raspe, Grant Richards (London),
1902 . . . . £125
ditto, Dutton (New York), 1903 . . . . . £40
Tales from Shakespeare, by C. and M. Lamb, Sands
(London), [1902]. £100
Rama and the Monkeys, edited by G. Hodgson, Dent
(London), 1903 . . . . £100
The Works of Mr Francis Rabelais, Grant Richards
(London), 1904 (2 vols) £200
Stories from Chaucer, edited by J.H. Kelman, Jack
(London), [1905]. £30
ditto, Dutton (New York), [1905] £30
Two Memoirs of Barry Lydon and Men's Wives, by W.M.
Thackeray, Caxton (London), [1906] . . . £75
Stories from the Iliad, edited by Jeanie Lang, Jack (London),
[1906] £25
Stories from the Odyssey, edited by Jeanie Lang, Jack
(London), [1906]. £25
The Monarchs of Merry England, by Roland Carse, Alf
Cooke (Leeds/London), [1907] (4 vols; stiff pictorial card
covers) £200
More Monarchs of Merry England, by Roland Carse, T.
Fisher Unwin (London), [1908] £175
Twelfth Night, by W. Shakespeare, Hodder & Stoughton
(London), [1908] £175
ditto, Hodder & Stoughton (London), [1908] (350 signed
copies, bound in vellum) £650
A Song of the English, by Rudyard Kipling, Hodder &
Stoughton (London), [c.1909] (30 colour plates) . . £200
ditto, Hodder & Stoughton (London), [c.1909] (deluxe
edition, 500 copies signed by the artist, 30 colour plates,
full vellum) £600
ditto, Hodder & Stoughton (London), [c.1909] (deluxe
edition, 50 copies signed by the artist and author, 30 colour
plates, full vellum) £1,000
ditto, Doubleday (New York), [c.1909] (30 colour plates) .
. . . . £200
ditto, Doubleday (New York), [c.1909] (deluxe edition, 500
copies signed by the artist, 30 colour plates, full vellum) .
. . . . £600
ditto, Hodder & Stoughton (London), [1912] (12 colour
plates) £45
ditto, Hodder & Stoughton/Daily Telegraph (London),
[1915] (16 colour plates) £65
ditto, Hodder & Stoughton (London), [1919] (16 colour
plates) £45
The Collected Verse of Rudyard Kipling, Doubleday Page
(New York), 1910 (9 colour plates). . . . £150
ditto, Doubleday Page (New York), 1910 (125 signed copies)
. . . . £750
The Dead King, by Rudyard Kipling, Hodder & Stoughton
(London), 1910 . . . . £65

ditto, Hodder & Stoughton (London), 1910 (wraps) . £50
Hans Andersen's Fairy Tales, Constable (London), 1913 .
. . . . £500
ditto, Constable (London), 1913 (100 signed copies, bound
in vellum) £2,500
ditto, Holt (New York), 1913 . . . . . £100
A Midsummer Night's Dream, by W. Shakespeare,
Constable (London), 1914 . . . . . . £300
ditto, Constable (London), 1914 (150 of 250 signed copies
bound in green boards) £1,250
ditto, Constable (London), 1914 (100 of 250 copies bound in
vellum) £2,000
The Water Babies, by Charles Kingsley, Constable
(London), 1915 . . . . £300
ditto, Houghton Mifflin (Boston), 1915 . . . . £200
Peacock Pie, by Walter de la Mare, Constable (London),
1916 . . . . £75
ditto, Holt (New York), 1924 . . . . £125/£20
Old-Time Stories, by C. Perrault, Constable (London), 1921
. . . . £250/£125
ditto, Dodd Mead (New York), 1921 . . £250/£125
Topsy Turvey Tales, by E.S. Munro, John Lane (London),
1923 . . . . £300/£150
The Incredible Adventures of Professor Branestawm, by
Norman Hunter, John Lane (London), 1933 . . £250/£75
Balbus, A Latin Reading Book, by G.M. Lyne, E. Arnold
(London), 1934 . . . . £75/£25
Heath Robinson's Book of Goblins, Hutchinson (London),
[1934] . . . . £350/£165
Once Upon A Time, by L.M.C. Clopet, Muller (London),
1934 . . . . £250/£125
How to Live in a Flat, by K.R.G. Browne, Hutchinson
(London), [1936] . . . . . . £100/£30
How to be a Perfect Husband, by K.R.G. Browne,
Hutchinson (London), [1937] . . . . £100/£30
How to Make a Garden Grow, by K.R.G. Browne,
Hutchinson (London), [1938] . . . . £75/£30
How to be a Motorist, by K.R.G. Browne, Hutchinson
(London), [1939] . . . . . . £75/£30
Mein Rant, by Richard F. Patterson, Blackie (London), 1940
. . . . £75/£25
How to make the Best of Things, by Cecil Hunt, Hutchinson
(London), [1940] . . . . . . £75/£20
How to Build a New World, by Cecil Hunt, Hutchinson
(London), [1941] . . . . . . £75/£20
How to Run a Communal Home, by Cecil Hunt, Hutchinson
(London), [1943] . . . . . . £75/£20

MARILYNNE ROBINSON
(b.1947)

An American author, Robinson's first novel, *Housekeeping*, won a PEN/Hemingway Award for best first novel
and was nominated for the Pulitzer Prize for Fiction. Her
second novel, *Gilead*, received the 2005 Pulitzer Prize and
the 2004 National Book Critics Circle Award for Fiction.

Novels
Housekeeping, Farrar, Straus, Giroux (New York), 1980 .
. . . . £500/£45
ditto, Faber (London), 1981 . . . . . £50/£15
Gilead, Farrar, Straus & Giroux (New York), 2004 £15/£5

ditto, Virago (London), 2005 . . . . . £15/£5
Home, Farrar, Straus & Giroux (New York), 2008 . £10/£5
ditto, Virago (London), 2008 . . . . . £10/£5

Others
*Mother Country: Britain, the Welfare State and Nuclear
Polluton*, Farrar, Straus, Giroux (New York), 1989 £20/£5
ditto, Faber (London), 1989 . . . . . £20/£5
The Death of Adam: Essays on Modern Thought, Houghton
Mifflin (New York), 1998 . . . . . £35/£10

SAX ROHMER
(b.1886 d.1959)

'Sax Rohmer' was the pseudonym for Arthur Ward, who
made his living initially by writing comedy sketches for
variety performers and short stories and serials for
magazines. He then wrote exotic thrillers which followed
the devilish exploits of the sinister Dr Fu Manchu, and
became one of the most successful and well-paid writers of
the 1920s and '30s.

'Fu Manchu' Novels
The Mystery of Dr Fu Manchu, Methuen (London), 1913 .
. . . . £1,000
ditto, as *The Insidious Dr Fu Manchu*, McBride (New
York), 1913 . . . . £800
The Return of Dr Fu Manchu, McBride (New York), 1916 .
. . . . £150
ditto, as *The Devil Doctor*, Methuen (London), 1916 . £150
The Si-Fan Mysteries, Methuen (London), 1917 . . £100
ditto, as *The Hand of Fu Manchu*, McBride (New York),
1917 . . . . £100
The Daughter of Fu Manchu, Doubleday (New York), 1931
. . . . £750/£45
ditto, Cassell (London), 1931 . . . . . £850/£45
The Mask of Fu Manchu, Doubleday (New York), 1932 .
. . . . £600/£40
ditto, Cassell (London), 1933 . . . . . £750/£40
Fu Manchu's Bride, Doubleday (New York), 1933 .
. . . . £600/£30
ditto, as *The Bride of Fu Manchu* Cassell (London), 1933 .
. . . . £700/£40
The Trail of Fu Manchu, Doubleday (New York), 1934 .
. . . . £200/£25
ditto, Cassell (London), 1934 . . . . . £400/£30
President Fu Manchu, Doubleday (New York), 1936 . .
. . . . £200/£25
ditto, Cassell (London), 1936 . . . . . £250/£25
The Drums of Fu Manchu, Doubleday (New York), 1939 .
. . . . £250/£75
ditto, Cassell (London), 1939 . . . . . £250/£75
The Island of Fu Manchu, Doubleday (New York), 1941 .
. . . . £600/£35
ditto, Cassell (London), 1941 . . . . . £600/£35
Shadow of Fu Manchu, Doubleday (New York), 1948 .
. . . . £175/£30
ditto, Jenkins (London), 1949 . . . . . £250/£30
Re-Enter Dr Fu Manchu, Fawcett (Greenwich, CT), 1957
(pbk) £20
ditto, Herbert Jenkins (London), 1957 . . . £250/£20

Emperor Fu Manchu, Herbert Jenkins (London), 1959 .
. . . . £150/£20
ditto, Fawcett (Greenwich, CT), 1959 (pbk) . . . £20
The Wrath of Fu Manchu, Tom Stacey (London), 1973 .
. . . . £65/£15
ditto, Daw (New York), 1975 (pbk) £10

Omnibus Editions
The Book of Fu Manchu, Hurst & Blackett (London), 1929
. . . . £500/£100
ditto, McBride (New York), 1929 (different contents) . .
. . . . £500/£100
The Golden Scorpion Omnibus, Grosset & Dunlap (New
York), 1938 . . . . . . £75/£20
The Sax Rohmer Omnibus, Grosset & Dunlap (New York),
1938 . . . . £75/£20

Other Novels
10.30 Folkestone Express, Lloyds Home Novels No. 41
(London), [no date] £1,000
The Sins of Severac Bablon, Cassell (London), 1914 . £150
ditto, Bookfinger (New York), 1967 (no d/w) . . . £20
The Yellow Claw, McBride (New York), 1915 . . £30
ditto, Methuen (London), 1915 . . . . . £45
Brood of the Witch Queen, Pearson (London), 1918 . £50
ditto, Doubleday (New York), 1924 . . . . £30
The Orchard of Tears, Methuen (London), 1919 . £75
ditto, Bookfinger (New York), 1970 (no d/w) . . . £20
The Quest of the Sacred Slipper, Pearson (London), 1919 .
. . . . £40
ditto, Doubleday (New York), 1919 . . . . £40
Dope, Cassell (London), 1919 . . . . £35
ditto, McBride (New York), 1919 . . . . £35
The Golden Scorpion, Methuen (London), 1919 . . £35
ditto, McBride (New York), 1920 . . . £600/£35
The Green Eyes of Bast, Cassell (London), 1920 . £400/£30
ditto, McBride (New York), 1920 . . . £300/£30
Bat-Wing, Cassell (London), 1921 . . . £200/£30
ditto, as ***Bat Wing***, Doubleday (New York), 1921 . £200/£30
Fire-Tongue, Cassell (London), 1921 . . . £400/£30
ditto, Doubleday (New York), 1922 . . £400/£30
Grey Face, Cassell (London), 1924 . . . £200/£30
ditto, Doubleday (New York), 1924 . . £200/£30
Yellow Shadows, Cassell (London), 1925. . . £250/£40
ditto, Doubleday (New York), 1926 . . £250/£40
Moon of Madness, Doubleday (New York), 1927 . £250/£40
ditto, Cassell (London), 1927 . . . £250/£40
She Who Sleeps, Doubleday (New York), 1928 . £250/£40
ditto, Cassell (London), 1928 . . . £250/£40
The Emperor of America, Doubleday (New York), 1929 .
. . . . £300/£50
ditto, Cassell (London), 1929 . . . £300/£50
The Day the World Ended, Doubleday (New York), 1930 .
. . . . £250/£40
ditto, Cassell (London), 1930 . . . £250/£40
Yu'an Hee See Laughs, Doubleday (New York), 1932. .
. . . . £225/£35
ditto, Cassell (London), 1932 . . . £225/£35
The Bat Flies Low, Doubleday (New York), 1935. £250/£40
ditto, Cassell (London), 1935 . . . £250/£40
White Velvet, Doubleday (New York), 1936 . £250/£40
ditto, Cassell (London), 1936 . . . £250/£40
Seven Sins, McBride (New York), 1943 . . £150/£35
ditto, Cassell (London), 1944 . . . £150/£35

Hangover House, Random House (New York), 1949 . .
. . . . £125/£20
ditto, Herbert Jenkins (London), 1950 . . £125/£20
Nude in Mink, Fawcett (Greenwich, CT), 1950 (pbk) . £25
ditto, as ***Sins of Sumuru***, Herbert Jenkins (London), 1951 .
. . . . £125/£20
ditto, Bookfinger (New York), 1977 (no d/w) . . . £20
Sinister Madonna, Fawcett (Greenwich, CT), 1950 (pbk) .
. . . . £20
ditto, Herbert Jenkins (London), 1956 . . £125/£20
Wulfheim, Jarrolds (London), 1950 (pseud 'Michael Furey')
. . . . £150/£35
ditto, Bookfinger (New York), 1972 (no d/w) . . . £20
Samuru, Fawcett (Greenwich, CT), 1951 (pbk) . . £20
ditto, as ***Slaves of Sumuru***, Herbert Jenkins (London), 1952
(different ending). . . . . £125/£20
ditto, Bookfinger (New York), 1979 (no d/w) . . . £20
Fire Goddess, Fawcett (Greenwich, CT), 1952 (pbk) . £25
ditto, as ***Virgin in Flames***, Herbert Jenkins (London), 1953.
. . . . £125/£20
ditto, Bookfinger (New York), 1978 (no d/w) . . . £20
The Moon is Red, Herbert Jenkins (London), 1954 £125/£20
ditto, Bookfinger (New York), 1976 (no d/w) . . . £20
Return of Samura, Fawcett (Greenwich, CT), 1954 (pbk) .
. . . . £20
ditto, as ***Sand and Satin***, Herbert Jenkins (London), 1955 .
. . . . £125/£20
ditto, Bookfinger (New York), 1978 (no d/w) . . . £20

Short Stories
The Exploits of Captain O'Hagan, Jarrolds (London), 1916
. . . . £350
ditto, Bookfinger (New York), 1968 (no d/w) . . . £20
Tales of Secret Egypt, Methuen (London), 1918 . . £100
ditto, McBride (New York), 1919 . . . . £100
The Dream Detective, Jarrolds (London), 1920 £600/£100
ditto, Doubleday (New York), 1925 . . . £350/£75
The Haunting of Low Fennel, Pearson (London), 1920 .
. . . . £600/£100
Tales of Chinatown, Cassell (London), 1922 . . £500/£25
ditto, Doubleday (New York), 1922 . . . £500/£25
Tales of East and West, Cassell (London), 1932 . £250/£65
ditto, Doubleday (New York), 1933 . . . £200/£65
Salute to Bazarada, Cassell (London), 1939 . . £125/£25
Egyptian Nights, Hale (London), 1944 (text presented as
novel) . . . . . . £200/£45
ditto, as ***Bim-Bashi Baruk of Egypt***, McBride (New York),
1944 (text presented as short stories) . . £200/£45
The Secret of Holm Peel, and Other Strange Stories, Ace
(New York), 1970 (pbk) £10

Non-Fiction Titles
Pause!, Greening (London), 1910 (anonymous) . . £500
Little Tich, Greening (London), 1911 (pbk) . . . £500
The Romance of Sorcery, Methuen (London), 1914 . £75
ditto, Dutton (New York), 1915 . . . . £75

FREDERICK ROLFE (BARON CORVO)

(b.1860 d.1913)

The author of a number of almost indigestible semi-autobiographical novels, Rolfe had a self-destructive paranoia. He is read for his 'Toto' tales and the minor classic *Hadrian the Seventh*. Sadly, he only really reached the level of genius in his vituperative letters to self-created enemies. He claimed that he had been given the title 'Baron Corvo' by an Italian countess, but there is nothing to back up his story.

Tarcissus: The Boy Martyr of Rome, privately printed (Saffron Walden, Essex), 1880 [1881] (stiff grey wraps) £2,000

ditto, Victim Press (London), 1972 (wrappers, in plastic wallet within printed card folder) £40

Stories Toto Told Me, Bodley Head (London), 1898 (paper wraps) £300

The Attack on St. Winefride's Well, privately printed (Holeywell), [1898] (anonymous; wraps) . . £2,500

In His Own Image, Bodley Head (London), 1901 (first printing with 1 advert leaf at end) £100

ditto, Knopf (New York), 1925 . . . . £65/£25

Chronicles of the House of Borgia, Grant Richards (London), 1901 . . . . £125

ditto, Dutton (New York), 1901 . . . . . £125

Hadrian the Seventh, Chatto & Windus (London), 1904 (first issue purple cloth with title and drawing stamped in white) £400

ditto, Chatto & Windus (London), 1904 (second issue with title and drawing blind stamped) £200

ditto, Knopf (New York), 1925 . . . . £75/£25

Don Tarquinio, Chatto & Windus (London), 1905 (first binding violet cloth) £250

ditto, Chatto & Windus (London), 1905 (second binding red cloth) £150

Don Renato, An Ideal Content, Francis Griffiths (London), 1909 . . . . £2,000

ditto, Chatto & Windus (London), 1963 (200 large paper copies in slipcase) . . . . . . £125/£75

ditto, Chatto & Windus (London), 1963 . . £40/£15

The Weird of the Wanderer, by Prospero and Caliban, William Rider (London), 1912 . . . . . £400

The Bull Against the Enemy of the Anglican Race, Corvine Society (London), 1929 (50 copies; wraps) . . £500

The Desire and Pursuit of the Whole, Cassell (London), [1934] (first binding, dark green cloth) . . £150/£45

ditto, Cassell (London), [1934] (second binding, light green cloth, no d/w) £30

ditto, New Directions (Norfolk, CT), 1953 . £25/£10

Hubert's Arthur, by Prospero and Caliban, Cassell (London), 1935 . . . . £125/£35

The Songs . . . of Meleager, First Editions Club (London), 1937 (750 copies; translations by Sholto Douglas extensively revised by Rolfe, cellophane d/w) £150/£125

Three Tales of Venice, The Corvine Press (Thames Ditton, Surrey), [1950] (150 numbered copies) . . . £200

Amico di Sandro, A Fragment of a Novel, The Peacocks Press (London), 1951 (150 numbered copies) . £150

ditto, The Peacocks Press (London), 1951 (10 numbered copies on parchment paper of 150) £650

Letters to Grant Richards, The Peacocks Press (Hurst, Berkshire), 1951 (200 numbered copies, no d/w) . £85

ditto, The Peacocks Press (Hurst, Berkshire), 1951 (10 numbered copies on azure handmade paper of 200) . £500

The Cardinal Prefect of Propaganda, Nicholas Vane (London), 1957 (262 copies) £100

ditto, Nicholas Vane (London), 1957 (12 lettered copies of 262) £600

Nicholas Crabbe, Chatto & Windus (London), 1958 £35/£10

ditto, Chatto & Windus (London), 1958 (215 numbered, large paper copies in slipcase) . . . £125/£100

ditto, New Directions (Norfolk, CT), 1958 . £15/£5

Letters to Pirie Gordon, Nicholas Vane (London), 1959 (350 numbered copies, glassine d/w) . . . £150/£125

ditto, Nicholas Vane (London), 1959 (14 deluxe, lettered copies) £600

Letters to Leonard Moore, Nicholas Vane (London), 1960 (350 numbered copies, glassine d/w) . £125/£100

ditto, Nicholas Vane (London), 1959 (14 deluxe, lettered copies) £600

A Letter to Father Beauclerk, Tragara Press (Edinburgh), 1960 (20 copies) £300

Letters of Baron Corvo to Kenneth Grahame, The Peacocks Press, 1962 (40 copies) £275

Letters to R.M. Dawkins, Nicholas Vane (London), 1962 (260 numbered copies) £125

ditto, Nicholas Vane (London), 1962 (14 deluxe, lettered copies) £600

Without Prejudice - One Hundred Letters from Frederick William Rolfe, Baron Corvo to John Lane, privately printed for Allen Lane (London), 1963 (600 copies, plain d/w) . . . . £125/£75

A Letter to a Small Nephew Named Claude, Typographic Library, The Univ of Iowa School of Journalism (Iowa City, IA), 1964 (134 copies; wraps) . . . £350

The Venice Letters, Cecil & Amelia Woolf (London), 1966 (25 copies) £200

ditto, Cecil & Amelia Woolf (London), 1974 . £45/£20

ditto, Cecil & Amelia Woolf (London), 1974 (200 numbered copies, slipcase) . . . . £100/£65

ditto, Cecil & Amelia Woolf (London), 1987 (first illustrated edition) . . . . £15/£5

ditto, Cecil & Amelia Woolf (London), 1987 (100 numbered copies) £40

Letters to James Walsh, Bertram Rota (London), 1972 (500 numbered copies) . . . . . . £45/£30

ditto, Bertram Rota (London), 1972 (26 lettered copies) £60

Ballade of Boys Bathing, Tragara Press (Edinburgh), 1972 (200 numbered copies) £45

Collected Poems of Fr Rolfe, Baron Corvo, Cecil & Amelia Woolf (London), 1974 . . . . . £25/£10

ditto, Cecil & Amelia Woolf (London), 1974 (200 numbered copies; slipcase) . . . . . . £50/£30

The Reverse Side of the Coin, Tragara Press (Edinburgh), 1974 (95 copies) £45

The Armed Hands, and Other Stories, Cecil & Amelia Woolf (London), 1974 . . . . . . £20/£5

ditto, Cecil & Amelia Woolf (London), 1974 (200 numbered copies) £45

Aberdeen Interval, Tragara Press (Edinburgh), 1975 (140 copies) £50

Frederick Rolfe and 'The Times' 4-12 Feb, 1901, Tragara Press (Edinburgh), 1975 (175 copies) . . . £45

Different Aspects: Frederick William Rolfe and the Foreign Office, Tragara Press (Edinburgh), 1977 (125 copies) £50

Letters to Harry Bainbridge, Enitharmon Press (London), 1977 (350 of 395 copies, glassine d/w) . . . £25/£20

ditto, Enitharmon Press (London), 1977 (45 numbered copies of 395, glassine d/w) . . . . . . £50/£45

Miscellaneous

The Rubaiyat of Umar Khaiyam, John Lane (London), 1903 (translated by Rolfe) £150

Agricultural and Pastoral Prospects of South Africa, by Col. Owen Thomas, Archibald Constable (London), 1904 (ghost-written by Rolfe) £250

CHRISTINA ROSSETTI
(b.1830 d.1894)

Christina Rossetti was rather over-shadowed during her lifetime by her brother, Dante Gabriel Rossetti, the poet and painter. Nevertheless, she was admired by contemporary poets such as Swinburne and Browning.

Poetry

Verses Dedicated to her Mother, privately printed at G. Polidori's (London) 1847 (pseud 'C.G.R.'; unlettered blue cloth wraps or lettered cloth boards) . . . £3,500

ditto, Eragny Press (London), 1906 (illustrated by Lucian Pissarro; 175 copies on paper) £500

ditto, Eragny Press (London), 1906 (10 copies on vellum) £1,750

Goblin Market, Macmillan (Cambridge), 1862 (with 16-page catalogue at rear) £1,250

ditto, London, 1893 (160 copies illustrated by Laurence Housman) £100

ditto, Harrap (London), 1933 (illustrated by Arthur Rackham; 4 colour and 19 b&w illustrations; wraps with d/w) . . . . £200/£65

ditto, Harrap (London), 1933 (400 signed, numbered copies; limp vellum, slipcase) . . . . . . £750/£600

ditto, Harrap (London), 1933 (10 numbered copies with original drawing; bound in publisher's full green morocco) £12,500

ditto, Lippincott (Philadelphia), 1933 (red boards with pictorial panel) . . . . £150/£65

The Prince's Progress and Other Poems, Macmillan (Cambridge), 1866 (green buckram) . . . £750

Poems, Roberts Bros (Boston), 1866 . . . . £300

Sing-Song, A Nursery Rhyme Book, Macmillan (Cambridge) 1872 (pictorial red cloth) . . . £500

Goblin Market, The Prince's Progress and Other Poems, Macmillan (Cambridge), 1881 . . . . £45

A Pageant and Other Poems, Macmillan (London), 1881 (dark blue cloth) £400

Verses: Chiefly Collected from Her Devotional Writings, SPCK (London), 1891 . . . . . . £35

New Poems, Macmillan (London), 1896 (dark blue cloth) £100

ditto, Macmillan (London), 1896 (dark green cloth) . £75

The Poetical Works of Christina Georgina Rossetti, Macmillan (London), 1904 . . . . . £30

Poems, Gregynog Press (Newtown, Wales), 1930 (25 copies in slipcase) £2,000

ditto, Gregynog Press (Newtown, Wales), 1930 (300 copies) £250

The Complete Poems of Christina Rossetti: A Variorum Edition, Louisiana State Univ Press (Baton Rouge, LA), 1979-1990 (3 vols) . . . . . . £60/£30

Prose

Commonplace and Other Short Stories, Ellis (London) 1870 . . . . £300

ditto, Roberts Bros (Boston), 1870 . . . . £150

Annus Domini: A Prayer for Each Day of the Year, James Parker (London), 1874 . . . . . . £75

Speaking Likenesses, Macmillan (London), 1874 (blue cloth binding) £200

ditto, Roberts Bros (Boston), 1875 . . . . £150

Seek and Find, SPCK (London), 1879 . . . £45

Called To Be Saints, SPCK (London), 1881 . . £45

Letter and Spirit, SPCK (London), 1883 . . . £45

Time Flies: a Reading Diary, SPCK (London), 1885 . £100

ditto, Roberts Bros (Boston) 1886 . . . . £100

The Face of the Deep: A Devotional Commentary on the Apocalypse, SPCK (London) £100

The Rossetti Birthday Book, privately printed, 1896 . £45

Maude: A Story for Girls, James Bowden (London) 1897 (limited to 500 copies) £45

Reflected Lights from 'The Face of the Deep', Dutton (New York) 1899 . . . . £65

Letters

The Family Letters of Christina Georgina Rossetti, Brown, Langham & Co., Ltd., 1908 . . . . . £60

ditto, Scribners (New York), 1908 . . . . £25

The Collected Letters of Christina Rossetti, Univ of Virginia Press (Charlottesville, VA), 1995 (2 vols) . . £45/£20

DANTE GABRIEL ROSSETTI
(b.1828 d.1882)

A painter and poet, Rossetti was one of the founders of the Pre-Raphelite Brotherhood. Brother of Christina, he married Elizabeth Siddal in 1860 (she died in 1862).

Poetry

Sir Hugh the Heron, G. Polidori's Private Press (London), 1843 (by 'Gabriel Rossetti, Junior'; wraps) . £1,750

Sister Helen: a ballad, Printed for Private Circulation (Oxford) 1857 (wraps; a forgery) £65

Hand and Soul, London, 1869 (wraps) . . £1,000

ditto, Kelmscott Press (for Way & Williams, Chicago) (London), 1895 (525 copies) £600

ditto, Kelmscott Press (for Way & Williams, Chicago) (London), 1895 (21 copies on vellum) . . . £2,000

Poems, privately printed (London), 1869 (printed wraps) £1,750

ditto, Ellis (London), 1870 (navy blue cloth) . . £350

ditto, Ellis (London), 1870 (green cloth) . . . £350

ditto, Ellis (London), 1870 (24 large paper copies) . £500

ditto, Boston, 1870 . . . . £100

Ballads and Sonnets, Ellis & White (London), 1881 (green cloth) £100
ditto, Ellis & White (London), 1881 (24 large paper copies) £500
ditto, Boston, 1881. . . . . £65
Verses, Privately Printed (London) 1881 (pink wraps; a forgery). £100
The Collected Works of Dante Gabriel Rossetti, Ellis & Scrutton (London) 1886 (2 vols; dark green cloth) . £250
ditto, Ellis & Scrutton (London) 1886 (large paper issue of 25 copies; 4 vols; grey paper spine, blue boards). £1,000
The Blessed Damozel, Dodd Mead (New York), 1886 (illustrated by Kenyon Cox) £100
Poetical Works of Dante Gabriel Rossetti, 1891 . £50
ditto, 1891 (large paper copies) £75
Ballads and Narrative Poems, Kelmscott Press (London), 1893 (limp vellum with ties; 310 copies) . . £1,000
ditto, Kelmscott Press (London), 1893 (6 copies on vellum). £4,000
Sonnets and Lyrical Poems, Kelmscott Press (London), 1894 (vellum with ties; 310 copies). . . . £750
ditto, Kelmscott Press (London), 1894 (6 copies on vellum). £2,500
The Blessed Damozel: A Book of Lyrics, Thomas B. Mosher (Portland, MA), 1895 (725 copies) £30
Complete Poetical Works, Roberts Bros (Boston), 1898 £30

Translations
The Early Italian Poets from Ciullo d'Alcamo to Dante Alighieri . . . Together With Dante's Vita Nuova, Smith, Elder (London) 1861 (translated by Rossetti; cloth) . £125
ditto, as *Dante and His Circle: With the Italian poets Preceding Him*, Ellis and White (London), 1874. . £50
Lenore: A Ballad by G.A. Burger, Ellis And Elvey (London), 1900 . . . . £75
Henry the Leper by Hartmann von Aue, Bibliophile Society (Boston, Ma), 1905 (447 sets; 2 vols in slipcase). . £100

Letters
Dante Gabriel Rossetti: Family Letters, Ellis And Elvey (London), 1895 . . . . £75
ditto, Roberts Bros (Boston, 1895 (2 vols) . . . £65
Letters of D.G. Rossetti to His Publisher, Ellis, Scholartis Press (London), 1928 (560 copies; no d/w) . . . £80
Letters, O.U.P. (London), 1965-7 (4 vols) . . £100/£50

HENRY ROTH
(b.1906 d.1995)

Henry Roth was an American novelist and short story writer whose first published novel, *Call It Sleep* (1934), had to wait until it was republished in the 1960s before it was hailed as a masterpiece of Jewish American literature. It was sixty years before he finished another novel.

Call It Sleep, Ballou (New York), 1934 (first printing d/w with text on front flap beginning 'Underlying the Splendid surface of this first novel...') . . . . £4,500/£400
ditto, Ballou (New York), 1934 (second printing d/w with blurb from the Minneapolis Star and text on front flap begins 'So excellently conceived and so beautifully executed...'). . . . . £1,000/£300

ditto, Joseph (London), 1963 . . . . . £150/£25
ditto, The Arion Press (San Francisco, CA), 1995 (300 signed, numbered copies in leather backed pictorial boards; pictorial cloth slipcase) . . . . £400/£350
ditto, The Arion Press (San Francisco, CA), 1995 (26 signed, lettered copies; slipcase) . . . . . £500/£450
Nature's First Green, Targ Editions (New York), 1979 (350 signed, numbered copies; unprinted yellow d/w) . £50/£40
Shifting Landscape; A Composite 1925-1987, Jewish Publication Society (Philadelphia, PA), 1987 . £15/£5
A Star Shines over Mt Morris Park, St Martin's Press (New York), 1994 . . . . £15/£5
ditto, St Martin's Press (New York), 1994 (150 signed, numbered copies bound in full leather; slipcase) . £100/£75
ditto, Weidenfeld & Nicolson (London), 1994. . £15/£5
A Diving Rock on the Hudson, St Martin's Press (New York), 1995 . . . . £15/£5
ditto, Weidenfeld & Nicolson (London), 1995. . £15/£5
From Bondage, St Martin's Press (New York), 1996 £15/£5
ditto, Weidenfeld & Nicolson (London), 1996. . £10/£5
Requiem for Harlem, St Martin's Press (New York), 1998 . . . . £10/£5
ditto, Weidenfeld & Nicolson (London), 1998. . £10/£5

PHILIP ROTH
(b.1933)

Philip Roth is a multi award-winning novelist who in 2001 received the highest award of the American Academy of Arts and Letters, the Gold Medal in fiction, given every six years 'for the entire work of the recipient'.

'David Kepesh' Novels
The Breast, Holt, Rinehart & Winston (New York), 1972 . . . . £15/£5
ditto, Holt, Rinehart & Winston (New York), 1972 (60 signed, numbered copies) . . . . . £250/£240
ditto, Cape (London), 1973 . . . . . £15/£5
The Professor of Desire, Farrar, Straus & Giroux (New York), 1977 . . . . £15/£5
ditto, Cape (London), 1978 . . . . . £10/£5
The Dying Animal, Houghton Mifflin (New York), 2001 . . . . £10/£5
ditto, Cape (London), 2001 . . . . . . £10/£5

'Zuckerman' Novels
My Life As a Man, Holt, Rinehart & Winston (New York), 1974 . . . . £15/£5
ditto, Cape (London), 1974 . . . . . £15/£5
The Ghost Writer, Farrar, Straus & Giroux (New York), 1979 . . . . £10/£5
ditto, The Franklin Library (Franklin Centre, PA), 1979 (full leather limited edition) £20
ditto, Cape (London), 1979 . . . . . £10/£5
Zuckerman Unbound, Farrar, Straus & Giroux (New York), 1981 . . . . £10/£5
ditto, Farrar, Straus & Giroux (New York), 1981 (350 signed, numbered copies; slipcase) . . . . £45/£25
ditto, The Franklin Library (Franklin Centre, PA), 1981 (full leather limited edition) £20
ditto, Cape (London), 1981 . . . . . £10/£5

The Anatomy Lesson, Farrar, Straus & Giroux (New York), 1983 . . . . £10/£5
ditto, The Franklin Library (Franklin Centre, PA), 1983 (full leather signed limited edition) £20
ditto, Cape (London), 1984 . . . . . £10/£5
Zuckerman Bound: A Trilogy and Epilogue, Farrar, Straus & Giroux (New York), 1985 . . . . £10/£5
ditto, Cape (London), 1987 . . . . . £10/£5
The Prague Orgy, Farrar, Straus & Giroux (New York), 1985 . . . . £10/£5
ditto, Cape (London), 1985 . . . . . £10/£5
Exit Ghost, Houghton Mifflin (New York), 2007 . £10/£5
ditto, Houghton Mifflin (New York), 2007 (750 signed presentation copies; unnumbered no d/w) . . . £100
ditto, Cape (London), 2007 . . . . . £10/£5

American Trilogy

American Pastoral, Houghton Mifflin (New York), 1997 .
. . . . £10/£5
ditto, The Franklin Library (Franklin Centre, PA), 1997 (full leather signed limited edition) £65
ditto, Cape (London), 1997 . . . . . £10/£5
I Married a Communist, Houghton Mifflin (New York), 1998 . . . . £10/£5
ditto, The Franklin Library (Franklin Centre, PA), 1998 (full leather signed limited edition) £65
ditto, Cape (London), 1998 . . . . . £10/£5
The Human Stain, Houghton Mifflin (New York), 2000 .
. . . . £10/£5
ditto, The Franklin Library (Franklin Centre, PA), 2000 (full leather signed limited edition) £65
ditto, Cape (London), 2000 . . . . . £10/£5

Other Novels

Letting Go, Random House (New York), 1962 . £100/£15
ditto, Deutsch (London), 1962 . . . . £45/£10
When She Was Good, Random House (New York), 1967 .
. . . . £25/£5
ditto, Cape (London), 1967 . . . . . £20/£5
Portnoy's Complaint, Random House (New York), 1969 .
. . . . £80/£10
ditto, Random House (New York), 1969 (600 numbered, signed copies) . . . . . £300/£200
ditto, Cape (London), 1969 . . . . . £35/£10
Our Gang (Starring Tricky and His Friends), Random House (New York), 1971 . . . . . £20/£5
ditto, Cape (London), 1971 . . . . . £15/£5
The Great American Novel, Holt, Rinehart & Winston (New York), 1973 . . . . . . £15/£5
ditto, Cape (London), 1973 . . . . . £15/£5
The Counterlife, Farrar, Straus & Giroux (New York), 1986
. . . . £15/£5
ditto, The Franklin Library (Franklin Centre, PA), 1986 (full leather signed limited edition) £20
ditto, Cape (London), 1987 . . . . . £10/£5
Deception, Simon & Schuster (New York), 1990 . £15/£5
ditto, Cape (London), 1990 . . . . . £10/£5
Patrimony: A True Story, Simon & Schuster (New York), 1991 . . . . £10/£5
ditto, Cape (London), 1991 . . . . . £10/£5
Operation Shylock: A Confession, Simon & Schuster (New York), 1993 . . . . £10/£5
ditto, The Franklin Library (Franklin Centre, PA), 1983 (full leather signed limited edition) £40

ditto, Cape (London), 1993 . . . . . £10/£5
Sabbath's Theater, Houghton Mifflin (New York), 1995 .
. . . . £10/£5
ditto, Cape (London), 1995 . . . . . £10/£5
The Plot Against America, Houghton Mifflin (New York), 2004 . . . . £10/£5
ditto, Cape (London), 2004 . . . . . £10/£5
Everyman, Houghton Mifflin (New York), 2006 . £10/£5
ditto, Cape (London), 2006 . . . . . £10/£5
Indignation, Houghton Mifflin (New York), 2008 . £10/£5
ditto, Cape (London), 2008 . . . . . £10/£5
The Humbling, Houghton Mifflin (New York), 2009 £10/£5
ditto, Cape (London), 2009 . . . . . £10/£5

Short Stories

Goodbye Columbus and *Five Short Stories*, Houghton Mifflin (Boston), 1959 . . . . . £600/£65
ditto, Deutsch (London), 1959 (title story only) . £350/£35
On the Air: A Long Story, New American Review (New York), 1970 (1,500 numbered copies, stapled wraps) . £25
Novotny's Pain, Sylvester & Orphanos (Los Angeles, CA), 1980 (300 signed, numbered copies; no d/w) . . £75
A Philip Roth Reader, Farrar, Straus & Giroux (New York), 1980 . . . . £10/£5
ditto, Cape (London), 1981 . . . . . £10/£5
The Conversion of the Jews, Creative Education, 1993 (Mankato, MN) . . . . £10/£5
His Mistress's Voice, The Press Of Appletree Alley (Lewisburg, PA), 1995 (195 signed, numbered copies; slipcase). . . . . £1,000/£750

Non-Fiction

Reading Myself and Others, Farrar, Straus & Giroux (New York), 1975 . . . . £15/£5
ditto, Cape (London), 1975 . . . . . £15/£5
The Facts: A Novelist's Autobiography, Farrar, Straus & Giroux (New York), 1988 . . . . . £10/£5
ditto, Farrar, Straus & Giroux (New York), 1988 (250 signed, numbered copies; slipcase) . . . £75/£50
ditto, Cape (London), 1989 . . . . . £10/£5
Shop Talk: A Writer And His Colleagues And Their Work, Houghton Mifflin (New York), 2001 . . . £10/£5
ditto, Cape (London), 2001 . . . . . £10/£5

J.K. ROWLING

(b.1965)

Rowling's books about Harry Potter, a young wizard, are a modern publishing phenomenon in terms of their huge sales and the enormous prices commanded by the first edition of the first title. Rowling has gained international attention and won multiple awards, as well as earnings that have reputedly made her wealthier than Queen Elizabeth II.

Harry Potter and the Philosopher's Stone, Bloomsbury (London), 1997 (laminated boards; no d/w; 500 copies) .
. . . . £15,000
ditto, Bloomsbury (London), 1997 (200 proof copies; pbk) .
. . . . £3,000
ditto, Bloomsbury (London), 1997 (first pbk edition) . £75
ditto, Bloomsbury (London), 1999 (collector's edition, no d/w) £400

ditto, as **Harry Potter and the Sorcerer's Stone**, Levine/Scholastic (New York), 1998   .   £1,500/£750
ditto, Levine/Scholastic (New York), 2000 (collector's edition, no d/w) £50
Harry Potter and the Chamber of Secrets, Bloomsbury (London), 1998   .   .   .   .   £1,500/£750
ditto, Bloomsbury (London), 1997 (300 proof copies; pbk) .
.   .   .   .   £1,500
ditto, Bloomsbury (London), 1999 (first pbk edition)   .   £25
ditto, Bloomsbury (London), 1999 (collector's edition, no d/w) £100
ditto, Levine/Scholastic (New York), 1999 (No 'Year 2' on spine of book or jacket)   .   .   .   .   £50/£15
Harry Potter and the Prisoner of Azkaban, Bloomsbury (London), 1999 (first issue with 'Joanne Rowling' on verso title-page)   .   .   .   .   .   £1,250/£750
ditto, Bloomsbury (London), 1999 (second issue with 'J.K. Rowling' on verso title-page)   .   .   .   £125/£30
ditto, Bloomsbury (London), 1999 (third issue with 'J.K. Rowling' on verso title-page, printer's name omitted, and adverts at the back)   .   .   .   .   .   £125/£30
ditto, Bloomsbury (London), 1999 (first state uncorrected proof; approx 50 copies; purple pbk)   .   .   .   £1,500
ditto, Bloomsbury (London), 1999 (second state uncorrected proof; approx 250 copies; green pbk)   .   .   .   £1,000
ditto, Bloomsbury (London), 2000 (first pbk edition)   .   £5
ditto, Bloomsbury (London), 1999 (collector's edition, no d/w) £750
ditto, Levine/Scholastic (New York), 1999   .   £50/£15
Harry Potter and the Goblet of Fire, Bloomsbury (London), 2000   .   .   .   .   .   .   £20/£5
ditto, Bloomsbury (London), 2000 (collector's edition, no d/w) £50
ditto, Levine/Scholastic (New York), 2000   .   .   £20/£5
ditto, Levine/Scholastic (New York), 2000 (25 copies with original artwork and certificate)   .   .   .   £2,500
Harry Potter and the Order of the Phoenix, Bloomsbury (London), 2003 (jacket for children)   .   .   £15/£5
ditto, Bloomsbury (London), 2003 (jacket for adults) £15/£5
ditto, Levine/Scholastic (New York), 2003   .   £15/£5
Harry Potter and the Half-Blood Prince, Bloomsbury (London), 2005 (jacket for children)   .   .   £10/£5
ditto, Bloomsbury (London), 2005 (jacket for adults) £10/£5
ditto, Bloomsbury (London), 2005 (collector's edition, no d/w) £45
ditto, Levine/Scholastic (New York), 2005   .   £15/£5
ditto, Levine/Scholastic (New York), 2005 (deluxe edition; slipcase).   .   .   .   .   .   £45/£20
Harry Potter and the Deathly Hallows, Bloomsbury (London), 2007 (jacket for children)   .   .   £10/£5
ditto, Bloomsbury (London), 2007 (jacket for adults) £10/£5
ditto, Bloomsbury (London), 2007 (collector's edition, no d/w) £25
ditto, Levine/Scholastic (New York), 2007   .   £10/£5
ditto, Levine/Scholastic (New York), 2005 (deluxe edition; slipcase; 7 prints).   .   .   .   .   £35/£20

'Harry Potter' Box Sets
Harry Potter Gift Set, Bloomsbury (London), 1998 (hardback of *Harry Potter and the Philosopher's Stone* and *Harry Potter and the Chamber of Secrets*)   .   .   £75
Harry Potter and the Goblet of Fire, Bloomsbury (London), 2001 (first edition and de-luxe edition together in slipcase

with signed watercolour by Jason Cockcroft as frontis and/or signed bookplate from Rowling).   .   .   £1,000
Harry Potter and the Order of the Phoenix, Bloomsbury (London), 2003 (hardback first edition multiple issue with poster in presentation box) £65
Harry Potter Deluxe Edition Box Set, Bloomsbury (London), 2004   .   .   .   .£150

Other Books
Quidditch Through the Ages, Bloomsbury (London), 2001 (pbk) £5
Fantastic beasts and Where to Find Them, Bloomsbury (London), 2001 (pbk). £5
Harry Potter's School Books, Bloomsbury (London), 2001 (by Kennilworthy Whisp'; above two books with Hogwarts library book plate; set sealed in satchel .   .   .   £20
Tales of Beedle the Bard, Privately Printed (London), 2007 (seven copies handwritten & illustrated by the author, in Italian handmade notebooks, bound in brown morocco, embellished with silver and moonstones)   £2 million
ditto, Children's High Level Group/Bloomsbury (London), 2008 (trade edition with the tales from the above edition and a commentary by Pofessor Albus Dumbledore; hardback without d/w) £5
ditto, Scholastic (Scranton, PA), 2008   .   .   .   £5
ditto, Children's High Level Group (London), 2008 (Collectors' Edition with 10 new illustrations, metalwork and clasp, replica gemstones; in slipcase disguised as wizarding textbook from Hogwarts library)   .   .   .£100

DAMON RUNYON
(b.1884 d.1946)

Runyon was best known for his post-Prohibition Broadway short stories of gangsters, hustlers and gamblers, written in vernacular in the present tense. Two of his stories were the basis for the musical *Guys and Dolls*.

Poetry
The Tents of Trouble, Fitzgerald (New York), 1911 (brown cloth; no d/w) £75
Rhymes of the Firing Line, Fitzgerald (New York), 1912 (blue cloth spine and tan paper boards; no d/w)   .   £65
Poems for Men, Duell, Sloan and Pearce (New York), 1947
.   .   .   .   £25/£10

Short Stories
Guys and Dolls, Stokes (New York), 1932   .   £3,500/£500
ditto, Jarrolds (London), 1932   .   .   .   .   £2,000/£250
Damon Runyon's Blue Plate Special, Stokes (New York), 1934   .   .   .   .£600/£75
Money From Home, Stokes (New York), 1935   .   £450/£50
More Than Somewhat, Constable (London), 1937.   £25/£10
Furthermore, Constable (London), 1938 .   .   .   £25/£10
Take It Easy, Stokes (New York), 1938   .   .   .£350/£40
ditto, Constable (London), 1938 .   .   .   .   £50/£10
My Wife Ethel, McKay (Philadelphia, PA), 1939   .   £45/£10
ditto, Constable (London), 1939 .   .   .   .   £50/£10
Runyon à la Carte, Lippincott (Philadelphia, PA), 1944   .
.   .   .   .   £75/£15
ditto, Constable (London), 1946 .   .   .   .   £50/£10

Three Wise Guys, Avon (New York), 1946 (pbk) .   . £10
Runyon First and Last, Lippincott (Philadelphia, PA), 1949
.   .   .   . £25/£10
ditto, Constable (London), 1954 .   .   .   .   . £50/£10
Runyon on Broadway, Constable (London), 1950 (contains
the stories from *More Than Somewhat*, *Furthermore* and
Take It Easy).   .   .   .   . £25/£10
The Turps, Constable (London), 1951   .   .   . £25/£10
More Guys and Dolls, Garden City Books (Garden City,
NY), 1951   .   .   .   . £25/£10

Play
A Slight Case of Murder, Dramatists Play Service (New
York), 1940 (with Howard Lindsay; wraps) .   .   . £10

Non-Fiction
My Old Man, Stackpole (New York), 1939   .   . £50/£10
ditto, Constable (London), 1940 .   .   .   .   . £40/£5
In Our Town, Creative Age Press (New York), 1946 £40/£10
Short Takes, Whittlesey House (New York), 1946.   . £15/£5
ditto, Constable (London), 1948 .   .   .   .   . £40/£5
All Horse Players Die Broke, The Del Mar Turf Club (Bel
Mar, CA), 1946 (no d/w) £30
Trials and Other Tribulations, Lippincott (Philadelphia,
PA), 1947   .   .   .   . £25/£10

Collected Editions
The Best of Runyon, Stokes (New York), 1938   . £25/£10
The Damon Runyon Omnibus, Blue Ribbon (New York),
1939   .   .   .   . £20/£5

RUPERT
see Mary Tourtel

SALMAN RUSHDIE
(b.1947)

Salman Rushdie, purveyor of postmodernist pyrotechnics,
was born in Bombay but migrated to Britain in 1965. His
writing is often described as 'Magic Realism', and has
brought him great literary respect. *Midnight's Children* was
awarded the 'Booker of Bookers' prize in 1993: it was
judged the best novel of the first 25 years of the Booker
Prize. He was knighted, controversially, in 2007.

Novels
Grimus, Gollancz (London), 1975   .   .   . £300/£35
ditto, Overlook Press (Woodstock, NY), 1979.   . £75/£20
Midnight's Children, Knopf (New York), 1981   . £500/£40
ditto, Cape (London), 1981 .   .   .   .   . £500/£40
Shame, Cape (London), 1983   .   .   .   . £25/£5
ditto, Knopf (New York), 1983   .   .   .   . £20/£5
The Satanic Verses, Viking (London), 1988   .   . £40/£5
ditto, Viking (London), 1988 (100 arabic numbered copies).
.   .   .   . £1,000
ditto, Viking (London), 1988 (12 leather-bound copies
signed and numbered I to XII; no d/w, printed on vellum
antique laid and bound in goatskin).   .   .   . £5,000
ditto, Viking (New York), 1988 .   .   .   .   . £20/£5

ditto, Penguin (London), 1988 (suppressed edition; pbk) £650
The Moor's Last Sigh, Cape (London), 1995 .   . £10/£5
ditto, Cape (London), 1995 (1,000 numbered proof copies;
pbk) £25
ditto, Cape (London), 1995 (200 signed copies, no d/w,
slipcase).   .   .   .   . £75/£50
ditto, Cape (London), 1995 (Limited Waterstone's Edition).
.   .   .   . £20
ditto, Pantheon (New York), 1995   .   .   . £10/£5
ditto, Pantheon (New York), 1995 (1,000 signed advance
reading copies; pbk, in slipcase)   .   .   . £25/£15
The Ground Beneath Her Feet, Cape (London), 1999 £10/£5
ditto, Cape (London), 1999 (150 signed copies, full leather-
bound, in slipcase)   .   .   .   .   . £125/£100
ditto, Holt (New York), 1999   .   .   .   . £10/£5
Fury, Cape (London), 2001 .   .   .   .   . £10/£5
ditto, Random House (New York), 2001   .   . £10/£5
Shalimar the Clown, Cape (London), 2005   .   . £10/£5
ditto, Random House (New York), 2005 .   .   . £10/£5
The Enchantress of Florence, Cape (London), 2008 £10/£5
ditto, Cape (London), 2008 (1000 signed copies)   . £35/£15
ditto, Blackwell (London), 2008 (100 signed copies)   .   .
.   .   .   . £125/£75
ditto, Random House (New York), 2008   .   . £10/£5

Children's Title
Haroun and the Sea of Stories, Granta (London), 1990   .
.   .   .   . £20/£5
ditto, Granta (London), 1990 (251 signed copies) .   . £250
ditto, Viking (New York), 1991 .   .   .   .   . £20/£5

Short Stories
Two Stories, privately printed (London), 1989 (60 signed
copies of 72; with 5 woodcuts and 3 linocuts by Bhupen
Khakhar) £500
ditto, privately printed (London), 1989 (12 specially bound,
signed copies of 72) £2,500
East, West, Cape (London), 1994   .   .   . £15/£5
ditto, Pantheon (New York), 1994   .   .   . £10/£5

Others
The Jaguar Smile: A Nicaraguan Journey, Picador
(London), 1987 .   .   .   . £10/£5
ditto, Viking (New York), 1987 .   .   .   . £10/£5
Is Nothing Sacred?, Granta (London & New York), 1990
(stapled wraps) £5
In Good Faith, Granta (London & New York), 1990 (stapled
wraps) £5
Imaginary Homelands: Essays and Criticism, Granta
(London), 1991   .   .   .   .   .   . £10/£5
ditto, Viking (New York), 1991 .   .   .   . £10/£5
The Wizard of Oz, B.F.I. (London), 1992 (pbk)   .   . £10
The Screenplay of Midnight's Children, Vintage (London),
1999 (pbk) £5
Conversations with Salman Rushdie, Univ Press of Missis-
sippi (Jackson, MS), 2000 (hardback; no d/w)   .   . £10
ditto, Univ Press of Mississippi (Jackson, MS), 2000 (pbk) £5
Step Across This Line: Collected Non-Fiction 1992-2002,
Cape (London), 2002 .   .   .   .   .   . £10/£5
ditto, Random House (New York), 2002   .   . £10/£5

R.R. RYAN

(b.1883 d.1950)

R.R. Ryan has gained a cult following in recent years as the author of 11 thriller novels. Recent research has found that R.R. Ryan was the *nom de plume* of Rex Ryan, itself a psuedonym used by Evelyn Bradley, a theatrical manager who was born in Waterloo, Lancashire, and who lived much of his adult life in Hove, Sussex.

Novels Published as 'R.R. Ryan'
The Right To Kill, Herbert Jenkins Limited (London), 1936
. . . . £1,000/£300
Devil's Shelter, Herbert Jenkins Limited (London), 1937 .
. . . . £1,500/£500
Death of a Sadist, Herbert Jenkins Limited (London), 1937.
. . . . £1,000/£300
The Subjugated Beast, Herbert Jenkins Limited (London), 1938 . . . . £1,200/£400
Freak Museum, Herbert Jenkins Limited (London), 1938 .
. . . . £1,500/£500
Echo of a Curse, Herbert Jenkins Limited (London), 1939 .
. . . . £1,500/£500
No Escape, Herbert Jenkins Limited (London), 1940 . .
. . . . £1,500/£500

Novels Published as 'Cameron Carr'
A New Face at the Door, Herbert Jenkins Limited (London), 1937 . . . . £200/£65
Gilded Clay, Herbert Jenkins Limited (London), 1938 . .
. . . . £200/£65
The Other, Herbert Jenkins Limited (London), 1938 . .
. . . . £200/£65

Novel Published as 'John Galton'
The Stars I Kneel To, Herbert Jenkins Limited (London), 1939 . . . . £100/£35

Novel Published as 'Noel Despard'
The Tyranny of Virtue, Willis (London), 1925 . £200/£65

VITA SACKVILLE-WEST

(b.1892 d.1962)

Vita Sackville-West received recognition with her volume of poetry *The Land*, which won the Hawthornden Prize. She also wrote prose, was a passionate gardener, and was the model for Virginia Woolf's *Orlando*. *All Passion Spent* is her best known work today; it is the story of an elderly lady who embraces freedom and whimsy after a lifetime of convention.

Novels
Heritage, Collins (London), 1919 . . . . . £100
ditto, Doran (New York), 1919 . . . . . . £65
The Dragon in Shallow Waters, Collins (London), 1921 .
. . . . £500/£75
ditto, Putnam's (New York), 1922 . . . £400/£65
Challenge, Doran (New York), 1923. . . . £500/£75
ditto, Collins (London), 1974 . . . . £15/£5
Grey Wethers, Heinemann (London), 1923 . . £350/£45

ditto, Doran (New York), 1923 . . . . £350/£45
Seducers in Equador, Hogarth Press (London), 1924 . .
. . . . £350/£40
ditto, Doran (New York), 1925 . . . . £250/£35
The Edwardians, Hogarth Press (London), 1930 . £150/£20
ditto, Hogarth Press (London), 1930 (125 signed copies, no d/w) £400
ditto, Doran (New York), 1930 . . . . £100/£15
All Passion Spent, Hogarth Press (London), 1931 . £250/£40
ditto, Doran (New York), 1931 . . . . £150/£25
Family History, Hogarth Press (London), 1932 . £300/£30
ditto, Doubleday Doran (New York), 1932 . £175/£20
The Death of Noble Godavary and Gottfried Kunstler, Benn (London), 1932 (pbk). £15
The Dark Island, Hogarth Press (London), 1934 . £250/£30
ditto, Doran (New York), 1934 . . . . £175/£20
Grand Canyon, Joseph (London), 1942 . . . £50/£15
ditto, Doran (New York), 1942 . . . . £35/£10
Devil at Westease, Doubleday Doran (New York), 1947 .
. . . . £125/£20
The Easter Party, Joseph (London), 1953 . £35/£15
ditto, Doubleday (New York), 1953 . . £30/£10
No Signposts in the Sea, Joseph (London), 1961 . £25/£10
ditto, Doubleday (New York), 1961 . . £20/£5

Short Stories
The Heir, privately printed, [1922] (100 signed copies) .
. . . . £400
ditto, Heinemann (London), 1922 (with four extra stories) .
. . . . £250/£35
ditto, Doran (New York), 1922 . . . . £200/£25
Thirty Clocks Strike the Hour and Other Stories, Doubleday Doran (New York), 1934 . . . £200/£25

Poetry
Chatterton, privately printed (Sevenoaks, Kent), 1909 (stapled wraps) £3,000
ditto, privately printed (Sevenoaks, Kent), 1909 (boards) .
. . . . £4,000
Constantinople, Eight Poems, privately printed, Complete Press (London), 1915 (stapled wraps) . . . £350
Poems of West and East, John Lane (London), 1917 . £125
Orchard and Vineyard, John Lane (London), 1921 . .
. . . . £300/£100
The Land, Heinemann (London), 1926 . . . £145/£30
ditto, Heinemann (London), 1926 (125 copies, slipcase) .
. . . . £750/£500
ditto, Doubleday (New York), 1927 . . . . £145/£30
King's Daughter, Hogarth Press (London), 1929 . £150/£30
ditto, Doubleday (New York), 1930 . . . £125/£25
Sissinghurst, Hogarth Press (London), 1931 (500 signed, numbered copies, hand-printed by the Woolfs, no d/w) .
. . . . £400
Invitation to Cast Out Care, Faber (London), 1931 £50/£20
ditto, Faber (London), 1931 (200 copies) . . . £150
V. Sackville-West, Benn (London), 1931 (stapled wraps) £5
Collected Poems, Volume One, Hogarth Press (London), 1933 . . . . £125/£40
ditto, Hogarth Press (London), 1933 (150 copies) . . £350
ditto, Doubleday (New York), 1934 . . . £100/£30
Solitude, Hogarth Press (London), 1938 . . £65/£15
ditto, Hogarth Press (London), 1938 (100 signed copies) .
. . . . £350/£225
Selected Poems, Hogarth Press (London), 1941 . £40/£10

The Garden, Joseph (London), 1946 . . . £60/£20
ditto, Joseph (London), 1946 (750 signed copies, plain d/w). . . . . £250/£145
ditto, Doubleday (New York), 1946 . . £50/£20

Travel
Passenger to Tehran, Hogarth Press (London), 1926 . . . . £500/£100
Twelve Days, Hogarth Press (London), 1928 £500/£100
ditto, Doubleday (New York), 1928 . . . £400/£75

Gardening
Some Flowers, Cobden-Sanderson (London), 1937 £75/£30
ditto, Abrams (New York), 1993. . . . £10/£5
ditto, Pavillon (London), 1993 (watercolours by Graham Rust) . . . . . . £10/£5
Country Notes, Joseph (London), 1939 . . £75/£30
ditto, Harper (New York), 1940 . . . . £40/£10
Country Notes in Wartime, Hogarth Press (London), 1940 . . . . . . £65/£15
ditto, Doubleday Doran (New York), 1941 . £50/£10
In Your Garden, Joseph (London), 1951 . . £45/£15
Hidcote Manor Garden, Country Life (London), 1952 . . . . £30/£10
In Your Garden Again, Joseph (London), 1953 . £45/£15
More For Your Garden, Joseph (London), 1955 . £35/£10
Even More For Your Garden, Joseph (London), 1958 . . . . £35/£10
A Joy of Gardening, Harper & Row (New York), 1958 . . . . £25/£10
ditto, as **A Joy of Gardening: A Selection for Americans**, Harper (New York), 1958 . £25/£10
V. Sackville-West's Garden Book, Joseph (London), 1968 . . . . £20/£5
ditto, Atheneum (New York), 1968 . . . £15/£5
The Illustrated Garden Book, Joseph (London), 1986 £15/£5
ditto, Atheneum (New York), 1986 . . . £15/£5

Historical and Biographical
Knole and the Sackvilles, Heinemann (London), 1922 . . . . £500/£125
ditto, Doran (New York), [1924]. . . . £350/£65
Aphra Benn, The Incomparable Astrea, Gerald Howe (London), 1927 . . . . £150/£45
ditto, Viking (New York), 1928 . . . £125/£40
Andrew Marvell, Faber (London), 1929 . . £100/£35
ditto, Faber (London), 1929 (75 signed copies) . £250
Saint Joan of Arc, Cobden-Sanderson (London), 1936. . . . . . . £45/£15
ditto, Cobden-Sanderson (London), 1936 (120 copies) . £150
ditto, Doubleday (New York), 1936 . . . £35/£10
Joan of Arc, Hogarth Press (London), 1937 . £65/£10
Pepita, Hogarth Press (London), 1937 . . £125/£15
ditto, Doubleday (New York), 1937 . . . £35/£10
English Country Houses, Collins (London), 1941. £35/£10
ditto, Random House (New York), 1949 . . £15/£5
The Eagle and the Dove, Joseph (London), 1943 . £30/£10
ditto, Doubleday (New York), 1944 . . . £30/£10
Daughter of France, Joseph (London), 1959 . £30/£10
ditto, Doubleday (New York), 1959 . . . £30/£10

Others
The Diary of the Lady Anne Clifford, Heinemann (London), 1923 (edited by V. Sackville-West). . . . £150/£35

Duineser Elegien, by Rainer Maria Rilke, Hogarth Press (London), 1931 (translated by Vita & Edward Sackville-West; 230 numbered copies signed by the translators) £1,500
The Women's Land Army, Joseph (London), 1944 £65/£15
Nursery Rhymes, Dropmore Press (London), 1947 (550 copies) . . . . £125/£45
ditto, Dropmore Press (London), 1947 (25 signed copies of the above) . . . . . . £1,250/£1,000
ditto, Joseph (London), 1950 . . . . £30/£10
Faces: Profiles of Dogs, Harvill Press (London), 1961 . . . . £25/£10
Dearest Andrew, Letters to Andrew Reiber, 1951-62, Joseph (London), 1979 . . . . £20/£10
ditto, Scribner's (New York), 1979 . . . £15/£5
Letters from V. Sackville-West to Virginia Woolf, Joseph (London), 1984 . . . . . . £20/£5
ditto, Morrow (New York), 1985 . . . £15/£5

SAKI
(b.1870 d.1916)

'Saki' was the pseudonym adopted by H.H. Munro for his predominantly humorous novels and short stories. He is considered by many to be a master of the short story and is often compared to O. Henry and Dorothy Parker. Although his writing is whimsical and satirical, some critics have noted a darker, more sinister undercurrent.

Novels
The Unbearable Bassington, John Lane (London), 1912 £75
When William Came, John Lane (London), 1913 . . £65
The Collected Novels and Plays, John Lane/Bodley Head (London), 1933. . . . . . £35/£15

Short Stories
Reginald, Methuen (London), 1904 . . . . £125
Reginald in Russia and Other Sketches, Methuen (London), 1910 . . . . £100
The Chronicles of Clovis, John Lane (London), 1911 . £125
Beasts and Superbeasts, John Lane (London), 1914 . £100
The Toys of Peace, John Lane/Bodley Head (London), 1919 . . . . £40
The Square Egg and Other Sketches, John Lane/Bodley Head (London), 1924 . . . . . £125/£40
The Collected Short Stories, John Lane/Bodley Head (London), 1930 . . . . . . £25/£10
Sredni Vashtar, Tartarus Press (Carlton-in-Coverdale), 2008 . . . . £30/£10

Others
The Rise of the Russian Empire, Grant Richards (London), 1900 . . . . £200
The Westminster Alice, Westminster Gazette (London), 1902 (wraps). £150
ditto, Westminster Gazette (London), 1902 (boards) . £125

J.D. SALINGER

(b.1919 d.2010)

Salinger is essentially a one-novel novelist. *The Catcher in the Rye* is narrated by an insightful but rebellious teenager and was banned in some countries because of its 'offensive' language. It was unpopular with critics upon publication, but quickly gained admirers and is still widely read, particularly in the U.S., where it is considered an acute depiction of teenage angst.

Novel
The Catcher in the Rye, Little, Brown (Boston), 1951 (first issue d/w with Salinger's photo on rear panel) £6,000/£750
ditto, Hamish Hamilton (London), 1951 . . £700/£85

Short Stories
Nine Stories, Little, Brown (Boston), 1953 . £1,250/£100
ditto, as *For Esme - With Love and Squalor and Other Stories*, Hamish Hamilton (London), 1953 . . £300/£40
Franny and Zooey, Little, Brown (Boston), 1961 £75/£20
ditto, Heinemann (London), 1962 . . . £65/£15
Raise High the Roof Beam, Carpenters and *Seymour: An Introduction*, Little, Brown (Boston), 1963 (first issue with no dedication page) . . . . . £750/£600
ditto, Little, Brown (Boston), 1963 (second issue with dedication page before half title) . . £100/£15
ditto, Little, Brown (Boston), 1963 (third issue with dedication page tipped in after the title page) . £65/£10
ditto, Heinemann (London), 1963 . . . £75/£15
The Complete and Uncollected Short Stories of J.D. Salinger, no publisher, 1974 (2 vols; wraps, vol.1 saddle-stitched, vol.2 perfect bound, pirated edition) . . £500

SAPPER

(b.1888 d.1937)

'Sapper' was the pseudonym of British author Herman Cyril McNeile, whose greatest literary creation was Bulldog Drummond. McNeile's first published works were successful war stories based upon his own experiences; realistic enough to seem authentic, yet managing to hide the true horror of trench warfare. Drummond's exploits were continued after McNeile's death by his friend Gerald Fairlie.

'Bulldog Drummond' Titles
Bull-Dog Drummond: The Adventures of a Demobilised Officer Who Found Peace Dull, Hodder & Stoughton (London), [1920] . . . . . £1,000/£75
ditto, Doran (New York), 1920 . . . . £1,000/£65
The Black Gang, Hodder & Stoughton (London), [1922] .
. . . . £350/£35
ditto, Doran (New York), 1922 . . . . £300/£25
The Third Round, Hodder & Stoughton (London), [1924] .
. . . . £350/£30
ditto, as *Bull-Dog Drummond's Third Round*, Doran (New York), 1920 . . . . £250/£25
The Final Count, Hodder & Stoughton (London), [1926] .
. . . . £350/£25
ditto, Doran (New York), 1926 . . . . . £300/£20

The Female of the Species, Hodder & Stoughton (London), [1928] . . . . £350/£35
ditto, Doubleday (New York), 1928 . . . . £300/£25
ditto, as *Bulldog Drummond and the Female of the Species*, Sun Dial (New York), 1943 . . . . . £50/£10
Temple Tower, Hodder & Stoughton (London), [1929]. .
. . . . £350/£30
ditto, Doubleday (New York), 1929 . . . . £300/£25
The Return of Bulldog Drummond, Hodder & Stoughton (London), 1932 . . . . £250/£20
ditto, as *Bulldog Drummond Returns*, Doubleday (New York), 1932 . . . . £225/£20
Knock-Out, Hodder & Stoughton (London), 1933 . £250/£20
ditto, as *Bulldog Drummond Strikes Back*, Doubleday (New York), 1933 . . . . £225/£20
Bulldog Drummond At Bay, Hodder & Stoughton (London), 1935 . . . . £250/£20
ditto, Doubleday (New York), 1935 . . . . £225/£20
Challenge, Hodder & Stoughton (London), 1937 . £250/£20
ditto, Doubleday (New York), 1937 . . . . £225/£20

Collected Editions
Bulldog Drummond: His Four Rounds With Carl Peterson, Hodder & Stoughton (London), 1937 . . . £125/£15
Sapper: The Best Short Stories, Dent (London), 1984 £25/£5

Other Novels
Jim Maitland, Hodder & Stoughton (London), 1923 £300/£25
ditto, Doubleday (New York), 1924 . . . . £250/£25
Tiny Carteret, Hodder & Stoughton (London), 1930 . .
. . . . £300/£25
ditto, Doubleday (New York), 1930 . . . . £250/£25
The Island of Terror, Hodder & Stoughton (London), 1931
. . . . £200/£20
ditto, as *Guardians of the Treasure*, Doubleday (New York), 1931 . . . . £200/£20

Other Short Stories
Sergeant Michael Cassidy, R.E., Hodder & Stoughton (London), 1915 . . . . £30
ditto, as *Michael Cassidy, Sergeant*, Doran (New York), 1916 . . . . £30
The Lieutenant and Others, Hodder & Stoughton (London), 1915 . . . . £30
Men, Women and Guns, Hodder & Stoughton (London), 1916 . . . . £25
ditto, Doran (New York), 1916 . . . . . £25
The Fatal Second, Doran (New York), 1916 (pbk) £75
The Motor-Gun, Doran (New York), 1916 (pbk) . £75
No Man's Land, Hodder & Stoughton (London), 1917. £20
ditto, Doran (New York), 1917 . . . . . £20
The Human Touch, Hodder & Stoughton (London), 1918 .
. . . . £20
ditto, Doran (New York), 1918 . . . . . £20
Mufti, Hodder & Stoughton (London), 1919 . . £35
ditto, Doran (New York), 1919 . . . . . £35
The Truce of the Bear, Doran (New York), 1919 (pbk) £75
The Dinner Club, Hodder & Stoughton (London), [1923] .
. . . . £200/£20
ditto, Doran (New York), [1923] . . . £150/£20
Mark Danver's Sin, and *The Madman of Coral Reef Lighthouse*, Doran (New York), 1923 (pbk). . . £75
Molly's Aunt at Angmering, Doran (New York), 1923 (pbk)
. . . . £75

Peter Cornish's Revenge, Doran (New York), 1923 (pbk) £75
The Man in Ratcatcher and Other Stories, Hodder & Stoughton (London), [1924]   .   .   .   . £200/£20
ditto, Doran (New York), [1924]   .   .   . £200/£20
Bulton's Revenge, Doran (New York), 1924 (pbk)   . £75
The Ducking of Herbert Folton, and *Coincidence*, Doran (New York), 1924 (pbk) £75
A Scrap of Paper, Doran (New York), 1924 (pbk).   . £75
That Bullet Hole Has a History!, Doran (New York), 1924 (pbk) £75
The Valley of the Shadow, Doran (New York), 1924 (pbk) .
    .   .   .   . £75
Out of the Blue, Hodder & Stoughton (London), [1925]   .
    .   .   .   . £150/£15
ditto, Doran (New York), 1925   .   .   .   . £150/£15
A Native Superstition, Doran (New York), 1925 (pbk). £75
The Other Side of the Wall, Doran (New York), 1925 (pbk)
    .   .   .   . £75
The Professor's Christmas Party, and *A Student of the Obvious*, Doran (New York), 1925 (pbk)   .   .   . £75
A Question of Identity, Doran (New York), 1925 (pbk) £75
Who Was This Woman?, *Two Photographs*, and *The Ring of Hearts*, Doran (New York), 1925 (pbk)   .   . £75
Word of Honour, Hodder & Stoughton (London), [1926]   .
    .   .   .   . £150/£15
ditto, Doran (New York), 1926   .   .   .   . £150/£15
The Eleventh Hour, Doran (New York), 1926 (pbk)   . £75
The Loyalty of Peter Drayton, and *Mrs Peter Skeffington's Revenge*, Doran (New York), 1926 (pbk)   .   . £75
The Message, Doran (New York), 1926 (pbk).   .   . £75
The Rout of the Oliver Samuelsons, Doran (New York), 1926 (pbk) £75
The Rubber Stamp, and *A Matter of Voice*, Doran (New York), 1926 (pbk) £75
The Saving Clause, Doran (New York), 1926 (pbk)   . £75
The Taming of Sydney Marsham, Doran (New York), 1926 (pbk) £75
Three of a Kind, and *The Haunting of Jack Burnham*, Doran (New York), 1926 (pbk) £75
Word of Honour, Doran (New York), 1926 (pbk) .   . £75
Jim Brent, Hodder & Stoughton (London), [1927]. £150/£15
The Saving Clause, Hodder & Stoughton (London), [1927]
    .   .   .   . £150/£15
Shorty Bill, Hodder & Stoughton (London), [1927] £150/£15
An Act of Providence, Doran (New York), 1927 (pbk) . £75
Billie Finds the Answer, Doran (New York), 1927 (pbk) £75
The Diamond Hair Slide, Doran (New York), 1927 (pbk) £75
Dilemma, Doran (New York), 1927 (pbk)   .   .   . £75
A Hundred Per Cent, Doran (New York), 1927 (pbk) . £75
Once Bit, Twice Hit, Doran (New York), 1927 (pbk)   . £75
Relative Values, Doran (New York), 1927 (pbk)   . £75
When Carruthers Laughed, Doran (New York), 1927 (pbk)
    .   .   .   . £75
John Walters, Hodder & Stoughton (London), [1928]   .
    .   .   .   . £150/£15
The Hidden Witness, Doubleday (New York), 1929 (pbk) .
    .   .   .   . £75
A Question of Mud, Doubleday (New York), 1929 (pbk) £75
The Undoing of Mrs Cransby, Doubleday (New York), 1929 (pbk) £75
Sapper's War Stories, Hodder & Stoughton (London), 1930
    .   .   .   . £75/£20
The Finger of Fate, Hodder & Stoughton (London), 1931 .
    .   .   .   . £150/£15

ditto, Doran (New York), [1931].   .   .   . £150/£15
The Great Magor Diamond, and *The Creaking Door*, Doubleday (New York), 1931 (pbk)   .   .   . £75
The Haunted Rectory, Doubleday (New York), 1931 (pbk).
    .   .   .   . £75
The Missing Chauffeur, Doubleday (New York), 1931 (pbk)
    .   .   .   . £75
51 Stories, Hodder & Stoughton (London), 1931   . £75/£10
The Brides of Mertonbridge Hall, Doubleday (New York), 1932 (pbk) £75
A Matter of Tar, Doubleday (New York), 1932 (pbk)   . £75
Uncle James's Golf Match, Hodder & Stoughton (London), 1932   .   .   .   . £175/£75
Ronald Standish, Hodder & Stoughton (London), 1933   .
    .   .   .   . £150/£20
The Man in Yellow, and *The Empty House*, Doubleday (New York), 1933 (pbk) £75
When Carruthers Laughed, Hodder & Stoughton (London), 1934   .   .   .   . £150/£15
ditto, Doran (New York), [n.d.]   .   .   . £150/£15
Ask For Ronald Standish, Hodder & Stoughton (London), 1936   .   .   .   . £150/£35

'Bulldog Drummond' Titles by Gerald Fairlie
Bulldog Drummond on Dartmoor, Hodder & Stoughton (London), 1938   .   .   .   .   .   . £125/£20
ditto, Hillman-Curl (New York), 1939   .   .   . £100/£15
Bulldog Drummond Attacks, Hodder & Stoughton (London), 1939   .   .   .   . £125/£20
ditto, Gateway (New York), 1940   .   .   . £100/£15
Captain Bulldog Drummond, Hodder & Stoughton (London), 1945   .   .   .   . £45/£10
Bulldog Drummond Stands Fast, Hodder & Stoughton (London), 1947   .   .   .   . £30/£10
Hands Off Bulldog Drummond, Hodder & Stoughton (London), 1949   .   .   .   . £25/£10
Calling Bulldog Drummond, Hodder & Stoughton (London), 1951   .   .   .   . £25/£10
The Return of the Black Gang, Hodder & Stoughton (London), 1954   .   .   .   . £25/£10

SARBAN

(b.1910 d.1989)

'Sarban' was the pseudonym used by John William Wall, a British diplomat for many years stationed in the Middle East. He wrote subtle stories of the supernatural and fantasy, and is best known for *The Sound of His Horn*, which explores the possibilities of what would have happened if Germany had won World War Two.

Ringstones and other Curious Tales, Davies (London), 1951
    .   .   .   . £65/£20
ditto, Coward-McCann (New York), [1951]   . £50/£20
ditto, Tartarus Press (Carlton-in-Coverdale, Yorkshire), 2000 (350 copies) .   .   .   . £65/£20
The Sound of His Horn, Davies (London), 1952   . £200/£30
ditto, Ballantine (New York), 1960 (pbk)   .   .   . £10
ditto, Tartarus Press (Horam, Sussex), 1999 (350 numbered copies) .   .   .   . £150/£40
The Doll Maker, Davies (London), 1953 .   .   . £250/£45
ditto, Ballantine (New York), 1960 (wraps)   .   . £10

ditto, Tartarus Press (Horam, Sussex), 1999 (250 numbered copies) . . . . £100/£25
The Sacrifice, Tartarus Press (Carlton-in-Coverdale, Yorkshire), 2002 (350 copies) . . . . £45/£15

WILLIAM SAROYAN
(b.1908 d.1981)

William Saroyan was an American author who set many of his stories and plays in Fresno, California, an Armenian-American community in which he grew up. In 1940 he won the Pulitzer Prize for Drama for *The Time of Your Life* but refused to accept it on the grounds that commerce had no right to patronise art.

Novels
The Human Comedy, Harcourt, Brace (New York), 1943 . . . . £65/£15
ditto, Armed Services Editions/Council on Books in Wartime (New York), 1943 (pbk) £20
ditto, Faber (London), 1943 . . . . £45/£10
The Adventures of Wesley Jackson, Harcourt, Brace (New York), 1946 . . . . . . £25/£5
ditto, Faber (London), 1947 . . . . £20/£5
The Twin Adventurers: The Adventures of William Saroyan, A Diary; The Adventures of Wesley Jackson, A Novel, Harcourt, Brace (New York), 1950 . . £50/£10
Rock Wagram, Doubleday (Garden City, NY), 1951 £25/£5
ditto, Faber (London), 1952 . . . . . £15/£5
Tracy's Tiger, Doubleday (Garden City, NY), 1951 £25/£5
ditto, Faber (London), 1952 . . . . . £20/£5
The Laughing Matter, Doubleday (Garden City, NY), 1953 . . . . £30/£5
ditto, Doubleday (Garden City, NY), 1953 (with signed label laid in) . . . . £60/£35
ditto, Faber (London), 1954 . . . . . £20/£5
ditto, as *A Secret Story (The Laughing Matter)*, Popular Library (New York), 1954 (pbk) £10
Mama I Love You, Little, Brown (Boston/Toronto), 1956 . . . . £25/£5
ditto, Faber (London), 1957 . . . . . £20/£5
Papa You're Crazy, Little, Brown (Boston/Toronto), 1957 . . . . £25/£5
ditto, Faber (London), 1958 . . . . . £20/£5
Boys and Girls Together, Harcourt, Brace & World (New York), 1963 . . . . . . £20/£5
ditto, Peter Davies (London), 1963 . . . £20/£5
One Day in the Afternoon of the World, Harcourt, Brace and World (New York), 1964 . . . . £20/£5
ditto, Cassell (London), 1965 . . . . £15/£5
After Thirty Years: The Daring Young Man on the Flying Trapeze, Harcourt, Brace and World (New York), 1964 . . . . £15/£5
Short Drive, Crazy Chariot, Phaedra (New York), 1966 . . . . £15/£5
Letters from 74 Rue Taitbout, or Don't Go, But If You Say You Must, Say Hello To Everybody, World Publishing Company (New York), 1969 . . . . £15/£5
ditto, Cassell (London), 1970 . . . . £20/£5
The Tooth and My Father, Doubleday (New York), 1974 . . . . £15/£5

Short Story Collections
The Daring Young Man On The Flying Trapeze, And Other Stories, Random House (New York), 1934 £200/£30
ditto, Random House (New York), 1934 (copies signed on a tipped-in leaf) . . . . . . £500/£450
ditto, Faber and Faber (London), 1935 . . . £150/£20
ditto, Yolla Bolly Press (Covelo, CA), 1984 (220 numbered copies signed by Herbert Gold and William Prochnow; slipcase; no d/w) . . . . . . £150/£100
ditto, Yolla Bolly Press (Covelo, CA), 1984 (25 numbered copies signed by Herbert Gold and William Prochnow; half leather; in a black oak box with leather label; also a separate suite of eight woodcuts signed and numbered by the artist) . . . . £300/£250
Inhale and Exhale, Random House (New York), 1936. . . . . £100/£15
ditto, Faber (London), 1936. . . . . £65/£10
Three Times Three, Conference Press (Los Angeles, CA), 1936 . . . . £60/£25
ditto, Conference Press (Los Angeles, CA), 1936 (250 signed, numbered copies) . . . . £125/£75
Little Children, Harcourt, Brace (New York), 1937 £50/£10
ditto, Faber (London), 1937. . . . . £60/£10
The Gay and Melancholy Flux, Faber (London), 1937. . . . . £65/£10
Love Here Is My Hat, Modern Age Books (New York), 1938 (pbk, in d/w) . . . . . £50/£10
ditto, Faber (London), 1938 . . . . . £50/£10
A Native American, George Fields (San Francisco, CA), 1938 (450 signed, numbered copies; no d/w) . . £125
The Trouble With Tigers, Harcourt, Brace (New York), 1938 . . . . £100/£10
ditto, Faber (London), 1939 . . . . . £65/£10
Peace, It's Wonderful, Modern Age Books (New York), 1939 (pbk) £25
ditto, Starling Press (New York), 1939 (first issue in fuchsia cloth, lettered in silver) . . . . £60/£10
ditto, Starling Press (New York), 1939 (second issue in brick red cloth, lettered in black) . . £35/£5
ditto, Faber (London), 1940 . . . . . £45/£10
3 Fragments and a Story, no publisher (no place), [1939] (wraps, in d/w) . . . . . . £100/£50
My Name is Aram, Harcourt, Brace (New York), 1940 (first edition d/w blurb on inside flap begins 'Aram, who is Aram Garoghlanian...'; d/w price $2.50) . . . £150/£30
ditto, Faber (London), 1941 . . . . . £75/£15
Saroyan's Fables, Harcourt, Brace (New York), 1941 (1,000 signed, numbered copies; slipcase) . . £125/£100
The Insurance Salesman And Other Stories, Faber (London), 1941 . . . . . . £50/£10
48 Saroyan Stories, Avon Books (New York), 1942 (pbk) £20
Best Stories of William Saroyan, Faber (London), 1942 . . . . £45/£10
Thirty-One Selected Stories, Avon (New York), 1943 (pbk) £15
34 More Great Stories: Some Day I'll Be A Millionaire, Avon (New York), 1943 (pbk) £15
Dear Baby, Harcourt, Brace (New York), 1944 . £35/£10
ditto, Editions for the Armed Services (New York), 1944 (pbk) £15
ditto, Faber (London), 1945 . . . . . £25/£5
The Saroyan Special, Harcourt, Brace (New York), 1948 (coloured illustrations) . . . . . £50/£10

The Fiscal Hoboes, Press of Valenti Angelo (New York),
1949 (250 numbered copies signed by author and
illustrator) £150
ditto, Press of Valenti Angelo (New York), 1949 (250 copies
in wraps) £75
The Assyrian And Other Stories, Harcourt, Brace (New
York), 1950 (first binding red/brown cloth) . £45/£10
ditto, Harcourt, Brace (New York), 1950 (remainder binding
dark blue cloth lettered in gilt) . . . . £30/£5
ditto, Faber (London), 1950 . . . . . £25/£5
Love, Lion Library Editions (New York), 1955 (pbk) . £10
The Whole Voyald And Other Stories, Little, Brown
(Boston/Toronto), 1956 . . . . . £25/£5
ditto, Faber (London), 1957 . . . . . £20/£5
17 and Other Stories, Yamaguchi Shoten (Tokyo), [c.1958]
(pbk; in d/w) . . . . £65/£25
My Kind of Crazy, Wonderful People, Harcourt, Brace &
World (New York), 1966 . . . . . £20/£5
*The Man With the Heart in the Highlands And Other
Stories*, Laurel Edition (Dell Publishing), (New York),
1968 (pbk) £15
Tales Out Of School, Nan'Un-Do (Tokyo), 1973 (pbk; with
others) £20
Best Short Stories, Aiikusha (Japan), 1976 (pbk) . £20
An Act or Two of Foolish Kindness, Penmaen Press
(Lincoln, MA), 1977 (200 copies) . . . £25/£5
ditto, Penmaen Press (Lincoln, MA), 1977 (300 numbered
copies signed by the author and illustrator, Helen Siegl) £35
Short Stories of William Saroyan, Shoseki (Tokyo), 1986
(60 pps, pbk; in d/w; issued with 28pps booklet) . £30
The Circus, Creative Education (Mankato, MN), 1986 (no
d/w) £10
Madness in the Family, New Directions (New York), 1988
. . . . £10/£5
My Heart's In the Highlands & Other Early Stories, New
Directions (New York), 1989 . . . . £10/£5
The Parsley Garden..., Creative Education (Mankato, MN),
1990 . . . . £10/£5
Fresno Stories, New Directions (New York), 1994 (pbk) £5

Plays
My Heart's In The Highlands, Harcourt, Brace (New York),
1939 . . . . £50/£10
ditto, Samuel French (New York), 1941 (first acting edition;
wraps) £30
The Hungerers, A Short Play, Samuel French (New York),
1939 (wraps). £65
The Time of Your Life, Harcourt, Brace (New York), 1939.
. . . . £150/£20
ditto, Samuel French (New York), 1941 (first acting edition;
stapled wraps) £20
ditto, Samuel French (London), 1941. . . . £15
Subway Circus, Samuel French (New York), 1940 (stapled
wraps) £25
A Special Announcement, House of Books Ltd (New York),
1940 (250 signed, numbered copies; glassine d/w) £76/£65
ditto, House of Books Ltd (New York), 1940 (26 signed,
lettered copies; glassine d/w) . . . £250/£225
The Ping-Pong Game, Samuel French (New York), 1940
(wraps) £25
*Three Plays: My Heart's in the Highlands, The Time of
Your Life, Love's Old Sweet Song*, Harcourt, Brace (New
York), 1940 . . . . £65/£10
ditto, as *The Time of Your Life, And Two Other Plays*,
Faber (London), 1942. . . . . . £40/£10

The People With Light Coming Out of Them, The Free
Company (New York), 1941 (wraps) . . . £25
The Beautiful People And Two Other Plays, Harcourt,
Brace (New York), 1941 . . . . . £75/£15
ditto, Samuel French (New York), 1942 (stapled wraps) £15
ditto, Faber (London), 1943 . . . . . £45/£10
Love's Old Sweet Song, Samuel French (New York), 1941
(wraps) £25
The Beautiful People, A Play, Samuel French (New York),
1942 (wraps). £20
Razzle-Dazzle, Harcourt, Brace (New York), 1942. £50/£10
ditto, as *Razzle-Dazzle*: The Human Opera, Ballet and
Circus, Faber (London), 1945 . . . . £50/£10
Get Away Old Man, Harcourt, Brace (New York), 1944 .
. . . . £50/£10
ditto, Faber (London), 1946. . . . . £35/£10
Jim Dandy, Fat Man in a Famine, Harcourt, Brace (New
York), 1947 . . . . £50/£10
ditto, Samuel French (New York), 1947 (wraps) . £15
ditto, Faber (London), 1948. . . . . £20/£5
Don't Go Away Mad and Two Other Plays, Harcourt, Brace
New York), 1949. . . . . . . £45/£10
ditto, Faber (London), 1951. . . . . £25/£5
Hello Out There, Samuel French (New York), 1949
(yellow/gold printed wraps) £25
ditto, Samuel French (New York), 1949 (grey printed wraps)
. . . . £10
Sam Ego's House, Samuel French (New York), 1949
(wraps) £25
A Decent Birth, A Happy Funeral, Samuel French (New
York), 1949 (wraps) £25
The Cave Dwellers, G.P. Putnam's (New York), 1958 £25/£5
ditto, as *The Cave Dwellers, A Play*, Samuel French (New
York), 1958 (wraps) £15
ditto, Faber (London), 1959. . . . . £20/£5
The Slaughter of the Innocents, Samuel French (New
York), 1958 (wraps) £20
Once Around the Block, Samuel French (New York etc)
(wraps) (fifty centre cover price) £25
*Sam, The Highest Jumper Of Them All, or The London
Comedy*, Faber (London), 1961 . . . £20/£5
Along the Wabash, Purdue Workshop (Lafayette, IA), 1961
(mimeographed script for actors) £75
Settled out of Court: A Play in Three Acts, Samuel French
(London), 1962 (wraps; with Henry Cecil) . . £30
The Time of Your Life and Other Plays, Bantam World
Drama (New York), 1967 (pbk) £15
*Three New Dramatic Works: The Dogs, or The Paris
Comedy and Two Other Plays...*, Phaedra (New York),
1969 (early issue with incorrect spelling of Lilian (for
Lillian) on the dedication page) . . . £15/£10
ditto, Phaedra (New York), 1969 (later issue with incorrect
spelling of Lillian) . . . . . . £10/£5
*Assassinations & Jim, Sam and Anna: Two Short Paris
Summertime Plays of 1974*, California State Univ
Northridge Libraries/The Santa Susana Press (CA), 1979
(300 signed, numbered copies; no d/w) . . . £30
ditto, California State Univ Northridge Libraries/The Santa
Susana Press (CA), 1979 (26 signed, lettered copies) . £125
Warsaw Visitor [and] *Tales from the Vienna Streets*, The
Press at California State Univ (Fresno, CA), 1991 £10/£5
ditto, The Press at California State Univ (Fresno, CA), 1991
(pbk) £5
Saroyan's Armenians, University Editions (Huntington,
WV), 1992 (pbk). £5

Other Fiction, Poetry etc

A Christmas Psalm, Gelber /Grabhorn Press (Lilienthal/San Francisco, CA) 1935 (200 signed, numbered copies; no d/w) £225

ditto, Gelber /Grabhorn Press (Lilienthal/San Francisco, CA) 1935 (3 copies printed on vellum, bound in red morocco) £500

Fragment by William Saroyan, Grabhorn Press (San Francisco, CA), 1938 (150 copies; wraps; broadside poem printed on a single-folded sheet laid loose into blue wraps) £125

Christmas, Quercus Press (San Mateo, CA), 1939 (100 copies; wraps) £150

The Way To Be Alive, The Albatross (Leipzig/Paris/ Bologna), 1939 . . . . £50/£15

Oh! Beauty!, Duchess Music ([London]), 1951 (sheet music) £50

The William Saroyan Reader, George Braziller (New York), 1958 . . . . £25/£5

Me, Saturday Evening Post (New York), 1963 (200 signed, numbered copies; grey wraps; privately printed by The Saturday Evening Post) £150

ditto, Crowell-Collier Press/Collier-Macmillan (New York/ London), 1963 (no d/w) £25

Horsey Gorsey and the Frog, Chicago Tribune (Chicago), November 7, 1965 (newspaper section 8A illustrated by Grace Davidian) £35

ditto, E.M. Hale (Eau Claire, WI), 1968 (pictorial cloth; no d/w) £20

Deleted Beginning and End of a Short Story, Lowell- Adams House Printers (no place), 1965 (hand printed) £75

The New Saroyan Reader: A Connoisseur's Anthology of the Writings of William Saroyan, Creative Arts (Berkeley, CA), 1984 . . . . £15/£5

ditto, Creative Arts (Berkeley, CA), 1985 (pbk) . . £5

An Armenian Trilogy, California State Univ (Fresno, CA), 1986 . . . . £15/£5

ditto, California State Univ (Fresno, CA), 1986 (pbk) . £5

The Pheasant Hunter, Redpath Press (Minneapolis, MN), 1986 (wraps; in envelope) . . . . . . £10/£5

Non-Fiction

Those Who Write Them and Those Who Collect Them, The Black Archer Press (Chicago), 1936 (50 numbered copies; stapled wraps) £200

William Saroyan Writes of Manuel Tolegian, Associated American Artists (New York), 1941 (exhibition catalogue) £50

Harlem As Seen by Hirschfield, The Hyperion Press (New York), 1941 (1,000 numbered copies; no d/w; in publisher's box; 24 original lithographs tipped-in) . . . . £3,000/£2,000

Hilltop Russians in San Francisco, James Delkin (Stanford Univ, CA), 1941 (500 copies) . . . £150/£125

Gentleman, Bibliotheca (Budapest), [c.1946] (wraps) . £40

The Bicycle Rider in Beverley Hills, Charles Scribner's Sons (New York), 1952 . . . . £30/£5

ditto, Faber (London), 1953 . . . . . . £20/£5

A Writer's Declaration, no publisher (no place), [c.1956] (wraps) £150

Here Comes, There Goes, You Know Who, Simon & Schuster (New York), 1961 . . . . £25/£5

ditto, Peter Davies (London), 1962 . . . £20/£5

Not Dying, Harcourt, Brace & World (New York), 1963 . . . . £20/£5

ditto, Cassell (London), 1966 . . . . . £15/£5

Who Is Varaz?, Studio H Gallery, New York, 1965 (wraps) £50

A Tribute to His Uncle, The Saroyan Family (Fresno, CA), 1965 (approx 100 copies; broadside) £35

Look At Us..., Cowles Education Corporation (New York), 1967 . . . . £15/£5

I Used to Believe I Had Forever, Now I'm Not So Sure, Cowles (New York), 1968 . . . . . £30/£5

ditto, Cassell (London), 1969 . . . . . £25/£5

Days of Life and Death and Escape to the Moon, Dial Press (New York), 1970 . . . . £15/£5

ditto, Dial Press (New York), 1970 (250 copies signed on a tipped-in leaf) . . . . . £125/£100

ditto, Michael Joseph (London), 1971 . . £15/£5

Escape to the Moon, Fresno '68, Gaku Shobo (Tokyo), [c.1970] (wraps; author's name printed as 'William Soroyan') £20

Places Where I've Done Time, Praeger (New York), 1972 . . . . £10/£5

ditto, Davis-Poynter (London), 1973 . . . £10/£5

Sons Come And Go, Mothers Hang In Forever, Franklin Library (Franklin Center, PA), 1976 (full leather limited edition) £25

ditto, McGraw-Hill (New York), 1976 . . £10/£5

Growing Up in Fresno; Reminiscences of the renowned Author William Saroyan, Fresno Free College Foundation (Fresno, CA), 1976 (26 unbound pages). . . . £75

Morris Hirchfield, Franco Maria Ricci (Milan), 1976 (3,000 numbered copies signed by the publisher; slipcase; no d/w) . . . . £75/£50

Chance Meetings, W.W. Norton (New York), 1978 £15/£5

Obituaries, Creative Arts (Berkeley, CA), 1979 . £15/£5

ditto, Creative Arts (Berkeley, CA), 1979 (pbk) . . £5

Births, Creative Arts (Berkeley, CA), 1983 . £15/£5

ditto, Creative Arts (Berkeley, CA), 1983 (pbk) . . £5

My Name is Saroyan, Coward-McCann (New York), 1983 . . . . £10/£5

Saroyan—Memoirs, Minerva Press (London), 1994 (pbk) £5

Where the Bones Go, The Press at California State Univ (Fresno, CA), 2002 (with Robert Setrakian) . £10/£5

SIEGFRIED SASSOON
(b.1886 d.1967)

In his youth Sassoon published a few volumes of indifferent poetry before finding some success with *The Daffodil Murderer*, a parody of *The Everlasting Mercy* by John Masefield. His First World War experiences changed his outlook and he subsequently became known as a writer of satirical anti-war verse. His prose also won acclaim, with *Memoirs of a Fox-Hunting Man* winning both the Hawthornden and Tait Black Memorial Prizes.

Novels

Memoirs of a Fox-Hunting Man, Faber (London), 1928 (anonymous). . . . . £600/£100

ditto, Faber (London), 1928 (second impression with 'A' on the blank leaf prior to the half-title page) . £500/£50

ditto, Faber (London), 1928 (260 signed, numbered copies). . . . . £1,250/£1,000

ditto, Faber (London), 1929 (300 signed, numbered copies, illustrated) . . . . £1,250/£600
ditto, Faber (London), 1929 (illustrated) . . . £100/£25
ditto, Coward-McCann (New York), 1929 . . £75/£15
Memoirs of an Infantry Officer, Faber (London), 1930 .
. . . . £150/£25
ditto, Faber (London), 1930 (750 signed copies) . . £350
ditto, Coward-McCann (New York), 1930 . . £100/£15
ditto, Faber (London), 1931 (illustrated by Freedman, 320 signed copies, d/w and slipcase) . . £1,500/£1,000
ditto, Faber (London), 1931 (illustrated by Freedman, 12 signed copies) £1,500
Sherston's Progress, Faber (London), 1936 . . £150/£25
ditto, Faber (London), 1936 (300 signed copies) . . £400
ditto, Doubleday (New York), 1936 . . . . £75/£10
The Complete Memoirs of George Sherston, Faber (London), 1937 . . . . £40/£10
ditto, Doubleday (New York), 1937 . . . . £30/£10

Poetry

An Ode for Music, privately printed (London), 1912 (50 copies) £1,250
The Daffodil Murderer, Richmond (London), 1913 (pseud 'Saul Kain'; wraps) £400
The Old Huntsman, Heinemann (London), 1917 (with errata) £200
ditto, Dutton (New York), 1917 . . . . . . £150
Counter-Attack, Heinemann (London), 1918 (wraps) . £275
ditto, Heinemann (London), 1918 . . . . . £250
ditto, Dutton (New York), 1918 . . . . . . £150
The War Poems of Siegfried Sassoon, Heinemann (London), 1919 . . . . £75
Picture Show, privately printed (Cambridge) 1919 (200 copies) £300
ditto, Heinemann (London), 1919 . . . . . £50
ditto, Dutton (New York), 1920 . . . . £400/£10
Recreations, privately printed [London)], 1923 (75 copies of 81) £1,000
ditto, privately printed [London], 1923 (6 copies of 81) .
. . . . £1,250
Selected Poems, Heinemann (London), 1925 . . £75/£15
Satirical Poems, Heinemann (London), 1926 . . £300/£50
ditto, Viking (New York), 1926 . . . . £200/£45
Nativity, Faber (London), 1927 (350 numbered copies; wraps) £40
ditto, Faber (London), 1927 (string-tied wraps) . . £20
ditto, William Edwin Rudge (New York), 1927 (27 copies to secure copyright). £200
The Heart's Journey, Heinemann (London) and Crosby Gaige (New York), 1928 (590 signed copies) £350/£150
ditto, Heinemann (London) and Crosby Gaige (New York), 1928 (9 copies on green paper). £600
ditto, Heinemann (London), 1928 . . . £75/£20
ditto, Harper (New York), 1929 . . . . £45/£15
To My Mother, Faber (London), 1928 (sewn wraps) . £15
ditto, Faber (London), 1928 (500 signed large paper copies)
. . . . £125
In Sicily, Faber (London), 1930 (wraps) . . . £20
ditto, Faber (London), 1928 (400 signed copies) . . £150
Poems by Pinchbeck Lyre, Duckworth (London), 1931 (glassine d/w) . . . . £55/£50
To the Red Rose, Faber (London), 1931(wraps) . . £25
ditto, Faber (London), 1931 (400 signed copies) . . £125
Prehistoric Burials, Knopf (New York), 1932 (Borzoi Chap Book; stitched wraps in envelope) . . . £20/£10

The Road to Ruin, Faber (London), 1933. . . £40/£10
Vigils, [Privately Published for the author by Douglas Cleverdon, Bristol], 1934 (272 signed copies, Niger morocco) £350
ditto, Heinemann (London), 1935 . . . . £50/£15
ditto, Viking (New York), 1936 . . . . . £45/£15
Rhymed Ruminations, Privately Printed at the Chiswick Press (London), 1939 (75 copies) . . . £600
ditto, Faber (London), 1940. . . . . . £35/£10
ditto, Viking (New York), 1941 . . . . . £25/£10
Poems Newly Selected, Faber (London), 1940. . £25/£10
Collected Poems, Faber (London), 1947 . . . £40/£15
ditto, Viking (New York), 1949 . . . . . £30/£10
Sequences, Privately printed at the C.U.P. by Brooke Crutchley (Cambridge, UK), 1956 (25 copies) . £1,250
ditto, Faber (London), 1956 . . . . . . £30/£10
ditto, Viking (New York), 1957 . . . . . £25/£10
Collected Poems, 1908-1956, Faber (London), 1961 £20/£10
An Octave, privately printed by the Shenval Press (London), 1966 (350 copies; slipcase) . . . . . £75/£50

Others

The Old Century and Seven More Years, Faber (London), 1938 . . . . £65/£20
ditto, Viking (New York), 1939 . . . . . £35/£10
The Weald of Youth, Faber (London), 1941 . . £40/£10
ditto, Viking (New York), 1942 . . . . . £25/£10
Siegfried's Journey, Faber (London), 1945 . . £35/£10
ditto, Viking (New York), 1946 . . . . . £15/£5
Meredith, Constable (London), 1948. . . . £20/£10
ditto, Viking (New York), 1948 . . . . . £20/£10
The Path to Peace, Stanbrook Abbey Press (Worcester, Worcs.), 1960 (500 copies, quarter vellum) . . £350
Something About Myself by Siegfried Sassoon, aged 11, Stanbrook Abbey Press (Worcester, Worcs.), 1966 (350 copies; wraps) £65
Diaries, 1920-1922, Faber (London), 1981 . £30/£15
Diaries, 1915-1918, Faber (London), 1983 . £25/£10
Diaries, 1923-1925, Faber (London), 1984 . £20/£10
Siegfried Sassoon: Letters to Max Beerbohm with a Few Answers, Faber (London), 1986 . . . . £20/£5

THE SAVOY

After leaving *The Yellow Book*, Aubrey Beardsley worked with Arthur Symons to produce *The Savoy*, published by Leonard Smithers (London). Sets of all eight issues were later published and bound in pictorial cloth in three volumes. The last issue is of special interest because Symons and Beardsley provided all of the material themselves.

No.1, January 1896 (including Christmas card) . . £250
No.1, January 1896 (without Christmas card) . . £165
No.2, April, 1896 . . . . £125
No.3, July, 1896 . . . . £100
No.4, August, 1896 . . . . £85
No.5, September, 1896 . . . . . . £85
No.6, October, 1896 . . . . £85
No.7, November 1896 . . . . £85
No.8, December 1896 . . . . £85
All 8 issues, 3 vols £850

DOROTHY L. SAYERS
(b.1893 d.1957)

Sayers was principally a writer of detective fiction: her novels follow the exploits of Lord Peter Wimsey, an English aristocrat who is also an amateur sleuth, and Harriet Vane, a crime novelist and detective. Jill Paton Walsh has completed and published two additional novels about Peter Wimsey and Harriet Vane: *Thrones, Dominations*, and *A Presumption of Death*.

Novels
Whose Body?, Boni & Liveright (New York), 1923 (first issue without 'Inc.' after Boni & Liveright on title-page) .
. . . . £3,000/£500
ditto, Boni & Liveright (New York), 1923 (second issue with 'Inc.' after Boni & Liveright on title-page) . £3,000/£200
ditto, Unwin (London), 1923 . . . £4,000/£600
Clouds of Witness, Unwin (London), 1926 . £3,000/£300
ditto, as *Clouds of Witnesses*, Dial Press (New York), 1927
. . . . £2,500/£100
Unnatural Death, Benn (London), 1927 . . £2,500/£250
ditto, as *The Dawson Pedigree*, Dial Press (New York), 1928
. . . . £1,750/£200
The Unpleasantness at the Bellona Club, Benn (London), 1928 . . . . £2,500/£250
ditto, Payson & Clarke (New York), 1928 . £1,000/£150
The Documents in the Case, Benn (London), 1930 (with Robert Eustace) . . . . . . £1,250/£150
ditto, Brewer & Warren (New York), 1930 . .£750/£75
Strong Poison, Gollancz (London), 1930 . . £1,500/£150
ditto, Brewer & Warren (New York), 1930 . .£750/£65
The Five Red Herrings, Gollancz (London), 1931. . .
. . . . £1,500/£125
ditto, as *Suspicious Characters*, Brewer & Warren (New York), 1931 . . . .£750/£45
Have His Carcase, Gollancz (London), 1932 . £1,500/£50
ditto, Brewer & Warren (New York), 1932 . .£600/£45
Murder Must Advertise, Gollancz (London), 1933. . .
. . . . £1,250/£50
ditto, Harcourt (New York), 1933 . . . .£500/£45
The Nine Tailors, Gollancz (London), 1934 . £1,250/£45
ditto, Harcourt (New York), 1934 . . . .£500/£40
Gaudy Night, Gollancz (London), 1935 . . .£700/£40
ditto, Harcourt (New York), 1936 . . . .£350/£40
Busman's Honeymoon: A Love Story with Detective Interruptions, Harcourt (New York), 1937 . .£300/£50
ditto, Gollancz (London), 1937 . . . .£350/£35
Thrones, Dominations, Hodder & Stoughton (London), 1998 (completed by Jill Paton Walsh) . . .£10/£5
ditto, St Martin's Press (New York), 1998 . .£10/£5

Collaborations
The Floating Admiral, Hodder & Stoughton (London), [1931] (chain novel; chapters by Sayers, G.K. Chesterton, Agatha Christie, John Rhode, Freeman Wills Crofts and others) . . . . . . £1,500/£100
ditto, Doubleday (New York), 1932 . . .£500/£30
Ask a Policeman, Barker (London), [1933] (chain novel; chapters by Sayers, Gladys Mitchell, John Rhode and others) . . . . £1,000/£100

ditto, Morrow (New York), 1933 . . . .£500/£65
Six against the Yard, Selwyn & Blount (London), 1936 (six stories by members of 'The Detection Club', one by Sayers).
. . . . £1,500/£100
ditto, as *Six against Scotland Yard*, Doubleday (Garden City, NY), 1936 . . . . . .£500/£35
Double Death, Gollancz, 1940 (chain novel; chapters by Sayers, Freeman Wills Crofts and others) . £800/£150
The Scoop and *Behind the Screen*, Gollancz (London), 1983 (chain novels; chapters by Dorothy L. Sayers, Agatha Christie, Hugh Walpole, E.C. Bentley, Freeman Wills Crofts and others) . . . . . . £25/£10
No Flowers by Request & Crime on the Coast, Gollancz (London), 1984 (chain novel; chapters by Dorothy L. Sayers, E.C.R. Lorac, Gladys Mitchell, John Dickson Carr, Elizabeth Ferrars and others) . . . . .£10/£5

Short Stories
Lord Peter Views the Body, Gollancz (London), 1928 . .
. . . . £1,500/£125
ditto, Payson & Clarke (New York), 1929 . £1,000/£75
Hangman's Holiday, Gollancz (London), 1933 £1,500/£100
ditto, Harcourt (New York), 1933 . . . .£600/£35
In the Teeth of the Evidence, Gollancz (London), 1939 .
. . . . £750/£45
ditto, Harcourt (New York), 1940 . . . .£250/£35
ditto, Gollancz (London), 1972 (3 additional stories) £25/£5
Lord Peter, A Collection of All the Lord Peter Wimsey Stories, Harper & Row (New York), 1972 . £30/£10
ditto, Harper & Row (New York), 1972 (adds 'Talboys') .
. . . . £25/£10
Talboys, Harper & Row (New York), 1972 (pbk) . .£30
Striding Folly, New English Library (London), 1972 (pbk).
. , ...£15

Plays
Busman's Honeymoon: A Detective Comedy in Three Acts, Gollancz (London), 1937 . . . . .£400/£75
ditto, Gollancz (London), 1937 (wraps) . . .£150
ditto, Harcourt Brace (New York), 1937 . . .£300/£65
The Zeal of Thy House, Gollancz (London), 1937 £35/£10
ditto, Harcourt Brace (New York), 1937 . . .£30/£10
The Devil to Pay, Gollancz (London), 1937 . .£35/£15
ditto, Harcourt Brace (New York), 1941 . . .£25/£10
He that Should Come, Gollancz (London), 1939 (wraps in d/w) . . . .£20/£10
The Man Born to be King, Gollancz (London), 1943 . .
. . . . £60/£15
ditto, Harper (New York), 1943 . . . . .£25/£10
The Just Vengeance, Gollancz (London), 1946 . £35/£10
ditto, Gollancz (London), 1946 (wraps) . . .£15
Four Sacred Plays, Gollancz (London), 1948 . .£15/£5
The Emperor Constantine, Gollancz (London), 1951 £20/£5

Poetry
Op. 1, Blackwell (Oxford, UK), 1916 (wraps). . .£400
Catholic Tales and Christian Songs, Blackwell (Oxford, UK), 1918 (stiff wraps and d/w) . . . £175/£100

Essays
The Greatest Drama Ever Staged, Hodder & Stoughton, 1938 (wraps in d/w) . . . . . .£20/£10
Begin Here, Gollancz (London), 1940 . . .£35/£10
ditto, Harcourt (New York), 1941 . . . .£25/£10

The Mind of the Maker, Methuen (London), 1941. £25/£10
ditto, Harcourt (New York), 1941 . . . . £15/£5
Unpopular Opinions, Gollancz (London), 1946 . £25/£10
ditto, Harcourt (New York), 1947 . . . £15/£5
Creed or Chaos and Other Essays, Methuen (London), 1947
. . . . £15/£5
ditto, Harcourt (New York), 1949 . . . £15/£5
Introductory Papers on Dante, Methuen (London), 1954 .
. . . . £50/£15
ditto, Harper (New York), 1955 . . . . £45/£10
Further Papers on Dante, Methuen (London), 1957 £45/£10
ditto, Harper (New York), 1957 . . . . £45/£10
The Poetry of Search and the Poetry of Statement, Gollancz
(London), 1963 . . . . £25/£10
Christian Letters to a Post-Christian World, William
Eerdmans (Grand Rapids, MI), 1969 . . . £15/£5
A Matter of Eternity, William Eerdmans (Grand Rapids,
MI), 1973 . . . . £15/£5
ditto, Mowbray (London), 1973 . . . . £15/£5
Wilkie Collins: A Critical and Bibliographical Study, Univ
of Toledo (Toledo, OH), 1977 . . . . £20/£5
Letters to a Diminished Church, W Publishing (Nashville,
TN), 2004 (wraps) £5

Children's Title
Even the Parrot, Methuen (London), 1944 . . £40/£10
The Days of Christ's Coming, Hamish Hamilton (London),
1960 . . . . £10/£5
ditto, Harpers (New York), 1960. . . . £10/£5

Translations
*Tristan in Brittany: Being the Fragments of the Romance
of Tristan, Written in the 12th Century*, Benn, 1929 . .
. . . . £25/£10
The Divine Comedy: Hell, Penguin (Harmondsworth,
Middlesex), 1949 (pbk) £5
The Divine Comedy: Purgatory, Penguin (Harmondsworth,
Middlesex), 1955 (pbk) £5
The Divine Comedy: Paradise, Penguin (Harmondsworth,
Middlesex), 1962 (pbk) £5
The Song of Roland, Penguin (Harmondsworth, Middlesex),
1957 (pbk) £5
ditto, Viking (New York), 1957 (pbk) . . . £5

Others
Papers Relating to the Family of Wimsey, privately printed,
Humphrey Milford (London), [1936] (approximately 500
copies; wraps) £500
Account of Lord Mortimer Wimsey, Hermit of the Wash,
'Printed by M. Bryan, 1816' [O.U.P. (Oxford, UK), 1937]
(250 copies; wraps) £500
*The Wimsey Family, A Fragmentary History Compiled
from Correspondence with Dorothy L. Sayers*, Gollancz
(London), 1977 (with C.W. Scott-Giles) . . £35/£10
ditto, Harper & Row (U.S.), 1977 . . . £25/£10

JACK SCHAEFER
(b.1907 d.1991)

American author Jack Schaefer started writing in order to
relax in the evenings while he was editor of a Virginian
newspaper. Most of his work consists of short poignant
stories about very individualistic characters in a wide range
of Western settings. In *Shane* he wrote one of the most famous Westerns of all time, and the most collectable first
edition of the genre.

Novels
Shane, Houghton Mifflin (Boston), 1949 . . £1,750/£250
ditto, Deutsch (London), 1954 . . . . . £200/£30
First Blood, Houghton Mifflin/Ballantine (New York), 1953
. . . . £425/£40
ditto, Deutsch (London), 1954 . . . . . £125/£20
The Canyon, Houghton, Mifflin/Ballantine (New York),
1953 . . . . £175/£25
ditto, Deutsch (London), 1955 . . . . . £100/£15
Company of Cowards, Houghton Mifflin (Boston), 1957 .
. . . . £150/£15
ditto, Deutsch (London), 1958 . . . . . £65/£10
Monte Walsh, Houghton Mifflin (Boston), 1963 . £250/£65
ditto, Deutsch (London), 1965 . . . . . £65/£10
The Short Novels of Jack Schaefer, Houghton Mifflin
(Boston), 1967 . . . . £45/£10
Mavericks, Houghton Mifflin (Boston), 1967 . . £65/£15
ditto, Deutsch (London), 1968 . . . . . £35/£10

Short Stories
The Big Range, Houghton, Mifflin/Ballantine (New York),
1953 . . . . £150/£25
ditto, Deutsch (London), 1955 . . . . . £65/£10
The Pioneers, Houghton Mifflin (Boston), 1954 . £125/£25
ditto, Deutsch (London), 1957 . . . . . £75/£15
The Kean Land, Houghton Mifflin (Boston), 1959 £100/£15
ditto, Deutsch (London), 1960 . . . . . £65/£10
The Plainsmen, Houghton Mifflin (Boston), 1963 . £50/£10
The Collected Stories of Jack Schaefer, Houghton, Mifflin
(Boston), 1966 . . . . £75/£10

Children's Titles
Old Ramon, Houghton Mifflin (Boston), 1960 . £200/£25
Stubby Pringle's Christmas, Houghton Mifflin (Boston),
1964 . . . . £200/£25

Others
The Great Endurance Horse Race, Stagecoach Press (Santa
Fe, NM), 1963 (750 numbered copies) . . . £40/£20
Heroes Without Glory, Houghton Mifflin (Boston), 1965 .
. . . . £20/£10
ditto, Deutsch (London), 1966 . . . . . £10/£5
Adolphe Francis Bandelier, The Press of the Territorian
(Santa Fe, NM), 1966 (1,000 copies; stapled wraps) . £10
New Mexico, Coward-McCann (New York), 1967 . £35/£10
An American Bestiary, Houghton Mifflin (Boston), 1975 .
. . . . £10/£5
Conversations With a Pocket Gopher, Capra Press (Santa
Barbara, CA), 1978 (wraps) £15
ditto, Capra Press (Santa Barbara, CA), 1978 (26 signed,
lettered hardback copies, no d/w) £125

Edited by Schaefer
Out West, Houghton Mifflin (Boston), 1955 . . £35/£10
ditto, Deutsch (London), 1959 . . . . £30/£10

PAUL SCOTT
(b.1920 d.1978)

Paul Scott was a British novelist, playwright and poet who received proper recognition for his writing only at the end of his life, when he won the 1977 Booker Prize with *Staying On*. His 'Raj' books became better known in the 1980s when they were dramatised for television as *The Jewel in the Crown*.

'The Raj Quartet'
The Jewel in the Crown, Heinemann (London), 1966 . .
. . . . £145/£25
ditto, Morrow (New York), 1966 . . . £45/£10
The Day of the Scorpion, Heinemann (London), 1968 .
. . . . £100/£25
ditto, Morrow (New York), 1968 . . . £25/£10
The Towers of Silence, Heinemann (London), 1971 £75/£20
ditto, Morrow (New York), 1972 . . . £25/£5
A Division of the Spoils, Heinemann (London), 1975 £75/£20
ditto, Morrow (New York), 1975 . . . £25/£5

Other Novels
Johnnie Sahib, Eyre & Spottiswoode (London), 1952 .
. . . .£200/£30
The Alien Sky, Eyre & Spottiswoode (London), 1953 .
. . . . £75/£20
ditto, as *Six Days In Marapore*, Doubleday (New York),
1953 . . . . £35/£5
A Male Child, Eyre & Spottiswoode (London), 1956 £50/£15
ditto, Dutton (New York), 1957 . . . . £35/£10
The Mark of the Warrior, Eyre & Spottiswoode (London),
1956 . . . . £50/£15
ditto, Morrow (New York), 1958 . . . £20/£5
The Chinese Love Pavilion, Eyre & Spottiswoode (London),
1960 . . . . £25/£10
ditto, as *The Love Pavilion*, Morrow (New York), 1962 .
. . . . £20/£5
The Birds of Paradise, Eyre & Spottiswoode (London),
1962 . . . . £25/£10
ditto, Morrow (New York), 1962 . . . £20/£5
The Bender, Secker & Warburg (London), 1963 . £25/£10
ditto, Morrow (New York), 1963 . . . £20/£5
The Corrida at San Feliu, Secker & Warburg (London),
1964 . . . . £25/£10
ditto, Morrow (New York), 1964 . . . £20/£5
Staying On, Heinemann (London), 1977 . . £45/£10
ditto, Morrow (New York), 1977. . . . £25/£5

Poetry
I, Gerontius, Favil Press (London), 1941 (wraps) . . £400

Others
After the Funeral, Whittington Press/Heinemann (London),
1979 (200 copies signed by illustrator; slipcase) . £100/£75
My Appointment with the Muse: Essays 1961-1975,
Heinemann (London), 1986 . . . . . £25/£10

WALTER SCOTT
(b.1771 d.1832)

Sir Walter Scott was a novelist, poet, editor and critic. It has been suggested that he turned to writing novels after his earlier poetic work had been eclipsed by Byron's *Child Harold's Pilgrimage*. Scott's career in prose proved to be phenomenal, however, and during his lifetime and for perhaps a century after his death he was acclaimed as one of the greatest novelists in the language.

Novels and Tales
Waverley; or, 'Tis Sixty Years Since, J. Ballantyne/
Constable… Longman etc (Edinburgh), 1814 (anon; first
issue with 'our' instead of 'your' in vol. 2, p.136, first line;
grey boards with straight-grain burgundy morocco spines
and tips, spines ruled and lettered in gilt; 3 vols) . . .
. . . . £4,000 the set
ditto, J. Ballantyne/Constable…Longman etc (Edinburgh),
1814 (rebound) . . . . . £1,000 the set
Guy Mannering, J. Ballantyne, (Edinburgh), 1815 (anon; 3
vols) . . . . £450 the set
The Antiquary, J. Ballantyne (Edinburgh), 1816 (anon; 3
vols) . . . . £275 the set
Tales of My Landlord: First Series; *The Black Dwarf* and
Old Mortality, Blackwood/John Murray, 1816 (pseud
'Jedediah Cleishbotham'; 4 vols) . . . £300 the set
Rob Roy, Constable/Longman, Hurst, Rees, Orme & Brown,
1818 [1817] (anon; 3 vols) . . . £325 the set
Tales of My Landlord: Second Series; *The Heart of Mid-
Lothian*, Constable (Edinburgh), 1818 (pseud 'Jedediah
Cleishbotham'; 4 vols) . . . . £200 the set
Tales of My Landlord: Third Series; *The of Lammermoor*
and *A Legend of Montrose*, Constable (Edinburgh), 1819
(pseud 'Jedediah Cleishbotham'; 4 vols) . £200 the set
Ivanhoe, Constable (Edinburgh), 1820 [1819] (pseud
'Laurence Templeton'; 3 vols) . . . £600 the set
The Monastery, Constable/J. Ballantyne/Longman, Hurst,
Rees, Orme & Brown, 1820 (anon; 3 vols) . £100 the set
The Abbot, Constable/J. Ballantyne/Longman, Hurst, Rees,
Orme & Brown, 1820 (anon; 3 vols) . . £100 the set
Kenilworth, Constable (Edinburgh), 1821 (anon; 3 vols) .
. . . . £200 the set
The Pirate, Constable (Edinburgh), 1822 [1821] (anon; 3
vols) . . . . £100 the set
The Fortunes of Nigel, Constable (Edinburgh), 1822 (anon;
3 vols) . . . . £100 the set
Peveril of the Peak, Constable (Edinburgh), 1822 [1823]
(anon; 3 vols) . . . . . £100 the set
Quentin Durward, Constable (Edinburgh), 1823 (anon; 3
vols) . . . . £100 the set
St Ronan's Well, Constable (Edinburgh), 1824 [1823] (anon;
3 vols) . . . . £100 the set
Redgauntlet, Constable (Edinburgh), 1824 (anon; 3 vols) .
. . . . £100 the set
Tales of the Crusaders: The Betrothed and The Talisman,
Constable/Hurst Robinson, 1825 (anon; 4 vols) . . .
. . . . £100 the set
Woodstock, (Edinburgh), 1826 (anon; 3 vols) . £100 the set

Chronicles of the Cannongate: First Series: The Highland Widow, The Two Drovers and The Surgeon's Daughter, Cadell (Edinburgh), 1827 (anon; 2 vols)   .   £100 the set
Chronicles of the Cannongate: Second Series: St Valentine's Day; or The Fair Maid of Perth, Cadell (Edinburgh), 1828 (anon; 3 vols)   .   .   .   £100 the set
Anne of Geierstein, Cadell (Edinburgh), 1829 (3 vols).   .
.   .   .   .   £175 the set
Tales of My Landlord: Fourth Series; *Count Robert of Paris* and *Castle Dangerous*, Constable (Edinburgh), 1832 [1831] (pseud 'Jedediah Cleishbotham'; 4 vols)   .   .   .
.   .   .   .   £175 the set

Collected Editions
Cadell Edition, Robert Cadell, 1829-33 (illustrated frontispiece and title-page only; 48 vols)   . £1,000 the set
Centenary Edition, Black, 1871 (illustrated frontispiece and title-page only; 25 vols)   .   .   .   . £250 the set
Border Edition, J.C. Nimmo, 1892-94 (edited by Andrew Lang; original etchings in text; 48 vols).   . £750 the set
ditto, J.C. Nimmo, 1892-94 (Large Paper Edition; limited to 365 sets on hand-made paper; with proof etchings; 48 vols)
.   .   .   .   £1,750

Poetry
The Lay of the Last Minstrel, Longman (Edinburgh), 1805.
.   .   .   .   £200
Ballads and Lyrical Pieces, J. Ballantyne/Longman, Hurst, Rees, Orme & Brown, 1806   .   .   .   .   . £100
Marmion: A Tale of Flodden Field, Constable (Edinburgh), 1809 [1808] £150
The Lady of the Lake, (Edinburgh), 1810   .   .   . £75
The Vision of Don Roderick, J. Ballantyne/Longman, Hurst, Rees, Orme & Brown (Edinburgh), 1811   .   .   . £50
Rokeby, J. Ballantyne (Edinburgh), 1813   .   .   . £40
The Bridal of Triermain, or The Vision of St John, J. Ballantyne (Edinburgh), 1813   .   .   .   .   . £100
The Lord of the Isles, Constable/Longman (Edinburgh), 1815   .   .   .   . £100
The Field of Waterloo, Constable (Edinburgh), 1815   . £50
Harold the Dauntless, Constable (Edinburgh), 1817   . £50
The Poetical Works, Cadell (Edinburgh), 1833-34 (edited by John G. Lockhart) £200

Non-Fiction
Rules and Regulations of the Royal Edinburgh Light Dragoons, 1798, (Edinburgh), 1799 (anon)   .   £1,000
The Border Antiquities of England and Scotland, Longman (London), 1814-17 (2 vols) £200
Lives of the Novelists, J. Ballantyne: 'Novelists' Library' series (Edinburgh), 1821-24 (4 vols)   .   . £100 the set
The Life of Napoleon Buonaparte, (Edinburgh), 1827 (9 vols)   .   .   .   . £400 the set
Letters on Demonology and Witchcraft, John Murray, 1830
.   .   .   .   £125
The Miscellaneous Prose Works, Cadell (Edinburgh), 1834-36 (28 vols)   .   .   .   .   .   . £200 the set
The Journal of Sir Walter Scott, D. Douglas (Edinburgh), 1890 (2 vols)   .   .   .   .   . £40 the set
The Letters of Sir Walter Scott, Constable, 1932-37 (12 vols)   .   .   .   . £100 the set

W.G. SEBALD
(b.1944 d.2001)

W.G. Sebald was a German writer and academic who gained acclaim for his novels depicting characters haunted by World War Two. Before his early death he was being cited by many literary critics as one of the greatest living authors, and had been tipped as a possible future winner of the Nobel Prize in Literature

Novels
The Emigrants, The Harvill Press (London), 1996 (translated by Michael Hulse)   .   .   .   . .£450/£65
ditto, New Directions (New York), 1996   .   .   £75/£15
The Rings of Saturn, The Harvill Press (London), 1998   .
.   .   .   . £400/£45
ditto, The Harvill Press (London), 1998 (pbk) .   .   . £40
ditto, New Directions (New York), 1998   .   . £45/£10
Vertigo, The Harvill Press (London), 1999   . £125/£20
ditto, The Harvill Press (London), 1999 (pbk) .   .   . £15
ditto, New Directions (New York), 1999   .   .   £15/£5
Austerlitz, Hamish Hamilton (London), 2001 (100 signed, numbered copies of the uncorrected proof in boards; no d/w) £500
ditto, Hamish Hamilton (London), 2001   .   .   £30/£5
ditto, Random House (New York), 2001   .   .   £10/£5

Poems
For Years Now, Short Books (London), 2001 (pbk; illustrations by Tess Jaray) £10
After Nature, Hamish Hamilton (London), 2002   £15/£5
ditto, Random House (New York), 2002   .   .   £10/£5
Unrecounted, Hamish Hamilton (London), 2004 (with lithographs by Jan Peter Tripp).   .   .   .   £10/£5
ditto, New Directions (New York), 2004   .   .   £10/£5

Others
On the Natural History of Destruction, Hamish Hamilton (London), 2003   .   .   .   .   .   .   £15/£5
ditto, Random House (New York), 2003   .   .   £10/£5
Campo Santo, Hamish Hamilton (London), 2005   . £10/£5
ditto, Random House (New York), 2005   .   .   £10/£5
Young Austerlitz, Penguin Books (London), 2005 (pbk)   £5

MAURICE SENDAK
(b.1928)

Maurice Sendak is an American writer and illustrator of children's books who is best known for *Where the Wild Things Are*. He spent the 1950s working as an artist for children's books, before beginning to write his own stories.

Books for Children written and illustrated by Sendak
Kenny's Window: A Tale for Children, Harper (New York), [1956] (d/w price $2.00)   .   .   .   .   . £300/£75
Happy Rain, Harper (New York), 1956 (d/w priced $2.50; blurb on book on front flap; illustrated blurb for book on back flap followed by '60/80/Harper & Brothers')   .   .
.   .   .   . £350/£75
ditto, The World's Work (Kingswood, Surrey), 1959 £65/£20
Very Far Away: A Tale, Harper (New York), 1957 (d/w priced $2.00, with blurb on book on front flap and '...40-

80/No.7316A' at bottom; 4 reviews of Kenny's Window on back flap with 'No.7317A' at bottom) . . . £300/£75

ditto, The World's Work (Kingswood, Surrey), 1960 £75/£25

The Acrobat, privately printed, 1959. . . . £125/£40

The Sign on Rosie's Door, Harper (New York), 1960 (d/w priced $2.50, with blurb on this book, and 'No.9759A/50-80' at the bottom; back flap with 4 para description of Sendak with 'No.9760A' at bottom) . . £200/£45

ditto, Hamish Hamilton (London), 1969 . £65/£20

The Nutshell Library, Harper (New York), 1962 (4 vols: *Alligators All Around, Chicken Soup with Rice, One Was Johnny* and *Pierre*; slipcase) . . . £145/£40 the set

ditto, Collins (London), 1964 . . . £125/£35 the set

Where The Wild Things Are, Harper (New York), 1963 (d/w priced $3.50, with 3 para blurb on book and '40/80/1163' at the bottom; no mention of Caldecott award) £2,000/£300

ditto, The Bodley Head (London), 1967 . . . £450/£75

Higglety Pigglety Pop!, or There Must be More to Life, Harper (New York), 1967. . . . . . £85/£25

ditto, The Bodley Head (London), 1969 . £75/£20

In the Night Kitchen, Harper (New York), 1970 . £125/£25

ditto, The Bodley Head (London), 1971 . . £50/£10

The Magician: A Counting Book, Rosenbach (New York), 1971 . . . . £45/£10

Pictures, Harper (New York), 1971 . . . . £60/£20

ditto, The Bodley Head (London), 1972 . . £35/£10

Really Rosie, Harper (New York), 1975 . . . £35/£10

Seven Little Monsters, Harper (New York), 1976 . £45/£15

ditto, The Bodley Head (London), 1977 . . £35/310

Some Swell Pup, or Are You Sure You Want a Dog?, by Maurice Sendak and Matthew Margolis, Farrar, Straus & Giroux (New York), 1976. . . . £50/£15

ditto, The Bodley Head (London), 1976 . . £35/£10

Outside Over There, Harper (New York), 1981 . £30/£10

ditto, The Bodley Head (London), 1981 . . £25/£10

We Are All in the Dumps with Jack and Guy, HarperCollins (London), 1993 . . . . £10/£5

Books for Adults written and illustrated by Sendak

Fantasy Sketches, Rosenbach (New York), 1972 (paperback) £25

Collection of Books, Posters and Original Drawings, Schiller (New York), 1984 (wraps). £25

Posters, Harmony (New York), 1986. . . . £35/£10

ditto, Harmony (New York), 1986 (wraps) . . £10

ditto, Bodley Head (London), 1987 . . . £25/£10

Caldecott and Co, Notes on Books and Pictures, Farrar, Straus & Giroux (New York), 1988 () . . £20/£5

ditto, Farrar, Straus & Giroux (New York), 1988 (250 signed, numbered copies; slipcase) . . £125/£100

Books by others, illustrated by Sendak

Atomics for the Millions, by M.C. Eidenoff, McGraw Hill (New York), 1947 (with statement on quality of the paper on copyrighd/w prices $3.50 on both flaps) . £300/£45

ditto, Harrap (London), 1950 . . . . . £200/£35

Wonderful Farm, by Marcel Ayme, Harper (New York), 1951 (translated by Norman Denny; with 'First Edition / I-A' on copyright page). . . . . £300/£45

Maggie Rose – Her Birthday Christmas, by R. Sawyer, Harper (New York), 1952 . . . . . £65/£20

A Hole is To Dig: A First Book of First Definitions, by Ruth Krauss, Harper (New York), 1952 ($1.50 on dj flap, green cloth spine, without 'grrr-r-r' on page 23) . £225/£75

ditto, Hamish Hamilton (London), 1963 . . . £200/£65

Shadrach, by Meindart de Jong, Harper (New York), 1953 . . . . £75/£15

ditto, Lutterworth (London), 1957 . . . . £45/£15

A Very Special House, by Ruth Krauss, Harper (New York), 1953 . . . . £100/£15

I'll Be You and You Be Me, by Ruth Krauss, Harper (New York), 1954 . . . . £150/£25

Magic Pictures, by Marcel Aymé, Harper (New York), 1954 . . . . £175/£30

The Wheel on the School, by Meindart de Jong, Harper (New York), 1954 . . . . £45/£10

ditto, Lutterworth (London), 1956 . . . . £45/£10

I Want to Paint My Bathroom Blue, by Ruth Krauss, Harper (New York), 1954 . . . . . . £75/£20

Tin Fiddle, by E. Tripp, O.U.P. (London), 1954 . £75/£20

The Little Cow and the Turtle, by Meindart de Jong, Harper (New York), 1955 . . . . . . £50/£15

ditto, Lutterworth (London), 1961 . . . £50/£15

What Can You So With A Shoe?, by B.S. de Regniers, Harper (New York), 1955 . . . . . £75/£20

Charlotte and the White Horse, by Ruth Krauss, Harper (New York), 1955 . . . .£145/£35

ditto, The Bodley Head (London), 1977 . . . £50/£15

The House of Sicty Fathers, by Meindart de Jong, Harper (New York), 1956 . . . . £50/£10

Little Bear, by Else Holmelund Minarik, Harper (New York), 1957 . . . . £75/£20

ditto, The World's Work (Kingswood, Surrey), 1958 £50/£15

What Do You Say Dear, by Sesyle Joslin, Faber (London), 1958 . . . . £50/£10

No Fighting, No Biting!, by Else Holmelund Minarik, Harper (New York), 1958 . . . . . .£175/£45

ditto, Tadworth (London), 1969 . . . . . £50/£10

Father Bear Comes Home, by Else Holmelund Minarik, Harper (New York), 1959. . . . . . £75/£20

ditto, The World's Work (Kingswood, Surrey), 1960 £50/£10

The Moon Jumpers, by Janice May Udry, Harper (New York), 1959 . . . . £50/£10

ditto, The Bodley Head (London), 1979 . . . £45/£10

Little Bear's Friend, by Else Holmelund Minarik, Harper (New York), 1960 . . . . £75/£20

ditto, The World's Work (Kingswood, Surrey), 1961 £50/£10

Dwarf Long-Nose, by Wilhelm Hauff, Random House (New York), 1960 (translated by Doris Orgel). . £60/£15

ditto, The Bodley Head (London), 1979 . . £35/£10

Little Bear's Visit, by Else Holmelund Minarik, Harper (New York), 1961 . . . . £75/£20

ditto, The World's Work (Kingswood, Surrey), 1962 £50/£10

The Big Green Book, by Robert Graves, Crowell-Crollier (New York), 1962 . . . . £35/£10

ditto, Kestrel (London), 1962 . . . . . £35/£10

The Grifffin and the Minor Canon, by Frank R. Stockton, Holt (New York), 1963 . . . . . .£100/£25

ditto, Collins (London), 1968 . . . . . £75/£20

The Bat-Poet, by Randall Jarrell, McMillan (New York), 1964 . . . . £50/£10

ditto, Kestrel (London), 1977 . . . . . £35/£10

The Bee-man of Orn, by Frank R. Stockton, Holt (New York), 1964 . . . . £50/£10

ditto, Collins (London), 1967 . . . . . £45/£10

Pleasant Fieldmouse, by Jan Wahl, Harper (New York), 1964 . . . . £40/£15

ditto, Tadworth (London), 1969 . . . . . £25/£10

Hector Protector and *As I Went Over the Water*, Harper (New York), 1965 . . . . . . £75/£20
ditto, The Bodley Head (London), 1967 . . . £50/£10
Animal People, by Randall Jarrell, Random House (New York), 1965 . . . . £50/£10
ditto, as *Animal Family*, by Randall Jarrell, Pantheon (New York), 1965 . . . . . . £75/£20
ditto, Hart-Davis (London), 1967 . . . . £50/£15
A Kiss for Little Bear, by Else Holmelund Minarik, Harper (New York), 1968 . . . . £50/£15
ditto, The World's Work (Kingswood, Surrey), 1969 £40/£10
Mr Rabbit and the Lovely Present, by Charlotte Zolotow, The Bodley Head (London), 1968 . . . . £40/£10
Lullabies and Night Songs, The Bodley Head (London), 1969 . . . . £50/£15
The Light Princess, by George MacDonald, The Bodley Head (London), 1969 . . . . . £50/£15
Zlateh The Goat and Other Stories, translated by Isaac Bashevis Singer and Elizabeth Shub, Harper and Row (New York), 1966 . . . . . £25/£10
ditto, Harper and Row (New York), 1966 (500 numbered copies signed by the author and Maurice Sendak; slipcase) . . . . £350/£300
ditto, Longman, Young (Harmondsworth, Middx), 1970 . . . . £25/£10
In Sarah's Room, The Bodley Head (London), 1972 . . £25/ £10
The Golden Key, by George MacDonald, The Bodley Head (London), 1972 (afterword by W.H. Auden; in d/w) . . £40/£15
The Juniper Tree and Other Tales from Grimm, Farrar, Straus & Giroux (New York), 1973 (selected by Segal and Sendak; translated by Lore Segal and Randall Jarrell; 2 vols; in d/ws and clipcase). . . . £75 the set
ditto, The Bodley Head (London), 1974 . . £75 the set
King Grisley-Beard, by Wilhelm and Jacob Grimm, Farrar, Straus & Giroux (New York), 1973. . . £45/£15
ditto, The Bodley Head (London), 1974 . . £25/£10
Fortunia, by Marie Aulnay, Frank Hallman (New York), 1974 (300 copies numbered and signed by translator and Sendak; wraps) £75
Fly By Night, by Randall Jarrell, Farrar, Straus & Giroux (New York), 1976 . . . . . £45/£15
ditto, The Bodley Head (London), 1977 . . £35/£10
Cinderella, Heinemann/Gallery Five (London), 1977 £20/£5
The Art of Maurice Sendak, by G. Selma Lanes, Harry N. Abrams (New York) 1980. . . . £100/£30
ditto, The Bodley Head (London), 1980 . £100/£30
The Nutcracker, by E.T.A. Hoffmann, Harper (New York), 1984 (translated by Ralph Manheim) . . £75/£20
ditto, The Bodley Head (London), 1984 . . £50/£10
Love For Three Oranges, Farrar, Strauss & Giroux (New York), 1984 . . . . . . £50/£15
ditto, The Bodley Head (London), 1984 . . £45/£10
The Cunning Little Vixen, by Rudolf Tesnohlidek, Farrar, Straus & Giroux (New York), 1985. . . £75/£20
ditto, The Bodley Head (London), 1986 . . £45/£10
In Grandpa's House, by P. Sendak, Harper & Row, 1985 . . . . £30/£10
ditto, The Bodley Head (London), 1986 . . £30/£10
Dear Mili, by Wilhelm Grimm, Michael di Capua/Farrar, Straus & Giroux (New York), 1988. . . £35/£15
ditto, Viking Kestrel (London), 1988. . . £25/£10
I Saw Esau, by Iona Opie, Walker (New York), 1992 £10/£5

ditto, Walker (New York), 1992 (300 numbered copies signed by Iona Opie and Sendak; slipcase) . £150/£125
ditto, Candlewick Press (Cambridge, Ma), 1992 . £10/£5
ditto, Candlewick Press (Cambridge, Ma), 1992 (300 numbered copies signed by Iona Opie and Sendak; slipcase). . . . . £100/£75

DR SEUSS
(b.1904 d.1991)

Dr Seuss was the pseudonym for the American Theodor Seuss Geisel, who also wrote as 'Theo Le Sieg' and 'Rosetta Stone'. A freelance magazine humorist and cartoonist from 1927, he became the founding president and editor-in-chief of Beginner Books at Random House in 1957. His most famous creation is 'The Cat in the Hat', and his books for children have now sold in the hundreds of millions.

Poetry for Children Illustrated by Seuss
And to Think That I Saw It on Mulberry Street, Vangueard Press (New York), 1937 (first issue with boy in white shorts on front cover; $1.00 price on d/w) . £3,000/£750
ditto, Country Life (London), 1939 . . . £1,000/£150
The 500 Hats of Bartholomew Cubbins, Vanguard Press (New York), 1938 . . . . . £1,000/£125
ditto, O.U.P. (London), 1940 . . . . £200/£30
The King's Stilts, Random House (New York), 1939 . . . . £650/£75
ditto, Hamish Hamilton (London), 1942 . . £450/£75
Horton Hatches the Egg, Random House (New York), 1940 . . . . £500/£65
ditto, Hamish Hamilton (London), 1942 . . £400/£50
McElligot's Pool, Random House (New York), 1947 (first issue with open-mouthed fish on front cover) . £250/£45
ditto, Collins (London), 1975 . . . . £35/£10
Thidwick, The Big-Hearted Moose, Random House (New York), 1948 . . . . . . £250/£45
ditto, Collins (London), 1968 . . . . £45/£10
Bartholemew and the Oobleck, Random House (New York), 1949 (blue boards and jacket) . . . . £250/£45
If I Ran the Zoo, Random House (New York), 1950 . . . . £250/£45
ditto, Collins (London), 1969 . . . . £40/£10
Scrambled Eggs Super!, Random House (New York), 1953 . . . . £200/£50
Horton Hears a Who!, Random House (New York), 1954 (first issue with complete ears on rear panel of d/w) . . . . £300/£50
ditto, Collins (London), 1976 . . . . £25/£10
On Beyond Zebra, Random House (New York), 1955 (first issue with $2.50 price on d/w) . . . £200/£40
If I Ran the Circus, Random House (New York), 1956 . . . . £175/£25
ditto, Collins (London), 1969 . . . . £45/£10
The Cat in the Hat, Random House (New York), 1957 (first issue with unlaminated boards and price on the d/w is '200/200') . . . . . . £2,500/£750
ditto, Hutchinson (London), 1958 . . . £200/£65
How the Grinch Stole Christmas, Random House (New York), 1957 . . . . . . £250/£45
ditto, Collins (London), 1973 . . . . £75/£40

The Cat in the Hat Comes Back!, Random House (New York), 1958 . . . . £400/£45
ditto, Collins (London), 1961 . . . . . £75/£20
Yertle the Turtle and Other Stories, Random House (New York), 1958 . . . . £75/£25
ditto, Collins (London), 1963 . . . . . £30/£10
Happy Birthday to You!, Random House (New York), 1959 . . . . £35/£15
One Fish, Two Fish, Red Fish, Blue Fish, Random House (New York), 1960 . . . . . £35/£15
ditto, Collins (London), 1962 . . . . . £25/£10
Green Eggs and Ham, Random House (New York), 1960 . . . . £65/£25
ditto, Collins (London), 1962 . . . . . £30/£10
The Sneetches and Other Stories, Random House (New York), 1961 . . . . £50/£20
ditto, Collins (London), 1965 . . . . . £30/£10
Sleep Book, Random House (New York), 1962 . £50/£20
ditto, Collins (London), 1964 . . . . . £25/£10
Hop on Pop, Random House (New York), 1963 . £50/£20
ditto, Collins (London), 1964 . . . . . £25/£10
ABC, Random House (New York*)*, 1963 . . £35/£15
ditto, Collins (London), 1964 . . . . . £25/£10
Fox in Socks, Random House (New York), 1965 . £35/£15
ditto, Collins (London), 1966 . . . . . £25/£10
I Had Trouble in Getting to Solla Sollew, Random House (New York), 1965 . . . . . . £65/£25
ditto, Collins (London), 1967 . . . . . £40/£20
I Can Lick 30 Tigers Today and Other Stories, Random House (New York), 1969 . . . . . £35/£15
ditto, Collins (London), 1970 . . . . . £25/£10
Mr. Brown Can Moo! Can You?, Random House (New York), 1970 . . . . £25/£10
ditto, Collins (London), 1971 . . . . . £20/£5
The Lorax, Random House (New York), 1971 . £60/£20
ditto, Collins (London), 1972 . . . . . £30/£10
Marvin K Mooney, Will You Please Go Now?, Random House (New York), 1972 . . . . . £25/£10
ditto, Collins (London), 1973 . . . . . £15/£5
Did I Ever Tell You How Lucky You Are?, Random House (New York), 1973 . . . . . . £35/£10
ditto, Collins (London), 1974 . . . . . £25/£10
The Shape of Me and Other Stuff, Random House (New York), 1973 . . . . £25/£10
ditto, Collins (London), 1974 . . . . . £10/£5
There's a Wocket in My Pocket!, Random House (New York), 1974 . . . . £20/£5
ditto, Collins (London), 1975 . . . . . £15/£5
Oh, The Thinks You Can Think, Random House (New York), 1975 . . . . £25/£10
ditto, Collins (London), 1976 . . . . . £15/£5
Because a Little Bug Went Ka-Choo!, Random House (New York), 1975 (pseud 'Rosetta Stone'; written with Michael Frith) . . . . £20/£5
ditto, Collins (London), 1976 . . . . . £10/£5
Oh Say Can You Say?, Random House (New York), 1979 . . . . £25/£10
ditto, Collins (London), 1980 . . . . . £15/£5
Dr Seuss Storybook, Collins (London), 1979 . £20/£10
Hunches in Bunches, Random House (New York), 1982 . . . . £35/£15
ditto, Collins (London), 1980 . . . . . £30/£10
The Butter Battle Book, Random House (New York), 1984 . . . . £40/£15

ditto, Collins (London), 1984 . . . . . £30/£10
ditto, Collins (London), 1988 . . . . . £15/£5
Daisy-Head Mayzie, Random House (New York), 1995 . . . . £20/£5
ditto, Collins (London), 1990 . . . . . £20/£5

Other Children's Books by Seuss
The Cat in the Hat Dictionary, by the Cat Himself, Random House (New York), 1964 (with Philip D. Eastman) £45/£20
The Cat in the Hat Beginner Book Dictionary in French, Random House (New York), 1965 . . . £30/£10
ditto, Collins (London), 1967 . . . . . £20/£5
The Cat in the Hat Beginner Book Dictionary in Spanish, Random House (New York), 1966 . . . . £30/£10
ditto, Collins (London), 1967 . . . . . £20/£5
Great Day for Up!, Random House (New York), 1974 (illustrated by Quentin Blake) . . . . £35/£10
ditto, Collins (London), 1975 . . . . . £25/£10
I Am Not Going to Get Up Today!, Random House (New York), 1987 (illustrated by James Stevenson) . £25/£10
ditto, Collins (London), 1988 . . . . . £15/£5

Books Written as Theo Le Sieg
Ten Apples Up on Top!, Random House (New York), 1961 (illustrated by Roy McKie) . . . . £45/£10
ditto, Collins (London), 1962 . . . . . £30/£5
I Wish That I Had Duck Feet, Random House (New York), 1965 (illustrated by B. Tobey) . . . . £35/£10
ditto, Collins (London), 1966 . . . . . £20/£5
Come Over to My House, Random House (New York), 1966 (illustrated by Richard Erdoes). . . . £25/£10
ditto, Collins (London), 1966 . . . . . £10/£5
The Foot Book, Random House (New York), 1968 £35/£15
ditto, Collins (London), 1969 . . . . . £25/£10
The Eye Book, Random House (New York), 1968 (illustrated by Roy McKie) . . . . . £25/£10
ditto, Collins (London), 1969 . . . . . £10/£5
I Can Write--By Me, Myself, Random House (New York), 1971 (as Theo Le Sieg) . . . . . £20/£5
ditto, Collins (London), 1972 . . . . . £10/£5
In a People House, Random House (New York), 1972 (illustrated by Roy McKie) . . . . . £25/£10
ditto, Collins (London), 1973 . . . . . £10/£5
The Many Mice of Mr Brice, Random House (New York), 1973 (illustrated by Roy McKie) . . . £25/£10
ditto, Collins (London), 1974 . . . . . £10/£5
Wacky Wednesday, Random House (New York), 1974 (illustrated by George Booth) . . . . £20/£10
ditto, Collins (London), 1975 . . . . . £10/£5
Would You Rather Be a Bullfrog?, Random House (New York), 1975 (illustrated by Roy McKie) . £20/£10
ditto, Collins (London), 1976 . . . . . £10/£5
Hooper Humperdink...? Not Him!, Random House (New York), 1976 (illustrated by Charles Martin) . £25/£10
ditto, Collins (London), 1977 . . . . . £15/£5
Please Try to Remember the First of Octemeber, Random House (New York), 1977 (illustrated by Arthur Cumings) . . . . £20/£5
ditto, Collins (London), 1978 . . . . . £10/£5
Maybe You Should Fly a Jet! Maybe You Should Be a Vet!, Random House (New York), 1980 (illustrated by Michael Smollin) . . . . £20/£5
ditto, Collins (London), 1981 . . . . . £10/£5

The Tooth Book, Random House (New York), 1981
(illustrated by Roy McKie)   .   .   .   .   £20/£5
ditto, Collins (London), 1982   .   .   .   .   £10/£5

Other non-Seuss Children's Books
The Cat in the Hat Songbook , Random House (New York),
1967   .   .   .   .   £50/£20
ditto, Collins (London), 1968   .   .   .   £25/£10
My Book about Me-By Me, Myself. I Wrote It! I Drew It!,
Random House (New York), 1969 (illustrated by Roy
McKie)   .   .   .   .   £25/£10
ditto, Collins (London), 1970   .   .   .   £20/£5
I Can Draw It Myself, Random House (New York), 1970   .
.   .   .   .   £25/£10
The Cat's Quizzer, Random House (New York), 1976 .   .
.   .   .   .   £35/£20
ditto, Collins (London), 1977   .   .   .   £30/£10
I Can Read with My Eyes Shut!, Random House (New
York), 1978 .   .   .   .   .   .   £25/£10
ditto, Collins (London), 1979   .   .   .   £20/£5

Other Books
Boners, Viking (New York), 1931   .   .   . £200/£35
More Boners, Viking (New York), 1931 .   . £150/£30
Still More Boners, Viking (New York), 1931 . £100/£20
The Seven Lady Godivas, Random House (New York), 1939
.   .   .   .   £450/£75
*Lost World Revisited: A Forward-Looking Backward
Glance*, Award Books (New York), 1967 (wraps)   . £40
You're Only Old Once!, Random House (New York), 1986
.   .   .   .   £35/£15
ditto, Fontana (London), 1986 (wraps)   .   .   . £5
*The Tough Coughs as He Ploughs the Dough: Early
Writings and Cartoons by Dr. Seuss*, Morrow (New York),
1986 (edited by Richard Marschall)   .   .   £20/£5
Oh, the Places You'll Go!, Random House (New York),
1990   .   .   .   .   .   .   £25/£10
ditto, Collins (London), 1991   .   .   .   £15/£5
Six by Seuss: A Treasury of Dr. Seuss Classics. Random
House (New York), 1991 .   .   .   .   £20/£5

ANNA SEWELL
(b.1820 d.1878)

Black Beauty was Anna Sewell's only novel, written in an
attempt to encourage the better treatment of horses. She
wrote it between 1871 and 1877 when her health was de-
clining and she was often so weak that she couldn't get out
of bed. She dictated the text to her mother and wrote on
slips of paper, which her mother then transcribed.

*Black Beauty: His Grooms and Companions. The Auto-
biography of a Horse*, Jarrold (London), 1877   . £7,500
ditto, American Humane Education Society (Boston), 1890
(orange printed wraps) £750
ditto, American Humane Education Society (Boston), 1890
(buff boards). £500
ditto, Jarrold (London), [1912] (18 colour plates by Cecil
Aldin) £100
ditto, Jarrold (London), [1912] (18 colour plates by Cecil
Aldin, 250 copies) £300

ditto, Dent (London), 1915 (illustrated by Lucy Kemp-
Welch) £100
ditto, Dent (London), 1915 (600 copies illustrated and signed
by Lucy Kemp-Welch) £450

TOM SHARPE
(b.1928)

Tom Sharpe became a full-time novelist in 1971 with the
publication of *Riotous Assembly*. His novels are often quite
bitter satires: his targets include apartheid, education,
British class snobbery, the literary world, political extrem-
ism, political correctness, bureaucracy and stupidity in
general. His books have been filmed and televised with
varying degrees of success.

Novels
Riotous Assembly, Secker & Warburg (London), 1971 .   .
.   .   .   .   £200/£25
ditto, Viking (New York), 1971 .   .   .   £60/£10
Indecent Exposure, Secker & Warburg (London), 1973   .
.   .   .   .   £150/£20
ditto, Atlantic Monthly Press (New York), 1987 (wraps)   . £5
Porterhouse Blue, Secker & Warburg (London), 1974 .   .
.   .   .   .   £75/£15
ditto, Prentice-Hall (Englewood Cliffs, NJ), 1974 . £25/£10
Blott on the Landscape, Secker & Warburg (London), 1975
.   .   .   .   £40/£10
ditto, Random House (New York), 1985 .   .   . £10/£5
Wilt, Secker & Warburg (London), 1976 .   .   £40/£10
ditto, Random House (New York), 1984 .   .   . £10/£5
The Great Pursuit, Secker & Warburg (London), 1977   .
.   .   .   .   £20/£5
ditto, Harper (New York), 1978   .   .   £15/£5
The Throwback, Secker & Warburg (London), 1978 £20/£5
ditto, Random House (New York), 1985 .   .   . £10/£5
The Wilt Alternative, Secker & Warburg (London), 1979   .
.   .   .   .   £20/£5
ditto, St Martin's Press (New York), 1979   .   . £15/£5
Ancestral Vices, Secker & Warburg (London), 1980 £20/£5
ditto, St Martin's Press (New York), 1980   .   . £15/£5
Vintage Stuff, Secker & Warburg (London), 1982 . £20/£5
ditto, Random House (New York), 1985 .   .   . £10/£5
Wilt on High, Secker & Warburg (London), 1984 . £15/£5
ditto, Random House (New York), 1985 .   .   . £10/£5
Grantchester Grind, A Porterhouse Chronicle,
Deutsch/Secker & Warburg (London), 1995 .   . £10/£5
The Midden, Deutsch/Secker & Warburg (London), 1996 .
.   .   .   .   £10/£5
ditto, Overlook Press (Woodstock, NY), 1997 .   . £10/£5
Wilt in Nowhere, Hutchinson (London), 2004 .   . £10/£5
The Gropes, 2009, Hutchinson (London), 2009   . £10/£5

GEORGE BERNARD SHAW
(b.1856 d.1950)

Primarily a playwright, Shaw's dramatic works are often satirical attacks on convention and cant. The Irishman's many other writings are often political, expressing his socialism. He was awarded the Nobel Prize in 1925, but declined offers of a peerage and the Order of Merit. He received an Academy Award for the screenplay of *Pygmalion* in 1938.

Novels

Cashel Byron's Profession, The Modern Press (London), 1886 (larger issue measuring approx. 24.8 x 15.4 cm; wraps) £600
ditto, The Modern Press (London), 1886 (smaller issue measuring approx. 23.3 x 14.8 cm; wraps) . . £500
ditto, Brentano's (New York), 1899 . . . . . £35
ditto, Stone (Chicago), 1901 . . . . . £40
An Unsocial Socialist, Swan, Sonnenschein, Lowrey & Co. (London), 1887 (first state with Shaw's first novel given incorrectly as 'The Confessions of Bryn Cashel's...' and publisher's name spelt wrong on spine). . . £1,250
ditto, Swan, Sonnenschein, Lowrey & Co. (London), 1887 (second state with errors corrected). £750
ditto, Brentano's (New York), 1900 . . . . . £50
Love Among the Artists, Stone (Chicago), 1905 . £50
ditto, Constable (London), 1914 . . . . . £65
The Irrational Knot, Constable (London), 1905 . £45
ditto, Brentano's (New York), 1905 . . . . £45
Immaturity, Constable (London), 1931 . . £65/£15
Unfinished Novel, Constable (London), 1958 (950 copies; acetate d/w) . . . . £25/£20
ditto, Constable (London), 1958 (25 lettered copies; acetate d/w) . . . . £75/£65

Plays

Widowers' Houses, Henry and Co (London), 1893 . £650
Plays Pleasant and Unpleasant, Grant Richards (London), 1898 (2 vols) £100
ditto, Stone (Chicago), 1898 (2 vols) £100
ditto, Brentano's (New York), 1905 (2 vols) . . . £65
Three Plays for Puritans, Grant Richards (London), 1901 . . . . £45
Mrs Warren's Profession, Grant Richards (London), 1902 . . . . £150
Man and Superman, Constable (London), 1903 . £30
ditto, Brentano's (New York), 1905 . . . . £25
John Bull's Other Island, and *Major Barbara*, Constable and Co. (London), 1907 (also contains *How He Lied to Her Husband*) £30
Press Cuttings, Constable (London), 1909 (first issue pink wraps; 'Price One Shilling' on upper cover). . £50
ditto, Constable (London), 1909 (second issue pink wraps; 'Price One Shilling. / Net.') £50
ditto, Constable (London), 1909 (third issue pink wraps; 'Price One Shilling net.') £25
ditto, Constable (London), 1909 (fourth issue grey wraps; 'Price One Shilling net.') £20
ditto, Brentano's (New York), 1909 (wraps) . . £65
The Doctor's Dilemma, Getting Married, and *The Shewing-Up of Blanco Posnet*, Constable and Co (London), 1911 £35

ditto, Brentano's (New York), 1911 . . . . . £25
Pygmalion, privately printed (London), 1912 (title-page reads 'Rough Proof-Unpublished'; wraps) . . £1,000
Androcles and the Lion, privately printed (London), 1913 (50 copies, title-page reads 'Rough Proof-Unpublished'; wraps) £600
Misalliance, The Dark Lady of the Sonnets, and *Fanny's First Plays*, Constable (London), 1914 . . . £25
ditto, Brentano's (New York), 1914 . . . . £25
Androcles and the Lion, Overruled, Pygmalion, Constable (London), 1916 . . . . £25
ditto, Brentano's (New York), 1916 . . . . £25
Heartbreak House, Great Catherine, and *Playlets of the War*, Constable (London), 1919 . . . . £25
ditto, Brentano's (New York), 1919 . . . . £25
Back to Methuselah. A Metabiological Pentateuch, Brentano's (New York), 1921 . . . . £125/£20
ditto, Constable (London), 1922 . . . . £125/£20
Saint Joan: A Chronicle Play in Six Scenes and an Epilogue, Constable (London), 1924 . £100/£20
ditto, Constable (London), 1924 (750 copies, with sketches by Charles Ricketts) . . . . £450/£250
ditto, Brentano's (New York), 1924 . . . £65/£15
Translations and Tomfooleries Constable (London), 1926 . . . . £50/£10
ditto, Brentano's (New York), 1926 . . . £50/£10
The Apple Cart, A Political Extravaganza, Constable (London), 1930 . . . . £65/£15
ditto, Brentano's (New York), 1931 . . . £50/£10
Too True To Be Good, Village Wooing, and *On the Rocks*, Constable (London), [1934] . . . . £45/£15
ditto, Dodd, Mead (New York), 1934 . . . £35/£10
The Simpleton of the Unexpected Isles, The Six of Calais, and *The Millionairess*, Constable (London), 1936 £40/£10
ditto, Dodd, Mead (New York), 1936 . . . £35/£10
'In Good King Charles's Golden Days', Constable (London), 1939 . . . . £35/£10
Geneva, Constable (London), 1939 (illustrated by Felix Topolski) . . . . £35/£10
ditto, Dodd, Mead (New York), 1947 . . . £25/£10
Buoyant Billions, Constable (London), 1949 (1,000 numbered copies of 1,025) . . . . £65/£25
ditto, Constable (London), 1949 (25 lettered copies of 1,025) £200
Buoyant Billions, Farfetched Fables, and *Shakes Versus Shav*, Constable (London), 1950 . . . £25/£10

Political Writings

A Manifesto, Fabian Society Tract No. 2 (London), 1884 (wraps) £100
To Provident Landlords and Capitalists, Fabian Society Tract No. 3 (London), 1885 (anonymous; wraps). £75
The True Radical Programme, Fabian Society Tract No. 6 (London), 1887 (anonymous; wraps) . . . £75
Fabian Essays in Socialism, Fabian Society (London), 1889 . . . . £100
ditto, Brown (Boston), 1904. . . . . . £75
Anarchism Versus State Socialism, Henry Seymour (London), 1889 . . . . £75
What Socialism Is, Fabian Society Tract No. 13 (London), 1890 (anonymous; wraps). £75
The Legal Eight Hours Question, R. Forder (London), 1891 (wraps) £75
Fabian Election Manifesto, Fabian Society Tract No. 40 (London), 1892 (anonymous; wraps) . . . £100

The Fabian Society: What it has Done, etc, Fabian Society Tract No. 41 (London), 1892 (wraps) . . . £65

Vote! Vote! Vote!, Fabian Society Tract No. 43 (London), 1892 (anonymous; wraps) £65

The Impossibilities of Anarchism, Fabian Society Tract No. 45 (London), 1893 (wraps) £65

A Plan of Campaign for Labour, Fabian Society Tract No. 49 (London), 1894 (wraps) £65

Report on Fabian Policy, Fabian Society Tract No. 70 (London), 1896 (anonymous; wraps) . . . £45

Women as Councillors, Fabian Society Tract No. 93 (London), 1900 (wraps) £65

Fabianism and the Empire: A Manifesto, Grant Richards (London), 1900 (wraps) £85

Socialism for Millionaires, Fabian Society Tract No. 107 (London), 1901 (wraps) £45

Common Sense of Municipal Trading, Constable (London), 1904 . . . . £45

Election Address, Fabian Society (London), 1904 (wraps) .
. . . . £45

Fabianism and the Fiscal Question, Fabian Society Tract No. 116 (London), 1904 (wraps) £35

Is Free Trade Alive or Dead?, George Standring (London), 1906 . . . . £50

The Sanity of Art, New Age Press (London), 1908 (cloth) .
. . . . £40

ditto, New Age Press (London), 1908 (paper) . . . £35

ditto, Benj. R. Tucker (New York), 1908 . . . £35

Rent and Value, Fabian Society Tract No. 142 (London), 1909 (stapled wraps) £35

Socialism and Superior Brains, Fabian Society Tract No. 146 (London), 1910 (stapled wraps) . . . £45

ditto, Lane (New York), 1910 . . . . . £45

The Case for Equality, Address to the Political & Economic Circle National Liberal Club (London), 1913 (wraps). £35

Common Sense about the War, 'New Statesman' supplement (London), 1914 (wraps) . . . £65

How to Settle the Irish Question, Talbot and Constable (Dublin), 1917 (first issue blue wraps) . . . £75

ditto, Talbot and Constable (Dublin), 1917 (second issue green wraps) £50

Peace Conference Hints, Constable (London), 1919 (wraps)
. . . . £30

Socialism and Ireland, 'New Commonwealth' supplement (London), 1919 (wraps) £25

Ruskin's Politics, Ruskin Centenary Council (London), 1921 (cloth with paper label) £45

A Discarded Defence of Roger Casement, privately printed by Clement Shorter (London), 1922 (25 copies) . . £200

The Unprotected Child & The Law, The Six Point Group (London), [1923] (wraps) £60

Bernard Shaw and Fascism, Favil Press (London), 1927 (wraps) £15

The Intelligent Woman's Guide to Socialism and Capitalism, Constable (London), 1928 ('were' for 'was' line 5, p.442) . . . . £150/£25

ditto, Brentano's (New York), 1928 . . . . £100/£20

The League of Nations, Fabian Society Tract No. 226 (London), 1929 (stapled wraps) £35

Bernard Shaw and Karl Marx, Random House (New York), 1930 (575 copies, slipcase) . . . . £65/£50

A Little Talk on America, Friends of the Soviet Union (London), 1931 (50 copies) £85

The Adventures of the Black Girl in Her Search for God, Constable (London), 1932 . . . . . £45/£10

ditto, Dodd, Mead (New York), 1933 . . . £35/£10

A Political Madhouse in America and Nearer Home, Constable (London), 1933 (boards and glassine d/w) . .
. . . . £40/£20

The Future of Political Science in America, Dodd, Mead (New York), 1933 . . . . £65/£20

Are We Heading for War?, Labour Party (London), 1934 (wraps) £30

Everybody's Political What's What?, Constable (London), 1944 . . . . £45/£10

ditto, Dodd, Mead (New York), 1944 . . . £35/£10

Fabian Essays, C. Allen & Unwin (London), 1948 £20/£5

Shaw on Censorship, Shavian Tract No. 3 (London), 1955 .
. . . . £25

The Matter with Ireland, Hart Davis (London), 1962 . .
. . . . £25/£10

ditto, Hill & Wang (New York), 1962 . . . £25/£10

The Road to Equality, Beacon Press (Boston), 1971 £20/£5

Other Prose

Quintessence of Ibsenism, Walter Scott (London), 1891 £35

ditto, Brentano's (New York), 1904 . . . . . £30

ditto, Constable (London), 1913 (extended edition) . £20

On Going to Church, Roycroft Printing Shop (East Aurora, NY), 1896 . . . . £45

ditto, Roycroft Printing Shop (East Aurora, NY), 1896 (26 copies on Japanese vellum) £750

The Perfect Wagnerite, Grant Richards (London), 1898 £85

ditto, Stone (Chicago), 1899 . . . . . . £40

Dramatic Opinions and Essays, Brentano's (New York), 1906 . . . . £30

ditto, Constable (London), 1907 (2 vols) . . . £45

On Shakespeare, Everett, 1907 (wraps) . . . £50

Statement of the Evidence in Chief of G.B.S. Before the Joint Select Committee on Stage Plays, privately printed (London), 1909 . . . . £200

Evidence Given Before the Joint Select Committee on Plays, The Stage (London), 1910 (wraps) . . . £30

To The Audience of the Kingsway Theatre: An Address, (London), 1913 (wraps) £25

Dying Tongue of the Great Elizabeth, London Shakespeare League (London), 1920 (wraps) £20

Nine Answers, privately printed by Jerome Kern (U.S.), 1923 (62 copies) £200

ditto, privately printed by Jerome Kern (U.S.), 1923 (150 copies) £100

Table-Talk of GBS, Chapman & Hall (London), 1925 . .
. . . . £40/£15

ditto, Harper (New York), 1925 . . . . . £40/£15

Experiments on Animals: Views for and Against, British Union for Abolition of Vivesection (London), [1927?] (wraps; with H.G. Wells) £50

Do We Agree? A Debate Between G.K. Chesterton and George Bernard Shaw, Cecil Palmer (London), 1928
. . . . £75/£25

ditto, Mitchell (New York), 1928 . . . . £75/£25

Music in London 1890-94, Constable (London), 1931 (3 vols) . . . . £100/£45

Ellen Terry and Bernard Shaw: A Correspondence, Fountain Press (New York), 1931 (3,000 numbered copies)
. . . . £35/£10

ditto, Putnam's (New York), 1931 . . . . £35/£10

ditto, Constable (London), 1931 . . . . . £35/£10

Our Theatre in the Nineties, Constable (London), 1932 (three vols) . . . . £200/£65

Prefaces, Constable (London), 1934 . . . £30/£10
Short Stories, Scraps and Shavings, Constable (London),
1934 (illustrated by John Farleigh) . . . £45/£10
ditto, Dodd, Mead (New York), 1934 . . £45/£10
London Music in 1888-1889, Constable (London), 1937 .
. . . . £45/£15
ditto, Dodd, Mead (New York), 1937 (pseud 'Bassetto') .
. . . . £45/£15
Florence Farr, Bernard Shaw and W.B. Yeats: Letters,
Cuala Press (Dublin), 1941 (500 numbered copies) . £100
ditto, Home & Van Thal (London), 1946 . . £30/£10
ditto, Dodd, Mead (New York), 1949 . . £30/£10
Sixteen Self Sketches, Constable (London), 1949 . £35/£10
ditto, Dodd, Mead (New York), 1949 . . £35/£10
*Bernard Shaw and Mrs Patrick Campbell: Their Corre-
spondence*, Gollancz (London), 1952 . . £25/£10
ditto, Knopf (New York), 1952 . . . . £25/£10
My Dear Dorothea, Pheonix House (London), 1956
(illustrated by Clare Winsten) . . . . £15/£5
ditto, Vanguard Press (New York), 1956 . . £15/£5
How to Become a Musical Critic, Hart Davis (London), 1960
. . . . £25/£10
ditto, Hill & Wang (New York), [1961] . . £25/£10
Shaw on Shakespeare, Dutton (New York), 1961 . £25/£10
ditto, Cassell (London), 1962 . . . . £25/£10
Collected Letters, Max Reinhardt, 1965-1988 (4 vols) .
. . . . £100/£40
ditto, Dodd, Mead (New York), 1965-1988 (4 vols) £100/£40
Shaw on Religion, Constable (London), 1967 . £20/£5
ditto, Dodd, Mead (New York), [1967] . . £20/£5
The Diaries, 1885-1897, Pennsylvania State Univ Press
(Philadelphia, PA), 1986 (2 vols) . . . £30/£10

MARY SHELLEY
(1797-1851)

Mary Wollstonecraft Shelley was the second daughter of
feminist, educator and writer Mary Wollstonecraft and the
liberal philosopher and dissenter, William Godwin. Famous
for *Frankenstein, or The Modern Prometheus,* her few
other works are also keenly sought by collectors. Some
doubt has been expressed about the authorship of her first
volume of poetry. She was the wife of Romantic poet Percy
Bysshe Shelley.

Poetry
Mounseer Nongtonpaw, Baldwin, Juvenile Series (London),
1808 (wraps). £5,000
ditto, Baldwin, (London), 1808 (rebound) . . £1,500

Fiction
Frankenstein, or, the Modern Prometheus, Lackington,
Hughes, Harding, Mayor & Jones (London), 1818 (anonymous, original boards, paper labels, 3 vols) . £125,000
ditto, Lackington, Hughes, Harding, Mayor & Jones
(London), 1818 (rebound, 3 vols) . . . £65,000
ditto, Whitaker (London), 1823 (second edition, 2 vols) .
. . . . £5,000
ditto, Carey, Lea and Blanchard (Philadelphia, PA), 1833 .
. . . . £12,500
*Valperga, or the Life and Adventures of Castruccio, Prince
of Lucca*, Whitaker (London), 1823 (3 vols). . £2,000

The Last Man, Colburn (London), 1826 ('By the Author of
Frankenstein', 3 vols). £2,500
The Fortunes of Perkin Warbeck, Colburn and Bentley
(London), 1830 (3 vols) £2,000
ditto, Carey, Lea and Blanchard (Philadelphia, PA), 1834 .
. . . . £650
Lodore, Bentley (London), 1835 ('By the Author of
Frankenstein', 3 vols). £1,000
ditto, Wallis & Newell (New York), 1835. . . £500
Falkner, Sanders and Ottley (London), 1837 ('The Author of
'Frankenstein;' 'The Last Man,' &c.' 3 vols) . . £750
ditto, Harper (New York), 1837 . . . . £500
Mathilda, University of North Carolina Press (Chapel Hill,
NC), 1959 (unfinished) . . . . . £30/£10
Collected Tales and Stories, Johns Hopkins Univ Press
(Baltimore), [1976] . . . . . . £20/£5

Others
History of a Six Weeks' Tour, Hookham (London), 1817
(anonymous, co-written by Percy Bysshe Shelley) £1,500
*Lives of the Most Eminent Literary and Scientific Men of
Italy, Spain, and Portugal*, Longman (London), 1835-37
(3 vols, with others, published as part of *The Cabinet of
Biography*) £125
*Lives of the Most Eminent Literary and Scientific Men of
France*, Longman (London), 1838-39 (2 vols, with others,
published as part of *The Cabinet of Biography*) . . £125
Rambles in Germany and Italy, 1840, 1842 and 1843,
Moxon (London), 1844 (2 vols) £300

ERNEST H. SHEPARD
(1879-1976)

Ernest Shepard was an English artist and book illustrator,
much-loved for his illustrations for *Winnie-the-Pooh* by
A.A. Milne and *The Wind in the Willows* by Kenneth
Grahame. Shepard grew to resent Pooh, 'that silly old bear'
and felt that these illustrations over-shadowed his other
work. He said that he modelled Pooh on a stuffed bear,
'Growler', owned by his son.

Books Written and Illustrated by Shepard
Fun and Fantasy: A Book of Drawings, Methuen (London),
1927 . . . . £75/£30
ditto, Methuen (London), 1927 (150 signed copies on
handmade paper). . . . . . £300/£200
Drawn from Memory, Methuen (London), 1957 . £35/£10
ditto, Lippincott (New York), 1957 . . . £35/£10
Drawn from Life, Methuen (London), 1961 . . £25/£10
ditto, Dutton (New York), 1962 . . . . £30/£10
Ben and Brock, Methuen (London), 1965 . . £25/£10
ditto, Doubleday (New York), 1966 . . . £15/£5
Betsy and Joe, Methuen, 1966 . . . . £25/£10
ditto, Dutton (New York), 1967 . . . . £15/£5

Books by Others, Illustrated by Shepherd
Smouldering Fires, or The Kinsmen of Kinthorne, by
Evelyn Everett-Green, Nelson (London), [1905] (6 colour
plates by Shepard) £30
Tom Brown's Schooldays, by Thomas Hughes, Nelson
(London), 1905 (black-and-white frontispiece by Shepard)
. . . . £45

ditto, Nelson (London), [1908] (4 colour plates by Shepard)
. . . . £35

'Play the Game!', by Harold Avery, Nelson (London),
[1906] (4 colour plates by Shepard) £20

Jeremy, by Hugh Walpole, Cassell (London), 1919 . £25

When We Were Very Young, by A.A. Milne, Methuen
(London), 1924 . . . . £4,000/£1,000

ditto, Methuen (London), 1924 (100 numbered copies,
signed by the author and artist). . . £6,000/£4,000

ditto, Dutton (New York), 1924 (100 numbered copies
signed by the author and artist, of 500) . .£2,500/£1,500

ditto, Dutton (New York), 1924 (400 unsigned copies of
500) . . . . £1,250/£650

Vespers: A Poem, by A.A. Milne, Methuen, [1924] (music
by H. Fraser-Simson). . . . . . £250/£65

ditto, Dutton (New York), 1925 . . . . . £45

Fourteen Songs, by A.A. Milne, Methuen (London), 1924
(music by H. Fraser-Simson) . . . . £200/£75

The King's Breakfast, by A.A. Milne, Methuen (London),
1925 (music by H. Fraser-Simson) . . . £175/£45

ditto, Methuen (London), 1925 (100 copies signed by Milne,
Shepard and Fraser-Simson) £600

ditto, Dutton (New York), 1925 . . . . £75/£35

Playtime and Company, by E.V. Lucas, Methuen (London),
1925 . . . . £75/£25

ditto, Doran (New York), 1925 . . . . . £65/£20

Winnie-the-Pooh, by A.A. Milne, Methuen (London), 1926
(first state d/w with '117th thousand' on advert for *When
We Were Very Young* at top of rear flap) . £2,500/£600

ditto, Methuen (London), 1926 (deluxe edition: red, green or
blue leather binding, in slipcase) . . £1,500/£1,000

ditto, Methuen (London), 1926 (350 copies, signed by the
author and artist, d/w and slipcase) . . £7,500/£3,500

ditto, Methuen (London), 1926 (20 special copies, signed by
the author and artist, on Japanese vellum) . . £8,000

ditto, Dutton (New York), 1926 (200 numbered copies,
signed by the author and artist). . . £6,500/£3,000

ditto, Dutton (New York), 1926 . . . £1,000/£300

ditto, Methuen (London), 1973 (illustrated in colour by
Shepard) . . . . £45/£10

ditto, Methuen (London), 1973 (300 copies signed by
Shepard; slipcase) . . . . . £750/£600

ditto, Methuen (London), 1976 (illustrated by Shepard, 300
numbered copies, signed by Christopher Milne; slipcase) .
. . . . £500/£300

**Teddy Bear and Other Songs From 'When We Were Very
Young'**, by A.A. Milne, Methuen (London), 1926 (music
by H. Fraser-Simson). . . . . . £200/£45

ditto, Methuen (London), 1926 (100 numbered copies,
signed by the author, artist and composer, d/w and slipcase)
. . . . £750/£450

ditto, Dutton (New York), 1926 . . . . £200/£45

Everybody's Pepys, edited by O.F. Morshead, Bell (London),
1926 . . . . £25/£10

ditto, Bell (London), 1926 (350 signed, large paper copies) .
. . . . £125

ditto, Harcourt, Brace (New York), 1926 . . £25/£10

The Holly Tree and Other Christmas Stories, by Charles
Dickens, Partridge (London), 1926. . . . £35/£10

ditto, Scribners (New York), 1926 . . . . £35/£10

Now We Are Six, by A.A. Milne, Methuen (London), 1927 .
. . . . £750/£125

ditto, Methuen (London), 1927 (deluxe edition: red, blue or
green leather binding, in slipcase) . . . £1,000/£750

ditto, Methuen (London), 1927 (200 numbered copies,
signed by the author and artist). . . £2,250/£1,500

ditto, Methuen (London), 1927 (20 special copies, signed by
the author and artist, on Japanese vellum) . . £4,500

ditto, Dutton (New York), 1927 (200 signed copies, acetate
d/w) . . . . £2,000/£1,000

ditto, Dutton (New York), 1928 . . . . . £450/£75

ditto, Methuen (London), 1976 (300 numbered copies,
signed by Christopher Milne) . . . . £400/£175

Songs from 'Now We Are Six', by A.A. Milne, Methuen
(London), 1927 (music by H. Fraser-Simson) . £200/£50

ditto, Methuen (London), 1927 (100 signed copies) . £750

ditto, Dutton (New York), 1927 . . . . £200/£45

The Little One's Log: Baby's Record, by Eva Erleigh
[Marchioness of Reading], Partridge (London), 1927. .
. . . . £30/£10

Let's Pretend, by Georgette Agnew, Saville (London), 1927
. . . . £45/£15

ditto, Saville (London), 1927 (160 signed, numbered copies)
. . . . £150

More Very Young Songs, by A.A. Milne, Methuen
(London), 1928 . . . . . . £200/£75

ditto, Methuen (London), 1928 (100 numbered copies,
signed by the author, artist and composer, d/w and slipcase)
. . . . £750

The House at Pooh Corner, by A.A. Milne, Methuen
(London), 1928 . . . . . . £750/£250

ditto, Methuen (London), 1928 (350 numbered copies,
signed by the author and artist). . . £3,500/£2,500

ditto, Methuen (London), 1928 (20 special copies, signed by
the author and artist) £6,000

ditto, Methuen (London), 1928 (deluxe edition: red, green or
blue leather binding, in slipcase) . . . £600/£400

ditto, Dutton (New York), 1928 (250 numbered copies,
signed by the author and artist). . . £2,000/£1,350

ditto, Dutton (New York), 1928 . . . . . £450/£75

ditto, Methuen (London), 1974 (illustrated in colour by
Shepard) . . . . £45/£10

The Christopher Robin Calendar 1929, by A.A. Milne,
Methuen 'Ephemerides' series (London), [1928]. . £150

The Christopher Robin Story Book, by A.A. Milne,
Methuen (London), 1928 (selections from *When We Were
Very Young*, *Now We Are Six*, *Winnie-the-Pooh* and *The
House at Pooh Corner*, new preface by the author) . .
. . . . £400/£75

ditto, Methuen (London), 1928 (350 copies signed by Milne
& Shepard; unprinted acetate d/w and slipcase) . . .
. . . . £1,750/£1,250

ditto, Dutton (New York), 1929 . . . . £350/£65

ditto, Dutton (New York), 1929 (350 copies signed by Milne
& Shepard; unprinted acetate d/w and slipcase) . . .
. . . .£1,750/£1,250

The Golden Age, by Kenneth Grahame, Bodley Head
(London), 1928 . . . . . . £75/£45

ditto, Bodley Head (London), 1928 (275 copies signed by
author and artist). £400

ditto, Dodd, Mead (New York), 1929 . . . £65/£35

Mr Punch's Country Songs, edited by E.V. Lucas, Methuen
(London), 1928 . . . . £35/£15

The Hums of Pooh, by A.A. Milne, Methuen (London),
1929 (music by H. Fraser-Simson) . . . . £200/£45

ditto, Methuen (London), 1929 (100 numbered copies,
signed by the author and artist and composer, d/w and
slipcase). . . . . £1,450/£1,000

ditto, Dutton (New York), 1930 . . . . £75/£35

Livestock in Barracks, by Anthony Armstrong, Methuen (London), 1929 . . . . £45/£15

Tales of Pooh, Methuen: 'Modern Classics' series (London), [1930] (selections from *Winnie-The-Pooh* and *The House at Pooh Corner*) . . . . . . £200/£65

The Christopher Robin Birthday Book, by A.A. Milne, Methuen (London), 1930 (selections from *When We Were Very Young, Now We Are Six, Winnie-the-Pooh* and *The House at Pooh Corner*) . . . . £125/£45

ditto, Dutton (New York), 1931 . . . . £125/£45

Dream Days, by Kenneth Grahame, Bodley Head (London), 1930 . . . . £125/£35

ditto, Bodley Head (London), 1930 (275 copies signed by author and artist) £450

ditto, Dodd, Mead (New York), 1930 . . £65/£35

Everybody's Boswell, edited by F.V. Morley, Bell (London), 1930 . . . . £25/£10

ditto, Bell (London), 1930 (350 signed, large paper copies) £125

ditto, Harcourt, Brace (New York), 1930 . . £25/£10

Wind in the Willows, by Kenneth Grahame, Bodley Head (London), 1931 . . . . . . £500/£200

ditto, Bodley Head (London), 1931 (200 copies signed by author and artist) . . . . £4,000/£3,000

Christmas Poems, by John Drinkwater, Sidgwick & Jackson (London), 1931 (sewn wraps) £10

The Christopher Robin Verses, Methuen (London), 1932 (contains *When We Were Very Young* and *Now We Are Six*, by A.A. Milne) . . . . £200/£65

ditto, Dutton (New York), 1932 . . . . £175/£50

Bevis: The Story of a Boy, by Richard Jefferies, Cape (London), 1932 . . . . £35/£10

Sycamore Square, by Jan Struther, Methuen (London), 1932 . . . . £30/£10

Everybody's Lamb, edited by A.C. Ward, Bell (London), 1933 . . . . £25/£10

ditto, Bell (London), 1933 (bound in publisher's leather) £65

ditto, Harcourt, Brace (New York), 1933 . . £25/£10

The Cricket in the Cage, by Patrick Chalmers, Black (London), 1933 . . . . £25/£10

Victoria Regina, by Laurence Housman, Cape (London), 1934 . . . . £20/£5

ditto, Scribners (New York), [c.1935] . . . £20/£5

The Seventh Daughter, by 'Euphan' [Barbara Euphan Todd], Burns Oates & Washbourne (London, 1935) . . . . £25/£10

The Modern Struwwelpeter, by Jan Struther, Methuen (London), 1936 . . . . . . £150/£75

Perfume from Provence, by Winifred Fortescue, Blackwood (London), 1935 . . . . . . £45/£20

Sunset House: More Perfume From Provence, by Winifred Fortescue, Blackwood (London), 1937 (frontispiece and d/w by Shepard) . . . . £45/£20

As the Bee Sucks, by E.V. Lucas, Methuen (London), 1937 . . . . £25/£10

Cheddar Gorge: A Book of English Cheeses, edited by John Squire, Collins (London), 1937 . . . £50/£15

ditto, Collins (London), 1937 (220 signed, numbered copies) £75

ditto, Macmillan (New York), 1938 . . . £25/£10

The Golden Sovereign, by Laurence Housman, Cape, 1937. . . . . £15/£10

ditto, Scribners (New York), 1937 . . . £10/£5

Gracious Majesty, by Laurence Housman, Cape, 1942 . . . . £10/£5

ditto, Scribners (New York), 1942 . . . . £10/£5

Happy and Glorious, by Laurence Housman, Cape, 1945 . . . . £10/£5

Bertie's Escapade, by Kenneth Grahame, Methuen (London), 1949 . . . . £75/£20

ditto, Lippincott (New York), 1949 . . . . £60/£15

The Islanders, by Roland Pertwee, Methuen (London), 1950 . . . . £30/£10

Enter David Garrick, by Anna Bird Stewart, Lippincott (New York), 1951 . . . . . . £15/£5

ditto, Lippincott (New York), 1951 . . . £10/£5

The Silver Curlew: A Fairy Tale, by Eleanor Farjeon, O.U.P. (London), 1953 . . . . . £50/£15

ditto, Viking (New York), 1954 . . . . £15/£5

The Reluctant Dragon, by Kenneth Grahame, Holiday House (New York), 1953 . . . . . £65/£15

Susan, Bill and the Wolf-Dog, by Malcolm Saville, Nelson (London), 1954 . . . . . £25/£10

Susan, Bill and the Ivy-Clad Oak, by Malcolm Saville, Nelson (London), 1954 . . . . . £25/£10

The Brownies and Other Stories, by J.H. Ewing, Dent, Children's Illustrated Classics series (London), 1954 £15/£5

The Cuckoo Clock, by Mrs Molesworth, Dent, Children's Illustrated Classics series (London), 1954 . £15/£5

Susan, Bill and the Vanishing Boy, by Malcolm Saville, Nelson (London), 1955 . . . . . £25/£10

Susan, Bill and the Golden Clock, by Malcolm Saville, Nelson (London), 1955 . . . . . £25/£10

Operation Wild Goose, by Roland Pertwee, Methuen (London), 1955 . . . . £25/£10

The Glass Slipper, by Eleanor Farjeon, O.U.P. (London), 1955 . . . . £15/£5

Frogmorton, by Susan Colling, Collins, 1955 . . £15/£5

Modern Fairy Stories, by R.L. Green, Dent, Children's Illustrated Classics series (London), 1955 . £15/£5

Mary in the Garden, by 'Golden Gorse', Country Life (London), 1955 . . . . £25/£10

Susan, Bill and the Dark Stranger, by Malcolm Saville, Nelson (London), 1956 . . . . . £25/£10

Susan, Bill and the 'Saucy Kate', by Malcolm Saville, Nelson (London), 1956 . . . . . £25/£10

At The Back of the North Wind, by George MacDonald, Dent, Children's Illustrated Classics series (London), 1956 . . . . £25/£10

The Crystal Mountain: A Tale for Children, by B.D. Rugh, Muller (London), 1956 . . . . . £20/£10

Tom Brown's Schooldays, by Thomas Hughes, Ginn (London), 1956 . . . . £15/£5

Royal Reflections, by Shirley Goulden, Methuen (London), 1956 . . . . £15/£5

The Secret Garden, by F.H. Burnett, Heinemann (London), 1957 . . . . £20/£5

The Pancake, edited by J.H., Ginn (London), 1957 £25/£10

Briar Rose, edited by J.H. Ginn (London), 1958 . £25/£10

Old Greek Fairy Tales, by R.L. Green, Bell (London), 1958 . . . . £15/£5

Fairy Tales, by Hans Christian Andersen, O.U.P. (London), 1961 (translated by L.W. Kingland) . . £30/£10

A Noble Company, edited by J. Compton, Ginn (London), 1961 . . . . £15/£5

The Flattered Flying Fish and Other Poems, by E.V. Rieu, Methuen (London), 1962 . . . . . £15/£5

M.P. SHIEL
(b.1865 d.1947)

The author of fantasy and science fiction, Matthew Phipps Shiel's early short stories are rather luxuriantly written. His 'Prince Zaleski' tales, for example, offer a detective far more decadent than that other drug-taking dilettante, Sherlock Holmes. In later years Shiel pared down his style and re-wrote some of his earlier books.

Short Stories

Prince Zaleski, John Lane (London), 1895 (decorated purple cloth; front and rear panels stamped in white; spine panel stamped in white and gold) £600

ditto, Roberts Brothers (Boston), 1895 (decorated blue-grey cloth; front panel stamped in black; spine panel stamped in gold; publisher's monogram stamped in black on rear panel) £200

ditto, Tartarus Press (Carlton-in-Coverdale, Yorkshire), 2002 . . . . £25/£10

Shapes in the Fire, John Lane (London), 1896 (pictorial yellow/brown cloth; front and rear panels stamped in red; spine stamped in red and gold). £800

ditto, Roberts Brothers (Boston), 1896 (pictorial brown cloth; front and rear panels stamped in black; spine panel stamped in gold) £200

ditto, Tartarus Press (Carlton-in-Coverdale, Yorkshire), 2000 . . . . £75/£25

The Pale Ape, T. Werner Laurie (London), [1911] (pictorial green cloth; front and rear panels and spine stamped in yellow) £500

ditto, Tartarus Press (Carlton-in-Coverdale, Yorkshire), 2006 . . . . £25/£10

Here Comes the Lady, The Richards Press (London), [1928] (light blue-green cloth; front and spine panels stamped in black) . . . . . . £350/£65

The Invisible Voices, The Richards Press (London), 1935 (with John Gawsworth; orange cloth; front panel stamped in black and blind; spine panel stamped in black) £350/£50

ditto, Vanguard Press (New York), 1936 . . . £300/£40

The Best Short Stories of M.P. Shiel, Gollancz (London), 1948 . . . . £50/£15

Xélucha and Others, Arkham House (Sauk City, WI), 1975 . . . . £10/£5

Prince Zaleski and Cummings King Monk, Mycroft & Moran (Sauk City, WI), 1977 . . . . £10/£5

Novels

The Rajah's Sapphire, Ward, Lock & Bowden (London), 1896 (decorated light green cloth; front and spine panels stamped in gold; top edge gilt; decorated endpapers printed in green) £250

ditto, Ward, Lock & Bowden (London), 1896 (second issue with decorated endpapers printed in blue) . . . £200

ditto, Highflyer Press (Kansas City, MO), 1981 (10 presentation copies; hardback; no d/w) . . . £60

ditto, Highflyer Press (Kansas City, MO), 1981 (500 copies; pbk) £25

The Yellow Danger, Grant Richards (London), 1898 (decorated brown cloth; front panel stamped in orange, red and black; spine stamped in black and gold). . . £225

ditto, R.F. Fenno & Co. (New York), 1899 (pictorial slate grey cloth; front panel stamped in red, green, gold and

black; spine panel stamped in gold; first issue with subtitle 'or, what might happen if the division of the Chinese Empire should estrange all European countries') . . £250

ditto, R.F. Fenno & Co. (New York), 1899 (second issue with subtitle 'The story of the world's greatest war.') £200

ditto, R.F. Fenno & Co. (New York), 1899 (pbk issue; published as No. 61 of 'Fenno Select Series,') . . £150

Contraband of War, Grant Richards (London), 1899 (pictorial dark grey cloth; front panel stamped in blue-grey and black; spine panel stamped in blue-grey) . . £75

ditto, The Gregg Press (Boston, MA), 1968 (no d/w) . £15

Cold Steel, Grant Richards (London), 1899 (pictorial tan cloth; front panel stamped in blue, orange, dark brown and black; spine panel stamped in dark brown and black; first issue with publisher's catalogue dated 1899) . . £150

ditto, Brentano's (New York), 1900 (pictorial grey cloth; front panel stamped in yellow, blue, brown and black; spine panel stamped in gold) £150

ditto, Gollancz (London), 1929 (revised edition, 105 signed copies, half vellum) £300

ditto, Vanguard Press (New York), 1929 (revised edition) . . . . £50/£10

The Man Stealers, Hutchinson & Co. (London), 1900 . £150

ditto, Lippincott (Philadelphia), 1900 . . . . £125

The Lord of the Sea, Grant Richards (London), 1901 (first issue with blank leaf preceding half title leaf; 'Yellow Danger' spelt correctly on verso half title) . . £175

ditto, Grant Richards (London), 1901 (second issue with no blank leaf preceding half title leaf; 'Yellow Dancer' for 'Yellow Danger' on verso half-title) . . . £150

ditto, Frederick A. Stokes Co. (New York), 1901 . £150

ditto, Gollancz (London), 1929 (revised edition, 105 signed copies, half vellum) £350

The Purple Cloud, Chatto & Windus (London), 1901 . £400

ditto, Gollancz (London), 1929 (revised edition) . £40/£10

ditto, Gollancz (London), 1929 (105 signed copies, half vellum) £400

ditto, Vanguard Press (New York), 1930 (revised). £75/£15

ditto, Tartarus Press (Carlton-in-Coverdale, Yorkshire), 2004 (illustrated) . . . . £30/£10

The Weird o' It, Grant Richards (London), 1902 . . £300

Unto the Third Generation, Chatto & Windus (London), 1903 . . . . £250

The Evil That Men Do, Ward, Lock & Co. Ltd (London), 1904 . . . . £250

The Lost Viol, Edward J. Clode (New York), 1905 (first issue with 'Edward J. Clode' on spine) £200

ditto, Edward J. Clode (New York), 1905 (second issue with 'E.J. Clode' on spine). £200

ditto, Ward, Lock & Co. Ltd (London), 1905 (copyright edition) £400

ditto, Ward, Lock & Co. Ltd (London), 1908 . . . £75

The Yellow Wave, Ward, Lock & Co. Ltd (London), 1905 (author's name spelt 'Sheil' on title-page) . . . £250

ditto, Ward, Lock & Co. Ltd (London), 1905 (author's name spelt correctly on title-page) £150

ditto, Thomas Langton (Toronto, Canada), 1905 (author's name spelt 'Sheil' on title-page) £125

The Last Miracle, T. Werner Laurie (London), 1906 [1907] £200

The White Wedding, T. Werner Laurie (London), [1908] £165

The Isle of Lies, T. Werner Laurie (London), [1909] . £100

This Knot of Life, Everett & Co. (London), [1909] (first binding with 'Everett & Co.' at base of spine) . . £145

ditto, Everett & Co. (London), [1909] (second binding with 'Everett') £100
The Dragon, Grant Richards (London), 1913 (advance copy, green cloth) £250
ditto, Grant Richards (London), 1913 . . . £100
ditto, Edward J. Clode (New York), 1914 . . . £75
ditto, as **The Yellow Peril**, Gollancz (London), 1929 (revised edition) . . . . . . £35/£10
ditto, as **The Yellow Peril**, Gollancz (London), 1929 (105 signed copies, half vellum) £300
Children of the Wind, Grant Richards (London), 1923 .
. . . . £250/£50
ditto, Knopf (New York), 1923 . . . . £225/£45
How The Old Woman Got Home, The Richards Press (London), 1927 . . . . £150/£40
ditto, Vanguard Press (New York), 1928 . . £125/£25
Dr Krasinski's Secret, The Vanguard Press (New York), 1929 . . . . £150/£30
ditto, Jarrolds (London), 1930 . . . . £150/£30
The Black Box, The Vanguard Press (New York), 1930 .
. . . . £200/£30
ditto, The Richards Press (London), 1931 . . £175/£25
Say Au R'Voir But Not Goodbye, Ernest Benn Ltd (London), 1933 (pbk) £40
This Above All, The Vanguard Press (New York), 1933 .
. . . . £75/£20
ditto, as **Above All Else**, Lloyd Cole (London), 1943 £65/£15
The Young Men Are Coming, Allen & Unwin (London), 1937 . . . . £75/£20
ditto, Vanguard Press (New York), 1937 . . £75/£20

Others
Richards' Shilling Selection from Edwardian Poets - M.P. Shiel, The Richards Press (London), 1936 (wraps) . £45
Science, Life and Literature, Williams & Norgate Ltd (London), 1950 . . . . £25/£10

NEVIL SHUTE
(b.1899 d.1961)

A popular novelist and scientist, Shute's *On the Beach*, about the survivors of a nuclear holocaust, is arguably his most important work. His adventure novels are written in a low-key style, often with an emphasis on technical details, although several of his novels also have a supernatural element. This is particularly true of *Round the Bend*, which concerns the creation of a new religion.

Novels
Marazan, Cassell (London), 1926 . . . £1,500/£225
ditto, Ballantine (New York), 1970 (pbk) £5
So Disdained, Cassell (London), 1926 . . £1,250/£125
ditto, as **The Mysterious Aviator**, Houghton Mifflin (Boston), 1928 . . . . . . £1,250/£125
Lonely Road, Heinemann (London), 1932 . £1,000/£100
ditto, Ballantine (New York), 1970 (pbk) £5
Ruined City, Heinemann (London), 1938 . . £800/£75
ditto, as **Kindling**, Morrow (New York), 1938 . £500/£50
What Happened to the Corbetts, Heinemann (London), 1939
. . . . £650/£65
ditto, as **Ordeal**, Morrow (New York), 1939 . £125/£25
An Old Captivity, Heinemann (London), 1940 . £250/£25

ditto, Morrow (New York), 1940 . . . £125/£25
Landfall, Heinemann (London), 1940 . . £125/£25
ditto, Morrow (New York), 1940 . . . £100/£15
Pied Piper, Heinemann (London), 1942 . . £100/£15
ditto, Morrow (New York), 1942 . . . £75/£15
Pastoral, Heinemann (London), 1944 . . £150/£20
ditto, Morrow (New York), 1944 . . . £100/£15
Most Secret, Heinemann (London), 1945 . . . £85/£15
ditto, Morrow (New York), 1945 . . . £65/£15
The Chequer Board, Heinemann (London), 1947 . £65/£10
ditto, Morrow (New York), 1947 . . . £50/£10
No Highway, Heinemann (London), 1948 . . £75/£15
ditto, Morrow (New York), 1948 . . . £60/£10
A Town Like Alice, Heinemann (London), 1950 . £300/£40
ditto, as **Legacy**, Morrow (New York), 1950 . £125/£20
Round the Bend, Heinemann (London), 1951 . . £65/£10
ditto, Morrow (New York), 1951 . . . £50/£10
The Far Country, Heinemann (London), 1952 . £75/£15
ditto, Morrow (New York), 1952 . . . £60/£10
In the Wet, Heinemann (London), 1953 . . £50/£10
ditto, Morrow (New York), 1953 . . . £45/£10
Requiem for a Wren, Heinemann (London), 1955 . £40/£5
ditto, as **The Breaking Wave**, Morrow (New York), 1955 .
. . . . £30/£5
Beyond the Black Stump, Heinemann (London), 1956 £35/£5
ditto, Morrow (New York), 1956 . . . £30/£5
On the Beach, Heinemann (London), 1957 . . £50/£10
ditto, Morrow (New York), 1957 . . . £30/£5
The Rainbow and the Rose, Heinemann (London), 1958 .
. . . . £25/£5
ditto, Morrow (New York), 1958 . . . £20/£5
Trustee from the Toolroom, Heinemann (London), 1960 .
. . . . £15/£5
ditto, Morrow (New York), 1960 . . . £15/£5
Stephen Morris, Heinemann (London), 1961 . . £15/£5
ditto, Morrow (New York), 1961 . . . £10/£5

Autobiography
Slide Rule, Heinemann (London), 1954 . . . £75/£10
ditto, Morrow (New York), 1954 . . . £65/£10

Drama
Vinland the Good, Heinemann (London), 1946 . £250/£35
ditto, Morrow (New York), 1946 . . . £45/£10

ALAN SILLITOE
(b.1928 d.2010)

Alan Sillitoe was one of the 'Angry Young Men' of the 1950s, whose reputation rests principally on *Saturday Night and Sunday Morning*. The novel describes the predicament of a young factory worker faced with the inevitable result of his youthful philandering. Sillitoe's story *The Loneliness of the Long Distance Runner* won the Hawthornden Prize in 1959.

Novels
Saturday Night and Sunday Morning, W.H. Allen (London), 1958 . . . . £250/£25
ditto, Knopf (New York), 1958 . . . . £50/£10
The General, W.H. Allen (London), 1960 . . £30/£5
ditto, Knopf (New York), 1961 . . . . £20/£5

Key to the Door, W.H. Allen (London), 1961 . . £25/£5
ditto, Knopf (New York), 1962 . . . . . £25/£5
The Death of William Posters, W.H. Allen (London), 1965
. . . . £20/£5
ditto, Knopf (New York), 1965 . . . . . £20/£5
A Tree on Fire, Macmillan (London), 1967 . . £20/£5
ditto, Doubleday (Garden City, NY), 1968 . . £20/£5
A Start in Life, W.H. Allen (London), 1970 . . £20/£5
ditto, Scribner's (New York), 1971 . . . £20/£5
Travels in Nihilon, W.H. Allen (London), 1971 . £20/£5
ditto, Scribner's (New York), 1972 . . . £20/£5
Raw Material, W.H. Allen (London), 1972 . . £20/£5
ditto, Scribner's (New York), 1973 . . . £20/£5
The Flame of Life, W.H. Allen (London), 1974 . £20/£5
The Widower's Son, W.H. Allen (London), 1976 . £15/£5
ditto, Harper & Row (New York), 1977 . . . £15/£5
The Storyteller, W.H. Allen (London), 1979 . £15/£5
ditto, Simon & Schuster (New York), 1980 . . £15/£5
Her Victory, Granada (London), 1982 . . . £15/£5
ditto, Watts (New York), 1982 . . . . . £15/£5
The Lost Flying Boat, Granada (London), 1983 . £15/£5
ditto, Little, Brown (Boston), 1983 . . . £15/£5
Down from the Hill, Granada (London), 1984 . £10/£5
Life Goes On, Granada (London), 1985 . . £10/£5
Out of the Whirlpool, Hutchinson (London), 1987 (illustra-
tions by Peter Farmer) . . . . . £10/£5
ditto, Harper & Row (New York), 1988 . . £10/£5
The Open Door, Grafton (London), 1989 . . £10/£5
Last Loves, Grafton (London), 1990 . . . £10/£5
Leonard's War – A Love Story, Harper Collins (London),
1991 . . . . £10/£5
Snowstop, Harper Collins (London), 1993 . £10/£5
The Broken Chariot, Flamingo (London), 1998 . £10/£5
Birthday, Flamingo (London), 2001 . . . £10/£5
The German Numbers Woman, Flamingo (London), 1999 .
. . . . £10/£5

Poetry
Without Beer or Bread, Outpost Publications (Dulwich
Village, UK), 1957 (wraps) £225
The Rats and Other Poems, W.H. Allen (London), 1960 .
. . . . £45/£15
A Falling Out of Love and Other Poems, W.H. Allen
(London), 1964 . . . . £20/£5
Love in the Environs of Voronezh, Macmillan (London),
1968 . . . . £10/£5
ditto, Doubleday (Garden City, NY), 1969 . . £10/£5
Poems, Rainbow Press (London), 1971 (with Ted Hughes
and Ruth Fainlight, 300 copies, numbered and signed by all
three poets, slipcase) . . . . . £125/£75
Shaman and Other Poems, Turret Books (London), 1968
(100 signed, numbered copies of 500, glassine d/w) £30/£15
ditto, Turret Books (London), 1968 (400 unsigned copies of
500, glassine d/w) . . . . . . £10/£5
Barbarians and Other Poems, Turret Books (London), 1973
(100 signed, numbered copies of 500) . . £30/£15
ditto, Turret Books (London), 1973 (400 unsigned copies of
500) . . . . £10/£5
From Canto Two of 'The Rats', published by the author
(Wittersham, Kent), 1973 (wraps) £15
Storm: New Poems, W.H. Allen (London), 1974 . £10/£5
Words Broadsheet Nineteen, Words Press (Bramley,
Surrey), 1975 (with Ruth Fainlight; 150 copies signed by
both poets; broadside) £25

Day-Dream Communiqué, Sceptre Press (Knotting,
Bedfordshire), 1977 (50 signed, numbered copies of 150;
stapled wraps) £20
ditto, Sceptre Press (Knotting, Bedfordshire), 1977 (100
unsigned copies of 150; stapled wraps) . . . £10
Snow on the North Side of Lucifer, Sceptre Press (Knotting,
Bedfordshire), 1977 (50 signed, numbered copies of 150;
stapled wraps) £20
ditto, Sceptre Press (Knotting, Bedfordshire), 1977 (100
unsigned copies of 150; stapled wraps) . . . £10
ditto, W.H. Allen (London), 1979 . . . . £20/£5
More Lucifer, Booth (Knotting, Bedford), 1980 (125
numbered copies; stapled wraps) £10
Israel: Poems on a Hebrew Theme, Steam Press (London),
1981 (with drawings by Ralph Steadman; 98 numbered
copies signed by Sillitoe and Steadman; slipcase) . .
. . . . £125/£100
Sun before Departure: Poems, 1974-1982, Granada
(London), 1984 . . . . £10/£5
Tides and Stone Walls, Grafton (London), 1986
(photographs by Victor Bowley) . . . . £10/£5
Three Poems, Words Press (Child Okeford, Dorset), 1988
(75 signed, numbered copies of 200; stapled wraps) . £25
ditto, Words Press (Child Okeford, Dorset), 1988 (125
unsigned, numbered of 200; stapled wraps) . . £15
Shylock the Writer, Turret Bookshop (London), 1991
(broadside) £35
The Mentality of the Picaresque Hero, Turret Bookshop
(London), 1993 (500 copies; wraps) . . . £15
Collected Poems, HarperCollins (London), 1993 . £10/£5

Short Stories
The Loneliness of the Long Distance Runner, W.H. Allen
(London), 1959 . . . . £200/£50
ditto, Knopf (New York), 1959 . . . . £100/£25
ditto, Easton Press (Norfolk CT), 2002 (full leather signed
edition, no d/w) £50
The Ragman's Daughter, W.H. Allen (London), 1963 .
. . . . £25/£5
ditto, Knopf (New York), 1964 . . . . £20/£5
Guzman Go Home, Macmillan (London), 1968 . £20/£5
ditto, Doubleday (Garden City, NY), 1969 . . £15/£5
Men, Women, and Children, W.H. Allen (London), 1973 .
. . . . £15/£5
ditto, Scribner's (New York), 1974 . . . £15/£5
The Second Chance and Other Stories, Cape (London),
1981 . . . . £10/£5
ditto, Simon & Schuster (New York), 1981 . . £10/£5
The Far Side of the Street, W.H. W.H. Allen (London),
1988 . . . . £15/£5
Collected Stories, Flamingo (London), 1995 . . £15/£5
Ron Delph and His Fight with King Arthur, Clarion
Publishing, 1996 (pbk) £40
ditto, Clarion Publishing, 1996 (150 signed copies, boards,
no d/w) £60
ditto, Clarion Publishing, 1996 (59 signed copies with loose
print, boards, no d/w) £75
Alligator Playground, A Collection of Short Stories,
Flamingo (London), 1997 . . . . . £15/£5

Plays
All Citizens Are Soldiers, Macmillan (London), 1969 (by
Lope de Vega; translation and adaptation by Sillitoe with
Ruth Fainlight) . . . . £25/£10

ditto, Dufour (Chester Springs, PA), 1969 . . £25/£10
Three Plays, W.H. Allen (London), 1978 (contains: *The Slot-Machine*, *The Interview* and *Pit Strike*) . . £10/£5

Children's Titles
The City Adventures of Marmalade Jim, Macmillan (London), 1967 . . . . £15/£5
ditto, Robson (London), 1977 (revised edition, illustrated by Shelagh McGee; decorated boards) £10
Big John and the Stars, Robson (London), 1977 (illustrated by Agnes Molnar; decorated boards) . . . £10
The Incredible Fencing Fleas, Robson (London), 1978 (illustrated by Mike Wilks; decorated boards) . . £5
Marmalade Jim at the Farm, Robson (London), 1980 (illustrated by Shelagh McGee; decorated boards) . £5
Marmalade Jim and the Fox, Robson (London), 1984 (illustrated by Tony Ross; decorated boards) . . £5

Others
Chopin's Winter In Majorca, by Luis Ripoll, Mossen Allcover (Palma De Mallorca, Spain), 1955 (translated by Sillitoe) . . . . £25/£10
The Road to Volgograd, W.H. Allen (London), 1964 £25/£5
ditto, Knopf (New York), 1964 . . . . . £20/£5
Mountains and Caverns: Selected Essays, W.H. Allen (London), 1975 . . . . £15/£5
The Saxon Shore Way: From Gravesend to Rye, Hutchinson (London), 1983 (photographs by Fay Godwin) . . . . £25/£10
Alan Sillitoe's Nottinghamshire, Grafton (London), 1987 (photographs by David Sillitoe) . . . £10/£5
Every Day of the Week: An Alan Sillitoe Reader, W.H. W.H. Allen (London), 1987 . . . . £10/£5
Life Without Armour, An Autobiography, Harper-Collins (London), 1995 . . . . £10/£5
Leading the Blind: A Century of Guide Book Travel 1815-1914, Macmillan (London), 1995 . . . £10/£5

SIDNEY SIME

(b.1865 d.1941)

Sidney Sime completed his training at the Liverpool School of Art in 1889, just in time to find regular work with the growing number of illustrated magazines that were starting up. He was a regular contributor of caricatures and grotesque sketches to *Pick-Me-Up*, *The Idler*, and his own magazine, *Eureka*. His career as a book illustrator took off when Lord Dunsany insisted that Sime's strange and macabre art was well-suited to his writings.

By Sime
Bogey Beasts, Goodwin and Tabb (London), nd [1923] (15 full page illustrations). . . . . . £225/£75
From An Ultima Dim Thule, Ferret Fantasy (London), 1973 (wraps) £30
ditto, Ferret Fantasy (London), 1973 (wraps, with additional insert) £60
Beasts That Might Have Been, Ferret Fantasy (London), 1974 (8 full page and 4 quarter page illustrations; pbk) £45
The Land of Dreams, Ferret Fantasy (London), 1975 (37 full page and 5 smaller illustrations; pbk) £35

ditto, Ferret Fantasy (London), 1975 (38 numbered copies in boards with d/w) £125
Sidney H Sime: Master of Fantasy, Ward Ritchie Press (Pasedena, CA), 1978 (pbk) £15
ditto, Ward Ritchie Press (Pasedena, CA), 1978 (200 numbered copies signed by Paul W. Skeeters and Ray Bradbury) £65
ditto, Ward Ritchie Press (Pasedena, CA), 1978 (26 lettered copies signed by Paul W. Skeeters and Ray Bradbury) £100
ditto, Ward Ritchie Press (Pasedena, CA), 1978 (50 copies with home-made d/w by Ferret Fantasy and extra tipped-in illustration) . . . . £75/£65
Sidney Sime, Master of the Mysterious, by Simon Heneage and Henry Ford, Thames & Hudson (London), 1980 (pbk) £10

Contributions to the Books of Others
Yule Tide Tales, The Favourite Publishing Co (London), 1897 (wraps). £100
Death and The Woman, by Arnold Golsworthy, Lawrence Greening (London), 1898 (cover design by Sime) . £35
Fancy Free, by Eden Philpotts, Methuen (London), 1901 (1 illustration) £25
The Gods of Pegana, by Lord Dunsany, Elkin Mathews (London), 1905 (8 illustration; grey boards with white cloth spine; drummer stamped in dark blue on front cover) . £400
ditto, Elkin Mathews (London), 1905 (grey boards with white cloth spine; drummer blind-stamped on front cover) £350
ditto, Elkin Mathews (London), 1905 (brown boards with white cloth spine; no drummer) £200
ditto, Luce (Boston), [1916]. £125
The House of Souls, by Arthur Machen, Grant Richards (London), 1906 (frontispiece by Sime and design in gilt, yellow and black on front board; 'E. Grant Richards' on spine) £250
ditto, Grant Richards (London), 1906 (second binding with 'Grant Richards' on spine) £225
Time and the Gods, by Lord Dunsany, Heinemann (London), 1906 (10 full page illustrations by Sidney Sime and one monochrome inlaid illustration on front cover; brown boards with green cloth spine) £250
ditto, Luce (Boston), 1913 . . . . . . £75
ditto, Putnam's (New York), 1922 [1923] (250 copies signed by Dunsany and Sime) £350
The Hill of Dreams, by Arthur Machen, Grant Richards (London), 1907 (frontispiece by Sime; dark red cloth, spine and front board lettered in gilt, 'E. Grant Richards' on spine, first binding without adverts after text) £200
ditto, Grant Richards (London), 1907 (second binding as above but with 20 pages of adverts after text) . . £150
ditto, Grant Richards (London), 1907 (third binding, various cloths, 'Grant Richards' on spine) £150
ditto, Tartarus Press (Horam, Sussex), 1998 (frontispiece, d/w illustration and two further illustrations by Sime; 350 copies) . . . . £50/£20
The Sword of Welleran, by Lord Dunsany, George Allen (London), 1908 (10 full page illustrations by Sidney Sime'; first issue with 'GEORGE ALLEN/& SONS' at base of spine; top edge gilt) £125
ditto, George Allen (London), 1908 (second issue with 'GEORGE ALLEN' at base of spine; top edge gilt) . £100
ditto, George Allen (London), 1908 (third issue with 'GEORGE ALLEN' at base of spine; top edge plain) . £90

ditto, George Allen (London), 1908 (fourth issue with 'GEORGE ALLEN/& UNWIN LTD' at base of spine; first line 3.2cm; top edge plain) £80

ditto, George Allen (London), 1908 (fifth issue with 'GEORGE ALLEN/& UNWIN LTD' at base of spine; first line 2.8cm; top edge plain) £75

ditto, Luce (New York), [no date] £75

The Ghost Pirates, by William Hope Hodgson, Stanley Paul (London), 1909 (frontispiece by Sime) . . £1,250

A Dreamer's Tales, by Lord Dunsany, George Allen (London), 1910 (9 full page illustrations by Sime) . £125

ditto, Luce (New York), 1911 . . . . . £75

The Book of Wonder, by Lord Dunsany, Heinemann (London), 1912 (10 full page illustrations by Sime; light brown boards with green cloth spine; inlaid illustration on front cover) £75

ditto, Luce (Boston), 1912 . . . . . . £45

The Children of the Don, by Thomas Evelyn Ellis, E Arnold (London), 1912 (frontispiece by Sime) £25

Tales of Wonder, by Lord Dunsany, Elkin Mathews (London), 1916 (six full page illustrations by Sime) . £75

ditto, as **The Last Book of Wonder**, Luce (Boston), 1916 £60

The Lunatic at Large, by J. Storer Clouston, Blackwood (London), nd [c.1916] (d/w by Sime) . . . £65/£10

The Chronicles of Rodriguez, by Lord Dunsany, Putnam's (London), 1922 (frontispiece by Sime; 500 copies numbered and signed by Dunsany and Sime) £400/£200

ditto, as **Don Rodriguez, Chronicles of Shadow Valley**, Putnam's (New York), 1924 . . . . . £125/£35

Bronwen, an opera by Joseph Holbrooke, London, 1922 (program with cover design by Sime; wraps) . . £75

The King of Elfland's Daughter, by Lord Dunsany, Putnam's (London), 1924 (frontispiece by Sime; 250 copies numbered and signed by Dunsany and Sime) . .
. . . . £500/£350

ditto, Putnam's (New York), 1924 . . . . £200/£25

The Blessing of Pan, by Lord Dunsany, Putnam's (London), 1927 (frontispiece by Sime) . . . . £250/£50

ditto, Putnam's (New York), 1928 . . . . £250/£50

My Talks with Dean Spanley, Heinemann (London), 1936 (frontispiece by Sidney Sime) . . . . £75/£15

ditto, Putnam's (New York), 1936 . . . . £65/£15

GEORGES SIMENON

(b.1903 d.1989)

Born in Belgium, Simenon's literary output was prodigious; he was able to write 60 to 80 pages a day and published around 450 novels and short stories. He is known especially for his 'Inspector Maigret' detective novels, although he also wrote a large number of psychological novels and several volumes of autobiography. He wrote in French and much of his work has not been translated into English.

'Maigret' Novels

The Crime of Inspector Maigret, Covici-Friede (New York), 1932 . . . . £1,250/£150

ditto, as **Introducing Inspector Maigret**, Hurst and Blackett (London), 1933 . . . . . . £1,250/£75

The Strange Case of Peter the Lett, Covici-Friede (New York), 1933 . . . . £1,000/£75

The Crossroad Murders, Covici-Friede (New York), 1933 .
. . . . £1,000/£75

Inspector Maigret Investigates, Hurst and Blackett (London), 1933 (the two above titles) . . . £750/£75

The Triumph of Inspector Maigret, Hurst and Blackett (London), 1934 . . . . . . £1,000/£75

The Patience of Maigret, George Routledge & Sons (London), 1939 . . . . £600/£65

ditto, Harcourt Brace (New York), 1940 . . . £350/£40

Maigret Travels South, George Routledge & Sons (London), 1940 . . . . £350/£40

ditto, Harcourt Brace (New York), 1940 . . . £350/£40

Maigret Abroad, George Routledge & Sons (London), 1940
. . . . £300/£35

ditto, Harcourt Brace (New York), 1940 . . . £300/£35

Maigret to the Rescue, George Routledge & Sons (London), 1940 . . . . £300/£30

ditto, Harcourt Brace (New York), 1941 . . . £275/£30

Maigret Keeps a Rendez-Vous, George Routledge & Sons (London), 1940 . . . . £265/£25

ditto, Harcourt Brace (New York), 1941 . . . £265/£25

Maigret Sits It Out, George Routledge & Sons (London), 1941 . . . . £250/£25

ditto, Harcourt Brace (New York), 1941 . . . £200/£20

Maigret and M. L'Abbé, George Routledge & Sons (London), 1941 . . . . £250/£25

ditto, Harcourt Brace (New York), 1942 . . . £200/£25

Maigret on Holiday, Routledge and Kegan Paul (London), 1950 . . . . £65/£10

ditto, as **No Vacation for Maigret**, Doubleday (New York), 1953 . . . . £45/£5

Maigret Right and Wrong, Hamish Hamilton (London), 1954 . . . . £45/£5

Maigret and the Strangled Stripper, Doubleday (New York), 1954 . . . . £45/£5

Maigret and the Killers, Doubleday (New York), 1954 .
. . . . £45/£5

ditto, as **Maigret and the Gangsters**, Hamish Hamilton (London), 1974 . . . . £20/£5

Maigret and the Young Girl, Hamish Hamilton (London), 1955 . . . . £45/£5

ditto, as **Inspector Maigret and the Dead Girl**, Doubleday (New York), 1955 . . . . . . £45/£5

The Fugitive, Doubleday (New York), 1955 . . £45/£5

Maigret and the Burglar's Wife, Hamish Hamilton (London), 1955 . . . . £45/£5

ditto, as **Inspector Maigret and the Burglar's Wife** Doubleday (New York), 1956 . . . . . . £45/£5

Inspector Maigret in New York's Underworld, Doubleday (New York), 1956 . . . . . . £45/£5

Maigret's Revolver, Hamish Hamilton (London), 1956.
. . . . £45/£5

ditto, Harcourt Brace (New York), 1984 . . . £10/£5

My Friend Maigret, Hamish Hamilton (London), 1956 .
. . . . £35/£5

ditto, as **The Methods of Maigret**, Doubleday (New York), 1957 . . . . £35/£5

Maigret Goes to School, Hamish Hamilton (London), 1957
. . . . £35/£5

ditto, Harcourt Brace (New York), 1988 . . . £10/£5

Maigret's Little Joke, Hamish Hamilton (London), 1957 .
. . . . £35/£5

ditto, as **None of Maigret's Business**, Doubleday (New York), 1958 . . . . £30/£5

Maigret and the Old Lady, Hamish Hamilton (London),
1958 . . . . £25/£5
Maigret's First Case, Hamish Hamilton (London), 1958 .
. . . . £25/£5
Maigret has Scruples, Hamish Hamilton (London), 1959 .
. . . . £25/£5
Maigret and the Reluctant Witnesses, Hamish Hamilton
(London), 1959 . . . . . . £25/£5
ditto, Harcourt Brace (New York), 1989 . . . £10/£5
Madame Maigret's Own Case, Doubleday (New York),
1959 . . . . £25/£5
ditto, as *Madame Maigret's Friend*, Hamish Hamilton
(London), 1960 . . . . . . £25/£5
Maigret Takes a Room, Hamish Hamilton (London), 1960 .
. . . . £25/£5
ditto, as *Maigret Rents a Room*, Doubleday (New York),
1961 . . . . £25/£5
Maigret in Court, Hamish Hamilton (London), 1961 £25/£5
ditto, Harcourt Brace (New York), 1983 . . . £10/£5
Maigret Afraid, Hamish Hamilton (London), 1961   £25/£5
ditto, Harcourt Brace (New York), 1983 . . . £15/£5
Maigret in Society, Hamish Hamilton (London), 1962 . .
. . . . £25/£5
Maigret's Failure, Hamish Hamilton (London), 1962 £25/£5
Maigret's Memoirs, Hamish Hamilton (London), 1963   .
. . . . £25/£5
ditto, Harcourt Brace (New York), 1985 . . . £15/£5
Maigret and the Lazy Burglar, Hamish Hamilton (London),
1963 . . . . £25/£5
Maigret's Special Murder, Hamish Hamilton (London),
1964 . . . . £25/£5
ditto, as *Maigret's Dead Man*, Doubleday (New York), 1964
. . . . £25/£5
Maigret and the Saturday Caller, Hamish Hamilton
(London), 1964 . . . . . . £25/£5
ditto, Harcourt Brace (New York), 1991 . . . £10/£5
Maigret Loses His Temper, Hamish Hamilton (London),
1965 . . . . £25/£5
ditto, Harcourt Brace (New York), 1974 . . . £25/£5
Maigret Sets a Trap, Hamish Hamilton (London), 1965   .
. . . . £25/£5
ditto, Harcourt Brace (New York), 1972 . . . £25/£5
Maigret on the Defensive, Hamish Hamilton (London), 1966
. . . . £25/£5
ditto, Harcourt Brace (New York), 1981 . . . £15/£5
Maigret and the Headless Corpse, Hamish Hamilton
(London), 1967 . . . . . . £25/£5
ditto, Harcourt Brace (New York), 1968 . . . £25/£5
Maigret and the Nahour Case, Hamish Hamilton (London),
1967 . . . . £25/£5
ditto, Harcourt Brace (New York), 1982 . . . £10/£5
Maigret's Pickpocket, Hamish Hamilton (London), 1968   .
. . . . £25/£5
ditto, Harcourt Brace (New York), 1968 . . . £25/£5
Maigret Has Doubts, Hamish Hamilton (London), 1968   .
. . . . £25/£5
ditto, Harcourt Brace (New York), 1982 . . . £10/£5
Maigret In Vichy, Harcourt Brace (New York), 1968 £25/£5
ditto, as *Maigret Takes the Waters*, Hamish Hamilton
(London), 1969 . . . . . . £25/£5
Maigret and the Minister, Hamish Hamilton (London), 1969
. . . . £20/£5
ditto, as *Maigret and the Calame Report*, Harcourt Brace
(New York), 1969 . . . . . . £20/£5

Maigret Hesitates, Hamish Hamilton (London), 1970 £20/£5
ditto, Harcourt Brace (New York), 1970 . . . £20/£5
Maigret's Boyhood Friend, Hamish Hamilton (London),
1970 . . . . £20/£5
ditto, Harcourt Brace (New York), 1970 . . . £20/£5
Maigret and the Wine Merchant, Hamish Hamilton
(London), 1971 . . . . . . £20/£5
ditto, Harcourt Brace (New York), 1975 . . . £20/£5
Maigret and the Killer, Hamish Hamilton (London), 1971 .
. . . . £20/£5
ditto, Harcourt Brace (New York), 1971 . . . £20/£5
Maigret and the Madwoman, Hamish Hamilton (London),
1972 . . . . £20/£5
ditto, Harcourt Brace (New York), 1972 . . . £20/£5
Maigret and the Flea, Hamish Hamilton (London), 1972 .
. . . . £15/£5
ditto, as *Maigret and the Informer*, Harcourt Brace (New
York), 1973 . . . . £15/£5
Maigret and Monsieur Charles, Hamish Hamilton
(London), 1973 . . . . . . £15/£5
Maigret and the Dosser, Hamish Hamilton (London), 1973
. . . . £15/£5
ditto, as *Maigret and the Bum*, Harcourt Brace (New York),
1973 . . . . £15/£5
Maigret and the Millionaires, Hamish Hamilton (London),
1974 . . . . £15/£5
ditto, Harcourt Brace (New York), 1974 . . . £15/£5
Maigret and the Loner, Hamish Hamilton (London), 1975 .
. . . . £15/£5
ditto, Harcourt Brace (New York), 1975 . . . £15/£5
Maigret and the Man on the Boulevard, Hamish Hamilton
(London), 1975 . . . . . . £15/£5
ditto, as *Maigret on the Bench*, Harcourt Brace (New York),
1975 . . . . £15/£5
Maigret and the Black Sheep, Hamish Hamilton (London),
1976 . . . . £15/£5
ditto, Harcourt Brace (New York), 1976 . . . £15/£5
Maigret and the Ghost, Hamish Hamilton (London), 1976 .
. . . . £15/£5
ditto, as *Maigret and the Apparition*, Harcourt Brace (New
York), 1976 . . . . £15/£5
Maigret and the Spinster, Hamish Hamilton (London), 1977
. . . . £15/£5
ditto, Harcourt Brace (New York), 1977 . . . £15/£5
Maigret and the Hotel Majestic, Hamish Hamilton
(London), 1977 . . . . . . £15/£5
ditto, Harcourt Brace (New York), 1978 . . . £15/£5
Maigret in Exile, Hamish Hamilton (London), 1978 £15/£5
ditto, Harcourt Brace (New York), 1979 . . . £15/£5
Maigret and the Toy Village, Hamish Hamilton (London),
1978 . . . . £15/£5
ditto, Harcourt Brace (New York), 1979 . . . £15/£5
Maigret's Rival, Hamish Hamilton (London), 1979   £15/£5
ditto, Harcourt Brace (New York), 1980 . . . £15/£5
Maigret in New York, Hamish Hamilton (London), 1979   .
. . . . £15/£5
Maigret and the Coroner, Hamish Hamilton (London), 1980
. . . . £15/£5
Maigret and the Mad Killers, Doubleday (New York), 1980
. . . . £15/£5
Maigret and the Death of a Harbor-Master, Harcourt Brace
(New York), 1989 . . . . . . £15/£5
Maigret and the Fortuneteller, Harcourt Brace (New York),
1989 . . . . £15/£5

Maigret and the Flemish Shop, Harcourt Brace (New York), 1990 . . . . £15/£5
Maigret and the Tavern by the Seine, Harcourt Brace (New York), 1990 . . . . . . £15/£5

'Maigret' Short Stories
Maigret's Christmas, Hamish Hamilton (London), 1976 . . . . £20/£5
ditto, Harcourt Brace (New York), 1977 . . £20/£5
Complete Maigret Short Stories, Hamish Hamilton (London), 1976 . . . . . . £15/£5
Maigret's Pipe, Hamish Hamilton (London), 1977. £15/£5
ditto, Harcourt Brace (New York), 1978 . £15/£5

Other Novels
The Disintegration of J.P.G. George, Routledge & Sons (London), 1937 . . £500/£75
In Two Latitudes, George Routledge & Sons (London), 1942 . . . . . . £350/£35
Affairs of Destiny, George Routledge & Sons (London), 1942 . . . . . . £250/£25
ditto, Harcourt Brace (New York), 1944 . . £250/£25
The Man who Watched the Trains Go By, George Routledge & Sons (London), 1942 . . £200/£25
ditto, Reynal & Hitchcock (New York), 1946 . £50/£10
Havoc by Accident, George Routledge & Sons (London), 1943 . . . . . . £200/£25
ditto, Harcourt Brace (New York), 1943 . . £150/£20
Escape in Vain, George Routledge & Sons (London), 1943 . . . . . . £150/£20
ditto, Harcourt Brace (New York), 1944 . . £150/£20
On the Danger Line, George Routledge & Sons (London), 1944 . . . . . . £125/£15
ditto, Harcourt Brace (New York), 1944 . . £125/£15
The Shadow Falls, George Routledge & Sons (London), 1945 . . . . . . £100/£15
ditto, Harcourt Brace (New York), 1945 . . £100/£15
The Lost Moorings, George Routledge & Sons (London), 1946 . . . . . . £75/£10
ditto, as *Blind Alley*, Reynal & Hitchcock (New York), 1946 . . . . . . £65/£10
Black Rain, Reynal & Hitchcock (New York), 1947 £50/£10
ditto, Routledge & Kegan Paul (London), 1949 . £50/£10
First Born, Reynal & Hitchcock (New York), 1947 £50/£10
Magnet of Doom, George Routledge & Sons (London), 1948 . . . . . . £50/£10
Chit of a Girl, Routledge & Kegan Paul (London), 1949 . . . . £50/£10
A Wife at Sea, Routledge & Kegan Paul (London), 1949 . . . . £50/£10
The Snow Was Black, Prentice-Hall (New York), 1950 . . . . £45/£10
ditto, as *The Stain on the Snow*, Routledge & Kegan Paul (London), 1953 . . . £45/£10
Strange Inheritance, Routledge & Kegan Paul (London), 1950 . . . . . . £35/£10
Poisoned Relations, Routledge & Kegan Paul (London), 1950 . . . . . . £35/£10
The Strangers in the House, Routledge & Kegan Paul (London), 1951 . . . . £35/£10
ditto, Doubleday (New York), 1954 . . £25/£5
The Window over the Way, Routledge & Kegan Paul (London), 1951 . . . . £35/£10

The Heart of a Man, Prentice-Hall (New York), 1951 . . . . £35/£10
Act of Passion, Prentice-Hall (New York), 1952 . £35/£10
ditto, Routledge & Kegan Paul (London), 1953 . £35/£10
The House by the Canal, Routledge & Kegan Paul (London), 1952 . . . . . . £35/£10
The Burgomaster of Furnes, Routledge & Kegan Paul (London), 1952 . . . . . £35/£10
The Trial of Bébé Donge, Routledge & Kegan Paul (London), 1952 . . . . . £35/£10
Aunt Jeanne, Routledge & Kegan Paul (London), 1953 . . . . £35/£10
ditto, Harcourt Brace (New York), 1983 . . £10/£5
The Girl in his Past, Prentice-Hall (New York), 1953 . . . . £35/£10
ditto, Hamish Hamilton (London), 1976 . . £10/£5
Four Days in a Lifetime, Prentice-Hall (New York), 1953 . . . . £35/£10
ditto, Hamish Hamilton (London), 1977 . . £10/£5
Belle, New American Library (New York), 1954 . £35/£10
Across the Street, Routledge & Kegan Paul (London), 1954 . . . . £35/£10
ditto, Harcourt Brace (New York), 1992 . . £10/£5
Ticket of Leave, Routledge & Kegan Paul (London), 1954 . . . . £35/£10
Tidal Wave, Doubleday (New York), 1954 . £35/£10
ditto, as *Violent Ends*, Hamish Hamilton (London), 1954 (drops one story) . . . . £30/£10
Destinations: The Hitchhiker and The Burial of Monsieur Bouvet, Doubleday (New York), 1955 . . £30/£10
Danger Ahead, Hamish Hamilton (London), 1955. £30/£10
A Sense of Guilt, Hamish Hamilton (London), 1955 (contains *Chez Krull* and *The Heart of a Man*) . £30/£10
The Magician and The Widow, Doubleday (New York), 1955 . . . . . . £15/£10
ditto, as *The Magician* only, Hamish Hamilton (London), 1974 . . . . . . £10/£5
Witnesses And The Watchmaker, Doubleday (New York), 1956 . . . . . . £15/£10
The Judge and the Hatter, Hamish Hamilton (London), 1956 (contains *The Witnesses* and *The Hatter's Ghosts*) . . . . £15/£5
ditto, as *The Hatter's Phantoms*, Harcourt Brace (New York), 1976 (single novel only) . . . £10/£5
The Sacrifice, Hamish Hamilton (London), 1956 . £15/£5
The Little Man from Archangel, Hamish Hamilton (London), 1957 . . . . . . £15/£5
The Stowaway, Hamish Hamilton (London), 1957. £15/£5
The Son, Hamish Hamilton (London), 1958 . £15/£5
Inquest on Bouvet, Hamish Hamilton (London), 1958 . . . . £15/£5
In Case of Emergency, Doubleday (New York), 1958 . . . . £15/£5
ditto, Hamish Hamilton (London), 1960 . . £15/£5
The Negro, Hamish Hamilton (London), 1959 . £15/£5
Striptease, Hamish Hamilton (London), 1959 . £15/£5
ditto, Harcourt Brace (New York), 1989 . . £10/£5
Sunday, Hamish Hamilton (London), 1960 . £10/£5
ditto, Harcourt Brace (New York), 1966 (with *The Little Man from Archangel*) . . . . . £10/£5
The Premier, Hamish Hamilton (London), 1961 . £15/£5
The Widower, Hamish Hamilton (London), 1961 . £15/£5
ditto, Harcourt Brace (New York), 1982 . . £15/£5

The Fate of the Malous, Hamish Hamilton (London), 1962
. . . . £15/£5
Pedigree, Hamish Hamilton (London), 1962 . . £15/£5
ditto, London House (New York), 1963 . . . £15/£5
Account Unsettled, Hamish Hamilton (London), 1962 . .
. . . . £15/£5
A New Lease of Life, Hamish Hamilton (London), 1963 .
. . . . £15/£5
The Iron Staircase, Hamish Hamilton (London), 1963 . .
. . . . £15/£5
ditto, Harcourt Brace (New York), 1977 . . . £10/£5
The Patient, Hamish Hamilton (London), 1963 . £15/£5
ditto, as *The Bells of Bicetre*, Harcourt Brace (New York),
1964 . . . . £15/£5
The Accomplices, Harcourt Brace (New York), 1964 £15/£5
ditto, Hamish Hamilton (London), 1966 . . . £15/£5
The Train, Hamish Hamilton (London), 1964 . . £15/£5
The Door, Hamish Hamilton (London), 1964 . . £15/£5
ditto, Harcourt Brace (New York), 1964 . . . £15/£5
The Blue Room, Harcourt Brace (New York), 1964 £15/£5
ditto, Hamish Hamilton (London), 1965 . . . £15/£5
Three Beds in Manhattan, Doubleday (New York), 1964 .
. . . . £15/£5
ditto, Hamish Hamilton (London), 1976 . . . £10/£5
The Man with the Little Dog, Hamish Hamilton (London),
1965 . . . . £15/£5
ditto, Harcourt Brace (New York), 1989 . . . £10/£5
The Little Saint, Harcourt Brace (New York), 1965 £15/£5
ditto, Hamish Hamilton (London), 1966 . . . £15/£5
The Cat, Harcourt Brace (New York), 1967 . . £15/£5
ditto, Hamish Hamilton (London), 1972 . . . £10/£5
The Confessional, Hamish Hamilton (London), 1967 £15/£5
ditto, Harcourt Brace (New York), 1968 . . . £15/£5
Monsieur Monde Vanishes, Hamish Hamilton (London),
1967 . . . . £15/£5
ditto, Harcourt Brace (New York), 1977 . . . £10/£5
The Old Man Dies, Harcourt Brace (New York), 1967 . .
. . . . £15/£5
ditto, Hamish Hamilton (London), 1968 . . . £15/£5
The Neighbours, Hamish Hamilton (London), 1968 £15/£5
The Prison, Hamish Hamilton (London), 1969 . £15/£5
ditto, Harcourt Brace (New York), 1969 . . . £15/£5
Big Bob, Hamish Hamilton (London), 1969 . . £15/£5
ditto, Harcourt Brace (New York), 1981 . . . £10/£5
The Man on the Bench in the Barn, Hamish Hamilton
(London), 1970 . . . . £10/£5
ditto, Harcourt Brace (New York), 1970 . . . £10/£5
November, Hamish Hamilton (London), 1970 . . £10/£5
ditto, Harcourt Brace (New York), 1970 . . . £10/£5
The Rich Man, Hamish Hamilton (London), 1971 . £10/£5
ditto, Harcourt Brace (New York), 1971 . . . £10/£5
Teddy Bear, Hamish Hamilton (London), 1971 . £10/£5
ditto, Harcourt Brace (New York), 1972 . . . £10/£5
The Disappearance of Odile, Hamish Hamilton (London),
1972 . . . . £10/£5
ditto, Harcourt Brace (New York), 1972 . . . £10/£5
The Glass Cage, Hamish Hamilton (London), 1973 £10/£5
ditto, Harcourt Brace (New York), 1973 . . . £10/£5
The Innocents, Hamish Hamilton (London), 1973 . £10/£5
ditto, Harcourt Brace (New York), 1974 . . . £10/£5
The Venice Train, Hamish Hamilton (London), 1974 £10/£5
ditto, Harcourt Brace (New York), 1974 . . . £10/£5
Betty, Harcourt Brace (New York), 1974 . . . £10/£5
ditto, Hamish Hamilton (London), 1975 . . . £10/£5

The Others, Hamish Hamilton (London), 1975 . £10/£5
The House on Quai Notre Dame, Harcourt Brace (New
York), 1975 . . . . £10/£5
The Bottom of the Bottle, Hamish Hamilton (London), 1977
. . . . £10/£5
The Girl with a Squint, Hamish Hamilton (London), 1978 .
. . . . £10/£5
ditto, Harcourt Brace (New York), 1978 . . . £10/£5
The Family Lie, Hamish Hamilton (London), 1978 £10/£5
ditto, Harcourt Brace (New York), 1978 . . . £10/£5
The Night Club, Hamish Hamilton (London), 1979 £10/£5
ditto, Harcourt Brace (New York), 1979 . . . £10/£5
The Grandmother, Hamish Hamilton (London), 1980 £10/£5
ditto, Harcourt Brace (New York), 1980 . . . £10/£5
The Delivery, Hamish Hamilton (London), 1981 . £10/£5
ditto, Harcourt Brace (New York), 1981 . . . £10/£5
The Long Exile, Hamish Hamilton (London), 1983 £10/£5
ditto, Harcourt Brace (New York), 1983 . . . £10/£5
The Lodger, Hamish Hamilton (London), 1983 . £10/£5
ditto, Harcourt Brace (New York), 1983 . . . £10/£5
The Reckoning, Hamish Hamilton (London), 1984 £10/£5
ditto, Harcourt Brace (New York), 1984 . . . £10/£5
The Couple from Poitiers, Hamish Hamilton (London), 1985
. . . . £10/£5
ditto, Harcourt Brace (New York), 1985 . . . £10/£5
Justice, Harcourt Brace (New York), 1985 . . £10/£5
The Outlaw, Hamish Hamilton (London), 1986 . £10/£5
ditto, Harcourt Brace (New York), 1987 . . . £10/£5
Maigret and the Yellow Dog, Harcourt Brace (New York),
1987 . . . . £10/£5
Uncle Charles, Hamish Hamilton (London), 1988 . £10/£5
ditto, Harcourt Brace (New York), 1987 . . . £10/£5
The Rules of the Game, Harcourt Brace (New York), 1989 .
. . . . £10/£5
ditto, Hamish Hamilton (London), 1989 . . . £10/£5
Donadieu's Will, Harcourt Brace (New York), 1991 £10/£5

Collected Editions
African Trio, Hamish Hamilton (London), 1979 . £10/£5
ditto, Harcourt Brace (New York), 1979 . . . £10/£5
The White Horse Inn, Hamish Hamilton (London), 1980 .
. . . . £10/£5
ditto, Harcourt Brace (New York), 1980 . . . £10/£5

Other Short Stories
The Little Doctor, Hamish Hamilton (London), 1978 £15/£5
ditto, Harcourt Brace (New York), 1981 . . . £10/£5

Autobiography
When I was Old, Harcourt Brace (New York), 1971 £15/£5
ditto, Hamish Hamilton (London), 1972 . . . £15/£5
Letter to my Mother, Hamish Hamilton (London), 1976 .
. . . . £15/£5
ditto, Harcourt Brace (New York), 1976 . . . £15/£5
Intimate Memoirs, Hamish Hamilton (London), 1984 £15/£5
ditto, Harcourt Brace (New York), 1984 . . . £15/£5

Essay
The Novel of Man, Harcourt Brace & World (New York),
1964 (limited edition, glassine d/w) . . . £15/£10

IAIN SINCLAIR
(b.1943)

Iain Sinclair is a British writer and film maker. His early work was mainly poetry, much of it published by his own small press, Albion Village Press. Much of his work is set in London.

Poetry

Back Garden: Poems and Stories, Albion Village Press (London), 1970 (wraps) £150
Muscat's Würm, Albion Village Press (London), 1972 (wraps). £125
The Birth Rug, Albion Village Press (London), 1973 (sewn wraps) £100
Lud Heat: A Book of the Dead Hamlets, Albion Village Press (London), 1975 (400 copies; wraps) . . . £75
ditto, Albion Village Press (London), 1975 (10 casebound copies containing additional holograph material). . £300
The Penances, The Many Press (London), 1977 (200 copies; stapled wraps) £75
Suicide Bridge: A Mythology of the South and East, Albion Village Press (London), 1979 (400 copies; pbk) . . £75
ditto, Albion Village Press (London), 1979 (15 casebound copies containing additional holograph material). . £250
Flesh Eggs and Scalp Metal: Selected Poems 1970-1987, Paladin (London), 1989 (pbk) £30
ditto, Paladin (London), 1989 (pbk; 26 lettered copies with handwritten poem) £125
Jack Elam's Other Eye, Hoarse Comerz Press (London), 1991 (stapled wraps; 200 copies) £75
The Ebbing of the Kraft, Equipage (Cambridge), 1997 (stapled wraps) £15
White Goods, Goldmark (Uppingham), 2002 (100 signed, numbered hardback copies; no d/w) . . . £60
ditto, Goldmark (Uppingham), 2002 (26 lettered copies signed by Sinclair and illustrator Emma Matthews; with additional material) £165
Saddling the Rabbit, Etruscan Books (Buckfastleigh, Devon), 2002 (pbk) £10
ditto, Etruscan Books (Buckfastleigh, Devon), 2002 (26 signed, lettered copies with handwritten poem) . £125/£85
The Firewall: Selected Poems 1979-2006, Etruscan Books (Buckfastleigh, Devon), 2006 (pbk) £15
ditto, Etruscan Books (Buckfastleigh, Devon), 2006 (pbk; 26 signed signed, lettered copies) . . . . £65/£45
Buried at Sea, The Worple Press (Tonbridge, Kent), 2006 (pbk) £10

Fiction

White Chappell, Scarlet Tracings, Goldmark (Uppingham), 1987 . . . . £40/£15
ditto, Goldmark (Uppingham), 1987 . . . . £40/£15
Downriver, Paladin (London), 1991 . . . . £15/£5
ditto, Random House (New York), 1993 . . . £10/£5
Radon Daughters, Cape, 1994 . . . . £10/£5
Slow Chocolate Autopsy, Phoenix House, 1997 . £10/£5
ditto, Phoenix House, 1997 (200 signed, numbered copies in slipcase). . . . . £60/£40
Landor's Tower, Granta (London), 2001 . . . £10/£5
Dining on Stones, Hamish Hamilton (London), 2004 £10/£5

Essays

Groucho Positive, Groucho Negative, The Village Press (London), 1973 (pbk). £30
Crash, British Film Institute (London), 1999 (pbk) . £5

Non-Fiction

The Kodak Mantra Diaries, Albion Village Press (London), 1971 (spiral bound) £50
Lights Out for the Territory: 9 Excursions in the Secret History of London, Granta (London), 1997 (pbk) . £10
ditto, Granta/Goldmark (London/Uppingham, 1997 (291 signed, numbered hardback copies; slipcase) . £100/£65
ditto, Granta/Goldmark (London/Uppingham), 1997 (26 signed, lettered hardback copies; slipcase) . £300/£250
Liquid City, Reaktion (London), 1999 (pbk) . . . £5
Rodinsky's Room, Granta (London), 1999 (with Rachel Lichtenstein). . . . . £10/£5
ditto, Granta (London), 1999 (250 signed, numbered copies; slipcase). . . . . £75/£50
ditto, Granta (London), 1999 (26 signed, lettered copies; slipcase). . . . . £200/£150
Dark-Lanthorns: Rodinsky as a Psychogeographer, Goldmark (Uppingham), 1999 (250 signed, numbered copies with facsimile Cadbury's Whole Nut wrapper laid-in) . . . . £75/£45
London Orbital: A Walk Around the M25, Granta London), 2002 . . . . £10/£5
ditto, Granta/Goldmark (London/Uppingham), 2002 (100 signed, numbered hardback copies; slipcase) . £45/£35
The Verbals, in conversation with Kevin Jackson, Worple Press (Tonbridge, Kent), 2003 (pbk) . . . £5
ditto, Worple Press (Kent), 2003 (60 signed, numbered copies and slipcased together with the short story 'View From My Window') £65
Edge of the Orison, Hamish Hamilton (London), 2005. . . . . £15/£5

ISAAC BASHEVIS SINGER
(b.1904 d.1991)

Isaac Bashevis Singer was a Polish-born American author. He was awarded the Nobel Prize in 1978 and is considered one of the leading figures in the Yiddish literary movement.

Novels

Di Familie Mushkat, Morris S. Sklarsky (New York), 1950 (2 cols; printed in Yiddish; no d/w) £500
ditto, as *The Family Moskat*, Knopf (New York), 1950 (translated by A.H.Gross, Maurice Samuels, Lyon Mearson and Nancy Gross) . . . . . . £350/£65
ditto, Secker & Warburg (London), 1966 . . £100/£20
Satan in Goray, Noonday Press (New York), 1955 £125/£35
ditto, Peter Owen (London), 1958 . . . . £100/£20
ditto, Sweetwater Editions (New York), 1981 (50 numbered copies (1-50) signed by Singer and illustrator Ira Moskowitz; includes a signed original drawing by Moskowitz and an extra suite of forty etchings; in box) £600/£500
ditto, Sweetwater Editions (New York), 1981 (75 numbered copies (51-125) signed by Singer and Ira Moskowitz; with

extra suite of 10 signed etchings; bound in full morocco; slipcase). . . . . . . £350/£300

ditto, Sweetwater Editions (New York), 1981 (350 numbered copies (126-475) signed by Singer and Ira Moskowitz; bound in full morocco; slipcase) . . . £175/£125

The Magician of Lublin, *ditto*, Noonday Press (New York), 1960 (translated by Elaine Gottlieb and Joseph Singer) .

. . . . £100/£15

ditto, Noonday Press (New York), 1960 (wraps) . . £10

ditto, Secker & Warburg (London), 1961 . . £75/£15

ditto, Limited Editions Club (New York), 1984 (1,200 numbered copies signed by Singer and the illustrator Larry Rivers; slipcase) . . . . . £150/£100

The Slave, Farrar, Straus & Cudahy (New York), 1962 (translated by the author and Cecil Hemley) . . £30/£5

ditto, Jewish Book Club (London), 1962 . . . £25/£5

ditto, Secker & Warburg (London), 1963 . . £25/£5

The Manor, Farrar, Straus (New York), 1967 (translated by Elaine Gottlieb and Joseph Singer) . . £20/£5

ditto, Jewish Publication Society of America (Philadelphia, PA), 1967 . . . . £20/£5

ditto, Secker & Warburg (London), 1968 . . . £15/£5

ditto, as *The Manor* and *The Estate*, Farrar, Straus & Giroux (New York), 1979 . . . . . . £15/£5

The Estate, Farrar, Straus (New York), 1969 (translated by Joseph Singer, Elaine Gottlieb and Elizabeth Shub) £20/£5

ditto, Jonathan Cape (London), 1970 . . . . £20/£5

Enemies: A Love Story, Farrar, Straus & Giroux (New York), 1972 . . . . £15/£5

ditto, Jonathan Cape (London), 1972 . . . . £15/£5

A Young Man In Search of Love, Doubleday (New York), 1978 . . . . £25/£5

ditto, Doubleday (New York), 1978 (300 numbered copies signed by the author and illustrator Raphael Soyer; slipcase). . . . . £125/£100

Shosha, Farrar, Straus & Giroux (New York), 1978 (translated by Joseph Singer) . . . £15/£5

ditto, Jonathan Cape (London), 1979 . . . . £15/£5

Isaac Bashevis Singer: Three Complete Novels, Avenel (New York), 1982 (*The Slave*, *Shosha*, and *Enemies: A Love Story*) . . . . £15/£5

Yentl The Yeshiva Boy, Farrar Straus & Giroux (New York), 1983 . . . . £15/£5

ditto, Farrar Straus & Giroux (New York), 1983 (450 signed, numbered copies; illustrated by Antonio; slipcase) £100/£75

The Penitent, Franklin Library (Franklin Center, PA), 1983 (signed limited edition in full leather) . . . £30

ditto, Farrar Straus & Giroux (New York), 1983 . £15/£5

ditto, Jonathan Cape (London), 1984 . . . £10/£5

The King of the Fields, Farrar, Straus & Giroux (New York), 1988 (translated by the author). . . . £10/£5

ditto, Farrar, Straus & Giroux (New York), 1988 (300 signed, numbered copies; slipcase) . . . £50/£35

ditto, Jonathan Cape (London), 1989 . . . £15/£5

Scum, Farrar, Straus & Giroux (New York), 1991 . £10/£5

ditto, Jonathan Cape (London), 1991 . . . £10/£5

The Certificate, Farrar, Straus & Giroux (New York), 1992 (translated by Leonard Wolf) . . . . £10/£5

ditto, Hamish Hamilton (London), 1993 . . £10/£5

Meshugah, Farrar, Straus & Giroux (New York), 1994. .

. . . . £10/£5

ditto, Hamish Hamilton (London), 1995 . . £10/£5

Shadows on the Hudson, Farrar, Straus & Giroux (New York), 1998 . . . . £10/£5

ditto, Hamish Hamilton (London), 1998 . . . £10/£5

Short Stories

Gimpel The Fool and Other Stories, Noonday Press (New York), 1957 (translated by Saul Bellow, Isaac Rosenfeld and others) . . . . £150/£30

ditto, Peter Owen (London), 1957 . . . . £75/£15

ditto, Franklin Library (Franklin Center, PA), 1980 (signed limited edition in full leather) £25

ditto, Franklin Library (Franklin Center, PA), 1980 (variant of above edition with additional 10 pps of notes) . . £35

The Spinoza of Market Street and Other Stories, Farrar, Straus & Cudahy (New York), 1961 (translated by Martha Glicklick, Cecil Hemley and others) . . . £30/£5

ditto, Jewish Publication Society (Philadelphia, PA), 1961 ($3.95 on d/w) . . . . £30/£5

ditto, Secker & Warburg (London), 1962 . . . £30/£5

Short Friday and Other Stories, Farrar, Straus & Giroux (New York), 1964 (translated by Cecil Hemley, Joseph Singer and others) . . . . . . £30/£5

ditto, Jewish Publication Society (Philadelphia, PA), 1965 .

. . . . £30/£5

ditto, Secker & Warburg (London), 1967 . . . £25/£5

Selected Short Stories, Modern Library (New York), 1966 .

. . . . £20/£5

The Séance and Other Stories, Farrar, Straus & Giroux (New York), 1968 (translated by Mirra Ginsburg, J.M. Lask and others) . . . . £20/£5

ditto, Jonathan Cape (London), 1970 . . . . £20/£5

A Friend of Kafka and Other Stories. Farrar, Straus & Giroux (New York), 1970 (translated by the author, Elizabeth Shub and others) . . . . . £45/£10

ditto, Jonathan Cape (London), 1972 . . . £30/£5

A Crown of Feathers and Other Stories, Farrar, Straus & Giroux (New York), 1973 . . . . . £15/£5

ditto, Jonathan Cape (London), 1974 . . . . £15/£5

Passions and Other Stories, Farrar, Straus & Giroux (New York), 1975 (translated by Blanche and Joseph Nevel, Joseph Singer and others) . . . . . £15/£5

ditto, Jonathan Cape (London), 1976 . . . . £15/£5

Old Love, Farrar, Straus & Giroux (New York), 1979 (translated by the author, Joseph Singer and others) £20/£5

ditto, Jonathan Cape (London), 1980 . . . . £20/£5

The Gentleman from Cracow and The Mirror, Limited Editions Club (New York), 1979 (2,000 numbered copies signed by the author and by illustrator Raphael Soyer; slipcase). . . . . £125/£100

ditto, Touchtone Press (New York), 1980 (150 signed, numbered copies; 12 lithographs hand-signed by Raphael Soyer; two folio boxes of which one contains Singer's text and the other Soyer's art) . . . . £1,250/£1,000

Reaches of Heaven, Landmark Press (New York), 1980 (250 numbered copies signed by Singer and artist Ira Moskowitz; 24 etchings signed by Moskowitz; two folio boxes of which one contains Singer's text and the other Soyer's art) . . . . . . £1,250/£1,000

ditto, Farrar, Straus & Giroux (New York), 1980 . £15/£5

ditto, Faber & Faber (London), 1982 . . . . £15/£5

The Collected Stories of Isaac Bashevis Singer, Farrar, Straus & Giroux (New York), 1982 (1,048 signed, numbered copies for the Book-of-the-Month Club; slipcase) . . . . £65/£45

ditto, Farrar, Straus & Giroux (New York), 1982 . £20/£5

ditto, Farrar, Straus & Giroux (New York), 1982 (450 signed, numbered copies) . . . . . £125/£100

ditto, Jonathan Cape (London), 1982 . . . . £20/£5

One Day of Happiness, Red Ozier Press (New York), 1982 (155 signed, numbered copies; with 3 coloured lithographs by Richard Callner each signed by artist; slipcase) . .
. . . . £400/£350

The Penguin Collected Stories of Isaac Bashevis Singer, Penguin Books (Harmondsworth, Middx), 1984 (pbk) £10

The Image and Other Stories, Farrar, Straus & Giroux (New York), 1985 (various translators) . . . . £10/£5

ditto, Farrar, Straus & Giroux (New York), 1985 (450 signed, numbered copies; slipcase) . . . . £50/£35

ditto, Jonathan Cape (London), 1986 . . . . £15/£5

The Death of Methuselah, Franklin Library (Franklin Center, PA), 1988 (signed limited edition in full leather; translated by the author, Deborah Menashe and Lester Goran) £25

ditto, Farrar, Straus & Giroux (New York), 1988 . £10/£5

ditto, Farrar, Straus & Giroux (New York), 1988 (200 signed, numbered copies; slipcase; no d/w) . £50/£35

ditto, Jonathan Cape (London), 1988 . . . . £15/£5

The Manuscript, Tamazunchale Press (Newton), [no date] (250 numbered copies; miniature book bound in full leather) £50

Children's

Zlateh The Goat and Other Stories, Harper and Row (New York), 1966 (translated by the author and Elizabeth Shub; illustrated by Maurice Sendak) . . . . £25/£10

ditto, Harper and Row (New York), 1966 (500 numbered copies signed by the author and Maurice Sendak; slipcase)
. . . . £350/£300

ditto, Longman, Young (Harmondsworth, Middx), 1970 .
. . . . £25/£10

Mazel and Schlimazel; or, The Milk of a Lioness, Farrar, Straus (New York), 1967 (translated by the author and Elizabeth Shub; illustrated by Margot Zemach) . £20/£5

ditto, Jonathan Cape (London), 1979 . . . £20/£5

The Fearsome Inn, Scribner (New York), 1967 (translated by the author and Elizabeth Shub) . . . £15/£5

ditto, Collins (London), 1970 . . . . £30/£10

When Shlemiel Went to Warsaw and Other Stories, Farrar, Straus & Giroux (New York), 1968 (translated by Elizabeth Shub and others; illustrated by Margot Zemach)
. . . . £20/£5

ditto, Longman (London), 1974 . . . . £15/£5

A Day of Pleasure: Stories of a Boy Growing Up in Warsaw, Farrar, Straus & Giroux (New York), 1969 (translated by the author, Elizabeth Shub and others) . £25/£5

ditto, Farrar, Straus & Giroux (New York), 1969 (pbk) . £5

ditto, Julia MacRae (London), 1980 . . . £25/£5

ditto, as *A Day of Pleasure* and other Stories for Children, Galahad Books (New York), 1992 . . . £10/£5

Joseph and Koza; or, The Sacrifice to the Vistula, Farrar, Straus & Giroux (New York), 1970 (translated by the author and Elizabeth Shub) . . . . £20/£5

ditto, Hamish Hamilton (London), 1984 . . £20/£5

Elijah The Slave: A Hebrew Legend Retold, Farrar Straus & Giroux (New York), 1970 (translated by the author and Elizabeth Shub; illustrated by Antonio Frasconi) . £20/£5

The Topsy-Turvy Emperor of China, Harper (New York), 1971 (translated by the author and Elizabeth Shub; illustrated by William Pene du Bois) . . . £20/£5

The Wicked City, Farrar, Straus & Giroux (New York), 1972 (translated by the author and Elizabeth Shub) . £15/£5

The Fools of Chelm and Their History, Farrar, Straus & Giroux (New York), 1973 (translated by the author and Elizabeth Shub; illustrated by Uri Shulevitz) . £20/£5

ditto, Abelelard (London), 1975 . . . . . £20/£5

Why Noah Chose the Dove, Farrar, Straus & Giroux (New York), 1974 (translated by Elizabeth Shub) . . £20/£5

A Tale of Three Wishes, Farrar, Straus & Giroux (New York), 1976 (translated by the author and Elizabeth Shub; illustrated by Irene Lieblich) . . . . . £15/£5

Naftali The Storyteller and His Horse, Sus and Other Stories, Farrar, Straus & Giroux (New York), 1976 (translated by the author, Joseph Singer and Ruth Finkel; illustrated by Margot Zemach) . . . . £15/£5

ditto, Jewish Publication Society (Philadelphia, PA), 1976 .
. . . . £15/£5

ditto, O.U.P. (London), 1977 . . . . £15/£5

The Power of Light, Eight Stories for Hanukkah, Farrar, Straus & Giroux (New York), 1980 (translated by the author and Elizabeth Shub; illustrated by Irene Lieblich) .
. . . . £15/£5

ditto, Robson Books (London), 1983 . . . . £15/£5

The Golem, Farrar, Straus & Giroux, New York, 1982 (translated by the author and Elizabeth Shub) . £15/£5

ditto, Farrar, Straus & Giroux, New York, 1982 (450 numbered copies signed by Singer and artist Uri Shulevitz)
. . . . £100/£75

ditto, Andre Deutsch (London), 1983 . . . £15/£5

Stories for Children, Farrar, Straus & Giroux (New York), 1984 (translated by author and Elizabeth Shub) . £15/£5

ditto, Farrar, Straus & Giroux (New York), 1984 (400 signed, numbered copies; slipcase; no d/w) . £75/£50

Shrewd Todie and Lyzer The Miser, Barefoot Books (Boston), 1994 . . . . £15

Autobiography

In My Father's Court, Farrar, Straus & Giroux (New York), 1966 (translated by Channah Kleinerman-Goldstein and others) . . . . £20/£5

ditto, Jewish Publication Society of America (Philadelphia, PA), 1966 . . . . £20/£5

ditto, Secker & Warburg (London), 1967 . . £20/£5

Love and Exile: The Early Years, A Memoir, Doubleday (New York), 1984 . . . . £15/£5

ditto, Doubleday (New York), 1984 (300 numbered copies signed by author and artist Raphael Soyer; slipcase) . .
. . . . £100/£75

ditto, Jonathan Cape (London), 1985 . . . . £15/£5

Remembrances of a Rabbi's Son, The UJA-Foundation Campaign (New York), 1984 (500 signed, numbered copies; with a signed lithograph by Chaim Gross laid in; slipcase) . . . . £175/£125

More Stories from My Father's Court, Farrar Straus Giroux (New York), 2000 . . . . . . £10/£5

Others

Mayses Fun Hintern Otvn, Y.L. Peretz (Tel-Aviv), 1970 (glassine d/w) . . . . £25/£20

An Isaac Bashevis Singer Reader, Farrar, Straus & Giroux (New York), 1971 . . . . £25/£5

Alone in the Wild Forest, Farrar, Straus & Giroux (New York), 1971 (translated by the author and Elizabeth Shub; illustrated by Margot Zemach) . . . . £20/£5

Tully Filmus, Selected Drawings, Jewish Publication Society of America (Philadelphia, PA), 1971 . . £25/£5

The Hasidim: Paintings, Drawings, and Etchings, Crown Publishers (New York), 1973 (paintings and drawings by Ira Moskowitz) . . . . . . £50/£10

National Book Award Acceptance Speech, no publisher (New York), 1974 (hand-sewn wraps) £100

Der Shpigl Un Andere Dertsylungen, Hebrew Univ Press (Jerusalem), 1975 . . . . . . £35/£10
A Little Boy In Search of God, Mysticism in a Personal Light, Doubleday (New York), 1976 . . . £15/£5
ditto, Doubleday (New York), 1976 (150 numbered copies signed by the author and illustrator Ira Moskowitz; slipcase). . . . . £75/£50
Yentl, A Play, Samuel French (New York), 1977 (pbk). £15
Nobel Lecture, Farrar, Straus (New York), 1979 . £15/£5
ditto, Jonathan Cape (London), 1980 (stapled wraps in d/w) . . . . £15/£5
Isaac Bashevis Singer on Literature and Life: An Interview, Univ of Arizona Press (Tucson, AZ), 1979 (with Paul Rosenblatt and Gene Koppel; no d/w) . . . £20
ditto, Univ of Arizona Press (Tucson, AZ), 1979 (pbk). £10
Lost In America, Doubleday (Garden City, NY), 1979 (translated by Joseph Singer) . . . . . . £15/£5
ditto, Doubleday (Garden City, NY), 1979 (500 numbered copies signed by Singer and illustratir Raphael Soyer) .
. . . . £125/£100
The Meaning of Freedom, United States Military Academy (West Point, NY), 1980 (wraps) £75
My Personal Concept of Religion, Southwestern Louisiana Univ Press (Lafayette, LA), 1982 (wraps; 100 copies signed by author and artist Rodrigue on back cover) . £150
Der Bal-Tshuve, I.L. Peretz Publishing House (Tel-Aviv), 1979 (no d/w) £30
Teibele and her Demons, A Play, Samuel French (New York etc), 1984 (wraps) £10
Gifts, Jewish Publication Society (Philadelphia, PA), 1985 (slipcase) . . . . £15/£10
Conversations With Isaac Bashevis Singer, Doubleday (New York), 1985 . . . . . . £10/£5
Conversations With Isaac Bashevis Singer, University Press of Mississippi (Jackson, MS), 1992 . . £20/£5
ditto, University Press of Mississippi (Jackson, MS), 1992 (pbk) £5

EDITH SITWELL

(b.1887 d.1964)

A poet and critic of aristocratic but eccentric parentage, Edith Sitwell co-founded the anthology *Wheels* with her brothers Osbert and Sacheverell in 1916 as a revolt against contemporary poetry. A penchant for experimentation and an outrageous dress-sense made her a well-known literary figure. She was made a Dame in 1954.

Poetry
The Mother and Other Poems, Blackwell (Oxford), 1915 (500 copies) £600
Twentieth Century Harlequinade and Other Poems, Blackwell (Oxford), 1916 (with Osbert Sitwell, 500 copies; wraps) £50
Clown's Houses, Blackwell (Oxford), 1918 (750 copies; wraps) £45
The Wooden Pegasus, Blackwell (Oxford), 1920 (750 copies) . . . . £175/£20
Façade, Favil Press (London), 1922 (150 signed copies; wraps) £600
Bucolic Comedies, Duckworth (London), 1923 . £45/£10
The Sleeping Beauty, Duckworth (London), 1924. £45/£10

ditto, Knopf (new York), 1924 . . . . . £40/£10
Troy Park, Duckworth (London), 1925 . . . £45/£10
ditto, Knopf (New York), 1925 . . . . . £40/£10
Poor Young People, The Fleuron (London), 1925 (with Osbert & Sacheverell Sitwell, 375 numbered copies) . £85/£50
The Augustan Books of Modern Poetry: Edith Sitwell, Benn (London), 1926 (stapled wraps) £5
Elegy on Dead Fashion, Duckworth (London), 1926 (225 signed copies) . . . . . . £200/£75
Poem for a Christmas Card, Fleuron, 1926 (wraps) . £75
Rustic Elegies, Duckworth (London), 1927 . £50/£10
ditto, Knopf (New York), 1927 . . . . . £40/£10
Popular Song, Faber & Gwyer (London), 1928 (sewn wraps) £10
ditto, Faber & Gwyer (London), 1928 (500 signed, numbered copies) £45
Five Poems, Duckworth (London), 1928 (275 copies) .
. . . . £100/£35
Gold Coast Customs and Other Poems, Duckworth (London), 1929 . . . . . . £30/£10
ditto, Houghton Mifflin (Boston), 1929 . . . £30/£10
In Spring, privately printed (London), 1931 (290 signed copies) £50
Jane Barston, 1719-1746, Faber (London), 1931 (sewn wraps) £10
ditto, Faber (London), 1931 (250 signed copies) . . £60
Epithalamium, Duckworth (London), 1931 (900 copies; wraps) £15
ditto, Duckworth (London), 1931 (100 signed copies) . £50
Five Variations on a Theme, Duckworth (London), 1933 .
. . . . £15/£5
Street Songs, Macmillan (London), 1942 . . . £20/£5
Green Song and Other Poems, Macmillan (London), 1944 .
. . . . £20/£5
ditto, Vanguard Press (New York), 1946 . . . £20/£5
The Shadow of Cain, John Lehmann (London), 1947 . .
. . . . £15/£5
Poor Men's Music, Fore Publications (London), 1950 (wraps) £10
Gardeners and Astronomers, Macmillan (London), 1953 .
. . . . £15/£5
ditto, Vanguard Press (New York), 1953 . . £15/£5
The Outcasts, Macmillan (London), 1962 . . £15/£5
ditto, as *Music and Ceremonies*, Vanguard Press (New York), 1963 . . . . £15/£5

Collected Poetry
Collected Poems, Duckworth (London), 1930 . . £25/£10
ditto, Duckworth (London), 1930 (320 signed copies; unprinted glassine d/w) . . . . £125/£100
Selected Poems, Duckworth (London), 1936 . . £30/£5
Poems New and Old, Faber (London), 1940 . . £20/£5
The Song of the Cold, Macmillan (London), 1945 . £10/£5
ditto, Vanguard Press (New York), 1948 . . £10/£5
The Canticle of the Rose, Macmillan (London), 1949 £10/£5
ditto, Vanguard Press (New York), 1949 . . . £10/£5
Façade and Other Poems, 1920-1935, Duckworth (London), 1950 . . . . £10/£5
Selected Poems, Penguin (Harmondsworth, Middlesex), 1952 (pbk) £5
Collected Poems, Vanguard Press (New York), 1954 £15/£5
ditto, Duckworth (London), 1957 . . . . £15/£5
The Pocket Poets, Vista (London), 1960 (pbk) . . £5

Others

Poetry and Criticism, Hogarth Press (London), 1925 (sewn wraps) £40

ditto, Holt (New York), 1926 . . . . .£100/£30

Alexander Pope, Faber (London), 1930 . . . £35/£10

ditto, Faber (London), 1930 (220 signed copies, d/w and slipcase). . . . .£100/£60

ditto, Cosmopolitan Book Corp (New York), 1930. £30/£10

The Pleasures of Poetry, Duckworth (London), 1930, 1931,1932 (3 vols) . . . . . . £75/£35

Bath, Faber (London), 1932. . . . . £35/£10

ditto, Harrison Smith (New York), 1932 . . £35/£10

The English Eccentrics, Faber (London), 1933 . £75/£15

ditto, as *English Eccentrics*, Vanguard Press (New York), 1957 . . . . £45/£10

Aspects of Modern Poetry, Duckworth (London), 1934 .
. . . . £20/£5

Victoria of England, Faber (London), 1936 . . £65/£15

ditto, Houghton Mifflin (Boston), 1936 . . £30/£10

I Live Under a Black Sun, Gollancz (London), 1937 £65/£15

ditto, Doubleday (New York), 1938 . . . £45/£10

Trio: Dissertations on Some Aspects of National Genius, Macmillan (London), 1938 (with Osbert and Sacheverell Sitwell) . . . . £30/£10

English Women, Collins (London), 1942. . . £20/£5

A Poet's Notebook, Macmillan (London), 1943 . £15/£5

ditto, Little, Brown (Boston), 1950 . . . £15/£5

Fanfare for Elizabeth, Macmillan (London), 1946 £15/£5

ditto, Macmillan (New York), 1946 . . . £15/£5

A Notebook on William Shakespeare, Macmillan, 1948 .
. . . . £15/£5

ditto, Beacon (Boston), 1961 (wraps). . . . £5

The Queens and the Hive, Macmillan (London), 1962 £15/£5

ditto, Little, Brown (Boston), 1962 . . . . £15/£5

Selected Letters, Macmillan (London), 1970 . . £10/£5

ditto, Vanguard Press (New York), 1970 . . . £10/£5

Autobiography

Taken Care Of, Hutchinson (London), 1965 . . £15/£5

ditto, Atheneum (New York), 1965 . . . £15/£5

OSBERT SITWELL

(b.1892 d.1969)

Sir Osbert Sitwell, fifth Baronet, was an English poet and novelist. His elder sister was Dame Edith Sitwell and his younger brother Sir Sacheverell Sitwell, and like them he devoted his life to art and literature. He also wrote a number of volumes of family memoirs.

Poetry

Twentieth Century Harlequinade and Other Poems, Blackwell (Oxford), 1916 (with Edith Sitwell, 500 copies; wraps) £50

The Winstonburg Line, Hendersons (London), 1919 (wraps)
. . . .£150

Argonaut and Juggernaut, Chatto & Windus (London), 1919 . . . . £20

ditto, Knopf (New York), 1920 . . . . £50/£10

At the House of Mrs Kinfoot, Favil Press (London), 1921 (101 signed copies; wraps) £150

Out of the Flame, Grant Richards (London), 1923. £30/£10

ditto, Doran (New York), [1923]. . . . . £30/£10

Poor Young People, The Fleuron (London), 1925 (with Edith & Sacheverell Sitwell, 375 numbered copies) .
. . . . £85/£50

Winter the Huntsman, The Poetry Bookshop (London), 1927 (wraps). £25

England Reclaimed: A Book of Eclogues, Duckworth (London), 1927 . . . . £45/£10

ditto, Duckworth (London), 1927 (165 signed copies) . .
. . . .£100/£65

ditto, as *England Reclaimed and Other Poems* Little, Brown (Boston), 1949 . . . . . . £25/£10

Miss Mew, Mill House Press (Stanford Dingley, Berkshire), 1929 (101 signed copies) £75

Collected Satires and Poems, Duckworth (London), 1931 .
. . . . £25/£5

ditto, Duckworth (London), 1931 (110 signed copies) . .
. . . . £75/£50

Three-Quarter Length Portrait of Michael Arlen, Heinemann/Doubleday Doran (London/New York), 1931 (520 numbered, signed copies) . . . . . £75/£30

Three-Quarter Length Portrait of the Viscountess Wimborne, Cambridge, 1931 (57 signed copies) . .£200

Mrs Kimber, Macmillan (London), 1937 (500 copies) . .
. . . . £35/£15

Selected Poems, Old and New, Duckworth (London), 1943.
. . . . £15/£5

Four Songs of the Italian Earth, Banyan Press (Pawlett, VT), 1948 (260 signed, numbered copies; sewn wraps) £40

Demos the Emperor, Macmillan (London), 1949 (wraps) .
. . . . £10

ditto, Macmillan (London), 1949 (500 signed copies; wraps)
. . . . £30

Wrack at Tidesend, Macmillan (London), 1952 . £15/£5

ditto, Caedmon Publishers (New York), 1953 . . £15/£5

On the Continent, Macmillan (London), 1958 . £15/£5

Poems about People or England Reclaimed, Duckworth (London), 1965 . . . . £15/£5

Autobiography

Left Hand, Right Hand!, Little, Brown (Boston), 1944 .
. . . . £20/£5

ditto, Macmillan (London), 1945 . . . . £15/£5

The Scarlet Tree, Little, Brown (Boston), 1946 . £10/£5

ditto, Macmillan (London), 1946 . . . . £10/£5

Great Morning, Little, Brown (Boston), 1947. . £10/£5

ditto, Macmillan (London), 1948 . . . . £10/£5

Laughter in the Next Room, Little, Brown (Boston), 1948 .
. . . . £10/£5

ditto, Macmillan (London), 1949 . . . . £10/£5

Noble Essences, Little, Brown (Boston), 1950 . £10/£5

ditto, Macmillan (London), 1950 . . . . £10/£5

Others

Who Killed Cock Robin?, C.W. Daniel (London), 1921 (plain boards with printed jacket pasted to spine only) £40

ditto, C.W. Daniel (London), 1921 (wrapper pasted to boards) £25

Triple Fugue, Grant Richards (London), 1924 . £50/£10

ditto, Doran (New York), 1925 . . . . £30/£5

Discursions on Travel, Art and Life, Grant Richards (London), 1925 . . . . £25/£5

ditto, Doran (New York), [1925]. . . . . £20/£5

Before the Bombardment, Duckworth (London), 1926. .
. . . . £25/£10

ditto, Doran (New York), 1926 . . . . £20/£10
**All at Sea: A Social Tragedy in Three Acts for First-Class
Passengers Only**, Duckworth (London), 1927 (with
Sacheverell Sitwell) . . . . . £45/£10
ditto, Doran (New York), 1928 . . . . £40/£10
The People's Album of London Statues, Duckworth
(London), 1928 (with Nina Hamnett) . . £40/£10
ditto, Duckworth (London), 1928 (116 signed copies) .
. . . . £200/£125
The Man Who Lost Himself, Duckworth (London), 1929 .
. . . . £25/£5
ditto, Coward-McCann (New York), 1930 . . £25/£5
Dumb Animal and Other Stories, Duckworth (London),
1930 . . . . £20/£5
ditto, Duckworth (London), 1930 (110 signed copies) .
. . . . £65/£45
ditto, Lippincott (Philadelphia), 1931 . . £20/£5
**Sober Truth: A Collection of Nineteenth-Century Episodes,
Fantastic, Grotesque and Mysterious**, Duckworth, 1930
(with Margaret Barton) . . . . £20/£5
ditto, Stokes (New York), [1930] . . . £20/£5
Victoriana: A Symposium of Victorian Wisdom,
Duckworth, 1931 (with Margaret Barton) . . £20/£5
**Belshazzar's Feast for Mixed Choir, Baritone Solo and
Orchestra**, O.U.P. (New York), 1931 (music by William
Walton) . . . . £35/£10
ditto, O.U.P. (New York), 1978 (350 numbered copies
signed by William Walton) £175
Dickens, Chatto & Windus (London), 1932 . . £30/£5
ditto, Chatto & Windus (London), 1932 (110 signed copies)
. . . . £65
**Winters of Content: More Discursions on Travel, Art and
Life**, Duckworth (London), 1932 . . . £25/£5
ditto, Lippincott (Philadelphia), 1932 . . £20/£5
Miracle on Sinaï: A Satyrical Novel, Duckworth (London),
1933 . . . . £40/£5
ditto, Holt (New York), 1934 . . . . £35/£5
Brighton, Faber (London), 1935 (with Margaret Barton) .
. . . . £25/£5
Penny Foolish, A Book of Tirades and Panegyrics,
Macmillan (London), 1935 . . . . £25/£5
Those Were the Days: Panorama with Figures, Macmillan
(London), 1938 . . . . £10/£5
Trio: Dissertations on Some Aspects of National Genius,
Macmillan (London), 1938 (with Edith and Sacheverell
Sitwell) . . . . £30/£10
Escape with Me: An Oriental Sketch Book, Macmillan
(London), 1939 . . . . £30/£5
ditto, Harrison-Hilton (New York), 1940 . . . £25/£5
Two Generations, Macmillan, 1940 (by Georgiana and
Florence Sitwell, edited by Osbert Sitwell) . £20/£5
Open the Door!, Macmillan (London), 1941 . £20/£5
ditto, Smith & Durrell (New York), 1941 . . £20/£5
A Place of One's Own, Macmillan (London), 1941 £20/£5
Gentle Caesar: A Play in Three Acts, Macmillan (London),
1942 (with R.J. Minney) . . . . . £20/£5
Sing High! Sing Low!, Macmillan (London), 1944 £15/£5
A Letter to My Son, Home & Van Thal (London), 1944
(wraps with d/w) . . . . £10/£5
**The True Story of Dick Whittington: A Christmas Story for
Cat Lovers**, Home & Van Thal (London), 1945 . £20/£5
Alive - Alive-Oh! and Other Stories, Pan (London), 1947
(pbk) £5
**The Novels of George Meredith and Some Notes on the
English Novel**, O.U.P. (Oxford, UK), 1947 (wraps) . £5

Death of a God and Other Stories, Macmillan (London),
1949 . . . . £15/£5
Collected Stories, Duckworth/Macmillan (London), 1953 .
. . . . £15/£5
ditto, Harper (New York), 1953 . . . . £15/£5
The Four Continents, Macmillan (London), 1954 . £15/£5
ditto, Harper (New York), 1954 . . . . £15/£5
Fee Fi Fo Fum! A Book of Fairy Stories, Macmillan
(London), 1959 . . . . . . £25/£10
A Place of One's Own and Other Stories, Icon (London),
1961 (wraps). £5
Tales My Father Taught Me, Hutchinson (London), 1962 .
. . . . £20/£5
ditto, Little, Brown (Boston), [1962] . . . £15/£5
Pound Wise, Hutchinson (London), 1963 . . . £15/£5
ditto, Little, Brown (Boston), [1963] . . . £15/£5
Queen Mary and Others, Joseph (London), 1974 . £15/£5
ditto, John Day (New York), 1975 . . . £15/£5
Rat week: An Essay on the Abdication, Joseph, 1986 . .
. . . . £10/£5

SACHEVERELL SITWELL

(b.1897 d.1988)

Sir Sacheverell Sitwell was a more traditional poet than his
brother Osbert and sister Edith. His work was severely
criticised by those who disliked the Sitwells in general, and
as a result he refused to publish any of his poems for many
years. His most important writings, however, were on art
and music criticism. He became the 6th Baronet, inheriting
the family title when Osbert died in 1969.

Poetry
The People's Palace, Blackwell (Oxford), 1918 (400 copies;
wraps) £85
Doctor Donne and Gargantua, First Canto, Favil Press
(London), 1921 (101 signed, numbered copies; wraps) £175
The Hundred and One Harlequins, Grant Richards
(London), 1922 . . . . £45/£10
ditto, Boni & Liveright (New York), [1923] . £45/£10
The Parrot, The Poetry Bookshop (London), 1923 (wraps) .
. . . . £45
The Thirteenth Caesar and Other Poems, Grant Richards
(London), 1924 . . . . £40/£10
ditto, Doran (New York), 1924 . . . . £45/£10
Exalt the Eglantine and Other Poems, The Fleuron
(London), 1926 (370 numbered copies) . . . £85/£50
Poor Young People, The Fleuron (London), 1925 (with
Osbert & Edith Sitwell, 375 numbered copies) . £85/£50
The Cyder Feast and Other Poems, Duckworth (London),
1927 . . . . £25/£10
ditto, Duckworth (London), 1927 (165 signed copies) .
. . . . £65/£30
ditto, Doran (New York), 1927 . . . . £25/£10
**The Augustan Books of Modern Poetry: Sacheverell
Sitwell**, Benn (London), 1928 (stapled wraps) . . £5
Two Poems, Ten Songs, Duckworth (London), 1929 (275
signed copies) £40
Dr Donne & Gargantua: The First Six Cantos, Duckworth
(London), 1930 . . . . £20/£5

ditto, Duckworth (London), 1930 (215 signed copies) . £100
ditto, Houghton Mifflin (New York), 1930 . . £20/£5
Canons of Giant Art: Twenty Torsos in Heroic Landscapes,
  Faber (London), 1933. . . . . . £30/£10
Collected Poems, Duckworth (London), 1936. . £20/£5
Selected Poems, Duckworth (London), 1948 . . £10/£5
ditto, Macmillan (New York), 1949 . . . £10/£5
An Indian Summer: 100 Recent Poems, Macmillan
  (London), 1982 . . . . . . £10/£5

Autobiography
**Journey to the Ends of Time, Volume One: Lost in the
  Dark Wood**, Cassell (London), 1959 . . . £15/£5
ditto, Random House (New York), 1959 . . . £15/£5

Others
Southern Baroque Art, Grant Richards (London), 1924 .
  . . . . £45/£15
ditto, Knopf (New York), 1924 . . . . £45/£15
All Summer in a Day: An Autobiographical Fantasia,
  Duckworth (London), 1926 . . . . £35/£10
ditto, Doran (New York), 1926 . . . . £35/£10
**All at Sea: A Social Tragedy in Three Acts for First-Class
  Passengers Only**, Duckworth (London), 1927 (with Osbert
  Sitwell) . . . . £45/£10
ditto, Doran (New York), 1928 . . . . £40/£10
German Baroque Art, Duckworth (London), 1927 £40/£10
ditto, Doran (New York), 1928 . . . . £40/£10
**A Book of Towers and Other Buildings of Southern
  Europe**, Etchells & Macdonald (London), 1928 (350
  numbered copies; slipcase) . . . . £200/£100
**The Gothick North: A Study of Medieval Life, Art and
  Thought**, Duckworth (London), 1929/30 (3 vols: *The Visit
  of the Gypsies; These Sad Ruins; The Fair-Haired Victory*)
  . . . . £85/£35 the set
ditto, Houghton Mifflin (Boston), 1929 (1 vol.) £25/£5
ditto, Duckworth (London), 1938 (1 vol.). . £25/£5
Beckford and Beckfordism, An Essay, Duckworth
  (London), 1930 (265 signed copies) . . . £75
Far from My Home, Stories: Long & Short, Duckworth
  (London), 1931 . . . . . . £25/£10
ditto, Duckworth (London), 1931 (110 signed, numbered
  copies, plain brown d/w) . . . . £65/£45
Spanish Baroque Art, Duckworth (London), 1931. £30/£10
Mozart, Peter Davies (London), 1932 . . £25/£10
ditto, Appleton (New York), 1932 . . . £25/£10
Liszt, Faber (London), 1934. . . . . £20/£5
ditto, Houghton Mifflin (Boston), 1934 . . £20/£5
Touching the Orient: Six Sketches, Duckworth (London),
  1934 . . . . £25/£5
A Background for Domenico Scarlatti, 1685-1757, Faber
  (London), 1935 . . . . . . £25/£5
**Dance of the Quick and the Dead: An Entertainment of the
  Imagination**, Faber (London), 1936 . . £50/£10
ditto, Houghton Mifflin (Boston), 1937 . . £25/£5
**Conversation Pieces: A Survey of English Domestic
  Portraits and Their Painters**, Batsford (London), 1936 .
  . . . . £50/£10
ditto, Scribner's (New York), 1937 . . . £50/£10
Narrative Pictures, Batsford (London), 1937 . £65/£15
ditto, Scribner's (New York), 1938 . . . £65/£15
La Vie Parisienne: A Tribute to Offenbach, Faber
  (London), 1937 . . . . . . £20/£5
ditto, Houghton Mifflin (Boston), 1938 . . £20/£5

Trio: Dissertations on Some Aspects of National Genius,
  Macmillan (London), 1938 (with Osbert and Edith Sitwell)
  . . . . £30/£10
Roumanian Journey, Batsford (London), 1938 £20/£5
ditto, Scribner's (New York), 1938 . . . £20/£5
Edinburgh, Faber (London), 1938 . . . £20/£5
ditto, Houghton Mifflin (Boston), 1938 . . £20/£5
German Baroque Sculpture, Duckworth (London), 1938
  (photographs by Anthony Ayscough, notes by Nicolaus
  Pevsner). . . . . £40/£10
The Romantic Ballet in Lithographs of the Time, Faber
  (London), 1938 (with Cyril Beaumont) . . £125/£50
Old Fashioned Flowers, Country Life (London), 1939. .
  . . . . £40/£10
ditto, Scribner's (New York), 1939 . . . £25/£10
Mauretania: Warrior, Man and Woman, Duckworth
  (London), 1940 . . . . . . £30/£10
**Poltergeists: An Introduction and Examination Followed
  by Chosen Instances**, Faber (London), 1940 . £40/£10
ditto, University Books (New York), 1959 . £20/£10
Sacred and Profane Love, Faber (London), 1940 . £20/£5
**Valse des Fleurs: A Day in St Petersburg and a Ball at the
  Winter Palace**, Faber (London), 1941 . . £15/£5
ditto, Fairfax Press (York, North Yorkshire), 1980 (60
  signed, roman numeralled deluxe copies of 400; slipcase).
  . . . . £300/£200
ditto, Fairfax Press (York, North Yorkshire), 1980 (340
  copies of 400) . . . . . . £100/£50
Primitive Scenes and Festivals, Faber (London), 1942. .
  . . . . £20/£5
The Homing of the Winds and Other Passages in Prose,
  Faber (London), 1942. . . . . . £20/£5
Splendours and Miseries, Faber (London), 1943 . £20/£5
**British Architects and Craftsmen: A Survey of Taste,
  Design and Style during Three Centuries 1600 to 1830**,
  Batsford (London), 1945 . . . . . £20/£5
ditto, Scribner's (New York), 1946 . . . £20/£5
The Hunters and the Hunted, Macmillan (London), 1947 .
  . . . . £20/£5
ditto, Macmillan (New York), 1948 . . . £20/£5
**The Netherlands: A Study of Some Aspects of Art, Costume
  and Social Life**, Batsford (London), 1948 . £20/£5
ditto, Hastings House (New York), 1974 . £15/£5
Morning, Noon and Night in London, Macmillan (London),
  1948 . . . . £15/£5
Theatrical Figures in Porcelain, Curtain Press (London),
  1949 . . . . £20/£10
Spain, Batsford (London), 1950 . . . £15/£5
ditto, Hastings House (New York), 1975 . . £15/£5
Cupid and the Jacaranda, Macmillan (London), 1952. .
  . . . . £20/£5
Truffle Hunt, Robert Hale (London), 1953 . £15/£5
Fine Bird Books 1700-1900, Collins (London), 1953 (with
  Handasyde Buchanan and James Fisher) . £400/£250
ditto, Collins (London), 1953 (295 signed copies, slipcase).
  . . . . £750/£500
ditto, Atlantic Monthly Press (New York), 1990 . £20/£5
Selected Works, Bobbs-Merrill (Indianapolis, IN), 1953 .
  . . . . £20/£5
Portugal and Madeira, Batsford (London), 1954 . £15/£5
Selected Works, Robert Hale (London), 1955 (different
  selection from above title). . . . . £15/£5
Old Garden Roses, George Rainbird, 1955 (2 vols, written
  with James Russell; vol. 2 published 1957 was not by
  Sitwell; 2000 copies) . . . . . £200/£125

ditto, Vol. 1, George Rainbird, 1955 (160 signed copies) . . . . £500/£350

Great Flower Books: A Bibliographical Record of Two Centuries of Finely-Illustrated Flower Books, Collins (London), 1956 . . . . . . £250/£150

ditto, Collins (London), 1956 (with Wilfrid Blunt and Patrick M. Synge, 295 signed copies, slipcase) . . £600/£400

ditto, Witherby, 1990 . . . . . £20/£5

ditto, Atlantic Monthly Press (New York), 1990 . £20/£5

Denmark, Batsford (London), 1956 . . . £20/£5

ditto, Hastings House (New York), 1956 . . . £20/£5

Arabesque and Honeycomb, Robert Hale (London), 1957 . . . . £20/£5

ditto, Random House (New York), 1958 . . £20/£5

Malta, Batsford (London), 1958 (with photographs by Tony Armstrong-Jones) . . . . . . £20/£5

Austria, Thames and Hudson (London), 1959 (with Toni Schneiders) . . . . £20/£5

ditto, Viking (New York), 1959 . . . . £20/£5

Bridge of the Brocade Sash: Travels and Observations in Japan, Weidenfeld & Nicolson (London), 1959 . £15/£5

ditto, World (Cleveland, OH), 1959 . . . £15/£5

Golden Wall and Mirador: From England to Peru, Weidenfeld & Nicolson (London), 1961 . £20/£5

ditto, World (Cleveland, OH), 1961 . . . £20/£5

The Red Chapels of Banteai Srei, Weidenfeld & Nicolson (London), 1962 . . . . . £20/£5

ditto, Obolensky (New York), 1963 . . . £20/£5

Monks, Nuns and Monasteries, Weidenfeld & Nicolson (London), 1965 . . . . . . £20/£5

ditto, Holt, Rinehart and Winston (New York), 1965 £20/£5

Southern Baroque Revisited, Weidenfeld & Nicolson (London), 1967 . . . . . . £20/£5

ditto, as ***Baroque and Rococo***, Putnam's (New York), 1967 . . . . £20/£5

Gothic Europe, Weidenfeld & Nicolson (London), 1969 . . . . £15/£5

ditto, Holt, Rinehart & Winston (New York), 1969. £15/£5

For Want of the Golden City, Thames and Hudson (London), 1973 . . . . . . £15/£5

ditto, John Day (New York), 1973 . . . £15/£5

CLARK ASHTON SMITH

(b.1893 d.1961)

An American poet, sculptor, painter and author of fantasy fiction, Clark Ashton Smith was a member of the circle of writers surrounding H.P. Lovecraft, whose work is made distinctive by its rich vocabulary. His short stories originally appeared in the pulp magazines *Weird Tales*, *Strange Tales*, *Astounding Stories*, S*tirring Science Stories* and *Wonder Stories*.

The Star-Treader and Other Poems, A.M. Robertson (San Francisco, CA), 1912 . . . . . . £100

Odes and Sonnets, The Book Club of California (San Francisco, CA), 1918 (300 numbered copies) . £250

Ebony and Crystal, Auburn Journal Press (Auburn, CA), 1922 (500 signed, numbered copies, no d/w). . £300

Sandalwood, privately printed (Auburn, CA), 1925 (250 signed, numbered copies; wraps) £450

The Immortals of Mercury, Stellar Publishing Corporation (New York), 1932 (stapled wraps) £100

The Double Shadow and Other Fantasies, Auburn Journal Press (Auburn, CA), 1933 (stapled wraps) . . . £200

The White Sybil, Fantasy Publications (Everett, PA), 1935 (with *The Men of Avalon* by D. Keller wraps) . . £125

Nero and Other Poems, Futile Press (Lakeport, CA), 1937 (dark tan boards with the title printed on the front and the spine covered in a light tan tape) . . . £425/£150

ditto, Futile Press (Lakeport, CA), 1937 (with a three-page printing of Ryder's 'The Price of Poetry' from *Controversy*, and an offprint of Smith's 'Adventure'). . . . . £500/£225

Out of Space and Time, Arkham House (Sauk City, WI), 1942 . . . . £750/£175

ditto, Spearman (London), 1971 . . . £45/£10

Lost Worlds, Arkham House (Sauk City, WI), 1944 . . . . £250/£75

ditto, Spearman (London), 1971 . . . . £45/£10

Genius Loci and Other Tales, Arkham House (Sauk City, WI), 1948 . . . . £95/£30

ditto, Spearman (London), 1972 . . . . £40/£10

The Ghoul and the Seraph, Gargoyle Press (Brooklyn, NY), 1950 (85 numbered copies; wraps) £500

The Dark Chateau, Arkham House (Sauk City, WI), 1958 . . . . £300/£100

Spells and Philtres, Arkham House (Sauk City, WI), 1958 . . . . £250/£75

Abominations of Yondo, Arkham House (Sauk City, WI), 1960 . . . . £100/£35

ditto, Spearman (London), 1972 . . . . £40/£10

Hesperian Fall, Clyde Beck (Pacific Grove, CA), 1961 (wraps) £150

The Hill of Dionysus: A Selection, Squires (Pacific Grove, CA), 1962 (100 hardback copies, half cloth, no d/w) . £150

ditto, Squires (Pacific Grove, CA), 1962 (15 hardback copies in full cloth with poem signed by Smith, no d/w). . £250

ditto, Squires (Pacific Grove, CA), 1962 (wraps) . £50

Cycles, Squires (Glendale, CA), 1963 (wraps). . . £50

¿Donde Duermos, Eldorado? y Otros Poemas, Squires (Glendale, CA), 1963 (176 copies, poems in Spanish; wraps) £100

Nero: An Early Poem, Squires (Glendale, CA), 1964 (381 copies; wraps) £40

ditto, Squires (Glendale, CA), 1964 (50 numbered copies; wraps) £125

Poems in Prose, Arkham House (Sauk City, WI), 1964 . . . . £75/£35

Tales of Science and Sorcery, Arkham House (Sauk City, WI), 1964 . . . . £50/£15

The Tartarus of the Suns, Squires (Glendale, CA), 1970 (165 copies; wraps) £45

The Palace of Jewels, Squires (Glendale, CA), 1970 (167 copies; wraps) £45

In the Ultimate Valleys, Squires (Glendale, CA), 1970 (160 copies; wraps) £45

To George Sterling: Five Poems, Squires (Glendale, CA), 1970 (199 copies; wraps) £100

Other Dimensions, Arkham House (Sauk City, WI), 1970 . . . . £45/£15

Zothique, Ballantine (New York), 1970 (pbk). . . £10

The Mortuary, Squires (Glendale, CA), 1971 (180 copies; wraps) £40

Selected Poems, Arkham House (Sauk City, WI), 1971 . . . . £75/£25

Hyperborea, Ballantine (New York), 1971 (pbk) . £10

Sadastor, Squires (Glendale, CA), 1972 (108 copies; wraps) £60

Xiccarph, Ballantine (New York), 1972 (pbk). . . £10

Planets and Dimensions, Mirage (Baltimore, MD), 1973 (500 numbered copies) . . . . . £50/£20

ditto, Mirage (Baltimore, MD), 1973 (wraps) . . £10

Poseidonis, Ballantine (New York), 1973 (pbk) . . £10

From the Crypts of Memory, Squires (Glendale, CA), 1973 (198 copies; wraps) £75

The Fantastic Art of Clark Ashton Smith, Mirage (Baltimore, MD), 1973 (wraps) £40

Grotesques and Fantastiques, De la Ree (Saddle River, NJ), 1973 (600 numbered copies; wraps) . . . £35

ditto, De la Ree (Saddle River, NJ), 1973 (50 hardback copies) £100

Klarkash-Ton and Monstro Ligriv, De la Ree (Saddle River, NJ), 1974 (500 numbered copies; wraps) . . £35

ditto, De la Ree (Saddle River, NJ), 1974 (50 copies in black buckram) £100

The Titans in Tartarus, Squires (Glendale, CA), 1974 (320 copies; wraps) £40

A Song From Hell, Squires (Glendale, CA), 1975 (296 copies; wraps) £40

The Potion of Dreams, Squires (Glendale, CA), 1975 (292 copies; wraps) £40

The Fanes of Dawn, Squires (Glendale, CA), 1976 (303 copies; wraps) £40

Seer of the Cycles, Squires (Glendale, CA), 1976 (321 copies; wraps) £40

The Burden of the Suns, Squires (Glendale, CA), 1977 (295 copies; wraps) £40

The Fugitive Poems of Clark Ashton Smith: Xiccarph Edition, Squires (Glendale, CA), 1974-1977 (contains: *The Titans in Tartarus, A Song From Hell, The Potion of Dreams, The Fanes of Dawn, Seer of the Cycles, The Burden of the Suns*, large paper, traycase, tipped-in signed poetry manuscript by C.A.S. from the series, limited to 51 copies) £450

The Black Book of Clark Ashton Smith, Arkham House (Sauk City, WI), 1979 (pbk) £25

The City of the Singing Flame, Timescape (New York), 1981 (pbk) £10

The Last Incantation, Timescape (New York), 1982 (pbk) £10

The Monster of the Prophecy, Timescape (New York), 1983 (pbk) £10

Clark Ashton Smith: Letters to H.P. Lovecraft, Necronomicon Press (West Warwick, RI), 1987 (wraps) . . £15

Mother of Toads, Necronomicon Press (West Warwick, RI), 1987 (stapled wraps) £15

The Dweller in the Gulf, Necronomicon Press (West Warwick, RI), 1987 (stapled wraps) . . . £15

The Vaults of Yoh-Vombis, Necronomicon Press (West Warwick, RI), 1988 (stapled wraps) . . . £10

The Monster of the Prophecy, Necronomicon Press (West Warwick, RI), 1988 (stapled wraps) . . . £10

Nostalgia of the Unknown, Necronomicon Press (West Warwick, RI), 1988 (stapled wraps) . . . £10

The Witchcraft of Ulua, Necronomicon Press (West Warwick, RI), 1988 (stapled wraps) . . . £10

Xeethra, Necronomicon Press (West Warwick, RI), 1988 (stapled wraps) £10

A Rendezvous in Averoigne, Arkham House (Sauk City, WI), 1988 . . . . £20/£10

Strange Shadows, Greenwood Press (Westport, CT), 1989 (no d/w) £100

The Hashish-Eater, Necronomicon Press (West Warwick, RI), 1989 (stapled wraps) £15

ditto, Sidney-Fryer (Sacramento, CA), 1990 (wraps) . £45

The Devil's Notebook, Starmont House (Mercer Island, WA), 1990 . . . . £100

ditto, Starmont House (Mercer Island, WA), 1990 (pbk) £25

Tales of Zothique, Necronomicon Press (West Warwick, RI), 1995 (pbk) £10

Live from Auburn: The Elder Tapes, Necronomicon Press (West Warwick, RI), 1995 (cassette with booklet) . £40

The Book of Hyperborea, Necronomicon Press (West Warwick, RI), 1996 (pbk) £10

DODIE SMITH
(b.1896 d.1990)

Dodie Smith was the author of *A Hundred and One Dalmations*, made into a classic cartoon by Disney, and subsequently filmed. Her novel, *I Capture the Castle* has also been made into a successful film, but her plays have been forgotten, except perhaps *Dear Octopus*.

Childrens Books

The Hundred and One Dalmations, Heinemann (London), 1956 . . . . £250/£40

ditto, Viking (New York), 1957 . . . . . £100/£20

The Starlight Barking: More About the Hundred and One Dalmatians, Heinemann (London), 1967 . . £75/£15

ditto, Simon & Schuster (New York), 1967 . . £65/£10

The Midnight Kittens, W.H. Allen (London), 1978 £20/£5

Adult Novels

I Capture the Castle, Little, Brown (Boston), 1948 £300/£45

ditto, Heinemann (London), 1949 . . . £1,000/£75

The New Moon with the Old, Heinemann (London), 1963 . . . . £20/£5

ditto, Little, Brown (Boston), 1963 . . . . £20/£5

The Town in Bloom, Heinemann (London), 1965 . £15/£5

ditto, Little, Brown (Boston), 1965 . . . . £15/£5

It Ends With Revelations, Heinemann (London), 1967 . . . . £10/£5

ditto, Little, Brown (Boston), 1965 . . . . £10/£5

A Tale of Two Families, Heinemann (London), 1970 £10/£5

ditto, Walker (New York), 1970 . . . . . £10/£5

The Girl from the Candle-Lit Bath, W.H. Allen (London), 1979 . . . . £10/£5

Plays

Call It A Day, Gollancz (London), 1936 . . . £45/£15

ditto, Samuel French (New York), 1936 . . . £35/£10

Bonnet Over the Windmill, Heinemann (London), 1937 . . . . £20/£5

Service, Samuel French (London), [1937] (wraps) . £5

Dear Octopus, Heinemann (London), 1938 . . £75/£20

Three Plays: Autumn Crocus; Service; Touch Wood, Heinemann (London), 1939 . . . . . £35/£10

Lovers and Friends, Samuel French (New York), [1947] (wraps) £5

Letter from Paris, Heinemann (London), 1954 ('Drama Library' series) . . . . £10/£5

I Capture the Castle, Heinemann (London), 1955 ('Drama Library' series) . . . . £20/£5

Amateur Means Lover, Samuel French (London), [1962] (wraps) £5

Autobiography

Look Back With Love: A Manchester Childhood, Heinemann (London), 1974 . . . . . . £20/£5
Look Back With Mixed Feelings, Heinemann (London), 1978 . . . . £15/£5
Look Back With Astonishment, W.H. Allen (London), 1979 . . . . £10/£5
Look Back With Gratitude, Muller, Blond & White (London), 1985 . . . . . . £10/£5

STEVIE SMITH

(b.1902 d.1971)

A poet, novelist and radio personality, Stevie Smith often illustrated her work with naive line drawings somewhat in the style of Edward Lear. *A Good Time Was Had By All* quickly established her as a poet with a dark style in which her characters are continually saying goodbye to friends or welcoming death. Her best known poem is the autobiographical 'Not Waving but Drowning'.

Novels

Novel on Yellow Paper, Cape (London), 1936 . £450/£50
ditto, Morrow (New York), 1937 . . . £150/£35
Over the Frontier, Cape (London), 1939 . . £125/£25
ditto, Pinnacle (New York), 1982 . . . £10/£5
The Holiday, Chapman & Hall (London), 1949 . £125/£30
ditto, Smithers (U.S.), 1950 . . . . . £100/£25

Poetry

A Good Time Was Had By All, Cape (London), 1937 . . . . £150/£35
Tender Only to One, Cape (London), 1938 . £150/£25
Mother, What is Man?, Cape (London), 1942. . £100/£15
Harold's Leap, Chapman & Hall (London), 1950 . £75/£15
Not Waving but Drowning, Deutsch (London), 1957 . . . . £200/£45
Selected Poems, Longmans (London), 1962 . £35/£10
ditto, New Directions (Norfolk, CT), 1964 (pbk) . . £10
The Frog Prince and Other Poems, Longmans (London), 1966 . . . . £35/£10
ditto, as *The Best Beast*, Knopf (New York), 1969. £35/£10
Francesca in Winter, Poem-of-the-Month-Club (London), 1970 (signed broadsheet) £60
Two in One, Longmans (London), 1971 . . £25/£10
Scorpion and Other Poems, Longmans (London), 1971 . . . . £25/£10
Collected Poems, Lane (London), 1975 . . £30/£10
ditto, O.U.P. (New York), 1976 . . . £25/£10

Others

Cats in Colour, Batsford (London), 1959. . £20/£5
ditto, Viking (New York), 1959 . . . . £15/£5
Me Again: Uncollected Writings, Virago (London), 1981 . . . . £20/£5
ditto, Farrar Straus (New York), 1982 . . £15/£5
Stevie Smith: A Selection, Faber (London), 1983 . £10/£5
ditto, Faber (New York), 1982 . . . . £10/£5

WILBUR SMITH

(b.1993)

Wilbur Smith is a best-selling novelist born in Northern Rhodesia, now Zambia. His very first novel was a success and his name is synonymous with adventure blockbusters. All of his work is set against the background of southern Africa.

When the Lion Feeds, Heinemann (London), 1964 . . . . £500/£100
ditto, Viking (New York), 1964 . . . . £200/£40
The Dark of the Sun, Heinemann (London), 1965 £500/£100
ditto, as *The Train From Katanga*, Viking (New York), 1965 . . . . £250/£35
The Sound of Thunder, Heinemann (London), 1966 . . . . £350/£65
ditto, as *The Roar of Thunder*, Simon & Schuster (New York), 1966 . . . . £200/£25
Shout At The Devil, Heinemann (London), 1968 . £300/£45
ditto, Coward-McCann (New York), 1968 . . £150/£20
Gold Mine, Heinemann (London), 1970 (dedication leaf present) . . . . £500/£350
ditto, Heinemann (London), 1970 (dedication leaf excised) . . . . £150/£20
ditto, Doubleday (Garden City, NY), 1970 . £125/£15
The Diamond Hunters, Heinemann (London), 1971 £150/£25
ditto, Doubleday (Garden City, NY), 1972 . £125/£15
The Sunbird, Heinemann (London), 1972 . £125/£25
ditto, Doubleday (Garden City, NY), 1973 . £100/£10
Eagle in the Sky, Heinemann (London), 1974. £125/£15
ditto, Doubleday (Garden City, NY), 1974 . £75/£10
The Eye of the Tiger, Heinemann (London), 1975. £125/£15
ditto, Doubleday (Garden City, NY), 1976 . £50/£5
Cry Wolf, Heinemann (London), 1976 . . £75/£15
ditto, Doubleday (Garden City, NY), 1977 . £45/£5
A Sparrow Falls, Heinemann (London), 1977. £75/£15
ditto, Doubleday (Garden City, NY), 1978 . £45/£5
Hungry As The Sea, Heinemann (London), 1978 . £75/£10
ditto, Doubleday (Garden City, NY), 1979 . £35/£5
Wild Justice, Heinemann (London), 1979 . £65/£10
ditto, as *The Delta Decision* (Garden City, NY), 1981 . . . . £50/£10
A Falcon Flies, Heinemann (London), 1980 . £65/£10
ditto, Doubleday (Garden City, NY), 1982 . £30/£5
Men of Men, Heinemann (London), 1981 . £60/£10
ditto, Doubleday (Garden City, NY), 1983 . £30/£5
The Angels Weep, Heinemann (London), 1982 . £60/£10
ditto, Doubleday (Garden City, NY), 1983 . £30/£5
The Leopard Hunts in Darkness, Heinemann (London), 1984 . . . . £45/£5
ditto, Doubleday (Garden City, NY), 1984 . £30/£5
The Burning Shore, Heinemann (London), 1985 . £45/£5
ditto, Doubleday (Garden City, NY), 1985 . £25/£5
Power of the Sword, Heinemann (London), 1986 . £30/£5
ditto, Little, Brown (Boston), 1986 . . . £15/£5
Rage, Heinemann (London), 1987 . . . £25/£5
ditto, Little, Brown (Boston), 1987 . . . £10/£5
A Time To Die, Heinemann (London), 1989 . £25/£5
ditto, Random House (New York), 1990 . . £10/£5
Golden Fox, Macmillan (London), 1990 . . £20/£5
ditto, Random House (New York), 1990 . . £10/£5
Elephant Song, Macmillan (London), 1991 . £15/£5
ditto, Random House (New York), 1991 . . £10/£5
River God, Macmillan (London), 1993 . . £15/£5

ditto, St Martin's (New York), 1994 . . . . £10/£5
The Seventh Scroll, Macmillan (London), 1995 £15/£5
ditto, St Martin's (New York), 1995 . . . £10/£5
Birds of Prey, Macmillan (London), 1997 . . £10/£5
ditto, St Martin's (New York), 1997 . . . £10/£5
Monsoon, Macmillan (London), 1999 . . £10/£5
ditto, St Martin's (New York), 1999 . . . £10/£5
Warlock, Macmillan (London), 2001. . . £10/£5
ditto, St Martin's (New York), 2001 . . . £10/£5
Blue Horizon, Macmillan (London), 2003 . £10/£5
ditto, St Martin's (New York), 2003 . . . £10/£5
Triumph of the Sun, Macmillan (London), 2005 . £10/£5
ditto, Macmillan (London), 2005 (1,000 signed, numbered copies; slipcase) . . . . £45/£25
ditto, St Martin's/Thomas Dunne (New York), 2005 £10/£5
The Quest, Macmillan (London), 2007 . . £10/£5
ditto, Macmillan (London), 2007 (1,500 signed, numbered copies; in d/w and slipcase) . . . £40/£20
ditto, Thomas Dunne (New York), 2007 . . . £10/£5

ZADIE SMITH
(b.1975)

Zadie Smith is an English novelist, widely regarded as one of England's most talented young authors. *White Teeth*, was an immediate bestseller and won the Whitbread First Novel Award 2000, the Guardian First Book Award, the Commonwealth Writers First Book Prize, the Betty Trask Award and the James Tait Black Memorial Prize for Fiction.

Novels
White Teeth, Hamish Hamilton (London), 2000 . £45/£10
ditto, Random House (New York), 2000 . . . £20/£5
The Autograph Man, Hamish Hamilton (London), 2002 .
. . . . £15/£5
ditto, Random House (New York), 2002 . . £10/£5
On Beauty, Hamish Hamilton (London), 2005 . £10/£5
ditto, Penguin (New York), 2005 . . . £10/£5

Collections
Martha and Hanwell, Penguin (London), 2005 (pbk) . £5

LEMONY SNICKET
(DANIEL HANDLER)
(b.1970)

Daniel Handler has written, under the pseudonym Lemony Snicket, the best-selling *A Series of Unfortunate Events*, a collection of books for children. He has also written three books for adults.

A Series of Unfortunate Events
The Bad Beginning, Harper Collins (New York), 1999 (laminated pictorial covers; no d/w) £125
ditto, Harper Collins (New York), 1999 (advance reading copy; bound with **The Reptile Room**; pbk) . . . £200
ditto, Egmont (London), 2001 (laminated pictorial covers; no d/w) £25

ditto, Egmont (London), 2003 ('Collector's Edition'; large format hardback; no d/w) £10
ditto, Egmont (London), 2003 (2,000 signed copies; bound in leather; slipcase) . . . . £100/£75
ditto, Harper Collins (New York), 2003 ('special edition'; slipcase). . . . . £60/£30
The Reptile Room, Harper Collins (New York), 1999 (laminated pictorial covers; no d/w) £20
ditto, Egmont (London), 2001 (laminated pictorial covers; no d/w) £15
The Wide Window, Harper Collins (New York), 2000 (laminated pictorial covers; no d/w) £20
ditto, Egmont (London), 2001 (laminated pictorial covers; no d/w) £15
The Miserable Mill, Harper Collins (New York), 2000 (laminated pictorial covers; no d/w) £15
ditto, Egmont (London), 2002 (laminated pictorial covers; no d/w) £15
The Austere Academy, Harper Collins (New York), 2000 (laminated pictorial covers; no d/w) £10
ditto, Harper Collins (New York), 2000 (advance reading copy; pbk) £25
ditto, Egmont (London), 2001 (laminated pictorial covers with wraparound band; no d/w) . . . . £20/£5
The Ersatz Elevator, Harper Collins (New York), 2001 (laminated pictorial covers first state priced at $8.95; no d/w) £10
ditto, Egmont (London), 2002 (laminated pictorial covers with wraparound band; no d/w) . . . . £10/£5
The Vile Village, Harper Collins (New York), 2001 (laminated pictorial covers first state priced at $9.95; no d/w) £10
ditto, Egmont (London), 2002 (laminated pictorial covers with wraparound band; no d/w) . . . . £10/£5
The Hostile Hospital, Harper Collins (New York), 2001 (laminated pictorial covers first state priced at $9.95; no d/w) £10
ditto, Egmont (London), 2003 (laminated pictorial covers; no d/w) £5
ditto, Egmont (London), 2003 (with reversible d/w) £10/£5
The Carnivorous Carnival, Harper Collins (New York), 2002 (laminated pictorial covers first state priced at $10.99; no d/w) £5
ditto, Egmont (London), 2003 (laminated pictorial covers; no d/w) £5
The Slippery Slope, Harper Collins (New York), 2003 (laminated pictorial covers; no d/w) £5
ditto, Egmont (London), 2004 (laminated pictorial covers; no d/w) £5
The Grim Grotto, Harper Collins (New York), 2004 (laminated pictorial covers; no d/w) £5
ditto, Egmont (London), 2004 (laminated pictorial covers; no d/w) £5
The Penultimate Peril, Harper Collins (New York), 2005 (laminated pictorial covers; no d/w) £5
ditto, Egmont (London), 2005 (laminated pictorial covers; no d/w) £5
The End, Harper Collins (New York), 2006 (laminated pictorial covers; no d/w) £5

Other Fiction by Lemony Snicket
Baby in the Manger, Monotreme Press (Iowa, IA), 2002 (65 numbered copies, 'signed'/embossed/dated by author and signed by illustrator) £500
The Latke Who Couldn't Stop Screaming, McSweeney's Books (San Francisco, CA), 2007 . . . . £10/£5

The Lump of Coal, HarperCollins (New York), 2008 £10/£5
The Composer is Dead, HarperCollins (New York), 2009 .
   .   .   .   . £10/£5

Non-Fiction
The Unauthorized Autobiography, Harper Collins (New
   York), 2002 (with reversible d/w) .   .   . £10/£5
ditto, Egmont (London), 2002 (boards which open out like
   cupboard doors; with wraparound band) .   . £25/£10
Behind the Scenes with Count Olaf, Egmont (London),
   2004 (pbk) £5
The Beatrice Letters, Harper Collins (New York), 2006 .
   .   .   .   . £10/£5
ditto, Egmont (London), 2006 (laminated pictorial covers; no
   d/w) £5
Horseradish: Bitter Truths You Can't Avoid, HarperCollins
   (New York), 2007 £10/£5

Novels as Daniel Handler
The Basic Eight, St Martin's (New York), 1999 . £75/£15
ditto, St Martin's (New York), 1999 (advance reading copy;
   pbk) £60
ditto, Allison & Busby (London), 2000 (pbk) .   . £5
Watch Your Mouth, St Martin's (New York), 2000 £10/£5
ditto, Allison & Busby (London), 2001 (pbk) .   . £5
Adverbs, Ecco (New York), 2006 .   .   . £10/£5
ditto, Fourth Estate (London), 2006 .   .   . £10/£5

Chapbook as Daniel Handler
How to Dress for Every Occasion by the Pope,
   McSweeney's (San Francisco, CA), 2005 .   . £10/£5

C.P. SNOW
(b.1905 d.1980)

Snow possessed a Ph.D in Chemistry and wrote a number
of technical papers before beginning his sequence of
political novels entitled *Strangers and Brothers*. These depict contemporary intellectuals in academic life and government. He was awarded a C.B.E. in 1943, a knighthood in
1957 and a Life Peerage in 1964.

'Strangers and Brothers' Titles
Strangers and Brothers, Faber (London), 1940 (later re-
   titled *George Passant*) .   .   .   . £1,250/£250
ditto, Scribner's (New York), 1960 .   .   . £35/£10
The Light and the Dark, Faber (London), 1947 . £200/£35
ditto, Macmillan (New York), 1948 .   .   . £75/£15
Time of Hope, Faber (London), 1949 .   . £100/£20
ditto, Macmillan (New York), 1950 .   .   . £65/£15
The Masters, Macmillan (London), 1951 .   . £75/£10
ditto, Macmillan (New York), 1951 .   .   . £65/£15
The New Men, Macmillan (London), 1954 . £45/£15
ditto, Scribner's (New York), 1954 .   .   . £35/£10
Homecomings, Macmillan (London), 1956 . £35/£10
ditto, as *Homecoming*, Scribner's (New York), 1956 £30/£10
The Conscience of the Rich, Macmillan (London), 1958 .
   .   .   .   . £30/£10
ditto, Scribner's (New York), 1958 .   . . £25/£10
The Affair, Macmillan (London), 1960 .   . £20/£5
ditto, Scribner's (New York), 1960 .   .   . £15/£5
Corridors of Power, Macmillan (London), 1964 . £15/£5

ditto, Scribner's (New York), 1964 .   .   . £10/£5
The Sleep of Reason, Macmillan (London), 1968 . £15/£5
ditto, Scribner's (New York), 1969 .   .   . £10/£5
Last Things, Macmillan (London), 1970 .   . £10/£5
ditto, Scribner's (New York), 1970 .   .   . £10/£5
Strangers and Brothers, Macmillan (London), 1972
   (omnibus edition, 3 vols) .   .   .   .   . £35/£10
ditto, Scribner's (New York), 1972 (3 vols) . £35/£10

Other Novels
Death Under Sail, Heinemann (London), 1932 £1,000/£150
ditto, Scribner's (New York), 1959 .   .   . £350/£40
New Lives for Old, Gollancz (London), 1933 (anonymous) .
   .   .   .   . £350/£75
The Search, Gollancz (London), 1934 .   . £100/£20
ditto, Bobbs-Merrill (Indianapolis, IN), 1935 .   . £45/£10
The Malcontents, Macmillan (London), 1972 .   . £10/£5
ditto, Scribner's (New York), 1972 .   .   . £10/£5
In Their Wisdom, Macmillan (London), 1974 .   . £10/£5
ditto, Scribner's (New York), 1974 .   .   . £10/£5
A Coat of Varnish, Macmillan (London), 1979 . £10/£5
ditto, Scribner's (New York), 1979 .   .   . £10/£5
ditto, Franklin Library (Franklin Centre, PA), 1979 (signed,
   limited edition) £15

Others
Richard Aldington, Heinemann (London), [1938] (stapled
   wraps) £15
Two Cultures and the Scientific Revolution, C.U.P.
   (London), 1959 (wraps) £15
ditto, C.U.P. (New York), 1959 .   .   .   . £20/£5
Science and Government, Harvard Univ Press (Cambridge,
   MA), 1961 .   .   .   . £10/£5
Variety of Men, Macmillan (London), 1968 .   . £15/£5
ditto, Scribner's (New York), 1968 .   .   . £15/£5
The State of Siege, Scribner's (New York), 1969 . £10/£5
Public Affairs, Macmillan (London), 1971 .   . £10/£5
ditto, Scribner's (New York), 1971 .   .   . £10/£5
Trollope, Macmillan (London), 1975 .   .   . £15/£5
ditto, Scribner's (New York), 1975 .   .   . £10/£5
The Realists, Macmillan (London), 1978 .   . £10/£5
ditto, Scribner's (New York), 1978 .   .   . £10/£5
The Physicists, Macmillan (London), 1981 .   . £10/£5
ditto, Little, Brown (Boston), 1981 .   .   . £10/£5

ALEXANDER SOLZHENITSYN
(b.1918 d.2008)

Solzhenitsyn was exiled from the Soviet Union in 1974,
after many years of trouble with the authorities as a result
of his writings. *The Gulag Archipelago*, an exposé of the
Soviet labour camp system, brought about his last arrest,
and he was flown, against his will, to West Germany. He
finally returned to Russia in 1994. He won the Nobel Prize
for Literature in 1970.

Novels
One Day in the Life of Ivan Denisovich, Praeger (New
   York), 1963 .   .   .   . £100/£15
ditto, Gollancz (London), 1963 .   .   .   . £100/£15

ditto, Dutton (New York), 1963 . . . . £85/£15
We Never Make Mistakes: Two Short Novels, Univ of South
    Carolina Press (Columbia, SC), 1963 . . . £65/£15
ditto, Sphere (London), 1972 (pbk) £5
For the Good of the Cause, Praeger (New York), 1964 .
    . . . . £25/£10
ditto, Pall Mall Press (London), 1964. . . . £25/£10
The First Circle, Harper & Row (New York), 1968 £35/£10
ditto, Collins (London), 1968 . . . . £25/£10
Cancer Ward, Dial Press (New York), 1968 (1 vol) £35/£10
ditto, Bodley Head (London), 1968-1969 (2 vols) . £65/£20
August 1914, Bodley Head (London), 1972 . . £35/£10
ditto, Farrar Straus (New York), 1972 . . . £35/£10
The Gulag Archipelago, Harper (New York), 1974 £20/£5
ditto, Collins (London), 1974 . . . . . £20/£5
The Gulag Archipelago, 2, Harper (New York), 1975 £15/£5
ditto, Collins (London), 1975 . . . . . £15/£5
The Gulag Archipelago, 3, Harper (New York), 1976 .
    . . . . £15/£5
ditto, Collins (London), 1978 . . . . . £15/£5
November 1916: The Red Wheel/Knot II, Farrar Straus
    (New York), 1998 . . . . . . £10/£5
ditto, Cape (London), 1999 . . . . . £10/£5

Plays
The Love-Girl and the Innocent, Bodley Head (London),
    1969 . . . . £15/£5
ditto, Farrar Straus (New York), 1970 . . . £15/£5
Candle in the Wind, Univ of Minnesota (Minneapolis, MN),
    1973 . . . . £15/£5
ditto, Bodley Head/O.U.P. (London/Oxford), 1973 £15/£5
Victory Celebrations, Bodley Head (London), 1983 £10/£5
Prisoners, Bodley Head (London), 1983 . . . £10/£5
Three Plays, Farrar Straus (New York), 1986 (Contains:
    *Victory Celebrations, Prisoners, The Love Girl And The
    Innocent*) . . . . £10/£5

Others
Stories and Prose Poems, Bodley Head (London), 1971 .
    . . . . £15/£5
ditto, Farrar Straus (New York), 1971 . . . £15/£5
'One Word of Truth ...', Bodley Head (London), 1972
    (stapled wraps) £10
ditto, as ***A World Split Apart***, Harper (New York), 1979 .
    . . . . £10/£5
Letter to Soviet Leaders, Index on Censorship (London),
    1974 (wraps). £5
ditto, Harper (New York), 1974 . . . . £10/£5
From under the Rubble, Little, Brown (Boston), 1975 . .
    . . . . £10/£5
ditto, Collins (London), 1975 . . . . . £10/£5
Lenin in Zurich, Farrar Straus (New York), 1976 . £10/£5
ditto, Bodley Head (London), 1976 . . . . £10/£5
Warning to the Western World, Bodley Head/BBC
    (London), 1976 (stapled wraps) £10
ditto, as ***Speeches to the Americans***, Farrar Straus (New
    York), 1976 . . . . £10/£5
A World Split Apart, Harper (New York), 1978 . £15/£5
ditto, as ***Alexander Solzhenitsyn Speaks to the West***, Bodley
    Head (London), 1979 . . . . . £10/£5
The Mortal Danger, Bodley Head (London), 1980 £10/£5
ditto, Harper (New York), 1980 . . . . £10/£5
The Oak and the Calf, Harper (New York), 1980 . £10/£5
ditto, Bodley Head (London), 1980 . . . . £10/£5

The Russian Question at the End of the Twentieth Century,
    Farrar Straus Giroux (New York), 1995. . . £10/£5
ditto, HarperCollins (London), 1995 . . . . £10/£5

Poetry
Prussian Nights, Collins/Harvill (London), 1977 . £15/£5
ditto, Farrar Straus (New York), 1977 . . . £15/£5

MURIEL SPARK
(b.1918 d.2006)

A Scottish novelist, poet and short story writer, Spark's
first novel, *The Comforters*, was very well received. She
considered that joining the Catholic Church in 1954 was
crucial in her progress towards becoming a novel writer.
All of her books are written with elegance and detachment,
and are full of black humour and irony.

Novels
The Comforters, Macmillan (London), 1957 . . £400/£40
ditto, Lippincott (Philadelphia), 1957 . . . £125/£15
Robinson, Macmillan (London), 1958 . . . £125/£20
ditto, Lippincott (Philadelphia), 1958 . . . £75/£15
Memento Mori, Macmillan (London), 1959 . . £100/£20
ditto, Lippincott (Philadelphia), 1959 . . . £45/£10
The Ballad of Peckham Rye, Macmillan (London), 1960 .
    . . . . £75/£20
ditto, Lippincott (Philadelphia), 1960 . . . £30/£10
The Bachelors, Macmillan (London), 1960 . . £45/£15
ditto, Lippincott (Philadelphia), 1961 . . . £15/£5
The Prime of Miss Jean Brodie, Macmillan (London), 1961
    . . . . £100/£20
ditto, Lippincott (Philadelphia), 1962 . . . £75/£15
The Girls of Slender Means, Macmillan (London), 1963 .
    . . . . £45/£10
ditto, Knopf (New York), 1963 . . . . . £15/£5
The Mandelbaum Gate, Macmillan (London), 1965 £20/£5
ditto, Knopf (New York), 1965 . . . . . £15/£5
The Public Image, Macmillan (London), 1968 . £20/£5
ditto, Knopf (New York), 1968 . . . . . £15/£5
The Driver's Seat, Macmillan (London), 1970 . £20/£5
ditto, Knopf (New York), 1970 . . . . . £15/£5
Not to Disturb, Macmillan (London), 1971 . £20/£5
ditto, Observer Books (London), 1971 (500 signed copies,
    glassine d/w). . . . . . . £100/£75
ditto, Viking (New York), 1972 . . . . . £15/£5
The Hothouse by the East River, Macmillan (London), 1973
    . . . . £15/£5
ditto, Viking (New York), 1973 . . . . . £15/£5
The Abbess of Crewe: A Modern Morality Tale, Macmillan
    (London), 1974 . . . . . . £15/£5
ditto, Viking (New York), 1974 . . . . . £15/£5
The Takeover, Macmillan (London), 1976 . . £15/£5
ditto, Viking (New York), 1976 . . . . . £10/£5
Territorial Rights, Macmillan (London), 1979 . £10/£5
ditto, Coward-McCann (New York), 1979 . . £10/£5
Loitering With Intent, Bodley Head (London), 1981 £10/£5
ditto, Coward-McCann (New York), 1981 . . £10/£5
The Only Problem, Bodley Head (London), 1984 . £10/£5
ditto, Franklin Library (Franklin Centre, PA), 1984 (signed,
    limited edition) £15
ditto, Coward-McCann (New York), 1984 . . £10/£5

A Far Cry from Kensington, Constable (London), 1988 .
. . . . £10/£5
ditto, London Limited Editions (London), 1988 (150 signed,
numbered copies, glassine d/w) . . . £50/£40
ditto, Houghton Mifflin (Boston), 1988 . . £10/£5
Symposium, Constable (London), 1990 . . £10/£5
ditto, Houghton Mifflin (Boston), 1990 . . £10/£5
Reality and Dreams, Constable (London), 1996 . £10/£5
ditto, Houghton Mifflin (Boston), 1996 . . £10/£5
Aiding and Abetting, Viking (London), 2000 . . £10/£5
ditto, Doubleday (New York), 2001 . . . £10/£5
The Finishing School, Viking (London), 2004 . £10/£5
ditto, Doubleday (New York), 2004 . . . £10/£5

Omnibus Editions
The Muriel Spark Omnibus, Volume 1, Constable
(London), 1993 . . . . . . £10/£5
The Muriel Spark Omnibus, Volume 2, Constable
(London), 1994 . . . . . . £10/£5
The Muriel Spark Omnibus, Volume 3, Constable
(London), 1996 . . . . . . £10/£5
The Muriel Spark Omnibus, Volume 4, Constable
(London), 1997 . . . . . . £10/£5

Poetry
Out of a Book, Millar & Burden (Leith, Midlothian), [1933]
(broadside, pseud 'Muriel Camberg') . . . £750
The Fanfarlo, Hand & Flower Press (Ashford, Kent), 1952
(first issue; sewn wraps printed in red) . . . £35
ditto, Hand & Flower Press (Ashford, Kent), 1952 (second
issue; sewn wraps printed in blue) £25
Collected Poems I, Macmillan (London), 1967 . £25/£10
ditto, Knopf (New York), 1968 . . . . £25/£10
Going Up to Sotheby's and Other Poems, Granada
(London), 1982 (pbk) £10

Short Stories
The Go-Away Bird with Other Stories, Macmillan (London),
1958 . . . . £75/£20
ditto, as *The Go-Away Bird and Other Stories*, Lippincott
(Philadelphia), 1960 . . . . . £35/£10
The Seraph and the Zambesi, Lippincott (Philadelphia),
1960 (privately printed; wraps) £20
Collected Stories I, Macmillan (London), 1967 . £20/£5
ditto, Knopf (New York), 1968 . . . . £15/£5
Bang-Bang You're Dead and Other Stories, Granada
(London), 1982 (wraps) £5
The Stories of Muriel Spark, Dutton (New York), 1985 .
. . . . £10/£5
ditto, Bodley Head (London), 1987 . . . £10/£5
The Portobello Road and Other Stories, Eurographica
(Helsinki), 1990 (350 signed copies; wraps) . . . £50
Harper and Wilton, Colophon Press (London), 1996 (100
signed copies of 110) £75
ditto, Colophon Press (London), 1996 (10 roman numbered
copies for the author, signed, of 110) . . . £450
The Quest for Lavishes Ghast, Cuckoo Press (London),
1998 (sewn wraps) £10
*The Young Man Who Discovered the Secret of Life and
Other Stories*, Travelman (London), 1999 (pbk) . . £5

Children's Titles
The Very Fine Clock, Knopf (New York), 1968 (drawings
by Edward Gorey) . . . . . . £45/£20

ditto, Macmillan (London), 1969 . . . . £25/£10
The French Window & The Small Telephone, Colophon
Press (London), 1993 (105 signed, numbered copies,
glassine d/w) £75
ditto, Colophon Press (London), 1994 (112 signed, lettered
copies, leather, slipcase) £200

Plays
Voices at Play: Stories and Ear-Pieces, Macmillan
(London), 1961 . . . . . . £25/£5
ditto, Lippincott (Philadelphia), 1962 . . . £10/£5
Doctors of Philosophy, Macmillan (London), 1963 £25/£5
ditto, Knopf (New York), 1966 . . . . £10/£5

Others
Reassessment, Reassessment Pamphlet No.1 (London),
[1948] (single sheet, folded) £450
*Child of Light: A Reassessment of Mary Wollstonecraft
Shelley*, Tower Bridge (Hadleigh,Essex), 1951 . £100/£25
ditto, Folcroft Library Editions (Folcroft, PA), 1976 £20/£5
ditto, as *Mary Shelley*, Dutton (New York), 1987 (revised
edition) . . . . £10/£5
ditto, Constable (London), 1988 . . . . £10/£5
Emily Brontë: Her Life and Work, Owen (London), 1953
(with Derek Stanford) . . . . . . £65/£15
ditto, Coward-McCann (New York), 1966 . . £25/£5
John Masefield, Nevill (London), 1953 . . . £35/£10
ditto, Folcroft Library Editions (Folcroft, PA), 1977 £20/£5
The Essence of the Brontës: A Compilation with Essays,
Owen (London), 1993 . . . . . £15/£5

Autobiography
Curriculum Vitae: A Volume of Autobiography, Constable
(London), 1992 . . . . £10/£5
ditto, Houghton Mifflin (Boston), 1993 . . . £10/£5

STEPHEN SPENDER
(b.1909 d.1995)

Sir Stephen Harold Spender was an English poet and essayist whose concerns were often social injustice and the
class struggle. He began as a lyrical poet, but in later years
put more of his energies into his critical writings. Spender
was made a C.B.E. in 1962 and knighted in 1983.

Poetry
*Nine Experiments by S.H.S.: Being Poems Written at the
Age of Eighteen*, hand-printed by Spender (Frognal,
Hampstead), 1928 (approx 18 copies; wraps) . £25,000
ditto, Elliston Poetry (Cincinnati, OH), 1964 (facsimilie; 500
numbered copies; boards, no d/w) £35
Twenty Poems, Blackwell (Oxford), 1930 (75 signed copies
of 135; wraps) £350
ditto, Blackwell (Oxford), 1930 (55 unsigned copies of 135;
wraps) £125
Poems, Faber (London), 1933 . . . . £85/£20
ditto, Random House (New York), 1934 . . £75/£15
Vienna, Faber (London), 1934 . . . . £100/£15
ditto, Random House (New York), 1935 . . £65/£10
The Still Centre, Faber (London), 1939 . . £65/£10
Selected Poems, Faber (London), 1940 . . £30/£10
Ruins and Visions, Faber (London), 1942 . . £65/£15

ditto, Random House (New York), 1942 (includes poems from *The Still Centre*). . . . . £50/£10
Spiritual Exercises, Curwen Press (London), 1943 (125 copies; wraps) £150
Poems of Dedication, Faber (London), 1947 . £35/£10
ditto, Random House (New York), 1947 . . £20/£5
The Edge of Being, Faber (London), 1949 . £25/£10
ditto, Random House (New York), 1949 . . £20/£5
Sirmione Peninsula, Faber (London), 1954 (wraps) . £15
Collected Poems, 1928-1953, Faber (London), 1955 £25/£10
ditto, Random House (New York), 1955 . . £25/£10
Inscriptions, Poetry Book Society (London), 1958 (stapled wraps) £10
Selected Poems, Random House (New York), 1964 £10/£5
ditto, Faber (London), 1965 . . . . £10/£5
The Generous Days, Godine (Boston), 1969 (50 signed & numbered copies, no d/w) £100
ditto, Godine (Boston), 1969 (200 numbered copies, no d/w) £25
ditto, Faber (London), 1971 . . . . £20/£5
ditto, Random House (New York), 1971 . . £20/£5
Art Student, Poem-of-the-Month-Club (London), 1970 (single sheet) £20
Recent Poems, Anvil Press Poetry (London), 1978 (400 signed copies; stapled wraps) £40
Collected Poems, 1928-1985, Faber (London), 1985 £20/£5
Dolphins, Faber (London), 1994. . . . £15/£5
ditto, Faber (London), 1994 (150 signed copies) . £50
ditto, St Martin's Press (New York), 1994 . . £15/£5

Novels
The Backward Son, Hogarth Press (London), 1940 £125/£30
The Temple, Faber (London), 1988 . . . £15/£5
ditto, Grove Press (New York), 1988. . . £15/£5

Short Stories
The Burning Cactus, Faber (London), 1936 . £50/£15
ditto, Random House (New York), 1936 . . £45/£15
Engaged in Writing and The Fool and The Princess, Hamish Hamilton (London), 1958 . . £25/£5
ditto, Farrar Straus (New York), 1958 . . £25/£5

Plays
Trial of a Judge, Faber (London), 1938 . . £35/£10
ditto, Random House (New York), 1938 . . £30/£10
Danton's Death, Faber (London), 1939 (adaptation with Goronwy Rees) . . . . . £35/£10
Oedipus Trilogy, Faber (London), 1985 . . £10/£5
ditto, Random House (New York), 1985 . . £10/£5

Prose
The Destructive Element, Cape (London), 1935 . £125/£25
ditto, Houghton Mifflin (Boston), 1935 . . £100/£25
Forward from Liberalism, Gollancz (London), 1937 . . . . £50/£15
ditto, Left Book Club (London), 1937 (wraps). . £25
ditto, Random House (New York), 1937 . . £25/£10
The New Realism: A Discussion, Hogarth Press (London), 1939 (wraps). £25
Life and the Poet, Secker & Warburg (London), 1942 (wraps in d/w) . . . . . . £15/£5
Citizens in War - And After, Harrap (London), 1945 £40/£10
European Witness: Impressions of Germany in 1945, Hamish Hamilton (London), 1946 . . . £20/£5

ditto, Reynal & Hitchcock (New York), 1946 . . £20/£5
Poetry Since 1939, Longmans (London), 1946 (wraps). £10
Returning to Vienna 1947: Nine Sketches, Banyan Press (Pawlett, VT), 1947 (500 signed copies; wraps) . . £50
World Within World, Hamish Hamilton (London), 1951 . . . . £10/£5
ditto, Harcourt Brace (New York), 1951 . . . £10/£5
Learning Laughter, A Study of Children in Israel, Weidenfeld & Nicolson (London), 1952 . . £15/£5
ditto, Harcourt Brace (New York), 1953 . . £15/£5
The Creative Element, Hamish Hamilton (London), 1953 . . . . £10/£5
ditto, British Book Center (New York), 1954 . £10/£5
The Making of a Poem, Hamish Hamilton (London), 1955 . . . . £15/£5
The Struggle of the Modern, Hamish Hamilton (London), 1963 . . . . . . £15/£5
ditto, Univ of California Press (Berkeley, CA), 1954 £15/£5
The Year of the Young Rebels, Weidenfeld & Nicolson (London), 1969 . . . £15/£5
ditto, Random House (New York), 1969 . . £10/£5
Love-Hate Relations: A Study of Anglo-American Sensibilities, Hamish Hamilton (London), 1974 . £10/£5
ditto, Random House (New York), 1974 . . £10/£5
T.S. Eliot, Fontana (London), 1975 (wraps) . . £5
ditto, Viking (New York), 1976 . . . . £15/£5
The Thirties and After: Poetry, Politics and People, 1933-75, Fontana (London), 1975 (wraps) . . . £5
ditto, Random House (New York), 1978 . . £10/£5
Henry Moore Sculptures in Landscape, Studio Vista (London), 1978 (illustrated by Geoffrey Shakerley) . . . . £25/£10
Letters to Christopher, Black Sparrow Press (Santa Barbara, CA), 1980 (wraps) £15
ditto, Black Sparrow Press (Santa Barbara, CA), 1980 (1,000 copies, glassine d/w) . . . . . £25/£20
ditto, Black Sparrow Press (Santa Barbara, CA), 1980 (200 numbered, signed copies) £25
ditto, Black Sparrow Press (Santa Barbara, CA), 1980 (50 hand-bound, numbered and signed copies, slipcase) . . . . £75/£45
China Diary, Thames & Hudson (London), 1982 . £10/£5
ditto, Abrams (New York), 1982. . . . £10/£5
Journals, 1939-83, Faber (London), 1985 . £10/£5
ditto, Faber (London), 1985 (150 signed copies, no d/w, slipcase). . . . . . £45/£35
ditto, Random House (New York), 1986 . . £10/£5
ditto, Franklin Library (Franklin Centre, PA), 1985 (signed, limited edition) £15

Others
W.H. Auden, A Memorial Address Delivered at Christ Church Cathedral, Oxford on 27 October, 1973, Faber (London), 1975 (wraps) £45
W.H. Auden, A Tribute, Weidenfeld & Nicolson (London), 1975 . . . . £15/£5
ditto, Macmillan (New York), 1975 . . . £10/£5

MICKEY SPILLANE
(b.1918 d.2006)

Spillane was an influential post-World War Two American mystery writer. His first novel *I, the Jury*, featured his detective Mike Hammer and began a series which, although tame by current standards, contained more sex and violence than its competitors. Literary critics did not like Spillane's work but at one point in America he had seven titles in a list of the top ten best-selling books of the 20th century.

Novels

I, The Jury, Dutton (New York), 1947 . . £1,250/£150
ditto, Barker (London), 1952 . . . . £500/£35
My Gun Is Quick, Dutton (New York), 1950 . £750/£75
ditto, Barker (London), 1951 . . . . £250/£20
Vengeance Is Mine, Dutton (New York), 1950 . £650/£35
ditto, Barker (London), 1951 . . . . £150/£20
One Lonely Night, Dutton (New York), 1951 . £750/£35
ditto, Barker (London), 1952 . . . . £100/£15
The Big Kill, Dutton (New York), 1951 . . £600/£35
ditto, Barker (London), 1952 . . . . £100/£15
The Long Wait, Dutton (New York), 1951 . £450/£30
ditto, Barker (London), 1953 . . . . £100/£15
Kiss Me, Deadly, Dutton (New York), 1952 . £350/£30
ditto, Barker (London), 1953 . . . . £100/£15
The Deep, Dutton (New York), 1961 . . . £40/£10
ditto, Barker (London), 1961 . . . . £30/£10
The Girl Hunters, Dutton (New York), 1962 . £35/£10
ditto, Barker (London), 1962 . . . . £30/£10
The Snake, Dutton (New York), 1964 . . £25/£10
ditto, Barker (London), 1964 . . . . £25/£10
The Day of the Guns, Dutton (New York), 1964 . £25/£10
ditto, Barker (London), 1965 . . . . £25/£10
Bloody Sunrise, Dutton (New York), 1965 . £25/£10
ditto, Barker (London), 1965 . . . . £25/£10
The Death Dealers, Dutton (New York), 1965 . £25/£10
ditto, Barker (London), 1966 . . . . £25/£10
The Twisted Thing, Dutton (New York), 1966 . £25/£10
ditto, Barker (London), 1966 . . . . £25/£10
The By-Pass Control, Dutton (New York), 1966 . £25/£10
ditto, Barker (London), 1967 . . . . £25/£10
The Body Lovers, Dutton (New York), 1967 . £25/£10
ditto, Barker (London), 1967 . . . . £25/£10
The Delta Factor, Dutton (New York), 1969 . £25/£10
ditto, Corgi (London), 1969 (pbk) £5
Survival . . . Zero!, Dutton (New York), 1970 . £25/£10
ditto, Corgi (London), 1970 (pbk) £5
The Erection Set, Dutton (New York), 1972 . £25/£10
ditto, Allen (London), 1972 . . . . £25/£10
The Last Cop Out, Dutton (New York), 1973 . £20/£5
ditto, Allen (London), 1973 . . . . £20/£5
The Killing Man, Dutton (New York), 1989 . £15/£5
ditto, Heinemann (London), 1990 . . . £15/£5
Black Alley, Dutton (New York), 1996 . . £10/£5
Something's Down There, Simon & Schuster (New York),
2003 . . . . £10/£5
ditto, Hale (London), 2004 . . . . £10/£5

Short Stories/Novellas

Me, Hood!, Corgi (London), 1963 (pbk) . . . £5
ditto, Signet (New York), 1969 (pbk). . . . £5
Return of the Hood, Corgi (London), 1964 (pbk) . £5

The Flier, Corgi (London), 1964 (pbk) £5
Killer Mine, Corgi (London), 1965 (pbk) . . . £5
ditto, Signet (New York), 1968 (pbk). . . . £5
The Tough Guys, Signet (New York), 1969 . . £5
Vintage Spillane, Allen (London), 1974 . . . £20/£5
Tomorrow I Die, Mysterious Press (New York), 1984 £10/£5
ditto, Mysterious Press (New York), 1984 (250 signed,
numbered copies, slipcase) . . . . £65/£45
ditto, Mysterious Press (New York), 1984 (26 signed,
lettered copies, slipcase) . . . . . £100/£65
*Together We Kill: The Uncollected Stories of Mickey
Spillane*, Five Star (New York), 2001 . . £15/£5
Primal Spillane, Gryphon Books (New York), 2003 (pbk) £5
Byline, Crippen & Landru, 2005 (250 signed, numbered
copies) . . . . £35/£20
ditto, Crippen & Landru, 2005 (pbk) £5

Children's Titles

The Day the Sea Rolled Back, Dutton (New York), 1979 .
. . . . £20/£5
ditto, Methuen (London), 1980 . . . . £15/£5
The Ship That Never Was, Bantam (New York), 1982 (pbk)
. . . . £5

GERTRUDE STEIN
(b.1874 d.1946)

Although American by birth Stein, writer, poet, feminist, playwright and catalyst in the development of modern art and literature, lived in France from 1903. Her life-long companion was Alice B. Toklas, and in 1932 she wrote *The Autobiography of Alice B. Toklas* which, despite the title, was about Stein's own life. The book was similar in style to *The Alice B. Toklas Cookbook*, which was, confusingly, written by Alice herself.

Fiction

*Three Lives: Stories of the Good Anna, Melanctha, and the
Gentle Lena*, The Grafton Press (New York), 1909 . £750
ditto, John Lane (New York), 1909 (300 copies with sheets
from the above edition) £600
ditto, Bodley Head (London), 1920 . . . £250/£40
*The Making of Americans, Being a History of a Family's
Progress*, Contact Editions/The Three Mountains Press
(Paris), [1925] (400 of 500 copies; wraps) . . £2,000
ditto, Boni (New York), 1925 (100 of 500 copies, no d/w) .
. . . . £2,000
ditto, Contact Editions/The Three Mountains Press (Paris),
[1925] (5 copies on vellum with a letter by Stein) £2,000
ditto, Peter Owen (London), 1968 . . . £75/£25
*A Book Concluding with As a Wife Has a Cow: A Love
Story*, Éditions de la Galerie Simon (Paris), 1926 (with
lithographs by Juan Gris; 102 numbered copies signed by
author and artist; wraps with glassine d/w) .£2,000/£1,500
ditto, Éditions de la Galerie Simon (Paris), 1926 (10
numbered copies on Japanese vellum signed by author and
artist; wraps). £10,000
ditto, Something Else Press, West Glover (VT), 1973 (sewn
warps) £20
Lucy Church Amiably, Imprimerie Union (Paris), 1930
(plain d/w) . . . . £300/£175
ditto, Something Else Press (New York), 1969 . £25/£10

Ida: A Novel, Random House (New York), 1941 . £100/£25
Brewsie and Willie, Random House (New York), 1946 .
. . . . £40/£10
Blood on the Dining Room Floor, Banyan Press (Pawlet, VT), 1948 (26 lettered copies, glassine d/w and slipcase) .
. . . . £300/£250
ditto, Banyan Press (Pawlet, VT), 1948 (600 numbered copies, glassine d/w and slipcase) . £150/£125
Things as They Are: A Novel in Three Parts, Banyan Press (Pawlet, VT), 1950 (26 lettered copies, glassine d/w). .
. . . . £300/£250
ditto, Banyan Press (Pawlet, VT), 1950 (490 numbered copies, glassine d/w) . . . . £175/£150
Mrs. Reynolds, and Five Early Novelettes, Yale Univ Press (New Haven, CT), 1952 (volume two of the unpublished works of Gertrude Stein) . . . . £25/£10
A Novel of Thank You, Yale Univ Press (New Haven, CT), 1958 (volume eight of the unpublished works of Gertrude Stein) . . . . £25/£10

Plays

Geography and Plays, Four Seas (Boston), 1922 (first binding with lettering on front cover) . . £350/£200
ditto, Four Seas (Boston), 1922 (second binding without lettering on front cover) . . £300/£150
A Village: Are You Ready Yet Not Yet, Éditions de la Galerie Simon (Paris), 1928 (with lithographs by Elie Lascaux; 90 numbered copies signed by author and artist; wraps) £1,250
ditto, Éditions de la Galerie Simon (Paris), 1928 (10 roman numbered signed copies; wraps) . . . £1,500
ditto, Éditions de la Galerie Simon (Paris), 1928 (10 numbered copies on Japanese vellum signed by author and artist) £2,000
Operas and Plays, Plain Edition (Paris), 1932 (wraps, slipcase). . . . . . . £350/£250
Four Saints in Three Acts, Random House (New York), 1934 (music by Virgil Thomson) . . . £75/£20
A Wedding Bouquet: Ballet, J. & W. Chester, Ltd (London), 1936 (music by Lord Berners; wraps) . . . £150
In Savoy, or 'Yes' Is for Yes for a Very Young Man, Pushkin Press (London), 1946 (wraps, in d/w) . £40/£25
The Mother of Us All, Music Press (New York), 1947 (music by Virgil Thomson; wraps) £75
ditto, Music Press (New York), 1947 (55 numbered copies signed by Thomson, bound in cloth) . . . £300
Last Operas and Plays, Rinehart (New York), 1949 £45/£10
In a Garden: An Opera in One Act, Mercury Music Corporation (New York), 1951 (music by Meyer Kupferman; wraps) £15
Selected Operas and Plays of Gertrude Stein, Univ. of Pittsburgh Press (Pittsburgh, PA), 1970 . . . £25/£10

Poetry and Prose Poems

Tender Buttons: Objects, Food, Rooms, Claire Marie (New York), 1914 . . . . £600
Have They Attacked Mary. He Giggled, Temple (West Chester, PA), 1917 (200 numbered copies, red stapled wraps) £750
Before the Flowers of Friendship Faded Friendship Faded, Plain Edition (Paris), 1931 (120 signed, numbered copies; wraps, glassine d/w) £1,000
Two (Hitherto Unpublished) Poems, Banyan Press/Gotham Book Mart (New York), 1948 (205 numbered copies; stitched blue wraps, printed in black & red) . . £65

Stanzas in Meditation and Other Poems (1929-1933), Yale Univ Press (New Haven, CT), 1956 (volume six of the unpublished works of Gertude Stein) . . . £60/£20

Other Titles

Portrait of Mabel Dodge, Galileiana (Florence), 1912 (300 copies; floral Florentine wallpaper wraps with printed label on the front cover) £1,000
Composition as Explanation, Hogarth Press (London), 1926 (green boards, no d/w) £125
An Elucidation, Transition (Paris), 1927 (stapled wraps) .
. . . . £125
Useful Knowledge, Payson & Clarke (New York), 1928 .
. . . . £250/£30
ditto, John Lane/Bodley Head (London), 1929 . £200/£30
An Acquaintance with Description, Seizin Press (London), 1929 (225 signed copies, glassine d/w) . . £750/£675
Dix Portraits, Éditions de la Montagne (Paris), [1930] (illustrated by Picasso and others, 10 signed, numbered copies, japanese vellum, autograph page of text by Stein, glassine d/w). £2,500
ditto, Éditions de la Montagne (Paris), [1930] (25 signed, numbered copies, glassine d/w) . . £1,500/£1,250
ditto, Éditions de la Montagne (Paris), [1930] (65 signed, numbered copies; wraps with d/w). . £1,000/£750
ditto, Éditions de la Montagne (Paris), [1930] (402 signed, numbered copies; wraps with glassine d/w) . £150/£125
How to Write, Plain Edition (Paris), 1931 (boards, no d/w) .
. . . . £125
ditto, Something Else Press, West Glover (VT), 1973 £20/£5
The Autobiography of Alice B. Toklas, Harcourt Brace (New York), 1933 . . . . . . £300/£30
ditto, Bodley Head (London), 1933 . . . . £200/£30
Matisse, Picasso, and Gertrude Stein, with Two Shorter Stories, Plain Edition (Paris), 1933 (wraps with glassine d/w and slipcase). . . . . . £275/£225
ditto, Something Else Press, West Glover (VT), 1972 £20/£5
Portraits and Prayers, Random House (New York), 1934 (cellophane d/w) . . . . . . £200/£150
Lectures in America, Random House (New York), 1935 (top edge stained grey, with frontispiece) . . £250/£65
ditto, Random House (New York), 1935 (top unstained, no frontispiece) . . . . £200/£15
Narration: Four Lectures, Univ of Chicago Press (Chicago), 1935 (introduction by Thornton Wilder) . £200/£45
ditto, Univ of Chicago Press (Chicago), 1935 (120 numbered copies signed by Stein and Wilder; slipcase). £650/£500
The Geographical History of America, or, The Relation of Human Nature to the Human Mind, Random House (New York), 1936 . . . . £1,000/£250
Everybody's Autobiography, Random House (New York), 1937 . . . . £150/£25
ditto, Heinemann (London), 1938 . . . £100/£15
Picasso, Librairie Floury (Paris), 1938 (text in French; wraps) £150
ditto, Batsford (London), 1938 (translated by Alice B. Toklas) . . . . £100/£25
ditto, Scribner's (New York), 1939 . . . £75/£20
The World Is Round, Willam R. Scott (New York), 1939 (juvenile; illustrated by Clement Hurd) . . £150/£35
ditto, Willam R. Scott (New York), 1939 (350 signed copies, slipcase). . . . . . . £600/£450
ditto, Batsford (London), 1939 . . . . £100/£25
Paris France, Scribner's (New York), 1940 . . £100/£25

ditto, Batsford (London), 1940 . . . . £75/£20

What Are Masterpieces?, Conference Press (Los Angeles, CA), 1940 . . . . . . £100/£25

ditto, Conference Press (Los Angeles, CA), 1940 (50 signed, numbered copies) . . . . . £650/£450

Wars I Have Seen, Random House (New York), 1945 . . . . £35/£10

ditto, Batsford (London), 1945 . . . £25/£10

The Gertrude Stein First Reader, and Three Plays, Fridberg (Dublin/London), 1946 . . . . . £30/£10

ditto, Houghton Mifflin (Boston), 1948 . . £30/£10

Selected Writings of Gertude Stein, Random House (New York), 1946 . . . . £25/£10

Four in America, Yale Univ Press (New Haven, CT), 1947 . . . . £45/£15

Literally True, Peter Holland et al. (Tujunga, CA), 1947 (folded leaflet) £50

Two: Gertrude Stein and Her Brother and Other Early Portraits (1908-1912), Yale Univ Press (New Haven, CT), 1951 (volume one of the unpublished works of Gertude Stein) . . . . £45/£15

Bee Time Vine and Other Pieces (1913-1927), Yale Univ Press (New Haven, CT), 1953 (volume three of the unpublished works of Gertrude Stein) . . £45/£15

As Fine as Melanctha (1914-1930), Yale Univ Press (New Haven, CT), 1954 (volume four of the unpublished works of Gertrude Stein) . . . . . £45/£15

Painted Lace and Other Pieces (1914-1937), Yale Univ Press (New Haven, CT), 1955 (volume five of the unpublished works of Gertrude Stein) . . £45/£15

To Bobchen Haas, Warren Press (Bethel, CT), 1956 (second state after suppression of first state, folded card) . . £25

Alphabets and Birthdays, Yale Univ Press (New Haven, CT), 1957 (volume seven of the unpublished works of Gertude Stein) . . . . . . £45/£15

On Our Way, Simon & Schuster (New York), 1959 (written by Stein & Alice B. Toklas; 100 numbered copies; wraps) £40

Gertrude Stein's America, Robert B. Luce (Washington, D.C.), 1965 . . . . . . £10/£5

Look at Me Now and Here I Am; Gertrude Stein: Writings and Lectures 1911-1945, Peter Owen (London), 1967 . . . . £45/£15

Motor Automatism, Phoenix Book Shop (New York), 1969 (with Leon M. Solomons; 500 copies; wraps) . . £15

Gertrude Stein on Picasso, Liveright (New York), 1970 . . . . £25/£10

A Primer for the Gradual Understanding of Stein, Black Sparrow Press (Santa Barbara, CA), 1971 (60 copies, slipcase). . . . . £75/£45

ditto, Black Sparrow Press (Santa Barbara, CA), 1971 (500 copies) . . . . £40/£25

Fernhurst, Q.E.D., and Other Early Writings, Boni & Liveright (New York), 1971 . . . . £25/£10

ditto, Peter Owen (London), 1972 . . . £25/£10

Sherwood Anderson/Gertrude Stein: Correspondence and Personal Essays, Univ of North Carolina Press (Chapel Hill, NC), 1972 . . . . . . £25/£10

Why Are There Whites to Console: A Portrait of Janet, Aloe Editions (n.p. [New York]), 1973 (26 lettered copies; sewn wraps) £100

ditto, Aloe Editions (n.p. [New York]), 1973 (74 numbered copies; sewn wraps) £75

Reflections on the Atomic Bomb, Black Sparrow Press (Santa Barbara, CA), 1973 (volume one of the previously uncollected writings of Gertrude Stein; 50 copies, with a copy of *Literally True*) . . . . . £75/£45

ditto, Black Sparrow Press (Santa Barbara, CA), 1973 (750 copies) . . . . £40/£25

ditto, Black Sparrow Press (Santa Barbara, CA), 1973 (pbk) £10

How Writing is Written, Black Sparrow Press (Santa Barbara, CA), 1974 (volume two of the previously uncollected writings of Gertrude Stein; 50 copies, with a copy of *Very Well I Thank You*) . . . £75/£45

ditto, Black Sparrow Press (Santa Barbara, CA), 1974 (750 copies) . . . . £40/£25

ditto, Black Sparrow Press (Santa Barbara, CA), 1974 (pbk) £10

Dear Sammy: Letters from Stein and Alice B. Toklas, Houghton Mifflin (Boston), 1977 . . . £25/£10

JOHN STEINBECK
(b.1902 d.1968)

The Grapes of Wrath is probably Steinbeck's best known work, and was later made into a classic film. He wrote in a naturalistic style, usually about the poor and working-class, but his books also reflect a wide range of interests, including marine biology, jazz, politics, philosophy, history, and myth. He was awarded the Nobel Prize for Literature in 1962.

Novels

Cup of Gold: A Life of Henry Morgan, Buccaneer, McBride (New York), 1929 (first issue, top edges stained blue and 'First published August, 1929' on copyright page) . . . . £12,500/£900

ditto, Covici Friede (New York), 1929 (second issue, using McBride sheets, maroon cloth). . . . £1,000/£100

ditto, Covici Friede (New York), 1936 (blue cloth) . . . . £250/£35

ditto, Heinemann (London), 1937 . . £1,000/£100

The Pastures of Heaven, Brewer (New York), 1932 (first issue with Brewer/Warren/Putnam on spine and bottom edges rough cut) . . . . £5,000/£500

ditto, Allan (London), 1933 . . . . £1,000/£100

To a God Unknown, Robert O. Ballou (New York), 1933 . . . . £3,500/£500

ditto, Heinemann (London), 1935 . . . £750/£150

Tortilla Flat, Covici Friede (New York), 1935 £4,000/£300

ditto, Covici Friede (New York), 1935 (500 advance review copies in pbk) £1,000

ditto, Heinemann (London), 1935 . . £1,000/£125

In Dubious Battle, Covici Friede (New York), 1936 . . . . £2,000/£150

ditto, Covici Friede (New York), 1936 (99 signed, numbered copies, tissue d/w and black slipcase) . £5,000/£4,000

ditto, Heinemann (London), 1936 . . . £650/£75

Of Mice and Men, Covici Friede (New York), 1937 (first state with line ending 'pendula' on page 9 and a dot between the numbers on page 88) . . £1,500/£500

ditto, Covici Friede (New York), 1937 (second state with line ending 'loosely' on page 9 and no dot between the numbers on page 88) . . . . . . £1,000/£150 *ditto*, Heinemann (London), 1937 . . . £1,000/£45

The Grapes of Wrath, Viking (New York), 1939 (first issue d/w with 'First Edition' at the foot of front flap) . . .

. . . . £2,250/£200

ditto, Heinemann (London), 1939 . . . . £500/£35

The Moon is Down, Viking (New York), 1942 (first state with large dot between 'talk' and 'this' on p.112, line 11) .

. . . . £175/£45

ditto, Viking (New York), 1942 (second state with large dot removed) . . . . £145/£15

ditto, Heinemann (London), 1942 . . . . £150/£20

Cannery Row, Viking (New York), 1945 (first issue, buff cloth) . . . . £1,000/£125

ditto, Viking (New York), 1945 (second issue, yellow cloth)

. . . . £750/£75

ditto, Heinemann (London), 1945 . . . . £225/£30

The Wayward Bus, Viking (New York), 1947 . £165/£25

ditto, Heinemann (London), 1947 . . . . £100/£15

The Pearl, Viking (New York), 1947 (first issue d/w with Steinbeck looking to his left) . . . . £200/£20

ditto, Heinemann (London), 1948 . . . . £75/£10

Burning Bright, Viking (New York), 1950 . £100/£15

ditto, Heinemann (London), 1951 . . . £35/£10

East of Eden, Viking (New York), 1952 (1st issue with 'bite' for 'bight' on p.281, line 38; 1st state dj with author's photo on rear panel and no reviews) . . . £650/£75

ditto, Viking (New York), 1952 (1,500 signed, numbered copies) . . . . £1,250/£850

ditto, Heinemann (London), 1952 . . . . £150/£25

Sweet Thursday, Viking (New York), 1954 . £125/£20

ditto, Heinemann (London), 1954 . . . . £75/£10

The Short Reign of Pippin IV: A Fabrication, Viking (New York), 1957 . . . . £75/£10

ditto, Heinemann (London), 1957 . . . . £35/£10

The Winter of Our Discontent, Viking (New York), 1961 .

. . . . £50/£10

ditto, Viking (New York), 1961 (500 copies, printed cellophane d/w) . . . . . . £400/£350

ditto, Heinemann (London), 1961 . . . . £30/£5

Short Stories

Saint Katy the Virgin, Covici Friede (New York), 1936 (199 signed, numbered copies, glassine d/w) . £1,750/£1,350

The Red Pony, Covici Friede (New York), 1937 (699 signed copies, glassine d/w, slipcase) . . . £1,500/£1,250

ditto, Covici Friede (New York), 1937 (26 signed, lettered copies, glassine d/w, slipcase) . . . £3,000/£2,500

ditto, Viking (New York), 1945 (enlarged edition, slipcase, no d/w) . . . . £150/£125

The Long Valley, Viking (New York), 1938 . £325/£100

ditto, Heinemann (London), 1939 . . . . £200/£30

How Edith McGillcuddy Met R.L.S., Rowfant Club (Cleveland, OH), 1943 (152 copies) . .£1,500/£1,000

Plays

Of Mice and Men: A Play in Three Acts, Covici Friede (New York), 1937 . . . . . . £650/£65

The Moon is Down: A Play in Two Parts, Dramatists Play Service (New York), 1942 (wraps) £225

ditto, English Theatre Guild (London), 1943 . . £100

Burning Bright, Dramatists Play Service (New York), 1951 (wraps) £100

Screenplays

The Forgotten Village, Viking (New York), 1941 . £75/£20

Viva Zapata!, Edizioni Filmcritica (Italy), 1952 . . £45

ditto, Viking (New York), 1975 (pbk) £25

ditto, as **Zapata: The Little Tiger**, Heinemann (London), 1991 . . . . £35/£10

Others

Sea of Cortez: A Leisurely Journal of Travel and Research, Viking (New York), 1941 (with Edward F. Ricketts) .

. . . .£600/£65

ditto, Viking (New York), 1941 (advance proof copy; pbk) .

. . . . £1,000

ditto, as **The Log from the Sea of Cortez**, Viking (New York), 1951 . . . .£200/£20

ditto, as **The Log from the Sea of Cortez**, Heinemann (London), 1958 . . . .£125/£20

Bombs Away: The Story of a Bomber Team, Viking (New York), 1942 (photographs by John Swope) . .£200/£25

A Russian Journal, Viking (New York), 1948 (photographs by Robert Capa) . . . . £75/£20

ditto, Heinemann (London), 1949 . . . . £50/£15

Once There Was a War, Viking (New York), 1958 £75/£20

ditto, Heinemann (London), 1959 . . . . £50/£15

Travels With Charley in Search of America, Viking (New York), 1962 . . . . £50/£15

ditto, Heinemann (London), 1962 . . . . £40/£10

Speech Accepting the Nobel Prize for Literature, Viking (New York), 1962 (wraps with d/w) . . £150/£100

America and Americans, Viking (New York), 1966 (first binding, with lettering running down the spine) . £40/£10

ditto, Heinemann (London), 1966 . . . £35/£10

Journal of a Novel: The 'East of Eden' Letters, Viking (New York), 1969 . . . . £25/£10

ditto, Viking (New York), 1969 (600 copies, glassine d/w and slipcase). . . . . . . £150/£125

ditto, Heinemann (London), 1970 . . . . £25/£10

Steinbeck: A Life in Letters, Viking (New York), 1975 .

. . . . £20/£5

ditto, Viking (New York), 1975 (1,000 numbered copies, slipcase, no d/w) . . . . . . £40/£30

ditto, Heinemann (London), 1975 . . . . £20/£5

The Acts of King Arthur and His Noble Knights, Farrar Straus (New York), 1976 . . . . . £20/£5

ditto, Heinemann (London), 1977 . . . . £20/£5

Working Days: The Journal of 'The Grapes of Wrath', Viking (New York), 1988 . . . . . £20/£5

Zapata: A narrative, in dramatic form, of the life of Emiliano Zapata, Yolla Bolly Press (Covelo, CA), 1991 (190 numbered copies signed by the artist, slipcase) .

. . . . £400/£300

ditto, Yolla Bolly Press (Covelo, CA), 1991 (40 signed deluxe copies signed by the artist, with *Zapata The Man, The Myth, and The Mexican Revolution*, signed) . £1,000

COUNT ERIC STENBOCK
(b.1860 d.1895)

Stenbock attended Balliol College, Oxford, succeeding to his title and inheriting the family estates in Estonia in 1885. After travelling there he returned to England in the summer of 1887, and descended into alcoholism and drug addiction. He was the most self-conscious of the 1890s decadents, impressing his contemporaries by his personality and wealth rather than his morbidly sensitive and self-financed poetry and prose.

Poetry

Love, Sleep and Dreams, Shrimpton & Son/Simpkin Marshall & Co. (London), 1881[?] . . . £1,000
ditto, Hermitage Books (Harleston, Norfolk), 1992 (60 numbered copies; wraps) £60
Myrtle, Rue and Cypress, privately printed by Hatchards (London), 1883 . . . . . . £1,000
ditto, Hermitage Books (Harleston, Norfolk), 1992 (60 numbered copies) £100
The Shadow of Death, The Leadenhall Press (London), 1893 . . . . £1,000
On the Freezing of the Baltic Sea, privately printed for Timothy d'Arch Smith (London), 1961 . . . £65
The Collected Poems of Eric, Count Stenbock, Durtro Press (London), 2001 (with 'Ballad of Creditors' tipped-in) £75

Short Stories

Studies of Death: Romantic Tales, David Nutt (London), 1894 . . . . £1,500
ditto, Durtro Press (London), 1996 [1997] (300 numbered copies) £150
The True Story of a Vampire, Tragara Press (Edinburgh), 1989 (110 numbered copies) £75
The Child of the Soul, Durtro Press (London), 1999 . £35
La Mazurka Des Revenants: A Serious Extravaganza In Six Parts, Durtro Press (London), 2002 (164 numbered copies; sewn wraps) £75
A Secret Kept, Durtro Press (London), 2002 (200 numbered copies; sewn wraps) £40
The King's Bastard or, The Triumph Of Evil, Durtro Press (London), 2004 (200 numbered copies; sewn wraps) . £25

Other

The Myth of Punch, Durtro Press (London), 1999 (120 numbered copies; sewn wraps). £75

LAURENCE STERNE
(b.1713 d.1768)

Sterne was an Anglo-Irish novelist and clergyman best known for *The Life and Opinions of Tristram Shandy, Gentleman*, and *A Sentimental Journey Through France and Italy*. His parishioners apparently saw little of him after he became a celebrity. He also published sermons and volumes of memoirs, and died in London after fighting tuberculosis for several years.

The Case of Elijah, Hilyard (York, UK), 1747 . . £450
The Abuses of Conscience, Ward (York, UK), 1750 . £450

A Political Romance (The History of a Good Warm Watchcoat), (York, UK), 1759. . . . £450
The Life and Opinions of Tristram Shandy, Gentleman, Ravanat & Dodsley ([York &]London), 1760-67 (9 vols) £8,000
The Sermons of Mr Yorick, Dodsley (London), [1760-69] (7 vols) £500
A Sentimental Journey Through France and Italy, Becket/Hondt (London), 1768 (pseud 'Mr Yorick', 2 vols) £1,000
ditto, Becket/Hondt (London), 1768 (350 large paper copies) £1,250
Letters from Mr Yorick to Eliza, Kearsley (London), 1775 . . . . £200
Letters to His Friends on Various Occasions, Johnson (London), 1775 . . . . £200
Letters to His Most Intimate Friends, Beckett (London), 1775 (3 vols) . . . . . . £350 the set

ROBERT LOUIS STEVENSON
(b.1850 d.1894)

Although he suffered from tuberculosis from childhood, Stevenson enjoyed a very full life. He studied engineering before turning to law, which he never practiced, but found his career in letters, becoming a novelist, essayist and poet. Many of Stevenson's romances have become classics of English literature, although novels such as *Treasure Island* and *Kidnapped* are often dismissed as children's fiction.

Fiction

New Arabian Nights, Chatto & Windus (London), 1882 (2 vols) £1,250
ditto, Holt (New York), 1882 . . . . . £200
Treasure Island, Cassell (London), 1883 (first issue with 'Dead Man's Chest' not capitalised on pp. 2 and 7; with 'rain' for 'vain' in the last line p.40; the 'a' not present in line 6, p.63; the '8' etc) . . . £4,500
ditto, Roberts Bros (Boston), 1884 . . . £1,000
Prince Otto, Chatto & Windus (London), 1885 . £200
ditto, Scribner's (New York), 1902 . . . . £100
The Dynamiter, More New Arabian Nights, Longmans Green & Co. (London), 1885 (with Fanny van de Grift Stevenson, boards) £250
ditto, Longmans Green & Co. (London), 1885 (with Fanny van de Grift Stevenson; wraps) . . . £275
ditto, Holt (New York), 1885 . . . . . £200
The Strange Case of Dr Jekyll and Mr Hyde, Scribner's (New York), 1886 (wraps). . . . £2,500
ditto, Scribner's (New York), 1886 (boards) . . £1,750
ditto, Longmans Green & Co. (London), 1886 (wraps, first issue with date on upper cover changed by hand to 1886) £3,250
ditto, Longmans Green & Co. (London), 1886 (boards). £2,000
Kidnapped, Cassell (London), 1886 (with folding frontispiece map, first issue with 'business' in line 11, p.40) £800
ditto, Cassell (London), 1886 (with folding frontispiece map, second issue with 'pleasure' in line 11, p.40) . £350

ditto, Scribner's (New York), 1886 (boards, with folding frontispiece map, 8 pages of ads) £450
ditto, Scribner's (New York), 1886 (wraps, no ads) . £300
The Merry Men and Other Tales, Chatto & Windus (London), 1887 . . . . £100
ditto, Scribner's (New York), 1887 . . . . . £100
The Black Arrow, Scribner's (New York), 1888 (wraps) .
. . . . £350
ditto, Scribner's (New York), 1888 (boards) . . . £200
ditto, Cassell (London), 1888 (wraps) . . . £250
ditto, Cassell (London), 1888 (boards) . . . £150
The Master of Ballantrae, Cassell (London), 1889 . £200
ditto, Scribner's (New York), 1889 (boards) . . £100
ditto, Scribner's (New York), 1889 (wraps) . . £175
The Wrong Box, Longmans Green & Co. (London), 1889 (with L. Osbourne) £75
ditto, Scribner's (New York), 1889 . . . . £75
The Wrecker, Cassell (London), 1892 (with L. Osbourne) .
. . . . £100
ditto, Scribner's (New York), 1892 . . . . £75
Three Plays, D. Nutt (London), 1892 (with W. Henley) £75
ditto, D. Nutt (London), 1892 (with W. Henley, 30 copies on Japanese vellum). £400
ditto, D. Nutt (London), 1892 (with W. Henley, 100 copies on Dutch handmade paper) £150
Catriona, Cassell (London), 1893 . . . . £125
ditto, as **David Balfour**, Scribner's (New York), 1893 . £100
Island Nights' Entertainments, Scribner's (New York), 1893 . . . . £125
ditto, Cassell (London), 1893 . . . . . £125
The Ebb-Tide, Stone & Kimball (Chicago), 1894 . . £45
ditto, Heinemann (London), 1894 (with L. Osbourne) . £45
Weir of Hermiston, Chatto & Windus (London), 1896 . £50
ditto, Scribner's (New York), 1896 . . . . . £45
St. Ives, Scribner's (New York), 1897 (with Quiller Couch)
. . . . £25
ditto, Heinemann (London), 1898 (with Quiller Couch) £25
The Suicide Club, Tartarus Press (Carlton-in-Coverdale, Yorkshire), 2004 . . . . £30/£10

Poetry
A Child's Garden of Verses, Longmans Green & Co. (London), 1885 . . . . £2,000
ditto, Scribner's (New York), 1885 . . . . . £650
Underwoods, Chatto & Windus (London), 1887 . £30
ditto, Chatto & Windus (London), 1887 (50 large paper copies) £150
ditto, Scribner's (New York), 1887 . . . . £30
Ballads, Scribner's (New York), 1890 . . . . £35
ditto, Chatto & Windus (London), 1890 . . . £35
Songs of Travel and Other Verses, Chatto & Windus (London), 1896 . . . . £30
Verses by R.L.S., privately printed, The De Vinne Press (New York), 1912 (100 presentation copies). . £300

Non-Fiction
The Pentland Rising, Elliot (Edinburgh), 1866 (anonymous; wraps) £2,500
The Charity Bazaar, privately printed [Edinburgh], 1868 (signed; wraps) £1,000
ditto, privately printed [Edinburgh], 1868 (unsigned; wraps)
. . . . £650
An Inland Voyage, Kegan Paul (London), 1878 . . £500
ditto, Roberts Bros (Boston), 1883 . . . . £225

Edinburgh: Picturesque Notes, Seeley & Co. (London), 1879 . . . . £125
Travels With a Donkey in the Cevennes, Kegan Paul (London), 1879 . . . . £400
ditto, Roberts Bros (Boston), 1879 . . . . £250
Virginibus Puerisque, Kegan Paul (London), 1881 . £75
ditto, Scribner's (New York), 1887 . . . . . £50
The Graver and the Pen, or Scenes from Nature with Appropriate Verses by ...., Osbourne & Co (Edinburgh), 1882 (wraps). £500
Familiar Studies of Men and Books, Chatto & Windus (London), 1882 . . . . £65
ditto, Chatto & Windus (London), 1882 (100 large paper copies) £125
ditto, Dodd Mead (New York), 1887. . . . . £45
ditto, Scribner's (New York), 1887 . . . . £45
The Silverado Squatters, Chatto & Windus (London), 1883 (first issue lacking 'his' on penultimate line, p.140) . £350
ditto, Roberts Bros (Boston), 1884 . . . . £200
Memories and Portraits, Chatto & Windus (London), 1887
. . . . £35
ditto, Scribner's (New York), 1887 . . . . £25
Memoir of Fleeming Jenkin, Scribner's (New York), 1887
. . . . £45
ditto, Longmans (London), 1912. . . . . £25
Father Damien, An Open Letter, privately printed (Sydney, Australia), 1890 (wraps, 25 copies). . . £1,500
ditto, privately printed (Edinburgh), 1890 (unbound sheets in portfolio, 30 copies) £750
ditto, Chatto & Windus (London), 1890 (wraps) . £75
In the South Seas, Cassell (London), 1890 (copyright edition) £1,000
ditto, Edinburgh Edition, 1896 (with 15 of 35 letters) . £75
ditto, Scribner's (New York), 1896 . . . . . £75
ditto, Chatto & Windus (London), 1900 . . . £35
Across the Plains, Chatto & Windus (London), 1892 . £65
ditto, Chatto & Windus (London), 1892 (100 large paper copies) £150
ditto, Scribner's (New York), 1892 . . . . £45
A Footnote to History, Cassell (London), 1892 . £40
ditto, Scribner's (New York), 1892 . . . . £35
Aes Triplex, privately printed, The De Vinne Press (New York), 1898 (160 copies) £300
ditto, as **Aes Triplex and Other Essays**, Mosher (Portland, ME), 1903 (wraps) £25
The Amateur Emigrant, Stone & Kimball (New York), 1895
. . . . £25
Vailima Letters, Methuen (London), 1895 . . £35
ditto, Methuen (London), 1895 (125 large paper copies) £75
ditto, Stone & Kimball (New York), 1895 (2 vols) £30 the set
Essays of Travel, Chatto & Windus (London), 1905 . £20
ditto, Scribner's (New York), 1905 . . . . . £20
Essays in the Art of Writing, Chatto & Windus (London), 1905 . . . . £20
ditto, Scribner's (New York), 1905 . . . . . £20
Lay Morals and Other Papers, Chatto & Windus (London), 1911 . . . . £20
ditto, Scribner's (New York), 1915 . . . . . £15
Records of a Family of Engineers, Chatto & Windus (London), 1912 . . . . £15

BRAM STOKER

(b.1847 d.1912)

Born and educated in Dublin, Abraham 'Bram' Stoker began his literary career as a journalist and drama critic. To supplement his income he wrote a number of novels of mystery and romance, the most famous of which was *Dracula*, the first Vampire novel. It has come to be regarded as one of the seminal works of the Horror genre.

Novels

The Snake's Pass, Harper (New York), 1890 (wraps) . £800
ditto, Sampson Low (London), 1891 [1890] . . . £500
The Watter's Mou', De Vinne & Co. (New York), 1894 .
. . . . £450
ditto, Constable (London), 1895 . . . . . £250
The Shoulder of Shasta, Constable (London), 1895 . £500
Dracula, Constable (London), 1897 (first issue with integral blank leaf at rear and no advertisement) . . £12,500
ditto, Constable (London), 1897 (second issue with eight-page catalogue beginning with an advert for *The Amazing Marriage* by George Meredith, ending with one for *The Whitehall Shakespeare*, and with no mention of *Dracula*) .
. . . . £7,500
ditto, Constable (London), 1897 (third issue with ad. for *Shoulder of Shasta* on p.392 [with/without extra 16-page catalogue]) £6,000
ditto, Doubleday & McClure (New York), 1899 . £4,000
Miss Betty, Pearson (London), 1898 . . . . £400
The Mystery of the Sea, Doubleday (New York), 1902. £300
ditto, Heinemann (London), 1902 . . . . . £300
The Jewel of Seven Stars, Heinemann (London), 1903. £400
ditto, Harper (New York), 1904 . . . . . . £200
The Man, Heinemann (London), 1905 . . . . £350
ditto, Century (New York), 1905 . . . not published
ditto, as *The Gates of Life*, Cupples & Leon (New York), 1908 (abridged by Stoker). £100
Lady Athlyne, Heinemann (London), 1908 . . £300
ditto, Reynolds (New York), 1908 . . . not published
ditto, Lovell (New York), 1909 . . . . . £600
The Lady of the Shroud, Rider (London), 1909 . . £250
The Lair of the White Worm, Rider (London), 1911 . £350
The Primrose Path and *Buried Treasures*, Desert Island Books (Westcliff-on-Sea), 2002 . . . . £15/£5

Short Stories

Under the Sunset, Sampson Low (London), 1882 [1881] .
. . . . £350
ditto, Newcastle (North Hollywood, CA), 1978 (pbk) . £5
Snowbound, Collier (London), 1908 (wraps) . . . £100
Dracula's Guest and Other Weird Stories, Routledge (London), 1914 . . . . £400
ditto, Hillman-Curl (New York), 1937 . . £2,000/£200
Shades of Dracula: Bram Stoker's Uncollected Stories, William Kimber (London), 1982 . . . . £25/£10
The Dualitists, Tragara Press (Edinburgh), 1986 (wraps) £45

Others

The Duties of the Clerks of Petty Sessions in Ireland, John Falconer (Dublin, Ireland), 1879 . . . . £225
A Glimpse of America, Sampson Low (London), 1886 (wraps) £75
Personal Reminiscences of Henry Irving, Heinemann (London), 1906 (two vols). £50

ditto, Macmillan (New York), 1906 . . . . . £40
Famous Impostors, Sidgwick and Jackson (London), 1910.
. . . . £75
ditto, Sturgis & Walton (New York), 1910 . . . £75
Dracula, or The Un-Dead, Pumpkin Books (Nottingham, UK), 1997 (Stoker's original playscript) . . £15/£5
ditto, Pumpkin Books (Nottingham, UK), 1997 (250 numbered copies signed by editor; slipcase) . . £25/£15
A Glimpse of America and Other Lectures, Interviews and Essays, Desert Island Books (Westcliff-on-Sea), 2002 (pbk) £15

ROBERT STONE

(b.1937)

Robert Stone is an American author whose work is critically well-regarded. His work is psychological complex, political, and darkly humorous.

A Hall of Mirrors, Houghton Mifflin (Boston), 1967 . .
. . . . £225/£45
ditto, Bodley Head (London), 1968 . . . £150/£25
Dog Soldiers, Houghton Mifflin (Boston), 1974 . £100/£15
ditto, Secker & Warburg (London), 1975 . . . £45/£10
A Flag for Sunrise, Knopf (New York), 1981. . £15/£5
ditto, Secker & Warburg (London), 1981 . . . £15/£5
Children of Light, Andre Deutsch (London), 1986. £50/£10
ditto, Knopf (New York), 1986 . . . . . £15/£5
Images of War, Vietnam Profile, Boston Book Co (Boston), 1986 (photos by Julene Fischer) . . . £25/£10
Deeds of War, Thames & Hudson (New York), 1989 (photos by James Nachtwey) . . . . . £125/£50
Day of the Locust, A New Introduction, Book-of-the-Month Club (no place), 1989 (stapled wraps) . . . £20
Outerbridge Reach, Ticknor & Fields (New York), 1992 .
. . . . £10/£5
ditto, Ticknor & Fields (New York), 1992 (300 signed, numbered copies; slipcase; no d/w). . . . £65/£45
ditto, Franklin Library (Franklin Center, PA), 1992 (signed limited edition in full leather) £30
ditto, Andre Deutsch (London), 1992. . . . £10/£5
'Carefully, he examined his imagined positions ...', Black Oak Books (Berkeley), 1992 (broadside) . . . £15
Helping, Dim Gray Bar Press ([New York]), 1993 (100 signed, numbered copies; errata slip laid in; slipcase). £100
Bear and His Daughter, Houghton Mifflin (Boston/New York), 1997 . . . . £10/£5
ditto, Bloomsbury (London), 1998 . . . . . £10/£5
Damascus Gate, Franklin Library (Franklin Center, PA), 1998 (signed limited edition in full leather) . . . £45
ditto, Houghton Mifflin (Boston/New York), 1998. £10/£5
ditto, Picador (London), 1998 . . . . . £10/£5
Bay of Souls, Houghton Mifflin (Boston), 2003 . £10/£5
Prime Green, Remembering the Sixties, Ecco Press (New York), 2007 . . . . £10/£5

TOM STOPPARD
(b.1937)

A prolific playwright, Stoppard was born in Czechoslovakia, taken to Singapore as an infant, and finished his education in England. His plays examine philosophical themes
and issues and brim with verbal wit, wordplay, puns, jokes,
innuendo and visual humour. Stoppard's achievements
were rewarded with a C.B.E. in 1978, a knighthood in 1997
and the Order of Merit in 2000.

Plays

Rosencrantz and Guildenstern are Dead, Faber (London),
1967 . . . . £1,000/£200
ditto, Faber (London), 1967 (pbk) £45
ditto, Grove Press (New York), 1967 . . . £150/£25
The Real Inspector Hound, Faber (London), 1968. £350/£50
ditto, Faber (London), 1968 (pbk) £30
ditto, Grove Press (New York), 1968 . . . £25/£10
Enter a Free Man, Faber (London), 1968 . . £150/£35
ditto, Faber (London), 1968 (pbk) £20
ditto, Grove Press (New York), 1972 (pbk) . . £15
If You're Glad I'll be Frank: A Play for Radio, Faber
(London), 1969 (stapled wraps) £5
Albert's Bridge, French (London), 1969 (stapled wraps) £10
Albert's Bridge and *If You're Glad I'll be Frank: Two Plays
for Radio*, Faber (London), 1969 . . . £100/£20
ditto, Faber (London), 1969 (pbk) £20
A Separate Peace: A Play in One Act, French (London),
1969 (stapled wraps) £20
After Magritte, Faber (London), 1971 (pbk) . . £40
ditto, French (New York), 1971 (pbk) . . . £15
Jumpers, Faber (London), 1972 . . . . £100/£20
ditto, Faber (London), 1972 (pbk) £25
ditto, Grove Press (New York), 1972 . . . £45/£10
ditto, Grove Press (New York), 1972 (pbk) . . £10
Artist Descending a Staircase and *Where Are They Now?:
Two Plays for Radio*, Faber (London), 1973 . £250/£35
ditto, Faber (London), 1973 (pbk) £25
Travesties, Faber (London), 1975 . . . £125/£25
ditto, Faber (London), 1975 (pbk) £25
ditto, Grove Press (New York), 1975 (pbk) . . £20
Dirty Linen and *New-Found-Land*, Ambiance/Almost Free
Playscript (London), 1976 (stapled wraps) . . £10
ditto, Inter Action, 1976 (1,000 signed, numbered copies;
stapled wraps) £20
ditto, Grove Press (New York), 1976 . . . £25/£10
ditto, Faber (London), 1976 (pbk) £5
The Fifteen Minute Hamlet, French (London), 1976 (stapled
wraps) £25
Albert's Bridge & Other Plays, Grove Press (New York),
1977 . . . . £35/£5
Every Good Boy Deserves Favour and *Professional Foul*,
Faber (London), 1978. . . . . . £50/£10
ditto, Faber (London), 1978 (pbk) £10
ditto, Grove Press (New York), 1978 . . . £30/£10
Night and Day, Faber (London), 1978 . . . £65/£15
ditto, Grove Press (New York), 1979 . . . £20/£5
Dogg's Hamlet, Cahoot's Macbeth, Inter-Action (London),
1979 (2,000 numbered copies; pbk) . . . £35
ditto, Faber (London), 1980 (pbk) £20
Undiscovered Country, Faber (London), 1980 (an adaptation
of *Das Weite Land* by Arthur Schnitzler; pbk) . £15

On the Razzle, Faber (London), 1981 (an adaptation of *Einen
Jux Will Er Sich Machen* by Johann Nestroy; pbk) . £10
The Real Thing, Faber (London), 1982 (stapled wraps) £10
ditto, Faber (London), 1982 (500 signed broadsides repro-
ducing a moment from the play) £125
ditto, Faber (New York), 1984 (revised edition) . £20/£5
The Dog It was That Died and Other Plays, Faber
(London), 1983 (pbk) £10
Four Plays for Radio, Faber (London), 1984 . £30/£10
ditto, Faber (London), 1984 (pbk) £10
Squaring the Circle, Faber (London), 1984 . £50/£15
ditto, Faber (London), 1984 (pbk) £10
ditto, Faber (New York), 1985 (pbk) . . . £10
Rough Crossing, Faber (London), 1985 (an adaptation of
Play at the Castle by Ferenc Molnàr) . . £35/£10
ditto, Faber (London), 1985 (pbk) £10
Dalliance and *Undiscovered Country*, Faber (London), 1986
. . . . £15/£5
ditto, Faber (London), 1986 (pbk) £5
Hapgood, Faber (London), 1988 . . . . £35/£10
ditto, Faber (London), 1988 (pbk) £5
Radio Plays 1964-1983, Faber (London), 1990 (pbk) . £5
In the Native State, Faber (London), 1991 (pbk) . £5
Television Plays, 1965-84, Faber (London), 1993 . £35/£10
ditto, Faber (London), 1993 (pbk) £5
Arcadia, Faber (London), 1993 (pbk) . . . £5
ditto, Arion Press (New York), 2001 (350 signed, numbered
copies with four prints) £500
ditto, Arion Press (New York), 2001 (50 signed, numbered
copies with an extra suite of larger prints) . . £1,500
Indian Ink, Faber (London), 1995 . . . £15/£5
ditto, Faber (London), 1995 (pbk) £5
The Invention of Love, Faber (London), 1997 . £15/£5
ditto, Faber (London), 1997 (pbk) £5
ditto, Grove Press (New York), 1998 (pbk) . . £5
Shakespeare in Love: A Screenplay, Hyperion/Miramax
(New York), 1999 (pbk) £10
ditto, Faber, 1999 (pbk) £5
Coast of Utopia, Faber (London), 2002 (3 vols: *Voyage,
Shipwreck* and *Salvage*) . . . . . £125/£40
ditto, Grove Press (New York), 2003 (3 vols in slipcase, no
d/ws) . . . . £100/£35
Rock 'n' Roll, Faber (London), 2006 (pbk) . . £5

Novels

Lord Malquist and Mr Moon, Blond (London), 1966 . .
. . . . £75/£15
ditto, Knopf (New York), 1968 . . . . £25/£10

Others

Rosencrantz and Guildenstern Are Dead: The Film, Faber
(London), 1991 (pbk) £10
Tom Stoppard in Conversation, Univ of Michigan Press
(Ann Arbor, MI), 1994 (edited by Paul Delaney; pbk) £5
Conversations with Stoppard, Nick Hern Books (London),
1995 (interviews with Mel Gussow) . . . £10/£5
ditto, Limelight Editions (New York), 1995 . £10/£5

DAVID STOREY
(b.1933)

British novelist and playwright Storey was one of the
'Angry Young Men' of the 1950s. Much of his writing
considers the problems of working-class characters as they
move into middle-class surroundings and/or a mid-life
crisis. *Saville* won the Booker prize in 1976.

Novels
This Sporting Life, Longmans (London), 1960 . £250/£35
ditto, Macmillan (New York), 1960 . . . . £35/£10
Flight into Camden, Longmans (London), 1960 . £100/£20
ditto, Macmillan (New York), 1961 . . . . £15/£5
Radcliffe, Longmans (London), 1963 . . . £35/£10
ditto, Coward-McCann (New York), 1964 . . £15/£5
Pasmore, Longman (London), 1972 . . . £15/£5
ditto, Dutton (New York), 1972 . . . . £10/£5
A Temporary Life, Lane (London), 1973 . . . £15/£5
ditto, Dutton (New York), 1974 . . . . £10/£5
Edward, Lane (London), 1973 . . . . £15/£5
Saville, Cape (London), 1976 . . . . £20/£5
ditto, Harper & Row (New York), 1976 . . £10/£5
A Prodigal Child, Cape (London), 1982 . . £15/£5
ditto, Dutton (New York), 1982 . . . . £10/£5
Present Times, Cape (London), 1984 . . . £15/£5
A Serious Man, Cape (London), 1998 . . . £10/£5
As It Happened, Cape (London), 2002 . . £10/£5
Thin-Ice Skater, Cape (London), 2004 . . £10/£5

Plays
The Restoration of Arnold Middleton, Cape (London), 1967
. . . . £30/£10
In Celebration, Cape (London), 1969 . . £15/£5
ditto, Grove Press (New York), 1975 . . . £15/£5
The Contractor, Cape (London), 1970 . . £15/£5
ditto, Random House (New York), 1970 . . £10/£5
Home, Cape (London), 1970 . . . . £15/£5
ditto, Random House (New York), 1971 . . £10/£5
The Changing Room, Cape (London), 1972 . £10/£5
ditto, Random House (New York), 1972 . . £10/£5
The Farm, Cape (London), 1973 . . . £10/£5
ditto, French (New York), 1974 (pbk) . . . £5
Cromwell, Cape (London), 1973 . . . . £10/£5
Life Class, Cape (London), 1975 . . . £10/£5
Mother's Day, Cape (London), 1977 . . . £10/£5
Early Days, Penguin (Harmondsworth, Middlesex), 1980
(pbk) £5
Sisters, Penguin (Harmondsworth, Middlesex), 1980 (pbk) .
. . . . £5
The March on Russia, French (London), 1989 (pbk) . £5

Poetry
Storey's Lives: Poems, 1951-1991, Cape (London), 1992 .
. . . . £15/£5

REX STOUT
(b.1886 d.1975)

Rex Stout was the American author of novels featuring,
among others, the detective Nero Wolfe. These Wolfe
books were nominated Best Mystery Series of the Century
and Stout was nominated Best Mystery Writer of the
Century at *Bouchercon 2000*, the world's largest mystery
convention. Stout was a longtime friend of the British
humorist P.G. Wodehouse.

Novels
How Like a God, Vanguard (New York), 1929 £2,500/£100
ditto, Kennerley (London), 1931 . . . . £1,000/£35
Seed on the Wind, Vanguard (New York), 1930 £1,000/£75
ditto, Kennerley (London), 1931 . . . . £1,000/£35
Golden Remedy, Vanguard (New York), 1931 . £750/£50
Forest Fire, Farrar & Rinehart (New York), 1933 . . .
. . . . £1,000/£75
ditto, Faber (London), 1934 . . . . . £250/£65
The President Vanishes, Farrar & Rinehart (New York),
1934 (anonymous) . . . . £750/£65
Fer-de-Lance, Farrar & Rinehart (New York), 1934 .
. . . . £8,000/£650
ditto, Cassell (London), 1935 . . . . £1,250/£100
The League of Frightened Men, Farrar & Rinehart (New
York), 1935 . . . . £6,500/£500
ditto, Cassell (London), 1935 . . . . £1,000/£85
O Careless Love, Farrar & Rinehart (New York), 1935. .
. . . . £1,250/£100
The Rubber Band, Farrar & Rinehart (New York), 1936 .
. . . . £7,000/£500
ditto, Cassell (London),1936 . . . . £1,250/£100
ditto, as *To Kill Again*, Hillman, 1960 (pbk) . . . £10
The Red Box, Farrar & Rinehart (New York), 1937 .
. . . . £7,500/£500
ditto, Cassell (London), 1937 . . . . £1,250/£100
The Hand in the Glove, Farrar & Rinehart (New York),
1937 . . . . £2,500/£200
ditto, as *Crime on Her Hands*, Collins Crime Club, 1939 .
. . . . £1,000/£100
Too Many Cooks, Farrar & Rinehart (New York), 1938 .
. . . . £1,250/£100
ditto, Collins Crime Club (London), 1938. . . £250/£45
Mr Cinderella, Farrar & Rinehart (New York), 1938 . .
. . . . £1,000/£75
Some Buried Caesar, Farrar & Rinehart (New York), 1939.
. . . . £1,250/£100
ditto, Collins Crime Club (London), 1939. . . £250/£45
ditto, as *The Red Bull*, Dell (New York), 1945 (pbk) . £10
Mountain Cat, Farrar & Rinehart (New York), 1939 . .
. . . . £750/£65
ditto, Collins Crime Club (London), 1940. . . £125/£25
ditto, as *The Mountain Cat Murders*, Pyramid (New York),
1971 (pbk) £10
Double for Death, Farrar & Rinehart (New York), 1939 .
. . . . £500/£45
ditto, Collins Crime Club (London), 1940. . . £125/£25
Over My Dead Body, Farrar & Rinehart (New York), 1939
[1940] . . . . £2,000/£250
ditto, Collins Crime Club (London), 1940. . . £125/£25
Where There's a Will, Farrar & Rinehart (New York), 1940
. . . . £2,000/£250
ditto, Collins Crime Club (London), 1941. . . £125/£25

The Broken Vase, Farrar & Rinehart (New York), 1941   .
.   .   .   .£450/£45
ditto, Collins Crime Club (London), 1942.   .   .£100/£15
Alphabet Hicks, Farrar & Rinehart (New York), 1941   .
.   .   .   .   £750/£100
ditto, Collins Crime Club (London) Sept. 1942   .£100/£15
ditto, as *The Sound of Murder*, Pyramid (New York), 1965
(pbk) £10
The Silent Speaker, Viking (New York), 1946   .£200/£40
ditto, Collins Crime Club (London), 1947.   .   £75/£15
Too Many Women, Viking (New York), 1947   .£200/£45
ditto, Collins Crime Club, 1948   .   .   .   £75/£15
And Be a Villain, Viking (New York), 1948   .   £150/£25
ditto, as *More Deaths than One*, Collins Crime Club
(London), 1949   .   .   .   .   .   £75/£15
The Second Confession, Viking (New York), 1949 £150/£25
ditto, Collins Crime Club (London), 1950.   .   £75/£15
In the Best Families, Viking (New York), 1950   .£150/£15
ditto, as *Even in the Best Families*, Collins Crime Club
(London), 1951   .   .   .   .   £65/£10
Murder By the Book, Viking (New York), 1951   .£200/£20
ditto, Collins Crime Club (London), 1952.   .   £65/£10
Prisoner's Base, Viking (New York), 1952   .   .£150/£15
ditto, as *Out Goes She*, Collins Crime Club (London), 1953
.   .   .   .   £65/£10
The Golden Spiders, Viking (New York), 1953   .£100/£10
ditto, Collins Crime Club (London), 1954.   .   £45/£10
The Black Mountain, Viking (New York), 1954   .£100/£10
ditto, Collins Crime Club (London), 1955.   .   £45/£10
Before Midnight, Viking (New York), 1955   .£100/£10
ditto, Collins Crime Club (London), 1956.   .   £45/£10
Might as Well Be Dead, Viking (New York), 1956 £100/£10
ditto, Collins Crime Club (London), 1957.   .   £45/£10
If Death Ever Slept, Viking (New York), 1957   .£100/£10
ditto, Collins Crime Club (London), 1958.   .   £45/£10
Champagne for One, Viking (New York), 1958   .£100/£10
ditto, Collins Crime Club (London), 1959.   .   £45/£10
Plot it Yourself, Viking (New York), 1959   .   .£100/£10
ditto, as *Murder in Style*, Collins Crime Club (London),
1960   .   .   .   .   £45/£10
Too Many Clients, Viking (New York), 1960 .   .£100/£10
ditto, Collins Crime Club (London), 1961.   .   £45/£10
The Final Deduction, Viking (New York), 1961   £75/£10
ditto, Collins Crime Club (London), 1962.   .   £35/£10
Gambit, Viking (New York) Oct 1962   .   .   £75/£10
ditto, Collins Crime Club (London), 1963.   .   £35/£10
The Mother Hunt, Viking (New York),1963 .   £75/£10
ditto, Collins Crime Club (London), 1964.   .   £35/£10
A Right to Die, Viking (New York), 1964   .   £75/£10
ditto, Collins Crime Club (London), 1965.   .   £35/£10
The Doorbell Rang, Viking (New York), 1965   £50/£10
ditto, Collins Crime Club (London), 1966.   .   £30/£5
Death of a Doxy, Viking (New York), 1966   .   £50/£10
ditto, Collins Crime Club (London), 1967.   .   £25/£5
The Father Hunt, Viking (New York), 1968 .   .   £50/£10
ditto, Collins Crime Club (London), 1969.   .   £25/£5
Death of a Dude, Viking (New York), 1969   .   £50/£10
ditto, Collins Crime Club (London), 1970.   .   £25/£5
Please Pass the Guilt, Viking (New York), 1973   .   £30/£5
ditto, Collins Crime Club (London), 1974.   .   £20/£5
A Family Affair, Viking (New York), 1975   .   £30/£5
ditto, Collins Crime Club (London), 1976.   .   £15/£5

Others

Red Threads, in *The Mystery Book*, Farrar & Rinehart (New
York), 1939   .   .   .   .   .   .£250/£25

ditto, Collins Crime Club (London), 1941.   .   .£125/£25
Bad for Business, in *The Second Mystery Book*, Farrar &
Rinehart (New York), 1940   .   .   .   .£250/£25
ditto, Collins Crime Club (London),1945 .   .   .£125/£25

Wolfe Novella Collections
Black Orchids, Farrar & Rinehart (New York), 1942   .   .
.   .   .   .   £1,500/£200
ditto, Collins Crime Club (London) Sept. 1943   .£100/£15
Not Quite Dead Enough, Farrar & Rinehart (New York),
1944   .   .   .   .£500/£45
Trouble in Triplicate, Viking (New York), 1949   .£150/£25
ditto, Collins Crime Club (London), 1949.   .   £75/£15
Three Doors to Death, Viking (New York), 1950 .£150/£25
ditto, Collins Crime Club (London), 1950.   .   £65/£10
Curtains for Three, Viking (New York), 1951   .£150/£25
ditto, Collins Crime Club (London), 1951.   .   £65/£10
Door to Death, Dell (New York), 1951 (pbk) .   .   £10
Triple Jeopardy, Viking (New York), 1952   .   .£150/£25
ditto, Collins Crime Club (London), 1952.   .   £65/£10
Three Men Out, Viking (New York), 1954   .   .£100/£15
ditto, Collins Crime Club (London), 1955.   .   £45/£10
Three Witnesses, Viking (New York), 1956   .   .£100/£15
ditto, Collins Crime Club (London), 1956.   .   £45/£10
Three for the Chair, Viking (New York), 1957   .£100/£10
ditto, Collins Crime Club (London), 1958.   .   £45/£10
And Four to Go, Viking (New York), 1958   .   .£100/£10
ditto, as *Crime and Again*, Collins Crime Club (London),
1959   .   .   .   .   .   .   £45/£10
Three at Wolfe's Door, Viking (New York), 1960 . £100/£10
ditto, Collins Crime Club (London) Jan. 1961 .   £45/£10
Homicide Trinity, Viking (New York), 1962   .   £75/£10
ditto, Collins Crime Club (London), 1963.   .   £35/£10
Trio for Blunt Instruments, Viking (New York), 1964.   .
.   .   .   .   £65/£10
ditto, Collins Crime Club (London), 1965.   .   £30/£5
Death Times Three, Bantam (New York), 1985 (pbk) .   £5

Story Collection
Justice Ends at Home, Viking, 1977.   .   .   £30/£10

Miscellany
The Nero Wolfe Cook Book, Viking (New York), 1973   .
.   .   .   .   £30/£10
Corsage, Rock (Bloomington, IN), 1977 .   .   .£200/£20

LYTTON STRACHEY
(b.1880 d.1932)

Giles Lytton Strachey was educated at Liverpool and
Cambridge Universities and became a prominent member
of the Bloomsbury Group. He is best known for
establishing a new form of biography in which psychological insight and sympathy for his subjects are combined
with irreverence and humour. He also wrote poetry, reviews
and essays.

Landmarks in French Literature, Williams and Norgate
(London), 1912 (first issue with top edge stained green and
8 pages of ads) £50
ditto, Williams and Norgate (London), 1912 (second issue
with top edge stained red) £20
ditto, Holt (New York), 1912   .   .   .   .   £20

Eminent Victorians, Chatto & Windus (London), 1918 £250
ditto, Putnam (New York), 1918 . . . . . . £100
Queen Victoria, Chatto & Windus (London), 1921 £125/£45
ditto, Harcourt (New York), 1921 . . . £100/£30
Books and Characters, Chatto & Windus (London), 1922 .
. . . . £50/£20
ditto, Harcourt (New York), 1922 . . . £35/£15
Pope: The Leslie Stephen Lecture, C.U.P. (Cambridge, UK),
1925 . . . . £35/£10
ditto, Harcourt (New York), 1926 . . . £30/£10
Elizabeth and Essex, Chatto & Windus (London), 1928 .
. . . . £50/£10
ditto, Harcourt Brace/Crosby Gaige (New York), 1928 . .
. . . . £40/£10
ditto, Harcourt Brace/Crosby Gaige (New York), 1928
(1,060 signed copies) £75
Portraits in Miniature, Chatto & Windus (London), 1931 .
. . . . £45/£10
ditto, Chatto & Windus (London), 1931 (260 signed copies)
. . . . £100
ditto, Harcourt (New York), 1931 . . . £30/£10
Characters and Commentaries, Chatto & Windus (London),
1933 . . . . £45/£15
ditto, Harcourt (New York), 1933 . . . £30/£10
Virginia Woolf and Lytton Strachey: Letters, Hogarth Press
(London), 1956 . . . . . . £75/£20
ditto, Harcourt (New York), 1956 . . . £45/£15
Spectatorial Essays, Chatto & Windus (London), 1964 £15/£5
ditto, Harcourt (New York), 1965 . . . £10/£5
Ermyntrude and Esmeralda, Blond (London), 1969 (17
illustrations by Erté) . . . . . £15/£5
ditto, Blond (London), 1969 (250 copies signed by Erté,
slipcase). . . . . . . £60/£45
ditto, Stein & Day (New York), 1969. . . £15/£5
Lytton Strachey by Himself, Heinemann (London), 1971
(edited Michael Holroyd) . . . . £15/£5
ditto, Holt, Rinehart & Winston (New York), 1971 £10/£5
Lytton Strachey: The Really Interesting Question,
Weidenfeld & Nicolson (London), 1972 (edited Paul Levy)
. . . . £15/£5
ditto, Coward-McCann (New York), 1973 . £15/£5
The Shorter Strachey, O.U.P. (Oxford, UK), 1980 (edited
Michael Holroyd) . . . . . £10/£5

GENE STRATTON-PORTER

(b.1863 d.1924)

Gene Stratton-Porter was an American author, amateur
naturalist and wildlife photographer. A best-selling novelist
in her day, she was considered one of the five most prominent American authors of the early twentieth century.

The Strike At Shane's, American Humane Education
Society (Boston), 1893 (green or brown cloth; anonymous)
. . . . £225
ditto, A. Flanagan (Chicago), 1896 (buff pictorial wraps
printed in black) £150
The Song of the Cardinal, Bobbs-Merrill (Indianapolis, IN),
1903 . . . . £125
ditto, Hodder & Stoughton (London), 1913 . . £65

Freckles, Doubleday, Page & Co (New York), 1904 . £125
ditto, Doubleday, Page & Co (London), 1904 . . . £65
What I Have Done With Birds, Bobbs-Merrill (Indianapolis,
IN), 1907 . . . . £125
At The Foot of the Rainbow, Outing Co (New York), 1907
. . . . £250
ditto, Hodder & Stoughton (London), 1913 . £175
Birds of the Bible, Jennings & Graham/Eaton & Mains
(Cincinnati/New York), 1909 . . . £250
ditto, Hodder & Stoughton (London), 1910 . . £150
A Girl of the Limberlost, Doubleday, Page & Co (New
York), 1909 . . . . £150
ditto, Doubleday, Page & Co (London), 1909 . . £125
Music of the Wild, Jennings & Graham/Eaton & Mains (Cin-
cinnati/New York), 1910 (green cloth, white spine) . £150
ditto, Jennings & Graham/Eaton & Mains (Cincinnati/New
York), 1910 (tan cloth; Abingdon imprint at base of spine)
. . . . £125
ditto, Doubleday, Page & Co (Garden City, NY), 1910. £75
ditto, Jennings & Graham/Eaton & Mains (Cincinnati/New
York), 1910 (100 signed, numbered copies; in box) . £350
ditto, Abingdon Press (New York/Cincinnati), 1910 (second
edition; blue cloth; pictorial cover) £65
ditto, Abingdon Press (New York/Cincinnati), 1910 (second
edition; green cloth; imprint of Doubleday, Page on spine)
. . . . £45
ditto, Abingdon Press (New York/Cincinnati), 1910 (100
signed, numbered copies of second edition) . . . £150
ditto, Hodder & Stoughton (London), 1910 . . . £50
The Harvester, Doubleday, Page & Co (Garden City, NY),
1911 (first state with copyright notice: 'Published August,
1911'; bottom of p.564 blank; printer's notice at foot of
copyright page; damaged type at bottom of pps. 7, 30, 411;
last word on page 25, 'work', in undamaged type) . £100
ditto, Doubleday, Page & Co (Garden City, NY), 1911
(second state with copyright notice: 'Published August,
1911'; bottom of copyright page blank; printer's notice at
bottom of p.564; damaged type at bottom of pps. 7, 25, 30
and 411). £75
ditto, Doubleday, Page & Co (Garden City, NY), 1911 (third
state with copyright notice: 'Published August, 1911'
deleted from copyright page; damaged type reset on pps. 7,
25, 30 and 411) £50
ditto, Hodder & Stoughton (London), 1911 . . . £65
After The Flood, Bobbs-Merrill (Indianapolis, IN), 1911 .
. . . . £150
ditto, The Indiana Society of Chicago (Chicago), 1912
(signed, numbered copies; red cloth) . . . £400
ditto, The Indiana Society of Chicago (Chicago), 1912
(signed, numbered copies; green leather) . . £750
Moths of the Limberlost, Doubleday, Page & Co (Garden
City, NY), 1912 (first state with four lines of copy at top of
p.333) £200
ditto, Doubleday, Page & Co (Garden City, NY), 1912
(second state as above but with errata slip bound in a
bottom of p.333) £150
ditto, Hodder & Stoughton (London), 1912 . . £125
Laddie, Doubleday, Page & Co (Garden City, NY), 1913
(blue cloth with spine title reading 'Laddie- A True Blue
Story') £65
ditto, Doubleday, Page & Co (Garden City, NY), 1913 (blue
cloth with spine title reading 'Laddie') £35
ditto, Doubleday, Page & Co (Garden City, NY), 1913
(brown, soft suede leather, stamped in gilt; top edges gilt).
. . . . £45
ditto, John Murray (London), 1913 . . . . £35

Birds of the Limberlost Especially Prepared for Katharine Minhan, Doubleday, Page & Co (New York), 1914 (buff wraps; only one known copy) £1,000

Birds of the Limberlost, Yestermorrow (New York), 1991 (425 numbered copies; no d/w; in box) . . . £125

Michael O'Halloran, Doubleday, Page (Garden City, NY), 1915 (green cloth) £50

ditto, Doubleday, Page (Garden City, NY), 1915 (brown suede stamped in giltl in cardboard folder with windmill illustration.) . . . . £100/£50

ditto, John Murray (London), 1915 . . . . . £30

Morning Face, Doubleday, Page & Co (Garden City, NY), 1916 (blue pictorial cloth) £125

ditto, Doubleday, Page & Co (Garden City, NY), 1916 (white cloth with design in gold and blue) . . £100

ditto, John Murray (London), 1916 . . . . £60

Friends in Feathers, Doubleday, Page & Co (Garden City, NY), 1917 . . . . £150

ditto, Curtis Brown (London), 1917 . . . . £100

ditto, John Murray (London), 1922 . . . . £30

A Daughter of the Land, Doubleday, Page & Co (Garden City, NY), 1918 (first binding state with publisher's name with ampersand in shape of open 'E', without diagonal cross line; lettering on cover and backstrip both orange; first issue with 'were' on page 304, line 20; perfect page number on p.11; text block bulks 1 inch when compressed) £150

ditto, Doubleday, Page & Co (Garden City, NY), 1918 (early binding state with normal ampersand on spine; lettering on cover and backstrip both orange; text block bulks 1 inch when compressed; perfect type in page number on p.11; 'was' on p.304, line 20) . . £100

ditto, Doubleday, Page & Co (Garden City, NY), 1918 (usual binding and text states: normal ampersand on spine; lettering on cover in orange and in yellow on spine; text block bulks 1¼ inches when compressed; broken type in page number on p.11; 'was' on p.304, line 20) . . £50

ditto, Doubleday, Page & Co (Garden City, NY), 1918 (1,000 signed copies) £150

ditto, John Murray (London), 1918 . . . . £75

Homing With The Birds, Doubleday, Page & Co (Garden City, NY), 1919 . . . . £150

ditto, John Murray (London), 1919 . . . . £100

ditto, Yestermorrow (New York), 1990 (300 copies) . £30

Her Father's Daughter, Doubleday, Page & Co (Garden City, NY), 1921 (grey/green cloth) . . . £250/£50

ditto, Doubleday, Page & Co (Garden City, NY/Toronto), 1921 (dark forest-green leather) . . . £235/£35

ditto, John Murray (London), 1921 . . . £150/£35

The Free Bird, Doubleday, Page & Co (Garden City, NY/Toronto), 1922 (glassine d/w and box) . £450/£100

The White Flag, Doubleday, Page & Co (New York), 1923 (pictorial cloth slipcase and d/w) . . . £250/£50

ditto, John Murray (London), 1923 . . . £150/£35

Jesus of the Emerald, Doubleday, Page & Co (New York), 1923 (glassine d/w and box) . . . £250/£100

ditto, John Murray (London), 1923 . . . £200/£75

Wings, Garden City Publishing Company (Garden City, NY), 1923 (wraps) £300

ditto, Garden City Publishing Company (Garden City, NY), 1923 (green cloth) . . . . . £250/£45

ditto, privately printed by Rollin King (Muncie, IN), 1976 (500 numbered copies; wraps) £30

Tales You Won't Believe, Doubleday, Page & Co (Garden City, NY), 1925 . . . . £250/£45

ditto, Heinemann (London), 1925 . . . £150/£35

The Keeper of the Bees, Doubleday, Page (Garden City, NY), 1925 . . . . £125/£20

ditto, Hutchinson & Co (London), 1925 . . £100/£15

The Magic Garden, Doubleday, Page (Garden City, NY), 1927 . . . . £250/£45

ditto, Hutchinson & Co (London), 1927 . . £150/£30

Let Us Highly Resolve, Doubleday, Page & Co (Garden City, NY), 1927 . . . . £275/£30

ditto, Heinemann (London), 1927 . . . £200/£30

ditto, Aeonian Press (New York), 1990 (325 numbered copies) £30

Euphorbia, Light and Life Press (Berne, IN), 1986 (1,000 numbered copies signed by the publisher; slipcase; no d/w) . . . . £35/£20

Coming Through the Swamp: The Nature Writings of Gene Stratton-Porter, Univ of Utah Press (Salt Lake City, UT), 1996 (pbk) £10

WILLIAM STYRON

(b.1925 d.2006)

William Styron was an American novelist and essayist. He received a Pulitzer Prize in 1968 for *The Confessions of Nat Turner*.

Lie Down in Darkness, Bobbs-Merrill (Indianapolis, IN), 1951 . . . . £200/£30

ditto, Hamish Hamilton (London), 1952 . . £150/£20

ditto, Franklin Library (Franklin Center, PA), 1982 (signed limited edition in full leather) £45

The Long March, Modern Library/Random House (New York), 1952 [1956] (pbk) £75

ditto, Hamish Hamilton (London), 1962 . . £125/£20

ditto, Random House (New York), 1968 . . £45/£10

Set This House on Fire, Random House (New York), 1960 (dark green d/w lettered in white, with additional text on flaps) . . . . £45£10

ditto, Random House (New York), 1960 (light green d/w lettered in red, title and publisher's information on flaps but no text) . . . . £300/£5

ditto, Hamish Hamilton (London), 1961 . . £45/£10

The Four Seasons, Pennsylvania State Univ Press (Pennysylvania, PA), 1965 (75 signed, numbered copies; boxed set of four etchings signed by the artist Harold Altman) £1,500

This Quiet Dust, Harper's Magazine (no place), [c.1965-67] (offprint in blue/grey stapled wraps) . . . £125

ditto, Random House (New York), 1967 (500 copies; wraps) £100

The Confessions of Nat Turner, Random House (New York), 1967 (presumed first state with 'woman' on p.262, line 11) . . . . £60/£20

ditto, Random House (New York), 1967 (presumed second state with 'women' on p.262, line 11) . . £50/£10

ditto, Random House (New York), 1967 (trade edition with extra leaf signed) . . . . £75/£20

ditto, Random House (New York), 1967 (500 signed, numbered copies; slipcase) . . . . £150/£125

ditto, Jonathan Cape (London), 1968 . . . £50/£10

ditto, Franklin Press (Franklin Center, PA), 1976 (limited edition in full leather) £30

ditto, Franklin Press (Franklin Center, PA), 1979 (signed limited edition in full leather) £50

ditto, Easton Press (Norwalk, CT), 2000 (signed, bound in full leather) £50
In The Clap Shack, Random House (New York) . £30/£5
Christchurch, An Address…, Briarpatch Press (Davidson, NC), 1977 (350 numbered copies; wraps) . . £60
ditto, Briarpatch Press (Davidson, NC), 1977 (26 signed, lettered copies; wraps) £125
Admiral Robert Penn Warren…, Palaemon Press (Winston-Salem, NC), 1978 (26 signed, lettered copies; wraps). £150
ditto, Palaemon Press (Winston-Salem, NC), 1978 (200 signed, numbered copies) £65
ditto, Palaemon Press (Winston-Salem, NC), 1978 (new edition; 50 numbered copies (Roman numerals) signed by Styron and Warren) £75
ditto, Palaemon Press (Winston-Salem, NC), 1981 (50 numbered copies (Roman numerals) signed by Styron and Warren) £75
ditto, Palaemon Press (Winston-Salem, NC), 1981 (26 lettered copies signed by Styron and Warren; decorated wraps) £75
ditto, Palaemon Press (Winston-Salem, NC), 1981 (74 numbered copies signed by Styron and Warren . . £35
Sophie's Choice, Random House (New York), 1979 £65/£10
ditto, Random House (New York), 1979 (500 signed, numbered copies; slipcase; no d/w) . . . £150/£125
ditto, Random House (New York), 1979 ('Advance Presentation Edition' in tissue d/w). . . . £45
ditto, Franklin Library (Franklin Center, PA), 1979 (limited edition in full leather). £30
ditto, Cape (London), 1979 . . . . . £30/£5
ditto, Easton Press (Norwalk, CT), 1999 (signed; bound in full leather) £100
Shadrach, Sylvester & Orphanos (Los Angeles), 1979 (300 signed, numbered copies; no d/w) . . . £60
ditto, Sylvester & Orphanos (Los Angeles), 1979 (24 signed, lettered copies; no d/w) £200
ditto, Sylvester & Orphanos (Los Angeles), 1979 (4 signed copies with name of recipient on each) . . . £300
The Message of Auschwitz, Press de la Warr (Blacksburg), 1979 (200 signed, numbered copies; wraps) . . £45
ditto, Press de la Warr (Blacksburg), 1979 (26 signed, lettered copies; wraps) £150
An Address at the 204th Commencement of Hampdensydney College, Hampden-Sydney College (Hampden-Sydney, VA), 1980 (950 numbered copies; wraps) . . £50
ditto, Hampden-Sydney College (Hampden-Sydney, VA), 1980 (50 signed, numbered copies; wraps) . . £150
Against Fear, Palaemon Press (Winston-Salem, NC), 1981 (50 signed, numbered copies; light blue sewn wraps). £60
ditto, Palaemon Press (Winston-Salem, NC), 1981 (250 signed, numbered copies; grey stapled wraps) . . £30
As He Lay Dead, A Bitter Grief, Albondocani, New York, 1981 (300 signed, numbered copies; wraps) . . £45
ditto, Albondocani, New York, 1981 (26 signed, lettered copies) £200
This Quiet Dust and Other Writings, Random House (New York), 1982 . . . . £15/£5
ditto, Random House (New York), 1982 (250 signed, numbered copies; slipcase; no d/w) . . . £100/£75
ditto, Cape (London), 1983 . . . . . £20/£5
Mr Jefferson and Our Times, Stuart Wright (Winston-Salem), 1984 (61 signed copies in marbled wraps) . £50
ditto, Stuart Wright (Winston-Salem), 1984 (14 signed, numbered copies; Japanese decorated wraps) . . £200

Conversations With William Styron, Univ Press of Mississippi (Jackson, MS/London), 1985 . . . £20/£10
ditto, Univ Press of Mississippi (Jackson, MS/London), 1985 (pbk) £10
Letter to the Editor of The Paris Review, Press de la Warr (Cambridge), 1986 (6 specially bound signed, lettered copies; sewn wraps) £200
ditto, Press de la Warr (Cambridge), 1986 (20 signed, lettered copies; sewn wraps) £150
ditto, Press de la Warr (Cambridge), 1986 (100 signed, numbered copies; sewn wraps). £75
Blankenship, Press de la Warr (no place), 1988 (100 signed, numbered copies; sewn wraps). £40
ditto, Press de la Warr (no place), 1988 (26 signed, lettered copies; sewn wraps) £125
Darkness Visible, Random House (New York), 1990 £10/£5
ditto, Cape (London), 1991 . . . . . £10/£5
Inheritance of Night; Early Drafts of Lay Down in Darkness, Duke Univ Press (Durham/London), 1993 (no d/w) £15
ditto, Duke Univ Press (Durham/London), 1993 (250 signed, numbered copies; slipcase; no d/w). . . £65/£50
ditto, Duke Univ Press (Durham/London), 1993 (26 signed, lettered copies; slipcase; no d/w) . . £175/£150
A Tidewater Morning, Eurographica (Helsinki), 1991 (350 signed, numbered copies; in heavy wraps and d/w) . £50
A Tidewater Morning: Three Tales From Youth, Random House, (New York), 1993 . . . . . £15/£5
ditto, Random House, (New York), 1993 (200 signed, numbered copies; slipcase; no d/w). . . £75/£50
ditto, Cape (London), 1993 . . . . . £15/£5
A Chance In A Million, Press de la Warr (Pennsylvania, PA), 1994 (200 signed, numbered copies; sewn blue wraps with printed label on front cover) . . . £25
ditto, Press de la Warr (Pennsylvania, PA), 1994 (26 signed, lettered copies; sewn red wraps with printed label on front cover) £65
Grateful Words About F. Scott Fitzgerald, F. Scott Fitzgerald Society (Hofstra Univ), 1997 (250 signed, numbered copies; cream stapled wraps). . . . £25
ditto, F. Scott Fitzgerald Society (Hofstra Univ), 1997 (26 signed, lettered copies; light blue stapled wraps) . . £100

MONTAGUE SUMMERS

(b.1880 d.1948)

A strange and scholarly character, Summers published many books on the supernatural as well as 17th century theatre and the Gothic novel. He claimed to be a Catholic priest and called himself the 'Reverend Alphonsus Joseph-Mary Augustus Montague Summers' although he was never a member of any order or diocese. He is best known for his translation of *Malleus Maleficarum*, the medieval manual for witch-hunters.

Major Works
The Marquis de Sade, The British Society for the Study of Sex Psychology (London), 1920 (stapled wraps) . . £100
The History of Witchcraft and Demonology, Kegan Paul (London), 1926 . . . . £145/£50
ditto, Knopf (New York), 1926 . . . . . £125/£40

The Geography of Witchcraft, Kegan Paul (London), 1927.
.   .   .   . £100/£35
ditto, Knopf (New York), 1927 .   .   .   . £100/£35
Essays in Petto, Fortune Press (London), [1928] . £150/£75
ditto, Fortune Press (London), [1928] (70 signed, numbered
copies) £200
The Discovery of Witches, Cayme Press (London), 1928
(wraps) £50
The Vampire: His Kith and Kin, Kegan Paul (London), 1928
.   .   .   . £100/£30
ditto, Dutton (New York), 1929 .   .   .   . £100/£30
The Vampire in Europe, Kegan Paul (London), 1929 .   .
.   .   .   . £125/£30
ditto, Dutton (New York), 1929 .   .   .   . £100/£30
The Werewolf, Kegan Paul (London), 1933 .   . £200/£45
ditto, Dutton (New York), 1934 .   .   .   . £175/£40
The Restoration Theatre, Kegan Paul (London), 1934 .   .
.   .   .   . £45/£20
ditto, Macmillan (New York), 1934 .   .   . £35/£20
A Bibliography of the Restoration Drama, Fortune Press
(London), [1935].   .   .   .   .   .   . £45/£20
ditto, Fortune Press (London), [1935] (250 copies). £65/£35
ditto, Fortune Press (London), [1943] (revised and enlarged
edition) .   .   .   . £30/£10
The Playhouse of Pepys, Kegan Paul (London), 1935 £45/£15
ditto, Macmillan (New York), 1935 .   .   . £40/£15
A Popular History of Witchcraft, Kegan Paul (London), 1937
.   .   .   . £75/£25
ditto, Dutton (New York), 1937 .   .   .   . £75/£25
The Gothic Quest, Fortune Press (London), [1938] (950
copies, no d/w) £150
A Gothic Bibliography, Fortune Press (London), [1940] (750
copies) £175
ditto, Russell & Russell (New York), 1964 (no d/w) . £50
Witchcraft and Black Magic, Rider (London), [1946] .   .
.   .   .   . £50/£20
ditto, Causeway (New York), 1974 .   .   . £30/£15
The Physical Phenomena of Mysticism, Rider (London),
[1950] .   .   .   . £35/£15
ditto, Barnes & Noble (New York), 1950 .   . £25/£10
The Galanty Show: An Autobiography, Cecil Woolf
(London), 1980 .   .   .   . £30/£10
ditto, Cecil Woolf (London), 1980 (30 signed copies) . £75
Letters to an Editor, Tragara Press (Edinburgh), 1986 (145
numbered copies; wraps) £20

Others
Antinous and Other Poems, Sisley's (London), [1907] £250
ditto, Cecil Woolf (London), 1995 .   .   . £15/£5
The Source of Southerne's The Fatal Marriage, C.U.P.
(Cambridge, UK), 1916 (wraps) £45
The Double Dealer, [Incorporated Stage Society] ([London]),
[1916] (wraps) £35
Orrey's The Tragedy of Zoroastres, C.U.P. (Cambridge,
UK), 1917 (wraps) £45
Love for Love, [Incorporated Stage Society] ([London]),
[1917] (wraps) £35
A Great Mistress of Romance, Royal Society of Literature
(London), [1917] (wraps) £45
The Way of the World, [Incorporated Stage Society]
([London]), [1918] (wraps) £35
Jane Austen: An Appreciation, Royal Society of Literature
(London), [1918] (wraps) £45
The Provok'd Wife, Incorporated Stage Society (London),
[1919] (wraps) £35

R.S. SURTEES
(b.1805 d.1864)

R.S. Surtees was a British sporting novelist and journalist
whose most successful character is arguably Mr Jorrocks, a
good-humoured and vulgar Cockney grocer who loves to
hunt. In 1832 Surtees co-founded the *New Sporting
Magazine*, of which he became editor for the following five
years. To this periodical he contributed the papers which
were later collected and published as *Jorrocks's Jaunts and
Jollities*.

Fiction
Jorrocks's Jaunts and Jollities, Spiers (London), 1838
(illustrated by Phiz) £350
ditto, E.L. Carey and A. Ha (Philadelphia, PA), 1838 (2 vols)
.   .   .   . £250
ditto, Ackermann (London), 1843 (15 coloured illustrations
by Henry Alken, first state) £750
ditto, Ackermann (London), 1843 (15 coloured illustrations
by Henry Alken, second state with ads announcing a new
edition of *The Life of John Mytton*) .   .   . £500
Handley Cross; or, Mr Jorrocks's Hunt, Colburn (London),
1843 (3 vols) £300
ditto, Bradbury & Evans (London), 1853 (17 monthly parts,
illustrated by John Leech) .   .   .   . £1,250 the set
ditto, Bradbury & Evans (London), 1854 (1 vol.) .   . £200
ditto, Edward Arnold (London), [1911] (12 colour plates by
Cecil Aldin in each of 2 vols) £100
Hillingdon Hall; or The Cockney Squire, Colburn
(London), 1845 (3 vols) £200
**Hawbuck Grange; or, The Sporting Adventures of Thomas
Scott, Esq.**, Longmans (London), 1847 (illustrated by Phiz)
.   .   .   . £250
Mr Sponge's Sporting Tour, Bradbury & Evans (London),
1852-3 (13 [12] monthly parts, illustrated by John Leech).
.   .   .   . £750 the set
ditto, Bradbury & Evans (London), 1853 (1 vol) .   . £200
Ask Mamma; or, The Richest Commoner in England,
Bradbury & Evans (London), 1857-8 (13 [12] monthly
parts, illustrated by John Leech) £1,000
ditto, Bradbury & Evans (London), 1858 (1 vol.) .   . £125
Plain or Ringlets?, Bradbury & Evans (London), 1858-60
(13 [12] monthly parts, illustrated by John Leech) . £600
ditto, Bradbury & Evans (London), 1860 (1 vol.) .   . £200
ditto, Bradbury & Evans (London), 1860 (1 vol.; wraps) £600
Mr Facey Romford's Hounds, Bradbury & Evans (London),
1864-5 (13 [12] monthly parts, illustrated by John Leech).
.   .   .   . £750
ditto, Bradbury & Evans (London), 1865 (1 vol.) .   . £200
Hunting with Mr Jorrocks, O.U.P. (Oxford, UK), 1956
(edited by Lionel Gough, illustrated by Edward Ardizzone)
.   .   .   . £50/£15

Non-Fiction
**The Horseman's Manual, being a treatise on Soundness,
the law of Warranty, and generally on the laws relating to
Horses**, Miller (London), 1831.   .   .   .   . £300
ditto, Treadway (New York), 1832 .   .   .   . £300
The Analysis of the Hunting Field, Ackermann (London),
1846 (colour plates by Henry Alken, first issue in green
cloth) £750

ditto, Ackermann (London), 1846 (colour plates by Henry Alken, second issue in red cloth) £500
Hints to Railway Travellers, Bradbury & Evans (London), 1852 (wraps). £100

PATRICK SÜSKIND
(b.1949)

Patrick Süskind studied medieval and modern history at the University of Munich. His play, *The Double Bass*, was an international success and his first novel, *Perfume* was an internationally acclaimed bestseller. He is the co-author of a hugely successful German television series *Kir Royal*.

Novels
Perfume: The Story of a Murderer, Hamish Hamilton, 1986 (translated by John E. Woods) . . . . £45/£10
ditto, Knopf (New York), 1986 . . . . . £40/£10
The Pigeon, Hamish Hamilton, 1988 (translated by John E. Woods) . . . . £10/£5
ditto, Knopf (New York), 1988 . . . . . £10/£5
The Story of Mr Sommer, Bloomsbury (London), 1992 (translated by Michael Hofmann) . . . . £10/£5
ditto, as **Mr Summer's Story**, Knopf (New York), 1993 .
. . . . £10/£5

Collections
Three Stories and a Reflection, Bloomsbury (London), 1996
. . . . £15/£5

Play
The Double-Bass, Hamish Hamilton, 1987 (translated by Michael Hofmann) . . . . £35/£10

Non-Fiction
On Love and Death, Old Street (London), 2006 (translated by Anthea Bell; pbk) £5
ditto, Overlook/Rookery (New York), 2006 (pbk) . . £5

GRAHAM SWIFT
(b.1949)

Graham Swift is an English novelist whose reputation was based largely on *Waterland* until *Last Orders* won the Booker and James Tait Black Memorial Prizes in 1996. *Last Orders* tells the story of a journey to the Kent coast from an East End pub made by four friends in order to scatter the ashes of their dead drinking-partner in the sea. It was filmed in 2001, starring Michael Caine and Bob Hoskins.

Novels
The Sweet Shop Owner, Allen Lane (London), 1980 . .
. . . . £350/£45
ditto, Washington Square (New York), 1985 (pbk). . £10
Shuttlecock, Allen Lane (London), 1981 . . . £250/£30
ditto, Washington Square (New York), 1985 (pbk). . £10
Waterland, Heinemann (London), 1983 . . . £125/£15
ditto, Poseidon (New York), 1984 . . . . . £15/£5

Out of This World, Viking (London), 1988 . . £10/£5
ditto, Poseidon (New York), 1988 . . . . . £10/£5
Ever After, Picador (London), 1992 . . . . £10/£5
ditto, Knopf (New York), 1992 . . . . . £10/£5
Last Orders, Picador (London), 1996 . . . £15/£5
ditto, Knopf (New York), 1996 . . . . . £10/£5
The Light of Day, Hamish Hamilton (London), 2003 £15/£5
ditto, Knopf (New York), 2003 . . . . . £10/£5
Tomorrow, Picador (London), 2007 . . . . £10/£5
ditto, Knopf (New York), 2007 . . . . . £10/£5

Short Stories
Learning to Swim and Other Stories, London Magazine Editions (London), 1982 . . . . . £250/£35
ditto, Poseidon (New York), 1982 . . . . £15/£5

Essays
Making An Elephant: Writing from Within, Picador (London), 2009 . . . . £10/£5
ditto, Knopf (New York), 2009 . . . . . £10/£5

A.J.A. SYMONS
(b.1900 d.1941)

A biographer, bibliographer and book collector, Symons' masterpiece is *The Quest for Corvo*, an unconventional biography of the English author Frederick Rolfe. The book was groundbreaking in its day because Symons' concentrated upon describing his own search for an understanding of his subject.

A Bibliography of the First Editions of Books by William Butler Yeats, First Edition Club (London), 1924 (500 copies)
. . . . £45/£20
Frederick Baron Corvo, The Curwen Press (London), 1927 (printed for the Sette of Odd Volumes, 199 copies; wraps)
. . . . £200
Emin: The Governor of Equatoria, The Fleuron (London), 1928 (300 numbered copies) £45
ditto, Falcon Press, 1950 . . . . . . £20/£5
An Episode in the Life of the Queen of Sheba Rediscovered by A.J.A. Symons, privately printed for Albert Ehrman and A.J.A. Symons, 1929 (150 copies; wraps) . . . £75
H.M. Stanley, Duckworth (London), 1933 . . £45/£15
ditto, Falcon Press (London), 1950 . . . . £25/£10
The Quest for Corvo, Cassell (London), 1934 . . £125/£25
ditto, Macmillan (New York), 1934 . . . . £100/£15
The Nonesuch Century; An Appraisal, Nonesuch Press (London), 1936 (with F. Meynell & D. Flower, 750 copies)
. . . . £450/£250
Essays and Biographies, Cassell (London), 1969 (edited by Julian Symons) . . . . £15/£5
A.J.A. Symons to Wyndham Lewis: Twenty-Four Letters, Tragara Press (Edinburgh), 1982 (120 copies; wraps). £35
Two Brothers: Fragments of a Correspondence, Tragara Press (Edinburgh), 1985 (105 copies; wraps) . . £20
ditto, Tragara Press (Edinburgh), 1985 (25 copies, signed by Julian Symons; wraps) £65

JULIAN SYMONS

(b.1912 d.1994)

Julian Symons was the younger brother (and biographer) of
A.J.A. Symons and is well known as a novelist specialising
in detective fiction. He was also a poet, critic, biographer
and the author of social and military history. Working first
as an advertising copywriter, he became a full-time writer
in 1947, co-founding the Crime Writers Association in
1953.

Novels

The Immaterial Murder Case, Gollancz (London), 1945   .
.   .   .   .   £75/£15
ditto, Macmillan (New York), 1957   .   .   £25/£10
A Man Called Jones, Gollancz (London), 1947   .   £65/£10
Bland Beginning, Gollancz (London), 1949   .   £50/£10
ditto, Harper (New York), 1949 .   .   .   £35/£10
The 31st of February, Gollancz (London), 1950   £50/£10
ditto, Harper (New York), 1950 .   .   .   £25/£5
The Broken Penny, Gollancz (London), 1953.   £45/£10
ditto, Harper (New York), 1953 .   .   .   £25/£5
The Narrowing Circle, Gollancz (London), 1954   £45/£10
ditto, Harper (New York), 1954 .   .   .   £25/£5
The Paper Chase, Collins Crime Club (London), 1956.
.   .   .   .   £45/£10
ditto, as *Bogue's Fortune*, Harper (New York), 1957 £25/£5
The Colour of Murder, Collins Crime Club (London), 1957
.   .   .   .   £45/£10
ditto, as *The Color of Murder*, Harper (New York), 1957   .
.   .   .   .   £25/£5
The Gigantic Shadow, Collins Crime Club (London), 1958.
.   .   .   .   £40/£5
ditto, as *The Pipe Dream*, Harper (New York), 1958 £25/£5
The Progress of a Crime, Collins Crime Club (London),
1960   .   .   .   .   £35/£5
ditto, Harper (New York), 1960 .   .   .   £25/£5
The Killing of Francie Lake, Collins Crime Club (London),
1962   .   .   .   .   £35/£5
ditto, as *The Plain Man*, Harper & Row (New York), 1962.
.   .   .   .   £25/£5
The End of Solomon Grundy, Collins Crime Club (London),
1964   .   .   .   .   £35/£5
ditto, Harper & Row (New York), 1964 .   .   £25/£5
The Belting Inheritance, Collins Crime Club (London),
1965   .   .   .   .   £35/£5
ditto, Harper & Row (New York), 1965   .   .   £25/£5
The Man Who Killed Himself, Collins Crime Club
(London), 1967   .   .   .   .   .   .   £35/£5
ditto, Harper & Row (New York), 1967   .   .   £25/£5
The Man Whose Dreams Came True, Collins Crime Club
(London), 1968   .   .   .   .   .   £35/£5
ditto, Harper & Row (New York), 1969   .   .   £25/£5
The Man Who Lost His Wife, Collins Crime Club (London),
1970   .   .   .   .   £30/£5
ditto, Harper & Row (New York), 1971   .   .   £25/£5
The Players and the Game, Collins Crime Club (London),
1971   .   .   .   .   £30/£5
ditto, Harper & Row (New York), 1972   .   .   £25/£5
The Plot against Roger Rider, Collins Crime Club
(London), 1973   .   .   .   .   .   £20/£5
ditto, Harper & Row (New York), 1973   .   .   £15/£5
A Three Pipe Problem, Collins Crime Club (London), 1975
.   .   .   .   £20/£5

ditto, Harper & Row (New York), 1975.   .   .   £15/£5
The Blackheath Poisonings, Collins Crime Club (London),
1978   .   .   .   .   £20/£5
ditto, Harper & Row (New York), 1978   .   .   £15/£5
Sweet Adelaide, Collins Crime Club (London), 1980 £20/£5
ditto, Harper & Row (New York), 1980   .   .   £15/£5
The Detling Murders, Macmillan (London), 1982 .   £20/£5
ditto, as *The Detling Secret*, Viking (New York), 1983.   .
.   .   .   .   £15/£5
The Name of Annabel Lee, Macmillan (London), 1983
.   .   .   .   £20/£5
ditto, Viking (New York), 1983 .   .   .   £15/£5
The Criminal Comedy of the Contented Couple, Macmillan
(London), 1985 .   .   .   .   .   £15/£5
ditto, as *A Criminal Comedy*, Viking (New York), 1986   .
.   .   .   .   £10/£5
The Kentish Manor Murders, Macmillan (London), 1988 .
.   .   .   .   £15/£5
ditto, Viking (New York), 1988 .   .   .   £10/£5
Death's Darkest Face, Macmillan (London), 1990. £15/£5
ditto, Viking (New York), 1990 .   .   .   £10/£5
Something Like a Love Affair, Macmillan (London), 1992 .
.   .   .   .   £15/£5
ditto, Mysterious Press (New York), 1992   .   £10/£5
Playing Happy Families, Macmillan (London), 1994 £15/£5
ditto, Mysterious Press (New York), 1995   .   £10/£5
A Sort of Virtue, Macmillan (London), 1996   .   £10/£5

Omnibus

The Julian Symons Omnibus, Collins (London), 1966.
.   .   .   .   £15/£5

Short Stories

Murder, Murder, Fontana (London), 1961 (pbk)   .   £5
Francis Quarles Investigates, Panther (London), 1965 (pbk)
.   .   .   .   £5
The Tigers of Subtopia and Other Stories, Macmillan
(London), 1981 .   .   .   .   .   £25/£5
ditto, Viking (New York), 1983 .   .   .   £15/£5
Somebody Else and Other Stories, Eurographica (Helsinki),
1990 (350 signed, numbered copies; wraps in d/w) £35/£20
Portraits of the Missing, Deutsch (London), 1991 . £20/£5
Murder under the Mistletoe, Severn House (London), 1993
.   .   .   .   £15/£5
The Man Who Hated Television and Other Stories,
Macmillan (London), 1995   .   .   .   £10/£5

Poems

Confusions About X, Fortune Press (London), [1939]
(frontispiece by Wyndham Lewis)   .   .   £125/£25
The Second Man, Routledge (London), 1943 .   £50/£10
The Object of an Affair and Other Poems, Tragara Press
(Edinburgh), 1974 (25 signed copies; wraps)   .   £40
ditto, Tragara Press (Edinburgh), 1974 (65 copies; wraps) .
.   .   .   .   £20
The Thirties and the Nineties, Carcanet (Manchester), 1990
.   .   .   .   £10/£5

Others

A.J.A. Symons: His Life and Speculations, Eyre &
Spottiswoode (London), 1950 .   .   .   £15/£5
Thomas Carlyle. The Life and Times of a Prophet, Gollancz
(London) Ltd., 1951 .   .   .   .   .   £15/£5

Horatio Bottomley: A Biography, The Cresset Press (London), 1955 . . . . . . £15/£5
The General Strike, The Cresset Press (London), 1957. .
. . . . £15/£5
The Thirties. A Dream Revolved, The Cresset Press (London), 1960 . . . . . £15/£5
Reasonable Doubt: Some Criminal Cases, The Cresset Press (London), 1960 . . . £15/£5
The Detective Story in Britain, Longmans, Green & Co. (London), 1962 (stapled wraps) £10
Buller's Campaign, The Cresset Press (London), 1963 £10/£5
England's Pride: The Story of the Gordon Relief Expedition, Hamish Hamilton (London), 1965 . £10/£5
Critical Occasions, Hamish Hamilton (London), 1966 £15/£5
Mortal Consequences, Harper & Row (New York), 1972 .
. . . . £15/£5
ditto, as *Bloody Murder: From the Detective Story to the Crime: A History*, Faber (London), 1972 . £15/£5
ditto, Viking (London), 1985 (revised edition) £10/£5
ditto, Mysterious Press (New York), 1993 . £10/£5
The Tell-Tale Heart: The Life and Works of Edgar Allan Poe, Faber (London), 1978 . . . £20/£5
ditto, Harper & Row (New York), 1978 . . . £15/£5
Portrait of an Artist: Conan Doyle, Whizzard Press/ Deutsch (London), 1979 . . . . £15/£5
ditto, Mysterious Press (New York), 1979 . £15/£5
The Modern Crime Story, Tragara Press (Edinburgh), 1980 (125 signed copies; wraps) £40
ditto, Eurographica (Helsinki), 1988 (350 signed copies; wraps) £10
1948 and 1984, Tragara Press (Edinburgh), 1984 (135 copies; wraps) £35
Two Brothers: Fragments of a Correspondence, Tragara Press (Edinburgh), 1985 (105 copies; wraps) . £20
ditto, Tragara Press (Edinburgh), 1985 (25 copies, signed by Julian Symons; wraps) £65
Makers of the New, Deutsch (London), 1987 . £10/£5
ditto, Random House (New York), 1987 . . £10/£5
Did Sherlock Holmes Meet Hercule...?, Yellow Barn Press (Council Bluffs, IA), 1987 (200 copies). . £50
Oscar Wilde: A Problem in Biography, Yellow Barn Press (Council Bluffs, IA), 1988 (200 copies). . £50
Does Literature Exist?, Yellow Barn Press (Council Bluffs, IA), 1993 (175 copies) £20

ELIZABETH TAYLOR
(b.1912 d.1975)

Elizabeth Taylor was a popular English novelist and short story writer whose work is often concerned with the nuances of ordinary life of middle and upper middle class English life.

At Mrs Lippincote's, Davies (London), 1945 . £125/£15
ditto, Knopf (New York), 1946 . . . . £65/£10
Palladian, Davies (London), 1946 . . . £45/£10
ditto, Knopf (New York), 1947 . . . £20/£5
A View of the Harbour, Davies (London), 1947 £45/£10
ditto, Knopf (New York), 1947 . . . £20/£5
A Wreath of Roses, Davies (London), 1949 . £25/£10
ditto, Knopf (New York), 1949 . . . £20/£5
A Game of Hide and Seek, Davies (London), 1951 £25/£10

ditto, Knopf (New York), 1951 . . . . £20/£5
The Sleeping Beauty, Davies (London), 1953 . £20/£5
ditto, Viking (New York), 1953 . . . . £20/£5
Angel, Davies (London), 1957 . . . . £15/£5
ditto, Viking (New York), 1957 . . . . £15/£5
In a Summer Season, Davies (London), 1961 . £15/£5
ditto, Viking (New York), 1961 . . . . £15/£5
The Soul of Kindness, Chatto & Windus (London), 1964 .
. . . . £15/£5
ditto, Viking (New York), 1964 . . . . £15/£5
The Wedding Group, Chatto & Windus (London), 1968 .
. . . . £10/£5
ditto, Viking (New York), 1968 . . . . £10/£5
Mrs Palfrey at the Claremont, Chatto & Windus (London), 1971 . . . . £10/£5
ditto, Viking (New York), 1971 . . . . £10/£5
Blaming, Chatto & Windus (London), 1976 . £10/£5
ditto, Viking (New York), 1976 . . . . £10/£5

Short Stories
Hester Lilly, Davies (London), 1954 . . . £25/£5
ditto, Viking (New York), 1954 . . . . £25/£5
The Blush, Davies (London), 1958 . . . £25/£5
ditto, Viking (New York), 1959 . . . . £25/£5
A Dedicated Man, Chatto & Windus (London), 1965 £15/£5
ditto, Viking (New York), 1965 . . . . £15/£5
The Devastating Boys and Other Stories, Chatto & Windus (London), 1972 . . . . . . £10/£5
ditto, Viking (New York), 1972 . . . . £10/£5
Dangerous Calm: Selected Short Stories of Elizabeth Taylor, Virago (London), 1997 . . . £15/£5

For Children
Mossy Trotter, Chatto & Windus (London), 1967 . £10/£5
ditto, Harcourt, Brace & World (New York), 1967 . £10/£5

G.P. TAYLOR
(b.1961)

G.P. Taylor was an Anglican vicar in North Yorkshire before taking up writing full-time. His work reflects his Christian faith and has offended neopagans in the same way that authors dealing with neopagans upset some Christian commentators.

Shadowmancer, Mount Publishing (Scarborough), 2002 (pbk) £200
ditto, Faber & Faber (London), 2003 . . . . £5
ditto, Faber & Faber (London), 2003 (hardback special edition) . . . . £15/£5
ditto, Charisma House (Lake Mary, FL), 2004. . £10/£5
Wormwood, Faber & Faber (London), 2004 . £10/£5
ditto, Faber & Faber (London), 2003 (pbk) . . £5
ditto, Putnam's (New York), 2004 . . . £10/£5
Tersias, Faber & Faber (London), 2005 . . £10/£5
ditto, Faber & Faber (London), 2005 (1,000 signed, numbered copies; slipcase) . . . . £30/£10
ditto, as *Tersias the Oracle*, Putnam's (New York), 2006 .
. . . . £10/£5
The Curse of Salamander Street, Faber & Faber (London), 2006 . . . . £10/£5
ditto, as *The Shadowmancer Returns: The Curse of Salamander Street*, Putnam's (New York), 2007 . £10/£5

PETER TAYLOR

(b.1917 d.1994)

Peter Taylor was an American short-story writer and
novelist who won the PEN/Faulkner Award (1986) and the
Pulitzer Prize for fiction (1987) for *A Summons to
Memphis*.

A Long Fourth and Other Stories, Harcourt, Brace (New
York), 1948 . . . . £300/£65
ditto, Routledge & Kegan Paul (London), 1948 . £200/£45
A Woman of Means, Harcourt, Brace (New York), 1950 .
. . . . £200/£45
ditto, Routledge & Kegan Paul (London), 1950 . £150/£25
The Widows of Thornton, Harcourt, Brace (New York),
1954 . . . . £125/£25
Tennessee Day in St Louis, Random House (New York),
1957 . . . . £100/£20
Happy Families Are All Alike, McDowell-Obolensky (New
York), 1959 . . . . £100/£20
ditto, McDowell-Obolensky (New York), 1959 (trial d/w
one-quarter inch taller than the book; blank flaps and back
panel) . . . . £150/£20
ditto, Macmillan (London), 1960 . . . £65/£10
Miss Lenora When Last Seen and Fifteen Other Stories,
Ivan Obolensky (New York), 1963 (light orange yellow
coarse linen cloth stamped in dark grey/red brown) . .
. . . . £100/£20
Miss Lenora When Last Seen and Fifteen Other Stories,
Ivan Obolensky (New York), 1963 [1967 or 1969] (second
issue in brilliant yellow linen cloth stamped in gold) .
. . . . £50/£10
The Collected Stories of Peter Taylor, Farrar, Straus and
Giroux (New York), 1969 . . . . . £45/£10
Literature, Sewanee and The World, University of the South
(Sewanee, TN), 1972 (wraps) £150
Presences; Seven Dramatic Pieces, Houghton Mifflin
(Boston), 1972 . . . . £150/£25
ditto, Houghton Mifflin (Boston), 1972 (pbk) . . £25
In The Miro District and Other Stories, Knopf (New York),
1977 . . . . £30/£5
ditto, Chatto & Windus (London), 1977 . . £15/£5
The Road and Other Modern Stories, C.U.P. (Cambridge),
1979 (pbk) £10
The Early Guest, Palaemon Press (Winston-Salem, NC),
1982 (140 signed, numbered copies; pbk in d/w) . . £65
ditto, Palaemon Press (Winston-Salem, NC), 1982 (26
signed, lettered copies; pbk in d/w) £150
Eudora Welty, Stuart Wright (no place), 1984 (5 numbered
copies; wraps) £150
The Old Forest and Other Stories, Dial (New York), 1985 .
. . . . £15/£5
ditto, Chatto & Windus/Hogarth (London), 1985 . £15/£5
A Stand in the Mountains, Frederic C. Beil (New York),
1985 (no d/w; in plain cardboard mailing box/slipcase) .
. . . . £25/£15
A Summons to Memphis, Knopf (New York) 1986 (first
issue d/w without mention of Pulitzer Prize on front flap;
text on rear flap beginning, 'now he gives us this...') £25/£5

ditto, Knopf (New York) 1986 (second issue d/w with
mention of Pulitzer Prize on front flap; text on rear flap
beginning, 'His highly acclaimed collection...') . £10/£5
ditto, Chatto & Windus/Hogarth (London), 1987 . £15/£5
"A Walled Garden", Tales For Travellers (Napa, CA), 1987
(single sheet folded map-style). £10
Conversations With Peter Taylor, Univ Press of Mississippi
(Jackson, MS/London), 1987 (hardback issue) . £15/£5
ditto, Univ Press of Mississippi (Jackson, MS/London), 1987
(pbk) £10
The Oracle of Stonleigh Court, Knopf (New York), 1993 .
. . . . £10/£5
ditto, Chatto & Windus (London), 1993 . . . £10/£5
In The Tennessee Country, Knopf (New York), 1994 . .
. . . . £10/£5
ditto, Chatto & Windus (London), 1994 . . . £10/£5

PHOEBE ATWOOD TAYLOR

(b.1909 d.1976)

Taylor was an American mystery author who wrote novels
under her own name, and the pseudonyms Freeman Dana
and Alice Tilton. Her first novel, The Cape Cod Mystery,
introduced the 'Codfish Sherlock', Asey Mayo, who
became a series character appearing in 24 novels. Taylor's
work was light and readable.

'Asey Mayo' novels
The Cape Cod Mystery, Bobbs Merrill (Indianapolis, IN),
1931 . . . . £400/£45
Death Lights a Candle, Bobbs Merrill (Indianapolis, IN),
1932 . . . . £350/£40
The Mystery of the Cape Cod Players, Norton (New York),
1933 . . . . £300/£35
ditto, Eyre and Spottiswoode (London), 1934 . £250/£25
The Mystery of the Cape Cod Tavern, Norton (New York),
1934 . . . . £200/£25
ditto, Eyre and Spottiswoode (London), 1935 . £175/£20
Sandbar Sinister, Norton (New York), 1934 . £150/£20
ditto, Gollancz (London), 1936 . . . £125/£20
The Tinkling Symbol, Norton (New York), 1935 . £150/£20
ditto, Gollancz (London), 1935 . . . £125/£20
Deathblow Hill, Norton (New York), 1935 . £150/£20
ditto, Gollancz (London), 1936 . . . £125/£20
The Crimson Patch, Norton (New York), 1936 . £150/£20
ditto, Gollancz (London), 1936 . . . £125/£20
Out of Order, Norton (New York), 1936 . . £150/£20
ditto, Gollancz (London), 1937 . . . £125/£20
Figure Away, Norton (New York), 1937 . . £135/£15
ditto, Collins Crime Club (London), 1938 . £100/£15
Octagon House, Norton (New York), 1937 . £125/£15
ditto, Collins Crime Club (London), 1938 . £100/£15
The Annulet of Gilt, Norton (New York), 1938 . £125/£15
ditto, Collins Crime Club (London), 1939 . £100/£15
Banbury Bog, Norton (New York), 1938 . £125/£15
ditto, Collins Crime Club (London), 1939 . £100/£15
Spring Harrowing, Norton (New York), 1939 . £75/£10
ditto, Collins Crime Club (London), 1939 . £65/£10
The Criminal C.O.D., Norton (New York), 1940 . £50/£10

ditto, as **Criminal C.O.D.**, Collins Crime Club (London), 1940 . . . . £45/£10

The Deadly Sunshade, Norton (New York), 1940 . £45/£10

ditto, Collins Crime Club (London), 1941 . . £40/£10

The Perennial Boarder, Norton (New York), 1941 £45/£10

ditto, Collins Crime Club (London), 1942 . . £40/£10

The Six Iron Spiders, Norton (New York), 1942 . £45/£10

ditto, Collins Crime Club (London), 1943 . . £40/£10

Three Plots for Asey Mayo, Norton (New York), 1942

. . . . £45/£10

Going, Going, Gone, Norton (New York), 1943 . £30/£5

ditto, Collins Crime Club (London), 1944 . . £25/£5

Proof of the Pudding, Norton (New York), 1943 . £20/£5

The Asey Mayo Trio, Messner (New York), 1946 . £25/£5

ditto, Collins Crime Club (London), 1946 . . £25/£5

Punch with Care, Farrar Strauss (New York), 1946 £20/£5

ditto, Collins Crime Club (London), 1947 . . £20/£5

Diplomatic Corpse, Little, Brown (New York), 1951 £20/£5

ditto, Collins Crime Club (London), 1951 . . £15/£5

Writing as 'Freeman Dana'

Murder at the New York World's Fair, Random House (New York), 1938 . . . . . . £150/£20

Writing as 'Alice Tilton'

Beginning with a Bash, Collins (London), 1937 . £200/£35

ditto, Norton (New York), 1972 . . . . £15/£5

The Cut Direct, Norton (New York), 1938 . . £125/£15

ditto, Collins Crime Club (London), 1938 . . £100/£15

Cold Steal, Norton (New York), 1939 . . . £75/£10

ditto, Collins Crime Club (London), 1940 . . £65/£10

The Left Leg, Norton (New York), 1940 . . . £45/£10

ditto, Collins Crime Club (London), 1941 . . £35/£10

The Hollow Chest, Norton (New York), 1941 . £45/£10

ditto, Collins Crime Club (London), 1942 . . £35/£10

File For Record, Norton (New York), 1943 . . £30/£5

ditto, Collins Crime Club (London), 1944 . . £25/£5

Dead Ernest, Norton (New York), 1944 . . . £30/£5

ditto, Collins Crime Club (London), 1945 . . £25/£5

The Iron Clew, Farrar Strauss (new York), 1947 . £20/£5

ditto, as **The Iron Hand**, Collins Crime Club (London), 1947

. . . . £20/£5

ALFRED TENNYSON

(b.1809 d.1892)

Tennyson was a Victorian poet who had achieved fame before the publication of his *Idylls of the King*, although it was this work that resulted in his contemporaries claiming him as one of the greatest poets of all time. Condemned by some critics after his death as embodying all that was wrong with his time (Empire and morality), his reputation nevertheless remains solid. His later books were published in huge print runs and are not at all rare. There are a number of forgeries, which are collectable in themselves.

Poetry

Poems by Two Brothers, Printed for W. Simpkin [London] and J. and J. Jackson (Louth), 1827 (with Charles Tennyson; boards, paper label, or cloth, or yellow wraps).

. . . . £1,750

Timbuctoo . . . A Poem which obtained the Chancellor's Medal..., John Smith (Cambridge, UK), 1829 (wraps) .

. . . . £1,750

Poems, Chiefly Lyrical, Effingham Wilson (London), 1830 (boards, paper label on spine; first issue with p91 numbered p19, and error p.72 of 'caronet' instead of 'carcanet').

. . . . £1,000

Poems, Moxon, 1833 (450 copies; boards, paper label on spine, or cloth) £850

Poems, Moxon (London), 1842 (2 vols; boards, paper label on spine) £650

The Princess: A Medley, Moxon (London), 1847 (green cloth) £250

ditto, Moxon (London), 1847 (50 large paper copies) . £300

In Memoriam, Moxon (London), 1850 (purple cloth; published in the 'Parchment Library'; first issue: p.2, line 13, has the words 'the sullen tree' instead of 'thee, sullen tree'; and p.198, line 3, has the word 'baseness' instead of 'bareness') £200

ditto, Macmillan (London), 1885 (large paper edition; 50 copies) £300

Ode on the Death of the Duke of Wellington, Moxon (London), 1852 (slate-coloured wraps) . . . £100

Maud, and Other Poems, Moxon (London), 1855 (green cloth; first issue with July list of books at rear) . . £65

The Charge of the Light Brigade, London, 1855 (wraps) £65

Poems, Moxon (London), 1857 (illustrated by Rossetti, Millais, Holman Hunt etc). £250

The Miller's Daughter, W. Kent (London), 1958 . £45

Idylls of the King, Moxon (London), 1868 (blind-stamped green cloth gilt; first issue with verso title-page blank (no printer's name) and 4 leaves of adverts dated July 1859) .

. . . . £35

ditto, Cassell, 1867-1869 (4 vols as *Elaine, Enid, Guinevere* and *Vivien*, illustrated by Gustave Doré) . £650 the set

The May Queen, Sampson Low (London), 1861 (illustrated by W. R. Thomms) £100

Helen's Tower, Clandeboye ... Privately Printed, [1861] (pink wraps) £250

Poems MDCCCXXX-MDCCCXXXIII, privately printed (Canada), 1862 (wraps) £150

Mariana, O. Breads (Worthing), 1863 (wraps) . . £45

A Welcome, Moxon (London), 1863 (wraps; first issue with diamond-shaped centre below the title is solid) . . £35

ditto, Moxon (London), 1863 (wraps; second issue with diamond-shaped centre hollow) £25

Enoch Arden, Moxon (London), 1864 (green cloth) . £25

Property, [1864] (wraps) £200

The Window, or The Loves of the Wrens, privately printed by Sir J. & Miss Guest, Canford Manor 1867 (6 copies; imp red cloth) £250

A Selection from His Works, Moxon's Miniature Poets (London), 1865 (illustrated by John Leighton) . . £50

The Victim, privately printed by Sir J. & Miss Guest, Canford Manor, 1867. . . . . £250

Tennysoniana, Basil Pickering (London), 1866 . . £45

The Holy Grail and Other Poems, Strahan (London), 1870.

. . . . £15

Gareth and Lynette, Strahan (London), 1872 (green cloth) .

. . . . £15

To the Queen, no printer, [1873] (wraps) . . . £175

Queen Mary: A Drama, H.S. King (London), 1875 (green cloth; first issue has the misprinted word 'Behled' on p.126, and no printers' imprint on p. 278.) . . . £25

The Poetical Works, H.S. King (London), 1875 (5 vols)   .
.   .   .   .   £45 the set
Harold: A Drama, H.S. King (London), 1877 (green cloth).
.   .   .   .   £10
Lord of Burghley, H. Johnson (Stamford), 1878 (wraps) £45
The Lover's Tale, Kegan Paul, 1879 .   .   .   .   £20
Ballads and Other Poems, Kegan Paul, 1880 (green cloth) .
.   .   .   .   £15
Early Spring, Macmillan (London), 1883.   .   .   £10
Beckett, Macmillan (London), 1884 (green cloth) .   .   £10
The Cup and the Falcoln, Macmillan (London), 1884 (green
cloth) £10
Tiresias and Other Poems, Macmillan (London), 1885
(green cloth). £10
Locksley Hall Sixty Years After, Macmillan (London), 1886
(green cloth). £10
The Brook, Macmillan (London), 1887 .   .   .   £10
The Throstle, Macmillan (London), 1889.   .   .   £10
Three Poems by Tennyson Illustrated by Edward Lear,
Bousson, Valadon & Co., Scribner's & Welford (London),
1889 (100 copies signed by Tennyson, 24 illustrations by
Lear) £1,500
Demeter and Other Poems, Macmillan (London), 1889
(green cloth). £10
The Foresters, Robin Hood and Maid Marian, Macmillan
(London), 1892 (green cloth) £10
The Death of Oenone, Akbar's Dream etc, Macmillan
(London), 1892   .   .   .   .   .   .   £10
Maud: A Monodrama, Kelmscott Press (London), 1893 (500
copies; slipcase) £1,500
The Works, Macmillan (London), 1898 (12 vols; 1,050
copies) £100
The Devil and the Lady, Macmillan (London), 1930 (1500
copies)   .   .   .   .   .   .   £20/£10

Forgeries
Morte d'Arthur, London, [1842] (stitched, without covers) .
.   .   .   .   £50
The Sailor Boy, 'Emily Faithfull', 1861 [1895] (cream
wraps) £45
Ode for the Opening of the International Exhibition,
'Moxon', 1862 [1890] (wraps).   .   .   .   £45
Idylls of the Hearth, Edward Moxon (London), 1864 (forged
'original' version of *Enoch Arden*) £200
Ode on the Opening of the Colonial and Indian Exhibition,
William Clowes, 1866   .   .   .   .   .   £45
Gareth and Lynette, Strahan (London), 1871 (a 'trial issue'
was forged by T J. Wise) £35
Lucretius, London, 1868 [1890] (brown cloth)   .   .   £45
The Lover's Tale, London, 1870 [1890]   .   .   .   £45
The Last Tournament, 'Strahan', 1871 [1895]   .   .   £45
England and America in 1782, Strahan & Co (London),
1872 (wraps). £50
The New Timon and the Poets, With Other Omitted Poems,
Privately Printed 1876   .   .   .   .   .   £40
A Welcome to Alexandrova, 'Henry S. King', 1863/1874
[1895] (40 copies; wraps). £45
Beckett, Macmillan (London), 1879 (green cloth) .   .   £10
The Falcoln, Printed for the author (London), '1879'
(wraps) £45
Child-Songs, Kegan Paul (London), 1880 (wraps).   .   £25
The Cup, Printed for the author (London), '1881' (wraps) .
.   .   .   .   £45

The Promise of May, Printed for the author (London),
'1882' (wraps) £45
Carmen Secularae, Printed for Private Distribution
(London), 1887 [1895] (wraps) £45
Child Songs, Kegan Paul (London), '1880' (wraps)   .   £45
Death of the Duke of Clarence and Avondale, London,
1893 (wraps). £25
The Antechamber, Printed for private circulation 1906
(wraps) £20

JOSEPHINE TEY
(b.1897 d.1952)

'Josephine Tey' was the pseudonym under which Scottish
author Elizabeth Mackintosh wrote popular mystery
novels. She had worked as a teacher until forced to give up
her job in order to care for her invalid father. Before
finding success as 'Josephine Tey' she wrote historical
plays as 'Gordon Daviot'.

Novels Written as 'Josephine Tey'
A Shilling for Candles, Methuen (London), 1936 . £500/£75
ditto, Macmillan (New York), 1954 .   .   .   .   £25/£10
Miss Pym Disposes, Peter Davies (London), 1946 . £200/£25
ditto, Macmillan (New York), 1948 .   .   .   .   £50/£10
The Franchise Affair, Peter Davies (London), 1948   .   .
.   .   .   .   £200/£20
ditto, Macmillan (New York), 1949 .   .   .   £50/£10
Brat Farrar, Peter Davies (London), 1949 .   . £150/£20
ditto, Macmillan (New York), 1950 .   .   . £125/£15
ditto, as *Come and Kill Me*, Pocket Books (New York), 1951
(pbk) £5
To Love and Be Wise, Peter Davies (London), 1950   .   .
.   .   .   .   £150/£20
ditto, Macmillan (New York), 1951 .   .   . £125/£15
The Daughter of Time, Peter Davies (London), 1951 .   .
.   .   .   .   £150/£20
ditto, Macmillan (New York), 1952 .   .   . £125/£15
The Singing Sands, Peter Davies (London), 1952 . £150/£20
ditto, Macmillan (New York), 1953 .   .   . £125/£15

Novels Written as 'Gordon Daviot'
The Man in the Queue, Methuen (London), 1929 £750/£125
ditto, Dutton (New York), 1929 .   .   .   . £250/£45
ditto, Peter Davies (London), 1953 (as 'Josephine Tey')   .
.   .   .   .   £50/£15
ditto, as *Killer in the Crowd*, Mercury (New York), 1954 (as
'Josephine Tey') .   .   .   .   .   £35/£10
Kif, An Unvarnished History, Benn (London), 1929 £50/£15
ditto, Appleton (New York), 1929 .   .   .   . £50/£15
The Expensive Halo, Benn (London), 1931   .   . £50/£15
ditto, Appleton (New York), 1931 .   .   .   . £50/£15
The Privateer, Peter Davies (London), 1952 .   . £25/£5
ditto, Macmillan (New York), 1952 .   .   .   £20/£5

Other Titles Written as 'Gordon Daviot'
Richard of Bordeaux, Gollancz (London), 1933   . £50/£10
ditto, Little, Brown (Boston), 1933 .   .   .   . £40/£10
The Laughing Woman, Gollancz (London), 1934 . £45/£10
Queen of Scots, Gollancz (London), 1934   .   . £40/£10

The Stars Bow Down, Duckworth (London), 1939   £40/£10
Claverhouse, Collins (London), 1937   .   .   .   £45/£10
Leith Sands, And Other Short Plays, Duckworth (London),
   1946   .   .   .   .   £40/£10
Plays, In Three Volumes, Peter Davies (London), 1953-54 .
   .   .   .   .   £50/£15 the set

W.M. THACKERAY
(b.1811 d.1863)

Thackeray was Charlotte Brontë's favourite author and she
dedicated the second edition of *Jane Eyre* to him. He was a
prolific writer under a number of pseudonyms, including
'Charles James Yellowplush, a footman', 'Michael Angelo
Titmarsh' and 'George Savage Fitz-Boodle'. Best known
for his novels, especially his masterly satire of middle-class
Victorian English society *Vanity Fair*, Thackeray also
travelled widely as a journalist.

Novels
Vanity Fair: A Novel Without a Hero, Bradbury & Evans
   (London), 1848 (20 parts in 19; yellow wraps)   .   £5,000
ditto, Bradbury & Evans (London), 1848 (first book edition,
   made up of the original parts; engraved title-page date
   1849; woodcut [later suppressed] of Lord Steyne on page
   336; 'Mr. Pitt' on p.453; green cloth)   .   .   £2,000
ditto, Bradbury & Evans (London), 1848 (second issue with
   'Sir Pitt' on p.453) £750
ditto, Harper & Bros (New York), 1848 (2 vols; green wraps)
   .   .   .   .£750
ditto, Harper & Bros (New York), 1848 (1 vols; cloth) .£500
*The History of Pendennis, His Fortunes and Misfortunes,
   His Friends and His Greatest Enemy*, Bradbury & Evans
   (London), 1850 (24 parts in 23; yellow wraps)   £2,000
ditto, Bradbury & Evans (London), 1849[-50] (blue patterned, gilt-stamped cloth; 2 vols)   .   .   .£750
ditto, Harper & Bros (New York), 1855   .   .   .£500
*The History of Henry Esmond, Esq. A Colonel In the
   Service of Her Majesty Q. Anne. Written by Himself*,
   Smith Elder (London), 1852 (olive-brown cloth with paper
   labels; 3 vols) £500
ditto, Harper & Bros (New York), 1852 (wraps)   .   .£300
The Newcomes: Memoirs of a Most Respectable Family,
   Bradbury & Evans (London), 1853-55 (24 parts in 23,
   yellow wraps) £1,250
ditto, Bradbury & Evans (London), 1854[-55] (slate-coloured
   cloth; 2 vols). £750
ditto, Harper & Bros (New York), 1855   .   .   .£100
*The Memoirs of Barry Lyndon, Esq., of The Kingdom of
   Ireland*, Appleton (New York), 1853 (2 vols)   .   £1,500
ditto, Bradbury & Evans (London), 1856 (wraps)   .£500
The Virginians: A Tale of the Last Century, Bradbury &
   Evans (London), 1859 (24 parts, yellow wraps)   .£750
ditto, Bradbury & Evans (London), 1858[-59] (blue cloth; 2
   vols) £500
ditto, Harper & Bros (New York), 1859   .   .   .£100
Lovel the Widower, Harper & Bros (New York), 1860 (violet
   cloth) £250
ditto, Smith Elder (London), 1861   .   .   .   .£250
*The Adventures of Philip on His Way Through the World;
   Shewing Who Robbed Him, Who Helped Him, and Who*

Passed Him By, Smith Elder (London), 1862 (brown or
   violet-blue cloth; 3 vols) £400
ditto, Harper & Bros (New York), 1862   .   .   .   £65
Denis Duval, Smith Elder (London), 1867 (red/pink cloth) .
   .   .   .   .£250

Christmas Books
Mrs Perkins's Ball, Chapman & Hall (London), [1847]
   (pseud 'Mr M.A. Titmarsh'; pink pictorial boards)   .£400
'Our Street', Chapman & Hall (London), 1848 (pseud 'Mr
   M.A. Titmarsh'; pink pictorial boards)   .   .£400
Doctor Birch and His Young Friends, Chapman & Hall
   (London), 1849 (pseud 'Mr M.A. Titmarsh'; pink pictorial
   boards) £400
The Kicklebury's on the Rhine, Chapman & Hall (London),
   1850 (pseud 'Mr M.A. Titmarsh'; pink pictorial boards)   .
   .   .   .   .£400
ditto, Stringer and Townsend (New York), 1851   .   £75
*The Rose and the Ring, or, The History of Prince Gigilo
   and Prince Bulbo: A Fireside Pantomime for Great and
   Small Children*, Chapman & Hall (London), 1855 (pseud
   'Mr M.A. Titmarsh'; pink pictorial boards)   .   .£500
Christmas Books, Chapman & Hall (London), 1857   .£250

Tales and Sketches
Comic Tales and Sketches, Hugh Cunningham (London),
   1841 (pseud 'Mr Michael Angelo Titmarsh'; no reference
   to *Vanity Fair*; dark brown cloth) £750
The Yellowplush Papers, Harper & Bros. (New York), 1848
   (brown boards with brown cloth spine)   .   .   £1,000
ditto, Harper & Bros (New York), 1848 (green cloth wraps)
   .   .   .   .   £1,500
The Book of Snobs, Punch Office (London), 1848 (green
   pictorial wraps) £350
ditto, Appleton (New York), 1852   .   .   .   .£100
The Great Hoggarty Diamond, Harper & Bros (New York),
   1848 (first issue with '82 Cliff Street' on title-page; wraps)
   .   .   .   .   £1,500
*The History of Samuel Titmarsh and the Great Hoggarty
   Diamond*, Bradbury & Evans (London), 1849 (pictorial
   boards or wraps) £350
Rebecca and Rowena: A Romance Upon Romance,
   Chapman & Hall (London), 1850 (pseud 'Mr Michael
   Angelo Titmarsh'; pictorial boards)   .   .   .£350
A Shabby Genteel Story, Appleton (New York), 1852 .£350
ditto, Bradbury & Evans, 1857 (wraps)   .   .   .£350
The Fatal Boots and *Cox's Diary*, Bradbury & Evans
   (London), 1855 (wraps) £350
The Little Dinner at Timmins's and *The Bedford-Row
   Conspiracy*, Bradbury & Evans (London), 1856 (wraps) .
   .   .   .   .£350
The Memoirs of Mr Charles J. Yellowplush and *The Diary
   of C. Jeames de la Pluche, Esq.*, Bradbury & Evans
   (London), 1856 (wraps) £350
The Fitz-Boodle Papers and *Men's Wives*, Bradbury &
   Evans (London), 1857 (wraps). £350

Non-Fiction
The Paris Sketch Book, John Macrone (London), 1840
   (pseud 'Mr Titmarsh', 2 vols; cloth)   .   .   .£750
The Irish Sketch Book, John Macrone (London), 1843
   (pseud 'Mr Titmarsh'; 2 vols; dark green cloth)   .£750
*Notes of a Journey from Cornhill to Grand Cairo, By Way
   of Lisbon, Athens, Constantinople, and Jerusalem,*

Chapman & Hall (London), 1846 (pseud 'Mr M.A. Titmarsh'; pictorial cloth) £500
ditto, Wiley & Putnam (New York), 1846. . . . £300
The English Humorists of the Eighteenth Century: A Series
of Lectures Delivered in England, Scotland and the
United States of America, Smith Taylor (London), 1853
(blue cloth) £250
ditto, Harper & Bros (New York), 1853 . . . £150
The Four Georges: Sketches of Manners, Morals, Court
and Town Life, Harper Bros (New York), 1860 (brown
cloth) £250
ditto, Smith Elder (London), 1861 (green cloth) . £250
The Roundabout Papers, Smith Elder (London), 1863 (blue
cloth) £250
ditto, Harper & Bros (New York), 1863 (brown cloth) . £150

Collected Editions
The Works of William Makepeace Thackeray, Smith Elder
'Library Edition' (London), 1869-86 (24 vols) . . £750
The Works of William Makepeace Thackeray, Smith Elder/
Ritchie Edition (London), 1898-99 (24 vols) . . £500
The Oxford Thackeray, O.U.P./Saintsbury Edition, O.U.P
(London), [1908] (17 vols) £250
The Works of William Makepeace Thackeray, Smith Elder
'Centenary Biographical Edition' (London), 1910-11 (26
vols) £750

PAUL THEROUX

(b.1941)

An American novelist and travel writer, Paul Theroux first
came to the attention of the critics with the publication of
The Great Railway Bazaar and *The Old Patagonian
Express*. His travel writing is appreciated for its rich
descriptions of people and places, although there is often a
strong element of irony in his work. His novels have been
filmed with varying degrees of success.

Novels
Waldo, Houghton Mifflin (Boston), 1967. . . . £150/£25
ditto, Bodley Head (London), 1968 . . . . £135/£20
Fong and the Indians, Houghton Mifflin (Boston), 1968 .
. . . . £85/£20
ditto, Hamish Hamilton (London), 1976 . . £65/£15
Girls at Play, Houghton Mifflin (Boston), 1969 . £86/£15
ditto, Bodley Head (London), 1969 . . . . £50/£10
Murder in Mount Holly, Alan Ross (London), 1969 . .
. . . . £1,750/£350
Jungle Lovers, Houghton Mifflin (Boston), 1971 . £75/£20
ditto, Bodley Head (London), 1971 . . . . £75/£20
Saint Jack, Bodley Head (London), 1973. . . £25/£10
ditto, Houghton Mifflin (Boston), 1973 . . . £25/£10
The Black House, Hamish Hamilton (London), 1974 £20/£5
ditto, Houghton Mifflin (Boston), 1974 . . . £20/£5
The Family Arsenal, Hamish Hamilton (London), 1976 .
. . . . £25/£5
ditto, Houghton Mifflin (Boston), 1976 . . . £25/£5
Picture Palace, Hamish Hamilton (London), 1978. £20/£5
ditto, Houghton Mifflin (Boston), 1978 . . . £20/£5
ditto, The Franklin Library (Franklin Centre, PA), 1978 (full
leather, signed, limited edition) £20

The Mosquito Coast, Hamish Hamilton (London), 1981 .
. . . . £20/£5
ditto, Houghton Mifflin (Boston), 1982 . . . £20/£5
ditto, Houghton Mifflin (Boston), 1982 (350 signed copies,
slipcase). . . . . £35/£20
Doctor Slaughter, Hamish Hamilton (London), 1984 £15/£5
ditto, as ***Half Moon Street***, Houghton Mifflin (Boston), 1984
(contains two novellas: 'Doctor Slaughter' & 'Doctor De
Marr') . . . . £15/£5
O-Zone, Hamish Hamilton (London), 1986 . . £15/£5
ditto, Putnam (New York), 1986 . . . . £15/£5
ditto, The Franklin Library (Franklin Centre, PA), 1986 (full
leather, signed, limited edition) £20
My Secret History, Hamish Hamilton (London), 1989 £15/£5
ditto, London Limited Editions (London), 1989 (150 signed,
numbered copies, tissue d/w) . . . . £50/£35
ditto, Putnam (New York), 1989 . . . . £15/£5
Dr. De Marr, Hutchinson (London), 1990 (revised edition).
. . . . £10/£5
Chicago Loop, Hamish Hamilton (London), 1990 . £15/£5
ditto, Random House (New York), 1991 . . . £15/£5
Millroy the Magician, Hamish Hamilton (London), 1993 .
. . . . £10/£5
ditto, Random House (New York), 1994 . . . £10/£5
My Other Life, Hamish Hamilton (London), 1996 . £10/£5
ditto, Houghton Mifflin (Boston), 1996 . . . £10/£5
Kowloon Tong, Hamish Hamilton (London), 1997. £10/£5
ditto, Houghton Mifflin (Boston), 1997 . . . £10/£5
ditto, Franklin Library (Franklin Centre, PA), 1998 (1,350
signed copies) £45
The Collected Short Novels, Hamish Hamilton (London),
1998 . . . . £10/£5
Hotel Honolulu, Hamish Hamilton (London), 2001 £10/£5
ditto, Houghton Mifflin (Boston), 2001 . . . £10/£5
Blinding Light, Houghton Mifflin (Boston), 2005 . £10/£5
ditto, Hamish Hamilton (London), 2005 . . . £10/£5

Short Stories
Sinning with Annie and Other Stories, Houghton Mifflin
(Boston), 1972 . . . . £100/£20
ditto, Hamish Hamilton (London), 1975 . . . £65/£15
The Consul's File, Hamish Hamilton (London), 1977 £20/£5
ditto, Houghton Mifflin (Boston), 1977 . . . £15/£5
World's End, Hamish Hamilton (London), 1980 . £15/£5
ditto, Houghton Mifflin (Boston), 1980 . . . £15/£5
The London Embassy, Hamish Hamilton (London), 1982 .
. . . . £10/£5
ditto, Houghton Mifflin (Boston), 1983 . . . £10/£5
The Collected Stories, Viking (New York), 1997 . £10/£5
ditto, Hamish Hamilton (London), 1990 . . . £10/£5
The Stranger at the Palazzo d'Oro: And Other Stories,
Hamish Hamilton (London), 2003 . . . . £10/£5
ditto, Houghton Mifflin (Boston), 2004 . . . £10/£5
The Elephanta Suite, Hamish Hamilton (London), 2007 .
. . . . £10/£5
ditto, as ***The Elephanta Suite: Three Novellas***, Houghton
Mifflin (New York), 2007 . . . . . . £10/£5

Travel
The Great Railway Bazaar: By Train Through Asia,
Hamish Hamilton (London), 1975 . . . . £100/£25
ditto, Houghton Mifflin (Boston), 1975 . . . £65/£20
The Old Patagonian Express: By Train Through the
Americas, Hamish Hamilton (London), 1979 . £25/£5

ditto, Houghton Mifflin (Boston), 1979 . . . £20/£5

The Kingdom by the Sea, Hamish Hamilton (London), 1983
. . . . £15/£5

ditto, Houghton Mifflin (Boston), 1983 . . . £15/£5

ditto, Houghton Mifflin (Boston), 1983 (250 signed, numbered copies, slipcase) . . . . £35/£25

Sailing through China, Russell (Wilton, Wilts.), 1983 . .
. . . . £15/£5

ditto, Russell (Wilton, Wilts.), 1983 (150 signed, numbered copies, glassine d/w) . . . . £35/£30

ditto, Houghton Mifflin (Boston), 1984 . . £15/£5

ditto, Houghton Mifflin (Boston), 1984 (250 signed, numbered copies) . . . . £35/£30

Patagonia Revisited, Russell (Wilton, Wilts.), 1985 (with Bruce Chatwin) . . . . £25/£10

ditto, Russell (Wilton, Salisbury, UK), 1985 (250 numbered copies signed by both authors, cellophane d/w) £200/£175

ditto, Houghton Mifflin (Boston), 1986 . . £20/£10

ditto, as ***Nowhere is a Place: Travels in Patagonia***, Sierra Club (San Francisco, CA), 1991 . . . £20/£10

Sunrise with Seamonsters, Hamish Hamilton (London), 1985 . . . . £10/£5

ditto, Houghton Mifflin (Boston), 1985 . . . £10/£5

The Imperial Way, Hamish Hamilton (London), 1985 (photographs by Steve McCurry) . . . £10/£5

ditto, Houghton Mifflin (Boston), 1985 . . . £10/£5

Riding the Iron Rooster: By Train Through China, Hamish Hamilton (London), 1988 . . . . £10/£5

ditto, Putnam (New York), 1988 . . . . £10/£5

Travelling the World, The Illustrated Travels of Paul Theroux, Sinclair-Stevenson (London), 1990 . £10/£5

ditto, as ***To the Ends of the Earth: The Selected Travels of Paul Theroux***, Random House (New York), 1990 £10/£5

The Happy Isles of Oceania: Paddling the Pacific, Hamish Hamilton (London), 1992 . . . . £10/£5

ditto, Putnam (New York), 1992 . . . . £10/£5

The Pillars of Hercules: A Grand Tour of the Mediterranean, Hamish Hamilton (London), 1995 . £10/£5

ditto, Putnam (New York), 1995 . . . . £10/£5

Fresh Air Fiend: Travel Writings, 1985-2000, Houghton Mifflin (Boston), 2000 . . . . . £10/£5

ditto, Hamish Hamilton (London), 2000 . . £10/£5

Dark Star Safari: Overland from Cairo to Cape Town, Hamish Hamilton (London), 2002 . . . £10/£5

ditto, Houghton Mifflin (Boston), 2003 . . £10/£5

Others

V.S. Naipaul: An Introduction to his Work, Deutsch (London), 1972 . . . . £500/£75

ditto, Africana (New York), 1972 . . . £750/£100

A Christmas Card, Hamish Hamilton (London), 1978 £20/£5

ditto, Houghton Mifflin (Boston), 1978 . . £20/£5

London Snow: A Christmas Story, Russell (Wilton, Wilts.), 1979 (450 signed, numbered copies, glassine d/w) £45/£40

ditto, Hamish Hamilton (London), 1980 . . . £15/£5

ditto, Houghton Mifflin (Boston), 1980 . . . £15/£5

The Shortest Day of the Year: A Christmas Fantasy, Sixth Chamber Press (Leamington Spa, Warwickshire), 1986 (175 signed copies) £75

ditto, Sixth Chamber Press (Leamington Spa, Warwickshire), 1986 (26 signed copies on handmade paper) . . . £150

The White Man's Burden, A Play in Two Acts, Hamish Hamilton (London), 1987 . . . . . £15/£5

Sir Vidia's Shadow, Hamish Hamilton (London), 1998 .
. . . . £10/£5

ditto, Houghton Mifflin (Boston), 1998 . . . £10/£5

The Romance of 'Martha's Vineyard': Vineyard Days, Vineyard Nights, Stewart Tabori & Chang (Edison, NJ), 2004 (photographs by Nancy Willard, text by Theroux) .
. . . . £10/£5

WILFRED THESIGER
(b.1910 d.2003)

Wilfred Patrick Thesiger was a British explorer and travel writer born in Addis Ababa, Ethiopia. He is best known for Arabian Sands which recounts his travels in the *Empty Quarter of Arabia* between 1945 and 1950 and describes the vanishing way of life of the Bedouins. *The Marsh Arabs* is an account of the traditional peoples who lived in the marshlands of southern Iraq.

Arabian Sands, Longmans (London), 1959 . . £100/£15

ditto, E P Dutton & Co (New York), 1959. . . £75/£15

The Marsh Arabs, Longmans (London), 1964 . . £45/£10

ditto, E P Dutton & Co (New York), 1964. . . £40/£10

Desert, Marsh and Mountain: The World of a Nomad, Collins (London), 1979 . . . . £30/£5

ditto, Collins (London), 1979 (120 full leather copies) . £300

ditto, as ***The Last Nomad***, E P Dutton & Co (New York), 1980 . . . . £10/£5

The Life of My Choice, Collins (London), 1987 . £10/£5

ditto, Norton (New York), 1988 . . . . . £10/£5

Visions of a Nomad, Collins (London), 1987 . . £20/£5

My Kenya Days, Collins (London), 1994 . . . £15/£5

The Danakil Diary, HarperCollins (London), 1996 . £20/£5

Among the Mountains, HarperCollins (London), 1998 £20/£5

Crossing the Sands, Motivate (London), 1999 . £25/£5

A Vanished World, HarperCollins (London), 2001 . £15/£5

My Life and Travels, Collins (London), 2002 . £15/£5

Thesiger in Arabia, Folio Society (London), 2005 (2 vols in slipcase) . . . . £20/£10

DYLAN THOMAS
(b.1914 d.1953)

Thomas was a Welsh poet and playwright widely considered to be one of the greatest poets of the 20th century. A notorious figure in London's Fitzrovia, Thomas died after taking morphine and drinking around a dozen whiskies in the White Horse Tavern in Greenwich Village, New York. One of his most well-known works, *Under Milk Wood*, was written as a radio play.

18 Poems, The Sunday Referee/The Parton Bookshop (London), 1934 (first issue, c.250 copies, flat spine, no advertisement leaf between half title and title) £2,500/£500

ditto, The Sunday Referee/The Parton Bookshop (London), 1934 (second issue, c.250 copies, round-backed spine, with advertisement leaf between half title and title) £1,000/£300

Twenty-Five Poems, Dent (London), 1936 . £450/£100

The Map of Love: Verse and Prose, Dent (London), 1939 (first issue in mauve cloth with very smooth texture, gilt blocking, top edge stained) . . . . £350/£250

ditto, Dent (London), 1939 (second issue in plum-coloured cloth with course texture, gilt blocking, top edge stained) .
.   .   .   .   .   .   £200/£100

ditto, Dent (London), 1939 (third issue, blue blocking, top edge stained).   .   .   .   .   £125/£75

ditto, Dent (London), 1939 (fourth issue, blue blocking, top edge unstained).   .   .   .   .   £75/£25

The World I Breathe, New Directions (Norfolk, CT), 1939 (first state binding with a single star to each side of the title on the spine).   .   .   .   .   £400/£100

ditto, New Directions (Norfolk, CT), 1939 (second state binding, with five stars on the spine)   .   .   £350/£75

Portrait of the Artist as a Young Dog, Dent (London), 1940
.   .   .   .   .   .   £400/£65

ditto, New Directions (Norfolk, CT), 1940   .   £225/£45

From In Memory of Ann Jones, Caseg Press (Llanllechid, Caernarvonshire), [1942] (500 copies, broadside)   . £200

New Poems, New Directions (Norfolk, CT), 1943 (paper boards, d/w) .   .   .   .   .   .   £175/£65

ditto, New Directions (Norfolk, CT), 1943 (stapled wraps in d/w)   .   .   .   .   .   £75/£45

Deaths and Entrances, Dent (London), 1946 .   . £275/£75

ditto, Gregynog Press (near Newtown, Montgomeryshire), 1984 (250 copies, John Piper illustrated edition, in slipcase).   .   .   .   .   .   £800/£600

ditto, Gregynog Press (near Newtown, Montgomeryshire), 1984 (28 roman numbered copies, in slipcase) £1,000/£900

Selected Writings of Dylan Thomas, New Directions (Norfolk, CT), 1946   .   .   .   .   £100/£25

Two Epigrams Of Fealty, privately printed for members of the Court of Redonda (London), 1947 (30 numbered copies, folded leaflet). £350

Twenty-Six Poems, Dent/New Directions (London/Norfolk, CT), [1950] (Nos I-X signed, numbered copies of 150, printed on Japanese vellum, in slipcase).   £6,000/£5,000

ditto, Dent/New Directions (London/Norfolk, CT), [1950] (Nos 11-60 signed, numbered copies of 150, slipcase)   .
.   .   .   .   .   .   £2,500/£2,000

ditto, Dent/New Directions (London/Norfolk, CT), [1950] (Nos 61-147 signed, numbered copies of 150, slipcase)   .
.   .   .   .   .   .   £2,500/£1,500

In Country Sleep and Other Poems, New Directions (Norfolk, CT), 1952   .   .   .   .   £200/£50

ditto, New Directions (Norfolk, CT), 1952 (100 signed, numbered copies, in slipcase)   .   .   £2,000/£1,750

Collected Poems, 1934-1952, Dent (London), 1952 £75/£15

ditto, Dent (London), 1952 (65 signed, numbered copies)   .
.   .   .   .   .   .   £2,500

ditto, New Directions (Norfolk, CT), 1953   .   £65/£10

The Doctor and the Devils, Dent (London), 1953 .   £30/£5

ditto, New Directions (Norfolk, CT), 1953   .   £25/£5

Galsworthy and Gawsworth, privately printed for members of the Court of Redonda (London), [1953] (30 numbered copies, folded leaflet). £350

Under Milk Wood: A Play for Voices, Dent (London), 1954
.   .   .   .   .   .   £150/£25

ditto, New Directions (Norfolk, CT), 1954 .   £125/£20

Quite Early One Morning, Dent (London), 1954   £45/£10

ditto, New Directions (Norfolk, CT), 1954   .   £20/£55

Conversation About Christmas, New Directions (Norfolk, CT), 1954 (stapled wraps, in envelope)   .   . £125/£65

A Child's Christmas in Wales, New Directions (Norfolk, CT), 1954 [1955].   .   .   .   .   £75/£20

ditto, New Directions (Norfolk, CT), [1969] (100 copies, illustrated by Fritz Eichenberg, with signed portfolio)   .
.   .   .   .   .   .   £350/£200

ditto, New Directions (Norfolk, CT), [1969] (trade edition illustrated by Fritz Eichenberg)   .   .   . £35/£10

ditto, Dent (London), 1978 (illustrated by Edward Ardizzone)   .   .   .   .   .   £50/£15

ditto, Godine (Boston), 1980 (illustrated by Ardizzone) .
.   .   .   .   .   .   £35/£10

Adventures in the Skin Trade and Other Stories, New Directions (Norfolk, CT), 1955   .   .   .   £100/£20

ditto, Putnam (London), 1955   .   .   .   £100/£20

A Prospect of the Sea, Dent (London), 1955 .   £35/£10

Letters to Vernon Watkins, Dent/Faber (London), 1957   .
.   .   .   .   .   .   £20/£10

ditto, New Directions (Norfolk, CT), 1957   .   £15/£5

The Beach of Falesa, Stein & Day (New York), 1963 (film script)   .   .   .   .   .   £15/£5

ditto, Cape (London), 1964 .   .   .   £15/£5

Twenty Years A-Growing, Dent (London), 1964 (film script)
.   .   .   .   .   .   £25/£10

Rebecca's Daughters, Triton (London), 1965 (film script with a foreword by Sidney Box)   .   .   . £15/£5

ditto, Little, Brown (Boston), 1965   .   .   . £15/£5

Me and My Bike, McGraw-Hill (New York), 1965 £20/£10

ditto, Triton (London), 1965 (film script) .   .   £20/£10

ditto, Triton (London), 1965 (500 numbered copies, in slipcase).   .   .   .   .   .   £40/£15

The Doctor and the Devils and Other Scripts, New Directions (Norfolk, CT), 1966   .   .   .   £15/£5

Selected Letters of Dylan Thomas, Dent (London), 1966   .
.   .   .   .   .   .   £25/£10

ditto, New Directions (Norfolk, CT), 1967   .   £25/£10

The Notebooks of Dylan Thomas, New Directions (Norfolk, CT), 1967   .   .   .   .   .   £15/£5

ditto, as *Poet in the Making: The Notebooks of Dylan Thomas*, Dent (London), 1968.   .   .   .   £15/£5

Twelve More Letters, Turret Books (London), 1969 (175 copies, acetate d/w)   .   .   .   .   £75/£60

ditto, Turret Books (London), 1969 (26 lettered copies, acetate d/w)   .   .   .   .   £125/£100

Dylan Thomas: Early Prose Writings, Dent (London), 1971
.   .   .   .   .   .   £20/£5

ditto, New Directions (Norfolk, CT), 1972   .   £20/£5

The Death of the King's Canary, Hutchinson (London), 1976 (with John Davenport)   .   .   .   £15/£5

ditto, Viking (New York), 1976 .   .   .   £15/£5

Drawings to Poems by Dylan Thomas by Ceri Richards, Enitharmon Press (London), 1980 (180 copies, slipcase)   .
.   .   .   .   .   .   £125/£75

ditto, Enitharmon Press (London), 1980 (500 hardback copies)   .   .   .   .   .   £25/£10

ditto, Enitharmon Press (London), 1980 (wraps)   .   £5

Collected Letters, Dent (London), 1985   .   .   £15/£5

ditto, Macmillan (New York), 1976   .   .   £15/£5

Dylan Thomas: The Notebook Poems, 1930-1934, Dent (London), 1989   .   .   .   .   .   £15/£5

Dylan Thomas: The Broadcasts, Dent (London), 1991   .
.   .   .   .   .   .   £15/£5

ditto, as *On Air With Dylan Thomas: The Broadcasts*, New Directions (Norfolk, CT), 1992   .   .   .   £15/£5

Dylan Thomas: The Filmscripts, Dent (London), 1995   .
.   .   .   .   .   .   £15/£5

EDWARD THOMAS

(b.1878 d.1917)

Not a 'War Poet', although he died in the First World War, Thomas's love of nature permeates his best work. Of Welsh extraction, he was born in London, and had already established himself as a journalist and poet before the outbreak of the War. He was killed in action at Arras in 1917 soon after his arrival in France.

Poetry

Six Poems, Pear Tree Press, [1916] (pseud 'Edward Eastway', copies in boards of total edition of 100) £1,500

ditto, Pear Tree Press, [1916] (pseud 'Edward Eastway', copies in wraps of total edition of 100) . . . £1,500

ditto, Pear Tree Press (London), 1927 . . . . £250

Poems, Selwyn & Blount (London), 1917 (525 copies, pseud 'Edward Eastway') £250

ditto, Holt (New York), 1917 (525 copies) . . £200

Last Poems, Selwyn & Blount (London), 1918 . £250

Collected Poems, Selwyn & Blount (London), 1920 £250/£75

ditto, Selwyn and Blount (London), 1920 (deluxe edition, 100 copies) £450

ditto, Seltzer (New York), 1921 . . . £200/£65

Augustan Books of Modern Poetry: Edward Thomas, Benn (London), [1926] (stapled wraps) £5

Selected Poems, Gregynog Press (near Newtown, Montgomeryshire), 1926 (275 copies) . . . £300

ditto, Gregynog Press (near Newtown, Montgomeryshire), 1926 (25 specially bound copies) £800

Two Poems, Ingpen & Grant (London), 1927 (85 copies; glassine d/w). . . . . . . £300/£250

Collected Poems, Ingpen & Grant (London), 1928. £70/£25

Others

The Woodland Life, Blackwood (London), 1897 (first issue, red cloth) £600

ditto, Blackwood (London), 1897 (second issue, blue/green buckram) £450

ditto, Blackwood (London), 1897 (second issue, smooth green cloth) £300

Horae Solitariae, Duckworth (London), 1902 (300 copies). £200

ditto, Dutton (New York), [1902] £135

Oxford, A. & C. Black (London), [1903] . . . £15

ditto, A. & C. Black (London), [1903] (deluxe edition, 300 copies) £175

Rose Acre Papers, Brown Langham (London), 1904 . £200

Beautiful Wales, A. & C. Black (London), 1905 . £75

The Heart of England, Dent (London), 1906 . . £50

ditto, Dutton (New York), [1906] £40

Richard Jefferies, Hutchinson (London), 1909 . £25

ditto, Little, Brown (Boston), 1909 . . . . £25

The South Country, Dent (London), 1909 . . £35

Rest and Unrest, Duckworth (London), 1910 . . £65

ditto, Dutton (New York), 1910 . . . . £65

Rose Acre Papers, Duckworth (London), 1910 . £30

Feminine Influence on the Poets, Secker (London), 1910 £40

ditto, John Lane (New York), 1911 . . . . £40

Windsor Castle, Blackie & Son (London), 1910 . £25

The Isle of Wight, Blackie & Son (London), 1911 . £15

ditto, Dana Estes (Boston), 1910. . . . . £10

Light and Twilight, Duckworth (London), 1911 . £30

Maurice Maeterlink, Methuen (London), [1911] . £30

ditto, Dodd, Mead (New York) 1911 . . . . £30

Celtic Stories, O.U.P. (Oxford and London), 1911 . £60

The Tenth Muse, Secker (London), [1911] . . £35

Algernon Charles Swinburne, Secker (London), 1912. £35

ditto, Mitchell Kennerley (New York) 1912 . . £30

George Borrow, Chapman & Hall (London), 1912. £25

Lafcadio Hearn, Houghton Mifflin (Boston), 1912 £20

ditto, Constable (London), 1912 . . . . . £20

Norse Tales, O.U.P. (Oxford and London), 1912 . £45

The Icknield Way, Constable (London), 1913. . £30

ditto, Dutton (New York), 1913 . . . . . £25

The Country, Batsford (London), [1913] . . . £20

The Happy-Go-Lucky Morgans, Duckworth (London), [1913] (green cloth; first issue with a frontispiece, the date on the title-page and twenty pages of adverts at the rear). £350

Walter Pater, Secker (London), 1913 . . . . £25

In Pursuit of Spring, Nelson (London), [1914] . £45

Four-and-Twenty Blackbirds, Duckworth (London), [1915] . . . . £500/£45

The Life of the Duke of Marlborough, Chapman & Hall (London), 1915 . . . . £20

Keats, T.C. & E.C. Jack (London), 1916 . . . £15

ditto, Dodge (New York), [1916] £15

A Literary Pilgrim in England, Dodd, Mead (New York), 1917 . . . . £25

ditto, Methuen (London), [1917]. £20

Cloud Castle and Other Papers, Duckworth (London), [1922] . . . . £100/£25

ditto, Dutton (New York), [1923] . . . . £65/£15

Essays of Today and Yesterday, Harrap (London), [1926] (black wraps) £25

ditto, Harrap (London), [1926] (brown binding with red and gold border) £20

ditto, Harrap (London), [1926] (imitation leather) . £20

ditto, Harrap (London), [1926] (brown binding with blue and gold border) £15

Chosen Essays, Gregynog Press (Newtown, Montgomeryshire), 1926 (350 numbered copies) £85

The Last Sheaf: Essays, Cape (London), [1928] . £35/£15

The Childhood of Edward Thomas, Faber (London), 1938 . . . . £125/£45

ditto, Faber (London), 1938 (pbk) £15

The Friend of the Blackbird, Pear Tree Press (London), 1938 . . . . £60

The Prose of Edward Thomas, Falcon Press (London), 1948 . . . . £30/£10

Letters from Edward Thomas to Gordon Bottomley, O.U.P. (Oxford, UK), 1968 . . . . £20/£5

Autumn Thoughts, Tragara Press (Edinburgh), 1975 (90 numbered copies on blue laid paper; wraps) . . £50

The Diary of Edward Thomas, Whittington Press (Andoversford, Gloucestershire), 1977 (50 roman numeralled copies of 575; slipcase) . . . . . . £225/£175

ditto, Whittington Press (Andoversford, Gloucestershire), 1977 (525 numbered copies of 575; slipcase) . £75/£50

Edward Thomas on the Countryside: A Selection, Faber (London), 1977 . . . . £10/£5

Edward Thomas: A Centenary Celebration, Eric and Joan Stevens (London), 1978 (75 copies signed by the artist) £75

Four Letters to Frederick Evans, Tragara Press (Edinburgh), 1978 (150 numbered copies; wraps) . . £40

Reading out of Doors, Tragara Press (Edinburgh), 1978 (110 numbered copies; wraps) £35

The Chessplayers, and Other Essays, Whittington Press (Andoversford, Gloucestershire), 1981 (375 copies) . £75

A Selection of Letters to Edward Garnett, Tragara Press
(Edinburgh), 1981 (175 numbered copies; wraps)   .   £30
The Letters of Edward Thomas to Jesse Berridge,
Enitharmon (London), 1981   .   .   .   .   .   £25/£10
The Fear of Death, Tragara Press (Edinburgh), 1982 (95
numbered copies; wraps) £45
A Sportsman's Tale, Tragara Press (Edinburgh), 1983 (125
numbered copies; wraps) £30
A Handful of Letters: Edward and Helen Thomas, Tragara
Press (Edinburgh), 1985 (165 numbered copies; wraps) £30

ROSS THOMAS

(b.1926 d.1995)

Ross Thomas was an American author of crime fiction and
was a two-time recipient of the Mystery Writers of
America's Edgar Allan Poe Award.

Novels

The Cold War Swap, Morrow (New York), 1966 £500/£100
ditto, as *Spy in the Vodka*, Hodder & Stoughton (London),
1967   .   .   .   .   £150/£35
Cast A Yellow Shadow, Morrow (New York), 1967 £150/£25
ditto, Hodder & Stoughton (London), 1968   .   £75/£10
The Seersucker Whipsaw, Morrow (New York), 1967 .   .
.   .   .   .   £250/£40
ditto, Hodder & Stoughton (London), 1968   .   £125/£25
The Singapore Wink, Morrow (New York), 1969 . £150/£35
ditto, Hodder & Stoughton (London), 1969   .   £65/£10
Warriors for the Poor; The Story of Vista, Morrow (New
York), 1969 (written with William Cook)   .   £150/£30
The Fools in Town Are On Our Side, Hodder & Stoughton
(London), 1970   .   .   .   .   .   .   £125/£20
ditto, Morrow (New York), 1971 (first issue d/w with review
on back of *The Singapore Wink*)   .   .   .   £125/£20
ditto, Morrow (New York), 1971 (second issue d/w with
review on back of this book)   .   .   .   .   £75/£20
The Backup Men, Morrow (New York), 1971   £65/£10
ditto, Hodder & Stoughton (London), 1971   .   £35/£10
The Porkchoppers, Morrow (New York), 1972   .   £65/£10
ditto, Hamish Hamilton (London), 1974   .   .   £30/£10
If You Can't Be Good, Morrow (New York), 1973 £65/£10
ditto, Hamish Hamilton (London), 1974   .   .   £30/£10
The Money Harvest, Morrow (New York), 1975   .   £50/£10
ditto, Hamish Hamilton (London), 1975   .   .   £30/£10
Yellow-Dog Contract, Morrow (New York), 1977   £60/£10
ditto, Hamish Hamilton (London), 1977   .   .   £25/£10
Chinaman's Chance, Simon & Schuster (New York), 1978
.   .   .   .   £45/£10
ditto, Hamish Hamilton (London), 1977   .   .   £25/£10
The Eighth Dwarf, Simon & Schuster (New York), 1979   .
.   .   .   .   £25/£10
ditto, Hamish Hamilton (London), 1979   .   .   £20/£5
The Mordida Man, Simon & Schuster (New York), 1981   .
.   .   .   .   £25/£10
ditto, Hamish Hamilton (London), 1981   .   .   £20/£5
Missionary Stew, Simon & Schuster (New York), 1983   .
.   .   .   .   £20/£5
ditto, Hamish Hamilton (London), 1984   .   .   £20/£5
Briarpatch, Simon & Schuster (New York), 1984 .   £20/£5
ditto, Hamish Hamilton (London), 1984   .   .   £20/£5
Out On The Rim, Mysterious Press (New York), 1987 £15/£5

ditto, Century Hutchinson (London), 1988   .   .   £10/£5
The Fourth Durango, Mysterious Press (New York), 1989
(500 signed, numbered copies; advance reading copy with
signed plate inside front cover) £20
ditto, Mysterious Press (New York), 1989 (first printing
p.44, last line 'Gear' for 'Bear'   .   .   .   £15/£5
ditto, Century (London), 1990   .   .   .   .   £10/£5
Twilight At Mac's Place, Mysterious Press (New York),
1990   .   .   .   .   £10/£5
ditto, Mysterious Press (New York), 1990 (100 signed,
numbered copies; slipcase; no d/w)   .   .   £50/£30
ditto, Mysterious Press (New York), 1990 (26 signed,
lettered copies; slipcase; no d/w)   .   .   £125/£100
Voodoo Ltd, Mysterious Press (New York), 1992 .   £10/£5
ditto, Little, Brown (London), 1993   .   .   .   £10/£5
Ah, Treachery!, Mysterious Press (New York), 1994 £10/£5
ditto, Little, Brown (London), 1994   .   .   .   £10/£5

Novels Written Under Pseudonym 'Oliver Bleeck'
The Brass Go-Between, Morrow (New York), 1969
(misprint 'Sociey' on p.208, line 3).   .   .   £125/£25
ditto, Hodder & Stoughton (London), 1970   .   £65/£10
Protocol for a Kidnapping, Morrow (New York), 1971 (first
state in red and tan boards)   .   .   .   £125/£25
ditto, Hodder & Stoughton (London), 1971   .   £45/£10
The Procane Chronicle, Morrow (New York), 1972   .   .
.   .   .   .   £150/£25
ditto, as *The Thief Who Painted Sunlight*, Hodder &
Stoughton (London), 1972   .   .   .   .   £35/£10
The Highbinders, Morrow (New York), 1974.   .   £65/£10
ditto, Hamish Hamilton (London), 1974   .   .   £30/£10
No Questions Asked, Morrow (New York), 1976 .   £50/£10
ditto, Hamish Hamilton (London), 1976   .   .   £30/£10

Others
Our Fair City, Universal Studio (Universal City), 1984
(wraps) £45
Brown Paper and Some String, California Mystery and
Suspense Writers Conference (San Rafael, CA), 1987 (400
copies; unbound wraps) £20
Spies, Thumbsuckers, etc, Lord John Press (Northridge,
CA), 1989 (300 signed, numbered copies)   .   .   £35
ditto, Lord John Press (Northridge, CA), 1989 (50 signed,
numbered copies) £125

FLORA THOMPSON

(b.1877 d.1947)

Flora Thompson began writing while living in Bournemouth, contributing essays and poems to magazines and
publishing her first collection, *Bog Myrtle and Peat*. Her
autobiographical writings, with their precise and unsenti-
mental descriptions of country life, are still enjoyed today.
They were collected together as *Lark Rise to Candleford*.

Prose
Guide to Liphook, Bramshott and Neighbourhood, Wil-
liams (Liphook, Hants), 1925 (wraps)   .   .   .   £40
Lark Rise, O.U.P. (Oxford, UK), 1939   .   .   £300/£50
Over to Candleford, O.U.P. (Oxford, UK), 1941   . £65/£15
Candleford Green, O.U.P. (Oxford, UK), 1943   . £65/£15
Lark Rise to Candleford, O.U.P. (Oxford, UK), 1945   .   .
.   .   .   .   £65/£10

ditto, Crown (New York), 1983 . . . . £15/£5
Still Glides the Stream, O.U.P. (Oxford, UK), 1948 £20/£5
ditto, Crown (New York), 1984 . . . . £10/£5
A Country Calendar, O.U.P. (Oxford, UK), 1979 . £10/£5
The Peverel Papers, Century (London), 1986 . . £10/£5

Poetry
Bog Myrtle and Peat, Allan (London), 1921 (wraps) . £175

HUNTER S. THOMPSON
(b.1937 d.2005)

Hunter S. Thompson was an American journalist and author, most famous for his novel *Fear and Loathing in Las Vegas*. He is credited as the creator of 'Gonzo' journalism; a style of reporting in which the reporter involves himself in the action so that they become the centre of the story.

Hell's Angels, Random House (New York), 1967 . £300/£65
ditto, Allen Lane/The Penguin Press (London), 1967 . .
. . . . £300/£65
Fear and Loathing in Las Vegas, Random House (New York), 1971 (illustrated by Ralph Steadman) . £500/£75
ditto, Paladin (London), 1972 (pbk) £50
Fear and Loathing: On The Campaign Trail, Straight Arrow Books (San Francisco, CA), 1973 (first issue d/w priced $6.95; white border around picture on back panel) .
. . . . £300/£10
ditto, Straight Arrow Books (San Francisco, CA), 1973 (second issue d/w priced $7.95; no border around picture on back panel) . . . . . £65/£10
ditto, Allison & Busby (London), 1974 . . £100/£15
America, by Ralph Steadman, Straight Arrow Books (San Francisco, CA), 1974 (Introduction (interview) by Hunter Thompson) . . . . . . £150/£30
ditto, Straight Arrow Books (San Francisco, CA), 1974 (pbk)
. . . . £10
ditto, Fantagraphics Books (Seattle, WA), 1989 (500 signed, numbered copies) . . . . . £50/£25
The Great Shark Hunt; The Gonzo Papers Volume 1, Summit Books (New York), 1979 . . . £45/£10
ditto, as ***The Great Shark Hunt; Strange Tales From A Strange Time***, Picador (London), 1980 (pbk) . £15
The Curse of Lono, Bantam Books (New York), 1983 (pbk; illustrated by Ralph Steadman). . . . £25
ditto, Picador/Pan (London), 1983 (pbk) . . . £25
Generation of Swine; The Gonzo Papers Volume 2, Summit Books (New York), 1988 . . . . £10/£5
ditto, as ***Generation of Swine; Tales of Shame and Degradation in the '80s***, Picador/Pan (London), 1988 (pbk) £10
Songs of the Doomed; The Gonzo Papers Volume 3, Summit Books (New York), 1990 . . . £10/£5
ditto, as ***Songs of the Doomed***, Picador/Pan (London), 1991
. . . . £15/£5
ditto, Picador/Pan (London), 1991 (pbk in d/w) . £20/£5
Screwjack, Neville (Santa Barbara, CA), 1991 (300 signed, numbered copies; red cloth; no slipcase or d/w) . £400
ditto, Neville (Santa Barbara, CA), 1991 (26 signed, numbered copies in full leather; no d/w or slipcase) . £750

ditto, as ***Screwjack: And Other Stories***, Simon & Schuster (New York/London etc), 2000 . . . . £10/£5
'Bats Over Barstow', Petro III Graphics (Lexington, KY), 1994 (77 numbered copies signed by artist Ralph Steadman; silkscreen print; Steadman's adaptation of the cover and frontispiece illustration for *Fear and Loathing in Las Vegas*) £2,500
ditto, Petro III Graphics (Lexington, KY), 1994 (20 numbered copies signed by Steadman) . . . £750
Better Than Sex; Confessions of a Political Junkie, Random House (New York), 1994 . . . £10/£5
I Told Him It Was Wrong, Dead-Eye 21 (no place), [1994] (broadside) £125
He Was A Crook, White Fields Press (Louisville, KY), 1995 (broadside) £25
ditto, White Fields Press (Louisville, KY), 1995 (200 numbered copies) £30
ditto, White Fields Press (Louisville, KY), 1995 (45 numbered copies signed 'H.S.T.' in silver paint) . £150
Kicking Nixon While He Was Up, White Fields Press (Louisville, KY), 1995 (broadside) £25
ditto, White Fields Press (Louisville, KY), 1995 (150 numbered copies) £35
ditto, White Fields Press (Louisville, KY), 1995 (35 numbered copies signed 'H.S.T.' in gold paint) . £150
'The Sheffiff', Petro III Graphics (Lexington, KY), 1995 (77 numbered copies signed by Thompson and artist Ralph Steadman; silkscreen print) £750
'Vintage Dr Gonzo', Petro III Graphics (Lexington, KY), 1995 (500 numbered copies signed by Thompson and artist Ralph Steadman; silkscreen print) £250
Open Letter: San Francisco, October 25, 1960, Whitefields Press (Louisville, KY), 1996 (broadside; 92 numbered copies signed 'H.S.T.' using a metallic felt-tip pen) . £60
ditto, Whitefields Press (Louisville, KY), 1996 (26 lettered copies signed 'H.S.T.') £150
Fear and Loathing in Las Vegas and Other American Stories, The Modern Library (New York), 1996 . £15/£5
Mistah Leary He Dead, X-Ray Book Company, San Francisco, 1996 (300 copies; sewn wraps) . . £150
ditto, X-Ray Book Company, San Francisco, 1996 (26 lettered copies; sewn wraps) £350
The Proud Highway; The Fear and Loathing Letters, Volume 1, Villard (New York), 1997 (approx 135 signed copies of the 'Advance Reader's Edition'; pictorial pbk) .
. . . . £150
ditto, Villard (New York), 1997 (approx 865 copies of the 'Advance Reader's Edition'; pictorial pbk) . . £30
ditto, Villard (New York), 1997 (trade issue with initialed bookplate) . . . . £75/£50
ditto, Villard (New York), 1997 (trade issue) . . £10/£5
ditto, Bloomsbury (London), 1997 . . . . £10/£5
The Rum Diary..., Simon & Schuster (New York), 1998 .
. . . . £10/£5
ditto, Simon & Schuster (New York), 1998 (signed by author on a tipped-in publisher's book plate) . . . £50/£45
ditto, Simon & Schuster (New York), 1998 (initialed by author on a bound-in leaf) . . . . £45/£40
ditto, Bloomsbury (London), 1998 . . . . £15/£5
Fear and Loathing in America, Simon & Schuster (New York/London etc), 2000 . . . . £10/£5
ditto, Simon & Schuster (New York/London etc), 2000 (300 signed copies; trade edition bound in full red leather). £125
ditto, Bloomsbury (London), 2000 . . . . £15/£5

The Proud Highway; The Fear and Loathing Letters, Volume 1, and *Fear and Loathing in America*, Villard/Simon & Schuster (New York etc) (15 signed, numbered sets; two vols; trade issues of both books signed and numbered by the author; in red leather slipcase chemises; each set different and 'enhanced')   £500/£400
ditto, Villard/Simon & Schuster (New York etc) (50 signed, numbered sets; two vol; trade issues of both books signed and numbered by the author; in black leather slipcase chemises) .   .   .   .   .   £400/£350
Kingdom of Fear, Simon & Schuster (New York/London etc), 2003 .   .   .   .   .   £10/£5
ditto, Allen Lane The Penguin Press (London), 2003 £10/£5

JIM THOMPSON

(b.1906 d.1977)

Jim Thompson was a successful writer for the pulp fiction houses of the 1950s, completing a dozen novels in just 19 months. He was highly thought-of, by critics and public alike, but never achieved great success. He also wrote two screenplays (for Stanley Kubrick's films *The Killing* and *Paths of Glory*). *Pop. 1280* became an acclaimed French film under the title *Coup de Torchon*.

Novels
Now and On Earth, Modern Age (New York), 1942 .   .
  .   .   .   .   £2,000/£350
Heed the Thunder, Greenberg (New York), 1946 . £850/£75
ditto, Armchair Detective Library (New York), 1991 £10/£5
ditto, Armchair Detective Library (New York), 1991 (100 numbered copies signed by James Elroy; slipcase) £40/£15
ditto, Armchair Detective Library (New York), 1991 (26 lettered copies signed by James Elroy; slipcase) . £75/£25
Nothing More Than Murder, Harper & Brothers (New York), 1949 .   .   .   .   .   £750/£85
The Killer Inside Me, Lion Books (New York), 1952 (#99; pbk) £250
ditto, Sphere (London), 1973 (pbk) .   .   .   £25
ditto, Zomba Books (London), 1983 .   .   £35/£10
ditto, Blood & Guts (Los Angeles, CA), 1989 (350 numbered copies signed by Stephen King; d/w and slipcase) £150/£75
ditto, Blood & Guts (Los Angeles, CA), 1989 (26 lettered copies signed by Stephen King; d/w and slipcase) . .
  .   .   .   .   £250/£200
Cropper's Cabin, Lion Books (New York), 1952 (#108; pbk)
  .   .   .   .   £75
Recoil, Lion Books (New York), 1953 (#120; pbk) . £75
ditto, Corgi (London), 1988 (pbk) .   .   .   £10
The Alcoholics, Lion Books (New York), 1953 (#127; pbk)
  .   .   .   .   £125
Bad Boy, Lion Books (New York), 1953 (#149; pbk) . £45
Savage Night, Lion Books (New York), 1953 (#155; pbk) .
  .   .   .   .   £125
ditto, Corgi (London), 1988 (pbk) .   .   .   £10
The Criminal, Lion Books (New York), 1953 (#184; pbk) .
  .   .   .   .   .   .   £100
The Golden Gizmo, Lion Books (New York), 1954 (#192; pbk) £75
Roughneck, Lion Books (New York), 1954 (#201; pbk) £45
A Swell-Looking Babe, Lion Books (New York), 1954 (#212; pbk) £75

A Hell of a Woman, Lion Books (New York), 1954 (#212; pbk) £125
The Nothing Man, Dell (New York), 1954 (#22; pbk) . £25
After Dark, My Sweet, Popular Library (New York), 1955 (#716; pbk) £75
The Kill-Off, Lion Library (New York), 1957 (#142; pbk) £25
Wild Town, Signet (New York), 1957 (#1461; pbk) . £25
The Getaway, Signet (New York), 1959 (#1584; pbk) . £25
ditto, Sphere (London), 1973 (pbk) .   .   £10
The Transgressors, Signet (New York), 1961 (#52034; pbk)
  .   .   .   .   £35
The Grifters, Regency (Evanston, IL), 1963 (#Rb322; pbk).
  .   .   .   .   £200
Pop. 1280, Fawcett Gold Medal (Greenwich, CT), 1964 (#K1438; pbk) £40
Texas by the Tail, Fawcett Gold Medal (Greenwich, CT), 1965 (#K1502; pbk) £40
South of Heaven, Fawcett Gold Medal (Greenwich, CT), 1967 (#D1793; pbk) £10
Ironside, Popular Library (New York), 1967 (#2244; pbk) .
  .   .   .   .   £10
The Undefeated, Popular Library (New York), 1969 (#8104; pbk) £10
Nothing but a Man, Popular Library (New York), 1970 (#8116; pbk). £25
Child of Rage, Lancer Books (New York), 1972 (#75342; pbk) £65
ditto, Blood & Guts (Los Angeles, CA), 1991 (500 numbered copies signed by contributor Gerald Petievich) . £50/£15
King Blood, Sphere Books (London), 1973 (pbk) .   . £20
ditto, Armchair Detective Library (New York), 1994 £10/£5
ditto, Armchair Detective Library (New York), 1994 (100 numbered copies signed by James Elroy; slipcase) £35/£20
ditto, Armchair Detective Library (New York), 1994 (26 lettered copies signed by James Elroy; slipcase) . £35/£20
The Rip-Off, Mysterious Press, 1987 (pbk) .   .   £5

Omnibus Editions
4 Novels, Zomba (London), 1983 (contains: *The Getaway, The Killer Inside Me, The Grifters, Pop. 1280*)   £10/£5
More Hardcore: 3 Novels, Donald I. Fine (New York), 1988 (contains *Ripoff, Roughneck, The Golden Gizmo*) £10/£5

Collections
Fireworks: The Lost Writings, Donald I. Fine (New York), 1988 .   .   .   .   £10/£5

KAY THOMPSON

(b.1908 d.1998)

Kay Thompson's Eloise series of children's books were inspired by her god-daughter Liza Minnelli. The four books in the series, illustrated by Hilary Knight, followed the adventures of a precocious six-year-old girl who lives at the Plaza Hotel in New York City, where Thompson herself lived. Although popular in the UK, they never achieved the bestseller status that they did in America.

Eloise Titles
Eloise: A Book for Precocious Grown-ups, Simon & Schuster (New York), 1955 .   .   .   £1,500/£250
ditto, Max Reinhardt (London), 1957.   .   .   £250/£40

ditto, Simon & Schuster (New York),1995 (250 copies signed by Thompson and Knight; slipcase) .   £150/£100
Eloise in Paris, Simon & Schuster (New York), 1957 £85/£25
ditto, Max Reinhardt (London), 1958.   .   .   . £65/£25
ditto, Simon & Schuster (New York),1999 (250 copies signed by Knight; slipcase)   .   .   . £145/£100
Eloise at Christmastime, Random House (New York), 1958
.   .   .   . £150/£35
ditto, Max Reinhardt (London), 1959.   .   . £150/£35
ditto, Simon & Schuster (New York),1999 (250 copies signed by Knight; slipcase)   .   .   . £145/£100
Eloise in Moscow, Simon & Schuster (New York), 1959 .
.   .   .   . £85/£25
ditto, Max Reinhardt (London), 1960.   .   . £65/£25
ditto, Simon & Schuster (New York), 2000 (250 copies signed by Knight; slipcase)   .   .   . £145/£100
The Absolutely Essential Eloise, Simon & Schuster (New York), 1999 .   .   .   .   .   . £10/£5
ditto, Simon & Schuster (New York), 1999 (250 copies signed by Knight; slipcase)   .   .   . £145/£100
Eloise's Guide to Life, Simon & Schuster (New York), 2000
.   .   .   . £10/£5
Eloise Takes A Bawth, Simon & Schuster (New York), 2002 .   .   .   . £10/£5

Others
Kay Thompson's Miss Pooky Peckinpaugh, and her secret private boyfriends complete with telephone numbers, Harper & Row (New York), 1970 .   .   . £25/£10

HENRY DAVID THOREAU
(b.1817 d.1862)

The two books published by American author and philosopher Henry Thoreau during his lifetime were not well received, but since his death *Walden* has come to be regarded as a classic. A lifelong advocate of the abolition of slavery, Thoreau's lasting contribution to literature is his writings on natural history and philosophy: it is argued that he anticipated modern environmentalism by a century.

A Week on the Concord and Merrimack Rivers, Munroe & Co. (Boston and Cambridge, MA.), 1849 .   . £4,000
ditto, Ticknor & Fields (Boston), 1862 (reissue of Munroe sheets) £1,250
ditto, Ticknor & Fields (Boston), 1868 .   .   . £250
ditto, Walter Scott (London), 1889 .   .   . £250
Walden, Ticknor & Fields (Boston), 1854 .   . £6,000
ditto, Ticknor & Fields (Boston), 1862 .   . £250
ditto, Douglas (Edinburgh), 1884 .   .   . £250
ditto, Walter Scott (London), 1886 .   .   . £125
Excursions, Ticknor & Fields (Boston), 1863 .   . £300
The Maine Woods, Ticknor & Fields (Boston), 1864 (in the first issue the books listed in the adverts are priced) . £300
Cape Cod, Ticknor & Fields (Boston), 1865 .   . £300
Letters to Various Persons, Ticknor & Fields (Boston), 1865
.   .   .   . £250
A Yankee in Canada, Ticknor & Fields (Boston), 1866 £800
Early Spring in Massachusetts, Houghton, Mifflin (Boston), 1881 .   .   .   . £200

Summer: From the Journal, Houghton, Mifflin (Boston), 1884 .   .   .   . £200
Winter: From the Journal, Houghton, Mifflin (Boston), 1888 .   .   .   . £200
Autumn: From the Journal, Houghton, Mifflin (Boston), 1892 .   .   .   . £200
Familiar Letters, Houghton, Mifflin (Boston), 1894 . £100
ditto, Houghton, Mifflin (Boston), 1894 (150 deluxe copies).
.   .   .   . £150
Poems of Nature, John Lane (London)/Houghton, Mifflin (Boston), 1895 .   .   .   .   .   . £250
Some Unpublished Letters, Marion Press (Jamaica, Queenborough, NY), 1899 (150 copies).   .   . £200
The Service, Goodspeed (Boston), 1902 (500 copies) . £75
ditto, Goodspeed (Boston), 1902 (20 copies on Japan vellum)
.   .   .   . £125
The First and Last Journeys of Thoreau, Bibliophile Society (Boston), 1904 (2 vols; 489 copies, slipcase)   £150/£100
Sir Walter Raleigh, Bibliophile Society (Boston), 1905 (489 copies, slipcase) .   .   .   .   . £100/£50
The Writings, Houghton, Mifflin (Boston), 1906 ('Walden Edition', blue cloth, 20 vols) £1,000
ditto, Houghton, Mifflin (Boston), 1906 ('Manuscript Edition', 400 of 600 numbered sets, green cloth with leaf of manuscript bound in, 20 vols) .   .   . £4,000
ditto, Houghton, Mifflin (Boston), 1906 ('Manuscript Edition Edition', approx 200 of 600 copies, custom bindings and extra set of frontispieces, 20 vols) .   £6,000
Unpublished Poems by Bryant and Thoreau, Bibliophile Society (Boston), 1907 (470 copies, slipcase) . £75/£45
Two Thoreau Letters, [Edwin Bliss Hill (Mesa, AZ), 1916] (c.250 copies; wraps) £125
The Moon, Houghton, Mifflin (Boston), 1927 (500 copies, slipcase).   .   .   .   .   . £125/£100
The Transmigration of the Seven Brahmans, Rudge (New York), 1931 (200 copies, slipcase) .   . £175/£150
ditto, Rudge (New York), 1932 (1,000 copies) . £65/£25
Collected Poems, Packard and Co. (Chicago), 1943 £100/£50
Consciousness in Concord, Houghton, Mifflin (Boston), 1958 .   .   .   . £20/£10
The Correspondence, New York Univ Press (New York), 1958 .   .   .   . £100/£35
Where I Lived and What I Lived For, Golden Cockerel Press (Waltham St Lawrence, Berks), 1924 (350 numbered copies bound in quarter parchment boards)   £200/£125
ditto, Golden Cockerel Press (Waltham St Lawrence, Berks), 1924 (30 numbered copies bound in blue morocco) . £300

COLIN THUBRON
(b.1939)

A popular travel writer, Thubron's novels have also been critical and commercial successes. Thubron is apparently a direct descendent of John Dryden and his first writings were appropriately enough poetry. Although published in a few journals, his poems have never been collected.

Travel
Mirror to Damascus, Heinemann (London), 1967 . £65/£15
ditto, Little, Brown (Boston), 1968 .   .   . £40/£10
The Hills of Adonis: A Quest In Lebanon, Heinemann (London), 1968 .   .   .   .   .   . £20/£5

ditto, Little, Brown (Boston), 1969 .   .   .   £15/£5
Jerusalem, Heinemann (London), 1969 .   .   £20/£5
ditto, Little, Brown (Boston), 1969 .   .   .   £15/£5
Journey into Cyprus, Heinemann (London), 1975 .   £20/£5
ditto, Atlantic Monthly Press (New York), 1990 (pbk) .   £5
Among the Russians, Heinemann (London), 1983 . £45/£15
ditto, as *Where the Nights are Longest: Travels by Car Through Western Russia*, Random House (New York), 1984 .   .   .   .   £10/£5
Behind the Wall: A Journey Through China, Heinemann (London), 1987 .   .   .   .   .   .   £15/£5
ditto, Atlantic Monthly Press (New York), 1988 .   £10/£5
The Silk Road—China: Beyond the Celestial Kingdom, Pyramid (London), 1989 (photographs by Carlos Navajas) .   .   .   .   £20/£5
ditto, as *The Silk Road: Beyond the Celestial Kingdom*, Simon & Schuster (New York), 1989 .   .   £20/£5
The Lost Heart of Asia, Heinemann (London), 1994 £10/£5
ditto, HarperCollins (New York), 1994 .   .   £10/£5
In Siberia, Chatto & Windus (London), 1999 .   .   £10/£5
ditto, HarperCollins (New York), 1999 .   .   £10/£5

Novels
The God in the Mountain, Heinemann (London), 1977 .
.   .   .   .   £25/£5
ditto, Norton (New York), 1977 .   .   .   £15/£5
Emperor, Heinemann (London), 1978 .   .   £25/£5
A Cruel Madness, Heinemann (London), 1984 .   £15/£5
ditto, Atlantic Monthly Press (New York), 1985 .   £10/£5
Falling, Heinemann (London), 1989 .   .   .   £10/£5
ditto, Atlantic Monthly Press (New York), 1990 .   £10/£5
Turning Back the Sun, Heinemann (London), 1991 £10/£5
ditto, HarperCollins (New York), 1992 .   .   £10/£5
Distance, Heinemann (London), 1996 .   .   £10/£5
To the Last City, Chatto & Windus (London), 2002 £10/£5

Edited by Thubron
Istanbul, Time Life (Amsterdam), 1978 (no d/w) .   .   £20
The Venetians, Time Life (Amsterdam), 1980 (no d/w) £10
The Ancient Mariners, Time Life (Amsterdam), 1981 (no d/w) £10

Others
The Royal Opera House, Covent Garden, Hamish Hamilton (London), 1982 .   .   .   .   .   .   £20/£10

JAMES THURBER
(b.1894 d.1961)

James Thurber was an American short story writer and cartoonist whose best known character, Walter Mitty, takes refuge in his daydreams. Thurber is remembered for his contributions (both cartoons and short stories) to the *New Yorker*. His idiosyncratic style was a result of his very poor eyesight: he drew his cartoons on large sheets of paper using a thick black crayon.

Fiction
Is Sex Necessary? Or Why Do You Feel the Way You Do, Harper (New York), 1929 (with E.B. White).   £450/£45
ditto, Heinemann (London), 1930 .   .   .   £300/£30
The Owl in the Attic and Other Perplexities, Harper (New York/London), 1931 .   .   .   .   .   £500/£75

The Seal in the Bedroom and Other Predicaments, Harper (New York/London), 1932 .   .   .   .   £400/£35
My Life and Hard Times, Harper (New York/London), 1933 .   .   .   .   £300/£45
The Middle-Aged Man on the Flying Trapeze, Harper (New York), 1935 .   .   .   .   .   £150/£25
ditto, Hamish Hamilton (London), 1935 .   .   £125/£20
Let Your Mind Alone! And Other More or Less Inspirational Pieces, Harper (New York), 1937 .£250/£35
ditto, Hamish Hamilton (London), 1937 .   .   £200/£25
The Last Flower: A Parable in Pictures, Harper (New York), 1939 .   .   .   .   .   .   £85/£15
ditto, Hamish Hamilton (London), 1939 .   .   £50/£10
Cream of Thurber, Hamish Hamilton (London), 1939 .   .
.   .   .   .   £45/£15
Fables for Our Time and Famous Poems Illustrated, Harper (New York), 1940 .   .   .   .   £150/£25
ditto, Hamish Hamilton (London), 1940 .   .   £75/£20
My World–And Welcome To It, Harcourt Brace (New York), 1942 .   .   .   .   £175/£35
ditto, Hamish Hamilton (London), 1942 .   .   £125/£25
Thurber's Men, Women and Dogs, Harcourt Brace (New York), 1943 .   .   .   .   .   .   £50/£25
ditto, Hamish Hamilton (London), 1943 .   .   £65/£15
The Thurber Carnival, Harper (New York), 1945 .   £65/£15
ditto, Hamish Hamilton (London), 1945 .   .   £45/£10
The Beast in Me and Other Animals, Harcourt Brace (New York), 1948 .   .   .   .   .   .   £45/£15
ditto, Hamish Hamilton (London), 1949 .   .   £25/£10
The Thurber Album: A New Collection of Pieces About People, Simon & Schuster (New York), 1952 .   £30/£10
ditto, Hamish Hamilton (London), 1952 .   .   £20/£5
Thurber Country: A New Collection of Pieces About Males and Females, Simon & Schuster (New York), 1953 .
.   .   .   .   £30/£10
ditto, Hamish Hamilton (London), 1953 .   .   £20/£5
Thurber's Dogs, Simon & Schuster (New York), 1955 .   .
.   .   .   .   £25/£5
ditto, Hamish Hamilton (London), 1955 .   .   £20/£5
A Thurber Garland, Hamish Hamilton (London), 1955 (no d/w) £35
Further Fables for Our Time, Simon & Schuster (New York), 1956 .   .   .   .   .   .   £25/£5
ditto, Hamish Hamilton (London), 1956 .   .   £20/£5
Alarms and Diversions, Harper (New York), 1957 £25/£5
ditto, Hamish Hamilton (London), 1957 .   .   £20/£5
Lanterns and Lances, Harper (New York), 1961 .   £25/£5
ditto, Hamish Hamilton (London), 1961 .   .   £20/£5
Credos and Curios, Harper (New York), 1962 .   £25/£5
ditto, Hamish Hamilton (London), 1962 .   .   £20/£5
Vintage Thurber, Hamish Hamilton (London), 1963 (2 vols)
.   .   .   .   £40/£10
Thurber and Company, Harper (New York), 1966 £25/£5
ditto, Hamish Hamilton (London), 1967 .   .   £20/£5

Children's Books
Many Moons, Harcourt Brace (New York), 1943 (illustrated by Louis Slobodkin) .   .   .   .   .   £300/£50
ditto, Hamish Hamilton (London), 1945 .   .   £200/£40
ditto, A.M. & R.W. Roe (St Joseph, MI), 1958 (illustrated by Philip Reed, 250 copies signed by illustrator, no d/w) £150
ditto, A.M. & R.W. Roe (St Joseph, MI), 1958 (trade edition, no d/w) £40

The Great Quillow, Harcourt Brace (New York), 1944
(illustrated by Doris Lee) . . . . . £145/£25
The White Deer, Harcourt Brace (New York), 1945
(illustrated by Thurber and Don Freeman) . . £100/£15
ditto, Hamish Hamilton (London), 1946 . . . £65/£15
The 13 Clocks, Simon & Schuster (New York), 1950
(illustrated by Mark [Marc] Simont) . . . £100/£15
ditto, Hamish Hamilton (London), 1951 . . . £65/£15
The Wonderful O, Simon & Schuster (New York), 1957
(illustrated by Marc Simont) . . . . £25/£10
ditto, Hamish Hamilton (London), 1958 . . . £25/£10

Plays
'Oh My, Omar': A Musical Comedy, Ohio State Univ
(Columbus, OH), 1921 (with Hayward M. Andersen; sewn
wraps) £400
Many Moons, Ohio State Univ (Columbus, OH), 1922
(wraps) £250
Tell Me Not: A Two Act Musical Comedy, Ohio State Univ
(Columbus, OH), 1924 (stapled wraps) £350
The Male Animal, Random House (New York), 1940 (with
Elliott Nugent) . . . . £45/£15
ditto, Hamish Hamilton (London), 1950 . . . £35/£10

Non-Fiction
Thurber on Humour, Ohioana Library Association
(Columbus, OH), 1953 (stapled wraps) £45
The Years with Ross, Little, Brown (Boston), 1959 £45/£15
ditto, Hamish Hamilton (London), 1959 . . . £45/£15
Selected Letters of James Thurber, Little, Brown (Boston),
1981 (edited by Helen Thurber & Edward Weeks) £15/£5
ditto, Franklin Library (Franklin Centre, PA), 1981 (limited
edition) £20
ditto, Hamish Hamilton (London), 1982 . . . £15/£10
*Collecting Himself, James Thurber on Writing, Writers,
Humor & Himself*, Harper (New York), 1989 (edited by
Michael J. Rosen) . . . . . . £10/£5
Thurber On Crime, Mysterious Press (New York), 1989
(edited by Robert Lopresti) . . . . £10/£5

WILLIAM M. TIMLIN
(b.1892 d.1943)

Although Timlin illustrated works by other authors, he is
best remembered for the beautiful fantasy *The Ship That
Sailed to Mars*, which he wrote and illustrated himself.
Timlin had begun work on another book, *The Building of a
Fairy City*, but it remained unfinished at his death.

Novels
The Ship That Sailed to Mars, Harrap (London), [1923]
(1,750 copies at 43/-) . . . . £2,500/£1,500
ditto, Stokes (New York), 1923 (250 copies at $12) . .
. . . . £2,000/£1,000
Others
South Africa, A. & C. Black (London), [1927] (24 pencil
sketches by Timlin) . . . . . . £45/£10
Out of the Crucible by Hedley A Chilvers, Cassell (London),
1929 (16 drawings by Timlin) . . . . £25/£5

J.R.R. TOLKIEN
(b.1892 d.1973)

John Ronald Reuel Tolkien was born in South Africa and
educated in Britain. He was appointed Professor of Anglo-
Saxon at Oxford in 1925 and published a number of academic works on the subject. He is best known for his
novels dealing with the mythical land of Middle-Earth, and
through the *Hobbit* and *The Lord of the Rings* he has become the father of modern high fantasy.

'Middle-Earth' Novels
The Hobbit, Allen & Unwin (London), 1937 (with b&w
illustrations by the author). . . £20,000/£5,000
ditto, Allen & Unwin (London), 1937 (second impression
with four new colour plates by the author) £5,000/£1,500
ditto, Houghton Mifflin (Boston), 1938 . £6,500/£1,000
*The Fellowship of the Ring, being the First Part of 'The
Lord of the Rings'*, Allen & Unwin (London), 1954 . .
. . . . £4,000/£600
ditto, Houghton Mifflin (Boston), 1954 . £1,250/£250
*The Two Towers, being the Second Part of 'The Lord of the
Rings'*, Allen & Unwin (London), 1954. . £3,000/£400
ditto, Houghton Mifflin (Boston), 1955 . £1,000/£200
*The Return of the King, being the Third Part of 'The Lord
of the Rings'*, Allen & Unwin (London), 1955 £3,000/£500
ditto, Houghton Mifflin (Boston), 1956 . . £1,000/£200
The Lord of the Rings, Allen & Unwin (London), 1962 (first
combined edition, three books in grey box) . £150/£75
ditto, Allen & Unwin (London), 1964 (deluxe combined
edition, three books bound in buckram, decorated box) .
. . . . £300/£150
The Silmarillion, Allen & Unwin (London), 1977 (printed
by Billing & Sons) . . . . . . £35/£10
ditto, Allen & Unwin (London), 1977 (printed by William
Clowes). . . . . £25/£5
ditto, Houghton Mifflin (Boston), 1977 . . . £25/£5

History of 'Middle-Earth' Titles
The Book of Lost Tales, Part 1, Allen & Unwin (London),
1983 . . . . £125/£75
ditto, Houghton Mifflin (Boston), 1984 . . . £75/£15
The Book of Lost Tales, Part 2, Allen & Unwin (London),
1984 . . . . £30/£35
ditto, Houghton Mifflin (Boston), 1984 . . £25/£10
The Lays of Beleriand, Allen & Unwin (London), 1985 .
. . . . £65/£10
ditto, Houghton Mifflin (Boston), 1985 . . £25/£10
The Shaping of Middle-Earth, Allen & Unwin (London),
1986 . . . . £75/£15
ditto, Houghton Mifflin (Boston), 1986 . . £25/£10
The Lost Road and Other Writings, Unwin Hyman
(London), 1987 . . . . £150/£25
ditto, Houghton Mifflin (Boston), 1987 . . £45/£15
*The Return of the Shadow: The History of the Lord of the
Rings, Part 1*, Unwin Hyman (London), 1988 . £125/£25
ditto, Houghton Mifflin (Boston), 1988 . . £25/£10
*Treason of Isengard: The History of the Lord of the Rings,
Part 2*, Unwin Hyman (London), 1989 . . . £30/£10
ditto, Houghton Mifflin (Boston), 1989 . . £25/£10
*The War of the Ring: The History of the Lord of the Rings,
Part 3*, Unwin Hyman (London), 1990 . . . £45/£15
ditto, Houghton Mifflin (Boston), 1990 . . £25/£10

Sauron Defeated: The History of the Lord of the Rings,
   Part 4, HarperCollins (London), 1992 . . . £65/£15
ditto, Houghton Mifflin (Boston), 1992 . . . £25/£10
Morgoth's Ring, HarperCollins (London), 1993 . £300/£45
ditto, Houghton Mifflin (Boston), 1993 . . . £20/£10
The War of the Jewels, HarperCollins (London), 1994 . .
   . . . . £300/£45
ditto, Houghton Mifflin (Boston), 1994 . . . £25/£10
The Peoples of Middle-Earth, HarperCollins (London),
   1996 . . . . £300/£45
ditto, Houghton Mifflin (Boston), 1996 . . . £20/£10

Other 'Middle-Earth' Titles
The Adventures of Tom Bombadil and Other Verses from
   'The Red Book', Allen & Unwin (London), 1962 £200/£25
ditto, Houghton Mifflin (Boston), 1963 . . . £125/£25
The Road Goes Ever On: A Song Cycle, Houghton Mifflin
   (Boston), 1967 . . . . £25/£10
ditto, Allen & Unwin (London), 1968 . . . . £35/£10
Bilbo's Last Song, Houghton Mifflin (Boston), 1974 £25/£5
ditto, Unwin Hyman (London), 1974 . . . . £25/£5
Unfinished Tales of Numenor and Middle-Earth, Allen &
   Unwin (London), 1980 . . . . . £25/£10
ditto, Houghton Mifflin (Boston), 1980 . . . £25/£10

Other Prose
Farmer Giles of Ham, Allen & Unwin (London), 1949 .
   . . . . £400/£50
ditto, Houghton Mifflin (Boston), 1950 . . . £175/£30
Tree and Leaf, Allen & Unwin (London), 1964 (pbk) . £15
ditto, Allen & Unwin (London), 1964 . . . £150/£30
ditto, Houghton Mifflin (Boston), 1965 . . . £45/£10
The Tolkien Reader, Ballantine (New York), 1966 £25/£10
Smith of Wootton Major, Allen & Unwin (London), 1967
   (no d/w) £25
ditto, Houghton Mifflin (Boston), 1967 . . . £25/£10
The Father Christmas Letters, Allen & Unwin (London),
   1976 (no d/w) £15
ditto, Houghton Mifflin (Boston), 1976 . . . £15/£5
Pictures by J.R.R. Tolkien, Allen & Unwin (London), 1979
   (slipcase) . . . . £75/£50
ditto, as *The Pictures of J.R.R. Tolkien*, Houghton Mifflin
   (Boston), 1979 (slipcase) . . . . . £75/£50
Poems and Stories, Allen & Unwin (London), 1980 (deluxe
   edition) . . . . £100/£35
ditto, Houghton Mifflin (Boston), 1980 . . . £25/£10
The Letters of J.R.R. Tolkien, Allen & Unwin (London),
   1981 . . . . £20/£5
ditto, Houghton Mifflin (Boston), 1981 . . . £20/£5
Mr Bliss, Allen & Unwin (London), 1982 . . £15/£5
ditto, Houghton Mifflin (Boston), 1983 . . . £15/£5

Other Poetry
Songs for the Philologists, privately printed, Univ College
   (London), 1936 . . . . £5,000
The Homecoming of Beorhtnoth, Allen & Unwin (London),
   1975 . . . . £20/£5

Academic Titles
A Middle English Vocabulary, O.U.P. (Oxford, UK), 1922
   (first issue with ads dated October 1921, 186 ornaments in
   cover design; wraps) £450
ditto, O.U.P. (Oxford, UK), 1922 (second issue with ads
   undated, 184 ornaments in cover design; wraps) . £225

ditto, O.U.P. (New York), 1922 . . . . . . £75
Sir Gawain and the Green Knight, O.U.P. (Oxford, UK),
   1925 (with errata slip) . . . . £450/£125
ditto, O.U.P. (New York), 1925 . . . . . £400/£75
Beowulf: The Monsters and the Critics, Milford (London),
   1937 (British Academy lecture, 1936; wraps) . . £400
ditto, Folcroft Library Editions (Folcroft, PA), 1972 . £10
Sir Gawain and the Green Knight, Pearl, and Sir Orfeo,
   Allen & Unwin (London), 1975 . . . . £15/£5
ditto, Houghton Mifflin (Boston), 1975 . . . £25/£5
Finn and Hengest: The Fragment and the Episode, Allen
   & Unwin (London), 1983 . . . . . £15/£5
ditto, Houghton Mifflin (Boston), 1983 . . . £15/£5

MARY TOURTEL
(b.1873 d.1948)

Rupert Bear is the best known creation of this British
author and illustrator: he first appeared in the *Daily
Express* in 1920. Tourtel ceased working on the cartoon
strip in 1935 due to failing eyesight. The very collectable
series of Rupert Annuals began in the following year, after
the strip had been taken over by Alfred Bestall. It is now
drawn by John Harrold.

'Rupert' Annuals
1936, Daily Express (London), 1936 (with d/w) . £2,000
ditto, Daily Express (London), 1936 (without d/w). . £400
1937, Daily Express (London), 1937 . . . . . £375
1938, Daily Express (London), 1938 . . . . . £325
1939, Daily Express (London), 1939 . . . . . £350
1940, Daily Express (London), 1940 . . . . . £350
1941, Daily Express (London), 1941 . . . . . £400
1942, Daily Express (London), 1942 (wraps) . . £450
1943, Daily Express (London), 1943 (wraps) . . £250
1944, Daily Express (London), 1944 (wraps) . . £250
1945, Daily Express (London), 1945 (wraps) . . £200
1946, Daily Express (London), 1946 (wraps) . . £150
1947, Daily Express (London), 1947 (wraps) . . £150
1948-49, Daily Express (London), 1948 (wraps) . . £75
1950-59, Daily Express (London), 1950-59 (boards) £75 each
1960-68, Daily Express (London), 1960-68 ('magic painting'
   pages not coloured in) . . . . . £100 each
1960-68, Daily Express (London), 1960-68 ('magic painting'
   pages coloured in) . . . . . . £35 each
1969, Daily Express (London), 1969 . . . . . £20
1970-89, Daily Express (London), 1970-89 . . . £5
1990, Daily Express (London), 1990 (anniversary issue) £10
1991-97, Daily Express (London), 1991-97 . . £5 each

'Rupert' Annuals - Facsimiles
1936, Daily Express (London), 1985 (numbered, limited
   edition with promotional band) . . . £100/£65
1937, Daily Express (London), 1986 (numbered, limited
   edition with promotional band) . . . . £95/£60
1938, Daily Express (London), 1989 (numbered, limited
   edition with promotional band) . . . . £70/£45
1939, Daily Express (London), 1991 . . . . . £35
1940, Pedigree Books (Exeter, Devon), 1992 . . . £30
1941, Pedigree Books (Exeter, Devon), 1993 (in soft
   slipcase). . . . . £45/£30

1942, Pedigree Books (Exeter, Devon), 1994 (numbered, limited edition in slipcase). . . . . £75/£45

1943, Pedigree Books (Exeter, Devon), 1995 (numbered, limited edition in slipcase). . . . . £75/£45

1944, Pedigree Books (Exeter, Devon), 1996 (numbered, limited edition in soft slipcase). . . . £60/£40

1945, Pedigree Books (Exeter, Devon), 1997 (numbered, limited edition in slipcase). . . . . £100/£45

1948, Pedigree Books (Exeter, Devon), 1998 (numbered, limited edition in slipcase). . . . . £85/£45

1949, Pedigree Books (Exeter, Devon), 1999 (numbered, limited edition in slipcase). . . . . £85/£45

1950, Pedigree Books (Exeter, Devon), 2000 (numbered, limited edition in slipcase). . . . . £75/£40

1951, Pedigree Books (Exeter, Devon), 2001 (numbered, limited edition in slipcase). . . . . £35/£20

1952, Pedigree Books (Exeter, Devon), 2002 (numbered, limited edition in slipcase). . . . . £35/£20

1953, Pedigree Books (Exeter, Devon), 2003 (numbered, limited edition in slipcase). . . . . £35/£20

1955, Pedigree Books (Exeter, Devon), 2004 (numbered, limited edition in slipcase). . . . . £20/£10

1957, Pedigree Books (Exeter, Devon), 2005 (numbered, limited edition in slipcase). . . . . £20/£10

1958, Pedigree Books (Exeter, Devon), 2006 (numbered, limited edition in slipcase). . . . . £30/£15

1959, Pedigree Books (Exeter, Devon), 2007 (numbered, limited edition in slipcase). . . . . £20/£10

1963, Pedigree Books (Exeter, Devon), 2008 (numbered, limited edition in slipcase). . . . . £20/£10

1965, Pedigree Books (Exeter, Devon), 2009 (numbered, limited edition in slipcase). . . . . £20/£10

'Monster Rupert' Annuals

Monster Rupert, Sampson Low (London), [1931] (Rupert with wolf) £850

Monster Rupert, Sampson Low (London), [1932] (Rupert on log). £700

Monster Rupert, Sampson Low (London), [1933] (Rupert with bird) £700

Monster Rupert, Sampson Low (London), [1934] (Rupert with small boy in storeroom) £700

Monster Rupert, Sampson Low (London), [1948] (Rupert on log, with d/w) £35

Monster Rupert, Sampson Low (London), [1949] (Rupert with fox, with d/w) £35

Monster Rupert, Sampson Low (London), [1950] (Rupert helping boy out of hole, all cut-outs intact, d/w) . £50/£20

Monster Rupert, Sampson Low (London), [1953] (all cut-outs intact) £40

'Rupert' Books

The Adventures of Rupert the Little Lost Bear, Nelson (London), [1921]. £500

The Little Bear and the Fairy Child, Nelson (London), [1922] £500

Margot the Midget and Little Bear's Christmas, Nelson (London), [1922]. £500

The Little Bear and the Ogres, Nelson (London), 1922 £500

'Rupert Little Bear's Adventures', Sampson Low (London), 1924-25 (3 books) . . . . . . £450 each

'Rupert - Little Bear Series', Sampson Low (London), 1925-27 (6 books) . . . . £400 each

'Little Bear Library' Titles, Sampson Low (London), [1928-1936] (numbered 1-46) . . . . £200/£75 each

The Rupert Story Book, Sampson Low (London), [1938] £450

Rupert Little Bear: More Stories, Sampson Low (London), [1939] £450

Rupert Again, Sampson Low (London), [1940] . . £450

'Adventure' Titles *(all in card covers)*

No. 1, Daily Express (London) £40

Nos. 2-9, Daily Express (London) . . . £15 each

No. 10, Daily Express (London) £25

Nos. 11-30, Daily Express (London) . . . £20 each

Nos. 31-40, Daily Express (London) . . . £25 each

Nos. 41-45, Daily Express (London) . . . £50 each

Nos. 46-48, Daily Express (London) . . . £60 each

No. 49, Daily Express (London) £100

No. 50, Daily Express (London) £125

Daily Express Children's Annuals

1930, Lane (London), 1930 . . . . . . £125

1931, Lane (London), 1931 . . . . . . £125

1932, Lane (London), 1932 . . . . . . £100

1933, Lane (London), 1933 . . . . . . £100

1934, Lane (London), 1934 . . . . . . £100

1935, Lane (London), 1935 . . . . . . £125

Other Collectable Titles by Mary Tourtel

A Horse Book, Grant Richards 'Dumpy Books for Children' series No. 10 (London), 1901 . . . . . £100

The Humpty Dumpty Book, Nursery Rhymes Told in Pictures, Treherne (London), [1902] . . . £100

The Three Little Foxes, Grant Richards 'Dumpy Books for Children' series No. 21 (London), 1903 . . . £100

B. TRAVEN

(b.1882 d.1969)

Little is known about B. Traven and it is not even certain whether he was German or just happened to write in that language. From his books it is obvious that he lived and travelled extensively in Europe, the United States and Mexico. He is best known for *The Treasure of the Sierra Madre* which was the basis for the John Huston film starring Humphrey Bogart. For all of the acclaim they have received, some of his works are still awaiting translation from German.

'Jungle/Mahogany' Novels

Der Karren, Buchergilde Guttenberg (Berlin), 1931 . . . . £750/£75

ditto, as **The Carreta**, Chatto & Windus (London), 1935 (translated by Basil Creighton). . . £1,000/£200

ditto, Hill & Wang (New York), 1970 . . . £50/£10

Regierung, Buchergilde Guttenberg (Berlin), 1931 £750/£75

ditto, as **Government**, Chatto & Windus (London), 1935 (translated by Basil Creighton). . . £1,000/£200

ditto, Hill & Wang (New York), 1971 . . . £45/£10

Der Marsch ins Reich der Caoba Ein, Buchergilde Guttenberg (Berlin), 1931 . . . . . . £600/£50

ditto, as **March to Caobaland**, Robert Hale (London), 1961 . . . . £75/£10 *ditto*, Hill & Wang (New York), 1971 . . . £40/£10

Die Troza, Buchergilde Guttenberg (Berlin), 1936 . £600/£65

ditto, as ***Trozas***, Allison & Busby (London), 1994 (translated by Hugo Young; pbk). £5

ditto, Ivan R. Dee (Chicago), [1994] . . . £10/£5

Die Rebellion der Gehenkten, Buchergilde Guttenberg (Berlin), 1936 . . . . . . £400/£45

ditto, as ***The Rebellion of the Hanged***, Robert Hale (London), [1952] (translated by Charles Duff) . £125/£35

ditto, Knopf (New York), 1952 . . . . £25/£10

Ein General Kommt aus dem Dschungel, Alex Holmstrom (Stockholm), 1939 . . . . . £400/£45

ditto, as ***The General from the Jungle***, Robert Hale (London), 1954 (translated by Desmond I Vesey) £125/£35

ditto, Hill & Wang (New York), 1972 . . . £25/£10

Aslan Norval, Kurt Desch (Vienna, Munich, Basel), 1960 . . . . £100/£15

Other Novels

Das Totenschiff, Buchergilde Guttenberg (Berlin), 1926 . . . . £1,250/£250

ditto, as ***The Death Ship***, Chatto & Windus (London), 1934 (translated by Eric Sutton). . . . £1,250/£250

ditto, Knopf (New York), 1934 (revised and rewritten by the author) . . . . £400/£45

ditto, Cape (London), 1940 . . . . . £200/£35

Der Wobbly, Buchmeister Verlag (Berlin and Leipzig), 1926 . . . . £750/£125

ditto, as ***The Cotton-Pickers***, Robert Hale (London), 1956 (translated by Eleanor Brockett) . . . £125/£35

ditto, Hill & Wang (New York), 1969 . . . £25/£10

Die Schatz der Sierra Madre, Buchergilde Guttenberg (Berlin), 1927 . . . . . . £750/£125

ditto, as ***The Treasure of the Sierra Madre***, Chatto & Windus (London), 1934 (translated by Basil Creighton) . . . . £3,000/£350

ditto, Knopf (New York), 1935 (revised and rewritten by the author) . . . . £2,000/£275

Die Brücke im Dschungel, Buchergilde Guttenberg (Berlin), 1929 . . . . £750/£100

ditto, as ***The Bridge in the Jungle***, Knopf (New York), 1938 (revised and rewritten by the author) . . . £400/£45

ditto, Cape (London), 1940 . . . . . £125/£35

Die Weisse Rose, Buchergilde Guttenberg (Berlin), 1929 . . . . £750/£100

ditto, as ***The White Rose***, Robert Hale (London), 1965 . . . . £125/£35

ditto, Lawrence Hill (Westport, CT), 1979 . £25/£10

Short Stories

Der Busch und Andere Erzählungen, Buchergilde Guttenberg (Berlin), 1928 . . . . . . £600/£75

Stories by the Man Nobody Knows, Regency Books (Evanston, IL), 1961 (pbk) £10

The Night Visitor and Other Stories, Hill & Wang (New York), 1966 . . . . . . £25/£10

ditto, Cassell (London), 1967 . . . . £100/£25

The Creation of the Sun and the Moon, Hill & Wang (New York), 1968 . . . . . £25/£10

ditto, Muller (London), 1971 . . . £100/£25

The Kidnapped Saint and Other Stories, Lawrence Hill (Westport, CT), 1968 . . . . . £25/£10

ditto, Allison & Busby (London), 1978 . . £50/£15

To the Honorable Miss S. . . . And Other Stories, Lawrence Hill (Westport, CT), 1968 (pseud 'Ret Marut') . £25/£10

Non-Fiction

Land des Frühlings, Buchergilde Guttenberg (Berlin), 1928 . . . . £750/£100

WILLIAM TREVOR
(b.1928)

A novelist, playwright and short story writer, Trevor's work often deals with the corruption of innocence. He was born William Trevor Cox in County Cork, Ireland and educated at Trinity College Dublin. He emigrated to England in the 1950s and now lives in Devon. In 2002 he was given an honorary knighthood, and an honorary C.B.E. in 1977.

Novels

A Standard of Behaviour, Hutchinson (London), 1958. . . . . £500/£100

ditto, Sphere (London), 1967 (revised edition; pbk) . £5

The Old Boys, Bodley Head (London), 1964 . £150/£25

ditto, Viking (New York), 1964 . . . . £50/£10

The Boarding House, Bodley Head (London), 1965 . . . . £125/£25

ditto, Viking (New York), 1965 . . . . £75/£15

The Love Department, Bodley Head (London), 1966 . . . . £100/£20

ditto, Viking (New York), 1967 . . . . £40/£10

Mrs Eckdorf in O'Neill's Hotel, Bodley Head (London), 1969 . . . . £65/£15

ditto, Viking (New York), 1970 . . . . £45/£10

Miss Gomez and the Brethren, Bodley Head (London), 1971 . . . . £75/£15

Elizabeth Alone, Bodley Head (London), 1973 £65/£15

ditto, as ***Dreaming***, Stellar Press (Hatfield, Herts), 1973 (extract from *Elizabeth Alone*, 225 copies; wraps with d/w) . . . . £95/£50

ditto, Viking (New York), 1974 . . . £35/£10

The Children of Dynmouth, Bodley Head (London), 1976 . . . . £20/£5

ditto, Viking (New York), 1977 . . . . £15/£5

Other People's Worlds, Bodley Head (London), 1980 £10/£5

ditto, Viking (New York), 1981 . . . . £10/£5

Fools of Fortune, Bodley Head (London), 1983 . £10/£5

ditto, Bodley Head (London), 1983 (40 numbered, signed copies, bound by Kenny's of Galway, slipcase) . . £125

ditto, Viking (New York), 1983 . . . . £10/£5

The Silence in the Garden, Bodley Head (London), 1988 . . . . £10/£5

ditto, London Limited Editions (London), 1988 (150 numbered, signed copies, glassine d/w) . . £65/£50

ditto, Viking (New York), 1988 . . . . £10/£5

Felicia's Journey, Viking (London), 1994 . £10/£5

ditto, Viking (New York), 1995 . . . . £10/£5

Death in Summer, Viking (London), 1998 . £10/£5

ditto, Viking (New York), 1998 . . . . £10/£5

The Story of Lucy Gault, Viking (London), 2002 . £10/£5

ditto, Viking (New York), 2002 . . . . £10/£5

Love and Summer, Viking (London), 2009 . £10/£5

ditto, Viking (New York), 2009 . . . . £10/£5

Short Stories

The Day We Got Drunk on Cake, Bodley Head (London), 1967 . . . . £500/£40

ditto, Viking (New York), 1968 . . . . . £50/£10

The Ballroom of Romance, Bodley Head (London), 1972 .
. . . . £175/£35

ditto, Viking (New York), 1972 . . . . . £35/£10

The Last Lunch of the Season, Covent Garden Press (London), 1973 (100 numbered, signed copies of 600; stapled wraps) £100

ditto, Covent Garden Press (London), 1973 (500 copies of 600; stapled wraps) £10

Angels at the Ritz and Other Stories, Bodley Head (London), 1975 . . . . £85/£20

ditto, Viking (New York), 1976 . . . . . £15/£5

Old School Ties, Lemon Tree Press (London), 1976 (illustrations by Magnus Lohkamp). . . . £50/£15

ditto, Lemon Tree Press (London), 1976 (pbk) . . £5

Lovers of Their Time and Other Stories, Bodley Head (London), 1978 . . . . £35/£10

ditto, Bodley Head (London), 1978 (extract, 225 copies; sewn wraps) £125

ditto, Viking (New York), 1978 . . . . . £20/£5

The Distant Past, Poolbeg Press (Dublin), 1979 (pbk) . £15

Beyond the Pale, Bodley Head (London), 1981 . £20/£5

ditto, Viking (New York), 1982 . . . . . £10/£5

The News From Ireland and Other Stories, Bodley Head (London), 1986 . . . . £15/£5

ditto, Bodley Head (London), 1986 (50 numbered, signed copies, bound by Kenny's of Galway, slipcase) £250/£175

ditto, Viking (New York), 1986 . . . . . £10/£5

Nights at the Alexandra, Hutchinson (London), 1987 (illustrations by Paul Hogarth) . . . . £10/£5

ditto, Harper (New York), 1987 . . . . . £10/£5

Family Sins and Other Stories, Bodley Head (London), 1990 . . . . £10/£5

ditto, Viking (New York), 1990 . . . . . £10/£5

The Collected Stories, Viking (London), 1990 . £15/£5

ditto, Viking (London), 1990 (100 signed copies) £250/£175

ditto, Viking (New York), 1992 . . . . . £15/£5

Two Lives, Viking (London), 1991 (contains 'Reading Turgenev' & 'My House in Umbria') . . £10/£5

ditto, Viking (New York), 1991 . . . . . £10/£5

Outside Ireland: Selected Stories, Penguin (London), 1995 (pbk) £5

Marrying Damian, Colophon Press (London), 1995 (175 numbered, signed copies; sewn wraps) £30

ditto, Colophon Press (London), 1994 (26 signed, lettered copies, slipcase) . . . . . . £175/£125

After Rain, Viking (London), 1996 . . . . £10/£5

ditto, Viking (New York), 1996 . . . . . £10/£5

The Piano Tuner's Wives, Clarion Press (Alton, Hants), 1996 (99 copies signed by author and illustrator out of 499 copies, with additional signed proof of one of the illustrations laid in) £90

ditto, Clarion Press (Alton, Hants), 1996 (150 copies numbered and signed by author and illustrator, of 499 copies) £60

ditto, Clarion Press (Alton, Hants), 1996 (250 copies numbered out of 499 copies) £25

Death of a Professor, Colophon Press (London), 1997 (200 numbered, signed copies; sewn wraps) . . . £35

ditto, Colophon Press (London), 1997 (26 signed copies, slipcase). . . . . £125/£75

Low Sunday, 1950, Colophon Press (London), 2000 (200 numbered, signed copies; sewn wraps) . . . £35

ditto, Colophon Press (London), 2000 (26 signed copies, slipcase). . . . . £125/£75

The Hill Bachelors, Viking (London), 2000 . . £10/£5

ditto, Viking (New York), 2000 . . . . . £10/£5

A Bit on the Side, Viking (London), 2004 . . £10/£5

ditto, Viking (New York), 2004 . . . . . £10/£5

Cheating at Canasta, Viking (London), 2007 . . £10/£5

ditto, Viking (New York), 2007 . . . . . £10/£5

Plays

The Girl, French (London), 1968 (wraps). . . £25

The Old Boys, Davis-Poynter (London), 1971 (pbk) . £15

Going Home, French (London), 1972 (wraps). . £10

A Night With Mrs Da Tonka, French (London), 1972 (wraps) £10

Marriages, French (London), 1973 (wraps) . . £10

Scenes from an Album, Co-op Books (Dublin), 1981 (pbk) £20

Children's Title

Juliet's Story, O'Brien Press (Dublin), 1991 . £15/£5

ditto, Bodley Head (London), 1992 . . . . £15/£5

ditto, Simon & Schuster (New York), 1992 . . £10/£5

Others

A Writer's Ireland, Viking (New York), 1984 . £15/£5

ditto, Thames & Hudson (London), 1984 . . . £10/£5

Excursions in the Real World, Hutchinson (London), 1993 . . . . £10/£5

ditto, Hutchinson/London Limited Editions (London), 1993 (150 signed copies) . . . . . . £65/£50

ditto, Knopf (New York), 1994 . . . . . £10/£5

ANTHONY TROLLOPE
(b.1815 d.1882)

Anthony Trollope was one of the most successful, prolific and respected English Victorian novelists. A civil servant who worked for the Post Office, his two best known series of books are based around the fictional cathedral town of Barchester. Arguably his greatest contribution to society, however, was the introduction of the pillar-box.

Novels

The Macdermots of Ballycloran, Newby (London), 1847 (3 vols, dark brown cloth) £10,000

ditto, Newby (London), 1848 (3 vols, second printing with 1848 title-page) £1,000

ditto, T. B. Peterson and Brothers (Philadelphia, PA), 1870 . . . . £850

The Kellys and the O'Kellys, Colburn (London), 1848 (3 vols, half cloth and boards) £4,000

ditto, Rudd & Carleton (New York), 1860 . . £350

La Vendée, Colburn (London), 1850 (3 vols) . £3,000

ditto, Colburn (London), 1850 (second issue with cancel title-page giving details of author's previous works, 3 vols) £500

The Warden, Longman (London), 1855 (first issue with ads dated September 1854) . . . . . £2,000 *ditto*, Longman (London), 1855 (later issue with ads dated March 1956 or no ads) £1,250

ditto, Longman (London), 1855 (later issue with ads dated October 1959) £1,000

Barchester Towers, Longman (London), 1857 (first issue with brick-red endpapers, some with ads dated 1857, pale brown cloth; 3 vols) £7,500

ditto, Longman (London), 1857 (second issue with dark brown endpapers, ads dated 1860, 3 vols) . . £4,500

The Three Clerks, Bentley (London), 1858 (quarter grey cloth, brown boards; 3 vols) £2,000

ditto, Bentley (London), 1858 (dark grey/purple cloth; 3 vols) £2,000

ditto, Harper (New York), 1860 . . . . . £300

Doctor Thorne, Chapman & Hall (London), 1858 (dark grey/purple cloth, first edition with 'mamma' on p.18, line 15, 3 vols) £7,500

ditto, Chapman & Hall (London), 1858 (second edition with 'mommon' on p.18, line 15, 3 vols). £650

ditto, Harper (New York), 1858 . . . . . £250

The Bertrams, Chapman & Hall (London), 1859 (dark grey/purple cloth, 3 vols) £2,000

ditto, Harper (New York), 1859 . . . . . £250

Castle Richmond, Chapman & Hall (London), 1860 (dark grey/purple cloth; first issue on spine, no line between 'Trollope' and 'Vol 1'; 16 pages of ads dated February 1860; on verso title, imprint is 'William Clowes & Sons'; 3 vols) £2,500

ditto, Chapman & Hall (London), 1860 (dark grey/purple cloth; second issue on spine a line between 'Trollope' and 'Vol 1'; 32 pages of ads dated May 1860; on verso title imprint is 'William Clowes & Sons'; 3 vols) . . £1,000

ditto, Chapman & Hall (London), 1860 (secondary binding, 3 vols in dark green cloth, no author on spine) . . £650

ditto, Harper (New York), 1860 . . . . . £200

Framley Parsonage, Smith Elder (London), 1861 (grey/purple cloth; 3 vols) £1,500

ditto, Smith Elder (London), 1861 (one vol; violet cloth; no illustrations) £300

ditto, Harper (New York), 1861 . . . . . £150

Orley Farm, Chapman & Hall (London), 1862 (20 parts, buff wraps) £6,000

ditto, Chapman & Hall (London), 1862 (bound from monthly parts; brown/purple cloth; 2 vols) £3,000

ditto, Harper (New York), 1862 . . . . . £65

The Struggles of Brown, Jones and Robinson, Harper (New York), 1862 (pirate edition; buff wraps). . £1,250

ditto, Smith Elder (London), 1870 (brown cloth) . . £750

Rachel Ray, Chapman & Hall (London), 1863 (pinkish maroon cloth; the dominant lines of the pattern are horizontal; 'VOL I' and 'VOL II' on the spine in roman capitals with serifs; 2 vols) £1,250

The Small House at Allington, Smith Elder (London), 1864 (green cloth; 2 vols) £2,000

ditto, Harper (New York), 1864 . . . . . £125

Can You Forgive Her, Chapman & Hall (London), 1864-65 (20 parts, buff wraps). £3,500

ditto, Chapman & Hall (London), 1864, 1865 (crimson cloth; 2 vols) £750

Miss Mackenzie, Chapman & Hall (London), 1865 (green cloth; 2 vols). £1,250

ditto, Harper (New York), 1865 . . . . . £75

The Belton Estate, Chapman & Hall (London), 1866 (red cloth; 24 pps of ads dated December 1, 1865; 3 vols) £2,500

The Last Chronicle of Barset, Smith Elder (London), 1866-67 (32 parts, white wraps). £2,500

ditto, Smith Elder (London), 1867 (powder blue cloth with gold church porch on front and spire on spine; 2 vols) £1,250

The Claverings, Harper (New York), 1866 (publication date considered suspect; 1 vol) £200

ditto, Smith Elder (London), 1867 (green cloth, gold scales on front; 2 vols). £2,500

Nina Balakta, Blackwood (Edinburgh), 1867 (anonymous, red/brown cloth, 8 pages of ads at rear of vol 2; 2 vols) £2,500

Linda Tressel, Blackwood (Edinburgh & London), 1868 (red/brown cloth; 2 vols) £750

Phineas Finn, The Irish Member, Virtue (London), 1869 (green cloth; author's name not on binding; 2 vols) £1,000

ditto, Harper (New York), 1869 . . . . . £150

He Knew He Was Right, Strahan (London), 1868-69 (32 weekly parts, pale grey/green wraps) . . £3,000

ditto, Strahan (London), [1869-70] (8 monthly parts, buff wraps) £1,500

ditto, Strahan (London), 1869 (green cloth; 2 vols). . £650

ditto, Harper (New York), 1869 (2 part; wraps) . £1,000

ditto, Harper (New York), 1869 (1 vol) . . . £250

The Vicar of Bullhampton, Bradbury, Evans (London), 1869-70 (11 parts, blue/grey wraps) . . . £3,500

ditto, Bradbury, Evans (London), 1870 (brown cloth) . £500

ditto, Harper (New York), 1870 . . . . . £125

Sir Harry Hotspur of Humblethwaite, Hurst and Blackett (London), 1871 (orange/red cloth) £750

ditto, MacMillan (New York), 1871 . . . . £250

Ralph the Heir, Hurst and Blackett (London), 1870-71 (19 parts, buff wraps). £2,500

ditto, Hurst and Blackett (London), 1871 (brown cloth; 3 vols) £2,000

The Golden Lion of Granpere, Tinsley (London), 1872 (red/brown cloth). £500

ditto, Harper (New York), 1872 . . . . . £125

The Eustace Diamonds, Harper (New York), 1872 (printed wraps) £1,000

ditto, Harper (New York), 1872 (cloth) . . . £750

ditto, Chapman & Hall (London), 1873 (salmon/brown cloth; 3 vols) £750

Phineas Redux, Chapman & Hall (London), 1874 (blue cloth; 24 illustrations; 2 vols) £750

ditto, Harper (New York), 1874 (26 illustrations, 1 vol). £300

Lady Anna, Chapman & Hall (London), 1874 (red/brown cloth; 2 vols). £1,500

Harry Heathcote of Gangoil, Harper (New York), 1874 £500

ditto, Sampson Low (London), 1874 (red or blue cloth). £500

The Way We Live Now, Chapman & Hall (London), 1874-75 (20 parts, blue wraps). £3,000

ditto, Chapman & Hall (London), 1875 (green or blue cloth; 2 vols) £1,000

ditto, Harper (New York), 1875 . . . . . £150

The Prime Minister, Chapman & Hall (London), 1875-76 (8 parts, grey wraps) £1,750

ditto, Chapman & Hall (London), 1875-76 (brown cloth with wraps bound in) £1,250

ditto, Chapman & Hall (London), 1876 (red/brown cloth; 4 vols) £1,500

The American Senator, Chapman & Hall (London), 1877 (3 vols; first binding pink/ochre cloth) . . . £1,000

ditto, Chapman & Hall (London), 1877 (3 vols; second binding blue, red/brown or pink cloth) . . . £750

Is He Popenjoy?, Chapman & Hall (London), 1878 (red/brown cloth; 3 vols) £1,000

Lady of Launay, Harper (New York), 1878 (wraps) . £400

An Eye for an Eye, Chapman & Hall (London), 1879 (green/ochre cloth; 2 vols). £750

John Caldigate, Chapman & Hall (London), 1879 (first binding grey cloth, 3 vols). £1,000

ditto, Chapman & Hall (London), 1879 (second binding dark green cloth, 3 vols) £750

Cousin Henry, Chapman & Hall (London), 1879 (blue or brown cloth; 2 vols) £750

The Duke's Children, Chapman & Hall (London), 1880 (blue/green cloth; 3 vols) £1,000

Dr Wortle's School, Chapman & Hall (London), 1881 (grey/green cloth; 2 vols). £1,000

Ayala's Angel, Chapman & Hall (London), 1881 (3 vols; orange or blue/grey cloth) £1,500

Kept in the Dark, Chatto & Windus (London), 1882 (olive/brown cloth; 2 vols) £1,000

Marion Fay, Chapman & Hall (London), 1882 (yellow/ochre or blue cloth; 3 vols) £1,250

The Fixed Period, Blackwood (Edinburgh & London), 1882 (red cloth; 2 vols) £1,000

Mr Scarborough's Family, Chatto & Windus (London), 1883 (blue/green cloth; 3 vols). . . . £1,500

The Landleaguers, Chatto & Windus (London), 1883 (green cloth; 3 vols). £1,500

An Old Man's Love, Blackwood (Edinburgh & London), 1884 (smooth red cloth; 2 vols) £650

ditto, Blackwood (Edinburgh & London), 1884 (red cloth with broad embossed lines; 2 vols) £650

The Noble Jilt, Constable (London), 1923 (red patterned cloth; 500 copies) . . . . £250/£150

Short Stories

Tales of All Countries, Chapman & Hall (London), 1861 (blue cloth) £650

Tales of All Countries: Second Series, Chapman & Hall (London), 1863 (blue cloth) £650

Tales of All Countries, Chapman & Hall (London), 1861 and 1963 (remaining sheets of first two series issued (with the original title-pages) as 1 vol; green cloth). . . £250

Lotta Schmidt and Other Stories, Strahan (London), 1867 (maroon cloth) £600

Christmas at Thompson Hall, Harper (New York), 1877 (wraps) £400

ditto, as *Thompson Hall*, Sampson Low (London), 1885 £500

Why Frau Frohmann Raised Her Prices and Other Stories, Isbister (London), 1882 (green, blue or red cloth; 1 vol) £1,000

ditto, Isbister (London), 1882 (2 vols) . . . £750

Others

The West Indies and the Spanish Main, Chapman & Hall (London), 1859 (maroon cloth) £450

ditto, Harper (New York), 1860 . . . . . £150

North America, Chapman & Hall (London), 1862 (pink/maroon patterned cloth; ads dated October; 2 vols) £1,000

ditto, Harper (New York), 1882 (grey cloth; 1 vol). . £200

ditto, Lippincott (Philadelphia), 1882 (first authorised edition; 2 vols) £200

Hunting Sketches, Chapman & Hall (London), 1865 (red cloth, bevelled edges, 32 pages of ads dated May 1865). £300

Travelling Sketches, Chapman & Hall (London), 1866 (red cloth, uniform with *Hunting Sketches*; 24 pages of ads dated February 1866) £300

Clergymen of the Church of England, Chapman & Hall (London), 1866 (red cloth, uniform with *Hunting Sketches*; 24 pages of ads dated March 30, 1866) . . . £250

An Editor's Tales, Strahan (London), 1870 (pink/brown cloth with author and title on the front) £350

ditto, Strahan (London), 1870 (dark brown cloth with just the publisher's device on front) £350

The Commentaries of Caesar, Blackwood (Edinburgh & London), 1870 (brown cloth; school book in series 'Ancient Classics For English Readers') £150

Australia and New Zealand, Chapman & Hall (London), 1873 (2 vols, 8 coloured maps; first issue dark green endpapers) £650

ditto, Chapman & Hall (London), 1873 (2 vols, 8 coloured maps; second issue yellow endpapers) £500

South Africa, Chapman & Hall (London), 1878 (2 vols; red cloth) £500

How the 'Mastiffs' Went to Iceland, Virtue (London), 1878 (blue cloth) £650

Thackeray, Macmillan (London), 1879 (cream cloth; paper label on spine) £250

ditto, Macmillan (London), 1879 (later issues in ochre or red cloth) £100

The Life of Cicero, Chapman & Hall (London), 1880 (maroon cloth with plain lettering on spine; 2 vols) . £250

ditto, Chapman & Hall (London), 1880 (later issue with darker maroon cloth with fancy lettering on spine; 2 vols). £125

Lord Palmerston, Isbister (London), 1882 (red/brown cloth; English Political Leaders series). £250

An Autobiography, Blackwood (Edinburgh & London), 1883 (first issue with smooth red cloth, green endpapers, 2 vols) £250

ditto, Blackwood (Edinburgh & London), 1883 (second issue with ribbed red cloth, green or brown endpapers, 2 vols) £150

London Tradesmen, Mathews & Marrot/Scribners (London/New York), 1927 (red linen spine, marbled boards, plain glassine d/w; 530 copies) . . . . £75/£25

The New Zealander, Clarendon Press (Oxford, UK), 1972 . . . . £25/£10

MARK TWAIN

(b.1835 d.1910)

An American humorist, novelist and travel writer, 'Mark Twain' was the pen name of Samuel Langhorne Clemens. He claimed that 'Mark Twain' was a reference to the depth of 'safe water', although other commentators have suggested that it referred to his bar tab in the wilder days of the West. At the height of his career Twain was possibly the most popular American celebrity of his day.

The Celebrated Jumping Frog of Calaveras Country and Other Sketches, Webb (New York), 1867 (first issue with single leaf of ads on cream paper inserted before title-page, last line on p.66 with 'life' unbroken, last line on p.198 with 'this' unbroken) . . . . . . £4,000 *ditto*, Webb (New York), 1867 (second issue with no ads and type broken or worn) £1,250

ditto, Routledge (London), 1867 (wraps) . . . £1,250

The Innocents Abroad or The New Pilgrim's Progress, American Publishing Company (Hartford, CT), 1868 (first issue, pp.xvii-xviii lacking page reference numbers; p.xviii with last entry reading 'Thankless Devotion - A Newspaper Valedictory'; p.129 with no illustration; p.643 reading Chapter XLI & p.654 reading 'Personal History') £1,000

ditto, Hotten (London), [1870] (2 vols) £650

ditto, as **Mark Twain's Pleasure Trip on the Continent**, Hotten (London), [1870] (1 vol.) £275

Mark Twain's (Burlesque) Autobiography & First Romance, Sheldon & Co. (New York), 1871 (first issue with no advert for Ball, Black & Co on verso title; wraps).
. . . . £450

ditto, Sheldon & Co. (New York), 1871 (first issue, cloth) .
. . . . £250

ditto, Hotten (London), [1871] (cloth) £200

ditto, Hotten (London), [1871] (wraps) £200

Memoranda From the Galaxy, Backas (Toronto), 1871 .
. . . . £1,000

Eye Openers/Good Things, Hotten (London), [1871] (wraps and cloth) £175

Screamers/A Gathering, Hotten (London), [1871] (wraps and cloth) £175

Roughing It, Routledge (London), 1872 (2 vols) . . £750

ditto, American Publishing Company (Hartford, CT), 1872 (cloth) £750

ditto, American Publishing Company (Hartford, CT), 1872 (various deluxe bindings) . . . £1,500-£1,000

The Innocents at Home, Routledge (London), 1872 . £500

A Curious Dream and Other Sketches, Routledge (London), [1872] £500

Mark Twain's Sketches, Routledge (London), 1872 . £450

The Choice Humorous Works, Hotten (London), [1873] .
. . . . £400

The Gilded Age, American Publishing Company (Hartford, CT), 1874 (cloth). £750

ditto, American Publishing Company (Hartford, CT), 1874 (various deluxe bindings) . . . £1,500-£1,000

ditto, Routledge (London), 1874 (3 vols) . . . £850

Mark Twain's Sketches. Number One, American News Co. (New York), [1874] (wraps, first state with rear wrapper blank) £650

ditto, American News Co. (New York), [1874] (wraps, second state with insurance ads on rear wrapper) . £500

Sketches, New and Old, American Publishing Company (Hartford, CT), 1875 . . . . £300

Old Times on the Mississippi, Belford (Toronto), 1876 £300

Information Wanted and Other Sketches, Routledge (London), 1876 . . . . £300

The Adventures of Tom Sawyer, Chatto & Windus (London), 1876 . . . . £7,500

ditto, American Publishing Company (Hartford, CT), 1876 (first printing on wove paper; blue cloth binding, edges gilt). £10,000

ditto, American Publishing Company (Hartford, CT), 1876 (various deluxe bindings) . . . £12,500-£17,500

A True Story, and the Recent Carnival of Crime, Osgood (Boston), 1877 . . . . £750

Punch, Brother, Punch, Slote, Woodman (New York), 1878 (wraps and cloth). £600

ditto, Slote, Woodman (New York), 1878 (wraps and cloth).
. . . . £400

ditto, Livingstone (London), 1878 (wraps) . . . £400

A Tramp Abroad, American Publishing Company (Hartford, CT), 1880 (first state with frontispiece captioned 'Moses')
. . . . £750

ditto, American Publishing Company (Hartford, CT), 1880 (first state in various deluxe bindings) . . . £1,250

ditto, American Publishing Company (Hartford, CT), 1880 (second state with frontispiece captioned 'Titian's Moses')
. . . . £300

ditto, Chatto & Windus (London), 1880 (2 vols) . £600

Conversation, As It Was by the Social Fireside in the Time of the Tudors, [Gunn (Cleveland, OH), 1880] (4 copies) .
. . . . £20,000

ditto, Charles Erskine Scott Wood (West Point, NY), 1882 (50 copies) £10,000

The Prince and the Pauper: A Tale for Young People of All Ages, Chatto & Windus (London), 1881 . . £1,000

ditto, Osgood (Boston), 1882 (green pictorial cloth with gilt edges) £1,000

ditto, Osgood (Boston), 1882 (various deluxe bindings)
. . . . £1,250-£1,500

ditto, Osgood (Boston), 1882 (6-14 copies on China paper, bound in white linen). £15,000

The Stolen White Elephant, Chatto & Windus (London), 1882 (first state, list of books on verso half title does not mention *The White Elephant*) £300

ditto, Chatto & Windus (London), 1882 (second state, list of books on verso half title mentions *The White Elephant*)
. . . . £150

ditto, Osgood (Boston), 1882 . . . . . . £150

Life on the Mississippi, Chatto & Windus (London), 1883 .
. . . . £500

ditto, Osgood (Boston), 1883 . . . . . . £1,000

The Adventures of Huckleberry Finn, Chatto & Windus (London), 1884 . . . . £1,250

ditto, Webster (New York), 1885 (blue cloth) . £4,500

ditto, Webster (New York), 1885 (green cloth) . £3,000

ditto, Webster (New York), 1885 (various deluxe bindings).
. . . . £5,000-£10,000

Mark Twain's Library of Humour, Chatto & Windus (London), 1888 . . . . £400

ditto, Webster (New York), 1888 . . . . . £500

A Connecticut Yankee in King Arthur's Court, Webster (New York), 1889 . . . . £750

ditto, Webster (New York), 1885 (various deluxe bindings).
. . . . £1,500-£3,000

ditto, as **A Yankee at the Court of King Arthur**, Chatto & Windus (London), 1889 . . . . . . £250

The American Claimant, Webster (New York), 1892 . £100

ditto, Chatto & Windus (London), 1892 . . . . £100

Merry Tales, Webster (New York), 1892 . . . . £100

The $1,000,000 Bank Note, Webster (New York), 1893 .
. . . . £100

ditto, Chatto & Windus (London), 1893 . . . . £100

Tom Sawyer Abroad, Chatto & Windus (London), 1894 .
. . . . £400

ditto, Webster (New York), 1894 . . . . . £500

The Tragedy of Pudd'nhead Wilson and the Comedy of Those Extraordinary Twins, Chatto & Windus (London), 1894 . . . . £200

ditto, American Publishing Company (Hartford, CT), 1894 .
. . . . £200

ditto, American Publishing Company (Hartford, CT), 1894 (various deluxe bindings) . . . . £500-£1,000

Personal Recollections of Joan of Arc, Harper (New York), 1896 (first state with 'The Abbey Shakespeare' advertised at head of p[463] and the first two volumes of 'The Memoirs of Barras' offered at $3.75 (the following two 'just ready') on p[464]) £200

ditto, Harper (New York), 1896 (second state with heading changed to 'George Washington' and 'The Memoirs of Barras' offered as a four volume set for $15) . £100

Tom Sawyer Abroad/Tom Sawyer, Detective/And Other Stories, Harper (New York), 1896 . . . . £1,000

Tom Sawyer, Detective, Chatto & Windus (London), 1897 . . . . £400

How to Tell a Story and Other Essays, Harper (New York), 1897 (first state, with spelling error of 'ciper' p187) . £300

ditto, Harper (New York), 1897 (second state, with error corrected to 'cipher') £125

Following the Equator, American Publishing Company (Hartford, CT), 1897 . . . . . . £175

ditto, American Publishing Company (Hartford, CT), 1897 (250 numbered, signed copies). . . . £3,000

ditto, American Publishing Company (Hartford, CT), 1897 (various deluxe bindings) . . . . £250-£500

ditto, as ***More Tramps Abroad***, Chatto & Windus (London), 1897 . . . . £150

The Man That Corrupted Hadleyburgh, Harper (New York), 1900 . . . . £150

ditto, Chatto & Windus (London), 1900 . . . £100

To the Person Sitting in Darkness, Anti-Imperialist League (New York), 1901 (wraps). £350

A Double Barrelled Detective Story, Harper (New York), 1902 . . . . £100

ditto, Chatto & Windus (London), 1902 . . . £75

My Debut as a Literary Person, American Publishing Company (Hartford, CT), 1903 (vol. 23 in a collected edition) £100

A Dog's Tale, National Anti-Vivesection Society (London), 1903 (wraps). £200

ditto, Harper (New York & London), 1904 . . £65

Extracts from Adam's Diary, Harper (New York & London), 1904 . . . . £65

King Leopold's Soliloquy, Warren (Boston), 1905. . £75

Eve's Diary, Harper (New York & London), 1906. . £65

What Is Man?, De Vinne Press (New York), 1906 (anonymous, 250 numbered copies) . . . £1,000

The $30,000 Bequest, Harper (New York & London), 1906 (first state without boxed advert on copyright page) . £100

ditto, Harper (New York & London), 1906 (second state) £50

Christian Science, Harper (New York & London), 1907 . . . . £125

A Horse's Tale, S.P.C.A./Harper (New York & London), 1907 . . . . £50

Is Shakespeare Dead? From My Autobiography, Harper (New York & London), 1909 . . . . . . £75

Extract from Captain Stormfield's Visit to Heaven, Harper (New York), 1909 . . . . £75

Queen Victoria's Jubilee, [privately printed (New York?), 1910] £650

Mark Twain's Speeches, Harper (New York), 1910 . £75

The Mysterious Stranger, a Romance, Harper (New York), 1916 . . . . £100

Mark Twain's Letters, Harper (New York), [1917] (2 vols). £100

ditto, Harper (New York), [1917] (350 copies, 2 vols) . £200

The Curious Republic of Gondour and Other Whimsical Sketches, Boni & Liveright (New York), 1919 . . £75

Europe and Elsewhere, Harper (New York), 1923 £200/£50

Mark Twain's Autobiography, Harper (New York), 1924 (2 vols, slipcase and d/ws) . . . . . . £200/£65

Mark Twain's Notebook, Harper (New York), 1935 . . . . £150/£50

ANNE TYLER
(b.1941)

Tyler is an American novelist, living in Baltimore, where her novels are set. She won a Pulitzer Prize for *Breathing Lessons*, and T*he Accidental Tourist* has been filmed. She is a member of the American Academy of Art and Letters.

Novels

If Morning Ever Comes, Knopf (New York), 1964 . . . . £750/£75

ditto, Chatto & Windus (London), 1965 . . £500/£65

The Tin Can Tree, Knopf (New York), 1965 . £450/£50

ditto, Macmillan (London), 1966 . . . £175/£20

A Slipping-Down Life, Knopf (New York), 1970 . £100/£15

ditto, Severn House (London), 1983 . . . £15/£5

The Clock Winder, Knopf (New York), 1972 . £600/£75

ditto, Chatto & Windus (London), 1973 . . £200/£35

Celestial Navigation, Knopf (New York), 1974 £65/£10

ditto, Chatto & Windus (London), 1975 . . £50/£10

Searching for Caleb, Knopf (New York), 1975 . £65/£10

ditto, Chatto & Windus (London), 1976 . . £50/£10

Earthly Possessions, Knopf (New York), 1977 . £45/£10

ditto, Chatto & Windus (London), 1977 . . £35/£10

Morgan's Passing, Knopf (New York), 1980 . £15/£5

ditto, Chatto & Windus (London), 1980 . . £10/£5

Dinner At the Homesick Restaurant, Knopf (New York), 1982 . . . . £10/£5

ditto, Chatto & Windus (London), 1982 . . £10/£5

The Accidental Tourist, Knopf (New York), 1985. £10/£5

ditto, Knopf (New York), 1985 (with tipped-in signed page) . . . . £75/£65

ditto, Chatto & Windus (London), 1985 . . £10/£5

Breathing Lessons, Knopf (New York), 1988. . £10/£5

ditto, The Franklin Library (Franklin Centre, PA), 1988 (signed, limited edition) £20

ditto, Chatto & Windus (London), 1989 . . £10/£5

Saint Maybe, Knopf (New York), 1991 . . £10/£5

ditto, The Franklin Library (Franklin Centre, PA), 1991 (signed, limited edition) £20

ditto, Chatto & Windus (London), 1991 . . £10/£5

Ladder of Years, Knopf (New York), 1995 . £10/£5

ditto, The Franklin Library (Franklin Centre, PA), 1995 (signed, limited edition) £25

ditto, Chatto & Windus (London), 1995 . . £10/£5

A Patchwork Planet, Knopf (New York), 1998 . £10/£5

ditto, The Franklin Library (Franklin Centre, PA), 1995 (signed, limited edition) £25

ditto, Chatto & Windus (London), 1998 . . £10/£5

Back When We Were Grownups, Knopf (New York), 2001 . . . . £10/£5

ditto, Chatto & Windus (London), 2001 . . £10/£5

The Amateur Marriage, Knopf (New York), 2004. £10/£5

ditto, Chatto & Windus (London), 2004 . . . £10/£5
Digging to America, Knopf (New York), 2006 . £10/£5
ditto, Chatto & Windus (London), 2006 . . . £10/£5
Noah's Compass, Chatto & Windus (London), 2009 £10/£5
ditto, Knopf (New York), 2010 . . . . . £10/£5

Others

A Visit with Eudora Welty, Pressworks (Chicago), 1980
(100 copies; sewn wraps) £100
Your Place Is Empty, William B. Ewert (Concord, NH),
1992 (uncollected story from *The New Yorker*; 40 signed,
numbered copies; handbound, no d/w) . . . £300
ditto, William B. Ewert (Concord, NH), 1992 (60 signed,
numbered copies; sewn wraps). £125
Tumble Tower, Orchard (New York), 1993 (illustrations by
Mitra Modarressi) . . . . . . £10/£5
ditto, Julia MacRae Books (London), 1995 (no d/w) . £5

BARRY UNSWORTH
(b.1930)

British novelist Unsworth is not as widely known as he
might be, despite being three-times shortlisted for the
Booker Prize and joint-winner with *Sacred Hunger* in 1992
(along with Michael Ondaatje's *The English Patient*). His
works often have historical themes; *Pascali's Island* is set
in the last years of the Ottoman Empire, *Morality Play* in
14th-century England, and *Sacred Hunger* deals with the
slave trade.

Novels

The Partnership, Hutchinson New Authors (London), 1966
. . . . £175/£25
The Greeks Have a Word For It, Hutchinson (London),
1967 . . . . £250/£45
The Hide, Gollancz (London), 1970 . . . . £165/£30
ditto, Norton (New York), 1996 . . . . £10/£5
Mooncranker's Gift, Lane (London), 1973 . £100/£20
ditto, Houghton Mifflin (Boston), 1974 . . £25/£5
The Big Day, Joseph (London), 1976 . . £45/£10
ditto, Mason/Charter (New York), 1976 . . £20/£5
Pascali's Island, Joseph (London), 1980 . . £65/£10
ditto, as ***The Idol Hunter***, Simon & Schuster (New York),
1980 . . . . £25/£5
The Rage of the Vulture, Granada (London), 1982 £20/£5
ditto, Houghton Mifflin (Boston), 1983 . . . £15/£5
Stone Virgin, Hamish Hamilton (London), 1985 . £25/£5
ditto, Houghton Mifflin (Boston), 1986 . . . £15/£5
Sugar and Rum, Hamish Hamilton (London), 1988 £25/£5
Sacred Hunger, Hamish Hamilton (London), 1992 £100/£15
ditto, Hamish Hamilton (London), 1992 (pbk). . £10
ditto, Doubleday (New York), 1992 . . . . £25/£5
Morality Play, Hamish Hamilton (London), 1995 . £15/£5
ditto, Doubleday (New York), 1995 . . . . £10/£5
After Hannibal, Hamish Hamilton (London), 1996 £15/£5
ditto, Doubleday (New York), 1997 . . . . £10/£5
Losing Nelson, Hamish Hamilton (London), 1999 . £10/£5
ditto, Doubleday (New York), 1999 . . . . £10/£5
The Songs of the Kings, Hamish Hamilton (London), 2002.
. . . . £10/£5
ditto, Random House (New York), 2003 . . . £10/£5

The Ruby in Her Navel, Hamish Hamilton (London), 2006.
. . . . £10/£5
ditto, Doubleday (New York), 2006 . . . . £10/£5
Land of Marvels, Hutchinson (London), 2009 . £10/£5
ditto, Doubleday (New York), 2009 . . . £10/£5

JOHN UPDIKE
(b.1932 d.2009)

An American novelist, short story writer and critic, John
Updike had a reputation as a keen observer of small-town,
Protestant, middle-class life. His best known works are his
'Rabbit' series, with *Rabbit is Rich* and *Rabbit at Rest* both
winning their author Pulitzer Prizes. As a critic Updike was
often involved in public duels with other writers.

Novels

The Poorhouse Fair, Knopf (New York), 1959 (first issue
d/w with one paragraph of copy on back flap) . £300/£40
ditto, Gollancz (London), 1959 . . . . . £200/£25
Rabbit, Run, Knopf (New York), 1960 (first issue d/w with
16-line blurb on front flap) . . . . £600/£50
ditto, Deutsch (London), 1961 . . . . £100/£15
ditto, Franklin Library (Franklin Centre, PA), 1977 (signed,
limited edition) £65
The Centaur, Knopf (New York), 1963 . . £100/£20
ditto, Deutsch (London), 1963 . . . . £60/£15
Of the Farm, Knopf (New York), 1965 . . . £75/£10
ditto, Deutsch (London), 1966 . . . . £40/£5
Couples, Knopf (New York), 1968 . . . . £35/£5
ditto, Deutsch (London), 1968 . . . . . £25/£5
Rabbit Redux, Knopf (New York), 1971 . . . £50/£10
ditto, Knopf (New York), 1971 (350 signed copies, slipcase,
clear d/w) . . . . £200/£150
ditto, Deutsch (London), 1972 . . . . £35/£10
ditto, Franklin Library (Franklin Centre, PA), 1981 (signed,
limited edition) £30
A Month of Sundays, Knopf (New York), 1975 . £25/£5
ditto, Knopf (New York), 1975 (450 signed, numbered
copies, slipcase, d/w) . . . . . £65/£45
ditto, Deutsch (London), 1975 . . . . £20/£5
Marry Me: A Romance, Knopf (New York), 1976. £20/£5
ditto, Knopf (New York), 1976 (300 signed, numbered
copies, slipcase, d/w) . . . . . £80/£50
ditto, Franklin Library (Franklin Centre, PA), 1976 (signed
limited edition) £25
ditto, Deutsch (London), 1977 . . . . £15/£5
The Coup, Knopf (New York), 1978. . . . £15/£5
ditto, Knopf (New York), 1978 (350 signed, numbered
copies, slipcase, d/w) . . . . . £45/£30
ditto, Deutsch (London), 1979 . . . . £10/£5
Rabbit is Rich, Knopf (New York), 1981 . . . £25/£5
ditto, Knopf (New York), 1981 (350 signed copies, slipcase,
d/w) . . . . £165/£100
ditto, Deutsch (London), 1982 . . . . £20/£5
The Witches of Eastwick, Knopf (New York), 1984 £25/£10
ditto, Knopf (New York), 1984 (350 signed copies, glassine
d/w and slipcase). . . . . . £125/£100
ditto, Franklin Library (Franklin Centre, PA), 1984 (signed
limited edition) £25
ditto, Deutsch (London), 1984 . . . . . £25/£10
Roger's Version, Knopf (New York), 1986 . . £10/£5

ditto, Knopf (New York), 1986 (350 signed copies, glassine d/w and slipcase).　.　.　.　.　.　.　£75/£50

ditto, Franklin Library (Franklin Centre, PA), 1986 (signed limited edition)　.　.　.　.　.　.　£25

ditto, Deutsch (London), 1986　.　.　.　.　£10/£5

S, Knopf (New York), 1988.　.　.　.　.　£10/£5

ditto, Knopf (New York), 1986 (350 signed copies, glassine d/w and slipcase).　.　.　.　.　.　£75/£50

ditto, Deutsch (London), 1988　.　.　.　£10/£5

ditto, Deutsch (London), 1988 (85 signed copies, slipcase)　.
.　.　.　.　.　.　.　.　£50/£40

Rabbit at Rest, Knopf (New York), 1990　.　.　£20/£5

ditto, Knopf (New York), 1990 (350 signed copies, glassine d/w and slipcase).　.　.　.　.　.　£75/£50

ditto, Franklin Library (Franklin Centre, PA), 1990 (signed, limited edition)　.　.　.　.　.　.　£70

ditto, Deutsch (London), 1991　.　.　.　£15/£5

Memories of the Ford Administration, Knopf (New York), 1992　.　.　.　.　.　.　.　£10/£5

ditto, Franklin Library (Franklin Centre, PA), 1992 (signed, limited edition)　.　.　.　.　.　.　£50

ditto, Hamish Hamilton (London), 1992　.　.　£10/£5

Brazil, Knopf (New York), 1994　.　.　.　£15/£5

ditto, Franklin Library (Franklin Centre, PA), 1994 (signed, limited edition)　.　.　.　.　.　.　£35

ditto, Hamish Hamilton (London), 1994　.　.　£15/£5

In the Beauty of the Lilies, Knopf (New York), 1996 £15/£5

ditto, Franklin Library (Franklin Centre, PA), 1996 (signed, limited edition)　.　.　.　.　.　.　£35

ditto, Hamish Hamilton (London), 1996　.　.　£15/£5

Toward the End of Time, Knopf (New York), 1997　£10/£5

ditto, Franklin Library (Franklin Centre, PA), 1998 (signed, limited edition)　.　.　.　.　.　.　£35

ditto, Hamish Hamilton (London), 1998　.　.　£10/£5

Gertrude and Claudius, Knopf (New York), 2000.　£10/£5

ditto, Franklin Library (Franklin Centre, PA), 2000 (signed, limited edition)　.　.　.　.　.　.　£35

ditto, Hamish Hamilton (London), 2000　.　.　£10/£5

Seek My Face, Knopf (New York), 2002.　.　£10/£5

ditto, Hamish Hamilton (London), 2002　.　.　£10/£5

Villages, Knopf (New York), 2004　.　.　.　£10/£5

ditto, Hamish Hamilton (London), 2004　.　.　£10/£5

Terrorist, Knopf (New York), 2006　.　.　.　£10/£5

ditto, Hamish Hamilton (London), 2006　.　.　£10/£5

The Widows of Eastwick, Knopf (New York), 2008　£10/£5

Short Stories

The Same Door, Knopf (New York), 1959　.　£225/£30

ditto, Deutsch (London), 1962　.　.　.　.　£100/£20

Pigeon Feathers and Other Stories, Knopf (New York), 1962　.　.　.　.　.　.　.　£125/£20

ditto, Deutsch (London), 1962　.　.　.　.　£65/£15

Olinger Stories: A Selection, Vintage (New York), 1964 (pbk)　.　.　.　.　.　.　.　.　£15

The Music School, Knopf (New York), 1966 (first issue with 'The state' on p. 46, line 15; first issue d/w with $4.95 price and 9/66 code listed on inside front flap and a black-and-white photo of the author on inside back flap)　.　.
.　.　.　.　.　.　.　.　£250/£150

ditto, Deutsch (London), 1967　.　.　.　.　£50/£15

The Angels, King & Queen Press (Pensacola, FL), 1968 (150 copies; sewn wraps in envelope)　.　.　.　£500/£400

Bech: A Book, Knopf (New York), 1970　.　.　£20/£5

ditto, Knopf (New York), 1970 (500 signed copies, slipcase)
.　.　.　.　.　.　.　.　.　£100/£65

ditto, Deutsch (London), 1970　.　.　.　.　£15/£5

The Indian, Blue Cloud Quarterly (Marvin, SD), 1971 (stapled wraps)　.　.　.　.　.　.　.　£35

Museums and Women and Other Stories, Knopf (New York), 1972　.　.　.　.　.　.　.　£15/£5

ditto, Knopf (New York), 1972 (350 signed copies, slipcase)
.　.　.　.　.　.　.　.　.　£90/£65

ditto, Deutsch (London), 1973　.　.　.　.　£15/£5

Warm Wine: An Idyll, Albondocani Press (New York), 1973 (26 signed, lettered copies)　.　.　.　.　.　£150

ditto, Albondocani Press (New York), 1973 (250 signed, numbered copies; sewn wraps).　.　.　.　.　£50

Couples, Halty Ferguson (Cambridge, MA), 1976 (26 signed, lettered copies of 276)　.　.　.　.　£125

ditto, Halty Ferguson (Cambridge, MA), 1976 (250 signed, numbered copies; sewn wraps).　.　.　.　£45

Domestic Life in America, New Yorker (New York), 1976 (wraps).　.　.　.　.　.　.　.　.　£250

Hub Fans Bid Kid Adieu, Lord John Press (Northridge, CA), 1977 (300 signed, numbered copies, no d/w)　.　£145

From the Journal of a Leper, Lord John Press (Northridge, CA), 1978 (26 signed, lettered copies)　.　.　.　£200

ditto, Lord John Press (Northridge, CA), 1978 (300 signed, numbered copies)　.　.　.　.　.　.　£50

Problems and Other Stories, Knopf (New York), 1979
.　.　.　.　.　.　.　.　.　£15/£5

ditto, Knopf (New York), 1979 (350 signed copies, glassine d/w and slipcase).　.　.　.　.　.　£60/£40

ditto, Deutsch (London), 1980　.　.　.　.　£10/£5

Too Far to Go: The Maples Stories, Fawcett Crest (New York), 1979 (pbk)　.　.　.　.　.　.　£10

ditto, as **Your Lover Just Called: Stories of Joan and Richard Maple**, Penguin (Harmondsworth, Middlesex), 1980 (pbk)　.　.　.　.　.　.　.　£5

The Chaste Planet, Metacom Press (Worcester, MA), 1980 (300 signed, numbered copies; sewn wraps).　.　.　£100

ditto, Metacom Press (Worcester, MA), 1980 (26 signed, lettered copies)　.　.　.　.　.　.　£250

Bech is Back, Knopf (New York), 1982　.　.　£15/£5

ditto, Knopf (New York), 1982 (500 signed, numbered copies, slipcase, d/w)　.　.　.　.　.　£50/£35

ditto, Deutsch (London), 1983　.　.　.　.　£10/£5

The Beloved, Lord John Press (Northridge, CA), 1982 (100 signed, numbered deluxe copies)　.　.　.　.　£125

ditto, Lord John Press (Northridge, CA), 1982 (300 signed, numbered copies)　.　.　.　.　.　.　£45

Getting Older, Eurographica (Helsinki), 1986 (350 signed, numbered copies; sewn wraps).　.　.　.　.　£125

A and P: Lust in the Isles, Redpath Press (Minneapolis, MN), 1986 (pbk)　.　.　.　.　.　.　£15

Trust Me, Knopf (New York), 1987　.　.　.　£10/£5

ditto, Knopf (New York), 1987 (350 signed, numbered copies, slipcase, d/w)　.　.　.　.　.　£65/£45

ditto, Deutsch (London), 1987　.　.　.　.　£10/£5

More Stately Mansions, Nouveau (Jackson, MS), 1987 (300 signed, numbered copies)　.　.　.　.　.　£45

ditto, Nouveau (Jackson, MS), 1987 (40 deluxe, signed, numbered copies)　.　.　.　.　.　.　£200

The Afterlife, Sixth Chamber Press (Leamington Spa, Warwickshire), 1987 (26 signed, lettered copies, no d/w) .£200

ditto, Sixth Chamber Press (Leamington Spa, Warwickshire), 1987 (175 signed, numbered copies, no d/w)　.　£50

Forty Stories, Penguin (London), 1987 (pbk)　.　.　£5

Going Abroad, Eurographica (Helsinki), 1988 (350 signed, numbered copies; sewn wraps).　.　.　.　.　£65

Brother Grasshopper, Metacom Press (Worcester, MA), 1990 (150 signed, numbered copies) . . . £100/£65

ditto, Metacom Press (Worcester, MA), 1990 (25 lettered, numbered copies) £200

The Alligators, Creative Education (Mankato, MN), 1990 . . . . £10/£5

Love Factories: Three Stories, with a Foreword, Eurographica (Helsinki), 1993 (350 signed, numbered copies; sewn wraps) £125

The Afterlife and Other Stories, Knopf (New York), 1994 . . . . £10/£5

ditto, Hamish Hamilton (London), 1994 . . . £10/£5

Friends from Philadelphia, Penguin (London), 1995 (pbk). £5

The Women Who Got Away, Ewert (Concord, NH), 1998 (90 signed, numbered copies; sewn wraps) . . . £75

ditto, Ewert (Concord, NH), 1998 (45 signed, numbered copies) £150

ditto, Ewert (Concord, NH), 1998 (15 signed, numbered copies; in box with original print) . . . £225/£200

Bech at Bay: A Quasi-Novel, Knopf (New York), 1999 . . . . £10/£5

ditto, Easton Press (Norwalk, CT), 1999 (1,100 signed, numbered copies) £65

ditto, Hamish Hamilton (London), 1999 . £10/£5

Bech: His Oeuvre, Ewert (Concord, NH), 2000 (90 signed, numbered copies; sewn wraps). £150

ditto, Ewert (Concord, NH), 2000 (20 signed, numbered copies; in box) . . . . . £500/£400

Licks of Love, Knopf (New York), 2000 . . £10/£5

ditto, Easton Press (Norwalk, CT), 2000 (1,650 signed, numbered copies) £65

ditto, Hamish Hamilton (London), 2000 . £10/£5

The Early Stories: 1953-1975, Knopf (New York), 2003 . . . . £10/£5

ditto, Hamish Hamilton (London), 2003 . £10/£5

Three Stories, Thornwillow Press (New York), 2003 (250 numbered copies; slipcase) . . . £350/£300

My Father's Tears and Other Stories, Knopf (New York), 2009 . . . . £10/£5

The Maples Stories, Fawcett Crest (New York), 2009 (pbk) £5

Poetry

The Carpentered Hen and Other Tame Creatures, Harper (New York), 1958 (first issue d/w with '…a wife and two small children' on the rear inside flap) . . £500/£45

ditto, as *Hoping for a Hoopoe*, Gollancz (London), 1959 . . . . £60/£15

Telephone Poles and Other Poems, Knopf (New York), 1963 . . . . £50/£15

ditto, Deutsch (London), 1964 . . . £35/£10

Dog's Death, Scott (Cambridge, MA), 1965 (100 signed copies, broadside) £450

Verse, Fawcett (Greenwich, CT), 1965 (pbk) . . £10

Bath after Sailing, Country Squires Press (Stevenson, CT), 1968 (125 signed copies; wraps) £300

ditto, Country Squires Press (Stevenson, CT), 1968 (15 signed copies; broadside, printed in italic font) . £500

ditto, Country Squires Press (Stevenson, CT), 1968 (3 signed copies; broadside, printed in roman font) . £650

Midpoint and Other Poems, Knopf (New York), 1969. . . . . £25/£10

ditto, Knopf (New York), 1969 (350 signed copies in d/w) . . . . £65/£45

ditto, Deutsch (London), 1969 . . . . £25/£10

The Dance of the Solids, Scientific American (New York), [1970] (wraps) £450

Seventy Poems, Penguin (Harmondsworth, Middlesex), 1971 (pbk) £5

Six Poems, Aloe Editions (New York), 1973 (26 signed, lettered copies; sewn wraps) £350

ditto, Aloe Editions (New York), 1973 (100 signed, numbered copies; sewn wraps). £125

Cunts, New York Quarterly (New York), 1973 (457 signed copies; wraps) £40

ditto, Hallman (New York), 1974 (26 signed, lettered copies) £400

ditto, Hallman (New York), 1974 (250 signed, numbered copies) £75

Query, Albondocani and Ampersand (New York), 1974 (greeting card in envelope, 400 [75] copies with upside-down cover artwork and publisher's letter) . £125/£90

ditto, Albondocani and Ampersand (New York), 1974 (correct cover art and publisher's colophon). . . £75

ditto, Albondocani and Ampersand (New York), 1974 (240 copies without colophon) £50

Flirt, International Poetry Forum, 1975 (approx 500 copies, broadside) £400

Sunday in Boston, Rook Press (Derry, PA), 1975 (100 copies signed by author and illustrator, broadside) . £100

ditto, Rook Press (Derry, PA), 1975 (100 copies signed by author only, broadside) £75

ditto, Rook Press (Derry, PA), 1975 (100 unsigned copies, broadside) £45

Scenic, Roxburghe Club (San Francisco, CA), 1976 (150 copies, broadside) £150

Tossing and Turning, Knopf (New York), 1977 . £20/£5

ditto, Deutsch (London), 1977 . . . £15/£5

Raining at Magens Bay, John Updike Newsletter (Northridge, CT), 1977 (200 numbered copies, broadside) . £45

ditto, John Updike Newsletter (Northridge, CT), 1977 (26 lettered copies, broadside). £200

The Lovelorn Astronomer, G.K. Hall (Boston), 1978 (400 copies with copyright notice; greeting card) . . £300

ditto, G.K. Hall (Boston), 1978 (1,400 copies; no copyright notice) £150

The Visions of Mackenzie King, John Updike Newsletter (Northridge, CT), 1979 (150 numbered copies, broadside) £75

Earthworm, Ontario Review Press (Ontario, Canada), 1979 (first state with 'God Bless'; postcard) . . . £175

ditto, Ontario Review Press (Ontario, Canada), 1979 (second state with 'God blesses'; postcard) £125

Sixteen Sonnets, Ferguson (Cambridge, MA), 1979 (250 signed, numbered copies; sewn wraps) . . . £60

ditto, Ferguson (Cambridge, MA), 1979 (26 signed, lettered copies) £200

Five Poems, Bits Press (Cleveland, OH, 1980 (135 signed copies) £50

ditto, Bits Press (Cleveland, OH, 1980 (50 signed copies) £100

An Oddly Lovely Day Alone, Waves Press (Richmond, VA), 1979 (250 numbered copies, broadside). . . . £25

ditto, Waves Press (Richmond, VA), 1979 (26 lettered copies, broadside) £75

Iowa, Press-22 (Portland, OR), 1980 (200 signed, numbered copies, broadside) £125

ditto, Press-22 (Portland, OR), 1980 (26 signed, lettered copies, broadside) £200

Styles of Bloom, Palaemon (Winston-Salem, NC), 1982 (55 signed, numbered copies, broadside) . . . £100
ditto, Palaemon (Winston-Salem, NC), 1982 (26 signed, lettered copies, broadside). £250
Spring Trio, Palaemon (Winston-Salem, NC), 1982 (150 numbered, signed copies; wraps) £75
ditto, Palaemon (Winston-Salem, NC), 1982 (10 roman numeralled, signed copies; wraps) £200
Small City People, Lord John Press (Northridge, CA), 1982 (100 signed, numbered copies, broadside) . . £125
ditto, Lord John Press (Northridge, CA), 1982 (26 signed, lettered copies, broadside). £200
Two Sonnets Whose Titles Came to Me Simultaneously, Palaemon (Winston-Salem, NC), 1982 (20 signed copies; broadside) £150
Jester's Dozen, Lord John Press (Northridge, CA), 1984 (50 signed, numbered copies of 200) £100
ditto, Lord John Press (Northridge, CA), 1984 (150 signed, numbered copies of 200) £75
Facing Nature, Knopf (New York), 1985 . . £15/£5
ditto, Deutsch (London), 1986 . . . . £10/£5
A Pear Like a Potato, Santa Susanna Press (Northridge, CA), 1986 (broadside, 26 signed, lettered copies) . £75
ditto, Santa Susanna Press (Northridge, CA), 1986 (broadside, 100 signed copies). £45
Two Sonnets, Northouse & Northouse (Dallas, TX), 1987 (40 signed, Roman numbered copies) . . . £250
ditto, Northouse & Northouse (Dallas, TX), 1987 . £40
On the Move, Bits Press (Cleveland, OH), 1988 (120 signed copies; sewn wraps) £50
In Memoriam Felis Felis, Sixth Chamber Press (Leamington Spa, Warwickshire), 1989 (200 unnumbered copies) . £25
ditto, Sixth Chamber Press (Leamington Spa, Warwickshire), 1989 (26 signed, lettered copies) £200
ditto, Sixth Chamber Press (Leamington Spa, Warwickshire), 1989 (12 roman numbered copies) £200
Mites and Other Poems in Miniature, Lord John Press (Northridge, CA), 1990 (26 signed, lettered copies) .£250
ditto, Lord John Press (Northridge, CA), 1990 (200 signed, numbered copies of 200) £45
Recent Poems, 1986-1990, Eurographica (Helsinki), 1990 (350 signed, numbered copies; sewn wraps). . . £100
Thanatopses, Bits Press (Cleveland, OH), 1991 (237 signed copies; sewn wraps) £45
Collected Poems 1953-1993, Knopf (New York), 1993 . . . . £15/£5
ditto, Hamish Hamilton (London), 1993 . . £15/£5
Poem Begun on Thursday, October 14, 1993 at O'Hare Airport, Terminal 3, Around Six O'Clock P.M., Literary Renaissance (Louisville, KY), 1994 (100 signed, numbered copies; sewn wraps) £40
ditto, Literary Renaissance (Louisville, KY), 1994 (26 signed, lettered copies; sewn wraps) . . . £75
ditto, Literary Renaissance (Louisville, KY), 1994 (26 signed, numbered copies; sewn wraps) . . . £125
In the Cemetery High above Shillington, Ewert (Concord, NH), 1995 (100 signed, numbered copies; sewn wraps) £50
ditto, Ewert (Concord, NH), 1995 (35 signed, numbered copies) £150
ditto, Ewert (Concord, NH), 1995 (15 signed, numbered copies; in a box) . . . . . £250/£200
January, Ewert (Concord, NH), 1997(100 signed, numbered copies; unfolded card) £25

ditto, Ewert (Concord, NH), 1997(40 signed, numbered copies; wraps sewn with red thread) £100
ditto, Ewert (Concord, NH), 1997(10 signed, numbered copies; wraps sewn with gold thread) . . . £150
Down Time, Ewert (Concord, NH), 1997 (30 copies signed by author and illustrator, broadside) . . . £125
ditto, Ewert (Concord, NH), 1997 (60 copies signed by author, broadside) £100
Upon Becoming a Senior Citizen, Tamarack Press (New York), 1998 (100 signed, numbered copies) . . . £50
ditto, Tamarack Press (New York), 1998 (26 signed, lettered copies) £100
Radiators, Ewert (Concord, NH), 1998 (130 copies folded as greeting card) £25
ditto, Ewert (Concord, NH), 1998 (40 signed, numbered copies; dewn wraps in d/w) . . . . £100/£65
ditto, Ewert (Concord, NH), 1998 (15 signed, personal copies; sewn wraps in d/w) £150
Religious Consolation, Ewert (Concord, NH), 1999 (150 copies folded as greeting card). £25
ditto, Ewert (Concord, NH), 1999 (50 signed, numbered copies; broadside) £100
ditto, Ewert (Concord, NH), 1999 (15 signed, numbered copies; broadside) £150
Rainbow, Ewert (Concord, NH), 1999 (85 signed copies; broadside) £150
Americana: And Other Poems, Knopf (New York), 2001 . . . . £10/£5
ditto, Penguin (London), 2001 . . . . . £5
Jesus and Elvis, Ewert (Concord, NH), 2001 (450 copies folded as greeting card) £20
ditto, Ewert (Concord, NH), 2001 (50 signed, numbered copies; broadside) £50
ditto, Ewert (Concord, NH), 2001 (15 signed, numbered; broadside) £100
Not Cancelled Yet, Limberlost Press (Boise, ID), 2003 (600 signed copies; wraps) £25
ditto, Limberlost Press (Boise, ID), 2001 (100 signed, numbered copies) £75
Flying to Florida, Lord John Press (Northridge, CA), 2003 (greeting card) £10
ditto, Lord John Press (Northridge, CA), 2003 (signed greeting card) £20
ditto, Lord John Press (Northridge, CA), 2003 (signed broadside) £50
December, Outdoors, Lord John Press (Northridge, CA), 2004 (signed greeting card) £20
Endpoint and Other Poems, Knopf (New York), 2009 . . . . £10/£5

Children's Titles

The Magic Flute, Knopf (New York), 1962 (no statement of printing on copyright page, cloth, in d/w) . £600/£250
ditto, Knopf (New York), 1962 (no statement of printing on copyright page, pictorial boards, no d/w) . . £500
ditto, Deutsch & Ward (London), 1964 . . £250/£40
The Ring, Knopf (New York), 1964 . . . £150/£45
A Child's Calendar, Knopf (New York), 1965 (no statement of printing on copyright page) . . . £125/£40
Bottom's Dream: Adapted from William Shakespeare's 'A Midsummer Night's Dream', Knopf (New York), 1969 (no statement of printing on copyright page). . £100/£30
A Helpful Alphabet of Friendly Objects, Knopf (New York), 1995 . . . . £15/£5

Plays

Three Texts from Early Ipswich: A Pageant, 17th Century Day Committee (Ipswich, MA), 1968 (950 copies; stapled wraps) £45

ditto, 17th Century Day Committee (Ipswich, MA), 1968 (50 signed, numbered copies; stapled wraps) . . £200

ditto, 17th Century Day Committee (Ipswich, MA), 1968 (26 signed, lettered copies, glassine d/w) . . £750/£650

Buchanan Dying, Knopf (New York), 1974 . . £25/£10

ditto, Deutsch (London), 1974 . . . . £20/£5

Others

Assorted Prose, Knopf (New York), 1965 . £35/£10

ditto, Knopf (New York), 1965 (signed copies, unspecified number) . . . . . . £125/£100

ditto, Deutsch (London), 1965 . . . . £20/£5

On Meeting Authors, Wickford Press (Newburyport, MA), 1968 (250 copies; stapled wraps) £500

A Conversation with John Updike, Union College (Schenectady, NY), 1971 (stapled wraps) . . . £25

A Good Place, Aloe Editions (New York), 1973 (26 signed, lettered copies; sewn wraps) £225

ditto, Aloe Editions (New York), 1973 (100 signed, numbered copies; sewn wraps). £150

Picked-Up Pieces, Knopf (New York), 1975 . £20/£5

ditto, Knopf (New York), 1975 (250 signed, numbered copies, slipcase) . . . . . . £125/£100

ditto, Deutsch (London), 1976 . . . . £15/£5

Talk from the Fifties, Lord John Press (Northridge, CA), 1979 (75 signed, numbered deluxe copies, boards, no d/w) £75

ditto, Lord John Press (Northridge, CA), 1979 (300 signed, numbered copies, boards, no d/w) £50

Three Illuminations in the Life of an American Author, Targ Editions (New York), 1979 (350 signed, numbered copies, glassine d/w) . . . . £40/£30

Ego and Art in Walt Whitman, Targ Editions (New York), 1980 (350 signed, numbered copies, glassine d/w) £40/£30

People One Knows: Interviews with Insufficiently Famous Americans, Lord John Press (Northridge, CA), 1980 (300 signed, numbered copies, boards, slipcase) . £50/£40

ditto, Lord John Press (Northridge, CA), 1980 (100 signed, numbered copies, leather spine, slipcase) . . £100/£75

Hawthorne's Creed, Targ Editions (New York), 1981 (250 signed, numbered copies, glassine d/w) . . £40/£30

Invasion of the Book Envelopes, Ewert (Concord, NH), 1981 (125 signed, numbered copies; sewn wraps) . £25

ditto, Ewert (Concord, NH), 1981 (10 signed, numbered copies) £300

Hugging the Shore, Knopf (New York), 1983 . £15/£5

ditto, Deutsch (London), 1984 . . . . £15/£5

Confessions of a Wild Bore, Tamazunchale Press (Newton, IA), 1984 (miniature book, 250 numbered copies) . £25

Emersonianism, Bits Press (Cleveland, OH), 1984 (200 signed, numbered copies, no d/w) . . . £45

Impressions, Sylvester & Orphanos (Los Angeles, CA), 1985 (300 signed, numbered copies, slipcase) £150/£100

A Soft Spring Night in Shillington, Lord John Press (Northridge, CA), 1986 (50 signed, numbered copies) £85

ditto, Lord John Press (Northridge, CA), 1986 (250 signed, numbered copies) £40

Howells as Anti-Novelist, William Dean Howells Memorial Committee, 1987 (150 copies; wraps) £40

Getting the Words Out, Lord John Press (Northridge, CA), 1988 (50 signed, numbered copies). £85

ditto, Lord John Press (Northridge, CA), 1988 (250 signed, numbered copies) £40

Self-Consciousness: Memoirs, Knopf (New York), 1989 . . . . £15/£5

ditto, Knopf (New York), 1989 (350 signed copies; slipcase) . . . . £65/£45

ditto, Easton Press (Norwalk, CT), 1989 (signed copies) £45

ditto, Deutsch (London), 1989 . . . . £10/£5

Just Looking: Essays on Art, Knopf (New York), 1989 . . . . £15/£5

ditto, Knopf (New York), 1989 (350 signed copies; slipcase) . . . . £65/£45

ditto, Deutsch (London), 1989 . . . . £10/£5

Odd Jobs: Essays and Criticism, Knopf (New York), 1991. . . . . £10/£5

ditto, Deutsch (London), 1991 . . . . £10/£5

Baby's First Step, James Cahill (CA), 1993 (100 signed, numbered copies; slipcase) . . . . £50/£35

Concert at Castle Hill, Lord John Press (Northridge, CA), 1993 (50 signed, numbered deluxe copies, boards, no d/w) £100

ditto, Lord John Press (Northridge, CA), 1993 (250 signed, numbered copies, boards, no d/w) £45

The Twelve Terrors of Christmas, Gotham Book Mart (New York), 1993 (with Edward Gorey; 500 copies signed by author and artist; stapled wraps) £150

ditto, Gotham Book Mart (New York), 1993 (50 numbered copies signed by author and artist) £250

ditto, Gotham Book Mart (New York), 1993 (26 lettered copies signed by author and artist) £350

Golf Dreams, Knopf (New York), 1996 . . . £10/£5

ditto, Knopf (New York), 1996 (500 signed, large print copies) . . . . £45/£25

ditto, Hamish Hamilton (London), 1997 . . . £10/£5

A Century of Arts and Letters, Columbia Univ Press (New York), 1998 . . . . £10/£5

Of Prizes and Print, Knopf (New York), 1998 (500 copies; stapled wraps) £20

On Literary Biography, Univ of South Carolina Press (Columbia, SC), 1999 (500 numbered copies, glassine d/w) . . . . £75/£50

More Matter: Essays and Criticism, Knopf (New York), 1999 . . . . £10/£5

ditto, Hamish Hamilton (London), 1999 . . . £10/£5

Humour in Fiction, Lord John Press (Northridge, CA), 2000 (100 copies) £45

ditto, Lord John Press (Northridge, CA), 2000 (26 lettered copies) £100

Three Trips: The Short Story Writer as Tourist, Penguin (London), 2005 (pbk). £5

In Love with a Wanton: Essays on Golf, Thornwillow Press (New York), 2005 (250 signed, numbered copies) . . . . £350/£300

Still Looking: Essays on American Art, Knopf (New York), 2005 . . . . £10/£5

ditto, Hamish Hamilton (London), 2006 . . . £10/£5

Due Considerations, Knopf (New York), 2007 . £10/£5

Hub Fans Bid Kid Adieu: John Updike on Ted Williams, Library of America (New York), 2010 . . . £10/£5

FLORENCE UPTON
(b.1873 d.1922)

Born in New York, Florence Upton moved to England in her twenties. She illustrated the 'Golliwogg' stories (in verse and prose) written by her mother, Bertha Upton. Thus began the whole 'Golliwogg' craze.

The Adventures of Two Dutch Dolls and a Golliwogg, Longmans (London), [1895] £450
ditto, De Wolfe, Fiske & Co. (Boston), [1895] . . £400
The Golliwogg's Bicycle Club, Longmans (London), [1896] £400
Little Hearts, Routledge (London), 1897 . . . £450
The Vege-Men's Revenge, Longmans (London), [1897] £400
The Golliwogg at the Sea-side, Longmans (London), 1898 . . . . £400
The Golliwogg in War!, Longmans (London), 1899 . £400
The Golliwogg's Polar Adventures, Longmans (London), [1900] £450
The Golliwogg's 'Auto-Go-Cart', Longmans (London), [1901] £400
The Golliwogg's Air-Ship, Longmans (London), [1902] £400
The Golliwogg's Circus, Longmans (London), [1903] . £400
The Golliwogg in Holland, Longmans (London), [1904] £400
The Golliwogg's Fox-Hunt, Longmans (London), [1905] £400
The Golliwogg's Desert Island, Longmans (London), [1906] £400
The Golliwogg's Christmas, Longmans (London), 1907 £400
The Adventures of Borbee and the Wisp: The Story of a Sophisticated Little Girl and an Unsophisticated Little Boy, Longmans (London), 1908 . . . . £350
Golliwogg in the African Jungle, Longmans (London), 1909 . . . . £450

ALISON UTTLEY
(b.1884 d.1976)

An author of children's books not unlike those of Beatrix Potter, Uttley's volumes were all illustrated by Margaret Tempest. Her stories are gentle and domestic, although among her many volumes of essays and memoirs her autobiography, *A Country Child*, reveals the harsher side of country life.

'Grey Rabbit' Books
The Squirrel, the Hare and the Little Grey Rabbit, Heinemann (London), 1929 . . . . . £200/£50
How Little Grey Rabbit Got Back Her Tail, Heinemann (London), 1930 . . . . £150/£45
The Great Adventure of Hare, Heinemann (London), 1931 . . . . £150/£35
The Story of Fuzzypeg the Hedgehog, Heinemann (London), 1932 . . . . £150/£35
Squirrel Goes Skating, Collins (London), 1934 . £150/£35
Wise Owl's Story, Collins (London), 1935 . £150/£35
Little Grey Rabbit's Party, Collins (London), 1936 £150/£35
The Knot Squirrel Tied, Collins (London), 1937 . £150/£35
Fuzzypeg Goes to School, Collins (London), 1938. £125/£35

Little Grey Rabbit's Christmas, Collins (London), 1939 . . . . £125/£35
My Little Grey Rabbit Painting Book, Collins (London), 1940 . . . . £125/£45
Moldy Warp The Mole, Collins (London), 1940 . £175/£45
Hare Joins the Home Guard, Collins (London), 1942 . . . . £150/£45
Little Grey Rabbit's Washing Day, Collins (London), 1942 . . . . £75/£20
Water-Rat's Picnic, Collins (London), 1943 . . £75/£20
Little Grey Rabbit's Birthday, Collins (London), [1944] . . . . £75/£20
The Speckledy Hen, Collins (London), [1945] . £65/£15
Little Grey Rabbit to the Rescue, Collins (London), 1946 . . . . £55/£15
Little Grey Rabbit and the Weasels, Collins (London), 1947 . . . . £55/£15
Grey Rabbit and the Wandering Hedgehog, Collins (London), 1948 . . . . £55/£15
Little Grey Rabbit Makes Lace, Collins (London), 1950 . . . . £55/£15
Hare and the Easter Eggs, Collins (London), 1952 £50/£15
Little Grey Rabbit's Valentine, Collins (London), 1953 . . . . £50/£15
Little Grey Rabbit Goes to the Sea, Collins (London), 1954 . . . . £50/£15
Hare and Guy Fawkes, Collins (London), 1956 . £50/£15
Little Grey Rabbit's Paint-Box, Collins (London), [1958] . . . . £50/£15
Grey Rabbit Finds a Shoe, Collins (London), [1960] £45/£15
Grey Rabbit and the Circus, Collins (London), [1961] . . . . £45/£15
Three Little Grey Rabbit Plays, Heinemann (London), 1961 . . . . £45/£15
Grey Rabbit's May Day, Collins (London), [1963] £45/£15
Hare Goes Shopping, Collins (London), 1965 . £45/£15
Little Grey Rabbit's Pancake Day, Collins (London), 1967. . . . . £45/£15
Little Grey Rabbit Goes to the North Pole, Collins (London), 1970 . . . . £45/£15
Fuzzypeg's Brother, Heinemann (London), 1971 . £45/£15
Little Grey Rabbit's Spring Cleaning Party, Collins (London), 1972 . . . . £45/£15
Little Grey Rabbit and the Snow-Baby, Collins (London), 1973 . . . . £45/£15
Hare and the Rainbow, Collins (London), 1975 . £45/£15

Other Children's Books
Moonshine and Magic, Faber (London), 1932 . £100/£35
The Advenures of Peter and Judy in Bunnyland, Collins (London), [1935]. . . . . . . £100/£35
Candlelight Tales, Faber (London), 1936. . £75/£25
The Adventures of No Ordinary Rabbit, Faber (London), 1937 . . . . £75/£25
High Meadows, Faber (London), 1938 . . £75/£20
Mustard, Pepper and Salt, Faber (London), 1938 . £75/£25
A Traveller in Time, Faber (London), 1939 . £75/£25
Tales of the Four Pigs and Brock the Badger, Faber (London), 1939 . . . . £50/£15
The Adventures of Sam Pig, Faber (London), 1940 £45/£15
Sam Pig Goes to Market, Faber (London), 1941 . £45/£15
Six Tales of Brock The Badger, Faber (London), 1941 . . . . £45/£15
Six Tales of Sam Pig, Faber (London), 1941 . . £45/£15

Six Tales of the Four Pigs, Faber (London), 1941 . £45/£15
Ten Tales of Tim Rabbit, Faber (London), 1941 . £50/£15
Nine Starlight Tales, Faber (London), 1942 . . £35/£10
Sam Pig and Sally, Faber (London), 1942 . . £45/£15
Ten Candlelight Tales, Faber (London), 1942. . £35/£10
Cuckoo Cherry-Tree, Faber (London), 1943 . . £35/£10
Sam Pig at the Circus, Faber (London), 1943 . £45/£15
Mrs Nimble and Mr Bumble, James (London), 1944 £50/£15
The Spice Woman's Basket and Other Tales, Faber
(London), 1944 . . . . £40/£15
Adventures of Tim Rabbit, Faber (London), 1945 . £45/£15
Some Moonshine Tales, Faber (London), 1945 . £30/£5
The Weather Cock and Other Stories, Faber (London), 1945
. . . . £35/£10
When All Is Done, Faber (London), 1945 . £35/£10
John Barleycorn: Twelve Tales of Fairy and Magic, Faber
(London), 1948 . . . . £45/£15
Sam Pig in Trouble, Faber (London), 1948 . £45/£15
Snug and Serena Meet a Queen, Heinemann (London),
1950 . . . . £65/£20
Snug and Serena Pick Cowslips, Heinemann (London),
1950 . . . . £65/£20
The Cobbler's Shop and Other Tales, Faber (London), 1950
. . . . £35/£10
Going to the Fair, Heinemann (London), 1951 . £45/£15
Toad's Castle, Heinemann (London), 1951 . £45/£15
Yours Ever, Sam Pig, Faber (London), 1951 . £45/£15
Christmas at the Rose and Crown, Heinemann (London),
1952 . . . . £45/£15
Mrs Mouse Spring Cleans, Heinemann (London), 1952 .
. . . . £45/£15
Snug and the Chimney-Sweeper, Heinemann (London),
1953 . . . . £45/£15
The Gypsy Hedgehogs, Heinemann (London), 1953 £45/£15
Little Red Fox and the Wicked Uncle, Heinemann (London),
1954 . . . . £75/£35
Sam Pig and the Singing Gate, Faber (London), 1955 . .
. . . . £45/£15
The Flower Show, Heinemann (London), 1955 . £45/£15
The Mouse Telegrams, Heinemann (London), 1955 £45/£15
Little Red Fox and Cinderella, Heinemann (London), 1956
. . . . £75/£35
Magic in My Pocket: A Selection of Tales, Puffin (London),
1957 (pbk) £5
Mr Stoat Walks In, Heinemann (London), 1957 . £40/£10
Snug and the Silver Spoon, Heinemann (London), 1957 .
. . . . £40/£10
Little Red Fox and the Magic Moon, Heinemann (London),
1958 . . . . £75/£35
Snug and Serena Count Twelve, Heinemann (London),
1959 . . . . £40/£10
Tim Rabbit and Company, Faber (London), 1959 . £40/£10
John at the Old Farm, Heinemann (London), 1960 £50/£15
Sam Pig Goes to the Seaside, Faber (London), 1960 £45/£10
Snug and Serena go to Town, Heinemann (London), 1961 .
. . . . £35/£10
Little Red Fox and the Unicorn, Heinemann (London), 1962
. . . . £75/£30
*The Little Knife Who Did All The Work: Twelve Tales of
Magic*, Faber (London), 1962 . . . £25/£10
Tim Rabbit's Dozen, Faber (London), 1964 . . £35/£10
The Sam Pig Storybook, Faber (London), 1965 . £45/£15
Enchantment, Heinemann (London), 1966 . . £25/£5
The Mouse, The Rabbit and the Little White Hen, Heine-
mann (London), 1966 . . . . . . £25/£5

Little Red Fox and the Big Tree, Heinemann (London),
1968 . . . . £75/£30
Lavender Shoes: Eight Tales of Enchantment, Faber
(London), 1970 . . . . £20/£5
The Brown Mouse Book, Magical Tales of Two Little Mice,
Heinemann (London), 1971 . . . . £30/£5
Fairy Tales, Faber (London), 1975 . . . £20/£5
Stories for Christmas, Faber (London), 1977 . £20/£5
From Spring to Spring: Stories of the Four Seasons, Faber
(London), 1978 . . . . £20/£5
Foxglove Tales, Faber (London), 1984 . . £20/£5

Others
The Country Child, Faber (London), 1931 . . £100/£30
Ambush of Young Days, Faber (London), 1937 . £50/£20
The Farm on the Hill, Faber (London), 1941 . £35/£10
Country Hoard, Faber (London), 1943 . . £45/£15
*The Washerwoman's Child: A Play on the Life and Stories
of Hans Christian Andersen*, Faber (London), 1946 .
. . . . £40/£15
Country Things, Faber (London), 1946 . . £45/£15
Carts and Candlesticks, Faber (London), 1946 . £45/£15
Buckinghamshire, Hale (London), 1950 . . £35/£10
Macduff, Faber (London), 1950 . . . . £35/£10
Plowmen's Clocks, Faber (London), 1952 . £45/£15
The Stuff of Dreams, Faber (London), 1953 . £35/£10
Here's a New Day, Faber (London), 1956 . £35/£10
A Year in the Country, Faber (London), 1957. . £35/£10
The Swan's Fly Over, Faber (London), 1959 . £45/£15
Something for Nothing, Faber (London), 1960 . £45/£15
Wild Honey, Faber (London), 1962 . . . £45/£15
Cuckoo in June, Faber (London), 1964 . . £45/£15
Recipes from an Old Farmhouse, Faber (London), 1966 .
. . . . £25/£10
A Peck of Gold, Faber (London), 1966 . . £45/£15
The Button-Box and Other Essays, Faber (London), 1968 .
. . . . £45/£15
A Ten O'clock Scholar and Other Essays, Faber (London),
1970 . . . . £45/£15
Secret Places and Other Essays, Faber (London), 1972 .
. . . . £50/£20
Country World: Memoirs of Childhood, Faber (London),
1984 . . . . £15/£5

LAURENS VAN DER POST

(b.1906 d.1996)

Sir Laurens Van der Post was a South African author, explorer, anthropologist, linguist and philosopher. An oppo-
nent of apartheid, in 1925 he helped found *Voorslag*, an
anti-apartheid magazine, and was forced to leave South
Africa because of his involvement with it.

Novels
In a Province, Hogarth Press (London), 1934 . £1,500/£200
ditto, Coward-McCann (New York), 1934 . £1,250/£125
The Face beside the Fire, Hogarth Press (London), 1953 .
. . . . £50/£10
ditto, Morrow (New York), 1953 . . . £25/£5
A Bar of Shadow, Hogarth Press (London), 1954 . £35/£10
ditto, Morrow (New York), 1956 . . . £20/£5

Flamingo Feather, Hogarth Press (London), 1955.   £25/£5
ditto, Morrow (New York), 1955   .   .   .   £20/£5
The Seed and the Sower, Hogarth Press (London), 1963   .
.   .   .   .   £20/£5
ditto, Morrow (New York), 1963   .   .   .   £15/£5
The Hunter and the Whale, Hogarth Press (London), 1967.
.   .   .   .   £15/£5
ditto, Morrow (New York), 1967   .   .   .   £15/£5
A Story Like the Wind, Hogarth Press (London), 1972 £15/£5
ditto, Morrow (New York), 1972   .   .   .   £15/£5
A Far-off Place, Hogarth Press (London), 1974   .   £15/£5
ditto, Morrow (New York), 1974   .   .   .   £15/£5
A Mantis Carol, Hogarth Press (London), 1975   .   £15/£5
ditto, Morrow (New York), 1975   .   .   .   £15/£5

Non-Fiction
Venture to the Interior, Morrow (New York), 1951 £50/£10
ditto, Hogarth Press (London), 1952   .   .   .   £30/£10
The Dark Eye in Africa, Hogarth Press (London), 1955   .
.   .   .   .   £25/£10
ditto, Morrow (New York), 1955   .   .   .   £20/£10
The Lost World of the Kalahari, Hogarth Press (London),
1958   .   .   .   .   £25/£5
ditto, Morrow (New York), 1958   .   .   .   £20/£5
The Heart of the Hunter, Hogarth Press (London), 1961   .
.   .   .   .   £20/£5
ditto, Morrow (New York), 1961   .   .   .   £15/£5
Patterns of Renewal, Pendel Hill Pamphlets (Wallingford,
PA), 1962 (wraps) £5
Journey into Russia, Hogarth Press (London), 1964 £20/£5
ditto, as *A View of All the Russians*, Morrow (New York),
1967   .   .   .   .   £15/£5
A Portrait of All the Russias, Hogarth Press (London), 1967
.   .   .   .   £15/£5
ditto, Morrow (New York), 1967   .   .   .   £15/£5
A Portrait of Japan, Hogarth Press (London), 1968 £15/£5
ditto, Morrow (New York), 1968   .   .   .   £15/£5
The Night of the New Moon: August 6 1945 . . Hiroshima,
Hogarth Press (London), 1970 .   .   .   .   £15/£5
ditto, as *The Prisoner and the Bomb*, Morrow (New York),
1971   .   .   .   .   £15/£5
Jung and the Story of Our Time: A Personal Experience,
Pantheon Books (New York), 1975.   .   .   £15/£5
ditto, Hogarth Press (London), 1976 .   .   .   £15/£5
First Catch Your Eland: A Taste of Africa, Hogarth Press
(London), 1977 .   .   .   .   .   .   £15/£5
ditto, Morrow (New York), 1977   .   .   .   £15/£5
Yet Being Someone Other, Hogarth Press (London), 1982 .
.   .   .   .   £15/£5
ditto, Morrow (New York), 1982   .   .   .   £15/£5
Testament to the Bushmen, Viking (London), 1984 (with
Jane Taylor) .   .   .   .   £25/£5
ditto, Viking (New York), 1984   .   .   .   £25/£5
*A Walk with a White Bushman: Laurens Van Der Post in
Conversation*, Chatto & Windus (London), 1986   £15/£5
ditto, Morrow (New York), 1986   .   .   .   £15/£5
About Blady: A Pattern out of Time, Chatto & Windus
(London), 1991 .   .   .   .   .   .   £15/£5
ditto, Morrow (New York), 1991   .   .   .   £15/£5
The Voice of the Thunder, Chatto & Windus (London),
1993   .   .   .   .   £15/£5
ditto, Morrow (New York), 1994   .   .   .   £15/£5
The Admiral's Baby, Murray (London), 1996.   .   £10/£5
ditto, Morrow (New York), 1996   .   .   .   £15/£5

S.S. VAN DINE
(b.1888 d.1939)
Van Dine was the pseudonym of Willard Huntington
Wright, a U.S art critic and author. His fictional detective
Philo Vance, an upper-class amateur sleuth with aesthetic
tastes, was very popular between the wars, but later
declined in popularity.

Vance Novels
The Benson Murder Case, Scribner's (New York), 1926   .
.   .   .   .   £2,500/£150
ditto, Benn (London), 1926 .   .   .   .   £1,000/£75
The Canary Murder Case, Scribner 1927   .   £200/£25
ditto, Benn (London), 1927 .   .   .   .   £150/£20
The Greene Murder Case, Scribner 1928.   .   £150/£20
ditto, Benn (London), 1928 .   .   .   .   £125/£15
The Bishop Murder Case, Scribner 1929 .   .   £125/£15
ditto, Cassell (London), 1929   .   .   .   £125/£15
The Scarab Murder Case, Scribner 1930 .   .   £100/£15
ditto, Cassell (London), 1930   .   .   .   £75/£10
The Kennel Murder Case, Scribner 1933 .   .   £100/£15
ditto, Cassell (London), 1933   .   .   .   £75/£10
The Dragon Murder Case Scribner 1933 .   .   £100/£15
ditto, Cassell (London), 1934   .   .   .   £75/£10
The Casino Murder Case, Scribner 1934 .   .   £100/£15
ditto, Cassell (London), 1934   .   .   .   £75/£10
The Garden Murder Case, Scribner 1935   .   £100/£15
ditto, Cassell (London), 1935   .   .   .   £75/£10
The Kidnap Murder Case, Scribner 1936.   .   £100/£15
ditto, Cassell (London), 1936   .   .   .   £75/£10
The Gracie Allen Murder Case, Scribner 1938   £100/£15
ditto, Cassell (London), 1938   .   .   .   £75/£10
ditto, as *The Smell of Murder*, Bantam (new York), 1950
(pbk) £5
The Winter Murder Case, Scribner 1939 .   .   £100/£15
ditto, Cassell (London), 1939   .   .   .   £75/£10

Collaborative Novel
The President's Mystery Story, Farrar & Rinehart (New
York), 1935 (with Franklin D Roosevelt, Rupert Hughes,
Samuel Hopkins Adams, Rita Weiman, John Erskine and
Erle Stanley Gardner).   .   .   .   .   £45/£10
ditto, Bodley Head (London), 1936 .   .   .   £45/£10

JULES VERNE
(b.1828 d.1905)

Born in Nantes, France, Verne studied law in Paris and
began his literary career while working at the Stock
Exchange. Famous for his escapist adventure novels and
short stories, Verne described space, air and underwater
travel long before they were possible. He also wrote opera
libretti and plays.

Fiction
Five Weeks in a Balloon, Appleton and Co. (New York),
1869   .   .   .   .   £3,000
ditto, Chapman & Hall (London), 1870   .   .   £2,500
*From the Earth to the Moon Direct in 97 Hours, 20
Minutes, and a Trip Round it*, Newark Publishing &

Printing Co. (Newark, NJ), 1870 (wraps, first book only) .
. . . . £800

ditto, Sampson Low (London), 1873 (complete edition). .
. . . . £1,450

ditto, Scribner's, Armstong & Co. (New York), 1874 £1,000

A Journey to the Centre of the Earth, Griffith & Farran
(London), 1872 [1871] £4,500

ditto, Scribner's, Armstong & Co. (New York), 1874 [1873]
(with no address under publisher's imprint or ads) £2,500

ditto, Scribner's, Armstong & Co. (New York), 1874 [1873]
(with address and ads) £1,500

Twenty Thousand Leagues Under the Sea, Sampson Low
(London), 1873 [1872] £7,500

ditto, Osgood (Boston), 1873 (10-15 copies only, with
central gilt vignette on the top board of a school of
jellyfish) £6,500

ditto, George Smith (Boston), 1873 (with central gilt vignette
on the top board: the image of Nemo with sextant) £1,500

*Meridiana: The Adventures of Three Englishmen and
Three Russians in South Africa*, Sampson Low (London),
1873 . . . . £1,250

ditto, Scribner's (New York), 1873 . . . . £450

The Tour of the World in Eighty Days, Osgood (Boston),
1873 (first issue with no mention of the translator, George
M. Towle, on title-page) £650

ditto as *Around the World in Eighty Days*, Sampson Low
(London), 1873 . . . . £7,500

ditto, Sampson Low (London), 1874 [1873] . £6,500

In Search of the Castaways, Lippincott (Philadelphia), 1873
. . . . £750

ditto, as *A Voyage Round the World*, Routledge (London),
1876-1877 (3 vols: *South America*, *Australia* and *New
Zealand*) . . . . £2,000 the set

The Fur Country, Sampson Low (London), 1874 [1873] .
. . . . £1,000

ditto, Osgood (Boston), 1873 . . . . . £400

A Floating City, and The Blockade Runners, Sampson Low
(London), 1874 . . . . £600

ditto, Scribner's, Armstong & Co. (New York), 1874 ('1875'
also on some title-pages) £450

Dr Ox's Experiment and Other Stories, Osgood (Boston),
1874 . . . . £750

ditto, Sampson Low (London), 1875 . . . . £750

ditto, as *A Winter Amid the Ice and Other Stories*, Sampson
Low (London), 1876 . . . . . . £400

The Mysterious Island, Sampson Low (London), 1875 (3
vols: *Dropped from the Clouds*, *Abandoned* and *The Secret
of the Island*) . . . . . . £2,000 the set

ditto, Scribner's, Armstong & Co. (New York), 1875-1876 (3
vols) . . . . £2,000 the set

*The Adventures of Captain Hatteras: The English at the
North Pole* and *The Field of Ice*, Routledge (London),
1875 [1874] (2 vols) . . . . . £750 the set

ditto, as *The Voyages and Adventures of Captain Hatteras*,
Osgood (Boston), 1875 [1874] (1 vol) . . . £500

The Survivors of the Chancellor [and *Martin Paz*],
Sampson Low (London), 1875 . . . . . £750

ditto, Osgood (Boston), 1875 . . . . . £400

Michael Strogoff, Frank Leslie's Publishing House (New
York), 1876 (wraps) £1,250

ditto, Sampson Low (London), 1877 [1876] . £1,000

ditto, Scribner's (New York), 1877 . . . . £750

The Child of the Cavern, Munro (New York), 1877 (wraps)
. . . . £1,000

ditto, Sampson Low (London), 1877 . . . . £750

*Hector Servadac, Travels and Adventures through the
Solar System*, Munro (New York), 1877 (wraps). . £750

ditto, as *To The Sun: A Journey Through Planetary Space*,
Claxton, Remsen & Haffelfinger (Philadelphia, PA), 1877
[1878] £500

ditto, as *Hector Servadac, etc*, Sampson Low (London),
1878 . . . . £500

ditto, Scribner's (New York), 1878 . . . . £500

Dick Sand; or A Captain at Fifteen, Munro (New York),
1877 (2 vols; wraps) £1,000

ditto, Munro (New York), 1877 (cloth) . . . £650

ditto, as *Dick Sands, The Boy Captain*, Sampson Low
(London), 1879 [1878] £650

ditto, Scribner's (New York), 1879 . . . . £650

500 Millions of the Begum, Munro (New York), 1879
(wraps, does not include 'Mutineers of the Bounty') £1,000

ditto, as *The Begum's Fortune*, Sampson Low (London),
1880 [1879] £1,250

ditto, Lippincott (Philadelphia, PA.), 1879 . . £650

The Tribulations of a Chinaman, Sampson Low (London),
1880 . . . . £650

ditto, Lee & Shepherd (Boston), 1880 . . . £500

ditto, Dutton (New York), 1880 . . . . . £350

The Steam House, Munro (New York), 1880-1881 (2 vols;
wraps) £1,500

ditto, as *Demon of Cawnpore* and *Tigers and Traitors*,
Sampson Low (London), 1881 (2 vols) . . £1,750

ditto, Scribner's (New York), 1881 (2 vols) . . £1,250

Down the Amazon and *The Cryptogram*, Sampson Low
(London), 1881 (2 vols) £750

ditto, Munro (New York), 1881-1882 (2 vols; wraps) . £750

ditto, Scribner's (New York), 1881-1882 (2 vols) . £650

Godfrey Morgan, A Californian Mystery, Sampson Low
(London), 1883 . . . . £800

ditto, as *Robinson's School*, Munro (New York), 1883
(wraps) £500

ditto, as *Godfrey Morgan, A Californian Mystery*,
Scribner's (New York), 1883 . . . . . £500

The Green Ray, Sampson Low (London), 1883 . . £750

ditto, Munro (New York), 1883 (wraps) . . . £650

ditto, with *The Blockade Runners*, Arco (New York), 1965
. . . . £50/£15

The Headstrong Turk, Munro (New York), 1883-1884 (2
vols: *The Captain of the Guidara* and *Scarpante the Spy*;
wraps) £1,250

ditto, as *Keraban the Inflexible*, Sampson Low (London),
1884-5 (2 vols) £2,000

The Vanished Diamond, Sampson Low (London), 1885 .
. . . . £1,000

ditto, as *The Southern Star or The Diamond Land*, Munro
(New York), 1885 (wraps). £850

ditto, Arco (New York), 1966 . . . . £50/£15

The Archipelago on Fire, Munro (New York), 1885 (wraps)
. . . . £800

ditto, Sampson Low (London), 1886 . . . . £1,000

Mathias Sandorf, Munro (New York), 1885 (wraps) . £800

ditto, Sampson Low (London), 1886 . . . . £1,000

Ticket No 9672, Munro (New York), 1886 (2 vols; wraps) .
. . . . £1,000

ditto, as *The Lottery Ticket*, Sampson Low (London), 1887.
. . . . £1,000

The Clipper of the Clouds, Sampson Low (London), 1887 .
. . . . £1,000

ditto, as *Robur the Conqueror or A Trip Round the World in
a Flying Machine*, Munro (New York), 1887 (wraps) £800

Texan's Vengeance, or North Versus South, Munro (New York), 1887 (2 vols; wraps) £1,000
ditto, as *North Against South*, Sampson Low (London), 1888 .   .   .   .£750
The Flight to France, Toronto National Publishing Co. (Toronto, Canada), 1888 .   .   .   .   .£750
ditto, Sampson Low (London), 1888 .   .   .   £1,000
ditto, Lovell (New York), 1888 (wraps) .   .   .£750
Adrift in the Pacific, Munro (New York), 1889 (wraps) £850
ditto, Sampson Low (London), 1889 .   .   .   £1,000
ditto, Bromfield & Co. (New York), 1889 .   .   .£650
A Family Without a Name, Lovell (New York), 1889 (wraps) £750
ditto, Sampson Low (London), 1891 [1890] .   .£750
Caesar Cascabel, Cassell (New York), 1890 .   .£400
ditto, Sampson Low (London), 1891 .   .   .   .£750
The Purchase of the North Pole, Sampson Low (London), 1891 [1890] £1,250
ditto, as *Topsy Turvy*, Ogilvie (New York), 1890 .   £1,250
ditto, Ogilvie (New York), 1890 (wraps) .   .   £1,000
Mistress Branican, Cassell (New York), 1891   .   .£400
ditto, Sampson Low (London), 1892 .   .   .   £1,250
The Castle of the Carpathians, Sampson Low (London), 1893 .   .   .   .   £1,250
ditto, Merriam (New York), 1894 .   .   .   .   £1,250
Claudius Bombarnac, Sampson Low (London), 1894 £1,250
ditto, as *The Special Correspondent, Or the Adventures of Claudius Bombarnac*, The U.S. Book Co. (no place, U.S.), 1894 .   .   .   .   £1,250
Foundling Mick, Sampson Low (London), 1895 .   £1,250
Captain Antifer, Sampson Low (London), 1895 .   £1,250
ditto, Fenno (New York), 1895 (wraps) .   .   £1,000
ditto, Fenno (New York), 1895 .   .   .   .   .£350
The Floating Island, Sampson Low (London), 1896 £1,000
ditto, Allison (New York), 1897 .   .   .   .   £1,250
Clovis Dardentor, Sampson Low (London), 1897 .   £1,000
Facing the Flag, Tennyson Neely (New York), 1897 .£100
ditto, as *For the Flag*, Sampson Low (London), 1897 .£400
An Antarctic Mystery, Sampson Low (London), 1898 £1,000
ditto, Lippincott (Philadelphia), 1898 .   .   .£500
The Will of an Eccentric, Sampson Low (London), 1900 .
   .   .   .   .   £1,500
The Chase of the Golden Meteor, Grant Richards (London), 1909 .   .   .   .£350
ditto, as *The Hunt for the Meteor*, Arco (London), 1965 .
   .   .   .   .   £50/£15
Master of the World, Parke & Co (New York), 1911 (as vol 14 of the 15 volume *Works of Jules Verne*) .   .   £500
ditto, Sampson Low (London), [1914] .   .   .£500
The Lighthouse at the End of the World, Sampson Low (London), [1923] .   .   .   .   .   £600/£100
ditto, Watt (New York), 1924 .   .   .   £600/£100
Their Island Home, Sampson Low (London), [1923] .
   .   .   .   .   £500/£75
ditto, Watt (New York), 1924 .   .   .   .   £500/£75
The Castaways of the Flag, Sampson Low (London), [1923]
   .   .   .   .   £500/£75
ditto, Watt (New York), 1924 .   .   .   .   £500/£75
Into the Niger Bend, Arco/Associated Booksellers (London/ Westport, CT), 1960 .   .   .   .   £50/£15
The City in the Sahara, Arco/Associated Booksellers (London/Westport, CT), 1960 .   .   .   £50/£15
The Masterless Man, Arco/Associated Booksellers (London/ Westport, CT), 1962 .   .   .   .   £50/£15

The Unwilling Dictator, Arco/Associated Booksellers (London/Westport, CT), 1962 .   .   .   .   £50/£15
The Golden Volcano: The Claim on Forty Mile Creek, Arco/Associated Booksellers (London/Westport, CT), 1962
   .   .   .   .   £50/£15
Flood and Fame, Arco/Associated Booksellers (London/ Westport, CT), 1962 .   .   .   .   £50/£15
The Secret of the Wilhelm Storitz, Arco/Associated Booksellers (London/Westport, CT), 1964 .   .   £50/£15
The Village in the Treetops, Arco/Associated Booksellers (London/Westport, CT), 1964 .   .   .   £50/£15
Salvage from the 'Cynthia', Arco/Associated Booksellers (London/Westport, CT), 1964 .   .   .   £50/£15
Yesterday and Tomorrow, Arco/Associated Booksellers (London/Westport, CT), 1965 .   .   .   £50/£15
Package Holiday, Arco/Associated Booksellers (London/ Westport, CT), 1965 .   .   .   .   £50/£15
End of the Journey, Arco/Associated Booksellers (London/ Westport, CT), 1965 .   .   .   .   £50/£15
Drama in Livonia, Arco/Associated Booksellers (London/ Westport, CT), 1967 .   .   .   .   £50/£15
The Danube Pilot, Arco/Associated Booksellers (London/ Westport, CT), 1967 .   .   .   .   £50/£15
The Sea Serpent, Arco/Associated Booksellers (London/ Westport, CT), 1967 .   .   .   .   £50/£15
Backwards to Britain, Chambers (Edinburgh), 1992 £20/£5
Adventures of the Rat Family, O.U.P. (New York/Oxford, UK), 1993 .   .   .   .   £20/£5
Paris in the 20th Century, Random House (London), 1996 .
   .   .   .   .   £20/£5

Non-Fiction
The Exploration of the World (B.C. 505 - A.D. 1700), Sampson Low (London), 1879 .   .   .   .   .£200
ditto, as *Famous Travels and Travellers*, Scribner's (New York), 1879 .   .   .   .£200
The Great Navigators of the Eighteenth Century, Sampson Low (London), 1880 .   .   .   .   .   .£200
ditto, Scribner's (New York), 1880 .   .   .   .£200
The Great Explorers of the Nineteenth Century, Sampson Low (London), 1881 .   .   .   .   .   .£200
ditto, Scribner's (New York), 1881 .   .   .   .£200

GORE VIDAL

(b.1925)

An acclaimed U.S. novelist and essayist, Vidal offers a sharp insight into contemporary American life. He wrote his first very well received novel *Williwaw* when only 21. A few years later *The City and the Pillar* caused controversy by dealing candidly with gay issues and as a result the *New York Times* refused to review a number of his later books.

Novels
Williwaw, Dutton (New York), 1946 .   .   .   £350/£40
ditto, Panther (London), 1965 (pbk) £10
ditto, Heinemann (London), 1970 .   .   .   £30/£10
In a Yellow Wood, Dutton (New York), 1947 .   .£250/£30
ditto, New English Library (London), 1967 (pbk) .   £5
ditto, Heinemann (London), 1979 .   .   .   £25/£10
The City and The Pillar, Dutton (New York), 1948 £150/£20

ditto, Lehmann (London), 1949 . . . . £45/£10
ditto, Dutton (New York), 1965 (revised edition) . £15/£5
ditto, Heinemann (London), 1965 (revised edition). £15/£5
The Season of Comfort, Dutton (New York), 1949 £125/£20
A Star's Progress, Dutton (New York), 1950 (pseud 'Katherine Everard') . . . . . £1,500/£150
A Search for The King: A 12th Century Legend, Dutton (New York), 1950 . . . . £100/£15
ditto, New English Library (London), 1967 (pbk) . . £5
Dark Green, Bright Red, Dutton (New York), 1950 . . £125/£20
ditto, Lehmann (London), 1950 . . . . . £45/£10
ditto, Signet (New York), 1968 (revised edition; pbk) . £5
ditto, New English Library (London), 1968 (pbk) . . £5
The Judgement of Paris, Dutton (New York), 1952 . . £100/£15
ditto, Heinemann (London), 1953 . . . . £75/£10
Death in The Fifth Position, Dutton (New York), 1952 (pseud 'Edgar Box') . . . . £300/£35
ditto, Heinemann (London), 1954 . . . £65/£15
ditto, Ballantine (New York), 1961 (revised and abridged; pbk) £5
ditto, Little, Brown (Boston), 1961 (revised and abridged edition) . . . . £10/£5
ditto, Heinemann (London), 1966 (revised and abridged edition) . . . . £10/£5
ditto, Armchair Detective Library (New York), 1991 (no d/w) £10
ditto, Armchair Detective Library (New York), 1991 (100 signed, numbered copies; slipcase) . . . £40/£30
ditto, Armchair Detective Library (New York), 1991 (26 signed, lettered copies; slipcase) . . . £60/£50
Death Before Bedtime, Dutton (New York), 1953 (pseud 'Edgar Box'). . . . . . . £300/£35
ditto, Heinemann (London), 1954 . . . £145/£20
ditto, Armchair Detective Library (New York), 1990 (no d/w) £10
ditto, Armchair Detective Library (New York), 1990 (100 signed, numbered copies; slipcase) . . . £40/£30
ditto, Armchair Detective Library (New York), 1990 (26 signed, lettered copies; slipcase) . . . £60/£50
Death Likes It Hot, Dutton (New York), 1954 (pseud 'Edgar Box') . . . . £300/£35
ditto, Heinemann (London), 1955 . . . £145/£20
ditto, Armchair Detective Library (New York), 1990 (no d/w) £10
ditto, Armchair Detective Library (New York), 1990 (100 signed, numbered copies; slipcase) . . . £40/£30
ditto, Armchair Detective Library (New York), 1990 (26 signed, lettered copies; slipcase) . . . £60/£50
Messiah, Dutton (New York), 1954 . . . £60/£15
ditto, Heinemann (London), 1955 . . . . £45/£15
ditto, Little, Brown (Boston), 1965 (revised and abridged edition) . . . . £10/£5
ditto, Heinemann (London), 1968 (revised and abridged edition) . . . . £10/£5
Three: Williwaw, A Thirsty Evil, Julian the Apostate, Signet (New York), 1962 (pbk) £5
Julian, Little, Brown (Boston), 1964. . . £40/£15
ditto, Heinemann (London), 1964 . . . £35/£10
ditto, The Franklin Library (Franklin Centre, PA), 1981 (full leather, signed, limited edition) £35
Washington, D.C., Little, Brown (Boston), 1967 . £30/£5
ditto, Heinemann (London), 1967 . . . £25/£5
Myra Breckinridge, Little, Brown (Boston), 1968 . £15/£5

ditto, Blond (London), 1968. . . . . £15/£5
Two Sisters: A Memoir in the Form of a Novel, Little, Brown (Boston), 1970 . . . . £15/£5
ditto, Heinemann (London), 1970 . . . £10/£5
Burr, Random House (New York), 1973 . . £15/£5
ditto, Heinemann (London), 1974 . . . £10/£5
Myron, Random House (New York), 1974 . £10/£5
ditto, Heinemann (London), 1975 . . . £10/£5
1876, Random House (New York), 1976 . . £10/£5
ditto, Random House (New York), 1976 (300 signed copies, slipcase). . . . . £75/£50
ditto, Heinemann (London), 1976 . . . £10/£5
Kalki, Random House (New York), 1978 . . £10/£5
ditto, Franklin Library (Franklin Centre, PA), 1978 (signed limited edition) £20
ditto, Heinemann (London), 1978 . . . £10/£5
Creation, Random House (New York), 1981 . £10/£5
ditto, Random House (New York), 1981 (500 signed copies, slipcase). . . . . £50/£40
ditto, Heinemann (London), 1981 . . . £10/£5
Duluth, Random House (New York), 1983 . £10/£5
ditto, Heinemann (London), 1983 . . . £10/£5
Lincoln, Random House (New York), 1984 . £10/£5
ditto, Random House (New York), 1984 (350 signed, numbered copies, slipcase) . . . . £75/£50
ditto, Franklin Library (Franklin Centre, PA), 1984 (signed limited edition) £25
ditto, Heinemann (London), 1984 . . . £10/£5
Empire, Random House (New York), 1987 . £10/£5
ditto, Random House (New York), 1987 (250 signed, numbered copies, slipcase) . . . . £75/£50
ditto, Franklin Library (Franklin Centre, PA), 1987 (signed limited edition) £20
ditto, Deutsch (London), 1987 . . . . £10/£5
Hollywood, Random House (New York), 1990 . £10/£5
ditto, Random House (New York), 1990 (200 signed, numbered copies, slipcase) . . . . £75/£50
ditto, Deutsch (London), 1990 . . . . £10/£5
Live from Golgotha, Random House (New York), 1992 . . . . £10/£5
ditto, Deutsch (London), 1992 . . . . £10/£5
The Smithsonian Institute, Random House (New York), 1998 . . . . £10/£5
ditto, Franklin Library (Franklin Centre, PA), 1998 (signed limited edition) £45
ditto, Little, Brown (London), 1998 . . . £10/£5
The Golden Age, Doubleday (New York), 2000 . £10/£5
ditto, Little, Brown (London), 2000 . . . £10/£5
ditto, Easton Press (Norwalk, CT), 2000 (1,100 signed copies) £65

Short Stories
A Thirsty Evil: Seven Short Stories, Zero Press (New York), 1956 . . . . £35/£10
ditto, Heinemann (London), 1958 . . . . £15/£5
The Ladies in The Library and Other Stories, Eurographica (Helsinki), 1985 (350 signed copies) . . . £50

Plays
Visit to a Small Planet and Other Television Plays, Little, Brown (Boston), 1956 . . . . £35/£10
The Best Man: A Play About Politics, Little, Brown (Boston), 1960 . . . . . . £40/£10
ditto, as **The Best Man**, Dramatists Play Service (New York), 1962 (revised edition; wraps) £10

Three Plays, Heinemann (London), 1962 . . .£150/£20
Romulus, Adapted from a Play of Friedrich Duerrenmatt: A New Comedy, Dramatists Play Service (New York), 1962 (wraps). £15
ditto, as *Romulus: The Broadway Adaptation*, Grove (New York), 1966 . . . . £15/£5
Weekend: A Comedy in Two Acts, Dramatists Play Service (New York), 1968 (wraps). £20
An Evening with Richard Nixon, Random House (New York), 1972 . . . . . . £20/£5

Essays

Rocking The Boat, Little, Brown (Boston), 1962 . £50/£10
ditto, Heinemann (London), 1963 . . . . £35/£10
Sex, Death and Money, Bantam (New York), 1968 (pbk) £5
Reflections Upon a Sinking Ship, Little, Brown (Boston), 1969 . . . . £20/£5
ditto, Heinemann (London), 1969 . . . . £15/£5
Homage to Daniel Shays: Collected Essays 1952-1972, Random House (New York), 1972 . . . £10/£5
ditto, as *Collected Essays 1951-1972*, Heinemann (London), 1974 . . . . £10/£5
ditto, as *On Our Own Now*, Panther (London), 1976 (pbk) £5
Matters of Fact and Fiction: Essays, 1973-1976, Random House (New York), 1977 . . . . £10/£5
ditto, Heinemann (London), 1977 . . . £10/£5
The Second American Revolution and Other Essays, Random House (New York), 1982 . . . £10/£5
Armageddon? Essays 1985-1987, Deutsch (London), 1987. . . . . £10/£5
ditto, as *At Home*, Random House (New York), 1988 £10/£5
View from the Diner's Club: Essays 1987 - 1991, Random House (New York), 1991 . . . . . £10/£5
ditto, Deutsch (London), 1991 . . . . £10/£5
United States: Essays, 1951-92, Deutsch (London), 1993 . . . . £10/£5
Virgin Islands, A Dependancy of the United States: Essays 1992-1997, Deutsch (London), 1997 . . £10/£5
Sexually Speaking: Collected Sex Writings, Cleis Press (San Francisco, CA), 1999 . . . . . £10/£5
The Last Empire: Essays 1992-2000, Doubleday (New York), 2001 . . . . . . £10/£5
Perpetual War for Perpetual Peace: How We Got to Be So Hated, Thunder Mouth Press (New York), 2002 (pbk) £5
Dreaming War: Blood for Oil and the Cheney-Bush Junta, Thunder Mouth Press (New York), 2002 (pbk) . £5
Inventing a Nation: Washington, Adams, Jefferson, Yale Univ Press (New Haven, CT), 2003 . . £10/£5
Imperial America: Reflections on the United States of Amnesia, Thunder Mouth Press/Nation Books (New York), 2004 . . . . £10/£5

Others

Views from a Window: Conversations, Lyle Stuart (Secaucus, NJ), 1980 . . . . . £15/£5
Vidal in Venice, Weidenfeld (London), 1984 . . £10/£5
ditto, Summit (New York), 1985. . . . £10/£5
Screening History, Harvard Univ Press (Cambridge, MA), 1992 . . . . £10/£5
ditto, Deutsch (London), 1992 . . . . £10/£5
Palimpsest, Random House (New York), 1995 . £10/£5
ditto, Deutsch (London), 1995 . . . . £10/£5
Point to Point Navigation: A Memoir 1964 to 2006, Random House (New York), 1995 . . . £10/£5

WILLIAM T. VOLLMANN
(b.1959)

William T. Vollmann is an American novelist, journalist, short story writer and essayist. His work is in part based upon experiences in the Afghan–Soviet War, and he has associated with drug abusers and prostitutes in rough districts of San Francisco.

You Bright and Risen Angels, Andre Deutsch (London), 1987 . . . . £50/£5
ditto, Atheneum (New York), 1987 . . . £30/£5
The Convict Bird, CoTangent Press (San Francisco, CA), 1987 (10 signed, numbered copies bound in steel with place markers made from chain, barbed wire, and hair purchased from street prostitutes) . . . £2,250
ditto, CoTangent Press (San Francisco, CA), 1987 (90 signed, numbered copies in hand-sewn wraps) . £175
ditto, CoTangent Press (San Francisco, CA), 1987 (12 signed out-of-series copies in wraps; 'Second Edition') . £125
The Rainbow Stories, Andre Deutsch (London), 1989 . . . . £65/£10
ditto, Atheneum (New York), 1987 . . . £25/£5
The Ice Shirt, Andre Deutsch (London), 1990 . £45/£10
ditto, Viking Press (New York), 1990 . . . £20/£5
The Happy Girls, CoTangent (New York), 1990 (3 copies signed by Vollmann and photographer Ken Miller; folio illustrated with 11 full-page paintings by Vollmann and three full-page photographs by Miller; enclosed in a wooden box with peephole, red lamp, buzzer and door knob; black lacquer box by artist James Lombino) £3,000
ditto, CoTangent (New York), 1990 (10 copies signed by Vollmann and Miller; folio) £2,000
Whores for Gloria, Pan-Picador (London), 1991 (pbk). £20
ditto, Pantheon (New York), 1991 . . . £10/£5
ditto, Pantheon (New York), 1991 (20 signed, numbered copies of trade edition rebound so that front cover has original watercolour drawing; limitation page handwritten and signed by Vollmann and Miller; photos also signed by Miller) £1,250
Thirteen Stories and Thirteen Epitaphs, Andre Deutsch (London), 1991 . . . . . . £15/£5
ditto, Pantheon (New York), 1991 . . . £10/£5
An Afghanistan Picture Show, Or How I Saved the World, Farrar, Straus and Giroux (New York), 1992 . £10/£5
Fathers and Crows, Viking (New York), 1992 . £10/£5
ditto, Andre Deutsch (London), 1992. . . £15/£5
Butterfly Stories, Andre Deutsch (London), 1993 (pbk) £10
ditto, Andre Deutsch (London), 1993 (26 signed, lettered copies; slipcase) . . . . £350/£300
ditto, Andre Deutsch (London), 1993 (100 signed, numbered copies; slipcase) . . . . . £150/£125
ditto, Grove Press (New York), 1993. . . £10/£5
The Grave of Lost Stories, CoTangent Press (Sacramento, CA), 1993 (15 numbered copies signed by author and binder; pictorial black wraps lettered in silver; illustrated with four original hand-coloured illustrations by Vollmann; cover hand-painted by Vollmann with snake bones laid into the illustration; book enclosed in chiselled marble covers by Ben Pax) £2,500
ditto, CoTangent Press (Sacramento, CA), 1993 (185 copies signed by author and binder; pictorial black wraps lettered in silver) £250

The Rifles, Viking Press (New York), 1994 . . £10/£5
ditto, Andre Deutsch (London), 1994. . . £10/£5
The Tale of the Dying Lungs, Vagabond Books (Los Angeles, CA), 1995 (26 signed, lettered copies; broadside) £200
ditto, Vagabond Books (Los Angeles, CA), 1995 (200 signed, numbered copies) £100
Open All Night, The Overlook Press (Woodstock/New York), 1995 (text by Vollmann; photographs by Ken Miller) . . . . £10/£5
ditto, The Overlook Press (Woodstock/New York), 1995 (pbk) £5
The Atlas, Viking (New York), 1996. . . £10/£5
The Royal Family, Viking (New York), 2000 . . £10/£5
Argall: The True Story of Pocahontas and Captain John Smith, Viking (New York), 2001 . . £10/£5
The Old Man: A Case Study from Rising Up and Rising Down, McSweeney's Books (San Francisco, CA), 2001 (wraps) £10
Yohnee Screen, CoTangent Press (Sacramento, CA), 2002 (5 copies; a hinged three-panel screen) . . . £7,500
Rising Up and Rising Down, McSweeney's Books (San Francisco, CA), 2003 (7 vols; slipcase; no d/ws) £250 the set
ditto, as *Rising Up and Rising Down: Some Thoughts on Violence, Freedom, and Urgent Means*, Ecco Press (New York), 2004 () . . . . . £15/£5
ditto, Ecco Press (New York), 2004 (wraps) . . £10
Expelled From Eden: A Wiliam T. Vollmann Reader, Thunder's Mouth Press/West Publishing Group (New York), 2004 (pbk) £10
Europe Central, Viking Press (New York), 2005 . £25/£5
ditto, Alma Books (Richmond, Surrey), 2006 . . £10/£5
Uncentering The Earth: Copernicus and the Revolution of the Heavenly Spheres, W.W. Norton (New York), 2006 . . . . £10/£5
ditto, Weidenfeld & Nicolson, London, 2006 . . £10/£5
Poor People, Ecco Press/HarperCollins (New York), 2007 . . . . £10/£5
Riding Toward Everywhere, Ecco Press/HarperCollins (New York), 2008 . . . . £10/£5
Imperial, Viking Press (New York), 2009 . . £10/£5
Kissing the Mask, Ecco Press/HarperCollins (New York), 2010 . . . . £10/£5

KURT VONNEGUT, Jr.

(b.1922 d.2007)

American novelist Vonnegut's experiences during World War Two influenced much of his writing. The bombing of the German city of Dresden, where he was held as a prisoner of war, was the inspiration for his best known novel, the acerbic *Slaughterhouse-Five*. Vonnegut was a humanist, socialist, world federalist and supporter of the American Civil Liberties Union.

Novels

Player Piano, Scribner's (New York), 1952 ('A' and publisher's seal on copyright page) . . . £750/£75
ditto, Macmillan (London), 1953 . . . £450/£60
ditto, as *Utopia 14*, Bantam Books (New York), [1954] (pbk) £15
The Sirens of Titan, Dell (New York), 1959 (pbk). . £85

ditto, Houghton Mifflin (Boston), 1961 . . £1,750/£200
ditto, Gollancz (London), 1962 . . . . . £600/£65
Mother Night, Fawcett (Greenwich, CT), 1962 (pbk) . £65
ditto, Harper & Row (New York), [1966] . . £200/£30
ditto, Cape (London), 1968 . . . . £75/£15
Cat's Cradle, Holt Rinehart (New York), 1963 . £500/£65
ditto, Gollancz (London), 1963 . . . . . £250/£35
God Bless You, Mr Rosewater or Pearls Before Swine, Holt Rinehart (New York), 1965 . . . . £300/£45
ditto, Cape (London), 1965 . . . . £150/£25
Slaughterhouse-Five or The Children's Crusade: A Duty-Dance with Death, Delacorte (New York), 1969. £500/£45
ditto, Cape (London), 1970 . . . . . £135/£20
ditto, Franklin Library (Franklin Centre, PA), 1978 (signed limited edition) £75
Breakfast of Champions or Goodbye Blue Monday, Delacorte (New York), 1973 . . . . £25/£5
ditto, Cape (London), 1973 . . . . . £25/£5
Slapstick or Lonesome No More, Delacorte (New York), 1976 . . . . £25/£5
ditto, Delacorte (New York), 1976 (250 signed, numbered copies, slipcase) . . . . . £165/£125
ditto, Franklin Library (Franklin Centre, PA), 1976 (signed limited edition) £25
ditto, Cape (London), 1976 . . . . . £30/£5
Jailbird, Delacorte (New York), 1979 . . £20/£5
ditto, Delacorte (New York), 1979 (500 signed copies, slipcase). . . . . £100/£75
ditto, Franklin Library (Franklin Centre, PA), 1979 (signed limited edition) £25
ditto, Cape (London), 1979 . . . . £20/£5
Deadeye Dick, Delacorte (New York), 1982 . . £15/£5
ditto, Delacorte (New York), 1982 (350 signed copies, slipcase). . . . . £150/£125
ditto, Cape (London), 1983 . . . . £15/£5
Galapagos, Delacorte (New York), 1985 . . . £15/£5
ditto, Delacorte (New York), 1985 (500 signed copies, slipcase). . . . . £100/£75
ditto, Franklin Library (Franklin Centre, PA), 1985 (signed limited edition) £40
ditto, Cape (London), 1985 . . . . . £15/£5
Bluebeard, Delacorte (New York), 1987 . . . £15/£5
ditto, Delacorte (New York), 1987 (500 signed copies, slipcase). . . . . £125/£100
ditto, Franklin Library (Franklin Centre, PA), 1987 (signed limited edition) £65
ditto, Cape (London), 1988 . . . . . £15/£5
Hocus Pocus; Or, What's The Hurry Son?, Putnam (New York), 1990 . . . . £10/£5
ditto, Putnam (New York), 1990 (250 signed copies, slipcase). . . . . £150/£125
ditto, Franklin Library (Franklin Centre, PA), 1990 (signed limited edition) £75
ditto, Cape (London), 1990 . . . . . £10/£5
Timequake, Putnam (New York), 1997 . . . £10/£5
ditto, Cape (London), 1997 . . . . . £10/£5
ditto, Easton Press (Norwalk, CT), 1997 (signed, numbered edition) £125

Short Stories

Canary in a Cathouse, Fawcett (Greenwich, CT), 1961 (pbk) £50
Welcome to the Monkey House: A Collection of Short Works, Delacorte (New York), 1968 . . £300/£45
ditto, Cape (London), 1969 . . . . . £125/£20

Bagombo Snuff Box: Uncollected Short Fiction, Putnam (New York), 1999 . . . . . £10/£5
ditto, Putnam (New York), 1999 (175 signed, numbered copies, slipcase) . . . . . £150/£100
ditto, Cape (London), 1999 . . . . . £10/£5

Plays
Happy Birthday, Wanda June, Delacorte (New York), 1971 (price at top on front flap of d/w) . . . £450/£50
ditto, Cape (London), 1973 . . . . . £150/£20
Between Time and Timbuktu or Prometheus-5: A Space Fantasy, Delacorte (New York), 1972 . . . £300/£65
ditto, Panther (London), 1975 . . . . . £15

Others
You've Never Been to Barnstable?, Crane Duplicating Service (Barnstable, MA), 1966 (two sheets folded once) £600
Wampeters, Foma, and Granfalloons (Opinions), Delacorte (New York), 1974 . . . £35/£10
ditto, Cape (London), 1975 . . . . . £25/£10
Sun Moon, Star, Harper & Row (New York), 1980 (with Ivan Chermayeff) . . . . . £15/£5
ditto, Hutchinson (London), 1980 . . . £15/£5
How to Write with Style, International Paper Company (Elmsford, NY), 1980 (single sheet, folded twice) . £20
Palm Sunday: An Autobiographical Collage, Delacorte (New York), 1981 . . . . . £15/£5
ditto, Delacorte (New York), 1981 (500 signed copies, slipcase). . . . . £125/£100
ditto, Cape (London), 1981 . . . . . £15/£5
Nothing Is Lost Save Honor: Two Essays, Nouveau Press (Jackson, MS), 1984 (300 signed copies; wraps) . £125
ditto, Nouveau Press (Jackson, MS), 1984 (40 signed deluxe copies, boards) £300
Fates Worse Than Death: An Autobiographical Collage of the 1980's, Putnam (New York), 1991 . . £10/£5
ditto, Putnam (New York), 1991 (200 signed, numbered copies, slipcase) . . . . £150/£100
ditto, Cape (London), 1991 . . . . . £10/£5
Like Shaking Hands with God: A Conversation about Writing, Seven Stories Press (New York), 1999 . £10/£5
God Bless You, Dr. Kevorkian, Seven Stories Press (New York), 1999 . . . . . £10/£5
ditto, Easton Press (Norwalk, CT), 2000 (full leather, signed limited edition) £200

LOUIS WAIN
(b.1860 d.1939)

Wain was a successful British illustrator, best known for his pictures of cats. He was at one time President of The National Cat Club of England. He suffered in later years from schizophrenia and was finally admitted to a psychiatric hospital where he worked sporadically until his death

Books Illustrated by Louis Wain (and either written by him, or with no author credited)
Madame Tabby's Establishment, Macmillan (London), 1886 (pseud 'Kari') £750
Aunt Louisa's Jumble Book, Frederick Warne (London), [c.1890] £175

Dreams by French Firesides, A. & C. Black (London), 1890 (pseud 'Richard Leander'). £225
Laugh and Grow Wise, McLoughlin (New York), [c.1890]. £200
Miss Lovemouse's Letters, Nelson (London), 1896 . £325
Puppy Dogs' Tales, Nelson (London), 1896 . . . £275
The Children's Tableaux: The Three Little Kittens, Nister (London), 1896 . . . . . . £300
The Dandy Lion, by Louis Wain and Clifton Bingham, Nister (London), [1900] £450
Fun All The Way, Nister (London), 1900. . . .£175
Pussies at Work, Raphael Tuck (London), [c.1900] . £325
Cats, Sands (London), [1901] (pseud 'Grimalkin'). £1,000
Catland, Raphael Tuck (London), 1901 (pseud 'Father Tuck') £700
Fun For Everyone, Nister (London), 1902 . . .£175
Fun and Frolic, by Louis Wain and Clifton Bingham, Nister (London), [1902]. £850
Pa Cats, Ma Cats, and Their Kittens, Raphael Tuck (London), [1902] (pseud 'Father Tuck'). . . .£900
The Louis Wain Nursery Book, Clarke (London), [1902] £275
Ever So Fun, Ernest Nister (London), [c.1902] . £200
Louis Wain's Cats and Dogs, Raphael Tuck (London), [1903] £450
Big Dogs, Little Dogs, Cats and Kittens, Raphael Tuck (London), [1903]. £1,000
Comic Animals ABC, by Louis Wain, Collins (London), [1903]. £400
Louis Wain's Baby's Picture Book, Clarke (London), 1903 . . . . £375
With Father Tuck to Animal Land, Raphael Tuck (London), 1903 (edited by Edric Vredenburg). . . £500
Louis Wain's Dog Painting Book, Raphael Tuck (London), [1903] £400
Louis Wain's Cat Painting Book, Raphael Tuck (London), [1903] £400
Father Tuck's Postcard Painting Book, Raphael Tuck (London), [1903]. £350
Louis Wain's Summer Book, Hutchinson (London), 1903 . . . . £275
The Louis Wain Kitten Book, Treherne (London), [1903] (printed on one side of the page) . . . £1,000
Catland ABC, Raphael Tuck (London), [1903] . £750
Cat Life, Raphael Tuck (London), 1903 . . . £450
Catland 'Panorama', Raphael Tuck (London), [c.1903] (folding board book) £700
Funny Animals and Stories About Them, Clarke (London), 1904 . . . . £350
Puss in Boots, Treherne, 1904 . . . . . £500
In Animal Land with Louis Wain, Partridge (London), [1904] £700
Kits and Cats, Raphael Tuck (London), 1904 . . £600
Nursery Rhymes Pictured by Louis Wain, Raphael Tuck (London), [c.1905] £400
Louis Wain's Animal Show: With Stories in Prose and Verse, Clarke (London), 1905 . . . . . £300
My Book of Funny Folk, Charles H. Kelly (London), 1905 . . . . £150
My Cat and Dog Book, Charles H. Kelly (London), 1905 . . . . £150
My Cat Book, Charles H. Kelly (London), 1905 . £225
Louis Wain's Summer Book for 1906, King (London), 1906 . . . . £350

Mixed Pickles Bottled by Louis Wain, Raphael Tuck (London), [c.1906] (edited by Edric Vredenburg)   . £275

Nursery Cats, Raphael Tuck (London), [c.1906]   . £325

In Cat and Dog Land with Louis Wain, Raphael Tuck (London), [c.1906] £400

Animal Playtime, Clarke (London), [1908]   . . . £325

A Little Book of Pussy Cats, Little Folks Library (London), 1908   . . . . £225

Louis Wain's Annual Street, King (London), 1911 . . £325

In Story Land with Louis Wain, Raphael Tuck (London), 1912   . . . . £650

Louis Wain's Painting Book, Shaw (London), 1912 . £350

Pussyland Pictures by Louis Wain, Raphael Tuck (London), [c.1912] £300

Louis Wain's Father Christmas, Shaw (London), 1912 £300

Animal Happyland, Clarke (London), [1913] . . . £325

Happy Hours with Louis Wain, Shaw (London), 1913 . £400

In Louis Wain Land, John F. Shaw (London), [c.1913] . £400

Pages of Fun, Ernest Nister (London), 1913   . . £200

A Cat Alphabet and Picture Book for Little Folk, Blackie & Sons (London), [1914] £350

Animal Picture-Land, Clarke (London), [1914]   . . £350

In Catland, John F. Shaw (London), [c.1914] (Father Tuck's Panorama Series) £325

Daddy Cat, Blackie & Sons (London), [1915]. . . £500

Busy Pussies, Blackie (London), [1915]   . . . £250

A Trip to Catland, Raphael Tuck (London), [c.1915] . £300

To Nursery Land with Louis Wain, Raphael Tuck (London), [c.1915] (edited by Edric Vredenburg)   . . . £250

Pussy Cats ABC, S.W. Partridge (London), [1915] . . £300

Pages to Please You, Raphael Tuck (London), [c.1916] . £175

Cats of All Sorts, Geographia (London), [c.1916]   . . £325

I'll Tell You A Story, Raphael Tuck (London), [c.1916] (edited by Edric Vredenburg) £150

Little Red Riding Hood and Other Tales, Gale & Polden (London), [1917]. £325

Rosy Cheeks Funny Book, Ernest Nister (London) [c.1917] £150

Cinderella and Other Fairy Tales, Gale & Polden (London), [1917] £325

Happy Schooldays, Gale and Polden (London), [1917] (pseud 'Freckles') £275

Billiecat Family Frolics, Gale and Polden (London), [c.1918] £300

Cats at Play, Blackie (London), [1918]   . . . £300

In Wain Land, John F. Shaw (London), [1919]   . . £300

Jock the Bow Wow, Valentine (London), 1919 . . . £175

The Farmyard Pussies: Tales for Little People, Aldine (London), [c.1919] £225

Tatters, The Puppy, Valentine (London), 1919 . . . £175

Flossy and Fluffy, Valentine (London), 1919   . . £225

Louis Wain's 'Doggie' Painting Book, Valentine (London), 1919   . . . . £200

Louis Wain's 'Kittens' Painting Book, Valentine (London), 1919.   . . . . £225

Louis Wain's 'Cats' Painting Book, Valentine (London), 1919   . . . . £250

The Jolly Cat Book, Geographia (London), [1919]   . £250

Fun in Catland, Geographia (London), [1919?]   . . £300

The Story of Tabbykin Town in School and at Play, Faulkner (London), [1920] (pseud 'Kittycat'; stapled wraps) £500

Pussy Land, Geographia (London), [1920]   . . . £400

I'll Tell You A Tale, Raphael Tuck (London), [c.1920] (edited by Edric Vredenburg) £175

Very Funny, Scott and Sleeman (London), 1920   . . £175

Louis Wain's Cat Mascot Postcard Painting Book, Raphael Tuck (London), [c.1920] £200

Louis Wain's Dog Mascot Postcard Painting Book, Raphael Tuck (London), [c.1920] £150

Louis Wain's Merry Mascot Postcard Painting Book, Raphael Tuck (London), [c.1920] £150

'Little People' Transfer Pictures, Raphael Tuck (London), [c.1920] (36 cat and dog transfers in printed wraps)   . £300

Somebody's Pussies, Raphael Tuck (London), [c.1920] . £200

Adventures of Peter Puss, Raphael Tuck (London), [c.1920] £250

The Kitten's House, Valentine (London), 1922   . . £450

Charlie's Adventures, Valentine (London), 1922 . . £600

Comical Kittens, Valentine (London), [1922] (painting book with paints and brush) £250

Louis Wain's Children's Book, Hutchinson (London), [1923] £300

Souvenir of Louis Wain's Work, Louis Wain Fund (London), [1925]. £150

ditto, as *Animals 'Xtra' and Louis Wain's Annual 1925*, Louis Wain Fund (London), [1925]. £150

Louis Wain's Animal Book, Collins (London), [1928] £175

Louis Wain's Great Big Midget Book, Dean (London), 1934 . . . . £175

Annuals

Louis Wain's Annual, Treherne (London), 1901   . . £325

Louis Wain's Annual for 1902, Treherne (London), 1902 . . . . £325

Louis Wain's Annual 1903, Hutchinson (London), 1903 . . . . £325

Louis Wain's Annual 1905, King (London), 1905.   . £235

Louis Wain's Annual for 1906, Shaw (London), 1906 . £225

Louis Wain's Annual 1907, Bemrose (London), 1907 . £225

Louis Wain's Annual 1908, Bemrose (London), 1908 . £225

Louis Wain's Annual 1909-10, Allen (London), 1909 . £200

Louis Wain's Annual 1910-11, Allen (London), 1910 . £200

Louis Wain's Annual 1911, Shaw (London), 1911   . £200

Louis Wain's Annual 1911-12, Shaw (London), 1911 . £200

Louis Wain's Annual 1912, Shaw (London), 1912   . £200

Louis Wain's Annual 1913, Shaw (London), 1913   . £200

Louis Wain's Annual 1914, Shaw (London), 1914   . £200

Louis Wain's Annual 1915, Shaw (London), 1915   . £200

Louis Wain's Annual 1921, Hutchinson (London), 1921   . . . . £200

Books Illustrated by Louis Wain (written by others)

Our Farm: The Trouble and Successes Thereof, by F.W. Pattenden, Clarke (London), [1888] £300

Peter, A Cat O' One Tail: His Life and Adventures, by Charles Morley, Pall Mall Gazette Extras (London), 1892. . . . . £700

Old Rabbit, The Voodoo and Other Sorcerers, by M.A. Owen, Unwin (London), 1893 . . . . . . £250

Lament of Billy Villy, by Emily Rowly Watson, Raphael Tuck (London), [1894] £325

More Jingles, Jokes and Funny Folks, by Clifton Bingham, Nister (London), 1898   . . . . £400

The Monkey That Would Not Kill, by Henry Drummond, Hodder & Stoughton (London), 1898   . . . . £125

Stories from Lowly Life, by C.M. Duppa, Macmillan (London), 1898   . . . . £225

Pussies and Puppies: With Verses and Tales by Various Writers, Partridge (London), [1899] £375

The Living Animals of The World, by C.J. Cornish, (London), [1901] £225

A Pussie's Diary, by Edith Warry, Dean (London), 1902 . . . . £300

ditto, as *A Cat's Diary*, by Edith Warry, Dean (London), 1907 (*A Pussie's Diary* on title-page) . . . £225

All Sorts of Comical Cats, by Clifton Bingham, Nister (London), 1902 . . . . . £1,000

Ping-Pong Calendar for 1903, by Clifton Bingham, Raphael Tuck (London), [1903] . . . £300

Ping-Pong As Seen By Louis Wain, by Clifton Bingham, Raphael Tuck (London), [1903] £600

Kittenland, by Clifton Bingham, Collins (London), [1903] £1,250

Fairy Tales, by Grace C. Floyd, Raphael Tuck (London), [c.1903] £250

Puppyland: Pictures and Play, by Clifton Bingham, Collins (London), 1903 . . . . £225

With Louis Wain to Fairyland, by Nora Chesson, Raphael Tuck (London), [1904] . . . £1,000

Funny Favourites, by Clifton Bingham, Nister (London), 1904 . . . . £650

Claws and Paws: Stories and Pictures from Kittenland and Puppyland, by C. Bingham, Nister (London), [1904] £1,000

Frolics in Fairyland, by Grace C. Floyd, Raphael Tuck (London), [c.1905] £250

Cat Tales, by W.L. Alden, Digby Long (London), 1905 £600

Fun at the Zoo, by Clifton Bingham, Collins (London), 1906 . . . . £250

At The Pantomime with Louis Wain, by Grace C. Floyd, Raphael Tuck (London), [c.1906] . . . £250

Pantomime Pussies, by Grace C. Floyd, Raphael Tuck (London), [c.1906] £250

Playtime in Pussyland, by Clifton Bingham, Alfe Cooke (London), [c.1906] £350

The Adventures of Friskers and His Friends, by Marian Hurrell, Culley (London), [1907] . . . £450

Mephistopheles: The Autobiography and Adventures of a Tabby Cat, by C.Y. Stephens, Jarrold (London), [1907] £600

The Kings and The Cats: Munster Fairy Tales for Young and Old, by John Hannon, Burns & Oates (London), 1908 . . . . £500

Cat's Cradle: A Picture Book for Little Folk, by May Clariss Byron, Blackie (London), [1908] . . £450

Full of Fun, by Clifton Bingham, Nister (London), [1908] £450

Holidays in Animal Land, by A.W. Ridler, Clarke (London), [1909] £400

Two Cats at Large: A Book of Surprises, by S.C. Woodhouse, Routledge (London), [1910] . . £600

The Merry Animal Picture Book, by A.W. Ridler, Clarke (London), [1910] £350

The Happy Family, by Edric Vredenburg, Raphael Tuck (London), 1910 . . . . . . £850

Such Fun with Louis Wain, by Norman Gale, Raphael Tuck (London), 1910 . . . . . £350

To Nursery Land with Louis Wain, edited by Edric Vredenburg, Raphael Tuck (London), 1910 .. . £325

Cats at School, by S.C. Woodhouse, Routledge (London), [1911] £650

Animals in Fun-Land, by A.W. Rider, Clarke (London), [1911] £350

With Louis Wain in Pussyland, by Norman Gale, Raphael Tuck (London), [c.1912] . . . £250

Cats of Many Lands, by Norman Gale, Raphael Tuck (London), [c.1912] £250

Life In Catland, by Norman Gale, Raphael Tuck (London), [c.1912] £275

Pleasures in Pussytown, by Norman Gale, Raphael Tuck (London), [c.1912] £250

Merry Times in Animal-Land, by A.W. Rider, Clarke (London), [1912] £300

The Cat Scouts: A Picture Book for Little Folk, by Jessie Pope, Blackie (London), [1912] . . £650

Louis Wain's Happy Land, by A.W. Ridler, Shaw (London), 1912 . . . . £250

Days in Catland With Louis Wain 'Panorama', by Arthur Barnaby, Raphael Tuck (London), [1912] £1,250

Tinker, Tailor, by Eric Vredenburg, Raphael Tuck (London), [1914] £650

Animal Fancy-Land, by A.W. Rider, Clarke (London), [1915] £300

Frolicsome Friends, by Jessie Pope, Blackie (London), 1915 . . . . £225

Little Soldiers, by May Crommelin, Hutchinson (London), [1915] £250

Merry Times with Louis Wain, by Dorothy Black, Raphael Tuck (London), 1916 . . . . £600

Terrier, VC, A Black and Tan Hero, by Julia Lowndes Tracey, Aldine (London), 1916 . . . £275

The Tale of Little Priscilla Purr, by Cecily M. Rutley, Valentine (London), 1920 . . . . £500

The Tale of Naughty Kitty Cat, by Cecily M. Rutley, Valentine (London), 1920 . . . . £250

The Tale of Peter Pusskin, by Cecily M. Rutley, Valentine (London), 1920 . . . . £250

The Tale of The Tabby Twins, by Cecily M. Rutley, Valentine (London), 1920 . . . . £250

Every Child's Own Picture Book, by Grace C. Floyd, Raphael Tuck (London), [c.1920] (24 perforated coloured picture labels for child to paste in) £250

The Pussy Rocker: Polly Puss, by Cecily M. Rutley, Valentine (London), [1921] (shape book) . . £300

The Puppy Rocker: Peter Pup, by Cecily M. Rutley, Valentine (London), [1921] (shape book) . . £300

The Teddy Rocker: Naughty Teddy Bear, by Cecily M. Rutley, Valentine (London), [1921] (shape book) . £300

Kits and Cats, by Anon [Norman Gale], Raphael Tuck (London), 1930s (with 'Louis Wain in Pussyland' on title-page) £175

Lost, Stolen or Strayed, by Marion Ashmore, Eyre & Spottiswoode (London), 1934 . . . . . £125

ALFRED WAINWRIGHT

(d.1907 d.1991)

Wainwright was the author and illustrator of numerous guides to the fells of England and Scotland. His handwritten and hand-drawn works have inspired and guided hillwalkers for the last four decades.

'A Pictorial Guide to the Lakeland Fells' Titles

The Eastern Fells, Henry Marshall (Kendal, Cumbria), 1955 (in 'second impression' d/w) . . . . £200/£165

The Far Eastern Fells, Henry Marshall (Kendal, Cumbria), 1957 . . . . £175/£75

The Central Fells, Henry Marshall (Kendal, Cumbria), 1958 . . . . £175/£75
The Southern Fells, Henry Marshall (Kendal, Cumbria), 1960 . . . . £175/£75
The Northern Fells, Henry Marshall (Kendal, Cumbria), 1962 . . . . £175/£75
The North-Western Fells, Westmorland Gazette (Kendal, Cumbria), 1964 . . . . . . £175/£75
The Western Fells, Westmorland Gazette (Kendal, Cumbria), 1966 . . . . . . £175/£75

'Lakeland Sketchbooks'
A Lakeland Sketchbook, Westmorland Gazette (Kendal, Cumbria), 1969 . . . . . . £75/£25
A Second Lakeland Sketchbook, Westmorland Gazette (Kendal, Cumbria), 1970 . . . . . £50/£20
A Third Lakeland Sketchbook, Westmorland Gazette (Kendal, Cumbria), 1971 . . . . . £45/£15
A Fourth Lakeland Sketchbook, Westmorland Gazette (Kendal, Cumbria), 1972 . . . . . £45/£15
A Fifth Lakeland Sketchbook, Westmorland Gazette (Kendal, Cumbria), 1973 . . . . . £45/£15

Scottish Mountain Drawings
The Northern Highlands, Westmorland Gazette (Kendal, Cumbria), 1974 . . . . . . £50/£20
The North-West Highlands, Westmorland Gazette (Kendal, Cumbria), 1976 . . . . . . £40/£15
The Western Highlands, Westmorland Gazette (Kendal, Cumbria), 1976 . . . . . . £40/£15
The Central Highlands, Westmorland Gazette (Kendal, Cumbria), 1977 . . . . . . £40/£15
The Eastern Highlands, Westmorland Gazette (Kendal, Cumbria), 1978 . . . . . . £40/£15
The Islands, Westmorland Gazette (Kendal, Cumbria), 1979 . . . . £40/£15

Others
Fellwanderer, The Story Behind the Guidebooks, Westmorland Gazette (Kendal, Cumbria), 1966 . £30/£10
Pennine Way Companion, Westmorland Gazette (Kendal, Cumbria), 1968 . . . . . . £75/£25
Walks in Limestone Country, Westmorland Gazette (Kendal, Cumbria), 1970 . . . . . £50/£20
Walks on the Howgill Fells, Westmorland Gazette (Kendal, Cumbria), 1972 . . . . . . £45/£15
A Coast to Coast Walk, St Bees Head to Robin Hood's Bay, Westmorland Gazette (Kendal, Cumbria), 1973 . £45/£15
The Outlying Fells of Lakeland, Westmorland Gazette (Kendal, Cumbria), 1974 . . . . . £45/£15
Westmorland Heritage, Westmorland Gazette (Kendal, Cumbria), 1974 (1,000 signed copies) . . £500/£200
ditto, Westmorland Gazette (Kendal, Cumbria), 1988 £20/£5
A Dales Sketchbook, Westmorland Gazette (Kendal, Cumbria), 1976 . . . . £45/£15
Kendal in the Nineteenth Century, Westmorland Gazette (Kendal, Cumbria), 1977 . . . . £75/£15
A Second Dales Sketchbook, Westmorland Gazette (Kendal, Cumbria), 1978 . . . . . . £40/£15
A Furness Sketchbook, Westmorland Gazette (Kendal, Cumbria), 1978 . . . . £40/£15
Walks from Ratty, Ravenglass and Eskdale Railway Co, 1978 . . . . £40/£15

A Second Furness Sketchbook, Westmorland Gazette (Kendal, Cumbria), 1979 . . . . . £40/£15
Three Westmorland Rivers, Westmorland Gazette (Kendal, Cumbria), 1979 . . . . . . £40/£15
A Lune Sketchbook, Westmorland Gazette (Kendal, Cumbria), 1980 . . . . £40/£15
A Ribble Sketchbook, Westmorland Gazette (Kendal, Cumbria), 1980 . . . . £40/£15
An Eden Sketchbook, Westmorland Gazette (Kendal, Cumbria), 1980 . . . . £40/£15
Lakeland Mountain Drawings, Westmorland Gazette (Kendal, Cumbria), 1980 (5 vols) . . . £40/£15 each
Welsh Mountain Drawings, Westmorland Gazette (Kendal, Cumbria), 1981 . . . . . . £40/£15
A Bowland Sketchbook, Westmorland Gazette (Kendal, Cumbria), 1981 . . . . £40/£15
A North Wales Sketchbook, Westmorland Gazette (Kendal, Cumbria), 1982 . . . . . . £40/£15
A Wyre Sketchbook, Westmorland Gazette (Kendal, Cumbria), 1982 . . . . £35/£10
A South Wales Sketchbook, Westmorland Gazette (Kendal, Cumbria), 1983 . . . . . . £35/£10
Wainwright in Lakeland, Abbott Hall Art Gallery (Kendal, Cumbria), 1983 (100 leather-bound, signed copies) . £500
ditto, Abbott Hall Art Gallery (Kendal, Cumbria), 1983 (signed, numbered copies) . . . . £300/£200
A Peak District Sketchbook, Westmorland Gazette (Kendal, Cumbria), 1984 . . . . . . £35/£10
Fellwalking with Wainwright, Joseph (London), 1984 (photographs by Derry Brabbs) . . . . £20/£5
Old Roads of Eastern Lakeland, Westmorland Gazette (Kendal, Cumbria), 1985 . . . . . £15/£5
Wainwright on the Pennine Way, Joseph (London), 1985 (photographs by Derry Brabbs) . . . . £15/£5
A Pennine Journey, Joseph (London), 1986 . £15/£5
Wainwright's Coast to Coast Walk, Joseph (London), 1987 (photographs by Derry Brabbs) . . . . £15/£5
Ex-Fellwanderer, Westmorland Gazette (Kendal, Cumbria), 1987 . . . . £15/£5
Wainwright in Scotland, Joseph (London), 1988 (photographs by Derry Brabbs) . . . . £15/£5
Fellwalking with a Camera, Westmorland Gazette (Kendal, Cumbria), 1988 . . . . . . £15/£5
Wainwright on the Lakeland Mountain Passes, Joseph (London), 1989 (photographs by Derry Brabbs) . £15/£5
Wainwright in the Limestone Dales, Joseph (London), 1991 (photographs by Ed Geldard) . . . . £10/£5
Wainwright's Favourite Lakeland Mountains, Joseph (London), 1991 (photographs by Derry Brabbs) . £10/£5
Wainwright in the Valleys of Lakeland, Joseph (London), 1992 (photographs by Derry Brabbs) . . £10/£5
Memoirs of a Fellwanderer, Joseph (London), 1993 £10/£5
Wainwright: His Tour of the Lake District, Whitsuntide, 1931, Joseph (London), 1993 (photographs by Ed Geldard) . . . . £10/£5
The Walker's Log Book, Joseph (London), 1993 . £10/£5

Other Titles Illustrated by Wainwright
Inside the Real Lakeland, by A.H. Griffin, Guardian Press (Preston, Lancs), 1961 . . . . . £25/£10
Scratch and Co., by Molly Lefebure, Gollancz (London), 1968 . . . . £20/£5
The Hunting of Wilberforce Pike, by Molly Lefebure, Gollancz (London), 1970 . . . . . . £15/£5

The Plague Dogs, by Richard Adams, Allen Lane (London), 1977 . . . . £15/£5

Guide to the View from Scafel Pike, Chris Jesty Panoramas (Bridport, Dorset), 1978 . . . £15

A.E. WAITE
(b.1857 d.1942)

An occultist, poet, bohemian and mystic, Waite's contribution to occult literature is voluminous. He was born in America but brought up in England, joining the Hermetic Order of the Golden Dawn in 1891. He became Grand Master in 1903. A number of his volumes on the occult have remained in print to the present day.

Principal Works

The Real History of The Rosicrucians, George Redway (London), 1887 . . . . £85

A Handbook of Cartomancy, George Redway (London), 1889 (pseud 'Grand Orient') £100

ditto, George Redway (London), 1889 (with the 16pp 'Chapter' advertisement) £400

The Interior Life from The Standpoint of The Mystics, 'Light' (London), [1891] £200

The Occult Sciences, Kegan Paul, Trench, Trübner and Co. (London), 1891 . . . . . £65

Azoth: or The Star in The East, Theosophical Publishing Society (London), 1893 . . . . . £75

Devil-Worship in France, George Redway (London), 1896 . . . . £75

The Book of Black Magic and Pacts, Redway (London), 1898 (500 copies) £500

The Life of Louis Claude de Saint-Martin, Philip Wellby (London), 1901 . . . . . £75

The Doctrine and Literature of The Kabalah, Theosophical Publishing Society (London), 1902. . . . . £75

Studies in Mysticism, Hodder & Stoughton (London), 1906 . . . . £60

The Hidden Church of The Holy Graal, Rebman Ltd (London), 1909 . . . . £90

The Key to The Tarot, William Rider & Son Ltd (London), 1910 . . . . £25

ditto, William Rider & Son Ltd (London), 1910 (with the Tarot pack, first printing only, in box). £500

The Pictorial Key to The Tarot, William Rider & Son Ltd (London), 1911 . . . . . . £75

The Book of Ceremonial Magic, William Rider and Son Ltd (London), 1911 . . . . . . £90

The Secret Tradition in Freemasonry, Rebman Ltd (London), 1911 . . . . . £250/£125

The Secret Doctrine in Israel, William Rider & Son Ltd (London), 1913 . . . .£100

The Way of Divine Union, William Rider & Son Ltd (London), 1915 . . . . £75

Deeper Aspects of Masonic Symbolism, privately printed (London), 1915 . . . . £75

New Encyclopaedia of Freemasonry, William Rider & Son Ltd (London), 1921 . . . . . . £90/£45

Robert Fludd and Freemasonry, offprint (1922) . . £45

Raymond Lully, William Rider & Son Ltd (London), 1922 . . . . £75/£25

Saint-Martin, William Rider & Son Ltd (London), 1922 . . . . £65/£25

Lamps of Western Mysticism, Kegan Paul, Trench, Trübner and Co. (London), 1923 . . . . . £60/£35

The Brotherhood of The Rosy Cross, William Rider & Son Ltd (London), 1924 . . . . . .£150/£75

Emblematic Freemasonry, William Rider & Son Ltd (London), 1925 . . . . . . £45/£20

The Secret Tradition in Alchemy, Kegan Paul, Trench, Trübner and Co. (London), 1926 . . £90/£45

The Holy Kabbalah, William & Norgate Ltd (London), 1929 . . . . £90/£50

The Holy Graal, William Rider & Son Ltd (London), 1933 . . . .£120/£50

The Secret Tradition in Freemasonry, Rider & Co. (London), 1937 . . . .£125/£75

Shadows of Life and Thought, Selwyn & Blount (London), 1938 . . . . £90/£50

Poetry

An Ode to Astronomy and Other Poems, 1877?, (100 copies) £2,000

A Lyric of The Fairyland, Catty (London), 1879 . .£650

Israfel, Letters, Visions and Poems, E.W. Allen (London), 1886 . . . .£150

ditto, James Elliot & Co. (London), 1894 (enlarged edition) £65

A Soul's Comedy, George Redway (London), 1887 . £75

Lucasta, James Burns (London), [1890] . £75

A Book of Mystery and Vision, Philip Wellby (London), 1902 . . . . £65

ditto, Philip Wellby (London), 1902 (10 signed copies on Japanese vellum). £350

Strange Houses of Sleep, Philip Wellby (London), 1906 (250 signed, numbered copies, with Arthur Machen) .£200

The Collected Poems of Arthur Edward Waite, Rider (London), 1914 (2 vols) . . . . £90/£50

The Book of The Holy Graal, J.M. Watkins (London), 1921 (500 copies) . . . . £75/£35

The Open Vision, Shakespeare Head Press (London), 1959 (500 copies) . . . . £30/£10

Fiction

Prince Starbeam, James Burns (London), 1889 . . £75

The Golden Stairs, Theosophical Publishing Society (London), 1893 . . . . £65

Belle and The Dragon, James Elliot (London), 1894 . £65

The Quest of The Golden Stairs, Theosophical Publishing House Ltd (London), [1927] . . . . . £35/£15

Others

The House of The Hidden Light, privately printed (London), 1904 (with Arthur Machen, 3 copies) . . . £5,000

ditto, Tartarus/Ferret (Carlton-in-Coverdale, North Yorks/ London), 2003 . . . .£100/£45

The Hermetic Text Society, Philip Wellby (London), 1907 . . . . £50

Steps to The Crown, Philip Wellby (London), 1906 . £45

DEREK WALCOTT
(b.1930)

Walcott is a West Indies poet, playwright, writer and visual artist. He won the Nobel Prize for Literature in 1992 'for a poetic oeuvre of great luminosity, sustained by a historical vision, the outcome of a multicultural commitment'.

Poetry

25 Poems, Guardian Commercial Printery (Port-of-Spain, Trinidad), 1948 . . . . £2,000
Epitaph for the Young: XXI Cantos, Advocate (Barbados), 1949 . . . . £1,500
Poems, City Printery (Kingston, Jamaica), 1951 . £1,000
In A Green Night: Poems 1948-1960, Jonathan Cape (London), 1962 . . . . . . £350/£65
Selected Poems, Farrar, Straus & Company (New York), 1964 . . . . £125/£20
The Castaway And Other Poems, Farrar, Straus (New York), 1965 . . . . £125/£20
ditto, Jonathan Cape (London), 1965 . . . £125/£20
The Gulf And Other Poems, Jonathan Cape (London), 1969
. . . . £65/£10
ditto, Farrar, Straus & Giroux (New York), 1970 . £30/£10
Another Life, Farrar, Straus & Giroux (New York), 1973 .
. . . . £45/£10
ditto, Farrar, Straus & Giroux (New York), 1973 (pbk) £10
ditto, Jonathan Cape (London), 1973 . . . £40/£10
Sea Grapes, Jonathan Cape (London), 1976 (pbk) . . £10
ditto, Farrar, Straus & Giroux (New York), 1976 . £30/£5
ditto, Farrar, Straus & Giroux (New York), 1976 (pbk) . £5
Selected Verse, Heinemann (London), 1976 (pbk) . . £10
The Star-Apple Kingdom, Farrar, Straus & Giroux (New York), 1979 . . . . £30/£5
ditto, Jonathan Cape (London), 1980 (pbk) . . . £10
The Fortunate Traveller, Farrar, Straus & Giroux (New York), 1981 . . . . £30/£5
ditto, Faber (London), 1982 (pbk) £10
Earth, The Silver Hands Press (New York), 1981 (12 signed, numbered copies; broadside) £200
Selected Poetry, Heinemann Educational (London), 1981 (pbk) £15
ditto, Heinemann Educational (London), 1993 (pbk; revised)
. . . . £10
Wales, Bookslinger Editions/Toothpaste Press (St Paul, MN), 1982 (90 signed, numbered copies; broadside) . £75
The Caribbean Poetry of Derek Walcott & The Art of Romare Bearden, Limited Editions Club (New York), 1983 (2000 numbered copies signed by Walcott and Bearden; slipcase; original numbered lithograph by Bearden laid in) . . . . . . £200/£100
Midsummer, Farrar, Straus & Giroux (New York), 1984 .
. . . . £30/£5
ditto, Faber (London/Boston), 1984 (pbk) . . . £10
Collected Poems 1948-1984, Farrar, Straus & Giroux (New York), 1986 . . . . £45/£10
ditto, Farrar, Straus & Giroux (New York), 1986 (in Faber d/w) . . . . £45/£10
ditto, Faber (London), 1990 (pbk) £10
The Arkansas Testament, Farrar, Straus, Giroux (New York), 1987 . . . . £15/£5
Salsa, Minnesota Center for Book Arts (Minneapolis, MN), 1988 (150 signed, numbered copies; broadside) . . £45

Omeros, Farrar, Straus & Giroux (New York), 1990 £15/£5
ditto, Farrar, Straus & Giroux (New York), 1990 (sixth printing with a signed extra leaf bound in for presentation to graduates). . . . . £50/£40
ditto, Faber (London), 1990 . . . . . £20/£5
Poems 1965-1980, Jonathan Cape (London), 1992 . £30/£5
The Bounty: Poems, Farrar, Straus & Giroux (New York), 1997 . . . . £10/£5
ditto, Faber (London), 1997 . . . . . £10/£5
Tieplo's Hound, Farrar, Straus & Giroux (New York), 2000
. . . . £10/£5
ditto, Faber (London), 2000. . . . . . £15/£5
ditto, Faber (London), 2000 (100 signed, numbered copies; acetate d/w) . . . . . . £150/£125
The Bounty, Faulkner House (New Orleans), 2002 (100 signed, numbered copies; broadside) £50
The Prodigal, Farrar, Straus Giroux (New York), 2004 (pbk)
. . . . £5
ditto, Faber (London), 2005. . . . . . £10/£5
White Egrets, Farrar, Straus Giroux (New York), 2010. .
. . . . £10/£5
ditto, Faber (London), 2010. . . . . . £10/£5

Plays

Henri Christophe; A Chronicle in Seven Scenes, Advocate (Barbados), 1950 (wraps) £1,250
Harry Dernier, Advocate (Barbados), 1952 (wraps) £1,000
The Sea at Dauphin, A Play in One Act, Univ College of The West Indies (Port-of-Spain), 1954 (wraps) £1,000
ditto, Univ College of the West Indies (no place), 1958 (wraps) £125
Ione: A Play in Music, Extra Mural Dept., Univ College of the West Indies (Mona, Jamaica), 1957 (wraps) . £750
The Charlatan, Extra Mural Dept., Univ College of the West Indies (Mona, Jamaica), 1957 (wraps) . . . £350
Ti-Jen: A Play In One Act, Extra Mural Dept, Univ College of the West Indies (Kingston, Jamaica), 1958 £750
Drums and Colours, Caribbean Quarterly (Port-of-Spain, Trinidad), 1961 ('Special Issue' of the Caribbean Quarterly; wraps). £450
Malcauchon: or The Six In the Rain (sic), Univ of the West Indies (Trinidad), 1966 (wraps) £250
Dream On Monkey Mountain And Other Plays, Farrar, Straus & Giroux (New York), 1970. . . . £30/£5
ditto, Jonathan Cape (London), 1972. . . . £35/£10
The Joker of Seville [and] *O Babylon; Two Plays*, Farrar, Straus & Giroux (New York), 1978. . . £45/£10
ditto, Farrar, Straus & Giroux (New York), 1978 (pbk). £10
ditto, Jonathan Cape (London), 1979 (pbk) . . . £10
The Joker of Seville and O Babylon!: Two Plays, Farrar, Straus & Giroux (New York), 1978. . . . £45/£10
ditto, Jonathan Cape (London), 1979 (pbk) . . . £10
Remembrance & Pantomime, Farrar, Straus & Giroux (New York), 1980 . . . . £30/£5
Three Plays: The Last Carnival, Beef, No Chicken [and] *A Branch of the Blue Nile*, Farrar, Straus & Giroux (New York), 1986 . . . . £20/£5
The Odyssey: A Stage Version, Farrar, Straus & Giroux (New York), 1993 . . . . £15/£5
ditto, Faber (London), 1993 (pbk) £10
The Capeman: A Musical, Farrar, Straus & Giroux (New York), 1998 (written with Paul Simon) . . £10/£5
ditto, Farrar, Straus & Giroux (New York), 1998 (pbk). £5

Walker and the Ghost Dance, Farrar, Straus Giroux (New York), 2002 (pbk) £5
The Haitian Trilogy: Plays, Farrar, Straus Giroux (New York), 2002 (pbk) £5

Others
The Poet in the Theatre, The Poetry Book Society/South Bank Centre (London), 1990 (stapled wraps) . . £25
The Antilles, Fragments of Epic Memory, Farrar, Straus Giroux (New York), 1993 . . . . . £10/£5
ditto, Faber (London), 1993 (pbk) £10
Conversations With Derek Walcott, Univ Press of Mississippi (Jackson, MS), 1996 . . . . £20/£5
ditto, Univ Press of Mississippi (Jackson, MS), 1996 (pbk) .
. . . . £5
Homage to Robert Frost, Farrar, Straus Giroux (New York), 1996 (written with Joseph Brodsky and Seamus Heaney) .
. . . . £10/£5
ditto, Faber (London), 1997 (pbk) £5
What The Twilight Says, Farrar, Straus Giroux (New York), 1998 . . . . £10/£5
ditto, Faber (London/Boston), 1998 (pbk) . . . £5

ALICE WALKER
(b.1944)

A novelist, poet, critic and essay-writer, Walker's third novel, *The Color Purple* secured her a Pulitzer Prize and a place amongst America's foremost living writers. Her work concentrates on the struggles of African-American women against racism, sexism and violence, emphasising their intrinsic strength and the importance of their cultural heritage

Novels
The Third Life of Grange Copeland, Harcourt, Brace, Jovanovich (New York), 1970 . . . . £150/£20
ditto, Women's Press (London), 1985 . . . £40/£10
Meridian, Harcourt, Brace, Jovanovich (New York), 1976 .
. . . . £125/£15
ditto, Deutsch (London), 1976 . . . . £75/£15
The Color Purple, Harcourt, Brace, Jovanovich (New York), 1982 . . . . £300/£30
ditto, Women's Press (London), 1983 . . . £50/£10
The Temple of My Familiar, Harcourt, Brace, Jovanovich (New York), 1989 . . . . . . £15/£5
ditto, Harcourt, Brace, Jovanovich (New York), 1989 (500 signed, numbered copies, slipcase) . . . £50/£35
ditto, Women's Press (London), 1989 . . . £15/£5
Possessing the Secret of Joy, Harcourt Brace (New York), 1992 . . . . £10/£5
ditto, Harcourt, Brace, Jovanovich (New York), 1992 (250 signed, numbered copies, slipcase) . . . £50/£35
ditto, Cape (London), 1992 . . . . . £10/£5
By the Light of My Father's Smile, Random House (New York), 1998 . . . . £20/£5
ditto, Women's Press (London), 1998 . . . £15/£5
Now Is the Time to Open Your Heart, Random House (New York), 2004 . . . . £10/£5
ditto, Weidenfeld & Nicolson, 2004 . . . £10/£5

Short Stories
In Love & Trouble: Stories of Black Women, Harcourt, Brace, Jovanovich (New York), 1973 . . . £125/£25
ditto, Women's Press (London), 1984 . . . £65/£15
You Can't Keep a Good Woman Down, Harcourt, Brace, Jovanovich (New York), 1981 . . . . £75/£15
ditto, Women's Press (London), 1982 . . . £45/£15
The Complete Stories, Women's Press (London), 1994 .
. . . . £10/£5
Alice Walker Banned, Aunt Lute Books (San Francisco, CA), 1996 . . . . £15/£5
The Way Forward Is with a Broken Heart, Random House (New York), 2000 . . . . . . £10/£5
ditto, Women's Press (London), 2000 . . . £10/£5

Poetry
Once, Harcourt, Brace & World (New York), 1968 £400/£45
ditto, Women's Press (London), 1986 (pbk) . . £5
Revolutionary Petunias and Other Poems, Harcourt, Brace, Jovanovich (New York), 1973 . . . . £225/£30
ditto, Women's Press (London), 1988 (pbk) . . £10
Good Night, Willie Lee, I'll See You in the Morning, Dial Press (New York), 1979 . . . . . £200/£25
ditto, Women's Press (London), 1987 (pbk) . . £10
Horses Make a Landscape Look More Beautiful: Poems, Harcourt, Brace, Jovanovich (New York), 1984 . £40/£10
ditto, Women's Press (London), 1985 . . . £25/£5
Her Blue Body Everything We Know: Earthling Poems 1965-1990, Harcourt, Brace, Jovanovich (New York), 1991
. . . . £10/£5
ditto, Harcourt, Brace, Jovanovich (New York), 1991 (111 signed copies, slipcase) . . . . . £90/£65
ditto, Women's Press (London), 1991 . . . £25/£5
Absolute Trust in the Goodness of the Earth, Random House (New York), 2003 . . . . . £10/£5
ditto, Women's Press (London), 2003 . . . £10/£5
A Poem Travelled Down My Arm: Poems And Drawings, Random House (New York), 2003 . . . £10/£5
Collected Poems, Pheonix (London), 2005 (pbk) . . £5

Children's Books
Langston Hughes, American Poet, Crowell (New York), 1974 . . . . £500/£45
To Hell with Dying, Harcourt, Brace, Jovanovich (New York), 1988 . . . . £20/£5
ditto, Hodder & Stoughton (London), 1988 . . £20/£5
Finding the Green Stone, Harcourt, Brace, Jovanovich (New York), 1991 . . . . £20/£5
ditto, Hodder & Stoughton (London), 1991 . . £15/£5

Others
In Search of Our Mother's Gardens: Womanist Prose, Harcourt, Brace, Jovanovich (New York), 1983 . £25/£10
ditto, Women's Press (London), 1984 . . . £20/£5
Living by the Word: Selected Writings 1973-1987, Harcourt, Brace, Jovanovich (New York), 1988 . . £15/£5
ditto, Women's Press (London), 1988 (pbk) . . £5
Warrior Marks: Female Genital Mutilation and the Sexual Blinding of Women, Harcourt Brace (New York), 1993 (with Pratibha Parmar) . . . . . £15/£5
The Same River Twice: Honoring the Difficult, Scribner's (New York), 1996 . . . . . . £20/£5
ditto, Women's Press (London), 1996 . . . £20/£5

Anything We Love Can Be Saved: A Writer's Activism, Random House (New York), 1997 . . . . £15/£5

ditto, Women's Press (London), 1997 (pbk) . . . £5

Sent By Earth: A Message from the Grandmother Spirit After the Bombing of the World Trade Center And Pentagon, Seven Stories Press (New York), 2001 (pbk) £5

We Are The Ones We Have Been Waiting For: Light In A Time of Darkness, New Press (New York), 2006   £10/£5

Overcoming Speechlessness : a poet encounters the horror in Rwanda, Eastern Congo, and Palestine/Israel, Seven Stories Press (New York), 2010 (pbk) £5

World Has Changed: Conversations with Alice Walker, The New Press (New York), 2010 . . . . . £10/£5

EDGAR WALLACE
(b.1875 d.1932)

Wallace's output of books was vast, and he made no attempt to disguise the fact that it was popular rather than critical success that he craved. In this ambition he was incredibly successful. There is a story to the effect that his house-guests sometimes observed him in the act of dictating a whole novel over the course of a weekend. He was also a very popular playwright

Novels

The Four Just Men, Tallis Press (London), 1905 (numbered competition slip) £100

ditto, Tallis Press (London), 1906 (includes chapter 12, a letter from Manfred as solution) £30

ditto, Tallis Press (London), 1911 (includes full chapter 12) £20

ditto, Small Maynard (Boston), 1920 . . . £75/£20

Angel Esquire, Arrowsmith (London), 1908 . . . £45

ditto, Holt (New York), 1908 . . . . . . £40

The Council of Justice, Ward Lock (London), 1908 . £100

Captain Tatham of Tatham Island, Gale & Polden (London), 1909 . . . . £200

ditto, as ***The Island of Galloping Gold***, Newnes (London), 1916 . . . . £25

ditto, as ***Eve's Island***, Newnes (London), 1926 (pbk) . £30

The Duke in the Suburbs, Ward Lock (London), 1909. £100

The Nine Bears, Ward Lock (London), 1910 . . . £100

ditto, as ***The Other Man***, Dodd, Mead (New York), 1911 . . . . £75

ditto, as ***Silinski, Master Criminal***, World Syndicate (New York), 1930 . . . . £35/£5

ditto, as ***The Cheaters***, Digit (London), 1964 (pbk) . £10

Private Selby, Ward Lock (London), 1912 . . . £100

Grey Timothy, Ward Lock (London), 1913 . . . £100

ditto, as ***Pallard the Punter***, Ward Lock (London), 1914 (pbk) £75

The River of Stars, Ward Lock (London), 1913 . . £100

The Fourth Plague, Ward Lock (London), 1913 . . £100

ditto, Doubleday Doran (New York), 1930 . . £65/£15

The Melody of Death, Arrowsmith (London), 1915 . £125

ditto, Dial Press (New York), 1927 . . . . £65/£25

1925: The Story of a Fatal Peace, Newnes (London), 1915 (pbk) £125

The Man Who Bought London, Ward Lock (London), 1915 . . . . £75

The Clue of the Twisted Candle, Small Maynard (Boston), 1916 . . . . £75

ditto, Newnes (London), 1917 . . . . . . £75

A Debt Discharged, Ward Lock (London), 1916 . . £75

The Tomb of Ts'in, Ward Lock (London), 1916 . . £400

The Just Men of Cordova, Ward Lock (London), 1917 £75

ditto, Doubleday Doran (New York), 1929 . . £65/£15

The Secret House, Ward Lock (London), 1917 . . £75

ditto, Small Maynard (Boston), 1919 . . . . £75

Kate Plus Ten, Small Maynard (Boston), 1917 . . £100

ditto, Ward Lock (London), 1919 . . . . . £100

Down Under Donovan, Ward Lock (London), 1918 . £85

Those Folk of Bulboro, Ward Lock (London), 1918 . £85

The Man Who Knew, Small Maynard (Boston), 1918 . £75

ditto, Newnes (London), 1919 . . . . . . £75

The Green Rust, Ward Lock (London), 1919 . . . £65

ditto, Small Maynard (Boston), 1920 . . . £250/£30

Jack O' Judgement, Ward Lock (London), 1920 . £500/£50

ditto, Small Maynard (Boston), 1921 . . . £350/£35

The Daffodil Mystery, Ward Lock (London), 1920 £750/£85

ditto, as ***The Daffodil Murder***, Small Maynard (Boston), 1921 . . . . £500/£50

The Book of All Power, Ward Lock (London), 1921 . . . . £450/£50

The Angel of Terror, Hodder & Stoughton (London), 1922. . . . . £450/£50

ditto, Small Maynard (Boston), 1922 . . . £350/£40

Sandi, The King-Maker, Ward Lock (London), 1922 . . . . £450/£40

Captains of Souls, Small Maynard (Boston), 1922. £450/£50

ditto, John Long (London), 1923 . . . . £500/£65

The Flying Fifty-Five, Hutchinson (London), 1922 £650/£85

The Crimson Circle, Hodder & Stoughton (London), 1922 . . . . £450/£45

ditto, Doubleday Doran (New York), 1929 . £200/£20

Mr. Justice Maxell, Ward Lock (London), 1922 £600/£100

The Valley of Ghosts, Odhams (London), 1922 . £450/£50

ditto, Small Maynard (Boston), 1923 . . . £350/£40

The Clue of the New Pin, Hodder & Stoughton (London), 1923 . . . . £400/£45

ditto, Small Maynard (Boston), 1923 . . . £200/£35

The Books of Bart, Ward Lock (London), 1923 . £450/£45

The Green Archer, Hodder & Stoughton (London), 1923 . . . . £425/£40

ditto, Small Maynard (Boston), 1924 . . . £225/£30

Blue Hand, Small Maynard (Boston), 1923 £450/£100

ditto, Ward Lock (London), 1925 . . . . £350/£75

The Fellowship of the Frog, Small Maynard (Boston), 1923 . . . . £450/£75

ditto, Ward Lock (London), 1925 . . . . £500/£85

The Missing Million, John Long (London), 1923 . £500/£85

ditto, as ***The Missing Millions***, Small Maynard (Boston), 1925 . . . . £350/£65

The Dark Eyes of London, Ward Lock (London), 1924 . . . . £450/£50

ditto, Doubleday Doran (New York), 1929 . £350/£45

The Sinister Man, Hodder & Stoughton (London), 1924 . . . . £300/£45

ditto, Small Maynard (Boston), 1925 . . . £200/£25

Room 13, John Long (London), 1924 . . . £450/£85

The Three Oak Mystery, Ward Lock (London), 1924 . . . . £450/£85

Double Dan, Hodder & Stoughton (London), 1924 £300/£45

HALF PRICE BOOKS
475 Sherry Lane
Fort Worth, TX 76114
817-732-4111

10/07/12 02:48 PM
#00003/SHAL003/00003

CUSTOMER: 0000000110
SALE: 0002049105

1	@20.00 NOST	20.00
	5784-(Nostalgia)	
1	@9.99 TITP	9.99
	10055736-Guide to First Edition Pri	

SHIP/HAND	0.00
TAX (8.25% on $0.00)	0.00
TOTAL	29.99

PAYMENT TYPE
VISA (**7271/REF:38756991)   29.99
AUTH CODE:588661

PAYMENT TOTAL	$	29.99
CHANGE DUE	$	0.00

THANK YOU!

Receipt is BPA free, recycled content

RETURNS-----ID REQUIRED FOR ANY REFUND

END OF TRANSACTION

by check are available after twelve (12) business days, and are then subject to the time limitations stated above. Please include original packaging and price tag when making a return. Proper I.D. and phone number may be required, where permitted. We reserve the right to limit or decline refunds.

*Gift cards cannot be returned for cash, except as required by law.

The personal information you provide is confidential and will not be sold, rented or disclosed to a third party for commercial purposes.

REFUND POLICY

Cash refunds and charge card credits on all merchandise* are available within 7 days of purchase with receipt. Merchandise charged to a credit card will be credited to your account. Exchange or store credit will be issued for merchandise returned within 30 days with receipt. Cash refunds for purchases made by check are available after twelve (12) business days, and are then subject to the time limitations stated above. Please include original packaging and price tag when making a return. Proper I.D. and phone number may be required, where permitted. We reserve the right to limit or decline refunds.

*Gift cards cannot be returned for cash, except as required by law.

The personal information you provide is confidential and will not be sold, rented or disclosed to a third party for commercial purposes.

REFUND POLICY

ditto, as *Diana of Kara-Kara*, Small Maynard (Boston), 1924 . . . . £200/£25
The Face in the Night, John Long (London), 1924 £450/£45
ditto, Doubleday Doran (New York), 1929 . . £350/£40
Flat 2, Doubleday Doran (New York), 1924 (pbk) . . £75
ditto, John Long (London), 1927 . . . . . £100/£15
The Strange Countess, Hodder & Stoughton (London), 1925 . . . . £250/£15
ditto, Small Maynard (Boston), 1926 . . . . £150/£10
A King by Night, John Long (London), 1925 . . £450/£50
ditto, Doubleday Page (New York), 1926 . . £350/£40
The Gaunt Stranger, Hodder & Stoughton (London), 1925 . . . . £300/£35
ditto, as *The Ringer*, Doubleday Page (New York), 1926 . . . . £150/£20
The Three Just Men, Hodder & Stoughton (London), 1925 . . . . £200/£15
ditto, Doubleday Doran (New York), 1929 . . . £200/£15
The Man from Morocco, John Long (London), 1925 . . . . £400/£40
ditto, as *The Black*, Doubleday Doran (New York), 1930 . . . . £150/£15
The Daughters of the Night, Newnes (London), 1925 (pbk) £100
The Hairy Arm, Small Maynard (Boston), 1925 . £300/£45
ditto, as *The Avenger*, John Long (London), 1926 . £450/£60
The Door with Seven Locks, Hodder & Stoughton (London), 1926 . . . . £200/£15
ditto, Doubleday Doran (New York), 1926 . £150/£10
We Shall See, Hodder & Stoughton (London), 1926 . . . . £200/£15
ditto, as *The Gaol-Breakers*, Doubleday Doran (New York), 1931 . . . . £100/£10
The Black Abbot, Hodder & Stoughton (London), 1926 . . . . £200/£15
ditto, Doubleday Page (New York), 1927 . . . £100/£10
The Terrible People, Hodder & Stoughton (London), 1926 . . . . £100/£10
ditto, Doubleday Page (New York), 1926 . . £100/£10
The Day of Uniting, Hodder & Stoughton (London), 1926 . . . . £200/£15
ditto, Mystery League (New York), 1930 . . £100/£10
Penelope of the Polyantha, Hodder & Stoughton (London), 1926 . . . . £200/£15
The Joker, Hodder & Stoughton (London), 1926 £200/£10
ditto, as *The Colossus*, Doubleday Doran (New York), 1932 . . . . £125/£10
The Square Emerald, Hodder & Stoughton (London), 1926 . . . . £200/£15
ditto, as *The Girl from Scotland Yard*, Doubleday Doran (New York), 1927 . . . . £125/£15
The Yellow Snake, Hodder & Stoughton (London), 1926 . . . . £200/£15
Barbara on Her Own, Newnes (London), [1926] . £150/£15
The Million Dollar Story, Newnes (London), 1926 (pbk) £100
The Northing Tramp, Hodder & Stoughton (London), 1926 . . . . £150/£15
ditto, Doubleday Doran (New York), 1929 . £100/£10
The Hand of Power, John Long (London), 1926 . £250/£75
ditto, Mystery League (New York), 1930 . . £125/£15
The Traitor's Gate, Hodder & Stoughton (London), 1927 . . . . £150/£10
ditto, Doubleday Page (New York), 1927 . . £100/£10

The Man Who Was Nobody, Ward Lock (London), 1927 . . . . £300/£75
The Feathered Serpent, Hodder & Stoughton (London), 1927 . . . . £200/£20
ditto, Doubleday Doran (New York), 1928 . £125/£15
Terror Keep, Hodder & Stoughton (London), 1927 £125/£10
ditto, Doubleday Page (New York), 1927 . . £120/£10
Big Foot, John Long (London), 1927 . . £200/£20
Number Six, Newnes (London), 1927 (pbk) . . £100
The Squeaker, Hodder & Stoughton (London), 1927 . . . . £125/£15
ditto, as *The Squealer*, Doubleday Doran (New York), 1928 . . . . £100/£10
The Forger, Hodder & Stoughton (London), 1927 . £200/£15
ditto, as *The Clever One*, Doubleday Doran (New York), 1928 . . . . £125/£10
The Double, Hodder & Stoughton (London), 1928 £125/£10
ditto, Doubleday Doran (New York), 1928 . £100/£10
The Thief in the Night, Readers Library (London), 1928 . . . . £75/£10
The Twister, John Long (London), 1928 . . £100/£10
ditto, Doubleday Page (New York), 1929 . . £75/£10
The Flying Squad, Hodder & Stoughton (London), 1928 . . . . £150/£10
ditto, Doubleday Doran (New York), 1928 . £10/£10
The Gunner, John Long (London), 1928 . . £100/£10
ditto, as *Gunman's Bluff*, Doubleday Doran (New York), 1929 . . . . £75/£10
Four Square Jane, Readers Library (London), 1929 . . . . £100/£10
ditto, World Wide (New York), 1929 . . . £75/£10
The India-Rubber Men, Hodder & Stoughton (London), 1929 . . . . £100/£10
ditto, Doubleday Doran (New York), 1930 . £65/£5
The Terror, Collins (London), 1929 . . . £75/£10
The Golden Hades, Collins (London), 1929 . £125/£10
The Green Ribbon, Hutchinson (London), 1929 . £300/£45
ditto, Doubleday Doran (New York), 1930 . £175/£25
Again the Ringer, Hodder & Stoughton (London), 1929 . . . . £100/£10
ditto, as *The Ringer Returns*, Doubleday Doran (New York), 1931 . . . . £75/£10
White Face, Hodder & Stoughton (London), 1930 . £100/£10
ditto, Doubleday Doran (New York), 1931 . £75/£10
The Calendar, Collins (London), 1930 . . £200/£15
ditto, Doubleday Doran (New York), 1931 . £150/£10
The Clue of the Silver Key, Hodder & Stoughton (London), 1930 . . . . £100/£10
ditto, as *The Silver Key*, Doubleday Doran (New York), 1930 . . . . £75/£10
The Lady of Ascot, Hutchinson (London), 1930 . £125/£15
The Devil Man, Collins (London), 1931 . . £650/£75
ditto, Doubleday Doran (New York), 1931 . £75/£15
On the Spot, John Long (London), 1931 . . £150/£15
ditto, Doubleday Doran (New York), 1931 . £100/£10
The Man at the Carlton, Hodder & Stoughton (London), 1931 . . . . £100/£10
ditto, Doubleday Doran (New York), 1932 . £75/£10
The Coat of Arms, Hutchinson (London), 1931 . £150/£10
ditto, as *The Arranways Mystery*, Doubleday Doran (New York), 1932 . . . . £125/£10
When the Gangs Came to London, John Long (London), 1932 . . . . £325/£100
ditto, Doubleday Doran (New York), 1932 . £250/£65

King Kong, Grosset & Dunlap (New York), 1932 (conceived by Wallace and Merian C. Cooper, written by Delos W. Lovelace) . . . . £4,000/£650

ditto, Corgi (London), 1966 (pbk) £10

The Frightened Lady, Hodder & Stoughton (London), 1932
. . . . £100/£10

ditto, as *The Mystery of the Frightened Lady*, Doubleday Doran (New York), 1933 . . . . £75/£10

The Man Who Changed His Name, Hodder & Stoughton (London), 1934 (with Robert Curtis) . . £350/£50

ditto, Doubleday Doran (New York), 1934 . £250/£25

The Mouthpiece, Hodder & Stoughton (London), 1935 (with Robert Curtis) . . . . . . £350/£50

ditto, Dodge (New York), 1936 . . . . £150/£15

Smoky Cell, Hodder & Stoughton (London), 1935 (with Robert Curtis) . . . . . . £250/£50

The Table, Hodder & Stoughton (London), 1936 (with Robert Curtis) . . . . . . £400/£50

The Sanctuary Island, Hutchinson (London), 1936 (with Robert Curtis) . . . . . . £300/£75

The Road to London, Kimber (London), 1986 . £15/£5

Short Stories

Smithy, Tallis Press (London), 1905 (card covers) . £200

Smithy Abroad, Hulton (London), 1909 (card covers) .£350

Sanders of the River, Ward Lock (London), 1911 . .£125

ditto, Doubleday Doran (New York), 1930 . £75/£15

The People of the River, Ward Lock (London), 1912 .£100

Smithy's Friend Nobby, Town Topics (London), 1914. £300

ditto, as *Nobby*, Newnes (London), [1916] . . . £25

The Admirable Carfew, Ward Lock (London), 1914 . £65

Bosambo of the River, Ward Lock (London), 1914 . £75

Bones, Ward Lock (London), 1915 . . . . £75

Smithy and the Hun, Pearson (London), 1915 (card covers)
. . . . £350

Smithy, Not to Mention Nobby Clark and Spud Murphy, Newnes (London), 1915 (card covers) £125

The Keepers of the King's Peace, Ward Lock (London), 1917 . . . . £75

Lieutenant Bones, Ward Lock (London), 1918 . . £75

Tam of the Scouts, Newnes (London), 1918 . . £75

ditto, as *Tam O' the Scoots*, Small Maynard (Boston), 1919
. . . . £65

The Fighting Scouts, Pearson (London), 1919 . . £75

The Adventures of Heine, Ward Lock (London), 1919. £75

Bones in London, Ward Lock (London), 1921 . £500/£75

Law of the Four Just Men, Hodder & Stoughton (London), 1921 . . . . £500/£45

ditto, as *Again the Three Just Men*, Doubleday Doran (New York), 1933 . . . . . . £200/£40

Chick, Ward Lock (London), 1923 . . . £400/£35

Bones of the River, Newnes (London), [1923] .£350/£35

Educated Evans, Webster (London), [1924] . £300/£30

The Mind of Mr. J.G. Reeder, Hodder & Stoughton (London), 1925 . . . . £250/£25

ditto, as *The Murder Book of Mr. J.G. Reeder*, Doubleday Doran (New York), 1929 . . . . £125/£15

More Educated Evans, Webster (London), [1926]. £250/£25

Sanders, Hodder & Stoughton (London), 1926 . £250/£25

ditto, as *Mr. Commissioner Sanders*, Doubleday Doran (New York), 1930 . . . . . £125/£15

The Brigand, Hodder & Stoughton (London), 1927 .
. . . . £125/£20

The Mixer, John Long (London), 1927 . . £125/£20

Good Evans, Webster (London), [1927] . . .£150/£15

Again the Three Just Men, Hodder & Stoughton (London), 1928 . . . . £150/£250

ditto, as *The Law of the 3 Just Men*, Doubleday Doran (New York), 1931 . . . . . . £65/£15

Again Sanders, Hodder & Stoughton (London), [1928]
. . . . £150/£15

ditto, Doubleday Doran (New York), 1929 . £75/£10

The Orator, Hutchinson (London), 1928 . . £200/£25

Elegant Edward, Readers Library (London), [1928] £75/£10

Forty Eight Short Stories, Newnes (London), 1929 £75/£10

Planetoid 127 and The Sweizer Pump, Readers Library (London), 1929 . . . . . . £65/£10

The Cat Burglar, Newnes (London), 1929 (pbk) . £65

Circumstantial Evidence, Newnes (London), 1929 (pbk) .
. . . . £65

ditto, as *Circumstantial Evidence and Other Stories*, World Syndicate (New York), 1934 . . . . £35/£10

Fighting Snub Reilly, Newnes (London), 1929 (pbk) . £65

ditto, as *Fighting Snub Reilly and Other Stories*, World Syndicate (New York), 1934 . . . . £35/£10

The Ghost of Down Hill, and The Queen of Sheba's Belt, Readers Library (London), 1929 . . £65/£10

The Little Green Man, Newnes (London), 1929 (pbk) . £65

The Prison-Breakers, Newnes (London), 1929 (pbk) . £65

Red Aces, Being Three Cases of Mr. Reeder, Hodder & Stoughton (London), 1929 . . . . £150/£15

ditto, Doubleday Doran (New York), 1930 . £100/£10

The Lone House Mystery, Collins (London), 1929. £150/£15

The Black, Readers Library (London), 1929 . £75/£10

ditto, Digit (London), 1962 (pbk) £5

For Information Received, Newnes (London), 1929 (pbk) .
. . . .£125

The Governor of Chi-Foo, Newnes (London), 1929 (pbk) .
. . . . £65

ditto, as *The Governor of Chi-Foo and Other Stories*, World Syndicate (New York), 1933 . . . . £35/£10

The Lady of Little Hell, Newnes (London), 1929 (pbk) £125

The Reporter, Readers Library (London), 1929 . £65/£10

The Big Four, Readers Library (London), 1929 . £65/£10

The Iron Grip, Readers Library (London), 1929 . £65/£10

Killer Kay, Newnes (London), 1930 (pbk) . . .£125

The Lady Called Nita, Newnes (London), 1930 (pbk) .£150

Mrs William Jones and Bill, Newnes (London), 1930 (pbk)
. . . .£125

The Guv'nor and Other Stories, Collins (London), 1932 .
. . . . £200/£20

ditto, as *Mr. Reeder Returns*, Doubleday Doran (New York), 1932 . . . . £150/£15

Sergeant Sir Peter, Chapman & Hall (London), 1932 .
. . . . £350/£35

ditto, Doubleday Doran (New York), 1933 . £250/£30

The Steward, Collins (London), 1932 . . £200/£20

Mr. J.G. Reeder Returns, Collins (London), 1934. £200/£15

The Last Adventure, Hutchinson (London), 1934 .£350/£35

The Woman from the East and Other Stories, Hutchinson (London), 1934 . . . . . . £250/£35

The Undisclosed Client, Digit (London), 1963 (pbk) . £5

The Man Who Married His Cook, White Lion (London), 1976 . . . . £30/£5

The Sooper and Others, Dent (London), 1984 . £10/£5

The Death Room: Strange and Startling Stories, Kimber (London), 1986 . . . . . . £10/£5

Poetry

The Mission that Failed, T. Maskew Miller (Capetown, South Africa), 1898 (pbk) £250
Nicholson's Nek, Eastern Press (London), 1900 . . £150
War and Other Poems, Eastern Press (London), 1900 . £150
Writ in the Barracks, Methuen (London), 1900 . . £100

Others

Unofficial Dispatches, Hutchinson (London), [1901] . £100
Famous Scottish Regiments, Newnes (London), 1914 (pbk) £125
Field Marshal Sir John French and His Campaigns, Newnes (London), 1914 (pbk) £125
Heroes All, Gallant Deeds of the War, Newnes (London), 1914 . . . . £45
My Life, Long (London), 1914 (pseud 'Evelyn Thaw') . £125
The Standard History of the War, Newnes (London), [1914-15] (4 vols) £45
Kitchener's Army and the Territorial Forces: The Full Story of a Great Achievement, Newnes (London), 1915 (6 vols; pbk) £50
War of the Nations, Newnes (London), 1915-17 (12 vols; pbk) £75
The Real Shell-Man, John Waddington (London), 1919 (pbk) £250
The Black Avons, George Gill (London), 1925 (4 pbks) £75
People: A Short Autobiography, Hodder & Stoughton (London), 1926 . . . . . £65/£15
ditto, Doubleday Doran (New York), 1929 . £50/£10
This England, Hodder & Stoughton (London), [1927] . . . . £150/£25
My Hollywood Diary, Hutchinson (London), [1932] . . . . £65/£15

HORACE WALPOLE
(b.1717 d.1797)

Considered one of the greatest letter-writers of the 18th century, Walpole will probably be remembered for his ground-breaking *The Castle of Otranto*, the first Gothic horror novel.

Aedes Walpoliane, or A Description of the Collection of Pictures at Houghton Hall, privately printed (London), 1747 [1748] (100 copies) £4,500
ditto, Dodsley (London), 1752 . . . . £1,500
A Letter from Xo Ho, A Chinese Philosopher at London, To His Friend Lien Chi at Peking, Middleton (London), 1757 . . . . £750
A Catalogue of Royal and Noble Authors of England, Scotland and Ireland, Strawberry Hill (London), 1758 (2 vols) . . . . . . £500 the set
ditto, Strawberry Hill (London), 1759 (2 vols). £200 the set
Fugitive Pieces in Verse and Prose, Strawberry Hill (London), 1758 . . . . . . £1,000
Catalogue of Pictures and Drawings in the Holbein Chamber, Strawberry Hill (London), 1760 . . £450
Anecdotes of Painting in England, Strawberry Hill (London), 1762-1771 [1780] (4 vols) . £750 the set
A Catalogue of Engravers Who Have Been Born or Resided in England, Strawberry Hill (London), 1763 £200

The Castle of Otranto, Lowndes (London), 1765 [1764] £7,500
ditto, Bathoe/Lowndes (London), 1765 . . £2,500
Historic Doubts on the Life and Reign of King Richard the Third, Dodsley (London), 1768 . . . . £200
The Mysterious Mother: A Tragedy, Strawberry Hill (London), 1768 (50 copies) £3,000
ditto, Strawberry Hill (London), 1781 . . . £500
A Description of the Villa at Strawberry Hill, Near Twickenham, Middlesex, Strawberry Hill (London), 1774 . . . . £500
Description of Strawberry Hill, Strawberry Hill (London), 1784 . . . . £450
Essay on Modern Gardening, Strawberry Hill (London), 1785 . . . . £600
Hieroglyphic Tales, Strawberry Hill (London), 1785 (7 copies) £15,000
ditto, Elkin Mathews (London), 1926 (250 copies). . £150
The Works of Horatio Walpole, Earl of Orford, Robinson/Edwards (London), 1798 (5 vols) . £500 the set
ditto, Robinson/Edwards (London), 1798 (large paper edition, 5 vols) . . . . . . £650 the set
Reminiscences, Richard Taylor (London), 1805 (25 copies) . . . . £1,000 the set
Memories in the Last Ten Years of the Reign of George the Second, Murray (London), 1822 (2 vols) . . £250
Memoirs of the Reign of King George the Third, Richard Bentley (London), 1845 (4 vols) . . £3000 the set
Journal of the Reign of King George the Third, from the Year 1771 to 1783, Richard Bentley (London), 1859 (2 vols) . . . . £300 the set
Journal of the Printing Office at Strawberry Hill, Constable (London), 1923 (650 copies) £75
ditto, Houghton Mifflin (Boston), 1923 (650 copies) . £125
Reminiscences, Written in 1788 for the Amusement of Miss Mary and Miss Agnes Berry, Milford/O.U.P. (Oxford, UK), 1925 (500 copies) . . . . . £65/£30
Strawberry Hill Accounts: A Record of Expenditure in Building, Furnishing, etc, from 1747 to 1795, O.U.P. (Oxford, UK), 1927 (500 copies) . . . £65/£30
Fugitive Verses, O.U.P. (Oxford, UK), 1931 . . . £50
ditto, O.U.P. (New York), 1923 (500 numbered copies) £75
Memoirs and Portraits, Batsford (London), 1963 . £20/£5

Letters

Letters from the Hon Horace Walpole to George Montagu, esq., From the Year 1736 to the Year 1770, Rodwell & Martin/Henry Colburn (London), 1818 . . . £125
Letters from the Hon Horace Walpole to the Rev William Cole, and Others, From the Year 1745 to the Year 1782, Rodwell & Martin/Henry Colburn (London), 1818 . £125
Private Correspondence of Horace Walpole, Earl of Orford, Now First Collected, Rodwell & Martin/Henry Colburn (London), 1820 (4 vols) . . £150 the set
Letters from the Hon Horace Walpole to the Earl of Hertford, During His Lordship's Embassy in Paris, Charles Knight (London), 1825 . . . . . £100
Letters to Sir Horace Mann, British Envoy at the Court of Tuscany, Richard Bentley (London), 1833 (3 vols) . . . . £150 the set
The Letters of Horace Walpole, Earl of Orford, Richard Bentley (London), 1840 (6 vols) . . £200 the set
Letters to Sir Horace Mann, Concluding Series, Richard Bentley (London), 1843-44 (4 vols) . . £150 the set

Letters Addressed to the Countess of Ossory, From the Year 1769 to 1797, Richard Bentley (London), 1848 (2 vols) .
. . . . £125 the set

Correspondence of Horace Walpole and William Mason, Richard Bentley (London), 1851 (2 vols)   £125 the set

The Letters of Horace Walpole, Now First Chronologically Arranged, Richard Bentley (London), 1857-59 (9 vols) .
. . . . £200 the set

ditto, Richard Bentley (London), 1891 . . . . £125

Horace Walpole and His World, Selected Passages from His Letters, Seeley Jackson (London), 1884 . . . £35

Letters of Sir Horace Walpole, T. Fisher Unwin (London), 1890 (2 vols) . . . . . . £30 the set

Some Unpublished Letters, Longmans (London), 1902   £20

The Letters of Sir Horace Walpole, Fourth Earl of Orford, Chronologically Arranged, Clarendon Press (Oxford, UK), 1903-5, 1919, 1925 (16 vols plus 3 supplementary vols) .
. . . . £150/£75

ditto, Clarendon Press (Oxford, UK), 1903-5, 1919, 1925 (19 vols, India Paper Edition) . . . . £100 the set

ditto, Clarendon Press (Oxford, UK), 1903-5, 1919, 1925 (19 vols, 260 sets signed by the editor) . . . £300/£200

Selected Letters, Dent, Everyman's Library (London), 1926 . . . . £15/£5

A Selection of Letters, O.U.P. (Oxford, UK), 1927 (two vols) . . . . £50/£25

Horace Walpole's Correspondence, Yale Univ Press (New Haven, CT), 1937-83 (43 vols, plus 5 vols of indices) .
. . . . . £2,000/£1,500 the set

HUGH WALPOLE

(b.1884 d.1941)

Hugh Walpole was a popular and critical success in his own time, and his 'Herries Chronicle' novels are still in print. His posthumous reputation, however, was blighted by Somerset Maugham's devastating portrayal of him in *Cakes and Ale*. Walpole's short stories are much appreciated by aficionados of supernatural fiction. He was knighted in 1937.

Novels

The Wooden Horse, Smith Elder (London), 1909 . .£150
Marradick at Forty, Smith Elder (London), 1910 . . £45
Mr Perrin and Mr Traill, Mills & Boon (London), 1911 £45
ditto, Doran (New York), 1911 . . . . . £25
The Prelude to Adventure, Mills & Boon (London), 1912 .
. . . . £25
ditto, Century (New York), 1912 . . . . £20
Fortitude, Secker (London), 1913 . . . . £25
ditto, Doran (New York), 1913 . . . . . £25
The Duchess of Wrexe, Secker (London), 1914 . . £25
ditto, Doran (New York), 1914 . . . . . £25
The Dark Forest, Secker (London), 1918. . . . £25
ditto, Doran (New York), 1916 . . . . . £25
The Green Mirror, Macmillan (London), 1918 . . £25
ditto, Doran (New York), 1918 . . . . . £25
The Secret City, Macmillan (London), 1919 . . £25
ditto, Doran (New York), 1919 . . . . . £20
Jeremy, Cassell (London), 1919 . . . . . £25
ditto, Doran (New York), 1919 . . . . . £20
The Captives, Macmillan (London), 1920. . . £75/£25

ditto, Doran (New York), 1920 . . . . . £65/£25
The Young Enchanted, Macmillan (London), 1921 £65/£20
ditto, Macmillan (London), 1921 (250 signed copies) .
. . . .£100/£40
ditto, Doran (New York), 1921 . . . . . £65/£20
The Cathedral, Macmillan (London), 1922 . . £50/£15
ditto, Macmillan (London), 1922 (250 signed copies) .
. . . .£100/£40
ditto, Doran (New York), 1922 . . . . . £50/£15
ditto, Doran (New York), 1922 (500 numbered copies).
. . . . £75/£35
Jeremy and Hamlet, Cassell (London), 1923 . . £35/£10
ditto, Doran (New York), 1923 . . . . . £35/£10
The Old Ladies, Macmillan (London), 1924 . . £35/£10
ditto, Macmillan (London), 1924 (250 signed copies) £75/£35
ditto, Doran (New York), 1924 . . . . . £35/£10
Portrait of a Man with Red Hair, Macmillan (London), 1925
. . . . £35/£10
ditto, Macmillan (London), 1925 (250 signed copies) .
. . . . £75/£35
ditto, Doran (New York), 1925 . . . . . £35/£10
ditto, Doran (New York), 1925 (250 numbered copies).
. . . . £65/£30
Harmer John, Macmillan (London), 1926 . . £35/£10
ditto, Macmillan (London), 1926 (250 signed copies) .
. . . . £60/£35
ditto, Doran (New York), 1926 . . . . . £30/£10
Jeremy at Crale, Cassell (London), 1927 . . . £30/£10
ditto, Doran (New York), 1927 . . . . . £30/£10
Wintersmoon, Macmillan (London), 1928 . . £35/£5
ditto, Macmillan (London), 1928 (175 signed copies) £45/£25
ditto, Doubleday Doran (New York), 1928 . . £30/£5
Farthing Hall, Macmillan (London), 1929 (with J.B. Priestley) . . . . £45/£10
ditto, Doubleday Doran (New York), 1929 . . £40/£10
Hans Frost, Macmillan (London), 1929 . . . £35/£5
ditto, Macmillan (London), 1929 (175 signed copies) . .
. . . . £35/£15
ditto, Doubleday Doran (New York), 1929 . . £30/£5
Rogue Herries, Macmillan (London), 1930 . . £30/£10
ditto, Macmillan (London), 1930 (200 signed copies) £50/£30
ditto, Doubleday Doran (New York), 1930 . . £30/£10
Above the Dark Circus, Macmillan (London), 1931 £30/£10
ditto, Macmillan (London), 1931 (200 signed copies) . .
. . . . £35/£20
ditto, as *Above the Dark Tumult*, Doubleday Doran (New York), 1930 . . . . £25/£10
Judith Paris, Macmillan (London), 1931 . . . £25/£5
ditto, Macmillan (London), 1931 (350 signed copies) . .
. . . . £30/£15
ditto, Doubleday Doran (New York), 1931 . . £25/£5
The Fortress, Macmillan (London), 1932. . . £25/£5
ditto, Macmillan (London), 1932 (310 signed copies) . .
. . . . £30/£15
ditto, Doubleday Doran (New York), 1932 . . £25/£5
Vanessa, Macmillan (London), 1933. . . . £25/£5
ditto, Macmillan (London), 1933 (315 signed copies) . .
. . . . £30/£15
ditto, Doubleday Doran (New York), 1933 . . £25/£5
Captain Nicholas, Macmillan (London), 1934 . £25/£5
ditto, Macmillan (London), 1934 (275 signed copies) £30/£15
ditto, Doubleday Doran (New York), 1934 . . £25/£5
The Inquisitor, Macmillan (London), 1935 . . £25/£5
ditto, Macmillan (London), 1935 (250 signed copies) £30/£15

ditto, Doubleday Doran (New York), 1935 . . £25/£5
A Prayer for My Son, Macmillan (London), 1936 . £25/£5
ditto, Macmillan (London), 1936 (200 signed copies) .
. . . . £30/£15
ditto, Doubleday Doran (New York), 1936 . £25/£5
John Cornelius, Macmillan (London), 1937 . £25/£5
ditto, Macmillan (London), 1937 (175 signed copies) £30/£15
ditto, Doubleday Doran (New York), 1937 . £25/£5
The Joyful Delaneys, Macmillan (London), 1938 . £25/£5
ditto, Macmillan (London), 1938 (180 signed copies) £30/£15
ditto, Doubleday Doran (New York), 1938 . £25/£5
The Sea Tower, Macmillan (London), 1939 . £25/£5
ditto, Doubleday Doran (New York), 1939 . £25/£5
The Bright Pavilions, Macmillan (London), 1940 . £25/£5
ditto, Doubleday Doran (New York), 1940 . £25/£5
The Blind Man's House, Macmillan (London), 1941 £25/£5
ditto, Doubleday Doran (New York), 1941 . £25/£5
The Killer and the Slain, Macmillan (London), 1942 £25/£5
ditto, Doubleday Doran (New York), 1942 . £25/£5
Katherine Christian, Macmillan (London), 1944 . £25/£5
ditto, Doubleday Doran (New York), 1944 . £25/£5

Short Stories
The Golden Scarecrow, Cassell (London), 1915 . . £40
ditto, Doran (New York), 1915 . . . . . . £40
The Thirteen Travellers, Hutchinson (London), 1921 .
. . . . £75/£25
ditto, Doubleday Doran (New York), 1921 . £65/£15
The Silver Thorn, Macmillan (London), 1928. . £40/£15
ditto, Macmillan (London), 1928 (175 signed copies) . £40
ditto, Doubleday Doran (New York), 1921 . £35/£10
All Soul's Night, Macmillan (London), 1933 . .£125/£20
ditto, Doubleday Doran (New York), 1921 . .£125/£15
Head in Green Bronze, Macmillan (London), 1938 £35/£15
ditto, Doubleday Doran (New York), 1938 . £35/£50
Mr Huffam, Macmillan (London), 1948 . . £35/£15
Tarnhelm, Tartarus Press (Carlton-in-Coverdale, North
Yorkshire), 2003 . . . . . . £35/£10

Plays
The Cathedral, Macmillan (London), 1937 . . £20/£5
The Haxtons, Deane (London), 1939 . . . £20/£5

Collaboration
The Scoop and *Behind the Screen*, Gollancz (London), 1983
(chain novels; chapters by Walpole, Dorothy L. Sayers,
Agatha Christie, E.C. Bentley, Freeman Wills Crofts and
others) . . . . £25/£10

Miscellaneous
Joseph Conrad, A Critical Study, Nisbet (London), 1916 .
. . . . £25
A Hugh Walpole Anthology, Dent (London), 1921 £35/£10
The Crystal Box, Glasgow Univ Press (Glasgow, Scotland),
1924 (150 signed, numbered copies) . . . £65
The English Novel: The Rede Lecture, C.U.P. (Cambridge,
UK), 1925 . . . . £35/£10
Reading: An Essay, Jarrold (london), 1928 . £25/£10
ditto, Harper (New York), 1926 . . . . £25/£10
Anthony Trollope: A Study, Macmillan (London), 1928 .
. . . . £25/£10
ditto, Macmillan (New York), 1928 . . . £25/£10
My Religious Experience, Ernest Benn (London), 1928 .
. . . . £15/£5

A Letter to a Modern Novelist, Hogarth Press (London),
1932 (wraps). £10
The Apple Trees, Golden Cockerel Press (Waltham St
Lawrence, Berks), 1932 (500 signed copies). . . £40
Extracts from a Diary, privately printed for the author by R.
Maclehose (Glasgow), 1934 . . . . . £35/£10
Roman Fountain, Macmillan (London), 1940 . £25/£10
ditto, Doubleday Doran (New York), 1940 . £25/£10
Open Letter of an Optimist, Macmillan (London), 1941
(stapled wraps) £20

MINETTE WALTERS
(b.1949)

Contemporary British crime writer Minette Walters owes
some of her popularity to highly successful television
adaptations of her books. She began by writing romantic
novelettes for the *Woman's Weekly Library* under a pseudonym. (These novelettes are essentially magazines but
could be seen as separate publications by die-hard collectors. Unfortunately, no records exist of which titles she
contributed to the series.)

Novels
The Ice House, Macmillan (London), 1992 . .£400/£35
ditto, Macmillan (London), 1992 (variant jacket, two heads
under the ice) . . . . . . £1,250/£35
ditto, St Martin's Press (New York), 1992 . .£125/£15
The Sculptress, Macmillan (London), 1993 . . £30/£5
ditto, St Martin's Press (New York), 1992 . . £15/£5
The Scold's Bridle, Macmillan (London), 1994 . £15/£5
ditto, Scorpion Press (Bristol, UK), 1994 (75 signed copies)
. . . . £100
ditto, Scorpion Press (Bristol, UK), 1994 (15 lettered copies)
. . . . £200
ditto, St Martin's Press (New York), 1994 . . £10/£5
The Dark Room, Macmillan (London), 1995 . . £15/£5
ditto, Putnam's (New York), 1996 . . . £10/£5
The Echo, Macmillan (London), 1997 . . . £15/£5
ditto, Putnam's (New York), 1997 . . . £10/£5
The Breaker, Macmillan (London), 1998 . . . £15/£5
ditto, Putnam's (New York), 1999 . . . £10/£5
Shape of Snakes, Macmillan (London), 2000 . . £10/£5
ditto, Macmillan (London), 2000 (600 signed copies of
second printing; slipcase; no d/w) . . . . £30/£15
ditto, Putnam's (New York), 2000 . . . £10/£5
Acid Row, Macmillan (London), 2001 . . . £10/£5
ditto, Putnam's (New York), 2002 . . . £10/£5
Fox Evil, Macmillan (London), 2002 . . . £10/£5
ditto, Putnam's (New York), 2003 . . . £10/£5
Disordered Minds, Macmillan (London), 2003 . £10/£5
ditto, Berkley (New York), 2004. . . . . £10/£5
The Devil's Feather, Macmillan (London), 2005 . £10/£5
ditto, Knopf (New York), 2006 . . . . . £10/£5
The Chameleon's Shadow, Macmillan (London), 2007 .
. . . . £10/£5
ditto, Knopf (New York), 2008 . . . . . £10/£5

Novella
The Tinder Box, Macmillan (London), 2004 . . £10/£5

REX WARNER
(b.1905 d.1986)

An English poet, novelist and translator, Warner is perhaps best known for his Kafkaesque novel *The Aerodrome*. He was educated at Wadham College, Oxford, where he associated with W.H. Auden and Cecil Day Lewis, and was published in *Oxford Poetry*. He was a contributor to *Left Review*.

Fiction

The Wild Goose Chase, Boriswood (London), 1937 . . . . £100/£25
ditto, Knopf (New York), 1938 . . . . . £30/£10
The Professor, Boriswood (London), 1938 . . £100/£25
ditto, Knopf (New York), 1939 . . . . . £30/£10
The Aerodrome, John Lane (London), 1941 . £250/£50
ditto, Lippincott (Philadelphia), 1946 . . £40/£10
Why Was I Killed? A Dramatic Dialogue, John Lane (London), 1943 . . . . £35/£10
ditto, as *Return of the Traveller*, Lippincott (Philadelphia), 1944 . . . . £25/£5
Men of Stones: A Melodrama, Bodley Head (London), 1949 . . . . £25/£5
ditto, Lippincott (Philadelphia), 1950 . . . £20/£5
Escapade: A Tale of Average, Bodley Head (London), 1953 . . . . £20/£5
The Young Caesar, Collins (London), 1958 . . £15/£5
ditto, Little, Brown (Boston), 1958 . . . £10/£5
Imperial Caesar, Collins (London), 1960. . . £15/£5
ditto, Little, Brown (Boston), 1960 . . . £10/£5
Pericles the Athenian, Collins (London), 1963 . £15/£5
ditto, Little, Brown (Boston), 1963 . . . £10/£5
The Converts, John Lane (London), 1967. . . £10/£5
ditto, Little, Brown (Boston), 1967 . . . £10/£5

Poetry

Poems, Boriswood (London), 1937 . . . . £45/£10
ditto, Knopf (New York), 1938 . . . . . £25/£10
ditto, as *Poems and Contradictions*, John Lane (London), 1945 . . . . £20/£5

Others

The Kite, Blackwell (Oxford), 1936 . . . . £100/£35
ditto, Hamish Hamilton (London), 1963 (revised edition) . . . . £25/£10
English Public Schools, Collins (London), 1945 . £15/£5
The Cult of Power: Essays, John Lane (London), 1946 . . . . £25/£10
ditto, Lippincott (Philadelphia), 1947 . . . £25/£10
John Milton, Parrish (London), 1949 . . . £15/£5
ditto, Chanticler Press (New York), 1950 . . £10/£5
Views of Attica and Its Surroundings, Lehmann (London), 1950 . . . . £15/£5
E.M. Forster, Longmans (London), 1950 (stapled wraps) £10
ditto, Longmans (London), 1960 (revised edition; stapled wraps) £5
Men and Gods, MacGibbon & Kee (London), 1950 £20/£5
ditto, Fararr Straus, Giroux (New York), 1959. . £15/£5
Ashes to Ashes: A Post-Mortem on the 1950-51 Tests, MacGibbon & Kee (London), 1951 (with Lyle Blair) . . . . £25/£10

Greeks and Trojans, MacGibbon & Kee (London), 1951 . . . . £10/£5
Eternal Greece, Thames & Hudson (London), 1953 (photographs by Martin Hurlimann) . . . £30/£10
The Vengeance of the Gods, MacGibbon & Kee (London), 1954 . . . . £10/£5
ditto, Michigan State (East Lansing, MI), 1955 . £10/£5
The Stories of the Greeks, Fararr Straus, Giroux (New York), 1967 (includes *Men and Gods*, *Greeks and Trojans*, *The Vengeance of the Gods*) . . . . £10/£5
Athens, Thames & Hudson (London), 1956 . . £10/£5
The Greek Philosophers, Michigan State (East Lansing, MI), 1958 . . . . £10/£5
Athens at War: Retold from Thucydides History of the Pelopennesian War, Bodley Head (London), 1970 £10/£5
ditto, Dutton (New York), 1971 . . . . . £10/£5
Men of Athens, Bodley Head (London), 1972. . £10/£5
ditto, Viking (New York), 1972 . . . . . £10/£5

Translations

The Medea of Euripides, John Lane (London), 1944 £20/£5
ditto, Univ of Chicago Press (Chicago), 1955 (with *Euripides Alcestis*, translated by Lattimore, *The Heracleidae* translated by Ralph Gladstone, *Hippolytus* translated by David Grene, etc.) . . . . £15/£5
Prometheus Bound, by Aeschylus, Bodley Head (London), 1947 . . . . £25/£5
The Persian Expedition, by Xenophon, Penguin (Harmondsworth, Middlesex), 1949 (pbk) £5
Hippolytus, by Euripides, Bodley Head (London), 1949 . . . . £20/£5
Helen, by Euripides, Bodley Head (London), 1951. £50/£5
The Peloponnesian War, by Thucydides, Penguin (Harmondsworth, Middlesex), 1954 (pbk, with d/w) £10/£5
Fall of the Roman Republic. Martus, Sulla, Crassus, Pompey, Caesar, Cicero: Six Lives, by Plutarch, Penguin (Harmondsworth, Middlesex), 1958 (pbk) . . . £5
ditto, Penguin (Harmondsworth, Middlesex), 1972 (revised edition; pbk) £5
Three Great Plays, New American Library (New York), 1958 (contains *Medea*, *Hippolytus* and *Helen*) . £10/£5
Poems of George Seferis, Little, Brown (Boston), 1960 . . . . £10/£5
ditto, Bodley Head (London), 1960 (pbk with d/w) £10/£5
War Commentaries of Caesar, New American Library (New York), 1960 . . . . £10/£5
Confessions of St Augustine, New American Library (New York), 1963 . . . . £10/£5
On the Greek Style: Selected Essays in Poetry and Hellenism, by George Seferis, Little, Brown (Boston), 1966 (with Th. D. Frangopoulos) . . . £10/£5
ditto, Bodley Head (London), 1967 . . . . £10/£5
History of My Times, by Xenophon, Penguin (Harmondsworth, Middlesex), 1966 (pbk). £5
Moral Essays, by Plutarch, Penguin (London), 1971 (pbk) £5

SYLVIA TOWNSEND WARNER

(b.1893 d.1978)

A left-wing author of novels, poetry and short stories, Warner wrote about ordinary and overlooked members of society. Her first novel, *Lolly Willowes*, the story of a modern witch, was a popular success. Most of her later short stories were first published in the *New Yorker* magazine.

Poetry

The Espalier, Chatto & Windus (London), 1925 . £125/£45
ditto, Dial Press (New York), 1925 . . . £30/£10
Time Importuned, Chatto & Windus (London), 1928 .
. . . . £100/£25
ditto, Viking Press (New York), 1928 . . £85/£25
Opus 7, Chatto & Windus (London), 1931 . . £20/£5
ditto, Chatto & Windus (London), 1931 (110 signed, numbered copies) £75
ditto, Viking Press (New York), 1931 . . £20/£5
Rainbow, Borzoi (New York), 1932 (wraps, in envelope) .
. . . . £75/£45
Whether a Dove or Seagull, Viking Press (New York), 1933 (with Valentine Ackland) . . . . £125/£45
ditto, Chatto & Windus (London), 1934 . . £125/£50
Two Poems, Grasshopper Broadsheet, Number Three, Fourth Series, March 1945 (broadside) £25
Boxwood, Monotype Corporation (London), 1957 (500 copies, withdrawn) £45
ditto, Monotype Corporation (London), 1958 (500 copies) £45
ditto, Chatto & Windus (London), 1960 (enlarged edition) .
. . . . £30/£10
King Duffus, privately printed by Clare and Co (Somerset) for the author [Dorset], 1968 (stapled wraps) . . £125
Twelve Poems, privately circulated booklet [Aldeburgh, Suffolk], 1977 (duplicated sheets, stapled) . . £65
ditto, as *Azrael*, Libanus Press (Newbury, Berkshire), 1978 (200 copies; sewn wraps) £75
ditto, as *Twelve Poems*, Chatto & Windus (London), 1980 (reissue). . . . . £10/£5
Collected Poems, Carcanet Press/Viking Press (Manchester, UK/New York), 1982 . . . . . £50/£20
Selected Poems, Carcanet Press (Manchester, UK), 1985 (pbk) £5

Novels

Lolly Willowes, Chatto & Windus (London), 1926. £125/£20
ditto, Viking Press (New York), 1926 . . £125/£20
Mr Fortune's Maggot, Chatto & Windus (London), 1927 .
. . . . £65/£15
ditto, Viking Press (New York), 1927 . . £45/£10
The True Heart, Chatto & Windus (London), 1929 £65/£15
ditto, Viking Press (New York), 1929 . . £45/£10
Summer Will Show, Chatto & Windus (London), 1936 .
. . . . £65/£15
ditto, Viking Press (New York), 1936 . . £35/£10
After The Death of Don Juan, Chatto & Windus (London), 1938 . . . . £45/£10
ditto, Viking Press (New York), 1938 . . £35/£10
The Corner that Held Them, Chatto & Windus (London), 1948 . . . . £25/£10

ditto, Viking Press (New York), 1948 . . . £20/£5
The Flint Anchor, Chatto & Windus (London), 1954 . .
. . . . £30/£10
ditto, Viking Press (New York), 1954 . . £20/£5
ditto, as *The Barnards of Loseby*, Popular Library (New York), 1954 (pbk) £5

Short Stories

The Maze, Fleuron (London), 1928 (signed; sewn wraps) .
. . . . £125
Some World Far From Ours and 'Stay Corydon, Thou Swain', Mathews & Marrot (London), 1929 (531 numbered, signed copies) . . . . . £55/£30
Elinor Barley, Cresset Press (London), 1930 (350 numbered, signed copies on mould-made paper, slipcase) . £125/£75
ditto, Cresset Press (London), 1930 (30 numbered and signed copies on handmade paper, extra set of engravings, slipcase) . . . . . . £750/£500
A Moral Ending, W. Jackson (London), 1930 (550 numbered, signed copies, glassine d/w with paper flaps) .
. . . . £75/£45
The Salutation, Chatto & Windus (London), 1932. £100/£40
ditto, Viking Press (New York), 1932 . . £75/£35
More Joy in Heaven, Cresset Press (London), 1935 £125/£50
ditto, as *24 Short Stories*, Cresset Press (London), 1939 (*More Joy in Heaven* is bound in with collections by James Laver and George Orwell). . . . £750/£125
The Cat's Cradle Book, Viking Press (New York), 1940 .
. . . . £35/£10
ditto, Chatto & Windus (London), 1960 . . £35/£10
A Garland of Straw, Chatto & Windus (London), 1943 .
. . . . £45/£15
ditto, Viking Press (New York), 1943 . . £30/£15
The Museum of Cheats, Chatto & Windus (London), 1947.
. . . . £30/£10
ditto, Viking Press (New York), 1947 . . £25/£10
Winter in The Air, Chatto & Windus (London), 1955 .
. . . . £30/£10
ditto, Viking Press (New York), 1956 . . £25/£5
A Spirit Rises, Chatto & Windus (London), 1962 . £25/£10
ditto, Viking Press (New York), 1962 . . £20/£5
Sketches from Nature, privately printed by Clare and Co (Somerset) for the author [Dorset], 1963 (stapled wraps) .
. . . . £125
A Stranger with a Bag, Chatto & Windus (London), 1966 .
. . . . £45/£15
ditto, as *Swans on an Autumn River*, Viking Press (New York), 1966 . . . . . . £20/£5
Two Conversation Pieces, privately printed by Clare and Co (Somerset) for the author [Dorset], 1967 (stapled wraps) .
. . . . £125
The Innocent and The Guilty, Chatto & Windus (London), 1971 . . . . £15/£5
ditto, Viking Press (New York), 1971 . . £15/£5
Kingdoms of Elfin, Chatto & Windus (London), 1977 .
. . . . £15/£5
ditto, Viking Press (New York), 1977 . . £15/£5
Scenes of Childhood, Chatto & Windus (London), 1981 .
. . . . £10/£5
ditto, Viking Press (New York), 1981 . . £10/£5
One Thing Leading to Another, Chatto & Windus (London), 1984 . . . . £10/£5
ditto, Viking Press (New York), 1984 . . £10/£5
Selected Stories, Chatto & Windus (London), 1989 £15/£5

ditto, Viking Press (New York), 1989 . . . £15/£5
The Music at Long Verney, Counterpoint (Washington, DC), 2001 . . . . . . £15/£5

Translations
By Way of Saint-Beuve, by Marcel Proust, Chatto & Windus (London), 1958 . . . £40/£20
ditto, as **Marcel Proust on Art and Literature 1896-1919**, Greenwich Editions/Meridian Books (New York), 1958 .
. . . . £35/£10
A Place of Shipwreck, by Jean Rene Huquenin, Chatto & Windus (London), 1963 . . . . . £25/£10

Other Works
Somerset, Paul Elek (London), 1949 (withdrawn) . £45/£15
Jane Austen, Longmans Green (London), 1951 (stapled wraps) £10
T.H. White, A Biography, Cape (London), 1967 . £25/£10
ditto, Viking Press (New York), 1968 . £25/£10
Letters, Chatto & Windus (London), 1982 . £25/£10
The Diaries of Sylvia Townsend Warner, Chatto & Windus (London), 1994 . . . . . . £20/£10
Sylvia and David, Sinclair Stevenson (London), 1994 £15/£5
I'll Stand by You, Pimlico (London), 1998 (pbk) . . £5
The Element of Lavishness: Letters of Sylvia Townsend Warner and William Maxwell, 1938-1978, Counterpoint (Washington, DC), 2001 . . . . . £15/£5

ROBERT PENN WARREN
(b.1905 d.1989)

Robert Penn Warren was an American poet, novelist, and literary critic. He won the Pulitzer Prize in 1947 for his novel *All the King's Men* (1946) and for poetry in 1957 and 1979, making him the only person to have won Pulitzer Prizes for both fiction and poetry.

John Brown: The Making of A Martyr, Payson & Clarke (New York), 1929 (approx 500 copies) . . £1,000/£200
Thirty-Six Poems, Alcestis Press (New York), 1935 (20 signed, numbered copies, 'I' to 'XX'; wraps; clear wax paper d/w) £1,500
ditto, Alcestis Press (New York), 1935 (135 signed, numbered copies, '1' to '135'; wraps; clear wax paper d/w)
. . . . £1,000
An Approach To Literature, Louisiana State Univ (Baton Rouge, LA), 1936 (with Cleanth Brooks and John Purser)
. . . . £250/£40
ditto, as **Notes On An Approach To Literature**, Prentice Hall (Englewood Cliffs, NJ), 1965 (pbk) . . . £25
Understanding Poetry; An Anthology for College Students, Louisiana State Univ/Holt (New York), 1938 (with Cleanth Brooks) . . . . £150/£30
Night Rider, Houghton Mifflin (Boston), 1939 . £500/£75
ditto, Eyre & Spottiswoode (London), 1940 . £250/£45
Eleven Poems on the Same Theme, New Directions (Norfolk, CT), 1942 . . . . . £150/£30
ditto, New Directions (Norfolk, CT), 1942 (stapled wraps, in d/w) . . . . £65/£10
Understanding Fiction, Louisiana State Univ/Crofts (Baton Rouge/New York), 1943 (with Cleanth Brooks; no d/w) .
. . . . £125

Statement of Ashby Wyndham, Univ Press (Sewanee, TX), 1943 (wraps). £150
At Heaven's Gate, Harcourt Brace (New York), 1943 (assumed first binding in light blue cloth) . . £350/£65
ditto, Harcourt Brace (New York), 1943 (second binding in green blue cloth) . . . . . . £325/£40
ditto, Eyre & Spottiswoode (London), 1946 . . £125/£25
Selected Poems 1923-1943, Harcourt Brace (New York), 1944 . . . . £125/£20
ditto, The Fortune Press (London), [1951] . £125/£25
All The King's Men, Harcourt, Brace (New York), 1946 (first issue d/w with 'What Sinclair Lewis Says' on back panel, no other reviews) . . . . £1,750/£125
ditto, Eyre & Spottiswoode (London), 1948 (blue and white d/w) . . . . £150/£35
ditto, Eyre & Spottiswoode (London), 1948 (pink and black d/w with English reviews). . . . . £125/£35
ditto, Franklin Library (Franklin Center, PA), 1977 (signed limited edition in full leather) £75
ditto, Limited Editions Club (New York), 1989 (600 numbered copies signed by Warren and artist Hank O'Neal; 2 vols; slipcase) . . . . £500/£400
Blackberry Winter, Cummington Press (Cummington, MA), 1946 (50 copies numbered in small Roman numerals i-l, signed by author and illustrator Wightman Williams; clear wax paper and plain white (unprinted) d/w) £1,250/£1,000
ditto, Cummington Press (Cummington, MA), 1946 (280 copies numbered 1-280; clear wax paper and plain white paper d/w) . . . . . . £300/£250
The Circus in the Attic, Harcourt, Brace (New York), 1947.
. . . . £200/£30
ditto, Eyre & Spottiswoode (London), 1952 . £75/£15
Modern Rhetoric, Harcourt (New York), 1949 (with an 'A' on copyright page; written with Cleanth Brooks; no d/w) .
. . . . £30
Fundamentals of Good Writing, Harcourt (New York), 1950 (written with Cleanth Brooks) . . . . £100/£20
ditto, Dennis Dobson (London), 1952 . . . £30/£5
World Enough and Time, Random House (New York), 1950
. . . . £30/£5
ditto, Random House (New York), 1950 (numbered, limited edition for booksellers in clear acetate d/w) . . £75/£65
ditto, Random House (New York), [1950] ('Kentucky Edition': 1,000 signed copies) . . . . £125/£100
ditto, Eyre & Spottiswoode (London), 1951 . . £35/£5
William Faulkner and His South, Univ of Virginia (Charlottesville, VA), 1951 (mimeographed sheets) . £150
Brother to Dragons, Random House (New York), 1953 .
. . . . £45/£10
ditto, Eyre & Spottiswoode (London), 1954 . £35/£5
Band of Angels, Random House (New York), 1955 £60/£10
ditto, Secker & Warburg (London), 1956 . . . £45/£10
Segregation, Random House (New York), 1956 . £45/£10
ditto, Eyre & Spottiswoode (London), 1957 . £45/£10
To A Little Girl, [Jane Doggett, Department of Graphic Arts, Yale Univ (New Haven, CT), 1956 (approx 175 copies; no d/w) £500
Promises; Poems 1954-1956, Random House (New York), 1957 . . . . £75/£10
ditto, Eyre & Spottiswoode (London), 1959 . £35/£5
Selected Essays, Random House (New York), 1958 £45/£10
ditto, Eyre & Spottiswoode (London), 1964 . £30/£5
Remember the Alamo!, Random House (New York), 1958 (blue/green cloth; 2 pps of ads at rear of book for 85

Landmark Books and 38 World Landmark Books and on verso of d/w) . . . . £100/£25

ditto, Random House (New York), 1958 (light green cloth; no ads at rear of book; list of 98 Landmark Books and 50 World Landmark Books on d/w verso; with 'Jacket illustration by Taylor Oughton' on rear d/w flap). £50/£10

How Texas Won Her Freedom, San Jacinto Museum (Texas), 1959 (green paper covered boards; green cloth spine; no d/w) £200

ditto, San Jacinto Museum (Texas), 1959 (pbk) . £65

The Cave, Random House (New York), 1959 . £25/£5

ditto, Eyre & Spottiswoode (London), 1959 . £25/£5

The Gods of Mount Olympus, Random House (New York), 1959 . . . . £100/£15

ditto, Frederick Muller (London), 1962 . . . £60/£10

All The King's Men: A Play, Random House (New York), 1960 . . . . £50/£10

ditto, Dramatists Play Service (New York), 1960 (wraps; script edition with 10 titles advertised on p.67; 7 titles on p.68; 10 titles on back cover) £30

You, Emperors, and Others, Random House (New York), 1960 . . . . £65/£10

The Scope of Fiction, Appleton-Century-Crofts (New York), 1960 (with Cleanth Brooks; no d/w) £30

The Legacy of the Civil War, Random House (New York), 1961 . . . . £50/£10

Wilderness: A Tale of The Civil War, Random House (New York), 1961 . . . . . £35/£5

ditto, Eyre & Spottiswoode (London), 1962 . £25/£5

Flood: A Romance of Our Time, Random House (New York), 1964 . . . . £30/£5

ditto, Random House (New York), 1964 (signed on tipped-in page) . . . . £75/£50

ditto, Collins (London), 1964 . . . . £20/£5

Who Speaks for the Negro?, Random House (New York), 1965 . . . . £30/£5

A Plea in Mitigation, Wesleyan College (Macon, GA), 1966 (stapled wraps; first issue with 'abstation' for 'abstraction' p.5 line 2) £60

ditto, Wesleyan College (Macon, GA), 1966 (stapled wraps; second issue with corrected text) . . . £35

Selected Poems New and Old 1923-1966, Random House (New York), 1966 . . . . . £25/£5

ditto, Random House (New York), 1966 (250 signed, numbered copies; in d/w and slipcase) . . £100/£75

Faulkner: A Collection of Critical Essays, Prentice-Hall (Englewood Cliffs, NJ), 1966 . . . . £25/£5

ditto, Prentice-Hall (Englewood Cliffs, NJ), 1966 (pbk) £10

Incarnations, Poems 1966-1968, Random House (New York), 1968 . . . . £20/£5

ditto, Random House (New York), 1968 (250 signed, numbered copies; in d/w and slipcase) . . £100/£75

ditto, W.H. Allen (London), 1970 . . . £25/£5

Audobon, A Vision, Random House (New York), 1969 . . . . £20/£5

ditto, Random House (New York), 1969 (300 signed, numbered copies; in d/w and slipcase) . . £75/£50

Man in Moonlight, no publisher (no place), 1969 (broadside) £75

Homage to Theodore Dreiser, Random House (New York), 1971 . . . . £20/£5

Meet Me in the Green Glen, Random House (New York), 1971 . . . . £20/£5

ditto, Random House (New York), 1971 (300 signed, numbered copies; in acetate d/w and slipcase) . £75/£50

ditto, Secker & Warburg (London), 1972 . . £15/£5

Hawthorne Was Relevant, no publisher (no place), 1972 (wraps) £60

Or Else, Poem/Poems 1968-1974, Random House (New York), 1974 . . . . £15/£5

ditto, Random House (New York), 1974 (300 signed, numbered copies; slipcase; no d/w) . . £60/£40

Democracy and Poetry, Harvard Univ Press (Cambridge, MA/London), 1975 . . . . . £20/£5

Selected Poems, 1923-1975, Random House (New York), 1976 . . . . £20/£5

ditto, Random House (New York), 1976 (pbk) . £5

ditto, Random House (New York), 1976 (250 signed and numbered copies; slipcase; no d/w). . . £65/£50

ditto, Franklin Library (Franklin Center, PA), 1976 (unsigned limited edition in full leather) . . £25

ditto, Secker & Warburg (London), 1976 . £15/£5

ditto, Franklin Library (Franklin Center, PA), 1981 (signed limited edition in full leather) . . . £20

Dream of a Dream, G.K. Hall (Boston), 1976 (single sheet folded to make a Christmas card) £30

A Conversation With Robert Penn Warren, WNET/13 (New York), 1976 (8 stapled mimeographed sheets) . £25

Rebuke of the Rocks, Colorado College (Colorado Springs, CO), 1976 (150 signed, numbered copies; broadside). £100

A Place To Come To, Secker & Warburg (London), 1977 . . . . £30/£5

ditto, Random House (New York), 1977 . . . £15/£5

ditto, Random House (New York), 1977 (350 signed, numbered copies; slipcase; no d/w). . . £50/£30

Now and Then, Poems, 1976-1978, Random House (New York), 1978 . . . . £15/£5

ditto, Random House (New York), 1978 (pbk) . £10

ditto, Random House (New York), 1978 (200 signed, numbered copies; slipcase; no d/w). . . £60/£50

Old Flame, Palaemon Press (no place), 1978 (100 signed, numbered copies; broadside) £75

ditto, Palaemon Press (no place), 1978 (26 signed, lettered copies) £200

For Aaron Copeland, Palaemon Press (Winston-Salem, NC), 1978 (50 signed, numbered copies; broadside) . £150

ditto, Palaemon Press (Winston-Salem, NC), 1978 (28 signed copies numbered I-XXVIII; reserved for authors in series) £200

Two Poems, Palaemon Press Ltd (no place), 1979 (200 signed copies numbered 1-200; no d/w) . . £45

ditto, Palaemon Press Ltd (no place), 1979 (30 signed copies numbered I-XXX; no d/w) £125

Jefferson Davis Gets His Citizenship Back, Univ Press of Kentucky (Lexington, KY), 1980 . . . £15/£5

Being Here: Poetry 1977-1980, Random House (New York), 1980 . . . . £15/£5

ditto, Random House (New York), 1980 (250 signed, numbered copies; slipcase) . . . . £50/£35

ditto, Secker & Warburg (London), 1980 . . £20/£5

Rumor Personified: Poems 1979-1980, Random House (New York), 1981 . . . . £15/£5

ditto, Random House (New York), 1981 (pbk) . . £5

ditto, Random House (New York), 1981 (250 signed, numbered copies; slipcase) . . . . £50/£35

ditto, Secker & Warburg (London), 1982 . . £15/£5

Prophecy, Palaemon Press (Lexington, KY), 1980 (45
numbered copies, broadside) £65

Robert Penn Warren Talking, Interviews 1950-1978,
Random House (New York), 1980 . . . £15/£5

Cycle, King Library Press (Lexington, KY), 1980 (broadside
on white deckle-edged paper) £100

ditto, King Library Press (Lexington, KY), 1980 (broadside
on brown unwatermarked paper) £50

Ballad of A Sweet Dream of Peace, Pressworks (Dallas,
TX), 1980 (350 signed and numbered copies; score laid in)
. . . . £75

ditto, Pressworks (Dallas, TX), 1980 (26 signed, lettered
copies; glassine d/w; score laid in) £250

Tell Me A Story, Univ of Kentucky (Lexington, KY), 1980
(broadside) £65

ditto, Coffee House Press (Lexington, KY), 1987 (broadside;
500 copies) £50

ditto, NEA/Library of Congress (Washington, DC), 1987
(500 signed, numbered copies; broadside) . . £75

Love: Four Versions, Palaemon Press (Winston-Salem, NC),
1981 (174 signed, numbered copies; no d/w) . £75

ditto, Palaemon Press (Winston-Salem, NC), 1981 (26
signed, lettered copies; no d/w) £150

Mountain Mystery, Palaemon Press (Winston-Salem, NC),
1981 (174 signed, numbered copies; no d/w) . . £75

ditto, Palaemon Press (Winston-Salem, NC), 1981 (26
signed, lettered copies; no d/w) £150

Chief Joseph of the Nez Perce, Georgia Review (no place),
1982 (stapled wraps) £125

ditto, Random House (New York), 1983 . £10/£5

ditto, Random House (New York), 1983 (pbk) . £5

ditto, Random House (New York), 1983 (250 signed,
numbered copies; slipcase; no d/w). . . . £60/£35

ditto, Random House (New York), 1983 (7 signed, lettered
copies in quarter leather) £200

ditto, Secker & Warburg (London), 1983 . . £15/£5

The Flower, Palaemon Press (Winston-Salem, NC), 1983 (3
signed copies printed for Rosanna Warren for private
circulation) £400

Little Girl Wakes Early, Palaemon Press (Winston-Salem,
NC), 1984 (10 signed, numbered copies; broadside) . £100

Snowfall, Parchment Gallery (no place), 1984 (80 signed,
numbered copies; broadside) £60

From Robert Penn Warren, Stuart Wright (Winston-Salem,
NC), 1984 (5 signed, numbered copies; wraps) . £125

New and Selected Poems 1923-1985, Random House (New
York), 1985 . . . . £15/£5

ditto, Random House (New York), 1985 (pbk) . £5

ditto, Random House (New York), 1985 (350 signed,
numbered copies; slipcase) . . . . £50/£30

ditto, Franklin Library (Franklin Center, PA), 1985 (signed
limited edition in full leather) £25

Poems, privately printed (Winston-Salem, NC), 1985 (15
copies in boards with leather spine). . . . £300

"Masts At Dawn", Library of Congress (Washington, DC),
1986 (broadside) £30

A Robert Penn Warren Reader, Random House (New
York), 1987 . . . . £10/£5

The Essential Melville, Ecco Press (New York), 1987 £15/£5

Six poems By Robert Penn Warren, Tamazunchale Press
(Newton, IA), 1987 (250 numbered copies; miniature book;
no d/w) £65

Little Boy and Lost Shoe, no publisher (no place), no date
(signed broadside) £75

Portrait of a Father, Univ Press of Kentucky (Lexington,
KY), 1988 . . . . £15/£5

New and Selected Essays, Random House (New York), 1989
. . . . £10/£5

ditto, Random House (New York), 1989 (350 signed,
numbered copies; slipcase; no d/w). . . . £45/£25

Talking With Robert Penn Warren, Univ of Georgia Press
(Athens, GA), 1990 . . . . £10/£5

Friends of Their Youth, The King Library Press (Lexington,
KY), 1993 (100 numbered copies signed by Cleanth
Brooks and Warren in facsimile; no d/w) . . . £50

The Collected Poems of Robert Penn Warren, Louisiana
State Univ Press (Baton Rouge, LA), 1998 . . £15/£5

**Selected Letters of Robert Penn Warren, Volume 1: The
Apprentice Years 1924-1934**, Louisiana State Univ Press
(Baton Rouge, LA), 2000 . . . . . £15/£5

ditto, Louisiana State Univ Press (Baton Rouge, LA), 2000
(pbk) £10

**Selected Letters of Robert Penn Warren, Volume 2: The
Southern Review Years, 1935-1942**, Louisiana State Univ
Press (Baton Rouge, LA), 2001 . . . . £15/£5

ditto, Louisiana State Univ Press (Baton Rouge, LA), 2001
(pbk) £10

Selected Poems of Robert Penn Warren, Louisiana State
Univ Press (Baton Rouge, LA), 2001 . . . £10/£5

COLIN WATSON

b.1920 d.1983

Watson was a British author of humorous detective fiction,
best-known for the twelve 'Flaxborough' novels set in a
fictional small town in England.

Flaxborough Novels

Coffin Scarcely Used, Eyre & Spottiswoode (London), 1958
. . . . £100/£20

ditto, Putnam (New York), 1967 . . . . £35/£10

Bump in the Night, Eyre & Spottiswoode (London), 1960
(no d/w). £50

ditto, Eyre & Spottiswoode (London), 1960 (second issue in
d/w) . . . . £50/£5

ditto, Walker (New York), 1962 . . . . £25/£10

Hopjoy Was Here, Eyre & Spottiswoode (London), 1962 .
. . . . £35/£10

ditto, Walker (New York), 1963 . . . . £30/£10

Lonelyheart 4122, Eyre & Spottiswoode (London), 1967 .
. . . . £35/£10

ditto, Putnam (New York), 1967 . . . . £25/£10

Charity Ends at Home, Eyre & Spottiswoode (London),
1968 . . . . £25/£10

ditto, Putnam (New York), 1968 . . . . £20/£5

The Flaxborough Crab, Eyre & Spottiswoode (London),
1969 . . . . £25/£10

ditto, as **Just What the Doctor Ordered**, Putnam (New
York), 1969 . . . . £20/£5

The Flaxborough Chronicle, Eyre & Spittiswoode
(London), 1969 (containing *Coffin Scarcely Used*, *Bump in
the Night* and *Hopjoy Was Here*) . . . . £30/£10

Broomsticks Over Flaxborough, Eyre Methuen (London),
1972 . . . . £25/£10

ditto, as **Kissing Covens**, Putnam (New York), 1972 £20/£5

The Naked Nuns, Eyre Methuen (London), 1975 . £25/£10

ditto, as **Six Nuns and a Shotgun**, Putnam (New York), 1975 . . . . £20/£5
It Shouldn't Happen to a Dog, Putnam (New York), 1977 .
. . . . £25/£10
ditto, as **One Man's Meat**, Eyre Methuen (London), 1977 .
. . . . £25/£10
Blue Murder, Eyre Methuen (London), 1979 . £25/£10
Plaster Sinners, Eyre Methuen (London), 1980 £15/£5
ditto, Doubleday (New York), 1981 . . . £10/£5
Whatever's Been Going On at Mumblesby?, Methuen (London) 1982 . . . . . . £15/£5
ditto, Doubleday (New York), 1983 . . . £10/£5

Other Fiction
The Puritan, Eyre & Spottiswoode (London), 1966 £30/£10
The Bell House Book, Hodder & Stoughton (London), 1979 (contains 'A Slight Case of Scotch') . . . £10/£5

Non-Fiction
Snobbery With Violence: English Crime Stories and Their Audience, Eyre & Spottiswoode (London), 1971. £25/£10
ditto, St Martin's Press (New York), 1972 . £20/£5

EVELYN WAUGH

(b.1903 d.1966)

Waugh is best known for his novels, although he also wrote a number of travel books. His first success was *Decline and Fall*, based on his experiences as a teacher. In the 1930s he was regarded as England's leading satirical novelist: his books offer an insight into the cynical and irresponsible mood of the English upper classes at the time.

Poetry
The World to Come: A Poem in Three Cantos, privately printed at the Westminster Press (London), 1916. £12,000

Novels
Decline and Fall, An Illustrated Novelette, Chapman & Hall (London), 1928 . . . . . £6,000/£1,000
ditto, Doubleday (New York), 1929 . . . £1,000/£75
ditto, Farrar (New York), 1929 . . . £500/£50
ditto, Chapman & Hall (London), 1937 (12 copies; pbk) .
. . . . £5,000
Vile Bodies, Chapman & Hall (London), 1930 £6,500/£300
ditto, Farrar (New York), 1930 . . . . £750/£65
ditto, Chapman & Hall (London), 1937 (12 copies; pbk) .
. . . . £7,500
Black Mischief, Chapman & Hall (London), 1932 . £800/£75
ditto, Chapman & Hall (London), 1932 (250 signed copies) .
. . . . £1,500/£750
ditto, Farrar (New York), 1932 . . . £450/£45
ditto, Chapman & Hall (London), 1937 (12 copies; pbk) .
. . . . £4,500
A Handful of Dust, Chapman & Hall (London), 1934 . .
. . . . £5,000/£250
ditto, Farrar (New York), 1934 . . . . £500/£75
ditto, Chapman & Hall (London), 1937 (12 copies; pbk) .
. . . . £4,000
Scoop: A Novel about Journalists, Chapman & Hall (London), 1938 (first issue with 's' in 'as' in last line of

p.88 and 'Daily Beast' logo in black letters on front of d/w) £1,500/
ditto, Chapman & Hall (London), 1938 (second issue wi 's' in 'as' in last line of p.88 and without 'Daily Beast d/w) . . . . £750/£
ditto, Little, Brown (Boston), 1938 . . . £250/£
Put Out More Flags, Chapman & Hall (London), 1942 .
. . . . £500/£5(
ditto, Little, Brown (Boston), 1942 . . £150/£30
Work Suspended, Chapman & Hall (London), 1942 (unfinished novel, 500 copies) . . . £1,500/£200
ditto, Chapman & Hall (London), 1948 . . £35/£10
Brideshead Revisited: The Sacred & Profane Memories of Capt Charles Ryder, privately printed for the author (London), 1945 [1944] (50 copies; pbk). . £8,000
ditto, Chapman & Hall (London), 1945 . £1,000/£125
ditto, Little, Brown (Boston), 1945 (600 copies) £400/£100
ditto, Little, Brown (Boston), 1946 . . £125/£25
Scott-King's Modern Europe, Chapman & Hall (London), 1947 . . . . £50/£15
ditto, Little, Brown (Boston), 1949 . . . £45/£10
The Loved One: An Anglo-American Tragedy, Chapman & Hall (London), 1948 . . . . . £75/£25
ditto, Chapman & Hall (London), 1948 (250 signed, numbered copies, glassine d/w) . . £500/£400
ditto, Little, Brown (Boston), 1948 . . . £35/£10
Helena, Chapman & Hall (London), 1950 . £45/£10
ditto, Chapman & Hall (London), 1950 (50 deluxe copies for presentation; unprinted glassine d/w) £1,500/£1,250
ditto, Little, Brown (Boston), 1950 . . . £25/£10
Men at Arms, Chapman & Hall (London), 1952 . £100/£20
ditto, Little, Brown (Boston), 1952 . . . £40/£10
Love Among The Ruins, Chapman & Hall (London), 1953 .
. . . . £35/£10
ditto, Chapman & Hall (London), 1953 (350 signed copies, glassine d/w). . . . . . £300/£250
Officers and Gentlemen, Chapman & Hall (London), 1955 .
. . . . £75/£15
ditto, Little, Brown (Boston), 1955 . . . £40/£10
The Ordeal of Gilbert Pinfold: A Conversation Piece, Chapman & Hall (London), 1957 . . . £35/£10
ditto, Chapman & Hall (London), 1957 (50 large copies for presentation). £1,500
ditto, Little, Brown (Boston), 1957 . . . £25/£10
Unconditional Surrender, Chapman & Hall (London), 1961 .
. . . . £45/£10
ditto, as **The End of The Battle**, Little, Brown (Boston), 1961 . . . . £25/£5
Basil Seal Rides Again, Chapman & Hall (London), 1963 (750 signed copies, glassine d/w) . . £250/£200
ditto, Chapman & Hall (London), 1963 . . £45/£15
ditto, Little, Brown (Boston), 1963 . . . £45/£15
ditto, Little, Brown (Boston), 1963 (1,000 signed copies, glassine d/w). . . . . . £225/£175
Sword of Honour, Little, Brown (Boston), 1961 . £35/£10
ditto, Chapman & Hall (London), 1965 (comprises *Men at Arms*, *Officers and Gentlemen* and *Unconditional Surrender*) . . . . £35/£10

Short Stories
Mr Loveday's Little Outing and Other Sad Stories, Chapman & Hall (London), 1936 . . £1,250/£100
ditto, Little, Brown (Boston), 1936 (750 copies) . £250/£35
Tactical Exercise, Little, Brown (Boston), 1954 . £45/£15

r's Schooldays and Other Stories, Little,
on), 1982 . . . . . £15/£5
Short Stories, Everyman's Library (London),
. . . . . £10/£5

ssay on The Pre-Raphaelite Brotherhood,
nted (London), 1926 (no d/w) . . £4,000
mple Press (Westerham, Kent), 1982 (475
d copies, acetate d/w) . . . . £50/£35
y Places, Queen Anne Press (London), 1952 (50
d, numbered copies) . . . . £650/£500
Queen Anne Press (London), 1952 (900 copies) . .
. . . . £100/£40
to, Queen Anne Press/British Book Centre (London/New
York), 1952 (950 copies) . . . . . £100/£40
ditto, Queen Anne Press/British Book Centre (London/New
York), 1952 (50 signed, numbered copies) . £650/£500

Travel
Labels, Duckworth (London), 1930 . . . £750/£75
ditto, Duckworth (London), 1930 (110 signed copies, page of
manuscript laid in) £1,750
ditto, as *A Bachelor Abroad*, Farrar (New York), 1932. .
. . . . £400/£40
Remote People, Duckworth (London), 1931 . £1,250/£125
ditto, as *They Were Still Dancing*, Farrar (New York), 1932
. . . . £150/£25
Ninety-Two Days, Duckworth (London), 1934 £1,000/£100
ditto, Farrar (New York), 1934 . . . . . £200/£30
Waugh in Abyssinia, Longman (London), 1936 £750/£100
ditto, Farrar (New York), 1936 . . . . £200/£25
Robbery Under Law, Chapman & Hall (London), 1939 .
. . . . £650/£75
ditto, as *Mexico: An Object Lesson*, Little, Brown (Boston),
1939 . . . . £200/£35
When The Going Was Good, Duckworth (London), 1946 .
. . . . £350/£100
ditto, Little, Brown (Boston), 1947 . . . £75/£20
A Tourist in Africa, Chapman & Hall (London), 1960 . .
. . . . £100/£20
ditto, Little, Brown (Boston), 1960 . . . £65/£15

Biography
Rossetti: His Life and Work, Duckworth (London), 1928 .
. . . . £1,500/£250
ditto, Dodd Mead (New York), 1928 . . . £500/£100
Edmund Campion, Longman (London), 1935 . . £650/£75
ditto, Longman (London), 1935 (50 signed copies). £1,500
ditto, Sheed and Ward (New York), 1935 . . £125/£35
The Life of the Right Reverend Ronald Knox, Chapman &
Hall (London), 1959 . . . . . £35/£5
ditto, Little, Brown (Boston), 1960 . . . £30/£5

Others
*An Open Letter to his Eminence the Cardinal Archbishop
of Westminster*, privately printed, 1933 . . . £5,000
Wine in Peace and War, Saccone & Speed (London), [1947]
. . . . £200/£150
ditto, Saccone & Speed (London), [1947] (100 signed
copies) £1,000
A Little Learning: The First Volume of an Autobiography,
Chapman & Hall (London), 1964 . . . £45/£10
ditto, Little, Brown (Boston), 1964 . . . £35/£10
Diaries, Weidenfeld (London), 1976 . . . £30/£10

ditto, Little, Brown (Boston), 1976 . . . . £30/£10
A Little Order: A Selection from his Journalism, Methuen
(London), 1977 . . . . . . £20/£5
ditto, Little, Brown (Boston), 1981 . . . . £15/£5
The Letters of Evelyn Waugh, Weidenfeld & Nicolson
(London), 1980 . . . . £20/£5
ditto, Ticknor & Fields (Boston), 1980 . . . £20/£5
The Essays, Articles and Reviews of Evelyn Waugh,
Methuen (London), 1983 . . . . . £20/£5
ditto, Little, Brown (Boston), 1984 . . . . £20/£5
*Mr Wu and Mrs Stitch: The Letters of Evelyn Waugh and
Diana Cooper*, Hodder & Stoughton (London), 1991 £15/£5
ditto, as *The Letters of Evelyn Waugh and Diana Cooper*,
Ticknor & Fields (New York), 1992 . . . £15/£5
The Letters of Nancy Mitford and Evelyn Waugh, Hodder
& Stoughton (London), 1996 . . . . £10/£5
ditto, Houghton Mifflin (Boston), 1996 . . . £10/£5

MARY WEBB
(b.1881 d.1927)

Mary Webb was an English novelist whose Hardyesque
stories powerfully describe nature and are peopled by
characters who battle grimly against fate. Although she
won the Prix Femina Vie Heureuse for *Precious Bane*, her
writing only came to prominence after her death, when she
was championed by Prime Minister Stanley Baldwin.

Novels
The Golden Arrow, Constable (London), 1916 . £100
ditto, Dutton (New York), 1918 . . . . . £50
Gone to Earth, Constable (London), 1917 (dark red cloth) .
. . . . £75
ditto, Dutton (New York), 1917 . . . . . £45
The House in Dormer Forest, Hutchinson (London), [1920]
. . . . £145/£35
ditto, Doran (New York), 1921 . . . . . £125/£30
Seven For A Secret, Hutchinson (London), 1922 . £125/£30
ditto, Doran (New York), 1923 . . . . . £100/£25
Precious Bane, Cape (London), 1924 . . £250/£100
ditto, Modern Library (New York), 1926 . . . £30/£10
Armour Wherein He Trusted, Cape (London), 1929 £50/£15
ditto, Dutton (New York), 1929 . . . . £40/£10

Short Stories
The Chinese Lion, Rota (London), 1937 (350 copies, glassine d/w and slipcase) . . . . . . £35/£20

Poetry
Poems and The Spring of Joy, Cape (London), 1928 £45/£15
ditto, Dutton (New York), 1929 . . . . . £35/£10
Fifty-One Poems, Cape (London), 1946 . . . £25/£5
ditto, Dutton (New York), 1946 . . . . £20/£5

Others
Spring of Joy: A Little Book of Healing, J.M. Dent & Sons
(London), 1917 . . . . £65
A Mary Webb Anthology, Cape (London), 1935 (illustrated
by Rowland Hilder and Norman Hepple) . . £20/£5
ditto, Dutton (New York), 1940 . . . . £20/£5
The Essential Mary Webb, Cape (London), 1949 . £15/£5

WEIRD TALES

Weird Tales was an American fantasy and horror fiction pulp magazine first published in 1923. Edwin Baird was the first editor of the monthly, assisted by Farnsworth Wright. Baird first published some of *Weird Tales'* best-known authors including H.P. Lovecraft, Clark Ashton Smith and Seabury Quinn. Under various editors *Weird Tales* struggled through to 1954. The magazine has been revived a number of times over the decades.

March, 1923, (1st issue, 1st state, on cover the word 'ooze' is in black surrounded by an orange rectangle, the woman's bow is black, the mans shirt orange and the faces are greenish) £3,000
ditto, (2nd state with rarer cover variant: 'ooze' in orange enclosed by black rectangle, the woman's bow is orange, the man's shirt grey and faces are flesh-toned) . £4,000
April, 1923 . . . . £2,500
May, 1923 . . . . £1,250
June, 1923 . . . . £1,000
July, 1923 (contains 2 poems by Clark Ashton Smith) £1,000
September, 1923 . . . . £750
October, 1923 (contains 'Dagon' by H.P. Lovecraft) £1,500
November, 1923 (contains 'The Invisible Monster' by H.P. Lovecraft) £1,000
January, 1924 (contains 'The Picture in the House' by H.P. Lovecraft) £750
February, 1924 (contains 'The Hound' by H.P. Lovecraft) .
. . . . £650
March, 1924 (contains 'The Rats in the Walls' by H.P. Lovecraft and article ghos-written for Houdini) . £650
April, 1924 (contains pseudonymous 'The Ghost-Eater', 'The White Ape' and poem by H.P. Lovecraft) . £500
May-June-July, 1924 (contains 'Imprisoned with the Pharaohs' ghost-written by Lovecraft for Houdini, 'The Loved Dead' ghost-written by Lovecraft for C.M. Eddy and Hypnas) £650
November, 1924 (contains work by Frank Belknap Long, Arthur J. Burks and Lovecraft). £800
December, 1924 . . . . £650
January, 1925 (contains 'The Festival' by H.P. Lovecraft) .
. . . . £650
February, 1925 (contains 'The Statement of Randolph Carter' by H.P. Lovecraft). £500
March, 1925 . . . . £300
April, 1925 (contains pseudonymous 'Deaf, Dumb and Blind' by H.P. Lovecraft) £250
May, 1925 (contains 'The Music of Erich Zann' by H.P. Lovecraft) £250
June, 1925 . . . . £325
July, 1925 (contains 'Spear and Fang' by Robert E. Howard, 'The Unnamable' by H.P. Lovecraft and 'The Werewolf of Ponkert' by H. Warner Munn).. . . . £650
August, 1925 (contains 'In the Forest of Villefere' by Robert E. Howard).. . . . . £325
September, 1925 (contains 'The Temple' by H.P. Lovecraft)
. . . . £175
October, 1925 (contains 'The Horror on the Links' by Seabury Quinn) £225
November, 1925 . . . . £125
December, 1925 . . . . £175
January, 1926 (contains 'The Tomb' by H.P. Lovecraft) .
. . . . £125

February, 1926 (contains 'The Cats of Ulthar' by H.P. Lovecraft) £125
March, 1926 . . . . £100
April, 1926 (contains 'The Outsider' by H.P. Lovecraft and 'Wolfshead' by Robert E. Howard). . . . £225
May, 1926 (contains 'Bat's Belfry' by August Dedeth). £125
June, 1926 (contains 'The Moon-Bug' by H.P. Lovecraft) .
. . . . £125
July, 1926 . . . . £100
August, 1926 (contains 'The Monster-god of Mamurth' by Edmond Hamilton, 'The Terrible Old Man' by H.P. Lovecraft and 'The Woman of the Wood' by A. Merritt) .
. . . . £175
September, 1926 (contains 'He' by H.P. Lovecraft and 'Jumbee' by Henry S. Whitehead) £125
October, 1926 . . . . £100
November, 1926 . . . . £100
December, 1926 (contains 'Metal Giants' by Edmond Hamilton) £150
January, 1927 (contains 'The Horror at Red Hook' by H.P. Lovecraft and 'The Lost Race' by Robert E. Howard) £100
February, 1927 . . . . £75
March, 1927 (contains 'The White Ship' by H.P. Lovecraft)
. . . . £75
April, 1927 . . . . £75
May, 1927 . . . . £65
June, 1927 . . . . £65
July, 1927 . . . . £65
August, 1927 . . . . £65
September, 1927 . . . . £75
October, 1927 (contains 'Pickman's Model' by H.P. Lovecraft, 'The Red Brain' by Donald Wandrei and 'Loup-Garou' by Wallace West) £100
November, 1927 (contains 'Back to the Beast' by Manly Wade Wellman) £75
December, 1927 . . . . £65
January, 1928 . . . . £50
February, 1928 (contains 'Call of Cthulhu' by H.P. Lovecraft and 'The Dream Snake' by Robert E. Howard) .
. . . . £125
March, 1928 (contains 'The Hyena' by Robert E. Howard) .
. . . . £75
April, 1928 . . . . £50
May, 1928 (contains 'The Sea Curse' by Robert E. Howard)
. . . . £75
June, 1928 (contains 'The Lurking Fear' by H.P. Lovecraft).
. . . . £75
July, 1928 . . . . £50
August, 1928 (contains 'Red Shadows' by Robert E. Howard and 'The Vengeance of Nitocris' by by Tennessee Williams under psudonym 'Thomas L. Williams') . £125
September, 1928 . . . . £50
October, 1928 (contains 'The Werewolf's Daughter' by H. Warner Munn) £75
November, 1928 . . . . £50
December, 1928 (contains 'The Copper Bowl' by George F. Eliot) £75
January, 1929 (contains 'The Silver Key' by H.P. Lovecraft and 'Skulls in the Stars' by Robert E. Howard) . £75
February, 1929 . . . . £50
March, 1929 (contains 'The Hounds of Tindalos' by Frank Belknap Long) £65
April, 1929 (contains 'The Dunwich Horror' by H.P. Lovecraft) £75
May, 1929 . . . . £50

June, 1929 (contains 'Rattle of Bones' by Robert E.
  Howard) £65
July, 1929 . . . . £50
August, 1929 (contains 'The Shadow Kingdom' by Robert
  E. Howard and 'The Inn of Terror' by Gaston Leroux) £75
September, 1929 (contains 'The Mirrors of Tuzun Thune' by
  Robert E. Howard) £65
October, 1929 (contains 'Skull-Face' by Robert E. Howard)
  . . . . £65
November, 1929 (contains 'The Curse of Yig' by H.P.
  Lovecraft ghost written for Zealia Brown Reed) . . £65
December, 1929 . . . . £65
January, 1930. . . . . £50
February, 1930 (contains 'The Fearsome Touch of Death'
  by Robert E. Howard). £75
March, 1930 . . . . £65
April, 1930 . . . . £50
May, 1930 . . . . £50
June, 1930 . . . . £75
July, 1930 . . . . £75
August, 1930 . . . . £75
September, 1930 . . . . £50
October, 1930. . . . . £50
November, 1930 . . . . £85
December, 1930 . . . . £50
January, 1931. . . . . £65
February, 1931 . . . . £50
March, 1931 . . . . £65
April, 1931 . . . . £50
May, 1931 . . . . £50
June - July, 1931 . . . . £50
August, 1931 (contains 'The Whisperer in Darkness' by H.P.
  Lovecraft) £75
September, 1931 . . . . £65
October, 1931. . . . . £65
November, 1931 . . . . £65
December, 1931 . . . . £65
January, 1932. . . . . £50
February, 1932 . . . . £50
March, 1932 . . . . £50
April, 1932 . . . . £50
May, 1932 . . . . £50
June, 1932 . . . . £50
July, 1932 . . . . £50
August, 1932 . . . . £50
September, 1932 . . . . £50
October, 1932. . . . . £50
November, 1932 . . . . £50
December, 1932 (contains 'The Phoenix on the Sword' by
  Robert E. Howard, the first appearance of Conan the
  Barbarian) £300
January, 1933. . . . .£100
February, 1933 . . . . £65
March, 1933 . . . . £75
April, 1933 . . . . £65
May, 1933 . . . . £40
June, 1933 . . . . £50
July, 1933 (contains 'The Horror in the Museum' by Hazel
  Heald ghost-written by Lovecraft and 'The Dreams in the
  Witch-House' by H.P. Lovecraft) £65
August, 1933 . . . . £40
September, 1933 . . . . £50
October, 1933 (classic bat-woman cover art by Margaret
  Brundage) £250
November, 1933 . . . . £50

December, 1933 . . . . £40
January, 1934. . . . . £50
February, 1934 . . . . £45
March, 1934 . . . . £45
April, 1934 . . . . £50
May, 1934 . . . .£100
June, 1934 . . . . £45
July, 1934 . . . . £45
August, 1934. . . . . £75
September, 1934 . . . . £45
October, 1934. . . . . £45
November, 1934 . . . . £45
December, 1934 . . . . £50
January, 1935. . . . . £65
February, 1935 . . . . £45
March, 1935 . . . . £45
April, 1935 . . . . £45
May, 1935 . . . . £45
June, 1935 . . . . £45
July, 1935 . . . . £30
August, 1935 . . . . £35
September, 1935 . . . . £65
October, 1935. . . . . £30
November, 1935 . . . . £45
December, 1935 . . . . £50
January, 1936. . . . . £35
February, 1936 . . . . £35
March, 1936 . . . . £45
April, 1936 . . . . £35
May, 1936 . . . . £35
June, 1936 . . . . £35
July, 1936 . . . . £50
August, 1936 . . . . £35
September, 1936 . . . . £35
October, 1936. . . . . £35
November, 1936 . . . . £35
December, 1936 . . . . £35
1937-1939 . . . . £35 each
1940-1945 . . . . £30 each
1946-1949 . . . . £25 each
1950-July 1953 . . . . . . £15 each
September 1953 –September 1954 . . . £10 each

DENTON WELCH

(b.1915 d.1948)

Welch studied painting at Goldsmiths' School of Art,
London, until a bicycle accident in 1935 severed his spine
and left him temporarily paralysed and permanently ill. He
took up writing, producing three highly autobiographical
books and numerous short stories and fragments. He is
admired for his often painfully precise descriptions of
people, objects, places and events.

Novels
Maiden Voyage, Routledge (London), 1943 . .£125/£30
ditto, Fischer (New York), 1945 . . . . . £50/£15
In Youth is Pleasure, Routledge (London), 1944 [1945] .
  . . . .£100/£20
ditto, Fischer (New York), 1946 . . . . . £45/£10
A Voice Through a Cloud, John Lehmann (London), 1950 .
  . . . . £50/£15
ditto, Dutton/Obelisk (New York), 1966 (pbk) . . £5

Short Stories/Miscellaneous

Brave and Cruel and Other Stories, Hamish Hamilton (London), 1948 [1949] . . . . . £100/£25

A Last Sheaf, John Lehmann (London), 1951 . . £75/£20

The Denton Welch Journals, Hamish Hamilton (London), 1952 (edited by Jocelyn Brooke) . . . . £65/£15

I Left My Grandfather's House, privately printed for James Campbell by The Lion & Unicorn Press (London), 1958 (130 of 150 copies) £100

ditto, privately printed for James Campbell by The Lion & Unicorn Press (London), 1958 (20 deluxe copies of 200) .
. . . . £250

ditto, The Lion & Unicorn Press (London), 1958 (200 numbered copies, 20pps of plates) £100

ditto, Allison & Busby (London), 1984 . . £15/£5

ditto, Allison & Busby (London), 1984 (pbk) . . . £5

Dumb Instrument, Enitharmon Press (London), 1976 (60 specially bound copies on blue paper of 600) . £250

ditto, Enitharmon Press (London), 1976 (540 copies of 600)
. . . . £75/£20

The Journals of Denton Welch, Allison & Busby (London), 1984 (edited by Michael De-la-Noy) . . £20/£10

ditto, Dutton (New York), 1984 . . . . £20/£5

The Stories of Denton Welch, Dutton (New York), 1985 .
. . . . £10/£5

Fragments of a Life Story: the Collected Short Writings of Denton Welch, Penguin (London), 1987 (edited and with an introduction by Michael De-la-Noy; pbk). . . £20

A Lunch Appointment, Elysium Press (North Pomfret, Vermont), 1993 (150 copies, bound in black silk) . £125

ditto, Elysium Press (North Pomfret, Vermont), 1993 (20 copies, bound in black silk), signed by Edmund White, with an extra signed etching by Le-Tan) . . £275

When I Was An Art Student, Elysium Press (North Pomfret, Vermont), 1998 (100 numbered copies in thin paper boards) £85

ditto, Elysium Press (North Pomfret, Vermont), 1998 (26 lettered cloth copies, slipcase) £125

Where Nothing Sleeps: The Complete Short Stories And Other Related Works, Tartarus Press (Carlton-in-Coverdale), 2005 (2 vols; d/ws and slipcase) . £70/£35

FAY WELDON
(b.1933)

A novelist, short story writer, playwright and essayist whose fiction often portrays contemporary women trapped in oppressive situations. Weldon worked in the advertising industry and then wrote for radio and television. Her popular success was the novel *The Life and Loves of a She Devil*, which was televised in the 1980s.

Novels

The Fat Woman's Joke, MacGibbon & Kee (London), 1967
. . . . £150/£35

ditto, as *... and the Wife Ran Away*, McKay (New York), 1968 . . . . £40/£10

Down Among the Women, Heinemann (London), 1971 .
. . . . £30/£5

ditto, St Martin's Press (New York), 1972 . . £15/£5

Female Friends, St Martin's Press (New York), 1974 £15/£5

ditto, Heinemann (London), 1975 . . . . £35/£10

Remember Me, Hodder & Stoughton (London), 1976 £15/£5

ditto, Random House (New York), 1976 . . . £10/£5

Words of Advice, Random House (New York), 1977 £10/£5

ditto, as *Little Sisters*, Hodder & Stoughton (London), 1977
. . . . £20/£5

Praxis, Hodder & Stoughton (London), 1978 . . £20/£5

ditto, Summit (New York), 1978. . . . . £15/£5

Puffball, Hodder & Stoughton (London), 1980 . £15/£5

ditto, Summit (New York), 1980. . . . . £15/£5

The President's Child, Hodder & Stoughton (London), 1982
. . . . £15/£5

ditto, Doubleday (Garden City, NY), 1983 . . £15/£5

The Life and Loves of a She Devil, Hodder & Stoughton (London), 1983 . . . . £25/£5

ditto, Pantheon (New York), 1984 . . . . £15/£5

The Shrapnel Academy, Hodder & Stoughton (London), 1986 . . . . £10/£5

ditto, Viking (New York), 1987 . . . . . £10/£5

The Heart of the Country, Century Hutchinson (London), 1987 . . . . £10/£5

ditto, Viking (New York), 1988 . . . . . £10/£5

The Hearts and Lives of Men, Heinemann (London), 1987.
. . . . £10/£5

ditto, Viking (New York), 1988 . . . . . £10/£5

The Rules of Life, Century Hutchinson (London), 1987 .
. . . . £10/£5

ditto, Harper & Row (New York), 1987 . . . £10/£5

Leader of the Band, Hodder & Stoughton (London), 1988 .
. . . . £10/£5

ditto, Viking (New York), 1989 . . . . . £10/£5

The Cloning of Joanna May, Collins (London), 1989 . .
. . . . £10/£5

ditto, Viking (New York), 1990 . . . . . £10/£5

Darcy's Utopia, Collins (London), 1990 . . . £10/£5

ditto, Viking (New York), 1991 . . . . . £10/£5

Growing Rich, HarperCollins (London), 1992 . £10/£5

Life Force, HarperCollins (London), 1992 . . £10/£5

ditto, Viking (New York), 1992 . . . . . £10/£5

Trouble, Viking (New York), 1993 . . . . £10/£5

ditto, as *Affliction*, HarperCollins (London), 1993 . £10/£5

Splitting, HarperCollins (London), 1995 . . . £10/£5

ditto, Atlantic Monthly Press (New York), 1995 . £10/£5

Worst Fears, HarperCollins (London), 1996 . . £10/£5

ditto, Atlantic Monthly Press (New York), 1996 . £10/£5

Big Women, HarperCollins (London), 1997 . . £10/£5

ditto, as *Big Girls Don't Cry*, Atlantic Monthly Press (New York), 1997 . . . . £10/£5

Rhode Island Blues, Flamingo (London), 2000 . £10/£5

ditto, Atlantic Monthly Press (New York), 2000 . £10/£5

The Bulgari Connection, Flamingo (London), 2001 £10/£5

ditto, Atlantic Monthly Press (New York), 2001 . £10/£5

Mantrapped, Fourth Estate (London), 2004 . . £10/£5

ditto, Grove (New York), 2004 . . . . . £10/£5

She May Not Leave, Fourth Estate (London), 2005 £10/£5

ditto, Atlantic Monthly Press (New York), 2006 . £10/£5

The Spa Decameron, Quercus (London), 2007 . £10/£5

The Stepmother's Diary, Quercus (London), 2008. £10/£5

Chalcot Crescent, Corvus (London), 2009 . . £10/£5

Short Stories

Watching Me Watching You, Hodder & Stoughton (London), 1981 . . . . £20/£5

ditto, Summit (New York), 1981. . . . . £15/£5

Polaris, Hodder & Stoughton (London), 1985. . £15/£5

ditto, Penguin (New York), 1989 (pbk) £5

Moon over Minneapolis Or Why She Couldn't Stay, Collins (London), 1991 . . . . . . £15/£5
ditto, Penguin (New York), 1992 (pbk) £5
A Question of Timing, Colophon Press (London), 1992 (125 unsigned, numbered copies of 231; wraps) . . . £10
ditto, Colophon Press (London), 1992 (100 signed, numbered copies of 231; wraps) £25
ditto, Colophon Press (London), 1992 (6 signed, numbered copies of 231; wraps) £150
Angel, All Innocence and Other Stories, Bloomsbury (London), 1995 (pbk) £5
Wicked Women, HarperCollins (London), 1995 . £10/£5
ditto, Atlantic Monthly Press (New York), 1997 . £10/£5
A Hard Time to Be a Father, Flamingo (London), 1998 .
. . . . £10/£5
ditto, Bloomsbury (New York), 1999. . . . £10/£5
Nothing to Wear & Nowhere to Hide, Flamingo (London), 2002 . . . . £10/£5

Children's Books
Wolf the Mechanical Dog, Collins (London), 1988 £15/£5
Party Puddle, Collins (London), 1989 . . . £15/£5
Nobody Likes Me!, Bodley Head (London), 1997 . £15/£5

Plays
Words of Advice, French (London), 1974 (pbk) . . £10
Action Replay, French (London), 1980 (pbk) . . . £10
I Love My Love, French (London), 1984 . . . £25/£10
The Reading Group, French (London), 1999 (pbk) . £5

Others
Letters to Alice: On First Reading Jane Austen, Joseph/ Rainbird Books (London), 1984 . . . . £15/£5
ditto, Taplinger (New York), 1985 . . . . £15/£5
Rebecca West, Viking (London), 1985 . . . £10/£5
ditto, Viking (New York), 1986 . . . . . £15/£5
Sacred Cows, Chatto & Windus (London), 1989 (pbk) £5
The Lady Is a Tramp: Portraits of Catherine Bailey, Thames & Hudson (London & New York), 1995 (photographs by David Bailey, text by Weldon) . . £20/£10
Godless in Eden: A Book of Essays, Flamingo (London), 1999 . . . . £10/£5
Auto Da Fay: A Memoir, Flamingo (London), 2002 £10/£5
ditto, Grove (New York), 2003 . . . . . £10/£5
What Makes Women Happy, Fourth Estate (London), 2006 . . . . £10/£5

H.G. WELLS

(b.1866 d.1946)

Wells was a versatile novelist whose writing ranged from innovative science fiction through to social realism, and he was also the author of works on politics, society and history. Towards the end of his life Wells grew increasingly pessimistic about the prospects for humanity: his last book was entitled *Mind at the End of its Tether*.

Novels
The Time Machine: An Invention, Henry Holt (New York), 1895 (first issue: bound in tan buckram, lettering stamped in purple, author's name misspelt 'H.S. Wells' on title-

page; 12 titles in the *Buckram Series* advertised on verso of half title, no mention of THE TIME MACHINE; six pages of ads at rear) £2,250
ditto, Henry Holt (New York), 1895 (second issue: bound as above; author's name correctly spelt on title-page; no ads at rear) £750
ditto, Henry Holt (New York), 1895 (third issue: bound in vertically ribbed red cloth) £500
ditto, Heinemann (London), 1895 (light tan cloth, 'H.S. Wells' on spine) £20,000
ditto, Heinemann (London), 1895 (light blue-grey wraps, printed in dark blue) £1,500
ditto, Heinemann (London), 1895 (grey cloth stamped in purple) £1,500
ditto, Heinemann (London), 1895 (second printing, red cloth)
. . . . £450
The Wonderful Visit, Dent (London), 1895 (front board blank) £300
ditto, Dent (London), 1895 (front board stamped with gilt angel by Arthur Rackham) £250
ditto, Macmillan (New York), 1895 . . . . .£100
The Island of Doctor Moreau, Heinemann (London), 1896 (monogram blind-stamped on back board) . . £750
ditto, Heinemann (London), 1896 (no monogram) . £450
ditto, Stone & Kimball (New York), 1896 (black cloth) £225
The Wheels of Chance: A Cycling Holiday Adventure, Dent (London), 1896 . . . . £150
ditto, Macmillan (New York), 1896 . . . . . £75
The Red Room, Stone & Kimball (New York), 1896 (12 copies only) £10,000
The Invisible Man: A Grotesque Romance, Pearson (London), 1897 . . . . £1,250
ditto, Arnold (New York), 1897 . . . . . . £750
The War of the Worlds, Heinemann (London), 1898 (16 pages of ads). £1,000
ditto, Heinemann (London), 1898 (32 pages of ads) . £750
ditto, Harper (New York), 1898 (15 illustrations by Warwick Goble, frontispiece by Cosmo Rowe) £400
When the Sleeper Wakes: A Story of Years to Come, Harpers (London), 1899 . . . .£175
ditto, Harper (New York), 1899 . . . . . .£125
ditto, Thomas Nelson (London), 1910 (revised edition). £25
Love and Mr Lewisham, Harpers (London), 1900 . . £65
ditto, Stokes (New York), 1900 . . . . . . £45
The First Men in the Moon, Bowen-Merrill (Indianapolis, IN), 1901 (first binding with 'Bowen Merrill' at base of spine panel) £750
ditto, Bowen-Merrill (Indianapolis, IN), 1901 (second binding with 'Bobbs / Merrill' at base of spine panel). £450
ditto, Newnes (London), 1901 (first issue in dark blue cloth, black endpapers) £450
ditto, Newnes (London), 1901 (second issue in dark blue cloth, white endpapers) £350
ditto, Newnes (London), 1901 (third issue in light blue cloth)
. . . . £325
ditto, Newnes (London), 1901 (fourth issue in blue/green cloth) £300
The Sea Lady: A Tissue of Moonshine, Methuen (London), 1902 . . . .£275
ditto, Appleton (New York), 1902 . . . . . £75
The Food of the Gods and How It Came to Earth, Macmillan (London), 1904 . . . . . .£150
ditto, Scribner's (New York), 1904 . . . . . £75
A Modern Utopia, Chapman & Hall (London), 1905 . £145
ditto, Scribner's (New York), 1905 . . . . . £65

Kipps: The Story of a Simple Soul, Macmillan (London), 1905 . . . . £65
ditto, Scribner's (New York), 1905 . . . . . £35
In The Days of The Comet, Macmillan (London), 1906 £75
ditto, Century (New York), 1906 . . . . . £50
The War in the Air and Particularly How Mr Bert Smallways Fared While It Lasted, George Bell (London), 1908 (first issue, blue cloth with lettering and decorations in gilt; no illustration on cover) . £225
ditto, George Bell (London), 1908 (second issue with blue cloth blind-stamped) £150
ditto, Macmillan (New York), 1908 . . . . . £150
Tono-Bungay, Macmillan (London), 1909 (with ads dated '1.09') £75
ditto, Macmillan (London), 1909 (with ads dated '2.09') £45
ditto, Duffield (New York), 1909 . . . . . £65
Ann Veronica, T. Fisher Unwin (London), 1909 . £65
ditto, Harper (New York), 1909 . . . . . £45
The History of Mr Polly, Thomas Nelson (London), 1910 . . . . £50
ditto, Duffield (New York), 1910 . . . . . £40
The New Machiavelli, Duffield (New York), 1910 (first issue with integral title-page without quotes by Lewes and James) £65
ditto, Duffield (New York), 1910 (second issue with cancel title-page with quotes) £30
ditto, John Lane/Bodley Head (London), 1911 . £45
Marriage, Macmillan (London), 1912 . . . £35
ditto, Duffield (New York), 1912 . . . . £25
The Passionate Friends, Macmillan (London), 1913 . £45
ditto, Harper (New York), 1913 . . . . . £45
The World Set Free, Macmillan (London), 1914 . £35
ditto, Dutton (New York), 1914 . . . . . £30
The Wife of Sir Isaac Harman, Macmillan (London), 1914 . . . . £35
ditto, Macmillan (New York), 1914 . . . . £30
Boon, T. Fisher Unwin (London), 1915 . . . £25
ditto, Doran (New York), 1915 . . . . . £25
Bealby: A Holiday, Methuen (London), 1915 . . £20
ditto, Macmillan (New York), 1915 . . . . £20
The Research Magnificent, Macmillan (London), 1915 £20
ditto, Macmillan (New York), 1915 . . . . £20
Mr Britling Sees It Through, Cassell (London), 1916 . £20
ditto, Macmillan (New York), 1916 . . . . £20
The Soul of a Bishop, Cassell (London), 1917 . £15
ditto, Macmillan (New York), 1917 . . . . £15
Joan and Peter: The Story of an Education, Cassell (London), 1918 . . . . £15
ditto, Macmillan (New York), 1918 . . . . £15
The Undying Fire, Cassell (London), 1919 . . £15
ditto, Macmillan (New York), 1919 . . . . £15
The Secret Places of the Heart, Cassell (London), 1922 . . . . £75/£15
ditto, Macmillan (New York), 1922 . . . £75/£15
Men Like Gods, Cassell (London), 1923 . . £125/£25
ditto, Macmillan (New York), 1923 . . . £125/£15
The Dream, Cape (London), 1924 . . . £100/£15
ditto, Macmillan (New York), 1924 . . . £100/£15
Christina Alberta's Father, Cape (London), 1925 . £75/£10
ditto, Macmillan (New York), 1925 . . . £75/£10
The World of William Clissold, Ernest Benn (London), 1926 (3 vols) . . . . £100/£25
ditto, Ernest Benn (London), 1926 (198 deluxe signed copies, 3 vols, slipcase) . . . . £250/£150
ditto, Doran (New York), 1926 (2 vols, slipcase) . £85/£20

Meanwhile, Ernest Benn (London), 1927 . . . £75/£10
ditto, Doran (New York), 1927 . . . . . £65/£10
Mr Blettsworthy on Rampole Island, Ernest Benn (London), 1928 . . . . £65/£10
ditto, Doubleday Doran (New York), 1928 . . £65/£10
The King Who Was a King, The book of a film, Ernest Benn (London), 1929 . . . . . . £65/£10
ditto, Doubleday Doran (New York), 1929 . . £65/£10
The Autocracy of Mr Parham, Heinemann (London), 1930. . . . . £50/£10
ditto, Doubleday Doran (New York), 1930 . . £50/£10
The Bulpington of Blup, Hutchinson (London), 1932 . . . . £40/£10
ditto, Macmillan (New York), 1933 . . . . £40/£10
The Shape of Things to Come, The Ultimate Revolution, Hutchinson (London), 1933 . . . £200/£30
ditto, Macmillan (New York), 1933 . . . £200/£25
ditto, as *Things to Come: A Film Story*, Cresset Press (London), 1935 . . . . £65/£10
The Croquet Player, Chatto & Windus (London), 1936 . . . . £50/£10
ditto, Viking (New York), 1937 . . . . . £50/£10
Man Who Could Work Miracles: A Film Story, Cresset Press (London), 1936 . . . . . . £45/£10
ditto, Macmillan (New York), 1936 . . . . £45/£10
Star Begotten: A Biological Fantasia, Chatto & Windus (London), 1937 . . . . £45/£15
ditto, Viking (New York), 1937 . . . . . £45/£15
Brynhild, Methuen (London), 1937 . . . . £40/£10
ditto, Scribner's (New York), 1937 . . . . £40/£10
The Camford Visitation, Methuen (London), 1937 £45/£15
The Brothers, Chatto & Windus (London), 1938 . £40/£10
ditto, Viking (New York), 1938 . . . . . £40/£10
Apropos of Dolores, Cape (London), 1938 . . £40/£10
ditto, Scribner's (New York), 1938 . . . . £40/£10
The Holy Terror, Joseph (London), 1939. . . £40/£10
ditto, Simon & Schuster (New York), 1939 . . £40/£10
The Final Men, Phantagraph Press (Rego Park, New York), 1940 (pbk) £50
Babes in the Darkling Wood, Secker & Warburg (London), 1940 . . . . £40/£10
ditto, Alliance Book Corp. (New York), 1940 . . £40/£10
All Aboard for Ararat, Secker & Warburg (London), 1940 . . . . £40/£10
ditto, Alliance Book Corp. (New York), 1941 . . £40/£10
You Can't Be Too Careful, Secker & Warburg (London), 1941 . . . . £35/£10
The Wealth of Mr Waddy, Southern Illinois Univ Press (Carbondale, IL), 1969 . . . . . . £25/£5

Omnibus Edition
Three Prophetic Novels of H.G. Wells, Dover (New York), 1960 (pbk) £5

Short Stories
Select Conversations with an Uncle, Now Extinct, and Two Other Remininiscences, Lane (London), 1895 . . £125
ditto, Merriam (New York), 1895 . . . . . £100
The Stolen Bacillus and Other Incidents, Methuen (London), 1895 . . . . £650
The Plattner Story and Others, Methuen (London), 1897 . . . . £350
Thirty Strange Stories, Edward Arnold (New York), 1897 . . . . £250

Tales of Space and Time, Harpers (London), 1900 [1899] .
. . . . £250
ditto, Doubleday (New York), 1899 . . . . £250
Twelve Stories and a Dream, Macmillan (London), 1903 .
. . . . £250
ditto, Scribner's (New York), 1905 . . . . £150
The Country of the Blind, and Other Stories, Nelson
(London), 1911 . . . . £50
ditto, privately printed (New York), 1915. . . £145
ditto, Golden Cockerel Press (Waltham St Lawrence, Berks),
1939 (30 signed copies) £1,000
ditto, Golden Cockerel Press (Waltham St Lawrence, Berks),
1939 (280 signed copies) £250
The Door in the Wall and Other Stories, Mitchell Kennerley
(New York), 1911 (240 copies with full set of plates by
Coburn) £750
ditto, Mitchell Kennerley (New York), 1915 (300 copies
with reduced set of plates). £125
ditto, Grant Richards (London), 1915 (60 signed copies with
full set of plates) £1,750
The Short Stories of H.G. Wells, Ernest Benn (London),
1927 . . . . £50/£20
The Desert Daisy, Beta Phi Mu (Urbana, IL), 1957 (1,413
numbered copies, glassine d/w) . . £20/£15
ditto, Beta Phi Mu (Urbana, IL), 1957 (no d/w) . £5
H.G. Wells: Short Stories, Folio Society (London), 1990
(with slipcase) . . . . . . £10/£5
*The Man Who Could Work Miracles: The Supernatural
Tales of...*, Tartarus Press (Carlton-in-Coverdale), 2006 .
. . . . £35/£10
ditto, as *A Dream of Armageddon*, Fall River Press (New
York), 2009 . . . . £10/£5

Children's Titles

Floor Games, Palmer (London), 1911 . . . £100
ditto, Small, Maynard (Boston), 1912 . . . £75
Little Wars, Palmer (London), 1913 . . . £100
ditto, Small, Maynard (Boston), 1913 . . . £100
The Adventures of Tommy, Harrap (London), 1929 . .
. . . . £125/£35
ditto, Amalgamated Press (London), 1929 (numbered copies
for private circulation; wraps) £150
ditto, Stokes (New York), 1929 . . . £125/£35

Others

Text-Book of Biology, W.B. Clive (London), 1893 (2 vols,
47 two-page plates, first binding dark green cloth) . £750
ditto, W.B. Clive (London), 1893 (2 vols, second binding
brown cloth). £500
ditto, W.B. Clive (London), 1894 (revised edition of Part 1)
. . . . £45
ditto, as *Text-Book of Zoology*, W.B. Clive (London), 1898
(revised edition) £35
Honours Physiography, Joseph Hughes (London), 1893
(with R.A. Gregory) £250
Certain Personal Matters, Lawrence & Bullen (London),
1898 [1897] £100
*Anticipations of the Reactions of Mechanical and Scientific
Progress upon Human Life and Thought*, Chapman &
Hall (London), 1902 [1901] £75
ditto, Harper (New York), 1902 . . . . £75
The Discovery of the Future, T. Fisher Unwin (London),
1902 (wraps and cloth) £125
ditto, Heubsch (New York), 1913 . . . . £45

Mankind in the Making, Chapman & Hall (London), 1903 .
. . . . £30
ditto, Scribner's (New York), 1904 . . . . £25
The Future in America: A Search after Realities, Chapman
& Hall (London), 1906 . . . . . £35
ditto, Harpers (New York), 1906. . . . . £25
Faults of The Fabian, Edward R. Pease (London), 1906 £30
Socialism and the Family, Fifield (London), 1906 (hard
covers) £30
ditto, Fifield (London), 1906 (paper covers) . . £30
Reconstruction of The Fabian Society, privately printed
(London), 1906 . . . . £35
The So-Called Science of Sociology, Macmillan (London),
1907 . . . . £35
The Misery of Boots, The Fabian Society (London), 1907 .
. . . . £30
Will Socialism Destroy the Home?, Independent Labour
Party (London), 1907. . . . . . £35
New Worlds for Old, Constable (London), 1908 . £45
ditto, Macmillan (New York), 1908 . . . . £40
*First and Last Things: A Confession of Faith and Rule of
Life*, Constable (London), 1908 . . . . £40
ditto, Putnams (New York), 1908 . . . . £35
The Labour Unrest, Associated Press (London), 1912 . £25
War and Common Sense, Associated Press (London), 1913
. . . . £25
Liberalism and It's Party, Good (London), 1913 . £25
An Englishman Looks at the World, Cassell (London), 1914
. . . . £25
The War That Will End War, Palmer (London), 1914
(wraps) £45
ditto, Duffield (New York), 1914 . . . . £35
The Peace of the World, Daily Chronicle (London), 1915
(wraps) £35
What Is Coming: A Forecast of Things after the War,
Cassell (London), 1916 . . . . . £30
ditto, Macmillan (New York), 1916 . . . . £25
The Elements of Reconstruction, Nisbet (London), 1916 .
. . . . £25
War and the Future, Cassell (London), 1917. . . £25
God the Invisible King, Cassell (London), 1917 . £25
ditto, Macmillan (New York), 1917 . . . . £20
In the Fourth Year: Anticipations of a World Peace, Chatto
& Windus (London), 1918 . . . . . £25
History is One, Ginn (Boston), 1919 (pamphlet) . £30
The Outline of History, Newnes (London), [1919-1920] (24
parts; stapled wraps) £100
ditto, Newnes (London), [1920] (2 vols) . . . £45
Russia in the Shadows, Hodder & Stoughton (London),
[1920] . . . . £100/£30
The Salvaging of Civilization, Cassell (London), 1921 . .
. . . . £75/£25
ditto, as *The Salvaging of Civilization: The Probable
Future of Mankind*, Macmillan (New York), 1921 .
. . . . £50/£15
University of London Election: An Electoral Letter, H.
Finer (London), 1922 (Single sheet folded to make 4pps;
wraps) £20
The Story of a Great Schoolmaster, Chatto & Windus
(London), 1924 . . . . . . £60/£20
ditto, Macmillan (New York), 1924 . . . £50/£15
A Year of Prophesying, T. Fisher Unwin (London), 1924 .
. . . . £45
Mr Belloc Objects to 'The Outline of History', Watts (New
York), 1926 . . . . £40/£15

ditto, Doran (New York), 1926 . . . . £40/£15
Democracy Under Revision, Hogarth Press (London), 1927
. . . . £75/£25
Experiments on Animals: Views for and Against, British
Union for Abolition of Vivesection (London), [1927?]
(wraps; with George Bernard Shaw) . . . £50
The Way the World is Going, Ernest Benn (London), 1928 .
. . . . £100/£25
ditto, Doran (New York), 1929 . . . £75/£20
The Open Conspiracy: Blue Prints for a World Revolution,
Gollancz (London), 1928 . . . . £65/£20
The Common Sense of World Peace, Hogarth Press
(London), 1929 . . . . . . £75/£30
**The Science of Life: A Summary of Contemporary
Knowledge about Life and Its Possibilities**, Amalgamated
Press (London), [1930] (with Julian Huxley and G.P.
Wells, 3 vols) . . . . . . £125/£50
ditto, Cassell (London), 1931 (1 vol.) . . £50/£15
ditto, Doubleday Doran (New York), 1931 (750 signed
copies, 4 vols) £250
ditto, Doubleday Doran (New York), 1931 (2 vols) . £250
The Problems of the Troublesome Collaborator, The
Society of Authors (London), 1930 (175 copies) . . £125
**Settlement of the Trouble between Mr Thring and Mr
Wells, A Footnote to The Problems of the Troublesome
Collaborator**, The Society of Authors (London), 1930 (225
copies) £75
The Work, Wealth and Happiness of Mankind, Doubleday
Doran (New York), 1931 . . . . . £30/£10
ditto, Doubleday Doran (New York), 1931 (250 signed
copies, 2 vols) £150
ditto, Heinemann (London), 1932 (1 vol.). . £45/£20
After Democracy, Watts (New York), 1932 . £50/£15
**Experiment in Autobiography: Discoveries and
Conclusions of a Very Ordinary Brain (since 1866)**,
Gollancz (London) & Cresset Press (London), 1934 (2
vols) . . . . £75/£30
ditto, Macmillan (New York), 1934 (1 vol.) . . £50/£15
The New America: The New World, Cresset Press (London),
1935 . . . . £50/£15
ditto, Macmillan (New York), 1935 . . . £50/£15
The Idea of a World Encyclopaedia, Hogarth Press
(London), 1936 (wraps) £45
The Anatomy of Frustration, Cresset Press (London), 1936
. . . . £40/£10
ditto, Macmillan (New York), 1936 . . . £40/£10
World Brain, Methuen (London), 1938 . . £45/£10
Travels of a Republican Radical in Search of Hot Water,
Penguin (Harmondsworth, Middlesex), 1939 (pbk with
d/w; d/w has title **In Search of Hot Water**) . £25/£10
The Fate of Homo Sapiens, Secker & Warburg (London),
1939 . . . . £50/£15
The New World Order, Secker & Warburg (London), 1940.
. . . . £45/£15
ditto, Knopf (New York), 1940 . . . . £45/£15
The Rights of Man, or What Are We Fighting For?
Penguin (Harmondsworth, Middlesex), 1940 (pbk with
d/w) . . . . £25/£10
**The Common Sense of War and Peace: World Revolution
or War Unending**, Penguin (Harmondsworth, Middlesex),
1940 (pbk with d/w) . . . . . £25/£10
**Guide to the New World: A Handbook of Constructive
Revolution**, Gollancz (London), 1941 . . £35/£15
The Outlook for Homo Sapiens, Secker & Warburg
(London), 1942 . . . . . . £30/£10

**Phoenix: A Summary of the Inescapable Conditions of
World Organisation**, Secker & Warburg (London), 1942 .
. . . . £40/£10
**A Thesis on the Quality of Illusion in the Continuity of the
Individual Life in the Higher Metazoa, with Particular
Reference to Species Homo Sapiens**, privately printed,
Watts (New York), 1942 (wraps) . . . £40
**Crux Ansata: An Indictment of the Roman Catholic
Church**, Penguin (Harmondsworth, Middlesex), 1943
(pbk) £5
'42 to '44: A Contemporary Memoir, Secker & Warburg
(London), 1944 . . . . . . £45/£10
Mind at the End of It's Tether, Heinemann (London), 1945
. . . . £40/£10
The Happy Turning: A Dream of Life, Heinemann
(London), 1945 . . . . . . £40/£10
ditto, as **Mind at the End of It's Tether** and **The Happy
Turning: A Dream of Life**, Didier (New York), 1946 .
. . . . £35/£10

IRVINE WELSH

(b.1958)

Welsh is a Scottish novelist who writes with black humour
about working-class Scottish life, often in his native
Edinburgh dialect. (Non-Scottish readers may have
difficulty deciphering the language, and may miss many of
the references to football, sectarianism etc.) His best known
work is *Trainspotting*, which is about a group of heroin
addicts and their attempts to give up using the drug.

Novels

Trainspotting, Secker & Warburg (London), 1993 (pbk) £200
ditto, Secker & Warburg (London), 1993 (110 hardcover
copies) . . . . . £2,000/£1,000
ditto, Norton (New York) 1996 (pbk, first state cover with
skeleton masks) £65
ditto, Norton (New York) 1996 (pbk, second state cover with
movie tie-in photo) £10
Marabou Stork Nightmares, Cape (London), 1995 (pbk) £5
ditto, Norton (New York), 1996 (pbk) . . . £5
Filth, Cape (London), 1998 . . . . £15/£5
ditto, Cape (London), 1998 (75 signed, numbered copies,
special binding) £65
ditto, Cape (London), 1998 ('obscene' limited edition: 50
signed, numbered copies with alternative d/w in addition to
the standard issue d/w.) . . . . £65/£5
ditto, Norton (New York), 1998 (pbk) . . . £5
Glue, Cape (London), 2001 . . . . £10/£5
ditto, Cape (London), 2001 (100 numbered, signed copies,
slipcase). . . . . . . £100/£65
ditto, Norton (New York), 2001 (pbk) . . . £5
Porno, Cape (London), 2002 . . . . £10/£5
ditto, Norton (New York), 2002 . . . . £10/£5
The Bedroom Secrets Of The Master Chefs, Cape (London),
2006 . . . . £10/£5
ditto, Norton (New York), 2006 . . . . £10/£5
Crime, Cape (London), 2008 . . . . £10/£5
ditto, Norton (New York), 2008 . . . . £10/£5

Short Stories

Past Tense, Clocktower Press (South Queensferry, Scotland), n.d. [1992] (stapled wraps, 300 copies) . £125

The Acid House, Cape (London), 1994 (pbk) . . . £5
ditto, Norton (New York), 1995 (pbk) . . . £5
Ecstasy: Three Tales of Chemical Romance, Cape (London), 1996 . . . . . . £20/£5
ditto, Cape (London), 1996 (50 numbered, signed copies, special binding) £150
ditto, Cape (London), 1996 (pbk) . . . £5
ditto, Norton (New York), 1996 (pbk) . . . £5
If You Liked School You'll Love Work, Cape (London), 2007 . . . . . . £10/£5
ditto, Norton (New York), 1996 . . . . £5
Reheated Cabbage, Cape (London), 2009 . . £10/£5

Plays

You'll Have Had Your Hole, Methuen Drama/Random House (London), 1998 (pbk) £5
Babylon Heights, Methuen (London), 2006 (with Dean Cavanagh; pbk) £5
ditto, Norton (New York), 2006 (pbk) . . . £5

EUDORA WELTY
(b.1909 d.2001)

Eudora Welty was an award-winning American author who wrote principally about the American South. During the 1930s she worked as a photographer but then devoted her time to writing fiction and over a full-time career which lasted for over fifty years she won numerous awards including the Pulitzer Prize in 1973 for her novel, *The Optimist's Daughter*.

Eudora Welty: A Note on the Author and Her Work, by Katherine Anne Porter, Doubleday Doran (Garden City, NY), 1941 (contains a single story by Welty, along with an appreciation by Porter; stapled wraps) . . . £1,500
A Curtain of Green, Doubleday Doran (Garden City, NY), 1941 . . . . £1,000/£165
ditto, John Lane Bodley Head (London), 1943 . £300/£75
The Robber Bridegroom, Doubleday Doran (Garden City, NY), 1942 . . . . . . £500/£100
ditto, Pennyroyal Press (West Hatfield, MA), 1987 (150 numbered copies signed by Welty and illustrator Barry Moser; full leather; no slipcase) £400
ditto, Harcourt Brace Jovanovich (San Diego/New York/London), 1987 (states 'First edition') . . £25/£5
ditto, Harcourt Brace Jovanovich (San Diego/New York/London), 1987 (states 'First edition'; signed by author on tipped-in leaf) £100
The Wide Net and Other Stories, Harcourt, Brace (New York), 1943 . . . . £600/£100
ditto, John Lane Bodley Head (London), 1945 (reverse of Welty d/w is for *Unlucky Farm* by F.E. Mills Young) .
. . . . £250/£35
Delta Wedding, Bodley Head (London), 1947. . £100/£20
Music From Spain, The Levee Press (Greenville, MS), 1948 (750 signed, numbered copies; glassine d/w) £400/£375
The Golden Apples, Harcourt, Brace (New York), 1949 .
. . . . £200/£20
ditto, Bodley Head (London), 1950 (first issue in brown cloth lacking front endpapers) . . . . £100/£20

ditto, Bodley Head (London), 1950 (second printing states 'First published in England'; red cloth stamped in black on spine; no endpapers) . . . . . . £20/£5
Short Stories, Harcourt, Brace (New York), 1949 (glassine d/w) . . . . £125/£100
ditto, Folcroft Library Editions (Folcroft, PA), 1971 (150 copies; no d.w) £20
The Ponder Heart, Harcourt, Brace (New York), 1954. .
. . . . £125/£25
ditto, Hamish Hamilton (London), 1954 . . £65/£15
ditto, as *The Ponder Heart: A Play*, Random House (New York) 1956 (adapted by Joseph Feilds and Jerome Chodorov) . . . . £30/£5
Selected Stories of Eudora Welty, Modern Library (New York), 1954 . . . . £30/£5
The Bride of Innisfallen and Other Stories, Harcourt, Brace (New York), 1955 (first edition, first state: copyright notice contains only one date 'copyright ... 1955, by Eudora Welty'; bound in blue and green mottled boards with green cloth spine and silver stamping) . £300/£150
ditto, Harcourt, Brace (New York), 1955 (first edition, second state: copyright contains 5 dates 'copyright...1949, 1951, 1952, 1954, 1955...'; copyright page tipped-in; bound as above) . . . . £125/£50
ditto, Harcourt, Brace (New York), 1955 (first edition, second printing: states 'first edition'; copyright notice with 5 dates as above but copyright page is integral; bound in light grey/brown cloth with blue and gold stamping) .
. . . . £75/£15
ditto, Hamish Hamilton (London), 1955 . . £100/£15
Place in Fiction, South Atlantic Quarterly (no place), [c.1956] (stapled wraps) £450
ditto, House of Books (New York), 1957 (26 signed, lettered copies in glassine d/w) . . . . £750/£700
ditto, House of Books (New York), 1957 (300 signed, numbered copies in glassine d/w) . . . £300/£250
October 7-25, 1958: Exhibition of Recent Sculpture, John Wood, The Contemporaries (New York), 1958 (wraps) .
. . . . £250
Henry Green: A Novelist ... , The Texas Quarterly (Austin, TX), 1961 (50 copies; stapled wraps) . . . £250
Three Papers on Fiction, Smith College (Northampton, MA), 1962 (stapled wraps) £50
The Shoe Bird, Harcourt, Brace & World (New York), 1964.
. . . . £150/£30
Thirteen Stories, Harcourt, Brace & World (New York), 1965 (pbk) £15
ditto, as *Moon Lake*, Franklin Library (Franklin Center, PA), 1980 (limited edition in full leather) . . . £25
A Sweet Devouring, Albondocani Press (New York), 1969 (26 signed, lettered copies; wraps) £750
ditto, Albondocani Press (New York), 1969 (150 signed, lettered copies; wraps) £500
Losing Battles, Random House (New York), 1970. £15/£5
ditto, Random House (New York), 1970 (300 signed, numbered copies in acetate d/w; slipcase) . £250/£200
ditto, Virago (London), 1982 . . . . . £20/£5
A Flock of Guinea Hens..., Albondocani Press (New York), 1970 (110 copies; wraps; with greeting and 'Albondocani Press/Ampersand Books' on first page) . . . £100
ditto, Albondocani Press (New York), 1970 (200 copies; wraps; with greeting only on first page) . . . £75
One Time, One Place..., Random House (New York), 1971 .
. . . . £30/£10

ditto, Random House (New York), 1971 (300 signed, numbered copies; acetate d/w; slipcase). . £200/£150

ditto, Univ Press of Mississippi (Jackson, MS), 1996 £20/£5

ditto, Univ Press of Mississippi (Jackson, MS), 1996 (125 numbered copies; slipcase) . . . . £75/£50

The Optimist's Daughter, Random House (New York), 1972 . . . . £125/£25

ditto, Random House (New York), 1972 (approx 225 signed, numbered copies; slipcase; no d/w). . . £200/£150

ditto, Andre Deutsch (London), 1973. . . . £25/£5

ditto, Franklin Library (Franklin Center, PA), 1978 (limited edition in full leather). £30

ditto, Franklin Library (Franklin Center, PA), 1980 (signed limited edition in full leather) £50

...The Southern Imagination, Southern Educational Communications Association (Columbia, SC), 1972 (wraps) £250

Some Notes on Time in Fiction, Mississippi Quarterly (Jackson, MS), 1973 (stapled wraps) . . . £250

A Pageant of Birds, Albondocani Press (New York), 1974 (300 signed, numbered copies; wraps, in d/w) £200/£150

ditto, Albondocani Press (New York), 1974 (26 signed, lettered copies; wraps, in d/w) . . . £600/£500

ditto, Albondocani Press (New York), 1974 (4 signed numbered copies marked 'out of series'; wraps, in d/w) . . . . £250/£150

Is Pheonix Jackson's Grandson Really Dead..., Critical Enquiry (Chicago), 1974 (wraps) £250

June Recital, Kenkyusha (Tokyo), 1974 . . £30

Fairy Tale of the Natchez Trace, The Mississippi Historical Society (Jackson, MS), 1975 (no d/w; in publisher's envelope) . . . . £60/£45

Images of the South, Center For Southern Folklore (Memphis, TN), 1977 (wraps; visits with Eudora Welty and Walker Evans) £45

Welty, An Exhibition at the Mississippi State Museum, Mississippi Department of Archives and History (Jackson, MS), 1977 (wraps) £45

Acrobats in a Park, Delta (no place), 1977 (wraps) . £150

ditto, Lord John Press (Northridge, CA), 1980 (100 signed, numbered copies; no d/w) £150

ditto, Lord John Press (Northridge, CA), 1980 (300 signed, numbered copies; no d/w) £75

The Eye of the Story, Random House (New York), 1978 . . . . £20/£5

ditto, Random House (New York), 1978 (300 signed, numbered copies; slipcase; no d/w). . . £175/£125

ditto, Virago (London), 1987 (pbk) £10

Ida M'Toy, Univ of Illinois Press (Urbana/Chicago/London), 1979 (350 signed, numbered copies; no d/w) £150

Women! Make Turban in Own Home!, Palaemon Press (Winston-Salem, NC), 1979 (35 signed copies numbered I-XXXV; no d/w) £300

ditto, Palaemon Press (Winston-Salem, NC), 1979 (200 signed, numbered copies; no d/w) £125

Critical Essays, Univ Press of Mississippi (Jackson, MS), 1979 . . . . £30/£10

Twenty Photographs, Palaemon Press (Winston-Salem, NC), 1980 (20 signed copies numbered I-XX; in clam-shell box; errata slip laid in). £6,000

ditto, Palaemon Press (Winston-Salem, NC), 1980 (75 signed, numbered copies; in clam-shell box; errata slip laid in) £5,000

The Collected Stories, Franklin Library, Franklin Center, 1980 . . . . £50

ditto, Harcourt Brace Jovanovich (New York/London), 1980 . . . . £30/£5

ditto, Harcourt Brace Jovanovich (New York/London), 1980 (500 signed, numbered copies; slipcase; no d/w) £225/£175

ditto, Marion Boyars (London/Boston), 1981 . . £30/£5

Bye-Bye Brevort, New Stage Theatre (Jackson, MS), 1980 (26 signed, lettered copies; no d/w). . . . £350

ditto, New Stage Theatre (Jackson, MS), 1980 (50 signed copies numbered I-L, in Roman numerals; no d/w) . £250

ditto, New Stage Theatre (Jackson, MS), 1980 (400 signed, unnumbered copies; no d/w) £125

White Fruitcake, Albondocani Press (New York), 1980 (175 copies; wraps; 'Albondocani Press/Ampersand Books' and greeting printed on first page; in mailing envelope) . . . . £75/£60

ditto, Albondocani Press (New York), 1980 (275 copies; wraps; greeting only printed on first page; in envelope) . . . . £65/£45

Retreat, Palaemon Press (Winston-Salem, NC), 1981 (7 signed, numbered copies; with signed numbered woodcut by Ann Carter Pollard tipped-in before title page) . £500

ditto, Palaemon Press (Winston-Salem, NC), 1981 (50 signed, numbered copies; with an original aquatint by Ann C. Pollard) £300

ditto, Palaemon Press (Winston-Salem, NC), 1981 (40 signed copies numbered i-xl) £250

ditto, Palaemon Press (Winston-Salem, NC), 1981 (150 signed copies numbered 1-150) £125

One Writer's Beginnings, Harvard Univ Press (Cambridge, MA/London), 1984 . . . . . . £45/£10

ditto, Harvard Univ Press (Cambridge, MA/London), 1984 (350 signed, numbered copies; slipcase; no d/w) £225/£175

ditto, Faber (London/Boston), 1985 (pbk). . . £10

Four Photographs, Lord John Press (Northridge, CA), 1984 (150 signed, numbered copies; broadside) . . . £65

Conversations With Eudora Welty, Univ Press of Mississippi (Jackson, MS), 1984. . . . . £20/£10

ditto, Univ Press of Mississippi (Jackson, MS), 1984 (pbk) £10

Eudora, Mississippi Department of Archives and History (Jackson, MS), 1984 (pbk) £10

The MacNeil/Lehrer New Hour, Transcript #2230, Journal Graphics (New York), 1984 (wraps; 300 copies). . £10

In Black and White, Lord John Press (Northridge, CA), 1985 (100 numbered copies signed by Welty and Anne Tyler; slipcase) . . . . £300/£250

ditto, Lord John Press (Northridge, CA), 1985 (300 numbered copies signed by Welty and Anne Tyler; no slipcase). £150

The Little Store, Tamazunchale Press (Newton, IA), 1985 (250 numbered copies; full leather miniature book) . £100

The Faulkner Investigation, Cordelia Editions (Santa Barbara, CA), 1985 (500 copies; wraps); written with Ross Macdonald) £20

Eudora Welty: A Keepsake, Univ of Mississippi, The John Davis Williams Library (no place), 1987 (500 numbered copies; stapled wraps) £20

No Place for You, My Love, Perfection Form Co (Logan, IA), 1987 . . . . £30

Morgana, Univ Press of Mississippi (Jackson, MS/London), 1988 . . . . £20/£5 *ditto*, Univ Press of Mississippi (Jackson, MS/London), 1988 (250 signed, numbered copies; slipcase; no d/w) £125/£100

ditto, Univ Press of Mississippi (Jackson, MS/London), 1988 (26 lettered copies signed by author and illustrator Mildred Nungester; slipcase; no d/w) . . . . £350/£300

The Complete Works of Eudora Welty, Rinsen Book Co. (Kyoto), 1988 (9 vols; no d/ws) £300

Photographs, Univ Press of Mississippi (Jackson/London), 1989 . . . . £50/£10

ditto, Univ Press of Mississippi (Jackson/London), 1989 (52 signed, lettered copies; bound in full leather; with separate photo; cloth covered box) . . . . £600/£500

ditto, Univ Press of Mississippi (Jackson/London), 1989 (375 signed, numbered copies; no d/w; slipcase) £350/£300

The Welty Collection, Univ of Mississippi (Jackson, MS), 1989 . . . . £30/£10

A Writer's Eye: Collected Book Reviews, Univ Press of Mississippi (Jackson, MS), 1994 . . . . £15/£5

Why I Live at the P. O. and Other Stories, Penguin Books (Harmondsworth, Middx), 1995 (pbk) . . . £10

More Conversations With Eudora Welty, Univ Press of Mississippi (Jackson, MS), 1996 . . . £15/£5

ditto, Univ Press of Mississippi (Jackson, MS), 1996 (pbk) £10

Complete Novels, Library of America (New York), 1998 . . . . £10/£5

Stories, Essays and Memoir, Library of America (New York), 1998 . . . . £10/£5

The First Story, Univ Press of Mississippi (Jackson, MS), 1999 (500 numbered copies; slipcase) . . . £50/£35

Country Churchyards, Univ Press of Mississippi (Jackson, MS), 2000 . . . . £10/£5

ditto, Univ Press of Mississippi (Jackson, MS), 2000 (150 numbered copies; slipcase) £75

On William Hollingsworth, Jr, University Press of Mississippi (Jackson, MA), 2002 . . . . £10/£5

On Writing, Modern Library (New York), 2002 . £10/£5

Some Notes on River Country, University Press of Mississippi (Jackson, MS), 2003 . . . £10/£5

On William Faulkner, University Press of Mississippi (Jackson, MS), 2003 . . . . . . £10/£5

ditto, University Press of Mississippi (Jackson, MS), 2003 (150 copies; slipcase) . . . . . . £100/£75

PATRICIA WENTWORTH

(b.1878 d.1961)

'Patricia Wentworth' was the pseudonym of Dora Amy Elles, who began her career as a romantic novelist. She is remembered as one of the great writers of 'Golden Age' detective fiction and for her creation of Miss Silver (a governess turned private eye) and Benbow Smith (an eccentric with a pet parrot).

'Miss Silver' Books

Grey Mask, Hodder & Stoughton (London), [1928] . . . . £750/£100

ditto, Lippincott (Philadelphia), 1929 . . . £250/£45

The Case is Closed, Hodder & Stoughton (London), 1937 . . . . £500/£50

ditto, Lippincott (Philadelphia), 1937 . . . £175/£35

Lonesome Road, Hodder & Stoughton (London), 1939 . . . . £350/£45

ditto, Lippincott (Philadelphia), 1939 . . . £175/£35

In The Balance, Lippincott (Philadelphia), 1941 . £150/£25

ditto, as *Danger Point*, Hodder & Stoughton (London), 1942 . . . . £165/£25

The Chinese Shawl, Hodder & Stoughton (London), 1943 . . . . £165/£25

ditto, Lippincott (Philadelphia), 1943 . . . £100/£20

Miss Silver Deals With Death, Lippincott (Philadelphia), 1943 . . . . £100/£20

ditto, as *Miss Silver Intervenes*, Hodder & Stoughton (London), 1944 . . . . £125/£20

The Clock Strikes Twelve, Lippincott (Philadelphia), 1944 . . . . £125/£20

ditto, Hodder & Stoughton (London), 1945 . £100/£15

The Key, Lippincott (Philadelphia), 1944 . . £100/£15

ditto, Hodder & Stoughton (London), 1946 . £100/£15

She Came Back, Lippincott (Philadelphia), 1945 . £75/£20

ditto, as *The Traveller Returns*, Hodder & Stoughton (London), 1948 . . . . £75/£15

Pilgrim's Rest, Lippincott (Philadelphia), 1946 . £45/£15

ditto, Hodder & Stoughton (London), 1948 . £75/£15

ditto, as *The Dark Threat*, Popular Library (New York), 1961 . . . . £50/£15

Latter End, Lippincott (Philadelphia), 1947 . £40/£15

ditto, Hodder & Stoughton (London), 1949 . £75/£15

Wicked Uncle, Lippincott (Philadelphia), 1947 . £35/£15

ditto, as *Spotlight*, Hodder & Stoughton (London), 1949 . . . . £75/£10

Eternity Ring, Lippincott (Philadelphia), 1948 . £35/£15

ditto, Hodder & Stoughton (London), 1950 . £45/£10

The Case of William Smith, Lippincott (Philadelphia), 1948 . . . . £35/£15

ditto, Hodder & Stoughton (London), 1950 . £35/£10

Miss Silver Comes To Stay, Lippincott (Philadelphia), 1949 . . . . £35/£15

ditto, Hodder & Stoughton (London), 1951 . £35/£10

The Catherine Wheel, Lippincott (Philadelphia), 1949 . . . . £35/£15

ditto, Hodder & Stoughton (London), 1951 . £35/£10

The Brading Collection, Lippincott (Philadelphia), 1950 . . . . £35/£15

ditto, Hodder & Stoughton (London), 1952 . £35/£10

ditto, as *Mr Brading's Collection*, Severn House (London), 1987 . . . . £10/£5

Through The Wall, Lippincott (Philadelphia), 1950 £35/£15

ditto, Hodder & Stoughton (London), 1952 . £35/£10

The Ivory Dagger, Lippincott (Philadelphia), 1951 £35/£15

ditto, Hodder & Stoughton (London), 1953 . £35/£10

Anna, Where Are You?, Lippincott (Philadelphia), 1951 . . . . £35/£15

ditto, Hodder & Stoughton (London), 1953 . £35/£10

ditto, as *Death at the Deep End*, Pyramid (New York), 1953 (pbk) £5

The Watersplash, Lippincott (Philadelphia), 1951 . £30/£10

ditto, Hodder & Stoughton (London), 1954 . £35/£10

Ladies' Bane, Lippincott (Philadelphia), 1952 . £30/£10

ditto, Hodder & Stoughton (London), 1954 . £35/£10

Out of the Past, Lippincott (Philadelphia), 1953 . £25/£10

ditto, Hodder & Stoughton (London), 1955 . £35/£10

Vanishing Point, Lippincott (Philadelphia), 1953 . £25/£10

ditto, Hodder & Stoughton (London), 1955 . £35/£10

The Silent Pool, Lippincott (Philadelphia), 1954 . £25/£10
ditto, Hodder & Stoughton (London), 1956 . £35/£10
The Benevent Treasure, Lippincott (Philadelphia), 1954 .
. . . . £25/£10
ditto, Hodder & Stoughton (London), 1956 . . £35/£10
Poison In The Pen, Lippincott (Philadelphia), 1955 £25/£10
ditto, Hodder & Stoughton (London), 1957 . . £35/£10
The Listening Eye, Lippincott (Philadelphia), 1955 £25/£10
ditto, Hodder & Stoughton (London), 1957 . . £35/£10
The Gazebo, Lippincott (Philadelphia), 1956 . £25/£10
ditto, Hodder & Stoughton (London), 1958 . . £35/£10
ditto, as *The Summerhouse*, Pyramid (New York), 1967
(pbk) £5
The Fingerprint, Lippincott (Philadelphia), 1956 . £25/£10
ditto, Hodder & Stoughton (London), 1959 . £35/£10
The Alington Inheritance, Lippincott (Philadelphia), 1958 .
. . . . £25/£10
ditto, Hodder & Stoughton (London), 1960 . . £25/£10
The Girl in the Cellar, Hodder & Stoughton (London), 1961
. . . . £25/£10

Others
The Astonishing Adventure of Jane Smith, Melrose
(London), 1923 . . . . . £2,500/£250
ditto, Small Maynard (Boston), 1923 . . . £1,250/£150
The Red Lacquer Case, Melrose (London), 1924 . . .
. . . . £1,000/£125
ditto, Small Maynard (Boston), 1925 . . . £300/£75
The Annam Jewel, Melrose (London), 1924 . £750/£100
ditto, Small Maynard (Boston), 1925 . . . £300/£65
The Dower House Mystery, Hodder & Stoughton (London),
[1925] . . . . £750/£100
ditto, Small Maynard (Boston), 1926 . . . £300/£65
The Black Cabinet, Hodder & Stoughton (London), [1925]
. . . . £600/£75
ditto, Small Maynard (Boston), 1926 . . . £200/£45
The Amazing Chance, Hodder & Stoughton (London),
[1925] . . . . £600/£75
ditto, Small Maynard (Boston), 1926 . . . £200/£45
Hue and Cry, Hodder & Stoughton (London), [1927] . .
. . . . £500/£75
ditto, Lippincott (Philadelphia), 1927 . . . £175/£40
Anne Belinda, Hodder & Stoughton (London), [1927] . .
. . . . £500/£75
ditto, Lippincott (Philadelphia), 1928 . . . £175/£40
Will O' The Wisp, Hodder & Stoughton (London), [1928] .
. . . . £500/£75
ditto, Lippincott (Philadelphia), 1928 . . . £175/£40
Fool Errant, Hodder & Stoughton (London), [1929] .
. . . . £500/£75
ditto, Lippincott (Philadelphia), 1929 . . . £175/£40
The Coldstone, Hodder & Stoughton (London), [1930] .
. . . . £450/£50
ditto, Lippincott (Philadelphia), 1930 . . . £150/£35
Beggar's Choice, Hodder & Stoughton (London), [1930] .
. . . . £450/£50
ditto, Lippincott (Philadelphia), 1931 . . . £150/£35
Kingdom Lost, Lippincott (Philadelphia), 1930 . £350/£45
ditto, Hodder & Stoughton (London), [1931] . £450/£50
Danger Calling, Hodder & Stoughton (London), [1931] .
. . . . £450/£50
ditto, Lippincott (Philadelphia), 1931 . . . £150/£35
Nothing Venture, Cassell (London), 1932 . £400/£45
ditto, Lippincott (Philadelphia), 1932 . . . £150/£35

Red Danger, Cassell (London), 1932 . . . £400/£45
ditto, as *Red Shadow*, Lippincott (Philadelphia), 1932 . .
. . . . £150/£35
Seven Green Stones, Cassell (London), 1933 . £300/£40
ditto, as *Outrageous Fortune*, Lippincott (Philadelphia),
1933 . . . . £125/£25
Walk With Care, Cassell (London), 1933 . . £400/£35
ditto, Lippincott (Philadelphia), 1933 . . . £125/£25
Fear By Night, Hodder & Stoughton (London), 1934 . .
. . . . £400/£35
ditto, Lippincott (Philadelphia), 1934 . . . £125/£25
Devil-In-The-Dark, Hodder & Stoughton (London), 1934 .
. . . . £400/£35
ditto, as *Touch And Go*, Lippincott (Philadelphia), 1934 .
. . . . £125/£25
Red Stefan, Hodder & Stoughton (London), 1935 . £400/£35
ditto, Lippincott (Philadelphia), 1935 . . . £125/£25
Blindfold, Hodder & Stoughton (London), 1935 . £400/£35
ditto, Lippincott (Philadelphia), 1935 . . . £125/£25
Dead Or Alive, Hodder & Stoughton (London), 1936 . .
. . . . £400/£35
ditto, Lippincott (Philadelphia), 1936 . . . £125/£25
Hole And Corner, Hodder & Stoughton (London), 1936 .
. . . . £300/£35
ditto, Lippincott (Philadelphia), 1936 . . . £125/£25
Down Under, Hodder & Stoughton (London), 1937 . . .
. . . . £350/£35
ditto, Lippincott (Philadelphia), 1937 . . . £125/£20
Run, Hodder & Stoughton (London), 1938 . . £300/£35
ditto, Lippincott (Philadelphia), 1938 . . . £100/£35
Mr Zero, Hodder & Stoughton (London), 1938 . £300/£35
ditto, Lippincott (Philadelphia), 1938 . . . £100/£35
The Blind Side, Hodder & Stoughton (London), 1939 . .
. . . . £300/£35
ditto, Lippincott (Philadelphia), 1939 . . . £100/£25
Rolling Stone, Hodder & Stoughton (London), 1940 . . .
. . . . £250/£30
ditto, Lippincott (Philadelphia), 1940 . . . £75/£20
Who Pays The Piper?, Hodder & Stoughton (London), 1940
. . . . £250/£35
ditto, as *Account Rendered*, Lippincott (Philadelphia), 1940
. . . . £65/£15
Unlawful Occasions, Hodder & Stoughton (London), 1941 .
. . . . £200/£25
ditto, as *Weekend With Death*, Lippincott (Philadelphia),
1941 . . . . £65/£15
Pursuit of a Parcel, Hodder & Stoughton (London), 1942 . .
. . . . £150/£25
ditto, Lippincott (Philadelphia), 1942 . . . £50/£15
Silence in Court, Lippincott (Philadelphia), 1945 . £50/£15
ditto, Hodder & Stoughton (London), 1947 . . £75/£15

Historical Fiction
A Marriage Under The Terror, Melrose (London), 1910 .
. . . . £125
ditto, Putnam (New York), 1910 . . . . . £125
A Little More Than Kin, Melrose (London), 1911 . . £150
ditto, as *More Than Kin*, Putnam (New York), 1911 . £100
The Devil's Wind, Melrose (London), 1912 . . . £125
ditto, Putnam (New York), 1912 . . . . . £100
The Fire Within, Melrose (London), 1913 . . . £125
ditto, Putnam (New York), 1913 . . . . . £100
Simon Heriot, Melrose (London), 1914 . . . £150
Queen Anne Is Dead, Melrose (London), 1915 . . £150

Poetry

A Child's Rhyme Book, Melrose (London), 1910 . . £75
Beneath the Hunter's Moon, Hodder & Stoughton (London), 1945 . . . . £65/£20
The Pool of Dreams, Hodder & Stoughton (London), 1953 .
. . . . £45/£10
ditto, Lippincott (Philadelphia), 1954 . . . £40/£10

Others

Earl or Chieftan? The Romance of Hugh O'Neill, Catholic Truth Society of Ireland (Dublin, Ireland), 1919 . . £45

MARY WESLEY
(b.1912 d.2002)

Mary Aline Mynors Farmar, better known as Mary Wesley, was a British novelist who became an author very late in life, after the death of her husband. She wrote two books for children before attempting adult fiction. Interest in her novels increased with their adaptation for television in the 1990s.

Novels for Adults

Jumping The Queue, Macmillan (London), 1983 . £65/£10
ditto, Penguin (New York), 1988 . . . £10/£5
The Camomile Lawn, Macmillan (London), 1984 . £90/£10
ditto, Summit (New York), 1985. . . . £65/£10
Harnessing Peacocks, Macmillan (London), 1985. £30/£5
ditto, Scribner's (New York), 1986 . . . £15/£5
The Vacillations of Poppy Carew, Macmillan (London), 1986 . . . . £30/£5
ditto, Penguin (New York), 1988 . . . £10/£5
Not That Sort of Girl, Macmillan (London), 1987 . £20/£5
ditto, Viking (New York), 1988 . . . . £10/£5
Second Fiddle, Macmillan (London), 1988 . £15/£5
ditto, Viking (New York), 1989 . . . . £10/£5
A Sensible Life, Bantam (London), 1990 . . £10/£5
ditto, Viking (New York), 1990 . . . . £10/£5
A Dubious Legacy, Bantam (London), 1992 . . £10/£5
ditto, Viking (New York), 1992 . . . . £10/£5
An Imaginative Experience, Bantam (London), 1994 £10/£5
ditto, Viking (New York), 1995 . . . . £10/£5
Part of the Furniture, Bantam (London), 1997 . £10/£5
ditto, Viking (New York), 1997 . . . . £10/£5

Novels for Children

The Sixth Seal, Macdonald (London), 1969 . . £45/£10
ditto, Stein & Day (New York), 1971. . . £30/£5
Speaking Terms, Faber (London), 1969 . . £20/£5
ditto, Gambit (Boston), 1971 . . . . £15/£5
Haphazard House, Dent (London), 1983. . . £10/£5

Others

Part of the Scenery, Bantam (London), 2001 (photographs by Kim Sayer) . . . . £10/£5

NATHANAEL WEST
(b.1903 d.1940)

West's reputation has become established since his death in 1940, with *Miss Lonelyhearts* widely regarded as his masterpiece, and *The Day of the Locust* considered one of the best novels written about the early years of Hollywood. Much of West's fiction can be seen as a response to the American Depression; the garish backdrop to *The Day of the Locust*, for example, contrasting with the reality of economic depression.

Novels

The Dream Life of Balso Snell, Contact Editions (New York/Paris), 1931 (500 numbered copies; sewn wraps; tissue d/w) . . . . . . £1,750/£1,250
ditto, Contact Editions (New York and Paris), 1931 (15 signed, numbered copies in boards). . . £5,000
Miss Lonelyhearts, Liveright (New York), 1933 £3,000/£350
ditto, Harcourt, Brace (New York), 1933 (Liveright plates used, but with Harcourt, Brace title page) . £1,000/£75
ditto, Greenberg (New York), 1934 (Liveright plates used, but with Greenberg title page) . . . . £500/£50
ditto, Grey Walls Press (London), 1949 . . £65/£15
A Cool Million, Covici Friede (New York), 1934 £750/£100
ditto, Neville Spearman (London), 1954 . . £150/£20
The Day of the Locust, Random House (New York), 1939 .
. . . . £850/£75
ditto, Grey Walls Press (London), 1951 . . £50/£10

Collections

The Complete Works, Farrar, Straus & Cudahy (New York), 1957 . . . . £35/£10
ditto, Secker & Warburg (London), 1968 . . £35/£10
Novels and Other Writings, Library of America (New York), 1997 (slipcase) . . . . . . £10/£5

REBECCA WEST
(b.1892 d.1983)

Cecily Isabel Fairfield assumed her pseudonym while training as an actress (the name 'Rebecca West' appears in an Ibsen play). She became a prolific author of novels, essays and articles for the *New Yorker* and other periodicals. Her writings are preoccupied with the idea of Original Sin. She was made a Dame in 1959.

Novels

The Return of the Soldier, Century Publishing (New York), 1918 . . . . £200/£45
ditto, Nisbet (London), 1918 . . . . £200/£35
The Judge, Hutchinson (London), 1922 . . £150/£30
ditto, Doran (New York), 1922 . . . . £125/£15
Harriet Hume, A London Fantasy, Hutchinson (London), 1929 . . . . £100/£20
ditto, Doran (New York), 1929 . . . . £75/£10
War Nurse, Cosmopolitan Book Co. (New York), 1930 (anonymous). . . . . £150/£45
The Harsh Voice: Four Short Novels, Cape (London), 1935
. . . . £35/£15
ditto, Doubleday (New York), 1935 . . . £35/£15

The Thinking Reed, Viking Press (New York), 1936 £40/£10

ditto, Hutchinson (London), [1936] . . . £40/£10

The Fountain Overflows, Viking (New York), 1956 £15/£5

ditto, Macmillan (London), 1957 . . . £15/£5

The Birds Fall Down, Macmillan (London), 1966 . £10/£5

ditto, Viking (New York), 1966 . . . . £15/£5

This Real Night, Macmillan (London), 1984 . . £15/£5

ditto, Viking (New York), 1985 . . . . £10/£5

Cousin Rosamund, Macmillan (London), 1985 . £10/£5

ditto, Viking (New York), 1986 . . . . £10/£5

Sunflower, Virago (London), 1986 . . . . £10/£5

ditto, Viking (New York), 1987 . . . . £10/£5

Others

Henry James, Nisbet (London), 1916 . . . . £35

ditto, Holt (New York), 1916 . . . . . £25

The Strange Necessity, Cape (London), 1928 . . £35/£10

ditto, Doran (New York), 1928 . . . . £30/£10

Lions and Lambs, Cape (London), 1928 . . . £45/£15

ditto, Harcourt Brace (New York), 1928 . . £45/£15

D.H. Lawrence, Secker (London), 1930 . . £40/£15

ditto, as *Elegy*, Phoenix Book Shop (New York), 1930 (250 signed copies, glassine d/w) . . . . £50/£40

Ending in Earnest: A Literary Log, Doubleday Doran (New York), 1931 . . . . £60/£20

Arnold Bennett Himself, John Day (New York), 1931 (stapled wraps) £15

St Augustine, Appleton (New York), 1933 . . £35/£10

ditto, Davies (London), 1933 . . . . £35/£10

A Letter to Grandfather, Hogarth Press (London), 1933 (stapled wraps) £20

The Modern 'Rake's Progress', Hutchinson (London), 1934 . . . . £75/£20

ditto, Hutchinson (London), 1934 (250 signed copies) . £175

Black Lamb and Grey Falcon, Viking Press (New York), 1941 (2 vols; d/ws and slipcase) . . . £75/£25

ditto, Macmillan (London), 1942 (2 vols; no slipcase) . . . . £75/£25

The Meaning of Treason, Viking Press (New York), 1947 . . . . £25/£5

ditto, Macmillan (London), 1949 . . . £20/£5

ditto, Macmillan (London), 1952 (enlarged; revised) £10/£5

A Train of Powder, Macmillan (London), 1955 . £20/£5

ditto, Viking (New York), 1955 . . . . £20/£5

The Court and the Castle, Yale Univ Press (New Haven, CT), 1957 . . . . £20/£5

ditto, Macmillan (London), 1958 . . . £20/£5

The Vassal Affair, Sunday Telegraph (London), 1963 (wraps) £10

McLuhan and the Future of Literature, The English Association (London), 1969 (wraps) . . . £15

Rebecca West, A Celebration, Macmillan (London), 1977 . . . . £10/£5

ditto, Viking (New York), 1977 . . . . £10/£5

1900, Weidenfeld & Nicolson (London), 1982 . £10/£5

ditto, Viking (New York), 1982 . . . . £10/£5

The Young Rebecca, Virago (London), 1982 . . £10/£5

ditto, Viking (New York), 1982 . . . . £10/£5

Family Memories, Virago (London), 1987 . . £10/£5

ditto, Viking (New York), 1988 . . . . £10/£5

The Only Poet and Short Stories, Virago (London), 1992 . . . . £10/£5

Selected Letters of Rebecca West, Yale Univ Press (New Haven, CT), 2000 . . . . . . £10/£5

EDITH WHARTON
(b.1862 d.1937)

Wharton was an American novelist and short story writer who, with *The Age of Innocence*, became the first woman to be awarded the Pulitzer Prize. She was also highly regarded as a landscape architect, and wrote on the decorative arts: her books *The Decoration of Houses* and *Italian Villas* were highly influential.

Novels and Novellas

The Touchstone, Scribner's (New York), 1900 . . £100

ditto, as *A Gift from The Grave*, Murray (London), 1900 . . . . £100

The Valley of Decision, Scribner's (New York), 1902 (2 vols) £150

ditto, Murray (London), 1902 . . . . . £100

Sanctuary, Scribner's (New York), 1903 . . . £125

ditto, Macmillan (London), 1903 . . . . £75

The House of Mirth, Scribner's (New York), 1905 . £100

ditto, Macmillan (London), 1905 . . . . £75

Madame de Treymes, Scribner's (New York), 1907 . £50

ditto, Macmillan (London), 1907 . . . . £50

The Fruit of The Tree, Scribner's (New York), 1907 . £65

ditto, Macmillan (London), 1907 . . . . £50

Ethan Frome, Scribner's (New York), 1911 (first issue with top edge gilt and perfect type in last line of p.135) . £500

ditto, Scribner's (New York), 1911 (second issue without gilt top edge, and with broken type in last line of p.135) . £75

ditto, Macmillan (London), 1911 . . . . £125

ditto, Scribner's (New York), 1922 (2,000 copies, new introduction, slipcase) . . . . £75/£50

ditto, Limited Editions Club (New York), 1939 (1,500 copies signed by illustrator Henry Varnum Poor, slipcase) £50/£40

The Reef, Appleton & Co. (New York), 1912 . . £40

ditto, Macmillan (London), 1912 . . . . £35

The Custom of The Country, Scribner's (New York), 1913. . . . . £40

ditto, Macmillan (London), 1913 . . . . £35

Summer, Appleton & Co. (New York), 1917 . . £45

ditto, Macmillan (London), 1917 . . . . £35

The Marne, Appleton & Co. (New York), 1918 . £35

ditto, as *The Marne: A Tale of the War*, Macmillan (London), 1918 . . . . £25

The Age of Innocence, Appleton & Co. (New York/ London), 1920 (first issue: 'burial', p.186, no mention of Pulitzer Prize on d/w) . . . £4,500/£1,000

The Glimpses of The Moon, Appleton & Co. (New York and London), 1922 . . . . £300/£40

A Son at The Front, Scribner's (New York), 1923. £175/£35

ditto, Macmillan (London), 1923 . . . £150/£25

Old New York, Appleton & Co. (New York and London), 1924 (4 vols in d/ws and slipcase) . . . £650/£150

The Mother's Recompense, Appleton & Co. (New York and London), 1925 . . . . £200/£25

Twilight Sleep, Appleton & Co. (New York and London), 1927 . . . . £150/£25

The Children, Appleton & Co. (New York and London), 1928 . . . . £150/£25

ditto, as *The Marriage Playground*, Grosset & Dunlap (New York), 1928 . . . . £125/£30

Hudson River Bracketed, Appleton & Co. (New York and London), 1929 . . . . . . £150/£25

The Gods Arrive, Appleton & Co. (New York and London), 1932 . . . . £150/£25

The Buccaneers, Appleton-Century (New York and London), 1938 . . . . . . £150/£25

Short Stories

The Greater Inclination, Scribner's (New York), 1899 (first issue: 'Wharton' only on spine) £300

ditto, John Lane (London), 1899. . . . . £150

Crucial Instances, Scribner's (New York), 1901 . . £125

ditto, Murray (London), 1901 . . . . . £75

The Descent of Man and Other Stories, Scribner's (New York), 1904 . . . . £75

ditto, Macmillan (London), 1904 . . . . £50

The Hermit and The Wild Woman, and Other Stories, Scribner's (New York), 1908 . . . . . £75

ditto, Macmillan (London), 1908 . . . . £75

Les Metteurs en Scène, Plon Nourrit (Paris), 1909 (in French) £45

Tales of Men and Ghosts, Scribner's (New York), 1910 £75

ditto, Macmillan (London), 1910 . . . . £50

Xingu and Other Stories, Scribner's (New York), 1916 £100

ditto, Macmillan (London), 1916 . . . . £75

Here and Beyond, Appleton & Co. (New York and London), 1926 . . . . £225/£35

Certain People, Appleton & Co. (New York and London), 1930 . . . . £150/£25

Human Nature, Appleton & Co. (New York and London), 1933 . . . . £150/£25

The World Over, Appleton-Century (New York and London), 1936 . . . . . . £150/£25

Ghosts, Appleton-Century (New York and London), 1937 . . . . £225/£35

Best Short Stories of Edith Wharton, Scribner's (New York), 1958 . . . . £45/£15

The Collected Short Stories of Edith Wharton, Scribner's (New York), 1968 (2 vols) . . . . £45/£15

The Ghost Stories of Edith Wharton, Scribner's (New York), 1973 . . . . £25/£10

ditto, Constable (London), 1975 . . . . £25/£10

Quartet: Four Stories, Allen Press (New York), 1975 (140 copies) £300

The Stories of Edith Wharton, Simon & Schuster (London), 1988 (selected by Anita Brookner) . . . £30/£10

The Ghost Feeler: Stories of Terror and Supernatural, Peter Owen (London), 1996 . . . . £10/£5

The Triumph of Night and Other Tales, Tartarus Press (Carlton-in-Coverdale), 2008 . . . . £30/£10

Poetry

Verses, privately printed (Newport, RI), 1878 (wraps; pseud 'Edith Newbold Jones') £30,000

Artemis to Actaeon and Other Verses, Scribner's (New York), 1909 . . . . £125

ditto, Macmillan (London), 1909 . . . . £125

Twelve Poems, The Medici Society (London), 1926 (130 signed copies) . . . . . £2,000/£1,250

Others

The Decoration of Houses, Scribner's (New York), 1897 (with Ogden Codman Jr.) £350

ditto, Batsford (London), 1898 . . . . . £350

Italian Villas and Their Gardens, Century (New York), 1904 . . . . £500

ditto, John Lane (London), 1904. . . . . £400

Italian Backgrounds, Scribner's (New York), 1905 . £175

ditto, Macmillan (London), 1905 . . . . £125

A Motor-Flight through France, Scribner's (New York), 1908 . . . . £100

ditto, Macmillan (London), 1908 . . . . £75

Fighting France: From Dunkerque to Belfort, Scribner's (New York), 1915 . . . . £75

ditto, Macmillan (London), 1915 . . . . £65

The Book of the Homeless, Scribner's (New York), 1916 (edited by Wharton) £100

ditto, Scribner's (New York), 1916 (125 copies, glassine d/w, slipcase) . . . . . £2,250/£1,750

ditto, Scribner's (New York), 1916 (50 copies, glassine d/w, slipcase). . . . . . £2,500/£2,000

ditto, Macmillan (London), 1916 . . . . £65

French Ways and Their Meaning, Appleton & Co. (New York), 1919 . . . . £65

ditto, Macmillan (London), 1919 . . . . £45

In Morocco, Scribner's (New York), 1920 . . £125/£35

ditto, Macmillan (London), 1920 . . . . £125/£30

The Writing of Fiction, Scribner's (New York and London), 1925 . . . . £125/£20

A Backward Glance, Appleton-Century (New York and London), 1934 . . . . . . £125/£20

An Edith Wharton Treasury, Appleton-Century-Crofts (New York), 1950 . . . . . . £25/£10

The Edith Wharton Reader, Scribner's (New York), 1965 . . . . £20/£5

The Letters of Edith Wharton, Simon & Schuster (London), 1988 . . . . £20/£5

Henry James and Edith Wharton Letters 1900-1915, Scribner's (New York), 1990 . . . . . £10/£5

DENNIS WHEATLEY

(b.1897 d.1977)

Wheatley's headstone describes him as the 'Prince of Thriller Writers', and with worldwide sales of more than 45 million few would argue with it. His novels can appear rather politically incorrect to modern readers, but they are still considered by many to be decently written pulp thrillers.

'Duke de Richleau' Titles

The Forbidden Territory, Hutchinson (London), [1933] . . . . £750/£75

The Devil Rides Out, Hutchinson (London), [1934] . . . . £750/£75

The Golden Spaniard, Hutchinson (London), [1938] . . . . £150/£15

Three Inquisitive People, Hutchinson (London), [1940] . . . . £50/£10

Strange Conflict, Hutchinson (London), [1941] . £175/£20

Codeword - Golden Fleece, Hutchinson (London), [1946] . . . . £50/£5

The Second Seal, Hutchinson (London), 1950 . £20/£5

The Prisoner in The Mask, Hutchinson (London), 1957 . . . . £10/£5

Vendetta in Spain, Hutchinson (London), 1961 . £10/£5

Dangerous Inheritance, Hutchinson (London), 1965 £10/£5
Gateway to Hell, Hutchinson (London), 1970 .   .   £10/£5

'Gregory Sallust' Titles
Black August, Hutchinson (London), [1934] .   . £275/£25
Contraband, Hutchinson (London), [1936]   .   . £100/£10
The Scarlet Impostor, Hutchinson (London), [1940] . .
      .   .   .   . £100/£10
Faked Passports, Hutchinson (London), [1940] . £100/£10
The Black Baroness, Hutchinson (London), [1940] .
      .   .   .   . £100/£10
'V' for Vengeance, Hutchinson (London), [1942] . £65/£5
Come into my Parlour, Hutchinson (London), [1946] £45/£5
The Island Where Time Stands Still, Hutchinson (London),
      1954   .   .   .   . £20/£5
Traitor's Gate, Hutchinson (London), 1958   .   . £15/£5
They Used Dark Forces, Hutchinson (London), 1964 £10/£5
The White Witch of The South Seas, Hutchinson (London),
      1968   .   .   .   . £10/£5

'Julian Day' Titles
The Quest of Julian Day, Hutchinson (London), [1939]   .
      .   .   .   . £125/£10
The Sword of Fate, Hutchinson (London), [1941] . £100/£10
The Bill for The Use of a Body, Hutchinson (London), 1964
      .   .   .   . £10/£5

'Roger Brook' Titles
The Launching of Roger Brook, Hutchinson (London),
      [1947] .   .   .   . £35/£5
The Shadow of Tyburn Tree, Hutchinson (London), [1948]
      .   .   .   . £30/£5
The Rising Storm, Hutchinson (London), [1949] . £25/£5
The Man Who Killed The King, Hutchinson (London), 1951
      .   .   .   . £20/£5
The Dark Secret of Josephine, Hutchinson (London), 1955
      .   .   .   . £20/£5
The Rape of Venice, Hutchinson (London), 1959 . £15/£5
The Sultan's Daughter, Hutchinson (London), 1963 £10/£5
The Wanton Princess, Hutchinson (London), 1966 £10/£5
Evil in a Mask, Hutchinson (London), 1969 .   . £10/£5
The Ravishing of Lady Mary Ware, Hutchinson (London),
      1971   .   .   .   . £10/£5
Desperate Measures, Hutchinson (London), 1974 . £10/£5

Other Titles
Such Power is Dangerous, Hutchinson (London), [1933] .
      .   .   .   . £275/£25
The Fabulous Valley, Hutchinson (London), [1934] .
      .   .   .   . £275/£25
The Eunuch of Stamboul, Hutchinson (London), [1935] .
      .   .   .   . £100/£10
They Found Atlantis, Hutchinson (London), [1936]   .   .
      .   .   .   . £100/£10
The Secret War, Hutchinson (London), [1937] . £100/£10
Uncharted Seas, Hutchinson (London), [1938] . £125/£10
Sixty Days to Live, Hutchinson (London), [1939] . £225/£25
The Man Who Missed The War, Hutchinson (London),
      [1945] .   .   .   . £30/£5
The Haunting of Toby Jug, Hutchinson (London), [1948] .
      .   .   .   . £35/£5
Star of Ill-Omen, Hutchinson (London), 1952.   £20/£5
To The Devil - A Daughter, Hutchinson (London), 1953   .
      .   .   .   . £25/£5

Curtain of Fear, Hutchinson (London), 1953 .   . £20/£5
The Ka of Gifford Hillary, Hutchinson (London), 1956   .
      .   .   .   . £20/£5
The Satanist, Hutchinson (London), 1960   .   . £20/£5
Mayhem in Greece, Hutchinson (London), 1962   . £10/£5
Unholy Crusade, Hutchinson (London), 1967. .   £10/£5
The Strange Story of Linda Lee, Hutchinson (London),
      1972   .   .   .   . £10/£5
The Irish Witch, Hutchinson (London), 1973 .   . £10/£5
The Deception Planners: My Secret War, Hutchinson
      (London), 1980 .   .   .   .   .   . £10/£5

Short Stories
Mediterranean Nights, Hutchinson (London), [1942] £65/£5
Gunmen, Gallants and Ghosts, Hutchinson (London),
      [1943] .   .   .   . £100/£10

Non-Fiction
Old Rowley: A Private Life of Charles II, Hutchinson
      (London), 1933 .   .   .   .   .   . £100/£10
Red Eagle: A Life of Marshal Voroshilov, Hutchinson
      (London), 1937 .   .   .   .   .   . £100/£10
Total War, Hutchinson (London), [1941] (wraps) .   . £10
The Seven Ages of Justerini's, Riddle Books (London),
      1949 (no d/w) £5
ditto, as *1749-1965: The Eight Ages of Justerini's*, Dolphin
      (Aylesbury, Bucks), 1965 .   .   .   .   . £10/£5
Stranger than Fiction, Hutchinson (London), 1959 £25/£5
Saturdays with Bricks and Other Days Under Shell-Fire,
      Hutchinson (London), 1961   .   .   .   . £30/£5
The Devil and All His Works, Hutchinson (London), 1971 .
      .   .   .   . £20/£5

Autobiography
The Young Man Said: 1897-1914, Hutchinson (London),
      1977   .   .   .   . £20/£5
Officer and Temporary Gentleman: 1914-1919, Hutchinson
      (London), 1978 .   .   .   .   .   . £20/£5
Drink and Ink: 1919-1977, Hutchinson (London), 1979   .
      .   .   .   . £20/£5
The Time Has Come, Arrow (London), 1981 (pbk) .   £5

Crime Dossiers
Murder Off Miami, Hutchinson (London), [1936] (with J.G.
      Links, sealed copy) £100
ditto, Hutchinson (London), [1936] (opened copy).   . £35
Who Killed Robert Prentice?, Hutchinson (London), [1937]
      (with J.G. Links, sealed copy) £100
ditto, Hutchinson (London), [1937] (with J.G. Links, opened
      copy) £35
The Malinsay Massacre, Hutchinson (London), [1938] (with
      J.G. Links, sealed copy) £100
ditto, Hutchinson (London), [1938] (opened copy).   . £35
Herewith The Clues!, Hutchinson (London), [1939] (with
      J.G. Links, sealed copy) £100
ditto, Hutchinson (London), [1939] (opened copy).   . £35

E.B. WHITE
(b.1899 d.1985)

Best known as the author of the children's books *Charlotte's Web* and *Stuart Little*, White was for many years a columnist on the *New Yorker*. A noted prose stylist, he is also known for the writers' guide, *The Elements of Style*. This was an edited and updated version of a book originally written and published by William Strunk Jr. in 1918.

Children's Novels

Stuart Little, Harper (New York), 1945 . . . £400/£50
ditto, Hamish Hamilton (London), 1946 . . . £150/£35
Charlotte's Web, Harper (New York), 1952 . . £600/£50
ditto, Hamish Hamilton (London), 1952 . . . £275/£30
The Trumpet of the Swan, Harper (New York), 1970 .
. . . . £25/£10
ditto, Hamish Hamilton (London), 1970 . . . £20/£5

Humour

Is Sex Necessary? Or Why Do You Feel the Way You Do?, Harper (New York), 1929 (with James Thurber) . £450/£45
ditto, Heinemann (London), 1930 . . . £300/£30
Ho-Hum: Newsbreaks from 'The New Yorker', Farrar & Rinehart (New York), 1931 . . . . £75/£15
Another Ho-Hum: More Newsbreaks from 'The New Yorker', Farrar & Rinehart (New York), 1932 . £65/£10

Poetry

The Lady Is Cold, Harper (New York), 1929 (first binding with Plaza Hotel statue, spine lettered in gold; pseud 'E.B.W.') . . . . £1,000/£175
ditto, Harper (New York), 1929 (second binding with city skyline, spine lettered in green; pseud 'E.B.W.') . £200/£65
The Fox of Peapack and Other Poems, Harper (New York), 1938 . . . . £65/£15
Poems and Sketches of E.B. White, Harper (New York), 1981 . . . . £15/£5

Others

Less Than Nothing, New York, 1927 (pseud 'Sterling Finney'; no d/w) £1,500
Alice Through the Cellophane, John Day (New York), 1933 (wraps) £300
Every Day Is Saturday, Harper (New York), 1934 . £200/£25
Farewell to Model T, Putnam (New York), 1936 . £200/£25
Quo Vadimus? Or The Case For The Bicycle, Harper (New York), 1939 . . . . £250/£30
One Man's Meat, Harper (New York), 1942 . . £100/£10
ditto, Gollancz (London), 1943 . . . . £100/£10
World Government and Peace: Selected Notes and Comment, 1943-1945, F.R. Publishing (New York), 1945 (wraps). £200
The Wild Flag, Houghton Mifflin (Boston), 1946 . £25/£5
Here Is New York, Harper (New York), 1949 . £25/£10
ditto, Hamish Hamilton (London), 1950 . . . £25/£5
The Second Tree From the Corner, Harper (New York), 1954 . . . . £10/£5
ditto, Hamish Hamilton (London), 1954 . . . £10/£5
The Elements of Style, Macmillan (New York), 1959 (with William Strunk Jr; wraps) £5

The Points of My Compass, Harper (New York), 1962 .
. . . . £10/£5
ditto, Hamish Hamilton (London), 1963 . . . £10/£5
An E.B. White Reader, Harper (New York), 1966 . £10/£5
Topics: Our New Countrymen At The U.N., Congressional Press (Portland, ME), 1968 (200 copies; wraps) . . £75
Letters of E.B. White, Harper (New York), 1976 . £15/£5
Essays of E.B. White, Harper (New York), 1977 . £15/£5
The Geese, Newton Tamazunchale Press, 1985 (250 numbered copies) £65
Writings From The New Yorker, 1925-1976, Harper (New York), 1990 . . . . £15/£5

ETHEL LINA WHITE
(b.1876 d.1944)

Welsh-born authoress Ethel Lina White began writing as a child, contributing to children's papers, and later wrote short stories and novels. Her first attempts were in the mainstream but she found success with crime and macabre fiction. *The Wheel Spins* was filmed by Alfred Hitchcock as *The Lady Vanishes*.

Novels

The Wish-Bone, Ward Lock (London), 1927 . . £500/£50
'Twill Soon Be Dark, Ward Lock (London), 1929 . £500/£50
The Eternal Journey, Ward Lock (London), 1930 . £500/£50
Put Out The Light, Ward Lock (London), 1931 . £500/£50
ditto, Harper (New York), 1933 . . . . . £250/£25
Fear Stalks the Village, Ward Lock (London), 1932 . .
. . . . £450/£45
ditto, Harper (New York), 1942 . . . . . £250/£25
Some Must Watch, Ward Lock (London), 1933 . £450/£30
ditto, Harper (New York), 1941 . . . . . £200/£20
ditto, as *The Spiral Staircase*, World (Cleveland, OH), 1946
. . . . £30/£5
Wax, Collins (London), 1935 . . . . . £350/£30
ditto, Doubleday (New York), 1935 . . . . £100/£25
The First Time He Died, Collins (London), 1935 . £350/£30
The Wheel Spins, Collins Crime Club (London), 1936 . .
. . . . £450/£45
ditto, Harper (New York), 1936 . . . . . £250/£20
ditto, as *The Lady Vanishes*, Fontana (London), 1962 (pbk)
. . . . £5
ditto, as *The Lady Vanishes*, Paperback Library (New York), 1966 (pbk) £5
The Third Eye, Collins Crime Club (London), 1937 . .
. . . . £300/£25
ditto, Harper (New York), 1937 . . . . . £125/£15
The Elephant Never Forgets, Collins Crime Club (London), 1937 . . . . £300/£25
ditto, Harper (New York), 1938 . . . . . £125/£15
Step in the Dark, Collins Crime Club (London), 1938 . .
. . . . £300/£25
ditto, Harper (New York), 1939 . . . . . £125/£15
While She Sleeps, Collins Crime Club (London), 1940. .
. . . . £250/£25
ditto, Harper (New York), 1940 . . . . . £125/£15
She Faded Into Air, Collins Crime Club (London), 1941 .
. . . . £200/£20
ditto, Harper (New York), 1941 . . . . . £100/£15

Midnight House, Collins Crime Club (London), 1942 .   .
.   .   .   .   £75/£10
ditto, as *Her Heart in Her Throat*, Harper (New York), 1942
.   .   .   .   £45/£10
The Man Who Loved Lions, Collins Crime Club (London),
1943   .   .   .   .   £75/£10
ditto, as *The Man Who Was Not There*, Harper (New York),
1943   .   .   .   .   £45/£10
They See In Darkness, Collins Crime Club (London), 1944
.   .   .   .   £75/£10

GILBERT WHITE
(b.1720 d.1793)

Gilbert White was for many years the curate of the small village of Selborne in Hampshire. His enduring classic is made up of his letters to fellow amateur naturalists about his interests. Rather than collecting specimens White believed in observing the local animal and bird life, and made many new discoveries.

The Natural History and Antiquities of Selborne,
Bensley/White (London), 1789   .   .   .   £2,500

PATRICK WHITE
(b.1912 d.1990)

Australian novelist, short story writer and dramatist Patrick White made use of a stream of consciousness technique in much of his writing. Although his work was well-received elsewhere, it was not until the publication of *Voss* that critics in his home country learnt to appreciate him. He won the Nobel Prize for Literature in 1973, the only Australian to have been so honoured.

Novels
Happy Valley, Harrap (London), 1939   .   . £2,500/£250
ditto, Viking (New York), 1940 .   .   .   £1,250/£200
The Living and the Dead, Viking (New York), 1941   .   .
.   .   .   .   £750/£75
ditto, Routledge (London), 1941.   .   .   £1,500/£250
The Aunt's Story, Viking (New York), 1948 .   . £250/£45
ditto, Routledge (London), 1948.   .   .   . £750/£65
The Tree of Man, Viking (New York), 1955 .   . £75/£20
ditto, Eyre & Spottiswoode (London), 1956   . £45/£10
Voss, Viking (New York), 1957 .   .   .   . £30/£10
ditto, Eyre & Spottiswoode (London), 1957   . £30/£10
Riders in the Chariot, Viking (New York), 1961 £35/£10
ditto, Eyre & Spottiswoode (London), 1961   . £25/£10
The Solid Mandala, Viking (New York), 1966   £20/£5
ditto, Eyre & Spottiswoode (London), 1966   . £20/£5
The Vivisector, Cape (London), 1970   .   . £20/£5
ditto, Viking (New York), 1970 .   .   .   . £15/£5
The Eye of the Storm, Cape (London), 1973 .   £20/£5
ditto, Viking (New York), 1974 .   .   .   . £15/£5
A Fringe of Leaves, Cape (London), 1976   . £20/£5
ditto, Viking (New York), 1976 .   .   .   . £15/£5
The Twyborn Affair, Cape (London), 1979 .   £20/£5
ditto, Viking (New York), 1980 .   .   .   . £15/£5

Memoirs of Many in One, Cape (London), 1986 . £15/£5
ditto, Viking (New York), 1986 .   .   .   . £15/£5

Short Stories
The Burnt Ones, Eyre & Spottiswoode (London), 1964   .
.   .   .   .   £35/£10
ditto, Viking (New York), 1964 .   .   .   . £20/£5
The Cockatoos, Cape (London), 1974   .   . £20/£5
ditto, Viking (New York), 1975 .   .   .   . £15/£5
Three Uneasy Pieces, Pascoe (Australia), 1987 (pbk) . £10
ditto, Cape (London), 1988 .   .   .   .   . £15/£5
ditto, Viking (New York), 1988 .   .   .   . £15/£5

Poetry
Thirteen Poems, privately printed, 1930 (pseudonym 'Patrick Victor Martindale'; wraps).   .   .   £3,000
The Ploughman and Other Poems, Beacon Press (Sydney, Australia), 1935 (200 copies)   .   .   £3,500/£2,000

Plays
Four Plays, Eyre & Spottiswoode (London), 1965. £35/£10
ditto, Viking (New York), 1966 .   .   .   . £30/£10
The Night of the Prowler, Penguin/Cape (London), 1978
(pbk) £10
Big Toys, Currency Press (Sydney, Australia), 1978 (pbk)
.   .   .   .   £10
Netherwood, Currency Press (Sydney, Australia), 1983 (pbk)
.   .   .   .   £10
Signal Driver, Currency Press (Sydney, Australia), 1983
(pbk) £10

Others
Flaws in the Glass, Cape (London), 1981   . £20/£5
ditto, Viking (New York), 1982 .   .   .   . £15/£5
Patrick White Speaks, Primavera Press (Sydney, Australia),
1989   .   .   .   . £15/£5
ditto, Cape (London), 1990 .   .   .   .   . £15/£5

T.H. WHITE
(b.1906 d.1964)

A novelist and children's writer, White's major success was the re-telling of Thomas Malory's *Le Morte d'Arthur* in a series of novels, beginning with *The Sword in the Stone*. A passionate naturalist, White's major interests were hunting, flying, hawking and fishing. *The Goshawk* is an account of his ill-fated attempt at the art of falconry.

Novels
Dead Mr Nixon, Cassell (London), 1931 (with R. McNair Scott)   .   .   .   . £1,500/£350
Darkness at Pemberley, Gollancz (London), 1932.   .   .
.   .   .   .   £1,000/£250
ditto, Century (New York), 1933   .   .   £750/£175
They Winter Abroad, Gollancz (London), 1932 (pseud 'James Aston')   .   .   .   .   .   . £400/£60
ditto, Viking (New York), 1932 .   .   .   . £150/£45
First Lesson, Gollancz (London), 1932 (pseud 'James Aston')   .   .   .   . £400/£60
ditto, Knopf (New York), 1933 .   .   .   . £150/£45
Farewell Victoria, Collins (London), 1933   . £200/£30
ditto, Smith & Haas (New York), 1934   .   . £125/£20

Earth Stopped, Or Mr Marx's Sporting Tour, Collins (London), 1934 . . . . . . £600/£75
ditto, Putnam (New York), 1935 . . . . £300/£50
Gone to Ground, Collins (London), 1935. . £250/£45
ditto, Putnam (New York), 1935. . . . £175/£40
The Elephant and The Kangaroo, Putnam (New York), 1947 . . . . £50/£10
ditto, Cape (London), 1948 . . . . . £60/£15

Children's Titles
The Sword in The Stone, Collins (London), 1938 . £600/£50
ditto, Putnam (New York), 1939 . . . . £200/£30
The Witch in The Wood, Putnam (New York), 1939 .
. . . . £325/£40
ditto, Collins (London), 1940 . . . . £500/£65
The Ill-Made Knight, Putnam (New York), 1940 . £300/£40
ditto, Collins (London), 1941 . . . . £500/£65
Mistress Masham's Repose, Putnam (New York), 1946 .
. . . . £50/£10
ditto, Cape (London), 1947 . . . . . £45/£10
The Master, An Adventure Story, Cape (London), 1957 .
. . . . £50/£10
ditto, Putnam (New York), 1957 . . . . £40/£10
The Once and Future King, Collins (London), 1958 .
. . . . £150/£25
ditto, Putnam (New York), 1958 . . . . £125/£20
The Book of Merlyn, Univ of Texas Press (Austin, TX), 1977 . . . . £20/£5
ditto, Collins (London), 1978 . . . . £15/£5
The Maharajah and Other Stories, Putnam (New York), 1981 . . . . £15/£5
ditto, Macdonald (London), 1981 . . . . £15/£5

Poetry
The Green Bay Tree, or The Wicked Man Touches Wood, Songs for Sixpence, No. 3, Heffer (Cambridge, UK), 1929 (wraps) £200
Cambridge Poetry, No. 8, Hogarth Living Poets, Hogarth Press (London), 1929 . . . . £225
Loved Helen and Other Poems, Chatto & Windus (London), 1929 . . . . £250/£50
ditto, Viking (New York), 1929 . . . . £250/£50
Verses, Shenval Press (Alderney), 1962 (100 numbered copies) £600
A Joy Proposed, Bertram Rota (London), 1980 (500 numbered copies) . . . . . £25/£10
ditto, Univ of Georgia Press (Athens, GA), 1983 . £20/£5

Non-Fiction
England Have My Bones, Collins (London), 1936. £125/£30
ditto, Macmillan (New York), 1936 . . . £100/£20
Burke's Steerage, Or The Amateur Gentleman's Introduction to Noble Sports and Pastimes, Collins (London), 1938 . . . . £75/£15
ditto, Putnam (New York), 1939 . . . . £65/£10
The Age of Scandal: An Excursion Through a Minor Period, Cape (London), 1950 . . . . £40/£10
ditto, Putnam (New York), 1950 . . . . £25/£10
The Goshawk, Cape (London), 1951 . . . £60/£15
ditto, Putnam (New York), 1952 . . . . £40/£10
The Scandalmonger, Cape (London), 1952 . £40/£10
ditto, Putnam (New York), 1952 . . . . £30/£5
The Godstone and The Blackymor, Cape (London), 1959 (illustrated by Ardizzone) . . . . £40/£15
ditto, Putnam (New York), 1959 . . . . £35/£10

America At Last, The American Journal of T.H. White, Putnam (New York), 1965. . . . . £15/£5
The White/Garnett Letters, Cape (London), 1968 . £15/£5
ditto, Viking (New York), 1968 . . . . £15/£5
Letters to a Friend, The Correspondence Between T.H. White and L.J. Potts, Putnam (New York), 1982. £20/£5
ditto, Alan Sutton (Gloucester, Gloucestershire), 1984 (enlarged edition) . . . . . . £15/£5

WALT WHITMAN
(b.1819 d.1892)

Whitman was not an immediate success in his native America, and it was only when he was taken up by Rossetti, Swinburne and others in England that his importance was widely recognised.

Poetry
Leaves of Grass, no publisher (Brooklyn, NY), 1855 (anon., first issue without adverts or reviews, with marbled endpapers, both front and back covers with triple gilt-stamped line, and frontis portrait on plain paper) . £70,000
ditto, no publisher (Brooklyn, NY), 1855 (second binding with both front and back covers with blind-stamped triple line) £35,000
ditto, no publisher (Brooklyn, NY), 1855 (third binding, copies with light yellowish-green or pink wraps). £25,000
ditto, Horsell, 1855 (as above but label pasted above Brooklyn imprint) £20,000
ditto, no publisher (Brooklyn, NY), 1856 (second edition with 20 additional poems) £6,500
Drum-Taps, Peter Eckler (New York), 1865 . . £1,500
Sequel to Drum Taps, privately printed (Washington, DC), 1865-6 (with 'When Lilacs Last in the Door-Yard Bloom'd' on title-page) £1,000
Poems, Camden Hotten (London), 1868 (edited by W.M. Rossetti, first issue with no price on spine) . . £275
After All, Not To Create Only, Pearson (Washington, DC), 1871 (11 folio sheets printed on one side only) . £1,750
ditto, Roberts Bros. (Boston), 1871 . . . . £400
ditto, Roberts Bros. (Boston), 1871 (wraps) . . £350
As a Strong Bird on Pinions Free & Other Poems, published by Whitman (Washington, DC), 1872 . £1,000
Memoranda. During the War, published by Whitman (Camden, NJ), 1875 (first issue with first page printed 'Remembrance Copy' and signed by Whitman below)
. . . . £2,000
ditto, published by Whitman (Camden, NJ), 1875 (second issue lacks portraits and the 'Remembrance Copy' leaf) .
. . . . £500
Two Rivulets, published by Whitman (Camden, NJ), 1876 (100 copies, signed frontispiece) £2,500
ditto, published by Whitman (Camden, NJ), 1876 (650 copies) £500
November Boughs, David McKay (Philadelphia, PA), 1888
. . . . £200
ditto, David McKay (Philadelphia, PA), 1888 (copies on large paper) £450
ditto, David McKay (Philadelphia, PA), 1888 (100 copies for the author bound in flexible gilt-stamped maroon cloth; signed) £3,000

Complete Poems and Prose of Walt Whitman, Ferguson (Philadelphia, PA), 1888 (600 signed copies) . £3,000

Leaves of Grass with *Sands at Seventy*, Ferguson Bros (Philadelphia, PA), 1889 (300 signed copies) . £3,000

Good-bye My Fancy, David McKay (Philadelphia, PA), 1891 . . . . £250

ditto, David McKay (Philadelphia, PA), 1891 (copies on large paper) £400

Selected Poems, Webster (New York), 1892 . . £75

Autobiographica, Webster (New York), 1892. . . £100

Poems, Chatto & Windus (London), 1895 . . . £65

When Lilacs Last in the Dooryard Bloomed, Essex House Press (London), 1900 (125 copies) £750

ditto, Goldsmith (New York), 1936 (325 copies) . £125

Memories of President Lincoln, Little Leather Library Corporation (New York), 1915 . . . . £45

The Uncollected Poetry and Prose of Walt Whitman, Doubleday (New York), 1921 (2 vols) . . £350/£150

Pictures: An Unpublished Poem, Faber/The June House (London), 1927 (700 copies, glassine d/w) . £45/£25

Walt Whitman's Workshop, Harvard Univ Press (Cambridge, MA), 1928 (750 copies) . . . £75/£20

Prose

Franklin Evans, or The Inebriate: A Tale of the Times, Winchester (New York), 1842 (original printed brown; wraps) £7,000

ditto, Winchester (New York), 1842 (rebound) . £2,500

Democratic Vistas, Redfield (Washington, DC), 1871 (first issue without author on title-page; wraps) . . £1,000

ditto, as *Democratic Vistas and Other Papers*, Walter Scott (London), 1888 . . . . £125

Specimen Days and Collect, Rees, Welsh (Philadelphia, PA), 1882-3 (cloth) £200

ditto, Rees, Welsh (Philadelphia, PA), 1882-3 (wraps) . £300

ditto, David McKay (Philadelphia, PA), 1883 . . £125

ditto, Wilson and McCormick (Glasgow, Scotland), 1883 . . . . £125

ditto, as *Specimen Days in America*, Walter Scott (London), 1887 . . . . £50

Complete Prose Works, David McKay (Philadelphia, PA), 1892 . . . . £100

ditto, David McKay (Philadelphia, PA), 1892 (60 numbered copies) £300

In Re Walt Whitman, David McKay (Philadelphia, PA), 1893 (1,000 numbered copies) £125

Notes and Fragments, Talbot & Co (U.S.), 1899 (250 copies) £650

The Complete Writings, Putnam (New York), 1902 (500 numbered sets, 10 vols) £1,500

Walt Whitman's Diary in Canada, Small, Maynard (Boston), 1904 (500 copies) £75

An American Primer, Small & Maynard (Boston), 1904 (500 copies) £75

Lafayette in Brooklyn, Smith (New York, 1905 (250 numbered copies) £100

The Gathering of the Forces, Putnam/Knickerbocker Press (New York), 1920 (2 vols, 1250 sets) . £200/£75

The Half-Breed and Other Stories, Columbia Univ Press (New York), 1927 (155 copies) . . . £45

ditto, Columbia Univ Press (New York), 1927 (30 copies) £125

Rivulets of Prose, Greenberg (New York), 1928 (499 copies) £40

A Child's Reminiscence, University of Washington Bookstore (Washington, DC), 1930 . . . . £100

I Sit and Look Out: Editorials from the Brooklyn Daily Times, Columbia Univ Press (New York), 1932 . £50/£20

Walt Whitman and the Civil War, Univ of Pennsylvania Press (Phil-adelphia, PA), 1933 . . . . £65/£30

New York Dissected, Rufus Rockwell Wilson, Inc. (New York), 1936 (750 numbered copies) . . . £125/£45

The Collected Writings of Walt Whitman, New York Univ Press (New York), 1963 . . . . . . £75/£35

Daybooks and Notebooks, New York Univ Press (New York), 1978 (3 vols; no d/w) £50

Letters

Calamus, Laurens Maynard (Boston), 1897 . . . £150

ditto, Laurens Maynard (Boston), 1897 (35 numbered large paper copies) £500

ditto, Putnam (London), 1897 . . . . . £125

The Wound Dresser, Small, Maynard (Boston), 1898 . £150

ditto, Small, Maynard (Boston), 1898 (60 large paper copies) £500

Letters ... To His Mother, Putnam (New York), 1902 (5 copies; wraps) £3,000

The Collected Writings of Walt Whitman: The Correspondence, New York Univ Press (New York), 1961 (6 vols) . . . . £250/£125

OSCAR WILDE

(b.1854 d.1900)

Known principally as a playwright, Wilde was also a fine essayist, poet and novelist. Born Oscar Fingal O'Flahertie Wills Wilde in Dublin, he was one of the greatest celebrities of his day, known for his cutting, rapier-quick wit. Even today his public persona often overshadows his considerable literary achievements.

Poetry

Ravenna, Thomas Shrimpton (Oxford), 1878 (wraps) £1,250

Poems, David Bogue (London), 1881 (first edition, first issue with the word 'may' in line three of page 136) £1,500

ditto, David Bogue (London), 1881 (second and third editions from same sheets as the first) . . . £250

ditto, Roberts Bros. (Boston), 1881 . . . . £100

ditto, Mathews and Lane (London), 1892 (220 signed copies) £3,000

The Sphinx, Mathews & Lane (London), 1894 (200 copies) £4,000

ditto, Mathews & Lane (London), 1894 (25 large paper copies) £6,000

ditto, John Lane/Bodley Head (London), 1910 (cheap edition) £30

ditto, John Lane (London), 1920 (1,000 copies, 10 illustrations by Alastair) £600

The Ballad of Reading Gaol, Leonard Smithers (London), 1898 (pseud 'C.3.3.' [800 copies]) £750

ditto, Leonard Smithers (London), 1898 (30 numbered copies) £5,000

ditto, Leonard Smithers (London), 1898 (third edition, 99 signed copies) £5,000

ditto, Alfred Bartlett (Boston), 1902 (550 copies) . . £150

Short Stories

The Happy Prince and Other Tales, David Nutt (London), 1888 (illustrated by Walter Crane) £1,500

ditto, David Nutt (London), 1888 (75 signed copies, large handmade paper edition) £6,000

ditto, Roberts Bros. (Boston), 1888 . . . . £400

ditto, Duckworth (London), 1913 (illustrated by Charles Robinson) £75

ditto, Duckworth (London), 1913 (250 copies signed by Robinson, in slipcase). . . . . £1,000/£700

ditto, Putnam's (New York), 1913 (illustrated by Robinson) £75

Lord Arthur Saville's Crime and Other Stories, Osgood, McIlvaine & Co. (London), 1891 . . . . £350

ditto, Dodd, Mead (New York), 1891 . . . . £300

A House of Pomegranates, Osgood, McIlvaine & Co. (London), 1891 . . . . £750

L'Anniversaire de L'Enfant, Black Sun Press (Paris), 1928 (9 illustrations by Alastair) £250

The Birthday of the Infanta, Black Sun Press (Paris), 1928 (100 copies, as above but text in English, 9 illustrations, slipcase). . . . . . . £1,000/£600

Plays

Vera, or The Nihilists Ranken & Co., 1880 (grey wraps) .
. . . . £15,000

ditto, privately printed (New York), 1882 (wraps) . £10,000

The Duchess of Padua, privately printed (New York), 1883 (20 copies printed as manuscript) . . . £12,500

ditto, Buckles (New York), 1906 . . . . £65

ditto, Methuen (London), 1908 (1,000 copies). . £250

Salome, Drame en Un Acte, Librairie de L'art Indépendant/ Elkin Mathews et John Lane (Paris/London), 1893 . £500

ditto, Librairie de L'art Indépendant/Elkin Mathews et John Lane (Paris/London), 1893 (50 tall copies on handmade paper) £1,500

Lady Windermere's Fan, Elkin Mathews & John Lane (London), 1893 . . . . . . £1,000

ditto, Elkin Mathews & John Lane (London), 1893 (50 deluxe copies on handmade paper) . . . £2,500

Salome, Elkin Mathews & John Lane (London)/Copeland & Day (Boston), 1894 (775 copies, illustrated by Beardsley). £1,750

ditto, Lane & Mathews (London)/Copeland & Day (Boston), 1894 (125 copies, on Japan vellum, large paper issue) .
. . . . £9,000

ditto, Melmoth & Co. (London), 1904 (250 numbered copies) £350

ditto, Melmoth & Co. (London), 1904 (50 numbered copies) £500

ditto, G. Crès (Paris), 1922 (9 illustrations by Alastair) . £100

ditto, G. Crès (Paris), 1922 (100 copies on Imperial Japon paper, 9 illustrations) £500

A Woman of No Importance, John Lane (London), 1894 .
. . . . £750

ditto, John Lane (London), 1894 (50 deluxe copies on handmade paper) £1,500

The Importance of Being Earnest, Smithers (London), 1899 (by the 'Author of Lady Windermere's Fan'; 1,000 numbered copies) £800

ditto, Smithers (London), 1899 (12 copies on Japanese vellum) £10,000

ditto, Smithers (London), 1899 (100 signed, deluxe copies).
. . . . £10,000

An Ideal Husband, Smithers (London), 1899 (by the 'Author of Lady Windermere's Fan'; 1,000 numbered copies) £650

ditto, Smithers (London), 1899 (12 copies on Japanese vellum). £10,000

ditto, Smithers (London), 1899 (100 signed, deluxe copies).
. . . . £10,000

Novel

The Picture of Dorian Gray, Ward, Lock (London), 1891 .
. . . . £1,250

ditto, Ward, Lock (London), 1891 (250 signed, numbered, large paper copies) £10,000

Essays

Intentions, Osgood, McIlvaine & Co. (London), 1891 . £350

ditto, Dodd, Mead (New York), 1891 . . . . £200

The Soul of Man Under Socialism, Humphreys (London), 1895 (50 copies, brown paper wraps) . . . £450

ditto, Luce (Boston), 1910 . . . . . . £100

Essays, Criticisms and Reviews, Wright & Jones (London), 1901 (300 numbered copies) £150

The Portrait of Mr W.H., privately printed [Smithers] (London), 1904 (200 copies) £300

ditto, Mitchell Kennerley (New York), 1921 . . £75

De Profundis, Methuen (London), [1905] (with ads dated February) £125

ditto, Methuen (London), [1905] (with ads dated March) £85

ditto, Methuen (London), [1905] (200 copies on handmade paper) £450

ditto, Methuen (London), [1905] (50 copies on Japanese vellum) £4,000

ditto, Putnams (New York), 1905 . . . . £100

The Suppressed Portions of De Profundis, Paul Reynolds (New York), 1913 (15 copies) . . . £1,500

De Profundis: A Facsimilie, British Library (London), 2000 (495 numbered copies) £75

ditto, British Library (London), 2000 (95 numbered copies signed by Merlin Holland). £200

Letters

Four Letters, privately printed, 1906 (wraps) . . £250

After Reading, Letters of Oscar Wilde to Robert Ross, Beaumont Press (London), 1921 (75 numbered copies on Japan vellum of 475) £300

ditto, Beaumont Press (London), 1921 (400 numbered copies of 475) £75

After Berneval, Letters of Oscar Wilde to Robert Ross, Beaumont Press (London), 1922 (75 copies on Japan vellum of 475) £300

ditto, Beaumont Press (London), 1922 (400 numbered copies of 475) £75

Some Letters from Oscar Wilde to Alfred Douglas, 1892-1897, privately printed for William Andrews Clark, Jr by John Henry Nash (San Francisco, CA), 1924 (225 copies, slipcase). . . . . . . £250/£200

Sixteen Letters from Oscar Wilde, Faber (London), 1930 (550 numbered copies; glassine d/w; slipcase) . £75/£50

ditto, Coward-McCann (New York), 1930 (500 unnumbered copies; glassine d/w; slipcase) . . . £65/£45

The Letters of Oscar Wilde, Hart Davis (London), 1962 .
. . . . £75/£25

ditto, Harcourt Brace (New York), 1962 . . . £75/£25

The Complete Letters of Oscar Wilde, Fourth Estate (London), 2000 . . . . £25/£10 *ditto*, Holt (New York), 2000 . . . . . £25/£10

Others

Phrases and Philosophies for The Use of The Young,
privately printed, A. Cooper (London), 1894 (wraps) . £200

Oscariana, privately printed by Humphreys (London), 1895
(50 copies in buff paper wraps) £200

ditto, Humphreys (London), 1910 (200 copies on Japanese
vellum; wraps) £250

ditto, Humphreys (London), 1910 (50 copies on Japanese
vellum) £300

Children in Prison and Other Cruelties of Prison Life,
Murdoch & Co. (London), [1898] (wraps) . . £1,000

Sebastian Melmoth, Humphries (London), 1904 . £75

Poems in Prose, Carrington (Paris), 1905 (50 copies on
vellum) £250

ditto, Carrington (Paris), 1905 (50 copies on paper) . £125

*Wilde and Whistler: An Acrimonious Correspondence in
Art*, Smithers (London), 1906 (400 copies; wraps) . £200

CHARLES WILLEFORD

(b.1919 d.1988)

Willeford had a hard upbringing, being orphaned as a child,
and by fifteen was living as a hobo and riding freight
trains. He joined the army and although horrified by war,
and the people who joined to fight, remained there and
started to write poetry. His career as a novelist was not
particularly successful until *Miami Blues* became a hit.

'Hoke Moseley' Series

Miami Blues, St Martin's Press (New York), 1984 £125/£25

ditto, Macdonald (London), 1985 . . . . £45/£10

New Hope for the Dead, St Martin's Press (New York),
1985 . . . . £100/£10

ditto, Futura (London), 1987 (pbk) £5

Sideswipe, St Martin's Press (New York), 1987 . £20/£5

ditto, Gollancz (London), 1988 . . . . £20/£5

The Way We Die Now, Random House (New York), 1988 .
. . . . £10/£5

ditto, Ultramarine (New York), 1988 (99 signed, numbered
copies) £85

ditto, Gollancz (London), 1989 . . . . £10/£5

Other Novels

High Priest of California, Royal Books (New York), 1953
(#20; bound with Talbot Mundy's *Full Moon*; pbk) . £75

Pick-up, Beacon (New York), 1955 (#B109; pbk) . £100

Wild Wives, Royal Books (New York), 1956 (#B130; bound
with *High Priest of California;* pbk) . . . £100

ditto, RE/Search Publications (San Francisco, CA), 1987
(250 signed, numbered copies). . . . £75/£45

Honey Gal, Royal Books (New York), 1958 (#B160; pbk) .
. . . . £100

ditto, as *The Black Mass of Brother Springer*, Black Lizard
(Berkley, CA), 1989 (pbk). £5

Lust is a Woman, Beacon Books (New York), 1958 (#B175;
pbk) £145

The Woman Chaser, Newsstand Library (Chicago), 1960
(#U137; pbk) £50

Understudy for Love, Newsstand Library (Chicago), 1961
(pbk) £150

The Whip Hand, Fawcett (Greenwich, CT), 1961 (#S-1087;
pseud 'W. Franklin Sanders'; pbk) £50

Cockfighter, Chicago Paperback House (Chicago), 1962
(#B120; pbk) £40

No Experience Necessary, Newsstand Library (Chicago),
1962 (#U182; pbk) £125

The Burnt Orange Heresy, Crown (New York), 1971 . .
. . . . £125/£20

The Hombre from Sonora, Lenox Hill Press (New York),
1971 (pseud 'Will Charles') . . . . £400/£65

ditto, as *The Difference*, Dennis McMillan Publications
(Tucson, AZ), 1991 . . . . . . £10/£5

Kiss Your Ass Good-bye, Dennis McMillan Publications
(Miami Beach, FL), 1987 (400 signed, numbered copies) .
. . . . £100/£25

ditto, Gollancz (London), 1989 . . . . £20/£5

The Shark-Infested Custard, Underwood-Miller (Novato,
CA), 1993 . . . . £10/£5

ditto, Cannongate (Edinburgh), 2000 (pbk) . . . £5

Collections

The Machine in Ward Eleven, Belmont Books (New York),
1963 (#90-286; pbk) £25

ditto, Consul (London), 1964 (#1309; pbk) . . £5

Everybody's Metamorphosis, Dennis McMillan Publications
(Miss-oula, MT), 1988 (400 signed, numbered copies) .
. . . . £100/£20

ditto, Dennis McMillan Publications (Missoula, MT), 1988
(26 signed, lettered copies) £200

A Charles Willeford Omnibus, MacDonald (London), 1991
. . . . £20/£5

The Second Half of the Double Feature, Wit's End
Publishing (New Albany, IN), 2003 . . . £15/£5

Poetry

The Outcast Poets, The Alicat Bookshop Press (Yonkers,
NY), 1947 (with other poets; loose sheets in a printed
envelope; includes five poems by Willeford) . . £50

Proletarian Laughter, The Alicat Bookshop Press (Yonkers,
NY), 1948 (stapled wraps). £65

Poontang and Other Poems, New Athenaeum Press
(Crescent City, FL), 1967 (500 copies; stapled wraps) £500

Non-Fiction

A Guide for the Undehemorrhoided, self-published
(Kendall, FL), 1977 . . . . £100

Off the Wall, Pegasus Rex Press (Montclair, NJ), 1980. .
. . . . £75/£10

Something About a Soldier, Random House (New York),
1986 . . . . £10/£5

New Forms of Ugly, Dennis McMillan Publications (Miami
Beach, FL), 1987 (350 signed, numbered copies) £100/£35

I Was Looking for a Street, The Countryman Press
(Woodstock, VT), 1988 . . . . . . £10/£5

ditto, Polygon (Edinburgh), 1991 (pbk) . . . £5

Cockfighter Journal: The Story of a Shooting, Neville
Publishing (Santa Barbara, CA), 1989 (300 signed,
numbered copies; unprinted acetate d/w) . . £75

ditto, Neville Publishing (Santa Barbara, CA), 1989 (26
signed, lettered copies) £300

Writing and Other Blood Sports, Dennis McMillan
(Tucson, AZ), 2000 . . . . . . £10/£5

CHARLES WILLIAMS
(b.1886 d.1945)

The author of many books on theological subjects, Charles Williams was also a poet, novelist, dramatist, critic and biographer. His best known works are his seven novels of Christian mysticism; supernatural thrillers dealing with the conflict between good and evil. He was a member of the Inklings, a literary discussion group which also included J.R.R. Tolkien and C.S. Lewis.

Poetry

The Silver Stair, Herbert & Daniel (London), [1912] . £500
Poems of Conformity, O.U.P. (Oxford, UK), 1917. . £125
Divorce, O.U.P. (Oxford, UK), 1920 .   .   . £500/£100
Windows of Night, O.U.P. (Oxford, UK), 1925 . £300/£75
Heroes and Kings, Sylvan Press (London), 1930 (300 copies) £250
Taliessin Through Logres, O.U.P. (Oxford, UK), 1938 .
.   .   .   . £125/£30
The Region of The Summer Stars, Editions Poetry (London), 1944 .   .   .   .   .   . £75/£25

Novels

War in Heaven, Gollancz (London), 1930 . . £600/£75
ditto, Pellegrini & Cudahy (New York), 1949 . . £50/£10
Many Dimensions, Gollancz (London), 1931 . £400/£60
ditto, Pellegrini & Cudahy (New York), 1949 . . £50/£10
The Place of The Lion, Gollancz (London), 1931 . £400/£60
ditto, Gollancz (London), 1931 (pbk).   .   .   . £45
ditto, Norton (New York), 1932 .   .   .   . £350/£50
The Greater Trumps, Gollancz (London), 1932 . £300/£50
ditto, Pellegrini & Cudahy (New York), 1950 . . £50/£10
Shadows of Ecstasy, Gollancz (London), 1933 . £200/£45
ditto, Pellegrini & Cudahy (New York), 1950 . . £50/£10
Descent into Hell, Faber (London), 1937 .   . £250/£40
ditto, Pellegrini & Cudahy (New York), 1949 . . £50/£10
All Hallows Eve, Faber (London), 1945 .   . £300/£35
ditto, Pellegrini & Cudahy (New York), 1948 . . £50/£10

Drama

The Masque of The Manuscript, privately printed for Amen House (London), 1927 (100 copies; wraps) .   . £350
A Myth of Shakespeare, O.U.P. (Oxford, UK), 1928 .
.   .   .   . £125/£45
The Masque of Perusal, privately printed for Amen House (London), 1929 (100 copies; wraps) .   . £350
Three Plays, O.U.P. (Oxford, UK), 1931 (red glassine d/w with paper flaps) .   .   .   .   . £200/£125
Thomas Cranmer of Canterbury, H.J. Goulden (Canterbury, Kent), 1936 (wraps) £45
ditto, O.U.P. (Oxford, UK), 1936 .   .   .   . £75/£25
Judgement at Chelmsford, O.U.P. (Oxford, UK), 1939 (wraps) £30
The House of The Octopus, Edinburgh House Press (London), 1945 .   .   .   .   .   . £30/£10
Seed of Adam and Other Plays, O.U.P. (Oxford, UK), 1948
.   .   .   . £30/£10
Collected Plays, O.U.P. (Oxford, UK), 1963 .   . £25/£10

Biography

Bacon, Barker (London), 1933 .   .   .   . £125/£25
James I, Barker (London), 1934 .   .   .   . £125/£25

Rochester, Barker (London), 1935 .   .   . £125/£25
Queen Elizabeth, Duckworth (London), 1936 . £100/£20
Henry VII, Barker (London), 1937 .   .   . £100/£20
Flecker of Dean Close, Canterbury Press (London), 1946 .
.   .   .   . £50/£10

Theology

He Came Down from Heaven, Heinemann (London), 1938
.   .   .   . £65/£15
The Descent of The Dove, Longmans, Green (London), 1939
.   .   .   . £65/£15
Witchcraft, Faber (London), 1941 .   .   . £125/£35
The Forgiveness of Sins, Bles (London), 1942 . £40/£10

Criticism

Poetry at Present, Clarendon Press (Oxford, UK), 1930 .
.   .   .   . £65/£15
The English Poetic Mind, Clarendon Press (Oxford, UK), 1932 .   .   .   . £125/£40
Reason and Beauty in The Poetic Mind, Clarendon Press (Oxford, UK), 1933 .   .   .   .   . £65/£20
Religion and Love in Dante, Dacre Press (London), [1941] (stitched wraps) £30
The Figure of Beatrice, Faber (London), 1943 . £75/£20
Arthurian Torso, O.U.P. (Oxford, UK), 1948 (with C.S. Lewis) .   .   .   . £125/£45
ditto, O.U.P. (New York), 1948 .   .   .   . £125/£45
The Image of The City, O.U.P. (Oxford, UK), 1958 £45/£10

TENNESSEE WILLIAMS
(b.1911 d.1983)

'Tennessee Williams' was the pen-name of Thomas Lanier Williams, an American playwright. Most of his work shows a sympathy with lost, lonely and self-punishing characters, and many of these are thought to have been modelled on his own family: the 'mad heroine' characters resemble his sister, Rose. He won the Pulitzer Prize for Drama for *A Streetcar Named Desire* in 1948 and *Cat On a Hot Tin Roof* in 1955.

Plays

Battle of Angels, Pharos (Murray, UT), 1945 (combined issue of Pharos 1 & 2; pale grey paper wraps printed in scarlet) £300
ditto, New Directions (Norfolk, CT), 1945 . . £50/£15
The Glass Menagerie, Random House (New York), 1945 .
.   .   .   . £500/£35
ditto, Lehmann (London), 1948 .   .   .   . £45/£10
27 Wagons Full of Cotton and other One Act Plays, New Directions (Norfolk, CT) [1945] (first issue, beige cloth boards; brown d/w) .   .   .   .   . £175/£20
ditto, New Directions (Norfolk, CT), 1945 (second issue with yellow boards with black cloth spine; introduction added; black d/w) .   .   .   .   .   . £100/£15
ditto, Lehmann (London), 1949 .   .   .   . £45/£10
ditto, New Directions (Norfolk, CT), 1953 (third edition, adds two more plays) .   .   .   .   . £45/£10
You Touched Me! A Romantic Comedy, French (New York), 1947 (with Donald Windham) .   . £350/£35
ditto, French (New York), 1947 (grey wraps) .   . £100

A Streetcar Named Desire, New Directions (New York), 1947 . . . . £1,500/£45

ditto, Lehmann (London), 1949 . . . . £35/£10

American Blues, Dramatists Play Services (New York), 1948 (author's name misspelled on front cover: 'Tennesse'; stapled wraps) £200

Summer and Smoke, New Directions (Norfolk, CT), 1948 (first issue d/w lists three plays by Williams on inside back flap) . . . . . . £175/£15

ditto, Lehmann (London), 1952 . . . . . £35/£10

The Rose Tattoo, New Directions (Norfolk, CT), 1951 (first binding rose cloth) . . . . . . £175/£65

ditto, New Directions (Norfolk, CT), 1951 (second binding tan cloth) . . . . £75/£10

ditto, Secker & Warburg (London), 1954 [1955] . £35/£10

I Rise in Flame, Cried the Phoenix, A Play about D.H. Lawrence, New Directions (Norfolk, CT), 1951 (300 signed copies) . . . . . . £300/£200

ditto, New Directions (Norfolk, CT), 1951 (10 signed copies, slipcase). . . . .£1,500/£1,250

Camino Real, New Directions (Norfolk, CT), 1953 £75/£15

ditto, Secker & Warburg (London), 1958 . . . £40/£10

Cat on a Hot Tin Roof, New Directions (Norfolk, CT), 1955 . . . . £250/£35

ditto, Secker & Warburg (London), 1956 . . . £175/£25

Four Plays, Secker & Warburg (London), 1956 . £40/£10

Suddenly Last Summer, New Directions (Norfolk, CT), 1958 . . . . £125/£25

A Perfect Analysis Given by a Parrot, Dramatists Play Services (New York), [1958] (wraps) . . . £25

Orpheus Descending/Battle of Angels, New Directions (Norfolk, CT), 1958 . . . . . £100/£20

Orpheus Descending, Secker & Warburg (London), 1958 . . . . £75/£15

Garden District, Secker & Warburg (London), 1959 £35/£10

Sweet Bird of Youth, New Directions (Norfolk, CT), 1959 . . . . £50/£15

ditto, Secker & Warburg (London), 1961 . . . £40/£10

Period of Adjustment/High Point over a Cavern/A Serious Comedy, New Directions (Norfolk, CT), 1960 . £50/£10

ditto, Secker & Warburg (London), 1961 . . . £35/£10

The Night of the Iguana, New Directions (Norfolk, CT), 1961 . . . . £65/£15

ditto, Secker & Warburg (London), 1963 . . . £45/£10

Five Plays, Secker & Warburg (London), 1962 . £35/£10

The Milk Train Doesn't Stop Here Anymore, New Directions (Norfolk, CT), 1964 (first issue, with pp.19-22 integral and scene 2 starting at p.22) . . £250/£200

ditto, New Directions (Norfolk, CT), 1964 (second issue, with pp.19-22 tipped-in and scene 2 starting at p.21) . . . . £50/£15

ditto, New Directions (Norfolk, CT), 1964 (third issue, with pp.19-22 bound in) . . . . . £45/£10

ditto, Secker & Warburg (London), 1964 . . . £45/£10

Three Plays: The Rose Tattoo, Camino Real, Sweet Bird of Youth, New Directions (Norfolk, CT), 1964. . £20/£5

The Eccentricities of a Nightingale; Summer and Smoke; Camino Real, New Directions (Norfolk, CT), 1964 £20/£5

The Mutilated, Dramatists Play Service (New York), 1967 (stapled wraps) £10

The Gnädiges Fräulein, Dramatists Play Service (New York), 1967 (stapled wraps) £10

Kingdom of Earth: The Seven Descents of Myrtle, New Directions (Norfolk, CT), 1968 . . . . £35/£10

ditto, as *The Kingdom of Earth: The Seven Descents of Myrtle*, Dramatists Play Service (New York), 1969 (wraps) £10

The Two-Character Play, New Directions (Norfolk, CT), 1969 . . . . £25/£5

In The Bar of a Tokyo Hotel, Dramatists Play Service (New York), 1969 (wraps) £10

Dragon Country: A Book of Plays, New Directions (Norfolk, CT), 1970 . . . . . . £20/£5

ditto, New Directions (Norfolk, CT), 1970 (pbk) . £10

Battle of Angels; The Glass Menagerie; A Streetcar Named Desire, New Directions (Norfolk, CT), 1971 . £20/£5

Cat on a Hot Tin Roof; Orpheus Descending/Suddenly Last Summer, New Directions (Norfolk, CT), 1971 . £20/£5

Small Craft Warnings, New Directions (Norfolk, CT), 1972 . . . . £25/£5

Vieux Carre, New Directions (Norfolk, CT), 1979. £20/£5

A Lovely Sunday for Creve Coeur, New Directions (Norfolk, CT), 1980 . . . . . . £15/£5

Steps Must Be Gentle, Targ (New York), 1980 (350 signed copies, with plain d/w) . . . . £125/£100

Clothes for a Summer Hotel, A Ghost Play, Dramatists Play Service (New York), 1981 (wraps) £10

It Happened the Day the Sun Rose, Sylvester & Orphanos (Los Angeles, CA), 1981 (330 signed copies) . £125

Clothes for a Summer Hotel, New Directions (Norfolk, CT), 1983 . . . . £20/£5

The Remarkable Rooming-House of Mme Le Monde, Albondocani Press (New York), 1984 (26 lettered copies of 176; wraps) £150

ditto, Albondocani Press (New York), 1984 (150 numbered copies of 176; wraps) £65

The Red Devil Battery Sign, New Directions (Norfolk, CT), 1988 . . . . £25/£5

Not About Nightingales, Methuen (London), 1998 (pbk) £5

Novels

The Roman Spring of Mrs Stone, New Directions (Norfolk, CT), 1950 . . . . £30/£10

ditto, New Directions (Norfolk, CT), 1950 (500 signed copies in slipcase) . . . . . £225/£175

ditto, Lehmann (London), 1950 . . . . . £30/£10

Moise and the World of Reason, Simon & Schuster (New York), 1975 . . . . £20/£5

ditto, Simon & Schuster (New York), 1975 (350 signed copies) £150

ditto, W.H. Allen (London), 1976 . . . . £20/£5

Short Stories

One Arm and Other Stories, New Directions (Norfolk, CT), 1948 . . . . £25/£10

ditto, New Directions (Norfolk, CT), 1948 (50 signed copies, slipcase). . . . . . . £1,000/£750

ditto, New Directions (Norfolk, CT), 1948 (1,500 copies, slipcase). . . . . £50/£30

Hard Candy, A Book of Stories, New Directions (Norfolk, CT), 1954 . . . . £20/£5

ditto, New Directions (Norfolk, CT), 1954 (1,500 copies on laid paper, slipcase) . . . . . £25/£10

ditto, New Directions (Norfolk, CT), 1948 (100 [10] signed copies, slipcase) . . . . . . £1,000/£750

ditto, New Directions (Norfolk, CT), 1948 (20 signed presentation copies, slipcase) . . . £1,000/£750

Man Brings This Up Road, Street & Smith (New York),
1959 . . . . £35/£10
Three Players of a Summer Game and Other Stories,
Secker & Warburg (London), 1960 . . . £25/£10
Grand, House of Books (New York), 1964 (26 signed
lettered copies, tissue d/w). . . . £160/£125
ditto, House of Books (New York), 1964 (300 signed copies,
tissue d/w) . . . . . £125/£100
The Knightly Quest, A Novella and Four Short Stories,
New Directions (Norfolk, CT), 1967 . . £25/£10
Eight Mortal Ladies Possessed, A Book of Stories, New
Directions (Norfolk, CT), 1974 . . . £20/£5
ditto, Secker & Warburg (London), 1975 . . £20/£5
Collected Stories, New Directions (Norfolk, CT), 1985 .
. . . . £15/£5
ditto, Secker & Warburg (London), 1986 . . £15/£5

Screenplays

Baby Doll, The Script for a Film, New Directions (Norfolk,
CT), 1956 . . . . . . £125/£25
ditto, Secker & Warburg (London), 1957 . . £100/£20
The Fugitive Kind, Signet (New York), 1960 (pbk) . £5
Stopped Rocking and Other Screenplays, New Directions
(Norfolk, CT), 1984 . . . . . £10/£5

Poetry

In The Winter of Cities, New Directions (Norfolk, CT),
1956 . . . . £75/£20
ditto, New Directions (Norfolk, CT), 1956 (500 signed
copies, slipcase) . . . . . £750/£600
Androgyne, Mon Amour, New Directions (Norfolk, CT),
1977 . . . . £25/£5
ditto, New Directions (Norfolk, CT), 1956 (200 signed
copies, slipcase) . . . . . £125/£100

Other Titles

Lord Byron's Love Letter, An Opera in One Act, Ricordi
(New York), [1955] (stapled wraps) . . . £25
Memoirs, Doubleday (New York), 1975 . . £20/£5
ditto, Doubleday (New York), 1975 (400 signed copies in
slipcase). . . . . . £250/£200
ditto, W.H. Allen (London), 1976 . . . £20/£5
*Tennessee Williams' Letters to Donald Windham, 1940-
1965*, Stamperia Valdonega (Verona), 1976 (500 numbered
copies; wraps; slipcase) . . . . £40/£25
ditto, Stamperia Valdonega (Verona), 1976 (26 lettered
copies signed by Williams and Windham; wraps; slipcase)
. . . . . . £1250/£1,000
ditto, Holt (New York), 1977 . . . £25/£5
Where I Live, Selected Essays, New Directions (Norfolk,
CT), 1976 . . . . . . £25/£5
Conversations with Tennessee Williams, Univ Press of
Mississippi (Jackson, MS), 1986 . . . £20/£5
*Five O'Clock Angel: Letters of Tennessee Williams to
Maria St. Just, 1948-1982*, Knopf (New York), 1990 .
. . . . £20/£5
ditto, Deutsch (London), 1991 . . . £20/£5
*The Selected Letters of Tennessee Williams, Volume I,
1920-1945*, New Directions (Norfolk, CT), 2000 £20/£5
ditto, Oberon (London), 2001. . . . £20/£5
*The Selected Letters of Tennessee Williams, Volume II,
1945-1957*, New Directions (Norfolk, CT), 2004 £20/£5

HENRY WILLIAMSON
(b.1895 d.1977)

Henry Williamson's most successful writings are his nature
novels, including *Tarka the Otter* and *Salar the Salmon*. It
is generally acknowledged that these owe a debt to the 19th
century naturalist Richard Jefferies. Williamson's right-
wing political sympathies in the 1930s did much to damage
his reputation.

'A Chronicle of Ancient Sunlight' Titles

The Dark Lantern, Macdonald (London), 1951 . £250/£20
Donkey Boy, Macdonald (London), 1952. . . £200/£20
Young Phillip Maddison, Macdonald (London), 1953 . .
. . . . £125/£15
How Dear is Life, Macdonald (London), 1954 . £100/£15
A Fox Under My Cloak, Macdonald (London), 1955 . .
. . . . £150/£15
The Golden Virgin, Macdonald (London), 1957 . £100/£15
Love and The Loveless: A Soldiers Tale, Macdonald
(London), 1958 . . . . . £100/£15
A Test To Destruction, Macdonald (London), 1960 . .
. . . . £100/£10
The Innocent Moon, Macdonald (London), 1961 . £45/£10
It Was The Nightingale, Macdonald (London), 1962 . .
. . . . £40/£10
The Power of The Dead, Macdonald (London), 1963 . .
. . . . £40/£10
The Phoenix Generation, Macdonald (London), 1965 . .
. . . . £35/£10
A Solitary War, Macdonald (London), 1966 . £35/£10
Lucifer Before Sunrise, Macdonald (London), 1967 £35/£10
The Gale of The World, Macdonald (London), 1969 £60/£15

'The Flax of Dream' Titles

The Beautiful Years, Collins (London), 1921 . £1,250/£200
ditto, Faber (London), 1929 (revised edition) . £65/£15
ditto, Faber (London), 1929 (200 signed copies, revised
edition) £125
ditto, Dutton (New York), 1929 (revised edition) . £65/£15
Dandelion Days, Collins (London), 1922. . £600/£15
ditto, Faber (London), 1930 (revised edition) . £35/£10
ditto, Faber (London), 1930 (200 signed copies, revised
edition).. . . . . . . £125
ditto, Dutton (New York), 1930 (revised edition) . £35/£10
The Dream of Fair Women, Collins (London), 1924 . .
. . . . £450/£125
ditto, Faber (London), 1931 (revised edition) . £35/£10
ditto, Faber (London), 1931 (200 signed copies, revised
edition) £125
ditto, Dutton (New York), 1931 (revised edition) . £35/£10
The Pathway, Cape (London), 1928 . . . £65/£10
ditto, Dutton (New York), 1929 . . . £50/£10
The Flax of Dream, Faber (London), 1936 (omnibus) . .
. . . . £35/£10
ditto, Faber (London), 1936 (200 copies) . . £150

Other Fiction

The Peregrine's Saga, Collins (London), 1923 (600 copies)
. . . . £1,000/£45
ditto, as *Sun Brothers*, Dutton (New York), 1925 (no d/w) .
. . . . £50
The Old Stag, Putnam (London), 1926 . . . £65/£15
ditto, Dutton (New York), 1927 . . . . £40/£15

Tarka The Otter, Putnams (London), 1927 (100 signed copies, privately printed for subscribers) . . £1,250
ditto, Putnam (London), 1927 (1,000 larger paper copies, no d/w) £100
ditto, Putnam (London), 1927 (first trade edition) . £300/£75
ditto, Dutton (New York), 1928 . . . . . £175/£30
The Linhay on The Downs and The Firing Gatherer, Elkin Mathews & Marrot (London): No. 12 in the Woburn Books series, 1929 (530 numbered copies initialled by the author) . . . . £55/£35
ditto, Cape (London), 1934 (revised and enlarged edition) . . . . £35/£10
The Patriot's Progress, Bles (London), 1930 . . £40/£10
ditto, Bles (London), [1930] (350 signed copies, slipcase) . . . . £200/£100
ditto, Dutton (New York), 1930 . . . . . £35/£10
The Star Born, Faber (London), 1933 . . £65/£15
ditto, Faber (London), 1933 (70 signed copies) . . £300
ditto, Faber (London), 1948 (revised edition) . . £15/£5
The Gold Falcon or The Haggard of Love, Faber (London), 1933 (anonymous) . . . . . . £75/£25
ditto, Smith & Haas (New York), 1933 . . . £65/£15
ditto, Faber (London), 1947 (revised edition) . . £15/£5
Salar The Salmon, Faber (London), 1935 . . £125/£20
ditto, Faber (London), 1935 (13 numbered copies signed and corrected by the author) £1,500
ditto, Little, Brown (Boston), 1936 . . . £65/£15
The Sun in The Sands, Faber (London), 1945 . £25/£10
The Phasian Bird, Faber (London), 1948 . . £25/£10
ditto, Little, Brown (Boston), 1950 . . . £25/£10
Scribbing Lark, Faber (London), 1948 . . £25/£10
Tales of Moorland and Estuary, Macdonald (London), 1953 . . . . £25/£10
Collected Nature Stories, Macdonald (London), 1970 . . . . £10/£5
The Scandaroon, Macdonald (London), 1972 . £20/£5
ditto, Macdonald (London), 1972 (250 signed copies, slipcase) . . . . £50/£35
ditto, Saturday Review Press (New York), 1973 £20/£5

Non-Fiction
The Lone Swallows, Collins (London), 1922 (500 copies) £65
ditto, Dutton (New York), 1926 . . . . £125/£25
ditto, Collins (London), 1928 (revised edition) . £100/£20
The Wet Flanders Plain, Beaumont Press (London), 1929 (80 of 320 signed copies on handmade parchment vellum) £400
ditto, Beaumont Press (London), 1929 (240 of 320 copies, numbered, on handmade paper) £150
ditto, Faber (London), 1929 (revised edition) . £100/£20
ditto, Dutton (New York), 1929 . . . . £85/£15

The Ackymals, Windsor Press [San Francisco, CA], 1929 (225 signed copies, slipcase) . . . £125/£100
The Village Book, Cape (London), 1930 . . . £65/£15
ditto, Cape (London), 1930 (504 signed copies) . . £75
ditto, Dutton (New York), 1930 . . . . £50/£10
The Wild Red Deer of Exmoor, Faber (London), 1931 (75 copies) £150
ditto, Faber (London), 1931 . . . . . £35/£10
The Labouring Life, Cape (London), 1932 . £45/£15
ditto, Cape (London), 1932 (122 signed copies, acetate d/w) . . . . £125/£75

ditto, as **As The Sun Shines**, Dutton (New York), 1933 . . . . £30/£10
On Foot in Devon, Maclehose (London), 1933 . £45/£15
Devon Holiday, Cape (London), 1935 . . . £40/£15
Goodbye West Country, Putnam (London), 1937 . £40/£15
ditto, Little, Brown (Boston), 1938 . . . . £40/£10
The Children of Shallowford, Faber (London), 1939 . . . . £60/£15
ditto, Faber (London), 1959 (revised edition) . . £15/£5
The Story of a Norfolk Farm, Faber (London), 1941 . . . . £35/£10
As The Sun Shines, Faber (London), 1941 . . £25/£10
Genius of Friendship - T.E. Lawrence, Faber (London), 1941 . . . . £75/£25
Norfolk Life, Faber (London), 1943 (with Lilias Rider Haggard) . . . . £20/£5
Life in a Devon Village, Faber (London), 1945 . £20/£5
Tales of a Devon Village, Faber (London), 1945 . £20/£5
A Clear Water Stream, Faber (London), 1958 . £20/£5
ditto, Ives Washburn (New York), 1958 . . . £20/£5
In The Woods, St Albert's Press (Llandeilo, Wales), 1960 (50 numbered and signed copies; cloth in glassine wraps) . . . . £100/£75
ditto, St Albert's Press (Llandeilo, Wales), 1960 (950 numbered copies; pbk in wraps) . . . . £35/£20

A.N. WILSON
(b.1950)

Andrew Norman Wilson is an English biographer, novelist and author of works of popular and cultural history. His biographies in particular are underpinned by his own early intention to follow a career in the Church of England: his lives of Tolstoy, Jesus, C.S. Lewis and Hillaire Belloc are notable for their deeply informed, sceptical attitude to religious belief.

'Lampitt' Chronicles
Incline Our Hearts, Hamish Hamilton (London), 1988. . . . . £10/£5
ditto, Viking (New York), 1989 . . . . . £10/£5
A Bottle in the Smoke, Sinclair-Stevenson (London), 1990 . . . . £10/£5
ditto, Viking (New York), 1990 . . . . . £10/£5
Daughters of Albion, Sinclair-Stevenson (London), 1991 . . . . £10/£5
ditto, Viking (New York), 1991 . . . . . £10/£5
Hearing Voices, Sinclair-Stevenson (London), 1995 £10/£5
ditto, Norton (New York), 1996 . . . . . £10/£5
A Watch in the Night, Sinclair-Stevenson (London), 1996 . . . . £10/£5
ditto, Norton (New York), 1996 . . . . . £10/£5

Other Novels
The Sweets of Pimlico, Secker & Warburg (London), 1977 . . . . £200/£25
Unguarded Hours, Secker & Warburg (London), 1978 . . . . £75/£15
Kindly Light, Secker & Warburg (London), 1979 . £45/£10
The Healing Art, Secker & Warburg (London), 1980 . . . . £30/£5

Who Was Oswald Fish?, Secker & Warburg (London), 1981
. . . . £30/£5
Wise Virgin, Secker & Warburg (London), 1982 . £30/£5
ditto, Viking (New York), 1983 . . . . . £15/£5
Scandal, Or Priscilla's Kindness, Hamish Hamilton (London), 1983 . . . . . . £20/£5
ditto, Viking (New York), 1984 . . . . . £15/£5
Gentlemen in England: A Vision, Hamish Hamilton (London), 1985 . . . . . . £15/£5
ditto, Viking (New York), 1986 . . . . . £15/£5
Love Unknown, Hamish Hamilton (London), 1986 £10/£5
ditto, Viking (New York), 1987 . . . . . £10/£5
The Vicar of Sorrows, Sinclair-Stevenson (London), 1993 .
. . . . £10/£5
ditto, Norton (New York), 1994 . . . . £10/£5
Dream Children, Murray (London), 1998 . £10/£5
ditto, Norton (New York), 1998 . . . . £10/£5
My Name Is Legion, Hutchinson (London), 2004 . £10/£5
ditto, Farrar Straus Giroux (New York), 2005 . £10/£5
A Jealous Ghost, Hutchinson (London), 2005 . . £10/£5
Winnie and Wolf, Hutchinson (London), 2007 . £10/£5
ditto, Farrar, Sraus & Giroux (New York), 2008 . £10/£5

Biography
The Laird of Abbottsford: A View of Walter Scott, O.U.P. (Oxford, UK), 1980 . . . . . £25/£5
The Life of John Milton, O.U.P. (Oxford, UK), 1983 £15/£5
Hilaire Belloc, Hamish Hamilton (London), 1984 . £15/£5
ditto, Atheneum (New York), 1984 . . . £15/£5
Tolstoy: A Biography, Hamish Hamilton (London), 1988 .
. . . . £15/£5
ditto, Norton (New York), 1988 . . . . . £15/£5
Eminent Victorians, BBC (London), 1989 . £10/£5
ditto, Norton (New York), 1990 . . . . £10/£5
C.S. Lewis; A Biography, Collins (London), 1990 . £10/£5
ditto, Norton (New York), 1990 . . . . £10/£5
Jesus, Sinclair-Stevenson (London), 1992 . £10/£5
ditto, Norton (New York), 1992 . . . . £10/£5
The Rise and Fall of the House of Windsor, Sinclair-Stevenson (London), 1993. . . . . £10/£5
ditto, Norton (New York), 1993 . . . . £10/£5
Paul: The Mind of the Apostle, Sinclair-Stevenson (London), 1997 . . . . . . £10/£5
ditto, Norton (New York), 1997 . . . . £10/£5
Iris Murdoch as I Knew Her, Hutchinson (London), 2003 .
. . . . £10/£5
Betjeman: A Life, Hutchinson (London), 2006 . £10/£5
ditto, Farrar, Straus & Giroux (New York), 2006 . £10/£5

Poetry
Lilibet: An Account in Verse of the Early Years of the Queen Until The Time of Her Accession, Blond & Briggs (London), 1984 (wraps) £10

Essays
How Can We Know? An Essay on The Christian Religion, Hamish Hamilton (London), 1985 . . . £10/£5
ditto, Atheneum (New York), 1985 . . . £10/£5
The Church in Crisis, Hodder & Stoughton (London), 1986 (with Charles Moore and Gavin Stamp; pbk) . . £5
Penfriends from Porlock: Essay and Reviews, 1977-1986, Hamish Hamilton (London), 1988 . . . £10/£5
ditto, Norton (New York), 1989 . . . . . £10/£5

Against religion: Why We Should Try to Live without It, Chatto & Windus (London), 1990 (pbk) . . . £5

Children's Titles
Stray, Walker (London), 1987 . . . . . £15/£5
ditto, Orchard (New York), 1989 . . . . . £10/£5
The Tabitha Stories, Walker (London), 1988 . . £15/£5
ditto, as *Tabitha*, Orchard (New York), 1989 . . £10/£5
Hazel the Guinea-pig, Walker, 1989 (illustrated by Jonathan Heale) . . . . £10/£5
ditto, Candlewick (Cambridge, MA), 1989 . . £10/£5

Others
Landscape in France, Elm Tree (London), 1987 (photographs by Charles Waite) . . . . . £10/£5
ditto, St Martin's Press (New York), 1988 . . £10/£5
God's Funeral, Murray (London), 1999 . . £10/£5
ditto, Norton (New York), 1999 . . . . . £10/£5
The Victorians, Hutchinson (London), 2002 . £20/£5
ditto, Norton (New York), 2003 . . . . . £15/£5
London: A Short History, Weidenfeld & Nicolson (London), 2004 . . . . £10/£5
ditto, Norton (New York), 2005 . . . . . £15/£5
After the Victorians: The Decline of Britain in the World, Hutchinson (London), 2005 . . . . £10/£5
ditto, Farrar Straus Giroux (New York), 2005 . . £10/£5
Our Times, Hutchinson (London), 2008 . . £10/£5
ditto, Farrar Straus Giroux (New York), 2010 . . £10/£5

ANGUS WILSON
(b.1913 d.1991)

A British novelist and short story writer, Angus Wilson attended Merton College, Oxford and worked as a librarian at the British Museum from 1937. His writing has a strongly satirical vein and several of his books have been successfully adapted for television. Wilson's critical writings are also highly regarded, particularly his studies of Zola and Dickens. He received a knighthood in 1980.

Novels
Hemlock and After, Secker & Warburg (London), 1952 .
. . . . £35/£10
ditto, Viking (New York), 1952 . . . . . £30/£5
Anglo-Saxon Attitudes, Secker & Warburg (London), 1956
. . . . £50/£10
ditto, Viking (New York), 1956 . . . . . £25/£5
The Middle Age of Mrs Eliot, Secker & Warburg (London), 1958 . . . . £25/£5
ditto, Viking (New York), 1959 . . . . . £15/£5
The Old Men at The Zoo, Secker & Warburg (London), 1961 . . . . £30/£5
ditto, Viking (New York), 1961 . . . . . £10/£5
Late Call, Secker & Warburg (London), 1964 . £20/£5
ditto, Viking (New York), 1965 . . . . . £10/£5
No Laughing Matter, Secker & Warburg (London), 1967 .
. . . . £15/£5
ditto, Viking (New York), 1967 . . . . . £10/£5
As if by Magic, Secker & Warburg (London), 1973 £15/£5
ditto, Viking (New York), 1973 . . . . . £10/£5

Setting The World on Fire, Secker & Warburg (London), 1980 . . . . £10/£5
ditto, Viking (New York), 1980 . . . . . £10/£5

Stories
The Wrong Set and Other Stories, Secker & Warburg (London), 1949 . . . . . £75/£20
ditto, Morrow (New York), 1950 . . . . £40/£10
Such Darling Dodos and Other Stories, Secker & Warburg (London), 1950 . . . . £35/£20
ditto, Morrow (New York), 1951 . . . £25/£10
A Bit Off The Map and Other Stories, Secker & Warburg (London), 1957 . . . . . £15/£5
ditto, Viking (New York), 1957 . . . . £10/£5
Death Dance: 25 Stories, Viking (New York), 1969 £15/£5
Collected Stories, Secker & Warburg (London), 1987 £10/£5
ditto, Viking (New York), 1987 . . . . £10/£5

Plays
The Mulberry Bush: A Play in 3 Acts, Secker & Warburg (London), 1956 . . . . . £30/£10

Others
Emile Zola, Secker & Warburg (London), 1952 . £45/£15
ditto, Morrow (New York), 1952 . . . £25/£10
For Whom The Cloche Tolls, Methuen (London), 1953 (with Philippe Jullian) . . . £45/£10
ditto, Curtis Books (New York), 1953 (pbk) . . £5
The Wild Garden: or, Speaking of Writing, Univ of California Press (Berkeley, CA), 1963 . . £15/£5
ditto, Secker & Warburg (London), 1963 . . £15/£5
Tempo: The Impact of Television on The Arts, Studio Vista (London), 1964 . . . . . . £20/£5
ditto, Dufour (Chester Springs, PA), 1966 . £15/£5
The World of Charles Dickens, Secker & Warburg (London), 1970 . . . . . . £10/£5
ditto, Viking (New York), 1970 . . . . £10/£5
ditto, Arcadia Press (London), 1970 (265 signed copies) £250
The Naughty Nineties, Methuen (London), 1976 . £15/£5
The Strange Ride of Rudyard Kipling: His Life and Works, Secker & Warburg (London), 1977 . . . £15/£5
ditto, Viking (New York), 1978 . . . . £10/£5
Diversity and Depth in Fiction: Selected Critical Writings, Secker & Warburg (London), 1983 . . . £10/£5
ditto, Viking (New York), 1983 . . . . £10/£5
Reflections in a Writer's Eye, Secker & Warburg (London), 1986 . . . . £10/£5
ditto, Viking (New York), 1986 . . . . £10/£5

EDMUND WILSON

(b.1895 d.1972)

Edmund Wilson was a writer and literary critic considered by many the pre-eminent American man of letters in his day. He was as interested in modern culture as he was in lierature and much of his work is influenced by Freud and Marx.

The Evil Eye, A Comedy in Two Acts, John Church Company (Cincinnati, Ohio)/Triangle Club (Princeton, NJ), 1915 (wraps; with lyrics by F. Scott Fitzgerald) . £1,250

The Undertaker's Garland, Knopf (New York), 1922 (written with John Peale) . . . . . £250/£50
ditto, Knopf (New York), 1922 (50 copies for 'Bookseller Friends'; no d/w) £150
Discordant Encounters, Plays and Dialogues, Albert & Charles Boni (New York), 1926 . . . . £500/£50
I Thought of Daisy, Charles Scribner's Sons (New York), 1929 . . . . £300/£75
ditto, W.H. Allen (London), [1952] . . . £60/£10
Galahad [and] *I Thought of Daisy*, Farrar Straus & Giroux (New York), 1967 . . . . . . £30/£5
Poets, Farewell!, Charles Scribner's Sons (New York), 1929 . . . . £300/£75
Axel's Castle, Charles Scribner's Sons (New York), 1931 ('A' on copyright page) . . . . £600/£100
The American Jitters, Charles Scribner's Sons (New York), 1932 . . . . £300/£65
ditto, as *Devil Take the Hindmost*, Charles Scribner's Sons (London), 1932 . . . . . . £300/£65
Travels in Two Democracies, Harcourt Brace (New York), 1936 . . . . £150/£20
This Room and This Gin and These Sandwiches: Three Plays, New Republic (New York), 1937 (100 signed, numbered copies; acetate d/w) . . . . £600/£500
ditto, New Republic (New York), 1937 (pbk) . . £125
The Triple Thinkers, Ten Essays on Literature, Harcourt Brace (New York), 1938 . . . . . £150/£25
ditto, New Republic (New York), 1937 (pbk) . . £125
ditto, John Lehmann (London), 1952 (revised and enlarged) . . . . £45/£10
To The Finland Station, Harcourt Brace (New York), 1940 . . . . £200/£30
ditto, Secker & Warburg (London), [1941] . £200/£30
The Boys in the Back Room, Colt Press (San Francisco, CA), 1941 . . . . £150/£30
ditto, Colt Press (San Francisco, CA), 1941 (100 signed, numbered copies; in acetate d/w) . . £350/£300
The Wound and the Bow, Houghton Mifflin (Boston), 1941 . . . . £150/£25
ditto, Secker & Warburg (London), [1942] . . £65/£10
Note-Books of Night, Colt Press (San Francisco, CA), 1942 (copies in decorated floral boards with cloth spine and d/w) . . . . £1,500/£1,250
ditto, Colt Press (San Francisco, CA), 1942 (21 signed copies in blue paper boards with a black leather spine stamped in gold) £500
ditto, Colt Press (San Francisco, CA), 1942 (inner tissue and outer d/w) . . . . £150/£25
ditto, Secker & Warburg (London), 1945 . . . £65/£10
Memoirs of Hecate County, Doubleday (Garden City, NY), 1946 . . . . £150/£25
ditto, W.H. Allen (London), 1952 (d/w priced '12/6 net' and '(in U.S.A. $4.00)' . . . . £30/£5
Europe Without Baedeker, Doubleday (Garden City, NY), 1947 . . . . £50/£10
ditto, Secker & Warburg (London), 1948 . . . £35/£5
ditto, as *Europe Without Baedeker ... Together With Notes ... 1963-1964*, Farrar, Straus & Giroux (New York), 1966 . . . . £15/£5
ditto, Rupert Hart-Davis (London), 1967 . . . £15/£5
The Little Blue Light, A Play, Farrar, Straus (New York), 1950 . . . . £25/£5
ditto, Gollancz (London), 1951 . . . . . £25/£5

Classics and Commercials, Farrar Straus (New York), 1950
. . . . £25/£5
ditto, W.H. Allen (London), 1951   . . . £25/£5
The White Sand, Thomas Todd (Boston), 1950 (12 copies; wraps) £250
Three Reliques of Ancient Western Poetry Collected by . . ., [Thomas Todd (Boston), 1951] (red stapled wraps) . £100
ditto, no publisher (no place), [c.1960] (wraps)   . £30
ditto, [Gotham Book Mart (New York), 1964] (green wraps)
. . . . £20
The Shores of Light, Farrar, Straus & Young (New York), 1952 . . . . £25/£5
ditto, W.H. Allen (London), 1952   . . . £20/£5
Wilson's Christmas Stocking, Thomas Todd (Boston), 1953 (red printed stapled wraps) £75
Five Plays, W.H. Allen (London), 1954   . £30/£5
ditto, Farrar Straus & Young (New York), 1954   £30/£5
Eight Essays, Anchor Books (Garden City, NY), 1954 (pbk)
. . . . £15
The Scrolls from the Dead Sea, O.U.P. (New York), 1955 .
. . . . £30/£5
ditto, W.H. Allen (London), 1955   . . . £25/£5
A Christmas Delirium, Thomas Todd (Boston), 1955 (wraps) £35
Red, Black, Blond and Olive, O.U.P. (New York), 1956   .
. . . . £30/£5
ditto, W.H. Allen (London), 1956   . . . £20/£5
A Literary Chronicle: 1920-1950, Anchor Books (Garden City, NY), 1956 (pbk) £10
ditto, Peter Smith (Gloucester), 1961 . . . £25/£5
A Piece of My Mind, Farrar Straus & Cudahy (New York), 1956 . . . . £20/£5
ditto, W.H. Allen (London), 1957   . . . £20/£5
The Ammerican Earthquake, Doubleday/Anchor Books (Garden City, NY), 1958 . . . . . £25/£5
ditto, Peter Smith (Gloucester), 1964 (rebound Anchor Books edition) . . . . £20/£5
"Legend and Symbol in Dr. Zhivago", Encounter (New York), 1959 (wraps) £10
Apologies to the Iroquois, Farrar, Straus & Cudahy (New York), 1960 . . . . £25/£5
ditto, W.H. Allen (London), 1960   . . . £15/£5
Night Thoughts, Farrar, Straus & Cudahy (New York), 1961
. . . . £20/£5
ditto, W.H. Allen (London), 1962   . . . £15/£5
Patriotic Gore, O.U.P. (New York), 1962   . £20/£5
ditto, O.U.P. (New York), 1962 (pbk)   . . . £5
ditto, Andre Deutsch (London), 1962 . . . £15/£5
The Cold War and the Income Tax, Farrar Straus (New York), 1963 . . . . £20/£5
ditto, W.H. Allen (London), 1964   . . . £15/£5
O Canada, Farrar Straus & Giroux (New York), 1965 . .
. . . . £20/£5
ditto, Rupert Hart-Davis (London), 1967 . . . £15/£5
The Bit Between My Teeth, Farrar Straus & Giroux (New York), 1965 . . . . £20/£5
ditto, W.H. Allen (London), 1966   . . . £15/£5
Holiday Greetings 1966, [Thomas Todd (Boston)], 1966 £75
A Prelude, Farrar, Straus & Giroux (New York), 1967 . .
. . . . £15/£5
ditto, W.H. Allen (London), 1967   . . . £15/£5
The Fruits of the MLA, New York Review (New York), 1968 (stapled wraps) £10

The Duke of Palermo, Farrar, Straus & Giroux (New York), 1969 . . . . £20/£5
ditto, W.H. Allen (London), 1969   . . . £20/£5
The Dead Sea Scrolls, 1947-1969, O.U.P. (New York), 1969
. . . . £15/£5
ditto, W.H. Allen (London), 1969   . . . £10/£5
Holiday Greetings and Desolating Lyrics, privately printed (no place), 1970 (stapled wraps) £65
Upstate; Records and Recollections of Northern New York, Farrar, Straus & Giroux (New York), 1971 . £15/£5
ditto, Macmillan (London), 1972   . . . £10/£5
A Window on Russia, Farrar, Straus & Giroux (New York), 1972 . . . . £15/£5
ditto, Macmillan (London), 1972   . . . £15/£5
The Devils and Canon Barham, Farrar (New York), 1973 .
. . . . £15/£5
ditto, Macmillan (London), 1973   . . . £15/£5
The Rats of Rutland Grange, Gotham Book Mart (New York), (26 signed, lettered copies; illustrated by Edward Gorey; in slipcase; no d/w) . . . £600/£500
ditto, Gotham Book Mart (New York), (100 signed, numbered copies; in slipcase; no d/w) . . £350/£300
ditto, Gotham Book Mart (New York), (1,000 pbk copies) .
. . . . £75
The Twenties, Farrar (New York), 1975 . . . £15/£5
ditto, Macmillan (London), 1975   . . . £15/£5
Corrections and Comments, University of Iowa (Iowa City, IA), 1976 (175 copies) £25
Letters on Literature and Politics, 1912-1972, Farrar Straus & Giroux (New York), 1977 . . . £15/£5
ditto, as *Letters on Literature and Politics*, Routledge & Kegan Paul (London), 1977 . . . . £15/£5
Israel and the Dead Sea Scrolls, Farrar Straus & Giroux (New York), 1978 . . . . . . £20/£5
The Nabokov-Wilson Letters, 1940-1971, Harper & Row (New York), 1979 . . . . . . £25/£5
ditto, Weidenfeld & Nicolson (London), 1980 . £20/£5
Dear Bunny, Dear Volodya: The Nabokov-Wilson Letters, 1940-1971, Univ of California Press (Berkley, CA), 2001 (pbk; revised and expanded) £5
The Thirties, Farrar, Straus & Giroux (New York), 1980 .
. . . . £15/£5
The Forties, Farrar, Straus & Giroux (New York), 1983 .
. . . . £15/£5
The Portable Edmund Wilson, Viking (New York), 1983 .
. . . . £15/£5
The Fifties, Farrar, Straus & Giroux (New York), 1986 .
. . . . £15/£5
The Sixties: The Last Journal 1960-1972, Farrar Straus & Giroux (New York), 1993 . . . . . £10/£5
From the Uncollected Edmund Wilson, Ohio Univ Press (Athens, OH), 1995 . . . . . . £10/£5
The Higher Jazz, Univ of Iowa Press (Ames, IA), 1998 (pbk) £5
Edmund Wilson: The Man in Letters, Ohio Univ Press (Athens, OH), 2001 . . . . . . £10/£5

JACQUELINE WILSON
(b.1945)

Wilson, a prolific and successful multi-award-winning author of books for children, was voted Children's Laureate in 2005. Perhaps her best-known work is *The Story of Tracy Beaker* about a very imaginative and determined girl who lives in care. She was made a Dame Commander of the British Empire in 2008.

Tracy Beaker Series
The Story of Tracy Beaker, Doubleday (London), 1991 . . . . £100/£20
ditto, Delacorte Press (New York), 2001 (pbk) . . £5
The Dare Game, Doubleday (London), 2000 (laminated boards; no d/w) £25
Starring Tracy Beaker, Doubleday (London), 2006 £10/£5

Mark Spark Series
Mark Spark, Hamish Hamilton (London), 1991 (laminated boards; no d/w) £20
Mark Spark in the Dark, Hamish Hamilton (London), 1993 (laminated boards; no d/w) £25

Freddy's Teddy Series
Freddy's Teddy, Longman (London), 1994 (pbk) . . £10
Teddy at the Fair, Longman (London), 1994 (pbk) . £10
Teddy Goes Swimming, Longman (London), 1994 (pbk) £10
Come Back, Teddy!, Longman (London), 1994 (pbk) . £10

Werepuppy Series
The Werepuppy, Blackie (London), 1991 (laminated boards; no d/w) £25
The Werepuppy on Holiday, Blackie (London), 1994 (laminated boards; no d/w) £20

Girls Series
Girls in Love, Doubleday (London), 1997 (laminated boards; no d/w) £20
ditto, Delacorte Press (New York), 2002 . . £10/£5
Girls Under Pressure, Doubleday (London), 1998 (laminated boards; no d/w) £15
ditto, Delacorte Press (New York), 2002 . . £10/£5
Girls Out Late, Doubleday (London), 1999 (laminated boards; no d/w) £10
ditto, Delacorte Press (New York), 2002 . . £10/£5
Girls in Tears, Doubleday (London), 2002 (laminated boards; no d/w) £10
ditto, Delacorte Press (New York), 2003 . . £10/£5

Adventure Holiday Series
Cliffhanger, Corgi Yearling (London), 1995 (pbk) . £10
Buried Alive!, Doubleday (London), 1998 (laminated boards; no d/w) £10

Stevie Day Series
Lonely Hearts, Armada (London), 1987 (pbk) . . £10
Supersleuth, Armada (London), 1987 (pbk) . . £10
Rat Race, Armada (London), 1988 (pbk) . . . £10
Vampire, Armada (London), 1988 (pbk) . . . £10

Non-Series Books
Hide and Seek, Macmillan (London), 1972 . . £65/£10

ditto, Doubleday (New York), 1973 . . . £15/£5
Ricky's Birthday, Macmillan (London), 1973 . £50/£10
Truth or Dare, Macmillan (London), 1973 . £75/£15
ditto, Doubleday (New York), 1974 . . . £15/£5
Snap, Macmillan (London), 1974 . . . . £40/£10
Let's Pretend, Macmillan (London), 1976 . £25/£10
Making Hate, Macmillan (London), 1977 . £25/£10
ditto, St. Martin's Press (New York), 1978 . £10/£5
Nobody's Perfect, O.U.P. (London), 1983 . £45/£10
Waiting for the Sky to Fall, O.U.P. (London/New York), 1983 . . . . £45/£10
The Killer Tadpole, Hamish Hamilton (London), 1984. . . . . £40/£10
The Other Side, O.U.P. (London), 1984 . . £50/£10
The School Trip, Hamish Hamilton (London), 1984 . £25
How to Survive Summer Camp, O.U.P. (London), 1985 . . . . £50/£10
Amber, O.U.P. (London), 1986 . . . . £40/£10
The Monster in the Cupboard, Blackie (London), 1986 £25
The Power of the Shade, O.U.P. (London), 1987 . £35/£5
This Girl, O.U.P. (London), 1988 . . . £35/£5
Falling Apart, O.U.P. (London), 1989 . . £35/£5
The Left Outs, Blackie (London), 1989 (laminated boards; no d/w) £15
The Party in the Lift, Blackie (London), 1989 (laminated boards; no d/w) £25
Is There Anybody There? Volume 1: Spirit Raising, Armada (London), 1989 (pbk) . . . £10
Is There Anybody There? Volume 2: Crystal Gazing, Armada (London), 1990 (pbk) . . . £10
Glubbyslyme, O.U.P. (London), 1987. . . . £125/£25
Take A Good Look, Blackie (London), 1990 (laminated boards; no d/w) £20
The Dream Palace, O.U.P. (London), 1991 . £25/£10
The Suitcase Kid, Doubleday (London), 1992. £45/£10
ditto, Delacorte (New York), 1997 . . . £10/£5
Video Rose, Blackie (London), 1992 (laminated boards; no d/w) £20
Deep Blue, O.U.P. (London), 1993 . . . £30/£5
The Mum-Minder, Doubleday (London), 1993 . £45/£10
The Bed and Breakfast Star, Doubleday (London), 1994 . . . . £50/£10
ditto, as *Elsa, star of the shelter!*, A. Whitman & Co. (Morton Grove, IL), 1996 (laminated boards; no d/w) £5
Twin Trouble, Methuen (London), 1994 (laminated boards; no d/w) £25
The Dinosaur's Packed Lunch, Doubleday (London), 1995 (laminated boards; no d/w) £35
Double Act, Doubleday (London), 1995 . . £35/£10
ditto, Delacorte Press (New York), 1998 . . £10/£5
Jimmy Jelly, Piccadilly Press (London), 1995 (laminated boards; no d/w) £10
Love from Katy, Ginn (London), 1995 (pbk) . . £5
My Brother Bernadette, Heinemann (London), 1995 (laminated boards; no d/w) £10
ditto, Crabtree Pub (New York), 2002 (laminated boards; no d/w) £5
Sophie's Secret Diary, Ginn (London), 1995 (pbk) . £5
Bad Girls, Doubleday (London), 1996 (laminated boards; no d/w) £40
ditto, Delacorte Press (New York), 2001 . . £10/£5
Beauty and the Beast, A. & C. Black (London), 1996 (pbk) £10

Connie and the Water Babies, Methuen/Mammoth
(London), 1996 (pbk) £10
Mr Cool, Kingfisher (London), 1996 (pbk) . . . £5
ditto, Kingfisher (Boston), 2004 (pbk) £5
The Lottie Project, Doubleday (London), 1997 (laminated
boards; no d/w) £20
ditto, Delacorte Press (New York), 1999 . . . £10/£5
The Monster Storyteller, Doubleday (London), 1997 (pbk) .
. . . . £5
Rapunzel, Scholastic (London), 1998 (pbk) . . . £5
The Illustrated Mum, Doubleday (London), 1999 (laminated
boards; no d/w) £10
ditto, Delacorte Press (New York), 2005 . . . £10/£5
Monster Eyeballs, Mammoth (London), 1999 (pbk) . £5
Lizzie Zipmouth, Corgi (London), 2000 (pbk). . . £10
Vicky Angel, Doubleday (London), 2000 (laminated boards;
no d/w) £5
ditto, Delacorte Press (New York), 2001 . . . £10/£5
Sleep-Overs, Doubleday (London), 2001 (laminated boards;
no d/w) £5
The Cat Mummy, Doubleday (London), 2001 (laminated
boards; no d/w) £5
Dustbin Baby, Doubleday (London), 2001 (laminated
boards; no d/w) £5
Secrets, Doubleday (London), 2002 (laminated boards; no
d/w) £5
The Worry Website, Doubleday (London), 2002 (laminated
boards; no d/w) £5
ditto, New York : Delacorte Press, 2003 . . . £10/£5
The Jacqueline Wilson Quiz Book, Corgi (London), 2005
(pbk) £5
Lola Rose, Doubleday (London), 2003 (laminated boards; no
d/w) £5
Midnight, Doubleday (London), 2003 (laminated boards; no
d/w) £5
Best Friends, Doubleday (London), 2004 (laminated boards;
no d/w) £5
ditto, Roaring Brook Press (New York), 2008 . . £10/£5
The Diamond Girls, Doubleday (London), 2004 . . £10
The World Of Jacqueline Wilson, Doubleday (London),
2005 (laminated boards; no d/w) £5
Clean Break, Doubleday (London), 2005 (laminated boards;
no d/w) £5
Love Lessons, Doubleday (London), 2005 . . £10/£5
Candyfloss, Doubleday (London), 2006 . . . £10/£5
ditto, Roaring Brook Press (New York), 2007 . . £10/£5
Kiss, Doubleday (London), 2007 . . . . £10/£5
Totally Jacqueline Wilson, Doubleday (London), 2007 .
. . . . £10/£5
My Sister Jodie, Doubleday (London), 2008 . . £10/£5
Cookie, Doubleday (London), 2008 . . . . £10/£5
ditto, Roaring Brook Press (New York), 2009 . . £10/£5
Hetty Feather, Doubleday (London), 2009 . . £10/£5
The Tracy Beaker Quiz Book, Corgi (London), 2009 (pbk).
. . . . £5
Little Darlings, Doubleday (London), 2010 . . £10/£5

Autobiography
Jacky Daydream, Doubleday (London), 2007. . £10/£5
My Secret Diary, Doubleday (London), 2009 . . £10/£5

R.D. WINGFIELD
(b.1928 d.2007)

Wingfield was the English author of several mystery novels
about Inspector Jack Frost, an unconventional policeman
who nevertheless manages to solve several crimes per
book. Before these Wingfield wrote crime plays for radio
in his spare time, their success prompting him to become a
full-time writer.

Frost at Christmas, Paperjacks (Toronto, Canada), 1984
(pbk) £175
ditto, Constable (London), 1989 . . . . .£100/£15
ditto, Bantam (New York), 1995 (pbk) £5
A Touch of Frost, Paperjacks (Toronto, Canada), 1987 (pbk)
. . . .£75
ditto, Constable (London), 1990 . . . £1,000/£100
ditto, Post Mortem Books (Hassocks, Sussex), 1998 (350
signed, numbered copies) £200
Night Frost, Constable (London), 1992 . . .£300/£45
ditto, Bantam (New York), 1995 (pbk) . . . £5
Hard Frost, Scorpion Press (Blakeney, Gloucestershire),
1995 (85 signed, numbered copies, acetate d/w) . £75/£65
ditto, Constable (London), 1995 . . . . £25/£5
ditto, Bantam (New York), 1995 (pbk) . . . £5
Winter Frost, Constable (London), 1999 . . . £10/£5

JEANETTE WINTERSON
(b.1959)

A winner of numerous awards, Winterson's first book, the
apparently autobiographical *Oranges Are Not The Only
Fruit* remains her classic. Much of her work has been categorised as 'magic realism', although she herself disagrees
with this description. One title in her bibliography is a
paperback on exercise, diet and lifestyle, although it is no
longer referred to by her publisher and is long out of print .

Novels
Oranges Are Not the Only Fruit, Pandora Press (London),
1985 (pbk) £175
ditto, Atlantic Monthly Press (New York), 1987 (price of
$6.95; pbk) £15
ditto, Guild (London), 1990 . . . . . £20/£5
Boating for Beginners, Methuen (London), 1985 .£250/£25
ditto, Methuen (London), 1985 (pbk). . . . £10
The Passion, Bloomsbury (London), 1987 . £65/£10
ditto, Atlantic Monthly Press (New York), 1988 . £15/£5
Sexing The Cherry, Bloomsbury (London), 1989 . £20/£5
ditto, Atlantic Monthly Press (New York), 1990 . £10/£5
Written on the Body, Cape (London), 1992 . £10/£5
ditto, Knopf (New York), 1993 . . £10/£5
Art and Lies: A Piece for Three Voices and a Bawd, Cape
(London), 1994 . . . . £10/£5
ditto, Knopf (New York), 1995 . . . . £10/£5
Gut Symmetries, Granta (London), 1997 . . £10/£5
ditto, Knopf (New York), 1997 . . . . £10/£5
The PowerBook, Cape (London), 2000 . . £10/£5
ditto, Knopf (New York), 2000 . . . . £10/£5
Lighthousekeeping, Fourth Estate (London), 2004 £10/£5
ditto, Harcourt (New York), 2005 . . . £10/£5

The Stone Gods, Hamish Hamilton (London), 2007   £10/£5
ditto, Harcourt (New York), 2007   .   .   .   £10/£5

Short Stories
The World and Other Places, Cape (London), 1998   £10/£5
ditto, Knopf (New York), 1998 .   .   .   .   £10/£5
The Dreaming House, Ulysses (London), 1998 (150 signed,
  numbered copies) £300
The King of Capri, Bloomsbury (London), 2003 (illustrated
  boards, no d/w) £10
ditto, Bloomsbury (New York), 2003.   .   .   £10/£5

Children's
Tanglewreck, Bloomsbury (London), 2006   .   £10/£5
ditto, Bloomsbury (New York), 2006.   .   .   £10/£5
The Battle of the Sun, Bloomsbury (New York), 2009 .   .
  .   .   .   .   £10/£5

Others
Fit for the Future, Pandora Press (London), 1986 . £250/£45
ditto, Pandora Press (London), 1986 (pbk)   .   .   . £45
Great Moments in Aviation and *Oranges Are Not the Only*
  Fruit: Two Filmscripts, Vintage (London), 1994 (pbk)   £5
Art Objects: Essays on Ecstasy and Effrontery, Cape
  (London), 1995   .   .   .   .   .   .   £10/£5
ditto, Knopf (New York), 1996 .   .   .   .   £10/£5
Weight, Cannongate (Edinburgh), 2005   .   .   £10/£5
ditto, Cannongate (New York), 2005 .   .   .   £10/£5
ditto, Knopf (Toronto), 2005   .   .   .   .   £10/£5
ditto, Cannongate (Edinburgh), 2005 (box set, also
  containing *A Word or Two About Myth* by Philip Pullman,
  A Short History of Myth by Karen Armstrong, and an
  introductory pamphlet, *The Penelopiad: The Myth of*
  Penelope and Odysseus by Margaret Atwood)   .   £45
ditto, Cannongate (Edinburgh), 2005 (1,500 numbered box
  sets, as above but each item signed by the authors)   . £85
The Lion, The Unicorn and Me: The Donkey's Christmas
  Story, Scholastic (London), 2009 (laminated boards; no
  d/w) £10
ditto, Scholastic (London), 2009 (100 signed, numbered
  copies with a signed print; in a keepsake box)   .   . £40

WISDEN CRICKETERS' ALMANACK

Wisden Cricketers' Almanack is perhaps the world's best
known sporting reference book. Regarded as the cricketers'
bible, it was initially published in paper wraps, with the
first hardback edition appearing in 1896. From 1938 the
limp edition cover was printed on linen rather than paper,
and the hardback acquired a dust wrapper from 1965.

1864-1895
1864 (paper wraps). £12,000
ditto (rebound) £6,000
1865 (paper wraps). £8,000
ditto (rebound) £4,000
1866-69   .   .   .   . £5,000
ditto (rebound) £2,500
1870-72.   .   .   .   . £2,250
ditto (rebound) £1,000

1873-74   .   .   .   . £2,000
ditto (rebound) £850
1875   .   .   .   . £5,000
ditto (rebound) £1,500
1876-7   .   .   .   . £2,000
ditto (rebound) £850
1878   .   .   .   . £1,750
ditto (rebound) £500
1879   .   .   .   . £1,750
ditto (rebound) £500
1880   .   .   .   . £1,650
ditto (rebound) £450
1881-1889   .   .   .   . £1,500
ditto (rebound) £400
1890-1895   .   .   .   . £1,000
ditto (rebound) £250

1896-1964
First value hardback (no d/w), second value paper wraps
  (linen from 1938)
1896   .   .   .   .   £5,000/£1,000
1897 .   .   .   .   £3,500/£750
1898-1901   .   .   .   .   .   .   £2,500/£350
1902-3   .   .   .   .   £2,000/£200
1904-05   .   .   .   .   £1,000/£200
1906-07   .   .   .   .   £750/£200
1908-15   .   .   .   .   £500/£200
1916   .   .   .   .   £3,500/£750
1917-19   .   .   .   .   £1,500/£250
1920-33   .   .   .   .   £500/£200
1934-39   .   .   .   .   £400/£200
1940   .   .   .   .   £750/£250
1941 .   .   .   .   £750/£350
1942 .   .   .   .   £600/£350
1943-45   .   .   .   .   £400/£250
1946 .   .   .   .   £300/£150
1947-48   .   .   .   .   £125/£100
1949 .   .   .   .   £100/£30
1950-64   .   .   .   . £50/£25

First value hardback with d/w, second value linen wraps
1965-76   .   .   .   . £60/£30
1977 to present   .   .   .   . £20/£10

P.G. WODEHOUSE
(b.1881 d.1975)

A prolific comic author, Pelham Grenville Wodehouse's
world is light, smart, superficial, and if you enjoy his
humour, highly addictive. The first 'Jeeves and Wooster'
story appeared in the collection *The Man With Two Left*
Feet. Wodehouse also found success as a lyricist and
worked with Cole Porter on the musical *Anything Goes*.

'Jeeves and Wooster' Novels
Thank You, Jeeves, Jenkins (London), 1934 .   £1,000/£75
ditto, Little, Brown (Boston), 1934 .   .   . £350/£40
Right Ho, Jeeves, Jenkins (London), 1934   .   . £850/£65
ditto, as *Brinkley Manor*, Little, Brown (Boston), 1934   .
  .   .   .   . £350/£40
The Code of The Woosters, Jenkins (London), 1938 .   .
  .   .   .   . £700/£45

ditto, Doubleday (New York), 1938 . . . . £350/£40
Joy in The Morning, Doubleday (New York), 1946. . .
. . . . £200/£30
ditto, Jenkins (London), 1947 . . . . £225/£25
The Mating Season, Jenkins (London), 1949 . £125/£20
ditto, Didier (New York), 1949 . . . . £100/£20
Ring for Jeeves, Jenkins (London), 1953 . . £175/£30
ditto, as ***The Return of Jeeves***, Doubleday (New York), 1953
. . . . £100/£20
Jeeves and The Feudal Spirit, Jenkins (London), 1954 .
. . . . £125/£25
ditto, as ***Bertie Wooster Sees It Through***, Simon & Schuster
(New York), 1955 . . . . . £50/£10
Jeeves in The Offing, Jenkins (London), 1960 . £75/£10
ditto, as ***How Right You Are, Jeeves***, Simon & Schuster
(New York), 1960 . . . . . . £50/£10
Stiff Upper Lip, Jeeves, Jenkins (London), 1963 . £65/£15
ditto, Simon & Schuster (New York), 1963 . £50/£10
Much Obliged, Jeeves, Barrie & Jenkins (London), 1971 .
. . . . £45/£10
ditto, as ***Jeeves and The Tie that Binds***, Simon & Schuster
(New York), 1971. . . . . . £35/£10
Aunts Aren't Gentlemen, Barrie & Jenkins (London), 1974
. . . . £45/£10
ditto, as ***The Cat-Nappers***, Simon & Schuster (New York),
1974 . . . . £35/£10

'Jeeves and Wooster' Short Stories
The Man With Two Left Feet, Methuen (London), 1917 .
. . . . £1,750
ditto, Burt (New York), 1933 . . . . £500/£75
My Man Jeeves, Newnes (London), 1919 (first printing by
Butler & Tanner). £600
The Inimitable Jeeves, Jenkins (London), 1923 £2,000/£75
ditto, as ***Jeeves***, Doran (New York), 1923. £2,000/£75
Carry On Jeeves, Jenkins (London), 1925 . £1,000/£75
ditto, Doran (New York), 1927 . . . . £750/£50
Very Good, Jeeves, Jenkins (London), 1930 . £750/£75
ditto, Doubleday (New York), 1930 . . . £650/£65
A Few Quick Ones, Jenkins (London), 1959 . £100/£15
ditto, Simon & Schuster (New York), 1959 . £75/£15
Plum Pie, Jenkins (London), 1966 . . £75/£15
ditto, Simon & Schuster (New York), 1967 . £65/£10

'Jeeves and Wooster' Omnibus Editions
Jeeves Omnibus, Jenkins (London), 1931 . . £600/£60
The World of Jeeves, Jenkins (London), 1967. . £100/£30

'Blandings' Novels
Something New, Appleton (New York), 1915. . . £650
ditto, as ***Something Fresh***, Methuen (London), 1915 £1,500
Leave it to PSmith, Jenkins (London), 1923 . £1,250/£150
ditto, Doran (New York), 1923 . . . . £1,000/£150
Summer Lightning, Jenkins (London), 1929 . £750/£125
ditto, as ***Fish Preferred***, Doubleday (New York), 1929. .
. . . . £500/£100
Heavy Weather, Jenkins (London), 1933 . . £650/£125
ditto, Little, Brown (Boston), 1933 . . . £500/£125
Uncle Fred in The Springtime, Jenkins (London), 1939 .
. . . . £500/£65
ditto, Doubleday (New York), 1939 . . . £250/£45
Full Moon, Jenkins (London), 1947 . . . £100/£25
ditto, Doubleday (New York), 1947 . . . £75/£25
Pigs Have Wings, Jenkins (London), 1952 . £75/£15

ditto, Doubleday (New York), 1952 . . . . £75/£15
Service with a Smile, Simon & Schuster (New York), 1961.
. . . . £50/£10
ditto, Jenkins (London), 1962 . . . . £45/£10
Galahad at Blandings, Jenkins (London), 1965 . £50/£10
ditto, as ***The Brinkmanship of Galahad Threepwood***, Simon
& Schuster (New York), 1965 . . . . £45/£10
A Pelican at Blandings, Jenkins (London), 1969 . £40/£10
ditto, as ***No Nudes is Good Nudes***, Simon & Schuster (New
York), 1970 . . . . £35/£10
Sunset at Blandings, Chatto & Windus (London), 1977
(unfinished novel, finished by Richard Usborne). £40/£10
ditto, Simon & Schuster (New York), 1977 . £35/£10

'Blandings' Short Stories
Blandings Castle and Elsewhere, Jenkins (London), 1935 .
. . . . £700/£75
ditto, Doubleday (New York), 1935 . . . £500/£65
Lord Emsworth and Others, Jenkins (London), 1937 . .
. . . . £700/£75
ditto, as ***Crime Wave at Blandings***, Doubleday (New York),
1937 . . . . £450/£50
Nothing Serious, Jenkins (London), 1950 . £200/£35
ditto, Doubleday (New York), 1951 . . . £125/£25

'Blandings' Omnibus
The World of Blandings, Barrie & Jenkins (London), 1975.
. . . . £40/£10

Other Novels
The Pothunters, Black (London), 1902 (first binding with
silver loving cup on front board and spine, no ads) £3,000
ditto, Black (London), 1902 (secondary binding with frontis
illustration on front cover, 8pps of ads) . . . £750
ditto, Macmillan (New York), 1924 . . £1,000/£100
A Prefect's Uncle, Black (London), 1903 (first issue, no
adverts). £2,000
ditto, Black (London), 1903 (second issue with 8pps of ads)
. . . . £1,000
ditto, Macmillan (New York), 1924 . . . £650/£65
The Gold Bat, Black (London), 1904. . . £1,250
ditto, Macmillan (New York), 1923 . . . £500/£65
William Tell Told Again, A. & C. Black (London), 1904
(first issue, off-white cloth lettered in gilt on spine and
front cover, top edge gilt, publisher's monogram on title-
page, 2pps of ads) £1,000
ditto, A. & C. Black (London), 1904 (second issue with
12pps of ads) £500
ditto, A. & C. Black (London), 1904 (third issue, tan/brown
cloth, gilt lettering on spine only, 2pps of ads, gilt on
cover) £350
ditto, A. & C. Black (London), 1904 (variant issue, buff
cloth, black lettering) £250
The Head of Kay's, A. & C. Black (London), 1905 . £750
ditto, Macmillan (New York), 1922 . . . £600/£65
Love Among The Chickens, Newnes (London), 1906 £3,000
ditto, Circle Publishing Co. (New York), 1909 . £750
The White Feather, A. & C. Black (London), 1907 £1,500
ditto, Macmillan (New York), 1922 . . . £600/£65
Not George Washington, Cassell (London), 1907 (written
with H. Westbrook, 'Cassell & Company' on spine) £2,500
ditto, Cassell (London), 1907 ('Cassell' only on spine). £750
ditto, Continuum (New York), 1980 . . . £25/£10
The Swoop, Alston Rivers (London), 1909 (wraps) £2,500

ditto, Heinemann (London), 1992 (400 copies, facsimile) £50

Mike, A. & C. Black (London), 1909. . . . £2,000

ditto, Macmillan (New York), 1924 . . . . £600/£65

ditto, as *Enter PSmith*, Black (London), 1935 (re-issue of second part of *Mike*) . . . . . £500/£65

ditto, as *Mike at Wrykyn*, Jenkins (London), 1953, and *Mike and PSmith*, Jenkins (London), 1953 (2 vol. re-issue, novel revised) . . . . £250/£35

A Gentleman of Leisure, Alston Rivers (London), 1910 . . . . £1,000

ditto, as *The Intrusion of Jimmy*, Watt (New York), 1910 . . . .£400

PSmith in The City, A. & C. Black (London), 1910 £1,250

The Prince and Betty, Mills and Boon (London), 1912 . . . . £1,250

The Prince and Betty, Watt (New York), 1912 (different from above) £600

ditto, as *PSmith Journalist*, A. & C. Black (London), 1915 . . . . £1,000

The Little Nugget, Methuen (London), 1913 . . £1,000

ditto, Watt (New York), 1914 . . . . . .£300

Uneasy Money, Appleton (New York), 1916 . . .£400

ditto, Methuen (London), 1917 . . . . £1,500

Piccadilly Jim, Dodd, Mead (New York), 1917 . .£400

ditto, Jenkins (London), 1918 . . . . . .£750

A Damsel in Distress, Doran (New York), 1919 . .£250

ditto, Jenkins (London), 1919 . . . . . .£500

Their Mutual Child, Boni & Liveright (New York), 1919 . . . .£250

ditto, as *The Coming of Bill*, Jenkins (London), 1920 . . . . £1,250/£150

The Little Warrior, Doran (New York), 1920 . £850/£200

ditto, as *Jill The Reckless*, Jenkins (London), 1921 . . . . £1,500/£350

The Girl on The Boat, Jenkins (London), 1922 £1,500/£300

ditto, as *Three Men and a Maid*, Doran (New York), 1922 (revised version) . . . . . £650/£125

The Adventures of Sally, Jenkins (London), 1922 . . . . £1,250/£250

ditto, as *Mostly Sally*, Doran (New York), 1923 £650/£125

Bill The Conqueror, Jenkins (London), 1924 . £1,000/£200

ditto, Doran (New York), 1925 . . . . £400/£100

Sam The Sudden, Methuen (London), 1925 . £750/£125

ditto, as *Sam in The Suburbs*, Doran (New York), 1925 . . . . £300/£50

The Small Bachelor, Methuen (London), 1927 £750/£125

ditto, Doran (New York), 1927 . . . . £300/£50

Money for Nothing, Jenkins (London), 1928 . £750/£125

ditto, Doran (New York), 1928 . . . . £300/£50

Big Money, Doubleday (New York), 1931 . £300/£50

ditto, Jenkins (London), 1931 . . . . £750/£100

If I Were You, Doubleday (New York), 1931 . £250/£40

ditto, Jenkins (London), 1931 . . . . £500/£75

Doctor Sally, Methuen (London), 1932 . . £450/£75

Hot Water, Jenkins (London), 1932 . . £450/£75

ditto, Doubleday (New York), 1932 . . . £350/£45

The Luck of The Bodkins, Jenkins (London), 1935 £400/£45

ditto, Little, Brown (Boston), 1935 . . . £200/£45

Laughing Gas, Jenkins (London), 1936 . .£500/£65

ditto, Doubleday (New York), 1936 . . . £200/£40

Summer Moonshine, Doubleday (New York), 1937 . . . . £300/£40

ditto, Jenkins (London), 1938 . . . . £500/£75

Quick Service, Jenkins (London), 1940 . . £250/£40

ditto, Doubleday (New York), 1940 . . . . £125/£20

Money in The Bank, Doubleday (New York), 1942 £250/£35

ditto, Jenkins (London), 1946 . . . . £200/£35

Spring Fever, Doubleday (New York), 1948 . £150/£25

ditto, Jenkins (London), 1948 . . . . £100/£25

Uncle Dynamite, Jenkins (London), 1948 . £100/£25

ditto, Didier (New York), 1948 . . . . £100/£25

The Old Reliable, Jenkins (London), 1951 . £75/£15

ditto, Doubleday (New York), 1951 . . . £65/£15

Barmy in Wonderland, Jenkins (London), 1952 . £75/£15

ditto, as *Angel Cake*, Doubleday (New York), 1952 £65/£15

French Leave, Jenkins (London), 1956 . . £50/£15

ditto, Simon & Schuster (New York), 1959 . £40/£10

Something Fishy, Jenkins (London), 1957 . £50/£15

ditto, as *The Butler Did It*, Simon & Schuster (New York), 1957 . . . . £50/£15

Cocktail Time, Jenkins (London), 1958 . . £50/£15

ditto, Simon & Schuster (New York), 1958 . £45/£10

The Ice in The Bedroom, Simon & Schuster (New York), 1961 . . . . £40/£10

ditto, as *Ice in The Bedroom*, Jenkins (London), 1961 . . . . £40/£10

Biffen's Millions, Simon & Schuster (New York), 1964 . . . . £45/£10

ditto, as *Frozen Assets*, Jenkins (London), 1964 . £45/£10

The Purloined Paperweight, Simon & Schuster (New York), 1967 . . . . £45/£10

ditto, as *Company for Henry*, Jenkins (London), 1967 . . . . £45/£10

Do Butlers Burgle Banks?, Simon & Schuster (New York), 1968 . . . . £40/£10

ditto, Jenkins (London), 1968 . . . . £45/£10

The Girl in Blue, Barrie & Jenkins (London), 1970 £25/£10

ditto, Simon & Schuster (New York), 1971 . £25/£10

Pearls, Girls and Monty Bodkin, Barrie & Jenkins (London), 1972 . . . . £25/£10

ditto, as *The Plot That Thickened*, Simon & Schuster (New York), 1973 . . . . £25/£10

Bachelors Anonymous, Barrie & Jenkins (London), 1973 . . . . £25/£10

ditto, Simon & Schuster (New York), 1974 . . £25/£10

The Luck Stone, Galahad Books (London), 1997 (250 numbered copies) £50

ditto, Galahad Books (London), 1997 (26 lettered copies bound in leather) £250

A Prince For Hire, Galahad Books (London), 2003 (200 copies) £50

ditto, Galahad Books (London), 2003 (16 copies bound in morocco) £250

ditto, Galahad Books (London), 2003 (pbk) . . £10

Other Short Stories

Tales of St Austin's, Black (London), 1903 . . .£750

ditto, Macmillan (New York), 1923 . . . £650/£50

The Man Upstairs, Methuen (London), 1914 . . £1,500

Indiscretions of Archie, Jenkins (London), 1921 . . . . £1,750/£125

ditto, Doran (New York), 1921 . . . . £1,250/£65

The Clicking of Cuthbert, Jenkins (London), 1922 . . . . £1,750/£100

ditto, as *Golf Without Tears*, Doran (New York), 1924. . . . .£750/£50

Ukridge, Jenkins (London), 1924 . . . £1,750/£75

ditto, as *He Rather Enjoyed It*, Doran (New York), 1926 .
. . . . £750/£50
The Heart of a Goof, Jenkins (London), 1926. £1,750/£75
ditto, as *Divots*, Doran (New York), 1927. . £1,000/£50
Meet Mr Mulliner, Jenkins (London), 1927 . £1,000/£45
ditto, Doran (New York), 1928 . . . . . £450/£35
Mr Mulliner Speaking, Jenkins (London), 1929 £1,000/£45
ditto, Doubleday (New York), 1930 . . . £450/£35
Homeopathic Treatment, Boy's Life (New York), 1931
(wraps) £1,000
Mulliner Nights, Jenkins (London), 1933. . £1,000/£50
ditto, Doubleday (New York), 1933 . . . £450/£45
The Great Sermon Handicap, Hodder & Stoughton
(London), 1933 . . . . . . £750/£100
Young Men in Spats, Jenkins (London), 1936. . £750/£50
ditto, Doubleday (New York), 1936 . . . £350/£45
Eggs, Beans and Crumpets, Jenkins (London), 1940 . .
. . . . £500/£50
ditto, Doubleday (New York), 1940 . . . £250/£30
Plum Pie, Jenkins (London), 1966 . . £75/£15
ditto, Simon & Schuster (New York), 1967 . £35/£10
Sir Agravaine, Blandford (Poole, Dorset), 1984 £25/£10
Plum Stones, Galahad Books (London), 1993 (12 booklets)
. . . . £200 the set
ditto, Galahad Books (London), 1993 (26 lettered copies, one
volume) £500

Other Omnibus Editions
Nothing but Wodehouse, Doubleday (New York), 1932 .
. . . . £250/£40
Methuen's Library of Humour: P.G. Wodehouse, Methuen
(London), 1934 . . . . £200/£35
Mulliner Omnibus, Jenkins (London), 1935 . . £400/£65
ditto, as *The World of Mr Mulliner*, Barrie & Jenkins
(London), 1972 (revised) . . . . . £20/£5
ditto, Taplinger (New York), 1974 . . . . £15/£5
Week-End Wodehouse, Jenkins (London), 1939 . £400/£65
ditto, Doubleday (New York), 1939 . . . . £300/£25
Wodehouse on Golf, Doubleday (New York), 1940 £350/£65
Selected Stories by P.G. Wodehouse, Random House,
Modern library (New York), 1958 . . . £25/£10
The Golf Omnibus, Barrie & Jenkins (London), 1973 £30/£5
ditto, Simon & Schuster (New York), 1974 . . £30/£5
The World of PSmith, Barrie & Jenkins (London), 1974 .
. . . . £30/£10
The World of Ukridge, Barrie & Jenkins (London), 1975 .
. . . . £30/£10
The Uncollected Wodehouse, Seabury Press (New York),
1976 . . . . £30/£5
Vintage Wodehouse, Barrie & Jenkins (London), 1977 .
. . . . £15/£5
Tales from The Drones Club, Hutchinson (London), 1982 .
. . . . £15/£5
Wodehouse Nuggets, Hutchinson (London), 1983 . £15/£5
The World of Uncle Fred, Hutchinson (London), 1983 .
. . . . £10/£5
Short Stories, Folio Society (London), 1983 (slipcase) . .
. . . . £10/£5
The World of Wodehouse Clergy, Hutchinson (London),
1984 . . . . £10/£5
The Hollywood Omnibus, Hutchinson (London), 1985. .
. . . . £10/£5
Wodehouse on Cricket, Hutchinson (London), 1987 £15/£5
The Aunts Omnibus, Hutchinson (London), 1989 . £10/£5

Plays
Hearts and Diamonds, Prowse (London), 1926 (with Laurie
Wylie) £35
The Play's The Thing, Brentano's (New York), 1927
(adapted from play by F. Molnar) £35
Good Morning Bill, Methuen (London), 1928 . £150/£45
A Damsel in Distress, Samuel French (London), 1930
(wraps) £40
Baa, Baa, Black Sheep, Samuel French (London), 1930
(wraps) £40
Leave it to Psmith, Samuel French (London), 1932 (wraps).
. . . . £65
Candlelight, Samuel French (New York), 1934 (adaptation
of play by S. Geyer; wraps) £40
Anything Goes, Samuel French (London), 1936 (with others;
wraps) £40
The Three Musketeers, Chappell (London)/Harms (New
York), 1937 (co-written with Clifford Grey and George
Grossmith) £40
Four Plays, Methuen (London), 1983 . . . £45/£10
ditto, Methuen (London), 1983 (pbk). £5

Autobiography
Performing Flea, Jenkins (London), 1953 . . £50/£15
ditto, as *Author! Author!*, Simon & Schuster (New York),
1962 (revised) . . . . £35/£10
Bring on the Girls, Simon & Schuster (New York), 1953
(with Guy Bolton) . . . . . . £45/£10
ditto, Jenkins (London), 1954 (revised) . . . £45/£10
America I Like You, Simon & Schuster (New York), 1956 .
. . . . £35/£10
ditto, as *Over Seventy*, Jenkins (London), 1957 (revised) .
. . . . £45/£15

Others
The Globe By The Way Book, Globe (London), 1907
(written with H. Westbrook; wraps) . . . £6,000
Louder and Funnier, Faber (London), 1932 . £600/£150
The Parrot and Other Poems, Hutchinson (London), 1988 .
. . . . £15/£5
Yours, Plum, Hutchinson (London), 1990 . . £15/£5

THOMAS WOLFE
(b.1900 d.1938)

Thomas Wolfe was an important 20th century American
novelist known for mixing highly original, poetic, rhapsodical, and impressionistic prose with autobiographical
writing. His books, written during the Great Depression,
depict the variety and diversity of American culture.

The Crisis in Industry, Univ of North Carolina (Chapel Hill,
NC), 1919 (200 copies; wraps). . . . £2,500
ditto, Ballinger's Books (Hillsborough, NC), 1978 (50
numbered copies) £30
ditto, Ballinger's Books (Hillsborough, NC), 1978 (50
numbered copies in a cardboard folder with a cloth
shelfback with signed copies of Richard Walser's
Prolegomena To...) £45
ditto, Ballinger's Books (Hillsborough, NC), 1978 (250
numbered copies with a reduced photo reprint of
Prolegomena To...) £20

ditto, Loom Press (Chapel Hill), 1978 (with *Prolegomena To...* in stapled wraps laid in) £20

ditto, Palaemon Press (Winston-Salem, NC), 1978 (200 numbered copies) £20

Look Homeward, Angel, Charles Scribner's (New York), 1929 (fore edges of book rough cut; first state d/w with portrait, printed price and biographical matter on back panel) . . . . . . £8,000/£400

ditto, Charles Scribner's (New York), 1929 (second state d/w with reviews and no portrait) . . . . £1,250/£400

ditto, Heinemann (London), 1930 . £600/£100

Of Time and The River, Charles Scribner's (New York), 1935 . . . . £450/£75

ditto, Heinemann (London), 1935 . . . £125/£20

From Death To Morning, Charles Scribners (New York), 1935 . . . . £150/£30

ditto, Heinemann (London), 1935 (12 copies; American sheets with cancel title leaf) £1,000

ditto, Heinemann (London), 1936 . . . £100/£15

The Story of a Novel, Charles Scribner's (New York), 1936 . . . . £100/£15

ditto, Heinemann (London), 1936 . . . £75/£15

A Note on Experts: Dexter Vespasian Joyner, House of Books (New York), 1939 (300 numbered copies; glassine d/w) . . . . £100/£75

The Web and The Rock, Harper & Brothers New York, 1939 (states 'First Edition' and has code letters 'E-O' . £150/£20

ditto, Heinemann (London), 1947 . . . £65/£10

The Face of a Nation, Scribner's (New York), 1939 ('CL' on copyright page, rather than Scribner's 'A') . £125/£25

You Can't Go Home Again, Harper & Brothers (New York), 1940 (states 'First edition' and code letters 'H-P' on copyright page) . . . . . £150/£20

ditto, Heinemann (London), 1947 . . £75/£15

ditto, Easton Press (Norwalk, CT), 1992 . . . £75

The Hills Beyond, Harper & Brothers (New York), 1941 (states 'First edition' and has code letters 'H-Q'). £125/£20

The Gentlemen of the Press, William Targ (Chicago), 1942 (350 unnumbered copies) £125

What Is Man?, James T. Mangan (Chicago), 1942 (100 copies; wraps) £250

America, Greenwood Press (San Mateo, CA), 1942 (150 numbered copies; wraps) £200

ditto, as **From Of Time and The River: America**, privately printed, Harrison Commercial Art Institute (Chicago), 1942 (red cloth and white d/w) . . . . . £125/£50

ditto, Malibu Press (Los Angeles, CA), 1952 (100 copies) . . . . £125/£50

Thomas Wolfe's Letters to His Mother Julia Elizabeth Wolfe, Charles Scribner's (New York), 1943 . £75/£15

ditto, Univ of North Carolina Press (Chapel Hill, NC), 1968 . . . . £45/£10

Stories by Thomas Wolfe, Avon (New York), 1944 (pbk) £10

A Stone, A Leaf, A Door, Charles Scribners (New York), 1945 . . . . £50/£10

The Portable Thomas Wolfe, Viking (New York), 1946 . £30/£5

ditto, as **The Indispensable Thomas Wolfe**, The Book Society (New York), 1950. . . . . £15/£5

ditto, as **Selections from The Work of Thomas Wolfe**, Heinemann (London), 1952 . . . . £25/£5

God's Lonely Man, San Jose College Laboratory Press (no place), 1947 (30 copies) £150

Thomas Wolfe Short Stories, Penguin Books (New York), 1947 (pbk) £10

ditto, Penguin Books (London), 1947 (pbk) . . £10

To Rupert Brooke, Richard Jean Picard (Paris), 1948 (100 numbered copies; wraps) £250

Mannerhouse: A Play in a Prologue and Three Acts, Harper & Brothers (New York), 1948 (states 'First edition and has publisher's code 'K-X') . . . £45/£10

ditto, Harper & Brothers (New York), 1948 (500 numbered copies; d/w and slipcase) . . . . £125/£100

ditto, Heinemann (London), 1950 . . . £30/£5

ditto, Louisiana State Univ Press (Baton Rouge, LA/ London), 1985 . . . . £15/£5

'...The Years of Wandering in Many Lands and Cities', Charles S. Boesen (New York), 1949 (600 copies; slipcase) . . . . £150/£125

A Western Journal, Univ of Pittsburgh Press (Pittsburgh, PA), 1951 . . . . £75/£15

The Correspondence of Thomas Wolfe and Homer Andrew Watt, New York Univ Press/Geoffrey Cumberlege/O.U.P. (New York/London), 1954 (issued in slipcase with *Thomas Wolfe at Washington Square* by Thomas Clark Pollock and Oscar Cargill) . . . . . . £50/£35

The Letters of Thomas Wolfe, Charles Scribner's (New York), 1956 ('A-7.56[V]' on copyright page) . £30/£5

ditto, as **The Selected Letters of Thomas Wolfe**, Heinemann (London), 1958 . . . . . £25/£5

'Dear Mabel': Letter of Thomas Wolfe to His Sister, South Atlantic Quarterly (no place), 1961 (wraps) . . . £100

The Short Novels of Thomas Wolfe, Charles Scribners (New York), 1961 . . . . £30/£5

The Thomas Wolfe Reader, Charles Scribners (New York), 1962 . . . . £25/£5

Thomas Wolfe's Purdue Speech: Writing and Living, Purdue Univ Studies (Lafayette, IN), 1964 . . £25/£5

The Mountains: A Play in One Act and **The Mountains: A Drama in Three Acts and A Prologue**, Univ of North Carolina Press (Chapel Hill, NC), 1970. . . £125/£30

The Notebooks of Thomas Wolfe, Univ of North Carolina Press (Chapel Hill, NC), 1970 (2 vols; slipcase; no d/w) . . . . £45/£30

Return, Thomas Wolfe Memorial (Asheville, NC), 1976 (wraps) £25

The Promise of America, Thomas Wolfe Festival, St Mary's College (Raleigh, NC), 1977 (single sheet printed on both sides) £60

Time... Thomas Wolfe, Thomas Wolfe Festival, St Mary's College (Raleigh, NC), 1978 (150 numbered copies; single sheet folded once to make four pages) . . . £75

A Prologue To America, Croissant Company (Athens, OH), 1978 (100 numbered copies; wraps) . . . £100

Confessio Amoris, Thomas Wolfe Society Univ of Akron (Akron, OH), 1979 (single page printed on both sides) £75

ditto, no publisher (no place), 1979 (broadside) . . £65

The Proem to 'O Lost', Thomas Wolfe Society (no place), 1979 (300 numbered copies; single sheet folded to make six pages) £75

Thomas Wolfe's Discovery of America, no publisher (no place), [c.1980] (single sheet folded once) . . £75

The London Tower, Thomas Wolfe Society (no place), 1980 (300 copies; wraps) £100

The Streets of Durham, Wolfe's Head Press (Raleigh, NC), 1982 (350 copies; wraps) £75

Welcome To Our City: A Play, Louisiana State Univ (Baton Rouge, LA/London), 1983 . . . . £20/£5

K-19: Salvaged Pieces, Thomas Wolfe Society (no place), 1983 (400 numbered copies; wraps) . . . £100

The Autobiography of An American Novelist, Harvard Univ Press (Cambridge, MA/London), 1983 (no d/w) . . £30

ditto, Harvard Univ Press (Cambridge, MA/London), 1983 (pbk) £10

Beyond Love and Loyalty, Univ of North Carolina Press (Chapel Hill, NC/London), 1983 . . . . £20/£5

My Other Loneliness, Univ of North Carolina Press (Chapel Hill, NC/London), 1983 . . . . £25/£5

ditto, Univ of North Carolina Press (Chapel Hill, NC/ London), 1983 (pbk) £5

The Train and The City, Thomas Wolfe Society (no place), 1984 (450 copies; wraps) £45

Holding On For Heaven, Thomas Wolfe Society (no place), 1985 (500 numbered copies; pbk) £20

Thomas Wolfe Interviewed 1929-1938, Louisiana State Univ (Baton Rouge, LA/London), 1985 . . . . £15/£5

ditto, Louisiana State Univ (Baton Rouge, LA/ London), 1985 (wraps) £5

The Hound of Darkness, Thomas Wolfe Society (no place), 1986 (600 numbered copies; black cloth; no d/w) . £30

The Complete Short Stories of Thomas Wolfe, Scribner (New York), 1987 . . . . . . £20/£5

Wolfe and Belinda Jeliffe, The Thomas Wolfe Society (no place), 1987 (500 numbered copies; wraps) . . £20

The Starwick Episodes, The Thomas Wolfe Society (no place), 1989 (650 numbered copies; no d/w). . . £20

ditto, Louisiana State Univ (Baton Rouge, LA), 1994 £15/£5

ditto, Louisiana State Univ (Baton Rouge, LA), 1994 (wraps) £5

Thomas Wolfe's Composition Books: The North State Fitting School 1912-1915, North Carolina Society and Thomas Wolfe Society (no place), 1990 (300 numbered copies signed by editor Alice R. Cotten) . . £25

The Autobiographical Outline of Look Homeward Angel, Thomas Wolfe Society (no place), 1991 (700 numbered copies; illustrated boards; no d/w) £25

The Good Child's River, Univ of North Carolina (Chapel Hill, NC), 1991 . . . . . . £10/£5

The Lost Boy, Univ of North Carolina Press (Chapel Hill, NC/London), 1992 . . . . . £10/£5

George Webber, A Writer: An Introduction by A Friend, The Thomas Wolfe Society (no place), 1994 (750 numbered copies; pictorial boards; no d/w) . . £25

The Party at Jack's, Univ of North Carolina Press (Chapel Hill, NC), 1995 . . . . . . £15/£5

Anyaeus, or A Memory of Earth, Thomas Wolfe Society (no place), 1996 (750 numbered copies; pictorial boards; no d/w) £25

Passage to England, A Selection, The Thomas Wolfe Society (no place), 1998 (600 numbered copies; pbk). £10

O Lost: The Story of the Buried Life, Univ of South Carolina Press (Columbia, SC), 2000 . . . £10/£5

An Anotated Chapter from O Lost: The Story of The Buried Life, Univ of South Carolina Press (Columbia), 2000 (signed by the editors) £10

To Loot My Life Clean: The Thomas Wolfe-Maxwell Perkins Correspondence, Univ of South Carolina Press (Columbia, SC), 2000. . . . . . . £15

The Medical Students, The Thomas Wolfe Society (no place), 2000 (600 numbered copies; wraps) . . . £5

Ca, C'est Paris: A Play Adapted From The Works of Thomas Wolfe, The Thomas Wolfe Society (no place), 2001 (500 numbered copies; pictorial boards; no d/w) £10

TOM WOLFE
(b.1930)

An American novelist and journalist, Wolfe developed the 'new journalism' style, reporting hard facts spectacularly and emotionally. He stumbled upon this technique by mistake when, on struggling with an article, he sent his editor a detailed letter on its subject. The impassioned letter was published unedited in place of the polished article Wolfe had originally envisaged.

Fiction

The Bonfire of the Vanities, Farrar Straus (New York), 1987 . . . . £20/£5

ditto, Farrar Straus (New York), 1987 (250 signed, numbered copies, slipcase) . . . . . . £200/£150

ditto, Franklin Library (Franklin Centre, PA), 1987 (signed, limited edition) £20

ditto, Cape (London), 1988 . . . . . £15/£5

A Man in Full, Farrar Straus (New York), 1998 . £10/£5

ditto, Farrar Straus (New York), 1998 (250 signed, numbered copies, slipcase) . . . . . . £75/£50

ditto, Franklin Library (Franklin Centre, PA), 1998 (signed, limited edition) £50

ditto, Cape (London), 1998 . . . . . £10/£5

I Am Charlotte Simmons, Farrar Straus (New York), 2004 . . . . £10/£5

ditto, Cape (London), 2004 . . . . . £10/£5

Non-Fiction

The Kandy-Kolored Tangerine Flake Streamline Baby, Farrar Straus (New York), 1965 . . . £100/£20

ditto, Cape (London), 1966 . . . . . £65/£10

The Electric Kool-Aid Acid Test, Farrar Straus (New York), 1968 . . . . £145/£25

ditto, Weidenfeld & Nicolson (London), 1969 . £100/£20

The Pump House Gang, Farrar Straus (New York), 1968 . . . . £30/£10

ditto, as *The Mid-Atlantic Man and Other New Breeds in England*, Weidenfeld & Nicolson (London), 1969 £35/£10

Radical Chic and Mau-Mauing the Flak Catchers, Farrar Straus (New York), 1970 . . . . . £25/£5

ditto, Joseph (London), 1971 . . . . . £25/£5

The New Journalism, Harper & Row (New York), 1973 . . . . £45/£10

ditto, Pan (London), 1975 (wraps) £10

The Painted Word, Farrar Straus (New York), 1975 £20/£5

Mauve Gloves and Madmen, Clutter and Vine and Other Stories, Farrar Straus (New York), 1976 . £25/£5

The Right Stuff, Farrar Straus (New York), 1979 . £20/£5

ditto, Cape (London), 1979 . . . . . £20/£5

In Our Time, Farrar Straus (New York), 1980 £10/£5

ditto, Picador (London), 1980 (wraps) . . . £5

From Bauhaus to Our House, Farrar Straus (New York), 1981 . . . . £20/£5

ditto, Farrar Straus (New York), 1981 (350 signed, numbered copies, slipcase) . . . . . £125/£100

ditto, Cape (London), 1982 . . . . . £15/£5

The Purple Decades, Farrar Straus (New York), 1982 . . . . £20/£10

ditto, Farrar Straus (New York), 1982 (450 signed copies, slipcase). . . . . £60/£45

ditto, Cape (London), 1983 . . . . . £15/£5

Hooking Up, Farrar Straus (New York), 2000 . £10/£5
ditto, Franklin Library (Franklin Centre, PA), 2000 (signed,
limited edition) £50
ditto, Cape (London), 2000 . . . . . £10/£5

TOBIAS WOLFF
(b.1945)

Tobias Wolff's short stories were first published at a time
when several American authors (such as Raymond Carver)
were working almost exclusively in the short story form
and he became associated with attempts to call this the
Dirty Realism movement. Today he is as well-known for
his books of memoirs.

Novels
Ugly Rumours, Allen & Unwin (London), 1975 £500/£100
Old School, Knopf (New York), 2004 . . . £10/£5
ditto, Bloomsbury (London), 2004 . . . £10/£5

Short Stories
In the Garden of the North American Martyrs, Ecco Press
(New York), 1981 (first state d/w with printed $14.95
price) . . . . £200/£20
ditto, Ecco Press (New York), 1981 (second state d/w price-
clipped with a $10.95 sticker affixed) . . £125/£20
ditto, Ecco Press (New York), 1981 (third state d/w with
printed $10.95 price) . . . . . £65/£20
ditto, as *Hunters in the Snow*, Jonathan Cape (London),
1982 . . . . £35/£10
The Barracks Thief, Ecco Press, US, 1984 . £50/£10
ditto, as *The Barracks Thief and Selected Stories*, Bantam
(New York), 1984 (pbk) £5
ditto, Jonathan Cape (London), 1987 . . . £20/£5
Back in the World, Houghton, US, 1985 . . £35/£10
ditto, Jonathan Cape (London), 1986 . . . £30/£10
The Other Miller, Babcock & Kunitz (Derry), 1986 (200
signed, numbered copies; boards without d/w) . £60
ditto, Babcock & Kunitz (Derry), 1986 (40 deluxe copies) .
. . . . £150
Collected Stories of Tobias Wolff, Picador (London), 1988
(pbk) £5
Two Boys and a Girl, Bloomsbury (London), 1996 (pbk) £5
The Night in Question: Stories, Knopf (New York), 1996 .
. . . . £10/£5
ditto, Picador (London), 1996 . . . . £10/£5
Our Story Begins: New and Selected Stories, Knopf (New
York), 2008 . . . . £15/£5
ditto, Bloomsbury (London), 1996 . . . £15/£5

Autobiography
This Boy's Life: A Memoir, Atlantic Monthly Press (New
York), 1989 . . . . £20/£5
ditto, Bloomsbury (London), 1989 . . . £15/£5
In Pharaoh's Army: Memories of a Lost War, Knopf (New
York), 1994 . . . . £15/£5
ditto, Bloomsbury (London), 1994 . . . £15/£5

VIRGINIA WOOLF
(b.1882 d.1941)

To the Lighthouse and *The Waves*, with their stream-of-
consciousness style, brought Woolf to the forefront of
Modernism. In exploring the emotional and psychological
motives of her characters, her innovations remain
influential even today. Virginia and Leonard Woolf's London home was the centre of the celebrated Bloomsbury
Group.

Novels
The Voyage Out, Duckworth (London), 1915 . . £1,150
ditto, Doran (New York), 1920 (revised text) . £4,000/£100
ditto, Duckworth (London), 1920 (revised text) £2,500/£75
Night and Day, Duckworth (London), 1919 . . . £800
ditto, Doran (New York), 1920 . . . . £3,500/£250
Jacob's Room, Hogarth Press (Richmond, Surrey), 1922 .
. . . . £22,500/£650
ditto, Hogarth Press (London), 1922 (40 copies with tipped-
in, hand printed slip for subscribers) . £30,000/£7,500
ditto, Harcourt Brace (New York), 1923 . . £6,000/£250
Mrs Dalloway, Hogarth Press (London), 1925. £15,000/£750
ditto, Harcourt Brace (New York), 1925 . £1,000/£150
To The Lighthouse, Hogarth Press (London), 1927 . .
. . . . £12,000/£650
ditto, Harcourt Brace (New York), 1927 . . £1,500/£150
Orlando: A Biography, Crosby Gaige (New York), 1928
(861 numbered, signed copies). £2,000
ditto, Hogarth Press (London), 1928 . . £1,000/£125
The Waves, Hogarth Press (London), 1931 . £1,000/£100
ditto, Harcourt Brace (New York), 1931 . . £250/£35
The Years, Hogarth Press (London), 1937 . . £400/£45
ditto, Harcourt Brace (New York), 1937 . . £200/£30
Between The Acts, Hogarth Press (London), 1941 . £400/£35
ditto, Harcourt Brace (New York), 1941 . . £200/£25
Melymbrosia: An Early Version of 'The Voyage Out', New
York Public Library (New York), 1982 . . £20/£5

Short Stories
Two Stories, Hogarth Press (Richmond, Surrey), 1917 (150
copies; sewn wraps or paper-backed cloth, one story by
Virginia and the other by Leonard Woolf) . £12,500
Kew Gardens, Hogarth Press (Richmond, Surrey), 1919 (150
copies, in wraps.). £12,500
Monday or Tuesday, Hogarth Press (Richmond, Surrey),
1921 (1,000 copies) £850
ditto, Harcourt Brace (New York), 1921 (cloth and boards) .
. . . . £750/£100
ditto, Harcourt Brace (New York), 1921 (full cloth) . .
. . . . £1,250/£125
A Haunted House, Hogarth Press (London), 1943 . £200/£30
ditto, Harcourt Brace (New York), 1944 . . £75/£15
Nurse Lugton's Golden Thimble, Hogarth Press (London),
1966 (glassine d/w) . . . . . £60/£45
Mrs Dalloway's Party, Hogarth Press (London), 1973 £25/£5
The Pargiters, Hogarth Press (London), 1977 . £25/£5
ditto, Harcourt Brace (New York), 1977 . . £20/£5

Essays
Mr Bennett and Mrs Brown, Hogarth Press (London), 1924
(wraps) £250
The Common Reader, Hogarth Press (London), 1925 . .
. . . . £1,500/£200

ditto, Harcourt Brace (New York), 1925 . . . £750/£85

A Room of One's Own, Fountain Press (New York)/Hogarth Press (London), 1929 (492 signed copies) . . £4,000

ditto, Hogarth Press (London), 1929 . . . £1,350/£75

ditto, Harcourt Brace (New York), 1929 . . . £250/£35

Street Haunting, Westgate Press (San Francisco, CA), 1930 (500 signed copies, slipcase) . . . £850/£750

On Being Ill, Hogarth Press (London), 1930 (250 signed, numbered copies) . . . . . £3,000/£2,000

Beau Brummell, Rimington & Hooper (New York), 1930 (550 signed copies, glassine d/w, slipcase) £1,250/£1,000

A Letter to A Young Poet, Hogarth Press (London), 1932 (stapled wraps) £65

The Common Reader: Second Series, Hogarth Press (London), 1932 . . . . . . £500/£50

ditto, Harcourt Brace (New York), 1932 . . . £125/£35

Walter Sickert: A Conversation, Hogarth Press (London), 1934 (stapled wraps) £50

The Roger Fry Memorial Exhibition, Garden City Press (Letchworth, Herts), [1935] £600

Three Guineas, Hogarth Press (London), 1938 . £250/£65

ditto, Harcourt Brace (New York), 1938 . . . £175/£35

Reviewing, Hogarth Press (London), 1939 (stapled wraps) .
. . . . £30

The Death of The Moth, Hogarth Press (London), 1942 .
. . . . £175/£25

ditto, Harcourt Brace (New York), 1942 . . . £75/£15

The Moment and Other Essays, Hogarth Press (London), 1947 . . . . £100/£20

ditto, Harcourt Brace (New York), 1948 . . . £65/£15

The Captain's Death Bed, Harcourt Brace (New York), 1950 . . . . £100/£15

ditto, Hogarth Press (London), 1950 . . . . £100/£15

Granite and Rainbow, Hogarth Press (London), 1958 . .
. . . . £100/£20

ditto, Harcourt Brace (New York), 1958 . . . £50/£15

Contemporary Writers, Hogarth Press (London), 1965 . .
. . . . £35/£10

ditto, Harcourt Brace (New York), 1966 . . . £25/£5

Collected Essays, Volumes 1-4, Harcourt Brace (New York), 1967 . . . . £80/£20 the set

Books and Portraits, Hogarth Press (London), 1977 £25/£5

ditto, Harcourt Brace (New York), 1977 . . . £15/£5

The London Scene, Hogarth Press (London), 1982 £15/£5

ditto, Random House (New York), 1982 . . . £10/£5

The Essays of Virginia Woolf, Volume I, Chatto & Windus (London), 1986 . . . . £30/£10

ditto, *Volume II*, Chatto & Windus (London), 1987 £30/£10

ditto, *Volume III*, Chatto & Windus (London), 1988 . .
. . . . £30/£10

ditto, *Volume IV*, Chatto & Windus (London), 1994 £30/£10

Biography

Flush: A Biography, Hogarth Press (London), 1933 . .
. . . . £300/£40

ditto, Harcourt Brace (New York), 1933 . . . £150/£25

Roger Fry: A Biography, Hogarth Press (London), 1940 .
. . . . £500/£45

ditto, Harcourt Brace (New York), 1940 . . . £200/£35

Autobiography

Moments of Being, Chatto & Windus for Sussex Univ Press (London), 1976 . . . . £30/£10

ditto, Harcourt Brace (New York), 1976 . . . £15/£5

Play

Freshwater, Hogarth Press (London), 1976 . . £20/£5

ditto, Harcourt Brace (New York), 1976 . . . £15/£5

Letters

Virginia Woolf and Lytton Strachey: Letters, Hogarth Press (London), 1956 . . . . . . £100/£20

ditto, Harcourt (New York), 1956 . . . £45/£15

The Flight of The Mind: The Letters of Virginia Woolf, 1888-1912, Hogarth Press (London), 1975 . . £25/£5

ditto, as *The Letters of Virginia Woolf, Volume I: 1888-1912*, Harcourt Brace Jovanovich (New York), 1975 .
. . . . £25/£5

The Question of Things Happening: The Letters of Virginia Woolf, 1912-1922, Hogarth Press (London), 1976
. . . . £25/£5

ditto, as *The Letters of Virginia Woolf, Volume II: 1912-1922*, Harcourt Brace Jovanovich (New York), 1976 .
. . . . £25/£5

A Change of Perspective: The Letters of Virginia Woolf, 1923-1928, Hogarth Press (London), 1977 . . £20/£5

ditto, as *The Letters of Virginia Woolf, Volume III: 1923-1928*, Harcourt Brace Jovanovich (New York), 1978 . .
. . . . £25/£5

A Reflection of The Other Person: The Letters of Virginia Woolf, 1929-1931, Hogarth Press (London), 1978 £25/£5

ditto, as *The Letters of Virginia Woolf, Volume IV: 1929-1931*, Harcourt Brace Jovanovich (New York), 1979 £25/£5

The Sickle Side of The Moon: The Letters of Virginia Woolf, 1931-1935, Hogarth Press (London), 1979 £20/£5

ditto, as *The Letters of Virginia Woolf, Volume V: 1931-1935*, Harcourt Brace Jovanovich (New York), 1979 . .
. . . . £25/£5

Leave The Letters Till We're Dead: The Letters of Virginia Woolf, 1936-1941, Hogarth Press (London), 1980 £15/£5

ditto, as *The Letters of Virginia Woolf, Volume VI: 1936-1941*, Harcourt Brace Jovanovich (New York), 1980 . .
. . . . £25/£5

Paper Darts: The Illustrated Letters, Collins & Brown (London), 1992 . . . . £15/£5

Diaries

A Writer's Diary, Hogarth Press (London), 1953 . £225/£45

ditto, Harcourt Brace (New York), 1954 . . . £125/£25

The Diary of Virginia Woolf, Volume 1, 1915-1919, Hogarth Press (London), 1977 . . . . . £25/£5

ditto, Harcourt Brace (New York), 1977 . . . £25/£5

The Diary of Virginia Woolf, Volume II, 1920-1924, Hogarth Press (London), 1978 . . . . . £20/£5

ditto, Harcourt Brace (New York), 1978 . . . £20/£5

The Diary of Virginia Woolf, Volume III, 1925-1930, Hogarth Press (London), 1980 . . . . . £15/£5

ditto, Harcourt Brace (New York), 1980 . . . £15/£5

The Diary of Virginia Woolf, Volume IV, 1931-1935, Hogarth Press (London), 1982 . . . . . £15/£5

ditto, Harcourt Brace (New York), 1982 . . . £15/£5

The Diary of Virginia Woolf, Volume V, 1936-1941, Chatto & Windus (London), 1984 . . . . . £15/£5

ditto, Harcourt Brace (New York), 1984 . . . £15/£5

CORNELL WOOLRICH
(b.1903 d.1968)

An American author of *noir* suspense fiction, Woolrich's story 'It Had to Be Murder', collected in *After-Dinner Story*, was filmed as *Rear Window* by Alfred Hitchcock. Woolrich lived for many years with his mother in a seedy hotel room, and after her death, alcoholism and an amputated leg turned him into something of a recluse.

Novels

Cover Charge, Boni & Liveright (New York), 1926 . . . . £2,000/£100

Children of the Ritz, Boni & Liveright (New York), 1927 . . . . £1,500/£100

Times Square, Boni & Liveright (New York), 1929 . . . . £1,500/£100

A Young Man's Heart, Mason (New York), 1930 . . . . £1,000/£100

The Time of Her Life, Boni & Liveright (New York), 1931 . . . . £1,000/£100

Manhattan Love Song, Godwin (New York), 1932 . . . . £1,000/£100

The Bride Wore Black, Simon & Schuster (New York), 1940 . . . . £1,500/£200

ditto, Hale (London), 1942 . . . . . . £250/£75

ditto, as *Beware the Lady*, Pyramid (New York), 1953 (pbk) £25

The Black Curtain, Simon & Schuster (New York), 1941 . . . . £1,000/£100

Black Alibi, Simon & Schuster (New York), 1942 . . . . £850/£100

ditto, Hale (London), 1951 . . . . . £250/£35

The Black Angel, Doubleday (New York), 1943 . £750/£85

ditto, Hale (London), 1949 . . . . . £250/£65

The Black Path of Fear, Doubleday (New York), 1944 . . . . £450/£65

Rendezvous in Black, Rinehart (New York), 1948. £150/£25

ditto, Hodder & Stoughton (London), 1950 . . £125/£25

Savage Bride, Fawcett Gold Medal (New York), 1950 (#136; pbk) £15

Death Is My Dancing Partner, Pyramid (New York), 1959 (#G374; pbk) £25

The Doom Stone, Avon (New York), 1960 (#T-408; pbk) £15

Into the Night, Mysterious Press (New York), 1967 (completed by Lawrence Block) . . . £10/£5

ditto, Simon & Schuster (London), 1988. . . £10/£5

Short Stories

Nightmare, Dodd Mead (New York), 1956 . . £150/£50

Violence, Dodd Mead (New York), 1958 . . . £150/£50

Hotel Room, Random House (New York), 1958 . £65/£20

Beyond the Night, Avon (New York), 1959 (#T-354; pbk) £10

The Ten Faces of Cornell Woolrich, Simon & Schuster (New York), 1965 . . . . £100/£20

ditto, Boardman (London), 1966. . . . £45/£10

The Dark Side of Love, Walker (New York), 1965 £400/£50

Nightwebs: A Collection of Stories, Harper (New York), 1971 . . . . £40/£10

ditto, Gollancz (London), 1973 . . . . £30/£10

Angels of Darkness, Mysterious Press (New York), 1979 . . . . £20/£10

ditto, Mysterious Press (New York), 1979 (250 numbered copies) . . . . £45/£35

ditto, Mysterious Press (New York), 1979 (lettered copies; d/w and slipcase) . . . . £80/£65

The Fantastic Stories of Colonel Woolrich, Southern Illinois Univ Press (Carbondale, IL), 1981 . . £80/£25

Rear Window and Four Short Novels, Ballantine (New York), 1984 (pbk) £5

Darkness At Dawn, Southern Illinois Univ Press (Carbondale, IL), 1985 . . . . . . £20/£5

ditto, Xanadu (London), 1988 . . . . . £10/£5

Blind Date With Death, Carroll & Graf (New York), 1985 (pbk) £5

Vampire's Honeymoon, Carroll & Graf (New York), 1985 (pbk) £5

Novels Written as 'William Irish'

Phantom Lady, Lippincott (Philadelphia), 1942 £850/£150

ditto, Hale (London), 1945 . . . . . £250/£75

Deadline at Dawn, Lippincott (Philadelphia), 1944 . . . . £450/£125

ditto, World (New York), 1946 (motion picture edition with photographs from the film) . . . . £25/£10

ditto, Hutchinson (London), 1947 . . . £200/£65

Waltz into Darkness, Lippincott (Philadelphia), 1947 . . . . £300/£75

ditto, Hutchinson (London), 1948 . . . £200/£50

I Married a Dead Man, Lippincott (Philadelphia), 1948 . . . . £300/£75

ditto, Hutchinson (London), 1950 . . . £200/£50

Strangler's Serenade, Rinehart (New York), 1951. £250/£75

ditto, Hale (London), 1952 . . . . . £250/£75

Short Stories Written as 'William Irish'

I Wouldn't Be In Your Shoes, Lippincott (Philadelphia), 1943 . . . . £500/£125

ditto, Hutchinson (London), 1946 . . . £250/£65

ditto, as *And So To Death*, Spivak (New York), 1947 (pbk) £25

ditto, as *Nightmare*, Spivak (New York), 1950 (pbk) . £25

After-Dinner Story, Lippincott (Philadelphia), 1944 . . . . £400/£100

ditto, Hutchinson (London), 1947 . . . £250/£65

ditto, as *Six Times Death*, Popular Library (New York), 1948 (pbk) £25

If I Should Die Before I Wake, Avon Murder Mystery Monthly No.31 (New York), 1945 (pbk) . . . £50

The Dancing Detective, Lippincott (Philadelphia), 1946 . . . . £275/£50

ditto, Hutchinson (London), 1948 . . . £75/£25

Borrowed Crime, Avon Murder Mystery Monthly No.42 (New York), 1946 (pbk) £125

Dead Man Blues, Lippincott (Philadelphia), 1948 . £275/£50

ditto, Hutchinson (London), 1950 . . . £75/£25

The Blue Ribbon, Lippincott (Philadelphia), 1949. £275/£50

ditto, as *Dilemma of the Dead Lady*, Graphic (New York), 1950 (#20; pbk) £15

ditto, Hutchinson (London), 1951 . . . £75/£20

Somebody on the Phone, Lippincott (Philadelphia), 1950 . . . . £400/£65

ditto, as *Deadly Night Call*, Graphic (New York), 1951 (pbk) £15

ditto, as *The Night I Died*, Hutchinson (London), 1951 .
. . . . £125/£35
Six Nights of Mystery, Popular Library (New York), 1950
(pbk) £40
Marihuana, Dell (New York), 1951 (pbk) . . . £100
You'll Never See Me Again, Dell (New York), 1951 (pbk) .
. . . . £45
Eyes That Watch You, Rinehart (New York), 1952 £275/£75
Bluebeard's Seventh Wife, Popular Library (New York),
1952 (pbk) £25

Novels Written as 'George Hopley'
Night Has a Thousand Eyes, Farrar & Rinehart (New York),
1945 . . . . £200/£45
ditto, Penguin (London), 1949 (pbk) £5
Fright, Rinehart (New York), 1950 . . . £250/£40
ditto, Foulsham (London), 1952 . . . . £75/£25

Collected Editions
The Best of William Irish, Lippincott (Philadelphia), 1960 .
. . . . £45/£15
Four Thrillers, Zomba Books (London), 1983 . £25/£10
Cornell Woolrich Omnibus, Penguin (London), 1998 (pbk)
. . . . £5

Non-Fiction
Blues of a Lifetime, Bowling Green State Univ Popular
Press (New York), 1991 . . . . . £35/£10

RICHARD WRIGHT

(b.1908 d.1960)

Richard Wright was an African-American author of
powerful, sometimes controversial novels, short stories and
non-fiction. Much of his work concerned racial themes and
helped redefine discussions of race relations in America in
the mid-20th century.

Uncle Tom's Children, Four Novellas, Harper & Brothers
(New York), 1938 (copyright page with date code 'B-N').
. . . . £1,250/£150
ditto, Gollancz (London), 1939 . . . . £600/£75
ditto, as *Uncle Tom's Children, Five Long Stories*, Harper
& Brothers (New York), 1940 (copyright page with code
'G-P') . . . . £450/£45
Bright and Morning Star, International Publishers (New
York), 1938 (wraps; 15¢ price on spine; 6 novels and 3
pamphlets advertised on rear cover) £60
Native Son, Harper & Brothers (New York), 1940 (ordinary
trade issue; copyright page with code 'A-P'; bound in blue
cloth with title imprint in red and white blocks on front
cover and spine; yellow and green d/w with 'A Book-of-
the-Month Club Selection' on front panel; no reviews on
spine of d/w). . . . . . . £1,250/£250
ditto, Harper & Brothers (New York), 1940 (Book-of-the-
Month Club issue; copyright page with code 'A-P'; bound
in grey cloth with front and rear covers blank; spine
stamped in gold over black block on spine; top edges
stained blue; top and bottom edges trimmed; fore edges
rough trimmed; no printed price on grey/brown d/w with
text printed in black; *Native Son* image centered on front
panel printed in rose, brown,black, and grey/blue; blurb

about *Native Son* on front flap, rear flap and rear panel) .
. . . . £20/£5
ditto, Gollancz (London), 1940 . . . . . £250/£25
Native Son: A Play, Harper & Brothers (New York), 1941
(with code 'C-Q'; first issue d/w with lettering printed in
yellow and green; flaps and rear panel printed in green;
front flap with three blurbs; yellow printed band on front
panel: 'A Mercury production...') . . . £350/£65
ditto, Harper & Brothers (New York), 1941 (second issue
d/w with front panel printed all yellow; flaps and rear panel
printed in red; front flap has seven blurbs) . £250/£65
How 'Bigger' Was Born, The Story of Native Son, Harper
& Brothers (New York), 1940 (stapled wraps; copyright
page code 'K-P') £125
12 Million Black Voices, Viking (New York), 1941 . .
. . . . £600/£100
ditto, Lindsay Drummond (London), 1947 . £300/£65
Black Boy; A Record of Childhood and Youth, Harper &
Brothers (New York), 1945 (copyright page code 'M-T'
and 'Copyright 1937, 1942, 1944, 1945, by Richard
Wright...'; first issue binding black cloth with publisher's
logo in light red on front cover; on p.229: 'Manufactured
by H. Wolff Book Manufacturing Co.'; all edges trimmed;
d/w price $2.50 on front flap) . . . . £200/£30
ditto, Harper & Brothers (New York), 1945 (presumed Book-
of-the-Month Club issue with 'Manufactured by Kingsport
Press' on p.229; top and bottom edges trimmed but fore
edges rough trimmed; no price on d/w) . . £20/£5
ditto, Gollancz (London), 1945 . . . . £125/£25
*A Hitherto Unpublished Manuscript by Richard Wright
Being A Continuation of Black Boy...*, no publisher
[Constance Webb], ([New York}), [1946] (numbered
copies but unknown limitation; mimeographed) . £1,500
The FB Blue Eyes, no publisher (no place), 1949 [printed
1969?] (one page folded to make eight; uncut) . . £25
The Outsider, Harper & Brothers (New York), 1953
(copyright page with code 'B-C') . . . . £100/£20
ditto, Angus and Robertson (London), 1954 . £50/£10
Savage Holiday, Avon Books (New York), 1954 (pbk). £25
Black Power: A Record of Reactions in a Land of Pathos,
Harper & Brothers (New York), 1954 (copyright page code
'H-D') . . . . £75/£15
ditto, Dennis Dobson (London), 1956 . . . £35/£10
*The Colour Curtain: A Report on the Bandung
Conference*, World (Cleveland/New York), 1956 £45/£10
ditto, Dennis Dobson (London), 1956 . . . £35/£10
Pagan Spain, Harper (New York), 1957 (copyright page
code 'A-G') . . . . £60/£10
ditto, Bodley Head (London), 1960 . . . . £40/£10
White Man, Listen!, Doubleday (Garden City, NY), 1957 .
. . . . £40/£10
ditto, Angus and Robertson (London), 1960 . £30/£10
Eight Men, World (Cleveland/New York), 1961 . £100/£15
Lawd Today, Walker (New York), 1963 . . £65/£10
ditto, Anthony Blond (London), 1965 . . . £30/£5
Letters to Joe C. Brown, Kent State Univ Libraries (Kent,
OH), 1968 (stapled wraps). £15
*The Man Who Lived Underground/L'Home qui vivait sous
terre*, Aubier-Flammarion (Paris), 1971 (pbk) . £65
American Hunger, Harper & Row, (New York), 1977 . .
. . . . £20/£5
ditto, Harper & Row, (New York), 1977 (pbk) . . £5
Richard Wright Reader, Harper & Brothers (New York),
1978 . . . . £30/£10

ditto, Harper & Row, (New York), 1978 (pbk) . . £5

Conversations With Richard Wright, Univ Press of
Mississippi (Jackson, MS), 1990 . . . . £25/£10

ditto, Univ Press of Mississippi (Jackson, MS), 1990 (pbk) .
. . . . £5

***Early Works; Native Son, Lawd Today!, Uncle Tom's
Children***, Library of America (New York), 1991. £15/£5

ditto, Library of America (New York), 1991 (subscriber
copies in slipcase without d/w). . . . . £15/£5

Later Works: Black Boy (American Hunger), The Outsider,
Library of America (New York), 1991 . . £15/£5

ditto, Library of America (New York), 1991 (subscriber
copies in slipcase without d/w). . . . £15/£5

Rite of Passage, HarperCollins (New York), 1994. £10/£5

Haiku: This Other World, Arcade (New York), 1998 £10/£5

Down By The River, Limited Editions Club (New York),
2001 (300 numbered copies signed by illustrator John
Wilson; in folding cloth-covered box) . . £1,000/£750

S. FOWLER WRIGHT

(b.1874 d.1965)

One of the key British authors of science fiction, Wright
paid for the publication of his earliest books himself.
Deluge was his first bestseller, and he went on to write
crime fiction (published under the name 'Sydney Fowler'
in the U.K.) as well as his scientific romances. He worked
as an accountant before taking up writing.

Poetry

Scenes from the Morte d'Arthur, Erskine Macdonald
(London), 1919 (pseud 'Alan Seymour') . . . £50

Some Songs of Bilitis, Poetry (Birmingham, UK), [1921] .
. . . . £145/£50

The Song of Songs and Other Poems, Merton Press
(London), [1925]. . . . . . . £145/£50

ditto, Cosmopolitan Book Corp. (New York), 1929 £125/£35

The Ballad of Elaine, Merton Press (London), 1926 . .
. . . . £125/£50

The Riding of Lancelot: A Narrative Poem, Fowler Wright
(London), 1929 . . . . . . £125/£50

Novels

The Amphibians, Swan Press (Leeds, UK), 1925 . . .
. . . . £1,500/£450

ditto, Merton Press (London), 1925 . . . £275/£45

Deluge, Fowler Wright (London), 1927 . . £200/£35

ditto, Cosmopolitan Book Corp. (New York), 1929 . .
. . . . £100/£20

The Island of Captain Sparrow, Gollancz (London), 1928 .
. . . . £175/£25

ditto, Cosmopolitan Book Corp. (New York), 1928 £75/£15

The World Below, Collins (London), 1929 . £200/£40

ditto, Longmans, Green & Co (New York), 1930 . £175/£40

ditto, Shasta (Chicago), 1949 . . . . £20/£5

ditto, Shasta (Chicago), 1949 (Limited, Autographed
Edition). . . . . £40/£25

Dawn, Cosmopolitan Book Corp. (New York), 1929 . .
. . . . £100/£30

ditto, Harrap (London), 1930 . . . . £100/£30

Elfwin, Harrap (London), 1930 . . . . £125/£25

ditto, Longmans, Green & Co. (New York), 1930 . £100/£25

Dream; or, The Simian Maid, Harrap (London), 1931 . .
. . . . £100/£25

Seven Thousand in Israel, Jarrolds (London), 1931 . .
. . . . £125/£35

Red Ike, Hutchinson (London), [1931] (with J.M. Denwood)
. . . . £35/£10

ditto, as ***Under the Brutchstone***, Coward-McCann (New
York), 1931 . . . . £35/£10

Beyond the Rim, Jarrolds (London), 1932 . £125/£35

Lord's Right in Languedoc, Jarrolds (London), 1933 . .
. . . . £100/£25

Power, Jarrolds (London), 1933 . . . . £75/£15

David, Butterworth (London), 1934 . . . £50/£10

Prelude in Prague: A Story of the War of 1938, Newnes
(London), 1935 . . . . . . £75/£25

ditto, as ***The War of 1938***, Putnam's (New York), 1936 .
. . . . £60/£20

Four Days War, Hale (London), 1936 . . £200/£45

Megiddo's Ridge, Hale (London), 1937 . . £350/£65

The Screaming Lake, Hale (London), [1937] . £250/£65

The Adventure of Wyndham Smith, Jenkins (London), 1938
. . . . £250/£65

The Hidden Tribe, Hale (London), 1938 . . £250/£65

Ordeal of Barrata, Jenkins (London), 1939 . £125/£40

The Siege of Malta, Muller (London), 1942 (2 vols) £60/£20

Spider's War, Abelard Press (New York), 1954 . £30/£10

Short Stories

The New Gods Lead, Jarrolds (London), 1932 . £100/£25

ditto, as ***The Throne of Saturn***, Heinemann (London), 1951
. . . . £45/£10

ditto, Arkham House (Sauk City, WI), 1949 . £35/£10

The Witchfinder, Books of Today (London), 1946 £30/£10

Novels Written as 'Sidney Fowler'

The King Against Anne Bickerton, Harrap (London), 1930
. . . . £125/£20

ditto, as ***The Case of Anne Bickerton***, Boni (New York),
1930 . . . . £75/£10

The Bell Street Murders, Harrap (London), 1931 . £125/£20

ditto, Macaulay (New York), 1931 . . . £75/£15

By Saturday, Lane (London), 1931 . . . £125/£20

The Hanging of Constance Hillier, Jarrolds (London), 1931
. . . . £125/£20

Crime and Co, Macaulay (New York), 1931 . . £125/£20

ditto, as ***The Hand-Print Mystery***, Jarrolds (London), [1932]
. . . . £125/£20

Arresting Delia, Jarrolds (London), 1933. . . £100/£20

ditto, Macaulay (New York), 1933 . . . £75/£10

The Secret of the Screen, Jarrolds (London), 1933. £100/£20

Who Else But She?, Jarrolds (London), 1934 . £100/£20

Three Witnesses, Butterworth (London), 1935 . £100/£20

Vengeance of Gwa, Butterworth (London), 1935 (pseud
'Anthony Wingrave'). . . . . . £100/£20

ditto, as ***The Vengeance of Gwa***, Books of Today (London),
1945 (by S. Fowler Wright) . . . . £25/£10

The Attic Murders, Temple (London), 1936 . . £100/£20

Was Murder Done?, Butterworth (London), 1936 . £100/£20

Post-Mortem Evidence, Butterworth (London), 1936 . .
. . . . £100/£20

Four Callers in Razor Street, Temple (London), 1937 . .
. . . . £100/£20

The Jordan's Murder, Jenkins (London), 1938 . £100/£20

The Murder in Bethnal Square, Jenkins (London), 1938 .
. . . . £100/£20
The Wills of Jane Kantwhistle, Jenkins (London), 1939 .
. . . . £100/£20
A Bout with the Mildew Gang, Eyre & Spottiswoode
(London), 1941 . . . . . . £100/£20
The Rissole Mystery, Rich & Cowan (London), 1941 . .
. . . . £100/£20
A Second Bout with the Mildew Gang, Eyre &
Spottiswoode (London), 1942 . . . . £100/£20
Dinner in New York, Eyre & Spottiswoode (London), 1943
. . . . £75/£20
The End of the Mildew Gang, Eyre & Spottiswoode
(London), 1944 . . . . . . £100/£20
The Adventure of the Blue Room, Rich & Cowan (London),
1945 . . . . £50/£15
Too Much for Mr Jellipot, Eyre & Spottiswoode (London),
1945 . . . . £75/£20
Who Murdered Reynard?, Rich & Cowan (London), 1947 .
. . . . £75/£20
With Cause Enough?, Harvill (London), 1954 . £75/£20

Non-Fiction
Police and Public: A Political Pamphlet, Fowler Wright
(London), 1929 . . . . £20
The Life of Sir Walter Scott: A Biography, Poetry League
(London), [1932] . . . . . . £40/£15
Should We Surrender Colonies?, Readers Library
Publishing Co. (London), [1939] £15

Translation
The Inferno From the Divine Comedy of Dante Alighieri,
Fowler Wright (London), 1928 . . . £100/£45
ditto, Cosmopolitan Book Corp. (New York), 1928 £25/£10

JOHN WYNDHAM
(b.1903 d.1969)

'John Wyndham' is the pen name used by British author
John Wyndham Parkes Lucas Beynon Harris, and he wrote
under several other variations of his name. He is best
known for his peculiarly British science fiction novels,
amongst them *The Day of the Triffids*, which describes a
world struck blind and battling against deadly walking
plants.

Novels
The Secret People, Newnes (London), [1935] (pseud 'John
Beynon') . . . . £2,000/£150
ditto, Lancer (New York), 1964 (pseud 'John Beynon
Harris'; pbk) £25
Foul Play Suspected, Newnes (London), [1935] (pseud
'John Beynon') . . . . £300/£75
Planet Plane, Newnes (London), [1936] (pseud 'John
Beynon') . . . . £2,000/£150
ditto, as *Stowaway to Mars*, Nova (London), 1953 (pbk) £20
The Day of The Triffids, Doubleday (New York), 1951 .
. . . . £500/£75
ditto, Joseph (London), 1951 . . . . £750/£75
The Kraken Wakes, Joseph (London), 1953 . £200/£35
ditto, as *Out of the Deeps*, Ballantine (New York), 1953
(cloth) . . . . £135/£30

ditto, Ballantine (New York), 1953 (pbk) . . . £10
Re-Birth, Ballantine (New York), 1955 (cloth) . £175/£35
ditto, Ballantine (New York), 1955 (pbk) . . . £10
ditto, as *The Chrysalids*, Joseph (London), 1955 . £175/£35
The Midwich Cuckoos, Joseph (London), 1957 . £250/£35
ditto, Ballantine (New York), 1957 . . . £100/£15
Trouble with Lichen, Joseph (London), 1960 . £100/£20
ditto, Ballantine (New York), 1960 (wraps) . . £10
A John Wyndham Omnibus, Joseph (London), 1964 (*The
Day of the Triffids*, *The Kraken Wakes*, *The Chrysalids*) .
. . . . £40/£10
ditto, Simon & Schuster (New York), 1966 . £30/£10
Chocky, Joseph (London), 1968 . . . £40/£10
ditto, Ballantine (New York), 1968 (pbk) . . . £5
Web, Joseph (London), 1979 . . . . £30/£5

Short Stories
Jizzle, Dennis Dobson (London), 1954 . . £200/£30
Seeds of Time, Joseph (London), 1956 . . £165/£25
Sometime, Never: Three Tales of Imagination, Eyre &
Spottiswoode (London), 1956 (with William Golding and
Mervyn Peake) . . . . . . £125/£35
ditto, Ballantine (New York), 1956 (pbk) . . . £20
Tales of Gooseflesh and Laughter, Ballantine (New York),
1956 (pbk) £10
The Outward Urge, Joseph (London), 1959 (with 'Lucas
Parkes') . . . . £75/£15
ditto, Science Fiction Books Club (London), 1959 (1 extra
story) . . . . £30/£10
ditto, Ballantine (New York), 1959 (pbk) . . . £10
Consider Her Ways, Joseph (London), 1961 . £35/£10
The Infinite Moment, Ballantine (New York), 1961 (pbk) .
. . . . £10
The Best of John Wyndham, Sphere (London), 1973 (pbk)
. . . . £5
ditto, as *The Man from Beyond*, Joseph (London), 1975 .
. . . . £40/£10
Wanderers of Time, Coronet (London), 1973 (pbk) . £5
ditto, Severn House (London), 1980 . . . £25/£5
Sleepers of Mars, Coronet (London), 1973 (pbk) . £5
ditto, Severn House (London), 1980 . . . £25/£5
Exiles on Asperus, Coronet (London), 1979 (pbk) . £5
ditto, Severn House (London), 1979 . . . £25/£5

Others
Love in Time, Utopian Publications (London), 1946 (pseud
'Johnson Harris'; wraps) £60

RICHARD YATES
(b.1926 d.1992)

Richard Yates was an American novelist and short story
writer whose work is considered by many to be some of the
most powerful, compassionate, and technically
accomplished of America's post-War generation.

Revolutionary Road, Little, Brown (Boston), 1961 £250/£30
ditto, Andre Deutsch (London), 1962 . . . £200/£30
Eleven Kinds of Loneliness, Little, Brown (Boston), 1962 .
. . . . £150/£25
ditto, Andre Deutsch (London), 1964 . . . £150/£25
A Special Providence, Knopf (New York), 1969 . £50/£10

Disturbing the Peace, Delacorte Press (New York), 1975 .
. . . . £35/£10
ditto, Methuen (London), 2007 (wraps) £5
The Easter Parade, Delacorte Press/Seymour Lawrence
(New York), 1976 . . . . . . £25/£5
ditto, Eyre Methuen (London), 1976 . . . . £20/£5
A Good School, Delacorte Press/Seymour Lawrence (New
York), 1978 . . . . £20/£5
ditto, Methuen (London), 2006 (wraps) £5
Liars in Love, Delacorte Press/Seymour Lawrence (New
York), 1981 . . . . £15/£5
ditto, Eyre Methuen (London), 1982 . . . £10/£5
Young Hearts Crying, Delacorte Press/Seymour Lawrence
(New York), 1984. . . . . . £10/£5
ditto, Eyre Methuen (London), 1986 . . . . £10/£5
Cold Spring Harbor, Delacorte Press/Seymour Lawrence
(New York), 1986 . . . . . . £10/£5
ditto, Methuen (London), 1987 . . . . £10/£5
The Collected Stories Of Richard Yates, Henry Holt (New
York), 2001.. . . . . . . £10/£5
ditto, Methuen (London), 2002 . . . . £10/£5

W.B. YEATS
(b.1865 d.1939)

Yeats was an Irish poet, dramatist and mystic associated in
his early career with the Decadent Movement of the 1890s.
In his forties his poetry took on a harder, more modern
style, influenced by his relationships with Modernist poets
like Ezra Pound, and his involvement in Irish Nationalism.
He was awarded the Nobel Prize for literature in 1923.

Poetry
Mosada, A Dramatic Poem, printed by Sealy, Bryers and
Walker (Dublin), 1886 (wraps). . . . £35,000
ditto, Cuala Press (Dublin), 1943 (50 copies; wraps in d/w).
. . . . £1,250/£1,000
The Wanderings of Oisin and Other Poems, Kegan, Paul,
Trench & Co. (London), 1889 (500 copies, first binding in
dark blue cloth with 'Kegan Paul Trech & Co.' and blind-
stamped publisher's device on back cover) . . £1,500
ditto, Kegan, Paul, Trench & Co. (London), 1889 (500
copies, later binding with 'Paul, Trench, Truber & Co. at
foot of spine and no blind-stamped device on back cover).
. . . . £1,000
The Countess Kathleen, T. Fisher Unwin (London), 1892
(500 of 530 copies) £500
ditto, T. Fisher Unwin (London), 1892 (30 copies on vellum
of 530) £2,500
ditto, Roberts (Boston), 1892 . . . . . £500
The Land of Heart's Desire, T. Fisher Unwin (London),
1894 (500 copies; wraps, design by Aubrey Beardsley,
presumed first state without two fleurons after 'Desire' on
front cover) £750
ditto, T. Fisher Unwin (London), 1894 (presumed second
state with two fleurons) £450
ditto, Stone & Kimball (Chicago), [1894] (450 copies in
glazed boards, date incorrect on title-page as 1814,
frontispiece by Aubrey Beardsley) £400
ditto, Mosher (Portland, ME), 1903 . . . . £45
ditto, Mosher (Portland, ME), 1903 (100 copies on Japan
paper) £100

ditto, Mosher (Portland, ME), 1903 (10 copies on vellum) .
. . . . £500
Poems, Unwin (London), 1895 (725 of 750 copies) £1,000
ditto, Unwin (London), 1895 (25 signed copies on Japan
vellum) £5,000
ditto, Copeland & Day (Boston), 1895 . . . . £650
ditto, Unwin (London), 1899 (second edition). . . £125
The Wind Among the Reeds, Elkin Mathews (London),
1899 . . . . £750
ditto, Bodley Head (New York), 1899 . . . . £300
The Shadowy Waters, Hodder & Stoughton (London), 1900
. . . . £450
ditto, Dodd, Mead (New York), 1901 . . . . £125
In the Seven Woods, Dun Emer Press (Dundrum, Ireland),
1903 (325 copies) £750
ditto, Macmillan (New York), 1903 . . . . £100
Poems, 1899-1905, Bullen (London), 1906 . . . £200
The Golden Helmet, John Quinn (New York), 1908 (50
copies) £2,500
The Green Helmet, Cuala Press (Dundrum, Ireland), 1910
(400 copies) £650
ditto, Macmillan (New York), 1912 . . . . £65
*Selections from the Love Poetry of William Butler Yeats,
1890-1911*, Cuala Press (Dundrum, Ireland), 1913 (300
copies) £350
Poems Written in Discouragement, Cuala Press (Dundrum,
Ireland), 1913 (100 copies) £2,500
Responsibilities: Poems and a Play, Cuala Press (Dundrum,
Ireland), 1914 (400 copies) £850
Easter, 1916, Clement Shorter (London), 1916 (25 copies
signed by Shorter; wraps fastened by a silk cord). . £200
Responsibilities and Other Poems, Macmillan (New York),
1916 . . . . £200
Eight Poems, Morland Press (London), [1916] (8 copies on
Dutch handmade paper; wraps) £1,500
ditto, Morland Press (London), [1916] (70 copies on Japan
vellum; wraps) £1,250
ditto, Morland Press (London), [1916] (170 copies on Italian
handmade paper; wraps) £1,000
The Wild Swans at Coole, Cuala Press (Dundrum, Ireland),
1917 (400 copies) £1,250
ditto, Macmillan (New York), 1919 . . . . £100
ditto, Macmillan (London), 1919 . . . . £100
Nine Poems, Clement Shorter (London), 1918 (25 copies;
wraps) £175
Later Poems, Macmillan (London), 1922. . . £100/£35
ditto, Macmillan (New York), 1922 (250 signed copies). .
. . . . £1,250
Seven Poems and a Fragment, Cuala Press (Dundrum,
Ireland), 1922 (500 copies) . . . £350/£250
The Cat and the Moon and Certain Poems, Cuala Press
(Dublin), 1924 (500 copies, glassine d/w) . £300/£200
Early Poems and Stories, Macmillan (London), 1925 .
. . . . £200/£45
ditto, Macmillan (New York), 1925 . . . £150/£40
ditto, Macmillan (New York), 1925 (250 signed copies;
slipcase). . . . .£1,750/£1,500
October Blast, Cuala Press (Dublin), 1927 (350 copies)
. . . . £300/£200
The Tower, Macmillan (London), 1928 . £1,200/£250
ditto, Macmillan (New York), 1928 . . . £750/£200
Selected Poems, Lyrical and Narrative, Macmillan
(London), 1929 . . . . . . £250/£45

Three Things, Faber (London), 1929 ('Ariel Poems'; wraps)
. . . . £35
ditto, Faber (London), 1929 (500 signed copies) . . £800
The Winding Stair, Macmillan (New York), 1929 £650/£150
ditto, Fountain Press (New York), 1929 (642 signed copies)
. . . . £1,250/£1,000
ditto, as ***The Winding Stair And Other Poems***, Macmillan
(London), 1933 . . . . . . £650/£150
The Collected Poems, Macmillan (London), 1933 . £200/£65
ditto, Macmillan (New York), 1933 . . . £200/£65
The King of the Great Clock Tower, Cuala Press (Dublin),
1934 (400 copies) . . . . . £300/£250
ditto, Macmillan (New York), 1935 . . . . £75/£25
A Full Moon in March, Macmillan (London), 1935 £200/£75
New Poems, Cuala Press (Dublin), 1938 (450 copies) . £450
Last Poems and Plays, Macmillan (London), 1940 £75/£25
ditto, Macmillan (London), 1940 . . . . £75/£25

Drama

Cathleen Ni Houlihan, Caradoc Press for A.H. Bullen
(London), 1902 (300 of 308 copies) . . . £1,000
ditto, Caradoc Press for A.H. Bullen (London), 1902 (8
copies on vellum of 308) £5,000
***Where There Is Nothing: Being Volume One of Plays for
an Irish Theatre***, John Lane (London), 1902 (15 copies;
wraps) £3,500
ditto, [John Lane] (London), 1902 (30 numbered copies) .
. . . . £3,500
ditto, Macmillan (New York), 1903 . . . . £35
ditto, Macmillan (New York), 1903 (100 numbered copies).
. . . . £650
ditto, Bullen (London), 1903 . . . . . £35
The Hour-Glass, Heinemann (London), 1903 (12 copies, the
title-page serves as front cover) . . . £4,000
ditto, privately printed [Cuala Press] (Dundrum, Ireland),
1914 (50 copies; wraps) £1,000
ditto, Bullen (London), 1907 (wraps). . . . £35
***The Hour-Glass, Cathleen Ni Houlihan, The Pot of Broth:
Being Volume Two of Plays for an Irish Theatre***, Bullen
(London), 1904 . . . . £75
ditto, Macmillan (New York), 1904 . . . . £65
ditto, Macmillan (New York), 1904 (100 numbered copies
printed on Japanese Vellum) £125
The King's Threshold, privately printed (New York), 1904
(100 copies; boards, glassine d/w, slipcase) . . £750
ditto, privately printed (New York), 1904 (signed copies of
the 100; boards, glassine d/w, slipcase) . . £1,500
***The King's Threshold: And on Baile's Strand: Being
Volume Three of Plays for an Irish Theatre***, Bullen
(London), 1904 . . . . £65
ditto, John Quinn (New York), 1904 . . . . £65
Deidre: Being Volume Five of Plays for an Irish Theatre,
Bullen (London), 1907 (first issue with printers' imprint
p.48) £100
ditto, Bullen (London), 1907 (second issue without printers'
imprint p.48). £50
The Unicorn from the Stars, Macmillan (New York), 1908
(with Lady Gregory) £100
Two Plays for Dancers, The Cuala Press (Dundrum,
Ireland), 1919 (400 copies) £300
Michael Robartes and the Dancer, The Cuala Press
(Dundrum, Ireland), 1920 (400 copies) . . .£750
Four Plays for Dancers, Macmillan (London), 1921
(illustrated by Dulac) . . . . . .£350/£50

ditto, Macmillan (New York), 1921 . . . .£200/£35
The Player Queen, Macmillan (London), 1922 (wraps). £30
Plays in Prose and Verse, etc., Macmillan (London), 1922 .
. . . .£150/£45
ditto, Macmillan (New York), 1924 (250 signed copies) .
. . . .£1,000/£650
ditto, Macmillan (New York), 1924 . . . .£125/£45
Plays and Controversies, Macmillan (London), 1923 . .
. . . .£200/£25
ditto, Macmillan (New York), 1924 . . . .£200/£25
ditto, Macmillan (New York), 1924 (250 signed copies,
slipcase). . . . .£1,000/£650
The Collected Plays, Macmillan (London), 1934 . £85/£25
ditto, Macmillan (New York), 1935 . . . . £85/£25
Wheels and Butterflies, New Plays, Macmillan (London),
1934 . . . . £75/£20
ditto, Macmillan (New York), 1934 . . . . £75/£20
Nine One-Act Plays, Macmillan (London), 1937 . £65/£20

Novels

John Sherman and Dhoya, T. Fisher Unwin (London), 1891
(356 copies in boards) £1,500
ditto, T. Fisher Unwin (London), 1891 (wraps) . £650
ditto, Cassell (New York), 1891 . . . . . £650
The Speckled Bird, Cuala Press (Dublin), 1973-74 (2 vols;
500 numbered sets in d/w and slipcase) . . £150/£100

Short Stories

The Secret Rose, Lawrence and Bullen (London), 1897
(illustrated by Jack B. Yeats) £500
ditto, Dodd, Mead & Company (New York), 1897 (English
sheets) £450
The Tables of the Law, privately printed [Lawrence and
Bullen] (London), 1897 (110 copies) . . . £1,000
ditto, Elkin Mathews (London), 1904 (blue-grey boards) .
. . . .£150
ditto, Elkin Mathews (London), 1904 (green cloth) . £125
ditto, Elkin Mathews (London), 1904 (wraps) . . £100
ditto, Shakespeare Head Press (Stratford-upon-Avon,
Warwickshire), 1904 (510 copies) £65
Stories of Red Hanrahan, Dun Emer Press (Dundrum,
Ireland), 1904 (500 copies) £200
***Stories of Red Hanrahan: The Secret Rose: Rose
Alchemica***, Bullen (London), 1913. . . . £40
ditto, Macmillan (New York), 1914 . . . . £35

Essays

The Celtic Twilight, Lawrence and Bullen (London), 1893
(illustrated by Jack B. Yeats, first binding with the name of
the publishers on the spine in upper case) . . .£750
ditto, Lawrence and Bullen (London), 1893 (second binding
with the name of the publishers in lower case) . £450
Ideas of Good and Evil, Bullen (London), 1903 . .£145
ditto, Macmillan (New York), 1903 . . . . £85
Discoveries; a Volume of Essays, Dun Emer Press
(Dundrum, Ireland), 1907 (200 copies) . . .£450
Poetry and Ireland: Essays. Cuala Press (Dundrum, Ireland),
1908 (250 copies) £350
The Cutting of an Agate, Macmillan (New York), 1912 .
. . . .£175
ditto, Macmillan (London), 1919 . . . . .£175
Per Amica Silentia Lunae, Macmillan (London), 1918. £150
ditto, Macmillan (New York), 1918 . . . .£150
Essays, Macmillan (London), 1924 . . . .£250/£85

ditto, Macmillan (New York), 1924 (250 signed copies) £750
If I Were Four and Twenty, Cuala Press (Dublin), 1940
(450 copies; glassine d/w) .   .   .   .   £250/£200

Autobiography
Reveries Over Childhood and Youth, Cuala Press (Dundrum, Ireland), 1915 (425 copies, 2 vols including portfolio) £1,000
ditto, Macmillan (New York), 1916 (1 vol, no portfolio) £75
ditto, Macmillan (London), 1916 (1 vol, no portfolio) . £75
Four Years, The Cuala Press (Dundrum, Ireland), 1921 (400 copies) .   .   .   .   .   .   £400/£300
The Trembling of the Veil, T. Werner Laurie (London), 1922 (1,000 signed copies)   .   .   £1,250/£1,000
Early Memories, Cuala Press (Dublin), 1923 (500 copies) .
.   .   .   .   £300/£200
A Vision, Macmillan (London), 1925 (600 signed copies) .
.   .   .   .   £1,250/£1,000
ditto, Macmillan (London), 1937   .   .   .   £100/£35
ditto, Macmillan (New York), 1938   .   .   .   £100/£35
Autobiographies: Reveries Over Childhood and Youth and The Trembling of the Veil, Macmillan (London), 1926 .
.   .   .   .   £165/£75
ditto, Macmillan (New York), 1927   .   .   .   £165/£75
Dramatis Personae, Cuala Press (Dublin), 1935 (400 copies)
.   .   .   .   £200
ditto, Macmillan (New York), 1936   .   .   .   £75/£25
ditto, Macmillan (London), 1936   .   .   .   £75/£25

Miscellaneous
Is the Order of R.R. & A.C. to Remain a Magical Order?, [privately printed for the Order Rubidae Rosae & Aureae Crucis, a section of the Order of the Golden Dawn] (no place), 1901 (wraps) £3,500
Collected Works in Prose and Verse, Shakespeare Head Press (Stratford-upon-Avon, Warwickshire), 1908 (8 vols, 1,060 copies, half vellum and cloth)   .   .   .   £1,000
ditto, Shakespeare Head Press (Stratford-upon-Avon, Warwickshire), 1908 (remainder binding cloth and boards)
.   .   .   .   £850
Synge and the Ireland of His Time, Cuala Press (Dundrum, Ireland), 1911 (350 copies) £450
The Bounty of Sweden, Cuala Press (Dublin), 1925 (400 copies, glassine d/w) .   .   .   .   £300/£200
Estrangement, Cuala Press (Dublin), 1926 (300 copies)   .
.   .   .   .   £500
The Death of Synge and Other Passages from an Old Diary, Cuala Press (Dublin), 1928 (400 copies) £250/£150
A Packet for Ezra Pound, Cuala Press (Dublin), 1929 (425 copies, glassine d/w) .   .   .   .   £400/£300
On the Boiler, Cuala Press (Dublin), 1939 (all but four copies of the first edition destroyed; wraps) .   .   £1,500
ditto, Cuala Press (Dublin), 1939 (second edition; wraps)   .
.   .   .   .   £100
Letters on Poetry from W.B. Yeats to Dorothy Wellesley, O.U.P. (Oxford, UK), 1940 .   .   .   .   £65/£20
ditto, O.U.P. (New York), 1940 .   .   .   .   £65/£20
Pages from a Diary Written in Nineteen Hundred and Thirty, Cuala Press (Dublin), 1944 (280 copies) .   £250
The Letters, Hart Davis (London), 1954   .   .   £45/£15
ditto, Macmillan (New York), 1955 .   .   .   £35/£10
The Collected Letters of W.B. Yeats, Volume I: 1865-1895, O.U.P. (Oxford, UK), 1986 .   .   .   .   £40/£20

The Collected Letters of W.B. Yeats, Volume III: 1901-1904, O.U.P. (Oxford, UK), 1994 .   .   .   £30/£15
The Collected Letters of W.B. Yeats, Volume II: 1896-1900, O.U.P. (Oxford, UK), 1998 .   .   .   .   £35/£15
The Collected Letters of W.B. Yeats, Volume IV: 1905-1907, O.U.P. (Oxford, UK), 2005 .   .   .   £25/£10

Edited by Yeats
Fairy and Folk Tales of the Irish Peasantry, Walter Scott (London), 1888 .   .   .   .   .   .   £300
Irish Fairy Tales, Fisher Unwin (London), 1892 (illustrated by Jack B. Yeats). £300
ditto, Cassell (New York), 1892 .   .   .   .   .   £200
The Poems of William Blake, Lawrence & Bullen (London), 1893 .   .   .   .   £200
ditto, Lawrence & Bullen (London), 1893 (200 numbered copies) £500
ditto, Scribner's (New York), 1893 .   .   .   .   £200

THE YELLOW BOOK

The Yellow Book was a literary and art periodical of the 1890s considered outrageous and decadent in its day: Aubrey Beardsley's distinctive artwork upset many commentators. Some contributors, such as Max Beerbohm, went on to become major literary figures, although several did not survive the decade.

Volume 1, Matthews & Lane (London), April, 1894 .   £75
Volume 2, Matthews & Lane (London), July, 1894 .   £60
Volume 3, Lane/Bodley Head (London), October, 1894 £50
Volume 4, Lane/Bodley Head (London), January, 1895. £45
Volume 5, Lane/Bodley Head (London), April, 1895 .   £40
Volume 6, Lane/Bodley Head (London), July, 1895 .   £35
Volume 7, Lane/Bodley Head (London), October, 1895 £35
Volume 8, Lane/Bodley Head (London), January, 1896 £35
Volume 9, Lane/Bodley Head (London), April, 1896 .   £35
Volume 10, Lane/Bodley Head (London), July, 1896 .   £35
Volume 11, Lane/Bodley Head (London), October, 1896 £35
Volume 12, Lane/Bodley Head (London), January, 1897 £35
Volume 13, Lane/Bodley Head (London), April, 1897 .   £35

Complete set of 13 volumes (evenly coloured spines) .   £750

APPENDIX I

SINGLE TITLE ENTRIES

2000 AD
Issue #1, IPC (London), 1977 . . . . . . £100

CHINUA ACHEBE
(b.1930)
Things Fall Apart, Heinemann (London), 1958 £850/£100
ditto, Obolensky (New York), 1959 . . . . £650/£65

GEORGE ADE
(b.1866 d.1944)
Fables in Slang, Stone (Chicago), 1900 . . . . £45
ditto, Stone (Chicago), 1900 (1,000 signed, numbered copies) £75

AESOP
(lived mid 6th century BC)
Aesop's Fables, 1485 . . . . . . £75,000
ditto, John Osborn (London), 1740 (edited by Samuel Richardson) £5,000
ditto, John Osborn (London), 1740 (rebound) . . £3,000

RICHARD HARRIS BARHAM
(b.1788 d.1845)
The Ingoldsby Legends, Bentley (London), 1840, 1842, 1847 (3 vols) £850

STAN BARSTOW
(b.1928)
A Kind of Loving, Joseph (London), 1960 . . £50/£10
ditto, Doubleday (New York), 1961 . . . £15/£5

THOMAS BEWICK
(b.1753 d.1828)
A General History of Quadrupeds, Bewick, Beilby & Hodgson (Newcastle, UK), 1790 . . . £1,000

WILLIAM BLAKE
(b.1757 d.1827)
Songs of Innocence and Experience, 1789 . . £250,000
Songs of Innocence and Experience, 1789 (with final plate 'A Divine Image') £750,000

ROLF BOLDREWOOD
(b.1826 d.1915)
Robbery Under Arms, Remington (London), 1888 (3 vols) .
. . . . £2,000

GEORGE BORROW
(b.1803 d.1881)
Wild Wales, Murray (London), 1862 (3 vols) . . £400

JAMES BOSWELL
(b.1740 d.1795)
The Life of Samuel Johnson, Baldwin, Dilly (London), 1791 (2 vols with 'gve' on p.235 of first volume). £5,000
ditto, Baldwin, Dilly (London), 1791 (with 'give' on p.235 of first volume) £3,000

E.R. BRAITHWAITE
(b.1922)
To Sir, With Love, Bodley Head (London), 1959 . £75/£10
ditto, Prentice-Hall (Englewood Cliffs, NJ), 1959 . £50/£10

PEARL S. BUCK
(b.1892 d.1973)
East Wind, West Wind, John Day (New York), 1930 . .
. . . . £500/£50
ditto, Methuen (London), 1931 . . . . £125/£20

EDWARD BULWER LYTTON
(b.1803 d.1873)
The Last Days of Pompeii, Bentley, 1834 (anonymous, 3 vols) £600
ditto, Harper's (New York), 1834 . . . . £150

JOHN BUNYAN
(b.1628 d.1688)
The Pilgrim's Progress, Nath. Ponder, Peacock (London), 1678 . . . . £100,000

SAMUEL BUTLER
(b.1835 d.1902)
Erewhon or Over the Range, Trubner & Co (London), 1872 (anonymous). £250
The Way of All Flesh, Grant Richards (London), 1903. £250

JAMES BRANCH CABELL
(b.1879 d.1958)
Jurgen, McBride (New York), 1919 (first issue with line rules on page 144 intact) £200

ERSKINE CALDWELL
(b.1903 d.1987)
Tobacco Road, Scribner's (New York), 1932 . £1,000/£100
ditto, Cresset Press (London), 1933 . . . £125/£25

LOUIS-FERDINAND CÉLINE
(b.1894 d.1961)
Journey to the End of the Night, Chatto & Windus (London), 1934 (translated by John Marks) . £250/£30
ditto, Little, Brown (Boston), 1934 . . . £175/£20

ERSKINE CHILDERS
(b.1870 d.1922)
The Riddle of the Sands, Smith Elder (London), 1903 £1,000
ditto, Dodd Mead (New York), 1915. . . . £250

CARLO COLLODI
(b.1826 d.1890)
Le Avventure di Pinocchio, Felice Paggi Librario-Editore (Florence), 1883 . . . . . . £20,000
ditto, as *The Story of a Puppet, or The Adventures of Pinocchio*, T. Fisher Unwin (London), 1892 [1891] . .
. . . . £4,000
ditto, Cassell (New York), 1892 . . . . £4,000

RICHARD CONDON
(b.1915 d.1996)
The Manchurian Candidate, McGraw-Hill (New York), 1959 . . . . £145/£25
ditto, Joseph (London), 1960 . . . . £65/£10

WILLIAM CONGREVE
(b.1670 d.1729)

The Way of the World, Tonson (London), 1700 . £2,000

CARROLL JOHN DALY
(b.1889 d.1958)

The Snarl of the Beast, Edward J. Clode (New York), 1927
. . . . £2,000/£100

CHARLES M. DOUGHTY
(b.1843 d.1926)

Travels in Arabia Deserta, C.U.P. (Cambridge, UK), 1888
(2 vols) £4,000

HOWARD FAST
(b.1914 d.2003)

Spartacus, privately printed (New York), 1951 . £200/£40
ditto, privately printed (New York), 1951 (autographed
edition: signed, and with $5 on d/w front flap) . £225/£65
ditto, Bodley Head (London), 1952 . . . £75/£15

EDWARD FITZGERALD
(b.1809 d.1883)

Rubáiyát of Omar Khayyám, Quaritch (London), 1859 .
. . . . £20,000

JOHN GALSWORTHY
(b.1867 d.1933)

Man of Property, Heinemann, 1906 . . . . £75
In Chancery, Heinemann, 1920 . . . . £65/£15
Awakening, Heinemann, [1920] . . . . £50/£10
To Let, Heinemann, 1921 . . . . . £50/£10
Forsyte Saga, Heinemann, 1922 (collects the above) . .
. . . . £100/£25
ditto, Heinemann, 1922 (large paper edition, 275 signed
copies; slipcase) £300

JOHN GAY
(b.1685 d.1732)

The Beggar's Opera, Watts (London), 1728 (three bars of
music on p.53; text ends p.59) £1,000

OLIVER GOLDSMITH
(b.1730 d.1774)

The Vicar of Wakefield, Newbery (Salisbury, Wiltshire),
1766 (2 vols, anonymous) £3,000
ditto, Mentz (Philadelphia, PA), 1772 . . £1,250

JOHN GRAY
(b.1866 d.1934)

Silverpoints, Elkin Mathews & John Lane (London), 1893
(250 numbered copies) £1,750

JACOB & WILHELM GRIMM
(b.1785 d.1863, b.1786 d.1859)

Kinder-und Hausmarchen, Realschulbuchhandlung (Berlin),
1812-14 (2 vols) £30,000
ditto, as *German Popular Stories*, Baldwin (London), 1823,
and Robbins (London), 1826 (2 vols; original boards) .
. . . . £20,000
ditto, Baldwin (London), 1823, and Robbins (London), 1826
(2 vols; rebound) £3,000

SUSAN HILL
(b.1942)

The Enclosure, Hutchinson (London), 1961 . £100/£20
The Woman in Black, Hamish Hamilton (London), 1983 .
. . . . £275/£35

E.T.A. HOFFMANN
(b.1776 d.1822)

The Devil's Elixir, Blackwood & Cadell (Edinburgh), 1824
(2 vols) £500
Hoffmann's Strange Stories from the German, Burnham
Brothers (Boston), 1855 . . . . . £250
Hoffmann's Fairy Tales, Burnham Brothers (Boston), 1857
. . . . £250

HEINRICH HOFFMANN
(b.1809 d.1894)

*The English Struwwelpeter, or Pretty Stories and Funny
Pictures for Little Children*, Friedrich Volckmar (Leipzig),
1848 (first English edition) £5,000

ANTHONY HOPE
(b.1863 d.1933)

The Prisoner of Zenda, Arrowsmith (Bristol, UK), 1894
(first issue with 16 titles advertised in the 3/6 list at rear of
book) £1,000
ditto, Holt (New York), 1894 . . . . . £25

W.H. HUDSON
(b.1841 d.1922)

The Purple Land, Sampson Low (London), 1885 (2 vols) .
. . . . £1,250

THOMAS HUGHES
(b.1822 d.1896)

Tom Brown's Schooldays, Macmillan (Cambridge, UK),
1857 ('nottable' for 'notable' p.24, line 15) . . . £750

LIONEL JOHNSON
(b.1867 d.1902)

Poems, Elkin Mathews/Copeland & Day (London), 1895 (25
signed copies) £2,500
ditto, Elkin Mathews/Copeland & Day (London), 1895 (750
copies) £250

SAMUEL JOHNSON
(b.1709 d.1784)

A Dictionary of the English Language, printed by Strahan
(London), 1755 (2 vols) £10,000

BEN JONSON
(b.1572 d.1637)

The Workes of Benjamin Jonson, [first volume], Will
Stansby (London), 1616 . . . . . . £3,500
ditto, [second volume], Richard Meighen (London), 1640 .
. . . . £1,500

NIKOS KAZANTZAKIS
(b.1885 d.1957)

Zorba the Greek, Lehman (London), 1952 . . £250/£35
ditto, Simon & Schuster (New York), 1953 . . £75/£15

CHARLES KINGSLEY
(b.1819 d.1875)
The Water Babies, Macmillan, 1863 (first issue, containing 'L'Envoi') £1,000

CHARLES AND MARY LAMB
(b.1775 d.1834, b.1764 d.1847)
Tales from Shakespeare, Hodgkins (London), 1807 (2 vols)
. . . . £4,000
ditto, Hodgkins (London), 1807 (2 vols rebound) . £2,500

Rev. C.R. MATURIN
(b.1782 d.1824)
Melmoth the Wanderer, Constable (Edinburgh), 1820 (4 vols) £1,750

JOHN MILTON
(b.1608 d.1674)
Paradise Lost, Parker (London), 1667 . . . £40,000
Paradise Regain'd, Starkey (London), 1671 . . £3,500

BILL NAUGHTON
(b.1910 d.1992)
Alfie, MacGibbon & Kee (London), 1966. . . £450/£65

BARONESS ORCZY
(b.1865 d.1947)
The Scarlet Pimpernel, Greening (London), 1905 . £2,000

CHARLES PERRAULT
(b.1628 d.1703)
Histoires, Ou Contes du Temps Passé, Avec des Moralitez, (Paris), 1697 . . . . £10,000

JOHN POLIDORI
(b.1795 d.1821)
The Vampyre, Sherwood, Neely & Jones (London), 1819 (unprinted drab paper wrappers) . . . £4,000

ALEXANDER POPE
(b.1688 d.1744)
The Rape of the Lock, Lintott (London), 1714 (wraps). .
. . . . £5,000
ditto, Lintott (London), 1714 (rebound) . . £2,500

COLE PORTER
(b.1893 d.1964)
Red Hot and Blue, Random House (New York), 1936 (300 signed deluxe copies). £2,500

SAMUEL RICHARDSON
(b.1689 d.1761)
Pamela, Rivington (London), 1741-1742 (4 vols) . £5,000

ANTOINE DE SAINT-EXUPÉRY
(b.1900 d.1944)
The Little Prince, Reynal & Hitchcock (New York), 1943 .
. . . . £1,000/£75
ditto, Reynal & Hitchcock (New York), 1943 (500 copies) .
. . . . £3,000/£2,000
ditto, as *The Little Prince*, Heinemann (London), 1945. .
. . . . £1,000/£75

RONALD SEARLE
(b.1920)
Hurrah for St Trinian's!, Macdonald (London), 1948 . .
. . . . £65/£15
ditto, Macdonald (New York), 1948 . . . . £35/£10

PETER SHAFFER
(b.1926 d.2001)
Equus, Deutsch (London), 1973 . . . . . £75/£15
ditto, Atheneum (New York), 1974 . . . . £45/£10

PERCY BYSSHE SHELLEY
(b.1792 d.1822)
Queen Mab, privately printed (London), 1813 (with title-page) £20,000
ditto, privately printed (London), 1813 (without title-page) .
. . . . £1,500
Poetical Works, Kelmscott Press (London), 1894-1895 (250 copies, 3 vols) £3,000

EDMUND SPENSER
(b.1552 d.1599)
The Faerie Queen, Ponsonbie (London), 1590-1596 (2 vols)
. . . . £17,500

RICCARDO STEPHENS
(b.1889 d.1958)
The Mummy, Eveleigh Nash (London), 1912 . . £1,500

WALLACE STEVENS
(b.1879 d.1955)
Harmonium, Knopf (New York), 1923 (first binding in chequered boards) . . . . £7,000/£1,750
ditto, Knopf (New York), 1923 (second binding in striped boards) . . . . . . £6,000/£1,000
ditto, Knopf (New York), 1923 (third binding in blue cloth)
. . . . £5,000/£450

HARRIET BEECHER STOWE
(b.1811 d.1896)
Uncle Tom's Cabin, Jewett (Boston), 1852 (2 vols; wraps, with Hobart and Robbins on copyright page) . £7,500
ditto, Jewett (Boston), 1852 (2 vols; cloth binding). £4,000
ditto, Jewett (Boston), 1852 (2 vols; 'gift' binding of gilt decorated brown cloth) £8,000
ditto, Cassell (London), 1852 (13 parts; wraps) . £2,000
ditto, Cassell (London), 1852 (cloth) £1,000

THEODORE STURGEON
(b.1918 d.1985)
The Dreaming Jewels, Greenberg (New York), 1950 . .
. . . . £75/£10
ditto, Gollancz (London), 1968 . . . . . £75/£10

LEW WALLACE
(b.1827)
Ben-Hur, Harper (New York), 1880 . . . . . £125

MARGERY WILLIAMS
(b.1912 d.1976)
The Velveteen Rabbit, Heinemann (London), 1922 . .
. . . . £10,000/£700

APPENDIX II

REFERENCES

General Reference Books

Ahearn, Allen and Patricia, *Collected Books, A Guide to their Values, 2002 Edition*, Putnam's, 2001.

Bédé, Jean-Albert, and Edgerton, William B., eds., *Columbia Dictionary of Modern European Literature*, Columbia Univ Press, 1980.

Breese, Martin, *Breese's Guide to Modern First Editions, 2000 Edition*, Breese Books, 1999.

Browning, D.C. (ed.), *Everyman's Dictionary of Literary Biography*, Everyman, 1970.

Bruccoli, Matthew J. et al., *First Printings of American Authors, Vols 1-5*, Gale Research, 1977-1987.

Cole, Michael (ed.), *Annual Register of Book Values, Modern First Editions*, The Clique (various editions).

Connolly, Joseph, *Modern First Editions*, Little, Brown, 1993.

Cooper, John, and Pike, B.A., *Detective Fiction: The Collector's Guide*, Scolar Press, 1994 (second edition). (*DF:TCG*)

Currey, Lloyd, *Science Fiction and Fantasy Authors, A Bibliography of First Printings of Their Fiction*, G.K. Hall, 1979. Updated by Rb Publishing, 2002 (cd rom).

Cutler and Stiles, *Modern British Authors, Their First Editions*, Allen & Unwin, 1930.

Foord, Peter and Williams, Richard, *Collins Crime Club: A Checklist of the First Editions*, Dragonby Press, 1999 (second edition).

Hamer, Martin, *The Hamer Comic Annual Guide*, Hamer 20th Century Books, 2000. Also *Comic Annual Supplement* No.2, 2002.

Hubin, Allen J., *The Bibliography of Crime Fiction, 1749-1980*, Garland, 1984.

Jackson, Crispin (ed.), and others, *The Book and Magazine Collector*, Diamond Publishing, various issues. (*B&MC*)

Jackson, Crispin (ed.), *Collecting Children's Books*, Book and Magazine Collector, 1995.

McBride, Bill and Arledge, Amy A., *Points of Issue: A Compendium of Points of Issue of Books by 19th-20th Century Authors*, McBride, 1996 (third edition; wraps).

McBride, Bill, *A Pocket Guide to the Identification of First Editions*, McBride, 2000 (sixth edition; wraps)

McBride, Bill, *Book Collecting for Fun & Profit: Building a Book Collection, Building a Book Business*, McBride, 2002 (wraps)

Nehr, Ellen, *Doubleday Crime Club Compendium, 1928-1991*, Offspring Press, 1992.

Ousby, Ian (ed.), *The Cambridge Guide to Literature in English*, Guild Publishing, 1989.

Peachment, Chris (ed.), and others, *The Book and Magazine Collector*, Warners, various issues. (*B&MC*)

Porter, Catherine, *Collecting Books*, Miller's, 1995 (2001 reprint).

Porter, Catherine, *Collecting Modern Books*, Miller's, 2003.

Pendergast, Sara & Pendergast, Tom (eds.), *St James Guide to Children's Writers*, St James Press, 1999 (fifth edition.)

Smiley, Kathryn (ed.), *Firsts: The Book Collector's Magazine*, Firsts (various issues). (*F:TBCM*)

Ward, K. Anthony, *First Editions, A Field Guide*, Scolar Press, 1994.

Zempel, Edward N., and Verkler, Linda A., *First Editions: A Guide to Identification*, Spoon River Press, 2001 (fourth edition).

On-line Resources

www.abebooks.com
www.AddAll.com
www.BookFinder.com
British Library Public Catalogue: www.blpc.bl.uk
Classic Crime Fiction: www.classiccrimefiction.com
Fantastic Fiction: www.fantasticfiction.co.uk
The Library of Congress: www.loc.gov

Author Bibliographies/References

EDWARD ABBEY
'Collecting Edward Abbey', by Spencer Maxwell, *F:TBCM*, September 1991, Vol.1, No.9, pps.20-23.

ANTHONY ABBOT
DF:TCG, by John Cooper and B.A. Pike, Scolar Press, 1994, pps13-14.

PETER ABRAHAMS
Peter Abrahams, by Michael Wade, Evans Brothers, 1972.
20th-Century Fiction, by George Woodcock, Macmillan, 1983.

J.R. ACKERLEY
Ackerley - A Life of J.R. Ackerley, by Peter Parker, Constable, 1994.
'J.R.Ackerley, Author and Editor', by Colin Wiles, *B&MC*, No. 152, November 1996, pps.28-36.

PETER ACKROYD
'Peter Ackroyd', by Crispin Jackson, *B&MC*, No.97, April 1992, pps.49-55.

DOUGLAS ADAMS
Don't Panic: Douglas Adams and the Hitch-Hiker's Guide to the Galaxy, by Neil Gaiman, Titan, 1993.

RICHARD ADAMS
'Richard Adams', by June Hopper, *B&MC*, No.187, October 1999, pps.16-27.

CHAS ADDAMS
'Chas Addams', by Richard Dalby, *B&MC*, No.103, October 1992, pps.65-73.

JAMES AGEE
James Agee, by Victor A. Kramer, Twayne/Gale, 1975.

ROBERT AICKMAN
Robert Aickman: An Introduction, by Gary William Crawford, Gothic Press, 2003.

CONRAD AIKEN
Conrad Aiken: A Bibliography, (1902-1978), by F.W. and F.C. Bonnell, Huntington Library, 1982.

JOAN AIKEN
'The Children's Books of Joan Aiken', by Daphne Stroud, *B&MC*, No.102, September 1992, pps.37-45.

KATHLEEN AINSLIE
www.blpc.bl.uk

W. HARRISON AINSWORTH
First Editions, A Field Guide, by K. Anthony Ward, Scolar Press, 1994, pps.2-5.

ALAIN-FOURNIER
Alain-Fournier: A Brief Life, by David Arkell, Carcanet, 1996.
'Alain-Fournier', by Martin Spence, *B&MC*, No.149, August 1996, pps.65-73.

ALASTAIR
Alastair, by Victor Arwas, Thames and Hudson, 1979.

EDWARD ALBEE
Edward Albee At Home and Abroad: A Bibliography, by Amacher, Richard E. & Margaret Rule, Ams Press, 1975.

LOUISA MAY ALCOTT
Louisa May Alcott A Bibliography, by Lucile Gulliver Lucile, Little, Brown, 1932.

CECIL ALDIN
Cecil Aldin, The Story of a Sporting Artist, by Roy Heron, Webb & Bowe, 1981.

RICHARD ALDINGTON
A Bibliography of the Works of Richard Aldington from 1915 to 1948, by Alister Kershaw, The Quadrant Press, 1950.

BRIAN ALDISS
Brian Aldiss, A Bibliography, 1954-62, by Margaret Manson, Dryden Press, 1962.

NELSON ALGREN
Nelson Algren: A Descriptive Bibliography, by Matthew J. Bruccoli, Univ of Pittsburgh Press, 1985.

GRANT ALLEN
Grant Allen: Hill-Top Philosopher: A Working Bibliography, by Phil Stephensen-Payne & Virgil Utter, Galactic Central Publications, 1999.

MARGERY ALLINGHAM
Ink in Her Blood: The Life & Crime Fiction of Margery Allingham, by Richard Martin, U.M.I. Research Press, 1988.

ERIC AMBLER
Eric Ambler, by Peter Lewis, Continuum, [n.d., c.1990.]
'Heroes Among Us: Eric Ambler's Novels of Intrigue', by Katherine Kominis, *F:TBCM*, June 1993, Vol.3, No.6, pps.24-19.

KINGSLEY AMIS
Kingsley Amis, A Checklist, by Jack Benoit Gohn, Kent State Univ Press, 1976.

MARTIN AMIS
Bruce Chatwin, Martin Amis, Julian Barnes, A Bibliography of their First Editions, by David Rees, Colophon Press, 1992.

ANNE ANDERSON
www.blpc.bl.uk

HANS CHRISTIAN ANDERSEN
'Hans Christian Andersen', by Richard Dalby, *B&MC*, No.254, April 2005, pps.36-52.

SHERWOOD ANDERSON
Sherwood Anderson: A Bibliography, by Eugene Sheehy and Kenneth Lohf, The Talisman Press, 1960.

MAYA ANGELOU
www.fantasticfiction.co.uk/a/maya-angelou

EDWARD ARDIZZONE
Edward Ardizzone, a preliminary hand-list of His Illustrated Books (1929-1970), by Brian Alderson, The Private Library, second series, Vol.5, No.1, Spring 1972.

MICHAEL ARLEN
Michael Arlen, by Henry Keyishian, Twayne, 1975.

DAISY ASHFORD
Daisy Ashford - Her Life, by R.M. Malcomson, Chatto & Windus/Hogarth Press, 1984.

ISAAC ASIMOV
Science Fiction and Fantasy Authors, A Bibliography of First Printings of Their Fiction, by Lloyd Currey, Rb Publishing, 2002 (cd rom).

MABEL LUCIE ATTWELL
Mabel Lucie Attwell, by Chris Beetles, Joseph, 1988

MARGARET ATWOOD
'A Preliminary Checklist of Writings by and About Margaret Atwood', by Alan J. Horne, *Malahat Review*, No.41, Univ of Victoria, 1977.

W.H. AUDEN
W.H. Auden: A Bibliography 1924-69, by B.C. Bloomfield and Edward Mendelson, Univ of Virginia Press, 1973.

JANE AUSTEN
Jane Austen: A Bibliography by Geoffrey Keynes, Nonesuch Press, 1929.

PAUL AUSTER
www.fantasticfiction.co.uk/a/paul-auster

REV. W. AWDRY & CHRISTOPHER AWDRY
The Thomas the Tank Engine Man, by Brian Sibley, Heinemann, 1995.

ALAN AYCKBOURN: http://www.alanayckbourn.net/

H.C. BAILEY
DF:TCG, by John Cooper and B.A. Pike, Scolar Press, 1994, pps.21-23.

BERYL BAINBRIDGE
'Beryl Bainbridge', by Martin Spence, *B&MC*, No.134, May 1995, pps.18-26.

FRANK BAKER
'Frank Baker: A Centenary Tribute', by Mark Valentine, *B&MC*, No.199, October 2008, pps.72-80.

JAMES BALDWIN
www.fantasticfiction.co.uk/b/james-baldwin

R.M. BALLANTYNE
R.M. Ballantyne, A Bibliography of First Editions, by Eric Quayle, Dawsons of Pall Mall, 1968.

J.G. BALLARD
Science Fiction and Fantasy Authors, A Bibliography of First Printings of Their Fiction, by Lloyd Currey, Rb Publishing, 2002 (cd rom).

IAIN BANKS
'Iain Banks', by David Howard, *B&MC*, No.148, July 1996, pps.76-85.

HELEN BANNERMAN
Sambo Sahib, The Story of Helen Bannerman, by Elizabeth Hay, Paul Harris, 1981.

JOHN BANVILLE
'John Banville', by David Howard, *B&MC*, No.215, February 2002, pps.110-119.

CICELY MARY BARKER
St James Guide to Children's Writers, St James Press, 1999 (fifth edition), pps.65.66.

CLIVE BARKER
Shadows in Eden, by Clive Barker and Stephen Jones, Underwood, 1991.

PAT BARKER
'Pat Barker', by Jane Roscoe, *B&MC*, No.176, November 1998, pps.86-94.

ROBERT BARNARD
DF:TCG, by John Cooper and B.A. Pike, Scolar Press, 1994, pps.23-25.

DJUNA BARNES
Djuna Barnes: A Bibliography, by Douglas Messeri, David Lewis, 1975.

JULIAN BARNES
Bruce Chatwin, Martin Amis, Julian Barnes, A Bibliography of their First Editions, David Rees, Colophon Press, 1992.

J.M. BARRIE
Sir James M. Barrie: A Bibliography, by B.D. Cutler, Franklin, 1931.

JOHN BARTH
John Bath: An Annotated Bibliography, by Richard AllanVine, The Scarecrow Press, Inc, 1977.

DONALD BARTHELME
Donald Barthelme: A Comprehensive Bibliography and Annotated Secondary Checklist, by Jerome Klinkowitz, Asa Pieratt and Robert Murray, Archon Books / The Shoe String Press, 1977.

H.E. BATES
A Bibliographical Study, by Peter Eades, St Paul's Bibliographies, 1990.

L. FRANK BAUM
Bibliographia Oziana, by Douglas G. Greene and Peter Hanff, The International Wizard of Oz Club, 1988.

'BB'
BB: A Celebration, by Tom Quinn (ed.), including a Bibliography by Tim Scott, Wharncliffe Publishing, 1993.

THE BEANO
The Hamer Comic Annual Guide, No.1, by Martin Hamer, Hamer 20th Century Books, 2000.

AUBREY BEARDSLEY
A Selective Checklist of the Published Wortks of Aubrey Beardsley, by Mark Samuels Lasner, Boston, 1995.

SAMUEL BECKETT
No Symbols Where None Intended, Carlton Lake, Humanities Research Center, 1984.

WILLIAM BECKFORD
A Bibliography of William Beckford of Fonthill, by Chapman, G. & Hodgkin, J., Constable, 1930.

FRANCIS BEEDING
'Hilary Saunders and Francis Beeding', by A.R. James, *B&MC*, No.152, November 1996, pps.52-62.

MAX BEERBOHM
A Bibliography of the Works of Max Beerbohm, by A.E. Gallatin and L.M. Oliver, Hart Davis, 1952.

BRENDAN BEHAN
Brendan, by Ulick O'Connor, Prentice Hall, 1971.

JOSEPHINE BELL
DF:TCG, by John Cooper and B.A. Pike, Scolar Press, 1994, pps.25-28.

GEORGE BELLAIRS
'George Bellairs: The Banker of Crime', by David Blake, *B&MC*, No.300, November 2008, pps.84-92.

HILLAIRE BELLOC
The English First Editions of Hillaire Belloc, by Patrick Cahill, published in London, 1953.

SAUL BELLOW
Bellow: A Comprehensive Bibliography, by B.A. Sokoloff and Mark E. Posner, Folcroft Library Editions, 1974.

LUDWIG BEMELMANS
Ludwig Bemelmans: A Bibliography, by Murray Pomerance, Heinemann, 1993.

ALAN BENNETT
'Alan Bennett', by Colin Wiles, **B&MC**, No.157, April 1997, pps.50-60.

ARNOLD BENNETT
Bennett, A Bibliography, by Norman Emery, Central Library, Stoke-on-Trent, 1967.

E.F. BENSON
The Life of E.F. Benson, by Brian Masters, Chatto & Windus, 1991.

E.C. BENTLEY
DF:TCG, by John Cooper and B.A. Pike, Scolar Press, 1994, pps.28-30.

THOMAS BERGER
www.fantasticfiction.co.uk/b/thomas-berger

ANTHONY BERKELEY
The Bibliography of Crime Fiction, 1749-1975, Allen J. Hubin, Publisher's Inc., 1979.

LORD BERNERS
'Lord Berners: Author and Eccentic', by Mark Valentine, **B&MC**, No.170, May 1998, pps.58-67.

JOHN BETJEMAN
Sir John Betjeman: A Bibliography of Writings By and About Him, by Margaret L. Stapleton, Scarecrow Press, 1974.

A.I. BEZZIRIDES
'Collecting A.I. Bezzerides', by Robin H. Smiley, **F:TBCM**, June 2003, Vol.13, No.6, pps.36-43.

AMBROSE BIERCE
Ambrose Bierce: A Bibliography, by Vincent Starrett, The Centaur Book Shop, 1929

EARL DERR BIGGERS
Earl Derr Biggers' Charlie Chan, by Otto Penzler, Mysterious Bookshop, c1999.

R.D. BLACKMOOR
'Lorna Doone', by David Ashford, **B&MC**, No.202, January 2001, pps.86-99.

ALGERNON BLACKWOOD
Algernon Blackwood, A Bio-Bibliography, by Mike Ashley, Greenwood Press, 1987.

NICHOLAS BLAKE *see C. Day Lewis*

ROBERT BLOCH
The Complete Robert Bloch, by Randall D. Larson, Fandom Unlimited, 1977.

EDMUND BLUNDEN
A Bibliography of Edmund Blunden, by B.J. Kirkpatrick, Clarendon Press, 1989.

ENID BLYTON
A Comprehensive Bibliography of the Books of Enid Blyton 1922-1970, by Tony Summerfield, 1997.

NELSON S. BOND
'Nelson S. Bond', by Mike Ashley, **B&MC**, No.221, August 2002, pps.54-64.

LUCY M. BOSTON
'Lucy M. Boston', by Daphne Stroud, **B&MC**, No.104, November 1992, pps.16-22.

ELIZABETH BOWEN
Elizabeth Bowen, by Jocelyn Brooke, Longmans, 1952.

JANE BOWLES
www.paulbowles.org/janebooks.html

PAUL BOWLES
Paul Bowles: A Descriptive Bibliography, by Jeffrey Miller, Black Sparrow Press, 1986.

WILLIAM BOYD
'The Novels of William Boyd', by David Howard, **B&MC**, No.81, December 1990, pps.18-22.

KAY BOYLE
Kay Boyle: A Bibliography, by Clark Chambers, Oak Knoll Press, 2001.

MALCOLM BRADBURY
www.fantasticfiction.co.uk/b/malcolm-bradbury

RAY BRADBURY
The Ray Bradbury Companion by William F. Nolan, Bruccoli Clark/Gale Research, 1975.

JOHN BRAINE
'John Braine', by Kenneth Fields, **B&MC**, No.86, May 1991, pps.28-35.

ERNEST BRAMAH
'Ernest Bramah', by Mark Valentine, **B&MC**, No.160, July 1997, pps.40-49.

CHRISTIANNA BRAND
'Christiana Brand: A Centeneray Tribute', by David Blake, **B&MC**, No.288, December 2007, pps.40-49.

RICHARD BRAUTIGAN
Richard Brautigan: An Annotated Bibliography, by John F. Barber, McFarland, 1990.

ANGELA BRAZIL
'The Schoolgirl Stories of Angela Brazil', by Katharine Gunn, **B&MC**, No.74, May 1990, pps.23-30.

ELINOR BRENT-DYER
Behind the Chalet School, by Helen McClelland, Bettany Press, 1996.

ANNE, CHARLOTTE & EMILY BRONTË
A Bibliography of the Writings of the Brönte Family, by Thomas J. Wise, Dawsons of Pall Mall, 1917.

JOCELYN BROOKE
'Jocelyn Brooke', by Colin Scott-Sutherland, **B&MC**, No.176, November 1998, pps.64-75.

RUPERT BROOKE
A Bibliography of the Works of Rupert Brooke, by Geoffrey Keynes, Hart Davis, 1964.

ANITA BROOKNER
'Anita Brookner: An 80th Birthday Tribute', by Nicola Lisle, **B&MC**, No.296, July 2008, pps.64-73.

DAN BROWN
'The Great Quest', by Mark Valentine, **B&MC**, No.269, June 2006, pps.36-46.

FREDRIC BROWN
A Key to Fredric Brown's Wonderland, by Newton Baird, Talisman Press, 1981.

ELIZABETH BARRETT BROWNING
A Bibliography of the Writings in Prose and Verse of Elizabeth Barrett Browning, by Wise, Thomas J., Printed for Private Circulation Only by Richard Clay & Sons, Ltd, 1918.

ROBERT BROWNING
Robert Browning: A Bibliography, 1830-1850, by Broughton, Leslie Nathan, et al., Cornell Univ Press, [1953]

JEAN de BRUNHOFF
The Art of Babar: the Work of Jean and Laurent de Brunhoff, Abrams, by Nicholas Fox Weber, 1999.

BILL BRYSON
'The Travel Books of Bill Bryson', by David Howard, **B&MC**, No.199, October 2008, pps.28-38.

JOHN BUCHAN
The First Editions of John Buchan, by Robert Blanchard, Archon, 1981.

ANTHONY BUCKERIDGE
The Jennings Companion, by David Bathurst, Summersdale, 1995.

CHARLES BUKOWSKI
A Bibliography of Charles Bukowski, by Charles Bukowski & Sanford Dorbin, Black Sparrow, 1969.
A Descriptive Bibliography of the Primary Publications of Charles Bukowski, by Aaron Krumhansl, Black Sparrow, 1999.

MIKHAIL BULGAKOV
Mikhail Bulgakov In English: A Bibliography 1891-1991, by Garth M. Terry, Astra Press, 1991

ANTHONY BURGESS
Anthony Burgess: A Bibliography, by Paul W. Boytinck, West, 1978.

JAMES LEE BURKE
'Collecting James Lee Burke', by Robin H. Smiley, **F:TBCM**, July 1991, Vol.1, No.7, pps.16-19.

W.J. BURLEY
DF:TCG, by John Cooper and B.A. Pike, Scolar Press, 1994, pps.55-56.

FRANCES HODGSON BURNETT
Frances Hodgson Burnett, by Phyllis Bixler, Twayne, 1984.

W.R. BURNETT
'Collecting W.R. Burnett', by Robin H. Smiley, **F:TBCM**, January 2002, Vol.12, No.1, pps.22-51 and February 2002, Vol.12, No.2, pps.22-51.

FANNY BURNEY
Fanny Burney: A Biography, by Clare Harman, HarperCollins, 2000.
ROBERT BURNS
A Bibliography of Robert Burns, by J.W. Egerer, Oliver & Boyd, 1965.
EDGAR RICE BURROUGHS
A Golden Anniversary Bibliography of Edgar Rice Burroughs, by Henry Hardy Heins, Donald Grant, 1964.
Edgar Rice Burroughs: The Exhaustive Scholar's and Collector's Descriptive Bibliography of American Periodical, Hardcover, Paperback and Reprint Editions, by Robert B. Zeuschner, McFarland, 1996.
WILLIAM S. BURROUGHS
William S. Burroughs: A Bibliography 1953-1973, by Joe Maynard and Barry Miles, Univ Press of Virginia, 1978.
ROBERT BURTON
Bibliographia Burtoniana: a Study of Robert Burton's The Anatomy of Melancholy with a Bibliography, by Paul Jordan-Smith, Stanford Univ Press, 1931.
CHRISTOPHER BUSH
DF:TCG, by John Cooper and B.A. Pike, Scolar Press, 1994, pps.57-60.
A.S. BYATT
A.S. Byatt, by Kathleen Coyne Kelly, Twayne, 1996.
LORD BYRON
A Bibliography of the Writings in Verse and Prose ..., by T.J. Wise, Privately Printed, London, 1933.
JAMES M. CAIN
'Collecting James M. Cain', by Robin H. Smiley and Christine Bell, *F:TBCM*, June 1995, Vol.5, No.6, pps.34-42.
PAUL CAIN
www.fantasticfiction.co.uk/c/paul-cain
RANDOLPH CALDECOTT
'Randolph Caldecott', by William H.P. Crewdson, *Antiquarian Book Monthly*, May 2000, pps32-36.
ALBERT CAMUS
Camus: A Bibliography, edited by Robert F. Roeming, Univ of Wisconsin Press, 1968.
TRUMAN CAPOTE
Truman Capote, A Checklist, by Kenneth Starosciak, Starosciak, 1974.
PETER CAREY
'Peter Carey', by David Howard, *B&MC*, No.169, April 1998, pps.30-39.
J.L. CARR
'The Books of J.L. Carr', by David Howard, *B&MC*, No.235, October 2003, pps.46-57.
JOHN DICKSON CARR
DF:TCG, by John Cooper and B.A. Pike, Scolar Press, 1994, pps.65-74.
LEWIS CARROLL
A Bibliography of the Writings of Lewis Carroll, by Sidney Herbert Williams, Bookman's Journal, 1924.
RACHEL CARSON
www.rachelcarson.org
ANGELA CARTER
Angela Carter, by Allison Lee, Twayne, 1997.
RAYMOND CARVER
'Collecting Raymond Carver', by Charles Michaud, *F:TBCM*, June 2002, Vol.12, No.6, pps.26-33.
JOYCE CARY
Joyce Cary: A Descriptive Bibliography, by Merja Makinen, Mansell, 1989.
WILLA CATHER
Willa Cather: A Bibliography, by Joan Crane, Univ of Nebraska Press, 1982.
NICK CAVE
www.fantasticfiction.co.uk/c/nick-cave
RAYMOND CHANDLER
Raymond Chandler: A Descriptive Bibliography, by Matthew J. Bruccoli, Univ of Pittsburgh Press, 1979.
LESLIE CHARTERIS
The Saint and Leslie Charteris, by W.O.G. Lofts and Derek Adey, Baker, 1970.

BRUCE CHATWIN
Bruce Chatwin, Martin Amis, Julian Barnes, A Bibliography of their First Editions, David Rees, Colophon Press, 1992.
GEOFFREY CHAUCER
Chaucer, A Bibliographical Manual, by E.P. Hammond, Peter Smith, 1933.
JOHN CHEEVER
'John Cheever: A Bibliographical Checklist', *American Book Collector*, Vol.7, No.8, New Series, August 1986.
G.K. CHESTERTON
G.K. Chesterton: A Bibliography, by John Sullivan, Univ of London Press, 1958.
PETER CHEYNEY
The Bibliography of Crime Fiction, 1749-1975, by Allen J. Hubin, 1979, pps.78-79.
AGATHA CHRISTIE
A Talent to Deceive: An Appreciation of Agatha Christie, by Robert Barnard, Collins, 1980.
WINSTON CHURCHILL
A Bibliography of the Works of Sir Winston Churchill, by Frederick Woods, Nicholas Vane, 1963.
TOM CLANCY
The Tom Clancy Companion, by Tom Clancy and Martin H. Greenberg, Fontana, 1992.
JOHN CLARE
'Nature Poet, John Clare', by F.N. Crack, *B&MC*, No.113, August 1993, pps.50-57.
ARTHUR C. CLARKE
Science Fiction and Fantasy Authors, A Bibliography of First Printings of Their Fiction, by Lloyd Currey, Rb Publishing, 2002 (cd rom).
HARRY CLARKE
A Bibliographical Checklist of the Work of Harry Clarke, by M. Steenson, Books & Things, London 2003.
MARY HIGGINS CLARK
www.fantasticfiction.co.uk/c/mary-higgins-clark
JAMES CLAVELL
www.fantasticfiction.co.uk/c/james-clavell
ROBERT M. COATES
www.fantasticfiction.co.uk/c/robert-m-coates
WILLIAM COBBETT
William Cobbett: A Bibliographical Account of His Life and Times, by M.L. Pearl, O.U.P., 1953.
LIZA CODY
'Liza Cody', by David Howard, *B&MC*, No.166, January 1998, pps.58-67.
J.M. COETZEE
J.M. Coetzee: A Bibliography, by Kevin Goddard & Jon Read,: National English Literary Museum, 1990.
SAMUEL TAYLOR COLERIDGE
A Bibliography of the Writings in Prose and Verse..., by Thomas J. Wise, The Bibliographical Society, 1913.
EOIN COLFER
www.fantasticfiction.co.uk/c/eoin-colfer
JOHN COLLIER
Science Fiction and Fantasy Authors, A Bibliography of First Printings of Their Fiction, by Lloyd Currey, Rb Publishing, 2002 (cd rom).
WILKIE COLLINS
Wilkie Collins: An Annotated Bibliography, 1889-1976, by Kirk H. Beetz, Scarecrow Press, 1978.
IVY COMPTON-BURNETT
Secrets of a Woman's Heart, by Hilary Spurling, Hodder & Stoughton, 1984.
MICHAEL CONNELLY
'Michael Connelly', by David Howard, *B&MC*, No.217, April 2002, pps.78-88.
CYRIL CONNOLLY
'Cyril Connolly, Critic and Novelist', by Kevin Nudd, *B&MC*, No.85, April 1991, pps.39-46.
JOSEPH CONRAD
A Bibliography of the Writings of Joseph Conrad 1895-1921, by Thomas J. Wise, Dawsons of Pall Mall, 1972.
PAT CONROY
www.fantasticfiction.co.uk/c/pat-conroy

JAMES FENNIMORE COOPER
A Descriptive Bibliography of the writings of James Fenimore Cooper, by Robert E Spiller and Philip C. Blackburn, R.R. Bowker, 1934.

A.E. COPPARD
The First Editions of A.E. Coppard, A.P Herbert and Charles Morgan, by Gilbert H. Fabes, Myers, 1933.

BERNARD CORNWELL
'A Bernard Cornwell Checklist', by Elizabeth Wessels and Jennifer Busick, *F:TBCM*, March 1999, Vol.9, No.3, pps.56-57.

PATRICIA CORNWELL
'Patricia Cornwell', *Breese's Guide to Modern First Editions*, Martin Breese, Breese Books, 1999, pps.247-249.

HUBERT CRACKANTHORPE
http://en.wikipedia.org/wiki/Hubert_Crackanthorpe

STEPHEN CRANE
'Collecting Stephen Crane', by Michael Quigley, *F:TBCM*, January 1996, Vol.6, No.1, pps.30-42.

WALTER CRANE
A Bibliography of the First Editions of Books Illustrated by Walter Crane, by Gertrude C.E. Masse, published in London, 1933.

JOHN CREASEY
John Creasey In Print, Hodder & Stoughton, 1969.

HARRY CREWS
Harry Crews: A First Bibliography, by Michael Hargraves, Michael Hargraves, 1981.

MICHAEL CRICHTON
'Michael Crichton', by Richard Dalby, *B&MC*, No.114, September 1993, pps.22-30.

EDMUND CRISPIN
DF:TCG, by John Cooper and B.A. Pike, Scolar Press, 1994, pps.97-98.

FREEMAN WILLS CROFTS
DF:TCG, by John Cooper and B.A. Pike, Scolar Press, 1994, pps.98-101.

RICHMAL CROMPTON
'Richmal Crompton', *Breese's Guide to Modern First Editions*, Martin Breese, Breese Books, 1999, pps.41-47.

HARRY CROSBY
Black Sun, The Brief Transit and Violent Eclipse of Harry Crosby, Geoffrey Wolff, Hamish Hamilton, 1976.
A Bibliography of the Black Sun Press, by George Robert Minkoff, Minkoff, 1970.

ALEISTER CROWLEY
Bibliography of the Published Works of Aleister Crowley, by Gerald Yorke, Black Cat Books, 2002.

JAMES CRUMLEY
www.fantasticfiction.co.uk/c/james-crumley/

COUNTEE CULLEN
A Bio-bibliography of Countee P. Cullen, by Margaret Perry, Greenwood, 1971.

E.E. CUMMINGS
E.E. Cummings, A Bibliography, George J. Firmage, Wesleyan Univ Press, 1960.

ROALD DAHL
'Roald Dahl', *Breese's Guide to Modern First Editions*, Martin Breese, Breese Books, 1999, pps.48-53.

CHARLES DARWIN
'Charles Darwin and Origin of Species', by Rupert Neelands, *B&MC*, No.249, December 2004, pps.66-79.

ROBERTSON DAVIES
'A Life Deeply lived: Collecting Robertson Davies', by John Conrad, *F:TBCM*, January 2001, Vol.11, No.1, pps.36-49.

W.H. DAVIES
W.H. Davies A Bibliography, by Sylvia Harlow, Oak Knoll Pr, 1993.

THE DANDY
The Hamer Comic Annual Guide, No.1, by Martin Hamer, Hamer 20th Century Books, 2000.

LINDSEY DAVIS
'Lindsey Davis', *Breese's Guide to Modern First Editions*, Martin Breese, Breese Books, 1999, pps.271-273

C. DAY LEWIS
C. Day Lewis, the Poet Laureate: A Bibliography by Geoffrey Handley-Taylor and Timothy d'Arch Smith, St James Press, 1968.
DF:TCG, by John Cooper and B.A. Pike, Scolar Press, 1994, pps.33-35.

LOUIS DE BERNIÈRES
'Louis de Bernières', by David Howard, *B&MC*, No.207, June 2001, pps.71-80.

WALTER DE LA MARE
Walter de la Mare: A Checklist Prepared on the Occasion of an Exhibition of His Books . . ., National Book League, 1956.

DON DELILLO
www.perival.com/delillo/ddbiblio.html

THOMAS DE QUINCEY
Thomas de Quincey. A Bibliography based upon the De Quincey Collection in the Moss Side Library, by J.A. Green, Free Reference Library & Moss Side Library, Manchester, 1908.

DANIEL DEFOE
A Checklist of the Writings of Daniel Defoe, by J.R. Moore, Archon Books, 1971 (second edition).

LEN DEIGHTON
Len Deighton: An Annotated Bibliography 1954-1985, by Edward Milward-Oliver, Sammler Press, 1985.
The Len Deighton Companion, by Edward Milford-Oliver, Grafton, 1987.

ANITA DESAI
www.fantasticfiction.co.uk/d/anita-desai

KIRAN DESAI
www.fantasticfiction.co.uk/d/kiran-desai/

MAURICE & EDWARD DETMOLD
The Fantastic Creatures of Edward Julius Detmold, edited by David Larkin, Peacock Press/Bantam Books, 1976.

COLIN DEXTER
'Colin Dexter and Peter Lovesey', *Breese's Guide to Modern First Editions*, Martin Breese, Breese Books, 1999, pps.54-60.

MICHAEL DIBDIN
'The Detective Fiction of Michael Dibdin', by David Howard, *B&MC*, No.150, September 1996, pps.60-67.

PHILIP K. DICK
PKD: A Philip K. Dick Bibliography by Daniel J.H. Levack, Underwood/Miller, 1981.

CHARLES DICKENS
The First Editions of the Writings of Charles Dickens, by John C. Eckel, published in Folkestone, 1993.
Charles Dickens in the Original Cloth: A Bibliographical Catalogue, Part I and II, by Walter E. Smith, Heritage Book Shop, 1982.

EMILY DICKINSON
Emily Dickinson: A Descriptive Bibliography, by Joel Myerson, Univ of Pittsburgh Press, 1984.

ISAK DINESEN
Isak Dinesen: A Bibliography, by Liselotte Henriksen, Univ of Chicago Press (Chicago), 1977.

BENJAMIN DISRAELI
Excursions in Victorian Bibliography, by M. Sadleir, Chaundy & Cox, 1922.

E.L. DOCTOROW
E.L. Doctorow: An Annotated Bibliography, by Michelle M. Tokarczyk and E.L. Doctorow, Taylor & Francis, 1988.

DAVID DODGE
'Nothing is Certain: Collecting David Dodge', by Robin H. Smiley, *F:TBCM*, April 2002, Vol.12, No.4, pps.36-49.

J.P. DONLEAVY
'J.P. Donleavy', by Colin Overall, *B&MC*, No.205, April 2001, pps.55-64.

LORD ALFRED DOUGLAS
'The Poetry of Lord Alfred Douglas', by John Stratford, *B&MC*, No.133, April 1995, pps.66-77.

GUSTAV DORÉ
Gustave Doré: Adrift on Dreams of Splendour, by Dan Malan, Malan Classical Enterprises, 1995.

JOHN DOS PASSOS
John DOS Passos: A Comprehensive Bibliography, by David Sanders, Taylor & Francis, 1987.

NORMAN DOUGLAS
A Bibliography of the Writings of Norman Douglas, by Edward D. McDonald, Centaur Book Shop, 1927.
ERNEST DOWSON
Bibliographies of Modern Authors, Second Series, C.A. & H.W. Stonehill, John Castle, 1925.
ARTHUR CONAN DOYLE
A Bibliographical Catalogue of the Writings of Sir Arthur Conan Doyle 1879-1928, by H. Locke, published in London, 1929.
A Bibliography of A. Conan Doyle, by Richard Lancelyn Green and John Michael Gibson, Clarendon Press, 1983.
RODDY DOYLE
'Roddy Doyle', by David Howard, *B&MC*, No.225, December 2002, pps.66-76.
MARGARET DRABBLE
Margaret Drabble:An Annotated Bibliography, by Joan Garrett Packer, Garland, 1988.
THEODORE DREISER
A Bibliography of the Writings of Theodore Dreiser, by Edward D. McDonald, Burt Franklin, 1968.
EDMUND DULAC
Edmund Dulac: His Book Illustrations: A Bibliography, by Anne Connolly Hughey, Buttonwood Press, 1995.
DAPHNE DU MAURIER
'The Early Books of Daphne du Maurier', by Tim Scott, *B&MC*, No.71, February 1990, pps.5-13.
'The Post-War Books of Daphne du Maurier', by Tim Scott, *B&MC*, No.90, September 1991, pps.34-44.
GEORGE DU MAURIER
'George du Maurier', by Brian Jones, *B&MC*, No.85, April 1991, pps.48-57.
LORD DUNSANY
Lord Dunsany: A Bibliography, by S.T. Joshi and Darrell Schweitzer, Scarecrow Press, 1993.
FRANCIS DURBRIDGE
The Bibliography of Crime Fiction, 1749-1975, by Allen J. Hubin, Publisher's Inc., 1979.
GERALD DURRELL
'Gerald Durrell', by Tim Scott, *B&MC*, No.68, November 1998, pps.45-52.
LAWRENCE DURRELL
Lawrence Durrell, A Study, by G.S. Fraser and Alan G. Thomas, Faber, 1968.
UMBERTO ECO
www2.dsc.unibo.it/dipartimento/people/eco
BERESFORD EGAN
Beresford Egan, by Adrian Woodhouse, Tartarus Press, 2005.
GEORGE ELIOT
George Eliot in Original Cloth: A Bibliographical Catalogue, by Brian Lake and Janet Nassau, Jarndyce Antiquarian Books, 1988.
T.S. ELIOT
T.S. Eliot: A Bibliography, by Donald Gallup, Faber, 1969.
ALICE THOMAS ELLIS
www.cas.sc.edu/engl/LitCheck/ellis.htm
BRET EASTON ELLIS
www.randomhouse.com/kvpa/eastonellis
RALPH ELLISON
A Ralph Waldo Ellison Bibliography (1914-1967), by R.S. Lillard, American Book Collector 1968.
JAMES ELLROY
www.fantasticfiction.co.uk/e/james-ellroy
ANNE ENRIGHT
www.fantasticfiction.co.uk/e/anne-enright
JOHN MEADE FALKNER
'John Meade Falkner', by Mark Valentine and Richard Dalby, *B&MC*, No.141, December 1995, pps.68-77.
G.E. FARROW
'G.E. Farrow', by Colin Scott-Sutherland, *B&MC*, No.146, May 1996, pps.58-68.
WILLIAM FAULKNER
Each in Its Ordered Place: A Faulkner Collector's Notebook, by Carl Petersen, Ardis, 1975.
SEBASTIAN FAULKS
'Sebastian Faulks', by David Howard, *B&MC*, No.216, March 2002, pps.64-74.

ELIZABETH FERRARS
DF:TCG, by John Cooper and B.A. Pike, Scolar Press, 1994, pps.121-124.
HENRY FIELDING
Henry Fielding: An Annotated Bibliography, by George H. Hahn, Scarecrow Press, 1979.
RONALD FIRBANK
A Bibliography of Ronald Firbank, by Miriam J. Benkowitz, Hart Davis, 1963.
Supplement to a Bibliography of Ronald Firbank, by Miriam J. Benkowitz, Enitharmon Press, 1980.
MARY FITT
'The Detective Novels of Mary Fitt', by David Blake, *B&MC*, No.268, May 2006, pps.60-68.
F. SCOTT FITZGERALD
Scott Fitzgerald: A Descriptive Bibliography, by Judith S. Baughman and Matthew J. Bruccoli, Gale, 1999.
PENELOPE FITZGERALD
'Penelope Fitzgerald', by David Howard, *B&MC*, No.153, December 1996, pps.70-78.
JAMES ELROY FLECKER
Modern British Authors, Their First Editions, Cutler and Stiles, Allen & Unwin, 1930.
IAN FLEMING
'The James Bond Books of Ian Fleming: A Descriptive Bibliography', by Lee Biondi and James M. Pickard, *F:TBCM*, November 1998, Vol.8, No.11, pps.38-51.
W. RUSSELL FLINT
More Than Shadows: A Biography of W. Russell Flint, by Arnold Palmer, The Studio, 1943.
FORD MADOX FORD
Ford Madox Ford, 1873-1939, by David Dow Harvey, Gordian Press, 1972.
C.S. FORESTER
C.S. Forester, by Allen and Patricia Ahearn, Quill & Brush, 1995.
E.M. FORSTER
A Bibliography of E.M. Forster, by B.J. Kirkpatrick, Clarendon Press, 1985.
FREDERICK FORSYTH
'Frederick Forsyth', by Craig Cabell, *B&MC*, No.203, February 2001, pps.4-12.
DION FORTUNE
'Dion Fortune: Mystic and Novelist', by Mark Valentine, *B&MC*, No.142, January 1996, pps.40-47.
JOHN FOWLES
'John Fowles', *Breese's Guide to Modern First Editions*, Martin Breese, Breese Books, 1999, pps.70-74.
ANNE FRANK
Anne Frank and After: Dutch holocaust literature in historical perspective, by Dick van Galen Last, Amsterdam Univ Press, c.1996
DICK FRANCIS
'Collecting Dick Francis', by Sheldon McArthur, *F:TBCM*, July/August 1993, Vol.3, No.7/8, pps.24-29.
GEORGE MACDONALD FRASER
'Collecting George MacDonald Fraser', by Kathryn Smiley, *F:TBCM*, February 1992, Vol.2, No.2, pps.20-25.
R. AUSTIN FREEMAN
DF:TCG, by John Cooper and B.A. Pike, Scolar Press, 1994, pps.137-141.
ROBERT FROST
Robert Frost: A Bibliography, by W.B.S. Clymer and C.R. Green, published in Amherst, 1937.
Robert Frost: A Descriptive Catalogue, by Joan Crane, Charlottesville, 1975.
WILLIAM GADDIS
www.fantasticfiction.co.uk/g/william-gaddis
GABRIEL GARCÍA MÁRQUEZ
'Collecting Gabriel García Márquez', by Don Klein, *F:TBCM*, February 1993, Vol.3, No.2, pps.24-30.
ERLE STANLEY GARDNER
Erle Stanley Gardner: A Checklist, by E.H. Mundell, Kent State Univ Press, 1968.
JOHN GARDNER
'Collecting John Gardner', by Clair Schilz, *F:TBCM*, April 1999, Vol.9, No.4, pps.36-43.

JOHN GARDNER
'John Gardner', by David Whitehead, *B&MC*, No.89, August 1991, pps.28-35.
ALAN GARNER
A Fine Anger: A Critical Introduction to the Work of Alan Garner, by Neil Philip, Collins, 1981.
DAVID GARNETT
'David Garnett', by George Jefferson, *B&MC*, No.97, April 1992, pps.24-32.
EVE GARNETT
'Eve Garnett', by June Hopper, *B&MC*, No.162, September 1997, pps.48-58.
JONATHAN GASH
'The 'Lovejoy' Novels of Jonathan Gash', by David Howard, *B&MC*, No.95, February 1992, pps.40-47.
ELIZABETH GASKELL
Elizabeth C. Gaskell: A Bibliographical Catalogue of First and Early Editions 1848-1866, by Walter E. Smith, Heritage Book Shop, 1998.
ROBERT GIBBINGS
Robert Gibbings: A Bibliography, by Agnes M. Kirkus, Dent, 1962.
LEWIS GRASSIC GIBBON
'Lewis Grassic Gibbon', by Mark Valentine, *B&MC*, No.203, February 2001, pps.40-50.
STELLA GIBBONS
'Stella Gibbons', by Crispin Jackson, *B&MC*, No.130, January 1995, pps.18-26.
MAY GIBBS
'May Gibbs: Creator of the Gumnut Babies', by Barbara Richardson, *B&MC*, No.237, December 2003, pps.50-64.
ANTHONY GILBERT
www.classiccrimefiction.com/anthonygilbertbib.htm
GILES' ANNUALS
'Giles Annuals', *B&MC*, No.65, August 1989, pps.14-19.
ERIC GILL
Bibliography of Eric Gill, by Evan R Gill, Cassell, 1953.
ALLEN GINSBERG
The Works of Allen Ginsberg, 1941-1994: A Descriptive Bibliography, by Bill Morgan, Greenwood Press, 1995.
WARWICK GOBLE
'The Illustrations of Warwick Goble', by Richard Dalby, *B&MC*, No.47, February 1988, pps.58-65.
RUMER GODDEN
'Rumer Godden: Author of *Black Narcissus* and *The Peacock Spring*', by Nicola Lisle, *B&MC*, No.165, December 1997, pps.48-58.
WILLIAM GOLDING
William Golding: A Bibliography 1934-1993, by R.A. Gekoski and P.A. Grogan, Deutsch, 1991.
NADINE GORDIMER
www.fantasticfiction.co.uk/g/nadine-gordimer
RODERICK GORDON and BRIAN WILLIAMS
www.fantasticfiction.co.uk/w/roderick-gordon-and-brian-williams
EDWARD GOREY
The World of Edward Gorey, by Ross, Clifford & Wilkin, Karen, Harry N. Abrams, 1996.
ELIZABETH GOUDGE
'Elizabeth Goudge', by Nicola Lisle, *B&MC*, No.294, May 2008, pps.68-79.
SUE GRAFTON
DF:TCG, by John Cooper and B.A. Pike, Scolar Press, 1994, pps.154-155.
KENNETH GRAHAME
Beyond the Wild Wood; the World of Kenneth Grahame, by Peter Green, Webb & Bower, 1982.
GÜNTER GRASS
Günter Grass, A Bibliography 1955-1975, by Patrick O'Neill, Univ of Toronto Press, 1976.
SHIRLEY ANN GRAU
www.fantasticfiction.co.uk/g/shirley-ann-grau
ROBERT GRAVES
Robert Graves: A Bibliography, by Fred H. Higginson and William P. Williams, St Paul's Bibliographies, 1987.
ALASDAIR GRAY
Brian Moore, Alasdair Gray, John McGahern, A Bibliography of their First Editions, David Rees, Colophon Press, 1991.

ANNA KATHERINE GREEN
www.classiccrimefiction.com/anna-katharine-green.htm
HENRY GREEN
Romancing, The Life and Work of Henry Green, by Jeremy Trelown, Faber, 2000.
KATE GREENAWAY
Printed Kate Greenaway: A Catalogue Raisonné, by Thomas Schuster and Rodney Engen, T.E. Schuster, 1986.
GRAHAM GREENE
Graham Greene: A Bibliography and Guide to Research, by R.A. Woobe, Garland, 1979.
ZANE GREY
Zane Grey a Bibliography, by Frank Gruber, Walter J. Black, 1969.
JOHN GRISHAM
jgrisham.com
GEORGE & WEEDON GROSSMITH
'George and Weedon Grosmith's *The Diary of a Nobody*', by A.R. James, *B&MC*, No.78, September 1990, pps.59-67.
DAVIS GRUBB
'Collecting Davis Grubb', by Timothy P. Slongo, *F:TBCM*, January 1992, Vol.2, No.1, pps.20-24.
THOM GUNN
Thom Gunn: A Bibliography 1940-1978, by Jack W.C. Hagstrom and George Bixby, Bertram Rota, 1979.
H. RIDER HAGGARD
Bibliography of the Works of Sir Henry Rider Haggard 1856-1925, by J.E. Scott, Elkin Mathews, 1947.
KATHLEEN HALE
'Kathleen Hale', by Kevin Nudd, *B&MC*, No.170, May 1998, pps.49-57.
RADCLYFFE HALL
'Radclyffe Hall', by Katharine Gunn, *B&MC*, No.160, July 1997, pps.59-67.
PATRICK HAMILTON
'The Novels and Plays of Patrick Hamilton', by Martin Loughlin, *B&MC*, No.93, December 1991, pps.30-37.
DASHIELL HAMMETT
Dashiel Hammett: A Descriptive Bibliography, by Richard Layman, Univ of Pittsburgh Press, 1997.
THOMAS HARDY
Thomas Hardy: A Bibliographical Study, by Richard Little Purdy, O.U.P., 1968.
A Bibliography of the Works of Thomas Hardy, by A.P. Webb, Burt Franklin, 1968.
CYRIL HARE
DF:TCG, John Cooper and B.A. Pike, Scolar Press, 1994, pps.162-164.
The Bibliography of Crime Fiction, 1749-1975, Allen J. Hubin, Publisher's Inc., 1979.
JOEL CHANDLER HARRIS
Joel Chandler Harris: An Annotated Bibliography of Criticism, 1977-1996 (with *Supplement, 1892-1976*), by Hugh T. Keenan, Greenwood Press, 1997.
ROBERT HARRIS
'Robert Harris', by David Howard, *B&MC*, No.211, October 2001, pps.109-117.
THOMAS HARRIS
'Thomas Harris', by David Whitehead, *B&MC*, No.204, March 2001, pps.18-24.
L.P. HARTLEY
L.P. Hartley, by Edward T. Jones, Twayne, 1978.
L.P. Hartley, by Paul Bloomfield, Longmans, Green & Co., 1970.
JOHN HARVEY
DF:TCG, by John Cooper and B.A. Pike, Scolar Press, 1994, p.165.
NATHANIEL HAWTHORNE
Nathaniel Hawthorne: A Descriptive Bibliography, by C.E. Frazer Clark Jr., Univ of Pittsburgh Press, 1978.
SEAMUS HEANEY
Seamus Heaney: A Bibliography 1959-2003, by Rand Brandes and Michael J. Durkan, Faber, 2008.
LAFCADIO HEARN
Lafcadio Hearn: A Bibliography of His Writings, by P.D. and Ione Perkins, Houghton Mifflin Co, 1934.

ROBERT A. HEINLEIN
Robert A. Heinlein: A Bibliography, by Mark Owings, Croatan House, 1973.
JOSEPH HELLER
Three Contemporary Novelists: An Annotated Bibliography, by Robert M. Scotto, Garland, 1977.
ERNEST HEMINGWAY
Ernest Hemingway: A Comprehensive Bibliography, by André Hanneman, Princeton Univ Press, 1967 and 1975 (supplement).
G.A. HENTY
G.A. Henty: A Bibliography, by Robert L. Dartt, John Sherratt, 1971.
FRANK HERBERT
Frank Herbert: A Voice from the Desert: A Working Bibliography, by Phil Stephensen-Payne, Galactic Central Publications, 1990
JAMES HERBERT
'Collecting James Herbert', by Craig Cabell, *B&MC*, No.128, November 1994, pps.23-31.
HERGÉ
'Happy Birthday Hergé: Tintin and his creator', by Vic Pratt, *B&MC*, No.283, July 2007, pps.28-47.
EDWARD HERON-ALLEN
'Edward Heron-Allen and Christopher Blayre', by R.B. Russell, *Antiquarian Book Monthly*, May 2000, pps.18-23.
HERMANN HESSE
Hermann Hesse: Biography and Bibliography, Joseph Mileck, Calif. Univ Press, 1977 (2 vols).
GEORGETTE HEYER
DF:TCG, by John Cooper and B.A. Pike, Scolar Press, 1994, pps.166-168.
PATRICIA HIGHSMITH
Patricia Highsmith, by Russell Harrison, Twayne, 1997.
CHARLIE HIGSON
www.fantasticfiction.co.uk/h/charles-higson
JOE HILL
www.fantasticfiction.co.uk/h/joe-hill
REGINALD HILL
DF:TCG, by John Cooper and B.A. Pike, Scolar Press, 1994, pps.168-170.
TONY HILLERMAN
Tony Hillerman: From The Blessing Way to Talking God: A Bibliography, by Louis A. Hieb, Vinegar Tom Press, 1992.
JAMES HILTON
'James Hilton: Author of *Goodbye Mr Chips*', by D.C. Hogg, *B&MC*, No.72, March 1990, pps.26-32.
CHESTER HIMES
Chester Himes: :An Annotated Primary and Secondary Bibliography, by Michel Fabre, R.E. Skinner and L. Sullivan, Greenwood Press, 1992.
WILLIAM HOPE HODGSON
Science Fiction and Fantasy Authors, A Bibliography of First Printings of Their Fiction, by Lloyd Currey, Rb Publishing, 2002 (cd rom).
ALAN HOLLINGHURST
www.fantasticfiction.co.uk/h/alan-hollinghurst
NICK HORNBY
'Nick Hornby', by Kevin Nudd, *B&MC*, No.227, February 2003, pps.102-111.
E.W. HORNUNG
'E.W. Hornung: Creator of Raffles, The Gentleman Crook', by Mark Valentine, *B&MC*, No.296, July 2008, pps.74-83.
KHALED HOSSEINI
www.fantasticfiction.co.uk/h/khaled-hosseini
MICHEL HOUELLEBECQ
www.fantasticfiction.co.uk/h/michel-houellebecq
GEOFFREY HOUSEHOLD
'Geoffrey Household', by D.C. Hogg, *B&MC*, No.58, November 1989, pps.52-58.
A.E. HOUSMAN
A.E. Housman: A Bibliography, by John Carter and John Sparrow, St Paul's Bibliographies, 1982.
ELIZABETH JANE HOWARD
'Elizabeth Jane Howard', by David Howard, *B&MC*, No.65, August 1989, pps.66-71.

ROBERT E. HOWARD
'Collecting Robert E. Howard', by Don Herron, *F:TBCM*, July/August 2000, Vol.10, No.7/8, pps.26-41.
L. RON HUBBARD
Science Fiction and Fantasy Authors, A Bibliography of First Printings of Their Fiction, by Lloyd Currey, Rb Publishing, 2002 (cd rom).
LANGSTON HUGHES
Langston Hughes: A Bio-Bibliography, by Thomas A. Mikolyzk, Greenwood Press, 1990.
RICHARD HUGHES
Richard Hughes: Novelist, by Richard Poole, Poetry Wales Press, 1987.
TED HUGHES
Ted Hughes: A Bibliography 1946-1995, by Keith M. Sagar and Stephen Tabor, Mansell, 1998 (second edition).
ZORA NEALE HURSTON
Zora Neale Hurston: An Annotated Bibliography and Reference Guide, by Rose Parkman Davis, Greenwood Press, 1997.
FERGUS HUME
'Pergus Hume: Mystery Man', by Jeremy Parrott, *B&MC*, No.232, July 2003, pps.38-50.
ALDOUS HUXLEY
Aldous Huxley: A Bibliography 1916-1959, by Claire John Eschelbach and Joyce Lee Shober, Univ of California Press, 1961.
J.K. HUYSMANS
J.K. Huysmans: A Reference Guide, by G. Cevasco, Hall, 1980.
HAMMOND INNES
'The Novels of Hammond Innes', by David Whitehead, *B&MC*, No.102, September 1992, pps.14-21.
MICHAEL INNES
DF:TCG, by John Cooper and B.A. Pike, Scolar Press, 1994, pps.174-176.
JOHN IRVING
'Collecting John Irving', by Charles Michaud, *F:TBCM*, January 1999, Vol.9, No.1, pps.36-43.
WASHINGTON IRVING
Washington Irving: A Bibliography, by William R. Langfeld, New York Public Library, 1933.
CHRISTOPHER ISHERWOOD
Christopher Isherwood: A Bibliography, by Selmer Westby and Clayton M. Brown, California State College, 1968.
KAZUO ISHIGURO
'Kazuo Ishiguro: A Checklist of First Editions', by Robin H. Smiley, *F:TBCM*, March 2001, Vol.11, No.3, p 30.
SHIRLEY JACKSON
'Collecting Shirley Jackson', by Karen Smiley, *F:TBCM*, March 1991, Vol.1, No.3, pps.20-23.
W.W. JACOBS
W.W. Jacobs: A Bibliography, by C. Lamerton, Greystone Press, 1988.
HENRY JAMES
A Bibliography of Henry James, by Leon Edel and Dan H. Laurence, O.U.P., 1982.
M.R. JAMES
Science Fiction and Fantasy Authors, A Bibliography of First Printings of Their Fiction, by Lloyd Currey, Rb Publishing, 2002 (cd rom).
P.D. JAMES
'Collecting P.D. James', by Kathryn Smiley, *F:TBCM*, June 1997, Vol.7, No.6, pps.38-48.
TOVE JANSSON
'Tove Jansson: Creator of the Moomins', by June Hopper, *B&MC*, No.204, March 2001, pps.26-39.
RICHARD JEFFERIES
The Forward Life of Richard Jefferies: A Chronological Study, by H. Matthews and P. Treitel, Petton Books, 1994.
JEROME K. JEROME
Jerome K Jerome, by Ruth Marie Faurot, Twayne, 1974.
RUTH PRAWER JHABVALA
Ruth Prawer Jhabvala, by Ralph J. Crane, Twayne, 1992.
CAPTAIN W.E. JOHNS
Biggles!: The Life Story of Capt. W.E. Johns; Creator of Biggles, Worrals, Gimlet & Steeley, by Peter Berresford Ellis and Jennifer Schofield, Veloce, 1993.

B.S. JOHNSON
B.S. Johnson: A Critical Reading, by Philip Tew, Manchester Univ Press, 2001.

JAMES JOYCE
A Bibliography of James Joyce 1882-1941, John Slocum and Herbery Cahoon, Rupert Hart Davis, 1953.

FRANZ KAFKA
A Kafka Bibliography 1908-1976, by Angel Flores, Gordian Press, 1976.

ERICH KÄSTNER
'Erich Kästner', by Martin Spence, *B&MC*, No.108, March 1993, pps.30-37.

JOHN KEATS
Keats: A Bibliography and Reference Guide with an Essay on Keats' Reputation, by J.R. MacGillivray, Univ of Toronto Press, 1949.

JAMES KELMAN
www.fantasticfiction.co.uk/k/james-kelman

THOMAS KENEALLY
Australian Melodramas: Thomas Keneally's Fiction, by Peter Pierce, Univ of Queensland Press, 1965.

WILLIAM KENNEDY
www.fantasticfiction.co.uk/k/william-kennedy

JACK KEROUAC
A Bibliography of Works by Jack Kerouac 1939-1975, by Ann Charters, Phoenix Bookshop, 1975 (revised and expanded second edition).

KEN KESEY
Ken Kesey, by Allen and Patricia Ahearn, Quill & Brush, 1995.

KEYNOTES
www.bodhranbooks.com

FRANCIS KILVERT
'William Plomer & Kilvert's 'Diary'', by Andrew Thomas, *B&MC*, No.220, July 2002, pps.84-97.

C. DALY KING
DF:TCG, by John Cooper and B.A. Pike, Scolar Press, 1994, pps.184-186.

STEPHEN KING
The Works of Stephen King: An Annotated Bibliography and Guide, Borgo Press, 1996.
Science Fiction and Fantasy Authors, A Bibliography of First Printings of Their Fiction, by Lloyd Currey, Rb Publishing, 2002 (cd rom).

RUDYARD KIPLING
A Bibliography of the Works of Rudyard Kipling, by Flora V. Livingstone, Burt Franklin, 1968.
Rudyard Kipling: A Bibliographical Catalogue, by James McG. Stewart, O.U.P., 1959.

C.H.B. KITCHIN
'The Novels of C.H.B. Kitchin', by David Whitehead, *B&MC*, No.139, October 1995, pps.62-69.

ARTHUR KOESTLER
Arthur Koestler: An International Bibliography, by Reed Merrill and Thomas Frazier, Ardis, 1979.

DEAN KOONTZ
A Checklist of Dean R. Koontz, by Christopher P. Stephens, Ultramarine Publishing Co., 1987.

MILAN KUNDERA
Milan Kundera: An Annotated Bibliography, by Glen Brand, Garland Publishing, 1988.

PHILIP LARKIN
Philip Larkin: A Bibliography 1933-76, by B.C. Blomfield, Faber, 1979.

STIEG LARSSON
www.fantasticfiction.co.uk/l/stieg-larsson

D.H. LAWRENCE
A Bibliography of D.H. Lawrence, by Warren Roberts, C.U.P., 1982.

T.E. LAWRENCE
T.E. Lawrence: A Bibliography, by Philip O'Brien, St Paul's Bibliographies, 1988.

EDWARD LEAR
Edward Lear, 1812-1888, by Vivien Noakes, Royal Academy of Arts, 1985.

JOHN LE CARRÉ
'John Le Carré and Len Deighton', *Breese's Guide to Modern First Editions*, Martin Breese, Breese Books, 1999, pps.111-118.

HARPER LEE
Harper Lee's To Kill a Mockingbird, edited by Harold Bloom, Chelsea House, 1996

LAURIE LEE
Laurie Lee, The Well-loved Stranger, by Valerie Grove, Viking/Penguin, 1999.

J. SHERIDAN LE FANU
J. Sheridan Le Fanu: A Bio-Bibliography, by Gary William Crawford, Greenwood Press, 1995.

RICHARD LE GALLIENNE
Modern British Authors, Their First Editions, Cutler and Stiles, Allen & Unwin, 1930.

URSULA LE GUIN
Ursula K. LeGuin: A Primary and Secondary Bibliography, by Elizabeth Cummins Cogell, Hall, 1983.

ROSAMOND LEHMANN
'Lehmann: A Bibliography' by M.T. Gustafson, in *Twentieth Century Literature 4*, 1959.

FRITZ LEIBER
Fritz Leiber: A Bibliography 1934-1979, by Chris Morgan, Morgenstein, 1979.

PATRICK LEIGH FERMOR
'Patrick Leigh Fermor', by David Howard, *B&MC*, No.291, February 2008, pps.76-84.

DONNA LEON
www.fantasticfiction.co.uk/l/donna-leon

ELMORE LEONARD
A Checklist of Elmore Leonard, by Christopher P. Stephens, Ultramarine, 1991.

GASTON LEROUX
'Gaston Leroux', by Richard Dalby, *B&MC*, No.38, May 1987, pps.14-22.

DORIS LESSING
Doris Lessing: A Bibliography of Her First Editions, by Eric T. Brueck, Metropolis, 1984.

IRA LEVIN
'Collecting the novels of Ira Levin', by Martin Naparsteck, *F:TBCM*, October 2008, Vol.18, No.8, pps.42-49.

C.S. LEWIS
C.S. Lewis: An Annotated Checklist of Writings About Him and His Works, by Joe R. Christopher and Joan K. Ostling, Kent State Univ Press, [n.d.].

MATTHEW GREGORY LEWIS
'Matthew Lewis', by Richard Dalby, *B&MC*, No.145, April 1996, pps.74-86.

NORMAN LEWIS
'Norman Lewis', by David Howard, *B&MC*, No.125, August 1994, pps.30-37.

SINCLAIR LEWIS
Sinclair Lewis: A Descriptive Bibliography: A Collector's and Scholar's Guide to Identification, by Stephen R. Pastore, Yale Books, 1997.

WYNDHAM LEWIS
A Bibliography of the Writings of Wyndham Lewis, by Bradford Morrow and Bernard LaFourcade, Black Sparrow Press, 1978.

THOMAS LIGOTTI
www.ligotti.net

DAVID LINDSAY
Science Fiction and Fantasy Authors, A Bibliography of First Printings of Their Fiction, by Lloyd Currey, Rb Publishing, 2002 (cd rom).

DAVID LODGE
David Lodge: An Annotated Primary and Secondary Bibliography, by Norbert Schürer, Peter Lang, 1995.

JACK LONDON
The Fiction of Jack London: A Chronological Bibliography, by Dale L. Walker and James E. Sisson III, Texas Western Press, 1972.
Jack London First Editions, by James E. Sisson III and Robert W. Martens, Star Rover House, 1979.

ANITA LOOS
'Anita Loos', by Brian Jones, *B&MC*, No.96, March 1992, pps.22-28.

E.C.R. LORAC
DF:TCG, by John Cooper and B.A. Pike, Scolar Press, 1994, pps.193-196.

H.P. LOVECRAFT
The Revised H.P. Lovecraft Bibliography, by Mark Owings and JacK L. Chalker, Mirage Press, 1973.

PETER LOVESEY
'Colin Dexter and Peter Lovesey', *Breese's Guide to Modern First Editions*, Martin Breese, Breese Books, 1999, pps.54-60.

MALCOLM LOWRY
Malcolm Lowry: A Bibliography, by J. Howard Woolmer, Woolmer/Brotherson, 1983.

ROBERT LUDLUM
'Robert Ludlum', by Roger Allen, *B&MC*, No.110, May 1993, pps.14-22.

ROSE MACAULAY
Rose Macaulay, by Alice R. Bensen, Twayne, 1969.

BETTY MACDONALD
'Laughing with Betty Macdonald', by Peter Bateman and Jenny Lerew, *F:TBCM*, December 2007, Vol.17, No.10, pps.22-34.

GEORGE MACDONALD
George Macdonald: A Bibliographical Study, by Raphael B. Shaberman, St Paul's Bibliographies, 1990.

PHILIP MACDONALD
DF:TCG, by John Cooper and B.A. Pike, Scolar Press, 1994, pps.199-201.

ROSS MACDONALD
Ross Macdonald/Kenneth Millar: A Descriptive Bibliography, by Matthew J. Bruccoli, Univ of Pittsburgh Press, 1983.

CORMAC McCARTHY
'The New McCarthyism: Collecting Cormac McCarthy', by Kenneth L. Pivratsky, *F:TBCM*, April 1993, Vol.3, No.4, pps.24-28.

FRANK McCOURT
www.fantasticfiction.co.uk/m/frank-mccourt

CARSON McCULLERS
'Collecting Carson McCullers', by Clair Schulz, *F:TBCM*, December 1996, Vol.6, No.12, pps.42-47.

IAN McEWAN
Muriel Spark, William Trevor, Ian McEwan, A Bibliography of their First Editions, David Rees, Colophon Press, 1992.

JOHN McGAHERN
Brian Moore, Alasdair Gray, John McGahern, A Bibliography of their First Editions, David Rees, Colophon Press, 1991.

ARTHUR MACHEN
A Bibliography of Arthur Machen, by Adrian Goldstone and Wesley Sweetser, Haskell House, 1973.

COLIN MACINNES
'Colin MacInnes', by Crispin Jackson, *B&MC*, No.116, November 1993, pps.40-47.

JULIAN MACLAREN-ROSS
Fear and Loathing in Fitzrovia: The Bizarre Life of Julian Maclaren-Ross, Paul Willetts, Dewi Lewis, 2003.

ALISTAIR MACLEAN
'Alistair Maclean', by David Whitehead, *B&MC*, No.157, April 1997, pps.16-26.

LARRY McMURTRY
Larry McMurtry: Unredeemed Dreams. A Collection of Bibliography, Essays, and Interview, by Larry McMurtry and Dorey Schmidt, School of Humanities, Pan American Univ, 1978.

LOUIS MACNEICE
A Bibliography of the Works of Louis MacNeice, by Christopher Armitage and Neil Clark, Kaye & Ward, 1973.

NORMAN MAILER
Norman Mailer: A Comprehensive Bibliography, by Laura Adams, Scarecrow Press, 1974.

BERNARD MALAMUD
Bernard Malamud: A Descriptive Bibliography, by Rita N. Kosofsky, Greenwood Press, 1991.

THOMAS MANN
Thomas Mann, by Andrew White, Grove Press, 1965.

OLIVIA MANNING
'Olivia manning: A Centenary Tribute', by Mark Valentine, *B&MC*, No.292, March 2008, pps.24-29.

KATHERINE MANSFIELD
Bibliographies of Modern Authors, Second Series, C.A. & H.W. Stonehill, John Castle, 1925.

CAPTAIN FREDERICK MARRYAT
Captain Frederick Marryat: Sea-Officer, Novelist, Country Squire: A Bio-Bibliographical Essay to Accompany an Exhi-bition . . . , by Alan Buster, Univ of California Press, 1980.

NGAIO MARSH
Ngaio Marsh: A Bibliography of English Language Publications in Hardback and Paperback, by Rowan Gibbs and Richard Williams, Dragonby Press, 1990.

RICHARD MARSH
'Richard Marsh', by Richard Dalby, *B&MC*, No.163, October 1997, pps.76-89.

PAULE MARSHALL
www.fantasticfiction.co.uk/m/paule-marshall

YANN MARTEL
www.fantasticfiction.co.uk/m/yann-martel

RICHARD MATHESON
Richard Matheson: He is Legend: An Illustrated Bio-Bibliography, by Mark Rathbun & Graeme Flanagan (eds.), Rathbun & Flanagan, 1984.

PETER MATTHIESSEN
'Collecting Peter Matthiessen', by Ken Lopez, *F:TBCM*, September 1993, Vol.3, No.9, pps.24-27.

W. SOMERSET MAUGHAM
A Bibliography of the Works of W. Somerset Maugham, by Raymond Toole Stott, Univ of Alberta Press, 1973.

WILLIAM MAXWELL
www.fantasticfiction.co.uk/m/william-maxwell

HERMAN MELVILLE
Herman Melville: An Annotated Bibliography, by Brian Higgins, G K Hall, 1979

H.L. MENCKEN
H.L. Mencken: An Annotated Bibliography, by S.T. Joshi, The Scarecrow Press, 2009.

ABRAHAM MERRITT
Science Fiction and Fantasy Authors, A Bibliography of First Printings of Their Fiction, by Lloyd Currey, Rb Publishing, 2002 (cd rom).

JAMES A. MICHENER
Bibliography: James A. Michener, by David A. Groseclose, State House Press, 1996.

ARTHUR MILLER
Arthur Miller: A Checklist of his Published Works, by Tetsumaro Hayashi, Kent, 1967.

HENRY MILLER
A Bibliography of Henry Miller 1945-1961, by Maxine Renken, Swallow, 1962.
Henry Miller: A Bibliography of Primary Sources, by Lawrence J. Shifreen and Roger Jackson, Alyscamps Press/Karl Orend Publishers, 1993

A.A. MILNE
Modern British Authors, Their First Editions, Cutler and Stiles, Allen & Unwin, 1930.

DAVID MITCHELL
www.fantasticfiction.co.uk/m/david-mitchell

GLADYS MITCHELL
DF:TCG, by John Cooper and B.A. Pike, Scolar Press, 1994, pps.214-218.

MARGARET MITCHELL
'Margaret Mitchell's *Gone With the Wind*', by Brian Jones, *B&MC*, No.130, January 1995, pps.28-37.

NAOMI MITCHISON
The Nine Lives of Naomi Mitchison, by Jenni Calder, Virago, 1997.

MARY RUSSELL MITFORD
First Editions, A Field Guide, by K. Anthony Ward, Scolar Press, 1994, pps.249-250.

NANCY MITFORD
Nancy Mitford: A Biography, by Selina Hastings, Dutton, 1986.

NICHOLAS MONSARRAT
'Nicholas Monsarrat', by David Whitehead, *B&MC*, No.203, February 2001, pps.14-25.

L.M. MONTGOMERY
'The Children's Books of L.M. Montgomery', by Monica Godfrey, *B&MC*, No.35, February 1987, pps.62-68.

MICHAEL MOORCOCK
Michael Moorcock: A Reader's Guide, by John Davey, Jayde Design, 2000.
BRIAN MOORE
Brian Moore, Alasdair Gray, John McGahern, A Bibliography of their First Editions, David Rees, Colophon Press, 1991.
WILLIAM MORRIS
The Books of William Morris by H.B. Forman, Holland Press, 1967.
ARTHUR MORRISON
DF:TCG, by John Cooper and B.A. Pike, Scolar Press, 1994, pps.221-223.
TONI MORRISON
Toni Morrison: An Annotated Bibliography, by David L. Middleton, Garland, 1987.
JOHN MORTIMER
'John Mortimer', by Dee Taylor, *B&MC*, No.100, July 1992, pps.50-57.
KATE MOSSE
www.fantasticfiction.co.uk/m/kate-mosse
PATRICIA MOYES
'The Detective Fiction of Patricia Moyes', by David Blake, *B&MC*, No.292, March 2008, pps.82-89.
HARUKI MURAKAMI
www.fantasticfiction.co.uk/m/haruki-murakami
IRIS MURDOCH
Iris Murdoch & Muriel Spark: A Bibliography, by Thomas A. Tominaga and Wilma Schneidermeyer, Scarecrow Press, 1976.
Iris Murdoch: A Descriptive Primary and Annotated Secondary Bibliography, by John Fletcher and Cheryl Bove, Garland, 1994.
VLADIMIR NABOKOV
Nabokov: A Bibliography, by Andrew Field, McGraw-Hill, 1974.
Vladimir Nabokov: A Descriptive Bibliography, by Michael Juliar, Garland, 1986.
SHIVA NAIPAUL
www.fantasticfiction.co.uk/n/shiva-naipaul
V.S. NAIPAUL
'V.S. Naipaul', by David Howard, *B&MC*, No.64, July 1989, pps.26-32.
VIOLET NEEDHAM
The Password is Fortitude: An evaluation of some children's books by Violet Needham, by Judith Crabb, Hermit Press, 1992.
EDITH NESBIT
'Edith Nesbit', *B&MC*, No.251, January 2005, pps.96-97.
KAY NIELSEN
'The Illustrated Books of Kay Nielsen', by Richard Dalby, *B&MC*, No.30, September 1986, pps.28-37.
ANAIS NIN
Anais Nin: A Bibliography, by Benjamin Franklin, Kent State Univ Press, 1973.
PATRICK O'BRIAN
Patrick O'Brian: Critical Appreciations and a Bibliography, by A.E. Cunningham, British Library, 1994.
EDNA O'BRIEN
'Edna O'Brien', by Kenneth Fields, *B&MC*, No.94, January 1992, pps.22-28.
FLANN O'BRIEN
'The Novels and Journalism of Flann O'Brien', by Crispin Jackson, *B&MC*, No.92, November 1991, pps.15-24.
TIM O'BRIEN
'Collecting Tim O'Brien', by Ken Lopez, *F:TBCM*, September 1996, Vol.6, No.9, pps.34-39.
FLANNERY O'CONNOR
Flannery O'Connor: A Descriptive Bibliography, by David Farmer, Garland Publishing, 1981.
LIAM O'FLAHERTY
Liam O'Flaherty: An Annotated Bibliography, by Paul A. Doyle, Whitston, 1972.
Liam O'Flaherty: A Descriptive Bibliography of His Works, by George Jefferson, Wolfhound Press, 1993.
JOHN O'HARA
John O'Hara: A Descriptive Bibliography, by Matthew J. Bruccoli, Univ of Pittsburg Press, 1978.
EUGENE O'NEILL
Eugene O'Neill: A Descriptive Bibliography, by Jennifer McCabe Atkinson, Univ of Pittsburgh Press, 1974.

MICHAEL ONDAATJE
The Annotated Bibliography of Canada's Major Authors, Volume Six, edited by Robert Lecker and Jack David, ECW Press, 1985.
JOE ORTON
Twenty Modern British Playwrights: A Bibliography, 1956-1976, by Kimball King, Garland, 1977.
GEORGE ORWELL
George Orwell: A Selected Bibliography, by Z.G. Zeke and W. White, published in Boston, 1962.
JOHN OSBORNE
John Osborne, by Simon Trussler, Longmans Green, 1969.
ELSIE J. OXENHAM
'The Hidden Gems of Elsie Jeanette Oxenham', by Clarissa Cridland, *B&MC*, No.198, September 2000, pps.48-65.
WILFRED OWEN
Wilfred Owen (1893-1918): A Bibliography, by William White, Kent State Univ Press, 1967.
SARA PARETSKY
DF:TCG, by John Cooper and B.A. Pike, Scolar Press, 1994, pps.235-236.
DOROTHY PARKER
'Dorothy Parker', by Val Tongue, *B&MC*, No.86, May 1991, pps.47-53.
THOMAS LOVE PEACOCK
'Thomas Love Peacock', by Martin Spence, *B&MC*, No.168, March 1998, pps.54-62.
MERVYN PEAKE
Mervyn Peake, by John Watney, St Martin's Press, 1976.
WALKER PERCY
Walker Percy: A Comprehensive Descriptive Bibliography, by Linda Whitney Hobson, Faust Publishing Company, 1988.
ELLIS PETERS
'Collecting Edith Pargeter/Ellis Peters', by Barbara G. Peters, *F:TBCM*, November 1995, Vol.5, No.11, pps.32-41.
DBC PIERRE
www.fantasticfiction.co.uk/p/d-b-c-pierre
HAROLD PINTER
Twenty Modern British Playwrights: A Bibliography, 1956-1976, by Kimball King, Garland, 1977.
SYLVIA PLATH
Sylvia Plath: A Bibliography, by Gary Lane and Maria Stevens, Scarecrow Press, 1978.
EDGAR ALLAN POE
Bibliography of the Writings of Edgar A. Poe, by John W. Robertson, Kraus Reprint, 1969.
WILLY POGÁNY
'The Book and Magazine Illustrations of Willy Pogany', *Imaginative Book Illustration Society Newsletter*, Autumn 1995, No.1, pps.11-24.
ELEANOR H. PORTER
'The Pollyanna Books of Eleanor H. Porter', by Barbara Richardson, *B&MC*, No.226, January 2003, pps.54-65.
CHARLES PORTIS
'Collecting Charles Portis', by Robin H. Smiley, *F:TBCM*, October 2006, Vol.16, No.8, pps.24-31.
BEATRIX POTTER
Beatrix Potter: A Bibliographical Checklist, by Jane Quinby, Sawyer, 1954.
A History of the Writings of Beatrix Potter, by Leslie Linder, Frederick Warne, 1971.
DENNIS POTTER
'Dennis Potter', by Andrew Thomas, *B&MC*, No.285, September 2007, pps.64-73.
EZRA POUND
A Bibliography of Ezra Pound, by Donald Gallup, Univ of Virginia Press, 1983.
ANTHONY POWELL
Anthony Powell-A Bibliography, by George Lilley, St Paul's, 1993.
JOHN COWPER POWYS
A Bibliography of the Writings of John Cowper Powys 1872-1963, by Dante Thomas, Paul P. Appel, 1975.
LLEWELYN POWYS
The Life of Llewelyn Powys, by Malcolm Elwin, Bodley Head, 1946.
T.F. POWYS
A Bibliography of T.F. Powys, by Peter Riley, Brimmell, 1967.

TERRY PRATCHETT
A Checklist of Terry Pratchett's Novels, Shorter Writings and Related Publications, Colin Smythe, privately printed by Colin Smythe, 2001.
ANTHONY PRICE
'Anthony Price', by David Howard, **B&MC**, No.161, August 1997, pps.50-59.
J.B. PRIESTLEY
J.B. Priestley, An Annotated Bibliography, by Alan Edwin Day, Hodgkins and Co., 1980.
V.S. PRITCHETT
V.S. Pritchett, by Dean R. Baldwin, Twayne, 1987.
MARCEL PROUST
The Magic Lantern of Marcel Proust, by Howard Moss, Faber, 1963.
PHILIP PULLMAN
'Philip Pullman', by Barbara Richardson, **B&MC**, No.218, May 2002, pps.20-34.
MARIO PUZO
'The Godfather: Mario Puzo', by Stephen Honey, **B&MC**, No.261, November 2005, pps.50-60.
THOMAS PYNCHON
Three Contemporary Novelists: An Annotated Bibliography, by Robert M. Scotto, Garland, 1977.
BARBARA PYM
Barbara Pym: A Reference Guide, by Dale Salwak, G.K. Hall, 1991.
ELLERY QUEEN
Royal Bloodline: Ellery Queen, by Francis M. Nevins, Jr., Bowling Green Univ Press, 1974.
JONATHAN RABAN
'Jonathan Raban', by David Howard, **B&MC**, No.89, August 1991, pps.14-20.
ARTHUR RACKHAM
Arthur Rackham, A New Bibliography, Richard Riall, Louise Ross and Co., 1994.
ANN RADCLIFFE
Ann Radcliffe: A Bio-Bibliography, by Deborah P. Rogers, Greenwood, 1996.
AYN RAND
Ayn Rand: First Descriptive Bibliography, by V.L. Perinn, Quill & Brush, 1990.
IAN RANKIN
DF:TCG, by John Cooper and B.A. Pike, Scolar Press, 1994, pps.251-252.
ARTHUR RANSOME
Arthur Ransome: A Bibliography, by Wayne G. Hammond, Oak Knoll Press, 2000.
SIMON RAVEN
'Simon Raven', by David Howard, **B&MC**, No.289, Christmas 2007, pps.93-103.
MARJORIE KINNAN RAWLINGS
'Collecting Marjorie Kinnan Rawlings', by Kathryn Smiley, **F:TBCM**, July/Aug 1995, Vol.5, No.7/8, pps.30-39.
FORREST REID
Forrest Reid: A Portrait and Study, by Russell Burlingham, Faber, 1953.
RUTH RENDELL
'Ruth Rendell', *Breese's Guide to Modern First Editions*, Martin Breese, Breese Books, 1999, pps.142-148.
JEAN RHYS
Jean Rhys: A Descriptive and Annotated Bibliography of Works and Criticism, by Elgin W. Mellown, Garland, 1984.
ANNE RICE
The Unauthorized Anne Rice Companion, by George Beahm, Andrews and McMeel, 1996.
CRAIG RICE
DF:TCG, by John Cooper and B.A. Pike, Scolar Press, 1994, pps.264-268.
FRANK RICHARDS
'Frank Richards', *Breese's Guide to Modern First Editions*, Martin Breese, Breese Books, 1999, pps.149-155.
LAURA RIDING
Laura Riding A Bibliography, by Joyce Piell Wexler, Garland Publishing, 1981.
W. HEATH ROBINSON
William Heath Robinson, by James Hamilton, Pavilion Books, 1992.

MARILYNNE ROBINSON
'The Blessing of language and memory: Marilynne Robinson', by Kathryn Smiley, **F:TBCM**, April 2008, Vol.18, No.4, pps.22-29.
SAX ROHMER
Masters of Villainy, by Cay Van Ash and Elizabeth Sax Rohmer, Bowling Green Univ Popular Press, 1972.
FREDERICK ROLFE (BARON CORVO)
A Bibliography of Frederick Rolfe Baron Corvo, by Cecil Woolfe, Rupert Hart Davis, 1957.
CHRISTINA ROSSETTI
First Editions, A Field Guide, by K. Anthony Ward, Scolar Press, 1994, pps.279-280.
DANTE GABRIEL ROSSETTI
Bibliography of the Works of Dante Gabriel Rossetti, by William Michael Rossetti, AMS Press, 1971.
HENRY ROTH
www.fantasticfiction.co.uk/r/henry-roth
PHILIP ROTH
Philip Roth: A Bibliography, by Bernard F. Rodgers, Scarecrow Press, 1984 (second edition).
J.K. ROWLING
'J.K. Rowling's 'Harry Potter' Books', by Barbara Richardson, **B&MC**, No.196, July 2000, pps.4-17.
DAMON RUNYON
'Damon Runyon: Gentleman Liar', by Robin H. Smiley, **F:TBCM**, February 2006, Vol.16, No.2, pps.22-37.
RUPERT *see Mary Tourtel*
SALMAN RUSHDIE
Contemporary World Writers: Salman Rushdie, by Catherine Cundy, Manchester Univ Press, 1996.
R.R. RYAN
'R.R. Ryan', by James Doig, **B&MC**, No.312, October 2009, pps.104-112.
VITA SACKVILLE-WEST
Vita Sackville West: A Bibliography, by Robert Cross and Ann Ravenscroft-Hulme, St Paul's Bibliographies, 1999.
SAKI
'Saki, A Life of Irony', by Jesse F. Knight, **F:TBCM**, September 1999, Vol.9, No.9, pps.50-57.
J.D. SALINGER
J.D. Salinger: A Thirty-Year Bibliography, 1938-1968, by Kenneth Starosciak, Croixside Press, 1971.
J.D. Salinger: An Annotated Bibliography 1938-1981, by Jack R. Sublette, Garland, 1984.
SAPPER
The Bulldog Drummond Encyclopedia, by Lawrence P. Treadwell Jr., McFarland, 2001.
SARBAN
'Brief Bibliography', by Mark Valentine, *The Doll Maker*, by Sarban, Tartarus Press, 1999, p.227.
WILLIAM SAROYAN
A Bibliography of William Saroyan, 1934-1964, by David Kherdian, Roger Beacham, 1965.
SIEGFRIED SASSOON
A Bibliography of Siegfried Sassoon, by Geoffrey Keynes, Hart Davis, 1962.
HILARY SAUNDERS *see Francis Beeding*
THE SAVOY
Publisher to the Decadents, by James G. Nelson, Rivendale Press, 2000.
DOROTHY L. SAYERS
A Bibliography of the Works of Dorothy L. Sayers, by Colleen B. Gilbert, Archon Books, 1978.
JACK SCHAEFER
'Collecting Jack Schaefer', by Larry Dingman and Robin H. Smiley, **F:TBCM**, May 1993, Vol.3, No.5, pps.24-29.
PAUL SCOTT
'Paul Scott', by Jeremy Parrott, **B&MC**, No.163, October 1997, pps.29-39.
WALTER SCOTT
'Sir Walter Scott', by Crispin Jackson, **B&MC**, No.155, February 1997, pps.32-42.
W.G. SEBALD
'W.G. Sebald', by Chris Griffiths, **B&MC**, No.303, January 2009, pps.92-101.

MAURICE SENDAK
'Maurice Sendak', by Martin Spence, **B&MC**, No.157, April 1997, pps.62-75.

DR SEUSS
St James Guide to Children's Writers, St James Press, 1999 (fifth edition), pps.965-967.

ANNA SEWELL
Anna Sewell and Black Beauty, by Margaret J. Baker, Longmans, Green & Company, 1957.

TOM SHARPE
'The Comic Novels of Tom Sharpe', by David Howard, **B&MC**, No.41, August 1987, pps.15-22.

GEORGE BERNARD SHAW
Bernard Shaw: A Bibliography, Dan H. Laurence, O.U.P., 1983.

MARY SHELLEY
Mary Shelley: An Annotated Bibliography, by W.H. Lyles, Garland, 1975.

ERNEST H. SHEPARD
The Work of E.H. Shepard, edited by Rawle Knox, Methuen, 1979.

M.P. SHIEL
The Works of M.P. Shiel, by A. Reynolds Morse, Fantasy Publishing Co., 1948.

NEVIL SHUTE
Nevil Shute, by Julain Smith, Twayne, 1976.

ALAN SILLITOE
Alan Sillitoe: A Bibliography, by David E. Gerard, Mansell, 1988.

SIDNEY SIME
'The Published Drawings of Sidney Sime', by Geoffrey Beare and Martin Steenson, *Imaginative Book Illustration Society Newsletter*, Winter 1998, No.10, pps.21-39.

GEORGES SIMENON
Georges Simenon: A Bibliography of the British First Editions . . . and of the Principal French and American Editions, by Peter Foord, Richard Williams and Sally Swan, Dragonby Press, 1988.

IAIN SINCLAIR
www.fantasticfiction.co.uk/s/iain-sinclair

ISAAC BASHEVIS SINGER
Bibliography of Isaac Bashevis Singer, 1924-1949, by David Neal Miller, Peter Lang Publishers, 1983.

EDITH, OSBERT and SACHEVERELL SITWELL
A Bibliography of Edith, Osbert and Sacheverell Sitwell by Robert Fifoot, Hart-Davis/O.U.P., 1971.
Sacheverell Sitwell: An Annotated and Descriptive Bibliography 1916-1986, by Neil Ritchie, Giardo Press, 1987

CLARK ASHTON SMITH
Emperor of Dreams, A Clark Ashton-Smith Bibliography, by Donald Sidney-Fryer, Grant, 1978.

DODIE SMITH
'Dodie Smith', by Valerie Grove, **B&MC**, No.154, January 1997, pps.17-26.

STEVIE SMITH
Stevie Smith: A Bibliography, by Jack Barbera et al., Mansell, 1987.

WILBUR SMITH
'Wilbur Smith', by David Whitehead, **B&MC**, No.181, April 1999, pps.17-26.

ZADIE SMITH
www.fantasticfiction.co.uk/s/zadie-smith

LEMONY SNICKET
'Lemony Snicket', by Simon Rogers, **B&MC**, No.251, January 2005, pps.38-44.

C.P. SNOW
The World of Snow, by Robert Greacen, Scorpion Press, 1962.

ALEXANDER SOLZHENITSYN
Alexander Solzhenitsyn: An International Bibliography of Writings By and About Him, by Donald M Fiene, Ardis, 1973.

MURIEL SPARK
Muriel Spark, William Trevor, Ian McEwan, A Bibliography of their First Editions, David Rees, Colophon Press, 1992.
Iris Murdoch & Muriel Spark: A Bibliography, by Thomas A. Tominaga and Wilma Schneidermeyer, Scarecrow Press, 1976.

STEPHEN SPENDER
Stephen Spender Works and Criticism: An Annotated Bibliography, by H.B. Kulkarni, Garland, 1976.

MICKEY SPILLANE
'Collecting Mickey Spillane', by Laurence Miller, **F:TBCM**, June 1996, Vol.6, No.6, pps.36-43.

GERTRUDE STEIN
Gertrude Stein: A Bibliography, by Robert A. Wilson, Quill & Brush, 1994.

JOHN STEINBECK
John Steinbeck: A Biographical Catalogue of the Adrian H. Goldstone Collection, by Adrian H. Goldstone and John R. Payne, Univ of Texas Press, 1974.

COUNT ERIC STENBOCK
'A Bibliography of Count Stenbock' by Timothy d'Arch Smith, *Stenbock Yeats and the Nineties*, by John Adlard, Woolf, 1969, pps.95-102.

LAURENCE STERNE
Laurence Sterne, by William Piper, Twayne, 1965.

ROBERT LOUIS STEVENSON
A Bibliography of the Works of Robert Louis Stevenson by Colonel W.F. Prideaux, Burt Franklin, 1968.

BRAM STOKER
Bram Stoker, A Bibliography of First Editions, by Richard Dalby, Dracula Press, 1983.

ROBERT STONE
Robert Stone: A Bibliography, 1960-1992, by Ken Lopez and Bev Chaney, Numinous Press, 1992.

TOM STOPPARD
Twenty Modern British Playwrights: A Bibliography, 1956-1976, by Kimball King, Garland, 1977.

DAVID STOREY
www.fantasticfiction.co.uk/s/david-storey

REX STOUT
DF:TCG, John Cooper and B.A. Pike, Scolar Press, 1994, pps.277-281.

LYTTON STRACHEY
'Lytton Strachey', by Helen Macleod, **B&MC**, No.35, February 1987, pps.53-61.

GENE STRATTON-PORTER
Gene Stratton-Porter: A Bibliography and Collector's Guide, by David G. MacLean, Americana Books, 1976.

WILLIAM STYRON
'William Styron: The Making of a Writer', by Peter Coveney, *F:TBCM*, January 2008, Vol.18, No.1, pps.18-31.

MONTAGUE SUMMERS
A Bibliography of the Works of Montague Summers, by Timothy d'Arch Smith, Aquarian, 1983.

R.S. SURTEES
R.S. Surtees, by Leonard Cooper, Arthur Barker Ltd., 1952.
The Sporting World of R.S. Surtees, by John Welcome, O.U.P., 1982.

PATRICK SÜSKIND
www.fantasticfiction.co.uk/s/patrick-suskind

GRAHAM SWIFT
'The Novels of Graham Swift', by David Howard, **B&MC**, No.92, November 1991, pps.62-67.

A.J.A. SYMONS
'A.J.A. Symons', by Richard Dalby, **B&MC**, No.119, February 1994, pps.74-84.

JULIAN SYMONS
Julian Symons: A Bibliography, by John J. Walsdorf, Oak Knoll Press/St Paul's Bibliographies, 1996.

ELIZABETH TAYLOR
www.fantasticfiction.co.uk/t/elizabeth-taylor

G.P. TAYLOR
www.fantasticfiction.co.uk/t/g-p-taylor

PETER TAYLOR
Peter Taylor: A Descriptive Bibliography, 1934-87, by Stuart Wright, Bibliographical Society of the Univ of Virginia, 1988.

PHOEBE ATWOOD TAYLOR
'The Detective Novels of Phoebe Atwood Taylor', by David Blake, **B&MC**, No.307, May 2009, pps.54-65.

ALFRED TENNYSON
A Bibliography of The Writings of Alfred, Lord Tennyson, edited by T.J. Wise, privately printed, 1907.

JOSEPHINE TEY
DF:TCG, John Cooper and B.A. Pike, Scolar Press, 1994, pps.287-288.
The Bibliography of Crime Fiction, 1749-1975, Allen J. Hubin, Publisher's Inc., 1979.
W.M. THACKERAY
A Thackeray Library by Henry Sayre Van Duzer, Burt Franklin, 1971.
PAUL THEROUX
Paul Theroux, by Allen and Patricia Ahearn, Quill & Brush, 1995.
WILFRED THESIGER
'The travel Books of Wilfred Thesiger', by David Howard, *B&MC*, No.295, June 2008, pps.78-88.
DYLAN THOMAS
Dylan Thomas: A Bibliography, by J. Alexander Rolph, Dent, 1956.
ditto, New Directions, 1956.
Dylan Thomas in Print: A Bibliographical History, by Ralph Maud, Dent, 1970.
ditto, Univ of Pittsburgh Press, 1970.
EDWARD THOMAS
Edward Thomas, A Biography and a Bibliography, by Robert P. Eckert, Dent, 1937.
ROSS THOMAS
The Bibliography of Crime Fiction, 1749-1975, Allen J. Hubin, Publisher's Inc., 1979.
FLORA THOMPSON
'Flora Thompson', by Paul Robinson, *B&MC*, No.158, May 1997, pps.14-24.
HUNTER S. THOMPSON
http://en.wikipedia.org/wiki/Hunter_S._Thompson_bibliography
JIM THOMPSON
'Collecting Thompson', by Craig Graham, *F:TBCM*, November 1993, Vol.3, No.11, pps.28-32.
KAY THOMPSON
'Eloise', by Barbara Richardson, *B&MC*, No.260, October 2005, pps.58-68.
HENRY DAVID THOREAU
'Collecting Henry David Thoreau', by Kevin MacDonnell, *F:TBCM*, September 1999, Vol.9, No.9, pps.22-55.
COLIN THUBRON
'Travel Writer and Novelist: Colin Thubron', by David Howard, *B&MC*, No.119, February 1994, pps.64-71.
JAMES THURBER
James Thurber: A Bibliography, by Edwin T. Bowden, Ohio State Univ Press, 1968.
WILLIAM M. TIMLIN
'William Timlin: Author-Artist Extraordinary', by Richard Dalby, *B&MC*, No.99, June 1992, pps.58-63.
J.R.R. TOLKIEN
J.R.R. Tolkien: A Descriptive Bibliography, by Wayne G. Hammond and Douglas Anderson, Oak Knoll Press/St Paul's Bibliographies, 1993.
MARY TOURTEL
The New Rupert Index, by John Beck, privately printed, 1991.
B. TRAVEN
B. Traven A Bibliography, by Edward N. Treverton, Rowman & Littlefield, 1999.
WILLIAM TREVOR
Muriel Spark, William Trevor, Ian McEwan, A Bibliography of their First Editions, David Rees, Colophon Press, 1992.
ANTHONY TROLLOPE
Trollope: A Bibliography by Michael Sadleir, Dawson, 1977.
MARK TWAIN
A Bibliography of the Works of Mark Twain, by Merle Johnson, Harper & Brothers, 1935.
BARRY UNSWORTH
www.fantasticfiction.co.uk/u/barry-unsworth
JOHN UPDIKE
John Updike: A Bibliography, by C. Clarke Taylor, Kent State Univ Press, 1968.
John Updike: A Bibliography of Primary and Secondary Materials, 1948-2007, By Jack De Bellis and Michael Broomfield, Oak Knoll Press, 2007 (including CD).

FLORENCE UPTON
A Lark Ascends, Florence Kate Upton, Artist and Illustrator, by Norma S. Davis, Scarecrow Press, 1992.
ALISON UTTLEY
Alison Uttley: The Life of a Country Child (1884-1976), by Denis Judd, Joseph, 1986.
LAURENS VAN DER POST
Laurens Van Der Post, by Frederic I. Carpenter, Twayne, 1969.
S.S. VAN DINE
DF:TCG, by John Cooper and B.A. Pike, Scolar Press, 1994, pps.290-292.
JULES VERNE
Jules Verne: A Bibliography, by Edward and Judith Myers, Country Lane Books, 1989.
GORE VIDAL
Gore Vidal: A Primary and Secondary Bibliography by Robert J. Stanton, Hall, 1978.
WILLIAM T. VOLLMANN
www.fantasticfiction.co.uk/v/william-t-vollmann
KURT VONNEGUT
Kurt Vonnegut Jr.: A Descriptive Bibliography and Annotated Secondary Checklist, by Asa B. Pieratt Jr. and Jerome Klinkowitz, Archon Books, 1987.
Kurt Vonnegut: A Comprehensive Bibliography, by Asa B. Pieratt Jr. et al., Archon Books, 1974.
LOUIS WAIN
Louis Wain: The Man Who Drew Cats, by Rodney Dale, William Kimber, 1968.
ALFRED WAINWRIGHT
Wainwright: The Biography, by Hunter Davies, Joseph, 1995.
A.E. WAITE
A.E. Waite A Bibliography, by R.A. Gilbert, Aquarian Press, 1983.
DEREK WALCOTT
Derek Walcott: An Annotated Bibliography of His Works, Critical Studies on Black Life and Culture (Vol. 14), Taylor & Francis, 1984.
ALICE WALKER
'An Addiction to Joy: Collecting Alice Walker', by Kathryn Smiley and Jerry Weinstein, *F:TBCM*, February 1995, Vol.5, No.2, pps.28-33.
Alice Malsenior Walker: An Annotated Bibliography, 1968-1986, by Louis & Darnell Pratt, Meckler, 1988.
EDGAR WALLACE
The British Bibliography of Edgar Wallace, by W.O.G. Lofts and Derek Adley, Howard Baker, 1969.
A Guide to the First Editions of Edgar Wallace, by Charles Kiddle, The Ivory Head Press, 1981.
HORACE WALPOLE
A Bibliography of Horace Walpole, A.T. Hazen, Yale Univ Press, 1948.
HUGH WALPOLE
Hugh Walpole: A Biography, by Rupert Hart-Davis, Macmillan, 1952.
MINETTE WALTERS
'Minette Walters', *Breese's Guide to Modern First Editions*, Martin Breese, Breese Books, 1999, pps.282-283.
REX WARNER
'Rex Warner', by Mark Valentine, *B&MC*, No.207, June 2001, pps.100-109.
SYLVIA TOWNSEND WARNER
A Bibliography, by R.B. Russell and J. Lawrence Mitchell, Tartarus Press [unpublished].
ROBERT PENN WARREN
Robert Penn Warren : A Descriptive Bibliography, 1922-1979, by James A. Grimshaw Jr., Univ of Virginia, 1985.
COLIN WATSON
DF:TCG, by John Cooper and B.A. Pike, Scolar Press, 1994, pps.304-306.
EVELYN WAUGH
A Bibliography of Evelyn Waugh, by Robert Murray Davis et al., Whitston, 1986.
MARY WEBB
Mary Webb, by Gladys Mary Coles, Seren Books/Poetry Wales Press, 1990.

WEIRD TALES
Bookery's Guide to Pulps & Related Magazines, Tim Cottrill. Bookery Press, 2005

DENTON WELCH
Denton Welch: Writer and Artist, by James Methuen-Campbell, Tartarus Press, 2002.

FAY WELDON
Fay Weldon, by Lana Faulks, Gale, 1998 (Twayne's English Authors Series).

H.G. WELLS
Comprehensive Bibliography of H.G. Wells, by M. Katanka, Katanka Ltd., 1968.

IRVINE WELSH
www.irvinewelsh.net

EUDORA WELTY
Eudora Welty: A Bibliography of Her Work, by Noel Polk, Univ Press of Mississippi, 1994.

PATRICIA WENTWORTH
DF:TCG, by John Cooper and B.A. Pike, Scolar Press, 1994, pps.306-310.

MARY WESLEY
'Mary Wesley', by David Howard, *B&MC*, No.156, March 1997, pps.14-22.

NATHANAEL WEST
Nathanael West: A Comprehensive Bibliography, by William White, Kent State Univ Press, 1975.

REBECCA WEST
Rebecca West, by Carl Rollyson, Scribner, 1995.

EDITH WHARTON
A Bibliography of the Writings of Edith Wharton, by Lavinia Davis, Southworth Press, 1933.
Edith Wharton: A Descriptive Bibliography, by Stephen Garrison, Univ of Pittsburgh Press, 1990.

DENNIS WHEATLEY
'The Historical and Adventure Novels of Dennis Wheatley', by Mike Stotter, *B&MC*, No.119, February 1994, pps.4-14.

E.B. WHITE
E.B. White: A Bibliographical Catalogue of Printed Materials in the Department of Rare Books, Cornell Univ Library, Garland, 1979.

ETHEL LINA WHITE
The Bibliography of Crime Fiction, 1749-1975, Allen J. Hubin, Publisher's Inc., 1979.

GILBERT WHITE
'Gilbert White's Natural History of Selborne', by A.R. James, *B&MC*, No.111, February 1994, pps.66-75.

PATRICK WHITE
Patrick White: A Bibliography, by Vivian Smith and Brian Hubber, Oak Knoll Press and Quiddlers Press 2004.

T.H. WHITE
T.H. White: An Annotated Bibliography, by François Gallix, Garland, 1986.

WALT WHITMAN
The Bibliography of Walt Whitman, by Frank Shay, Friedmans, 1920.

OSCAR WILDE
Bibliography of Oscar Wilde, Stuart Mason (pseud of Christopher Millard), Bertram Rota, 1967.

CHARLES WILLEFORD
'Collecting Charles Willeford', by Don Herron, *F:TBCM*, June 1998, Vol.8, No.6, pps.36-45.

CHARLES WILLIAMS
Charles W.S. Williams, A Checklist, by Lois Glenn, Kent State Univ Press, 1975.

TENNESSEE WILLIAMS
Tennessee Williams: A Bibliography, by Drewey Wayne Gunn, Scarecrow Press, 1980.

HENRY WILLIAMSON
A Bibliography and a Critical Survey of the Works of Williamson, by I. Waveney Girvan, Alcuin Press, 1931.

A.N. WILSON
www.fantasticfiction.co.uk/w/a-n-wilson

ANGUS WILSON
Angus Wilson, by K.W. Gransden, Longmans, Green & Co., 1969.

EDMUND WILSON
Edmund Wilson, A Bibliography, by Richard David Ramsey, David Lewis, 1971.

JACQUELINE WILSON
'Jacqanory', by Barbara Richardson, *B&MC*, No.264, January 2006, pps.54-67.

R.D. WINGFIELD
DF:TCG, by John Cooper and B.A. Pike, Scolar Press, 1994, pps.311-312.

JEANETTE WINTERSON
British Writers, Supplement IV, Eric Ambler to Jeanette Winterson, by George Stade and Carol Howard, Scribner's, 1997.

WISDEN CRICKETERS'ALMANACK
'Collecting Wisden Cricketers' Almanacks', by Deryk Brown, *B&MC*, No.111, June 1993, pps.74-83.

P.G. WODEHOUSE
A Bibliography and Reader's Guide to the First Editions of P.G. Wodehouse, by David A. Jasen, Greenhill Books, 1986 (revised and expanded second edition).
P.G. Wodehouse: A Comprehensive Bibliography and Checklist, by Eileen McIlvaine and James H. Heineman, Heineman, 1991.

THOMAS WOLFE
Thomas Wolfe: A Descriptive Bibliography, by Carol Johnston, Oak Knoll Press, 1987.

TOM WOLFE
Tom Wolfe, by William McKeen, Twayne, 1995.

TOBIAS WOLFF
www.fantasticfiction.co.uk/w/tobias-wolff

VIRGINIA WOOLF
A Bibliography of Virginia Woolf, by B.J. Kirkpatrick, Clarendon Press, 1989.

CORNELL WOOLRICH
Cornell Woolrich: A Descriptive Bibliography and Price Guide, by Otto Penzler, Mysterious Bookshop, 1999.

RICHARD WRIGHT
Richard Wright: A Primary Bibliography, by Charles T. Davis & Michel Fabre, G.K. Hall & Co., 1982.

S. FOWLER WRIGHT
Science Fiction and Fantasy Authors, A Bibliography of First Printings of Their Fiction, by Lloyd Currey, Rb Publishing, 2002 (cd rom).

JOHN WYNDHAM
Science Fiction and Fantasy Authors, A Bibliography of First Printings of Their Fiction, by Lloyd Currey, Rb Publishing, 2002, (cd rom).

RICHARD YATES
'Collecting Richard Yates', by Martin Naparsteck, *F:TBCM*, January 2008, Vol.18, No.1, pps.32-39.

WILLIAM BUTLER YEATS
A Bibliography of the Writings of W.B. Yeats, by Allan Wade, Ruper Hart Davis, 1958.

THE YELLOW BOOK
The Yellow Book: A Checklist and Index, by Mark Samuels Lasner, The Eighteen Nineties Society, 1998.

APPENDIX III

PUBLISHERS' CONVENTIONS FOR IDENTIFYING A FIRST EDITION

The following list suggests the different conventions adopted by various publishers to denote a First Edition, but you should also establish whether any later editions are referred to or indicated in the book. If they are, then the book is not a First Edition. Unless otherwise noted, the relevant information can be found on the copyright or verso title page.

Abelard-Schuman
States 'First published' with the year, **or** no statement.

George Allen & Unwin
States 'First published' with the year.

W.H. Allen
States 'First edition' with the year, **or** no statement.

Allison & Busby
States 'First published'.

D. Appleton & Co
Usually a numerical identification in brackets at foot of last page, ie first printing = '(1)', second printing = '(2)'.

D. Appleton-Century Co
Before 1980s usually a numerical identification in brackets at foot of last page, ie first printing = '(1)', second printing = '(2)'. Number line since 1980s.

Arkham House
Apart from collected works of Lovecraft, Arkham House did not publish reprints. Before 1980s a colophon at the back of book. From late 1970s first edition statement.

Atheneum
States 'First edition'. Number line from mid-1980s.

Atlantic Monthly Press
Before 1925 no statement (or publication date on the title page and did not consistently list later printings.) Little, Brown published Atlantic Monthly Books from 1925 and used their own methods for first edition identification.

Avon (hardbacks)
Before June 1981 no statement. 1981-1995 a number line. From 1996 states 'First Printed' with month/year **or** 'First edition' with number line.

Avon (paperbacks)
Early first editions have no statement. Later editions state 'First Avon Printing' with month/year.

Ballantine Books
Hardbacks state 'First edition' **or** 'First edition' with month/year. Paperbacks have no statement.

Ernest Benn
States 'First published' with the year, **or** the date with Benn imprint, **or** no statement.

A. & C. Black
States 'First edition' with the year, **or** no statement.

William Blackwood
No statement.

Bobbs-Merrill
Before 1920s sometimes a bow-and-arrow device on the copyright page. From 1920s states 'First edition' **or** 'First printing'.

Bodley Head
States 'First published' with year **or** 'First published in Great Britain' with year.

Albert & Charles Boni
No statement.

Boni & Liveright
Usually no statement.

Bowes & Bowes
States 'First published' with the year.

Boydell & Brewer
States 'First published' with the year.

Brentano's
Before 1928 no statement. From 1928 states 'First printed' with year.

Edgar Rice Burroughs, Inc
Only published the books of Edgar Rice Burroughs. Before 1933 no statement. From 1933 states 'First edition'.

A.L. Burt
Mainly a reprint publisher.

John Calder
States 'First published' with the year.

Calder & Boyars
States 'First published' with year **or** 'First published in Great Britain' with year.

Jonathan Cape
States 'First published' with year, **or** 'First published in Great Britain' with year. From 1994 also includes number line.

Jonathan Cape & Harrison Smith
States 'First published' with year, **or** 'First published in America' with year, **or** no statement.

Cassell & Co
Before early 1920s the year of publication is on the title page and the verso title page is blank. In early 1920s stated 'First published' with year, **or** 'First published in Great Britain' with year.

Chapman & Hall
Before 1935 no statement. From 1935 either states 'First published' with year **or** no statement.

Chatto & Windus
No statement. Now uses a number line.

City Lights
Early first editions have no statement. Some later titles state 'First edition'.

Collins
No statement.

Constable
Same date on front and verso of title page, **or** states 'First published' with year, **or** no statement.

Contact editions
Limited editions include a colophon page. No statement on trade editions.

Copeland & Day
States 'First published' with month/year.

Pascal Covici
Sometimes stated, but usually no statement.

Covici Friede
No statement.

Covici McGee
No statement.

Coward-McCann
Before mid-1930s a torch design on the colophon page, which was removed for later printings. No consistency afterwards.

Crime Club (U.K.)
See Collins.

Crime Club (U.S.)
(Published under the name 'Sydney Fowler' in the U.K.)
See Doubleday, Doran & Co.

Thomas Y. Crowell
Usually no statement. Appear to have sometimes used a number line as early as the 1940s.

Peter Davies
No statement, **or** states 'First published' with month/year **or** 'First Printed' with month/year.

John Day Co/John Day & Co/John Day in association with Reynal and Hitchcock
Early titles may state 'First published' with month/year but from 1930s no statement. Used number line from the 1970s.

Delacorte Press/Seymour Lawrence
States 'First printing' **or** 'First American Printing', but now uses number line.

J.M. Dent
From 1929 states 'First published' with year.

Andre Deutsch
States 'First published' with year.

Dial Press
Occasionally stated 'First printing' before mid-1960s but usually the same date on the title page and the copyright page. In the late 1960s states 'First printing' with year. Now uses a number line.

Dodd, Mead

Before 1976 no statement and often later printings were not noted. In late 1976 added a number line to the verso title page. In the 1970s first-print d/ws of some titles were issued without a price on the flap, making them look like book club editions.

George H. Doran

Usually printed a colophon with the initial 'GHD' on the copyright page, though not consistently until the early 1920s. Occasionally states 'First printing'.

Doubleday & Co

States 'First edition'.

Doubleday, Doran & Co

States 'First edition'.

Doubleday & McClure Co

Usually the date on the title page should match the date on the copyright page.

Doubleday, Page & Co

Before the early 1920s no statement. In early 1920s states 'First edition'.

Duckworth

States 'First published' with year, or no statement.

Duell, Sloan and Pearce

Usually states 'First edition' or placed a Roman numeral 'I'.

E.P. Dutton

Before 1929 the date on the title page should match the date on the copyright page. 1929-1993 as before but states 'First edition' or 'First Published' with year. From 1993 states 'First published' with month/year and number line.

Editions Poetry

States 'First published' with year.

Duell, Sloan and Pearce

Usually states 'First edition' or places a Roman numeral 'I' on the copyright page.

Egoist Press

Limited editions include a colophon page. No statement on trade editions.

Eyre & Spottiswoode

Prints the year of publication under their name at the bottom of the title page or states 'This book, first published' with year.

Eyre Methuen

No statement or states 'First Published' with year.

Faber & Faber, Ltd

States 'First published' with month/year. Before 1968 the year of publication is in Roman numerals. From 1968 the year of publication is in Arabic numerals. Now uses number line

Faber & Gwyer, Ltd

States 'First published by Faber & Gwyer' with month/year.

Farrar & Rinehart

Publisher's logo on copyright page. Infrequently states 'First edition'.

Farrar, Strauss

Publisher's stylised initials, FS, on the copyright page.

Farrar, Strauss & Cudahy

States 'First published' with year or 'First printing'.

Farrar, Strauss & Giroux

States either 'First published' with year, or 'First printing' with year, or 'First edition' with year.

Fawcett (hardbacks)

States 'First edition' with month/year, and number line.

Fawcett Gold Medal Books

States 'First published' or no statement. Reprints often noted on last page of text.

Fleet Publishing Corp

No statement up to c.1955. From 1955 states 'First printing'.

Folio Society

No statement or states 'First published' with year.

Franklin Library

First editions are limited to an unstated number and are not reprinted. Standard works are reprinted without indication.

Funk & Wagnalls

Used a Roman numeral 'I' on copyright page. From 1929 states 'First published' with month/year.

Bernard Geis

States 'First printing' or 'First Publication'.

Golden Cockerel Press

No statement.

Victor Gollancz, Ltd

Before 1984 no statement. From 1984 states 'First published' with date.

Gotham Book Mart

No statement or states 'First edition' or details on colophon page.

Grosset & Dunlap

Mainly a reprint publisher. No statement in their few first editions. A later printing can only be identified by detective work, i.e. if it advertises other books published after the first edition of the title in question.

Grove Press

No statement before 1960. 1961-1985 states 'First edition' with year or 'First published' with year. From 1985 adds number line.

Grove Weidenfeld

States 'First edition' with year, and uses a number line.

Hamish Hamilton

States 'First published' with year, or 'First published in Great Britain' with year. Adds a number line from 1988.

Harcourt, Brace & Co

From 1921-1931 no statement. From 1931 states 'First edition' or 'First American Edition'.

Harcourt, Brace & World.

States 'First edition' or 'First American Edition'

Harcourt Brace Jovanovich

States 'First edition' or 'First American Edition'. Some state 'First edition/ABCDE', dropping 'First edition' and the letter 'A' for later printings. Between 1973-1983 they state 'First edition/BCDE', dropping 'First edition' and the letter 'B' for later printings.

Harper & Brothers

Before 1912 the date on the title page should be the same as the last date on the copyright page. Between 1912-1922 a two-letter code appears on the colophon page corresponding to, or earlier than, the date on the title page. 1st letter=month: A=Jan, B=Feb, C=Mar, D=Apr, E=May, F=Jun, G=Jul, H=Aug, I=Sept, K=Oct, L=Nov, M=Dec. 2nd letter=year: M=1912, N=1913, O=1914, P=1915, Q=1916, R=1917, S=1918, T=1919, U=1920 V=1921, W=1922.

Began stating 'First edition' on copyright page in 1922.

Harper & Row

States 'First edition' (and see Harper & Brothers date code above). Added a number line to the bottom of the last page (directly before the rear free endpaper) in 1969, but often did not remove the 'First edition' statement from later printings. By 1975 the number line was usually on the copyright page (still often did not remove 'First edition' statement from later printings).

HarperCollins

States 'First edition' and uses a number line. Sometimes fails to remove 'First edition' statement from later printings, but number line is altered.

HarperFlamingo

States 'First edition' and uses a number line.

HarperPrism

States 'First edition' with month/year and uses a number line.

Rupert Hart-Davis

States 'First edition' with year on copyright page and/or the date on title page.

Hart-Davis, MacGibbon Limited

States 'First published' with year.

Heinemann

From 1890 to 1921 states year of publication on title page, removing it from later printings and adding a note to the copyright page. From 1920s states 'First published' with year or 'First published in Great Britain' with year.

Her Majesty's Stationery Office

States 'First published' with year.

Hodder & Stoughton Ltd

Before 1940s no consistent practice. 1940s-1976 states 'First Printed' with year or 'First published' with year. From 1976 states 'First published' with year.

Hogarth Press

No statement. Now uses number line.

Henry Holt

Before 1945 no statement. 1945 to 1985 states 'First Printed' or 'First edition' with number line. From 1985 'First edition' with year and number line.

Holt, Rinehart & Winston

Before the 1970s states 'First edition' or 'First printing'. In 1970s began using a number line.

Houghton Mifflin
Before 1953 the same date on the title page as the copyright page. 1953-1970s states 'First printing' **or** 'First printing' with month/year. From 1970s adds number line.

B.W. Huebsch
No statement.

Hutchinson and Co
States 'First published' with year **or** 'First published in Great Britain' with year.

Michael Joseph Ltd
States 'First published' with year. From 1990 adds a number line.

Knopf
Before 1933/34 no statement. From 1933/34 states 'First edition', usually in capital letters. If the book is preceded by or is simultaneous with the British edition the statement reads 'First American edition'.

John Lane
Before 1925 no statement. From 1925 states 'First publ-ished' and year.

T. Werner Laurie
States 'First published' and year.

Limited Editions Club
Does not publish reprints. Colophon at back of book.

J.B. Lippincott
Before c.1925 date on title page should be the same as on the copyright page, although for autumn titles the title page date may be one year earlier. From c.1925 states 'First edition' **or** 'Printed' with month/year. Later adds number line.

Lippincott and Crowell
States 'First edition', later adds number line.

Little, Brown
Before c.1930 the same date should appear on title page and copyright page. c.1930-1940 states 'Published' with month/year. From 1940 states 'First edition' **or** 'First printing'. Added number line in 1970s.

Horace Liveright, Inc./Liveright Publishing Corp
Before 1970s no statement. From 1970s states 'First edition' with number line.

Longmans Green Co (U.K.)
Before late 1920s no statement. From late 1920s states 'First published' with year.

Longmans Green Co (U.S.)
Before late 1920s no statement. From late 1920s states 'First edition' with year.

Macaulay
No statement.

MacGibbon & Kee
States 'First published' with year.

Macmillan (U.K.)
Before mid 1920s no statement. From mid 1920s states 'First published' with year.

Macmillan (U,S.)
Before late 1880s date on title page should match date on copyright page. From 1936 states 'First printing'. Added number line in 1970s.

Macmillan (Canada)
No statement.

Robert M. McBride
States 'First published', with year, **or** 'Published' with month/year, **or** 'First edition'.

McClure, Phillips
No statement **or** states 'First printing'.

McDowell Obolensky
No statement **or** states 'First printing'.

McGraw-Hill
Before 1956 no statement. From 1956 states 'First edition'.

Methuen & Co
States 'First published' with year.

William Morrow
Before 1973 no statement **or** states 'First printing' with year. From 1973 states 'First edition' and uses number line.

New American Library
States 'First published' with month/year and number line.

New Directions
Before 1969 inconsistent. From 1970 states 'First published' with year.

New English Library
States 'First published' with year which should match copyright year.

W.W. Norton
States 'First edition' with month/year **and/or** number line.

Peter Owen
States 'First published' with year.

O.U.P. (U.K. and U.S.)
Before late 1980s no statement. From late 1980s number line.

Kegan Paul, Trench, Trubner & Co
No statement **or** states 'First published' with year.

Pelligrini & Cudahy
No statement.

Philtrum
States 'First published'.

Picador
States 'Published' with year **or** 'First published' with year.

G.P. Putnam's Sons
Before 1985 no statement. From 1985 number line.

Random House
States 'First published' **or** 'First edition', sometimes with year. Later books have a number line which should begin with '2', so that the first printing states 'First edition/ 23456789', the second printing states '23456789', the third '3456789' etc.

Reynal & Hitchcock
Before 1948 no statement. From 1948 states 'First edition' **or** 'First American Edition'

Grant Richards
No statement.

Rinehart & Co
Printed an 'R' in a circle which is removed from later editions.

St Martin's Press
Before 1980s no statement. From early 1980s number line and a first edition statement.

Sampson, Low, Marston, Searle & Rivington
No statement.

Sampson, Low, Son & Co
Same date appears on title page as copyright page.

Scribners
Before 1930 the Scribners seal and the date. From 1930 an 'A' on the copyright page, with the Scribner seal **and/or** a code representing the month and year of publication. Number line used from 1970s.

Martin Secker, Ltd/Secker & Warburg
Before 1940s no statement In 1940s states 'First published' with year.

Sheed & Ward (U.K.)
States 'First published' with month/year.

Sheed & Ward (U.S.)
No statement.

Simon & Schuster
Before 1952 no statement (a few titles in the 1930s had a series of dots or asterisks to indicate later printings.) From 1952 states 'First edition'. In early 1970s began to use a number line (occasionally with a first edition statement.)

Small, Maynard
No statement.

Smith, Elder
No statement.

Harrison Smith & Robert Haas
Inconsistent use of first edition statement

Colin Smythe
States 'First published' with year.

S.P.C.K.
States 'First published' with year, or no statement.

Frederick A. Stokes Co
No statement.

Stone & Kimball
Same date appears on title page as copyright page.

T. Fisher Unwin
No statement before 1914. From 1914 states 'First published' with year.

Vanguard
No statement. Number line from mid-1970s.

Viking Press
Before late 1930s no statement. From 1937 states 'First published' with year **or** 'Published by' with year. In 1980s a number line on later printings only.

Ward, Lock
Before 1930s year of publication on title page, removed for later printings. From mid-1930s states 'First published' with year.

Weidenfeld & Nicolson
States 'First published' or no statement.

APPENDIX IV

PSEUDONYMS

This is an aid to identifying some of the alternative names which writers sometimes use.

Alternative Name	Usual Name
352087 A/C Ross	T.E. Lawrence
A Lady of Fashion	Djuna Barnes
Abhavananda	Aleister Crowley
Agapida, Fray Antonio	Washington Irving
Andrézel, Pierre	Isak Dinesen
Ashdown, Clifford	R. Austin Freeman
Ashe, Gordon	John Creasey
Aston, James	T.H. White
Axton, David	Dean Koontz
Bachman, Richard	Stephen King
Barclay, Bill	Michael Moorcock
Bassetto	George Bernard Shaw
Barum Browne	Hilary Saunders
Bastable, Bernard	Robert Barnard
'BB'	D.J. Watkins-Pitchford
Beeding, Francis	Hilary Saunders
Bell, Acton	Anne Brontë
Bell, Currer	Charlotte Brontë
Bell, Ellis	Emily Brontë
Beynon, John	John Wyndham
Bishop, George Archibald	Aleister Crowley
Blake, Nicholas	C. Day Lewis
Bland, Fabian	Edith Nesbit
Blayre, Christopher	Edward Heron-Allen
Blixen, Karen	Isak Dinesen
Box, Edgar	Gore Vidal
Boz	Charles Dickens
Bradbury, Edward P.	Michael Moorcock
Brown, Fr. Aloysius	David Lodge
Brown, Danielle	Dan and Blythe Brown
Brust, Harold	Peter Cheyney
Bryan, Michael	Brian Moore
Burke, Leda	David Garnett
Burton, Miles	John Rhode
C.3.3.	Oscar Wilde
C.G.R.	Christina Rossetti
Camberg, Muriel	Muriel Spark
Carnac, Carol	E.C.R. Lorac
Carr, H.D.	Aleister Crowley
Carr, Jolyon	Ellis Peters
Catherall, Arthur	D.J. Watkins-Pitchford
Charles, Will	Charles Willeford
Chaucer, Daniel	Ford Madox Ford
Cherry	Benjamin Disraeli
Chris, Leonard	Dean Koontz (disputed by author)
Cleishbotham, Jedediah	Walter Scott
Cleri, Mario	Mario Puzo
Clerihew, E.	E.C. Bentley
Clerk, N.W.	C.S. Lewis
Clifford, Martin	Frank Richards
Coffey, Brian	Dean Koontz
Coffyn, Cornelius	Hilary Saunders
Colvin, James	Michael Moorcock
Comte de Fénix	Aleister Crowley
Comus	R.M. Ballantyne
Conquest, Owen	Frank Richards
Cooke, M.E.	John Creasey
Cooke, Margaret	John Creasey
Cousins, Sheila	Graham Greene
	(with Ronald Matthews)

Coyle, William	Thomas Keneally
Crayon, Geoffrey	Washington Irving
Credo	John Creasey
Crosby, Henry Grew	Harry Crosby
Daviot, Gordon	Josephine Tey
Davison, Lawrence H.	D.H. Lawrence
Deane, Norman	John Creasey
Democritus Junior	Robert Burton
Derry Down Derry	Edward Lear
Dickson, Carr	John Dickson Carr
Dickson, Carter	John Dickson Carr
Douglas, Michael	Michael Crichton
Douglass, G. Norman	Norman Douglas
Doyle, John	Robert Graves
Dwyer, Deanna	Dean Koontz
Dwyer, K.R.	Dean Koontz
E.B.W.	E.B. White
Earle, William	Captain W.E. Johns
Early, Jon	Captain W.E. Johns
Eastway, Edward	Edward Thomas
Eireann, Coras Jompair	John Betjeman
Everard, Katherine	Gore Vidal
Fair, A.A.	Earle Stanley Gardner
Fairbairn, Roger	John Dickson Carr
Farran, Richard M.	John Betjeman
Father Tuck	Louis Wain
Felcamps, Elise	John Creasey
Finney, Sterling	E.B. White
Firth, Violet M.	Dion Fortune
Fleming, Oliver	Philip MacDonald
Flying Officer 'X'	H.E. Bates
Fowler, Sidney	S. Fowler Wright
Frazer, Robert Caine	John Creasey
Freckles	Louis Wain
French, Paul	Isaac Asimov
Furey, Michael	Sax Rohmer
Gaunt, Graham	Jonathan Gash
Gentleman of the University Of Cambridge, A	Aleister Crowley
Gibbon, Grassic	J. Leslie Mitchell
Gill, Patrick	John Creasey
Goldsmith, Peter	J.B. Priestley
Graham, Tom	Sinclair Lewis
Grand Orient	A.E. Waite
Grant, Jonathan	Jonathan Gash
Grimalkin	Louis Wain
H.B.	Hillaire Belloc
Haig, Fenil	Ford Madox Ford
Halliday, Michael	John Creasey
Hamilton, Clive	C.S. Lewis
Hammond, Ralph	Hammond Innes
Harris, John Beynon	John Wyndham
Harris, Johnson	John Wyndham
Harvey, Jack	Ian Rankin
Haycraft, Anna	Alice Thomas Ellis
Heldmann, Bernard	Richard Marsh
Hill, John	Dean Koontz
Hockaby, Stephen	Gladys Mitchell
Hogarth, Charles	John Creasey
Home, Michael	Christopher Bush
Hope, Brian	John Creasey
Hopley, George	Cornell Woolrich
Hornem, Horace	Lord Byron
Hudson, Jeffery	Michael Crichton
Hueffer, Ford Madox	Ford Madox Ford
Hueffer, H. Ford	Ford Madox Ford
Hughes, Colin	John Creasey
Hunt, Kyle	John Creasey
Husson, Jules Francois Felix	R.M. Ballantyne

Irish, William	Cornell Woolrich
Jenks, Agneta Mariana	William Beckford
Jones, Edith Newbold	Edith Wharton
Kain, Saul	Siegfried Sassoon
Kari	Louis Wain
Kell, Joseph	Anthony Burgess
Kells, Susannah	Judy & Bernard Cornwell
Kendrake, Carleton	Earle Stanley Gardner
Kenny, Charles J.	Earle Stanley Gardner
Kerouac, John	Jack Kerouac
Khan, Khaled	Aleister Crowley
Kittycat	Louis Wain
Knickerbocker, Diedrich	Washington Irving
Lady, A	Jane Austen
Lady of Fashion, A	Djuna Barnes
Lange, John	Michael Crichton
Lawless, Anthony	Philip MacDonald
Leander, Richard	Louis Wain
Lear, Peter	Peter Lovesey
Lee, William (Willy)	William S. Burroughs
Lennox, Terry	John Harvey
Lincoln, Geoffrey	John Mortimer
Lucas, Victoria	Sylvia Plath
Lutiy, the late Major	Aleister Crowley
MacBetjeman, Ian	John Betjeman
Macdonald, John Ross	Ross Macdonald
Macdonald, John	Ross Macdonald
Mactaggart, Norma Doris	Elizabeth Ferrars
Mahatma Guru Sri	
Parahamsa Shivaji	Aleister Crowley
Mallowan, A.C.	Agatha Christie
Malone, Louis	Louis Macniece
Mann, Abel	John Creasey
Mann, James	John Harvey
Manton, Peter	John Creasey
Mara, Bernard	Brian Moore
March, Maxwell	Margery Allingham
Market-gardener, A	R.D. Blackmore
Markham, Robert	Kingsley Amis
Marlow, the Right Hon	
Lady Harriet	William Beckford
Marric, J.J.	John Creasey
Marsden, James	John Creasey
Martindale, Patrick	Patrick White
Marut, Ret	B. Traven
Master Therion	Aleister Crowley
Mattheson, Rodney	John Creasey
McClure, S.S.	Willa Cather
McCoy, Edmund	John Gardner
Melanter	R.D. Blackmore
Millar, Kenneth	Ross Macdonald
Mitchell, James Leslie	Lewis Grassic Gibbon
Moorland, Dick	Reginald Hill
Morgan, Claire	Patricia Highsmith
Morton, Anthony	John Creasey
Myles na gCopaleen	Flann O'Brien
Nabokoff-Sirin, Vladimir	Vladimir Nabokov
Nichols, Leigh	Dean Koontz
Norden, Charles	Lawrence Durrell
Normyx	Norman Douglas
North, Anthony	Dean Koontz
O'Casey, Brenda	Alice Thomas Ellis
Paige, Richard	Dean Koontz
Palinurus	Cyril Connolly
Pargeter, Edith	Ellis Peters

Peeslake, Gaffer	Lawrence Durrell
Perdurabo, Frater	Aleister Crowley
Pilgrim, David	Hilary Saunders
Platts, A. Monmouth	Anthony Berkeley
Pollock, Mary	Enid Blyton
Porlock, Martin	Philip MacDonald
Power, Cecil	Grant Allen
Ramal, Walter	Walter de la Mare
Rampling, Anne	Abbe Rice
Ranger, Ken	John Creasey
Rayner, Olive Pratt	Grant Allen
Redfern, John	Ellis Peters
Reed, Eliot	Eric Ambler
Reid, Desmond	Michael Moorcock
Reilly, William K.	John Creasey
Rich, Barbara	Robert Graves
	(with Laura Riding)
Richards, Hilda	Frank Richards
Riley, Tex	John Creasey
Roquelaire, A.N.	Anne Rice
Ross, Barnaby	Ellery Queen
Ruell, Patrick	Reginald Hill
Russ, Patrick	Patrick O'Brian
Russ, Richard Patrick	Patrick O'Brian
Sanders, W. Franklin	Charles Willeford
Seymour, Alan	S. Fowler Wright
Siluriensis, Leolinus	Arthur Machen
Somers, Jane	Doris Lessing
Sopht, Ensign	R.M. Ballantyne
Sparks, Timothy	Charles Dickens
St John Cooper, Henry	John Creasey
St. E. A. of M. & S	Aleister Crowley
Steele, V.M.	Dion Fortune
Stone, Rosetta	Dr Seuss
Street, C.J.C.	John Rhode
Stuart, Ian	Alistair Maclean
Swanson, Logan	Richard Matheson
Tanner, Lt-Col., William	Kingsley Amis
Temple, Paul	Francis Durbridge
Templeton, Laurence	Walter Scott
Thaw, Evelyn	Edgar Wallace
Titmarsh, Mr M.A.	W.M. Thackeray
Torrie, Malcolm	Gladys Mitchell
Traherne, Michael	D.J. Watkins-Pitchford
Underhill, Charles	Reginald Hill
Verey, Rev. C.	Aleister Crowley
Vine, Barbara	Ruth Rendell
Warborough, Martin Leach	Grant Allen
Warddel, Nora Helen	E. Heron-Allen
Watson, John H., M.D.	Michael Moorcock
Waye, Cecil	John Rhode
Weary, Ogdred	Edward Gorey
West, Owen	Dean Koontz
Westmacott, Mary	Agatha Christie
Wilson, John Burgess	Anthony Burgess
Wingrave, Anthony	S. Fowler Wright
Wolfe, Aaron	Dean Koontz
Yorick, Mr	Laurence Sterne
York, Jeremy	John Creasey
Young, Collier	Robert Bloch

APPENDIX V

THE NOBEL PRIZE FOR LITERATURE

Alfred Nobel's will stipulated that prizes for literature should be given to those who, during the preceding year, 'shall have conferred the greatest benefit on mankind' and who 'shall have produced in the field of literature the most outstanding work in an ideal direction'. The Nobel Prize for Literature is therefore awarded to an author rather than a book.

2009 Herta Müller
2008 J.M.G. Le Clézio
2007 Doris Lessing
2006 Orhan Pamuk, Turkey
2005 Harold Pinter, United Kingdom
2004 Elfriede Jelinek, Austria
2003 J.M. Coetzee, United Kingdom
2002 Imre Kertész, Hungary
2001 V.S. Naipaul, United Kingdom
2000 Gao Xingjian, China
1999 Günter Grass, Germany
1998 José Saramago, Portugal
1997 Dario Fo, Italy
1996 Wislawa Szymborska, Poland
1995 Seamus Heaney, Ireland
1994 Kenzaburo Oë, Japan
1993 Toni Morrison, U.S.
1992 Derek Walcott, The Antilles/U.S.
1991 Nadine Gordimer, South Africa
1990 Octavio Paz, Mexico
1989 Camilo José Cela, Spain
1988 Naguib Mahfouz, Egypt
1987 Joseph Brodsky, U.S.
1986 Wole Soyinka, Nigeria
1985 Claude Simon, France
1984 Jaroslav Seifert, Czechoslovakia
1983 William Golding, England
1982 Gabriel Garcia Márquez, Colombia
1981 Elias Canetti, Bulgaria
1980 Czeslaw Milosz, U.S.
1979 Odysséus Elýtis, Greece
1978 Isaac Bashevis Singer, U.S.
1977 Vicente Aleixandre, Spain
1976 Saul Bellow, U.S.
1975 Eugenio Montale, Italy
1974 Henry Martinson, Sweden
1974 Eyvind Johnson, Sweden
1973 Patrick White, Australia
1972 Heinrich Böll, Germany
1971 Pablo Neruda, Chile
1970 Aleksandr Solzhenitsyn, U.S.S.R.
1969 Samuel Beckett, France
1968 Yasunari Kawabata, Japan
1967 Miguel Angel Asturias, Guatemala
1966 Shmuel Yosef Agnon, Israel
1966 Nelly Sachs, Sweden
1965 Mikhail Sholokov, U.S.S.R.
1964 Jean-Paul Sartre, France
1963 Giorgios Seféris, Greece
1962 John Steinbeck, U.S.
1961 Ivo Andric, Yugoslavia
1960 St.-John Perse, France
1959 Salvatore Quasimodo, Italy
1958 Boris Pasternak, U.S.S.R.
1957 Albert Camus, France
1956 Juan Rámon Jiménez, Spain
1955 Halldór Kiljan Laxness, Iceland
1954 Ernest Hemingway, U.S.
1953 Winston Churchill, England

1952 François Mauriac, France
1951 Pär Lagerkvist, Sweden
1950 Bertrand Russell, England
1949 William Faulkner, U.S.
1948 T.S. Eliot, England
1947 André Gide, France
1946 Hermann Hesse, Switzerland
1945 Gabriela Mistral, Chile
1944 Johannes V. Jensen, Denmark
1943 no award given
1942 no award given
1941 no award given
1940 no award given
1939 Frans Eemil Sillanpaä, Finland
1938 Pearl S. Buck, U.S.
1937 Roger Martin Du Gard, France
1936 Eugene O'Neill, U.S.
1935 no award given
1934 Luigi Pirandello, Italy
1933 Ivan Bunin, Russia
1932 John Galsworthy, England
1931 Erik Karlfeldt, Sweden
1930 Sinclair Lewis, U.S.
1929 Thomas Mann, Germany
1928 Sigrid Undset, Norway
1927 Henri Bergson, France
1926 Grazia Deledda, Italy
1925 George Bernard Shaw, England
1924 Wladyslaw Reymont, Poland
1923 William Butler Yeats, Ireland
1922 Jacinto Benavente, Spain
1921 Anatole France, France
1920 Knut Hamsun, Norway
1919 Carl Spitteler, Switzerland
1918 no award given
1917 Karl Gjeilerup, Denmark
1917 Henrik Pontoppidan, Denmark
1916 Verner von Heidenstam, Sweden
1915 Romain Rolland, France
1914 no award given
1913 Rabindranath Tagore, India
1912 Gerhart Hauptmann, Germany
1911 Maurice Maeterlinck, Belgium
1910 Paul von Heyse, Germany
1909 Selma Lagerlöf, Sweden
1908 Rudolf Eucken, Germany
1907 Rudyard Kipling, England
1906 Giosuè Carducci, Italy
1905 Henryk Sienkiewicz, Poland
1904 José Echegaray, Spain
1904 Frédéric Mistral, France
1903 Bjørnstjerne Bjørnson, Norway
1902 Theodor Mommsen, Germany
1901 Sully Prudhomme, France

APPENDIX VI

THE BOOKER PRIZE

The Booker Prize for Fiction is perhaps the world's most famous and prestigious literary prize. It is awarded to the best novel of the year written by a citizen of the U.K., British Commonwealth, Eire, Pakistan or South Africa.

2009 *Wolf Hall* by Hilary Mantel
2008 *The White Tiger* by Aravind Adiga
2007 *The Gathering* by Anne Enright
2006 *The Inheritance of Loss* by Kiran Desai
2005 *The Sea* by John Banville
2004 *The Line of Beauty* by Alan Hollinghurst

2003 *Vernon God Little* by D.B.C. Pierre
2002 *Life of Pi* by Yann Martel
2001 *True History of the Kelly Gang* by Peter Carey
2000 *The Blind Assassin* by Margaret Atwood
1999 *Disgrace* by J.M. Coetzee
1998 *Amsterdam* by Ian McEwan
1997 *The God of Small Things* by Arundhati Roy
1996 *Last Orders* by Graham Swift
1995 *The Ghost Road* by Pat Barker
1994 *How Late It Was, How Late* by James Kelman
1993 *Paddy Clarke Ha Ha Ha* by Roddy Doyle
1992 *The English Patient* by Michael Ondaatje/
       Sacred Hunger by Barry Unsworth
1991 *The Famished Road* by Ben Okri
1990 *Possession* by A.S. Byatt
1989 *The Remains of the Day* by Kazuo Ishiguro
1988 *Oscar and Lucinda* by Peter Carey
1987 *Moon Tiger* by Penelope Lively
1986 *The Old Devils* by Kingsley Amis
1985 *The Bone People* by Keri Hulme
1984 *Hotel du Lac* by Anita Brookner
1983 *Life and Times of Michael K* by J.M. Coetzee
1982 *Schindler's Ark* by Thomas Keneally
1981 *Midnight's Children* by Salman Rushdie
1980 *Rites of Passage* by William Golding
1979 *Offshore* by Penelope Fitzgerald
1978 *The Sea, the Sea* by Iris Murdoch
1977 *Staying On* by Paul Scott
1976 *Saville* by David Storey
1975 *Heat and Dust* by Ruth Prawer Jhabvala
1974 *The Conservationist* by Nadine Gordimer
1973 *The Siege of Krishnapur* by J.G. Farrell
1972 *G* by John Berger
1971 *In a Free State* by V.S. Naipaul
1970 *The Elected Member* by Bernice Rubens
1969 *Something to Answer for* by P.H. Newby

APPENDIX VII

THE PULITZER PRIZE

The prize is named after Hungarian newspaper publisher Joseph Pulitzer and honours books that depict the positive and negative aspects of the human condition, giving preference to those which portray American life.

2010 *Tinkers* by Paul Harding
2009 *Olive Kitteridge* by Elizabeth Strout
2008 *The Brief Wondrous Life of Oscar Wao* by Junot Diaz
2007 *The Road* by Cormac McCarthy
2006 *March* by Geraldine Brooks
2005 *Gilead: A Novel* by Marilynne Robinson
2004 *The Known World* by Edward P. Jones
2003 *Middlesex* by Jeffrey Eugenides
2002 *Empire Falls* by Richard Russo
2001 *The Amazing Adventures of Kavalier and Clay* by Michael Chabon
2000 *Interpreter of Maladies* by Jhumpa Lahiri
1999 *The Hours* by Michael Cunningham
1998 *American Pastoral* by Philip Roth
1997 *Martin Dressler: The Tale of an American Dreamer* by Stephen Millhauser
1996 *Independence Day* by Richard Ford
1995 *The Stone Diaries* by Carol Shields
1994 *The Shipping News* by E. Annie Proulx
1993 *A Good Scent from a Strange Mountain* by Robert Olen Butler
1992 *A Thousand Acres* by Jane Smiley
1991 *Rabbit at Rest* by John Updike
1990 *The Mambo Kings Play Songs of Love* by Oscar Hijuelos

1989 *Breathing Lessons* by Anne Tyler
1988 *Beloved* by Toni Morrison
1987 *A Summons to Memphis* by Peter Taylor
1986 *Lonesome Dove* by Larry McMurtry
1985 *Foreign Affairs* by Alison Lurie
1984 *Ironweed* by William Kennedy
1983 *The Color Purple* by Alice Walker
1982 *Rabbit is Rich* by John Updike
1981 *Confederacy of Dunces* by John Kennedy Toole
1980 *The Executioner's Song* by Norman Mailer
1979 *The Stories of John Cheever* by John Cheever
1978 *Elbow Room* by James Alan McPherson
1977 no award given
1976 *Humboldt's Gift* by Saul Bellow
1975 *The Killer Angels* by Michael Shaara
1974 no award given
1973 *The Optimist's Daughter* by Eudora Welty
1972 *Angle of Repose* by Wallace Stegner
1971 no award given
1970 *Collected Stories* by Jean Stafford
1969 *House Made of Dawn* by N. Scott Momaday
1968 *Confessions of Nat Turner* by William Styron
1967 *The Fixer* by Bernard Malamud
1966 *The Collected Stories of Katherine Anne Porter* by Katherine Anne Porter
1965 *The Keepers of the House* by Shirley Ann Grau
1964 no award given
1963 *The Reivers* by William Faulkner
1962 *The Edge of Sadness* by Edwin O'Connor
1961 *To Kill a Mockingbird* by Harper Lee
1960 *Advise and Consent* by Allen Drury
1959 *The Travels of Jaimie McPheeters* by Robert Lewis Taylor
1958 *A Death in the Family* by James Agee
1957 no award given
1956 *Andersonville* by MacKinlay Kantor
1955 *A Fable* by William Faulkner
1954 no award given
1953 *The Old Man and the Sea* by Ernest Hemingway
1952 *The Caine Mutiny* by Herman Wouk
1951 *The Town* by Conrad Richter
1950 *The Way West* by A.B. Guthrie, Jr.
1949 *Guard of Honor* by James Gould Cozzens
1948 *Tales of the South Pacific* by James A. Michener
1947: *All the King's Men* by Robert Penn Warren
1946: no award given
1945: *A Bell for Adano* by John Hersey
1944: *Journey in the Dark* by Martin Flavin
1943: *Dragon's Teeth* by Upton Sinclair
1942: *In This Our Life* by Ellen Glasgow
1941: no award given
1940: *The Grapes of Wrath* by John Steinbeck
1939: *The Yearling* by Marjorie Kinnan Rawlings
1938: *The Late George Apley* by John Phillips Marquand
1937: *Gone with the Wind* by Margaret Mitchell
1936: *Honey in the Horn* by Harold L. Davis
1935: *Now in November* by Josephine Winslow Johnson
1934: *Lamb in His Bosom* by Caroline Miller
1933: *The Store* by Thomas Sigismund Stribling
1932: *The Good Earth* by Pearl S. Buck
1931: *Years of Grace* by Margaret Ayer Barnes
1930: *Laughing Boy* by Oliver La Farge
1929: *Scarlet Sister Mary* by Julia Peterkin
1928: *The Bridge of San Luis Rey* by Thornton Wilder
1927: *Early Autumn* by Louis Bromfield
1926: *Arrowsmith* by Sinclair Lewis (declined)
1925: *So Big* by Edna Ferber
1924: *The Able McLaughlins* by Margaret Wilson
1923: *One of Ours* by Willa Cather
1922: *Alice Adams* by Booth Tarkington
1921: *The Age of Innocence* by Edith Wharton
1920: no award given
1919: *The Magnificent Ambersons* by Booth Tarkington
1918: *His Family* by Ernest Poole